MW01010224

Dick Findlay '89

This edition of the book is dedicated
to Anton Rupert
academic, conservationist
and entrepreneur

289

Elephant (*Loxodonta africana*) Olifant

# THE MAMMALS OF THE SOUTHERN AFRICAN SUBREGION

BY

JOHN D. SKINNER
M.Sc. Ph.D. F.I.Biol. F.Z.S. F.R.S.(SA)

Director
Mammal Research Institute
University of Pretoria

AND

THE LATE REAY H.N. SMITHERS
D.Sc. M.I.Biol.

Senior Research Officer
Mammal Research Institute
University of Pretoria

WITH COLOUR PLATES BY
DICK FINDLAY

University of Pretoria, Pretoria
Republic of South Africa

1990

Published by the University of Pretoria
Pretoria, Transvaal, Republic of South Africa



First edition 1983
Reprinted 1986
Second edition 1990

English editions:

| | |
|---|---|
| Special Presentation edition | ISBN 0 86979 793 X |
| Subscriber's edition | ISBN 0 86979 801 4 |
| Ordinary edition | ISBN 0 86979 802 2 |

Origination and colour:
Sparhams Cape

Printing and bookbinding:
CTP Book Printers Cape, Republic of South Africa

Dust cover and end papers:
The ordinary and "King" cheetahs *Acinonyx jubatus* in their natural habitat illustrated from examples seen at the De Wildt Cheetah Breeding Research Station of the National Zoological Gardens of S.A. and photographs taken by Mr Anthony Bannister

# CONTENTS

# Foreword

In my foreword to the first edition I mentioned how privileged I was to be associated with the project on *The Mammals of the Southern African Subregion* from the outset in 1972, when Professor John Skinner first approached the Council of Management of the University of Pretoria's Mammal Research Institute with a view to producing a text embracing all the published information on the mammalian fauna within the compass of a single encyclopaedia. For the record, I should mention that, through Professor Skinner's persistence and motivation during the first phase of this project, the Council for Scientific and Industrial Research (C.S.I.R.) of which I was then Vice President, gave his project their blessing and support in 1976. The following year, having obtained approval and financial support for the second phase of the project from the University, whom I might add were enthusiastic from the outset, Professor Skinner started to plan for the execution of this phase.

Professor Skinner himself was then heavily committed to both undergraduate and postgraduate student training as well as the administration of the Mammal Research Institute. He realised that no single person could undertake a project of this magnitude; in particular the complex ramification of mammalian taxonomy was one of the subjects the team led by him was not equipped to unravel.

At the time Dr Reay Smithers, having retired as the Director of the National Museums of Rhodesia, was engaged in a project on small carnivores under Professor Skinner's direction in that country. Realising the information obtained could be included in the book and that Dr Smithers was a scientist with exceptional all-round ability and knowledge, Professor Skinner persuaded the University to appoint him as Senior Scientific Officer, an offer which he accepted. The University then transferred the Smithers family to an official house on campus, and the execution of the project with the back-up of the Institute team and outside support commenced. That it took three years longer to complete than Professor Skinner had anticipated and for which Dr Smithers was contracted, only emphasises the enormity of their task. The first book will always, therefore, serve as a monument to Dr Smithers.

When the University invited Dr Smithers to undertake a comprehensive revision of the book, Professor Skinner resolved to complete the project in the event of anything happening to Dr Smithers who was then in his 80th year. It was a tragedy when he passed away before the comprehensive revision required by the University could really commence, but we were fortunate to have Professor Skinner who had played a major part in the production of our first edition, far more than simply editing the text. Moreover, with his wide ranging contacts in the zoological field, he was in a position to seek appropriate advice whenever needed, quite apart from the magnificent team of colleagues he has assembled in the Mammal Research Institute over the years and on whom he could rely for support.

Over eleven hundred references have been added to those listed in the first edition and again some 10 percent of these had their origin in the Mammal Research Institute: either as theses from post graduates, or as projects emanating from research programmes. Indeed it is worth mentioning here that this is by no means the only dynamic, long-term project being undertaken by scientists in the Institute.

Much of the text has been rewritten, but for some species few new facts have been published. Some changes are more subtle, for example the publication in 1986 of an excellent monograph by Prof J.A.J. Meester and his co-authors on mammalian taxonomy has reduced the need for detailed discussion of taxonomy. On the other hand greater emphasis has been placed in the revised edition on behavioural ecology, ecophysiology and conservation, particularly the commendable part played by countries and their scientists in the subregion. Most sections have been extensively revised and those on cetacea, pachyderms, primates and artiodactyls have been largely rewritten.

The University also appointed a new artist for this edition in the person of Mr Dick Findlay, and the number of colour plates and other illustrations has been increased. The new 3-dimensional approach to the ungulate spoor illustrations is particularly impressive and will hopefully be extended to other species in future editions. The illustrations were completed under the guidance of Professor Skinner and other experts, with final vetting by Professor Murray Schoonraad of our Department of Fine Arts. As one would expect of an artist of Mr Findlay's ability and stature, the results are quite outstanding.

Again I would like to report our indebtedness first to the University of Pretoria for their major sponsorship of this magnificant project. The University advanced over half a million rand to bring the second phase to fruition and one can anticipate they will be no less generous with this third phase for which an order of ten thousand books has been placed. Secondly, thanks are due to the Foundation for Research Development, until recently a branch of the C.S.I.R., which has whole-heartedly financially supported Professor Skinner's research projects with comprehensive grants since 1984. However, long before that date, since its launch in 1966, the C.S.I.R. has given the team in the Mammal Research Institute unstinting support. There has indeed been an admirable commitment from these two institutions in particular, but I would like to report also our gratitude for the generous financial support from many sponsors and donors to this and other projects which contribute indirectly to the quality of the book. In addition, many institutions provide invaluable logistical support, enabling us to undertake .our various research projects. The continuation of this project and production of the superb second edition of *The Mammals of the Southern African Subregion* is a vindication of faith in the University's ability to pursue long-term research projects indefinitely. Moreover, now that the text of this comprehensively revised edition is on magnetic tape, it will be revised continuously and progressively by Professor Skinner and eventually his succesors.

Professor D.M. Joubert
Vice-Chancellor and Principal
University of Pretoria

# Lists of Sponsors, Donors and Subscribers

## Sponsors and Donors

The Rupert Family Foundation for Nature Conservation
African Oxygen Ltd
Barlow Rand Ltd
Cemcrete (Pty) Ltd
Division of Nature Conservation of the Transvaal Provincial Administration
Hammond, Dr C A
Hersov, Basil
Londolozi Game Reserve
Martin, Tomas Walter
Slack, Mr & Mrs H R
Safmarine
South African Breweries Ltd
Zoological Society of Southern Africa

## Subscribers

### A

AECI Ltd
Africana Book Collectors
Aiken, T E
Alexander, Prof A
Anderson, J L
Andrag, Mrs J
Ansell, W F H

### B

Baldwin, T R
Bannister, A
Barry, E A
Barnwell, Peter
Basson, Mrs P
Bell, L
Bendall, G D
Bernitz, Drs H & Z
Biggs, R C
Bishop, I R
Borkum, M M
Bowker, W M D
Boyes, Mr & Mrs Des
Bradshaw, J R
Bristow, Dr J W
Broster, J
Brown, A J V

### C

Carrington, C
Churcher, Dr D S
Coetzee, C G
Croal, P

### D

De la Harpe, D
Delany, Prof M J
De Villiers, P S
Dewar, Mr J & Mrs S
Doepel, W R
Drummonds, I M McK
Du Plessis, G van E
Du Plessis, Ms M
Du Preez, D J
Du Toit, Mr & Mrs G J

### E

Els, Leon M
Embleton, C A

### F

Faure, Mrs C
Ferreira, N A
Ferrer, Ms M A
F H Chamberlain Trading (Pty) Ltd
Foster, M
Fraser, John & Candy
Fulton, D R
Funston, Dr M

### G

Geldenhuys, F
Glanvill, L
Glenton, J
Goulding, A M
Greig Fester (SA) (Pty) Ltd
Grossett, P
Grieve, G R H

### H

Haagner, C
Haagner, P C
Haagner, P
Haagner, S B
Halton, R G
Harraway, D
H E Joosub Charitable Trust
Hepplewhite, Mr & Mrs M
Hersov, Basil
Hes, A D
Hoets, N v R
Howe, Mrs L
Hunt Leuchars & Hepburn Holdings Ltd

### J

Jobling, B
Johnson, I M
Jones, Mrs J E Fraser
Jooste, J M
Jordan, R

### K

Kahn, S H
Kieviet, D
King, Les & Ilana
King, K W
Klapwijk, D J
Klapwijk, M
Knight, Mr & Mrs M H
Kreher, R K

### L

Lamprecht, Dr D S
Lawrie, R M
Lee, G M
Lincoln, L A J
Logan, Ms M

### M

Mackenzie, I
MacWhirter, A D
Marde, Booyse
Maree, A M I
Martin, R G K
Melass, I K
Mentis, Mr & Mrs R
Mia, S Y
Miller D B
Mitchell, Prof D
Mitchell, Prof G
Morford, Dr R A
Mumford, Mrs L A

### N

National Co-op Dairies Ltd
National Museum, Bloemfontein
National Zoological Gardens of SA
Naylor, Dr G A
Niebuhr, Dr H F

### O

Oake, K

### P

Pakenham, A
Partridge, K J
Patz, Dr I M
Peacocke, K M
Pelser, P C
Porter, B W
Porter, G F Lambert
Pretorius, T L
Prozesky, Dr O W
Pullinger, P J

### R

Rae, J
Redgment, Mr F & Mrs M
Rijksmuseum van Natuurlike Historie
Library, Leiden, Netherlands
Rosseau, Dr P E

### S

Sansbury, R
Schaary, Mrs H L
Schwabland, J
Searle, R
Segal, N C
Serge, D
Simms, B
Slotow, L
Slotow, Dr M
Smith, Mrs A M Wallington
Smith, P A
Spencer, F D
Stagg, Ms R
Stannard, Ms J
Stegmann, Mr & Mrs D E
Stephen, D J F
Stevenson-Hamilton Memorial Library
Steyn, T
Stowe, J G
Stretton, J H
Stretton, S
Struwig, Andries
Stuart, Miss P
Sussman, Q H
Swanepoel, C M

### T

Tagg, D M T
Taute, Dr A H
Taylor, V R C
Trautmann, Miss J
Turner, J J

### U

University of Port Elizabeth

### V

Van Bergen, Dr C O
Van Bruggen, Dr A C
Van der Byl, J H
Van der Jagt, Dr & Mrs D R
Van der Reyden, Dr P R
Van Kerken, H
Van Rooyen, N
Van Wyk, Brig. J A
Van Wyk, Dr L
Varrie, Dr & Mrs S M L
Vegter, Ms M C E
Viljoen, Dr A C
Vorster, Dr & Mrs P

### W

Walker, Dr J B
Wedderburn, W M
Weyers, The Hon. Justice L
Wildlife Society of SA: Natal Branch
Wildlife Society of SA: Northern Cape Branch
Williams, Mr & Mrs P
Wilmot, Ms H
Wingate, L
Winskill, N G
Wise, Mr R & Mrs V
Wolstenholme, Dr B N

### Z

Zway, S D

# Author's Preface

Dr Austin Roberts' monumental pioneering work *The Mammals of South Africa*, published in 1951, was a singular achievement in the history of mammalogy in southern Africa. The team project which led to the publication 30 years later of *The Mammals of the Southern African Subregion*, under the authorship of Dr Reay H.N. Smithers, was similarly a milestone. Indeed, with the advance of knowledge over three decades it required teamwork to carry that second project to a conclusion. Information has been published at an ever increasing rate, necessitating another great team effort to bring the third phase of the project to fruition and publish this revised edition within a decade. Emphasis has been placed increasingly on the living mammal which will be evident in this book and even more so with the passage of time. Over 1 100 new references covered for this edition have an asterisk placed next to them. Mammalogists in southern Africa have made a great contribution to our knowledge and may deficiencies in this knowledge continue to be redressed in the future.

John D. Skinner
Mammal Research Institute
University of Pretoria
0002 Pretoria
August 1990

# Acknowledgements

In a dynamic, ongoing project of this nature there will be those to whom the author(s) and the University will be indebted at each particular phase. Acknowledgements made in the first edition therefore will not necessarily be repeated here.

The revision of this book has been an immense task which could not have been contemplated without the full backing of the University and the outstanding support from my staff and colleagues. As with the first edition, it took a great team effort to bring this encyclopaedic project to fruition.

Professor D.M. Joubert, Vice-Chancellor and Principal, has taken a personal interest in the continuing success of this major academic project since the outset in 1972 and I am immensely grateful to him for his unstinting support. In the decision to comprehensively revise our "encyclopaedia", Professor H.P. van der Schijff, then Vice-Principal, was equally enthusiastic, as was Professor P.J. Zietsman, then Dean of the Faculty of Science, and their successors Professors O.W. Prozesky and N. Sauer. The latter two, with Professor M. Schoonraad of the Department of Fine Arts, were later joined by Professor T. Erasmus with his appointment as Director of Research, to serve on the Steering Committee for this phase of the project, under Professor Prozesky's chairmanship. Latterly this function was no less ably performed by Professor L. van Biljon, Vice-Principal, who gave the project every support. The Steering Committee's ability to make quick and effective decisions whenever necessary greatly enhanced the smooth administration of the undertaking.

It was essential to continue to obtain support, both financial and moral, from sponsors other than the University. In this regard it is a particular pleasure to acknowledge the personal support of Dr Anton Rupert, Chancellor of the University of Pretoria and then Vice President of the World Wildlife Fund for Nature; the Foundation for Research Development and, in particular, its Chief Executive, Dr R.R. Arndt, and the Transvaal Provincial Administration Division of Nature Conservation who have supported my personal research and that of the Mammal Research Institute for almost twenty years. The whale and seal research on which these sections of the book are based has been sponsored by the Department of Environment Affairs on the advice of the South African Scientific Committee for Antarctic Research, and the whale research latterly by Safmarine and the Southern African Nature Foundation. I would also like to record our appreciation to Barlow Rand for their support and continued interest in the success of this project. In addition, the support of our many subscribers has been invaluable.

I would like to pay special tribute to the late Dr Reay H.N. Smithers. Thanks to his diligence, the second phase of this project was successfully concluded and we have built on the foundations he helped lay to complete the third phase.

No project of this nature can be accomplished single-handed. This involved teamwork from the outset of the second phase and putting together the first edition, an effort which has continued unabated since then. I am immensely grateful to my team at the Mammal Research Institute, as well as overseas scientists associated with the Institute, for their loyal and unstinting support and advice and for checking parts of the typescript appertaining to their own specialist interests and areas of expertise. Among these I would like to thank:

Prof. R.J. van Aarde, Drs P.B. Best, whose advice and help on cetaceans proved indispensible, M.N. Bester, W. Ferguson, A.A. McKenzie, P.R.K. Richardson, M. van der Merwe, Messrs M.A. Haupt, G. van Dyk, A. van Jaarsveld and C.K. Willis; postgraduate students Messrs M. Anderson, R.A.G. Davies, A. Duthie, G.T.H. Ellison, A. Grimbeek, T.P. Jackson, W. Kilian, M.H. Knight, A. van Rooyen, Mss Colette Grobler, Annette K. Knight, Paulette Prinsloo and Brigitta Wenhold; and foreign associates Profs K. Hodges, R.R. Hofmann, P.A. Racey, Drs S.K. Bearder, M.J. Coe, D.H.M. Cumming, Barbara Herzig-Straschil and P.J. Woodall.

Scientists from other universities and institutions who generously gave of their time and expertise in advising on particular sections are: Profs G.A. Doyle, Jennifer U.M. Jarvis, H. Klingel, J.A.J. Nel, B. Penzhorn, M. Webb, Drs N.C. Bennett, G. Calef, Jane Carruthers, N. Fairall, D. Gordon, J. Henschel, S.P. Henzi, Hillary Keogh, M.J. Lawes, A. Kitchener, N. Leader-Williams, M. Lindeque, C. Lynch, Judith Masters, G. Murray, N. Owen-Smith, L.C. Rookmaaker, G.J.B. Ross, Alison M. Rosser, D.T. Rowe-Rowe, J.D. Skead, Lilian Westlin-van Aarde, D. Williamson, B. Wou Wa Musiti, The Hon. R.H. Emslie, Messrs A. Bannister, A.E. Bowland, J. Culverwell, D.J. de Villiers, R. du Toit, R.A. Goss, J.J. Herholdt, I.F. Lyle, P. le S. Milstein, D. Pepler, R.H. Taylor, R.J. Teede, H. van der Heiden, C. van Ee, S. Vrahemis, V.J. Wilson, I. Whyte, Ms C.M. Craig, Mrs Karin Trendler, Ms Ann van Dyk, and all other zoologists and naturalists who have assisted me in various ways.

My best thanks go to my staff who undertook the administrative and other chores associated with a vast project of this nature. Due to their selfless support which exceeded even my demanding schedule, we were able to complete this project within a reasonable time-scale. They are a credit to the University and I am immensely grateful for their support. When I was called on to fulfil my commitment to the University on the death of Dr Reay Smithers, Dr H.M. Dott willingly accepted the responsibility for managing the project, in itself a vast task, thereby freeing me to spend all my spare time on revising the script. I shall be grateful forever to him for the enthusiasm and responsibility with which he undertook this task, freeing me from much anguish in the process. His advice on preparation of parts of the text was also invaluable. Furthermore, we were fortunate to be served by willing and experienced secretaries in Mss Ingrid Vis and Karin Serfontein, and we had an exceptional proof reader in Mrs Patsy Skinner, with an acute perception for errors. Ms Vis and Mrs Skinner also exceeded their responsibilities in directing my attention to many important matters in the script, thereby improving the final result immeasurably. No expression of thanks can ever convey my gratitude to Mrs Skinner for her dedication to the task in hand during the final important months of the project when she was under extreme personal stress from a devastating illness.

Apart from these staff members directly involved, I enjoyed the support of a superb back-up staff. Mrs Nita Brosnan and Brenda Coetzee, secretaries in the Institute and Department respectively, were always prepared to lend a hand and to shoulder some of the administration. Together with Mrs Babsie Potgieter, these five women saved me much stress and anxiety. I have always been blessed with the women in my life! I would also like to record my thanks to Messrs A. Meyer and C. Hildyard for their help.

I am indebted to Mrs Elna Randall and her colleagues in the Merensky Library who spared no efforts in the support of this project. No research is feasible without this support and we have a superb library at the University of Pretoria. Reprints were obtained from all over the world. I would also like to express my appreciation to the director of the Cambridge University Library for their assistance. The more than 1 100 references covered in this new edition is a measure of the research being carried out on our indigenous mammalian fauna.

The 38 new plates, the dust cover and several new line drawings are the work of Mr Dick Findlay of Pretoria who, in his customary immutable style, acquitted himself with aplomb. I would like to express our appreciation for criticism endured from those of us less gifted artistically yet not averse to passing judgement and he was always happy to oblige in making changes. For the cetacean plates, we sought the advice and approval of Drs P.B. Best and G.J.B. Ross, and Prof Evert F. Potgieter advised us on the preparation of the four plates on ungulate spoor and that on the elephant, in three dimensions. For use of the colour photograph of a painting by Jacques-Laurent Agasse of the extinct quagga I am indebted to the President of the Royal College of Surgeons in London and to Dr Andrew Kitchener for drawing my attention to its existence. Professor Murray Schoonraad advised on and supervised the artwork; in particular he designed the dustcover to give due credit to the University.

We are indebted to the Director of the Transvaal Museum, the

Curator of Mammals and his Collection Manager, Drs C.K. Brain, I.L. Rautenbach and Mrs E. Jones for giving access to material in their mammal collection which proved invaluable in the preparation of plates, and for their advice. It was often necessary to borrow specimens for examination and illustration and we are grateful for their support. Similarly, the Director of the National Zoological Gardens, Mr W. Labuschagne, gave us access to their collection whenever necessary and we thank him and his staff. The cheetahs on the dust cover were painted from animals held at their de Wildt Cheetah Breeding Station and a photograph taken by Mr Anthony Bannister. The Curator of the Johannesburg Zoological Gardens, Mr. R. Wilkinson, gave us access to the sitatunga.

Credit for the other black and white drawings repeated from the first edition goes to Mrs Clare Abbott, except those listed below:

Mr L Penny for the skull illustrations of species nos 250–253, 255, 257, 260–275, 277–280, and Figs 277.1 and 278.1;
Mr M.T. Liversedge for Figs 255.2 and XXXIII.1;
Ms P Chesselet for Figs 302.2, 303.2

Mrs H J Smithers drew the black spoor drawings, as well as the original maps on which much of the distribution data was plotted.

Finally I would like to acknowledge the help and advice received from our experienced Cape & Transvaal Printers and particularly the personal interest shown in this project by Mr Len Clout, their Managing Director. What a pleasure it has been to work with such an experienced firm!

**This is an ongoing, non profit-making project of the University of Pretoria. To obtain perfection in future editions, the help of all mammalogists is required to improve the text and add new information. Please send comments and reprints to:**

The Director
Mammal Research Institute
University of Pretoria
0002 Pretoria
Republic of South Africa

# Explanatory notes

## The Southern African Subregion (Map i)

The Southern African Subregion is defined, for purposes of this book, as the mainland region of the African Continent south of the Cunene/Zambezi rivers and its coastal waters, including those of the Prince Edward Islands. It includes, therefore, within the mainland area the whole of Namibia and the Caprivi Strip, Botswana, Zimbabwe, that part of Mozambique which lies south of the Zambezi River, the Republic of South Africa, and the self-governing states that lie within its borders.

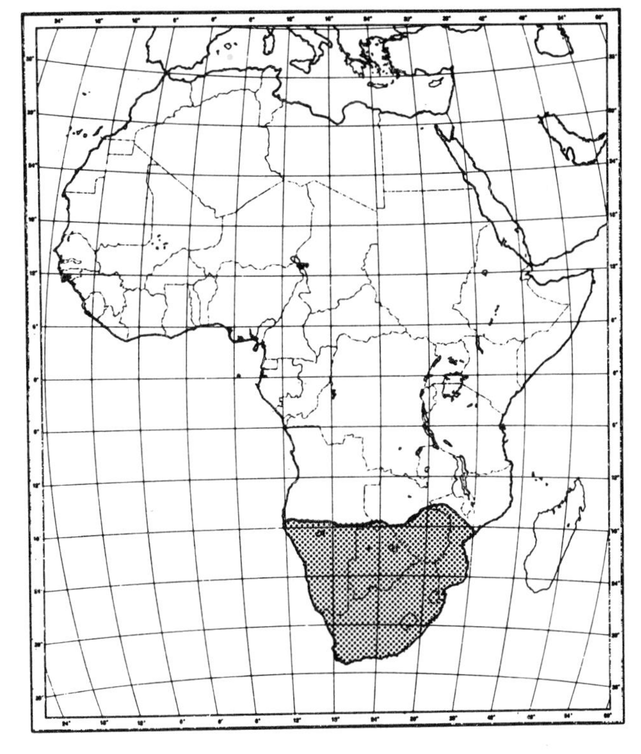

Map i
The mainland sector of the Southern African Subregion

The Prince Edward Islands (Map ii), annexed by the Republic of South Africa in 1947, consist of two islands, Marion and Prince Edward, the former named after the captain of the French ship *Mascarin*, Captain Nicolas Marion Dufresne, who visited the islands in January 1772; the latter after the fourth son of King George III of Great Britain, Prince Edward Augustus (van Zinderen Bakker sr, 1971). The position of Marion Island, which has an area of 290 km$^2$, is 46°52′3″, 37°51′32″E and that of Prince Edward Island, which is smaller and lies 22 km NNE of Marion, 46°38′00″, 37°59′35″E (Langenegger & Verwoerd, 1971).

While Marion Island has a terrestrial mammalian fauna of two introduced species, the house mouse, *Mus musculus*, and the feral domestic cat, *Felis catus*, Prince Edward Island is devoid of terrestrial mammals. Both islands, however, have a rich fauna of marine mammals in their coastal waters and fur seals and elephant seals visit their beaches to moult and breed.

The map (Map ii) showing the locating of the Prince Edward Islands also shows the summer and winter limits of the pack ice and the Antarctic Convergence. Oceanographical research has shown the existence of a layer of cold, poorly saline surface water some 100–250 m deep surrounding the Antarctic Continent. At its northern boundary this cold water sinks below the warmer sub-Antarctic water and the band where the two converge is known as the Antarctic Convergence. The convergence zone may displace from 80 160 km either way, the difference in temperature on either side varying between about 0,8 °C–5,2 °C depending on the location and season. A 360° map of Antarctica is provided at the end of the section on Cetacea, the whales and dolphins (See Species No. 243).

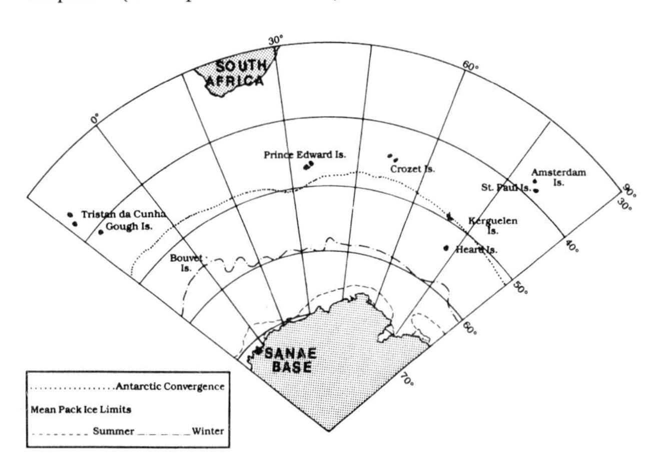


Map ii
The southern tip of the African Continent and a sector of Antarctica to show the location of the Prince Edward Islands, the South African National Antarctic Expedition (SANAE) base, the location of the Antarctic Convergence, and the mean summer and winter limits of the pack ice.

## Changes in place names

The newest names applied to places have been applied in the text as far as possible.

## The numbering system

Numbering of the Families and species:
Each of the 47 Families is given a roman number (I-XLVII), those figures relating to Family characteristics having the same roman number:
e.g. XVI. Family Bathyergidae: Fig. XVI.I. . .Fig. XVI.2. . .*etc.*

Each of the 338 species is given an arabic number (1–338), those figures relating to a particular species having the same arabic number:
e.g. 134 *Hystrix africaeaustralis*: Fig. 134.1. . .Fig. 134.2 . . .*etc.*

In the first edition each species was given a number which appeared immediately above the scientific name. As nine species new to the Subregion list have been added, in order not to disturb this numbering system, when a new species is added it is given the same number as its nearest relative, with the addition of the Suffix A. For example, *Crocidura occidentalis* (Pucheran, 1855) which is now being added is given the number 12A and follows immediately on 12 *Crocidura flavescens; C. occidentalis* at one time was thought to be a subspecies of *C. flavescens*, but is now accorded full specific rank.

Conversely it is necessary to withdraw from the list species listed in the first edition. The yellow baboon, *Papio cynocephalus*, was included in the first edition as it was thought erroneously that its distribution extended south of the Zambezi River and therefore into the Subregion. In such cases the number and heading are retained, the heading is shown as WITHDRAWN, and a brief explanation is given as to why this has been necessary.

## Colloquial names

Colloquial names have come to be applied as a convenient means of the identification of species. Unlike the scientific name they are not precise for, even within a restricted area such as the Subregion, different names come into general use in different areas for the same species and eventually become deeply entrenched in the language. While it is utopian to expect that one can dictate a standardisation of colloquial names that will find general acceptance, the desirability of standardisation is obvious. In this regard we have sought the advice of the English Academy of South Africa. They advised the use of the Afrikaans suffix where the prefix is Afrikaans; for example springbok, steenbok etc. This protocol has been followed throughout. In addition, Swanepoel, Smithers & Rautenbach (1980), by the publication of a list of colloquial names in English and Afrikaans, attempted a standardisation and this list, with modifications, has been used as a guideline in this edition. These modifications arise from new knowledge which recently has come to hand. Species of the genus *Pronolagus* and *Bunolagus*, for example, have long been referred to as "hares", but studies by Robinson (1981) show clearly that they are rabbits, not hares. There has long been confusion between the wild cat, *Felis lybica*, and the black-footed cat, *Felis nigripes*, because both species have black feet. To try and avoid this it is suggested that the colloquial name of *F. nigripes* be changed to the small spotted cat which is aptly descriptive of this, our smallest felid.

There is a school of thought which believes that colloquial names should be descriptive and, while subscribing in general to this view, the names of individuals who have become synonymous with particular species have been retained in this edition. Examples of this include Smith's red rock rabbit for *Pronolagus rupestris*, named after Sir Andrew Smith who wrote the *Illustrations of the Zoology of South Africa* (1838–1849); Selous' mongoose, *Paracynictis selousi*, after the famous hunter, naturalist and collector, F.C. Selous; Rudd's mouse, *Uranomys ruddi*, after C.D. Rudd of De Beers Consolidated Mines who financed a number of expeditions to the eastern parts of the Subregion.

## Taxonomic notes

The publication of the *Classification of Southern African Mammals* by Meester, Rautenbach, Dippenaar & Baker (1986) has provided the most comprehensive and up-to-date taxonomic treatment of African mammals available. The treatment afforded them in the present edition is based largely on the information given in this book and, where there is a departure from this treatment, due reference is made to the authorities responsible for the changes. This edition makes no pretence at being a taxonomic treatise and the reader is referred in all instances to Meester *et al.* (1986) and other taxonomic papers cited for further clarification.

At the same time, rapid progress using modern technology has highlighted the necessity for covering new methods of analysis. Within recent years the status and relationships of genera and species have been resolved using new methods. Traditional criteria such as morphometric analysis and external characters are still used, but are gradually being replaced. Examples of the use of these new techniques can be seen in the treatment of the Lagomorpha in the first edition of this work which is based on the work of Robinson (1981) who applied comparative karyology, sperm morphology, electrophoretic analysis of blood proteins and red blood cell enzymes to establish the status and relationships of the species included in this Order, or in the work of Gordon (1984) on the cytogenetics of the *Praomys (Mastomys) natalensis* species complex. The murids and other Families are currently the subject of intense genetic investigation and while only briefly considered here, will be dealt with in greater depth in future editions of this book.

The diploid chromosome number of the species is provided, where available, irrespective of whether the investigation of this has been carried out with or without the techniques of G-banding, C-banding or silver nitrate staining of somatic chromosomes. Where these techniques have not been employed the data are of limited value in phylogenetic assessments, as their absence precludes unequivocable identification of the shared derived chromosomal traits and grossly underestimates the degree of chromosomal divergence among species (Robinson, Skinner & Haim, 1986; Wenhold & Robinson, 1987). Readers are referred to the original papers which will show whether G-banding and other techniques have been applied and in which a fuller assessment of the situation is given. As an addition to the information provided in the first edition, where there have been changes in the acceptance of subspecies, a list is provided of those listed in Meester *et al.* (1986), together with a broad indication of their limits of distribution.

## Distribution

As many of the species which occur in the Subregion occur in other parts of Africa as well, the text, therefore, lists the countries, or parts of them outside the Subregion, in which the various species are found. The maps show the broad limits to the best of our knowledge within which they occur.

For those who would like more detailed information, a list is provided at the end of this section of the papers from which the information has been compiled, under the names of the countries concerned, and giving the names of the authors and the dates of publication of their papers. Reference to the Bibliography will give the detailed reference as to where these papers are to be found. This list is not comprehensive and may no longer be relevant, many species' distributions being altered or destroyed or becoming locally extinct.

With the growing appreciation of wildlife as a natural resource much has been done by International and National Organisations to ensure the survival of species by translocating them from areas where their future is insecure to National Parks and Reserves and latterly to private game farms. Surplus stock has been made available for introduction to suitable terrain or for reintroduction to areas where they formerly occurred but in which they no longer exist. Where species are considered to be endangered mention is made of translocations. It will be necessary to prepare new maps for future editions.

Some mammals are found only where there is suitable habitat. This cannot be represented adequately on small scale maps and only the general limits within which they occur can be given. The text qualifies the distribution in these cases. The section dealing with **Habitat** indicating the type of habitat in which they may be expected to be found.

While there is a greater tendency for the distributional range of species to shrink, for reasons already given, some, for example the bat-eared fox, *Otocyon megalotis*, have extended their range within recent years, colonising areas beyond their former limits of occurrence. Where there are only a few records of a species, the individual records only are plotted on the maps. It is unwise, until pan African revisions are undertaken, to try and give their distribution other than on a Subregion basis. In such cases the caption to the maps indicates that their distribution is on a Subregion basis only.

In order to avoid the repetitive use of the name the Republic of South Africa, for convenience the four provinces of the country, the Transvaal, Orange Free State, Natal and Cape are considered as major units of the same status as surrounding countries.

The location of the countries mentioned in the text is given on Map iii. Map iv shows the location of the four provinces of the Republic of South Africa and the self-governing states lying within its borders.

The location of major National Parks and Game Reserves in the Subregion is illustrated in map v.

**Countries, authors and publication dates**

**Africa**

Allen (1939), Ellerman, Morrison-Scott & Hayman (1953), Dekeyser (1955), Dorst & Dandelot (1970).

**Angola**

Hill & Carter (1941), Hayman (1963), da Silva (1970), Cabral (1989a).

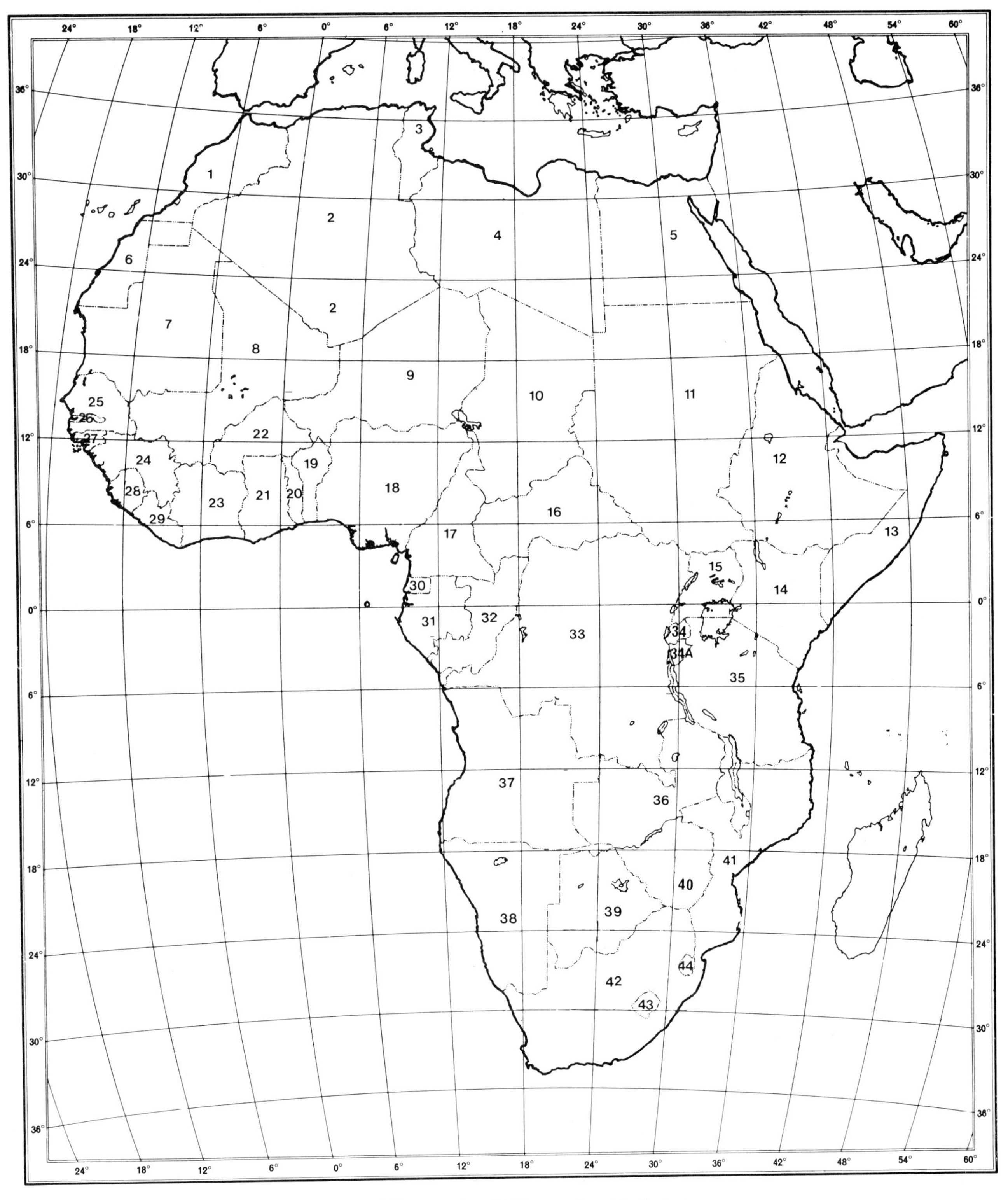


Map iii. The countries of Africa mentioned in the text

1. Morocco
2. Algeria
3. Tunisia
4. Libya
5. Egypt
6. Western Sahara
7. Mauritania
8. Mali
9. Niger
10. Chad
11. Sudan
12. Ethiopia
13. Somalia
14. Kenya
15. Uganda
16. Central African Republic
17. Cameroun
18. Nigeria
19. Benin
20. Togo
21. Ghana
22. Burkina Faso
23. Ivory Coast
24. Guinea
25. Senegal
26. Gambia
27. Guinea Bissau
28. Sierra Leone
29. Liberia
30. Equatorial Guinea
31. Gabon
32. Congo Republic
33. Zaire
34. Rwanda
34A. Burundi
35. Tanzania
36. Zambia
37. Angola
38. Namibia
39. Botswana
40. Zimbabwe
41. Mozambique
42. Republic of South Africa
43. Lesotho
44. Swaziland

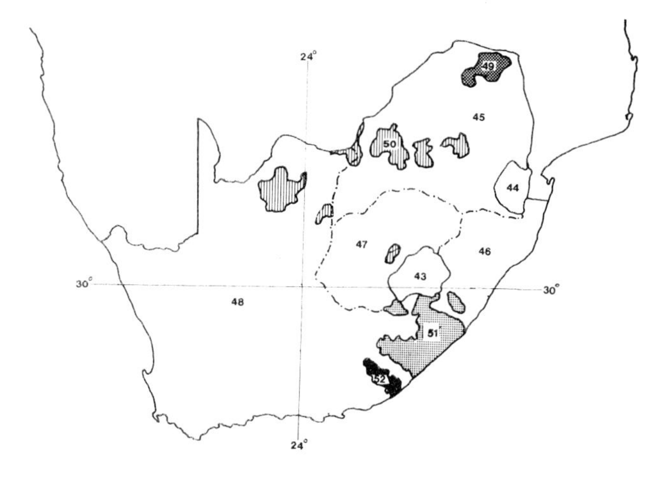


Map iv
The Republic of South Africa showing its four Provinces and the self-governing states lying within its borders:

43. Lesotho
44. Swaziland
45. Transvaal (Province)
46. Natal (Province)
47. Orange Free State (Province)
48. Cape (Province)
49. Venda
50. Bophuthatswana
51. Transkei
52. Ciskei

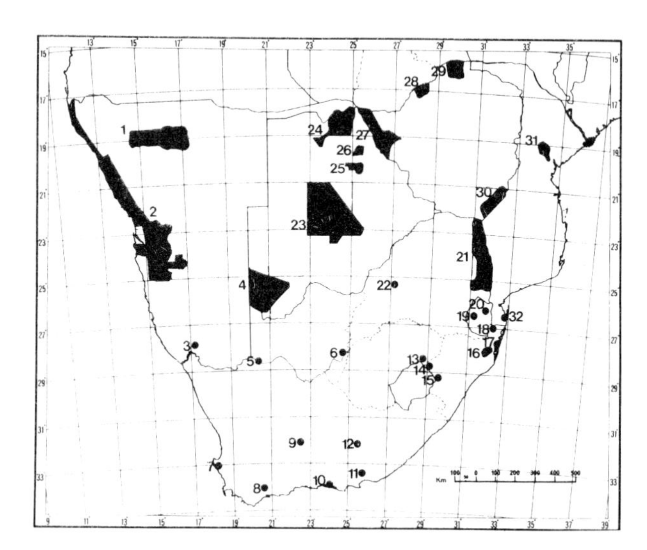


Map v
Location of the major National Parks and Game Reserves in the Subregion.

1. Etosha National Park
2. Skeleton Coast National Park/ Namib-Naukluft Park
3. Fish River Canyon Park
4. Kalahari Gemsbok National Park/Gemsbok National Park
5. Augrabies Falls National Park
6. Vaalbos National Park
7. West Coast National Park
8. Bontebok National Park
9. Karoo National Park
10. Tsitsikamma Coastal and Tsitsikamma Forest National Parks
11. Addo Elephant National Park
12. Mountain Zebra National Park
13. Golden Gate Highlands National Park
14. Royal Natal National Park
15. Giants Castle Game Reserve
16. Hluhluwe/Umfolozi Game Reserves
17. Mkuzi/Sodwana Complex
18. Ndumu Game Reserve
19. Mlilwane National Park
20. Hlane National Park
21. Kruger National Park
22. Pilanesberg National Park
23. Central Kalahari/Khutse Game Reserves
24. Chobe/Moremi National Parks
25. Makgadikgadi Pans Game Reserve
26. Nxai Pan National Park
27. Hwange/Matetsi/ Zambezi National Parks and Safari Area
28. Matusadona National Park
29. Mana Pools National Park
30. Gona-re-zhou National Park
31. Gorongosa National Park
32. Maputo Elephant Reserve

**Botswana**

Smithers (1971).

**Burundi**

Hayman, Misonne & Verheyen (1966).

**Cameroun**

Eisentraut (1942), Aellen (1952), Dekeyser (1955), Perret & Aellen (1956), Hill (1968).

**Central African Republic**

Bourgoin (1955), Barber, Buchanan & Galbreath (1980).

**Congo Republic**

Malbrant & MacLatchy (1949), Aellen & Brosset, 1968.

**East Africa**

Corbet & Neal (1965), Kingdon (1971, 1974, 1977, 1979, 1982).

**Egypt**

Hoogstraal, Wassif & Kaiser (1957), Happold (1967), Harrison (1968).

**Ethiopia**

Corbet & Yalden (1972), Largen, Kock & Yalden (1974), Yalden, Largen & Kock (1976, 1977, 1980, 1984, 1986).

**Bioko Island**

Eisentrout (1964).

**Gabon**

Brosset (1966).

**Gambia**

Sclater & Thomas (1899), Clarke (1953).

**Ghana**

Cansdale (1948), Grubb (1971).

**Guinea**

Eisentrout & Knorr (1957), Prunier (1946).

**Guinea Bissau**

Monard (1938, 1939, 1940, 1943).

**Guinea, Equatorial**

Basilio (1952), Jones (1971), Jones (1972).

**Ivory Coast**

Edmond-Blanc (1954).

**Kenya**

Hollister (1918), Stewart & Stewart (1963), Williams (1967).

**Liberia**

Allen & Coolidge (1930), Kuhn (1965).

**Libya**

Hufnagl (1972).

**Madagascar**

Dorst (1953).

**Malawi**

Thomas (1898), Sweeney (1959), Hanney (1965), Hayes (1978).

**Morocco**

Cabrera (1932), Panouse (1957).

**Mozambique**

Peters (1852), Dalquest (1965), Smithers & Tello (1976).

**Niger**

Poché (1975).

**Nigeria**

Rosevear (1953), Happold (1989).

**Republic of South Africa**

Sparrman (1786), Holub (1881), Bryden (1893), Roberts (1951), du Plessis (1969), Davis (1974). **Cape Province:** Anderson (1888), Bryden (1893), Bigalke (1955), Rautenbach & Nel (1978), Stuart & Lloyd (1979), Herselman (1980), Skead (1980), Stuart (1980), Stuart, Lloyd & Herselman (1980), Stuart (1981). **Natal:** Cowles (1936), Vincent (1962), Dixon (1966), Laycock (1973), Mentis (1974), Pringle (1977),

Rowe-Rowe (1978a), Scotcher (1978). **Orange Free State:** Lynch (1975). **Transvaal:** Rautenbach (1978).

**Rwanda**

Hayman, Misonne & Verheyen (1966).

**Sahara**

Pocock (1964).

**Sahara, Western**

Valverde (1957).

**Sierra Leone**

Haywood (1933), Jones (1966).

**Somalia**

Azzaroli & Simonetta (1966), Funaioli & Simonetta (1966), Funaioli & Lanza (1968).

**Namibia**

Shortridge (1934), Joubert & Mostert (1975).

**Sudan**

Hinton & Kinshaw (1920), Setzer (1956), Kock (1969), Koopman (1975).

**Tanzania**

Swynnerton & Hayman (1950).

**Chad**

Felix (1953), Vielliard (1974).

**Uganda**

Watson (1950), Bere (1962).

**Burkina Faso**

Koopman (1978).

**West Africa**

Cansdale (1948), Rosevear (1953), Dekeyser (1955), Rosevear (1965), Rosevear (1969).

**Zaire**

Frechkop (1944), Schouteden (1945), Hayman (1954), Koopman 1965).

**Zambia**

Ansell (1960), Hanks (1969), Ansell (1978).

**Zimbabwe**

Harrison (1959), Harrison (1960), Fenton (1975), Smithers & Wilson (1975), Wilson (1975).

## The Biotic Zones of the Subregion (Map vi)

A number of attempts have been made to divide the southern parts of Africa into biotic zones on the basis of major vegetation types (Chapin, 1932; Moreau, 1952; Keay, 1959; Davis, 1962; Meester, 1965). Rautenbach (1978) tested mathematically the validity of the generally accepted Southern African Biotic Zones based on the mammalian faunal resemblances and recognised six to be viable biogeographic entities with full zonal status (Map vi). Rautenbach's (1978) zones and the nomenclature of these are used in the text, with the limits of each shown on the map, but with a slight extension northeastwards of the South West Arid Zone to encompass the Makgadikgadi Pan, Botswana. In the caption to the map Davis' (1962) zonation is given to show how it corresponds to that of Rautenbach (1978). In addition, as distribution is dealt with on a Continental basis, Rosevear's (1953) zonation as it applies to Central and West Africa is given and the map follows these limits.

Rautenbach's (1978) six biotic zones of the Subregion are as follows:

### Southern Savanna Woodland (F)

This zone covers the northern and northeastern parts of the Subregion, with a narrow extension coastally in the east through Natal and Transkei as far as Port Elizabeth, Cape Province, with a marginal extension northwestwards in this sector.

North of the Subregion this zone forms a continuum, through western Tanzania, Kenya and Uganda, with the Northern Savannas (E) which extend westward through West Africa.

In the Subregion the mean annual rainfall within the Zone is variable, tending to be lower westwards than eastwards, in the former as low as 375 mm, but throughout the Zone usually about 500 mm, increasing eastwards to about 900 mm.

At lower altitudes the vegetation consists of an open woodland association of mopane, *Colophospermum mopane;* in the warmer areas with baobabs, *Adansonia digitata*, a sparse grass cover and little underbush. At higher altitudes, the drier western areas carry an open woodland on scrub *Acacia* association and in the eastern areas an open woodland association of *Brachystegia/Julbernardia*. West of this across the northern parts of the Subregion this association includes the false mopane, *Guibourtia* spp, in increasing proportion. This Zone supports a good grass cover, the woodland forming, in parts, a mozaic with grassland and is abundantly interspersed with grassy vleis.

### Southern Savanna Grassland (F1)

Rautenbach (1978) showed that this Zone was worthy of separation from the Southern Savanna Woodland Zone of which it had been part formerly. This zone is one of mixed grassland, the dominant species being red grass, *Themeda triandra*, which has been replaced in parts due to burning and over-utilisation, by inferior and hardier species. Bush and tree growth is confined largely to riverine areas or to rocky ridges. The mean annual rainfall exceeds 500 mm, with an average annual temperature of about 18 °C.

### South West Cape (J)

This Zone, also known as the Cape Macchia or *fynbos* zone, extends from just north of Clanwilliam broadly following the coastline eastwards to about Port Elizabeth, and is characterised by having a cool mediterranean type of climate, with relatively humid winters and hot, dry summers. Often this area is referred to as being a winter rainfall area, but winter rains are only experienced by the extreme southwestern tip of the continent west of Cape Agulhas. Swellendam and Mossel Bay have rainfall maxima in spring and autumn and Port Elizabeth has rain throughout the year. A true summer maximum is first evident eastwards at East London (Fuggle & Ashton, 1979). Precipitation which is related to the topography is in excess of a mean of 200 mm per annum, in parts rising to over 3 000 mm (e.g. Dwarsberg, Stellenbosch 3 300 mm). The area has a unique and particularly rich flora consisting of 6 000 species of plants. Today the association is fragmented by development and only about 40% of the original vegetational area remains (Taylor, 1978).

### South West Arid (H)

This Zone covers the greater part of central and western Botswana and Namibia, and extends into the southwestern parts of Angola east of the coastal desert. Southward it covers parts of the western Orange Free State and most of the Cape Province west of about 26 °E, and extends southward to the limits of the South West Cape Zone and in parts west to the limit of the Namib Desert Zone, which was included in it at one time.

The mean annual rainfall in the northern part of this Zone is from about 200 mm to 500 mm. A large part of the northern area has a covering of Kalahari sand, with a vegetational cover of *Acacia* woodland or low scrub and patches of camelthorn trees, *A. erioloba*, and a good grass cover. In the south the area is one of Karoo scrub or succulent Karoo vegetation, the former in areas with a mean annual rainfall of about 250 mm–375 mm, the latter in lower rainfall areas of under 250 mm.

### Namib Desert (I)

This Zone was first recognised as a separate unit by Meester (1965). It extends as a narrow coastal strip into southwestern Angola as far north as about 12 °S and southward through Namibia to the Orange River which forms the border with

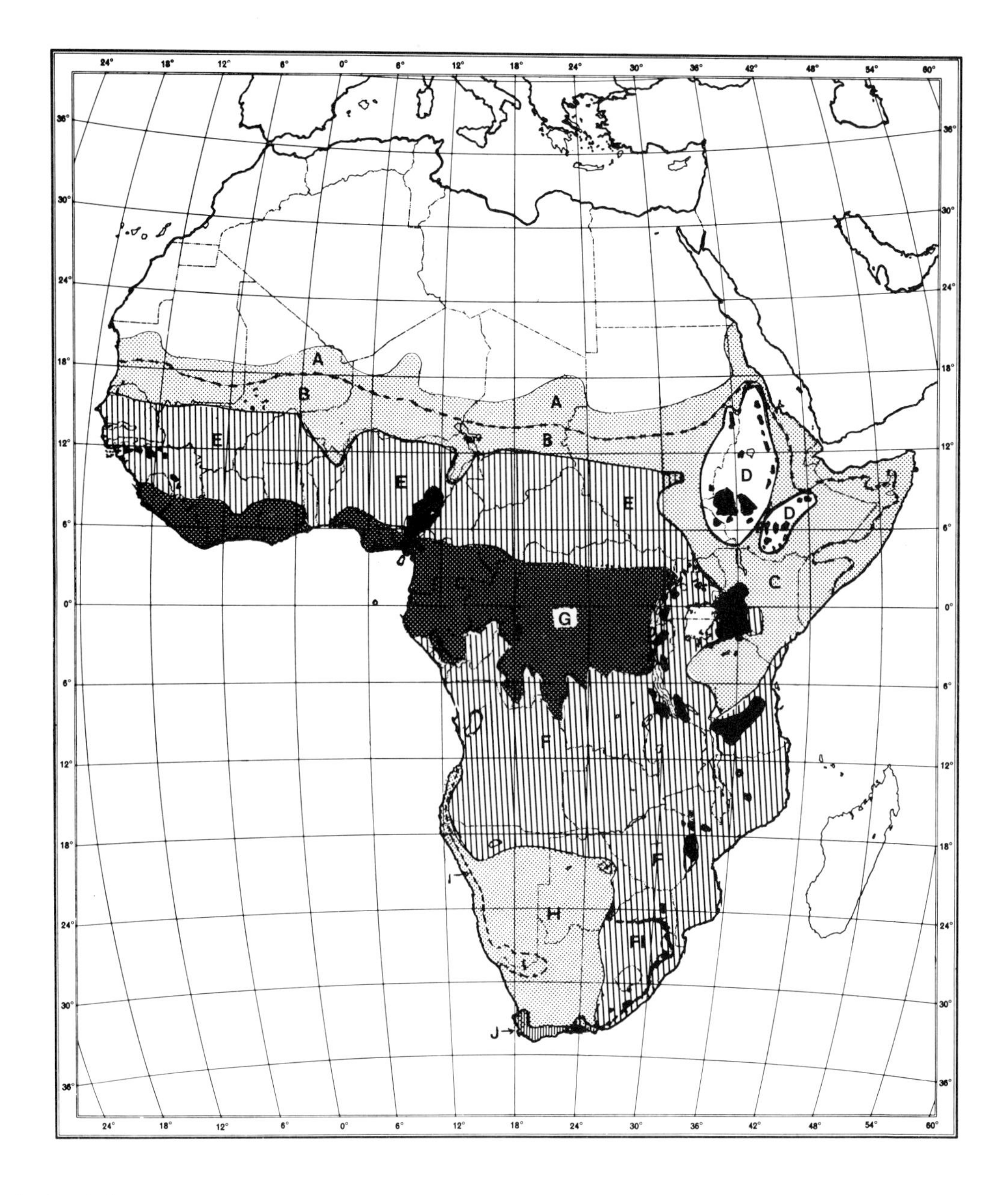


**Key to the Symbols**

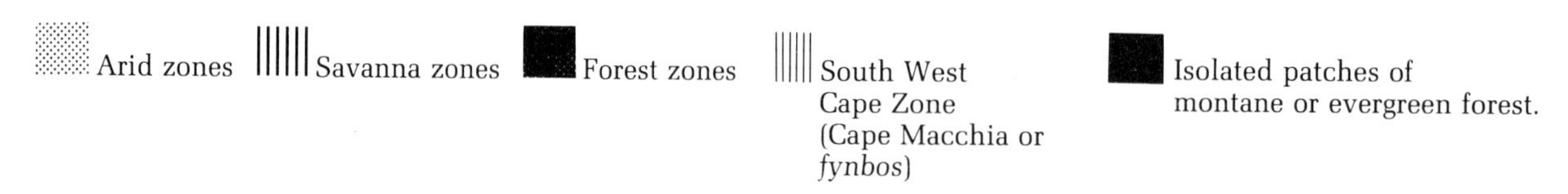


**Map vi**

The main biotic zones of Africa south of the Sahara (after Chapin, 1932; Moreau, 1952; Rosevear, 1953; Keay, 1959; Davis, 1962 and Rautenbach, 1978).

**Nomenclature:**

| | Rautenbach (1978) | Davis (1962) | Rosevear (1953) for West and Central Africa |
|---|---|---|---|
| | **Zones** | **Zones** | **Zones** |
| A+B | — | Sudanese Arid | — |
| A | — | — | Sahelian |
| B | — | — | Sudan |
| C | — | Somali Arid | — |
| D | — | Ethiopian Highlands | — |
| E | — | Northern Savanna | Guinea Savanna |
| F | Southern Savanna Woodland | Southern Savanna | — |
| F1 | Southern Savanna Grassland | | |
| G | Forest | Lowland Forest | High Forest |
| H | South West Arid | South West Arid | — |
| I | Namib Desert | — | — |
| J | South West Cape | South West Cape (Cape Macchia or *fynbos*) | — |

the Cape Province. It covers both banks of the Orange River as far inland as about Upington. The mean annual rainfall is less than 125 mm, and in the coastal areas much lower than this. The area supports a sparse vegetation predominantly supported by moisture from advective fog caused by the action of the cold waters of the Benguela Current which sweeps northwards up the coast (Louw & Seely, 1982).

**Forest** (solid black on map)

This zone is not a continuum but consists of scattered, relatively small areas of forest in the eastern parts of the Subregion. It includes the temperate evergreen forest at Knysna, which lies in an area with a mean annual rainfall of between 760 mm and 1 016 mm. This forest has a closed canopy at an average height of about 20 m, with yellowwood, *Podocarpus* sp; stinkwood, *Ocotea* sp, and cedar trees, *Widdringtonia* sp. Some yellowwoods attain a height of nearly 40 m. The forest has a dense underbush in parts, with abundant ferns.

Between the eastern parts of the Cape Province and the highland areas of eastern Zimbabwe there are scattered, fairly small areas of montane and evergreen forest, the former occurring at high altitudes where the temperature is low and the mean annual rainfall over 1 000 mm.

**The Biotic Zones of West and Central Africa**

Rosevear (1953) defined the biotic zones found in West and Central Africa and provided a series of photographs of each. His nomenclature is used in the sections dealing with the distribution of species in these regions.

## Endangered, Vulnerable and Rare Mammals

The publication of Red Data Books for the Republic of South Africa followed a decision by the International Union for the Conservation of Nature and Natural Resources (IUCN) taken in the early 1960's. This was done through the Foundation for Research Development (FRD), the most recent edition being that by Smithers (1986) which covers only the terrestrial mammals. On the basis of the IUCN's definitions, Smithers (1986) showed that apart from the two species that had become extinct within historical times, the quagga and the blue antelope, and Lichtenstein's hartebeest (extinct in the Republic of South Africa), three species are listed as **Endangered:** the riverine rabbit, the wild dog and the roan antelope. A further 14 species are listed as **Vulnerable** and 25 species as **Rare.**. So little is known about 45 species that it is impossible at this juncture to list them as anything but **Indeterminate.** This publication reflects the outstanding efforts by organisations such as the National Parks Board of S.A., Provincial Conservation authorities, and the National Zoological Gardens of S.A., among others, that have allowed the removal of species such as the Cape mountain zebra and the hook-lipped rhinoceros from the **Endangered** category, and, for example, the removal from the list altogether of the cheetah. Mention is made in the text of species listed in the higher categories of **Endangered, Vulnerable** and **Rare**; it is important to interpret these in terms of the definitions as laid down by the IUCN.

## Measurements and Abbreviations

**Position of mammae** (Fig. i)

The position of the mammae is recorded in accordance with their position in relation to the regions of the under surface of the body and may be expressed, in the case of the individual illustrated, as P2 A2 I2 = 12 or simply 2–2–2 = 12, which indicates 2 pairs pectoral, 2 pairs abdominal, 2 pairs inguinal = total 12. Where the mammae are not paired the total number on each side may be recorded as follows: L9, R8 = 17, indicating nine on the left side of the body, eight on the right.

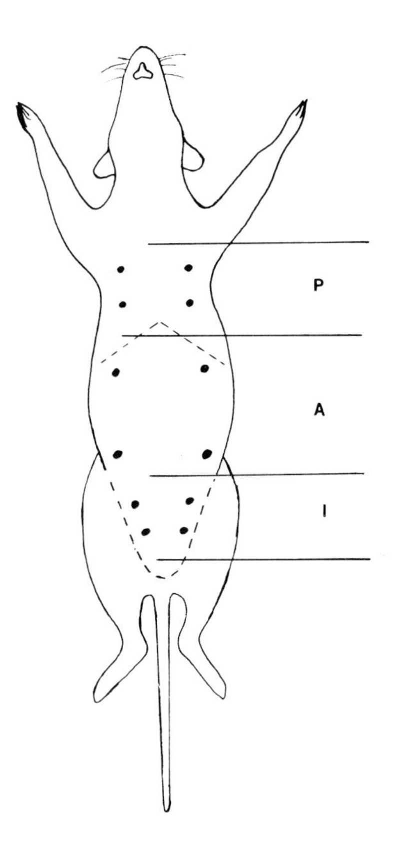


Fig. i. Position of the mammae:
P = pectoral region.
A = abdominal region.
I = inguinal region.
This individual would have a mammary formula of 2P 2A 21 = 12, which indicates two pairs in each region.

**Body measurements**

The tables of measurements and mass given for the species reflect the data obtained from specimens measured in the flesh. It is internationally accepted that mammal measurements are expressed in millimetres (mm). Where in the text, as opposed to the tables, it is desirable to indicate the size, metres (m) are used for large specimens.

Some measurements can be taken more accurately than others. Ansell (1965a) suggested certain standards which he felt worthy of attainment. In publishing measurements it is convenient to use abbreviations and these and the methods used in obtaining the measurements are set out in the following list. Where there is a deviation from these methods this is stated in the text.

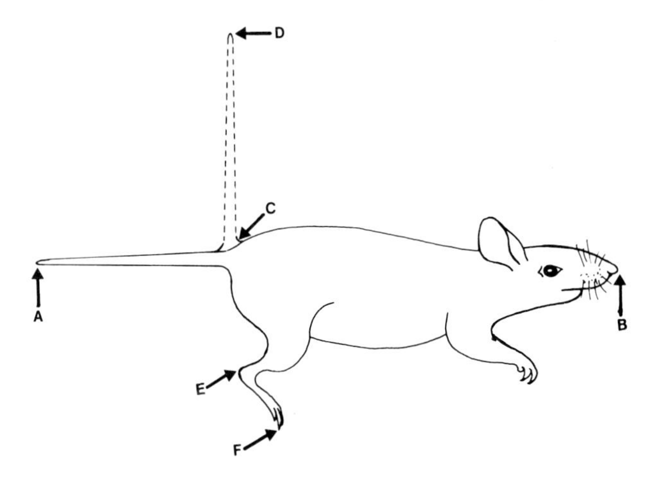


Fig.ii. Measurements of a mammal:
A–B = TL, the total length.
B–C = HB, the length of the head and body.
C–D = T, the length of the tail.
E–F = HF c/u, the length of the hind foot (*cum unguis*).

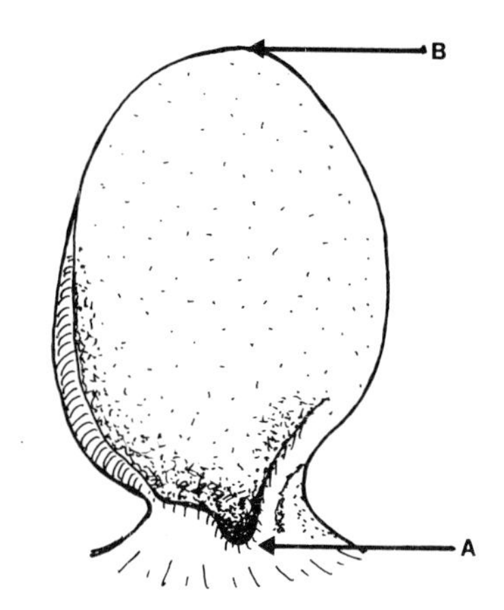


Fig.iii. Measurements of a mammal:
A–B = E, the length of the ear.

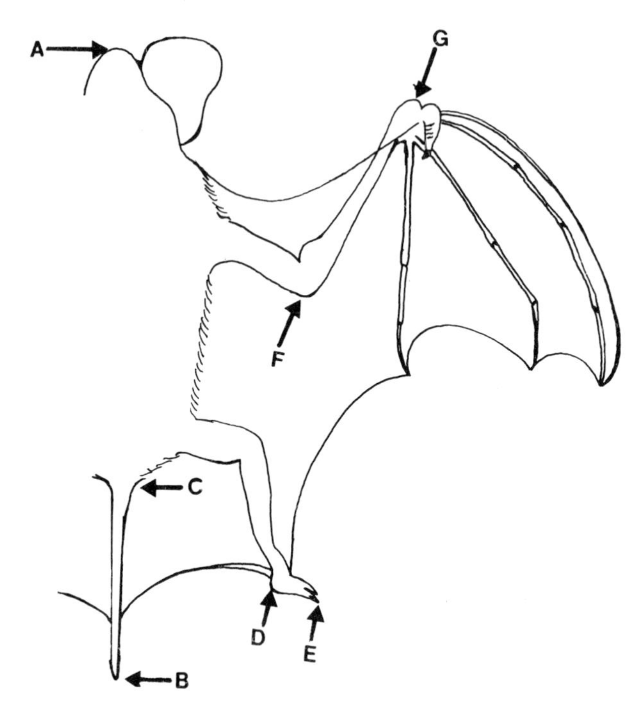


Fig. iv. Measurements of a bat:
A–B = TL, the total length.
A–C = HB, the length of the head and body.
B–C = T, the length of the tail.
D–E = HF c/u, the length of the hind foot (*cum unguis*).
F–G = F/a, the length of the forearm.

TL — The total length of the specimen, laid out on its side in a natural position, the measurement taken as between pegs from the tip of the nose to the end of the vertebrae of the tail. In small specimens such as rodents, shrews *etc.* pins are inserted in soft board or celotex at the positions indicated. This measurement is subject to some individual variation, but is useful in giving a general idea of the size of the specimen (Fig. (ii): A–B).

HB — The length of the head and body is measured from the tip of the snout to the base of the tail. It can also be derived by subtraction of T from TL (Fig. (ii): B–C).

T — The length of the tail, held at an angle to the line of the body, is measured from the base of the tail to the end of the vertebrae of the tail. (Fig. (ii): C–D).

T M/A — Because of the configuration of the tail, in some species such as pangolin, otters, porcupine and aardvark, it is impossible to ascertain the base of the tail. The measurement is taken from the centre of the anus to the end of the vertebrae of the tail and the result expressed as "Tail from mid-anus" or "T M/A".

Hf — The length of the hind foot is measured from the heel to the:
(1) end of the longest claw and then expressed as Hf/cu (*cum unguis*). (Fig. (ii): E-F).
(2) end of the longest digit or to the base of the claw or hoof and then expressed as Hf s/u (*sine unguis*).

E — The length of the ear is measured from the notch of the ear to the tip. (Fig. (iii): A–B).

Mass — The mass is recorded in grams (g) for the smaller species, kilograms (kg) for the larger.

F/a — This is recorded only in bats and its length is a valuable character in the identification of some species. It is the total length of the radius and ulna bones in the wing and may be taken either in the flesh or in the drier specimen. (Fig. (iv): F–G).

$\bar{x}$ — This is the average measurement or mass based on the sample size n.

n — The sample size from which the average measurement or mass is calculated.

Range — The minimum and maximum measurements or mass within the sample examined.

Sh.ht — The height at the shoulder, measured as the specimen lies on its side, from the sole of the hoof or paw to the top of the shoulder, or in life while standing in a natural position.

Ht hq. — The height at the hindquarters, measured as for the shoulder height.

**Skull measurements**

TL skull The greatest length of the skull.
CB skull The length from the back of the occipital condyles to the bases of the incisor teeth where they emerge from the maxillary bone (Figs XXXII.2 & 3).
Cl skull The length from the back of the occipital condyle to the front face of the upper first incisor tooth.

**Dentition**

Symbols are used to denote the category of the teeth referred to: I incisor; C canine; P premolar and M molar, and in the lower case i, c, p and m for deciduous teeth. Reference to an individual tooth is made by referring to its position by number reckoned from front to back and whether it lies in the upper or lower jaw by placing its number above or below a line. For example $P^4$ refers to the fourth premolar tooth in the upper jaw, $P_4$ the same tooth in the lower jaw.

The term cheekteeth refers to all the teeth lying posterior to the canine, when it is undesirable to differentiate between the premolars and molars.

The number of teeth possessed by a mammal is very variable and is expressed by a formula, which in the case of a black-backed jackal, *Canis mesomelas*, is:

$I\frac{3}{3}\ C\frac{1}{1}\ P\frac{4}{4}\ M\frac{2}{3} = 42$

This indicates that this species has three incisor teeth in each half of the upper and lower jaws and two molar teeth in each half of the upper jaw and three in each half of the lower jaw. The total number of teeth is twice that in each jaw half.

**The vertebral formula in Cetacea** (Fig. v)

The bones of Cetacea are different in structure to those of terrestrial mammals. Covered on the outside with a compact

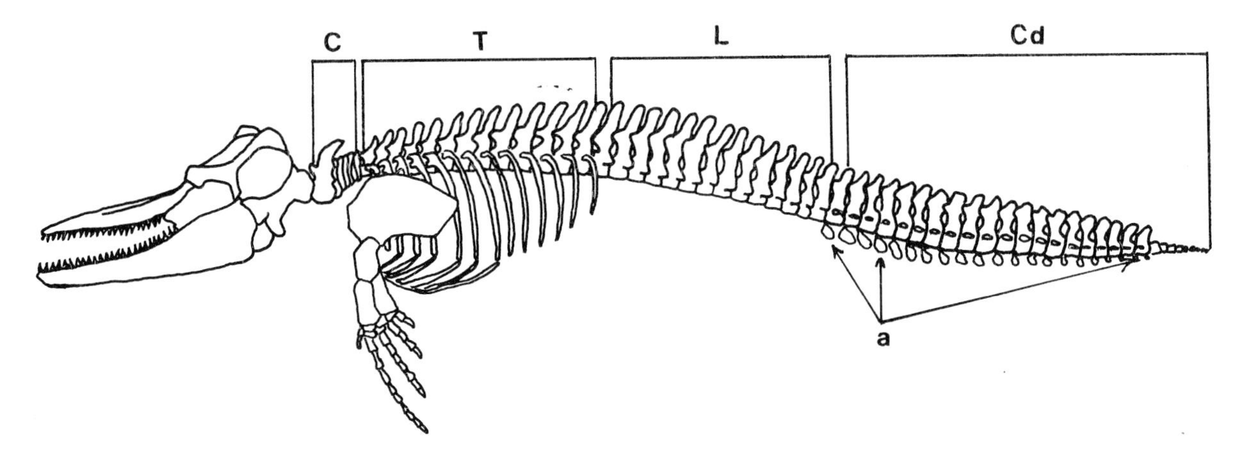


Fig. v. Skeleton of an odontocete cetacean to show the four regions of the vertebral column used in arriving at the vertebral formula (after Watson, 1981)).
C = cervical vertebrae.
L = lumbar vertebrae.
T = thoracic vertebrae.
Cd = caudal vertebrae.
a = chevron bones.

bony covering, they are honeycombed inside, the interstices in life filled with fatty marrow. The total number of bones in the vertebral column varies throughout the Order, for example, the pygmy right whale, *Caperea marginata*, has 41, the melon-headed whale, *Pepenocephala electra*, 82.

Like terrestrial mammals all Cetacea have seven neck bones or cervical vertebrae. In species such as the fin whale, *Balaenoptera physalus*, all these bones are separate, while in others varying numbers are fused together. In the killer whale, *Orcinus orca*, for example, three or four of the bones are fused together, in the long-finned pilot whale, *Globicephala melaena*, six are fused together, and in the southern right whale, *Balaena glacialis*, all seven are fused into one. This factor has a direct bearing on the mobility of the head of the individual species. Those with the greatest number of free cervical vertebrae have the most mobile heads, the movement, however, generally being restricted to an up and down movement.

The number of bones in the other parts of the vertebral column varies and can be expressed as a formula—the vertebral formula—the various regions of the vertebral column shown as letters and the number of bones in each as numbers:

C cervical vertebrae or neck bones.

T thoracic vertebrae. These are bones in the vertebral column on which the rib bones articulate. The southern bottlenosed whale, *Hyperoodon planifrons*, has nine thoracic vertebrae (T9) whereas the blue whale, *Balaenoptera musculus*, has 15 (T15).

L lumbar vertebrae. In the Cetacea the lumbar or waist region is enlarged compared with this region in terrestrial mammals. This is necessary to allow for an expanded region for the attachment of the muscles which actuate the tail, the principal swimming organ. The number of bones varies. In fast swimming species they may have up to about 29 lumbar vertebrae, in slow swimming a correspondingly lesser number.

Cd caudal vertebrae. These can be distinguished from the lumbar vertebrae by the presence of V shaped bones (chevron bones) which lie beneath a series of the anterior caudal vertebrae. Those at the extremity of the tail lack chevron bones but can always be recognised as they are small compared with those anterior to them. The flukes are supported entirely by ligaments and fibrous tissue and lack bones.

The small bones at the extremity of the tail often get lost in preparation and it is not always possible therefore to express the number of caudal vertebrae with accuracy.

## Food

The information on this aspect of the species is very extensive and it is not possible nor desirable to provide, within the space available, detailed lists of food, particularly in the case of all the herbivorous species. Many species feed on particular plant parts and these are more important than the actual plant species. In addition different species may be eaten in different seasons and by different sexes. Due reference is made to important papers in which readers will find more detailed information than can be provided here. The colloquial names of trees are those used by Palgrave (1977) and of grasses as they appear in Meredith (ed.) (1955) and Lightfoot (1975).

Information available on the food of non-herbivorous species is presented either as the number of times a particular food item occurs in a given number of stomach contents or scats or, where large samples are available, as a percentage occurrence.

## Bibliography

This is a list of works of which we are aware, although there may be no explicit reference in the text. Those marked with a * have been added to the bibliography published with the first edition.
Anyone interested in obtaining a bibliography on a particular Order, Family, or Species should contact the Secretary, Mammal Research Institute, University of Preoria. We would also like to receive notice of any publications, old or new, which ought to be included.

## The geological time table

In discussing in brief the fossil antecedents of certain of our mammals it is necessary to have a time scale so that their occurrence in the various Eras, Periods and Epochs of the world may become more meaningful to the reader. The time table provided is part of a much more extensive table prepared by Van Eysinga (1978) and published by the Elsevier Scientific Publishing Company, Amsterdam, with whose permission it is used.

| T | ERA | PERIOD | | EPOCH |
|---|---|---|---|---|
| .01 | CAINOZOIC | QUATERNARY | | HOLOCENE |
| .2 | | | | PLEISTOCENE |
| .4 | | | | |
| .6 | | | | |
| .8 | | | | |
| 1.0 | | | | |
| 1.2 | | | | |
| 1.4 | | | | |
| 1.5 | | | | |
| 1.8 | | | | |
| 3 | | TERTIARY | NEOGENE | PLIOCENE |
| 4 | | | | |
| 5 | | | | |
| 10 | | | | MIOCENE |
| 15 | | | | |
| 20 | | | | |
| 22.5 | | | | |
| 30 | | | PALAEOGENE | OLIGOCENE |
| 35 | | | | |
| 40 | | | | EOCENE |
| 45 | | | | |
| 50 | | | | |
| 55 | | | | |
| 60 | | | | PALEOCENE |
| 65 | | | | |

Geological time table:
T= Geological time in millions of years
(after Van Eysinga, 1978; Amsterdam: Elsevier Publishing Company).

# Glossary of terms used

**abomasum**
Fourth, glandular, stomach of a ruminant.

**acrosome**
The complex cytoplasmic structure at the tip of a mature spermatozoa.

**adpressed**
Lying closely applied to a surface.

**aestivate**
To enter a state of torpor in summer.

**agonistic**
A broad class of behaviour patterns including all types of attack, threat, appeasement and flight.

**alates**
The winged reproductive caste of social insects e.g. ants, termites.

**allele**
Gene which occupies the same relative position on homologous chromosomes.

**allopatric**
Having separate and mutually exclusive areas of geographical distribution.

**altricial**
Requiring care or nursing after birth; at birth helpless, usually with the eyes and ears closed and partially naked.

**ambient**
Surrounding; used with temperature: the ambient temperature being the temperature of the air surrounding the animal.

**Amphibia**
The Class which includes the frogs and toads.

**Amphisbaenidae**
A Family of the Suborder Sauria or lizards.

**androgen**
The male hormone.

**angular process**
The extreme posterior lower corner of the mandibular ramus.

**annulated**
Ringed.

**anoestrus**
The physiological state in a non pregnant mature female when she will not breed.

**anterior**
To the front

**anterior palatal foramina**
The two foramina on the ventral part of the skull, in the rodents situated in that part of the bony palate which lies between the incisors and the cheekteeth.

**antero-internal cusp**
The most anterior cusp of a cheektooth situated on the inside or lingual side of the tooth.

**antitragus**
A lobe near the base of the outer fringe of the ear.

**antorbital**
Situated in front of the orbit or eye-socket.

**Arachnida**
The Class which includes spiders, sun spiders, scorpions, ticks and mites.

**Araneae**
The Family of true spiders.

**arboreal**
Living in or being adapted to living in trees.

**argentophilic** (granules)
Granules which combine with silver stains.

**asdic**
Type of hydrophone.

**astragalus**
The talus, the ankle bone.

**auditory bulla**
A globular, capsular bone adjacent to the middle and inner ear situated on the ventral side of the skull.

**auditory meatus**
The tubular ear passage or in a more restricted sense the opening of the ear to the exterior.

**autosomal**
Any chromosome not a sex chromosome.

**Aves**
The Class of animals with feathers and wings—the birds.

**bezoar**
Compact ball of hair or fibrous material; can measure up to 15 mm.

**bicuspid**
Having two points or cusps.

**bifid**
Divided into two by an emargination.

**bimodal reproduction**
Twice within the year.

**biome**
A broad ecological unit characterised by the distinctive life forms of the climax species, plant or animal.

**biotic zone**
A continuous geographic area that contains ecological associations distinguishable from those of adjacent zones especially at the species and subspecies level.

**biotope**
Habitat, the kind of ecological surroundings in which any particular species lives.

**bipedal**
Walking on two feet.

**braincase**
That part of the skull that houses the brain.

**braks, brackish**
salty areas, having a salty flavour.

**buccal**
On the cheek side of the mouth or teeth or penetrating to the cheek or sometimes used broadly as pertaining to the cavity of the mouth.

**bulla**
See **auditory bulla**

**bursa (of the ear)**
A small pocket situated on the external rim of the ear pinna.

**calcaneum (calcar)**
A bony or cartilaginous spur which arises from the ankle of a bat which helps to support the interfemoral membrane.

**callosities**
Hardening and thickened area on the skin.

**canine**
The tooth immediately posterior to the incisors.

**caravanning**
An action whereby the young of shrews attach themselves to their mother; the group moving around in a line.

**carbonic anhydrase**
An enzyme system found in red blood cells which can be analysed using electrophoresis.

**carnassial shear or carnassial mechanism**
Found in some carnivores and formed by the blade-like cusps of the fourth upper premolar teeth and first lower molar teeth which, occluding together like the blades of a pair of scissors, provide a shearing action for cutting through tough skin or bone.

**caudal**
Concerning the tail, or in the direction of the tail.

**cellulose**
A complicated polyose which forms the cell walls in all plants $(C_6H_{10}O_5)_x$.

**Cephalopoda**
Squids, cuttlefish, octopus.

**cheekteeth**
Those teeth lying posterior to the canine teeth.

**Chilopoda**
A subclass of the Myriapoda—the centipedes.

**choana**
A funnel-shaped aperture.

**cingulum**
The ridge around the base of the crown of a tooth.

**cline**
A gradual and sequential change of character without a significant break.

**Coleoptera**
The Order which includes beetles.

**commensal**
An organism living with another and sharing the same food, one or both benefitting by the association.

**compression**
Confinement of a population within narrow margins.

**conch**
The external ear flap or pinna.

**Condylar process**
A process of the mandible forming the lower portion of the hinge of the lower jaw.

**condyle**
The rounded process on a bone serving as an articulation with another bone.

**conspecific**
Of the same species.

**coprophagy**
Eating faeces, usually as a means of increasing digestive efficiency or replenishing the microbial fauna of the intestinal tract.

**cotery, coteries**
Small groups of animals.

**courser**
An animal that chases its prey.

**crenated**
Having the margin notched or with rounded teeth.

**crepuscular**
Active around sunrise or sunset.

**crescentic**
Crescent-shaped.

**croup**
That part of an animal that lies immediately behind the upper part of the pelvis (the ilium).

**cusp**
A point of elevation on the crown of a tooth.

**dambo**
Low-lying swampy depression (=vlei).

**deciduous**

Shed: refers to the elements of the first or "milk" dentition. In most placental mammals the incisors, canines and premolars are shed and are replaced by permanent teeth.

**demersal**

Living in the bottom layers of the sea.

**dental formula**

A brief and convenient method of expressing the number and kinds of teeth in the form of fractions representing the teeth on one side of both the upper and lower jaws. The total number doubled gives the total number of teeth possessed by the individual species. I=incisor, C=canine, P=premolar, M=molar.

$I\frac{3}{3}\ C\frac{1}{1}\ P\frac{4}{4}\ M\frac{3}{3} = 44$

**diapause**

Interruption to the normal sequence of development.

**diaspore**

Any spore, seed, fruit or other portion of a plant when being dispersed is able to produce a new plant.

**diastema**

The gap between two adjacent teeth, especially between incisors and cheekteeth of herbivores.

**digit**

A finger or toe in mammals.

**dilambdodont**

Having oblong molar teeth with two V-shaped ridges (hedgehog)

**Diplopoda**

A subclass of Myriapoda, the millipedes.

**Diptera**

The Order which includes flies.

**displacement activity**

The performance of a behaviour pattern out of its normal functional context of behaviour.

**distal**

Furthest away from a given point, usually the main axis of the body.

**dorsal**

On, towards, or pertaining to the back.

**dune streets or straits**

The valley area running between two parallel dunes.

**ecosystem**

An area of nature which includes living organisms and non-living substances interacting to produce an exchange of materials between the living and non-living parts.

**ecotone**

A boundary between two plant communities of major rank.

**ectoparasites**

A parasite that lives on the exterior of an organism.

**elaphine snakes**

The front fanged snakes eg. the cobras and mambas.

**electrophoresis**

In general terms a movement of charged particles under the influence of an electric field.

**emargination**

A notch

**endemic**

Restricted to a particular region or country.

**endoparasite**

A parasite that lives in the interior of an organism.

**entoconoid**

A cusp on the lower molar teeth in mammals.

**epipelagic**

Living in the upper layers of the sea.

**erythristic (erythrism)**

The reddening of the hair caused by the abnormal presence of red pigment.

**Eutheria**

The taxon which includes all placental mammals.

**evagination**

an outgrowth.

**eversible**

Capable of being everted (see below).

**evert**

Turn an organ (gland) outwards or inside out.

**exocarp**

The superficial layer of the pericarp.

**extant**

Still existing, not extinct.

**falcate**

Curved like a sickle.

**fecund**

Fertile.

**feral**

Wild, escaped from domestication/introduction and reverted to the wild state.

**fetlock**

That joint of a horse's leg, where a tuft of hair grows, between the metacarpal/metatarsal and proximal phalange.

**flange**

A projecting rim (of bone).

**flehmen**

An act performed by many species of mammals whereby an adult male sniffs the vulva and urine of a female to test if she is in oestrus. In the act the head of the male is raised, the nose pointed upwards, the lips retracted and the nose wrinkled. This muscular contraction opens the *ductus incisivus* ensuring that scent molecules reach the Jacobsen's organ for olfactory analysis.

**foramen**

An aperture or hole.

**forb**

Any herb other than a grass.

**fossorial**

Adapted to digging.

**fovea**

A small pit, or depression.

**to fox**

The reddening which takes place in the hair of a specimen with age.

**fulvous**

Reddish-yellow or tawny.

**genome**

Either of two sets of chromosomes in a zygote.

**genotype**

The sum total of the hereditary factors of an organism.

**genus** (pl. **genera**)

Category of classification above the species level.

**geophagia**

The eating of soil engaged in by herbivorous animals.

**glenoid fossa**

The subcylindrical cavity on the underside of the skull which receives the mandibular condyle to form the hinge connecting the lower and upper jaws.

**graminivorous**

Subsisting on grasses.

**gregarious**
Living together in colonies or other types of assemblage.

**gular**
Appertaining to the upper part of the throat.

**gustatory**
A sense of taste.

**habitat**
The kind of place with respect to vegetation and climate in which a given species of animal lives.

**hallux**
The great toe (digit I) on the hind foot.

**herbivorous**
Subsisting on plants.

**holotype**
A single type specimen used and designated as such by an author in describing a new species or subspecies.

**home range**
The area over which an animal normally travels in pursuit of its routine activities.

**hycium**
Dassie urine.

**hypocone**
A fourth cusp arising on the cingulum on the postero-internal side of an upper molar tooth producing a quadri-tubercular pattern.

**incisive foramina**
Anterior palatal foramina.

**incisors**
The most anterior teeth emerging in the upper jaw from the premaxillary bone in the lower from the front of the mandible.

**infundibulum**
A funnel-shaped cavity or depression

**inguinal**
Situated in the groin, that is the area between the lower lateral part of the abdomen and the thigh.

**insectivorous**
Subsisting entirely or mainly on insects.

**interfemoral**
Situated between the legs.

**interorbital constriction**
The least distance between the upper rims of the orbits measured across the top of the skull.

**isabelline**
Greyish-yellow.

**isohet**
A line drawn on a map through places having equal amounts of rainfall.

**Isoptera**
The Order which includes termites (white ants).

**karyogram**
Synonymous with karotype.

**karyotype**
Display of the chromosomes or chromosome types seen at metaphase arranged in an orderly manner.

**labial**
Pertaining to the lips, sometimes used instead of buccal as indicating the outer side of the mouth as opposed to the lingual side.

**labile**
Liable to change.

**lachrymal**
A small bone situated at the upper anterior corner of the eye orbit.

**lambdoid**
The cranial structure joining the occipital and parietal bones.

**lanceolate**
Having the form of the blade of a lance.

**lanceolate-pectinate**
Lanceolate (see above) with a comb-like margin.

**lateral**
Situated on the side of the medium axis.

**lekking**
Behavioural activity where males gather at specific sites (leks) to display.

**Lepidoptera**
The Order which includes butterflies and moths.

**lignin**
A complex substance which, associated with cellulose, causes the thickening of plant cell walls, and so forms wood.

**lingual**
Pertaining to the tongue, situated on the tongue side as opposed to the buccal (or labial) side.

**lophs**
Transverse ridge on a (molar) tooth.

**lordosis**
Dorsi-flexion of the spine, often performed by females prior to copulation.

**malleus**
An ear ossicle (a small bone).

**mammae**
Strictly the milk bearing glands but usually represented by the nipples alone.

**mandible**
The lower jaw.

**mandibular condyle**
The process on the lower jaw which fits into the glenoid fossa to form the hinge between the upper and lower jaws.

**mandibular ramus**
One of the two symmetrical branches of the mandible joined anteriorly at the mandibular symphysis.

**mandibular symphysis**
The anterior junction of the two branches of the mandible where they join anteriorly.

**masseter**
A muscle which raises the lower jaw and assists in chewing.

**mastoid**
A bone situated posterior to the auditory meatus, often small but sometimes greatly inflated.

**matrilinal**
Based on the maternal line of descent.

**maxilla (maxillary)**
The bone of the upper jaw which carries the upper canines and the upper cheekteeth and forms the major part of the palate.

**meatus**
A short canal.

**melanistic (melanism)**
Darkening caused by an excessive development of black pigment (melanin).

**melon**
Used in connection with marine mammals, the swollen bulbous head of some Cetacea.

**mesic**
Description of a habitat which is not harsh or arid (moist).

**mesopelagic**
Living in the middle depths of the sea.

**metacone**
In mammals, the postero-external cusp of a lower molar tooth.

**miombo (mjombo woodland)**
An association dominated by *Brachystegia spp.*

**molar**
A tooth adapted to grinding, the most posterior teeth in the cheekteeth row, not preceded by milk teeth.

**montane**
Of mountainous country.

**muffle**
The thickest part of the upper lip and nose in ruminants and rodents.

**Muridae**
The Family of the Order Rodentia which includes the rats and mice.

**muzzle**
That part of the face that lies anterior to the eyes.

**Myriapoda**
The Order which includes the millipedes and centipedes.

**nares**
Nostrils.

**nasals**
The two bones which form a roof to the nasal apertures on the top of the muzzle.

**nasute**
Referring to termites with an anterior projection on the head.

**neritic**
Pertaining to a strip of shallow water immediately adjacent to a seacoast.

**nipple cling**
The act of the young of murids remaining in a state of semi-permanent attachment to the nipples of the female after birth.

**nuchal**
Pertaining to the neck.

**nuchal patch**
A patch of hair on the nape of Lagomorphs which contrasts in colour with the colour of the upper parts of the body.

**occipital condyles**
The pair of smooth rounded processes of the occipital bone at the posterior end of the skull on either side of the occipital foramen which acts as a hinge between the head and the neck.

**occipital crest**
A flange-like process of the supra-occipital bone which forms the upper posterior portion of the cranium.

**ochraceous**
Yellowish.

**oestrus**
The period when a female will mate for the purpose of fertilisation of the ova.

**opisthodont**
Of the incisors, directed posteriorly.

**oribatid mites**
A group of sarcoptiform mites—the beetle mites.

**orthodont**
Used in relation to the incisors when directed in a more or less vertical plane.

**Orthoptera**
The Order which includes grasshoppers, locusts and crickets.

**osteophagia**
The chewing on bones engaged in by herbivorous animals suffering from a deficiency of phosphorus and calcium in their diet.

**palate**
The roof of the mouth.

**palatine**
In the region of the palate.

**paracone**
In mammals, the antero-external cusp of an upper molar tooth.

**paratype**
All the specimens of a type-series used by an author in the original description of a species or subspecies, except that specimen designated as the holotype.

**paroccipital process**
A narrow finger-like downward projection of bone at the posterior end of the skull behind the ear bullae.

**parturition**
The act or processes of giving birth.

**pastern**
That part of an ungulate's foot between the fetlock and the hoof.

**pectinate**
Comb-like structure.

**pectoral**
Pertaining to or situated on the chest.

**pedal glands**
Glands which are situated in the feet opening between the hooves.

**pelage**
The hairy coat.

**pericarp**
Wall of a fruit if derived from the wall of the ovary.

**phalanx**
One of the bones in a finger.

**phenotype**
All the observable, measurable and in any way recordable aspects of an organism in contrast to its genotype.

**philtrum**
A narrow downward extension of the rhinarium which contacts the margin of the mouth.

**phloem**
Part of the vascular of plants.

**phonation**
Production of sounds.

**piloerection**
The erection at will of the hair of a mammal under stress.

**pinna**
The external ear flap or conch.

**plantain**
The fruit of a tree-like tropical plant allied to the banana which bears a similar fruit.

**plantar**
Pertaining to the sole of the foot.

**pollex**
innermost forelimb digit; thumb.

**polyethism**
Display of different patterns of behaviour by particular individuals within a social group.

**posterior**
To the back.

**postorbital bar**
The bony process which in some species encloses the back of the eye socket.

**postorbital constriction**
A narrowing of the skull posterior to the postorbital processes—not to be confused with the interorbital constriction.

**postorbital process**
A bony projection situated immediately above and slightly posterior to the eye socket.

**posterior palatal foramina**
Two, sometimes inconspicuous, foramina situated in the palate between the cheekteeth.

**postorbital**
Posterior to the eye socket.

**precocial**
Born in an advanced stage of development with all its faculties operative, eg. wildebeest, elephant shrew, dassie.

**prehensile**
Capable of grasping.

**premolar**
The teeth lying between the canines and the molars, preceded by milk teeth.

**preputial gland**
A gland situated adjacent to the penis or vaginal opening.

**proodont**
Of the incisors when directed anteriorly.

**protocone**
The inner cusp of an upper molar tooth.

**proximal**
Closer to the median axis or a given point.

**proximate factor**
Nearest, next, before or after; immediate operative factor.

**purse-seine**
A type of fishing net which has a purse-shaped holding section.

**ramus**
Branch.

**refection**
Synonymous with coprophagy.

**Reptilia**
The Class which includes the lizards and snakes.

**rete or rete mirabilia**
A net-like structure of blood vessels.

**rhinarium**
The naked fleshy area of the tip of the muzzle which encloses the nostrils.

**riparian**
Growing on or living on the banks of streams or rivers.

**rostrum**
That portion of the skull which lies anterior to the eye orbits, the upper portion of the muzzle.

**rugose**
Wrinkled, corrugated.

**sagittal**
A longitudinal ridge of bone situated on the medial axis of the cranium which is sometimes developed into an erect plate and is sometimes absent.

**saltatorial**
Jumping.

**Sauria**
The Suborder of the Order Squamata which includes the lizards.

**scatter hoard**
The act of establishing small stores of food in many places.

**S.D.**
Standard deviation: the square root of the arithmetic mean of the squares of the deviation from the arithmetic mean of a frequency distribution. A measure of the variation of measurements about the mean.

**senescence**
ageing.

**series**
A number of specimens available for examination.

**Serpentes**
The Suborder of the Order Squamata which includes the snakes.

**species**
Composed of potentially or actually interbreeding populations at a particular point in time.

**sounder**
Group of pigs.

**spermatogenesis**
Sperm formation.

**stolons**
The underground stems of plants (grasses).

**stotting**
Bouncing up and down with legs held stiffly Afrikaans *pronk*

**supra occipital crest**
A flange-like process of the supraoccipital bone which forms the upper posterior portion of the cranium.

**symbionts**
See symbiosis.

**symbiosis**
An internal partnership between two organisms (symbionts) in which the mutual advantages normally outweigh the disadvantages.

**sympatric**
Having the same or overlapping areas of geographical distribution.

**symphysis**
The line of junction of two pieces of bone separated in early life, often applied to the junction of the two halves of the mandible or pelvis.

**synonym**
A word or name identical with another of the same language.

**talanoid**
The posterior heel of a molar tooth.

**taxon (pl. taxa)**
A group of organisms which are classified together, at a specified rank in a Linnaean hierarchy, eg. a particular species, genus, Family.

**taxonomy**
The classification and naming of animals.

**telegony**
The supposed influence of a previous sire on offspring borne by a female to other sires.

**temporalis**
A broad radiating muscle arising from the coronoid process of the lower jaw and attaching to the upper part of the skull.

**thermolabile**
A situation in which the body temperature is variable

**thermoregulation**
A mammal's ability to regulate its body temperature under differing ambient temperatures.

**thoracic**
Appertaining to the chest.

**topotype**
A specimen collected at the type locality.

**torus (pl. tori)**
A projecting ridge above the eye sockets in a Primate.

**tragus**
A small cartilaginous process found in the external opening of the ear.

**trifid**
Divided into three by two emarginations.

**type**
The specimen from which the original description of a species or subspecies is made (=holotype).

**type locality**
The locality from which the type specimen was collected.

**umbel**
An arrangement of flowers springing from a common centre and forming a flat rounded cluster.

**ungulates**
Hoofed animals such as members of the Orders Perissodactyla and Artiodactyla.

**unicuspid**
Having one cusp on the crown, a simple tooth.

**ventral**
On or pertaining to the abdominal or under side.

**vibrissae**
Stout, stiff, generally long, tactile bristles growing singly or in small clusters on the body or head of a mammal. Whiskers are mystacial vibrissae.

**xeric**
Description of a habitat which is arid.

**zygomatic arch** (=zygoma)
The arched composite bone supporting the cheeks on either side of the skull made up of processes of the maxillary bone, the jugals and the squamosal.

**zygomatic plate**
The expanded flattened lower branch of the maxillary process typically found in the Murinae and Gerbillinae.

# Order INSECTIVORA

## Shrews, hedgehogs and golden moles

Linnnaeus failed to recognise this group of mammals, and included the pigs, armadillos, opossums and insectivores in his "Bestiae", a grouping which Simpson (1945) considers his least successful attempt to bring order into classification. Eighteenth century authors included the insectivores, as we know them today, with the rodents and it was not until the 19th century that Cuvier (1817) recognised the Insectivora under the vernacular name *insectivora*, a name they have borne ever since.

Simpson (1945) recognised them as a difficult group to classify logically and one of extremely ancient origin and differentiation. The characters which unite them are in great part primitive and today they are recognised as the most primitive of all placental mammals and as a group standing near the origin of all other groups. The fossil history of the Insectivora is less well known than that of the large mammals and only a very limited number of localities have yielded their fossil remains. In the Subregion, the Erinaceidae, Soricidae and Chrysochloridae are first known from the Pliocene/Early Pleistocene beds dated about two million years ago (Butler, 1978).

In reviewing the Order, Heim de Balsac & Meester (1977) followed Findley (1967) and used the ordinal name Insectivora to include the Families represented in the Subregion: the Soricidae; Erinaceidae; Chrysochloridae and Macroscelididae, and extralimitally the Tenrecidae, which includes the otter shrews of the Subfamily Potamogalinae of Africa and two Subfamilies of tenrecs which occur on Madagascar and other islands in the Indian Ocean. The Potamogalinae includes the otter shrew, *Potamogale velox*, an aquatic species with an oar-like tail which lives in rivers and streams in forested areas, the nearest records to the Subregion being from the Mwinilunga District of Zambia and two smaller species: *Micropotomogale lamottei* of West Africa and *M. ruwenzorii* of East Africa. The Macroscelididae, the elephant shrews, were elevated to full ordinal rank by Butler (1956) an arrangement that subsequently has been accepted generally and is followed in this work. In the Subregion, the Order is well represented by members of the three Families and includes 12 genera and 32 species.

Key to the Families after Meester, Rautenbach, Dippenaar, Baker (1986).

1. Zygomatic arches incomplete; no more than 32 teeth (nine upper and seven lower per jaw half); upper molars with cusps in W-pattern (dilambdodont); front upper incisors strongly bilophodont, anterior cusp forming a pronounced forward-projecting hook.
   ... Family SORICIDAE

   Zygomatic arches complete; 36–44 teeth
   ... 2

2. Back densely covered with spines; eyes and ears normal
   ... Family ERINACEIDAE

   Back covered with fur, forming a thick, iridescent pelage over entire body; modified for fossorial life, with no visible eyes or external ears, and with strong forelimbs and claws for digging
   ... Family CHRYSOCHLORIDAE

# I. Family SORICIDAE

## Shrews

### Subfamily CROCIDURINAE

Shrews are the most numerous species of insectivores in Africa. In the Subregion the Family is well represented by four genera and 15 species. All the African species belong to the Subfamily Crocidurinae, having unpigmented teeth, unique characters of the mandibular condyle, the hinge of the lower jaw, and the lower fourth premolar teeth.

Repenning (1967) thought that shrews had their origin outside the African Continent, only entering Europe in the Miocene and being first represented in Africa in the mid-Miocene Epoch, some 12 to 15 million years ago, by *'Sorex' dehmiafricanus* from Morocco. Although its dentition is primitive, however, there is no good evidence that this form is close to the ancestry of the many living Crocidurinae (Butler, 1978).

The four genera of living Crocidurinae represented in the Subregion are *Myosorex*, *Sylvisorex*, *Suncus* and *Crocidura*. The genus *Myosorex* has a wide distribution in tropical Africa, where most of the species are confined to high altitudes (Heim de Balsac & Lamotte, 1956). Three species occur in the Subregion: *M. cafer*, *M. varius* and *M. longicaudatus*. The possibility of other species being recognised cannot be ruled out and is under investigation by A. Wolhuter of the Transvaal Museum, Pretoria. *Myosorex longicaudatus* is of particular interest as it was only discovered and described by Meester & Dippenaar in 1978 and is, therefore, the latest new species of mammal to be discovered in the Subregion, an event which is as unexpected today as it is worthy of note.

The fossil *Myosorex robinsoni* from the Plio-Pleistocene deposits of the Transvaal is an early member of this group of species, but had characters from which Butler (1978) judged that it was not a direct ancestor of either *M. cafer* or *M. varius*, but was a representative of an earlier migration from further north. Living members of the genus *Myosorex* have fossorial adaptations and generally are confined to damp places in forested areas or to the vicinity of streams and rivers.

*Sylvisorex* has certain archaic characters which were thought, by Heim de Balsac & Lamotte (1957), to suggest that it was broadly ancestral to *Suncus* and in part to *Crocidura*. *Sylvisorex* is restricted mainly to tropical Africa, five of the eight known species living on mountains and two in damp forests, the remaining species *S. megalura*, extending into savanna and occurring in the Subregion. While *Sylvisorex* is confined to Africa, *Suncus* has a much wider distribution, occurring in Eurasia and in the Oriental region, where Butler (1978) thought the genus originated. Fossil remains from the

Transvaal cave brecchias are close to the living *S. varilla* and *S. infinitesimus* and these are related to *E. etruscus*, a species that occurs in the Mediterranean region and Asia and which has extended its distribution into West Africa. Butler (1978) suggested that this group of species entered Africa rather late.

The genus *Crocidura* is by far the largest genus of African shrews and one of the largest genera of living mammals. It is well represented in the Subregion by eight species. From the diversity of species found in Africa, Butler (1978) suggested that the genus is African in origin, although it occurs both in Asia and Europe.

Heim de Balsac & Lamotte (1957) thought that *Crocidura* had its ancestry in the *Sylvisorex-Suncus* group from which it differs by the loss of the third upper premolar teeth. These teeth reappear in several of the species, however, which Meester (1953) suggested is a recurrence of an ancestral character. In the Transvaal fossil deposits, *Crocidura* is represented by a small species rather similar to the living *C. bicolor* (Davis & Meester, unpublished).

One of the most remarkable fossil shrews so far discovered in Africa is *Diplomesodon fossorius* from the Late Pliocene beds at Makapansgat in the Transvaal. The only other species of the genus is known from central Asia. Butler (1978) warned, however, that its apparent close affinity with this Asian species could be due to parallel evolution, which is prevalent in the Soricidae, and that it could well be a derivative of the *Crocidura* group, paralleling *Diplomesodon* as a result of adaptation to a dry environment.

Both sexes of shrews have musk glands situated on their flanks between the fore and hind limbs. They are small, elongated areas, bordered by rows of stiff hairs whose tips close over them (Crowcroft, 1957). They are developed better in males than in females and, although they may be difficult to find in the live individual, they can be seen clearly on the flesh side of the skin, when it is dead. The action of these glands is controlled by sex hormones, for Pearson (1946) recorded that in anoestrous females they were better developed than when they were in oestrus. The injection of testosterone, the male hormone, increased the blood supply to these glands in females. Under stress, shrews have a strong odour of musk which emanates from these glands, a factor which probably makes them distasteful to most mammalian predators. Dogs and cats, while avidly hunting shrews, normally deposit them on the door mat uneaten. On the other hand avian predators such as barn owls, *Tyto alba*, appear to be undeterred by this factor and shrew remains occur regularly in their casts. Hamilton (1940) and others suggested that the main function of these glands is to help the sexes to find one another during the breeding season. Crowcroft (1957) on the other hand suggested that the odour helps shrews to avoid individuals unsuitable for mating, the glands being developed better in the males, the scent-marking of their paths may be unattractive to other males for a time. The enlargement of the glands in non-breeding females probably serves to deter males from seeking these unsuitable females.

All shrews are capable of burrowing but, at most, this consists of the excavation of short, blind escape tunnels from the nests. Some construct open cup-shaped nests (*C. hirta; C. flavescens*), others (*C. mariquensis*) ball-shaped nests made of soft, pliable vegetable debris (Meester, 1963). While most species can climb well, under certain circumstances, they are all generally terrestrial. They have a high metabolic rate and remain active, in bursts, throughout the 24 hour period and soon die if deprived of food or water, even for short periods. Meester (1963) recorded that, in captivity, shrews eat one to two thirds of their body weight of meat per day. They are voracious feeders and even the small species will attack and eat large grasshoppers almost as big as themselves. They will drink water and do so rather like a bird, dipping the mouth and then raising the head to allow it to trickle down their throats. Their life span in the wild is of the order of 16 months, although in captivity they live much longer. Meester (1963) kept *C. flavescens* and *C. hirta* in containers for up to two and a half years.

None of our shrews have poisonous saliva, although the American shrew, *Blarina brevicauda*, has submaxillary glands which secrete a venom similar to that of the venom of elaphine snakes (cobras, mambas), and can inflict poisonous bites.

Shrews can be distinguished easily from rats and mice as they have long, narrow, pointed muzzles, very small eyes, five digits on each of the feet and narrow skulls with continuous rows of teeth. When captured by domestic pets they emit a characteristic piercing squeak (Skinner, pers. comm.).

Key to the genera (Meester *et al.* 1986)

1. Skull with braincase sharply angled laterally in squamosal region; paired dorsal foramina in frontal region; interparietal large, parieto-occipital suture follows a sigmoid curve; second upper unicuspid ($I^3$) clearly smaller than first ($I^2$) and third (C); fourth unicuspid ($P^3$) present, minute

   ... *Myosorex*,

   Skull with braincase smoothly curved or only slightly angled in squamosal region; no paired foramina in frontal region; parieto-occipital suture follows a simple curve

   ... 2

2. Fourth upper unicuspid present

   ... 3

   Fourth upper unicuspid absent

   ... *Crocidura*

3. Long hairs on tail, scattered sparsely among short bristles; braincase somewhat flattened; protocone of $P^4$ reduced, in some cases virtually lost; blade of $I_1$ without denticulations on cutting surface

   ... *Suncus*

   No long hairs on tail; braincase inflated; talon of $P^4$ well developed, with prominent protocone and hypocone; blade of $I_1$ with two or three denticulations on cutting surface

   ... *Sylvisorex*

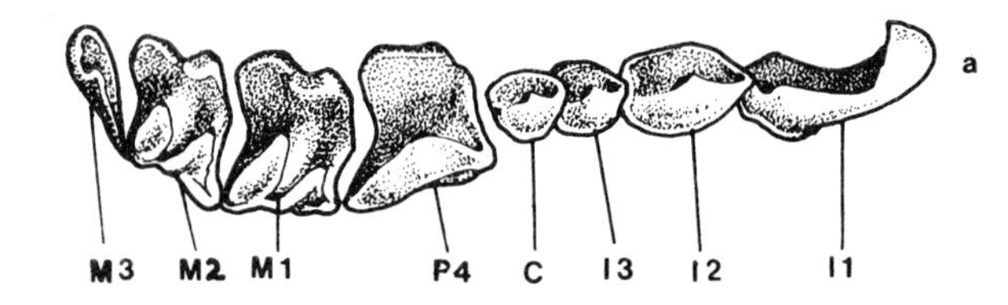


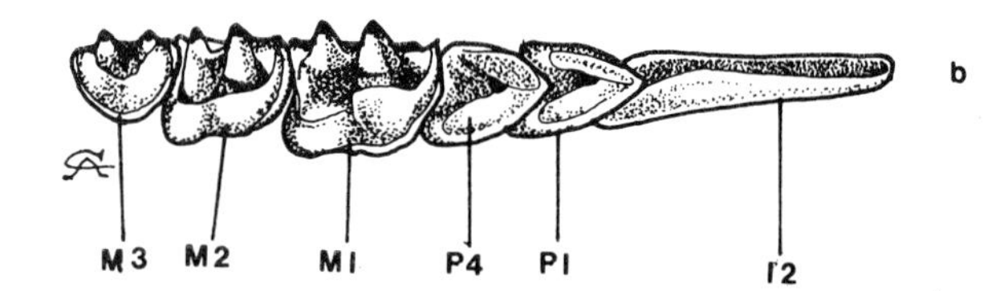


Fig. 1.1 Teeth in the genus *Crocidura*
(a) Left upper jaw. Note: *Myosorex, Suncus* and *Sylvisorex* have an extra unicuspid tooth No. 4 which lies between the canine (C) and the upper fourth premolar.
(b) Right lower jaw. Note: *Myosorex* has three unicuspid teeth in the lower jaw.

## Genus *Myosorex* Gray, 1837

This genus is represented in the Subregion by three species: *M. longicaudatus, M. cafer* and *M. varius*. The first named, which, at the present juncture, is only known from a restricted area in the southern Cape Province, can be distinguished readily from the other two by features of its tail. In the case of the other two it is not easy to distinguish them in parts of their distributional range. In the eastern Cape Province the two species are distinct and can be recognised on the basis of the colour of the upper and under parts of the body and feet, the colour pattern of their tails and to a lesser extent on the relative position of the palatine fissures. In the northeastern Transvaal and eastern Zimbabwe, however, populations are very variable in respect of these characters. In Inyanga, Zimbabwe, there is complete intergradation between the extremes of variability represented by the two species, the population occurring here being assigned to *M. cafer* (Heim de Balsac & Meester, 1977). Wolhuter (pers. comm.) confirmed this identification on the evidence of the karyotype which is similar to *M. cafer* at 2n = 38.

As in *Sylvisorex* the tails in *Myosorex* lack long bristles seen in the other genera. They have an extra tiny premolar tooth on each side in the upper and lower jaws giving them eight pairs in the upper set and seven in the lower. These tiny teeth lie internal to the toothrow in the upper jaw between the canine tooth and the premolar and in the lower between the two premolars.

The dental formula is:

$I\frac{3}{2}\ C\frac{1}{1}\ P\frac{2}{1}\ M\frac{3}{3} = 32$

Although at the moment only three species are listed chromosome analysis shows that other sympatric species may occur (Wolhuter, pers. comm.). In the northern extension of the distribution of *M. cafer* in the Transvaal from about Wakkerstroom to Entabeni, Wolhuter (pers. comm.) has found a second species, which may be shown eventually to be *M. tenuis* Thomas & Schwann, 1905, which has a karyotype of 2n = 40, as compared with *M. cafer* of 2n = 38. A further form which has a karyotype of 2n = 38 occurs within the distributional range of *M. cafer* in estuarine reedbeds and other wet habitats in KwaZulu/Natal which may be *M. sclateri* Thomas & Schwann, 1905. In the western range of *M. varius* in the Cape Province, material from the Cedarberg Mountains from preliminary examination seems to have a karyotype of 2n = 24 compared with *M. varius* of 2n = 42. Further specimens are required to confirm this. Studies are being conducted in an attempt to resolve these issues.

Key to the species after Meester *et al.* (1986)

1. Colour duller and paler, more greyish-brown or brown; ventral colour greyish-fawn; hind feet off-white; tail bicoloured; anterior palate with lateral fissures overlapping median fissure
   ... *Myosorex varius*

   Colour richer, more reddish-brown or blackish-brown; ventral colour yellowish-brown; hind feet and tail brown to black; tail not bicoloured; anterior palate with lateral palatal fissures anterior to median fissure(s)
   ... 2

2. Tail shorter (< 60 mm), slender, not prehensile; a single median palatal fissure behind paired lateral fissures (Fig. 1.2)
   ... *Myosorex cafer*

   Tail longer (> 53 mm), thickened at base, prehensile; median palatal fissures paired, and an additional unpaired fissure occasionally present (Fig. 1.2)
   ... *Myosorex longicaudatus*

---

No. 1

## *Myosorex longicaudatus* Meester & Dippenaar, 1978

## Long-tailed forest shrew
## Langstertbosskeerbek

Plate 1

---

### Colloquial Name

The unique feature of this forest-dwelling species is the long, basally thick semi prehensile tail.

### Taxonomic Notes

This species closely resembles *M. cafer* in general appearance but can be distinguished readily from it by its long tail and by certain features of the skull.

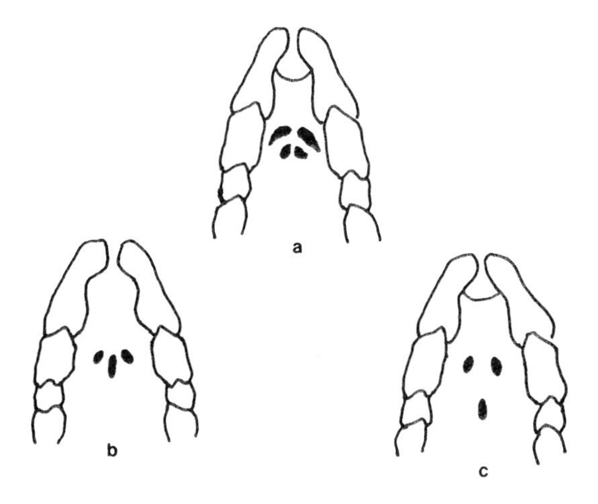


Fig. 1.2. Diagrammatic representation of the relative positions of the palatal fissures:
(a) *Myosorex longicaudatus* (b) *M. varius* (c) *M. cafer*
after Meester (1963) and Meester & Dippenaar (1978).

### Description

Long-tailed forest shrews have a total length of about 150 mm and, as the name suggests, have longer tails than the other two species of the forest shrews that occur in the Subregion. Expressed as a percentage of the length of the head and body, the tail in *M. longicaudatus* is 74,3%; in *M. varius* 46,1% and *M. cafer* 49,7% (Table 1.1). The colour of the upper parts of the body is dark blackish-brown, the under parts slightly paler and tinged brown with no clear line of demarcation between them. The hind feet are overall brown to blackish-brown, the upper surface of the forefeet similar to the upper surface of the hind feet, but the under surface of the latter is paler. The upper surface of the tail is blackish-brown, only slightly paler on the under surface, and the tail is noticeably thickened near the base (Meester & Dippenaar, 1978).

The interparietal region of the skull is wide (Fig. 1.3.a.), the snout comparatively long and slender. A characteristic feature is the number and relative positioning of the palatal fissures (Fig. 1.2.a.). This species has two small fissures situated in line with the posterior edge of the larger anterior pair or in 76% of cases entirely posterior to them. Occasionally a third fissure is present situated directly behind the posterior pair or between the anterior and posterior pairs.

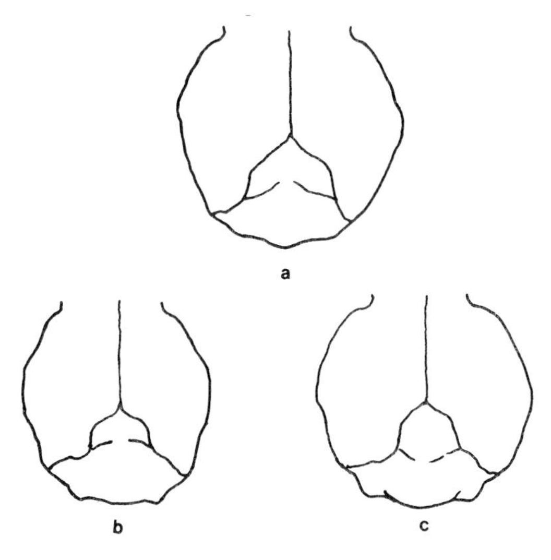


Fig. 1.3. Comparison of the interparietal bones in:
(a) *Myosorex longicaudatus* (b) *M. varius* (c) *M. cafer*
after Meester & Dippenaar (1978).

**Table 1.1**

Measurements (mm) of the long-tailed forest shrew, *M. longicaudatus* Meester & Dippenaar, 1978

**Topotypical series**

| | Males | | | Females | | |
|---|---|---|---|---|---|---|
| | x̄ | n | Range | x̄ | n | Range |
| (TL | 150 | 21) | | (145 | 7) | |
| HB | 86 | 21 | 79–93 | 83 | 7 | 75–87 |
| T | 64 | 21 | 57–66 | 62 | 7 | 59–67 |
| Hf c/u | 17,3 | 21 | 16–18 | 16,4 | 7 | 16–17 |
| E | 11,5 | 21 | 10–12 | 10,4 | 7 | 10–12 |
| 100 × T / HB | 74,3% | 28 | 67,7–89,3% | | | |

## Distribution

*Southern African Subregion*

So far known only from a range of localities in the southern parts of the **Cape Province**: Diepwalle State Forest; the Knysna Forest; the forest near George and at the mouth of the Storms River; from Boesmansbos in the Langeberg Mountains; from near Heidelberg and from the Robertson Pass near Mossel Bay.

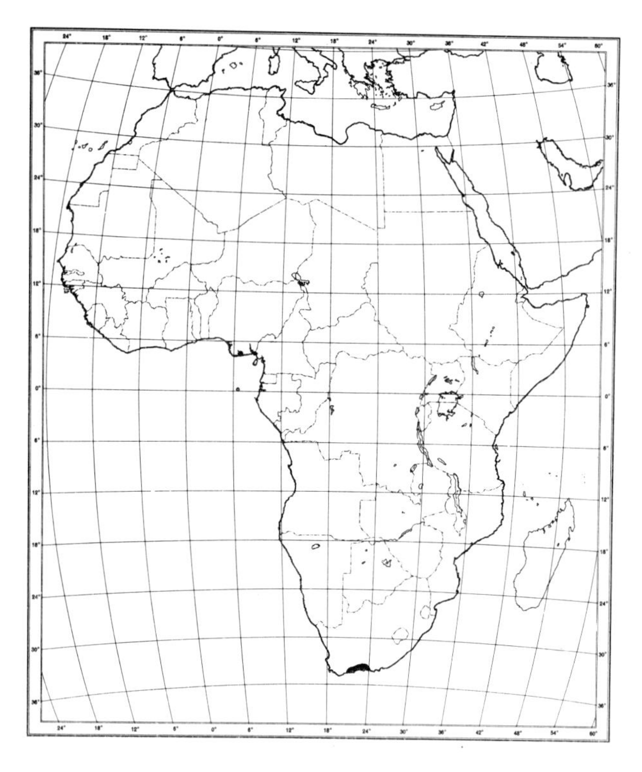

## Habitat

They are closely confined to the ecotone of forest and fynbos, living predominantly in the cover of dense matted clumps of fern.

## Habits

Little is known about the habits of this species. The increase in the length of the tail, its thickness and its semi-prehensile nature suggests an arboreal way of life (Meester & Dippenaar, 1978).

## Food

Breytenbach (*in litt.*) recorded that four of 11 stomachs contained, in addition to insects, over 64% of seeds.

## Reproduction

No information available.

---

No. 2

# *Myosorex cafer* (Sundevall, 1846)

## Dark-footed forest shrew
## Donkerpootbosskeerbek

Plate 1

---

## Colloquial Name

So named as their feet are darker in colour than the colour of the upper parts of the body.

## Taxonomic Notes

Two subspecies are recognised: *M. c. cafer* from the species' range and *M. c. sclateri* Thomas & Schwann, 1905 from the Ngoye Forest, Umfolozi and Sibudeni areas of KwaZulu/Natal. No characters in the teeth are marked or constant enough to allow a clear separation of this species from the forest shrew, *M. varius* (Meester, 1958a.).

## Description

Dark-footed forest shrews have a total length of about 130 mm with tails that are about 46% to 51% of the length of the head and body and a mass of about 13,0 g (Table 2.1). The upper parts of the body are dark brown, the under surface buffy-brown. The feet are dark in colour, the lateral surfaces of the hind feet are darker than the upper surfaces, the forefeet paler overall than the hind feet. The tail is an even dark brown colour.

## Table 2.1

Measurements (mm) and mass (g) of the dark-footed forest shrew, *M. cafer*

**Eastern Zimbabwe** (Smithers & Wilson, 1979)

| | Males | | | Females | | |
|---|---|---|---|---|---|---|
| | x̄ | n | Range | x̄ | n | Range |
| TL | 126 | 10 | 117–131 | 127 | 91 | 125–133 |
| (HB | 86 | 10) | | (84 | 9) | |
| T | 40 | 10 | 37–47 | 43 | 93 | 9–47 |
| Hf c/u | 14 | 10 | 14–15 | 15 | 10 | 14–15 |
| E | 10 | 10 | 9–12 | 11 | 10 | 10–11 |
| Mass | 12,8 | 10 | 10,0–15,0 | 12,8 | 9 | 11,0–15,0 |
| 100 × T / HB | 46,5 | 10 | | 51,2% | 9 | |

**Port St Johns, Transkei** (Meester & Dippenaar, 1978)

**Irrespective of sex**

| | x̄ | n | Range |
|---|---|---|---|
| (TL | 132 | 46) | |
| HB | 88 | 46 | 78–105 |
| T | 44 | 46 | 36–50 |
| Hf c/u | 14,7 | 46 | 13–16 |
| E | 10,1 | 46 | 9–11 |
| 100 × T / HB | 49,7% | 45 | 34,3–58,1% |

## Distribution

In **Zimbabwe** they occur narrowly in the eastern, highland parts of the country from Inyanga south to the Melsetter District and into **Mozambique**, south of the Zambezi River, eastwards to the Gorongoza National Park in the Beira District. South of this there is a break in their distribution, the species reoccurring in the eastern **Transvaal** and extending southwards into **Natal** and coastally as far as King William's Town District in the eastern **Cape Province.** The distributional range of this species falls within that of the more widespread *M. varius* with which it is sympatric in various localities.

## Habitat

Dark-footed forest shrews are confined to moist, densely vegetated habitat and, in parts of their distributional range, are like most of their East and Central African relatives, restricted to mountainous country (Heim de Balsac & Lamotte, 1956). In eastern Zimbabwe, they occur in dense scrub and grass in damp areas fringing mountain streams and in montane grassland where there are wet sponges within the mist belt, at altitudes over about 1 200 m. In Mozambique they occur on Gorongoza Mountain up to about 1 600 m in montane grassland.

## Habits

In eastern Zimbabwe they are active both during the day and at night, having been trapped at various times throughout the 24 hour period. They appear to forage solitarily and to be purely terrestrial. At Inyanga, Zimbabwe they were seen to forage in the thickest tangles of vegetation on the stream banks and not necessarily to use the runways of the vlei rat, *Otomys irroratus*, which were clearly visible in the under

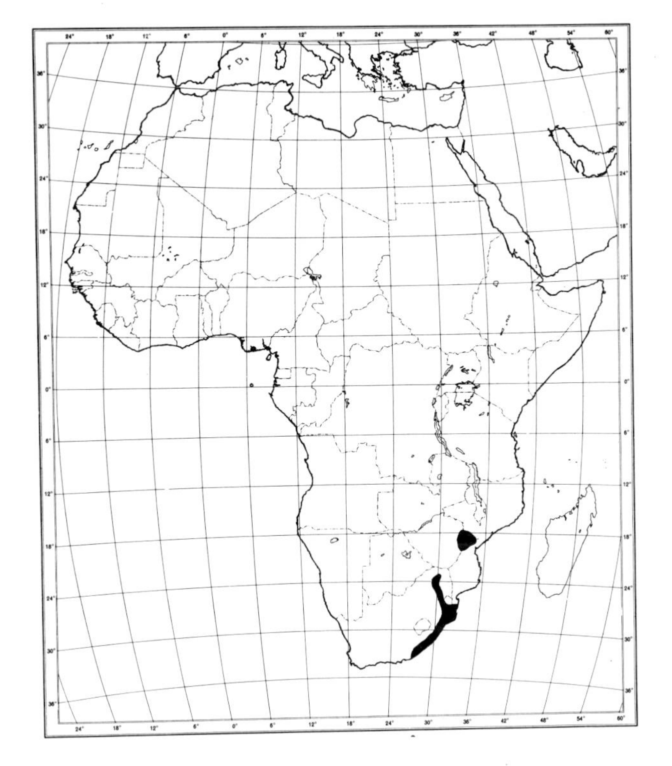

growth. A ball-shaped nest, believed to be of this species, constructed of soft grass, was found on the raised bank of the stream among rocks with a heavy overhead cover of grass and undergrowth. It was tucked under the shelter of an overhanging boulder. While their habits have not been studied in detail they are probably very similar to those of the forest shrew, *M. varius*.

### Food
Churchfield (1985) found that in Zimbabwe 19 different foods were taken including coleoptera, isoptera, lepidoptera larvae, lithiobiomorphs and isopods as well as spiders, worms and a small amount of seeds and green plant material.

### Reproduction
In eastern Zimbabwe gravid females were taken in October and November, the average number of foetuses being three (n = 3) with a range of from two to four. In the Transvaal, Rautenbach (1978) recorded a lactating female in March.

---

No. 3

## *Myosorex varius* (Smuts, 1832)

## Forest shrew
## Bosskeerbek

Plate 1

---

### Colloquial Name
So named for their close association with forests and a moist, densely vegetated environment.

### Taxonomic notes
No subspecies are recognised. The eastern Zimbabwe populations are assigned to *M. cafer*.

### Description
Forest shrews have a total length of about 120 mm, with tails that are about 46% of the length of the head and body and a mass of about 15,0g (Tablc 3.1). The colour of the upper parts of the body is dark brown to greyish brown depending on their place of origin, the hair on the under parts in the browner specimens with light brown tips, in the greyer with off white or very pale buffy tips, in both cases the grey bases of the hairs showing through. The feet are paler in colour than the upper parts of the body, the tail dark brown on the upper surface, paler on the lateral and ventral surfaces, which may be fawn or whitish.

### Table 3.1
Measurements of the forest shrew, *M. varius*

**Port St Johns, Transkei** (Meester & Dippenaar, 1978)

**Irrespective of sex**

| | $\bar{x}$ | n | Range |
|---|---|---|---|
| (TL | 124 | 22) | |
| HB | 85 | 22 | 72–95 |
| T | 39 | 21 | 34–46 |
| Hf c/u | 13,6 | 22 | 12–14 |
| E | 9,4 | 22 | 8–10 |
| $\frac{100\times T}{HB}$ | 46,1% | 21 | 38,2–56,2% |

### Distribution
They occur in the southern and eastern parts of the **Transvaal**; in the **northeastern Orange Free State**; **Natal**; **Lesotho** and in the **Cape Province** from the Eastern Province, where they occur inland to Murraysburg and Beaufort West, and coastally to the northwestern parts of the province, as far as Port Nolloth. This species has a wider distribution than *M. cafer*, its distribution overlapping that of *M. cafer* the two species being sympatric in parts of their ranges.

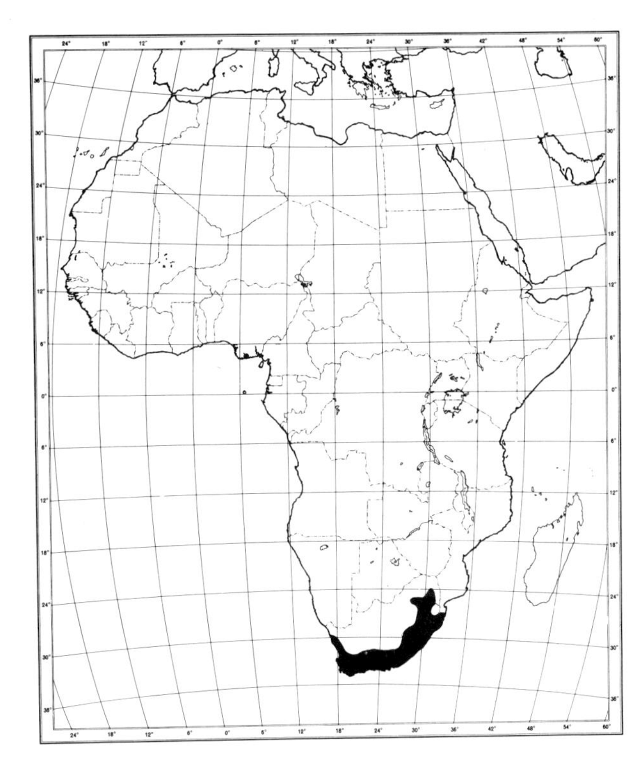

### Habitat
Like *M. cafer* this species prefers a moist, densely vegetated habitat. On the Transvaal Highveld they occur in dense grass along the banks of streams and in the Cape Province on coastal mountains under drier conditions, where there is a continuous cover of low succulent bushes subsisting on a low rainfall, but where mists are frequent.

### Habits
From observations in captivity, Goulden & Meester (1978) found that the forest shrew, *M. varius*, is intermittently active throughout the day and night. They are most active during the night when bouts of activity lasting from one to two hours would be interspersed with periods of rest lasting up to 15 minutes. During the day they would remain in the nest for one or two hours at a time, coming out to forage or defecate for a few minutes at a time. They rest in a relaxed crouch with the feet and tail tucked under the body. When sleeping they lie on their bellies, the head tucked under their

chest, the feet and tail under the body or with their head, tail and legs to one side. They sleep very heavily and when there is a pair in the nest they sleep head to tail.

They are active burrowers but never achieve the excavation of more than very shallow blind tunnels leading under rocks or other objects. They dig with their front claws and the snout. They will use existing burrows and holes and have been dug out of molerat burrows. The nests are constructed of soft, pliable grass with one or more entrances usually alongside rocks, one of the entrances giving access to a blind tunnel under them. Given the choice of stony ground or soil on which to build their nests, they invariably choose the latter (Goulden & Meester, 1978).

They groom their fur by scratching with their hind feet and nibbling with their teeth, and wash their faces by passing the forepaws over them. They scratch constantly, often stopping in mid-run to do so, then nibbling on the paws. Both sexes have lateral glands on the side of their bodies which Pearson (1946) suggested may, by rubbing against grasses and other objects, leave an individual odour which may serve to demarcate territories. They also rub their bodies on the ground and this habit, and by huddling close to objects in their home range, may transfer their scent to these.

They vocalise with a short, sharp squeak when alarmed or when fighting and make comfort noises when a pair are together and will chitter when settling into the nest. They sometimes adopt an offensive or defensive posture with their mouths wide open, no audible sound being emitted (Goulden & Meester, 1978).

In captivity they deposit their faeces in a specific corner of the cage, usually urinating at the same time. Although coprophagy is found amongst most shrews it was not noted in this species. They are a particularly aggressive species (Wolhuter, pers. comm.).

### Food

In captivity, Goulden & Meester (1978) stated that they readily ate earthworms, locusts, grasshoppers, bagworms, termites and beetles in addition to the mincemeat provided. Small insects were beheaded and bitten rapidly down the abdomen before being eaten. Large insects such as locusts were tossed in the air, the hind legs broken off by twisting or jerking, then dealt with in the same way as the smaller. They seldom ate earthworms, slugs or snails unless very hungry. While feeding they crouch in front of the food and nibble at it *in situ* but would carry large food items back to the nest to be eaten. They are cannibalistic and will eat rodent carcasses. They drink frequently but never take large amounts at a time, sometimes taking a mouthful, raising the head and allowing the water to trickle down their throats.

### Reproduction

In captivity, Goulden & Meester (1978) noted that in establishing pairs the two individuals at first would react aggressively towards each other before settling down, this occasionally leading to brief physical encounters, but usually only to squeaking contests. In courting behaviour the male would chase the female and try to catch her by the loose skin around the neck. This was accompanied by sharp high-pitched squeaking and a strong musk odour. No successful matings were observed.

In the Transvaal, Rautenbach (1978) recorded gravid females during the months from September to March, suggesting that the young are born during the warm, wet, summer months.

## Genus *Suncus* Ehrenberg, 1833

Heim de Balsac & Meester (1977) recognised six species as occurring on the continent, three of which occur in the Subregion; *S. lixus*, *S. varilla* and *S. infinitesimus*. All three are tiny species, the largest, *S. lixus*, with an average length of head and body of 69 mm, the smallest, *S. infinitesimus*, about 58 mm. Very little is known about their life histories.

Key to the species (Meester & Lambrechts, 1971)

1. Size largest, condylo-incisive length (C1) 19–21 mm, length of upper tooth row 7,4–8,8 mm, mandible and incisor length 11,0–12,6 mm; colour greyish above, paler grey below, dorsal and ventral colour intergrading gradually

   ... *lixus*

   Size smaller, condylo-incisive length 13,9–17,5 mm, length of upper tooth row, mandible and incisor length 8,1–10,4 mm.

   ... 2

2. Size larger, condylo-incisive length 15,1–17,5 mm, length of upper toothrow 6,0–7,1 mm, mandible and incisor length 8,7–10,4 mm; colour greyish-chestnut above, silvery-fawn below, dorsal and ventral colour sharply demarcated

   ... *varilla*

   Size smaller, condylo-incisive length 13,9–15,2 mm, length of upper tooth row 5,3–6,3 mm, mandible and incisor length 8,1–9,2 mm; colour greyish-brown above, greyish below, dorsal and ventral colour intergrading gradually

   ... *infinitesimus*

No. 4

## *Suncus lixus* (Thomas, 1898)

## Greater dwarf shrew
## Groter dwergskeerbek

Plate 1

### Colloquial Name

The colloquial name indicates that, although they are a very tiny shrew, this species is the largest of the three species of the genus that occurs in the Subregion.

### Taxonomic Notes

This species originally was described from a specimen from the Nyika Plateau, northern Malawi. Two subspecies are recognised by Meester *et al.* (1986): *S.l. lixus*, which is recorded from Zimbabwe and northern Botswana, and *S.l. gratulus* (Thomas & Schwann, 1907) from the Transvaal.

### Description

Greater dwarf shrews have a total length of about 110 mm, with tails that are about 65% of the length of the body and a mass of about 8,0 g (Table 4.1). The upper parts of the head and body are grey with a brown tinge which gradually disappears to give way to the paler grey of the under parts. The upper surface of the hands and feet are white or off-white, the tail bi-coloured, brown on the upper surface and yellowish on the under, with sparse short hairs closely applied to its surface and a few long hairs scattered over the basal half to two thirds of its length (Meester & Lambrechts, 1971).

**Table 4.1**

Measurements (mm) of greater dwarf-shrews, *S. lixus*, from the Transvaal (Meester & Lambrechts, 1971)

**Irrespective of sex**

| | $\bar{x}$ | n | Range |
|---|---|---|---|
| (TL | 114 | 6) | |
| HB | 69 | 6 | 52–81 |
| T | 45 | 6 | 36–51 |

### Distribution

Throughout their distributional range there are only few and scattered records of this species.

*South of the Sahara, excluding the Southern African Subregion*

They are recorded from **Malawi, Zambia, Tanzania** and **Kenya** (if *S. aequatorius* Heller, 1912 is considered to be a synonym).

*Southern African Subregion*

There are two records of this species from northeastern **Botswana**; one from the Fort Victoria District, **Zimbabwe**, and one from western Gaza District of **Mozambique** near the Transvaal border. They are recorded as occurring widely in the eastern **Transvaal** with an extension in a southwesterly direction from the northeast of the province through Tzaneen to Rustenburg.

### Habitat

Rautenbach 1978 recorded that, in the Transvaal, they occur in damp situations in riverine forest. In Zimbabwe they were taken in savannna woodland and in the Makgadikgadi Pan area, Botswana, in open dry scrub.

### Food

Insectivorous.

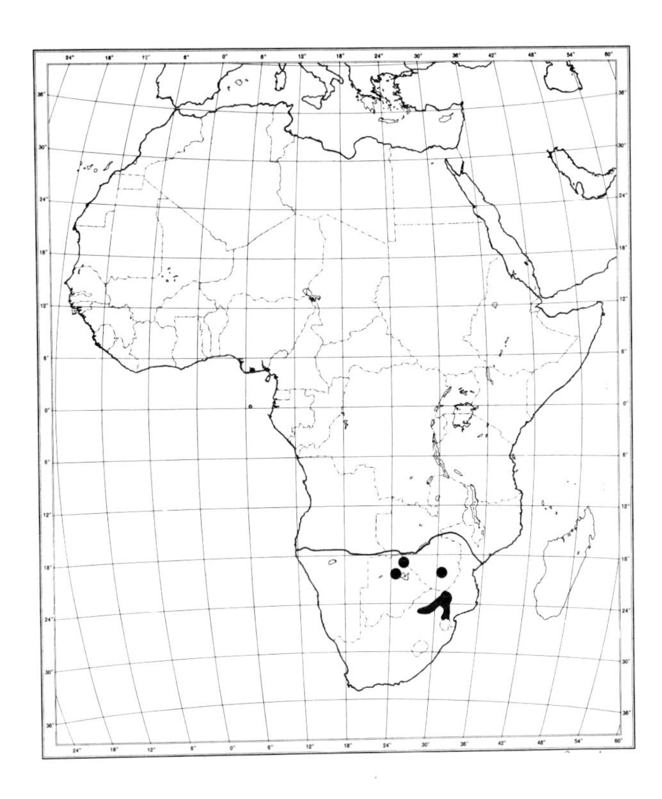

### Habits and Reproduction

No information available.

---

No. 5

## *Suncus varilla* (Thomas, 1895)

## Lesser dwarf shrew
## Kleiner dwergskeerbek

Plate 1

---

### Colloquial Name

In size this species ranks between the greater dwarf shrew, *S. lixus*, and the least dwarf shrew, *S. infinitesimus*.

### Taxonomic Notes

Meester *et al.* (1986) listed four subspecies: *S.v. varilla* (Thomas, 1985) from East London; *S. v. orangiae* (Roberts, 1924) from southern Natal, the Orange Free State; northeastern Zimbabwe and the Beira District of Mozambique, south of the Zambezi River; *S.v. warreni* Roberts, 1929 from the southwestern Cape Province north to Port Nolloth and *S.v. tulbaghensis* Roberts, 1946 from Eendekuil, southeastern Cape Province.

### Description

Adult lesser dwarf shrews have an average total length of 89 mm with tails that are about 60% of the length of the head and body and a mass of some 6,5 g (Table 5.1). The colour of the upper parts is greyish-chestnut, the under parts pale silvery-fawn, the two colours sharply demarcated one from another. The hands and feet are white, the tail brown or buffy on the upper surface, paler on the under, and more hairy than in *C. lixus* with more numerous short closely adpressed hairs and more numerous long bristles over most of its length (Meester & Lambrechts, 1971).

### Table 5.1

Measurements (mm) of lesser dwarf shrews, *S. varilla*, from the Orange Free State.

**Irrespective of sex**

| | $\bar{x}$ | n | Range |
|---|---|---|---|
| (TL | 89) | 79 | – |
| HB | 56 | 79 | (44–68) |
| T | 34 | 79 | (25–45) |
| Af c/u | 9 | 22 | (9–10) |
| E | 8 | 19 | (7–9) |

### Distribution

There are relatively few records of this species from some parts of its distributional range and these are scattered, making it impossible to delimit its full range in the Subregion.

*South of the Sahara, excluding the Southern African Subregion*

Recorded from northern **Malawi; Zambia** and southwestern **Tanzania.**

*Southern African Subregion*

Recorded from the western, southern central and northeastern sectors and the East London district of the **Cape Province**; the **Orange Free State**; the southern **Transvaal** and northern and southern parts of **Natal;** northeastern **Zimbabwe** and central **Mozambique**.

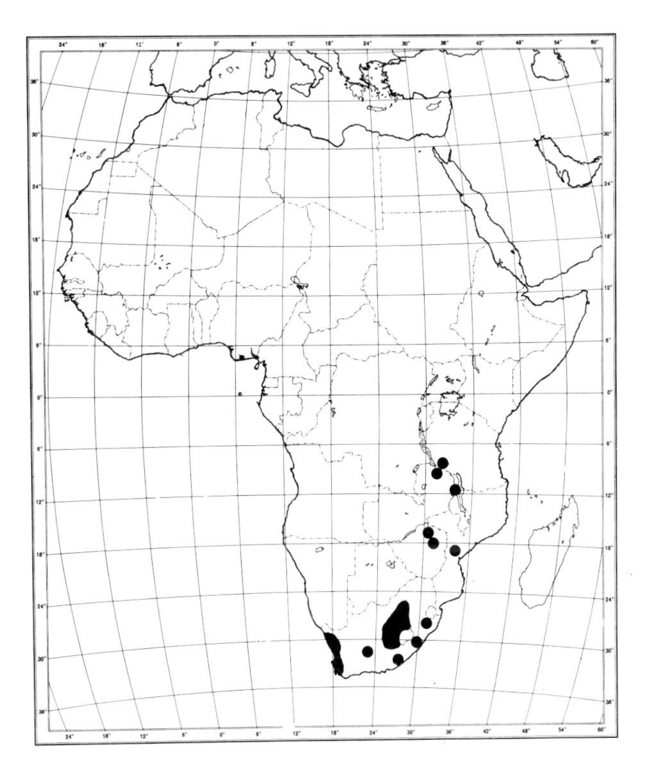

### Habitat

Lynch (1986) found that in the Orange Free State they lived in the dead mounds of the snouted harvester termite, *Trinervitervoides* which were situated in open grassland. Evidence of their occupation of these mounds was often given by the presence of their droppings which were deposited on the dome of the mounds. They appeared to choose the larger sized mounds of a diameter from 0,52 m to 1,81 m and a height of 0,12 m to 0,66 m.

### Habits

Lynch (1986) stated that they built round ball-shaped nests approximately 70 mm to 100 mm in diameter, within the dead termite mounds either above or below ground level. These nests are constructed of blades of green grass, sometimes with feathers, leaves or shreds of paper woven into them, up to three nests being constructed within a single mound.

Lynch (1986) believes that this species spends the major part of their lives within the mounds which provide a suitable stable microclimate for this tiny shrew, thus relieving it to some degree of the need of having to thermoregulate to maintain a constant body temperature.

### Food

Insectivorous.

### Reproduction

No information is available.

---

No. 6

## *Suncus infinitesimus* (Heller, 1912)

## Least dwarf shrew
## Kleinste dwergskeerbek

Plate 1

---

### Colloquial Name

This is the smallest of the three species of dwarf shrews that occur in the Subregion.

### Taxonomic Notes

Heim de Balsac & Meester (1977) listed three subspecies, only one of which, *S.i. chriseos* (Kershaw, 1921), occurs in the Subregion.

### Description

This tiny shrew has an average total length of 79 mm with a tail about 55% of the length of the head and body and a mass of from 3,0 g–4,0 g (Table 6.1). The upper parts are darker in colour than either *S. lixus* or *S. varilla*, a dark greyish-brown, and the under parts are greyish, the two colours intergrading gradually. The feet are lighter in colour than the upper parts, the tail brown on the upper surface and slightly lighter on the under surface.

### Table 6.1

Measurements (mm) of least dwarf shrews, *S. infinitesimus*, from the Subregion.

| | Males | | | Females | | |
|---|---|---|---|---|---|---|
| | $\bar{x}$ | n | Range | $\bar{x}$ | n | Range |
| (TL | 82) | | | (82) | | |
| HB | 53 | 12 | (46–60) | 53 | 9 | (45–61) |
| T | 29 | 12 | (24–35) | 29 | 9 | (23–37) |
| Hf c/u | 9 | 12 | (7–10) | 9 | 9 | (8–10) |
| E | 8 | 8 | (6–9) | 8 | 7 | (6–8) |

### Distribution

Records are few and scattered but indicate a wide distribution on the continent.

*South of the Sahara, excluding the Southern African Subregion*

They are recorded from northern **Nigeria**, if Morrison-Scott's (1946) *S. etruscus* is considered to be synonymous; the **Central African Republic** and **Kenya**.

*Southern African Subregion*

They are recorded from the southern **Transvaal**, western **Orange Free State**, southern **Natal** and the eastern coastal parts of the **Cape Province** as far west as Knysna.

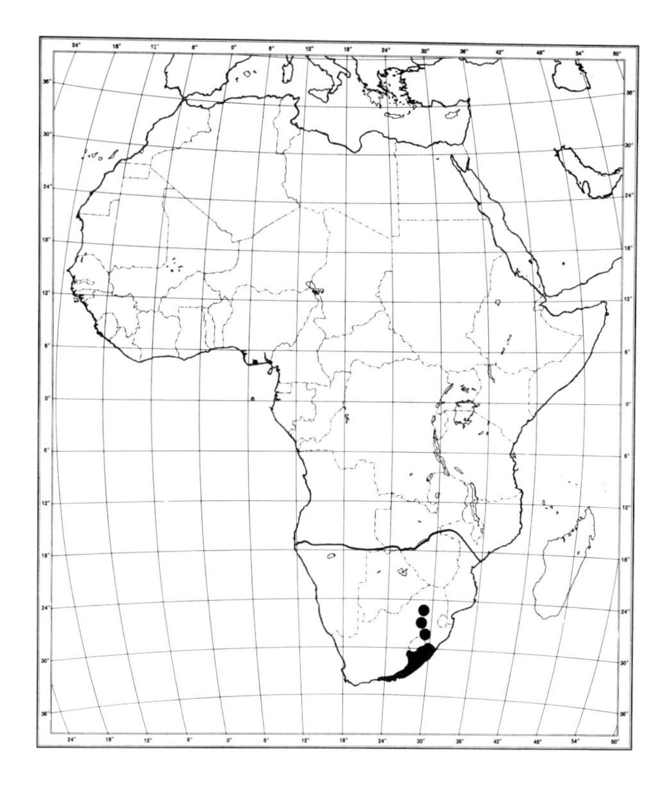

### Habitat

In the Transvaal, Rautenbach (1978) recorded taking them in termite mounds and in the Knysna area they occur in forest.

### Plate 1

1. Long-tailed forest shrew, *Myosorex longicaudatus*
   Langstertbosskeerbek
2. Dark-footed forest shrew, *Myosorex cafer*
   Donkerpootbosskeerbek
3. Forest shrew, *Myosorex varius*
   Bosskeerbek
4. Greater dwarf shrew, *Suncus lixus*
   Groter dwergskeerbek
5. Lesser dwárf shrew, *Suncus varilla*
   Kleiner dwergskeerbek
6. Least dwarf shrew, *Suncus infinitesimus*
   Kleinste dwergskeerbek
7. Swamp musk shrew, *Crocidura mariquensis*
   Vleiskeerbek
8. Tiny musk shrew, *Crocidura fuscomurina*
   Dwergskeerbek
9. Maquassie musk shrew, *Crocidura maquassiensis*
   Maquassie-skeerbek
10. Reddish-grey musk shrew, *Crocidura cyanea*
    Rooigrysskeerbek

PLATE · I
1
2
3
4
5
6
7
8
9
10
Dick Findlay '86.

### Habits

Rautenbach (1978) stated that they are terrestrial, usually occur solitarily, and are active for short periods throughout both the day and night.

### Food

Insectivorous.

### Reproduction

No information available.

## Genus *Crocidura* Wagler, 1832

This genus has a very wide distribution, not only in Africa but in Europe and Asia extending eastwards through China to the coast of the Pacific Ocean and to Japan. It is represented in the Subregion by nine species which range in size from the largest, the greater musk shrew, *C. flavescens*, which has a total length of about 200 mm and a mass of about 35,0 g, to small species such as the tiny musk shrew, *C. bicolor*, at 100 mm and a mass of about 6,0 g. A great deal remains to be learnt about the relationships of the species, their distribution and geographic variation, and compared with other mammalian species we know very little about their life histories in the wild. Allen (1939) listed no less than 162 species and subspecies from Africa, Roberts (1951) 23 from the Subregion alone. Heim de Balsac & Meester (1977) in their review of the genus remarked that it was the most complex of any of the African shrew genera and perhaps of any mammalian species, including as it does an overwhelming diversity of often poorly defined forms. They concluded that much more collecting will have to be carried out before the taxonomy of the genus can be satisfactorily clarified. As an example of this, Meester (1963) in his Thesis on the genus *Crocidura*, had 367 specimens of *C. flavescens* on which to base his findings, but on the other hand only three *C. maquassiensis*. Work towards this end is now proceeding and modern techniques of chromosome and multi-variate analyses are being applied in an effort to sort out the present complex situation (Dippenaar, 1980).

In their review Heim de Balsac & Meester (1977) recognised 85 species from the continent, remarking that certainly not all of these are valid, of which they recognise eight as occurring in the Subregion. A ninth being added subsequently by the recognition of *C. occidentalis* as a valid species which, in the first edition, was considered synonymous with *C. flavescens*.

Members of this genus are very adaptable and are found in a wide variety of habits which range from areas in which the terrain is arid or semi-desert with a mean annual rainfall of about 100 mm to moist forests in the northeastern parts of the Subregion where this may be as much as 1 500 mm per year. However, they do not occur in the Namib Desert in the western coastal areas of Namibia. In some cases up to three or four species occur sympatrically. While some of them can be recognised reasonably easily on account of their size and other features, others present difficulties as their characters are ill-defined. Colour varies and, in some cases, is similar in different species and the minutae of differences in the dentition are difficult to appreciate except to the specialist conversant with the group. As in the case of the bats, therefore, it is recognised that the layman will have difficulties in identifying some of the species.

The dental formula of members of the genus is:

$I\frac{3}{1}\ C\frac{1}{0}\ P\frac{1}{2}\ M\frac{3}{3} = 28$

While in the upper jaw all three incisor teeth are present, in the lower jaw only $I_2$ is present, the canine absent. The single premolar in the upper jaw is $P^4$, the two in the lower jaw $P_1$. In the upper jaw $I^1$ is hooked, the forward curve of the tooth projecting beyond the tip of the jaw. In the lower jaw $I_2$ projects far forward from the tip of the jaw, being elongated in a forward direction from the root of the tooth (Heim de Balsac & Lamotte, 1957; Meester, 1963). Dippenaar (1979a) points out that there still remains much confusion as to the homologies of the "unicuspidate" teeth in the lower jaw but, until the issue is resolved, follows this plan (Fig. I.1).

Males of the genus have abdominal testes, the females three pairs of inguinal mammae. Their skulls do not have either auditory bullae or zygomatic arches.

Shrews of this genus are territorial, with well developed home ranges that are defended vigorously. Within the range they establish ill-defined pathways on which they move around (Meester, 1963). Intruders are chased off with squeaking and if necessary, energetic attacks. Strange male lesser musk shrews, *C. hirta*, introduced to containers with an established male will squeak at each other first, then rise on their back legs and slash at each other's heads with the teeth (Smithers, 1983). They are vociferous and vocalise with a soft twittering with the mouth closed or staccato squeaks with the mouth open, which in the young becomes a soft chirring (Meester, 1963).

In most species the moult is well marked in the pelage, the shorter, brighter, new hair contrasting with the old. In *C. mariquensis*, Dippenaar (1977) found that the variation in colour usually can be accounted for by the obvious differences between juvenile and adult pelages. In juveniles the pelage is usually greyer on the upper and under parts of the body and generally paler than in the adults. Most of the variation is accounted for, however, by the adult moults: the new long fur on the upper parts of the body in the winter pelage and the new short fur of the summer pelage which is darker and blacker than the fur it replaces. New fur on the under parts is usually paler and greyer than the fur it replaces. Meester (1963) found that, in some species, moulting individuals are found in all months of the year, but that post-juvenile and spring moults can be recognised. The time of the post-juvenile moult is determined by the age of the young, the spring moult taking place most commonly from about August to November.

Coprophagy or the eating of faeces is common and in the giant musk shrew, *C. flavescens*, and lesser musk shrew, *C. hirta*, Meester (1963) recorded that they would lick their everted rectum. This allows for the augmenting of the bacillus population in the digestive system which is responsible for the breaking down of chitin into substances which can be utilised by the body.

Like other mammals shrews have ectoparasites in the form of ticks and fleas. Among the latter *Dinopsyllus ellobius*, *D. longifrons* and *Xenopsyllus brazileinsis* have been identified, all of which play a part in the transmission of plague.

Key to the species after Meester *et al.* (1986)

1. Larger, condylo-incisive skull length (C1) normally greater than 25 mm

   ... 2

   Smaller, C1 normally less than 25 mm

   ... 3

2. Larger, C1 greater than 30 mm; dorsally dull dark brown, ventrally buffy-brown washed with dark grey

   ... *Crocidura occidentalis*

   Smaller, C1 less than 30 mm; dorsally cinnamon-brown, ventrally silvery-grey

   ... *Crocidura flavescens*

3. Larger, C1 *c.* 22–25 mm

   ... 4

   Smaller, C1 less than 22 mm

   ... 5

4. Dorsally cinnamon-brown or pale fawn, ventrally silvery-grey or cream; $M^3$ not particularly robust, $M_3$ with simple, conical hypoconid, entoconid minute or absent

   ... *Crocidura hirta*

   Dorsally grey-brown, ventrally grey; $M^3$ robust $M_3$ with hypoconid adjoined by an anterolingual fovea

   ... *Crocidura luna*

5. Dorsally blackish-brown or black, ventrally dark brown

   ... *Crocidura mariquensis*

   Dorsally greyish-fawn, grey-brown, buffy-brown or brown, ventrally silvery-grey or grey

   ... 6

6. Larger, C1 *c.* 19–22 mm

   ... 7

   Smaller, C1 *c.* 15,5–19,0 mm

   ... 8

7. (In above 500 mm mean annual rainfall zone) Dorsally buffy-brown, ventrally silvery-grey, $M_3$ normally lacking entoconid; or (in below 500 mm m.a.r. zone) dorsally grey-brown, ventrally grey, $M_3$ with or without entoconid

   ... *Crocidura cyanea*

   (Occurs only in above 500 mm m.a.r. zone) Dorsally brown, ventrally light grey; $M_3$ usually with traces of an entoconid

   ... *Crocidura silacea*

8. Slightly smaller, C1 *c.* 15,5–18,0 mm; dorsally grey-brown or greyish-fawn, ventrally silvery-grey; $M_3$ lacking entoconid

   ... *Crocidura fuscomurina*

   Slightly larger, C1 *c.* 17,5–19,0 mm; dorsally grey-brown, ventrally grey; $M_3$ with well-developed entoconid

   ... *Crocidura maquassiensis*

*C. cyanea* and *C. silacea* are difficult to distinguish, hence cannot be keyed out easily. This is particularly evident when the sympatric *C.c. infumata* and *silacea* are compared. However, detailed comparison, particularly using multivariate methods, confirms that they are valid species (Meester *et al.*, 1986).

No. 7

## *Crocidura mariquensis* (A. Smith, 1844)

## Swamp musk shrew
## Vleiskeerbek

Plate 1

### Colloquial Name

This species is associated particularly with a swampy environment.

### Taxonomic Note

Meester *et al.* (1986) recognised subspecies as occurring in the Subregion; *C.m. mariquensis* which occurs in Natal, the northern Orange Free State, Transvaal and Mozambique, and *C.m. shortridgei* St. Leger, 1932 which occurs from northeastern Namibia to the extreme northwestern parts of Zimbabwe. Dippenaar (1979a) recognised a third subspecies, *C.m. neavei* Wroughton, 1907, from Zambia.

### Description

Swamp musk shrews have a total length of about 140 mm with tails that are up to 69% of the length of the head and body, the males with a mass in *C.m. mariquensis* of about 12,0 g; in *C.m. shortridgei* males 11,7 g, females 9,0 g (Table 7.1). In *C.m. mariquensis* the upper parts of the body are blackish-brown, lightly grizzled with reddish-fawn in the worn pelage and fuscous-black in the new pelage. The individual hairs have slaty-grey bases, with reddish-fawn to reddish-brown subterminal annulations and blackish-brown tips. The under parts are slightly paler in colour with a silvery sheen. The individual hairs have slaty-brown bases and fawn or light brown tips. The upper surfaces of the hands and feet are light reddish-brown to black. The tail is blackish-brown on the upper surface, sometimes slightly paler below, the two colours merging gradually.

In *C.m. shortridgei* the upper parts of the body are dark brown, the under parts slightly paler with a silvery sheen. The individual hairs are slaty-grey at the bases, with a reddish-fawn or reddish-brown subterminal annulation and dark brown tips. The under parts are paler than the upper, with a fawn grizzling, the individual hairs slaty-grey at the bases with fawn-coloured tips, the colour of the upper and under parts merge gradually. The hair on the upper parts of the hands and feet varies from light brown to black. The tail is dark brown to black, sometimes paler below, well haired, with long caudal bristles on the quarter to two thirds of the basal length. The fresh summer pelage is browner and less reddish than the worn winter pelage.

**Table 7.1**

Measurements (mm) and mass (g) of swamp musk shrews, *C. mariquensis*, *C.m. mariquensis* from the Transvaal (Meester, 1963) and *C.m. shortridgei*, northern Botswana (Smithers, 1971).

*C.m. mariquensis*

**Irrespective of sex**

| | $\bar{x}$ | n | Range |
|---|---|---|---|
| (TL | 128 | 11) | |
| HB | 76 | 11 | 60–87 |
| T | 52 | 11 | 40–60 |
| Hf c/u | 15 | 11 | 13–16 |
| E | 7 | 10 | 6–8 |

*C.m. shortridgei*

| | Males | | | Females | | |
|---|---|---|---|---|---|---|
| | $\bar{x}$ | n | Range | $\bar{x}$ | n | Range |
| TL | 144 | 51 | 128–156 | 133 | 50 | 112–155 |
| T | 61 | 50 | 50–72 | 56 | 50 | 42–71 |
| Hf c/u | 17 | 52 | 15–19 | 16 | 50 | 13–18 |
| E | 9 | 52 | 7–11 | 8 | 50 | 6–10 |
| Mass | 11,7 | 46 | 9,8–16,5 | 9,0 | 50 | 6,1–13,9 |

### Distribution

This species occurs in two discrete areas in the Subregion, separated by a broad area of unsuitable terrain; the two populations are sub-specifically differentiated, the northern as *C.m. shortridgei*, the southern *C.m. mariquensis*.

*South of the Sahara, excluding the Southern African Subregion*

This species is recorded from south central **Angola; Zambia;** and southeastern **Zaire**.

*Southern African Subregion*

*C.m. shortridgei* occurs in northeastern **Namibia**; in the Okavango Delta in northern **Botswana** south to Maun and along the Chobe River to the Zimbabwe border and in the extreme northwestern parts of **Zimbabwe** in the Zambezi Valley east to Nampini farm, about 60 km west of the Victoria Falls. *C.m. mariquensis* occurs in the central and southern parts of the Transvaal; the extreme northern parts of the Orange Free State and in central and coastal **Natal**, south to about 30 °S.

### Habitat

Swamp musk shrews live in moist habitats, such as in thick grass along river banks, in reedbeds and in swamp. In the Okavango Swamp and along the Chobe River, in northern Botswana, *C. m. shortridgei* abounds in the tangled masses of semi-aquatic grasses along the fringes of the water, and in the litter piles deposited by the receding floods. They were trapped frequently in the runways of vlei rats, *Otomys* sp and were not averse to occurring where the substrate was wet but were also found in the drier grassland back from the water's edge. Of the two subspecies, *shortridgei* on the whole appears to prefer a wetter habitat.

### Habits

Like other musk shrews they are active both at night and by day, being trapped at a wide variety of times throughout the 24 hour period. They were trapped regularly in the runways made by vlei rats. *Otomys* sp, and water rats, *Dasymys incomtus*.

### Food

Insectivorous.

### Reproduction

*C. m. shortridgei* appears to have an extended breeding season, gravid females having been taken on the Chobe river

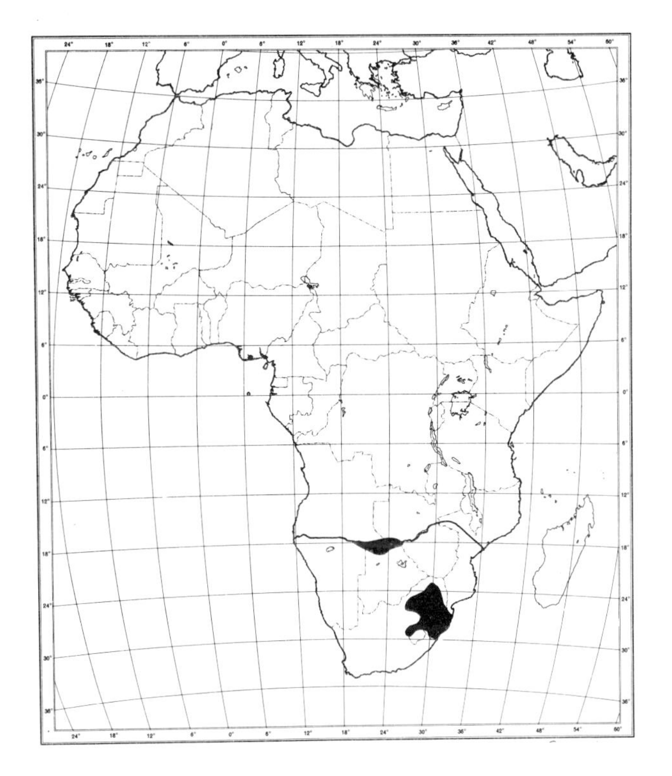

in northeastern Botswana in every month from August to December and from February to April. Although a series of females was examined, taken during the months of May to July, the colder months of the year, no gravid females were recorded. In the sample the average number of foetuses per female was $\bar{x}$ = 3,3 (n = 22) with a range of from two to five (Smithers, 1971). The young are born in nests constructed from soft vegetable debris deep in clumps of tussock grasses on slightly raised patches of ground on the fringes of swamp. In the eastern parts of the Okavango Swamp a nest was found in a pile of debris deposited by floods on top of the grass about 300 mm above the ground.

No. 8

## *Crocidura fuscomurina* (Heuglin, 1865)

## Tiny musk shrew
## Dwergskeerbek

Plate 1

### Colloquial Name

As the name indicates this is a very small species, the smallest member of the genus that occurs in the Subregion.

### Taxonomic Notes

Meester *et al* (1986) listed two subspecies from the Subregion: *C. f. bicolor* Bocage, 1889 which occurs in the northern Orange Free State, Transvaal, Zimbabwe, Mozambique and in eastern and northeastern Botswana and *C. f. woosnami* Dollman, 1915 from the southern Orange Free State, northern and central Botswana, the Caprivi and northern Namibia. The nominate *C.f. fuscomurina* (Heuglin, 1865) was described originally from material from the Sudan.

### Description

Adults of this tiny species have a total length of about 100 mm with tails that are between 17% (*C. f. bicolor*) and 18% (*C. f. woosnami*) of the length of the head and body and have a mass of between 4,0 g (*C. f. bicolor*) and 6,0 g (*C. f. woosnami*) (Table 8.1). Judging from the average measurements given in Table 8.1 *C. f. woosnami*, in most respects, is slightly larger than *C. f. bicolor*.

*C. f. bicolor* is grey-brown on the upper parts of the body, grizzled with grey; the individual hairs are slaty-grey at their bases, with fawn-coloured subterminal annulations and brown or buffy-brown tips. The under parts are silvery-grey, some specimens with a yellowish tinge, the individual hairs with slaty-grey bases with white or off-white tips. The upper surfaces of the hands and feet are off-white to light brown. The tail is light to dark brown above, paler below with a sharp demarcation between the two colours. The basal three quarters of the tail is sparsely covered with long bristles.

*C. f. woosnami* is greyish-fawn on the upper parts of the body; the individual hairs have slaty-grey bases with pale fawn subterminal annulations and brown or buffy-brown tips. The under parts are pale silvery-grey lightly grizzled with grey, the individual hairs with slaty-grey bases and broad white or off-white tips. The upper surfaces of the hands and feet are off-white. The tail is pale fawn or light brown above, slightly paler below, with a gradual transition between the two colours. The basal three quarters or more of the tail is sparsely covered with long bristles.

**Table 8.1**

Measurements (mm) and mass (g) of tiny musk shrews, *C. f. woosnami* (Smithers, 1971) and *C. f. bicolor* (Meester, 1963)

*T. f. woosnami* (Smithers, 1971)

| | Males | | | Females | | |
|---|---|---|---|---|---|---|
| | $\bar{x}$ | n | Range | $\bar{x}$ | n | Range |
| TL | 108 | 9 | 90–100 | 105 | 8 | 93–115 |
| T | 45 | 8 | 36–49 | 43 | 8 | 40–46 |
| Hf c/u | 13 | 9 | 12–14 | 12 | 8 | 1–12 |
| E | 9 | 7 | 8–10 | 9 | 8 | 7–10 |
| Mass | 5,8 | 8 | 4,5–6,8 | 5,7 | 7 | 4,2–6,8 |

*T. f. bicolor* (Meester, 1963)

**Irrespective of sex**

| | $\bar{x}$ | n | Range |
|---|---|---|---|
| (TL | 97) | | |
| HB | 58 | not given | 48–75 |
| T | 39 | not given | 28–50 |
| Hf c/u | 10 | not given | 8–11 |
| E | 7 | not given | 7–9 |

Rautenbach (1978) gives the mass (g) of *C. f. bicolor* for the Transvaal as:

| | Males | | | Females | | |
|---|---|---|---|---|---|---|
| | $\bar{x}$ | n | Range | $\bar{x}$ | n | Range |
| Mass | 4,4 | 3 | 4,0–5,0 | 3,0 | 5 | 2,0–3,0 |

### Distribution

*South of the Sahara, excluding the Southern African Subregion*

They are recorded from **Kenya;** northern **Tanzania; Zambia; Angola; Malawi;** and **Mozambique,** north of the Zambezi River.

*Southern African Subregion*

They occur in northern **Namibia;** in northern and northeastern **Botswana,** with records from the extreme southeastern parts of the country; widely in **Zimbabwe** and in **Mozambique,** south of the Zambezi River. In the **Transvaal** they occur widely in the eastern parts of the Province and throughout parts of the central and southwestern sectors, in the northern and southwestern **Orange Free State** and in the extreme northeastern parts of the **Cape Province**.

### Habitat

In northern Botswana, they live on the fringe of the Okavango Swamp and along rivers in fallen, matted "litindi" grass, *Vossia cuspidata*, which provides good overhead cover and also in the thick cover of couch grass, *Cynodon dactylon*, along the water's edge. Shortridge (1934) stated that they favour dry, sandy soil near water and Vesey-Fitzgerald (1962) recorded the species from rubbish heaps and wood piles and also from under the herb mat in grassland, where the grass remains green throughout the year. The type of *C. f. woosnami* was taken in swampy country among reeds, but it also occurs in the western Okavango in Botswana in arid terrain where water is only available seasonally (Smithers, 1971). In general terms *C. f. bicolor* occurs in the Southern Savanna Zone, *C. f. woosnami* in the South West Arid Zone.

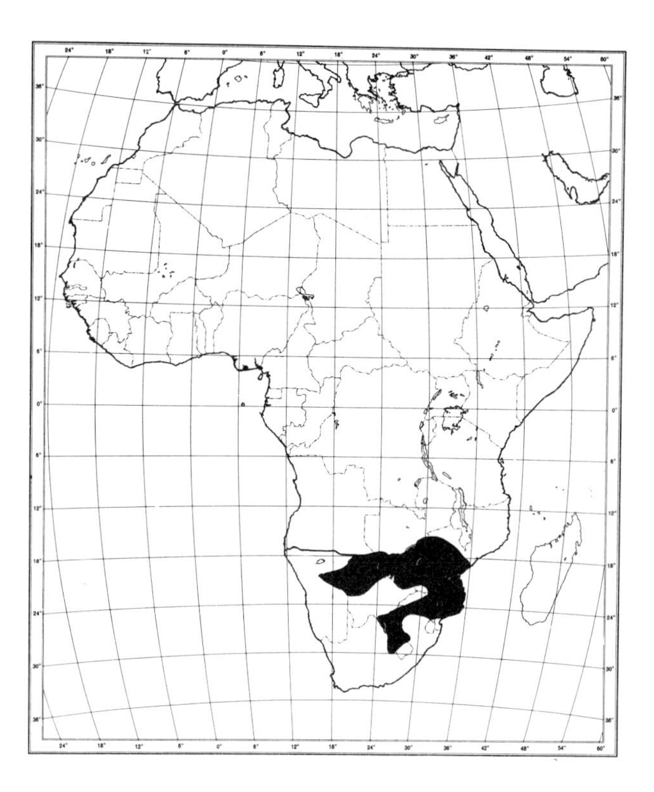

## Habits

Little is known about the habits of this species but, like other shrews of the genus *Crocidura*, they appear, from trapping records, to be active both nocturnally and diurnally.

## Food

Insectivorous.

## Reproduction

Meester (1963) recorded gravid females in November and December and a specimen from Kasane, Botswana was gravid with four foetuses in December. Watson & Watson (1986) recorded that a female taken in March in the Kruger National Park gave birth to two altricial young which weaned in 23 to 27 days after birth. The one survivor was carried round on the back of the female until it was 24 days old, there being no sign of caravanning. This meagre information suggests that the young are born during the warm, wet months of the year.

Dippenaar (1979b) recorded the post-natal development of a litter of four young, which were born in a clothing cupboard in a house in the Transvaal in February 1974. The female and the litter were brought into captivity and the following observations made. The young were born naked at a mass of about 1,4 g. At birth the snout is bulbous, gradually becoming more slender and mobile and by the 13th day resembled that of the adults. The young left the nesting box for the first time on the 17th day, first attempting to eat solid food on the 19th day. Caravanning was witnessed on the third day, when the young were placed outside the nest box. Upon hearing their squeaking, the female approached them and presented her rump whereupon one of the young bit into it above the tail and was caravanned back to the nest box. A second young would join the caravan either biting into the rump of the female alongside the first, when it usually would fall off, then biting into the rump of the first young which was still attached, to be dragged back to the nest. In this species caravanning continued up to the 19th day.

On the first day after birth the skin on the back had a grey pigmentation which progressively darkened up to the seventh day. The upper parts of the body were sparsely covered with short whitish hairs. By the seventh day the body had acquired a covering of short greyish-brown hair on the upper parts and whitish hair on the under parts and, by the 10th day, the pelage was similar to that of the adults. Their eyes were closed at birth, eye slits appearing on the fourth day and the eyes opened on the 12th day.

---

No. 9

# *Crocidura maquassiensis* Roberts, 1946

## Maquassie musk shrew
## Maquassie-skeerbek

Plate 1

---

## Colloquial Name

Named after the type locality Maquassie, Wolmaransstad district, western Transvaal.

## Taxonomic Notes

There is still some doubt as to the validity of this species which may well be a variant of *C. cyanea* or a southern form of *C. suaveolens* (Pallas, 1811). (Meester *et al.* 1986). Ellerman *et al.* (1953) considered it a subspecies of the Palaearctic *C. russula*, noting that it has a longer tail. Meester (1963) prefers to consider it a valid species until such time as the links between the widely separated distributional ranges of this species and *C.russula* are shown and further data are available to show that this relationship is more than just a superficial similarity.

## Description

This is a very small species, only slightly larger than the tiny musk shrew, *C. bicolor*, and smaller than the reddish-grey musk shrew, *C. cyanea*. Adults have a total length of about 100 mm with tails which are about 71% of the length of the head and body(Table 9.1). The colour of the upper parts of the body is grey-brown, washed with grey. The individual hairs are slaty-grey at their bases, with a fawn-coloured subterminal annulation and brown tips. The under parts are grey, tinged with fawn. The individual hairs have slaty-grey bases and light grey tips, the colour of the upper and under parts merging gradually. The upper parts of the hands and feet are light brown. The tail is dark brown above, not much paler below, the two shades of colour merging gradually. The basal two-thirds to three-quarters of the tail has a sparse sprinkling of long bristles (Meester, 1963).

## Table 9.1

Measurements (mm) of three Maquassie musk shrews, *C. maquassiensis* (Meester, 1963).

**Irrespective of sex**

| | $\bar{x}$ | n | Range |
|---|---|---|---|
| (TL | 106 | 3) | |
| HB | 62 | 3 | 55–74 |
| T | 44 | 3 | 43–46 |
| Hf c/u | 11 | 3 | 11–12 |
| E | 8 | 3 | 8–9 |

## Distribution

This is a rare species and is at present known from only six localities, all lying within the Subregion: Bulawayo and Inyanga, **Zimbabwe**; Motlateng, Blouberg, Krugersdorp and Maquassie, **Transvaal**, and Mbabane, **Swaziland**.

## Habitat

With so few records it is impossible to assess the habitat requirements of this species properly. The original type was collected in a house, the Motlateng specimen on a mountainside under a rock, among grass and sparse trees at an altitude of 1 580 m. While there is no record as to exactly where the Inyanga specimen was taken, the area is montane grassland with rocky substrate and relic patches of forest at an altitude of 1 800 m. The Bulawayo specimen was taken in a rocky area (Dippenaar, *in litt.*).

### Habits, Food and Reproduction

Except for the fact that they are probably insectivorous, like other species of *Crocidura*, there is no information available on these aspects of their life history.

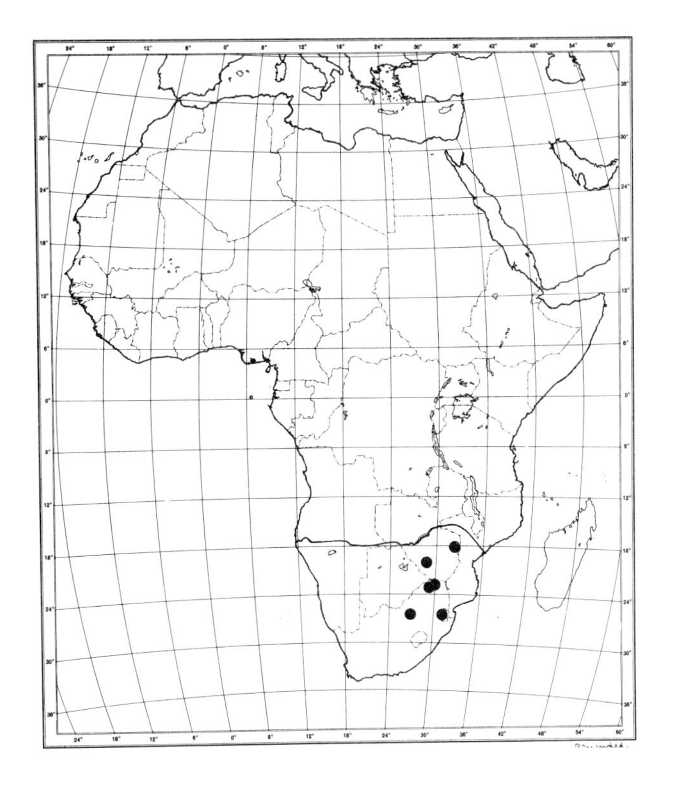

No. 10

## *Crocidura cyanea* (Duvernoy, 1838)

## Reddish-grey musk shrew
## Rooigrysskeerbek

Plate 1

### Colloquial Name

There is unfortunately a considerable variation in colour of the upper parts of the body, but there is a tendency in individuals from the western parts of the species range, from which the species originally was described (Citrusdal, western Cape Province), to have a reddish tinge. In the later described *C. c. infumata* the name is barely appropriate as they are reddish-fawn in colour.

### Taxonomic Notes

Heim de Balsac & Meester (1977) listed nine subspecies from the continent of which two occur in the Subregion: *C. c. cyanea*, which has a wide distribution in the Subregion from northern Namibia through the Cape Province to the Orange Free State and *C. c. infumata* (Wagner, 1841) from parts of the southern Cape Province northwards to the northern Transvaal, Zimbabwe and northern Botswana and Mozambique.

### Description

Reddish-grey musk shrews have a total length of about 130 mm with tails that are about 65% of the length of the head and body and a mass of 8,0 g to 9,0 g (Table 10.1). The colour of the upper parts of the body in the western *C. c. cyanea* is paler than those from the eastern parts of the Subregion and is grey with a wash of reddish-brown. In those from the eastern parts, *C. c. infumata*, they are less grey and more reddish-brown in colour. In both, the upper parts are slightly grizzled with fawn. Corresponding with the lighter colour of *C. c. cyanea*, the under parts are paler and greyer and have less of the fawn tinge seen in *C. c. infumata*. In both the subspecies the tail is paler below than on the upper surface. In the darker *C. c. infumata* it is darker on the upper surface, the two colours in both blending gradually one into the other. The upper surfaces of the feet in both are distinctly lighter in colour than the upper parts of the body and both have long hairs present on one third to seven eighths of the basal section of the tail.

**Table 10.1**

Measurements (mm) and mass (g) of reddish-grey musk shrews. *C. cyanea*, from the Transvaal (Rautenbach, 1978)

| | Males | | | Females | | |
|---|---|---|---|---|---|---|
| | $\bar{x}$ | n | Range | $\bar{x}$ | n | Range |
| TL | 132 | 25 | 110–159 | 126 | 20 | 105–143 |
| T | 52 | 24 | 42–60 | 49 | 20 | 40–55 |
| Hf c/u | 13 | 24 | 11–16 | 12 | 20 | 9–15 |
| E | 9 | 25 | 6–10 | 8 | 19 | 5–10 |
| Mass | 8,8 | 19 | 5,0–11,0 | 9,4 | 11 | 5,0–11,0 |

### Distribution

*South of the Sahara, excluding the Southern African Subregion*

They are recorded from **Ethiopia; Somalia;** southern **Sudan**; northeastern **Zaire; Uganda; Kenya; Tanzania; Angola; Zambia** and **Mozambique,** north of the Zambezi River.

*Southern African Subregion*

They occur in **Namibia;** the **Cape Province; Natal**; the **Transvaal; Botswana; Zimbabwe** and in parts of **Mozambique**, south of the Zambezi River, excluding most of the Gaza, Inhambane and southern parts of the Vila Pery and Beira districts, but occurring in the extreme south of the Maputo District.

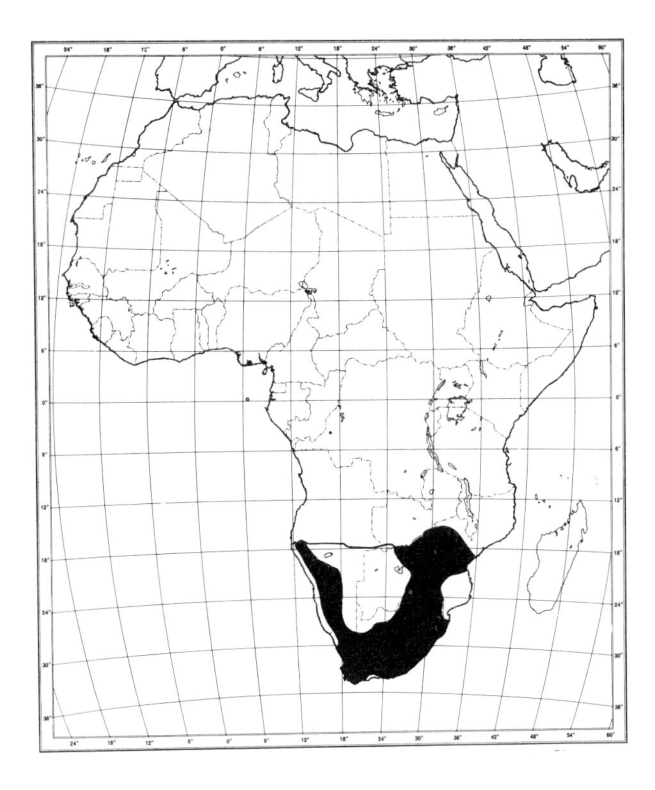

### Habitat

*C. c. cyanea* occurs in the South West Arid Zone in relatively dry terrain, with a mean annual rainfall of less than 500 mm, compared with *C. c. infumata* which replaces it in the Southern Savanna Zone in the eastern parts of the Subregion where the mean annual rainfall is in excess of this (Meester, 1963). Roberts (1936a) caught a specimen under a flat stone and others are recorded among rocks, in dense scrub and grass, in damp places and in hedges around farmlands (Meester, 1963). Rautenbach (1978) added montane forest to this. Smithers & Wilson (1979) recorded that, in Zimbabwe, they occur in grassland and in thick scrub bordering streams in the eastern parts of the country, where they were taken at an altitude of 2 430 m on Inyangani Mountain. They also occur in wet vleis with a good grass cover. In the dry western sector, Wilson (1975) collected them in scrub on Kalahari Sand as well as in reedbeds around water holes. In the drier western areas they occur in karroid scrub and in the Cape Macchia Zone, often in association with rocks. These diverse types of habitat indicate that the species has a wide habitat tolerance.

### Habits

Very little is known about this aspect of their life history. As they have been trapped both at night and by day it seems that like other crocidurids they are active sporadically throughout the 24 hour period.

### Food

Insectivorous.

### Reproduction

In the Transvaal a gravid female was taken in December with two foetuses (Rautenbach, 1978); in Namibia, Hoesch & Leymann (1956) took three gravid females in November, December and January, one with six foetuses, two with four; and in western Zimbabwe, Smithers & Wilson (1979) recorded a gravid female with two foetuses in March. This meagre information suggests that the young are born during the warm, wet summer months, but further information is required to confirm this.

---

No. 11

## *Crocidura silacea* Thomas, 1895

## Peters' musk shrew
## Peters se skeerbek

---

### Colloquial Name

Named after W.C.H. Peters who travelled widely and collected zoological material in Mozambique.

### Taxonomic Notes

Four subspecies are listed by Heim de Balsac & Meester (1977) of which only one, *C. s. silacea*, occurs in the Subregion.

### Description

This is a small species slightly smaller than *C. cyanea*. About 120 mm overall, their tails are about 70% of the length of the head and body (Table 11.1). The colour of the upper parts of the body is buffy-brown or brown lightly grizzled with pale grey or fawn. The individual hairs have slaty-grey bases, with a pale grey or fawn subterminal band and buffy-brown or brown tips. The under parts are light grey or grey with a light brown or olive tinge in worn fur, the colour of the upper and lower parts of the body merging gradually. The upper surface of the fore and hind feet is brown, yellow or white, the tail light to dark brown on the upper surface, slightly or markedly paler below, the two colours merging gradually, with long bristles over the basal half to seven eighths of its length. The fresh summer pelage is darker than the old fur. There is considerable individual variation in colour; some are more buffy-brown on the upper parts, the under parts tinged light brown, others browner on the upper parts, lacking the buffy tinge, the under parts often tinged olive (Meester, 1963).

**Table 11.1**

Measurements (mm) of Peters' musk shrews, *C. silacea*, from the subregion.

| | Males | | |
|---|---|---|---|
| | $\bar{x}$ | n | Range |
| TL | 117 | 11 | (104–125) |
| HB | 70 | 12 | (65–76) |
| T | 48 | 11 | (43–55) |
| Hf c/u | 12 | 12 | (11–13) |
| E | 9 | 11 | (8–11) |

### Distribution

*South of the Sahara, excluding the Southern African Subregion*

The extralimital distribution of this species is imperfectly known but is recorded from **Angola; Zambia; Malawi; Mozambique,** north of the Zambezi River; northeastern **Zaire; Tanzania; Kenya; Uganda;** southern **Sudan;** southern **Ethiopia;** western **Somalia; Cameroun; Guinea Bissau** and **Guinea.**

*Southern African Subregion*

They are recorded from the extreme southeastern parts of **Botswana**; from parts of the western and central and widely throughout the eastern **Transvaal**; from Umlalazi, **Natal** and the Maputo District of **Mozambique,** south of the Zambezi River and from **Zimbabwe.**

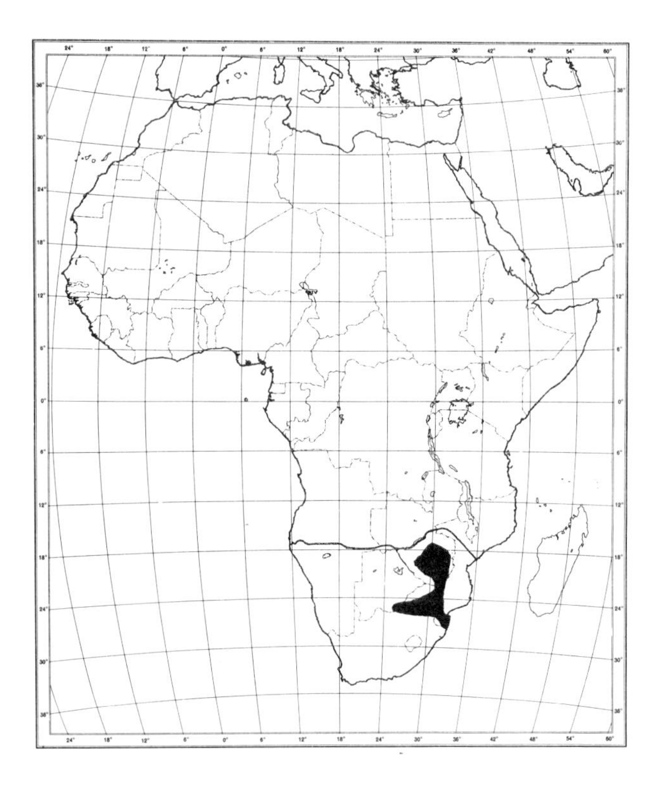

### Habitat

There is a paucity of information on the habitat requirements of this species. They have been taken in coastal forest, savanna woodland, montane evergreen forest and other montane communities and in grassland. They have been taken under trees, in old timber and under rocks and stones.

### Habits

No information is available from the Subregion.

### Food

Insectivorous.

### Reproduction

No information is available from the Subregion.

---

No. 12

## *Crocidura flavescens* (I. Geoffroy, 1827)

## Greater musk shrew
## Groter skeerbek

---

### Colloquial Name

Two large shrews occur in the Subregion, this species and *C. occidentalis*, the latter being the larger of the two.

### Taxonomic Notes

Originally described by Geoffroy from "La Cafrérie et le pays des Hottentots", Roberts (1951) fixed the type locality as King William's Town, eastern Cape Province. This species is endemic to the Southern African Subregion and no subspecies are recognised.

### Description

Adults have a total length of about 160 mm with tails of about 60 mm and an average mass of 26,7 g for males and 22,2 g for females. The colour of the body is variable but the upper parts are generally a lighter or darker shade of cinnamon-brown. In the lighter coloured specimens the under parts have a whitish wash, in the darker a wash of yellowish, the lighter colour of the under parts tending to extend upwards narrowly on to the flanks. The upper parts of the tail are the same colour as the upper parts of the body, the under parts paler and the tail is shorter than in *C. occidentalis*.

**Table 12.1**

Measurements (mm) and mass (g) of greater musk shrews, *C. flavescens*, from the Transvaal (Rautenbach, 1978).

| | Males | | | Females | | |
|---|---|---|---|---|---|---|
| | $\bar{x}$ | n | Range | $\bar{x}$ | n | Range |
| TL | 161 | 12 | 130–177 | 163 | 9 | 150–170 |
| T | 56 | 12 | 45–65 | 55 | 9 | 52–59 |
| Hf c/u | 16 | 12 | 12–18 | 17 | 9 | 14–17 |
| E | 11 | 11 | 8–12 | 11 | 9 | 10–13 |
| Mass | 26,7 | 7 | 20,0–30,0 | 22,2 | 5 | 18,0–25,0 |

### Distribution

*Southern African Subregion*

Occurs from the southwestern **Cape Province,** narrowly eastwards along the coast to **Natal;** eastern **Lesotho** and northwards through western **Swaziland** into the southeastern **Transvaal**; and the southern parts of the Inhambane district in the southern **Mozambique**.

### Habitat

Meester (1963) stated that this species is confined to the areas with a mean annual rainfall of between 500 mm and 750 mm. Within this they are found in broken or mountainous country with a dense cover of vegetation and especially where there are areas of decaying leaf litter in damp places, in dense vegetation fringing forest or where there are stands of dense low vegetation such as ferns on shrub covered hillsides, in thick undergrowth in vleis or along the banks of streams. While they prefer a moist habitat they appear to be able to utilise a slightly drier type than *C. occidentalis*, whose requirements are for a decidedly wet substrate.

### Habits

Active sporadically throughout the 24 hour period, being trapped both during the day and at night. Open cup-shaped rather untidy nests are constructed in the shelter of dense vegetation raised well above the ground so as to remain dry.

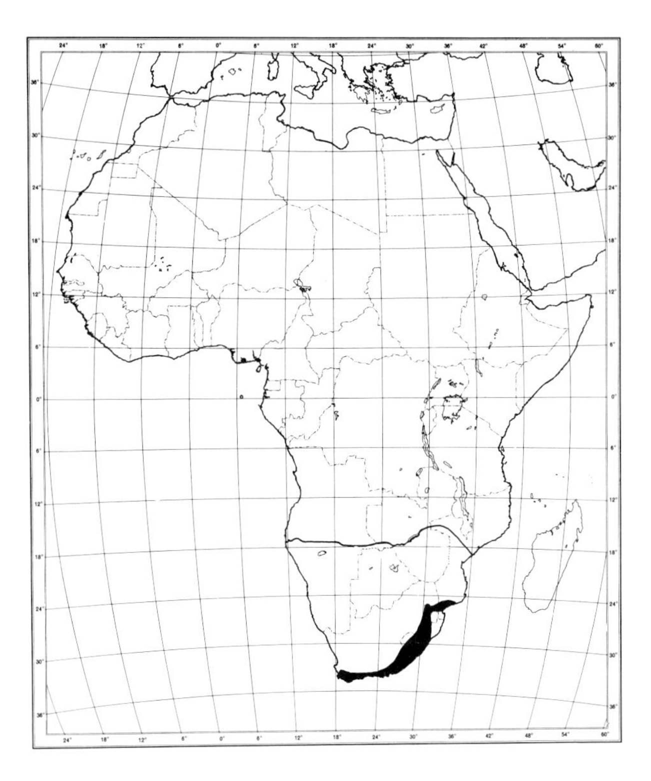

### Food

Insectivorous and like other shrews have carnivorous tendencies for they can be trapped on baits of mouse flesh.

### Reproduction

Few records of gravid females are available but these, dating both from the winter and summer months, suggest that they may breed throughout the year but confirmation of this is required. Gravid females carried up to five foetus.

---

No. 12A

## *Crocidura occidentalis* (Pucheran, 1855)

## Giant musk shrew
## Reuse skeerbek

---

### Colloquial Name

So named as it is the largest species of shrew found in the Subregion.

### Taxonomic Notes

Some authors, including Honacki, Kinman & Koeppl (1982) considered this species and *C. flavescens* (I. Geoffroy, 1827) to be conspecific, others Meester (1963; 1986) as each being worthy of specific rank, the latter view being followed here. *C. occidentalis* was described originally from material from the Gabon and has a wide distribution in Sub-Saharan Africa. Two subspecies are currently recognised, the nominate form and *C. occidentalis zuleika* Dollman, 1915 described from the Chrinda Forest, Melsetter, Zimbabwe. Specimens from the Haroni/Lusito confluence, Melsetter at 20 °S is the most southerly locality on the continent from which the species has been recorded.

### Description

Adult *C. o. zuleika* have a total length of about 200 mm with a tail about 80 mm, and an average mass of 35,4 g for males,

33,8 g for females. The upper parts of the body are buffy brown, the tail a shade darker, the under parts lighter in shade than the upper parts, with a grey tinge. The colour of the under parts is paler and blends imperceptibly into the colour of the upper parts on the flanks. The individual hairs of the upper parts are slaty-grey at the base and have a fawn subterminal band and buffy brown tips, those on the under parts with slaty-grey bases and pale buffy brown tips.

**Table 12A. 1**

Measurements (mm) and mass (g) of giant musk shrews, *C. o. zuleika*, from eastern Zimbabwe (Smithers & Wilson, 1979)

| | Males | | | Females | | |
|---|---|---|---|---|---|---|
| | x̄ | n | Range | x̄ | n | Range |
| TL | 201 | 5 | 190–218 | 202 | 7 | 185–212 |
| T | 82 | 5 | 75–87 | 78 | 6 | 70–83 |
| Hf c/u | 21 | 5 | 20–23 | 21 | 7 | 18–22 |
| E | 12 | 5 | 10–14 | 11 | 6 | 9–12 |
| Mass | 35,4 | 3 | 33,3–37,0 | 33,8 | 4 | 31,0–37,0 |

### Distribution

*North Africa*

The species is recorded from the valley of the Nile in **Egypt**.

*South of the Sahara, excluding the Southern African Subregion*

Recorded from **Senegal** eastwards to the **Sudan** and **Ethiopia** and southwards in all countries to the borders of the Subregion, their distribution is scattered and discontinuous.

*Southern African Subregion*

They occur in the extreme northeastern parts of **Namibia**, on the Grootfontein-Caprivi border; in the northern parts of the Okavango Swamp and on the Chobe River in **Botswana** and in the swamps of the eastern **Caprivi**. There is a break in distribution eastwards, the species reoccurring in eastern **Zimbabwe** and in adjacent parts of **Mozambique**, east to the Gorongoza district.

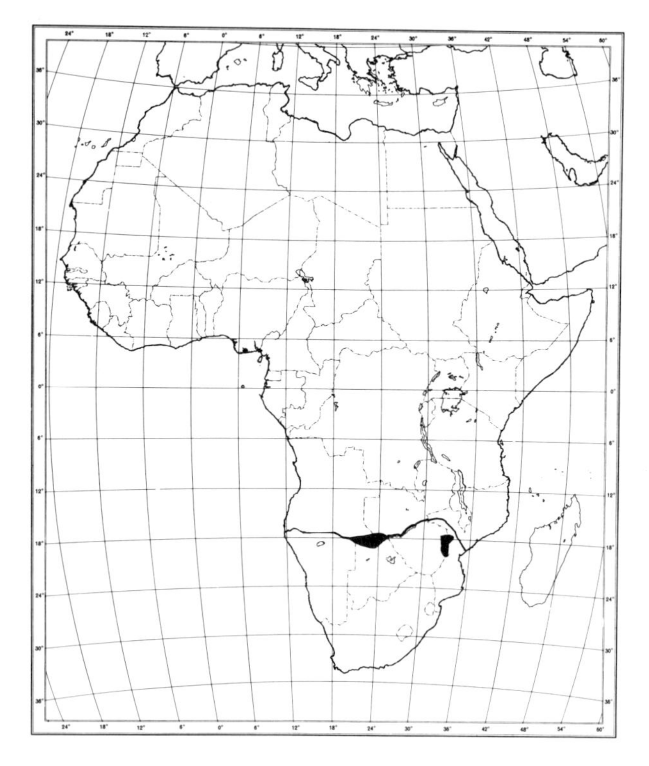

Southern African Subregion distribution only

### Habitat

Everywhere associated with damp places, in northeastern Namibia, the northern parts of Botswana and the eastern Caprivi they occur along the Okavango and Chobe Rivers and on the fringes of swamp in wet grassland. In the highlands of eastern Zimbabwe they were taken on the fringes of montane forest, along streams in dense tangled vegetation and in the dense cover of rank grasses in sponges.

The scattered nature of their occurrence is no doubt due to their requiring damp places in which to live. In eastern Zimbabwe they are found where the mean annual rainfall is in excess of 1 500 mm and where they occur in areas of lower rainfall, such as in northeastern Namibia and northern Botswana, they are closely confined to wet places.

### Habits

In parts such as in the Okavango swamp and in the eastern Caprivi they are quite numerous where there is suitable habitat. Like other shrews they appear to be active sporadically throughout the 24 hour period, being trapped both diurnally and nocturnally.

### Food

Predominantly insects but it was very noticable in eastern Zimbabwe that where species such as vlei rats, *Otomys* spp, were being caught in deadfall traps in habitat frequented by this species, unless trap lines were visited frequently catches were badly chewed. In captivity they are known to exhibit carnivorous and cannibalistic tendencies.

### Reproduction

Meester (1963) on the basis of a range of juveniles from extralimital localities suggested that they breed throughout the year. So far the few records of gravid females taken in the Subregion show that the young are born at least during the summer months of November to January but whether breeding is confined to this period of the year remains to be confirmed.

---

No. 13

## *Crocidura luna* Dollman, 1910

## Grey-brown musk shrew
## Grysbruinskeerbek

---

### Colloquial Name

The colloquial name refers to the colour of the upper parts of the body.

### Taxonomic Notes

Five subspecies are listed by Heim de Balsac & Meester (1977) of which only one, *C. l. luna*, occurs in the Subregion.

### Description

Grey-brown musk shrews have an overall length of about 90 mm with tails that are about 63% of the length of the head and body (Table 13.1). The colour of the upper parts of the body is grey-brown heavily grizzled with grey; the individual hairs have slaty-grey bases, a light fawn or light grey subterminal band and a light or darker brown tip. The under parts are grey washed with olive or fawn, the colour of the upper and under parts merging gradually. The upper surfaces of the hind and forefeet are pale brownish-grey to yellowish-brown. The tail is brown to dark blackish-brown on the upper surface, merging into a paler shade of either colour below and is sparsely covered with long bristles over about 60% of its length from the base (Dippenaar, 1980).

**Table 13.1**

Measurements (mm) of grey-brown musk shrews, *C. luna*, from the Eastern Districts of Zimbabwe (Meester, 1963)

| | Males | | | Females | | |
|---|---|---|---|---|---|---|
| | x̄ | n | Range | x̄ | n | Range |
| TL | 85 | 6 | 80–90 | 86 | 7 | 80–90 |
| T | 54 | 6 | 50–60 | 51 | 7 | 45–55 |
| Hf c/u | 15 | 6 | 15–16 | 15 | 7 | 14–15 |
| E | 10 | 6 | 9–11 | 10 | 7 | 9–11 |

## Distribution

*South of the Sahara, excluding the Southern African Subregion*

This species is recorded from **Angola;** northern and eastern **Zambia; Malawi; Mozambique,** north of the Zambezi River; southern, eastern and northeastern **Zaire; Tanzania** and southern, central and western **Kenya** and southern and eastern **Uganda.**

*Southern African Subregion*

They are confined to the eastern highlands of **Zimbabwe,** from the Inyanga south to the Melsetter District, and in adjacent parts of **Mozambique,** south of the Zambezi River, in the western and nortwestern parts of the Vila Pery and central Beira districts.

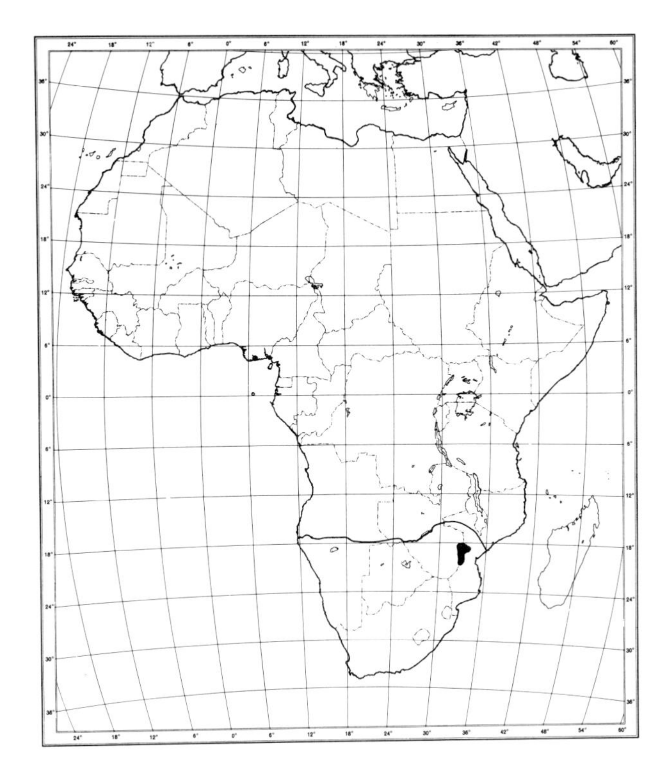

## Habitat

In the Eastern Districts of Zimbabwe and in western Mozambique they occur on the fringes of montane forest in tangled undergrowth, in areas with a mean annual rainfall of between 1 200 mm and 1 400 mm. Elsewhere they have been taken in areas where it is about 700 mm. In Zambia, Ansell (1957) stated that they occur in gallery forest, in damp, grassy plains usually along the edges of streams. Vesey-Fitzgerald (1962) recorded them from wood piles in old cultivated areas, grass and sedge sward bordering a lake, under boulders in a stream bed, tussock grass and in bog and in thickets of termitaria, all of which are cool and damp even during the hottest weather.

## Habits

Very little is known about the habits of this species. Trapping shows that, like other shrews, they are active intermittently throughout the 24 hour period and appear to forage solitarily.

## Food

Insectivorous.

## Reproduction

No information is available from the Subregion.

No. 14

# *Crocidura hirta* Peters, 1852

## Lesser red musk shrew
## Klein rooiskeerbek

## Colloquial Name

Named lesser to distinguish them from the greater musk shrew, *Crocidura flavescens*, to which they are closely related.

## Taxonomic Notes

Heim de Balsac & Meester (1977) listed four subspecies from the continent, of which two occur in the Subregion: *C. h. hirta*, which occurs in Natal, the Orange Free State, the Transvaal, Zimbabwe and parts of Mozambique, and *C. h. deserti* Schwann, 1906 from the more arid western parts of the Subregion.

## Description

Musk shrews, *C. hirta*, have a total length of about 130 mm with tails that are about half the length of the head and body and a mass of about 16,0 g (Table 14.1). Specimens from the eastern parts of the Subregion, *C. h. hirta*, are cinnamon-brown on the upper parts of the body, lightly grizzled with fawn, there being some variation, however, from a pale reddish-fawn to a dark brown. The individual hairs are slate-grey at the base with a fawn subterminal band and a brown or buffy-brown tip. The under parts are paler, usually with a yellow or fawn tinge. The transition from the colour of the upper to that of the under parts may be gradual or sharply demarcated. At the spring moult the new fur is darker than the old. Specimens from the more arid western parts of the Subregion are markedly lighter in colour (*C. h. deserti*). In Botswana the upper parts of the body are pale fawn, washed with buffy, the under parts whitish or off-white with a yellowish tinge. There is a gradual transition in colour from the darker, redder eastern *C. h. hirta* to the lighter western *C. h. deserti* in western Zimbabwe, the western Transvaal and in eastern Botswana, suggesting that, when more adequate material is available, it may be possible to demonstrate an east-west cline in this character.

**Table 14.1**

Measurements (mm) and mass (g) of lesser red musk shrews, *C. h. hirta*, from the Transvaal (Rautenbach, 1978) and *C. h. deserti*, from Botswana (Smithers, 1971)

*C. h. hirta*

| | Males | | | Females | | |
|---|---|---|---|---|---|---|
| | $\bar{x}$ | n | Range | $\bar{x}$ | n | Range |
| TL | 137 | 73 | 112–163 | 137 | 71 | 110–155 |
| T | 48 | 73 | 39–62 | 46 | 71 | 35–55 |
| Hf c/u | 15 | 73 | 12–16 | 13 | 70 | 10–17 |
| E | 10 | 73 | 5–12 | 9 | 70 | 5–13 |
| Mass | 16,1 | 26 | 11,1–24,0 | 14,9 | 34 | 8,0–22,0 |

*C. h. deserti*

| | Males | | | Females | | |
|---|---|---|---|---|---|---|
| | $\bar{x}$ | n | Range | $\bar{x}$ | n | Range |
| TL | 129 | 14 | 122–140 | 132 | 18 | 118–149 |
| T | 44 | 14 | 42–48 | 46 | 18 | 42–51 |
| Hf c/u | 15 | 14 | 14–17 | 16 | 18 | 15–17 |
| E | 11 | 14 | 10–13 | 12 | 18 | 10–14 |
| Mass | 16,9 | 12 | 14,0–20,0 | 15,1 | 14 | 12,0–20,0 |

## Distribution

*South of the Sahara, excluding the Southern African Subregion*

This species is recorded from **Angola; Zambia; Malawi; Mozambique,** north of the Zambezi River; **Tanzania; Zaire;** and from parts of **East Africa** and southern **Somalia.**

*Southern African Subregion*

They are recorded from northern **Namibia** and they occur widely throughout **Botswana; Zimbabwe; Mozambique,** south of the Zambezi River; throughout most of the **Transvaal**, except the southern parts of the province; in the northwestern **Orange Free State;** northern and northeastern **Cape Province**; from northern **Natal** southwards coastally to Durban.

### Habitat

The musk shrew, *C. hirta*, is catholic in its habitat requirements, the darker *C. h. hirta* being found in the eastern parts of the Subregion in forest, in damp situations along rivers and streams and in a wide range of situations in the Southern Savanna Zone. They appear to require cover in the form of low bushes, dense undergrowth, piles of debris and fallen logs and are recorded as using holes in termitaria, disused rodent burrows and holes under rocks. They are commonly found in compost heaps in suburban gardens. *C. h. deserti* occurs in the open scrub bushes of arid parts of Botswana, appearing to favour areas where there are low bushes but they also occur on the fringes of the Okavango Swamp in the north in riverine woodland and where piles of debris have been washed up when the swamps flood. Although there might appear to be a tendency to be associated with damp situations, they also occur in the central Kalahari where water is available only seasonally and, therefore, they are not dependent on a water supply, probably relying on dew for their moisture requirements.

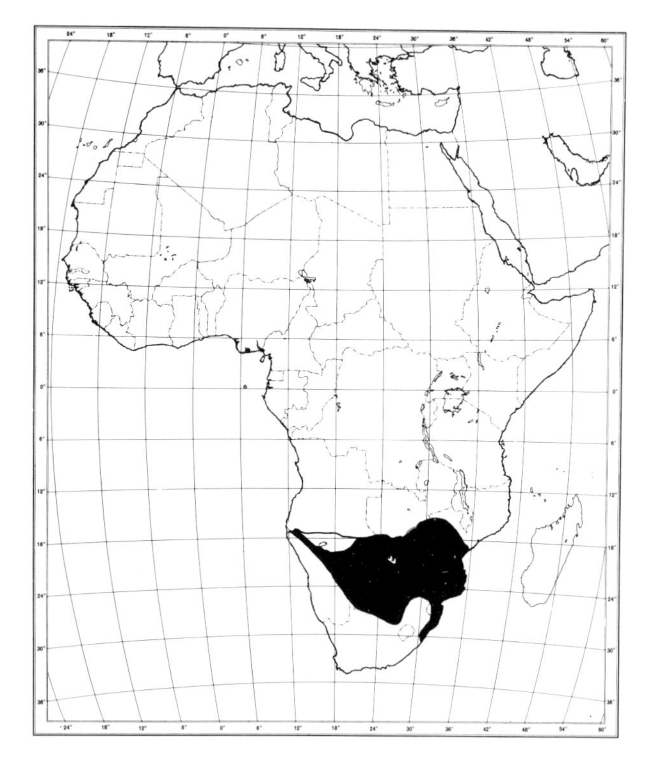

### Habits

They appear to be active on and off throughout the 24 hour period, being caught in traps both during the day and at night. Normally they forage solitarily but Meester (1963) has shown that they will live together amicably in groups of two or more.

In captivity, strangers introduced to individuals already established, leads to fighting. The antagonists rise up on their back legs, with their mouths open, and slash at each others' necks and heads with their teeth.

### Food

In captivity, Meester (1963) recorded that they will eat earthworms, insects and termites and that they will feed on the carcasses of other rodents and bats and are at times cannibalistic. They can be maintained for considerable periods of time on a diet of minced beef or beef liver. Stomach contents of wild caught specimens consist predominantly of the remains of insects.

### Reproduction

Gravid females have been recorded in Botswana in November and April (Smithers, 1971); in Zimbabwe between September and February (Smithers & Wilson, 1979) and in the Transvaal between November and May (Rautenbach, 1978). This suggests that the young are born during the warm, wet months of the year between about September and May.

Average litter size in Botswana was 3,6 (n = 5) with a range of from one to nine in the Transvaal. The gestation period is 18 days and females can have two litters in the course of a single breeding season (Meester, 1963).

---

No. 15

## *Sylvisorex megalura* (Jentink, 1888)

## Climbing shrew
## Klimskeerbek

---

### Colloquial Name

The long tail of this species suggests that it has climbing habits. Ansell (1978) believed that they are predominantly, although not perhaps entirely, arboreal.

### Taxonomic Notes

Heim de Balsac & Meester (1977) listed seven subspecies from the continent of which Meester *et al.* (1986) listed two from the Subregion: *S. m. sheppardi* Kershaw, 1921, from eastern Zimbabwe and *S. m. sorella* (Thomas, 1898) from the Tete District, Mozambique.

### Description

Climbing shrews have a total length of about 160 mm with tails that are slightly longer than the length of the head and body and a mass of between 5,0 g and 7,0 g (Table 15.1). The upper parts of the body are greyish with a distinct brownish tinge, the head and sides of the face are pale brown, the individual hairs narrowly grey at the base with broad buffy-brown tips. The flanks are greyer than the upper parts of the body, the under parts pale buffy or off-white, the individual hairs with grey bases and broad, pale buffy or off-white tips. The upper surfaces of the hands and feet are the same colour as the upper parts of the body, the long, thin tail is dark brown above and distinctly paler and buffier below, the two colours sharply demarcated one from the other.

In the skull the lower canine teeth are absent, the dental formula is:

$I\frac{3}{2}\ C\frac{1}{0}\ P\frac{2}{1}\ M\frac{3}{3} = 30$

### Table 15.1

Measurements (mm) and mass (g) of climbing shrews, *S. megalura*, from Zimbabwe

| | Males | | | Females |
|---|---|---|---|---|
| | $\bar{x}$ | n | Range | (one only) |
| TL | 158 | 3 | 158 | 142 |
| T | 84 | 3 | 84 | 75 |
| Hf c/u | 16 | 3 | 15–16 | 19 |
| E | 9 | 3 | 9–10 | – |
| Mass | 5,7 | 3 | 5,0–7,0 | – |

### Distribution

*South of the Sahara, excluding the Southern African Subregion*

They are recorded from **Guinea; Liberia;** the **Ivory Coast; Central African Republic; Rwanda; Uganda; Kenya; Ethiopia; Cameroun; Gabon;** in northern and western **Angola;**

eastern and northeastern **Zaire**; northwestern and northeastern **Zambia; Malawi** and **Mozambique**, north of the Zambezi River.

*Southern African Subregion*

They are recorded from eastern **Zimbabwe** and from the Tete District, Mozambique.

**Habitat**

Dieterlen & Heim de Balsac (1979) recorded that extralimitally to the Subregion they occur commonly in cultivated areas at altitudes of 1 600 to 1 900m above sea level in regenerating bush. They also recorded them in gallery forest, and in stands of high grass and savanna scrub. At higher altitudes of up to 2 300 m they have been found in forest and in regenerating forest with a single record from a swamp.

In Zimbabwe they were taken in thick scrub in areas with a mean annual rainfall of from 1 200 mm to 1 400 mm close to the Mozambique border, and near Harare on the plateau where the rainfall is 800 mm to 1 000 mm. All the localities were between altitudes of from 1 200m to 1 500 m. The Harare specimens were taken on the fringe of an orchard surrounded by areas of tall *Hyparrhenia* sp grass.

**Habits**

Little is known about their habits. The Harare specimens were trapped at night on the ground at the base of a line of mulberry trees fringing an orchard. A ball-shaped nest was found in a low scrub bush on the fringe of the orchard nearby, which it was thought might have been constructed by this species. It was ball-shaped and situated in the entwined twigs of a bush about 1 m above the ground. Its construction was markedly different from that of the chestnut climbing mouse, *Dendromus mystacalis*, which was common in the area, being constructed of lengths of broad leaved grasses. Apparently it was not in use as it was slightly disintegrated, but appeared to have had a single entrance. This type of nest is very similar to those described by Dieterlen & Heim de Balsac (1979).

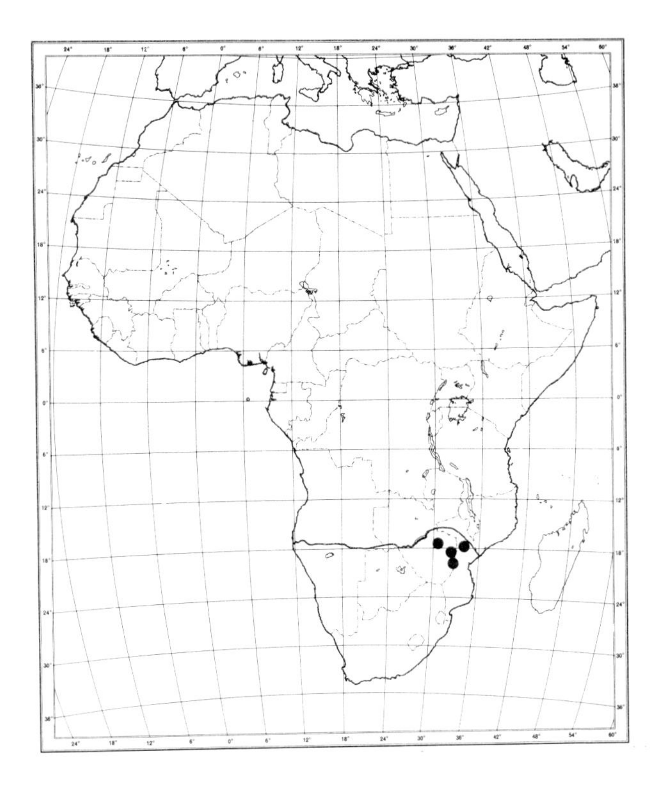

**Food and Reproduction**

No data are available on this aspect of their life history in the Subregion.

# II. Family ERINACEIDAE

## Hedgehog

### Subfamily ERINACEINAE
### Genus *Atelerix* Pomel, 1848

No. 16

### *Atelerix frontalis* (A. Smith, 1831)

### South African hedgehog
### Suid-Afrikaanse krimpvarkie

Plate 2

**Colloquial Name**

It is necessary to call the hedgehog that occurs in the Subregion the South African hedgehog to distinguish it from the other genera and species of hedgehogs that occur in Africa, Europe and Asia.

**Taxonomic Notes**

Meester *et al.* (1986) listed two subspecies from the Subregion: *A. f. frontalis* (A. Smith, 1831) from the eastern parts of the species range which occurs in the Cape Province, excluding the southwest, the Orange Free State, Transvaal, western Zimbabwe and Eastern Botswana and *A. f. angolae* (Thomas, 1918) from northern Namibia and extralimitally south western Angola. Corbet (1974a) noted that these two subspecies are doubtfully distinguishable.

**Description**

The South African hedgehog is unmistakable with its covering of short spines. The maximum size is about 200 mm overall, with a mass of up to about 400 g (Table 16.1). The spiny coat extends from the forehead, round behind the ears and covers the whole of the upper parts of their bodies. Their faces, limbs and tails are covered with dark brown or greyish brown hair. The hair on the under parts varies in colour from white, interspersed with a few black hairs, to totally black, their chins either white or black. Characteristically they have a band of white hair across their foreheads, extending on either side to below their ears, which contrasts with their otherwise dark brown or black faces. Their snouts are sharp pointed.

The spines are white at the base, with a broad black or dark brown band in the middle, and white or buffy tips. Some of the spines are white throughout their length and, in some individuals, tend to lie in lines from the forehead to the tail. In others the white spines are scattered throughout the spiny coat. On account of the variability of the width of the bands and their colour there is considerable variation in the general colour of South African hedgehogs. Some look black, others brownish and, where the white tip bands are broad, they are lighter in colour.

In some other African hedgehogs there is a broad parting running back from the forehead between the spines. In the

South African hedgehog it is narrow and inconspicuous. They have five toes on their back feet, unlike *E. albiventris* of West and East Africa and Zambia which has only four.

**Table 16.1**

Measurements (mm) and mass (g) of adult hedgehogs, *A. frontalis*, from various localities

**Botswana**

| | Males | | | Females | | |
|---|---|---|---|---|---|---|
| | $\bar{x}$ | n | Range | $\bar{x}$ | n | Range |
| TL | 193 | 7 | 177–212 | 185 | 5 | 170–215 |
| T | 19 | 7 | 17–21 | 21 | 5 | 19–24 |
| Hf c/u | 32 | 7 | 26–38 | 30 | 5 | 27–33 |
| E | 25 | 7 | 19–28 | 25 | 5 | 22–27 |
| Mass | 348,0 | 4 | 324,0–399,0 | 2 only 236,0 and 286,0 | | |

**Zimbabwe** (Smithers, 1971)

| | Males | | | Females | | |
|---|---|---|---|---|---|---|
| | $\bar{x}$ | n | Range | $\bar{x}$ | n | Range |
| TL | 209 | 7 | 190–220 | 220 | 4 | 206–235 |
| T | 24 | 7 | 20–30 | 24 | 4 | 20–25 |
| Hf c/u | 34 | 7 | 32–36 | 34 | 4 | 31–36 |
| E | 25 | 9 | 20–27 | 27 | 4 | 25–29 |
| Mass | 362,0 | 9 | 291,0–479,0 | 2 only 410,0 and 450,0 | | |

**Northern Namibia** (Shortridge, 1934)

**Irrespective of sex**

| | $\bar{x}$ | n |
|---|---|---|
| TL | 210 | 9 |
| T | 25 | 9 |
| Hf c/u | 30 | 9 |
| E | 25 | 9 |

Mass and observed range not provided

## Distribution

The South African hedgehog occurs in parts of the Subregion and Angola but has not been recorded from the extreme eastern and southwestern sectors of the Subregion and has a discontinuous distribution throughout its distributional range.

*South of the Sahara, excluding the Southern African Subregion*

They occur in southwestern **Angola**, from near Benguela southwards to the Namibian border.

*Southern African Subregion*

In **Namibia** they occur in the nortwestern and central parts of the country, not penetrating into the coastal Namib desert. In **Botswana** they are confined to the eastern sector and, in **Zimbabwe**, have a scattered distribution from the western border areas with Botswana eastwards to about Fort Victoria, which is the furthest east they have been recorded at this latitude. In the **Transvaal** they are confined to west of longitude 31 °E, and in the **Orange Free State** they occur throughout, extending into western **Lesotho**. In the **Cape Province** they occur in the northeast and southwards of this to the Grahamstown district. So far they have not been recorded in Natal and Sclater's (1901) record from there is believed to be an error. The break in distribution shown on the map may be due to their being overlooked. A skin was picked up in the western Okavango but the record is not plotted as Bushmen eat them and it may have been discarded far from its place of collection.

## Habitat

The South African hedgehog occurs in such a wide variety of habitats that it is difficult to assess its requirements. They are common in suburban gardens in western Zimbabwe, in the scrub bush of the southeastern and eastern Botswana, in the western Karoo in the Cape Province, and in grassland in the Transvaal. In the Subregion all the localities from which they have been taken to date lie within the 300 mm to 800 mm limits of mean annual rainfall, their distribution in the Cape Province falling within these limits southwards to near the coast. To some extent rainfall may limit their distribution for, in the Subregion, they do not occur in desert and are absent from areas of forest where the rainfall is generally over 1 000 mm. They avoid wet ground.

The one factor that is common to all the habitats in which they have been taken is dry cover, which they require for resting places and in which to have their young. This habitat must at the same time provide a plentiful supply of insects and other food. Suburban gardens provide both these requirements and this may explain their common occurrence in this type of habitat.

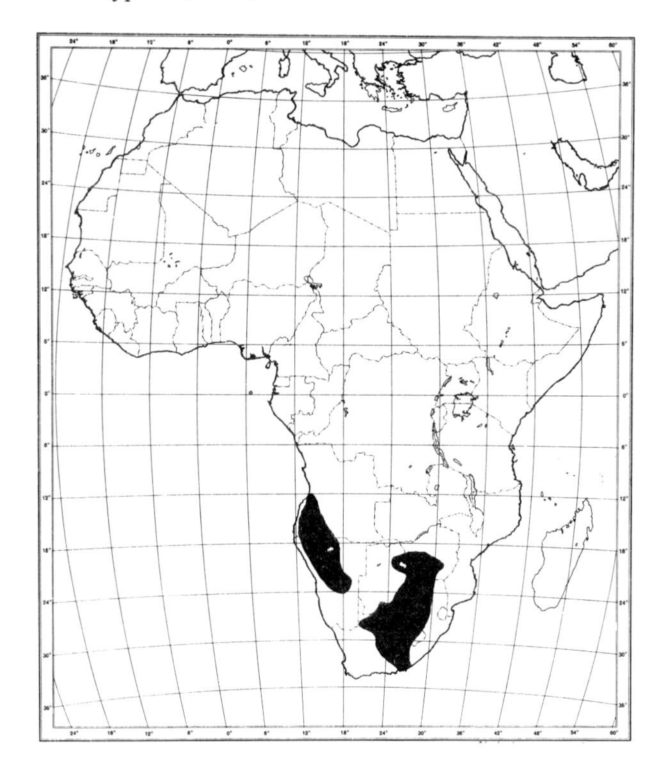

## Habits

South African hedgehogs are predominantly nocturnal, becoming active after sundown, although, after light showers of rain at the commencement of the wet season, they may be active during daylight hours, no doubt to take advantage of emerging insects and surfacing earthworms. Large numbers are killed annually at night on roads in the Bulawayo District, Zimbabwe, especially after the first rains in October. They rest during the day curled up like a ball under matted grass, in debris under the shade of bushes or in holes in the ground. In suburban situations they are found often under heaps of garden rubbish. They work their way into the debris until they are covered completely. These resting places are changed daily, the only semi-permanent sites being those used by a female in which to have her young and these only until the young can move with her, and those used during periods of hibernation which may last at least up to six weeks at a stretch.

Although hedgehogs move around slowly they are capable, nevertheless, of a surprising turn of speed, which they accomplish by rising high on their long legs. Their sense of smell is acute and they will locate food under debris or even shallowly underground, scratching and digging for it. Hearing may also play a part in food location. Their sight is poor and often they will not notice a hand lowered to catch them until it is quite close, when probably it is located by scent. They take little notice of a dazzling light shone on them at night.

Hedgehogs, in areas where they are quite common, are seen rarely during the colder, drier months from May to July. Reviewing the dates on which specimens were collected shows that of the 360 in collections of organisations in the Subregion, 335 or 93,1%, were taken during the months from August to April, only 25 or 6,9%, during May to July, at least three of the latter having been flooded out of their resting places by unseasonable rains.

It is well known that the European hedgehog, *E. europaeus*, hibernates during the cold winter months. This hibernation is not deep and often does not begin until December, ending in March or April, and, during this period, individuals are frequently seen abroad (Lawrence & Brown, 1967). From observations in captivity South African hedgehogs *A. frontalis*, behave somewhat similarly. During the warm, wet summer months from about October to April when food is plentiful, they lay down a thick layer of fat under the skin, which gives it a translucent appearance, reaching their maximum mass just prior to the onset of the colder weather in May. With the approach of the colder weather they lose their enthusiasm for food and by June have become lethargic, remaining in the resting places, under debris or in holes and ceasing to eat altogether. While the weather remains cold they will remain in the resting places but, with the advent of a warm spell, they will emerge and move around and, if the warm spell continues over a period of some days, they will feed, albeit with less enthusiasm than during the summer. With the return of colder weather they return to the resting places and may remain in a state of hibernation in these for periods up to at least six weeks at a time. During the months of May to about October they obviously are relying on their fat reserves for their energy requirements for, at the time of the return of warm weather in October, they have used up most of these and the skin has lost ists translucent appearance. In captivity a female in a large outside enclosure had a mass of 410,0 g in April and in October, on finally emerging for the summer season after the first rains, 350,0 g.

A recent study by Gillies (1988) has revealed that *A. frontalis* do become torpid in captivity, under simulated winter conditions. Torpid animals were characterised by a large reduction in metabolism together with a loss of coordination and responsiveness. When disturbed and placed outside their nests, torpid animals took two hours to regain "consciousness" and return to their nest chambers (Gillies, 1988). Food restriction increased the duration of torpor during winter, but no individuals were observed in true torpor under summer conditions, which suggests that temperature alone is the factor controlling the periodicity of torpor. Furthermore, some torpor bouts exceeded 24 hours which indicates that this species may indeed enter prolonged hibernation during the colder months of winter.

An encounter between two hedgehogs is a noisy affair, accompanied by much snuffling, snorting and growling as they butt each other with their heads. The alarm call is a high-pitched scream, uttered as if they are in pain.

Their means of defence is very effective and is accompanied by rolling up into a ball, the head, legs and soft under parts of the belly well protected inside the ball of outstanding, sharp spines. They uncoil from this ball with the greatest caution, quickly enclosing themselves if they are not satisfied that the danger has passed. In the Hwange National Park, a lion was seen rolling a balled hedgehog between his paws and trying to bite it, getting pricked in both endeavours and eventually leaving it in disgust. Examination showed that the hedgehog was none the worse for this treatment. This balling is, however, no defence against the long talons and scaly feet of the milky eagle owl, *Bubo lacteus*. In Botswana, as in East Africa, they appear to be a favourite prey of this owl, the stripped spiny skins featuring on the ground under their feeding perches and the bones and teeth showing up in their casts (Smithers, 1971).

**Food**

South African hedgehogs eat such a wide variety of food that they may almost be considered as omnivores. Invertebrates, however, form the bulk of their food and include beetles, termites, centipedes and millipedes, grasshoppers, moths and earthworms. They will take small mice, lizards and the eggs and chicks of ground-living birds as well as frogs, slugs and some vegetable matter, including fungi. Millipedes are sought after soon after they emerge with the onset of the rains, but later are disregarded. This may be due to the development of the obnoxious fluid which the millipedes secrete when handled, which is less in evidence when they first emerge, only developing later. In captivity hedgehogs flourish on a diet of mealworms, grasshoppers, mincemeat, brown sugar and brown bread moistened with water. Food is located predominantly by scent and, as they move around, they snuffle loudly in searching for it. Although they will drink in captivity, they occur in areas where water is not available, or may only be available seasonally, but they are not dependent on it.

**Reproduction**

The South African hedgehog is a seasonal breeder and in the northern parts of the Subregion the young are born during the warm, wet summer months from October to March. The gestation period lasts about 35 days and litter size varies from one to 11. At birth the young weigh 9,0 ± 1,4g and are oval in shape with the tips of the spines just showing in the skin (van der Colf, 1989). They are born blind and naked in well hidden, sheltered nests in dry debris or in holes lined with dry leaves. Lactating females spend most of the day with the young and lie on their side to suckle their young. Females have two pairs of pectoral and a pair of abdominal mammae, sometimes with extra abdominal mammae, irregularly placed. Males do not participate in parental care.

The infant spines are shed at about a month or six weeks old and are replaced by the darker adult spines. The eyes open at 10 days and the infants begin to accompany their mothers on foraging excursions at four to six weeks of age when they weigh 104 ± 12,1g (n=1, van der Colf, 1989). They are weaned when five weeks old and adult females can produce more than one litter annually.

Females are seasonally polyoestrus (van der Colf, 1989) and males experience seasonal changes in gonadal activity with peak activity during the breeding season (van der Colf & Van Aarde, 1989).

# III. Family CHRYSOCHLORIDAE

## Golden moles

The Family Chrysochloridae, the golden moles, is endemic to Africa south of the Sahara and is comprised of seven genera and 18 species, 15 of which occur in the Subregion (Meester *et al.*, 1986).

The three species found north of the limits of the Subregion are: Stuhlmann's golden mole, *Chrysochloris stuhlmanni*, which occurs in Uganda and adjacent parts of Zaire and Tanzania; the Congo golden mole, *Chlorotalpa leucorhina*, from southern Zaire, northern Angola and Cameroun; and Simonetta's golden mole, *Chlorotalpa tytonis*, which is only known to occur in the vicinity of Giohar in Somalia.

Knowledge of many species occurring in the Subregion is based on only a few specimens from scattered localities. Visagie's golden mole, *Chrysochloris visagiei*, is known only from a single specimen taken near Calvinia. With one or two exceptions little is known about their life histories. Most of them are difficult to trap and such specimens as are available have been taken fortuitously, such as when moving on the surface of the ground after rain or at night or dug up by chance. The Cape golden mole, *Chrysochloris asiatica*, is one of the exceptions. A nuisance in gardens, they are caught easily in commercially available traps. These same traps fail to catch Arends' golden moles, *Chlorotalpa arendsi*, which are similar in size and apparently in habits, as they appear to be more than normally sensitive to disturbance of their runs and invariably circumnavigate the traps. So far no trap has proved effective in catching the smaller species, such as the yellow golden mole, *Calcochloris obtusirostris*, although many ingenious designs have been tried. Study of their habits in their natural environment is well nigh impossible owing to their subterranean habits, although a few interesting observations have been made in captivity.

All the golden moles have sheens of various colours on their fur. This is long and coarse in the giant golden mole, *Chrysospalax trevelyani*, and rough-haired golden mole, *Chrysospalax villosus*, and soft and woolly in the remainder. All have dense underfur. Not all are golden in colour; the Cape golden mole, *Chrysochloris asiatica*, and Arends' golden mole, *Chlorotalpa arendsi*, for example are very dark brown, with sheens of green, violet and purple. All are blind, the eyes degenerate and covered with skin and fur. Their bodies are cylindrical with no external tail, although tail vertebrae are present under the skin. The head is pointed with a horny pad on the point of the muzzle which encloses the nostrils. The ears are simple tiny openings, without pinnae.

The forelimbs are short and muscular, the ribs and sternum bent inwards to accommodate their heavy muscles (Fig.III.1). Each forelimb has four digits, the fifth digit in all members of the Family being absent. The claws on the third digits are well developed, those on the first and second digits smaller, and the fourth digits in most species are reduced to stumps. The claws are sharply pointed and hollowed out underneath, the outside edges of those on the second and in particular the third digits knife-like, adapted to cutting through the soil. The hind limbs are not as well developed as the forelimbs and have five digits, joined by membraneous skin, each digit with a small claw. The membraneous skin between the digits makes the back feet ideal for pushing back the soil which is first loosened by the claws of the front feet in burrowing.

Golden moles differ from true moles in having only four digits on their front feet; true moles, which are members of the Family Talpidae and which do not occur in the Subregion, have five. Otherwise they look very similar, as both are adapted to a similar way of life.

All the species are insectivorous, but most of them will take earthworms. The largest species, *Chrysospalax trevelyani* eats the giant earthworm, *Microchaetus* sp, and de Winton's golden mole, *Cryptochloris wintoni*, eats legless lizards, *Typhlosaurus* sp (Roberts, 1951). Food is usually dragged underground to be eaten. In captivity, beetle larvae buried in the containers in which yellow golden moles, *Calcochloris obtusirostris*, are kept, are taken and eaten. However, they do take insects and earthworms moving on the surface of the ground. They are extremely sensitive to surface disturbances and the yellow golden mole will emerge quickly to the fluttering of a moth or the movement of an earthworm laid on the ground surface of the container, seizing it and either eating it *in situ* or dragging it underground to be consumed.

Very little is known about the time at which the young are born and such information as is available is based on their reproductive status at the time of capture.

Most of the species move in subsurface runs, which show on the surface as raised dome-like elevations of the soil. If the soil is compacted it tends to crack as it is pushed up by their movement under it. If disturbed while on the move, they will retreat back along these runs, but more commonly tunnel deeply to escape. These surface runs do not appear to be used as permanent paths of movement and new ones are continually being made until in some areas the ground is a maze of raised runs. Golden moles prefer to live in light soils such as sandy loam, sandy alluvium or, in some cases such as Grant's golden moles, *Eremitalpa granti*, in pure, loose dune sand. They are not capable of burrowing in the heavier clay soils or other types that are hard and compacted.

Fossil Chrysochloridae are known from the Pleistocene deposits in southern Africa, the remains showing that they have changed very little in their morphology over geological ages.

Petter (1981a) synonymises the genera *Calcochloris* and *Chlorotalpa* with *Amblysomus*, the present treatment, however, follows Meester (1974).

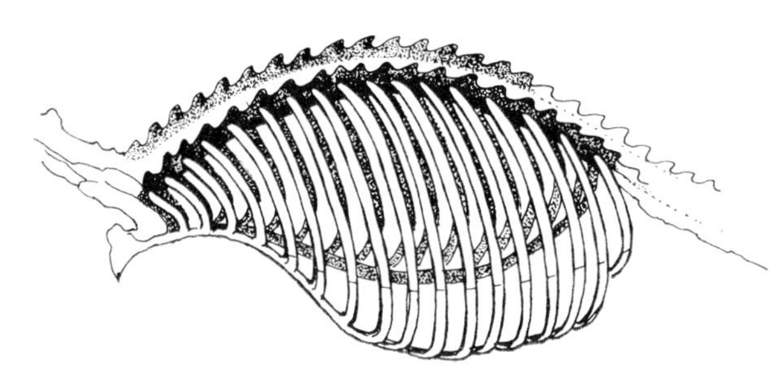

Ill.1. Ribcage: *Chrysospalax villosus*.

Key to the genera (Meester *et al.* (1986))

1. Larger; total length of skull 32,8 mm and more, width 20,2 mm and more; length of upper toothrow 12,7 mm and more; zygomatic arch produced upward posteriorly and meeting the lambdoid crest at the back
   ... *Chrysospalax*

   Smaller; total length of skull 30,5 mm and less, width 20 mm and less; length of upper toothrow under 12 mm; zygomatic arch not produced upward posteriorly to meet the lambdoid crest
   ... 2

2. With temporal bullae showing clearly in dorsal aspect of skull
   ... 3

   Without externally visible temporal bullae
   ... 4

3. First claw of forefoot nearly as long as second; temporal bullae not pronounced; frontal region greatly expanded
   ... *Cryptochloris*

   First claw much shorter than second; temporal bullae pronounced; frontal region not greatly expanded
   ... *Chrysochloris*

4. Forefoot with three well-developed claws, first not very much smaller than second and third; skull short, 20,6 mm and less in length, but broad, 16,1–18,2 mm wide, with breadth/length index 85–90%
   ... *Eremitalpa*

   Forefoot with two well-developed claws; skull longer, 21 mm or more in length, but narrower, breadth/length index below 83%
   ... 5

5. Ten upper and lower teeth in each jaw half
   ... *Chlorotalpa*

   Normally only 9 upper and lower teeth in each jaw half; if a tenth is present (in *Amblysomus gunningi*) it differs in appearance from those preceding it, and also from the homologous tooth in the preceding genus
   ... 6

6. $P^1$ and $P_1$ molariform; skull broad, breadth/length index 69–76%; bases of hair yellow
   ... *Calcochloris*

   $P^1$ and $P_1$ triconid and sectorial; skull narrower, breadth/length index 58–71%; bases of hairs slate-grey
   ... *Amblysomus*

## Genus *Chrysospalax* Gill, 1883

Key to the species (Meester, 1974)

1. Larger, adults with head and body length 198 mm and more, skull length 40 mm and more
   ... *trevelyani*

Smaller, adults with head and body length 175 mm and less, skull length 37 mm and less

. . . *villosus*

---

No. 17

## *Chrysospalax trevelyani* (Günther, 1875)

## Giant golden mole
## Reuse-gouemol

---

### Colloquial Name

So named as they are by far the largest species of golden mole occurring on the continent.

### Taxonomic Notes

No subspecies are recognised.

### Description

This is by far the largest of all the golden moles, adults measuring up to 230 mm in head and body length. The upper parts are dark glossy brown, slightly darker on the head, where there are two dull yellow patches of hair in the position that would have been occupied by the eyes, and a yellow patch around the small ear openings. The throat and under parts of the front limbs are dull yellow with a darker line down the mid-throat. The remainder of the upper parts are only slightly lighter in colour than the upper parts. Corresponding with their large size the claws on the third digits are large, about 17 mm long and 7 mm across the base, and heavily built. The claw on the second digit is slightly smaller than that on the third, while the first digit is very small with a small rounded claw. The fourth digit is reduced to a tubercle with a rounded claw.

The guard coat is harsh in texture, the individual hairs on the mid-back about 20 mm long and evenly coloured. The underfur is dense and buffy-grey in colour, the individual hairs with buffy-yellow bases.

### Distribution

So far they are only known from a series of restricted areas in the **Cape Province** from King William's Town, East London districts eastwards to Port St Johns in **Transkei** (Poduschka, 1980).

### Habitat

They are associated throughout their range with forests, occurring within them and in their immediate vicinity.

### Habits

In the Amatola Forest, Ciskei, Maddock & Hickman (1985) recorded that they were predominantly nocturnal and lived in a series of short burrows, each about 10 m in length, which were linked by surface runways. Maddock (1986) recorded that the burrows varied in length from 1 m to 13,6 m and had chambers, nests and dead ends and were connected to the surface by open holes. No mole hills were seen out of 140 burrows investigated.

Burrow entrances were linked by direct surface runways, small meandering runways ran from there, which were thought to lead to foraging areas.

From studies in the field and captivity, Maddock & Hickman (1985) found that there was a gradual increase in their activity from about 16h00 till 20h00, thereafter decreasing until 06h00 with a slight increase between 23h00 and 01h00. Some diurnal activity was noted between 09h00 and 16h00 but this was at a minor level.

After dark a male moved 128,4 m along the surface runways passing two burrows and remaining in the area of the fourth for 36 hours. Thereafter it moved a further 32,8 m to a fifth burrow, moving over seven nights, an average distance of 36,6 m per night. Oblivious to normal forest noises the mole was sensitive to the observers movements, the rustle of clothing and took to the nearest burrow. No diurnal

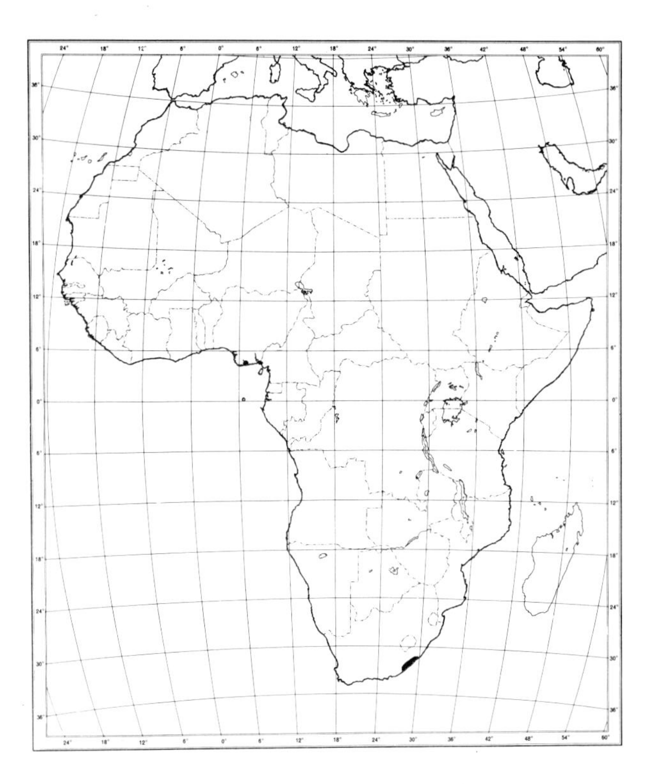

surface activities were noted in the wild, whereas in captivity this was recorded throughout the 24 hour period. Foraging activities included digging around the burrow entrance and foraging in leaf litter. While ambient summer temperatures during the day reached 23,1 °C (±2,8 °C) they found that burrow temperatures remained constant and similar to nocturnal surface temperatures at 18,1 °C (±0,8 °C).

### Food

Although Roberts (1951) recorded that they fed on the giant earthworm, *Microchaetes* sp, in the area in which Maddock (1986) worked these earthworms did not occur but they, nevertheless, were favoured in laboratory experiments and were followed by house mice, *Mus musculus*. In captivity they had a wide dietary range and in the wild they are believed to have a similar preference.

### Reproduction

Unknown.

---

No.18

## *Chrysospalax villosus* (A. Smith, 1833)

## Rough-haired golden mole
## Grasveldgouemol

Plate 2

---

### Taxonomic Notes

Meester *et al.* (1986) listed six subspecies: *C. v. villosus* from near Durban; *C. v. dobsoni* (Broom, 1918) from Pietermaritzburg, which he suggests is a synonym of *C. v. villosus*; *C. v. leschae* (Brown, 1918) from the eastern Cape Province; *C. v. rufopallidus* (Roberts, 1924), *C. v. rufus* (Meester, 1953) and *C. v. transvaalensis* (Brown, 1913) all from the Transvaal.

### Description

The rough-haired golden mole is a large species with a head and body length of about 150 mm (Table 18.1). As the name suggests the hair is long and coarse. The glossy individual hairs of the guard coat on the mid-back are about 15 mm long and are slate-grey at the base with a broad band of yellowish-brown or reddish-brown and narrow dark brown tips. The underfur is dense, woolly and grey in colour. The under parts are greyer than the upper, the sides of the face and top of the muzzle pale buffy-grey with a dark patch around the base of the horny nasal pad. The claws on the third digits of the front feet are 16 mm long and 4 mm across the base. Those on the second are slightly smaller and on the first distinctly smaller, barely reaching a third of the length of those on the second. The fourth digit is reduced to a tubercle, but carries a stout rounded claw about 1,5 mm in length.

**Table 18.1**

Measurements (mm) and mass (g) of rough-haired golden moles, *C. villosus*

| | Males | | |
|---|---|---|---|
| | $\bar{x}$ | n | Range |
| HB | 151 | 2 | 148–154 |
| Hf c/u | 18 | 2 | 15–20 |
| Mass | 125,0 | 2 | 108,0–142,0 |

### Distribution

*Southern African Subregion*

Recorded from the extreme eastern parts of the **Cape Province** through southern and central **Natal** to the southeastern **Transvaal**.

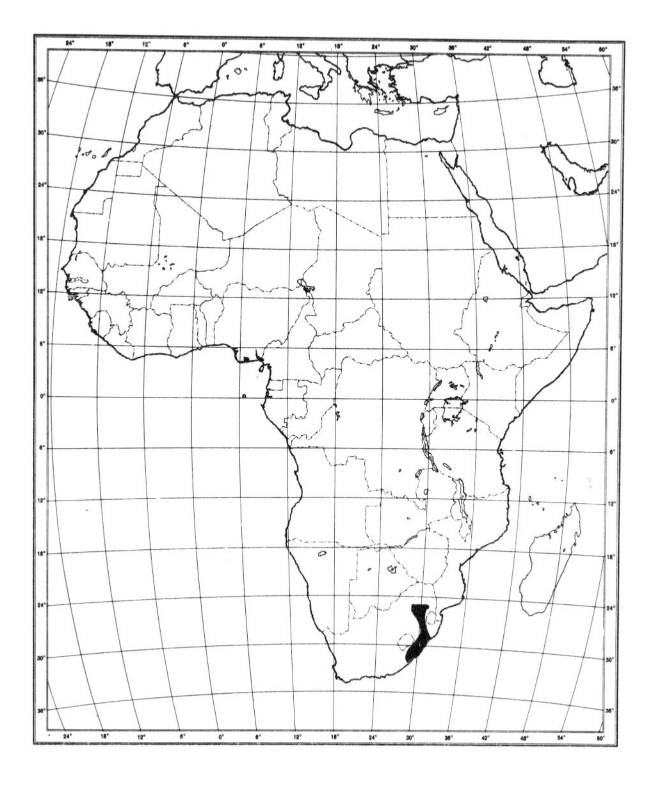

### Habitat

Grassland, with a preference for the use of dry ground on the fringes of marshes or damp vleis.

### Habits

They apparently do not make subsurface runs like other golden moles, but excavate burrows, the entrances to which are characterised by loose piles of soil thrown up at the sides and back and which are left open when they leave the burrows to forage. Roberts (1951) thought that they lived in chambers within their burrow systems from which they emerge only after rain. From the entrances, through repeated use, tracks are formed to feeding areas which are marked by the disturbance of the soil in rooting with the horny pad on their noses. If suddenly alarmed when out of the burrows they are quick to return to their shelter. In captivity, Roberts (1951) noted that, irrespective of the direction in which they faced, when they were disturbed their reactions were so rapid and the location of the burrow entrance apparently so well known that it was difficult to follow them as they sought refuge within it.

### Food

Insects and earthworms. They emerge from the burrows to feed on the surface normally only after rain when they become particularly active.

### Reproduction

Practically nothing is known about this aspect of their life history. Roberts (1951) recorded a female with two foetuses, but gave no date of recovery of the specimen. The females have two pairs of mammae, one pair inguinal, one pair situated far forward on the abdominal region.

## Genus *Cryptochloris* Shortridge & Carter, 1938

Key to the species (Meester, 1974)

1. Paler, more fawn coloured; head of the malleus bulbous ... *wintoni*

   Darker, browner in colour; head of the malleus elongated ... *zyli*

---

No. 19

## *Cryptochloris wintoni* (Broom, 1907)

## De Winton's golden mole
## De Winton se gouemol

---

### Colloquial Name

Named after Mr W.E. de Winton who contributed substantially to the study of South African mammals.

### Taxonomic Notes

The genus *Cryptochloris* is distinguished from *Chrysochloris* by having the frontal region of the skull expanded, the temporal bullae reduced in size and the first claws of the front feet nearly as long as the second. Meester (1974) listed two species, *C. wintoni* and *C. zyli*, distinguished on colour and the shape of the malleus of the inner ear but expressed doubt as to their specific distinctness. No subspecies have been described.

### Description

In size and colour they are very similar to Grant's golden mole, *Eremitalpa granti*, with which they share the same sand dune habitat. About 90 mm in length of head and body, the upper parts are pale fawn with a tinge of yellow and a silvery sheen. In one of the series of specimens there is an indistinct and diffused brown line from the nape of the neck to the shoulder.

The hair on the upper parts is grey at the base, then white with broad pale fawn tips. The tips of the hair on the under parts are whitish giving the under parts an overall lighter colour than the upper. The sides of the face are pale yellow with lighter spots of the same colour in the position that the eyes would occupy if present. The forefeet have large pads on the inner sides of the first digits, presumably to facilitate digging in the loose sandy substrate. The claws on the first digits of the front feet are thin and lightly built but are nearly as long as those on the second digit, which are broader and nearly as long as those on the third. The claws on the third digits are the broadest of all, especially at their bases, and measure 11 mm in length and 5 mm across the base.

### Distribution

Only known to occur at Port Nolloth, northwestern **Cape Province**.

### Habitat

Lives in coastal and adjacent sand areas.

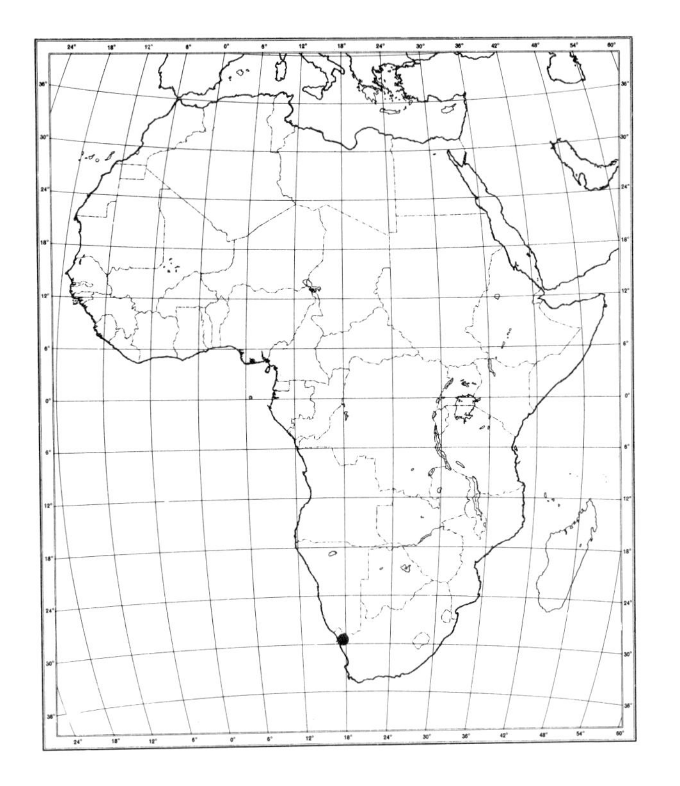

**Habits**

Roberts (1951) stated that they make subsurface runs which may extend for 50 m to 60 m and which may pass under bushes where their prey tends to be more plentiful.

**Food**

Roberts (1951) stated that their food consists of insects, including their larvae and pupae, and legless lizards, *Typhlosaurus vermis*. He suggested that the long slender claws may be an adaptation to holding these reptiles.

**Reproduction**

Unknown.

---

No. 20

## *Cryptochloris zyli* Shortridge & Carter, 1938

## Van Zyl's golden mole
## Van Zyl se gouemol

---

**Taxonomic Notes**

This species is darker and browner in colour than de Winton's golden mole. The malleus of the inner ear is elongated and not bulbous as in de Winton's.

**Description**

They are about 80 mm in head and body length. The colour of the upper parts of the body is dark lead with a violet sheen. The under parts are very slightly paler than the upper parts. The sides of the face are buffy-white.

**Distribution**

The single and only known specimen came from Companies Drift, Lamberts Bay, **Cape Province**.

**Habitat, Habits and Reproduction**

Unknown.

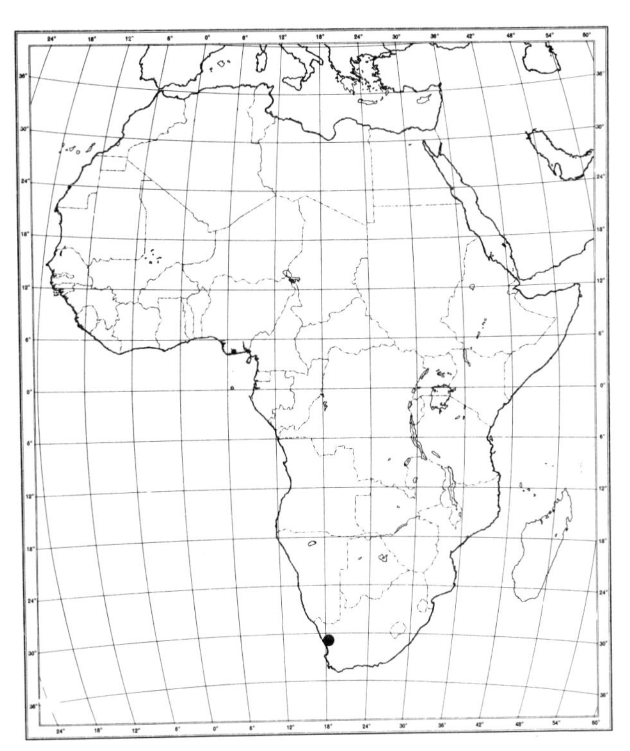

## Genus *Chrysochloris* Lacépède, 1799

Key to the species (Meester, 1974)

1. Colour pale greyish-brown to dark brown, with no trace of buffy; head of the malleus relatively slender (Fig. 22.1.a)

   ... *asiatica*

   Colour pale yellowish-buffy; head of malleus robust and broad, width about half of its length (Fig. 22.1.b)

   ... *visagiei*

---

No. 21

## *Chrysochloris asiatica* (Linnaeus, 1758)

## Cape golden mole
## Kaapse gouemol

Plate 2

---

**Colloquial Name**

So called as they are confined in their distribution to the southwestern Cape Province.

**Taxonomic Notes**

Meester *et al.* (1986) do not recognise any of the many subspecies that have been described, showing that there is a cline in colour and size running from the southern parts of their distributional range northwards.

This was the first species of golden mole to be described, the locality given to the original specimen by Linnaeus being "Siberia" usually considered to be the Cape of Good Hope.

The skulls of this genus are distinguished by temporal bullae which form bulges in the braincase toward the rear of the eye orbits.

**Description**

Specimens from the southwestern Cape Province have a head and body length of about 110 mm (Table 21.1). They are dark brown in colour on the upper parts with a sheen of green, bronze and purple. The under parts are lighter in colour and duller than the upper parts, the chin, throat and fore limbs light buffy. On the sides of the face there are two distinct light buffy bands running from the cheeks to the position which the eyes would occupy if present.

The claws on the third digits of the front feet are the largest, about 10 mm in length and 3 mm across their bases. The claws on the second digits are smaller than those on the third, while those on the first are smaller still. The fourth digit is represented by a tiny and barely perceptible tubercle. The malleus of the ear is narrower than in *C. visagiei* (Fig. 22.1.a).

**Table 21.1**

Measurements (mm) of Cape golden moles, *C. asiatica*

| | Males | | | Females | | |
|---|---|---|---|---|---|---|
| | $\bar{x}$ | n | Range | $\bar{x}$ | n | Range |
| HB | 105 | 10 | 100–110 | 105 | 7 | 99–110 |
| Hf c/u | 13 | 8 | 11–16 | 13 | 7 | 11–14 |

### Distribution

They are confined to the southwestern parts of the **Cape Province**, including Robben Island and Table Bay.

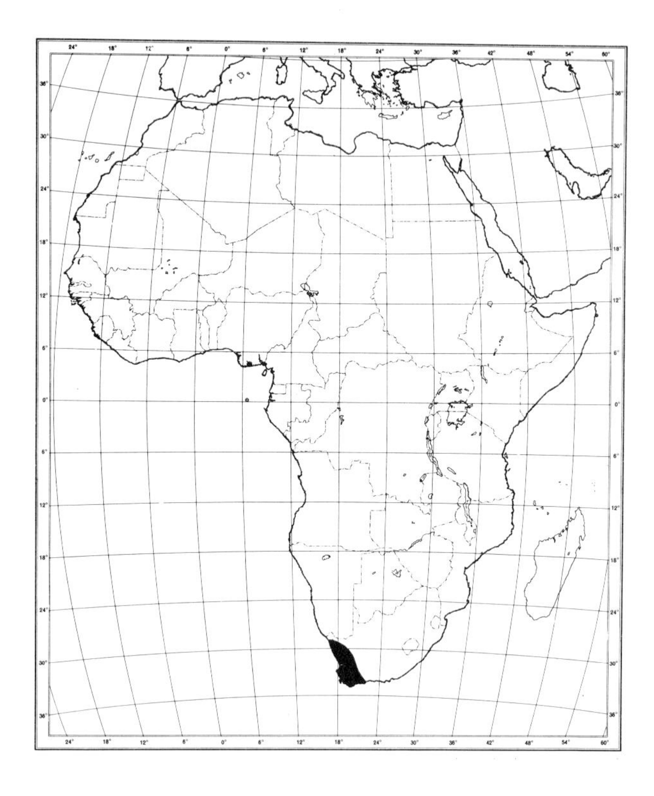

### Habitat

They are found in sandy soil, especially where this has been loosened by cultivation. They are very common in gardens and especially in seed beds where their subsurface runs press up the young plants and cause them to wilt.

### Habits

They tunnel below the surface and these runs may extend for considerable distances; they also burrow downwards and throw up mounds. They are particularly active after rain.

### Food

In captivity they will take practically any type of insect as well as earthworms.

### Reproduction

Broom (In Roberts, 1951) recorded that the young are born during the wet winter months. Females have two pairs of mammae, one pair inguinal and one pair situated far forward on the abdomen towards the flanks.

No. 22

## *Chrysochloris visagiei* Broom, 1950

## Visagie's golden mole
## Visagie se gouemol

This species remains known only from the original type specimen which was taken at Gouna, 86 km east of Calvinia, **Cape Province.** Meester (1974) suggested that it may be an aberrant *C. asiatica*. Nothing is known about its ecology. It was named after Mr I.H.J. Visagie on whose farm the original specimen was collected.

### Description

The type specimen of Visagie's golden mole has a head and body length of 106 mm and a hind foot c/u of 13 mm. The upper parts of the body are a pale tawny-olive colour, the top of the head and the face paler than the upper parts. The base of the individual hairs is pale slate-grey, the tips a light fawn. The under parts are paler in colour than the upper, the grey colour of the bases of the hairs on the belly showing through giving the belly a grey appearance.

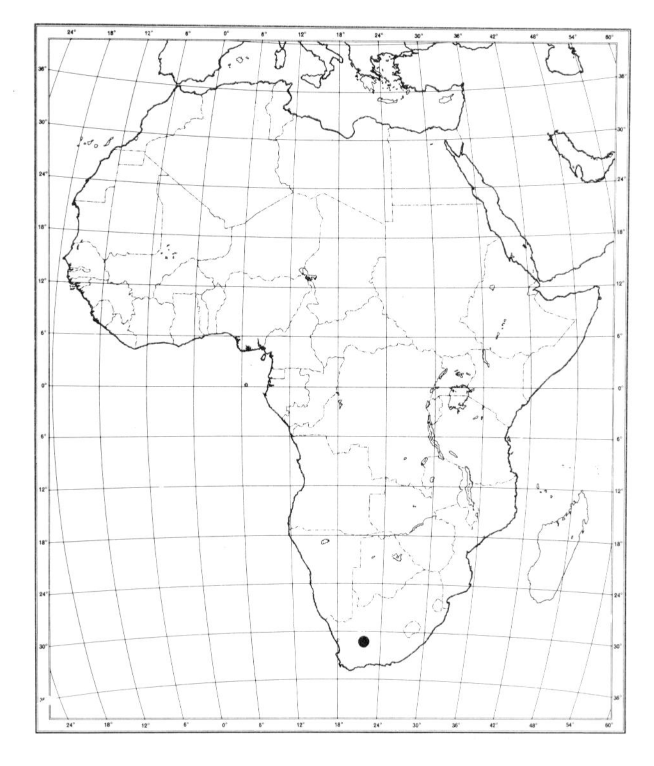

The claw on the fourth digit of the forefoot is very small; the malleus of the ear some twice as long as broad; the head, however, is particularly broad compared with that of other *Chrysochloris* spp (Fig. 22.1.b).

The total length of the skull is 22,8 mm, the width 17,7 mm. They have 10 teeth on each side of the upper and lower jaws, the length of the upper tooth row 10,0 mm, the lower 8,0 mm.

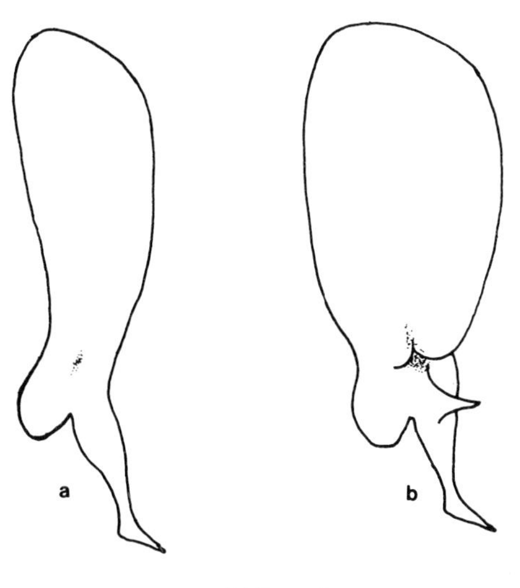


22.1. Malleus of ear
(a) *Chrysochloris asiatica*
(b) *C. visagiei* after Broom, 1950.

## Genus *Eremitalpa* Roberts, 1924

No. 23

## *Eremitalpa granti* (Broom, 1907)

## Grant's golden mole
## Grant se gouemol

Plate 2

### Colloquial Name

Named after Capt. C.H.B. Grant, Hon. Associate of the Zoological Department, British Museum (Nat. Hist.) London, who collected zoological material in southern Africa and became the co-author with C.W. Mackworth Praed of books on African birds.

### Taxonomic Notes

Meester *et al.* (1986) listed two subspecies: *E. g. granti* from Little Namaqualand and southwestern Cape Province and *E. g. namibensis* Bauer & Niethammer, 1959 from the Namib Desert, Namibia.

### Description

A very small pale-coloured species with a head and body length of about 85 mm (Table 23.1). The upper parts are a pale greyish-yellow with a silvery sheen; the flanks and under parts are paler than the upper parts with a slightly more intense yellow tinge. The claw on the first digit of the front feet is flat and blade-like with a rounded tip, the claws on the second and third digits about the same length, or the third slightly longer, both these claws pointed and hollowed out underneath and broad towards the base. The fourth digit is vestigial but bears a scraper-like claw that is about as broad as it is long, with a broad rounded end. The broad hollowed out claws are an adaptation to burrowing in loose sand and would be hardly effective in a more consolidated substrate.

**Table 23.1**

Measurements (mm) of Grant's golden moles, *E. granti*

| | Males | | | Females | | |
|---|---|---|---|---|---|---|
| | $\bar{x}$ | n | Range | $\bar{x}$ | n | Range |
| HB | 83 | 7 | 76–85 | 80 | 10 | 77–86 |
| Hf c/u | 11 | 4 | 9–12 | 10 | 3 | 9–10 |

### Distribution

*Southern African Subregion*

They are confined to the Namib Desert in **Namibia** from about Walvis Bay south to the Orange River and south of this in the coastal area to St Helena Bay in the western **Cape Province**, with a single inland record from Garies, where a skull was recovered from a barn owl, *Tyto alba*, pellet (Roberts, 1951).

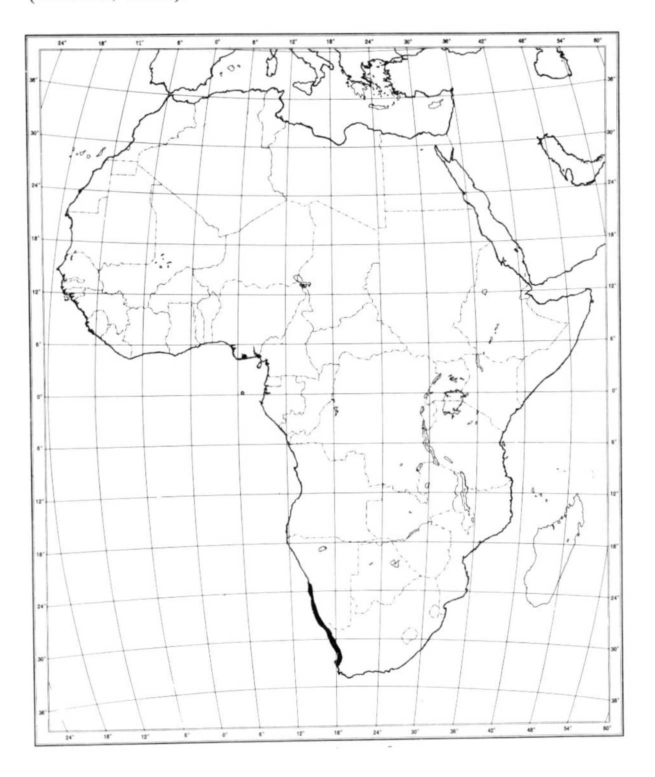

### Habitat

They are confined to sand dunes, occurring in dunes devoid of vegetation, but with a preference for those with scattered clumps of dune-grass, *Stipagrostis sabulicola* (Coetzee, 1969).

### Habits

Holm (1969) stated that they are strictly nocturnal and that he could find no evidence of diurnal activity. Their skulls and bones are common items in the casts of barn owls, *Tyto alba*.

They are active from 21h00 throughout the hours of darkness. In the dune system Holm (1969) followed the spoor of individuals, showing that they moved over distances up to 5 800 m in foraging. In the riverbed the maximum distance observed was 300 m, owing to the more plentiful food supply available there. Coetzee (1969) stated that they appear to have a preference for wandering on the more consolidated windward side of the dunes and in the loose sand would emerge and submerge in it while moving. When foraging in loose sand their subsurface runs are obliterated behind them as they "swim" through it. In more consolidated sand telltale cracking of the surface marks the runs. They will burrow to depths of over 500 mm.

### Food

Holm (1969) recorded a wide range of food eaten by Grant's golden mole. The web-footed gecko, *Pelmatogecko rangei*, figures as the largest prey taken. He recorded that one per night was taken on three successive nights. Crickets, and the larvae of beetles including *Tenebrio mollitor* and *Omymacris laeviceps* were taken frequently. In the river beds they foraged in piles of debris for dynastid beetles, eating only the abdomens. Termites and ants, the bodies of moths, spiders, legless lizards and mealy-bugs foraged from the roots of dune grass, *Stipagrostis sabulicola*, were recognised in stomach contents. Stomach contents invariably include a high percentage of sand, as they so often dragged the prey into it before eating.

### Reproduction

The only indication of the time at which the young are born is provided by Holm (1969) who recorded two gravid females, each with a single, near full-term foetus, taken in October. Where the young are born is not known but the loose sandy nature of the substrate in which they live appears unsuitable for the construction of chambers.

## Genus *Chlorotalpa* Roberts, 1924

Key to the species (Meester, 1974)

1. Larger, greatest skull length more than 26 mm; $P_1$ molariform, four-cusped; the head of the malleus elongated ... *arendsi*
   Smaller, greatest skull length less than 25 mm ... 2
2. Colour uniformly glossy black or brownish-black ... *duthiae*
   Colour reddish-yellow, darker (dark reddish-brown) towards the mid-back ... *sclateri*

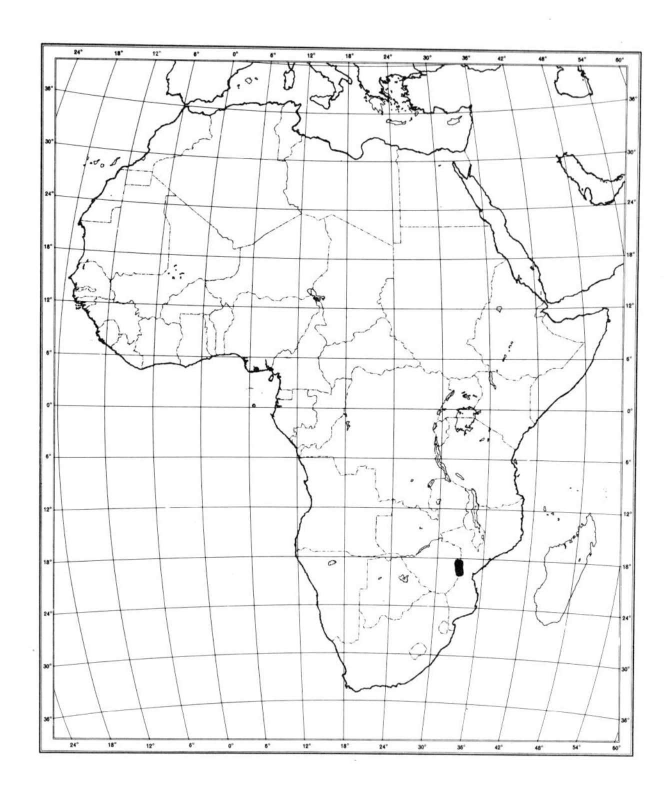

No. 24

## *Chlorotalpa arendsi* Lundholm, 1955

## Arends' golden mole
## Arends se gouemol

**Colloquial Name**

Named after the collector, Mr Nicholas Arends, then Technician at the Kaffrarian Museum, King William's Town.

**Taxonomic Notes**

No subspecies have been described (Meester *et al.*, 1986).

**Description**

About 120 mm in head and body length (Table 24.1), Arends' golden moles are glossy black or very dark brown with a bronze sheen, the underfur dark grey. The sides of the face, throat and limbs are lighter in colour than that of the upper parts; the under parts are only a shade lighter than the upper and have a faint green sheen. The claw on the first digit is short, narrow but stoutly built, the second the longest claw, the third about three-quarters the length of the second and the fourth digit is vestigial, its claw appearing as a round knob.

**Table 24.1**

Measurements (mm) and mass (g) of Arends' golden moles, *C. arendsi*, from eastern Zimbabwe (Smithers & Wilson, 1979)

| | Males | | | Females | | |
|---|---|---|---|---|---|---|
| | $\bar{x}$ | n | Range | $\bar{x}$ | n | Range |
| TL | 127 | 8 | 118–138 | 121 | 6 | 109–139 |
| Hf c/u | 16 | 8 | 14–17 | 15 | 6 | 14–16 |
| Mass | 58,2 | 6 | 50,0–76,0 | 46,5 | 6 | 38,3–55,8 |

**Distribution**

*Southern African Subregion*

They are confined to the eastern parts of **Zimbabwe** and occur narrowly along the Mozambique border from about 18 °S to 20 °S and in the adjacent parts of **Mozambique**, south of the Zambezi River.

**Habitat**

The original specimen was taken in montane grassland at an altitude of 2 000 m just above the eastern forest clad slopes at Inyanga, Zimbabwe. It was found in open spaces between clumps of tussock grass. Near Penhalonga, Zimbabwe they occurred in riverine forest which had a dense undercover and a deep substrate of leaf litter.

**Habits**

They form subsurface runs between clumps of tussock grass in montane grassland. Lundholm (1955a) noted that they-constructed subsurface runs in the loose soil thrown up in road making. He suggested that, while their runs were found predominantly in open areas, they may more generally keep to the denser vegetation. This was the situation at Penhalonga where their main activity was in the loam of the underbush. Some runs, however, extended far into the adjacent grassland.

**Food**

No information is available on the food of this species, but it is likely to be similar to that of other golden moles of the same size and to consist principally of earthworms and insects.

**Reproduction**

No information is available.

No. 25

## *Chlorotalpa duthiae* (Broom, 1907)

## Duthie's golden mole
## Duthie se gouemol

**Plate 2**

16. South African hedgehog, *Atelerix frontalis*
    Suid-Afrikaanse krimpvarkie
18. Rough-haired golden mole, *Chrysospalax villosus*
    Grasveldgouemol
21. Cape golden mole, *Chrysochloris asiatica*
    Kaapse gouemol
23. Grant's golden mole, *Eremitalpa granti*
    Grant se gouemol
27. Yellow golden mole, *Calcochloris obtusirostris*
    Geel gouemol
29. Zulu golden mole, *Amblysomus iris*
    Zoeloelandse gouemol
30. Hottentot golden mole, *Amblysomus hottentotus*
    Hottentot gouemol

PLATE 2
16
18
21
23
27
29
30
Dick Findlay '86.

This species is represented in collections by only a few specimens, all taken in the coastal area between Knysna and Port Elizabeth. Nothing is known of their ecology.

### Description

About 100 mm in head and body length (Table 25.1), the colour of the upper parts is a very dark brown, almost black, with a very distinct green sheen. The sides of the face are yellowish, this colour extending upwards on either side as triangular patches, their apices at the position which would have been occupied by the eyes. The under parts are a shade lighter in colour than the upper. The first digits on the front feet are reduced, the tip of the claw barely reaching halfway up that of the second digit.

**Table 25.1**

Measurements (mm) of Duthie's golden moles, *C. duthiae*

| | Males | | | Females | | |
|---|---|---|---|---|---|---|
| | $\bar{x}$ | n | Range | $\bar{x}$ | n | Range |
| HB | 101 | 8 | 92–111 | 100 | 5 | 95–109 |
| Hf c/u | 11 | 8 | 9–12 | 12 | 4 | 12 |

### Distribution

Apparently restricted to the coastal belt of the **Cape Province** between Knysna and Port Elizabeth.

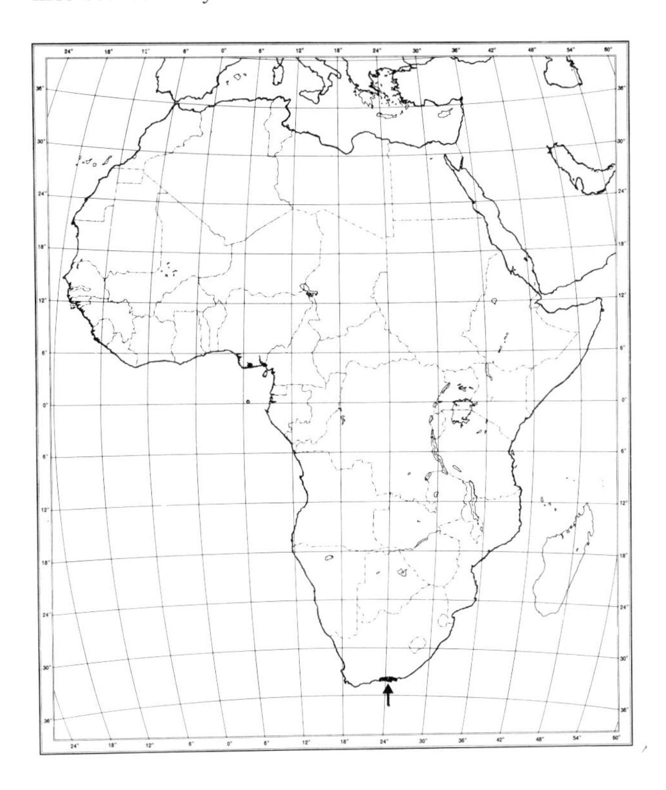

### Habitat

Alluvial sand and sandy loam.

### Habits and Reproduction

Unknown.

No.26

## *Chlorotalpa sclateri* (Broom, 1907)

Sclater's golden mole
Sclater se gouemol

### Colloquial Name

Named after W.L. Sclater, a former Director of the South African Museum, Cape Town.

### Taxonomic Notes

Meester *et al.* (1986) listed three subspecies: *C. s. sclateri* from the western, central and east-central parts of the Cape Province and Lesotho, *C. s. montana* Roberts, 1924 from the Wakkerstroom area in the southeastern Transvaal and *C. s. shortridgei* Broom, 1950 from the western-central parts of the Cape Province.

### Description

Specimens from the Cape Province are a glossy reddish-brown on the upper parts, while those from Wakkerstroom are glossy dark brown. Both are about 100 mm in head and body length. The sides of the face are not so clearly different in colour from the rest of the head as in some other species, being a dull buffy colour with two light spots in the position which would have been occupied by the eyes. The chin is buffy-yellow in the Cape Province specimens, grey in those from southeastern Transvaal, and both have a tinge of brown on the lower throat. The flanks are tinged reddish, the under parts are a dull grey with a faint reddish tinge.

The third digits on the front feet are armed with curved claws about 9 mm long and 3 mm across the base, the fourth digit showing as a minute knob, with a tiny nail. The claw of the first digit barely reaches halfway up that of the second digit.

Too few specimens are available to allow an assessment of mean measurements.

### Distribution

*Southern African Subregion*

Sclater's golden mole occurs in the western, central and central-eastern parts of the **Cape Province** with records from the northeastern **Orange Free State, Lesotho** and the south-eastern **Transvaal**. This distribution, represented by a series of scattered records, is shown as continuous, until more information becomes available.

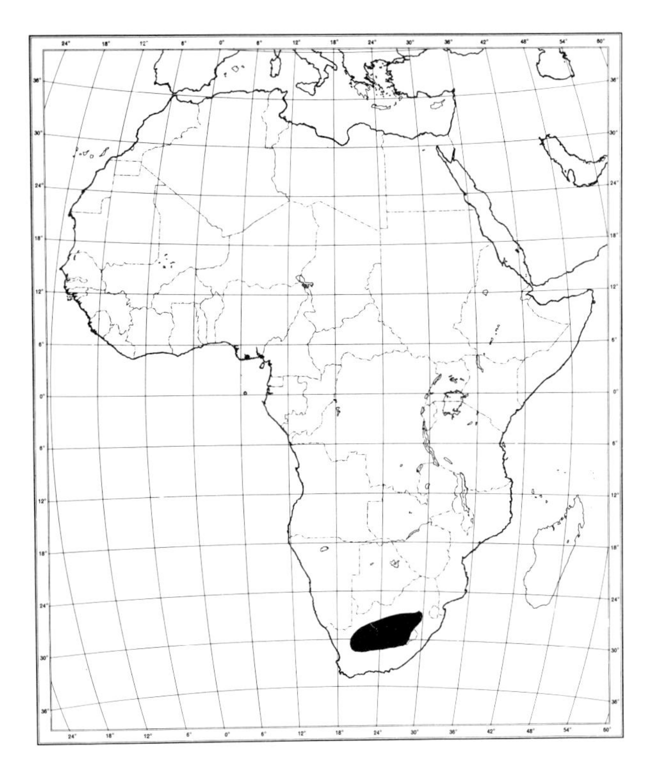

### Habitat

The species occurs in the Drakensberg at high altitudes in moist kloofs (Roberts, 1951) and on the escarpment near Beaufort West. Data recorded on specimens from Wakker-stroom associate them with rocky hillsides, but apart from these scant observations, no other information is available.

### Habits
Unknown.

### Reproduction
Unknown. Females have one pair of inguinal and one pair of abdominal mammae.

## Genus *Calcochloris* Mivart, 1867

No. 27

## *Calcochloris obtusirostris* (Peters, 1851)

## Yellow golden mole
## Geel gouemol

Plate 2

### Taxonomic Notes
Meester (1974) listed three subspecies: *C. o. obtusirostris* from southern Mozambique; *C. o. chrysillus* (Thomas & Schwann, 1905) from coastal Mozambique and south of the Umfolozi River, Natal; and *C. o. limpopoensis* (Roberts, 1946) from the northeastern Kruger National Park northwards into Mozambique.

### Description
Yellow golden moles are about 100 mm in head and body length (Table 27.1). They vary in colour, depending on the locality from which they originate, from a glossy brown to a bright golden-yellow. This variation is imparted to the upper parts of the individual by the presence or absence of dark glossy tips to the hairs of the guard coat, the underfur and bases of the hairs of the guard coat being yellow. The under parts are golden, in the darker coloured specimens with a wash of reddish-brown. The chest and upper parts of the belly are darker than the remainder of the under parts and the individual hairs in this region have darker tips. The sides of the face are yellow, with a broad yellow or buffy band across the top of the snout. The claws on the third digits of the front feet are about 10 mm long and 4 mm broad at their bases. The fourth digit, which is reduced to a stump in most species of golden moles, while small, is armed with a claw about 2 mm in length.

### Table 27.1
Measurements (mm) and mass (g) of yellow golden moles, *C. obtusirostris*, from southeastern Zimbabwe (Smithers & Wilson, 1979).

| | Males | | | Females | | |
|---|---|---|---|---|---|---|
| | $\bar{x}$ | n | Range | $\bar{x}$ | n | Range |
| HB | 102 | 6 | 100–108 | 100 | 3 | 97–100 |
| Hf c/u | 12 | 6 | 12 | 11 | 3 | 11–12 |
| Mass | 27,3 | 6 | 24,0–30,0 | One | only | 20,8 |

### Distribution
*Southern African Subregion*

In **Zimbabwe** they are confined to a restricted area in the southeastern lowveld and in the **Transvaal** to the extreme northern parts of of the Kruger National Park. They occur in northern **Natal**, northwards through the Maputo, Gaza and Inhambane Districts of **Mozambique**, south of the Zambezi River, to the confluence of the Busi and Revue rivers in the Vila Pery District.

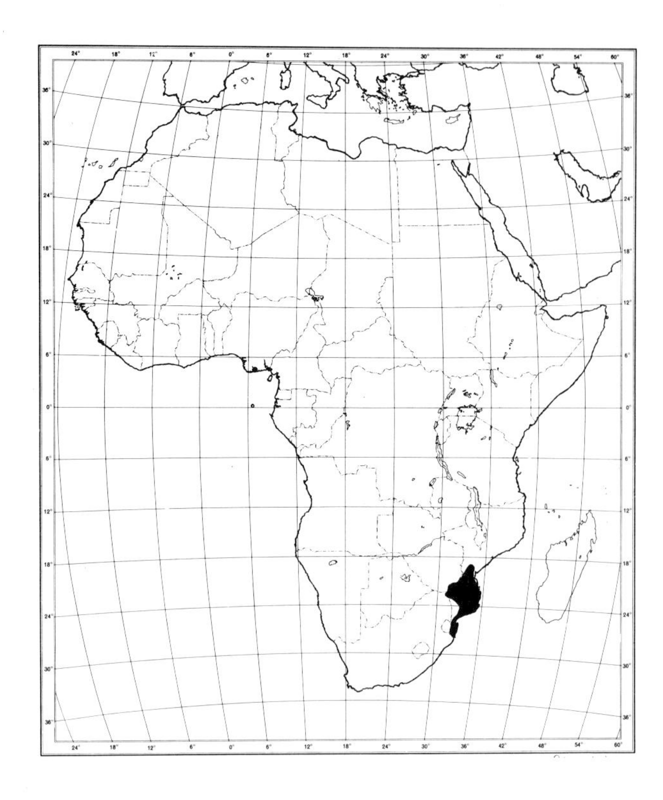

### Habitat
They are confined to light sandy soils, sandy alluvium, and coastal sand dunes. In Zimbabwe they have been taken in dry, sandy river beds. In captivity, when transferred to containers with heavy clay or schist soils, they made no attempt to burrow into these and would do so only into sandy substrates.

### Habits
They move in subsurface runs like other species of golden moles. If disturbed in these while moving they burrow deeply into the substrate. Roberts (1936) observed that they occupy chambers around the bases of trees from which the subsurface runs lead off for long distances. He noted that they regularly used the same runs for, if they were flattened, they would be reopened later. While there are no observations of mounds on record, the fact that they construct chambers suggests that mounds must be present somewhere along the burrow system. The loose structure of the soil in which they live may make the mounds less obvious than in other substrates.

In captivity they tunnel up to a depth of 200 mm into loose, sandy soil. They are highly sensitive to the movements of earthworms, moths and other insects dropped on to the surface of the soil, quickly burrowing up to their vicinity and then dragging them below the surface to be eaten or, if they are large, eating them *in situ*. At times they would emerge and, porpoise-like, would move at a surprising speed in and out of the surface of the sandy soil around the containers, continuing to do this for up to a minute at a time. Watering of the soil surface in the containers appeared to stimulate them and they would continue to tunnel in the dampened soil until it was churned up. When handled they vocalised with a high-pitched series of squeaks.

### Food
In captivity they would take earthworms, cockroaches, grasshoppers, moths, mealworms, flies and small beetles, but would not touch odiferous insects, such as plant-sucking bugs. They ate ground-up meat and, while they would take this if presented on a small dish on the surface, appeared to prefer to take it if it was set in a depression in the soil surface covered with a flat stone. They squeak quietly when handled.

### Reproduction
No information available.

## Genus *Amblysomus* Pomel, 1848

Key to the species (Meester *et al.*, 1986)

1. Thirty-six teeth; $M_3$ and $M^3$ absent; well-developed talonid on lower cheekteeth ... 2

   Thirty-eight to forty teeth; $M_3$ sometimes, and $M^3$ usually present, but if so, differing from those molars in front of it; talonid of lower cheekteeth feebly developed or absent ... *gunningi*
2. Dorsal colour brown to blackish, without any reddish, and not becoming markedly paler on sides than on midback ... *iris*

   Dorsal colour pale to darker reddish-brown, not brown or blackish; if dark, becoming paler on sides than on midback ... 3
3. Usually darker, rich reddish-brown in colour, paler on sides than on midback; larger, greatest skull length 22–31 mm; braincase narrower, breadth/length index usually 57–66%, exceptionally up to 68% in large skulls; upper toothrow shorter in relation to palate length, usually 87–103%, exceptionally up to 107% in very large skulls ... *hottentotus*

   Paler, lacking the rich reddish-brown of the midback; pale cinnamon-brown above and on sides; smaller, greatest skull length 21,5–23,5 mm; braincase wider, breadth/length index 67–71%; upper toothrow longer in relation to palate length, about 104–105% in three available specimens ... *julianae*

No. 28

## *Amblysomus gunningi* (Broom, 1908)

## Gunning's golden mole
## Gunning se gouemol

### Colloquial Name

Named after Dr J.W.B. Gunning, a former Director of the Transvaal Museum, Pretoria.

### Taxonomic Notes

Ellerman & Morrison-Scott (1951) pointed out that the dental formula is not necessarily a valid generic or specific character in the Order. In the original series, collected in the Woodbush Forest, eastern Transvaal, there were specimens with 10 upper teeth and 10 lower on each side, others with 10 upper and 10 lower on one side and nine upper and 10 lower on the other, and still others with nine upper and 10 lower on each side.

Meester (1974) in his revision used size, length of upper toothrow and other skull characters to separate the genera. In dealing with *Chlorotalpa*, *Calcochloris* and *Amblysomus* he separated *Chlorotalpa* from the other two in having 10 upper and 10 lower teeth in each jaw half, the others normally having nine. In *Calcochloris* and *Amblysomus* he added the proviso that if the 10th tooth is present, as in *A. gunningi*, it differs in appearance from the preceding teeth and also from the 10th tooth, as in the genus *Eremitalpa*.

As all the known specimens originate from a very restricted area, no subspecies have been described.

### Description

Adult Gunning's golden moles have a head and body length of about 120 mm (Table 28.1). Their colour is a dark golden-brown on the upper parts of the body, the fur having the characteristic sheen common to all the golden moles; in this case a rich brown tinged with bronze. The cheeks and front parts of the muzzle are distinctly lighter in colour than the upper parts and are tinged yellow. The under parts of the neck and limbs are light fawn; the remainder of the under parts is fawn, tinged with light golden-brown.

The claw on the first digit of the front feet is short and narrow, that on the second digit about three-quarters the length of the claw on the third, which is the longest. The fourth digit is vestigial and has a knob-like claw. The claws on the second and third digits are highly efficient tools for loosening the soil as they burrow. There are five digits on the hind feet joined by a membrane, each digit with a thin, slightly curved claw; the claw on the third digit is distinctly larger than the remainder.

**Table 28.1**

Measurements (mm) of Gunning's golden moles, *A. gunningi*

| | Males | | | Females | | |
|---|---|---|---|---|---|---|
| | $\bar{x}$ | n | Range | $\bar{x}$ | n | Range |
| HB | 127 | 31 | 125–130 | 121 | 3 | 120–123 |
| Hf c/u | 14 | 3 | 13–14 | 14 | 3 | 14–15 |

### Distribution

*Southern African Subregion*

An inhabitant of montane forest and grassland, this species originally was described from the Woodbush Forest in the eastern **Transvaal**. It was known only from this restricted locality until 1974 when it was taken in the Agatha Forest Reserve some 20 km south of the original locality (Rautenbach, 1978).

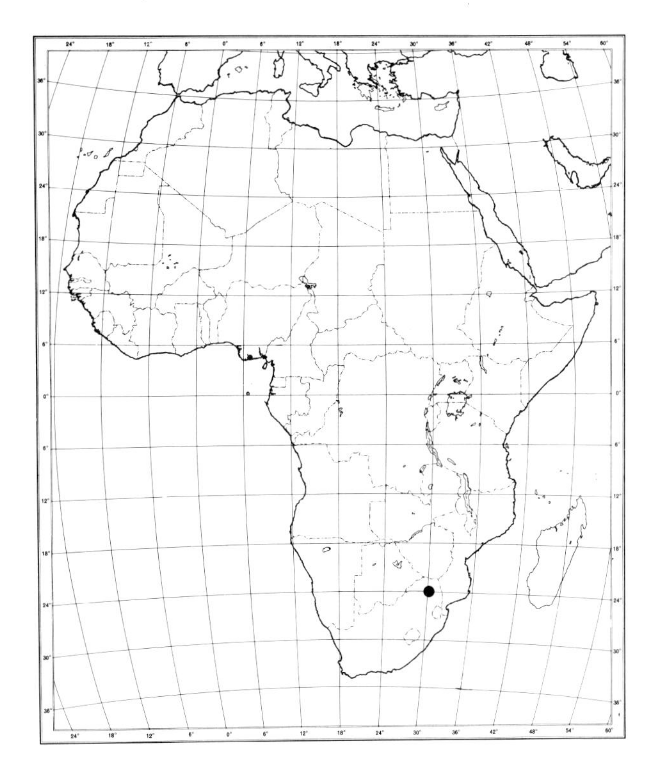

### Habitat

The locality recorded for the original specimens suggests that this species is associated with montane forest but they were taken subsequently in ploughed lands and in open montane grassland (Rautenbach, 1978). In both montane and lowland forest in Zimbabwe, Arends' golden mole, *Chlorotalpa arendsi*, occurs within the forest but has extensive surface runs and burrow systems extending far out into grassland or cultivated lands, where these abut on to the forest fringes. In the Agatha Forest Reserve, Rautenbach (1978) recorded that they occur alongside the common molerat, *Cryptomys hottentotus*.

### Habits

The subsurface runs wind and twist over considerable distances and, in addition to these, deeper burrows are excavated, and the soil pushed out into mounds which are smaller than those of the common molerat, *Cryptomys* spp.

**Food**

Insectivorous.

**Reproduction**

Unknown.

---

No. 29

## *Amblysomus iris* Thomas & Schwann, 1905

## Zulu golden mole
## Zoeloelandse gouemol

Plate 2

---

**Taxonomic Notes**

Three subspecies are listed by Meester *et al.* (1986): *A. i. iris* which occurs from the eastern Cape Province; *A. i. corriae* Thomas, 1905 from the southern Cape Province, and *A. i. septentrionalis* Roberts, 1913 from the southeastern Transvaal.

**Description**

The Zulu golden mole is a small species with a head and body length of about 100 mm (Table 29.1). The colour of the upper parts is a very dark smoky-brown with a distinctly greenish sheen. The sides of the face and chin are lighter in colour and tinged yellow. In the position the eyes would occupy, if present, there are two tiny buffy spots. The under parts are lighter in colour than the upper. The claw on the first digit of the front feet is about half the length of the second and is narrow, the claw on the second is about three quarters the length of the claw on the third, which is the longest. The fourth digit is vestigial and has a knob-like claw.

**Table 29.1**

Measurements (mm) and mass (g) of Zulu golden moles, *A. iris*

| | Males | | | Females | | |
|---|---|---|---|---|---|---|
| | $\bar{x}$ | n | Range | $\bar{x}$ | n | Range |
| HB | 114 | 3 | 106–119 | 114 | 9 | 105–122 |
| Hf c/u | 15 | 3 | 14–15 | 15 | 9 | 13–16 |
| Mass | – | | | One only 44,0 | | |

**Distribution**

*Southern African Subregion*

In the **Cape Province** they occur in the vicinity of George, Knysna and Grahamstown; in **Transkei** at Port St. Johns and in **Natal** in the Hluhluwe Game Reserve and further north. There is a single record from the southeastern **Transvaal** at Wakkerstroom, which is as far north as it has been recorded so far. From Natal westwards to the Cape Province the records all fall in a narrow sector along the coast, with the exception of the single specimen from Grahamstown.

**Habitat**

Nothing appears to be known about the habitat requirements of this species. From the localities in which they have been taken they appear to be associated with light sandy soils. Roberts (1951) indicated that they are associated with coastal sandy areas in the eastern parts of their range.

**Habits**

As for the Hottentot golden mole, *A. hottentotus*.

**Reproduction**

No information available.

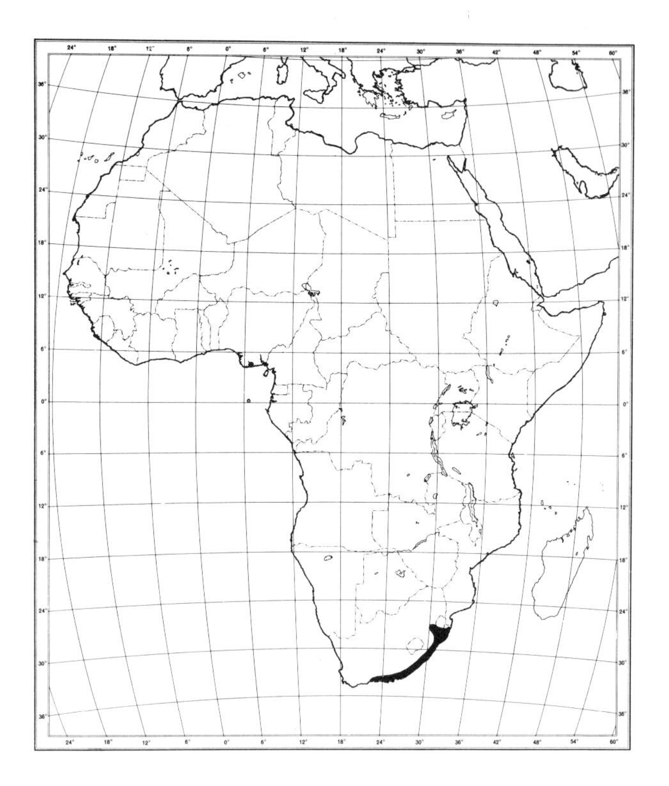

---

No. 30

## *Amblysomus hottentotus* (A. Smith, 1829)

## Hottentot golden mole
## Hottentot gouemol

Plate 2

---

**Taxonomic Notes**

This species is closely related to Gunning's golden mole, *A. gunningi*, from which it differs by having 36 teeth compared with Gunning's which has 38 to 40. Meester *et al.* (1986) recognised three subspecies: *A. h. hottentotus* which has a wide distribution from Port Elizabeth eastwards through Natal and the Orange Free State to the eastern Transvaal, *A. h. devilliersi* Roberts, 1946 from the southwestern Cape Province and *A. h. marleyi* Roberts, 1931 from KwaZulu.

**Description**

The head and body length of this species is about 120 mm (Table 30.1). The colour of the upper parts is a rich dark reddish-brown, with a predominantly bronze sheen mixed with green and purple. The flanks are lighter in colour than the back, the cheeks off-white or tinged yellow, the top of the snout greyish-brown. They have distinct patches of off-white hair covering the minute ear openings and tiny white spots in the position which the eyes would occupy, if present. The under parts are lighter than the upper and have a faint grey tinge. In some specimens there is a diffused white band running centrally from the upper chest to the belly. The claw on the first digit of the front feet reaches about half way up the claw on the second digit which is nearly the length of the third claw which is the largest, being stoutly built, broad at its base, with a thick leading edge and a knife-like trailing edge. The fourth digit is vestigial, armed with a knob-like claw.

**Table 30.1**

Measurements (mm) of Hottentot golden moles, *A. hottentotus*

| | Males | | | Females | | |
|---|---|---|---|---|---|---|
| | $\bar{x}$ | n | Range | $\bar{x}$ | n | Range |
| HB | 129 | 10 | 115–145 | 122 | 3 | 120–125 |
| Hf c/u | 16 | 10 | 14–18 | 14 | 3 | 13–15 |

## Distribution

*Southern African Subregion*

The Hottentot golden mole has a distribution which extends from the southwestern parts of the Cape Province to the Transvaal. In the **Cape Province** they occur in the vicinity of Stellenbosch, extending narrowly eastwards along the coast to the Eastern Province. In this province the furthest inland they have so far been taken is Somerset East. They occur in the central and northeastern **Orange Free State;** throughout **Natal**, and in the extreme northern parts of **Lesotho**. In the **Transvaal** they occur in the eastern and southeastern parts of the Highveld, the records from Haenertsburg (23°50′S) being the furthest north they have been recorded so far. They occur in **Swaziland** in the Mbabane District and in the southern parts of **Mozambique** in the Maputo District.

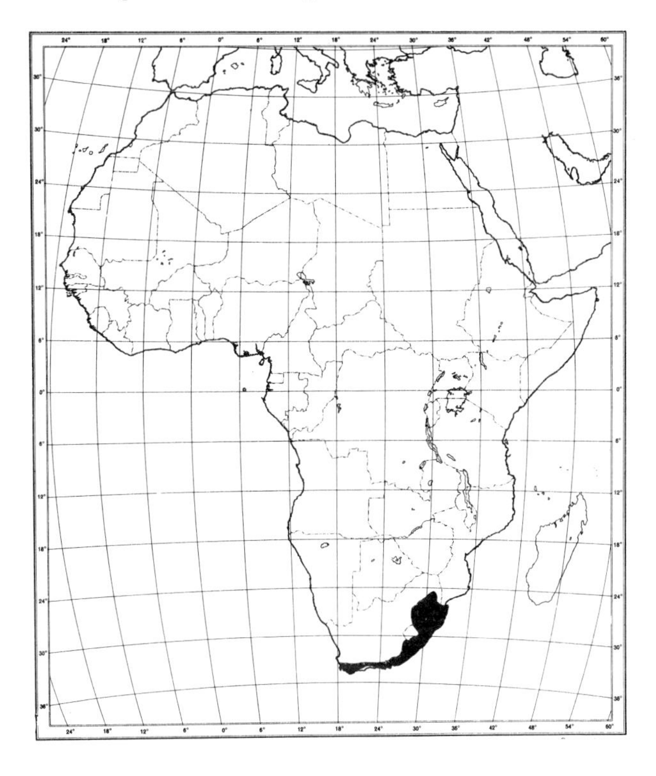

## Habitat

Roberts (1951) stated that they sometimes occur in forest although the great majority of records are from grassland. In Natal, Kuyper (1979) recorded them from forest, with little ground cover, but more commonly in adjacent grassland. Most of her observations were made on the fairways of a golf course. Rautenbach (1978), in the Transvaal, associated them with soft ground, mostly sandy soils or sandy loam, although he took them in black clayey soil. All the records lie in areas with a mean annual rainfall of over 500 mm, in parts up to 1 000 mm. They occur from sea level to over 3 000 m above sea level (Sani Pass, Lesotho).

## Habits

The Hottentot golden mole uses subsurface runs of about-four to six centimetres in diameter a few centimeters below the ground surface and burrows of up to 500 mm deep. The run and burrow system may extend in length to over 200 m. The burrows have many blind side-tunnels, some of which they may use as resting places, others as latrines. Some may later be filled in with surplus soil from new excavations. The subsurface runs show above ground as raised dome-like ridges. Where the soil is light the mole opens them up with its horny nose pad. In heavier soil the front claws assist in the process, loosening the soil ahead of it. Where soil accumulates it may be pushed to the surface of the ground with the back feet into small heaps at intervals along the subsurface run. The burrows run well under the surface of the ground. They dig with the front claws, making openings to the surface through which surplus soil is moved to form the mounds. In digging the burrows, the individual braces the back feet against the burrow wall, using the claws of the front feet and nose pad to push the soil under its body. It is then pressed back with the back feet along the burrow to the surface. This excavation may be carried out with the individual lying in the normal position, sideways or even upside down (Kuyper, 1979). If they wish to turn in the burrow they tuck their heads under their bodies, somersaulting to regain their normal position.

In pushing out the soil to the surface they never expose themselves. When a sufficient length of burrow has been excavated they open a new hole to the surface to get rid of surplus soil. The direction of the burrow is clearly shown on the surface by the line of these mounds. They invariably plug up the burrow, through which the soil has been expelled, just below the mound. The burrows are constructed neatly and finished off by stamping the floors with the feet and smoothing the sides by pressing their bodies against them. Kuyper (1979) estimated that they can burrow at the rate of 1 to 1,5 m/h.

Hottentot golden moles co-exist on the same ground as common molerats, *Cryptomys hottentotus*, and sometimes may share a burrow with them. They are active much less in winter than in summer and during the winter months appear to burrow deeper. During winter they may lie up in the nests for periods in a state of torpor. After rain they are particularly active, as can be seen by the appearance of extensive subsurface runs. Korn (1986) reported on an individual, caught by hand after a heavy rainfall, which kept in captivity entered a state of torpor at night in cold weather which lasted up to 10 hours. Mobility and feeding were observed 30 minutes after exposure to warm conditions.

Kuyper (1979) stated that there appeared to be three periods during which they are more active than at other times: early in the morning around sunrise, at sunset and again at midnight. During the 24 hour period they are intermittently active, punctuated by rest periods of an hour or two. They certainly have some surface activity at night as their skulls and bones are found frequently in the casts of barn owls, *Tyto alba*. Like other golden moles they are attracted to the surface by the movements of worms and insects and may fall victim during these emergences to feed. When food becomes scarce they emerge, usually at night, to move on the surface in search of new areas in which to settle and this also makes them prone to predation.

Like other golden moles they are extremely sensitive to disturbance and will retreat quickly from the subsurface runs to the deeper burrows if disturbed by surface vibrations of observers walking too close. If their retreat is blocked their usual reaction is to burrow vertically downwards. On the surface of the ground they can move suprisingly quickly and Kuyper (1979) has shown that they can swim, which is to their advantage as their burrows are subject to flooding.

## Food

Like other golden moles they live on insects and earthworms, but unlike some of them they will also eat snails and vegetable matter. Kuyper (1979) included in their diet the bulbs of the pig lily, *Zantedeschia rehmanni*, and *Homeria* sp, as well as potatoes. In captivity they will drink water, but may obtain their moisture requirements under natural conditions from their food or from dew.

## Reproduction

Little is known about this aspect of their life history. Roberts (1951) stated that the young are born during the rains and Rautenbach (1978) took a gravid female with two foetuses in November and a lactating female in the same month in the Golden Gate National Park. Kuyper (1979) recorded a gravid female in August. From this meagre information it appears that they may have their young during the early part of the warm summer months in the eastern part of their distributional range.

The young are born in an enlarged side tunnel of the burrow system in a ball-like nest of dry grass with a single entrance towards the open burrow end. The newly born have a head and body length of about 47 mm and a mass of about 4,5 g. They are altricial, being pale pink and naked except for a few hairs on the forehead and on the sides of the muzzle. The ear openings are marked by small protuberances on the sides of the head. The claws are well developed but soft (Kuyper, 1979).

No. 31

## *Amblysomus julianae* Meester, 1972

## Juliana's golden mole
## Juliana se gouemol

### Colloquial Name

Named by the describer of the species after his wife, Mrs Juliana Meester.

### Taxonomic Notes

No subspecies are recognised (Meester, *et al.*, 1986).

### Description

A small species, adults reaching a head and body length of about 100 mm (Table 31.1). In Pretoria specimens the upper parts are cinnamon-brown, slightly darker down the mid-back, the flanks paler than the upper parts, the colour fading imperceptibly into the fawn colour of the under parts. The sides of the face and across the top of the snout, the chin, throat and upper parts of the chest are off-white. The upper chest is tinged yellow. The upper parts of the fore limbs are off-white and the tops of the hind feet have short off-white bristles. The colour varies with locality, those taken at the Numbi Gate, Kruger National Park are slightly darker above, the under parts browner and the white facial marking not continuous over the snout, which is brown. The claw on the first digit of the front feet barely reaches the insertion of the second which is nearly the length of the third claw, the largest and heaviest. The fourth digit is vestigial, armed with a knob-like claw.

### Table 31.1

Measurements (mm) and mass (g) of Juliana's golden moles, *A. julianae*

| | Males | | | Females | | |
|---|---|---|---|---|---|---|
| | $\bar{x}$ | n | Range | $\bar{x}$ | n | Range |
| HB | 102 | 2 | 98–106 | 100 | 2 | 99–100 |
| Hf c/u | 14 | 2 | 13–14 | 12 | 2 | 11–13 |
| Mass | One | only | 21,0 | One | only | 23,0 |

### Distribution

*Southern African Subregion*

So far only recorded from three localities in the **Transvaal**: the Willows, Pretoria; Numbi Gate and Machulwane, Kruger National Park.

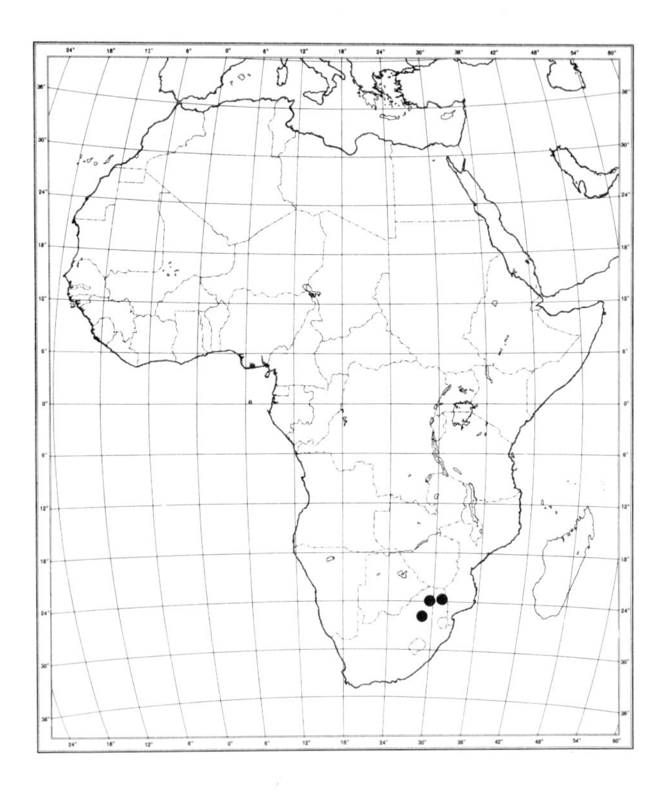

### Habitat

One specimen taken at Numbi Gate was found dead on the ground, the other was taken live and kept for observation. The area in which they were taken lies in the Transvaal Lowveld with a bush savanna association. Those from the Willows occurred in sandy soil with rock outcrops. The vegetation was grassland with bush intrusions (Meester, 1972c).

### Habits

Meester (1972c) found subsurface runways which he believed were made by this species but he made no mention of mounds. They probably do tunnel deeply as well as using subsurface runs, throwing up small mounds like other golden moles.

### Food

From observations on the live Numbi Gate individual, which was kept in captivity, they eat earthworms, cockroaches, grasshoppers and other insects. This individual also took mealworms and ground beef, but would not eat snails or slugs. The food was held in the forefeet when eaten and usually was dragged into the burrow to be eaten (Meester, 1972c).

### Reproduction

Unknown.

# Order MACROSCELIDEA

Elephant-shrews

## IV. Family MACROSCELIDIDAE

For a long time elephant-shrews were included as a Family of the Order Insectivora although their relationships to other groups of mammals has been the subject of some controversy. The Family at one time was associated with the Tupaiidae, a group of shrew-like mammals found in parts of India and southeastern Asia, in the Order Menotyphla. Subsequently the Tupaiidae were placed in a separate Order, the Scandentia, and Butler (1956) suggested that the macroscelids were worthy of full ordinal rank, a suggestion that subsequently has found wide acceptance and been followed by authorities such as McKenna (1975); Honacki, Kinman & Koeppl (1982) and Meester *et al.* (1986). Recent opinion places the elephant-shrews near to the lagomorphs and rodents, a view supported by morphological evidence (Novacek & Wyss, 1986) and a relatively large, functional caecum (Woodall & Mackie, 1987).

The Macroscelididae is a small Family whose members occur only on the African Continent. It is comprised of two Subfamilies, only one of which, the Macroscelidinae, is represented in the Subregion. Their fossil history is poorly known, although better so than that of most insectivores.

The earliest known were recovered from the Early Oligocene beds in Egypt of some 35 to 30 million years ago. Other remains were taken from Early Miocene beds in the Namib Desert, Namibia dating about 22 to 20 million years ago.

By the time that representatives of the Subfamily Macroscelidinae appear in the fossil record the main radiation had taken place already. Both *Macroscelides* and *Elephantulus* are well differentiated in the Makapansgat, Transvaal, brecchias (Butler, 1978). The Makapansgat *Elephantulus antiquus* has some resemblance to the East African *E. rufescens* on the one hand and *E. edwardii*, which occurs in the southern parts of the Subregion, on the other. The fossil species *E. broomi* closely resembles the living *E. intufi*. Similarly the fossil *Macroscelides* from Makapansgat is only subspecifically distinct from the living *Macroscelides proboscideus*.

The lower third molar teeth are absent in most Macroscelidinae, but occur in one fossil form, *Palaenothentoides* and in two living species which occur in the Subregion, *E. brachyrhynchus* and *E. fuscus*, which were long differentiated on the basis of this character under the genus *Nasilio*. Corbet (1974b), however, considered them both as belonging to the genus *Elephantulus*, a treatment followed here.

*Mylomygale*, a fossil Macroscelidinae from the late Pliocene deposits in the Transvaal, from the Taungs deposits (Broom, 1948) and Sterkfontein, Transvaal (de Graaff, 1960a) has been placed by authorities in various Subfamilies and remains a problematical species whose relationships remain to be determined (Butler, 1978). The first member of the Family to be discovered was the short-eared elephant-shrew, *Macroscelides proboscideus* (Shaw, 1800), which was purported to come from the "Cape of Good Hope". In fact they do not occur there and it must have been brought from the hinterland. Many years later Roberts (1951) fixed the locality as Roodewal in the Oudtshoorn District.

As further species were discovered it was realised that they could be placed in two natural groups or subfamilies. The first, the Macroscelidinae, is well represented in the Southern African Subregion by the genera *Macroscelides*, *Elephantulus* and *Petrodromus*. *Macroscelides* is represented by a single species the short-eared elephant-shrew, *M. proboscideus*, which is confined in its distribution to within the limits of the Subregion. *Elephantulus* is represented by six species, and has a wide distribution in other parts of Africa, with an additional four species, the East African, *E. fuscipes* and *E. rufescens*, the Somali, *E. revoili*, and the North African, *E. rozeti*. The largest member of the Family which occurs in the Subregion, the four-toed elephant-shrew, *Petrodromus tetradactylus*, extends northwards to East Africa, with an isolated population westwards in Zaire.

The second Subfamily, the Rhynchocyoninae includes only one genus, *Rhynchocyon*, with two species, neither of which has been recorded so far in the subregion. The checkered elephant-shrew, *R. c. cirnei*, was taken originally at Quelimane, Mozambique, which is just north of the limits of the Subregion, and there remains the possibility that one day it may be taken in forest south of the Zambezi River. Against this possibility, it has been found that larger rivers can be barriers of their spread.

As the colloquial name suggests their characteristic feature is the possession, by all members of the Family, of an elongated, trunk-like, and exceedingly mobile snout, on the extremity of which is carried the tiny rhinarium, which encloses the nostrils. This snout is constantly in motion, twisting up and down and from side to side as the individual tests the air. Several glands discharge their secretions at the tip of the snout, these may protect the rhinarium from the chemical defences of ants and termites (Kratzing & Woodall, 1988). The broad, upstanding ears are as mobile as the snout and are expressive of their mood. In the infrequent encounters witnessed in captivity the ears are folded back, but, when the individual is sitting, they are held upright and are twitching and turning continually. The eyes are large for the size of the head and they are keen-sighted, quickly spotting the slightest movements of ants and other small insects, which are their principal food. They have nictitating membranes which can be passed over the surface of the eyes to protect them. All southern African species examined in detail are active both day and night, at varying levels, and only *Rhynchocyon* seems to be exclusively diurnal (Woodall *et al.*, 1989).

The hind limbs are much longer than the fore, and the hind feet are long and slender. In the genera *Elephantulus* and *Macroscelides* there are five digits on the hind feet armed with claws, the first located well back of the other four. In *Petrodromus* there are only four toes on the fore and hind feet. In all members of the Family the tail is covered sparsely with bristles and is usually fairly long and, characteristically in all members, there is a naked patch on the rump at the base of the tail. In some individuals this naked area tends to become covered with tiny, bright red oribatid mites, which attach firmly to its surface. The bullae are developed well, exceptionally so in *Macroscelides*, where they are so large that they can be seen when the skull is viewed from above as two rounded, bony domes lying on either side of the posterior end of the braincase (Fig.IV.1.a).

*Elephantulus myurus* and *E. brachyrhynchus* occur in the same general area, but are separated clearly by their habitat requirements, *E. myurus* living in rocky terrain and *E. brachyrhynchus* on the adjacent sandy ground.

*Macroscelides proboscideus* lives in arid country with a mean annual rainfall as low as 100 mm, whereas the much larger *Petrodromus tetradactylus* is confined to forest in

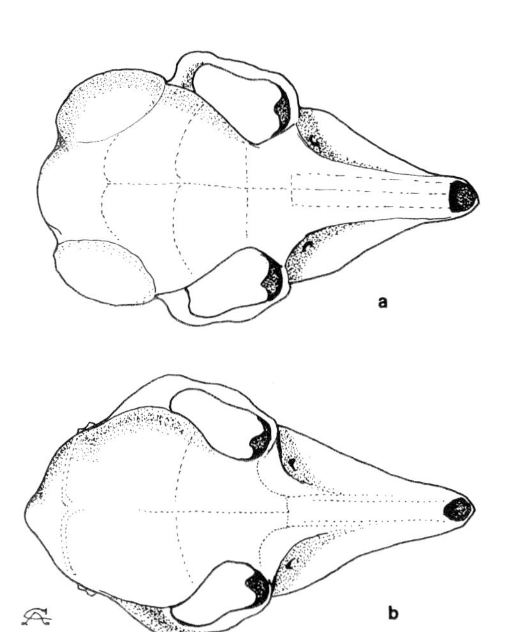


Fig.IV.1. Dorsal view skulls:
(a) *Macroscelides proboscideus*
(b) *Elephantulus myurus*.

high rainfall areas over 1 000 mm and is believed by Butler (1978) to be, in some respects, the most primitive of all our elephant-shrews. Its early fossil history is unknown.

Three species of *Elephantulus: E. myurus, E. edwardii* and *E. rupestris* live in a rocky habitat, their distributions not overlapping in the Subregion. *Elephantulus brachyrhynchus, E. fuscus* and *E. intufi* live on sandy soils, *E. intufi* generally confined to the lower rainfall areas and able to exist in areas with as low a mean annual rainfall as 100 mm, conditions which the other two species cannot tolerate. In Botswana, for example, the distributions of *E. intufi* and *E. brachyrhynchus* are mutually exclusive, *E. intufi* replacing *E. brachyrhynchus* in the more arid parts of the country.

The dental formula is:

$I\frac{3}{3}\,C\frac{1}{1}\,P\frac{4}{4}\,M\frac{2}{2} = 40$

except in *E. brachyrhynchus* and *E. fuscus* which have a third lower molar on each side of the lower jaw, a tiny simple tooth, much smaller than the molar immediately in front of it. For a long time the possession of this tooth was considered to be of sufficient importance to separate them from *Elephantulus* under the genus *Nasilio*, a view that is not accepted generally today.

In all the species which occur in the Subregion, the hind limbs are much longer than the fore. This suggests movement by jumping but, although they are capable of prodigious leaps, the normal method of locomotion in all the smaller species is by running on all four feet. The four-toed elephant-shrew, *Petrodromus tetradactylus*, however, as can be seen from the pattern on their paths on the forest floor, do proceed in a series of jumps (see text). This pattern may be produced only when they are moving quickly, for they walk around normally on all fours when searching for food.

If suddenly alarmed they jump straight up into the air before making for shelter. They are all very fast movers, especially when out in the open, running from the shelter of one bush to another or from one rock to another with lightening speed.

They all have exceedingly long, thinly tapering, pink tongues. These are so long that they can curl them around the top of their muzzles to lick their fur clean after eating.

## Subfamily MACROSCELIDINAE

Key to the genera after Corbet (1974b)

1. Four toes on the hind feet; larger; length of head and body over 160 mm; two pairs mammae

   ... *Petrodromus*

   Five toes on the hind feet; smaller; length of head and body less than 160 mm; three pairs mammae

   ... 2

2. Auditory bullae enormously inflated, to the extent that, in life, they can be seen as rounded swellings at the back of the skull (Fig. IV.1.a); second and third upper incisors broad and bilobed at their cutting edges (Fig. IV.2.a)

   ... *Macroscelides*

   Auditory bullae of normal size; second and third upper incisors not bilobed at their cutting edges (Fig. IV.2.b)

   ... *Elephantulus*

## Genus *Petrodromus* Peters, 1846

*Petrodromus* is a well defined genus, distinguished throughout its wide distributional range from the two genera *Macroscelides* and *Elephantulus* by the absence of a big toe (the hallux), by their greater overall size and by the fact that the females have two pairs of mammae as compared with three pairs in the other two genera. Eleven species have been described but Corbet & Hanks (1968), following a review of members of the genus, came to the conclusion that they were all subspecies of the oldest named, *P. tetradactylus*.

No. 32

## *Petrodromus tetradactylus* Peters, 1846

## Four-toed elephant-shrew
## Bosklaasneus

Plate 3

### Colloquial Name

The name derives from the fact that, unlike all other members of the Family, they have only four toes on their hind feet.

### Taxonomic Notes

Nine subspecies are listed from the continent by Corbet (1974b) of which six occur in the Subregion: *P. t. beirae*, Roberts, 1913 from central Mozambique, south of the Zambezi River; *P. t. schwanni* Thomas & Wroughton, 1907 from coastal southern Mozambique; *P. t. swynnertoni* Thomas, 1918 from the Melsetter District, Zimbabwe; *P. t. tetradactylus* Peters, 1846 from central Mozambique, originally taken at Tete on the Zambezi River; and *P. t. warreni* Thomas, 1918 from coastal Natal. *P. occidentalis* Roberts, 1913 is recorded from the eastern Caprivi Strip (Shortridge, 1934).

The subspecies are characterised mainly by variation in colour and size. *P. t. schwanni* has knobs on the bristles under the tail which differentiates this subspecies from all the others in the Southern African Subregion. The diploid chromosome number is 2n = 28 (Wenhold & Robinson, 1987).

### Description

This is by far the largest species of elephant-shrew that occurs in the Subregion. Males and females are about the same size, having a total length of about 350 mm and tails about three-quarters the length of the head and body, but the females tend to be heavier than the males with a mean mass of about 200,0 g as against 120,0 g in the males (Table 32.1).

They vary in colour geographically. *P. t. tetradactylus* from the extreme northeastern parts of the Subregion has rusty-reddish upper parts, bordered on the sides from the shoulders to the rump by a broad band of buffy-grey; the sides of the neck, cheeks, forearms, flanks and thighs are orange-buff, the cheeks tinged with brown. They have a conspicuous white ring around the eyes and the upper lip, chin, throat and middle parts of the under parts are white, tinged buffy in some individuals. In front of the eyes the reddish colour of the snout is darker and, behind the eyes

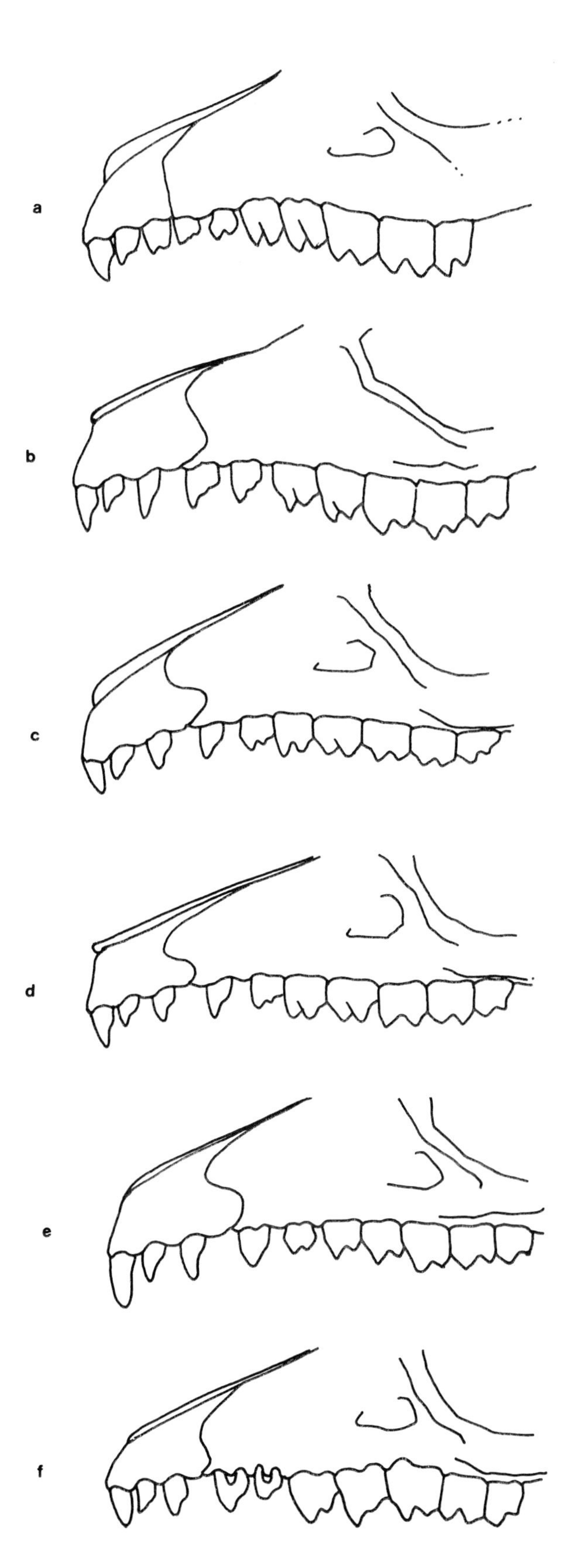


Fig.IV.2. Left hand upper toothrow and profile of rostrum:
(a) *Macroscelides proboscideus*
(b) *Elephantulus brachyrhynchus*
(c) *E. intufi*
(d) *E. rupestris*
(e) *E. myurus*
(f) *E. edwardii* after Corbet & Hanks (1968).

below the white extension of the eye ring, there is a black line bordered by chestnut-red, the black line broadening below the ears. The ears are rusty-brown, with pure white hair on the bases of the inner margins.

The upper parts of the hands and feet are buffy-yellow, the tail blackish on the upper surface, the under surface buffy, darkening in the middle and black towards the tip, covered with bristles which are especially numerous towards the tip. The under parts of the hind feet are naked and they have a naked patch on the rump at the base of the tail.

In *P. t. occidentalis*, which occurs in the eastern Caprivi Strip, the upper parts are paler than *P. t. tetradactylus* ; *P. t. beirae* from Mozambique is slightly larger in size. *P. t. swynnertoni* from eastern Zimbabwe is darker on the upper parts and slightly smaller; and *P. t. warreni* from Natal is paler than *P. t. beirae* and has a shorter muzzle.

*P. t. schwanni* from the Imhambane District of Mozambique has knobs on the tips of the tail bristles, the posterior foramina of the palate closed and they have a short skull. They are closely confined to a forest habitat. The club-shaped hairs on the ventral surface of the tail have a specialised structure and may facilitate scent marking with secretions from the tail glands (Sokolov *et al.*, 1980).

The first upper incisor teeth are large, the second small and close behind them, the third isolated and much larger than the second, the canines resembling the third incisor. The first premolar resembles the canine, the second double the size, the third molariform, the fourth like the first. They have two molar teeth. The lower incisors are bifid.

**Table 32.1**

Measurements (mm) and mass (g) of four-toed elephant-shrews, *P. tetradactylus*, from eastern Zimbabwe (Smithers & Wilson, 1979)

| | Males | | | Females | | |
|---|---|---|---|---|---|---|
| | $\bar{x}$ | n | Range | $\bar{x}$ | n | Range |
| TL | 350 | 10 | 324–370 | 355 | 10 | 33 |
| (HB | 188) | | | (192) | | |
| T | 162 | 10 | 160–176 | 163 | 10 | 162–170 |
| Hf c/u | 59 | 10 | 57–67 | 58 | 10 | 55–62 |
| E | 35 | 10 | 33–37 | 35 | 10 | 32–37 |
| Mass* | 182,1 | 8 | 160,2–202,3 | 203,6 | 9 | 176,0–280,0 |

*Corrected from National Museum, Bulawayo records

**Distribution**

Within the distributional limits as shown on the map the occurrence of the four-toed elephant-shrew is dependent on the availability of forest or woodland with dense underbush. As a consequence their occurrence is discontinuous throughout.

*South of the Sahara, excluding the Southern African Subregion*

In East Africa their northern limits lie in the extreme southern parts of **Uganda** and east of Lake Victoria in southeastern **Kenya**. Generally distributed throughout **Tanzania** they occur in southeastern **Zaire** with an isolated population in the west, south of the Congo River, extending into the **Congo Republic** and probably into the extreme northern parts of **Angola** and their distribution may extend from Zambia into the west of the country. In **Zambia** they occur throughout, except in the southwest, west of the Zambezi River. In **Mozambique**, north of the Zambezi River, they occur coastally and in the south, and, as they are known from the southern Tanzania, may well, in time be shown to have a wider occurrence, where there is suitable habitat. They are widespread in the Southern Province of **Malawi** and may well occur further north, as they are known from adjacent parts of Zambia.

*Southern African Subregion*

In **Zimbabwe** they are known only from the more southerly parts of the Eastern Districts. Although they occur on the Transvaal bank of the Limpopo River west to near Beit Bridge they so far have not been shown to occur on the northern bank of the river, although there is, in parts, suitable habitat. In **Mozambique**, south of the Zambezi River, they occur widely, except in the northern parts of the Vila Pery District along the Zimbabwe border, and in the drier western parts of the Gaza and Inhambane District. Their distribution in the south is predominantly coastal, continuing to the northern Natal border. In the **Transvaal** there is an isolated population in the northeast in the riparian forests of the Limpopo River and adjacent thickets, which extend westwards in the valley to near Beit Bridge. They occur marginally in northeastern and northern **Natal** near the Mozambique border and in the eastern **Caprivi Strip**.

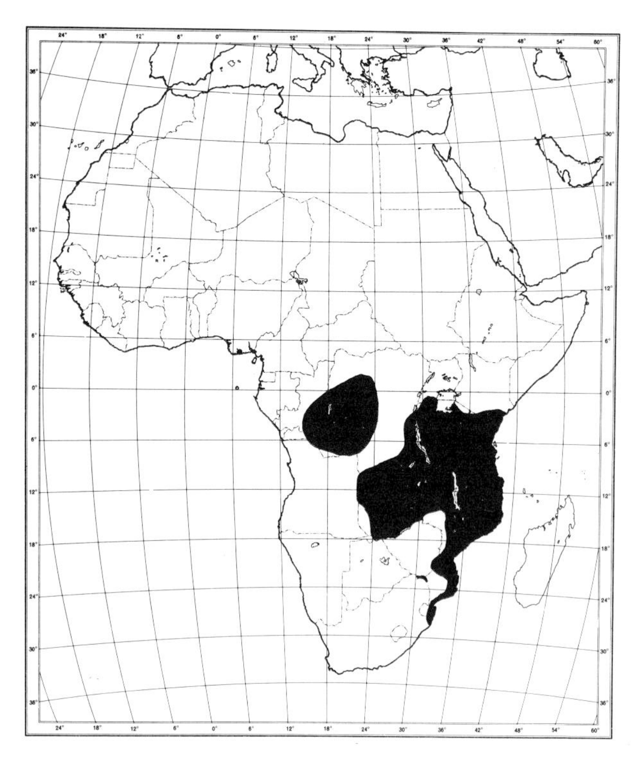

**Habitat**

They are associated closely with well developed riparian and evergreen forests with dense underbush, and in coastal forests and scrub. They are generally absent in areas with a mean annual rainfall of less than about 700 mm.

**Habits**

They are a terrestrial species which occur singly or in pairs and are active both day and night (Woodall *et al.*, 1989). They rest up in holes under roots of trees, in termite mounds, under fallen logs, in hollow logs or in patches of dense underbush. Distinct runs are formed from these resting places radiating to areas where food is available. These runs are marked by bare patches in the ground litter, about 240 mm long and about 700 mm between their centres (Ansell & Ansell, 1969) and mark the take-off and landing points as they proceed in jumps along them. Where low obstacles lie across these paths they jump over them. The normal method of locomotion is, however, a walk or they will run on all four feet and it is only when they are in a hurry that they resort to leaping. When alarmed they stamp their hind feet, the sound of which can be heard from several metres away and they may utter a loud shrill squeak. When under stress they make a soft purring noise. This is not vocal but produced by vibrating the hind feet on the ground (see *Elephantulus myurus* No. 38).

**Food**

Four-toed elephant-shrews are insectivorous. Stomachs of specimens from the eastern Zimbabwe forests were crammed with ants with smaller amounts of other insects, which were masticated so finely that identification was impossible. In captivity they take crickets and grasshoppers, which are taken more readily if they move. This indicates that, although they will smell potential food items with their long snouts, sight may be more important in locating food.

**Reproduction**

From such meagre information as is available from the Subregion the young are born just before and at the commencement of the rains from about August to October. Ansell (1960a) recorded foetuses in Zambia in January, July and October, and it may be that when further information is available a more extended breeding season may become evident. One or at most two young are produced at a birth. These are precocial being fully haired like the adults and have their eyes open.

## Genus *Macroscelides* A. Smith, 1829

The most characteristic feature of members of this genus is the inflated auditory region; the bullae are enlarged to the extent that they can be seen when the skull is viewed from above (Fig. IV.1.a). Adaptations for an arid habitat include a relatively long large intestine, probably to resorb faecal moisture (Woodall, 1987), and long renal papillae like those of desert rodents. The females, like those of the genus *Elephantulus*, have three pairs of mammae, two pairs pectoral and one abdominal, compared with *Petrodromus* which have two pairs of pectoral mammae.

---

No. 33

## *Macroscelides proboscideus* (Shaw, 1800)

## Round-eared elephant-shrew
## Ronde-oorklaasneus

Plate 3

---

**Colloquial Name**

The former colloquial name, short-eared elephant-shrew, widely used for this species, is unfortunate because, compared with other smaller species of elephant-shrews, the ears are not shorter. Roberts (1951) recorded ear lengths of up to 29 mm in this species from Namibia which surpassed the maximum recorded for the rock elephant-shrew, *E. myurus*, or the bushveld elephant-shrew, *E. intufi*. In fact the ears are very broad and expanded, almost circular in shape and this differentiates them from the other elephant-shrews.

**Taxonomic Notes**

Meester *et al.* (1986) listed two subspecies: *M. p. proboscideus* from the South West Arid Zone in the Cape Province, southeast to Grahamstown, the extreme southwestern parts of Botswana and southwestern Namibia and *M. p. flavicaudatus* Lundholm, 1955 from the northern parts of Namibia in the vicinity of the mouth of the Omaruru River and northwards to about 18 °S. The diploid chromosome number is 2n = 26 (Wenhold & Robinson, 1987).

**Description**

Adults have a total length of about 230 mm with tails about 20% longer than the length of the head and body and a mass of about 40,0 g (Table 33.1). They vary in colour throughout their distributional range. Specimens from the Cape Province are buffy-grey on the upper parts of the body, the flanks lighter in colour, the under parts white, with dark grey bases to the hairs showing through irregularly. The tail is dark and tends to be darker towards the tip. The ears are dark with a fringe of white hairs on their inner edges and towards the base of the outer edges. Some of the specimens have a richer brown colour, with light buffy-brown flanks. The pelage has a sprinkling of long black hairs interspersed throughout the guard coat and, where these tend to lie together as they do on the rump, they impart to the coat a dark wash of colour. Specimens from Namibia are much paler than those from the Cape Province; a series from Omaruru are pale creamy-buff on the upper parts, with yellowish tinged flanks and correspondingly pale tails. They have no white ring around the eyes, which is a feature in *Elephantulus* spp. The under parts of the feet are naked to the ankle, the skin paler in the lighter coloured specimens from Namibia than in those from the Cape Province.

The shape of the supratragus of the ear is characteristic, being square at the end and sparsely haired, unlike any possessed by species of *Elephantulus*, (Fig. IV.4.a).

The rostrum is short and the teeth are crowded together (Fig.IV.2.a). The first upper incisor is unicuspid, the second and the first premolar bicuspid; the incisors have one root, the canines two. The second upper premolar is molariform, with two lingual cusps. In the lower jaw the second and third premolars are narrow and sectorial.

**Table 33.1**

Measurements (mm) and mass (g) of round-eared elephant-shrews, *M. proboscideus*

| | Males | | | Females | | |
|---|---|---|---|---|---|---|
| | $\bar{x}$ | n | Range | $\bar{x}$ | n | Range |
| TL | 234 | 8 | 222–245 | 235 | 6 | 222–248 |
| (HB | 114) | | | (113) | | |
| T | 120 | 8 | 114–128 | 122 | 6 | 115–129 |
| Hf c/u | 36 | 8 | 34–39 | 36 | 6 | 34–37 |
| E | 23 | 8 | 21–23 | 25 | 6 | 20–29 |
| Mass | 38,0 | 4 | 32,0–47,0 | 38,4 | 5 | 31,0–47,0 |

**Distribution**

The round-eared elephant-shrew is confined in its distribution to within a comparatively narrow sector of the southwestern parts of the Subregion within the South West Arid Zone.

*Southern African Subregion*

They occur in the eastern and southern sector of **Namibia**; in the extreme southwestern parts of **Botswana** and widely throughout the central and western parts of the **Cape Province**.

**Habitat**

Round-eared elephant-shrews are a species of open country with a shrub bush and sparse grass cover. They are not confined to any particular type of ground, occurring on hard gravel plains as well as on loose sandy soils providing there is some cover of bush, which is an essential habitat requirement.

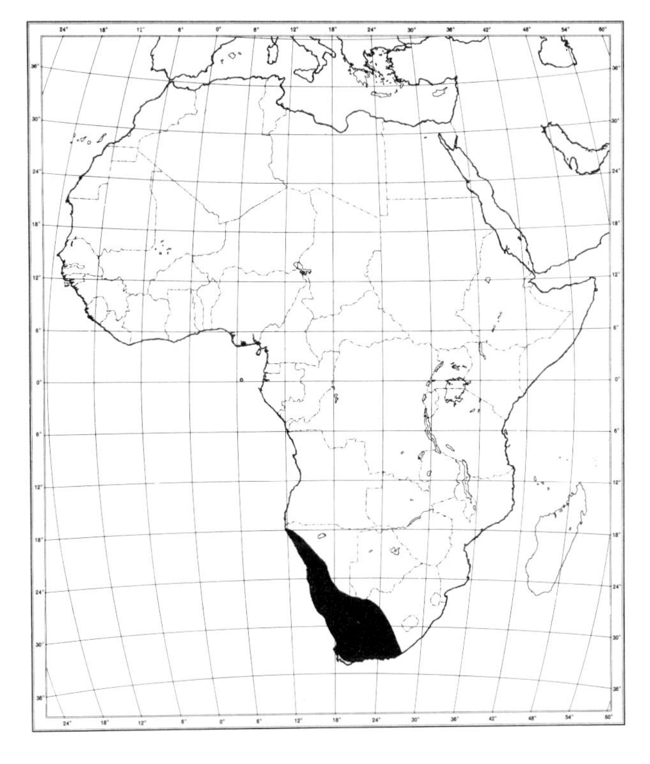

**Habits**

They are solitary or at times occur in pairs and are most active at dawn, dusk and at night (Sauer & Sauer, 1972; Woodall *et al.*, 1989). They live in burrows, the entrances of which lie under the cover of low, karroid, scrub bushes. Shortridge (1934) recorded that, in captivity, they are adept burrowers, from which one may reasonably assume that they excavate their own burrows in the wild. He stated that these burrows have an entrance and an emergency exit, the latter inconspicuously situated and entering the ground perpendicularly. This type of excavation is typical of the burrows of certain rodents e.g. the short-tailed gerbil, *Desmodillus auricularis*. They are known to use the disused burrows of rodents. Like other species, such as the bushveld elephant-shrew, *E. intufi*, they tend to use the cover of bushes, avoiding exposing themselves in open situations. When disturbed they move from bush to bush at great speed, eventually diving into their burrows. Like other elephant-shrews they are sun lovers and will sit on the fringe of bush cover sunning themselves in the early mornings.

**Food**

Insects, including ants and termites.

**Reproduction**

Information on breeding is scanty. In Namibia, Shortridge (1934) recorded a series of eight specimens each carrying twin foetuses in August and September. This suggests that they follow the general pattern of the smaller elephant-shrews, the young being born during the warm, wet months of the year from about September to February. The young are precocial, being born fully haired with the eyes open.

## Genus *Elephantulus* Thomas & Schwann, 1906

This genus is represented in the Subregion by six species, two of which, *E. brachyrhynchus* and *E. fuscus*, can be distinguished from the remainder by the possession in the adults of three molar teeth, giving a total of 11 teeth on either side of the lower jaw compared with the remainder which have only two molar teeth, a total of 10. The remainder can be distinguished from each other by the possession or absence of lingual cusps on their first and second upper premolar teeth (Fig.IV.3); the formation of the second upper premolars, which may be molariform or sectorial; and the formation of the supratragus of the ear (Fig. IV.4).

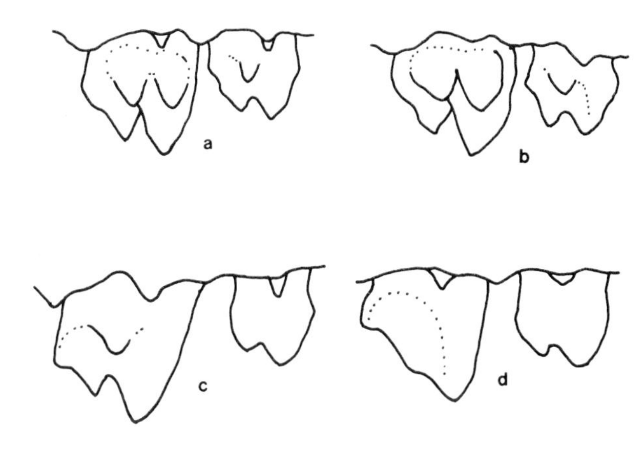


Fig.IV.3. Lingual aspect of the first upper premolar tooth (right) and second (left) of: (a) *E. rupestris* (b) *E. intufi* (c) *E. myurus* (d) *E. edwardii*. after Corbet (1974).

Key to the species, adapted from Corbet (1974b)

1. Eleven teeth in each side of the lower mandible in adults ... 2

   Ten teeth in each side of the lower mandible in adults ... 3

2. Supratragus of the ear swollen and twisted backwards on a constricted stalk (Fig.IV.4.d); darker and greyer in colour ... *fuscus*

   Supratragus of the ear not as above; browner, not grey in colour ... *brachyrhynchus*

3. First upper premolar with a cusp on its inner face, second upper premolar molariform with two well developed cusps on its inner face (Fig. IV.3.a & b); under parts whitish ... 4

   First upper premolar without a cusp on its inner face, second upper premolar sectorial with or without small

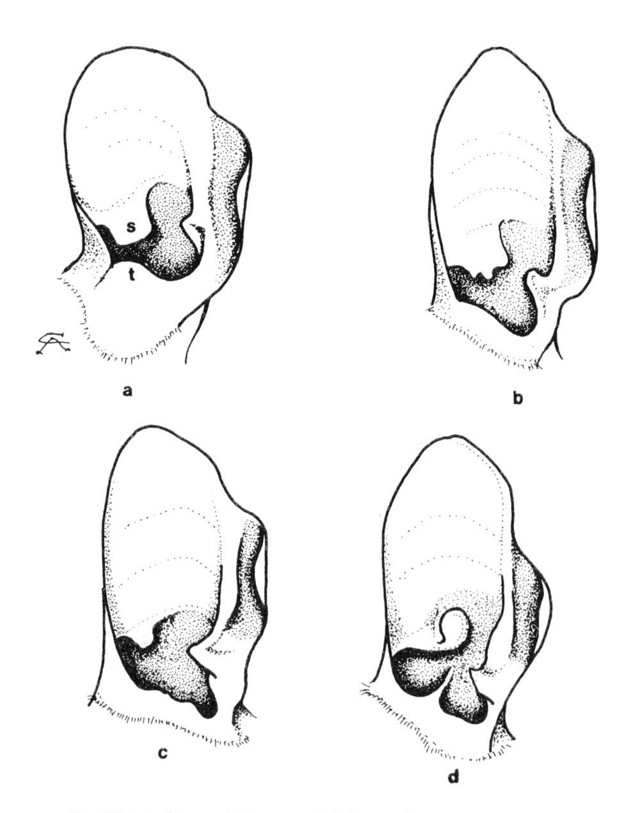


Fig.IV.4. Left ear of Macroscelididae to show supratragus s and tragus t in: (a) *Macroscelides proboscideus* (b) *Elephantulus edwardii* (c) *E. brachyrhynchus* (d) *E. fuscus* after Corbet & Hanks (1968).

cusps on its inner face (Fig. IV.3.c & d); under parts greyish

... 5

4. Body-size larger, upper toothrow over 18,7 mm; tail 115% of the length of the head and body, distinctly tufted and black on the top; with a narrow white ring around the eyes, broken above and below; the lower second and third premolar with three cusps arranged in a triangle behind the principal cusp

   ... *rupestris*

   Size smaller, upper toothrow less than 18,7 mm; tail about 106% of the length of the head and body, not distinctly tufted, speckled on the top; white rings around the eyes conspicuous and unbroken; the lower second and third premolars with only two cusps arranged transversely behind the principal cusp

   ... *intufi*

5. Upper second premolar with one, occasionally two cusps on its inner face (Fig. IV.3.c); lower first premolar with two roots; supratragus small and thick; premaxillary suture sinuous; upper parts greyish; soles of hind feet black

   ... *myurus*

   Upper second premolar without a cusp on its inner face (Fig. IV.3.d); lower first premolar with only one root; supratragus large and thin (Fig. IV.4.b); premaxillary suture straight; upper parts and soles of hind feet brown

   ... *edwardii*

---

No. 34

## *Elephantulus fuscus* (Peters, 1852)

### Peters' short-snouted elephant-shrew
### Peters se kortneus klaasneus

---

Very little is known about the ecology of this species which has only a marginal distribution in the Subregion. It is a close relative of *E. brachyrhynchus* from which it differs in the form of the supratragus of the ear (Fig. IV.4.d). It is likely that, in many respects, the life histories of the two species are very similar. Both species occur together in the vicinity of Tete, Mozambique, where a comparative examination would be interesting.

#### Description

No reliable external measurements are available, but Corbet & Hanks (1968) estimated that they are about 210 mm in total length with tails that are shorter than the length of the head and body.

They are darker and greyer in colour and slightly smaller than *E. brachyrhynchus* from the same area. The infraorbital foramen is diagonal in lateral view and triangular when viewed from in front, whereas in *E. brachyrhynchus* it is oval, the longer axis lying vertically. The tail is lighter below than in *E. brachyrhynchus*, with some wholly black hairs in the mid-dorsal line (Corbet, 1974). The supratragus is characteristic in shape, swollen and twisted backward on a narrow stalk (Fig. IV.4.d).

#### Distribution

*South of the Sahara, excluding the Southern African Subregion*

They are recorded from southern **Malawi**; and from the Tete and Zambezia districts of **Mozambique,** north of the Zambezi River, and from Southeastern **Zambia**.

*Southern African Subregion*

They occur in **Mozambique**, south of the Zambezi River, in the central parts of the Vila Pery and Beira districts, and in the Tete District.

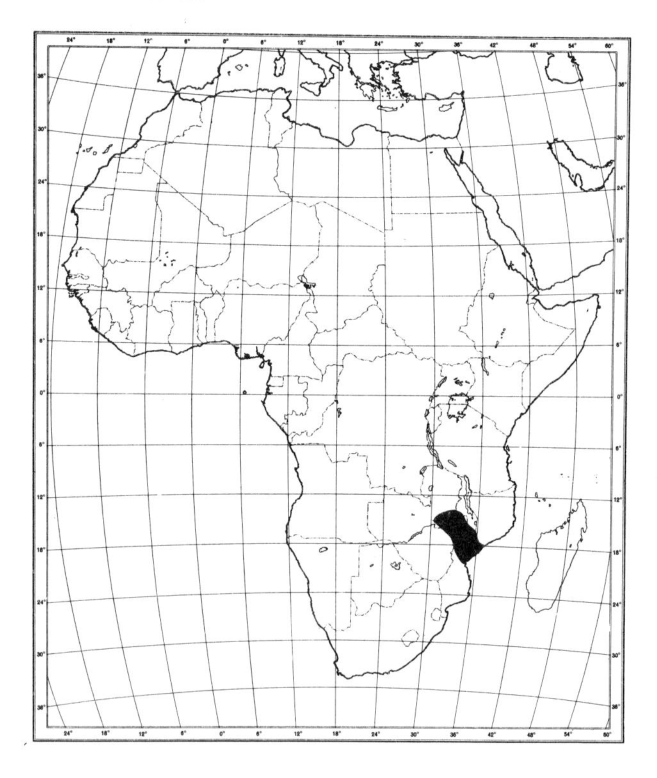

#### Habitat

They are found in grassland with scattered bushes and trees on a sandy substrate.

#### Food

Insects, including termites and ants.

#### Reproduction

No information is available at present on the breeding of this species. However, it is likely to be very similar to that of the short-snouted elephant-shrew, *E. brachyrhynchus*.

No. 35

## *Elephantulus brachyrhynchus* (A. Smith, 1836)

## Short-snouted elephant-shrew
## Kortneus klaasneus

Plate 3

### Colloquial Name

The name refers to the fact that the snout is shorter than in the other species of *Elephantulus* and, in this respect, they more closely resemble the round-eared elephant-shrew, *Macroscelides proboscideus*. This feature is reflected when the skulls are compared, the rostrum of this species being shorter than in other *Elephantulus* (Fig. IV.2.b).

### Taxonomic Notes

No subspecies are recognised, the variation seen from one end of the distributional range to the other, grades imperceptively through the intermediate stages. The diploid chromosome number is 2n = 26 (Stimson & Goodman, 1966).

### Description

Adults have a total length of about 210 mm, with tails shorter or about the same length as the length of the head and the body and a mass of about 44,0 g (Table 35.1). They are very variable in colour geographically; specimens from Namibia and northern Botswana are reddish-yellow on the upper parts, with a profuse sprinkling of black hairs scattered throughout the pelage; those from the Transvaal are darker, a yellowish-brown and darker brown from the northeastern parts of the province; and greyer from Mozambique. The under parts are white, the upper surface of the tail deep brown in the darker specimens to yellowish-grey in the lighter, the under surface paler.

A conspicuous feature of all the colour forms is the white, buffy or off-white ring around the eyes and the white upper lip and the buffy-yellow or white patch of hair behind at the bases of the ears, which contrast with the colour of the upper parts. In all cases the bases of the individual hairs on the upper parts are deep slate-grey, the general colour of the individual depending on the colour of the tips of the hairs. The naked soles of the hind feet in this species are brown as opposed to black in *E. myurus*.

### Table 35.1

Measurements (mm) and mass (g) of short-snouted elephant-shrews, *E. brachyrhynchus*, from Botswana (Smithers, 1971)

| | Males | | | Females | | |
|---|---|---|---|---|---|---|
| | $\bar{x}$ | n | Range | $\bar{x}$ | n | Range |
| TL | 210 | 25 | 200–227 | 210 | 23 | 200–222 |
| (HB | 111) | | | (113) | | |
| T | 99 | 24 | 89–108 | 97 | 24 | 90–105 |
| Hf c/u | 30 | 25 | 28–34 | 30 | 25 | 27–33 |
| E | 21 | 25 | 19–23 | 20 | 26 | 18–22 |
| Mass | 44,5 | 20 | 33,0–52,0 | 42,7 | 10 | 30,0–52,0 |

### Distribution

The short-snouted elephant-shrew has a wide distribution in Africa south of the Sahara.

*South of the Sahara, excluding the Southern African Subregion*

The northern limits of distribution lie in central **Uganda** and central **Kenya,** in the latter occurring through to the southeastern parts of the country. In **Tanzania** they occur centrally and in the northeast, from the coast westwards to the Rift Valley, extending into southeastern **Zaire.** Widespread in western **Angola**, their distribution in the south extends to the Humpata plateau, being absent in the northwest, most of the south and from the coastal desert. They occur throughout **Zambia** and **Malawi** but are absent from most of the northeastern sector of **Mozambique**, north of the Zambezi River,

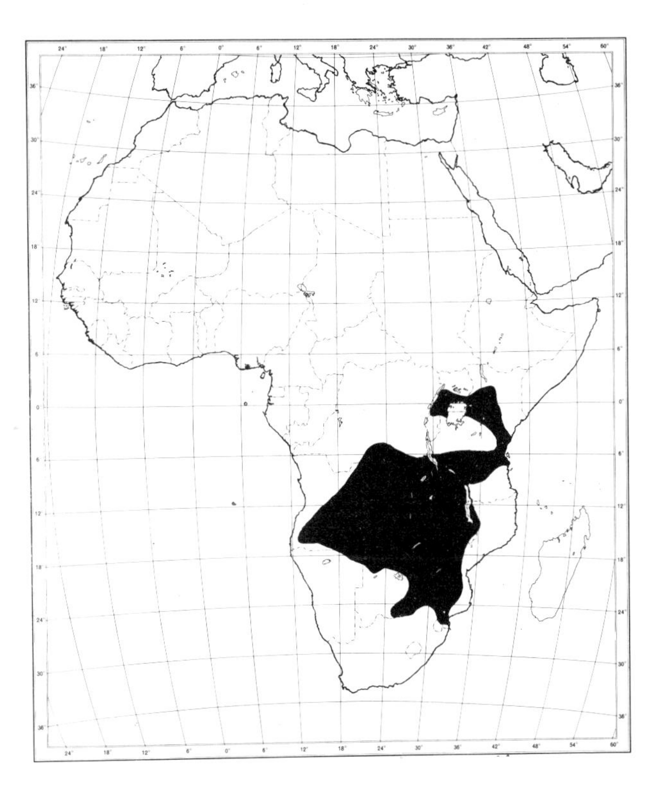

only occurring here narrowly along the southeastern shores of Lake Malawi.

*Southern African Subregion*

In **Namibia** they are confined to the northeast; in **Botswana** they occur widely in the north, northeast and eastern parts of the country, south to the border with the Cape Province. In the **Transvaal** they occur in the west, north and eastern parts of the province extending southwards to northeastern **Swaziland**. In **Mozambique**, south of the Zambezi River, they occur in the western areas south to the western parts of the Maputo District but not as far as the border with northern Natal. This marks their most southerly limits on the continent.

### Habitat

Although the short-snouted elephant-shrew, *E. brachyrhynchus*, occurs in the same general areas as the rock elephant-shrew, *E. myurus*, and the bushveld elephant-shrew, *E. intufi*, they are segregated by their habitat requirements. This species is associated in the Subregion with denser cover than the bushveld elephant-shrew. They occur in areas where there is a dense grass cover with scrub bush and scattered trees. They will use the cover afforded by the underbush of riparian woodland, and, in the Transvaal, are found more generally in this type of habitat. This segregation is marked in Botswana at the southern extremity of the Okavango Delta. Here the short-snouted elephant-shrew is associated with the richer vegetation of well-watered delta, the bushveld elephant-shrew, *E. intufi*, with the adjacent dry, open grassland and scrub association of the northern parts of the Kalahari.

Although in parts their habitat abuts on to rocky koppies or rocky hillsides, they do not use the cover afforded by rocks, where they are replaced by the rock elephant-shrew, *E. myurus*. Where these diverse types of habitat lie adjacent to one another this species and *E. myurus* are often found living within a few metres of each other.

Although in parts of their distributional range they occur on sandy ground or sandy alluvium, they are also found on the hard substrate of mopane scrub. The nature of the ground does not seem to be a factor in limiting their occurrence as it does in the case of the bushveld elephant-shrew, *E. intufi*, which has a marked preference for sandy soils.

### Habits

Short-snouted elephant-shrews are active both day and night, with most activity at dawn (Woodall *et al.*, 1989). On cold, cloudy days they are much less in evidence and during rain they tend to remain in cover.

Generally solitary, pairs may temporarily occupy resting places of holes under the cover of bushes, fallen trees, thorn fences or piles of debris. It is not known whether they excavate these holes themselves or whether they are using disused rodent burrows, which so often are located in these situations. In captivity they use the cover of grass tussocks or piles of dry grass and in the wild, they may well use similar cover. Except in the immediate vicinity of the holes or cover, which they use under bushes, they do not form the defined runways which are a feature of the bushveld elephant-shrew, *E. intufi*. This may be a factor of the type of substrate on which they so often occur, which does not mark so clearly as it does on the looser sandy substrate on which *E. intufi* is found. Like other members of the Family they are fast movers, running quickly from the cover of one bush to another and avoiding areas with no overhead cover. When disturbed they remain in the cover of bush, sitting motionless in the shade where they are difficult to see.

### Food

Their food consists predominantly of insects, in particular ants and termites. In captivity they take grasshoppers and crickets freely, and, although no evidence of this has been found in the Subregion, in East Africa they are recorded as eating vegetable matter, including seeds and the fruits of *Strychnos* sp and *Flacourtia indica* (Kingdon, 1974).

### Reproduction

In the Transvaal, Rautenbach (1978) recorded gravid females during the months of October to March and, in Botswana, Smithers (1971) took one in June. In Zambia, Ansell (1960a) recorded gravid females in October and juveniles in October, November and February. A gravid female was taken in the Fort Victoria district, Zimbabwe in September.

It is to the advantage of insectivores to have their young during the warm, wet summer months when food is plentiful. The June record may be atypical, caused possibly by the female having lost a previous litter and being covered late in the season. Further information is required on the time at which the young are born.

Usually two young are produced, the foetuses implanted one each in the left and right horn of the reproductive tract, but there are a number of records of a single foetus. The young are precocial, being born fully haired with their eyes open. They move around soon after birth and very soon thereafter feed independently.

---

No. 36

## *Elephantulus rupestris* (A. Smith, 1831)

## Smith's rock elephant-shrew
## Smith se klipklaasneus

Plate 3

---

### Colloquial Name

Three species of elephant-shrews live in a rocky habitat: this species, the Cape rock elephant-shrew, *E. edwardii*, and the rock elephant-shrew, *E. myurus*. Andrew Smith's surname is applied to this species to distinguish it from the others.

### Taxonomic Notes

Many subspecies have been described, but Corbet (1974b) stated that few of these are likely to be valid. Until a revision is undertaken none are recognised. Great confusion was caused by the fact that Andrew Smith's type specimen of *E. rupestris* later turned out to be a rock elephant-shrew, *E. myurus*. As a consequence later authors referred all the named subspecies of *E. rupestris* to *E. intufi* and all the subspecies of *E. myurus* and *E. edwardii* to *E. rupestris*. This confusion was resolved by Corbet (1974b) and is the basis of the present treatment of the Family. The diploid chromosome number is 2n = 26 (Wenhold & Robinson, 1987).

### Description

Adults have a total length of about 270 mm with tails about 150 mm and a mass of about 65,0 g (Table 36.1). In the Cape Province the upper parts of the body and forehead are yellowish-brown, profusely pencilled with black, caused by the narrow black tips of the individual hairs lying in juxtaposition. The most conspicuous feature of the upper parts is the broad patches of rufous-yellow hair at the base of the ears which extend on to the nape of the neck on either side. The flanks and sides of the face are light grey tinged with yellow, the under parts greyish-white. The lower parts of the limbs are whitish on the upper surface, the naked portion of the hind feet black. The ears are brown and naked behind with white hair on their inner margins. They have indistinct whitish rings around their eyes. The proboscis has a narrow dark line on top and is tawny-greyish on the sides. The tail is dark on its upper surface, slightly lighter towards it base on the under surface and from about its middle is covered profusely with dark bristly hair which lengthens towards the tip where it forms an elongated brush. In Namibia they are much paler in colour, the white tips to the hairs of the under parts broader giving the whole a whiter appearance. The first upper premolar teeth have a single lingual cusp, the second two (Fig. IV.3.a).

### Table 36.1

Measurements (mm) and mass (g) of Smith's rock elephant-shrews, *E. rupestris*

| | Males | | | Females | | |
|---|---|---|---|---|---|---|
| | $\bar{x}$ | n | Range | $\bar{x}$ | n | Range |
| TL | 275 | 9 | 251–297 | 278 | 4 | 269–288 |
| (HB | 128) | | | (131) | | |
| T | 147 | 9 | 130–161 | 147 | 4 | 139–154 |
| Hf c/u | 38 | 9 | 34–40 | 38 | 4 | 36–40 |
| E | 27 | 9 | 22–31 | 27 | 4 | 24–28 |
| Mass | 62,8 | 8 | 54,0–68,0 | 70,0 | 4 | 63,0–77,0 |

### Distribution

*Southern African Subregion*

Smith's rock elephant-shrews are confined in their distribution to within the limits of the Subregion, occurring in a narrow sector of territory that runs from Kaokoland, in the northwest of **Namibia** through the central parts of the **Cape Province** to the coast in the vicinity of East London. They do not occur in the Namib Desert or in the nórtheastern part of Namibia or in the southwestern part of the Cape Province. They occur through to the coast in the northwestern Cape Province, in parts of Namaqualand.

### Habitat

Closely confined to a habitat of rocky koppies, rocky outcrops or piles of boulders, where these offer sufficient holes and crannies to provide refuges.

### Habits

Very similar to the rock elephant-shrew, *E. myurus*

### Plate 3

32. Four-toed elephant shrew, *Petrodromus tetradactylus*
    Bosklaasneus
33. Round-eared elephant shrew, *Macroscelides proboscideus*
    Ronde-oorklaasneus
35. Short-snouted elephant-shrew, *Elephantulus brachyrhynchus*
    Kortneus klaasneus
36. Smith's rock elephant-shrew, *Elephantulus rupestris*
    Smith se klipklaasneus
37. Bushveld elephant-shrew, *Elephantulus intufi*
    Bosveldklaasneus
38. Rock elephant-shrew, *Elephantulus myurus*
    Klipklaasneus
39. Cape rock elephant-shrew, *Elephantulus edwardii*
    Kaapse klipklaasneus

PLATE 3
32
33
35
36
37b
37a
38
39
Dick Findlay

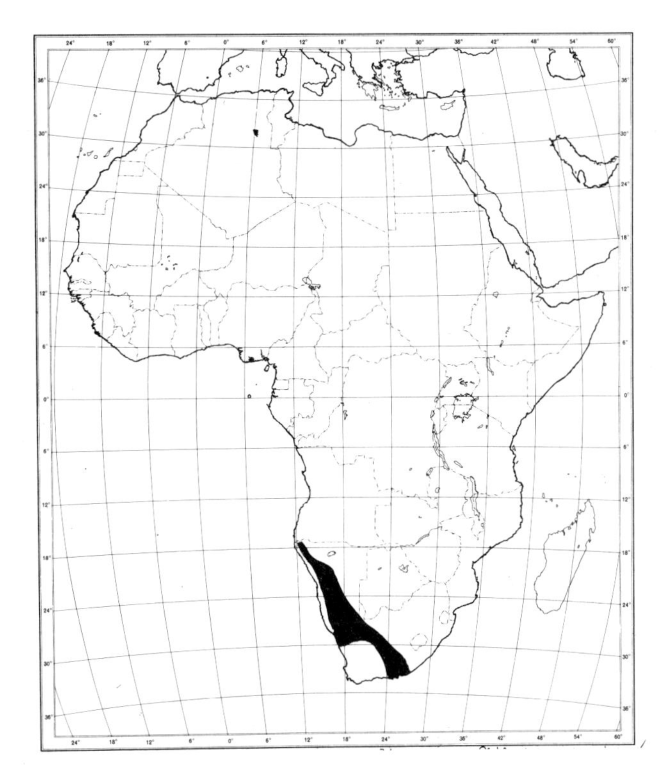

## Food

Insects, including in particular ants and termites.

## Reproduction

In Namibia, Shortridge (1934) recorded females with one and two foetuses in September.

---

No. 37

# *Elephantulus intufi* (A. Smith, 1836)

## Bushveld elephant-shrew
## Bosveldklaasneus

Plate 3

---

## Colloquial Name

Bushveld is used to indicate the type of habitat in which this species lives, as opposed to others which are associated with a rocky habitat.

## Taxonomic Notes

A number of subspecies have been described but, Meester *et al.* (1986) did not recognise any of them.

## Description

Adults have a total length of about 240 mm, with tails slightly longer than the length of the head and body and a mass of about 50,0 g (Table 37.1). The upper parts of the body of specimens from the Transvaal are yellowish-buffy in colour with a tendency to be dark down the mid-back caused by the long black hairs, which are scattered throughout the coat, lying irregularly in juxtaposition. The flanks are paler, and the under parts and chin white, the grey bases of the hair showing through. They have a conspicuous russet patch at the posterior base of the ears which contrasts with the general colour of the body. They have white rings around their eyes and their tails are dark above and buffy underneath. The ears have conspicuous white hairs on their inner margins.

Specimens from Namibia are much paler than those from the Transvaal, an overall pale yellowish-buff and from Kaokoland are much greyer. They have a white ring around the eyes, which shows up more conspicuously in the greyer specimens than in the paler ones.

The soles of the hind feet are naked and pale brown in colour, not black as in *E. myurus*.

**Table 37.1**

Measurements (mm) and mass (g) of bushveld elephant-shrews, *E. intufi*, from Botswana (Smithers, 1971) and the Transvaal (Rautenbach, 1978)

**Botswana**

| | Males | | | Females | | |
|---|---|---|---|---|---|---|
| | $\bar{x}$ | n | Range | $\bar{x}$ | n | Range |
| TL | 230 | 14 | 211–248 | 242 | 25 | 222–272 |
| (HB | 110) | | | (117) | | |
| T | 120 | 14 | 97–132 | 125 | 25 | 113–142 |
| Hf c/u | 35 | 14 | 33–37 | 36 | 25 | 34–37 |
| E | 24 | 14 | 23–25 | 24 | 25 | 21–26 |
| Mass | 47,0 | 8 | 41,0–56,0 | 52,0 | 10 | 42,0–56,0 |

**Transvaal**

| | Males | | | Females | | |
|---|---|---|---|---|---|---|
| | $\bar{x}$ | n | Range | $\bar{x}$ | n | Range |
| TL | 230 | 14 | 212–249 | 235 | 20 | 204–256 |
| (HB | 115) | | | (118) | | |
| T | 115 | 14 | 102–128 | 117 | 20 | 103–129 |
| Hf c/u | 31 | 14 | 29–34 | 31 | 19 | 29–34 |
| E | 23 | 14 | 21–24 | 23 | 19 | 20–25 |
| Mass | 46,0 | 9 | 35,0–55,0 | 52,0 | 10 | 40,0–74,0 |

## Distribution

Bushveld elephant-shrews are confined in their distribution to within the limits of the Subregion, except for a marginal extension into southwestern Angola.

*South of the Sahara, excluding the Southern African Subregion*

They occur in **Angola** where they are confined to a narrow sector in the southwest, inland from the coastal desert, from the Cunene River northwards to just north of Lobito Bay.

*Southern African Subregion*

They occur widely in **Namibia,** excluding the coastal Namib Desert, the northeast and parts of the south, extending eastwards into the central and southern parts of **Botswana** and parts of the northern **Cape Province**. In the **Transvaal** they are found only in the northwest.

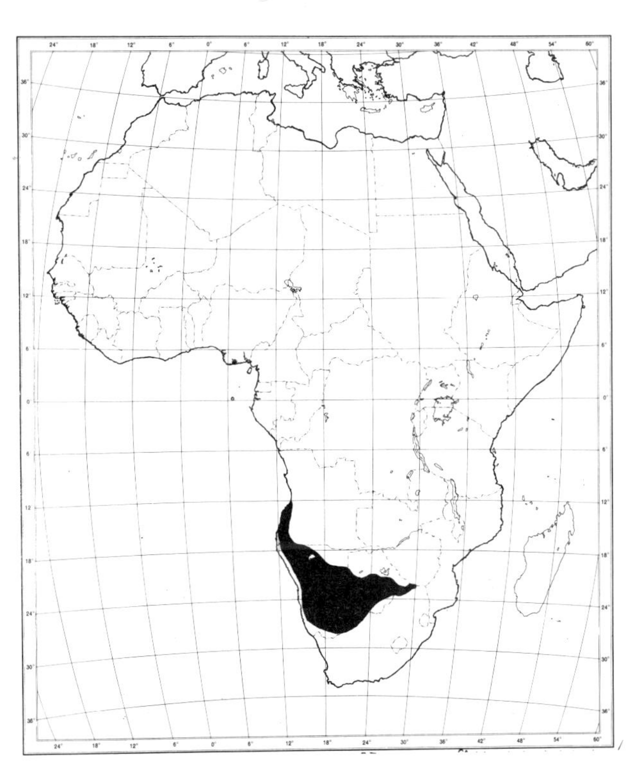

### Habitat

As can be seen from the distribution of this species they can utilise more arid terrain than any of the other species of *Elephantulus*. This is exemplified quite dramatically when the situation in Botswana is examined in relation to the distribution of the short-snouted elephant-shrew, *E. brachyrhynchus*. *E. brachyrhynchus* occurs in the well-watered Okavango Delta and in the eastern parts of the country which have a mean annual rainfall of 450 mm and over. *E. intufi*, on the other hand, occupies the dry central areas, where the mean annual rainfall is less than 450 mm, and, west of this, they occupy areas where it falls below 200 mm.

In the central Kalahari, where they are the only species of elephant-shrew which occurs, they live in a habitat of scrub bush with a thin grass cover and a sandy substrate. The area is devoid of surface water except seasonally, where it may lie temporarily in pans, otherwise seeping away into the sand.

Cover is an essential habitat requirement and is provided by the low bushes which lie scattered in the open grassland. They occupy far thinner cover than *E. brachyrhynchus*, but are not found on the open areas around pans where the grass is short. In these situations they tend to use the raised sandy fringes, where the grass is slightly higher and there is a scattering of low bush.

### Habits

The bushveld elephant-shrew is exclusively diurnal, not being in evidence until after sunrise, when the day starts to warm up, and retiring well before sunset, but a captive individual was active both day and night (Woodall *et al*., 1989). They live in burrows, the entrances situated under bushes, but whether they excavate these themselves or whether they are disused rodent burrows has not been determined. Like the short-snouted elephant-shrew, *E. brachyrhynchus*, they tend to move and feed within the shelter of bushes, avoiding spending time in the open. They form clearly defined runs radiating out from the burrow entrances, these leading from bush to bush. If they are disturbed while away from their burrows, they seek the shelter of the deepest shade within these bushes, sitting tightly against or under the branches and, in traversing the open ground between them, do so at lightning speed. Sitting in the shade they are very difficult to see, their presence usually being detected by the slight movements of their ears, which never seem to remain completely motionless. They run on all fours but will jump over obstacles in their paths. Shortridge (1934) recorded that this species, like some of the others, will stamp its hind feet when alarmed. In captivity when they are alarmed they vibrate the hind feet on the substrate which creates a loud purring noise (Smithers, 1983). They often utter a high-pitched squeak under these circumstances.

### Food

They eat insects, predominantly ants. When they catch grasshoppers or anything larger than ants away from cover, they carry them back to the safe shelter of bushes to be eaten. Small scatterings of chitinous wing cases of insects are found often, which mark the sites where these have been consumed.

### Reproduction

Shortridge (1934) recorded three females with two foetuses each taken in eastern Namibia in November. In Botswana gravid females were taken during the months from August to February, the average number of foetuses per female being 1,9 (n = 9) with a range of one to three (Smithers, 1971). In the Transvaal, Rautenbach (1978) recorded gravid females in August and March, the average number of foetuses per female being 1,6 (n=6) with a range of one or two. From this it appears that they are seasonal breeders, the young being born during the warm, wet summer months from about August to March.

No. 38

## *Elephantulus myurus* Thomas & Schwann, 1906

## Rock elephant-shrew
## Klipklaasneus

Plate 3

### Colloquial Name

So named from their close association with rocky habitat.

### Taxonomic Notes

While numbers of subspecies have been recognised in the past their validity is in doubt and Meester *et al*. (1986) did not recognise any of them. The diploid chromosome number is 2n = 30 (Ford & Hamerton, 1956).

### Description

Adult rock elephant-shrews have a total length of about 260 mm and a mass of about 60,0 g (Table 38.1). The upper parts of the body are buffy-grey, greyer towards the rump. The flanks are paler than the upper parts and greyer. They have buffy patches behind at the bases of the ears, but these do not contrast with the colour of the upper parts to the same extent as they do in other species. The head is buffy-grey, the forehead washed with paler buff, the eyes conspicuously ringed with white. The ears are brown with a fringe of white hairs on their inner margins. The under parts are white, the slate-grey bases of the hair showing through. The tail is slightly longer than the length of the head and body, and is sparsely haired, darker above than below and darker towards the tip. The upper surface of the hands and feet is whitish, the naked under surfaces of the hind feet black. The hair on the upper parts of the body is soft and woolly and about 13 mm long, the individual hairs shiny black for most of their length with buffy tips, many of the hairs with narrow black tips. Interspersed throughout the coat there are a series of long black hairs which may have a tactile function. They have five digits on the fore and hind feet armed with short curved claws, each digit with a conspicuous swollen digital pad. Externally this species can be distinguished from *E. rupestris* by its less hairy tail, less conspicuous light coloured patches behind the ears and generally greyer colour.

This species, as opposed to *E. rupestris* and *E. intufi*, has no lingual cusps on the upper first premolar teeth; the second upper premolar teeth usually have a single lingual cusp, but sometimes two set very close together and less than half the height of the labial cusps. In this species the posterior labial cusps of the second upper premolars are distinctly smaller than the anterior, the difference much more marked than in *E. rupestris* (Fig. IV.3.c).

**Table 38.1**

Measurements (mm) and mass (g) of rock elephant-shrews, *E. myurus*, from the Transvaal (Rautenbach, 1978) and Zimbabwe (Smithers & Wilson, 1979)

**Transvaal**

| | Males | | | Females | | |
|---|---|---|---|---|---|---|
| | $\bar{x}$ | n | Range | $\bar{x}$ | n | Range |
| TL | 263 | 56 | 202–291 | 263 | 58 | 219–290 |
| (HB | 126) | | | (127) | | |
| T | 137 | 55 | 104–153 | 136 | 59 | 101–156 |
| Hf c/u | 37 | 59 | 29–40 | 36 | 61 | 31–40 |
| E | 25 | 59 | 18–30 | 25 | 61 | 19–29 |
| Mass | 60,9 | 60 | 48,0–80,0 | 60,0 | 59 | 41,0–98,0 |

**Zimbabwe** (Zimbabwe National Monument)

**Irrespective of sex**

| | $\bar{x}$ | n | Range |
|---|---|---|---|
| TL | 268 | 6 | 261–274 |
| T | 138 | 6 | 127–144 |
| Hf c/u | 37 | 6 | 35–38 |
| E | 25 | 6 | 38,0–26 |
| Mass | 47,1 | 6 | 38,0–56,0 |

## Distribution

Within the limits shown on the map the rock elephant-shrew only occurs where there is suitable habitat. In the Transvaal, for example, they are absent from the southern and central parts of the province owing to this factor. Their limits of distribution lie predominantly within the Sub-region, with a marginal extension into northwestern Mozambique.

*South of the Sahara, excluding the Southern African Subregion*

The only area outside the Subregion in which this species occurs lies in **Mozambique** just north of the Zambezi River in the Tete District.

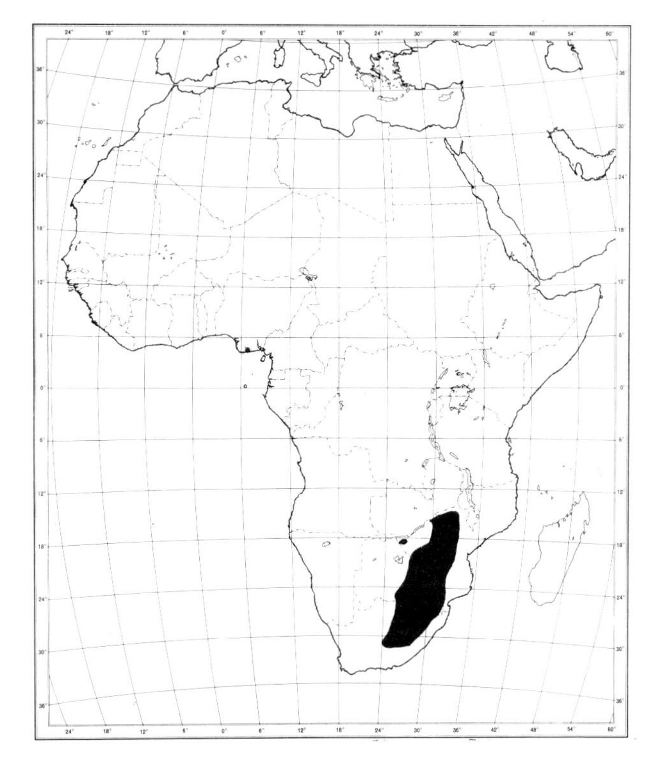

*Southern African Subregion*

In **Zimbabwe** they are widespread in the eastern parts of the country, and are absent in the north and northwest except for an isolated population in granite koppies in the Hwange National Park. They occur in eastern **Botswana** and the western parts of **Mozambique**, south of the Zambezi River, south to the northwestern parts of the Maputo District. They occur widely in the **Transvaal**, except in the grassland areas in the central and southern parts of the province; and in the **Orange Free State**, as in the Transvaal, they are absent from grassland but otherwise have a wide distribution in the western parts of the province. They occur in the mountain-ous parts of western **Natal** and in **Lesotho** and in the northeastern **Cape Province**, south to about Deelfontein and Burghersdorp.

## Habitat

Rock elephant-shrews, as the name suggests, are confined closely to a habitat of rocky koppies or piles of boulders. They only occur in this type of association if there are sufficient holes and crannies to provide safe shelter. In granite formations, where the boulders or *dwalas* rise from the ground level and do not provide this type of shelter, they are absent, yet they may be present in adjacent parts of the rocky terrain where the formation is more broken or exfoliated. They have a preference for living in those parts of their rocky habitat that have overhanging ledges or vegetation which provide them with cover from aerial predation. They occasionally occur on flat ground, using the cover of isolated boulders or small rocky outcrops.

Although they occur in the same general area as the short-snouted elephant-shrew, *E. brachyrhynchus*, the two species are segregrated by their habitat requirements, this species being confined to the rocky parts of the terrain, the short-snouted elephant-shrew to the adjacent sandy, flat ground.

## Habits

Rock elephant-shrews are predominantly diurnal, with a peak of activity at dawn, but they are also active at night (Woodall *et al.*, 1989). However, they noticeably are more active during the warmer hours of the day, this activity tailing off during the cooler hours before sunset.

Characteristically, they tend to keep to the shady cover of overhanging rocks or the shade of bushes or trees overhang-ing their rocky habitat. Sitting in this cover they blend into the background and are difficult to see. Often only the twitching of their sensitive ears reveals their presence. From this cover they will sally forth with lightning-quick hops to seize their prey which, if it is the size of a grasshopper or larger, they will carry back to the shade to be consumed at leisure. They are very quick in their movements and leap with agility from boulder to boulder over distances of up to about a metre. If disturbed they run for the cover of their refuges but, when left undisturbed, will reappear soon. In the early mornings they sit quietly on sheltered rocks sunning themselves, looking like little stones. They are always very much on the alert and speed for shelter when disturbed. They vocalise in a series of high-pitched squeaks, tailing off at the end of the sequence to one that is barely audible. In doing so the head is held high, the trunk curled back over the top of the muzzle,the mouth held wide open (Fig. 38.1). When alarmed they make a loud "purring" noise by vibrating the hind feet against the substrate.

## Food

Small insects with a high proportion of ants and termites, often foraging for these in dassie middens (Wright, pers. comm.).

## Reproduction

From information available from eastern Botswana (Smith-ers, 1971) and the Transvaal (van der Horst, 1946; Rauten-bach, 1978) the young are born during the warm, wet summer months from September to March. The gestation period is long for the size of the species, being given by van der Horst (1946) as eight weeks. Usually two young are produced at a birth, but there are numerous records of only one. At birth the length of the head and body is about 50 mm. They are precocial, being born fully haired with the eyes open and they walk about soon after they are born. They apparently remain within the shelter of the rocks for a time as very small individuals are not seen with the adults. By the time they are about a third of the size of adults, however, they move about freely and independently and feed with them. Females become sexually mature at between five and six weeks old.

During their short lives the females may have up to three litters. Most of them have one litter, there being a small drop in the number of those having a second, and a substantial drop in those having a third. With the optimum possibility of a female having six offspring during her breeding period, this rarely happens, van der Horst (1946) giving the mean number of offspring from a pair as 4,5.

Male rock elephant-shrews have relatively small, abdom-inal testes with active spermatogenesis throughout the year, but with a significant reduction in testis and prostate size, and sperm numbers and viability in winter (Woodall & Skinner, 1989).

38.1. Rock elephant-shrew,
*E. myurus* vocalising.

No. 39

## *Elephantulus edwardii* (A. Smith, 1839)

## Cape rock elephant-shrew
## Kaapse klipklaasneus

Plate 3

### Colloquial Name

The first specimen of this elephant-shrew was collected by Edward Verreaux and named after him by Andrew Smith. Verreaux was a well known collector after whom a number of other mammals and birds are named, including Verreaux's mouse, *Praomys verreauxi*, and the black eagle, *Aquila verreauxi*. The locality of *E. edwardii* was given as the Olifants River which Shortridge (1934) and Roberts (1951) decided was the river by this name in the Oudtshoorn District. They are associated with rocky terrain, as is the rock elephant-shrew, *E. myurus*, from which it is appropiate to distinguish them under the name Cape rock elephant-shrew as they are confined in their distribution to the Cape Province.

### Taxonomic Notes

No subspecies are recognised by Corbet (1974b). Rautenbach & Nel (1980) presented evidence from their material from the Cedarberg Mountains that there is variation in one of the characters of the teeth which, in the past, has been used among others to separate them from the rock elephant-shrew, *E. myurus*.

### Description

Adults have a total length of about 250 mm and tails slightly longer than the length of the head and body and a mass of about 50 g (Table 39.1). The upper parts of the body and forehead are greyish-brown, tinged yellowish and pencilled with blackish-brown. The sides of the head and flanks are ashy-grey tinged with pale tawny. The under parts are white, the dark grey bases to the hairs showing through. The chin and the eye rings are greyish-white, the legs light ashy-grey. Posterior to the bases of the ears there are patches of tawny-rufous hair. The whiskers are black, the proboscis black on the top, whitish on the sides. The large ears are broad at the base and rise to rounded tips. The tail is proximally black above and paler below but completely black towards the tip. It is densely covered with short, dark coloured hair which is longer towards the tip where it forms a small tuft. The fur is long, soft and silky, the individual hairs on the upper parts slate-grey at the base, annulated towards the tip with greyish-brown, and narrowly tipped with black.

In the first and second upper premolars the anterior labial cusps are well developed, the posterior poorly so, neither having lingual cusps (Fig. IV.3.d). The first lower premolar tooth is single rooted compared with that of *E. myurus* in which it is double rooted.

**Table 39.1**

Measurements (mm) and mass (g) of Cape rock elephant-shrews, *E. edwardii*

| | Males | | | Females | | |
|---|---|---|---|---|---|---|
| | x̄ | n | Range | x̄ | n | Range |
| TL | 252 | 7 | 235–261 | 260 | 9 | 220–288 |
| (HB | 122) | | | (124) | | |
| T | 130 | 7 | 120–140 | 136 | 9 | 126–144 |
| Hf c/u | 34 | 7 | 33–36 | 35 | 9 | 34–36 |
| E | 27 | | 25–30 | 29 | 9 | 25–31 |
| Mass | 47,0 | 7 | 36,0–52,0 | 53,0 | 9 | 40,0–65,0 |

### Distribution

*Southern African Subregion*

Appears to occur in two discrete areas in the southwestern **Cape Province**, one in the northwest, the other in the Richmond, Port Elizabeth sector.

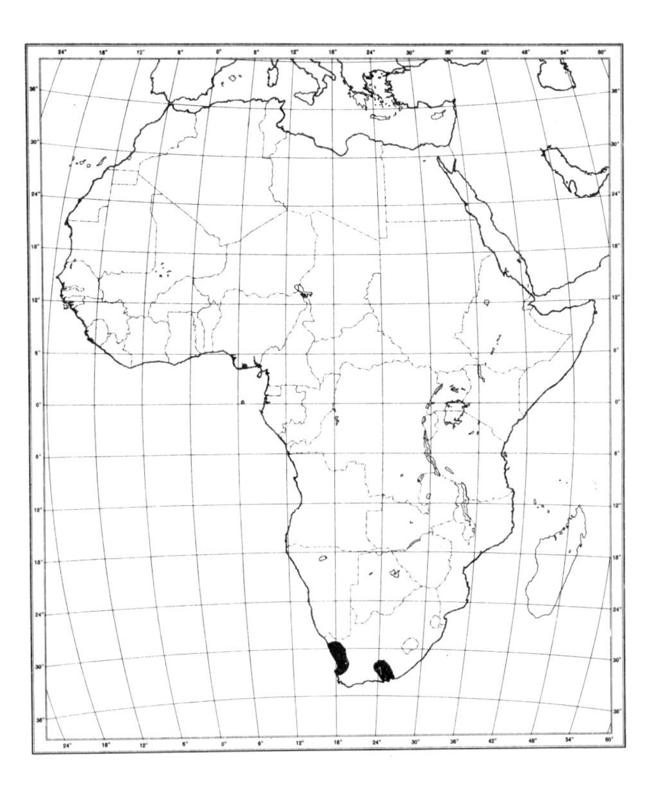

### Habitat

Cape rock elephant-shrews originally were recorded as coming from a locality "bearing little or no vegetation, except a few dwarf shrubs". There was no suggestion that they were associated with rocky terrain. Dieckmann (1979) collected them in the Hester Malan Nature Reserve in Namaqualand in the vicinity of low rocky outcrops, where he noted that they formed indistinct runways. He also took them on hard sandy ground with a sparse cover of vegetation. In the Cedarberg Mountains, Rautenbach & Nel (1980) recorded them from rocky slopes, with or without a cover of vegetation. It seems that, unlike the rock elephant-shrew, *E. myurus*, this species will use quite small rocky outcrops provided they have shelter in the form of cracks and crannies. Verreaux may have missed the significance of this in his original notes.

### Habits

This species is predominantly nocturnal with much reduced activity during the day (Rickart, 1981; Woodall *et al.*, 1989) and occurs singly or in pairs.

### Food

Insects, predominantly ants and termites. In captivity they would also feed on locusts and cockroaches, discarding the more heavily chitinised parts of these insects (Woodall & Currie, 1989).

### Reproduction

A single young, sometimes two, are born during the summer months from November to January.

# Order CHIROPTERA

## Bats

### The fossil record

The earliest known fossil bat was discovered in the early Eocene deposits in America (Jepsen, 1966). In relative dating this is 75 million years after the appearance of the first mammals. From the structure of its teeth and skeleton it was certainly an insect eater although, unlike present day insect-eating bats, it had two claws on the forearm, one on the thumb, the other on the first finger, which is a characteristic of modern fruit eaters. In all respects, however, it closely resembles bats as we know them today but gives us no clues as to the origin of flight in the Order or their origin prior to this time.

The oldest fossil bat known from Africa is *Vampyravus orientalis* which was recovered from the Oligocene deposits of Egypt, but whose relationships remain problematical. For a long time it was thought that bats were related to the Tupaiidae, the tree shrews, a Family of insectivores that occur in Asia and India, and to the Dermoptera, the flying lemurs of the Far East and that the Chiroptera and Insectivora evolved from a common, probably arboreal, ancestor (Anderson & Knox Jones, 1967).

Pettigrew (1986) and Pettigrew, Robson, Hall & Mc Anally, (in press) have shown that the Megachiroptera have a Primate-like visual system and musculo-skeletal adaptations of the flight apparatus, neither of which are found in the Microchiroptera. They believe that the Megachiroptera evolved from early Primates, which were moderate sized gliders, of which the other living descendants are the Dermoptera; the Microchiroptera from small, agile insectivores with forelimbs modified for gliding during leaps. This means that the power of flight must have evolved in parallel in two separate lines of mammals, one of them ancestral Primates.

Four Families have been recognised from the early Miocene beds of East Africa. The fruit-eaters, the Pteropodidae, are represented by *Propotto leakeyi*, whose fossil remains were thought to be those of a lemur originally (Simpson, 1967), but were later shown to be those of a fruit bat (Walker, 1969). Its cheekteeth were set closer together than in modern forms, the molar teeth low with blunt cusps and lacking the longitudinal groove seen in our living pteropodids. Butler (1978) nevertheless, did not believe that the Pteropodidae were of African origin as it is in the Oriental Region that the greatest diversity is found.

In the Microchiroptera the six Families that are represented in the Subregion occur in the fossil record as follows:

The Emballonuridae, the sheath-tailed and tomb bats, are known from the early Miocene beds of Rusinga, on the shores of Lake Victoria, and in Europe from the early Oligocene.

The Nycteridae, the slit-faced bats, are known from undescribed material from the Pliocene beds of East Africa (Butler, 1978).

The Rhinolophidae, the horseshoe bats, are known from the early Eocene or early Oligocene of Europe and the late Pliocene deposits of Makapansgat, Transvaal (De Graaff, 1960a).

The Hipposideridae occur in the middle Eocene beds of Europe, but no fossil remains have been recovered so far from the Subregion.

The two largest Families of bats that occur in the Subregion, the Vespertilionidae and the Molossidae, which are known from fossil remains from the beginning of the Oligocene in Europe and from scanty remains from the Mio-Pliocene of North Africa, are not known from East Africa until much later, in the early Pleistocene (Butler, 1978).

### Dentition

Young bats have milk teeth like most young mammals. Those of the Megachiroptera are simpler than those of the Microchiroptera and are peg-like with hooked ends. In the Microchiroptera they are similarly hooked, but have one or two cusps lower down on the sides of the teeth below the primary cusp, which is located near the tip. It is thought that this hooking assists the young in clinging more firmly to the teat or fur of their mothers when being carried around.

In some Families, e.g. the Rhinolophidae, milk teeth are present in the young prior to birth, but are reabsorbed before they are born (Spillman, 1927). Slaughter (1970) suggested that, as females of this Family have a pair of dummy teats situated low down on the belly not connected to the mammary glands, there may be less need for the clinging milk set (see Family Hipposideridae, Fig. III.1).

While many species retain the maximum number of three incisor teeth on either side of the lower jaw, none of them have more than two on either side in the upper jaw. Which incisor has been lost in the course of evolution has been the subject of controversy among authorities.

In many bats the cutting faces of the lower incisors are divided into two (bifid) or three (trifid) sections, which may be used like combs in grooming. The canine teeth are well developed and, in many insect-eating bats, have a broad collar near the base, better developed inside than on the front of the teeth. Slaughter (1970) suggested that it protects the gums from damage by the hard exoskeletons of beetles. Fruit-eating bats do not require this protection and have canines that are smooth to their bases.

No bat has more than three premolar teeth on either side of both jaws, although the basic number for placental mammals is four. Again there is some controversy as to which has been lost, the most widely accepted theory being that it is the first (Miller, 1907).

In the fruit-eating bats the molar teeth have flat faces, an adaptation to masticating soft food. In the insect-eaters, the cheekteeth are equipped with high cusps to deal with their harder insect diet. In the fossil record there are no types of dentition which are intermediate between the two widely different types.

### Location of prey

Those who study and therefore have to handle bats grow to appreciate their cleanliness and the delicacy of the complicated structures of the nose and ears which are part, in many species, of the sophisticated mechanism known as echolocation which allows them to navigate and catch their prey in total darkness. Clicks or bleeps made by bats bounce off objects in their path and their positions are then located by perception of the echo from them.

The time lag between the emission of the clicks or bleeps by the bat, their reception after bouncing back from the object ahead of them and the bat's reaction to the stimulus is something to the order of 1/100th of a second. The bat is both the transmitter of the impulses and their receiver. The outer ears are the amplifiers, the inner ear the receiver and booster, and the brain the computer that sorts, files and transmits the information to the body. Deprived of the use of one ear, a bat perceives direction but cannot pinpoint the object.

The calls of bats are mostly far above the range of sound audible to the human ear, which is from about 20 vibrations a second, in some people with acute hearing, up to 18 000 vibrations per second. The sound a bat emits to locate obstacles and its prey may extend up to as much as 230 000 vibrations per second. Bats can vary the length of their calls, sending out pulses of less than 1/1000th of a second when nearing the prey, at the same time making adjustments to their course to compensate for the prey's violent evasions.

Bats use different kinds of sound to obtain different kinds of information. A steady call allows them to estimate the speed and direction of the prey. This system exploits the Doppler effect which causes the fall in pitch of an automobile horn as it passes the listener. Another call employs frequency modulation or change of pitch. Echoes of this call are heard slightly differently by the bat's two ears and its brain interprets the difference in terms of heading and range of the moving prey. Some bats improve on their accuracy by adding a harmonic call to the basic call or by raising the pitch of the call. In doing the latter they must sacrifice range since high frequency sound dissipates faster in air than low frequency. Using low frequency calls, bats can detect prey at up to about 10 m but with high frequency not over about 0,6 m (Fullard, 1981).

### Wing and flight membranes

The flight membranes of a bat extend from the shoulder around the tips of the digits to the foot, continuing as the interfemoral membrane from the inside of the hind limbs and partially or wholly enclosing the tail vertebrae. The relationship of the membrane to the tail vertebrae is a most important character in distinguishing between the Families and the manner in which it attaches to the foot is constant within a genus or species. The membrane is elastic and contracts as the digits are folded together, and is supplied liberally with blood vessels. When at rest, the wings are folded against the body.

Reference is made in the text to the bony structure supporting the membrane, the various parts of which are illustrated and named as follows:

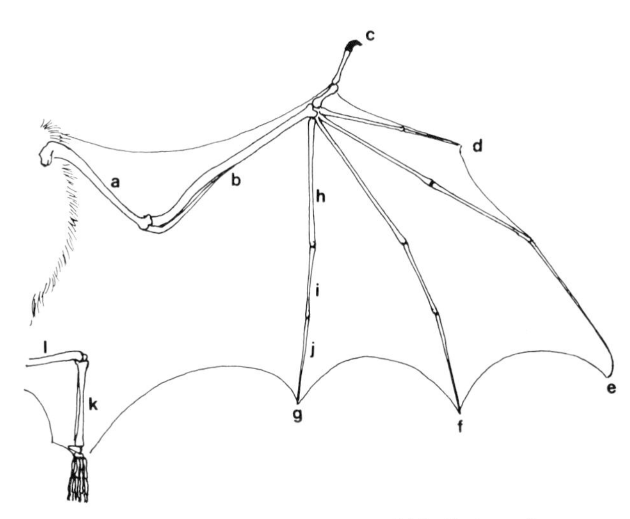


| | |
|---|---|
| a upper arm or humerus | g fifth digit or finger |
| b forearm | h metacarpal |
| c first digit or thumb | i first phalanx |
| d second digit or finger | j second phalanx |
| e third digit or finger | k shin bone or tibia |
| f fourth digit or finger | l thigh bone or femur |

### Classification

The Order Chiroptera is divided into two Suborders, the Megachiroptera, the fruit-eaters, and the Microchiroptera, the insect-eaters.

Key to the Suborders in the Subregion, after Hayman & Hill (1971)

1. Second digit on forearm terminating in a claw (Fig. V.1), margin of the ear forming a complete ring; ear tragus absent; interfemoral membrane greatly reduced, little more than a narrow band along the margin of the hind legs; tail absent or rudimentary (Fig. 45.1); cheekteeth simple, without well-developed cusp pattern (Fig. V.3)
   ... Suborder Megachiroptera
   The fruit-eating bats

2. Second digit on forearm without a claw; margin of the ear not forming a complete ring; ear tragus generally present (absent in Family Rhinolophidae); interfemoral membrane and tail generally well developed; cheekteeth cuspidate, with generally well developed W pattern
   ... Suborder Microchiroptera
   The insect-eating bats

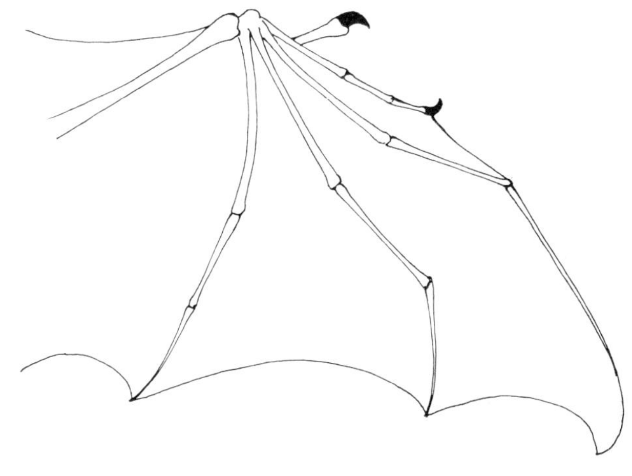

Fig. V.1. Wing of a fruit bat, Pteropodidae: *Eidolon helvum*; note claws on first and second fingers.

Fig. V.2. Head of a fruit bat, Pteropodidae: *Epomophorus* sp.

# Suborder MEGACHIROPTERA

## Fruit-eating bats

All members of this Suborder belong to the Family Pteropodidae, the general account given of the Suborder applying to all members of this Family. The muzzle in all the members occurring in the Subregion is simple, tapering and dog-like without noseleaves (Fig. V.2).

These are characterised by the fact that most of them have

two claws on the wing structure, one on the thumb, the other on the first or index finger (Fig. V.1). All Megachiroptera of the Subregion have these two claws, the Microchiroptera have only one.

The ears of the Megachiroptera are simple tubular structures and lack the ear tragus possessed by all the Microchiroptera, with the exception of the members of the Family Rhinolophidae.

There are other important features which differ in the two Suborders. Mossman (1937) for example, showed that the foetal membranes are fundamentally different, differences which involve the development of the yolk sac and the structure of the placenta.

Most of the Megachiroptera rely on sight for orientation, the exception being the Egyptian fruit bat, *Rousettus aegyptiacus*, which has in addition powers of echolocation. They orient visually, when there is sufficient light to allow for this, but emit "clicks" with their tongues in total darkness which, picked up by the ears as the sound bounces back, give them powers of orientation.

In the Microchiroptera the "clicks" are produced by the larynx and they rely on their powers of echolocation in total darkness for their orientation, their sight being less well developed than in the Megachiroptera.

Although the Megachiroptera are classed generally as fruit-eaters, and for most of them fruit is their principal food, some of them eat flowers, flower buds and pollen and others lap nectar. There are no true nectar lappers in the Subregion (see *Epomophorus gambianus*), but they have interesting adaptations to their feeding habits. The long-tongued bat, *Glossophaga soricina*, of South America and other nectar lappers have extremely long thin tongues, the tips of which are equipped with long spinous papillae which act like absorbent brushes. Their muzzles are long and narrow and their molar teeth are to all intents and purposes non-functional.

The Megachiroptera include among its members some of the world's largest bats, as well as some very small species. The flying fox, *Pteropus neohibernicus*, of New Guinea, has a wing span of some 1,8 m; the African *Nanonycteris veldkampi* a wing span of about 180 mm. The largest species that occurs in the Subregion is the straw-coloured fruit bat, *Eidolon helvum*, which has a wingspan of up to 0,66 m.

The Megachiroptera tend to be gregarious, occurring in huge colonies.

In the Subregion one of the species, Peter's epauletted fruit bat, *Epomophorus crypturus*, regularly occurs in colonies numbering hundreds and the cave dweller, the Egyptian fruit bat, *Rousettus aegyptiacus*, in thousands.

In the Subregion eight species of Megachiroptera, or fruit-eating bats occur. As far as is known the straw-coloured fruit bat, *Eidolon helvum*, only visits the Subregion on migration, returning to the forested regions further north to have their young. They are not common in the Subregion.

All eight members of the Family Pteropodidae that occur in the Subregion can be recognised by their dog-like faces (Fig. V.2), with elongated snouts. They are fairly large with total lengths, measured from the tip of their snouts to the end of their small tails, where they protrude sufficiently to be measured, of over 120 mm.

The diagnostic feature used in differentiating between the four species of *Epomophorus* and the one species of *Epomops* is the arrangement and positioning of the ridges on the skin of the palate (Figs 40.1; 41.1).

# V. Family PTEROPODIDAE

Key to the genera after Meester *et al.* (1986)

1. Ears with white basal tufts ... 2

   Ears without white basal tufts ... 3

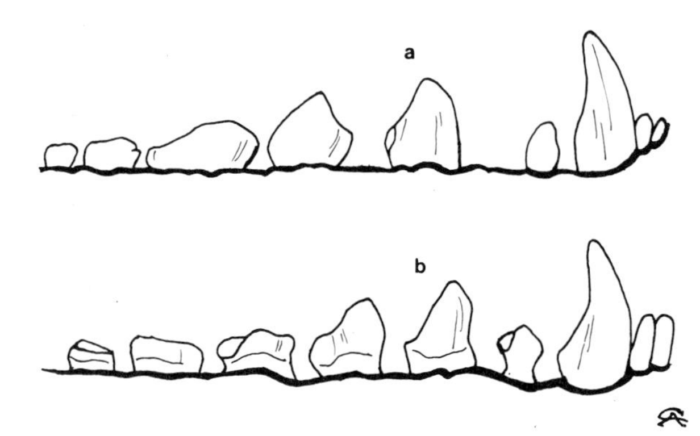


Fig. V.3. Pteropodidae, teeth of lower jaw, right hand side, (a) *Eidolon helvum* (b) *Rousettus aegyptiacus*.

2. Six prominent palatal ridges, one or two being post-dental, and these are no different from inter-dental ridges; post-dental palate strongly concave posteriorly ... *Epomophorus*

   Five palatal ridges, the last two post-dental, these being differentiated from interdental ridges, thick, and each bearing two triangular projections; post-dental palate flattened posteriorly ... *Epomops*

3. Forearm generally 110–130 mm; colour generally tawny, with dorsal fur restricted to a narrow median band, sharply demarcated from naked wing membranes ... *Eidolon*

   Forearm 65–102 mm; ruff of stiff hair present or absent on lower neck of adult males ... *Rousettus*

## Genus *Epomophorus* Bennett, 1836

Key to the species after Hayman & Hill (1971)
(Measurements in mm)

1. One palatal ridge behind the last tooth (Fig. 40.1.a); length of forearm 77–89 in males, 72–86 in females ... *wahlbergi*

   Two palatal ridges behind the last tooth (Fig. 40.1.b) ... 2

2. Fourth palatal ridge midway between the third and fifth (Fig. 40.1.b) ... 3

   Fourth palatal ridge much nearer the third than the fifth; length of forearm 87–91 in males, 82 in females (Fig. 41.1.b) ... *angolensis*

3. Length of forearm 87–93 in males, 81–86 in females ... *gambianus*

   Length of forearm 81–85 in males, 79–80 in females ... *crypturus*

---

No. 40

## *Epomophorus wahlbergi* (Sundevall, 1846)

### Wahlberg's epauletted fruit bat
### Wahlberg se witkolvrugtevlermuis

Plate 5

---

**Colloquial Name**

Named after Johan August Wahlberg, explorer, hunter and outstanding collector of zoological material in southern

Africa. He was killed in 1856 by a wounded elephant near the Savuti in northeastern Botswana (Gyldenstolpe, 1934).

### Taxonomic Notes

Hayman & Hill (1971) listed two subspecies: *E. w. haldemani* (Halowell, 1846) from the northern and western parts of their distributional range on the continent, and *E. w. wahlbergi*, mainly from the southern and eastern parts. There is considerable overlapping, both in characters and distribution and *E. w. haldemani* eventually may be shown to be untenable (Hayman & Hill, 1971).

### Description

Buffy-brown to brown on the upper parts and pale buffy-brown on the under parts. In the field it is impossible to distinguish Wahlberg's epauletted fruit bat from Peters' epauletted fruit bat, with which it so often associates. The males, as in Peters', have glandular pouches on the shoulders covered with long white hairs which, when open, resemble white rosettes. Both sexes have whitish patches at the base of the brownish ears.

The only way the two species can be recognised readily is that in Wahlberg's there is only one ridge on the palate behind the last molars, whereas there are two ridges in *E. crypturus* (Fig. 40.1). Wahlberg's is slightly smaller than Peters', the comparative lengths of the forearms being 77–89 mm in males and 72–86 mm in females, whereas in Peters' it is 81–85 mm in males and 79–80 in females (Table 40.1).

**Table 40.1**

Measurements (mm) and mass (g) of Wahlberg's epauletted fruit bats, *E. wahlbergi*

| | Males | | | Females | | |
|---|---|---|---|---|---|---|
| | $\bar{x}$ | n | Range | $\bar{x}$ | n | Range |
| TL | 138 | 7 | 120–156 | 140 | 8 | 122–144 |
| Hf c/u | 23 | 7 | 20–25 | 21 | 8 | 18–23 |
| E | 23 | 7 | 20–27 | 24 | 8 | 22–28 |
| F/a | 84 | 3 | 81–85 | 78 | 8 | 68–85 |
| Mass | 93,9 | 5 | 67,7–113,9 | 112,3 | 4 | 94–140 |

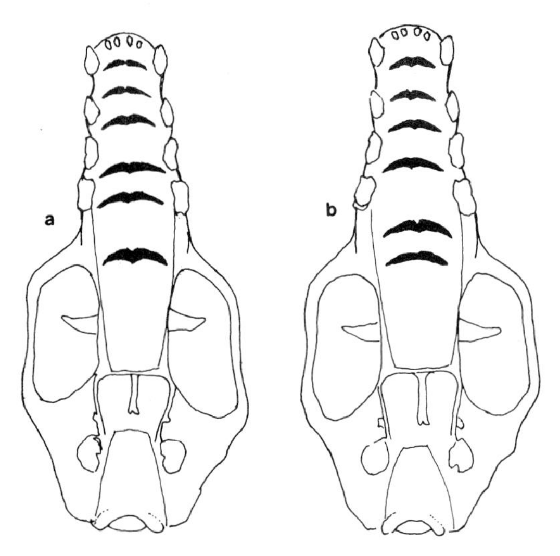


Fig. 40.1. Palatal ridges:
(a) *Epomophorus wahlbergi* (b) *E. crypturus*.

### Distribution

*South of the Sahara, excluding the Southern African Subregion*

This species is confined to the continent south of the Sahara and has been recorded coastally in the **Gabon**; **Central African Republic**, and in parts of northern and southern **Zaire**. It occurs in **Uganda; Kenya; Somalia**; in the eastern parts of **Tanzania**; widely in **Malawi** and **Zambia**, excluding the southern parts of the country and parts of the Northern Province, and in **Angola**. There are no records from north-eastern Mozambique, north of the Zambezi River, but it is likely that they occur there, at least in the east, as they are recorded from adjacent parts of southern Tanzania and Malawi.

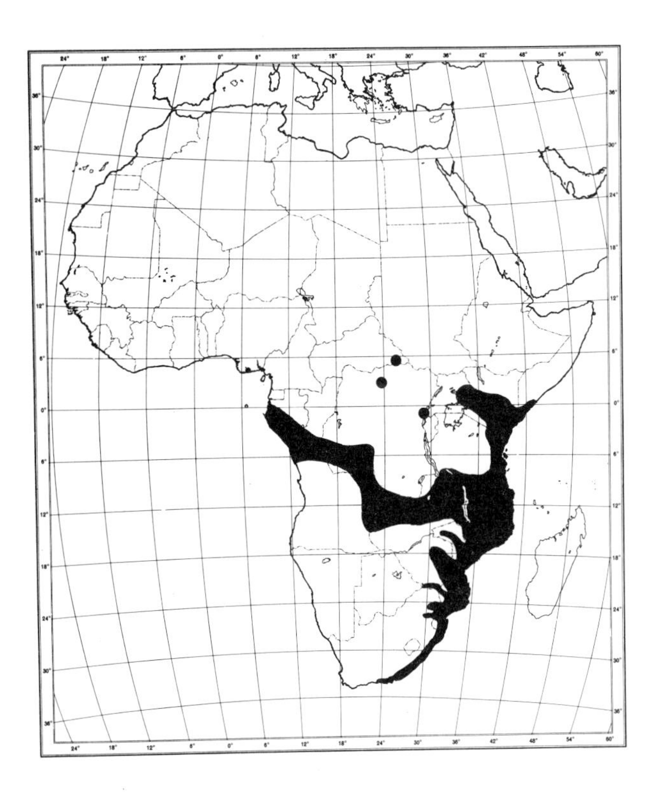

*Southern African Subregion*

In this sector they tend to be confined to the eastern parts of the continent, penetrating westwards into the drier areas up river valleys such as those of the Zambezi and Limpopo rivers and their tributaries. They occur widely in **Mozambique**, south of the Zambezi River, penetrating into the eastern parts of **Zimbabwe**, where they also occur in the Limpopo River Valley as far west as its confluence with the Shashi River. In the **Transvaal** they occur in the Limpopo River Valley and in the eastern parts of the province penetrate westwards to Tzaneen in the Letaba District and southwards to the Groblersdal District. Their distribution in the Transvaal and in adjacent parts of Mozambique suggests that they eventually will be shown to occur in Swaziland, but there are no records to substantiate this at the moment. They occur at least in the eastern parts of **Natal** and narrowly along the coastal fringe as far as the Uitenhage District in the **Cape Province**.

### Habitat

Tropical forest and evergreen riverine forests where there are fruit-bearing trees. While their occurrence lies largely within areas with a mean annual rainfall in excess of 700 mm, they penetrate up river valleys carrying evergreen forest into otherwise much drier country with a minimum annual rainfall as low as 250 mm (Limpopo Valley).

### Habits

They hang up during the day in the dense canopy of evergreen trees, sometimes in colonies numbering dozens of individuals and often in association with Peters' epauletted fruit bat, *E. crypturus*, which is always in far greater numbers. In coastal cities in Mozambique they roost in evergreen trees in the cities' parks, and even in the trees along busy streets.

Like *E. crypturus* they exhibit considerable local movements actuated by their search for food. At preferred feeding sites they may settle in the cover of evergreen trees during the day and then quite suddenly, when the supply is exhausted, move off elsewhere (Fenton, Brigham, Mills & Rautenbach, 1985).

### Food

Soft and pulpy wild fruits such as wild figs, *Ficus* spp, are favoured in particular and they have also been observed to take mahobohobo, *Uapaca kirkiana* and *U. sansibarica*; mobola plum, *Parinari curatellifolia* and kudu berries, *Pseudolachnostylis maprouneifolia*. Among orchard fruits they will take guavas, plums and apricots. Their feeding habits are similar to those of Peters' epauletted fruit bat, *E. crypturus*.

### Reproduction

Gravid females with a single foetus have been taken in Zimbabwe in June and December which suggests that they may breed widely throughout the year but further information is required to substantiate this.

No. 41

## *Epomophorus angolensis* Gray, 1870

## Angolan epauletted fruit bat
## Angola-witkolvrugtevlermuis

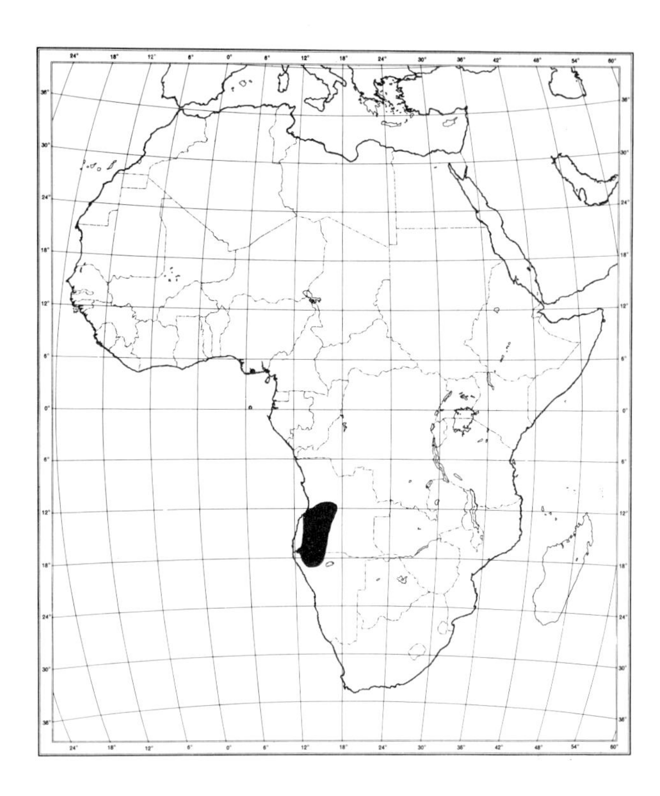

### Colloquial Name

Named Angolan as it was described originally from a specimen taken at Benguela, Angola.

### Taxonomic Notes

No subspecies have been described.

### Description

Very similar externally to *E. crypturus* and *E. wahlbergi*, but slightly larger, the males with forearm lengths of 87–91 mm, the females about 82 mm. Males have a total length of about 190 mm; about 150 mm in females (Table 41.1). They have two palatal ridges behind the last molar teeth as in *E. crypturus* and *E. gambianus*, but differ from them in that the third and fourth ridges from the front are nearer together than to the second and fifth (Fig. 41.1.b). In other skull characters they are similar to *E. gambianus* and different from *E. wahlbergi* which has only one palatal ridge behind the last molar teeth.

### Table 41.1

Measurements (mm) of a series of female *E. angolensis*, from northern Namibia (Shortridge, 1934)

| | Females | | |
|---|---|---|---|
| | $\bar{x}$ | n | Range |
| HB | 146 | 12 | 130–155 |
| T | 3 | 12 | 3–4 |
| Hf c/u | 22 | 12 | 21–23 |
| E | 24 | 12 | 23–26 |

A single male measured Hb 185; T 5; Hf c/u 23; E 28.

### Distribution

Restricted in their occurrence to the southwestern parts of **Angola** and the northwestern parts of **Namibia**. Not occurring in the western desert areas of the country, except possibly where there is riverine forest, or rivers running through them. Not recorded east of 17 °E.

### Habitat

Little is on record regarding the habitat requirements of this species, but as they are a fruit-eating species, they are probably confined to areas of riverine and other types of evergreen forest where there are fruit-bearing trees.

### Habits

Shortridge (1934) recorded that in Ovamboland they hung up singly from the bare branches of large *Acacia* sp trees near the Cunene River. Apart from this brief observation nothing seems to have appeared in literature concerning their habits.

### Food

Like other species of the genus *Epomophorus* they probably live predominantly on wild fruits.

### Reproduction

Shortridge (1934) recorded that newly-born young were found clinging to their mothers in September and October in Ovamboland, Namibia.

No. 42

## *Epomophorus gambianus* Gray, 1870

## Gambian epauletted fruit bat
## Gambiaanse witkolvrugtevlermuis

### Colloquial Name

So named as the species was described from a specimen from Gambia in West Africa.

### Taxonomic Notes

Hayman & Hill (1971) listed two subspecies, *E. g. gambianus* from the northern parts of the species' range which is replaced in the southern parts by *E. g. parvus* described by Ansell (1960c) from Zambia; the limits of the two subspecies are not known.

*E. g. parvus* has been described as being smaller than *E. g. gambianus* (Ansell, 1960c). Later Ansell (1978) thought that they might be conspecific with *E. crypturus*, the difference being in the proportion of the zygomatic breadth to the total length of the skulls in the males. In *E. g. parvus* it is less than half the total length of the skull, whereas in *E. crypturus* it is more than half. The matter remains unsolved and in the meantime Smithers (1983) followed Hayman & Hill (1971) in recognising *E. g. parvus* as a valid subspecies, although Meester *et al.* (1986) do not agree and place it as a subspecies of *E. wahlbergi*.

### Description

The Gambian epauletted fruit bat has a head and body of about 160 mm and a wingspan about 560 mm. The colour of the upper parts varies considerably from a sepia to a yellowish-cream, the under parts from off-white to about the same colour as the upper parts. The long, soft fur extends on to the upper and under parts of the upper arm and half of the forearm, and on to the upper parts of the legs, but only on to the proximal half of the legs underneath. It also extends sparsely on to the wing membranes, where on the upper surface it is similar in colour to the upper parts of the body, white on the under surface. They have the epaulettes on their shoulders like other members of the genus (see *E. crypturus*). The dark brown wings are short and broad with rounded tips. Most individuals have no noticeable tail, in others it may reach a length of about 5 mm. The muzzle, particularly in the male, is long and tapering, the nostrils enclosed in soft pads.

They have two ridges on the palate behind the last molar teeth, the first subtriangular in shape, the second of normal form, divided into two sections one on either side of the midline (Fig. 41.1.a). The posterior portion of the palate is deeply hollowed out which is the main distinction between this genus and *Epomops*, in which it is shallow or flattish.

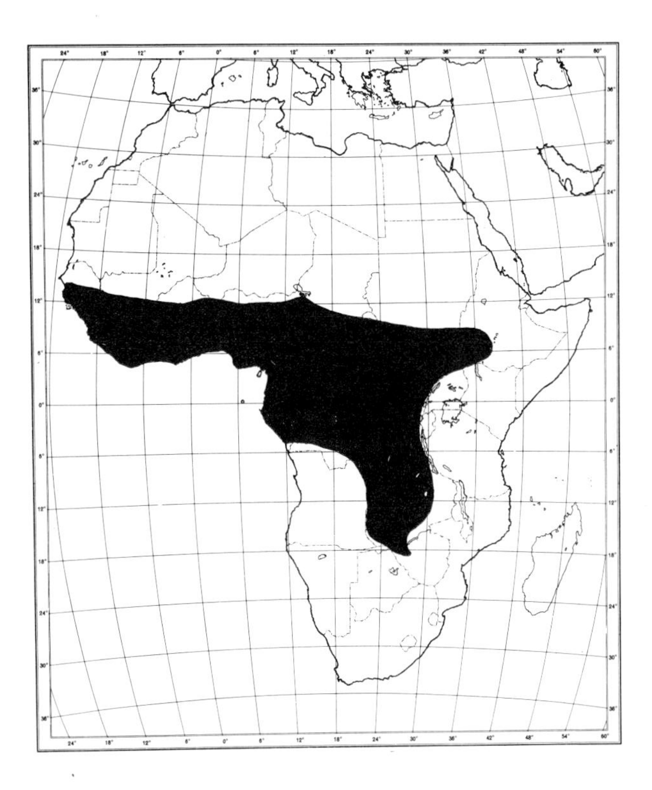

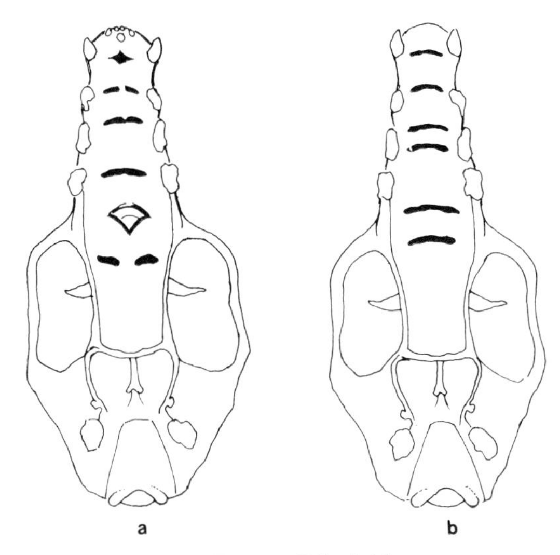


Fig. 41.1. Palatal ridges:
(a) *Epomophorus gambianus* (b) *E. angolensis*.

### Distribution

*South of the Sahara, excluding the Southern African Subregion*

They occur from **Senegal** and **Gambia** in West Africa eastwards in the High Forest and Guinea Savanna Zones to the **Sudan** and **Ethiopia** and southwards in northwestern **Uganda** and **Zaire**. They have been recorded in **Zambia** near the border with Angola, but not in the eastern sector, and no doubt in time will be shown to occur within Angolan limits in the southeast. In the extreme northeast of the country they are recorded in adjacent parts of Zaire.

*Southern African Subregion*

There are only two records of the occurrence of this species in the Subregion, both from **Zimbabwe** where a single specimen was taken in the riverine forest of the Zambezi River some 60 km up river from the Victoria Falls and another from the Sengwa Research Station in the northwest of the country (18 28 Aa).

### Habitat

In the northern and western parts of their range Gambian epauletted fruit bats occur both in open savanna woodland and in forest (Rosevear, 1965). One of the two specimens taken in the Subregion was taken in the well developed riverine forest of the Zambezi River, the other in much drier woodland associated with a tributary of that river. Rosevear (1965) noted that they appeared to be indifferent to their vegetational surroundings, possibly because they are both fruit-eaters and nectar-suckers. Their occurrence in drier woodland, like other fruit bats, will be governed by the availability of food.

### Habits

From the observations made in Zimbabwe by Thomas & Fenton (1978) they appear to be solitary in habit. In West Africa, Rosevear (1965) recorded that they occurred in colonies of 12 to 20, roosting during the day in clumps of bamboo and in the canopy of evergreen trees. In Zimbabwe, Thomas & Fenton (1978) noted that this species roosted in Natal mahogany, *Trichilia emetica* and sausage trees, *Kigelia africana*. One individual used five different trees in six days, another used a Natal mahogany on two consecutive days and then moved 150 m and 400 m between two sausage trees and a Natal mahogany. In Sierra Leone, Rosevear (1965) recorded that individuals in colonies hung singly, not close together like other members of the genus. They appear to be early movers in the evening, for they have been seen feeding as daylight fades.

### Food

In Zimbabwe, Thomas & Fenton (1978) by telemetry recorded that the species began foraging less than 45 min. after dark. Individual bats visited the same *Diospyros senensis* shrub on two successive nights, spending between 90 min. and 105 min. in feeding on the fruits, with breaks of 10 min. and 15 min. while they rested in adjacent Natal mahogany trees, *Trichilia emetica*. They appeared to feed solitarily and to have access to this food resource for almost two hours before the arrival of the Egyptian fruit bat, *Rousettus aegyptiacus*. In West Africa, Rosevear (1965) recorded that in addition to eating wild fruits, they lapped nectar from flowers and may possibly eat the anthers and fleshy petals of some species. They will eat the fruit of wild figs, *Ficus* spp, and have been observed to eat bananas.

In lapping nectar they visit each flower in turn for a quarter to three quarters of a minute, holding on by their feet and lapping the nectar with their long tongues. He recorded a specimen in the British Museum (Nat. Hist.) that was taken on the flower of a baobab, *Adansonia digitata* and they may also sip nectar from the flowers of the sausage tree, *Kigelia africana*. Both these trees occur in the area in the Subregion from which they have been taken.

### Reproduction

No information available.

---

No. 43

## *Epomophorus crypturus* Peters, 1852

## Peters' epauletted fruit bat
## Peters se witkolvrugtevlermuis

---

### Colloquial Name

Named after W.C.H. Peters who in 1852 published a monumental work on zoological material collected mainly in the Tete District of Mozambique. In the course of his career he was the first to describe eight new species of bats, six rodents, the porcupine, the bushy-tailed mongoose and Lichtenstein's hartebeest.

### Taxonomic Notes

No subspecies are recognised.

### Description

Peters' epauletted fruit bats are a common species in parts of the Subregion. The males are considerably larger than the females, adult males measuring about 150 mm in total length with mean masses of about 105 g and maximum masses of up to 140 g. The females measure about 120 mm in total length and have mean masses of about 76 g (Table 43.1).

The colour of the body is very variable and although usually a brownish-buff on the upper parts, it may be pale buffy and, in the extreme, nearly white. Both sexes have white patches at the base of the funnel-shaped ears, but only the males have the epaulettes on the shoulders. These are sunken glandular pouches in the skin covered with long white hairs. When under stress, when vocalising or possibly under sexual stimulus, these pouches are everted, the white hair, which in this species is 9 mm long, forms the conspicuous white epaulettes. They share this feature with the other three species of *Epomophorus*, *E. angolensis*, *E. gambianus* and *E. wahlbergi* that occur in the Subregion. The under parts are lighter in colour than the upper parts and in adult males the lower part of the throat has a collar of russet brown which is less obvious in juveniles and in the females.

They have two ridges on the palate behind the last molar teeth (Fig. 40.1.b).

### Table 43.1

Measurements (mm) and mass (g) of Peters' epauletted fruit bats, *E. crypturus*, from the northern parts of the Subregion (Smithers & Wilson, 1979)

| | Males | | | Females | | |
|---|---|---|---|---|---|---|
| | $\bar{x}$ | n | Range | $\bar{x}$ | n | Range |
| TL | 149 | 12 | 130–170 | 122 | 12 | 110–125 |
| Hf c/u | 22 | 12 | 20–23 | 21 | 12 | 20–22 |
| E | 24 | 12 | 22–27 | 24 | 12 | 22–25 |
| F/a | 83 | 12 | 80–86 | 79 | 12 | 76–82 |
| Mass | 104,5 | 12 | 80–140 | 75,5 | 12 | 64–88 |

### Distribution

Confined to the southern part of the continent, being replaced northwards by the eastern epauletted fruit bat, *E. anurus*, which extends from the northern parts of the Rift Valley in eastern Zaire and Rwanda into Kenya, Tanzania, the southern Sudan and Ethiopia and westwards to Nigeria.

*South of the Sahara, excluding the Southern African Subregion*

They occur in southeastern **Zaire** and widely in **Zambia** and **Malawi**, while at present there are no records from northeastern Mozambique, east of Lake Malawi. They have been taken in the Tete District, north of the Zambezi River. While there are no records from southeastern **Angola**, they occur on the Zambian border and in the valley of the Okavango River in Botswana right to the Angolan border and no doubt occur in Angola, if only marginally.

*Southern African Subregion*

While there are no records from Namibia, as they occur in the valley of the Okavango River in Botswana, they may well be found to occur along the river into that country. In **Botswana** they are common throughout the valley of the Okavango River and in its delta south to Maun and on the Chobe River in the northeast. In **Zimbabwe** they occur throughout except in parts of the dry west and in the central parts of **Mozambique**, south of the Zambezi River. They are found along the borders of the Transvaal south to the Maputo District. In the **Transvaal** they occur in the north in the Limpopo River valley and in the east as far south as Gollela. This indicates a possible occurrence in Swaziland from which at the moment there are no records. Southwards there are isolated records from **Natal** and the eastern **Cape Province**.

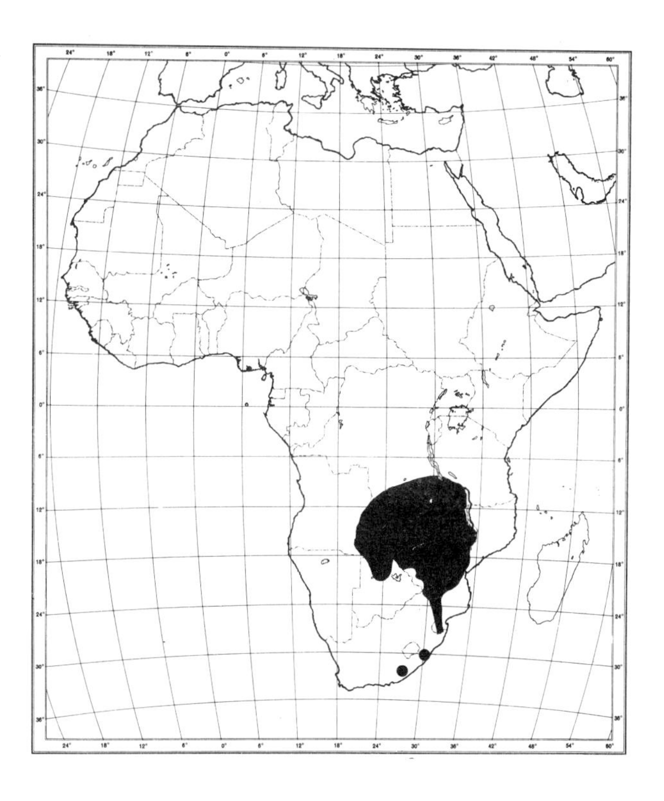

### Habitat

Peters' epauletted fruit bats are governed in their occurrence by the availability of fruit-bearing trees. They are associated predominantly with evergreen forests in the higher rainfall areas but occur in evergreen riverine forests deep into otherwise dry and unsuitable terrain. Their requirements are nowhere better exemplified than in northern Botswana where they are common throughout the Okavango Delta, with its rich riverine vegetation. They are not found in the drier associations of mopane, *Colophospermum mopane*, *Acacia* spp or *Terminalia* spp that surround it and which offer insufficient cover and food to satisfy their needs. Where there are isolated areas of slightly higher rainfall within otherwise drier country, such as in the Masvingo or Matopos Hills areas in Zimbabwe, where the run-off from the granite bosses supports an evergreen vegetation around their bases, they settle in these moister woodlands and move into the dry surrounding country to preferred feeding sites. In parts man has provided additional suitable conditions for them in orchard development where fruits such as guavas, plums, mangoes and other soft fleshy fruits provide them with food and surrounding exotic trees such as *Cyperus* sp the deep foliage shelter which they require in which to roost. They are independent of surface water, obtaining all their moisture requirements from their food.

### Habits

Peters' epauletted fruit bats are gregarious, occurring in colonies numbering up to hundreds of individuals. During the day they hang up by their feet, slightly spaced out one from another, on the thinner branches of evergreen trees where the thick foliage provides surrounding cover. In Zimbabwe they commonly use trees such as the wild fig, *Ficus* spp or the sausage tree, *Kigelia africana*, but they will use any evergreen tree provided it has thick foliage to provide cover and thin enough twigs to allow them to cling on to them. In Botswana they were found using the outer finer twigs of a clump of high growing bamboo in a garden fringing the Okavango River, strung out on these in such numbers that the poles were weighed down to within 3 m of the ground.

The colonies are very noisy, the males vocalising with a repeated musical bark which is uttered predominantly when hanging, but also occasionally when on the wing. As they settle after a night's foraging, there is much bickering among members of the colony. The clawed first digit on the forelimb and wings are used to slash other members who attempt to hang up too close and it takes a considerable time for the colony to settle quietly for the day.

### Food

The food of Peters' epauletted fruit bats consists almost entirely of wild or cultivated fruits which are soft and pulpy. The fruit of wild figs, *Ficus* sp; marula, *Sclerocarya birrea*; mabola plum, *Parinari curatellifolia*; kudu berry, *Pseudolachnostylis maprouneifolia*; mahobohobo, *Uapaca kirkiana*; bird plum, *Berchemia discolor*; red milkwood, *Mimusops zeyheri*, and quinine tree, *Rauvolfia caffra*, are sought after.

In feeding on small fruits they maintain their position on the outside of the canopy by wing flapping, pluck the fruit with their teeth and fly with it to a nearby feeding site. These sites are open branches of a size convenient for them to hang by the back feet. They fly to these carrying the fruit in their mouths, where it is manipulated by the claws on the first and second digits of the wings as they eat. In Zimbabwe the same bat would use the same feeding site over a period of a few nights and may well do so until the fopd source is depleted. They are wasteful feeders and when eating fruits such as mobola plums, the ground under the site gets covered in the discarded hard skins and pips and small bundles of chewed pulp as if, in eating the rather stringy pulp of this fruit, they are utilising the juices only. With very soft fruits such as figs they may cling to the fruit cluster or twigs and eat *in situ* or if the fruit becomes loosened in the process it is held in the mouth and carried to a feeding site.

They are great raiders of orchard or garden fruits such as guavas, apricots, peaches and loquats and if pawpaws are left to ripen on the tree, they damage these by biting into them and scratching them as they cling. Apples, pears and other hard fruits remain untouched.

### Reproduction

In a sample of 155 females taken throughout the year in Zimbabwe gravid females were observed from late July through to March. There was in this series a pronounced peak about August and from observations of juveniles, the main bulk of the young are born about September (Smithers & Wilson, 1979). In the Transvaal, Rautenbach (1982) observed lactating females with their young during November.

A single young is produced at a birth. The young are born with their eyes closed, with a sparse coat of hair on the back and naked under parts. In the early stages of their lives they fix firmly on to one of the female's nipples, clinging to her with their clawed digits of the forearms and the claws on the feet and are carried by her while she is feeding. Later as they grow and become too large to be conveniently carried, she will leave them hanging in the roost. Twins are known.

## Genus *Epomops* Gray, 1870

Only one species of this genus occurs in the Subregion.

---

No. 44

## *Epomops dobsonii* (Bocage, 1889)

## Dobson's fruit bat
## Dobson se vrugtevlermuis

---

### Colloquial Name

Named after G.G. Dobson who among his many other papers on bats published a *Catalogue of the Chiroptera in the collection of the British Museum* in 1878.

### Taxonomic Notes

Hayman & Hill (1971) stated that the relationship of this species with others that occur in West Africa is not clear and the possibility of intergrading must be taken into account. The palatal ridge pattern is apparently not as fixed a character as was formerly supposed. In the meantime until further information becomes available it is considered as a valid species.

### Description

Adult males have a head and body length of about 160 mm and forearms of 86 mm. The females are slightly smaller than the males (Table 44.1).

The upper parts are greyish-brown, the under parts a drab cinnamon colour washed with grey. The males have dark greyish-brown throats, in the females the throats are greyish. The wings, ears and rhinarium are dark brown. The muzzle is elongate and broad, the sides nearly parallel. It is not, however, as elongated as in *Epomophorus* spp.

They have three cheekteeth on either side of the upper jaw and five in the lower, the palate strongly arched from back to front and side to side. The post dental palate in this species has converging margins and is flat with five to seven palatal ridges posterior to the last tooth. In *Epomophorus* spp the post dental palate is almost parallel sided and is concave posteriorly and they have only up to two ridges posterior to the teeth.

The hair that covers the glandular region on the shoulders of the males and forms the epaulettes is much longer than in *E. crypturus*, measuring up to 18 mm as against 9 mm in *E. crypturus*. It is in addition tinged yellow as against the pure white hair in *E. crypturus*, and when extended forms a much larger epaulette.

**Table 44.1**

Measurements (mm) of male Dobson's fruit bats, *E. dobsonii*, from Zambia (Harrison, 1959) and females from Angola (Hill & Carter, 1941)

| | Males | | | Females | | |
|---|---|---|---|---|---|---|
| | $\bar{x}$ | n | Range | $\bar{x}$ | n | Range |
| HB | 160 | 4 | 146–168 | 142 | 3 | 137–145 |
| E | 28 | 3 | 27–28 | 26 | 3 | 25–27 |
| F/a | 86 | 5 | 82–88,2 | 83 | 3 | 81,5–83,0 |

### Distribution

*South of the Sahara, excluding the Southern African Subregion*

Occurs widely in central **Angola** and **Zambia** eastwards to the borders of Malawi from which country there are no records at the moment, although they may occur there. Recorded from Katanga in southeastern **Zaire**, and from **Rwanda** and **Tanzania**.

*Southern African Subregion*

Represented from the Subregion by a solitary specimen from Kasane on the Chobe River in the extreme northeast of **Botswana**.

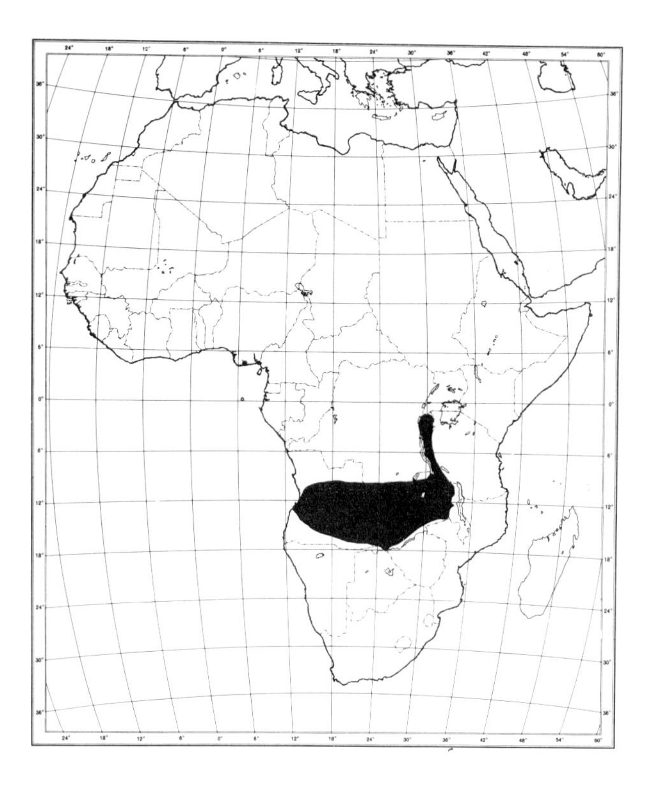

### Habitat

Practically nothing is known about the habitat requirements of this species. In Angola they occur in savanna woodland but as they are fruit-eaters, this association must include fruit-bearing trees. The single record from the Subregion was taken in a colony of Peters' epauletted fruit bats, *Epomophorus crypturus*, in the riparian evergreen woodland of the Chobe River and certainly they will be associated in other parts of their distributional range with similar conditions.

### Habits

Judging from the number of specimens in collections, *E. dobsonii* is nowhere so numerous as other fruit-eating bats such as *E. crypturus* or *E. helvum*.

### Food

Apart from the fact that they eat fruit like other members of the Family, there is nothing specific on record.

### Reproduction

Unknown.

## Genus *Eidolon* Rafinesque, 1815

No. 45

## *Eidolon helvum* (Kerr, 1792)

## Straw-coloured fruit bat
## Geel vrugtevlermuis

### Colloquial Name

They are not entirely straw-coloured, only on the shoulders and back, the rump and hind limbs normally being various shades of brown.

### Taxonomic Notes

Hayman & Hill (1971) listed three subspecies, one from Madagascar, *E. h. dupreaneanum* Schlegel & Pollen, 1866; one from the African Continent, *E. h. helvum*, and one from Arabia, *E. h. sabaeum* Andersen, 1907. There have been differing opinions advanced, some authorities (Eisentraut, 1964) suggesting that no subspecies should be recognised; Andersen (1912) on the other hand believed that the Madagascar and Arabian forms should be recognised as distinct species.

### Description

Straw-coloured fruit bats are by far the largest species of bats found in the Subregion. While it is difficult to judge the sexes in the field, there is a greater difference in size between them in this species than in the other fruit bats. Jones (1972) in West Africa recorded that the forearm in the males averages about 13% longer than in the females. The small number measured in the Subregion shows an average of 4% greater length in the males.

They have a total length of about 190 mm with forearms in the males of about 116 mm, in females 113 mm and a mass of between 243 g and 280 g (Table 45.1).

Although the colloquial name suggests that they are an overall pale golden-yellow colour, there is a considerable variation in colour between individuals and between one area of the body and another. On the upper parts the fur covers the head and shoulders and lies in a band down the mid-back extending on to the upper parts of the forearms, legs and narrow interfemoral membrane, but not on to the wing membranes. In some specimens there is a distinct yellow or orange collar on the throat which extends upwards on to the back of the neck but the remaining fur on the upper parts is either various shades of grey or brown, edged at the back of the shoulders and on the mid-back by a yellowish fringe. The fur on the rump and legs is often darker in shade than on the shoulders. The under parts are lighter in colour, in some the collar of slightly longer hair on the throat contrasts with the remainder, which is tinged paler yellow or orange. The skin underlying the collar on the throat is glandular and has been observed to secrete a sticky fluid with a musky smell (Allen, Lang & Chapin, 1917).

**Table 45.1**

Measurements (mm) and mass (g) of straw-coloured fruit bats, *E. helvum*, from Zimbabwe (Smithers & Wilson, 1979)

| | Males | | | Females | | |
|---|---|---|---|---|---|---|
| | $\bar{x}$ | n | Range | $\bar{x}$ | n | Range |
| TL | 190 | 5 | 165–205 | 189 | 6 | 181–207 |
| T | 15 | 5 | 14–18 | 15 | 6 | 11–20 |
| Hf c/u | 30 | 5 | 24–34 | 34 | 6 | 30–39 |
| E | 28 | 5 | 26–29 | 28 | 6 | 26–32 |
| F/a | 116 | 5 | 110–122 | 113 | 6 | 102–118 |
| Mass 2 | only 247,3 and 243,0 | | | 2 only 267,7 and 280,5 | | |

The naked wing membranes are dark blackish-brown, the wings long and pointed. Large specimens may have a wing span of up to 0,75 m. When resting the ends of the wings are folded back. The interfemoral membrane runs narrowly up the insides of the thighs and is only a few millimetres wide where it joins across the body. The tail which is about 15 mm long projects beyond this membrane for about half its length (Fig. 45.1). The first finger on the forearm is long and has a powerful curved claw which is used in clambering around in tree branches; the claw on the second digit is less well developed (Fig. V.1).

The dental formula is:

$I\frac{2}{2}\ C\frac{1}{1}\ P\frac{3}{3}\ M\frac{2}{3} = 34$

### Distribution

As is shown under **Habitat** the distribution of this species has to be dealt with in a different manner from other species

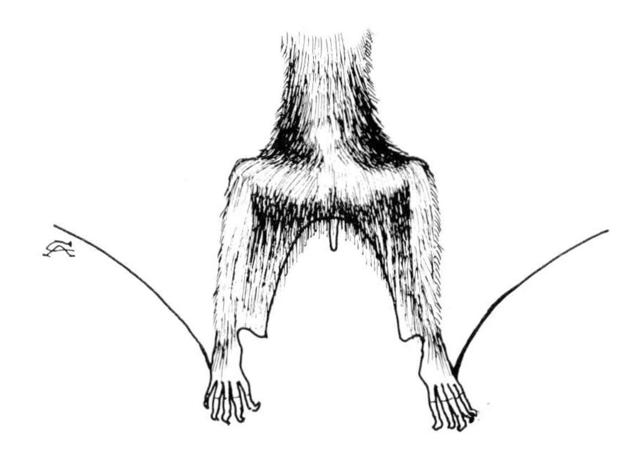

Fig. 45.1. Tail and interfemoral membrane of *Eidolon helvum*.

which are resident in the Subregion. The straw-coloured fruit bat is a migrant from its focus of distribution which lies to the north of the Subregion in the tropical forests of the continent and they are only seen on migration and not as residents. This means in effect that they are prone to turn up almost anywhere in the Subregion from time to time. At the moment most records are from the eastern and southern parts of the Subregion, for these areas with their higher rainfall than in the west, provide a better supply of wild fruits, their principal food. Nevertheless they have been recorded from the Subregion's most arid terrain, the Namib Desert in Namibia.

In Zaire, Allen, Lang & Chapin (1917) observed that immense numbers journey about irregularly and then become abundant in regions from which they were previously absent. Even the vast colony at Kampala, Uganda, moves out during the months of June to September (Kingdon, 1974). They are recorded from sea level to altitudes of 2 000 in East Africa.

*South of the Sahara, excluding the Southern African Subregion*

Straw-coloured fruit bats occur in forests from **Guinea** in West Africa eastwards to **Nigeria** and throughout the tropical forests of **Cameroun; Gabon; Zaire** to the Rift Valley and parts of the **Sudan; Uganda; Kenya; Tanzania** and northern **Angola**.

While it is impossible at the moment to clearly define the southern limits of the area in which they may be considered to be resident on a year round basis, this may well include parts of northeastern **Zambia, Malawi** and possibly northeastern **Mozambique**. South of this they are considered as occurring on migration, only remaining in areas for a shorter or longer period depending on the local availability of food.

*Southern African Subregion*

Of sporadic occurrence in **Namibia**; in **Zimbabwe**, as far west as the Matopo Hills, and in **Mozambique**, south of the Zambezi River, in the central and southern parts of the country. In the **Transvaal** they have been taken as solitary wanderers in the southwest of the province. They appear commonly in northeastern **Natal** and have been taken in the **Orange Free State** and the eastern **Cape Province**, with records from as far west, coastally, as the Bredasdorp district.

**Habitat**

Straw-coloured fruit bats occur in the Subregion in a wide variety of habitats from coastal forests in Natal and Mozambique to parts of the dry South West Arid Zone in Namibia. In the Subregion we only see them while they are on migration, when they tend to scatter widely, not being truly resident and only remaining in an area if held there temporarily by the availability of a plentiful food supply. Their prime habitat is in the tropical forests of the continent which supply them with a variety of wild pulpy fruits during the greater part of the year, and it is the availability of food that determines their occurrence more than any other factors. Their prime habitat covers a very extensive

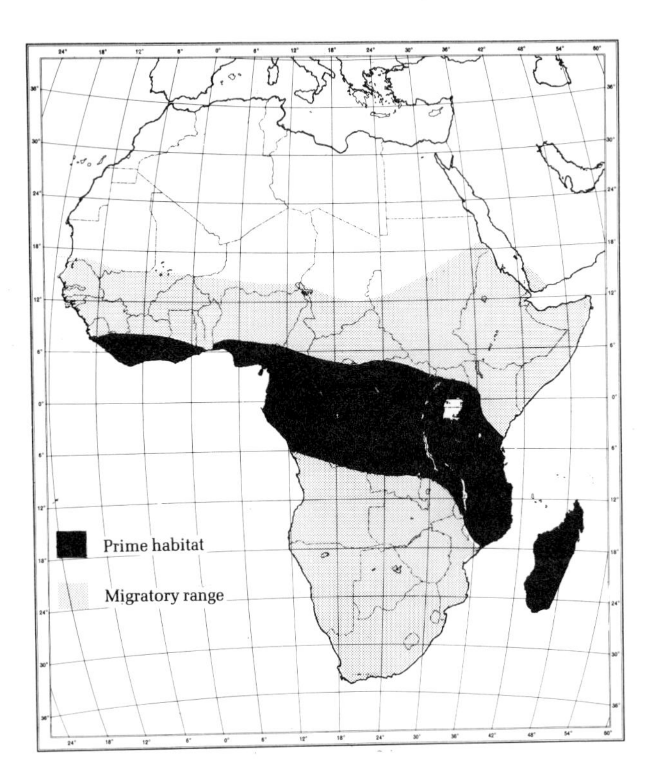


area ranging from Guinea in West Africa eastwards to the Rift Valley in East Africa, a distance of some 5 000 km which is up to 650 km wide in parts. In their search for food resources they cover great distances, crossing country that is totally unsuitable for them and in which, were they to settle, they would perish. At times this movement is ill directed, for Rosevear (1965) recorded that they have been taken at sea some 250 km from the nearest land. He stated that in West Africa they have been found in the Sudan Savanna Zone which borders on the southern fringes of the Sahara, so that their sudden appearance in some of the more arid parts of the Subregion is not surprising.

**Habits**

Straw-coloured fruit bats are gregarious and subject to wide migration and movements in search of food supplies. The classic colony at Kampala, which roosts during the day in a grove of saligna gums, *Eucalyptus saligna*, was estimated by Ogilvie & Ogilvie (1964) to number some 200 000 individuals. They return to the grove about 07h00 in the morning and leave to forage about 18h30 in the evening. They hang in the grove in clumps of 1–50, chattering continuously, with some individuals always flying around in search of new places to hang. Fighting is common, contestants battering each other with their wings. In the Subregion they never occur in such huge numbers and colonies of up to 20 or 30 are exceptional. More often up to half a dozen is the rule and often single individuals are seen.

Even in the Kampala colony, which was known prior to European settlement, they are subject to movement, for Kingdon (1974) recorded that they are absent from June to September, as they are too from other large colonies such as those at Avakupi in Zaire (Allen, Lang & Chapin 1917). In the forest habitat in West Africa, Rosevear (1965) noted that they tend to prefer clumps of very high trees to roost in, relic patches of ancient forest being preferred. In the Subregion they have a habit of hanging on power lines and pylons which accounts for the number of individuals that get electrocuted annually in Zimbabwe, where no less than seven of the 12 specimens in the collection of the National Museums were recovered after death by electrocution. Their huge wingspan of 0,75 m renders them prone to death in this manner when alighting to rest (Smithers & Wilson, 1979).

Their wings are long and pointed, adapted to a rather slow but steady flight, interspersed with short periods of gliding which carry them over great distances. The powerful hooked claw of the thumb is used in clambering around branches and in clinging on to trees while feeding. Rosevear (1965) described the evening flight of the colony as a remarkable sight. Most of them take off as if by a common signal, the flying colony when seen from a distance looks like a black cloud over the forest.

Jones (1972) stated that, in roosting in trees, they tend to use the more sturdy branches, hanging with their wings half folded away from their bodies or along the sides of their bodies with the wing tips folded back. They remain alert and active during the day, hanging with their eyes open, ears erect and constantly moving. In addition to the daytime roosts, they rest from time to time during the night between bouts of feeding, hanging in trees. On taking to the wing they drop for distances up to 2 m from the roosts before flying.

### Food

Digestion in the straw-coloured fruit bat is extremely rapid (Rodhain & Bequaert, 1916), which is probably the reason why stomachs examined from Zimbabwe and Mozambique were invariably empty. Allen, Lang & Chapin (1917) found the same state of affairs in the specimens they examined in Zaire.

We have to rely on the observations of Rosevear (1965) in West Africa who reported on their feeding habits., There they are a pest in banana plantations, a food which captive individuals eat with avidity. They eat the fibrous pulp of the fruits of the Borasses palm, *Borassus* sp, dates, and wild figs, *Ficus* spp. They will take large succulent flowers or flower buds such as those of the baobab, *Adansonia digitata*, and the silk cotton tree, *Bombax* sp. He recorded that they were reported to eat the fresh leaves of *Erythrina* sp, completely stripping the trees. Jones (1972) in West Africa reported that they eat mangoes, pawpaws, avocado pears, figs, passion fruit, custard apples and loquats. In feeding they hang by the claws on their thumbs and use both feet. They chew noisily, discarding fibrous material.

In Zaire and West Africa the bats are eaten by the indigenous people, Allen, Lang & Chapin (1917) recording that at Leopoldville they saw bunches of them tied together being sold in the markets.

### Reproduction

There are no indications at the moment that straw-coloured fruit bats breed in the Subregion. No specimens examined were gravid and it may be that they only breed within the limits of better developed and more extensive forested regions to the north. Allen, Lang & Chapin (1917) recorded that at Avakubi, in Zaire, from the presence of gravid females, they appeared to have a definite breeding season, the young being born about November. Rosevear (1965) stated that the young are carried about by their mothers until the stage when they are able to take care of themselves. The females usually have one young, occasionally two.

## Genus *Rousettus* Gray, 1821

This genus is represented on the continent by three species, two of which, *R. aegyptiacus* and *R. angolensis* occur in the Subregion. Members have a wide distribution: *R. aegyptiacus* is found from the Cape Province to Egypt and westwards to Senegal, extralimitally on the Mediterranean island of Cyprus, in parts of the Middle East and eastwards to Pakistan.

The generic name *Rousettus* was applied to the group as the earliest known representatives were red in colour; the two species that occur in the Subregion, however, are brown or dark brown on the upper parts of the body.

They are medium-sized bats with wingspans up to about 450 mm. The wing membranes are dark in colour, almost black. They have very short tails and narrow interfemoral membranes. In both species the eyes are large, as in other fruit-eating bats. The Egyptian fruit bat, *R. aegyptiacus*, has powers of echolocation which are brought into play in total darkness. This allows them to roost in caves that are totally dark, a shelter denied to other fruit-eating bats. Bocage's fruit bat, *R. angolensis*, on the other hand has no powers of echolocation and when using caves can only use parts that are adequately illuminated.

The dental formula is:

$I\frac{2}{2}\ C\frac{1}{1}\ P\frac{3}{3}\ M\frac{2}{3} = 34$

and is the same as in the straw-coloured fruit bat, *Eidolon helvum*. The anterior upper premolar is very small and roughly equal in size to the upper incisor, whereas in *E. helvum* it is appreciably larger. The two upper and three lower molars and last premolar in *R. aegyptiacus* are distinctly longer than broad, whereas in *R. angolensis* they are only as long as broad.

Key to the species after Hayman & Hill (1971)
(Measurements in mm)

1. Wing membranes arise from the first toe; hair short and sleek; cheekteeth heavy; length of forearm generally above 89 and up to 96; adult males with no collar of bristly hairs on the throat
   ... *aegyptiacus*

   Wing membranes arise from the second toe; hair longer and coarser; cheekteeth reduced in bulk; length of forearm less than 90; adult males with a distinct collar of bristly hairs on the throat
   ... *angolensis*

No. 46

## *Rousettus aegyptiacus* (E. Geoffroy, 1810)

## Egyptian fruit bat
## Egiptiese vrugtevlermuis

Plate 4

### Colloquial Name

The name derives from the fact that the species was described originally from a specimen from the Great Pyramid of Giza in Egypt.

### Taxonomic Notes

Hayman & Hill (1971) listed four subspecies, only one of which, *R. a. leachi* (A. Smith, 1829), occurs in the Subregion. This was described from a specimen from "gardens about Cape Town".

### Description

Egyptian fruit bats are the second largest species of fruit bat that occurs in the Subregion, only being exceeded in size by the straw-coloured bat, *Eidolon helvum*. Adults are about 150 mm in total length with masses of about 130 g. There are little or no differences between the sexes (Table 46.1). They have a wingspan of about 0,6 m.

Their colour varies throughout their wide range, those from the Subregion are dark brown on the upper parts, sometimes tinged with slate-grey, the under parts smoke-grey. The fur extends along the top of the forearm for about half of its length and along the top of the legs to the ankles. Underneath it extends half way along the forearm and only on to the upper parts of the legs. The rounded ears are naked except at their bases, the fur on the face is short and longer on the forehead and the upper parts of the body. The fur extends narrowly on to the dark brown wing membranes. The eyes are noticeably large. They have a distinct pale buffy or yellowish collar around the throat and neck which contrasts markedly on the upper parts with the general dark brown colour. The wings are rounded at the tips.

The dental formula is:
$I\frac{2}{2}\ C\frac{1}{1}\ P\frac{3}{3}\ M\frac{2}{3} = 34$

**Table 46.1**
Measurements (mm) and mass (g) of Egyptian fruit bats, *R. aegyptiacus*, from the northeastern parts of the Subregion (Smithers & Wilson, 1979)

| | Males | | | Females | | |
|---|---|---|---|---|---|---|
| | $\bar{x}$ | n | Range | $\bar{x}$ | n | Range |
| TL | 150 | 17 | 140–162 | 150 | 19 | 140–162 |
| T | 18 | 14 | 15–22 | 19 | 17 | 16–24 |
| Hf c/u | 23 | 16 | 20–27 | 24 | 18 | 22–26 |
| E | 22 | 17 | 20–25 | 22 | 18 | 19–24 |
| F/a | 89 | 17 | 83–96 | 90 | 19 | 88–95 |
| Mass | 133,4 | 11 | 88,1–166,0 | 129,3 | 18 | 117,7–166,0 |

## Distribution

The Egyptian fruit bat has a very wide distribution from the Cape Province to Egypt and westwards to Senegal and beyond Continental limits to the countries at the eastern end of the Mediterranean, to Arabia, southeastern Iran, Baluchistan and west Pakistan. They do not occur in the Sahara or in the northwestern parts of the continent or in the southwestern sector except coastally.

*Northeastern Africa*

They occur in **Egypt** in association with the Nile Valley right to the coast of the Mediterranean.

*South of the Sahara, excluding the Southern African Subregion*

They occur from **Senegal** and are recorded from most of the countries eastwards to the **Sudan** and **Ethiopia**, in the High Forest Zone, Guinea savanna and in parts of the Sudan savanna. Southwards they are recorded widely in most countries to the borders of the Southern African Subregion. In **Angola** they have been taken in the central and northern parts of the country with the situation in the south not being known. In **Zambia**, although there are only a few records from the southeast, Ansell (1978) believed that eventually they would be shown to occur throughout the country. At the moment there are no records from Malawi or from northeastern Mozambique, but there is good reason to believe that they will be found there eventually.

*Southern African Subregion*

They appear to have an eastern distribution in the Subregion, not being recorded from Namibia, Botswana or the more arid parts of the Cape Province.

They occur in the central and eastern parts of **Zimbabwe**, and in the central and southeastern parts of **Mozambique**, south of the Zambezi River. In the latter area they are absent from the more arid parts of the Banhine Flats in the west. In the **Transvaal** they are recorded from Pafuri in the northern parts of the Kruger National Park and from the Letaba and Barberton Districts. They occur in **Natal** and in the **Cape Province** narrowly westwards along the southern coast to Cape Town.

## Habitat

Although from their distribution Egyptian fruit bats appear to be catholic in their habitat requirements, two factors at least are essential for them. As a fruit-eater the habitat must provide this and at the same time caves or similar structures must be available as cover in which to roost during the day. In Botswana and Namibia the semi-desert areas, while they have suitable caves, do not provide the necessary food, and in areas such as the Okavango Delta in Botswana where fruit is plentiful, the nature of the terrain is such that suitable caves are almost non-existent. So far they have not been recorded from the Drodtsky Caves in western Ngamiland which are certainly within reach of the food supply in the Okavango Delta and which are extensive enough to accommodate them. Where cover and a plentiful food supply occur together they are found in very large numbers.

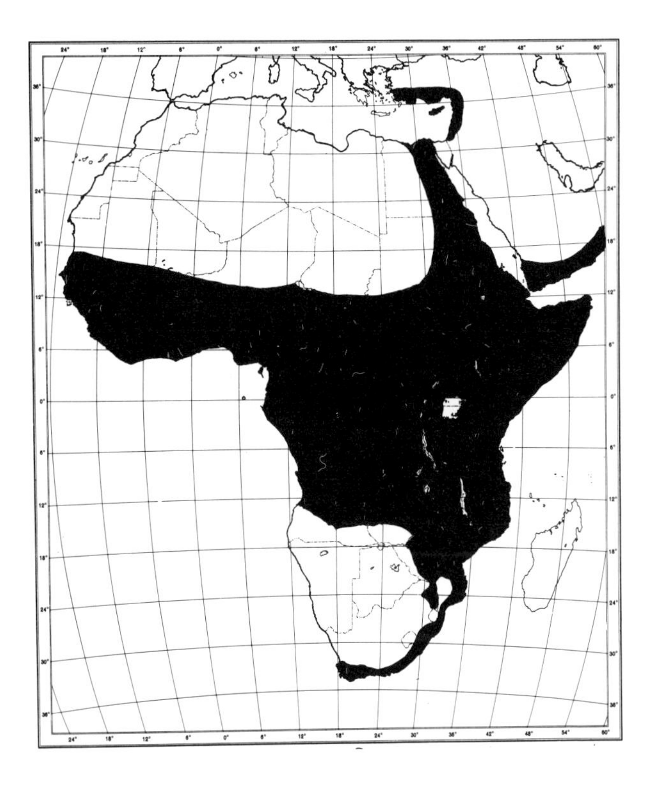

## Habits

Egyptian fruit bats are gregarious, occurring in colonies numbering up to thousands of individuals in caves or other similar structures. They hang up from the ceilings or the walls, usually by one foot, the wings closely folded around the body, and the other foot folded across the front of the body outside the enfolding wings. They pack tightly together in clusters, usually deep in the caves in total darkness. The colony is very restless and extremely noisy, chirping and chattering continuously, a noise which can be heard long before the cave entrance is approached. They avoid light, this sometimes resulting in continuous fighting for the darkest niches and crevices in a cave. Indeed, availability of dark places may act as a rough regulator of numbers in a cave (Herzig-Straschil & Robinson, 1978).

As sundown approaches the restlessness and noise become more apparent as individuals start to groom themselves prior to the night's foraging. In the Tsitsikama National Park activity data indicated a different winter and summer pattern. In winter they became active on average 90 minutes after sunset, and activity ceased about 216 minutes before sunrise. In summer the period of activity was appreciably longer regardless of the shortened dark phase, starting 30 minutes after sunset and ending 12 minutes before sunrise. The delayed onset of emergence under the influence of moonlight in winter was quite pronounced (Herzig-Straschil & Robinson, 1978). This latter was also suspected in the eastern Transvaal (Jacobsen & du Plessis, 1976).

Rousette bats are the only species of fruit bat that have powers of echolocation, which allow them to move in total darkness. The system used is different from that found in Microchiroptera which emit high frequency sound from the mouth in the case of the Vespertilionidae, or from the complicated nasal structures in the Hipposideridae. In the case of the rousette bats Möhres & Kulzer (1956a) found that the Egyptian fruit bat was not inconvenienced when its eyes were covered and it was able to fly around in complete darkness, avoiding obstacles with ease. If, however, its ears were obstructed, it was helpless in complete darkness. The system of echolocation used is by repetitive tongue "clicks", those of lower frequency audible to the human ear, the echo of these being picked up by the ears which allows them to pinpoint obstacles ahead of them. The clicks are emitted through the corners of the mouth with the jaws closed.

The Egyptian fruit bats have a well developed eyesight and when returning to their caves, providing there is sufficient light, they will locate these by sight. As they enter they will switch to echolocation to find their way around and eventually to pinpoint the location of suitable hanging places. They therefore are fully equipped to find their way around either by sight or echolocation. Egyptian fruit bats are agile, fast fliers and can negotiate narrow openings between the branches of trees with ease.

### Food

In feeding they will circle a fruiting tree, then hover before alighting and snuffling about on the branches to discover suitable fruit (Rosevear, 1965). Once secured, it may either be eaten *in situ* or conveyed in the mouth to a feeding site. The fruit is manipulated in one of the back feet, the other clinging to the branch while the food is eaten, or the food may be held against the chest by the back feet while it is eaten.

The hard skin and seeds of fruit are discarded, the pulp chewed and any fibrous material dropped. Under favourite feeding sites quite large accumulations of discarded material may be found.

Herzig-Straschil & Robinson (1978), in the eastern Cape, observed several individuals at a Cape ash tree (*Ekebergia capensis*) bearing ripe fruit in June and these bats also ate fruit from saffronwood (*Cassine crocea*), Bushman's poison (*Acokanthera oppositifolia*) and mistletoe (*Viscum obscurum*). In the Eastern Transvaal figs formed the basis of the bats' diet (Jacobsen & du Plessis, 1976), in particular the Cape fig (*Ficus capensis*), while *F. petersii* and *F. sansibarica* were also eaten at certain times of the year; other fruits utilised were from the Cape ash tree, water berry (*Syzigium cordatum*), red stinkwood (*Prunus africana*) and wild plum (*Harpephyllum caffrum*). In Zimbabwe, Thomas & Fenton (1978) recorded their eating the fruits of *Diospyros senensis*. Soft garden and orchard fruits are also eaten. Egyptian fruit bats have cheek pouches in which food can be stored temporarily.

Lombard (1961) reported that, after eating, the hair on the chest which tends to become matted with the fruit juices, is thoroughly combed with the claws on the feet and the toes cleaned in the mouth. They also pick out fibrous material from between the teeth with the claws on the feet.

### Reproduction

During the mating season, which in the Cape Province is from June to mid-September, Lombard (1961) noted that the males tended to form groups, ignoring the females and juveniles, which formed nursery groups on their own.

Using Mutere's (1968) forearm age relationship it was estimated that birth in the Tsitsikama National Park occurs from October to June (Herzig-Straschil & Robinson, 1978), whereas in the eastern Transvaal the period was slightly shorter, with a peak in mid-summer (Jacobsen & du Plessis, 1976) and further north parturition is given as from September to December (Penzhorn & Rautenbach, 1988). A single young is produced at birth, occasionally twins, after a gestation period given by Kingdon (1974) as 105 to 107 days. In East Africa they breed twice a year and in Egypt throughout the year (Kingdon, 1974).

The young are born with their eyes closed and their ears folded back, the eyes opening and ears erecting at about 10 days of age. At birth they cling tightly to the ventral surface of their mothers and are carried around by them for about six weeks during the suckling period. The mother then leaves the young bat in the cave while she forages, bringing back food for it. At first it licks the juices from her mouth and later eats mouthfuls for itself (Lombard, 1961). At this time of their lives the young bats usually lose weight and do not start to gain weight until they start to fly at about nine to 10 weeks of age. They recognise their young by smell as was shown in Kulzer's (1958) experiment when a female's own and a strange young were enclosed in bags. The mother correctly identified her own offspring as was shown by her frenzied attempts to release it.

No. 47

## *Rousettus angolensis* (Bocage, 1898)

## Bocage's fruit bat
## Bocage se vrugtevlermuis

### Colloquial Name

Named after J.V. Barboza du Bocage who originally described the species *Cynonycteris angolensis* (=*R. angolensis*) from Angola.

### Taxonomic Notes

Hayman & Hill (1971) listed three subspecies from the continent, only one of which, *R. a. angolensis*, occurs in the Subregion and then only marginally into Zimbabwe. Some doubt has been expressed in the past as to whether this species should be retained in the genus *Rousettus* or whether it deserves full recognition as a genus, *Lissonycteris*, on its own. It differs from *R. aegyptiacus* and other rousette bats in the possession by the males of a distinct neck ruff of coarse sticky hairs and the fact that it does not possess powers of echolocation. In addition it has a long, silky fur and the wing membranes arise from the second toe of the hind foot and not from the outside toe as in *R. aegyptiacus*; the cheekteeth are squarish, not rectangular, and the premaxilla is ossified across the front. As Meester *et al.* (1986) included it in the genus *Rousettus*, this view is followed.

### Description

Slightly smaller than the Egyptian fruit bat, *R. aegyptiacus*, Bocage's, *R. a. angolensis*, has a head and body length of about 120 mm and a wingspan of about 400 mm.

The relative size is perhaps best illustrated in the length of the forearm which in the Egyptian fruit bat measures 90–105 mm and in Bocage's fruit bat from the Subregion 81–85 mm (Table 47.1). The West African subspecies, *R. a. smithi* Thomas, 1908, is smaller still with a forearm length of 72–82 mm (Rosevear, 1965).

The characteristic feature of male Bocage's fruit bats is the collar of stiff coarse hairs on the throat and sides of the neck, which forms whorls below the ears. It is dusky-orange in colour and is sticky, suggesting that it arises from a glandular area of skin. The colour of the upper parts in specimens from the Subregion is a rich brown, with the under parts lighter in shade than the upper, the collar in the males orange. The throat and sides of the neck in the females are sparsely haired.

**Table 47.1**
Forearm and skull measurements (mm) of a series of four male and three female specimens of Bocage's fruit bat, *R. angolensis*, from Zimbabwe (Smithers & Wilson, 1979)

| | Males | | | Females | | |
|---|---|---|---|---|---|---|
| | $\overline{x}$ | n | Range | $\overline{x}$ | n | Range |
| F/a | 83 | 4 | 81–84 | 84 | 3 | 82–87 |
| TL skull | 43 | 4 | 42–44 | 43 | 3 | 42–46 |

### Distribution

In the eastern part of the continent there are no records of this species between northern Tanzania and eastern Zimbabwe. It is likely however that they do occur, if only coastally, where there is suitable forest habitat. Their occurrence in the western Vila Pery District of Mozambique suggests that they may in time be taken in parts of the Dondo and Amatonga forests further east.

*South of the Sahara, excluding the Southern African Subregion*

They occur from **Sierra Leone** eastward in the High Forest Zone to **Nigeria** and from thence eastward to **Ethiopia**; southern **Sudan**; southern **Uganda** and southern **Kenya**. South of this they have been taken in **Cameroun; Gabon; Congo Republic; Zaire** and in northern **Angola** from whence at Pongo Andongo (9°40'S 15°40'E) the type specimen of *R. angolensis* was taken. They occur in the Mwinilunga

District on the Zaire border in **Zambia** and Ansell (1978) stated that they may also occur in the extreme northern parts of the country.

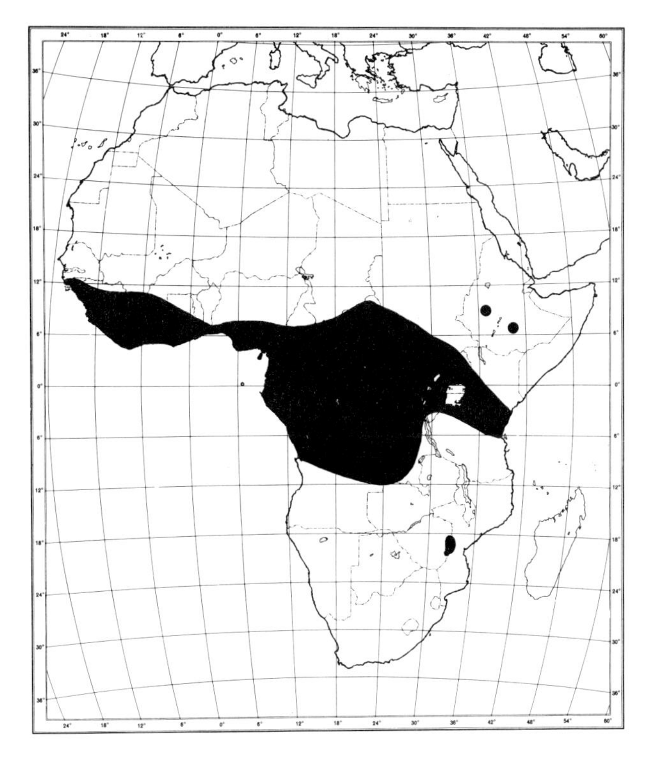

*Southern African Subregion*

They have been recorded from the Eastern Districts of **Zimbabwe** in the Inyanga and Mutare districts and south to Birchenough Bridge on the Sabi River and in adjacent parts of **Mozambique**, where they have been taken in the western Vila Pery District. These populations are far south of the general limits of their distribution.

### Habitat

Like the Egyptian fruit bat the more important habitat requirements of Bocage's fruit bat are the availability of substantial shelter in the form of caves or hollow trees in which to roost during the day and a plentiful food supply in the form of wild fruits. In West Africa they occur in the High Forest Zone (Rosevear, 1965) and they have also been taken in gallery forests, montane and lowland forest and in gardens in residential areas (Mutare, Zimbabwe). These types of habitat provide the necessary food supply and they can find roosting places in hollow trees if caves are not available in the vicinity. Unfortunately as all the specimens taken in the Subregion to date have been netted, there is no information on their roosting places. In West Africa they occur from sea level to over 900 m and in East Africa, on Mount Ruwenzori, to 1 800 m (Rosevear, 1965). In the Subregion they appear to be confined to lower altitudes of up to 1 200 m.

### Habits

While no information is available from the Subregion, in West Africa, Eisentraut & Knorr (1957) recorded that these bats hang up near the entrance to caves, which one would expect in a species that has no powers of echolocation to navigate in the dark. They are gregarious, occurring in small colonies of up to about six together, and in the case of the Zimbabwe specimens from Mutare, were associated with far larger numbers of Peters' epauletted fruit bats, *E. crypturus*, feeding on guavas in an orchard. In other parts of eastern Zimbabwe eight were netted together in a forest clearing. In East Africa, Kingdon (1974) noted that they hang free in the roosting places and assume this posture immediately on alighting in trees, not crawling around among the branches like the straw-coloured fruit bat, *Eidolon helvum*, or the Egyptian fruit bat, *R. aegyptiacus*.

### Food

In Mutare, Zimbabwe they were observed to eat wild figs, *Ficus* spp, and orchard fruits such as guavas and mangoes. Mangoes appeared to be chewed *in situ*. Kingdon (1974) stated that they stuff their cheek pouches full of food and then fly to a feeding site to eat at leisure. The food is manipulated by one foot as they hang from the other. Fibrous material is chewed and then discarded.

### Reproduction

No information is available from the Subregion. Kingdon (1974) in East Africa observed that the stickiness of the collar increased and decreased from time to time, and thought it might be due to glandular secretion connected with sexual behaviour. Eisentraut (1956) in Cameroun found that females formed nurseries.

# Suborder MICROCHIROPTERA

## Insect-eating bats

In the Subregion the Suborder Microchiroptera is represented by six Families, the Emballonuridae, the sheath-tailed bats; the Nycteridae, the slit-faced bats; the Rhinolophidae, the horseshoe bats; the Hipposideridae, the leaf-nosed bats; the Vespertilionidae, a diverse Family which includes the serotines, the long-eared bats, hairy bats and others and the Molossidae, the free-tailed bats. Collectively 65 species occur in the Subregion.

These are characterised by the possession of a single claw on the thumb of the forearm and, except in the case of members of the Family Rhinolophidae, a tragus in the ear. The differences in the foetal membranes between members of this Suborder and the Megachiroptera as pointed out by Mossman (1937) have been mentioned in dealing with that Suborder.

The Microchiroptera rely, when it is totally dark, on echolocation for their orientation, many of them having complicated and most delicate structures around the nose which play a part in this process. As opposed to the "clicks" produced by the tongue of the only fruit bat that uses echolocation, the Egyptian fruit bat, *Rousettus aegyptiacus*, the "clicks" in the Microchiroptera originate in the larynx.

Fenton (1975) showed, however, that some of the Microchiroptera that occur in the Subregion, including the common slit-faced bat, *Nycteris thebaica*, rely to some extent on vision for orientation when there is adequate light.

Generally classed as insect-eaters, the Microchiroptera include species that eat fish, frogs, fruit, birds, drink blood and some are cannibals. Most of those that occur in the Subregion eat insects, although species such as the large slit-faced bat, *Nycteris grandis*, have been known to eat fish and frogs, albeit this is a departure from their normal insect diet. We have no blood-sucking bats in Africa, they are found only in the New World.

Key to the Families after Meester *et al.* (1986)

1. With a distinct tail extending free of the interfemoral membrane

   . . . 2

   Tail almost entirely enclosed within the interfemoral membrane

   . . . 3

2. Free terminal part of tail emerging upwards from near the middle of the interfemoral membrane (Fig. VI.1)

   . . . Emballonuridae

   Free terminal part of tail emerging from the posterior part of the interfemoral membrane and extending well beyond it (Fig. VII.2)

   . . . Molossidae

3. No noseleaves (Fig. VIII.1)

   . . . Vespertilionidae

   Face with noseleaves

   . . . 4

4. Face with a deep central slit (Fig. IX.1)

   . . . Nycteridae

   Face without a deep central slit, but with noseleaves

   . . . 5

5. Posterior noseleaf subtriangular with an erect point (Fig. X.1); toes with three phalanges

   . . . Rhinolophidae

   Posterior noseleaf elliptical (Fig. XI.1); toes with two phalanges

   . . . Hipposideridae

# VI. Family EMBALLONURIDAE

## Sheath-tailed bats

The name of this Family is derived from the Greek *emballo* to throw and *oura* a tail, referring to the tail structure of all its members which resembles a spear thrown into the ground at an angle. This characteristic feature of the tail marks members of the Family from all other bats (Fig. VI.1)

Representatives of this Family are found in the New World, in Africa, Madagascar, the Middle East through to India, Malaya and Australia and, within these regions, are confined almost entirely to the tropics. It is represented in the Subregion by two genera and three species. Their heads are dog-like and are unadorned by noseleaves (Fig. VI.2), the ears rounded at the tips and roughly triangular with a distinct tragus which differs in shape between the two genera *Coleura* and *Taphozous* and between the two species of the latter (Fig. 48.1).

The wings are long and narrow. At rest the first phalanx of the third digit folds upwards, the second phalanx downward upon it, thereby making the long wing more manageable when crawling around. In *Taphozous mauritianus* there is a small flap of skin near the distal joint of the forearm and stretched between the forearm and the metacarpal of the fifth digit called the radio-metacarpal pouch (Fig. VI.3). The function of this is unknown. The interfemoral membrane, which partially encloses the tail, is supported at the sides of its posterior edge by two spurs (calcanea) arising from the ankles on either side (Fig. VI.1.a).

The fur of emballonurid bats is short and soft and does not spread much beyond the body, either on to the wing or interfemoral membranes.

Pel's pouched bat, *Taphozous peli*, which occurs in Zaire and West Africa, which has a forearm of up to 95 mm and a wingspan of about 0,7 m, is the largest insectivorous bat found in Africa.

The skulls of all members of this Family have a unique feature in the well developed postorbital process which is long and slender and curves outward and downward around the eye sockets. The frontal arc is concave, forming in *Taphozous* a deep saucer-shaped depression, which shows in life. The palate is incomplete showing a deep U-shaped emargination between the upper incisor teeth and ends posteriorly at the level of the base of the canines (Fig. 49.1).

The lower jaw may have two or three incisors on either side, the dental formula being

$I\frac{1}{3}\ C\frac{1}{1}\ P\frac{2}{2}\ M\frac{3}{3} = 32$ or

$I\frac{1}{2}\ C\frac{1}{1}\ P\frac{2}{2}\ M\frac{3}{3} = 30$

The upper incisors are minute, the lower trilobed. The anterior upper premolar is very small, the posterior much larger. In *Coleura* the posterior upper molar has the normal N pattern, in *Taphozous* a V pattern.

Some emballonurids have the power of echolocation but their eyes are strikingly large and vision probably plays an important role in their movements.

Key to the genera (Measurements in mm)

1. Smaller, forearm less than 55; two upper and six lower incisor teeth

   . . . *Coleura*

   Larger, forearm over 57; two upper incisors which may be minute or absent, four lower incisor teeth

   . . . *Taphozous*

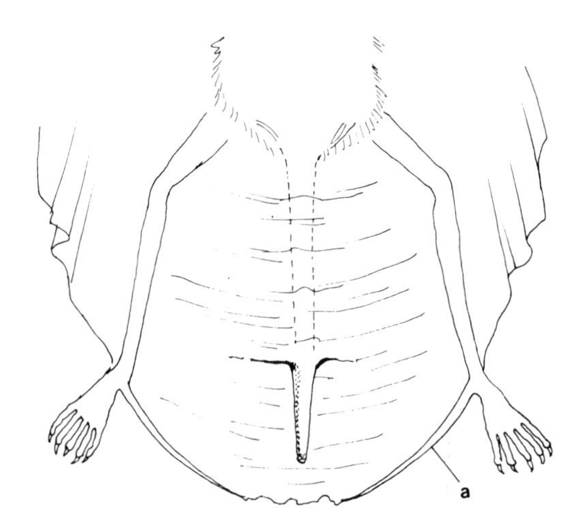


Fig. VI.1. Tail of the Emballonuridae: *Taphozous* sp showing calcaneum (a).

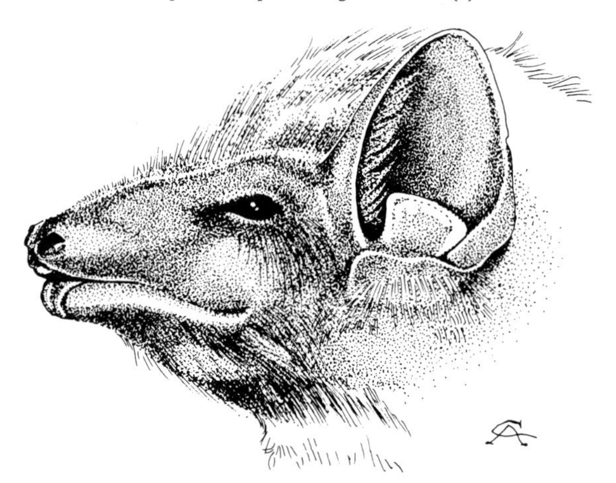

Fig. VI.2. Head of *Taphozous mauritianus*.

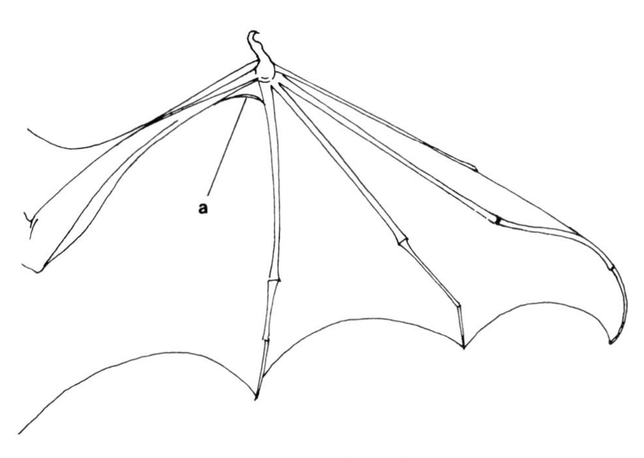


Fig. VI.3. Emballonuridae: *Taphozous mauritianus* wing showing radio-metacarpal pouch (a).

## Genus *Coleura* Peters, 1867

No. 48

## *Coleura afra* (Peters, 1852)

## Sheath-tailed bat
## Skedestertvlermuis

### Colloquial Name

The name refers to the peculiar situation of the tail which is enclosed in part by the interfemoral membrane between the back legs, a feature common to all the three species of Emballonuridae that occur in the Subregion.

### Taxonomic Notes

Hayman & Hill (1971) stated that it is doubtful if any subspecies can be recognised.

### Description

The sheath-tailed bat is the smallest of the three species of Emballonuridae that occur in the Subregion, never exceeding about 70 mm in total length, with a wingspan of some 220 mm.

They are brown in colour, the under parts slightly lighter than the upper parts, the wing membranes a translucent light brown. The ears are moderately large, their margins extending forward along the side of the head above and below the eye, the lower lobe nearly reaching the corner of the mouth. The ear tragus is characteristic in shape (Fig. 48.1)

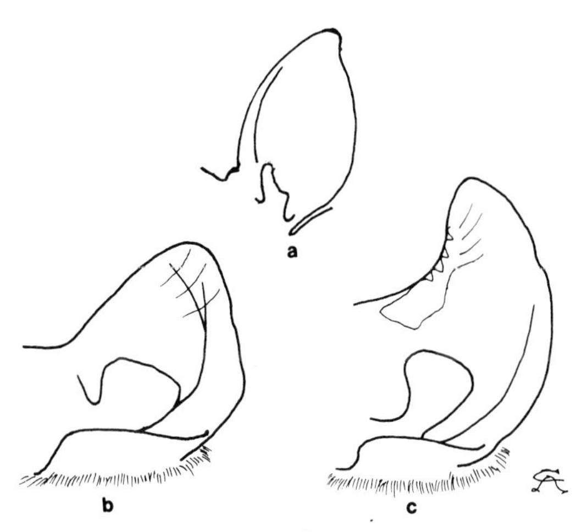


Fig. 48.1. Ears and tragus: (a) *Coleura afra* (b) *Taphozous mauritianus* (c) *T. perforatus*.

They have three incisor teeth on either side of the lower jaw which distinguishes them from *Taphozous* which has only two. In the skull the tiny anterior upper premolar teeth are situated in the tooth row separating the canines from the next premolar.

### Distribution

The sheath-tailed bat, *C. afra*, the original specimen having come from Tete on the Zambezi River, was long considered to have an eastern distribution on the continent, the great majority of specimens coming from localities in East Africa. Subsequently it has been recorded from Guinea in West Africa and from Benguela in Angola. The species remains very poorly represented in collections, however, and it is not possible to draw up an overall distribution map.

Outside the continent they have been known to occur on the Seychelles Islands in the Indian Ocean from where Peters described *C. seychellensis* in 1869, which is considered now to be doubtfully separable from the continental species, even as a subspecies (Hayman & Hill, 1971).

*South of the Sahara, excluding the Southern African Subregion*

They occur in **Guinea; Ghana; Central African Republic;** in the northern and eastern parts of **Zaire**, in the southeastern **Sudan**, and in **Ethiopia** and **Somalia**, excluding the desert areas. Recorded from **Uganda, Kenya** and northern **Tanzania**, with a record from Benguela on the western coast of **Angola**.

*Southern African Subregion*

Originally they were taken from Tete, which lies on the northern bank of the Zambezi River in **Mozambique**, but no doubt they occur south of the river. This remains the only part of the Subregion from which the species is known.

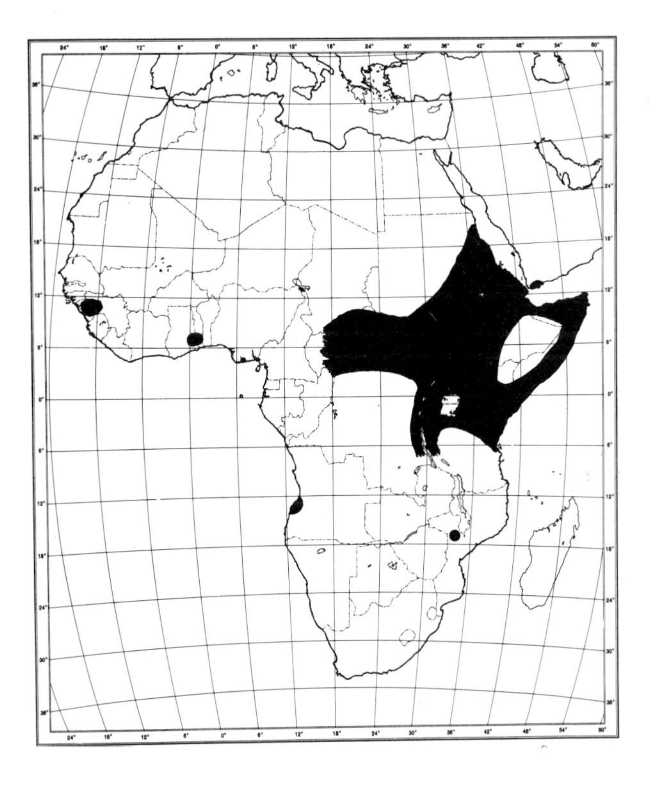

### Habitat

Nothing is known about the habitat requirements of the species in the Subregion and we have to rely on information from other parts of their distributional range. Rosevear (1965) stated that in West Africa they occur in woodland, but only where there are acceptable roosting places in the shape of caverns or disused dark rooms in which to shelter during daylight hours.

Peters (1852) took his specimens from a dark cellar in Tete, Mozambique, and Rosevear (1965) quoted Anderson (1902) who found hundreds in the cellars of Government House in Suakin in the Sudan. In Guinea they originated from a cave and Monard (1939) took specimens from a native hut. Kingdon (1974) in Kenya recorded that they roosted in caves on the sea and lake shores, in rocky outcrops and in houses. Allen & Loveridge (1933) collected specimens from a cave in East Africa where they were hanging from the ceiling, well separated from one another.

### Habits

Sheath-tailed bats are gregarious, occurring in colonies numbering hundreds. At Tete, Peters (1852) recorded that of 100 specimens he handled, he took only 20 females, which indicates that the colony probably numbered in hundreds. Kingdon (1974) recorded colonies numbering thousands of individuals in Kenya, and stated that in using caves, they hang predominantly on the walls, rarely from the roof, the adults well-spaced out and the young in clusters. They tend to use the lighter parts of caves near the entrance and remain segregated from other species using the same shelter.

### Food

Insectivorous.

### Reproduction

The information that is available from eastern Africa may well not apply in the southern parts of their range. In Tanzania it appears that the young are born during the dry spell between the short and long rains and in the Sudan at the end of the rains about October (Kingdon, 1974). One young is produced at birth and is carried by the mother during the early part of its life.

## Genus *Taphozous* E. Geoffroy, 1818

Key to the species (Measurements in mm)

1. Fur on upper parts grizzled greyish, the tips of the hair whitish, under parts pure white; total length of the skull over 21,5, forearm 58–64; gular sac in males ... *mauritianus*

   Fur on upper parts unicolour dark brown, the under parts not pure white; total length of the skull less than 21,5, forearm 60–67; no gular sac in males ... *perforatus*

---

No. 49

## *Taphozous mauritianus* E. Geoffroy, 1818

## Tomb bat
## Witlyfvlermuis

Plate 5

---

### Colloquial Name

The name tomb bat or Mauritian tomb bat, as they are so often called, probably originates from the generic name *Taphozous*, which is derived from the Greek *taphos*, a grave and *zoos*, living.

The specimen from which the species was described came from the Island of Mauritius and the appellation tomb bat is unfortunate, as they are by no means associated with tombs, although, as will be seen under **Habits**, they will use buildings on which to roost. The Afrikaans name is singularly appropriate, referring as it does to their pure white under parts.

### Taxonomic Notes

While numbers of subspecies have been described, Koopman (1975) believed that they are of doubtful value.

### Description

Tomb bats have a total length of about 110 mm and a mean mass of about 28 g, the largest specimens with a mass of up to about 36 g (Table 49.1). The fur on the upper parts looks grey, the individual hairs pale brown at the base, greyish-brown in the middle, with white tips, which gives them a grizzled, greyish appearance. The under parts are pure white, the wing membranes parchment white. The ears are short, broad and rounded at the tips, and unlike the closely allied Egyptian tomb bat, *T. perforatus*, have no papillae on their inner edges (Fig. VI.2). The eyes are larger than in other bats of similar size. The males have a deep glandular sac on the throat which in the female is reduced to a small fold in the skin (Rosevear, 1965).

The skull sometimes has a slight trace of a sagittal crest. The anterior emargination of the palate is a broad U (Fig. 49.1), in *T. perforatus* it is narrow and more V-shaped (Rosevear, 1965).

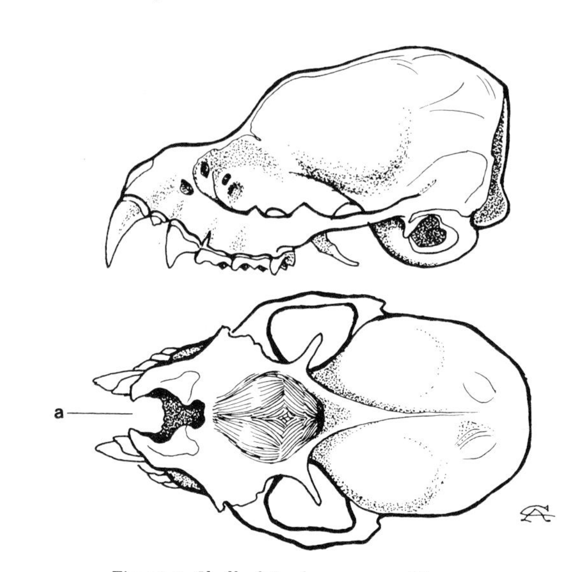


Fig. 49.1. Skull of *Taphozous mauritianus*: (a) palatal emargination; (b) postorbital process.

**Table 49.1**

Measurements (mm) and mass (g) of tomb bats, *T. mauritianus*, from Zimbabwe (Smithers & Wilson, 1979)

| | Males | | | Females | | |
|---|---|---|---|---|---|---|
| | $\bar{x}$ | n | Range | $\bar{x}$ | n | Range |
| TL | 105 | 13 | 101–109 | 108 | 8 | 100–112 |
| T | 23 | 13 | 21–27 | 25 | 8 | 22–27 |
| Hf c/u | 14 | 13 | 12–19 | 16 | 8 | 14–19 |
| E | 17 | 13 | 14–20 | 18 | 8 | 17–20 |
| F/a | 62 | 10 | 60–64 | 62 | 7 | 61–63 |
| Mass | 27,1 | 11 | 20,0–36,1 | 28,5 | 7 | 27,5–31,6 |

### Distribution

The species has a very wide distribution in Africa, but there are few records from the Subregion, where they may occur deeper into the South West Arid Zone than present information indicates. Their absence in the drier parts of Botswana, where they have not been taken in spite of diligent search, suggests, however, that they are associated with better watered terrain in this part of their distributional range. They also occur on islands in the Indian Ocean such as Madagascar, Mauritius, Reunion, Assumption and Aldabra (Hayman & Hill, 1971).

*South of the Sahara, excluding the Southern African Subregion*

Hayman & Hill (1971) recorded the species from **Senegal** eastwards to the southern **Sudan** and **Somalia** and there is a record from northeastern **Ethiopia**. Southwards they have been recorded in all the countries to the borders of the Subregion, although there are only scattered records from many of them. Although there are no records from eastern Zambia, Ansell (1978) believed that they must occur throughout. They are not represented from Malawi or

Mozambique, north of the Zambezi River, but probably they will be found to occur there in time.

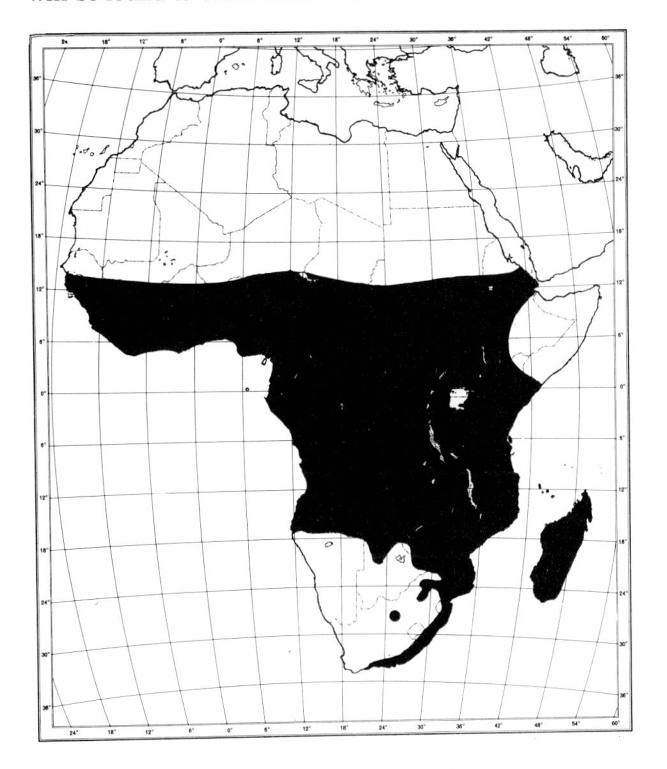

*Southern African Subregion*

Their occurrence in adjacent parts of Angola and Botswana suggests that eventually they will be taken at least in the northern parts of Namibia from whence at the moment there are no records. In **Botswana** they occur in the Okavango Delta, on the Chobe River and in the Tati Concession in the northeast. They occur widely throughout **Zimbabwe** except in parts of the dry western areas, in central and southern **Mozambique**, central and eastern **Transvaal, Natal** and narrowly along the south coast of the **Cape Province** to about Mossel Bay, with an isolated record from Hartswater in the northern parts of the province which suggests a wider distribution in this sector than is at present known (Erasmus & Rautenbach, 1984).

**Habitat**

Tomb bats are associated predominantly with open savanna woodland, but they are found in parts of Mozambique and eastern Zimbabwe on the fringes of and in clearings in forests. Present records suggest that in the Subregion they cannot utilise the drier western areas where the food supplies are less plentiful than in the east with its higher rainfall. In West Africa, however, Rosevear (1953) showed that in Nigeria they are found in parts of the Sahel Zone which has a mean annual rainfall of some 500 mm which is lower than in some parts of our arid western areas. Other factors therefore must be playing a part in their exclusion from our drier areas, or it may be that they have simply not been traced.

**Habits**

Tomb bats are usually found in pairs, or two or more pairs may be found occupying a convenient roosting place, but when they do, the close association of the pair is very obvious. They roost during the day clinging by their feet to the vertical surfaces of tree trunks, rock faces or the external walls of buildings where there is some overhead shelter from the sun and rain. In the Subregion they are found hanging on the walls under the eaves of houses and on tree trunks where an overhanging branch gives shade, and on rock faces. Where the walls of houses, which have been white-washed or painted are used, their preferred hanging places are marked by a characteristic brown urine staining over a rectangular area some 150 mm long and 100 mm wide.

They hang from their two feet, belly against the vertical surface and if disturbed move quickly sideways, crab-like to take cover around the corner or deeper up under the eaves, or if they fly off, will alight on the trunk of a nearby tree and clamber around it out of sight. When roosting they remain on the alert and often will disappear before they are seen, the tell-tale urine stain remaining to mark their presence. At Robin's Camp in Hwange National Park, Zimbabwe, where there was a wide choice of different types of building, they preferred rondavels with thatched roofs where the beams jutted out through the walls behind which they took refuge. They soon become used to disturbance and, apart from turning their heads to view observers, take no avoidance action.

They are sharp and alert in their movements and fast fliers. In the roosting position the ends of their long narrow wings fold upwards, lying on the outside of the remainder of the wing, so reducing its length for convenience of movement. Their eyes are large and their eyesight good. While they have powers of echolocation, it is not known how the two senses complement each other, but the fact that they roost in full daylight suggests that eyesight plays a large part in location of the roosting place and in their look-out for danger. In subdued lights, echolocation is brought into play.

Aggression is accompanied by screeching and at rest, when relaxed, they chirrup. In flight when making quick turns, the wings produce a whirring sound. Usually tomb bats move to forage after dark, but they have been seen taking off and catching butterflies passing their roosting places during the day (D. Rushworth, pers. comm.). They drop from the roosting place before swooping off on their swift flight. Fenton, Bell & Thomas (1980) showed that the bats use multiharmonic constant frequency echolocation search calls, followed by multiharmonic approach and terminal calls as they near the target. These calls combine shallow and steep frequency modulated sweeps as the target is approached. A component of these calls makes the call audible to the human ear. The combination of characters, particularly the constant frequency search calls, distinguishes them from the calls of other insectivorous bats. They found that this species is capable of detecting its prey at distances of up to three metres.

**Food**

Insectivorous

**Reproduction**

Very little information is available from the Subregion except that females carrying a single foetus were taken in February, and females carrying a single young in October in Zimbabwe. Ansell (1960a) collected a juvenile in February. One at birth is probably the general rule and it is certainly to the advantage of an insectivorous species to have their young during the warm, wet summer months from about October to March.

---

No. 50

## *Taphozous perforatus* E. Geoffroy, 1818

## Egyptian tomb bat
## Egiptiese witlyfvlermuis

---

**Colloquial Name**

The specimen from which this species was described was taken by Geoffroy from a Royal tomb in Egypt. We now know that, far from being specially associated with this country, they have a wide distribution beyond its borders. The derivation of the generic name is given under *T. mauritianus*, the specific name *perforatus* referring to the peculiar situation of the tail which seems to perforate the interfemoral membrane, a feature common to all members of the Family Emballonuridae (Fig. VI.1).

**Taxonomic Notes**

Hayman & Hill (1971) did not recognise any of the subspecies that have been described. Harrison (1961) considered *T. sudani* a distinct sibling species which occurs alongside *T. perforatus*, but Rosevear (1965) did not consider that it warranted this treatment. Meester *et al.* (1986) included all material from the Subregion in *T. p. sudani* Thomas, 1915.

**Description**

Egyptian tomb bats are almost identical in size with the tomb bat, *T. mauritianus* (Table 50.1), but in the Subregion they are dark brown in colour and lack the grizzling on the upper parts seen in *T. mauritianus*. In the northern parts of their distributional range they are a paler, ashy-brown (Rosevear, 1965). In the Subregion the outer two-thirds of the wing membranes are white, the inner third blackish, the tips dusky, and there is no sign either in the males or females of the glandular sac on the throat found in the tomb bat. The under parts are lighter in colour than the upper parts, the throat and neck brown, the remainder light brown washed with ashy-grey, with some white hair on the lower belly. There is a band of ashy-grey hair on the inner parts of the wing membranes.

The anterior emargination of the palate is narrower than in *T. mauritianus* and is more V-shaped. The ears are more pointed than in *T. mauritianus* and have a series of minute papillae on their inner edges which are lacking in *T. mauritianus*, the tragus not so broad at its apex (Fig. 48.1.c).

**Table 50.1**

Measurements (mm) and mass (g) of a series of eight female Egyptian tomb bats, *T. perforatus*, taken in Zimbabwe (Smithers & Wilson, 1979)

| | Females | | |
|---|---|---|---|
| | $\bar{x}$ | n | Range |
| TL | 103 | 8 | 95–108 |
| T | 26 | 8 | 22–30 |
| Hf c/u | 14 | 8 | 13–15 |
| E | 18 | 8 | 15–20 |
| F/a | 63 | 8 | 62–63 |
| Mass | 30,2 | 6 | 23,4–33,2 |

**Distribution**

Outside the continent the Egyptian tomb bat occurs along the west coast of **Arabia** and eastwards to northeastern **India**. Except in the northeast of the continent there are only scattered records of the occurrence of this species and there is a lack of information from countries immediately north of the limits of the Subregion.

*Northeastern Africa*

They occur throughout the valley of the Nile in **Egypt** from the Sudan border to the coasts of the Mediterranean Sea.

*South of the Sahara excluding the Southern African Subregion*

They occur from **Senegal** in West Africa eastwards to **Ethiopia** and **Somalia** and southwards to **Cameroun**; in the northern, eastern and southeastern parts of **Zaire**, in **Uganda, Kenya** and central and northern **Tanzania** and in parts of northern **Zambia**. At the moment there are no records of the species between northern Zambia and the two apparently isolated populations in the Subregion.

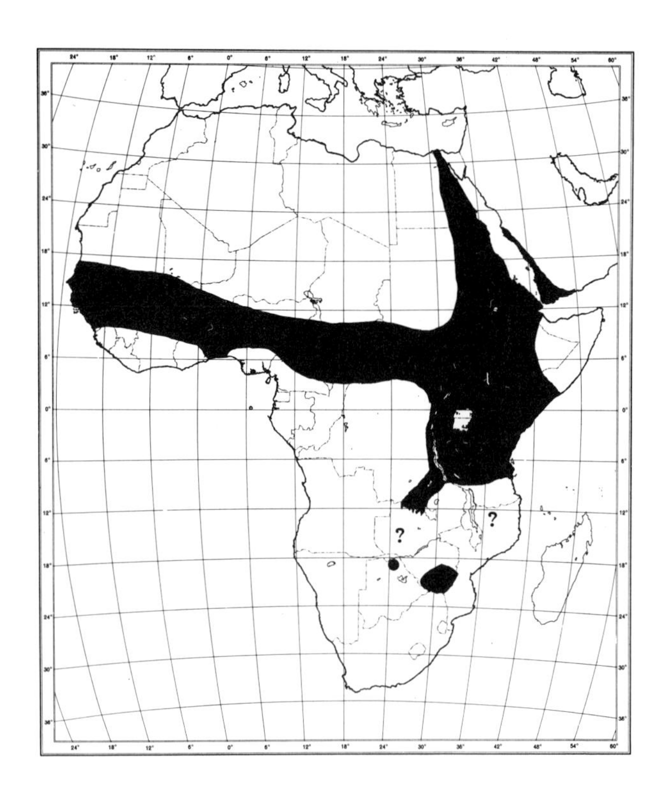

*Southern African Subregion*

They occur in northern **Botswana**, in the Okavango Delta and, in the east of the country, at the Shashi/Limpopo confluence area and in the southern parts of **Zimbabwe**.

**Habitat**

The Egyptian tomb bat is associated throughout its range with open woodland, avoiding forest, semi-desert and desert areas. As they require the shelter of rocks or stone buildings in which to roost during the day, they only occur where these are available. Specimens taken at the Shashi/Limpopo confluence were collected near a range of sandstone hills with an open association of *Acacia* woodland, on the flat country adjacent to the dry river bed. The well-developed riverine woodland included many large trees such as wild figs, *Ficus* sp, with a dense undergrowth of climbers and thickets.

**Habits**

Although, like their close relatives the tomb bats, *T. mauritianus*, Egyptian tomb bats use rocky outcrops and stone or brick buildings to shelter in during the day, their use of these differs markedly. While the tomb bat hangs from the ceiling or walls or against rock faces, where there is overhead cover, the Egyptian tomb bat crawls to more substantial shelter into rock crevices, the gaps in stonework or the dark corners of caves where they are totally hidden. Although Rosevear (1965) recorded that in West Africa they occur in hundreds, in the Subregion they are seldom found in colonies of more than six or eight together, bunched tightly in their secure retreats.

**Food**

Insectivorous.

**Reproduction**

The only evidence of the time the young are born are two gravid females taken in November in southeastern Zimbabwe. Each carried a single foetus, implanted in the right uterine horn.

# VII. Family MOLOSSIDAE

## Free-tailed bats

The name of the Family is derived from the Greek *molossus*, a kind of dog used by Greek shepherds in ancient times. The head of molossids is reminiscent of a bull-dog, the face being heavily wrinkled and often they are referred to as mastiff bats or bull-dog bats (Fig. VII.1). They can best be recognised, however, by the stout tail, one third to one half of which is enclosed in the interfemoral membrane, the remainder projecting beyond its posterior margin. The tail is, therefore, not entirely free as the colloquial name suggests, but it is certainly more obviously so than in any other Family of bats (Fig. VII.2).

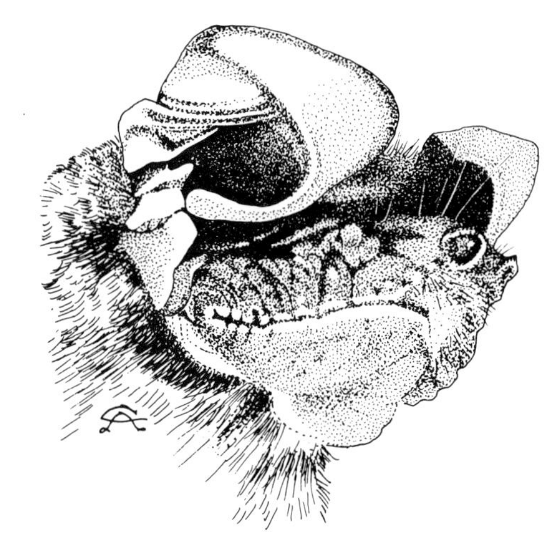

Fig. VII.1. Head of a Molossidae: *Tadarida bivittata*

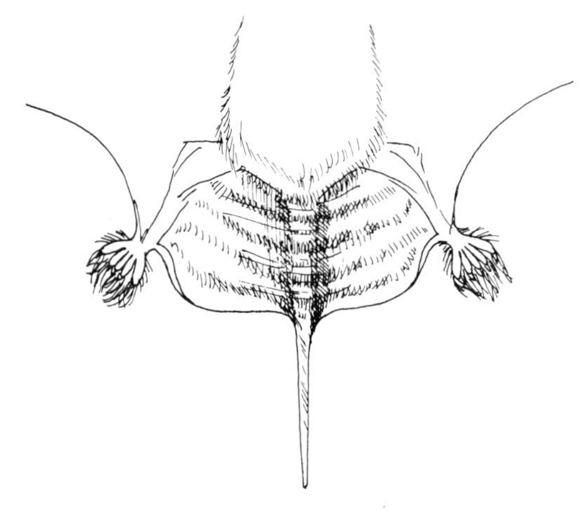

Fig. VII.2. Tail of a Molossidae.

The jowl is heavy with thick lips which are deeply wrinkled, the nostrils carried on smooth prominences. The upper lips have a series of stiff bristles, some circular in section, others of spatulate shape with flattened and slightly curved ends (Rosevear, 1965). The ears are characteristic of the Family, in some species exceptionally large and about as broad as they are high with rounded tips. They have a series of creases on their inner sides, their outer margins with a subrectangular antitragus at their bases. The tragus is small and varies in shape within the species. The inner margins of the ears are often connected together across the top of the head by a broad band of skin and in some there is a crest of long hair on the posterior face of this band or on the top of the head immediately behind it, which is erectile at will.

The wings are long, narrow and pointed, the second finger with a single bony phalanx. The wing membranes in some species are whitish or transparent and in some species there is a band of long hair on the under side of the wing extending from the upper arm to the thigh. The interfemoral membrane has a sparse covering of bristly hairs on its under side and is supported on either side by calcanea arising from the ankles. The two outer toes on the feet are stouter than the three middle ones and are fringed on their outer sides with white bristly hair and, towards the end of these digits, with a brush of long white hair curved towards the tips.

The fur of the molossids is short and lies closely adpressed to the body; the general colour is very dark brown or reddish-brown. Most of them show a sparsely haired yoke across the top of the neck, just in front of the shoulders, which looks pale and contrasts with the general colour of the remainder of the upper parts.

In the Subregion there is a considerable size range from the little free-tailed bat, *T. pumila*, with a wingspan of about 180 mm to the Midas free-tailed bat, *T. midas*, of about 450 mm.

There are no outstanding characters in the skull. The braincase is broad and rather flat, the palate emarginated deeply between the upper incisors in some species, shallowly in others, features that are useful in identification of the subgenera (Fig. VII.3). More valuable, however, is the degree of development of the crowns of the posterior molars which is different in the three subgenera (see key to subgenera) (Fig. VII.4).

The dental formula varies from:

$I\frac{1}{2}\ C\frac{1}{1}\ P\frac{2}{2}\ M\frac{3}{3} = 30$, to

$I\frac{1}{1}\ C\frac{1}{1}\ P\frac{2}{2}\ M\frac{3}{3} = 28$, to

$I\frac{1}{1}\ C\frac{1}{1}\ P\frac{1}{2}\ M\frac{3}{3} = 26$

Molossids are gregarious, sometimes occurring in roosts in huge numbers. They are adept crawlers and climbers and are able to progress forwards, backwards or sideways with equal ease and quite quickly. Laid on the ground they normally do not attempt to fly off like other bats but scurry to the nearest sheltered corner.

Representatives of this Family are found both in the Old and New Worlds. They occur widely in Africa and on Madagascar; in parts of southern Europe; the Middle East; India; southern and eastern Asia to Australia.

The Family is comprised of four genera, *Otomops, Sauromys, Mormopterus* and *Tadarida*. *Tadarida* is divided into three subgenera: *Mops, Chaerephon and Tadarida; Mops* is represented in the Subregion by two species, *Chaerephon* by five, *Tadarida* by four; a total of 14 species occurring. They all have faces like mastiff dogs and tails in which one third

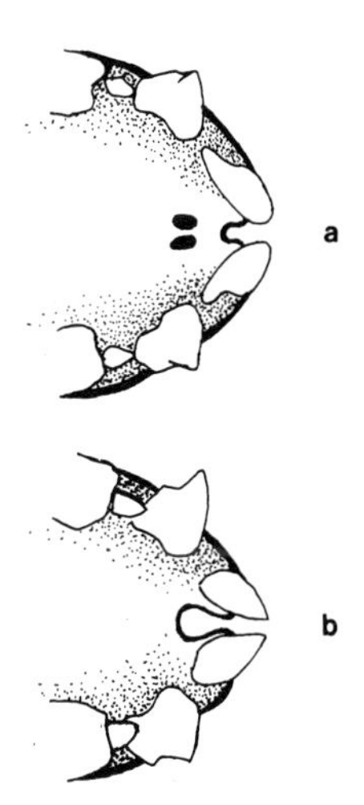


Fig. VII.3. Molossidae: anterior palatal emargination
(a) *Tadarida (Chaerephon)* sp (b) *Tadarida (Mops)* sp.

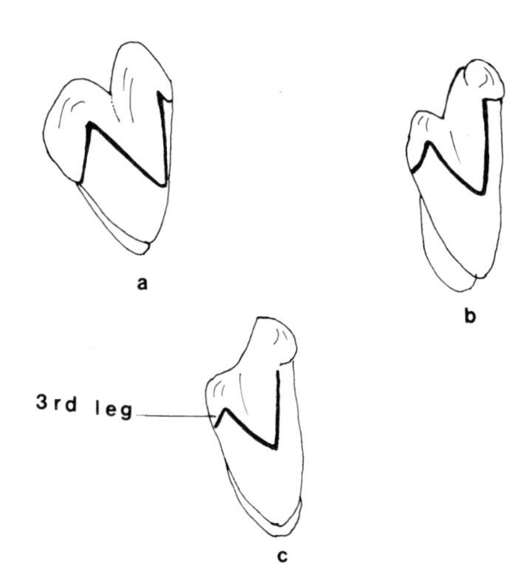


Fig. VII.4. *Tadarida*: posterior upper molars, showing subgeneric modification of W pattern (a) *T. (Tadarida) aegyptiaca* (b) *T. (Chaerephon) major* (c) *T. (Mops) leonis* (Rosevear, 1965).

to a half is enclosed in the interfemoral membrane, the remainder projecting free beyond its posterior margin.

Key to the genera after Meester *et al.* (1986)
(Measurements in mm)

1. Prominent vertical projection on zygoma; size very large, forearm 62–73 mm; ears very large, 38–40 mm, conjoined on extended snout; conspicuous bicoloured dorsal pelage pattern with pale collar separating dark anterior and posterior regions of body
 ... *Otomops*

 Not combining the above characters
 ... 2

2. Skull conspicuously flattened, greatest depth of braincase not more than one-third of greatest width; 5 upper cheekteeth ($P^1$ well developed); ears separate, not widely spaced; forearm 36–42
 ... *Sauromys*

 Skull not conspicuously flattened; 4–5 upper cheekteeth; ears separate or conjoined; forearm 30–66 mm
 ... 3

3. Only one upper premolar; three pairs of lower incisors; large palatal emargination; ears separate; size small, forearm *c.* 38 mm, condylobasal length less than 15 mm
 ... *Mormopterus*

 Almost always two upper premolars; not more than two pairs of lower incisors; condylobasal length generally more than 15 mm
 ... *Tadarida*

## Genus *Otomops* Thomas, 1913

No. 51

## *Otomops martiensseni* (Matschie, 1897)

## Large-eared free-tailed bat
## Bakoor-losstertvlermuis

### Colloquial Name
So named from their possessing outstandingly large round-pointed ears which are attached at their bases along the side of the head and lie in the plane of the face.

### Taxonomic Notes
Hayman & Hill (1971) listed three subspecies, *O. m. martiensseni* of East Africa and Zimbabwe; *O. m. icarus* Chubb, 1917 of Natal and central Angola and *O. m. madagascarensis* Dorst, 1953 of Madagascar.

### Description
A medium sized species about 140 mm in total length with a mass of some 30 g (Table 51.1). The upper parts are blackish-brown with a paler band across the top of the shoulders. The back of the head and lower back is a shade darker than the remainder of the upper parts, the individual hairs with whitish bases. The under parts are similar in colour to the upper parts. The dark fur on the upper parts is bordered along its outer edge by a sharply defined white band of fur from the shoulder to the knee. The ears have small spines along their anterior borders.

The ear tragus and antitragus are absent but they have a semi-circular flap of skin extending from the base of the ear which, when depressed, can seal off the wide ear opening (Fig. 51.1). The skull has a helmet at the back of the dorsal surface, the top of the braincase domed. The anterior upper premolars are missing, the canines and remaining premolars well separated.

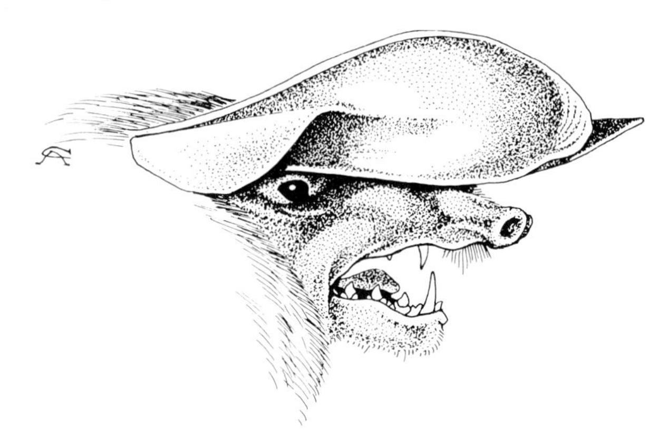

Fig. 51.1. Head of *Otomops martiensseni*

**Table 51.1**
Measurements (mm) and mass (g) of large-eared free-tailed bats, *Otomops martiensseni*, from Durban, Natal (ex formalin)

| | Males | | | Females | | |
|---|---|---|---|---|---|---|
| | x̄ | n | Range | x̄ | n | Range |
| HB | 84 | 4 | 78–93 | 98 | 6 | 94–103 |
| T | 36 | 4 | 35–37 | 37 | 6 | 33–42 |
| F/a | 55 | 4 | 52–58 | 63 | 6 | 62–64 |
| Mass | 29,1 | 4 | 22,2–37,2 | 31,9 | 6 | 30,1–33,4 |

### Distribution
*Extralimital to the continent*
The species occurs on **Madagascar**.

*South of the Sahara, excluding the Southern African Subregion*
Recorded from eastern **Zaire; Rwanda**; the **Central African Republic**; southwestern **Uganda**; **Ethiopia**; southern and southeastern **Kenya**; northeastern **Tanzania**; central **Angola** and **Malawi**.

*Southern African Subregion*
Recorded from the eastern end of Lake Kariba and the Sengwa Research Station, **Zimbabwe**; and from Durban and Westville, **Natal**.

### Habitat
Kingdon (1974) recorded the habitat of this species in East Africa as ranging from semi-arid areas to montane forest and from sea level to an altitude of 2 000 m. Nothing is on record as far as the Subregion is concerned as, so far, only a few specimens have been taken, 11 of them from Durban, Natal, and one from Lake Kariba, Zimbabwe, where it was netted.

### Habits
A gregarious species in East Africa where colonies numbering in hundreds have been recorded from lava tunnels on

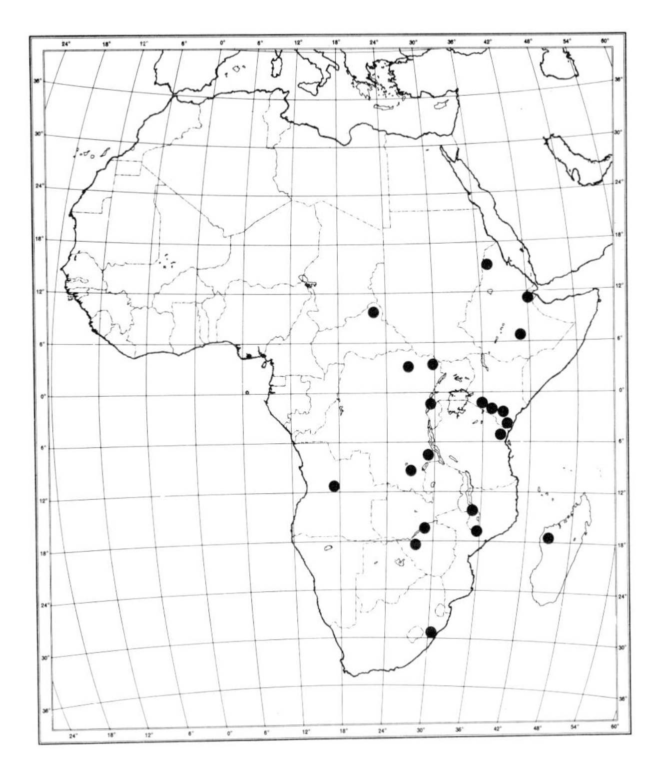

Mount Suswa, Kenya. They roost packed closely together and are fast, straight fliers (Kingdon, 1974). The first specimen, from Durban, was picked up dead from a gutter, the others taken from the loft of a dwelling house in the same city.

### Food

Insectivorous.

### Reproduction

No data available.

## Genus *Sauromys* Roberts, 1917

No. 52

## *Sauromys petrophilus* (Roberts, 1917)

## Flat-headed free-tailed bat
## Platkop-losstertvlermuis

### Colloquial Name

The skull of this species is distinctly flattened, an adaptation to its roosting in very narrow rock crevices.

### Taxonomic Notes

Originally described by Roberts (1917) as *Platymops petrophilus*, a genus with representatives in the Sudan, Ethiopia and other parts of East Africa. Peterson (1965) in reviewing the Family Molossidae restricted the distribution of the genus *Platymops* to East Africa, and included material from the Subregion in the genus *Sauromys*. *Sauromys* differs from *Platymops* in the absence, among other features, of wart-like granulations on the forearm, the absence of a gular sac and in having a well developed anterior upper premolar, which is reduced or absent in *Platymops*. Meester *et al.* (1986) listed five subspecies from the Subregion: *S. p. petrophilus* (Roberts, 1917) from the Transvaal, southeastern Botswana, southern Zimbabwe and the Tete District, Mozambique; *S. p. haagneri* (Roberts, 1917) from Namibia; *S. p. umbratus* from the western Cape Province; *S. p. erongensis* (Roberts, 1946) from Namibia, which is probably a synonym of *S. p. haagneri* and *S. p. fitzsimonsi* (Roberts, 1946) from the southwestern Cape Province, possibly a synonym of *S. p. umbratus*.

### Description

Flat-headed free-tailed bats have a total length of about 110 mm and masses from about 13 g to 15 g (Table 52.1). The colour of the upper parts varies depending on the area from which they originate, those from the Transvaal being a tawny-olive, from Namibia brownish-grey and from the southwestern Cape Province a dark seal brown. Specimens from the Tete District, Mozambique, are darker in colour than any from further south and are dark brown, more like those from the Cape Province.

The Namibian specimens are greyish-white on the under parts, those from the Transvaal slightly lighter in colour, and those from the Cape Province whitish. In the Mozambique specimens the under parts are the same colour as the upper parts with a faint grey wash. Even in series from the same locality there is some variation in the colour, some darker, some lighter. This variation in the colour has led to the description of five subspecies. The characteristic feature of the species shows in the skull which unlike other Molossids is distinctly flattened. They have five upper cheekteeth, the anterior upper premolar well developed.

**Table 52.1**

Measurements (mm) and mass (g) of flat-headed free-tailed bats, *S. petrophilus*, from the Transvaal (Rautenbach, 1982)

| | Males | | | Females | | |
|---|---|---|---|---|---|---|
| | $\bar{x}$ | n | Range | $\bar{x}$ | n | Range |
| TL | 110 | 9 | 103–127 | 114 | 7 | 100–131 |
| T | 38 | 9 | 30–49 | 37 | 7 | 29–45 |
| Hf c/u | 9 | 9 | 6–13 | 9 | 7 | 8–10 |
| E | 17 | 9 | 15–22 | 18 | 7 | 15–22 |
| F/a | 43 | 8 | 38–48 | 44 | 7 | 41–50 |
| Mass | 12,8 | 9 | 9,0–16,0 | 15,0 | 6 | 13,0–22,0 |

### Distribution

The only record outside the borders of the Subregion at the moment is a specimen from Chiutu, Tete District, **Mozambique**, which lies just north of the Zambezi River.

*Southern African Subregion*

Recorded from Ombu farm, Omaruru district, the Brandberg and the Namib Desert Park, **Namibia**; Molepolole, southeastern **Botswana**; seven localities in **Zimbabwe** south of the central plateau; in the northern **Transvaal** and in the Pretoria area; and in the **Cape Province** from Goodhouse and the Augrabies Falls on the Orange River, Clanwilliam and Ceres.

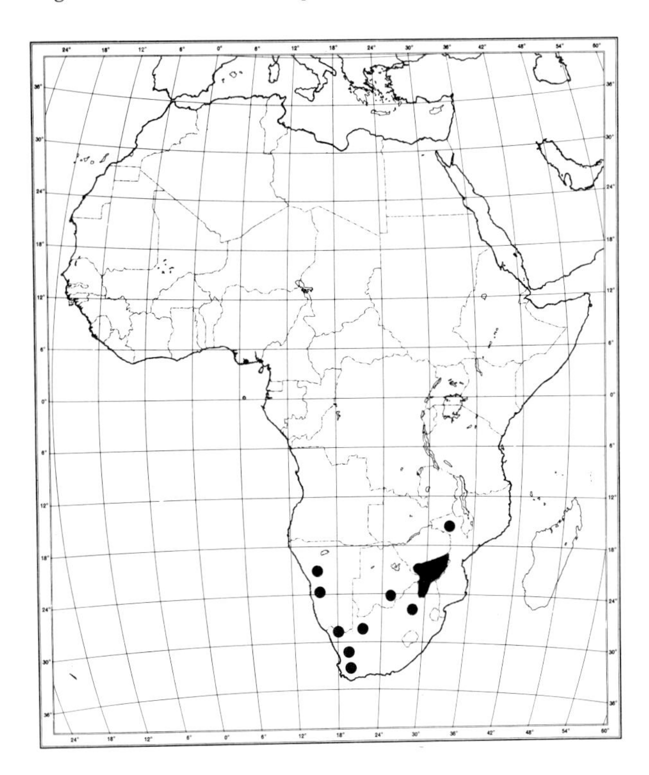

### Habitat

All the specimens known from the Subregion were taken in rocky areas and, apart from a plentiful food supply, the availability of narrow rock fissures and crevices to roost in during the day appears to be among their essential habitat requirements.

### Habits

They generally occur in small numbers, most records being of up to four, but Rautenbach (1982) recorded a colony in the Transvaal that may have numbered over this figure. They roost during the day under slabs of exfoliated rock or in narrow rock crevices or fissures. If disturbed they tend to scramble back into the narrowest parts of these shelters, making them impossible to reach. They pack tightly together in the crevices, but scatter when disturbed.

### Food

Insectivorous.

### Reproduction

No information is available from the Subregion.

## Genus *Mormopterus* Peters, 1865

No. 53

## *Mormopterus acetabulosus* (Hermann, 1804)

## Natal free-tailed bat
## Natalse losstertvlermuis

Formerly included in the genus *Tadarida*.

Only two specimens of this species have been taken on the mainland of **Africa**, the first by Andrew Smith in 1833 on the edge of a forest near Durban, Natal, the second by P.C. Zaphiro in 1905 between the district of Shoa and Lake Rudolph in southern **Ethiopia** (Hayman & Hill, 1971). The species occurs on the Indian Ocean islands of **Madagascar, Mauritius** and **Reunion**, and apart from the fact that the two specimens exist to show that it does occur on the mainland, nothing is known of its life history under mainland conditions and no specimens are available for examination.

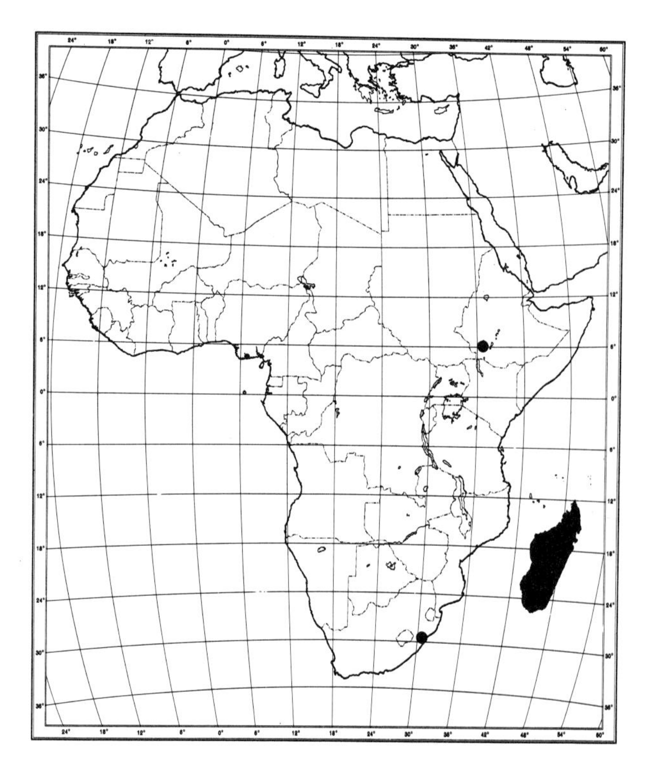

The extralimital *M. a. acetabulosus* originally was described from Port Louis, Mauritius, the Natal specimen being relegated to the subspecies *M. a. natalensis* (A. Smith, 1847).

## Genus *Tadarida* Rafinesque, 1814

Key to the subgenera and species (Meester *et al.*, 1986) (Measurements in mm)

1. Anterior palatal emargination well developed, extending beyond upper incisors, and including area of incisive foramina; third commissure of last upper molar well developed, almost as long as second commissure ... 2

   Anterior palatal emargination greatly reduced, not extending behind upper incisors and separated from incisive foramina by a bony bar ... 7

2. Condylobasal length more than 21 mm ... 3

   Condylobasal length less than 21 mm ... 5

3. Interdental palatal length more than twice palatal width at anterior end; ears very large, united at base close to nostrils, and projecting well beyond muzzle when laid forward; basisphenoid pits shallow; lower canines almost touching at base; forearm 63 mm ... *Tadarida (Tadarida) lobata*

   Interdental palatal length less than twice palatal width at anterior end ... 4

4. Larger, total skull length 23,5–25,7 mm, forearm 63–66 mm. ... *Tadarida (T.) ventralis*

   Smaller, total skull length 22–22,9 mm, forearm 57–62 mm ... *Tadarida (T.) fulminans*

5. Forehead flat; width of anterior palatal emargination more than diameter of upper incisor; forearm 44–53 mm; lower canines widely separated at base ... *Tadarida (T.) aegyptiaca*

   Forehead elevated; width of anterior palatal emargination less than diameter of upper incisor; condylobasal length more than 17 mm ... 6

6. Zygomatic breadth more than 12 mm ... *Tadarida (Chaerephon) bivittata*

   Zygomatic breadth less than 12 mm ... *Tadarida (C.) ansorgei*

7. Third commissure of last upper molar well developed, almost as long as second commissure; basisphenoid pits shallow, separated at most by a low ridge ... 8

   Third commissure of last upper molar reduced, clearly shorter, and usually much shorter, than second commissure ... 10

8. Forehead virtually flat; maxillary toothrow length more than 6,3 mm; interdental palate (measured at anterior end of posterior premolar) approximately twice as long as it is wide ... *Tadarida (C.) nigeriae*

   Forehead distinctly elevated; maxillary toothrow less than 6,3 mm ... 9

9. Interdental palate (measured at anterior end of posterior premolar) approximately twice as long as it is wide; males with long (13–14 mm) bicoloured postaural crest, dark basally, pale apically ... *Tadarida (C.) chapini*

   Interdental palate approximately one-and-half times as long as it is wide; males with short (10 mm or less) unicoloured postaural crest ... *Tadarida (C.) pumila*

10. Condylobasal length more than 23 mm; forearm 58–66 mm

... *Tadarida (Mops) midas*

Condylobasal length less than 21 mm; forearm 45–50 mm; third commissure of last upper molar clearly present and approximately half as long as second commissure

... *Tadarida (M.) condylura*

No. 54

## *Tadarida (Mops) midas* (Sundevall, 1843)

## Midas free-tailed bat
## Midas se losstertvlermuis

### Taxonomic Notes

Hayman & Hill (1971) listed two subspecies, *T. m. miarensis* Grandidier, 1861 from Madagascar and *T. m. midas*, the subspecies that occurs on the mainland of Africa.

### Description

The Midas free-tailed bat is the largest of the molossid bats that occur in the Subregion. Total length is about 140 mm, adult males have a mean mass of 48,5 g, females 44,5 g, and wingspans of up to 450 mm (Table 54.1). Within any one colony the colour is relatively uniform, the upper parts dark brown sparsely flecked with white, the under parts lighter and more tawny; the individual hairs from the chest to the belly are tipped with white, this being more pronounced on the flanks. Characteristically there is a band across the top of the shoulders where the hair is sparse, giving it the appearance of being naked. In other parts of Africa red and orange-red phases are known.

The wing membranes and interfemoral membranes are dark brown, the under side of the wing membranes near the body with bands of white hair extending from the forearm to the thigh. In West African specimens Rosevear (1965) recorded that there is a further band of white hair behind the forearm from the elbow to the wrist which is lacking in specimens from southern Africa. The ears are large and rounded and are connected together by a band of skin across the top of the head; the antitragus is large. The legs are short and stout, the feet heavy.

The sagittal crest on top of the skull is well developed, the supraoccipital crest in the males is large and projects posteriorly, but is less developed in the females. The minute anterior upper premolar lies in the toothrow; the two premolars in the lower jaw are about equal in size.

**Table 54.1**
Measurements (mm) and mass (g) of Midas free-tailed bats, *T. (M.) midas*, from Maun, Botswana (Smithers, 1971)

| | Males | | | Females | | |
|---|---|---|---|---|---|---|
| | $\bar{x}$ | n | Range | $\bar{x}$ | n | Range |
| TL | 144 | 38 | 127–160 | 142 | 44 | 126–150 |
| T | 49 | 49 | 45–58 | 47 | 44 | 40–52 |
| Hf c/u | 15 | 26 | 13–17 | 15 | 31 | 13–17 |
| E | 28 | 38 | 25–32 | 27 | 44 | 25–30 |
| F/a | 61 | 30 | 59–61 | 60 | 29 | 59–61 |
| Mass | 48,5 | 4 | 42,0–52,3 | 44,5 | 4 | 41,0–48,0 |

### Distribution

This species is not represented well in collections and there are few records from any part of its distributional range except Botswana.

*Extralimital to the continent*

Recorded from the northern borders of Yemen in **Arabia** and **Madagascar**.

*South of the Sahara, excluding the Southern African Subregion*

Recorded from **Senegal; Nigeria; Chad**; northeastern **Zaire**; southeastern **Sudan**; western **Ethiopia; Uganda**, **Kenya** and **Rwanda**. There do not appear to be any records from Tanzania, but they occur in the Southern Province of **Malawi** and in southwestern **Zambia**.

*Southern African Subregion*

Recorded from the Okavango Delta and Savuti in northern **Botswana** and from the southern parts of **Zimbabwe**. In the **Transvaal** they have been recorded in the northern parts of the province and from Skukuza in the Kruger National Park, a record which appears to mark their most southerly limits on the continent.

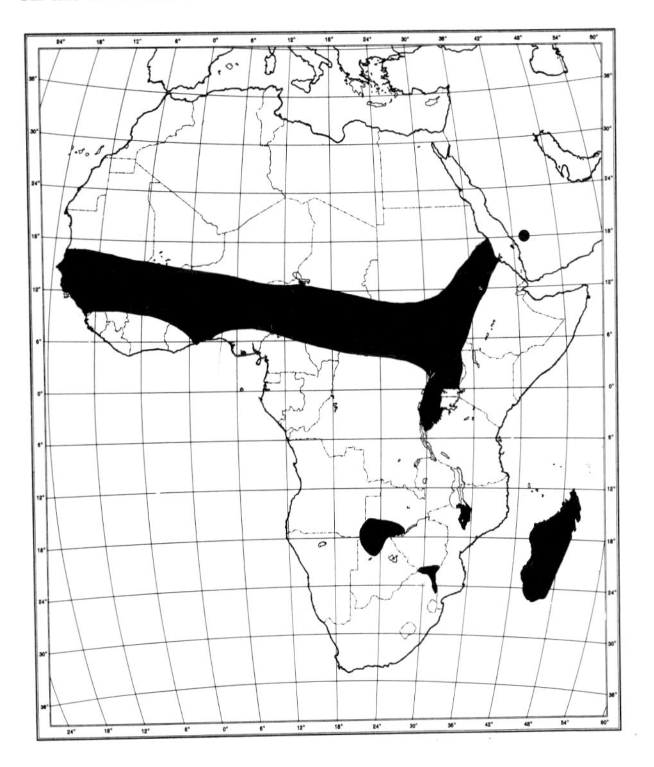

### Habitat

In West Africa, Rosevear (1965) associated them with the open woodlands of the Guinea and Sudan savannas and the records from the Subregion all lie in the savanna woodland zone. Noticeably most records from the southern parts of their range lie in association with major rivers or in Botswana with the extensive swamps of the Okavango Delta.

### Habits

Midas free-tailed bats are gregarious, occurring in parts of the Subregion in colonies estimated to number in hundreds (Maun, Botswana). In other localities they occurred in dozens. The Maun colony illustrated very clearly their preference for roosting in total darkness, the bulk of this very large colony was in the fourth compartment of an attic; none were in the half light of the first and second compartments.

The only openings to this attic were through the louvered ventilator at the end of the first compartment and two small holes near the pitch of the corrugated iron roof in the fourth compartment. The bats entered the attic, on returning to the roost, through the louvered ventilator, but invariably departed through the two small apertures in the fourth compartment. Samples were caught monthly from this colony by hanging four gallon petrol tins under two openings in the fourth compartment and catching them as they dropped from there, prior to opening their wings in flight.

In Zimbabwe, a colony of a few dozen roosted packed tightly together head upwards in the 50 mm wide joints of a concrete bridge which were covered at road level with rubber strips. The joints were about 600 mm deep, open at the sides, and provided cool but slightly light roosting places (Wright *in litt.*). At Maun the bats packed themselves tightly together between the rafters and other woodwork of the roof and the corrugated iron between it and the top of the walls and into corners in the brickwork or in crevices in it. The colonies are very noisy, especially when disturbed and even if not, squeak and jostle for position continuously. The individuals become exceedingly aggressive when handled, threatening the approaching hand with open mouths and if given the opportunity bite fiercely. Aldridge & Rautenbach (1987) found them, like most molossids, not to be agile fliers, preferring to fly in an uncluttered open airspace at heights of 40 m and above. They are fast, ranging over considerable distances in their excursions.

### Food

Insectivorous.

### Reproduction

Gravid females were taken from the Maun, Botswana, colony between December and February, the largest percentage being found in January and February. This suggests that the young are born about February/March. Birth weights, from the evidence of near full-term foetuses, appeared to be between 9,6–10,0 g, the females carrying a single foetus.

---

No. 55

## *Tadarida (Mops) condylura* (A. Smith, 1833)

## Angola free-tailed bat
## Angola-losstertvlermuis

Plate 4

---

### Colloquial Name

Originally described from Natal, it might more appropriately have been called the Natal free-tailed bat, but this name is preoccupied by *Mormopterus acetabulosus*.

### Taxonomic Notes

Numbers of subspecies have been described but, owing to the wide range of size and colour known to occur within one locality, they are of doubtful validity (Rosevear, 1965). None are recognised here.

### Description

The Angola free-tailed bat has a total length of some 100 mm with a tail about 40 mm long (Table 55.1). The upper parts are a rich dark brown colour and show clearly a band across the body just in front of the shoulders where the hair is so sparse that this band appears naked. The under parts are much lighter in colour than the upper parts, the upper chest grey or grey-brown, the throat tawny and the remainder of the under parts whitish. The band of hair on the wing membranes near the body is, in some specimens, white, in others tawny or greyish-white. The wing and interfemoral membranes are light brown.

The length of the forearm shows the size difference between this species at 45–50 mm and *T. midas* at 59–61 mm.

The skull sometimes has a well developed sagittal crest and the supraoccipital crest is large and projects posteriorly. The anterior upper premolar is minute, lies squeezed out externally to the toothrow and in some specimens is missing. The ridges on the posterior upper molars are of the V pattern (Fig. VII.4.c), but the third leg is longer than in any other African *Mops* (Rosevear, 1965).

**Table 55.1**
Measurements (mm) and mass (g) of Angola free-tailed bats, *T. (M.) condylura*, from the Kruger National Park, Transvaal

| | Males | | | Females | | |
|---|---|---|---|---|---|---|
| | $\bar{x}$ | n | Range | $\bar{x}$ | n | Range |
| TL | 123 | 15 | 112–131 | 120 | 12 | 114–124 |
| T | 46 | 15 | 39–55 | 42 | 12 | 38–45 |
| Hf c/u | 11 | 15 | 10–12 | 12 | 12 | 11–13 |
| E | 18 | 15 | 16–20 | 19 | 12 | 15–18 |
| F/a | 47 | 15 | 43–49 | 47 | 12 | 45–48 |
| Mass | 22,1 | 15 | 17,0–28,0 | 20,3 | 12 | 16,0–28,0 |

### Distribution

*South of the Sahara, excluding the Southern African Subregion*

They occur from **Guinea Bissau** and **Senegal**; southern **Niger; Nigeria** eastwards to **Ethiopia** and **Somalia** and in most countries southward to the borders of the Subregion.

*Southern African Subregion*

Not recorded from Namibia; they occur in the Okavango Delta in northern **Botswana**; in southeastern **Zimbabwe**; widely in **Mozambique**, south of the Zambezi River; in the eastern **Transvaal; Swaziland; Natal** and the eastern **Cape Province**.

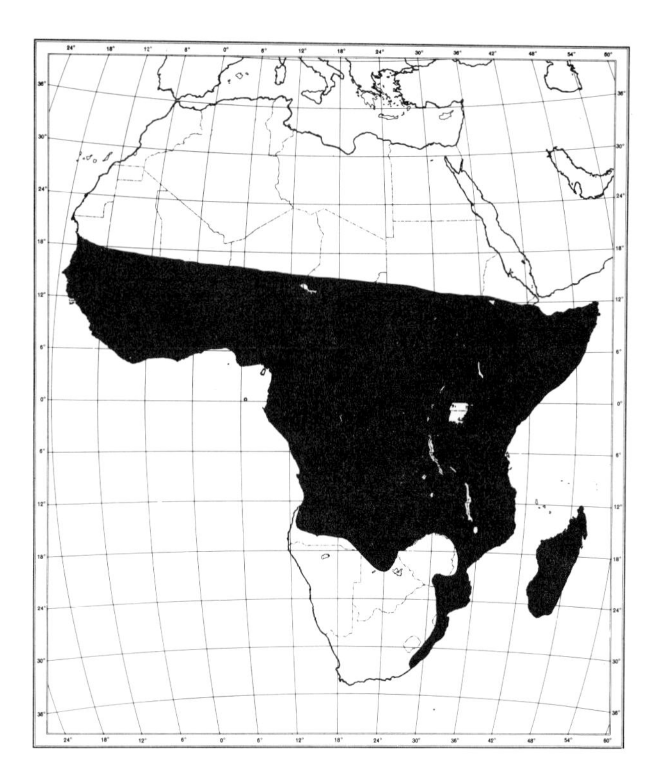

### Habitat

Both in the northern part of their distributional range and in the Subregion they do not appear to have a preference for any particular type of vegetational association. Rosevear (1965) noted that in West Africa they are as at home in the arid Sahel woodland as in the rain forest, and in the Subregion they occur in dry savanna woodland, but also in the rich riverine vegetation of the Okavango Delta in Botswana with its associated extensive swamps.

Although they have been taken in caves in the Kruger National Park (Rautenbach, 1982) they are by no means restricted to the occurrence of this type of shelter for they will use narrow crevices in trees or similar roosting places in buildings. They appear to be catholic in their habitat requirements, providing there is a plentiful food supply.

### Habits

Angola free-tailed bats are gregarious and although usually found in colonies numbering up to a dozen, where there is ample shelter in the form of nooks and crevices in caves and mine shafts, as in Mozambique, they occur in hundreds. Like the Midas free-tailed bat, *T. midas*, they roost during the day packed tightly together in crevices. In addition to secluded crevices in caves and mine shafts, they will use cracks in trees, the crevices between the stone or brickwork of buildings, or between the rafters or brickwork and the corrugated iron roof, or where the iron sheets overlap each other. The temperatures reached between the iron sheets must at times rise very high, yet they have been taken from such situations where the iron sheets are unpleasantly hot to handle, but this does not seem to deter them. Verschuren (1957) noted that in the use of tree cracks they prefer those that are so situated as to allow them a free drop as they take to flight. This factor appears to be as necessary to them as to *T. midas*.

In the use of caves they use crevices high up near the ceiling which allow them the free drop in taking to flight. They leave their roosting places after sundown, returning shortly before sunrise. Members of a colony all arrive within a minute of each other (Verschuren, 1957). In crawling in to roost the tips of the narrow wings fold back and tuck under the remainder of the wing. Colonies are restless and noisy, squeaking and jockeying for position continuously.

### Food

Insectivorous.

### Reproduction

Smithers (1971) took three gravid females on the Chobe River, Botswana, in January, each with a single foetus, but otherwise there is no information available from the Subregion. M. van der Merwe found them to be strictly seasonal breeders in southern latitudes with females producing more than one offspring per summer.

## Subgenus *Chaerephon* Dobson, 1874

The characters separating this subgenus and *Mops* are not well defined. Originally it relied solely on the broad band of skin connecting the ears across the top of the head and on the size of the ear tragus. While these differentiate *Chaerephon* from the subgenus *Tadarida*, they are commonly shared with members of the subgenus *Mops*. The degree of development of the ridges on the molars and the size of the anterior palatal notch remain the best method of recognising members of this subgenus (Figs. VII.3 & VII.4.b).

No. 56

## *Tadarida (Chaerephon) nigeriae* (Thomas, 1913)

## Nigerian free-tailed bat
## Nigeriese losstertvlermuis

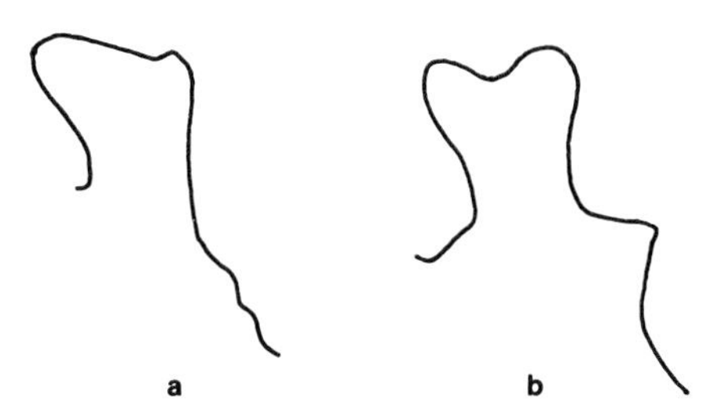


Fig. 56.1. Ear tragus:
(a) *Tadarida pumila* (b) *T. nigeriae*.

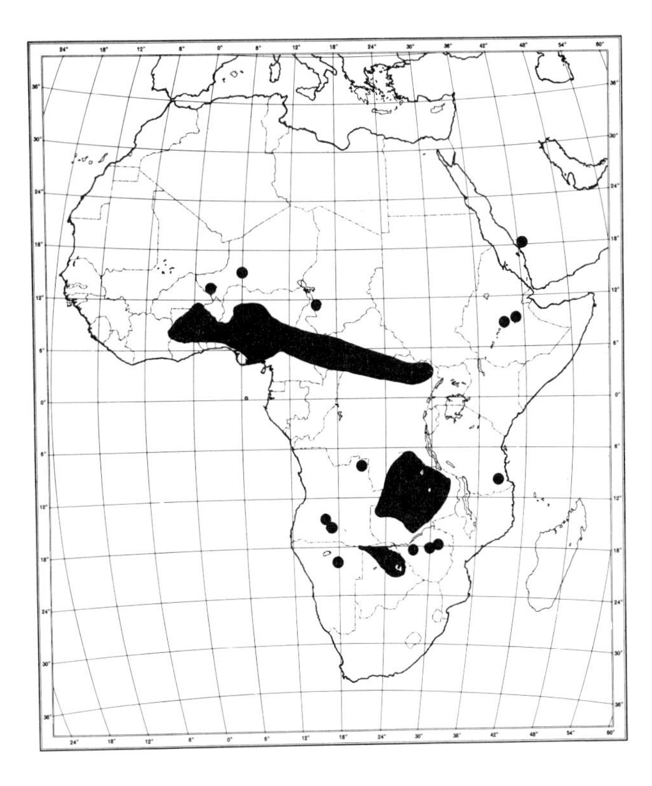

### Colloquial Name

Originally described from a specimen from Nigeria, the name is useful in distinguishing the species from other members of the genus.

### Taxonomic Notes

Hayman & Hill (1971) listed two subspecies from the continent, *T. m. spillmani* from the southern parts of its distributional range and *T. n. nigeriae* from the northern parts. *T. n. spillmani* (Morard, 1932) has whitish wing membranes against the dark membranes of *T. n. nigeriae*.

### Description

Adults of this species have a total length of some 100 mm with tails of about 35 mm. As only a few specimens have been taken in the Subregion, a table of measurements and mass is not given until more material is available. They are particularly dark in colour, the upper and under parts a dark sepia-brown, the under parts characterised by bands of long white hair on the flanks, which extend onto the wing membranes in narrow bands. The wing and interfemoral membranes are off-white, the under parts of the membranes slightly lighter in colour, especially near the body. The ears are connected across the top of the head by a band of skin which is rolled back at its top edge and which conceals behind it a tuft of hair which is erectile at will and then forms a crest. The ear tragus is bilobed at its tip (Fig. 56.1.b).

The skull has a poorly developed sagittal crest, but the supraoccipital crest is well developed and projects posteriorly. The anterior upper premolar is small and lies in the toothrow, separating the canine and the posterior premolar. The anterior lower premolar is only slightly smaller than the posterior one.

### Distribution

*Extralimital to the continent*

Recorded from southwestern **Arabia**.

*South of the Sahara, excluding the Southern African Subregion*

Occurs from **Niger** and **Ghana** eastwards to **Ethiopia** and in northeastern and southeastern **Zaire; Zambia; Angola** and **Tanzania**.

*Southern African Subregion*

Recorded from **Namibia** and **Zimbabwe** and are distributed widely in northern **Botswana**.

### Habitat

A savanna woodland species associated in the southern parts of their range with *Brachystegia* woodland.

### Habits

Nigerian free-tailed bats are gregarious, Ansell (1960a) recording large colonies. They roost during the day in the roofs and under the eaves of houses and in thatched huts. At one of the localities in Zimbabwe a colony of about six emerged from under the bark of a dead tree standing in water, and one was secured. Presumably they pack tightly together in the roosting places; the loose bark of the dead tree from which they emerged did not allow any other type of roosting attitude. Ansell (1960a) recorded their association with trees in Zambia.

### Food

Insectivorous.

### Reproduction

In Zambia, Ansell (1960a) recorded a juvenile in January, but there is no information available from the Subregion.

---

No. 57

## *Tadarida (Chaerephon) bivittata* (Heuglin, 1861)

## Spotted free-tailed bat
## Gevlekte losstertvlermuis

---

### Colloquial Name

So called from the tiny white and sometimes barely distinguishable flecks on the upper parts of the body.

### Taxonomic Notes

No subspecies are recognised.

### Description

They are about 100 mm in total length with a tail of 37 mm. The adult males have a mean mass of 15,4 g, females 14,6 g (Table 57.1). The upper parts are dark umber-brown and have a variable pattern of tiny white flecks or short stripes on the sides of the crown of the head, on the shoulders and sometimes on the flanks. The under parts may be the same colour as the upper parts or may be tinged with grey. The wing and interfemoral membranes are dark brown.

### Table 57.1

Measurements (mm) and mass (g) of spotted free-tailed bats, *T. (C.) bivittata*, from Zimbabwe (Smithers & Wilson, 1979)

| | Males | | | Females | | |
|---|---|---|---|---|---|---|
| | $\bar{x}$ | n | Range | $\bar{x}$ | n | Range |
| TL | 105 | 10 | 102–108 | 105 | 21 | 100–111 |
| T | 37 | 10 | 34–40 | 37 | 21 | 34–40 |
| Hf c/u | 11 | 10 | 11 | 10 | 21 | 9–11 |
| E | 22 | 10 | 21–23 | 21 | 21 | 20–22 |
| F/a | 47 | 10 | 45–47 | 46 | 21 | 43–47 |
| Mass | 15,4 | 10 | 13,5–16,7 | 14,6 | 21 | 13,1–17,0 |

### Distribution

*South of the Sahara, excluding the Southern African Subregion*

Recorded from **Eritrea; Ethiopia;** the southeastern **Sudan** southwards to **Zambia**. Not so far recorded from Malawi or Mozambique, north of the Zambezi River.

*Southern African Subregion*

Recorded from six widely scattered localities in **Zimbabwe**, Bulawayo marking its most southerly known limit of distribution at the moment.

### Habitat

A savanna woodland species, occurring in *Brachystegia* woodland in Zambia and Zimbabwe.

### Habits

A gregarious species, occurring in small numbers, not usually more than about six. Roosts during the day tucked away in the crevices of rocks, in caves and mine shafts.

### Food

Insectivorous.

### Reproduction

No information available from the Subregion.

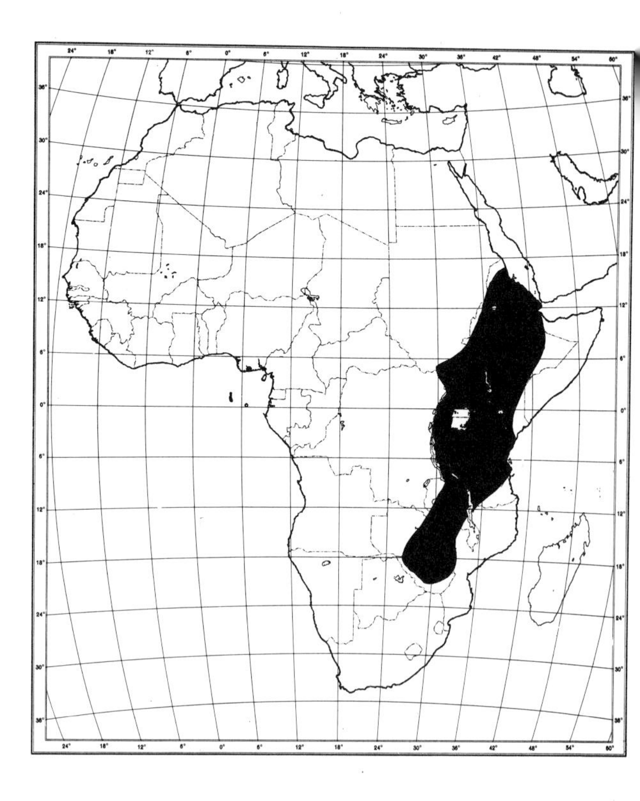

---

No. 58

## *Tadarida (Chaerephon) chapini* (J.A. Allen, 1917)

## Pale free-tailed bat
## Bleek losstertvlermuis

---

### Colloquial Name

So called because of their pale body colour and the whitish wing and interfemoral membranes.

### Taxonomic Notes

Hayman & Hill (1971) listed three subspecies from the continent, *T. c. chapini* from Zaire and Uganda; *T. c. lancasteri* Hayman, 1938 from Zambia and Angola, and *T. c. shortridgei* (Thomas, 1926) from northern Namibia.

### Description

A medium-sized species with a total length of about 150 mm, including a tail of just over 30 mm. The upper parts are pale cinnamon-brown, the hair off-white at the base, the

### Plate 4

46. Egyptian fruit bat, *Rousettus aegyptiacus*
    Egiptiese vrugtevlermuis
55. Angola free-tailed bat, *Tadarida (Mops) condylura*
    Angola-losstertvlermuis
67. Schreibers' long-fingered bat, *Miniopterus schreibersii*
    Schreibers se grotvlermuis
71. Temminck's hairy bat, *Myotis tricolor*
    Temminck se langhaarvlermuis
75. Banana bat, *Pipistrellus nanus*
    Piesangvlermuis
86. Cape serotine bat, *Eptesicus capensis*
    Kaapse dakvlermuis
90. Schlieffen's bat, *Nycticeius schlieffenii*
    Schlieffen se vlermuis
93. Lesser woolly bat, *Kerivoula lanosa*
    Klein wolhaarvlermuis
102. Geoffroy's horseshoe bat, *Rhinolophus clivosus*
    Geoffroy se saalneusvlermuis
112. Short-eared trident bat, *Cloeotis percivali*
    Drietand-bladneusvlermuis

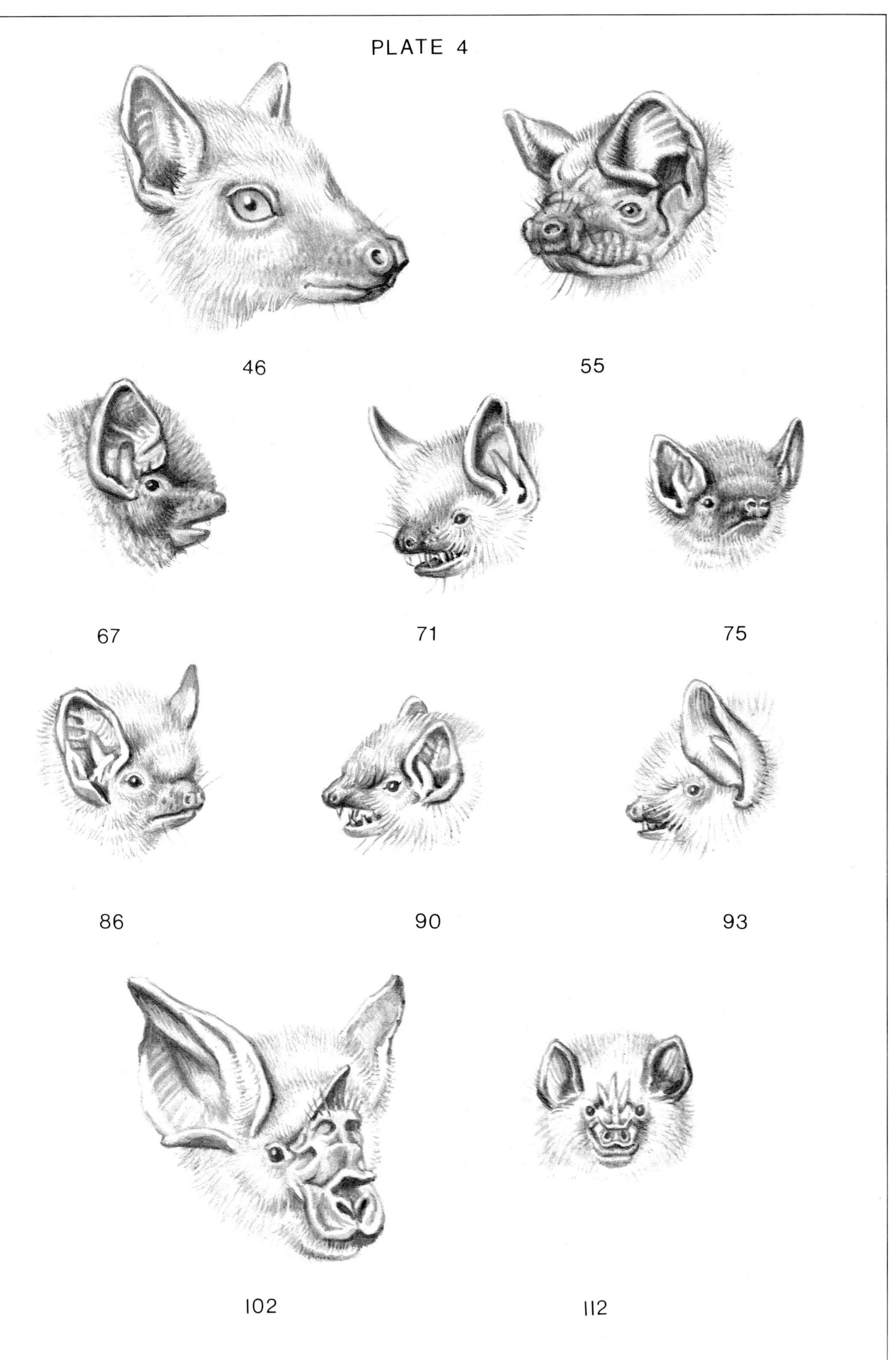
PLATE 4
46
55
67
71
75
86
90
93
102
112
Dick Findlay.

under parts greyish-brown with a whitish band down the mid-belly and a narrow band of white along the fringe of the wing membranes next to the body, running from the forearm to the hind legs. The wing membranes are white, tinged yellow near the body, and between the forearms and the legs near the body are punctuated with tiny black specks. The interfemoral membrane is dark brown.

The ears are joined by a band of skin across the top of the head and from this rises a crest of long hair, 12 mm in length, the basal half of the hair reddish-chestnut, the remainder white (Fig. 58.1). This long hair lies back on the head, reaching the base of the ears on either side. Just behind the base of this crest the hair on the head is white. The minute anterior upper premolars lie in the toothrow; the anterior lower premolar is smaller than the posterior.

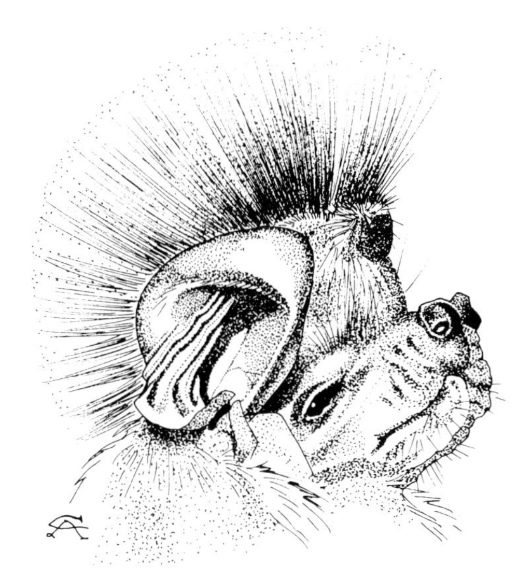

Fig. 58.1. Head: *Tadarida chapini*

**Distribution**

Too few specimens of this beautiful crested bat are known from too few localities to be able to assess the limits of their occurrence.

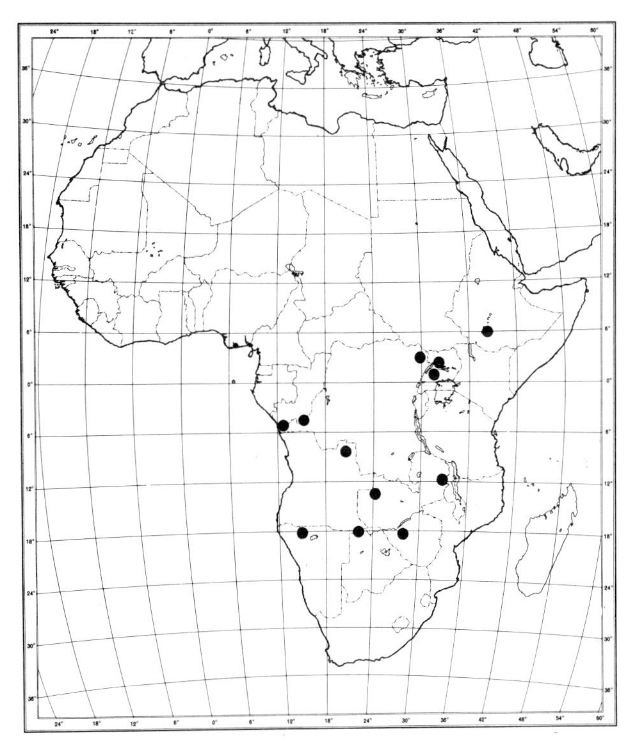

*South of the Sahara, excluding the Southern African Subregion*

Recorded from northeastern and eastern **Zaire; Uganda**; southern **Ethiopia**; northeastern **Angola** and northwestern and eastern **Zambia**. Kingdon (1974) stated that it was taken in **Kenya**, but did not give localities.

*Southern African Subregion*

Known only from northern **Namibia**, northwestern **Zimbabwe** and northern **Botswana**.

**Habitat**

Too little information is available to allow an assessment of the habitat in which they occur. In northeastern Zaire, the type locality of the species, Allen, Lang & Chapin (1917) observed that the two specimens were taken in an "open district" (open savanna woodland?) and not in the forest. One specimen was caught in a house, the other taken from the crop of a bat hawk, *Macheirhamphus alcinus*. In Botswana and Zimbabwe they were taken in mopane woodland.

**Food**

Insectivorous.

**Habits and Reproduction**

Unknown.

---

No. 59

## *Tadarida (Chaerephon) pumila* (Cretzschmar, 1830–1831)

## Little free-tailed bat
## Klein losstertvlermuis

---

**Colloquial Name**

The smallest of the molossids that occur in the Subregion.

**Taxonomic Notes**

Hayman & Hill (1971) treated the name *pumila* in its widest possible sense as the earliest name for a large group of the commonest African molossid bats whose relationships have been the subject of varying interpretations. They point out that attempts at subspecific separation based on colour are profitless. As here understood *T. pumila* includes both the dark and white winged forms, the latter previously known under the name *T. limbata*.

**Description**

The smallest of the free-tailed bats with a total length of about 90 mm including the tail which measures up to 39 mm (Table 59.1). As the species includes both the dark winged and light winged forms, the colour of these small bats can vary from those that have deep blackish-brown upper parts, the under parts slightly paler, to those that are browner above and whose slightly paler brown under parts have a broad irregularly edged band of white from the anus to the chest, this character coupled with having translucent white wing membranes. This band itself is variable and in some white-winged specimens is absent or barely discernible as a narrow white line. They all have a narrow band of hair on the wing membranes from the forearm to the thighs which varies in colour from white to tawny. The rounded ears are large for the size of their heads, are connected together across the top of the head by a band of skin and their outer edges are folded in upon the ears giving them a clumsy appearance. The antitragus is large and tends to conceal the tiny tragus which is asymmetrically bilobed at the tip (Fig. 56.1.a).

**Table 59.1**

Measurements (mm) and mass (g) of little free-tailed bats, *T. (C.) pumila*, from Botswana (Smithers, 1971) and Zimbabwe (Smithers & Wilson, 1979)

**Botswana**

| | Males | | | Females | | |
|---|---|---|---|---|---|---|
| | $\bar{x}$ | n | Range | $\bar{x}$ | n | Range |
| TL | 87 | 48 | 70–100 | 91 | 91 | 70–102 |
| T | – | | | — | | |
| F/a | 37 | 10 | 36–39 | 37 | 12 | 36–38 |
| Mass | 11,5 | 20 | 10,3–13,9 | 12,1 | 65 | 10,1–16,1 |

**Zimbabwe**

| | Males | | | Females | | |
|---|---|---|---|---|---|---|
| | $\bar{x}$ | n | Range | $\bar{x}$ | n | Range |
| TL | 93 | 10 | 90–98 | 95 | 20 | 90–100 |
| T | 36 | 10 | 35–39 | 35 | 20 | 31–39 |
| F/a | 38 | 10 | 37–39 | 38 | 20 | 37–39 |
| Mass | 11,1 | 11 | 10,1–12,7 | 11,3 | 12 | 10,1–14,8 |

**Mass of gravid females**
**Botswana**

| | $\bar{x}$ | n | Range |
|---|---|---|---|
| Mass | 13,6 | 46 | 12,1–16,7 |

**Zimbabwe**

| | $\bar{x}$ | n | Range |
|---|---|---|---|
| Mass | 12,5 | 19 | 11,2–15,1 |

## Distribution

*Extralimital to the continent*

Recorded from **Yemen** in southwestern Arabia.

*South of the Sahara, excluding the Southern African Subregion*

Recorded from **Gambia**; southern **Niger; Nigeria; Chad**; southeastern **Sudan; Ethiopia; Eritrea; Uganda; Kenya; Tanzania; Congo Republic; Zaire; Angola; Zambia; Malawi** and **Mozambique**, north of the Zambezi River.

*Southern African Subregion*

They occur throughout the Okavango Delta in northern **Botswana**, south to Lake Ngami; north and south of the plateau in **Zimbabwe**; widely in **Mozambique**, south of the Zambezi River; in the eastern **Transvaal, Swaziland** and northern **Natal**. There appears to be a break in their distribution westwards, the next records being in the southwest of the **Cape Province** and northwestwards to near Springbok in Namaqualand.

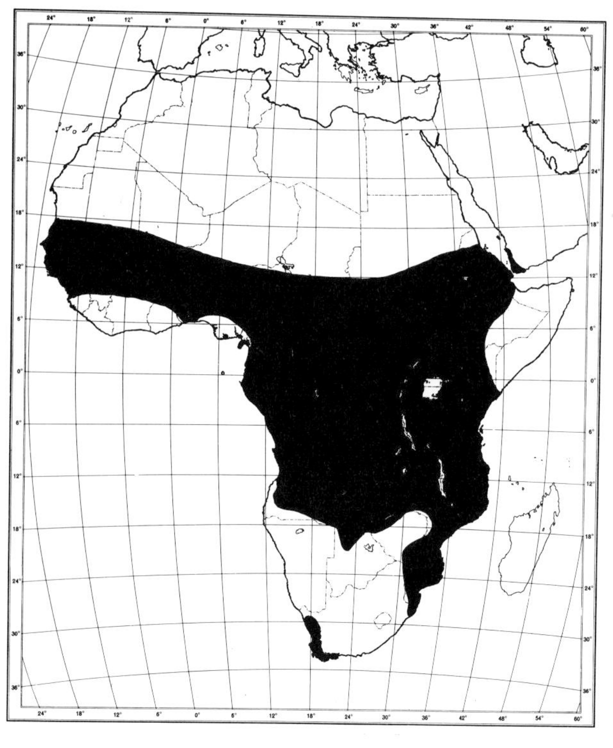

## Habitat

Although apparently not occurring in the High Forest Zone of West Africa, they occur widely in the Guinea and Sudan savannas and in the forests of the Congo basin in Zaire (Rosevear, 1965). Southwards they are found in savanna woodland in Zambia and in dry mopane woodland at altitudes of less than 1 000 m in Zimbabwe. In the Cape Province they occur in the mountainous areas in the Cape Macchia Zone as well as in the more arid open country further north. They appear to be catholic in their choice of habitat. In Zimbabwe they showed a clear preference for lowveld conditions, never being taken on the plateau over the 1 000 m level.

## Habits

Little free-tailed bats are gregarious, occurring in colonies in favourable areas in hundreds (Triangle, Zimbabwe) (Smithers & Wilson, 1979). Other colonies of 100 to 150 are known (Maun, Botswana) (Smithers, 1971). They roost during the day tucked away in crevices in brickwork under roofs, between the rafters and the corrugated iron roofing sheets, between the overlap of the sheets or in any other type of crevice that presents itself. Verschuren (1957) found them in Zaire in colonies of up to half a dozen in cracks in trees, the entrances to which were very narrow. The size of the colony may well depend on the amount of crevice space available. They appear to be indifferent to high temperatures, for the Maun colony lived in a badly ventilated attic where the temperature in the room underneath reached 40 °C and was certainly higher where they were roosting.

About an hour before leaving the roost the colony becomes very restless, individuals squeaking and jockeying for position and generally being very noisy. Verschuren (1957) noted that the entrances to the crevices in trees were through small cracks. Both in the Triangle and Maun colonies the entrances to the attic were through very small apertures between the corrugated iron sheets and the brickwork which allowed only one or two to drop into flight at a time.

They appear to forage singly, there being numerous records of solitary individuals entering houses. At the Savuti swamp in Botswana their solitary foraging habits were very noticeable. Their flight is fast and erratic, making them difficult to shoot as they flew past about 12 m above the ground with sudden swoops to within 3 m of it. A random sample of 165 adults, taken during the months of October to February showed a sex ratio of 45 males : 120 females, in August of 3 males : 12 females and in June of 1 male : 4 females.

## Food

Insectivorous.

## Reproduction

In northern Botswana gravid females were taken in August and from October to February, by far the larger number in December. Many hairless young were seen in the colonies at Maun in February, some clinging to their mothers, others on their own in the roosts. This indicates that the young are born during the warm, wet summer months from about October to March. Van der Merwe, Rautenbach & Van der Colf (1986) showed that, in the Transvaal Lowveld, there were three peaks of parturition: in early November, late January and early April. The gestation period is about 60 days, females giving birth to a single young at a birth, with a birth mass of about 3,2 g. Females become sexually mature at the age of 5–12 months.

The potential for mature females to produce up to three singletons per summer, is ascribed to their ability to undergo post-partum oestrus (Van der Merwe, Giddings & Rautenbach, 1987).

No. 64

## *Tadarida (Chaerephon) ansorgei* (Thomas, 1913)

# Ansorge's free-tailed bat
# Ansorge se losstertvlermuis

Included in the first edition in the subgenus *Tadarida*, Meester *et al.* (1986) followed Freeman (1981) who showed the relationship of this species to other subgenus *Chaerephon* species. For convenience its original number (No. 64) is retained.

### Colloquial Name

Named after Dr. W.J. Ansorge, a collector of zoological specimens, who collected specimens of this species in Malange, northern Angola.

### Taxonomic Notes

No subspecies have been described. Hayman & Hill (1971), Largen, Kock & Yalden (1974) and Corbet & Hill (1980) placed this species in the subgenus *Tadarida*, a treatment followed here. Koopman (1975) and Freeman (1981) noted its relationship with *T. bivitatta* and the extralimital *T. bemmeleni* and placed it in *Chaerephon*, a treatment followed by Meester *et al.* (1986).

### Description

Ansorge's free-tailed bats are a small species, their total length about 106 mm with a tail 36 mm long (Table 64.1). The upper parts of the body are dark umber-brown, the top of the head, neck and throat darker, almost black, and contrasting with the colour of the upper parts. The under parts are a shade lighter than the upper parts. The wing membranes are a translucent light brown, the ears large and rounded.

They are very similar to the Egyptian free-tailed bat in colour, but they are smaller, a feature illustrated by the total length of the skull which in this species measures 18–20 mm in length, in the Egyptian free-tailed bat 19–21 mm. The braincase in this species is elevated, while it is flat in the Egyptian species. In this species the canines in the lower jaw are almost touching at their bases, whereas in the Egyptian species they are widely separated.

**Table 64.1**

Measurements (mm) of two Ansorge's free-tailed bats, *T. (C.) ansorgei*

| | TL | T | Hfc/u | E | F/a |
|---|---|---|---|---|---|
| Male | 102 | 36 | — | 20 | 43 |
| Female | 102 | 36 | — | 20 | 44 |

### Distribution

This is not a common bat anywhere in its distributional range and many of the apparent blanks in its distribution may be due to its not having been collected so far.

*South of the Sahara, excluding the Southern African Subregion*

Recorded from Oku Lake, **Cameroun**; the **Central African Republic**; southern **Sudan; Ethiopia**; southeastern and northeastern **Zaire; Kenya**; western **Uganda**; northeastern **Tanzania; Zambia** and Malanje, **Angola**, the type locality.

*Southern African Subregion*

Recorded from four localities in **Zimbabwe**, one on the Mozambique border, which suggests that they will turn up there in due course; the Kruger National Park, and from the Mkuzi Game Reserve, **Natal**.

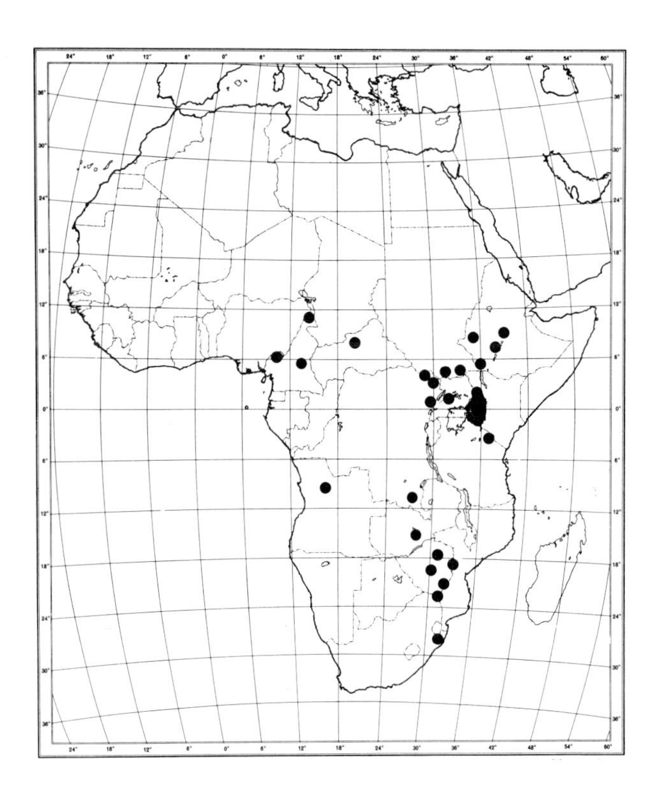

### Habitat

As this species usually roosts during the day in rock clefts, caves and mine adits the availability of this type of shelter may well be a primary habitat requirement, in addition to the availability of a plentiful food supply.

### Habits

Ansorge's free-tailed bat, judging from the comments of Allen, Lang & Chapin (1917) who recorded a colony of hundreds in a pitch dark rock cleft in northeastern Zaire, is a gregarious species. They recorded how the people there suffocate the bats in their rocky roosting place, collecting basketfuls as food. In Zimbabwe they roosted in caves and mine adits. Like other closely related species, they probably pack tightly into crevices, which is suggested by Allen, Lang & Chapin's (1917) observations. Their colony had been in residence over a long period as there was a layer of dry guano on the floor over 0,3 m thick. This colony became very noisy when approached, individuals squeaking and jostling.

### Food

Insectivorous.

### Reproduction

No information available.

## Subgenus *Tadarida* Rafinesque, 1814

In members of this subgenus the palatal emargination is deep and well developed, the ridging on the upper posterior molars forming a full W pattern (Fig. VII.4.a).

No. 60

## *Tadarida (Tadarida) lobata* (Thomas, 1891)

## Big-eared free-tailed bat
## Grootoor-losstertvlermuis

So far this species is only known from some 23 specimens from four localities in **Kenya** and one in **Zimbabwe**. Originally it was taken in Turkwell in northwestern Kenya and until 1970 remained known only from three specimens, the first described by Thomas in 1891, the second which was collected live in a house in Hatfield, Harare, Zimbabwe, some 2 000 km to the south, and the third from the Cherangami Hills, Kenya, collected by the Oxford University Expedition in 1969. Since then a specimen was collected in the Kapenguria district of Kenya and 19 from Maungu Hill in southeastern Kenya (Peterson, 1974). While the appearance of this species in Zimbabwe so far out of its usual range is surprising and may be a natural phenomenon in a species which is a fast, high flier, the possibility of its being transported in an aircraft cannot be ruled out. During the time it was taken there were regular air services from Nairobi to Harare, Zimbabwe, and as it is a species that uses substantial cover in which to roost, it could have made use of the shelter of an aircraft parked at night. Wiles & Hill (1986) recorded the transport of the North American small brown bat, *Myotis lucifugus*, to Guam, Mariana Islands, a distance of about 10 000 km by air. The transport of bats by ship is a well-known phenomenon, species reaching New Zealand from Japan, from Panama to the Bass Strait off southeastern Australia, and from Canada to Holland (Vaute, 1982).

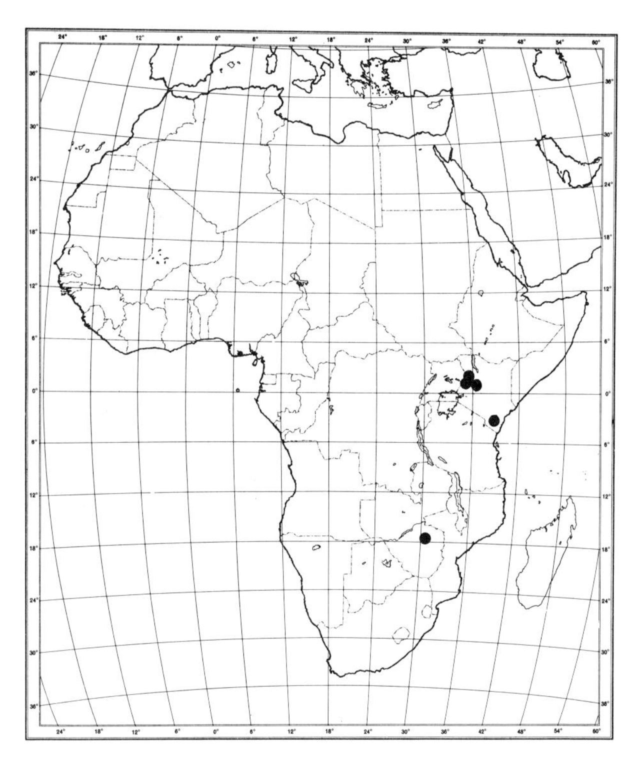

All the recent specimens were shot near water and therefore there is no information on their roosting places. Peterson (1974) suggested that, like their nearest relatives, *T. fulminans*, they probably used rock crevices. He recorded that the specimens taken at the Maungu Hill flew high over the water after dark, only three or four descending within 7 m of the ground. Their flight was fast and straight and while flying they uttered a distinctive single or double noted, loud squeak.

This species has very large ears which, like the wing membranes, are translucent. The ears arise well forward on the rostrum near the nostrils. The colour of the upper parts is cinnamon-brown with a conspicuous white spot on the shoulders, the under parts buffy, the buffy hair extending marginally onto the wing membranes. The upper lips are plain, not wrinkled. Peterson (1974) remarked that they appear to inhabit arid or semi-arid terrain.

No. 61

## *Tadarida (Tadarida) ventralis* (Heuglin, 1861)

## Transvaal free-tailed bat
## Transvaalse losstertvlermuis

Only 16 specimens of this species are known. The original specimen from which the species *T. africana* (Dobson, 1876) (*T. ventralis*) was described came from the Transvaal, no exact locality being given. No others have turned up in the province since that date.

It is the rarest of the African molossids, single specimens being known from **Ethiopia**; eastern **Zaire; Kenya; Malawi**; the **Transvaal** and two localities in **Mozambique**; five from Katire in the southern **Sudan** and four from the Lake Manyara National Park in **Tanzania** (Table 61.1). It is also the largest of the three closely related species *T. ventralis*, *T. lobata* and *T. fulminans*.

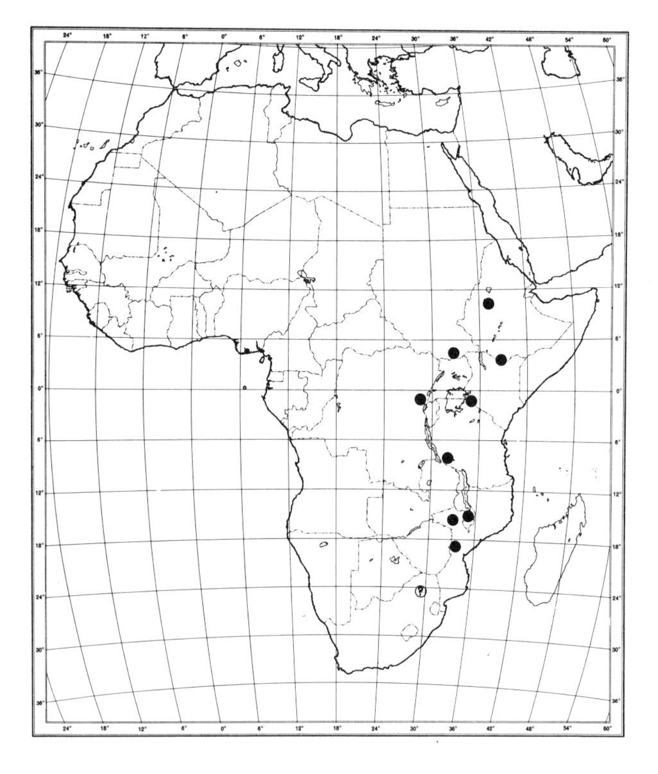

They average in total length 140 mm, with a forearm of 62 mm. The colour of the upper parts is variable. In the four specimens from Tanzania examined by Harrison (1971), three were umber-brown with a distinct gloss, the under parts lighter brown with a distinct median white streak of varying width. The fourth specimen had bright fulvous upper parts, almost orange-brown, the under parts fulvous, the streak white washed with fulvous, the flanks lighter in shade. This colour difference was not related to sex.

In the middle of the throat they had a circular tuft of hair around a bare patch of skin, which may be glandular. In the fulvous specimen these hairs formed a beard and were ash-grey. In the other three specimens these hairs were white at the base with pale umber-brown tips. The colour of the Transvaal specimen is reddish-brown on the upper parts, the under parts lighter in colour and brighter. The wing membranes are light brown. Its measurements (mm) are as follows:

| TL | T | Hf c/u | E |
|---|---|---|---|
| 147 | 61 | 12 | 25 |

**Table 61.1**

Measurements (mm) of a series of four specimens of the Transvaal free-tailed bat, *T. (T.) ventralis*, from Lake Manyara National Park, Tanzania (Harrison, 1971)

| | Irrespective of sex | | |
|---|---|---|---|
| | x̄ | n | Range |
| TL | 140 | 4 | 137–152 |
| T | 55 | 4 | 53–63 |
| Hf c/u | 12 | 4 | 11–13 |
| E | 20 | 4 | 18–24 |
| F/a | 62 | 4 | 61–65 |

## Food

Insectivorous.

## Habitat, Habits, Reproduction

Unknown.

---

No. 62

# *Tadarida (Tadarida) fulminans* (Thomas, 1903)

## Madagascar large free-tailed bat
## Madagaskarse grootlosstertvlermuis

---

## Colloquial name

Originally this species was described from Fianarantsoa, Madagascar.

## Taxonomic Notes

No subspecies are recognised.

## Description

Madagascar large free-tailed bats are about 150 mm in total length, with a tail about 56 mm long and a mass of about 33 g (Table 62.1). The upper parts of the body vary in colour from reddish-brown to dark chocolate-brown. Individuals occur in which the upper parts are reddish; chocolate-brown, however, is the more usual colour. The under parts are similar in colour to the upper parts and have a distinct median white, irregularly edged band from the anus to the chest. The upper lips are plain, not wrinkled as in the Egyptian free-tailed bat.

The skull has a well developed sagittal crest, the anterior upper premolars set in the toothrow, but slightly to the outside of it. The anterior lower premolar is only about half the height of the posterior premolar.

**Table 62.1**

Measurements (mm) and mass (g) of a series of six male and eight female Madagascar free-tailed bats, *T. (T.) fulminans*, taken in Zimbabwe (Smithers & Wilson, 1979)

| | Males | | | Females | | |
|---|---|---|---|---|---|---|
| | x̄ | n | Range | x̄ | n | Range |
| TL | 147 | 6 | 145–150 | 143 | 8 | 138–150 |
| T | 56 | 6 | 54–59 | 55 | 8 | 53–57 |
| Hf c/u | 13 | 6 | 12–15 | 13 | 8 | 11–14 |
| E | 24 | 6 | 22–25 | 24 | 8 | 22–25 |
| F/a | 60 | 6 | 59–61 | 59 | 8 | 58–60 |
| Mass | 32,3 | 5 | 31,2–34,1 | 33,1 | 8 | 25,7–39,0 |

## Distribution

*Extralimital to the continent*

Recorded from eastern **Madagascar.**

*South of the Sahara, excluding the Southern African Subregion*

Recorded from northeastern **Zaire; Rwanda**; southern **Kenya**; northeastern **Tanzania**, **Malawi** and northeastern and southwestern **Zambia**.

*Southern African Subregion*

Recorded from four localities centred on Harare, **Zimbabwe**, and one locality in the Hwange National Park in the northwest; and in the **Transvaal** from Pafuri in the northern sector of the Kruger National Park (Pienaar, Joubert, Hall-Martin, de Graaff & Rautenbach, 1987).

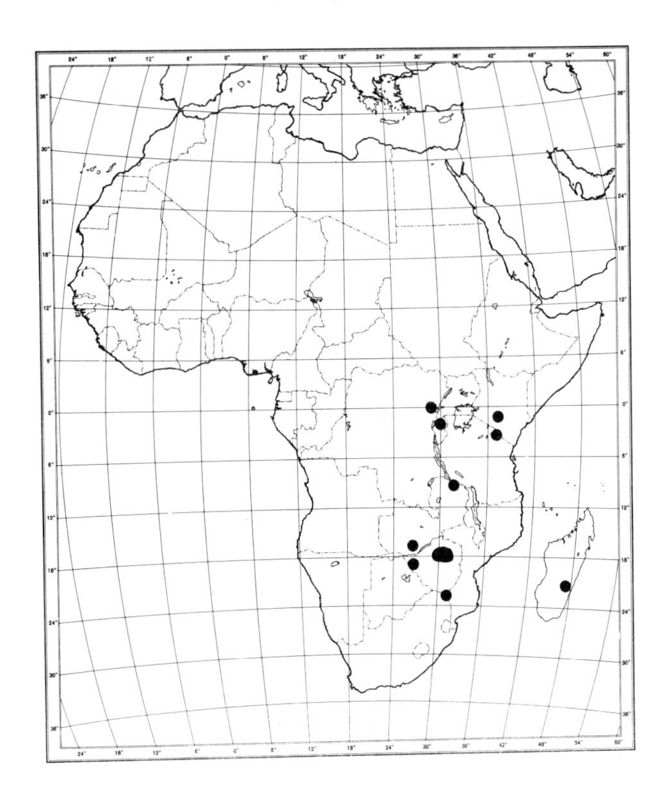

## Habitat

A savanna woodland species, associated in Ethiopia with mountainous country and probably more dependent on rocky terrain than on the vegetational association, as they require rock crevices to roost in during the day. The specimens from Zimbabwe were all taken from areas of granite hills in the savanna woodland zone.

## Habits

Madagascar large free-tailed bats are gregarious, but never occur in colonies of more than about 20. In the Chikupo caves, Zimbabwe, a colony packed into a crack in the granite, the opening of which was some 7 to 8 m above the floor and situated at the entrance. This allowed them a free fall in taking to flight. They left the roosting place at sundown, returning before first light in the morning. Their flight was fast and direct and they appeared to be high fliers.

## Food

Insectivorous.

## Reproduction

Six gravid females were taken at the Chikupo caves, Zimbabwe, in October, each carrying a single foetus.

No. 63

## *Tadarida (Tadarida) aegyptiaca* (E. Geoffroy, 1818)

## Egyptian free-tailed bat
## Egiptiese losstertvlermuis

Plate 5

### Colloquial Name

The original specimens were collected in Egypt during the Napoleonic wars by Geoffroy, who served under Napoleon.

### Taxonomic Notes

Hayman & Hill (1971) listed two subspecies, *T. a. aegyptiaca* from Algeria and Egypt and mainly on the eastern parts of the continent to the Cape and *T. a bocagei* (Seabra, 1900) from the central and western regions. *T. a. bocagei* is slightly smaller and darker than *T. a. aegyptiaca*.

### Description

Egyptian free-tailed bats have a total length of about 110 mm, tails 38 mm long and a mass of about 15 g (Table 63.1). The upper parts are dark sooty-brown, the top of the head and back of the neck darker still, nearly black. The under parts are generally the same colour as the upper parts, or they may be a shade lighter. In some individuals the throat is buffy, the mid-belly off-white, the flanks tinged grey or tawny. The wing and interfemoral membranes are a translucent light brown, the fur of the under parts spreading thickly but narrowly on to the wing membranes where it is generally the same colour as that on the under parts, but in some cases lighter and in exceptional cases white. The rounded ears are set closely together on the top of the head, the ear tragus larger than in the subgenera *Chaerephon* or *Mops* and not concealed by the antitragus.

The braincase is broad and flat, tending to be depressed in the middle. It has no sagittal crest and there is no noticeable supraoccipital crest. The palatal emargination is large and reaches back to the level of the canines. The anterior upper premolars are minute and lie in the toothrow, the posterior premolar large. The ridge pattern on the molar is a full development of the W-pattern (Fig. VII.4.a).

### Table 63.1

Measurements (mm) and mass (g) of Egyptian free-tailed bats, *T. (T.) aegyptiaca*, from Zimbabwe (Smithers & Wilson, 1979)

| | Males | | | Females | | |
|---|---|---|---|---|---|---|
| | $\bar{x}$ | n | Range | $\bar{x}$ | n | Range |
| TL | 112 | 11 | 106–115 | 111 | 16 | 105–118 |
| T | 38 | 11 | 33–40 | 39 | 16 | 35–43 |
| Hf c/u | 10 | 11 | 9–11 | 10 | 16 | 8–12 |
| E | 21 | 11 | 19–22 | 20 | 16 | 18–22 |
| F/a | 48 | 10 | 48–54 | 48 | 16 | 46–52 |
| Mass | 14,9 | 11 | 13,8–17,3 | 15,6 | 16 | 13,8–18,1 |

### Distribution

Although locally Egyptian free-tailed bats can be very numerous, records of their occurrence in some countries such as Angola and Zambia are restricted to a very limited range of localities. There remain large areas in the Subregion from which they have not been taken, such as parts of the Transvaal and Botswana, but there is no good reason to explain this, except lack of collecting.

*Extralimital to the continent*

Recorded from southwestern **Arabia** and **India**.

*North Africa*

Recorded from **Algeria** and **Egypt**, extending to the coast of the Mediterranean.

*South of the Sahara, excluding the Southern African Subregion*

There is a single record from central **Nigeria**, east of which they occur in the central and southeastern parts of the **Sudan; Ethiopia; Eritrea; Somalia**; northeastern **Zaire; Uganda; Kenya** and in northeastern **Tanzania**. There appears to be a break in distribution south, the next records being from eastern **Zambia**, on the Malawi border, and from the south of the country. They occur in central and southern **Angola**. There are no records at the moment from southern Tanzania, northeastern Mozambique or Malawi.

*Southern African Subregion*

They occur widely throughout the whole of the Subregion.

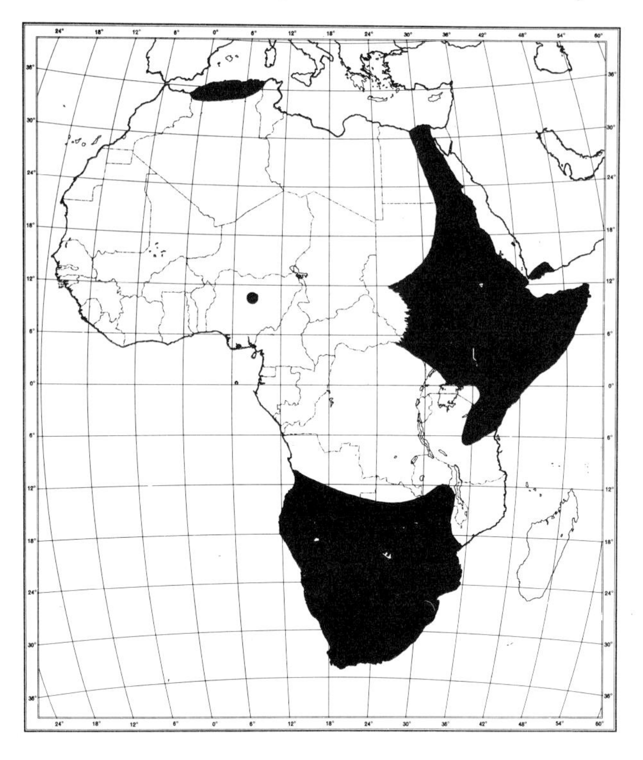

### Habitat

In the southern parts of their distributional range they occur in all the vegetational associations available, excluding forest. They do occur, however, on forest fringes and can be as locally common in such areas as they are in the arid scrub savanna of the southern parts of Botswana or on the open grassland of the Makgadikgadi Pan and Lake Ngami.

In the more arid areas in Botswana there was a noticeable association of this species with water holes, even with boreholes and reservoirs. At Tshane in southwestern Botswana the borehole was the only water available on a year round basis. Here they came to sip water from the surface of the round reservoir, 6 m in diameter. When the water dropped a metre they were able to reach the water surface, but unable to pull out at the other side and a large series was collected as a result. In dry country they were netted frequently over temporary pools. They may be dependent on water in arid areas, not only as a source of moisture, but for the richer insect life associated with it.

### Habits

Egyptian free-tailed bats are gregarious, occurring in colonies numbered in dozens. They roost during the day in caves, rock crevices, under rock exfoliation, in hollow trees and behind the bark of dead trees. Shortridge (1934) stated that in Namibia the colonies can number in hundreds, and Herselman (1980) recorded several colonies numbering in hundreds in the Cape Province. In Zimbabwe, Wright (*in litt.*) reported that in the Pesu River gorge they roosted in nearly vertical cracks in the rock, 15 mm to 20 mm wide, packed in tightly. This colony was located by the noisy squeaking of its members. In western Zimbabwe they were taken from hollow trees by smoking them out. They will also roost in the attics of houses, in crevices in the brick or in any other type of crevice available. Where they are found in caves they seek crevices and crannies in the rock in which to roost. Colonies have a very strong smell.

**Food**

Insectivorous.

**Reproduction**

In the Transvaal, Rautenbach (1982) took gravid females in September, October and December; Smithers & Wilson (1979), in Zimbabwe, a female with a single foetus in November and lactating females in December; and Wright (pers. comm.) recorded lactating females with young in northern Botswana in December. In the Cape Province, Herselman (1980) recorded heavily pregnant females in several localities in November. These data indicate that the young are born during the warm, wet summer months. Apparently maternity colonies are established as Herselman (1980) found all female colonies in November in two localities.

No. 64

## *Tadarida (Tadarida) ansorgei* (Thomas, 1913)

Ansorge's free-tailed bat
Ansorge se losstertvlermuis

Freeman (1981) showed that this species is better placed in the subgenus *Chaerephon* and therefore it is transferred to follow *T. (Chaerephon) pumila* (No. 59), for convenience retaining its original number (No. 64)

# VIII. Family VESPERTILIONIDAE

## Vesper bats

This is by far the largest Family of the insect-eating bats and the most diverse. In the Subregion three Subfamilies are recognised, comprising 10 genera and 29 species and including a range of woolly, long-fingered, serotine, long-eared, hairy, house and other forms, making it difficult to apply a general colloquial name that is applicable to all members. Rosevear (1965) uses the name Vesper bats, borrowing it from the name for the Family which is derived from the Latin for a bat, *vespertilio* which seems appropriate.

Members of the family occur throughout the world, except in the Arctic and Antarctic regions, where there is insufficient insect life to support them. Because of their diversity and the fact that many of the species can only be recognised by examination of their dental and cranial characters, it is impossible to present a key that can be used in the field to distinguish them. The head is devoid of noseleaves, the nostrils circular or crescent-shaped (Fig. VIII.1). The ears are separated widely with fairly conspicuous tragi varying in shape according to the species involved. Their tails are long, the vertebrae enclosed within the interfemoral membrane which is supported on either side by a calcaneum which arises from the ankle.

Fig. VIII.1. Head of *Eptesicus capensis*

In the Subfamily Kerivoulinae the fur is erect and frizzy, the ends of the hair curled; in most of the other species the hair is adpressed to the body.

The wings vary in shape from the long pointed form found in the Miniopterinae to others in which they are more rounded. In all of them the second finger has a metacarpal and one phalanx.

There are no characters by which a Vespertilionid skull can be recognised, there being great diversity within the Family. Even the dentition is variable, the number of teeth varying according to the genus from 30 to 38. Some genera, for example *Nycticeius*, *Scotophilus* and *Scotoecus* have one incisor in the upper jaw while the remainder have two and, although the tooth characters are used in distinguishing the genera, they are very variable. In the genus *Eptesicus* there are no first upper premolars (Fig. VIII.2); in *Pipistrellus* on the other hand they are present (Fig. VIII.3), a character used to differentiate between the two genera. However, specimens of *Eptesicus* are known that possess this tooth on one side only and *Pipistrellus* that lack it or in which it is present again on one side only. Authorities are agreed, however, that it is convenient to retain the two genera (Ellerman & Morrison-Scott, 1951; Rosevear, 1965).

Key to the Subfamilies (Meester *et al.*, 1986)

1. Second phalanx of third digit about three times as long as first; braincase high and rounded
   ... MINIOPTERINAE

   Second phalanx of third digit not especially elongated
   ... 2

2. Ears not funnel-shaped, without deep emargination below tip; tragus short and broad or long and narrow, but not sharply pointed; braincase not particularly high and rounded
   ... VESPERTILIONINAE

   Ears funnel-shaped, with deep emargination below tip; tragus long, narrow, sharply pointed; braincase high and rounded
   ... KERIVOULINAE

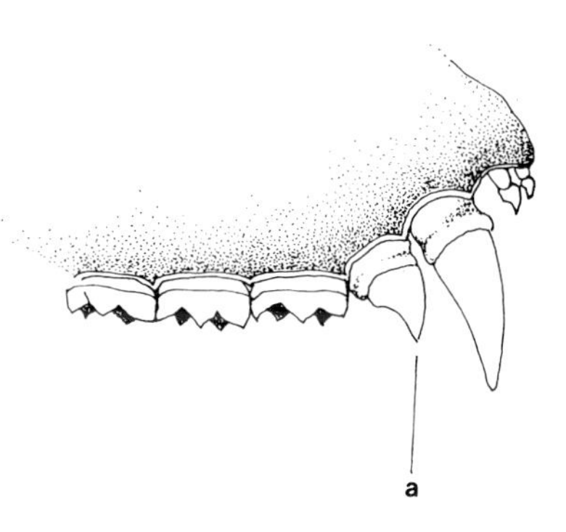


Fig. VIII.2. Upper toothrow of *Eptesicus capensis*, with one upper premolar (a) and no anterior upper premolar.

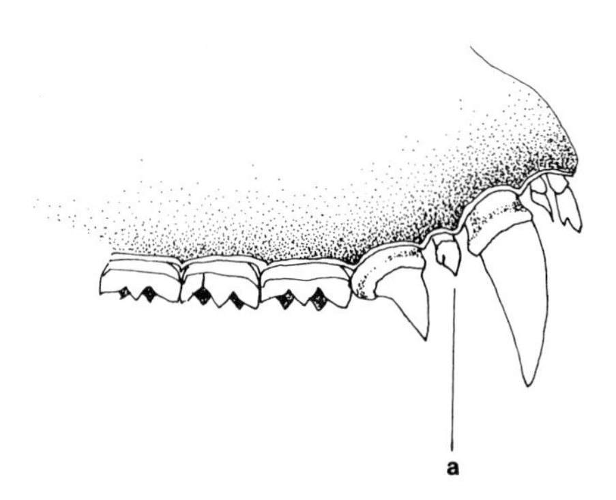


Fig. VIII.3. Upper toothrow of *Pipistrellus nanus* to show small anterior upper premolar (a), between canine and posterior premolar.

## Subfamily MINIOPTERINAE

### Genus *Miniopterus* Bonaparte, 1837

Superficially most members of this genus appear very much alike but there is a wide size range which has in the past led to the description of over a dozen species. Hayman & Hill (1971) recognised only four species, three of which occur in the Subregion. These three species have overlapping forearm lengths and they cannot be separated on this basis alone, as is possible in other genera of bats. The mean length of the skull in fact remains the only criterion by which separation is possible at this juncture. Further study may well show that it is only possible to recognise two species, a large and a small, these being found occurring together in parts of their range (Hayman & Hill, 1971).

Schreibers' long-fingered bat, *M. schreibersii*, which is very common in parts of the Subregion, has a very wide distribution from the Cape Province to Morocco and extralimitally in Europe, Asia, in the Australasian region and in Madagascar.

In all members of the genus the braincase rises abruptly from the rostrum, as in the genus *Kerivoula* from which they can be distinguished, because in *Miniopterus* there are two normal-sized premolars and a third tiny vestigial premolar on either side of the upper jaw compared with *Kerivoula* which has three normal sized premolars. In addition, in *Miniopterus* the two anterior lower premolars are much smaller than the third compared with *Kerivoula* in which they are all approximately equal in size. (See *Kerivoula* Fig. 93.1).

The dental formula is

$I\frac{2}{3}\ C\frac{1}{1}\ P\frac{3}{3}\ M\frac{3}{3} = 38$

Van der Merwe (1985a) recorded the presence of a tiny, vestigial tooth lying between the upper canine and the following premolar on either side of the jaw in all three species of *Miniopterus*. He believed this to be $P^2$ and that therefore the premolar following it should be $P^3$ and not $P^2$ as recorded by Miller (1907).

The lower incisors are trifid, the anterior upper premolar much smaller than the posterior, which exceeds the molars in height.

Key to the species after Meester *et al.* (1986)

1. Size larger, forearm 45–50 mm; skull length 16 mm and more

   ... *inflatus*

   Size smaller, forearm 42–47 mm; skull length *c.* 14–15 mm

   ... 2

2. Forearm 42–44 mm; skull length *c.* 14 mm; colour brownish black and/or russet

   ... *fraterculus*

   Forearm 42–47 mm; skull length *c.* 15 mm; colour slaty-black

   ... *schreibersii*

No. 65

## *Miniopterus inflatus* Thomas, 1903

## Greater long-fingered bat
## Groot grotvlermuis

**Colloquial Name**

The largest of the three species of long-fingered bats occurring in the Subregion.

**Taxonomic Notes**

Meester *et al.* (1986) listed two subspecies from the continent, only one of which occurs in the Subregion, *M. i. rufus* Sanborn, 1936 which has a marginal distribution in the northeast.

**Description**

As the name implies this is the largest of the three species of long-fingered bats that are found in the Subregion. In average measurements of total length they are in fact the same size as Schreibers' long-fingered bat (Table 65.1), but when the lengths of the forearms, their masses and in particular the lengths of their skulls are considered, the size difference is noticeable. This species has a total skull length of 16 mm or more, Schreibers' about 15 mm and the lesser about 14 mm.

The colour of the upper parts is deep chocolate or sooty-brown, a little lighter on the under parts. Like other members of the genus, the wings are long and pointed, the wing and interfemoral membranes very dark brown, almost black. Their ears are small with rounded tips, the ear tragus long and parallel-sided with a round tip and slightly expanded at the base of the outer edge (Fig. 65.1).

Fig. 65.1. Ear tragus of *Miniopterus inflatus*

In the skull the braincase rises abruptly from the rostrum as in *Kerivoula*, but can be distinguished from members of this genus as *Miniopterus* has only two premolars in the upper jaw as compared with *Kerivoula* which has three. They have three in the lower jaw, the two anterior ones smaller than the third, whereas in *Kerivoula* they are all about the same size. The lower incisors are trifid, the outer one indistinctly so. The anterior upper premolar is much smaller than the posterior one, which is taller than the molars.

The dental formula is

$I\frac{2}{3}\ C\frac{1}{1}\ P\frac{3}{3}\ M\frac{3}{3} = 38$

**Table 65.1**

Measurements (mm) and mass (g) of greater long-fingered bats, *M. inflatus*, from Zimbabwe (Smithers & Wilson, 1979)

| | Irrespective of sex | | |
|---|---|---|---|
| | x̄ | n | Range |
| TL | 112 | 4 | 111–116 |
| T | 56 | 4 | 56 |
| Hf c/u | 11 | 4 | 10–11 |
| E | 12 | 4 | 11–12 |
| F/a | 47 | 4 | 45–48 |
| Mass | 14,7 | 4 | 12,5–16,8 |
| Skull TL | 16 | 4 | 16 |

**Distribution**

Very few records of the greater long-fingered bat are available and these are so scattered that it is impossible at the moment to assess their distributional limits.

*South of the Sahara, excluding the Southern African Subregion*

Recorded from **Cameroun; Gabon; Ethiopia;** southern **Somalia; Kenya;** western and eastern **Zaire; Uganda** and from Kilwa Island, Lake Mweru, **Zambia**.

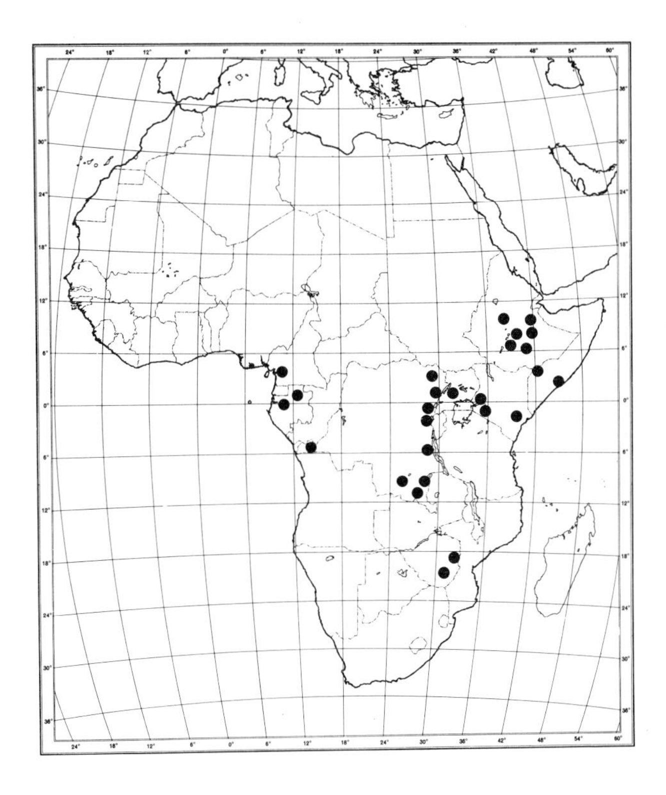

*Southern African Subregion*

Recorded from Mutare and the Zimbabwe National Monument, **Zimbabwe**, where in both localities they were taken in association with *M. schreibersii*.

**Habitat**

The availability of caves or mine adits and a plentiful food supply are probably the more important habitat requirements of this species; the type of vegetational association less important.

**Habits**

Practically nothing is known of the habits of this species. Where it occurs with Schreibers' long-fingered bat, *M. schreibersii*, in the Subregion it does so in very small numbers. Hanging in a cave with *M. schreibersii*, the size difference is not noticeable and it is only when the skulls are examined that this becomes apparent.

**Food**

Insectivorous.

**Reproduction**

No information available.

---

No. 66

## *Miniopterus fraterculus* Thomas & Schwann, 1906

## Lesser long-fingered bat
## Klein grotvlermuis

---

**Colloquial Name**

The smallest of the three species of long-fingered bats that occur in the Subregion.

**Taxonomic Notes**

No subspecies have been described.

**Description**

About 90 mm in total length with a tail of about 50 mm, the lesser long-fingered bat, as the name implies, is smaller than the commoner Schreibers' long-fingered bat, *M. schreibersii* (Table 66.1). Their upper parts are a rich russet-brown, the hair soft and woolly, the top of the head tending to be slightly darker than the back. The under parts are a rich light brown, darker on the throat. The wings are long and pointed with black membranes, the interfemoral membrane translucent dark brown. The light brown hair of the under parts extends sparsely onto the wing membranes between the elbow and the thighs.

The ears are small for their size, strongly curved on their inner edges, the tips bluntly pointed.

**Table 66.1**

Measurements (mm) of a male and female lesser long-fingered bat, *M. fraterculus*, from the Transvaal (Rautenbach, 1982)

| | TL | T | Hfc/u | E | F/a |
|---|---|---|---|---|---|
| Male | 98 | 48 | 8 | 8 | 42 |
| Female | 99 | 52 | 8 | 8 | 42 |

**Distribution**

With the exception of records from southern **Kenya** and southern **Malawi**, all the other known records to date are from the Subregion.

*Southern African Subregion*

Recorded from Mutare, **Zimbabwe**; 25 km southwest of Covane, Inhambane District, **Mozambique**, south of the Zambezi River; the Barberton District, **Transvaal**; from the **Natal** midlands, and from localities in the southern and eastern parts of the **Cape Province**.

**Habitat**

Dependent on the shelter of caves or mine adits and a plentiful food supply, these factors may rank as their principal habitat requirements.

**Habits**

Like *M. schreibersii* and *M. inflatus* this is a cave dwelling species which occurs, like *M. inflatus*, alongside *M. schreibersii*, in small numbers. Nothing is known of its habits.

**Food**

Insectivorous.

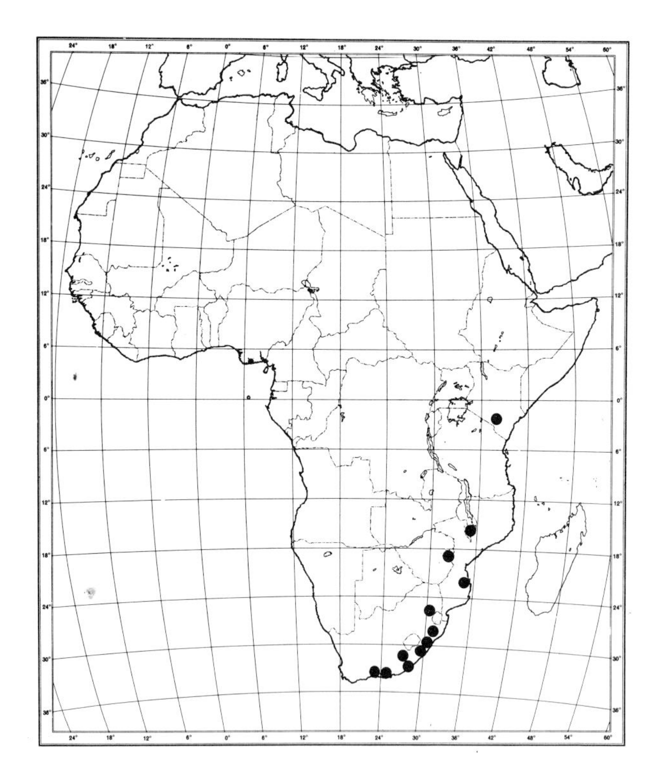

## Reproduction

Bernard (1980a) showed that in Natal copulation and ovulation took place about mid-May to the beginning of June. This was followed by a period of delayed implantation of the embryo of some two and a half months, parturition occurring in December. The females carried a single foetus in the right uterine horn (Bernard, 1980b).

No. 67

# *Miniopterus schreibersii* (Kuhl, 1819)

## Schreibers' long-fingered bat
## Schreibers se grotvlermuis

Plate 4

## Taxonomic Notes

Meester *et al.* (1986) included all the material from the Subregion in *M. s. natalensis* (A. Smith, 1833).

## Description

Schreibers' long-fingered bats have a total length of some 110 mm, with tails of about 50 mm and a mean mass of 10 g (Table 67.1). The upper parts are very dark brown, the under parts slightly lighter, especially towards the lower belly. The wings are long and pointed, the wing and interfemoral membranes very dark brown, nearly black. The ears are small for the size of the body and have rounded ends. The shape of the skull is typical for members of this genus (Fig. 67.1).

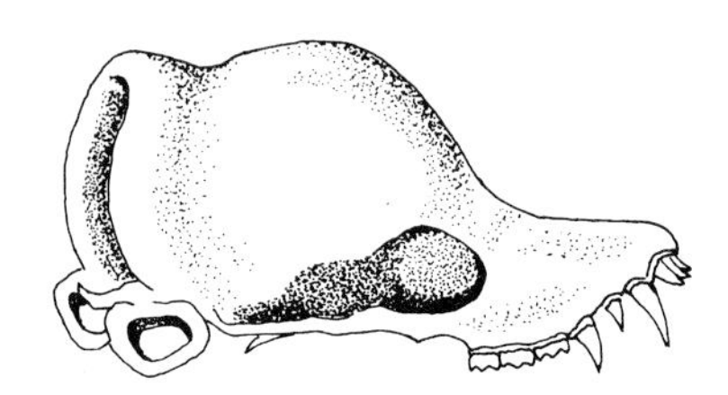

Fig. 67.1. Skull of *Miniopterus schreibersii*

**Table 67.1**

Measurements (mm) and mass (g) of Schreibers' long-fingered bats, *M. schreibersii*, from the Transvaal (Rautenbach, 1982)

| | Males | | | Females | | |
|---|---|---|---|---|---|---|
| | $\bar{x}$ | n | Range | $\bar{x}$ | n | Range |
| TL | 112 | 54 | 102–128 | 109 | 39 | 93–118 |
| T | 53 | 55 | 46–60 | 52 | 41 | 46–58 |
| Hf c/u | 10 | 55 | 8–11 | 10 | 35 | 8–11 |
| E | 11 | 56 | 8–13 | 11 | 38 | 9–12 |
| F/a | 45 | 25 | 42–48 | 45 | 12 | 44–47 |
| Mass | 10,1 | 33 | 6,0–13,0 | 10,2 | 19 | 7,8–12,6 |

## Distribution

Schreibers' long-fingered bat has extralimitally to the continent a very wide distribution extending eastwards from Europe through India and the Far East southwards through Malaya to northern and eastern Australia. Between the European and western North African populations there is a break in their distribution southwards, occurring again from Cameroun and Ethiopia south to the Cape Province.

*Extralimital to the continent*

Recorded from **Spain** and **France** eastwards to **Turkey** and south to **Israel** and from there through southern **Asia; India** and **Sri Lanka** east to **Malaya** and north to **Japan** and south to northern and eastern **Australia**.

*North Africa*

Recorded from **Morocco; Algeria** and **Tunisia**.

*South of the Sahara, excluding the Southern African Subregion*

Recorded from **Cameroun; Central African Republic**; southern **Sudan; Ethiopia**; northeastern, southeastern and southern **Zaire; Rwanda; Uganda**; southeastern **Kenya**; parts of **Tanzania; Mozambique**, north of the Zambezi River; **Malawi; Zambia** and **Angola**.

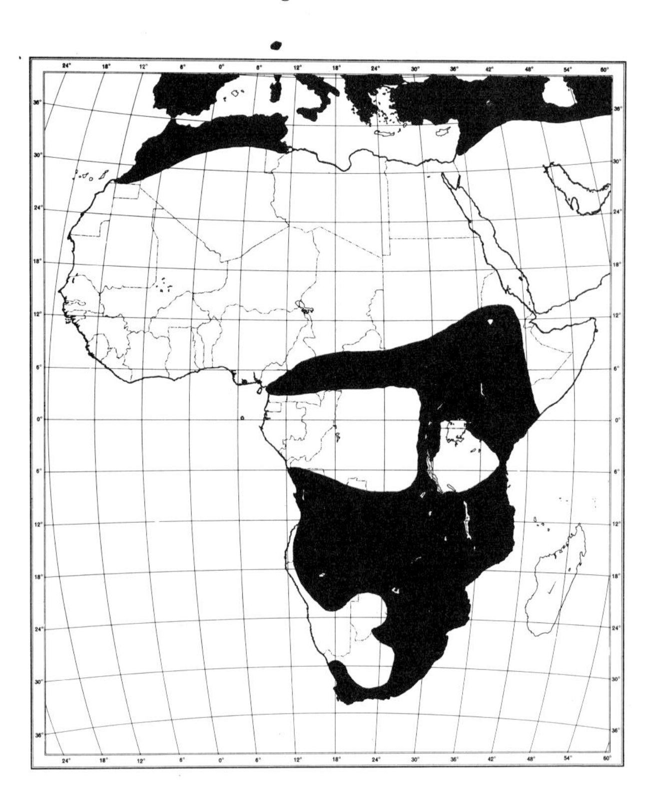

*Southern African Subregion*

They occur in northern **Namibia**, about as far south as Gobabis; in northern, eastern and parts of southern **Botswana**; throughout **Zimbabwe** and **Mozambique**, south of the Zambezi River; in parts of the **Transvaal**; in **Natal** and the **Orange Free State**. In the **Cape Province** they occur widely except in the central and in parts of the north of the province.

### Habitat

Schreibers' long-fingered bats are cave dwellers and the availability of caves or other similar substantial shelter such as mine adits are an essential habitat requirement. These and a plentiful food supply may well govern their occurrence, for otherwise they are found in a wide range of vegetational associations and in areas with a mean annual rainfall as low as 300 mm to over 1 000 mm. The maternity caves in which the females give birth must provide the correct conditions of temperature (Van der Merwe, 1973c), and the availability of such caves must be an important habitat requirement. Dwyer (1966) showed that suitable maternity caves could attract females from an area with a radius of up to 300 km. Herselman (1980) showed that in the Cape Province banded individuals moved up to distances of 250 km to sites for winter hibernation.

### Habits

Schreibers' long-fingered bats are gregarious. In a study in the Transvaal, Van der Merwe (1975) found that movements involve both long distance seasonal migrations as well as local inter-cavern movements.

Annual migrations take place between caves situated on the southern Transvaal Highveld and caves situated in the northern Transvaal bushveld. These long distance migrations occur during the periods late winter and spring, for movement towards the bushveld caves, and late summer migrations for movement towards the Highveld caves (Van der Merwe, 1975). These long distance migrations range over 150 km and are undertaken by pregnant females en route to maternity caves situated in the northern Transvaal bushveld.

Later the same females and their weaned young return to caves in the southern Transvaal Highveld where mating and hibernating colonies are formed. Females from various Highveld caves, and perhaps further afield, aggregate in the same maternity caves year after year to give birth and raise their young. In some of the maternity caves the number of adult females alone is more than 100 000 (Van der Merwe, 1973a; 1978).

These north-bound migrations start at the end of July (Van der Merwe, 1973a; 1978) when the hibernation period comes to an end and the hibernating colonies start breaking up. Females do not necessarily migrate directly to the maternity caves but, in some cases, make use of pre-maternity caves in the northern Transvaal bushveld where they stay temporarily until the urge to give birth drives them to the maternity caves (Van der Merwe, 1973a). Many females, however, do not migrate immediately after breaking up of the hibernation colonies, but stay on in some Highveld caves even as late as November before migrating directly to the maternity caves (Van der Merwe, 1975). At this stage (November) many juveniles have already been born in the maternity caves (Van der Merwe, 1975).

Many males also undertake this migration with the females. Some of them, however, migrate directly to the maternity caves to be there well in advance of the females. The vast majority of them do not stay long at the maternity caves, but start leaving them as there is an increased influx of pregnant females.

Movements of the males after leaving the maternity caves are somewhat obscure. They may either stay in some other, still unknown, bushveld caves, or more possibly migrate directly back to the Highveld where they stay in bachelor groups, awaiting the return of the females towards late summer. Many males, however, do not seem to migrate long distances at all, but stay on in the Highveld caves after the hibernating colonies have broken up (Van der Merwe, 1975). The absence of males in the maternity caves is most probably to avoid any form of competition with the full-term or lactating females, especially competition for food, as these females have a very high metabolic rate during that stage.

On the southern Transvaal Highveld local inter-cavern movements are common, even during winter when they are supposed to be in hibernation (Van der Merwe, 1973a; 1975). Hibernation has been found not to be a continuous period of torpidity, but is characterised by much activity such as intra and inter-cavern movements (Van der Merwe, 1973a; Norton & Van der Merwe, 1978). During periods of torpidity, however, these bats can be handled with ease for periods of more than 20 minutes before they will start waking up. Much of these activities during the hibernation period may be attributed to the relatively high cave temperatures prevailing in some of the Highveld caves during the winter months (Norton & Van der Merwe, 1978). In some of these Highveld caves their numbers vary from a few individuals up to an estimated number of 4 000 (Van der Merwe, 1973a).

During the day they roost in caves and mine adits where total darkness prevails. They have been recorded from vertical mine shafts and in the roofs of houses (Smithers & Wilson, 1979). Roberts (1951) stated that they will also roost in crevices in rocks and trees.

They hang from the ceilings of caves in tightly packed clusters, using their hind claws for anchorage. They may also use the walls and then the claws of both feet and thumbs are used to secure a hold. Cluster formation starts when a few individuals land on all fours on the ceiling, holding with the claws of both feet and thumbs. They clamber around until a suitable anchorage is found for the claws on the feet, then drop into the hanging position with the head down. New arrivals aggregate around them causing the cluster to expand rapidly. Late arrivals may land on the middle of the growing cluster in an attempt to secure a foothold on the ceiling. They use the claws of both feet and thumbs to cling to the heads and shoulders of other individuals in the clusters until a foothold is found, or they may crawl over the heads and shoulders of those already hanging towards the perimeter where they can secure a position.

When landing on the walls, they do so with their heads upwards, then turn around until the head is down and crawl around until a secure hold is found. Occasionally individuals use crevices, crawling into them backwards, others following, until the crevice is full of bats (Van der Merwe, 1973b).

In disbanding of the clusters the individuals on the outside tend to take to flight first, working towards the centre. In large clusters however, some of the individuals in the centre may wriggle loose, leaving a gap, from the edges of which individuals detach themselves.

Schreibers' long-fingered bats are extremely fast fliers, their long, pointed wings adapted for this purpose. They tend to fly high, swooping in the air like swallows. When they hang in the roosting places, the long, tapering ends of the wings fold back, the tail and its interfemoral membrane rolling up against their bellies.

In the caves they hang in closely packed clusters, estimated at densities of up to 2 800 individuals/m$^2$ (Norton & Van der Merwe, 1978).

The winters can be very cold on the Transvaal Highveld, and Twente (1955a) postulated that hibernating bats in temperate regions must roost in cool places in order to keep their body metabolism at a sufficiently low level to prevent over-utilisation of their fat resources before the onset of the next favourable feeding season. Conversely during their feeding season, when insect life is plentiful, as it is in the Transvaal during the summer months from about September to March, they must roost up in places warm enough for digestion and assimilation to proceed.

Van der Merwe (1973c), after study of the temperature and humidity in a cave used for hibernation, came to the conclusion that low temperature was the deciding factor in its choice.

### Food

Insectivorous.

### Reproduction

In the Transvaal, Rautenbach (1982) found gravid females in October and November. Smithers & Wilson (1979) recorded them in September and October in Zimbabwe, and Herselman (1980) in the Cape Province in October. The females normally produce one young at birth, but Herselman (1980) found one female, out of 150 examined, carrying twins.

The pattern of reproduction is similar to that of temperate zone *Miniopterus* in that ovulation and fertilisation follow immediately upon copulation in the autumn, and neither sex stores sperm for prolonged periods (Van der Merwe, 1980). The females enter hibernation already pregnant, with the blastocyst lying unattached in the right uterine horn (Van der Merwe, 1980). On the Transvaal Highveld, Van der Merwe (1979) found that mating takes place in mixed clusters of males and females during late summer and autumn. Ovulations and conceptions peak towards the end of March and terminate towards the end of April.

Copulation and fertilisation are followed by a long gestation period of eight months, with the peak of births during the last half of November terminating towards mid December (Van der Merwe, 1979). After fertilisation the conceptus only develops as far as the bilaminar blastocyst stage and then shows no conspicuous development for four months while lying unattached in the right uterine horn (Van der Merwe, 1979, 1980). This period of delayed implantation overlaps to some extent with the winter hibernation period (Van der Merwe, 1980). Implantations occur during the winter with a peak towards the end of July when the hibernation period normally comes to an end (Van der Merwe, 1979). For the next four months embryonic and foetal development occur during which time the foetuses reach an average mass of 2,7 g at birth (Van der Merwe, 1979).

At birth the juveniles are pink, the only signs of pigmentation being a faint coloration around the rostrum where there are a few faint vibrissae. The ears are fully erect and the eyes closed. The milk teeth are sharp and the thumbs and hind feet well developed. The feet and thumbs are very important as the females deposit their young on the roof only a few hours after being born and they are especially dependent on their hind feet for attachment (Van der Merwe, 1978). After birth the juveniles remain attached to their mothers for only a few hours, after which they are placed in a separate juvenile cluster. Normally a more secluded place within a maternity cave is selected to serve as the maternity chamber. This phenomenon is to promote high and stable temperatures within the chamber, which is important for maximum growth of the juveniles. In these chambers the adult females control the temperature by hanging at various distances from the juveniles. When the temperature drops too low, they will hang nearer to the juveniles, sometimes closely surrounding them, and when the temperature increases too much, they will move away. When the juveniles are older and more active they generate more heat themselves, which may result in the females hanging on the outside of the chamber to prevent it from overheating (Van der Merwe, 1978).

Maternity colonies break up towards the end of the summer and the females and weaned young start migrating back to caves on the southern Transvaal Highveld where mating and hibernating colonies are formed (Van der Merwe, 1975).

## Subfamily VESPERTILIONINAE

Key to the genera, after Meester *et al.* (1986)

1. Six upper, six lower cheekteeth on each side
   ... *Myotis*

   Fewer than six upper and six lower cheekteeth
   ... 2

2. Five upper, five lower cheekteeth; ears not lengthened; two upper incisors on each side; wing with fifth finger not shortened; ears not joined at base
   ... *Pipistrellus*

   Four upper, five lower cheekteeth; ears notably lengthened only in exceptional cases
   ... 3

3. Two upper incisors on each side
   ... 4

   One upper incisor on each side
   ... 6

4. Rostrum very short and broad; braincase very high, more than two-thirds of condylobasal length; lower lip with lobe at posterior angle; frequently with body pattern of spots and/or stripes, or conspicuous reticulation of wing membranes
   ... *Chalinolobus*

   Rostrum not shortened; braincase not elevated; no body or wing pattern
   ... 5

5. Ears 18 mm or more, about half length of forearm
   ... *Laephotis*

   Ears less than 18 mm, much less than half length of forearm
   ... *Eptesicus*

6. Size larger, forearm not less than 46 mm; first and second upper molars with W-pattern obsolescent; tragus long and tapering
   ... *Scotophilus*

   Size smaller, forearm less than 46 mm; first and second upper molars with normal W-pattern; tragus either sickle-shaped or short and broad
   ... 7

7. Skull with rostrum not broadened; palatal emargination narrow; anterior lower premolar about half the crown area of the next premolar; upper canines with rounded anterior surface; tragus halfmoon-shaped; penis not enlarged; forearm 29–33 mm
   ... *Nycticeius*

   Skull with rostrum notably broadened, particularly across lachrymals; palatal emargination broader; lower premolars equal in crown area; upper canines with broad, flat anterior face; tragus short and broad; penis greatly lengthened; forearm 28–38 mm
   ... *Scotoecus*

## Genus *Myotis* Kaup, 1829

The generic name is derived from the Greek *os otis* an ear, and *mys* a mouse, referring to their large ears.

Members of this genus can be separated from other vespertilionids by the elongated muzzle, the rich coppery-red colour of the body, the soft fur, which stands out from the body and the characteristic shape of the ear tragus. In the skull the braincase rises from the elongated muzzle in a rather even slope and they have three premolars in both the upper and lower jaws (Fig. 72.1).

The dental formula is

$I\frac{2}{3}\ C\frac{1}{1}\ P\frac{3}{3}\ M\frac{3}{3} = 38$

the great number of teeth accounting for the elongated muzzle. The upper two incisors are bifid, the lower incisors trifid. The skull has no sagittal or supraoccipital crests.

Key to the species after Hayman & Hill (1971)
(Measurements in mm)

1. Size larger, forearm over 52
   ... *welwitschii*

   Size smaller, forearm 52 or less
   ... 2

2. Wings with glands; first two upper premolars greatly reduced and closely crowded together laterally
   ... 3

   Wings without glands; first two upper premolars not greatly reduced, not crowded together laterally (Fig. 72.1)
   ... 4

3. Size smaller, forearm 32,5–32,9; upper parts dull drab
   ... *seabrai*

   Size larger, forearm 34,5; upper parts honey-yellow
   ... *lesueuri*

4. Size larger, forearm 47–52 ... *tricolor*

Size smaller, forearm less than 47 ... *bocagei*

No. 68

## *Myotis welwitschii* (Gray, 1866)

## Welwitsch's hairy bat
## Welwitsch se langhaarvlermuis

Plate 5

### Colloquial Name

Named after Welwitsch, an Austrian botanist, who made extensive collections in Angola.

### Taxonomic Notes

Meester *et al.* (1986) did not recognise any subspecies.

### Description

Welwitsch's hairy bat is about 120 mm in total length, with a tail about 60 mm and a mass of 14,0 g (Table 68.1). It is the largest of the four species that occur in the Subregion. As in the other species of *Myotis*, the hair stands erect giving it a hairy look from which the colloquial name originates. The upper parts are a pale coppery-red, very similar to *M. tricolor*, but if anything, a shade darker. The individual hairs are black at the base and broadly tipped with coppery-red. The top of the head and neck tend to be paler in colour than the remainder of the body. The under parts are whitish, tinged with coppery-red.

The skin over the bones of the wings is light reddish-brown, the membranes dark, nearly black, and are reticulated with a profuse series of faint white lines, and with a few tiny yellow spots between the forearm and the fifth digit. The interfemoral membrane is coppery-red with a sparse coating of hair near the body and profusely covered with a series of small, irregularly shaped black dots. The ears are large with rounded points and are coppery-red in colour with narrow black edges.

**Table 68.1**

Measurements (mm) and mass (g) of Welwitsch's hairy bat, *M. welwitschii*, from Zimbabwe (Smithers & Wilson, 1979)

| | Irrespective of sex | | |
|---|---|---|---|
| | $\bar{x}$ | n | Range |
| TL | 119 | 7 | 105–127 |
| T | 58 | 7 | 52–63 |
| Hf c/u | 13 | 7 | 11–15 |
| E | 21 | 6 | 19–22 |
| F/a | 55 | 6 | 52–58 |
| Måss | 14,1 | 6 | 12,0–16,5 |

### Distribution

Records of this species are too few and scattered to allow an understanding of the limits within which they may occur. The original specimen from which the species was described is labelled "Angola", without further details of the locality from which it originated. It was taken, however, in this country by Hayman (1963).

*South of the Sahara, excluding the Southern African Subregion*

Recorded from the Ulurugu Mountains and from the east and southwest of **Tanzania**; from southeastern and northeastern

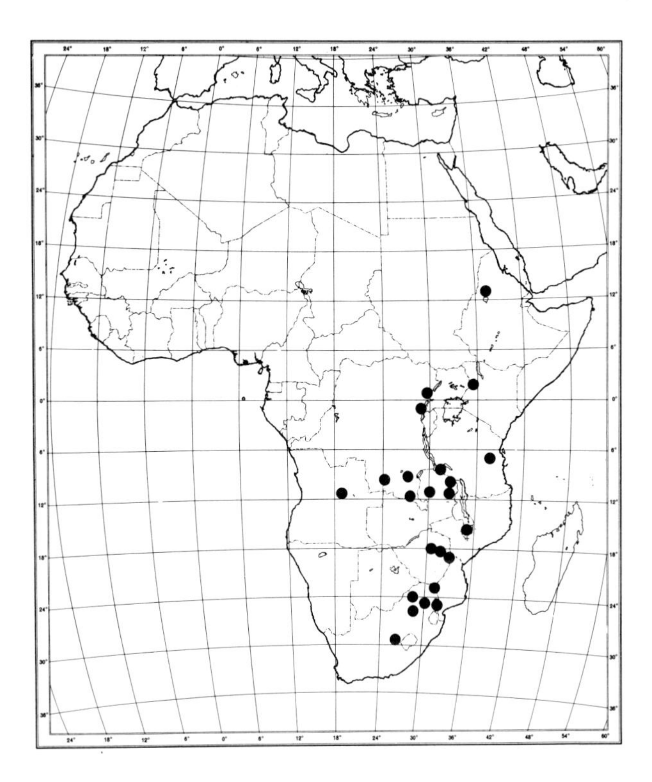

**Zaire; Kenya; Ethiopia**; central **Angola**; northwestern **Zambia** and the Southern Province of **Malawi**.

*Southern African Subregion*

Recorded from Mashonaland and the Eastern Districts of **Zimbabwe**; parts of the central and eastern **Transvaal**; and the **Orange Free State**.

### Habitat

A savanna woodland species.

### Habits

A solitary species that has been taken roosting during the day hanging in bushes and trees (Rautenbach, 1982; Smithers & Wilson, 1979). They enter houses at night when foraging.

### Food

Insectivorous.

### Reproduction

No information available.

No. 69

## *Myotis seabrai* (Thomas, 1912)

## Angola hairy bat
## Angola-langhaarvlermuis

### Colloquial Name

So called as the original specimen originated from Mossamedes on the southwestern coast of Angola.

### Taxonomic Notes

No subspecies have been described.

### Description

*M. seabrai* and *M. lesueuri* are very similar, *M. seabrai*, however, being slightly smaller with a forearm length of 32,5 to 32,9 mm as opposed to that of *M. lesueuri* at 34,5 mm. *M. seabrai* is, in addition, darker in colour, a dull drab with a tinge of yellow, the base of the hairs a pale slate-grey. Too few specimens of either species are available to properly assess any variation in characters or factors which might assist in separating these two closely allied species.

**Distribution**

*Angola*

Only known in **Angola** from the type locality Mossamedes in the southwest.

*Southern African Subregion*

Recorded from Berseba in **Namibia** and from three localities in the northwestern **Cape Province**, namely Goodhouse on the Orange River, Steyerskraal, Goegab and east and south of this (Herselman, 1980).

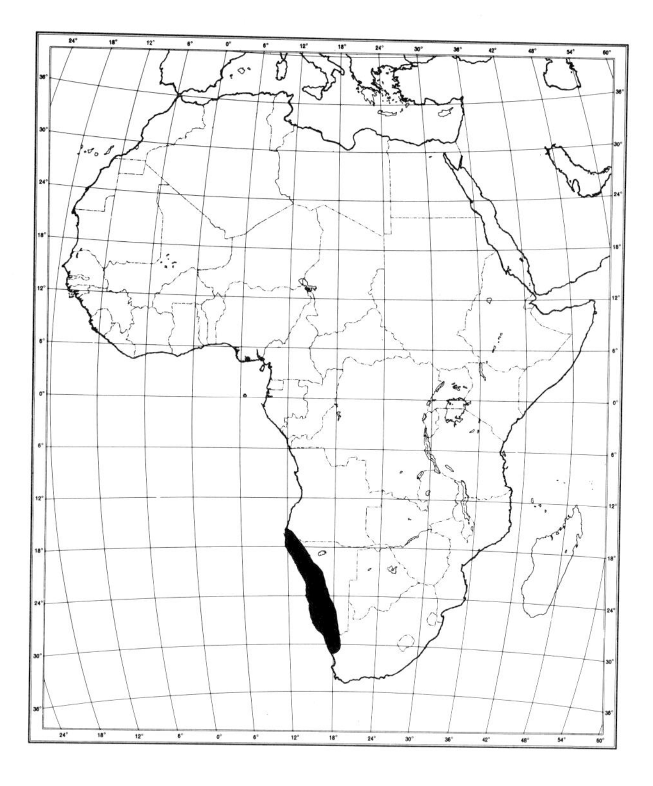

**Habitat**

Too little information is available to allow an assessment of the habitat requirements of this species. All the localities from which it has been taken lie in areas with a mean annual rainfall of less than 100 mm. Mossamedes is a coastal town lying in desert surroundings, Goodhouse a settlement on the Orange River with irrigated citrus orchards and riverine associations, and the other localities all lying in arid terrain.

**Habits**

Shortridge (1934) collected two at Berseba, Namibia, flying around a church, and he suspected that they roosted in the steeple during the day. Roberts (1951) stated that their flight was not so strong or erratic as the Cape serotine bat, *E. capensis*, and on emerging in the evening, they had a comparatively steady, direct flight. He observed that as dusk descended they circled low around trees and bushes, at Goodhouse around orange trees, snapping insects from the leaves.

**Food**

Insectivorous.

**Reproduction**

No information available.

---

No. 70

## *Myotis lesueuri* (Roberts, 1919)

## Lesueur's hairy bat
## Lesueur se langhaarvlermuis

---

**Colloquial Name**

Named after J.S. le Sueur of L'Ormarins in the Paarl District, Cape Province, who recovered the original specimen from his cat.

**Taxonomic Notes**

The two species *M. lesueuri* and *M. seabrai* are differentiated purely on a matter of size, *M. lesueuri* being the larger of the two, with a forearm length of 34,5 mm against that of *M. seabrai* at 32,5 to 32,9 mm. Hayman & Hill (1971) questioned the status of this species, noting that there has been some doubt as to whether it possesses wing glands. Herselman & Norton (1985) showed that some individuals had a gland on one or other of the wings, whereas in others it was absent. Hayman & Hill (1971) listed both species on the basis of difference in size.

**Description**

Lesueur's hairy bats have a total length of some 90 mm and tails 43 mm in length. The upper parts are honey-yellow in colour, the under parts much paler, a pale yellowish-white. The head is pale like the under parts, the face brown. The individual hairs on the body are black at the base. The wing and interfemoral membranes are dark brown. The two species *M. lesueuri* and *M. seabrai* are so alike that they can only be distinguished on size, the best criterion being the length of the forearm (see **Taxonomic notes**).

**Distribution**

*Southern African Subregion*

Confined in their distribution to parts of the southwestern **Cape Province** where they occur from the vicinity of Franschhoek north to Citrusdal and northeast to Beaufort West and Mazelsfontein in the Great Karoo. Herselman (1980) in spite of the scarcity of this species, believed that in time they will be shown to occur more widely in the Cape Province.

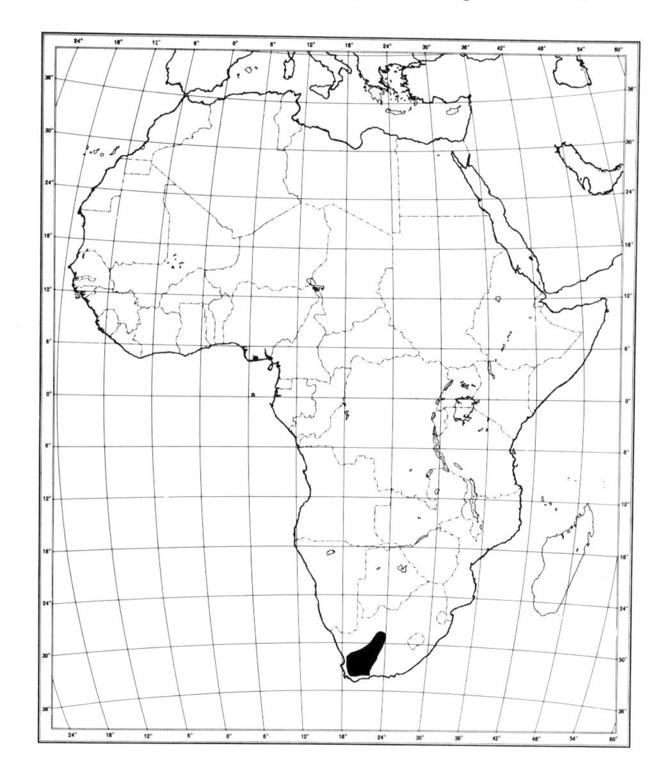

## Food

Insectivorous.

## Habitat, Habits and Reproduction

No information is available as the majority of the specimens have either been trapped or picked up dead.

---

No. 71

# *Myotis tricolor* (Temminck, 1832)

## Temminck's hairy bat
## Temminck se langhaarvlermuis

Plate 4

---

## Colloquial Name

Named after C.J. Temminck who was the author of the *Monographies de Mammalogie* (1827) and whose name is perpetuated in that of the pangolin, *Manis temminckii*.

## Taxonomic Notes

No subspecies are recognised.

## Description

Temminck's hairy bats have a total length of about 100 mm with a tail about half this length. The upper parts are a pale coppery-brown, the individual hairs narrowly light grey at their bases, then broadly pale buff with coppery-brown tips. The under parts are lighter in colour, pale brown washed faintly with coppery-brown. The wing membranes are dark brown, the interfemoral membrane with a dense covering of coppery-brown hair, near the body naked towards the hind margin. The ears have rounded tips and are brown in colour.

## Distribution

All records to date, with the exception of the single record from western Zaire (Hayman, Misonne & Verheyen, 1966) indicate an easterly distribution on the continent from western Ethiopia, from where there are a number of records, to the southwestern Cape Province where it has been taken in a number of localities. It is not, however, well represented from the intervening areas, records being few and scattered.

*South of the Sahara, excluding the Southern African Subregion*

They have been taken in western **Ethiopia**; in **Kenya; Uganda; Zaire**; **Zambia; Malawi**, but are not recorded from Tanzania or the northeastern parts of Mozambique, but probably do occur.

*Southern African Subregion*

They occur in eastern **Zimbabwe** and adjacent parts of **Mozambique** south of the Zambezi River, in parts of the **Transvaal, Orange Free State, Natal** and **Transkei** and in the southern and southwestern parts of the **Cape Province**. Not so far recorded from Lesotho, but may well occur.

## Habitat

They occur predominantly in savanna woodland, but penetrate into drier, more open terrain in the southern parts of their range. Their occurrence is probably governed more by the availability of caves and mine adits, in which to roost during the day, than the vegetational associations in which they are found.

## Habits

A gregarious species, occurring in colonies numbering dozens, roosting during the day in caves and mine adits. They appear to have a preference for those that are waterlogged and where they are undisturbed (Roberts, 1951; Herselman, 1980). They hang from the ceilings or walls; in the former case Roberts (1951) stated that they clung either with the claws of the feet or with the aid of these as well as the claws

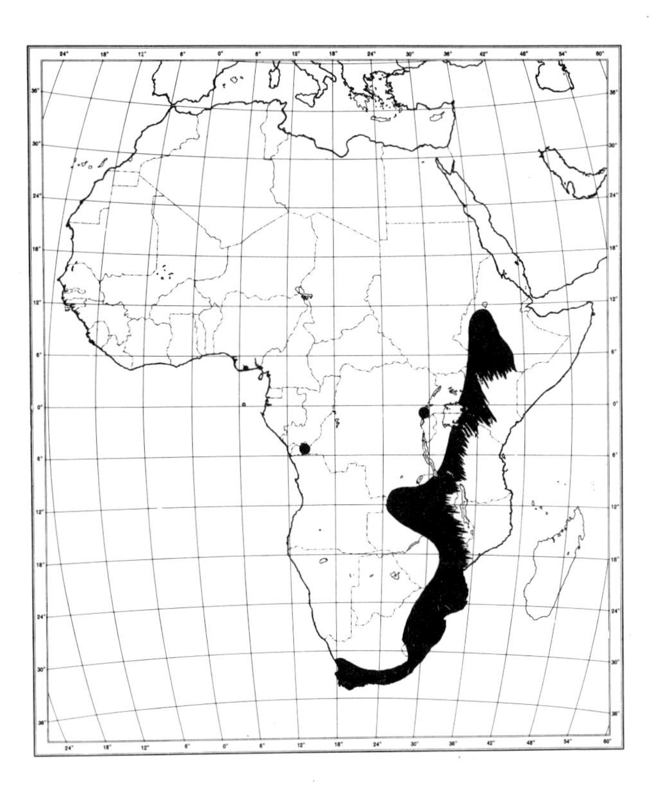

on the thumbs. There is evidence of local movement, for Herselman (1980) reported that an individual ringed in De Hoop Cave, Cape Province, was recaptured in a cave at Montagu, a distance of 90 km away. In the roosting places they are often found in association with Schreibers' long-fingered bats, *Miniopterus schreibersii*, and Cape horseshoe bats, *Rhinolophus capensis*.

## Food

Insectivorous.

## Reproduction

Bernard (1982b) found that copulation took place in mid-April in Natal and ovulation and fertilisation in mid-September. The gestation period was estimated to be 63 days, parturition occurring between mid-November to mid-December, followed by a six weeks period of lactation. He assumed that the females stored the sperm in their uterine horns between mid-April and mid-September, a reproductive strategy reported for north-temperate members of the genus.

Herselman (1980) reported gravid females and juveniles in the Cape Province towards the end of October, females giving birth to their young from late October to the middle of November.

---

No. 72

# *Myotis bocagei* (Peters, 1870)

## Rufous hairy bat
## Rooi langhaarvlermuis

---

## Colloquial Name

This species is often called Bocage's hairy bat or Bocage's banana bat. J.V. Barbosa du Bocage was an eminent Portuguese zoologist who worked during the 19th century, and who named material from the Congo and Angola collected by his Portuguese colleague Snr M. Jose d'Anchieta.

### Taxonomic Notes

Hayman & Hill (1971) listed two subspecies, *M. b. cupreolus* Thomas, 1904 from West Africa and *M. b. bocagei* from the remainder of the species' range.

### Description

Rufous hairy bats have a total length of about 100 mm, with tails 40 mm in length and a mass of about 7,0 g. They are a very beautiful species with their coppery-red upper parts and almost black ears, wing and interfemoral membranes. The under parts are lighter in colour than the upper parts and are off-white washed with coppery-red. The hair on the body is narrowly black at the base with broad coppery-red tips. The inner margins of the ears are strongly convex, sweeping out to the broadly rounded tips, the outer edges strongly concave, giving the ear the appearance of a blunt-pointed sickle.

In members of the genus *Myotis* there are three premolars in each side both in the upper and lower jaw (Fig. 72.1). The ear tragus is long and has a rounded tip (Fig. 72.2).

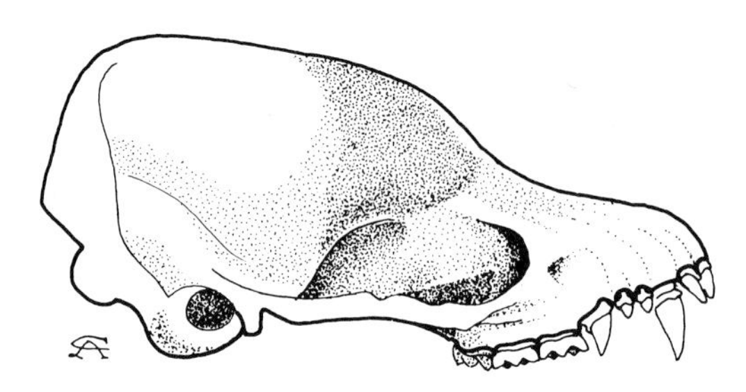

Fig. 72.1. Skull of *Myotis bocagei*.

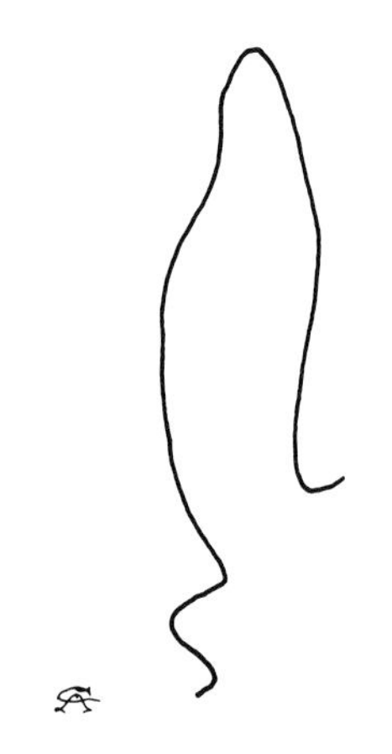

Fig. 72.2. Ear tragus of *Myotis bocagei*.

### Distribution

Particularly in the eastern and southern parts of their distributional range Bocage's hairy bats are poorly represented in collections and it is not possible at the moment to show their limits of occurrence. In West Africa, Rosevear (1965) showed that *M. b. cupreolus* occurs from Liberia eastwards in the forest zone.

*Extralimital to the continent*

They occur in **Aden** in southwestern Arabia.

*South of the Sahara, excluding the southern African Subregion*

Recorded from **Niger; Guinea** and **Liberia** eastwards to southern **Cameroun; Equatorial Guinea** and **Zaire**. The original specimen was collected at Duque de Braganza, northern **Angola**, and remains the only record from that country. They are recorded from the **Central African Republic; Uganda; Rwanda; Burundi**; central **Kenya** and southwestern **Tanzania**; and in **Zambia** from Chingi on the

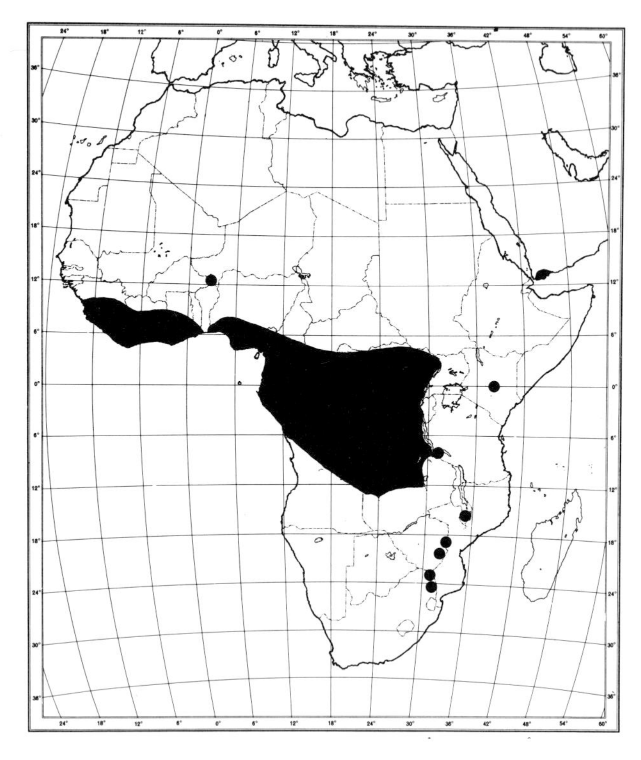

Angola border in the west and from the Southern Province of **Malawi**.

*Southern African Subregion*

Recorded from the Eastern Districts of **Zimbabwe** and Pafuri and Skukuza in the Kruger National Park, **Transvaal**.

### Habitat

The West African subspecies, *M. b. cupreolus*, is a forest species; *M. b. bocagei*, the subspecies occurring in the Subregion, is associated predominantly with open savanna woodland.

### Habits

Bocage's hairy bats occur solitarily or at most two occur together. They roost during the day in hollow trees, in the shelter of the leaves of *Hyphaene* palms, or in bunches of bananas, and have been taken from the sheath of an arum lily, and from damp undercover in thickly overgrown swamp (Rosevear, 1965). While there is no information on the roosting places in the Subregion as the specimens were netted, it is perhaps significant that in both localities bananas were being grown. In Zaire, Allen, Lang & Chapin (1917) recorded that the indigenous people know them as the "big red brother" of the banana bat, *Pipistrellus nanus*, as both occur together in bunches of bananas. They noted that they appear to avoid villages and therefore do not come to the notice of travellers.

### Food

Insectivorous.

### Reproduction

No information is available from the Subregion.

## Genus *Pipistrellus* Kaup, 1829

The name is derived from the Italian *pipistrello* from *vispitrello*, the diminutive form of the Latin *vespertilio*, a bat (Rosevear, 1965). Members of the genus are all small bats, difficult to distinguish from one another, the differences between them being slight. In this genus, as compared with *Eptesicus*, members have an anterior upper premolar (Fig. 75.1) which is generally lacking in *Eptesicus*. It is, however, sometimes absent in *Pipistrellus*, but for convenience the identity of the two genera is maintained.

Members of the genus have two upper premolars, the dental formula being

$I\frac{2}{3}\ C\frac{1}{1}\ P\frac{2}{2}\ M\frac{3}{3} = 34$

The position of the anterior upper premolar is variable, sometimes lying in the toothrow, in other specimens internal to the toothrow. The skull has no sagittal or supraoccipital crest. Studies in progress by I.L. Rautenbach and R.L. Peterson suggest the presence of other species of *Pipistrellus* in southern Africa.

Key to the subgenera

1. Inner upper incisors unicuspid or not very deeply bicuspid (Fig. 75.2); the under parts brown or grey
   ... *Pipistrellus*

   Inner upper incisors deeply bifid; the under parts pure white
   ... *Vansoni*

## Subgenus *Pipistrellus* Kaup, 1829

Key to the species after Meester *et al.* (1986)

1. Outer upper incisor more than half length of inner upper incisor; forehead strongly concave; upper canine and posterior upper premolar separated by a gap through which anterior upper premolar can be seen clearly rising above cingula of adjoining teeth; interdental palate clearly longer than broad
   ... *nanus*

   Outer upper incisor less than half length of inner upper incisor; forehead usually flat or weakly concave; upper canine and posterior upper premolar in contact or barely separated, anterior upper premolar seen from the side only with difficulty, usually not rising appreciably above cingula of adjoining teeth
   ... 2
2. Interdental palate as broad as long; forehead flat; total length of skull 12 mm or less
   ... *rusticus*

   Interdental palate longer than broad; forehead at least slightly concave; total length of skull more than 12 mm
   ... 3
3. Posterior upper incisor barely extending beyond cingulum of anterior upper incisor; anterior upper premolar a pointed tooth rising above cingulum of canine but not above cingulum of posterior upper premolar; maxillary toothrow more than 4,5 mm
   ... *kuhlii*

   Posterior upper incisor extending well beyond cingulum of anterior upper incisor; anterior upper premolar a flat-crowned tooth, completely below cingula of adjoining teeth; maxillary toothrow less than 4,5 mm
   ... *anchietai*

No. 73

## *Pipistrellus kuhlii* (Kuhl, 1819)

## Kuhl's bat
## Kuhl se vlermuis

### Taxonomic Notes

Hayman & Hill (1971) listed five subspecies from the continent, of which two occur in the Subregion, *P. k. broomi* Roberts, 1948 from Natal and *P. k. subtilis* (Sundevall, 1846) from other parts of the Subregion.

### Description

Kuhl's bats are very similar in size and colour to rusty bats. They are only very slightly larger, with total lengths averaging about 76 mm in males to 80 mm in females and a mean mass of 4,6 g and 5,8 g respectively (Table 73.1). The colour of the upper parts is light brown to russet, the under parts lighter coloured, in some buffy-white. Their ears are broader than in the rusty bat, but similarly rounded at the tips. The wing and interfemoral membranes are dark, nearly black, the former with a narrow white border. The ear tragus is knife-shaped with a rounded point (Fig. 76.1.c).

**Table 73.1**

Measurements (mm) and mass (g) of Kuhl's bats, *P. kuhlii*, from the Transvaal (Rautenbach, 1982)

| | Males | | | Females | | |
|---|---|---|---|---|---|---|
| | $\bar{x}$ | n | Range | $\bar{x}$ | n | Range |
| TL | 76 | 16 | 63–80 | 80 | 5 | 76–84 |
| T | 29 | 16 | 20–33 | 30 | 5 | 26–32 |
| Hf c/u | 6 | 6 | 5–7 | 6 | 4 | 5–8 |
| E | 11 | 15 | 9–12 | 10 | 5 | 7–12 |
| F/a | 29 | 13 | 25–31 | 31 | 3 | 31 |
| Mass | 4,6 | 14 | 4,0–6,0 | 5,8 | 4 | 4,0–7,0 |

### Distribution

*Extralimital to the continent*

Kuhl's bat originally was described from a specimen from Trieste at the north end of the Adriatic and has a wide distribution in **Europe**, the **Middle East** and eastwards to **India**.

*North of the Sahara*

They occur throughout **Morocco; Tunisia**; in **Libya**, being common in the coastal towns, and in **Egypt** to the shores of the Mediterranean. In **Algeria** they occur coastally and deep into the Sahara southward to the oasis of Messad and the Ahaggar Massif.

*South of the Sahara, excluding the Southern African Subregion*

Recorded from the northeastern and southeastern **Sudan; Ethiopia; Cameroun**; and in parts of **Somalia** and **Kenya**. There is a single record from northeastern **Tanzania** and although they are at present only recorded from western and northeastern **Zambia**, Ansell (1978) believed that they are more widespread than present records indicate. They occur in southern **Malawi** with a single record from the extreme north of the country. At present there are no records from Mozambique, north of the Zambezi River.

*Southern African Subregion*

Recorded from central and eastern **Zimbabwe** and the Maputo District of **Mozambique**, south of the Zambezi River. In the **Transvaal** they occur across the middle of the province from near the Botswana border to the Mozambique border just north of Swaziland, and in the northeastern **Orange Free State**. They occur in **Natal** and coastally westwards in the **Cape Province** to about Knysna, being comparatively rare in this part of their range.

### Habitat

It is difficult to assess the habitat requirements of a species that can utilise such diverse habitats as those found in Europe, in the deserts of Arabia or the Sahara and the forested terrain of the Knysna area on the south coast of the Cape Province. In Arabia, Harrison (1964) noted that although they foraged over the desert, they never moved far from the oasis with which they were associated. All the records from Zimbabwe were made in the vicinity of streams and rivers and their eastern distribution in the Subregion suggests that they prefer well-watered terrain. It seems likely that a water supply, the availability of suitable roosting places and a plentiful food supply are among their primary requirements.

### Habits

Kuhl's bats are gregarious, occurring in small colonies in Zimbabwe numbering up to about 12. They are apparently far commoner in North Africa where Hufnagl (1972) stated that they are the commonest species in Libya, roosting in the roofs of bazaars and old houses. In the Cape Province on the other hand Herselman (1980) recorded them as being very rare. Judging from the number of specimens in collections in the Subregion, they are nowhere common. There is a scarcity of information on their daylight roosting places in the

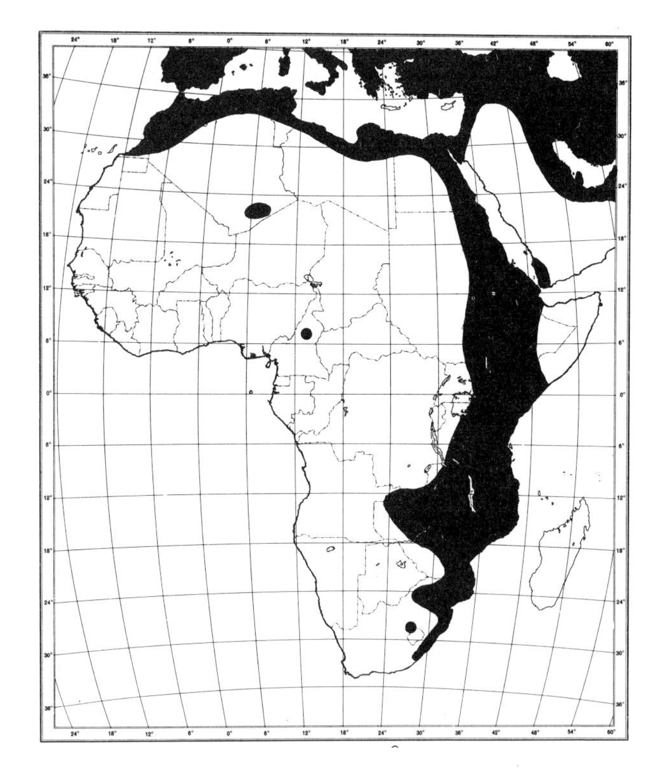

Subregion. In Zimbabwe a colony of about 12 occupied a vertical narrow crack in an exfoliated granite boss. This colony became very noisy when approached, squeaking and nickering as they scrambled deeper into the crack. They were huddled together in a tight mass. Harrison (1955) found them huddling in this manner between the coral blocks used to build the houses in coastal Arabia, the colony being similarly noisy when disturbed. Both Smithers (1971) and Rautenbach (1982) recorded collecting them under the loose bark of dead trees and Rautenbach (1982) observed an individual emerging from under the roof of an old farmhouse. He noted that they were the first to emerge at dusk, being slow but acrobatic in flight as they hawked insects about 8 m above the ground. He netted specimens over water at dusk and during the first two hours of darkness.

### Food

Insectivorous.

### Reproduction

Rautenbach (1982) took two gravid females in October in the Transvaal, each with a single foetus which suggests that, like other insect-eating species, the young are born during the warm wet months of the year.

---

No. 73A

## *Pipistrellus anchietai* (Seabra, 1900)

## Anchieta's bat
## Anchieta se vlermuis

---

### Colloquial Name

This species is named after Snr Anchieta, a Portuguese national, who was a prolific collector of zoological material in Angola in the 1860's and who has numerous reptiles, birds and mammals named after him.

### Taxonomic Notes

Koopman (1975) was inclined to regard *Eptesicus bicolor* (Bocage, 1889), still known only from the type specimen from Caconda, Angola, and *Pipistrellus anchietai* as conspecific. *P. anchietai* has the anterior upper premolars, which are situated internal to the toothrow, which are missing in *E. bicolor*, but the presence or absence of these teeth is a variable factor in the two genera and it may be that *E. bicolor* is simply a *P. anchietai* in which they are missing.

### Description

A small species comparable in size to the banana bat, *P. nanus*, with a total length of 76 mm, a tail of 33 mm and a forearm length of an average of 32,5 mm (Table 73A.1). The upper parts of the body are light brown, the individual hairs broadly dark brown and nearly black at their bases, with broad light brown tips. The under parts are lighter in colour, the individual hairs black at their bases with off-white or cream tips. The wing membranes are dark brown. The ears are small and rounded at their tips, the ear tragus with a distinct bulge on its outermost margin and an emargination below it. The upper part has a rounded tip and roughly parallel sides (Fig.73A.1). The small anterior upper premolars are broad and flat crowned. The skull has a broad rostrum, and the braincase is slightly elevated above the level of the rostrum.

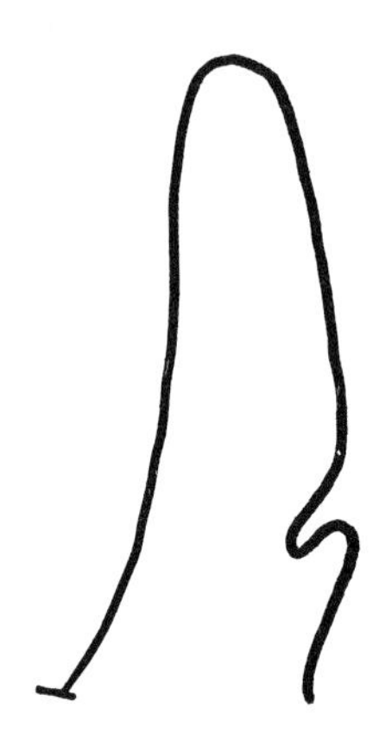

Fig. 73 A.1. Ear tragus of *Pipistrellus anchietai*

**Table 73A.1**

Measurements (mm) of Anchieta's bats, *P. anchietai*, from Angola (Hill & Carter, 1941)

| | Irrespective of sex | | |
|---|---|---|---|
| | x̄ | n | Range |
| (TL | 76) | | |
| HB | 43 | 6 | 41–46 |
| T | 33 | 6 | 31–36 |
| Hf c/u | 8 | 1 | |
| E | 10 | 6 | 9–11 |
| F/a | 32,5 | 6 | 30,4–34,5 |

A specimen from Skukuza, Kruger National Park, eastern Transvaal had a forearm length of 32,4 mm.

### Distribution

*South of the Sahara, excluding the southern African Subregion*

Recorded from **Angola**; western **Zambia** and southeastern **Zaire**.

*Southern African Subregion*

So far only recorded from Skukuza, Kruger National Park, eastern **Transvaal**.

### Habitat, Habits, Food, Reproduction

Nothing appears to have been published on these aspects of the ecology of this species. The single specimen from Skukuza was netted and no other information recorded.

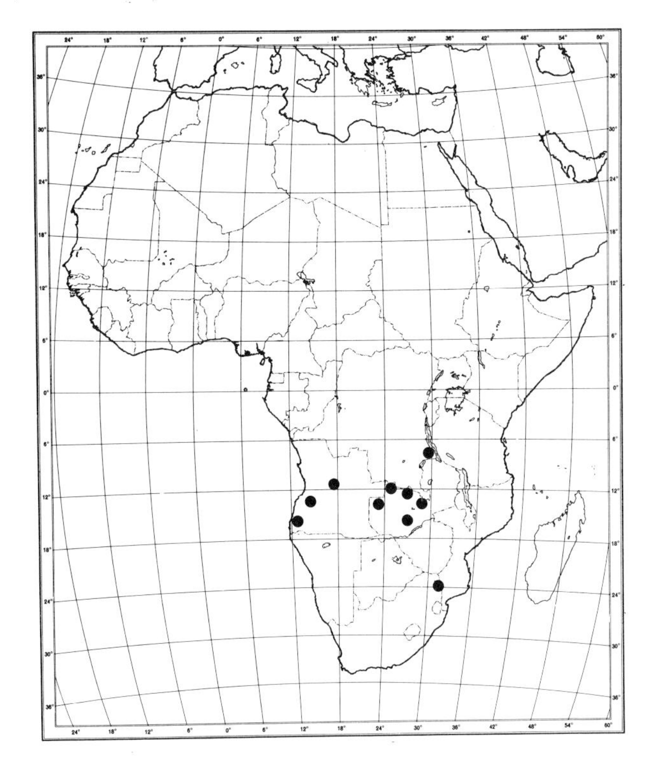

the course of time may be shown to have a wider distribution than present records indicate.

*South of the Sahara, excluding the Southern African Subregion*

Recorded from localities in **West Africa** eastwards to the southern **Sudan**; western **Ethiopia** and northern **Kenya**. No records are available between this and western **Zambia** where they have been taken adjacent to the Zaire and Angola borders; however no records are available from these countries at the moment.

*Southern African Subregion*

They occur in the northeastern parts of **Namibia**; in northern and northeastern **Botswana**; widely in **Zimbabwe**, excluding the eastern sector and in parts of the **Transvaal**.

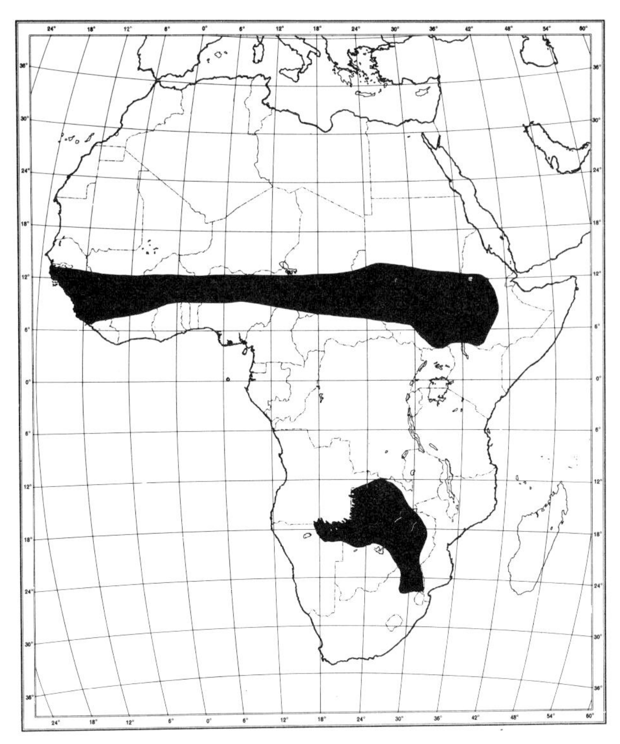

No. 74

## *Pipistrellus rusticus* (Tomes, 1861)

## Rusty bat
## Roeskleurvlermuis

### Colloquial Name

So named on account of the rusty colour of their fur.

### Taxonomic Notes

Hayman & Hill (1971) listed two subspecies, one of which *P. r. rusticus* occurs in the Subregion, the other *P. r. marrensis* Thomas-Hinton, 1923 in Ethiopia and the Sudan.

### Description

Rusty bats are about 70 mm in total length and have tails of about 27 mm in length and a mass of between 3,0 and 4,0 g (Table 74.1). The colour of the upper parts is a pale rust, the under parts a shade lighter in colour and tinged with grey. The wing and interfemoral membranes are dark in colour, nearly black. The ears are rounded at the tips. The individual hairs on both the upper parts and under parts are black at their bases, the general colour imparted by their broad, pale rusty tips. The ear tragus is sickle-shaped with a rounded point (Fig. 76.1.d).

**Table 74.1**

Measurements (mm) of rusty bats, *P. rusticus*, from Zimbabwe (Harrison, 1962)

| | Males | | | Females | | |
|---|---|---|---|---|---|---|
| | $\bar{x}$ | n | Range | $\bar{x}$ | n | Range |
| TL | 72 | 9 | 70–75 | 75 | 4 | 70–80 |
| T | 27 | 9 | 25–30 | 27 | 4 | 25–31 |
| Hf c/u | 6 | 9 | 5–6 | 6 | 4 | 5–7 |
| E | 10 | 9 | 8–10 | 9 | 4 | 8–10 |
| F/a | 28 | 9 | 27–29 | 29 | 4 | 28–29 |

### Distribution

The rusty bat appears to occur in two discrete populations, the northern in parts of West Africa and the Sudan and Ethiopia, the southern in Zambia and in the northern parts of the Subregion. It is not a common species anywhere and in

### Habitat

The southern populations occur in savanna woodland, in all cases in Zimbabwe associated with riverine associations. Too little information is presently available to comment further on their habitat requirements.

### Habits

No information is available on their habits in the Subregion.

### Food

Insectivorous.

### Reproduction

M. van der Merwe & Rautenbach (unpubl.) found this species to be a seasonal breeder and that females give birth to twins during November. Copulations are initiated during April when both uterine horns are full of spermatozoa. The uterine horns stay full of spermatozoa until August when ovulation and fertilization occur.

No. 75

## *Pipistrellus nanus* (Peters, 1852)

## Banana bat
## Piesangvlermuis

Plate 4

### Colloquial Name

Characteristically this species roosts during the day in the rolled-up, fresh sprouting terminal leaves of banana plants and has become associated with them in particular.

### Taxonomic Notes

Hayman & Hill (1971) noted that a considerable number of probable synonyms or, at the most, doubtful subspecies have been listed. Koopman (1975) believed that the recognition of subspecies serves no useful purpose until the geographical variation of the species throughout its extensive range is undertaken. Until such time no subspecies are recognised.

### Description

Banana bats are tiny, about 77 mm in total length, with tails 36 mm and a mass of about 4,0 g (Table 75.1). The colour of the upper parts varies widely, individuals being reddish-brown, light brown, or dark brown, in some the colour being darker on the rump than on the shoulders. The individual hairs are black at their bases, the general colour of the upper parts being imparted to it by their broadly coloured tips. The under parts are lighter in colour, their colour being similar to that of the upper parts, but a shade lighter, some with a distinct greyish tinge. The wing and interfemoral membranes are brown. The ears are roughly triangular, the outer edge slightly convex, the tips pointed. The ear tragus is hatchet-shaped with an abrupt angle on its outer edge (Fig. 76.1.b). They have a minute first upper premolar lying between the canine and the posterior premolar (Fig. 75.1). The inner upper incisors are shallowly bifid (Fig. 75.2).

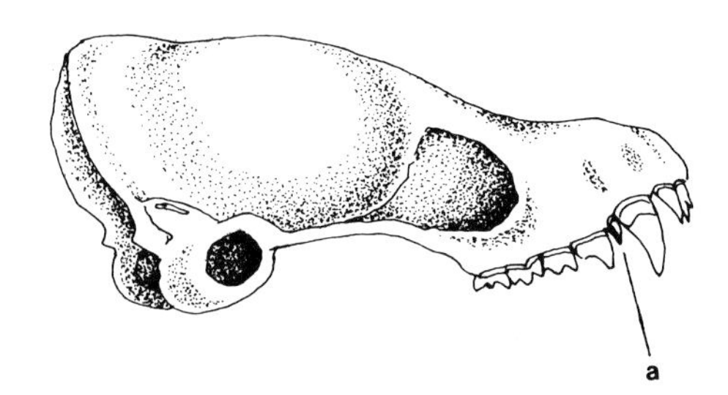


Fig. 75.1. Skull of *Pipistrellus nanus*, to show minute first upper premolar (a).

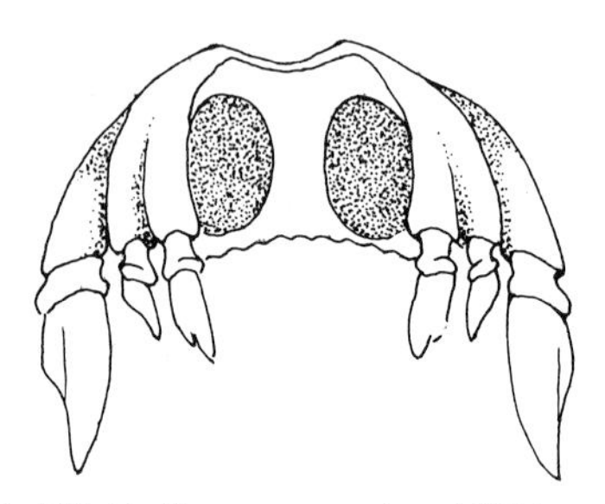

Fig. 75.2. Skull of *Pipistrellus nanus*, to show bifid inner upper incisors and simple outer incisors together with the canines.

### Table 75.1

Measurements (mm) and mass (g) of banana bats, *P. nanus*, from Zimbabwe (Smithers & Wilson, 1979)

| | Males | | | Females | | |
|---|---|---|---|---|---|---|
| | $\bar{x}$ | n | Range | $\bar{x}$ | n | Range |
| TL | 77 | 10 | 72–82 | 80 | 10 | 74–84 |
| T | 36 | 10 | 34–38 | 36 | 10 | 36–38 |
| Hf c/u | 6 | 10 | 5–7 | 6 | 10 | 5–7 |
| E | 11 | 10 | 10–11 | 11 | 10 | 11–12 |
| F/a | 32 | 10 | 30–32 | 32 | 10 | 31–32 |
| Mass | 4,0 | 10 | 3,0–4,0 | 4,0 | 10 | 3,0–4,0 |

### Distribution

Banana bats have a wide distribution on the continent from Sierra Leone to Ethiopia and parts of Somalia, and southwards to northern Namibia and the eastern parts of the Cape Province.

*South of the Sahara, excluding the Southern African Subregion*

Recorded from **Sierra Leone; Liberia;** the **Ivory Coast; Nigeria** and eastwards to the southern **Sudan**; southern and northern **Somalia; Zaire; Uganda; Kenya; Tanzania; Angola; Zambia; Malawi** and northeastern **Mozambique.**

*Southern African Subregion*

Confined to the northern parts of **Namibia**; throughout the Okavango Delta and south to Lake Ngami in northern **Botswana**; widespread in **Zimbabwe**; except in parts of the dry west and throughout **Mozambique** south of the Zambezi River. Recorded from the Limpopo Valley, in the northern **Transvaal** and in eastern parts of the province; in **Natal** and southwards to the eastern parts of the **Cape Province** at Bedford.

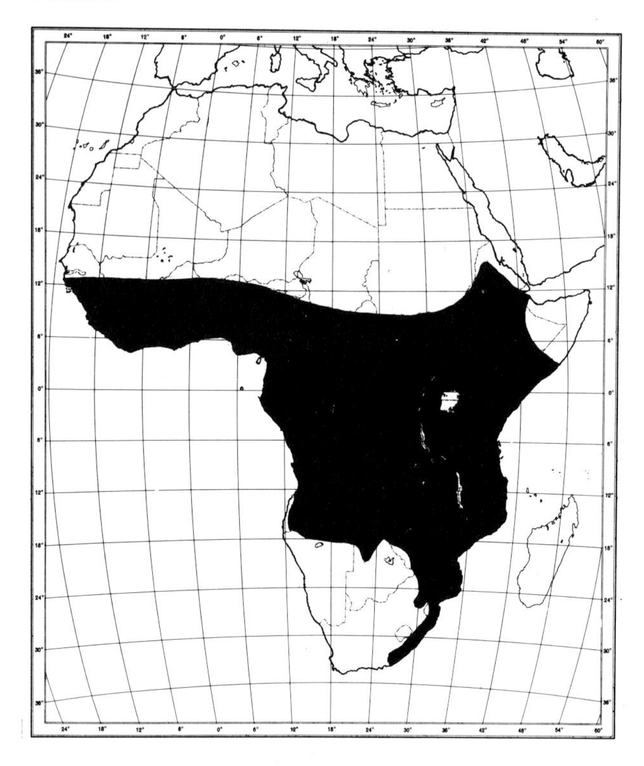

### Habitat

Throughout their wide distributional range they occur in a variety of vegetational associations, including forest and woodland savanna. Within this range they are associated particularly with areas where bananas or plantains are grown, or where the naturally occurring association contains as components strelitzia trees, *Strelitzia caudata* or *S. nicolai*, the leaves of which provide them with shelter during the day. Either these domestic fruits or the strelitzias require moist conditions and in the drier parts of their range they therefore tend to occur in riverine associations, where irrigation provides the necessary water or where the mean annual rainfall is sufficient to support forest in which the strelitzias occur. A dozen or so banana plants in a farm garden is often sufficient to provide shelter for a small colony. While particularly associated with these plants, they can find shelter in other situations (see **Habits**).

### Habits

Banana bats are gregarious, occurring in small numbers. They will roost during the day tucked into the thatch of huts, under rafters or in other crevices in roofs and have been taken from oil palms in West Africa (Rosevear, 1965). Allen, Lang & Chapin (1917) found them roosting huddled together under the dry leaves of plantains. Characteristically however their preferred roosting places are in the rolled up, freshly sprouting, terminal leaves of banana plants or inside the bunches of fruit. These terminal leaves roll in a funnel shape and the tiny banana bats, up to six or seven per leaf, tuck themselves into the inside roll of the leaf towards the narrow end, head downward and one on top of another.

These terminal leaves grow quickly and soon open out to the broad, spreading leaf characteristic of this plant, so that they have of necessity to find another leaf that is still rolled up in which to roost. There is apparently a critical stage of unrolling when they vacate the leaf, for when the end is too open to the sky above, they leave, their faeces accumulated at the narrow end, marking its former use. Banana leaves have a very smooth, slippery surface and to effect escape from the rolled leaf, which stands upright, the thumb on the wing and the soles of the feet are equipped with sucker pads to assist them in clambering up the steep sides. Their flight is rather slow and fluttering even when handled in nets. They have the ability to open their mouths very wide, to an angle it is said of 120° (Allen, Lang & Chapin, 1917) which may be advantageous to them in catching insects in flight. Small as they are this allows them to latch on to the end of a finger, their needle sharp teeth easily breaking the skin.

### Food

They are insectivorous. Fenton, Boyle, Harrison & Oxley (1977) recorded that, in Zimbabwe, a colony roosting between the eaves, troughs and fascia boards of a building emerged to forage between 19h00 and 19h05. Individuals returned to this roost at 19h45 with full stomachs. The foraging time was punctuated by returns to the roost during the night and there appeared to be three periods of foraging activity, the first shortly after they emerged, the second later and the third just before dawn.

### Reproduction

In Zimbabwe, a sample of 26 out of 30 females were pregnant in September, a smaller percentage being gravid in August. In Namibia, Shortridge (1934) recorded gravid females in October. Of the 26 gravid females, the average number of foetuses was 1,9 with a range of one to two. In Natal, South Africa, Banana bats were found to be monoestrous and seasonal, with births of single or twin infants in November and December (LaVal & LaVal 1977).

## Subgenus *Vansoni* Roberts, 1946

Members of this subgenus are at once recognisable among members of the genus *Pipistrellus* by their white under parts and by the upper incisors, the inner ones being very long and so deeply bifid that they appear to be two teeth, the outer ones minute and tucked tightly against the base of the inner. The anterior upper premolar is very small, lying in some specimens in the toothrow, in others internal to it.

---

No. 76

## *Pipistrellus rueppellii* (Fischer, 1829)

## Rüppell's bat
## Rüppell se vlermuis

---

### Colloquial Name

The type (*Vespertilio temminckii*) was described in Rüppell's (1827) *Atlas zu der Reise im Nördlichen Afrika* and renamed by Fischer (1829) after Rüppell (*V. rüppellii*).

### Taxonomic Notes

Meester *et al.* (1986) recognized two subspecies from the Subregion: the nominate *P. r. rueppellii* from eastern Zimbabwe and the northern parts of the Kruger National Park, Transvaal, and *P. r. vernayi* Roberts, 1932 from northeastern Botswana.

### Description

The pure white under parts of Rüppell's bats render them easily distinguishable from other pipistrelline bats.

They are small bats, some 100 mm in total length, with tails 38 mm and a mass of about 7,0 g (Table 76.1).

The subspecies *P. r. vernayi* from Botswana has light brownish-grey upper parts, *P. r. rueppellii* from other parts of the Subregion is much darker in colour, a deep sepia. The hairs on the upper parts have darker bases, the terminal portion lighter and greyer in the former subspecies and darker and browner in the latter. The white fur of the under parts extends marginally on to the wing membranes which are paler in *P. r. vernayi* than in *P. r. rueppellii*. The division between the darker upper parts and white under parts is defined clearly. The ears contrast with the colour of the upper parts, being dark, rather triangular in shape and broadly rounded at their tips. The ear tragus is long and knife-shaped with a rounded point (Fig. 76.1.a).

The inner upper incisors are deeply bifid, the outer very small in comparison (Fig. 76.2).

**Table 76.1**

Measurements (mm) and mass (g) of Rüppell's bats, *P. rueppellii*, from Zimbabwe (Smithers & Wilson, 1979)

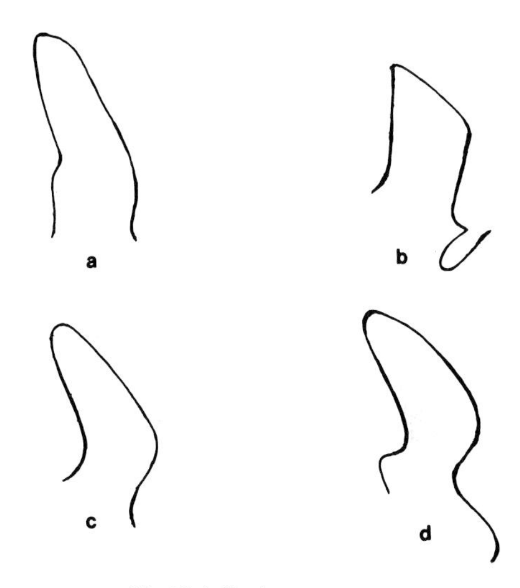


Fig. 76.1. Ear tragus:
(a) *Pipistrellus rueppellii* (b) *P. nanus* (c) *P. kuhlii* (d) *P. rusticus*

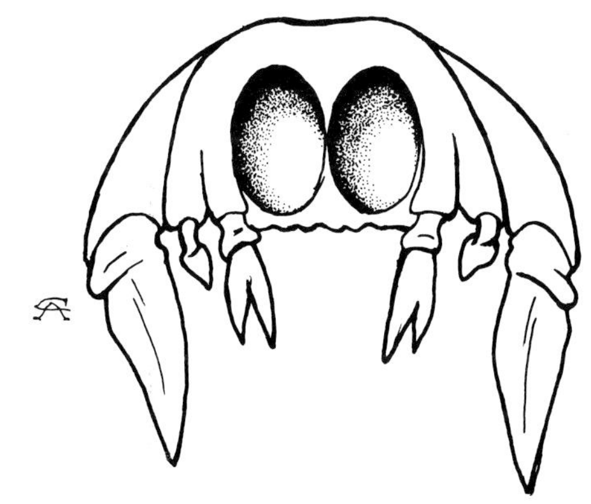

Fig. 76.2 Upper incisors and canine teeth, *Pipistrellus rueppellii*

| | Irrespective of sex | | |
|---|---|---|---|
| | $\bar{x}$ | n | Range |
| TL | 96 | 5 | 90–110 |
| T | 38 | 5 | 32–40 |
| Hf c/u | 9 | 5 | 9 |
| E | 11 | 5 | 11 |
| Mass | 7,1 | 5 | 6,8–7,3 |

### Distribution

*Extralimital to the continent*

Recorded from localities in **Iraq** at the northern end of the Persian Gulf.

*North Africa*

They occur in the valley of the Nile in **Egypt** to the shores of the Mediterranean with an isolated record from Beni Abbes, **Algeria**.

*South of the Sahara, excluding the Southern African Subregion*

Recorded from **Senegal; Chad**; the **Sudan**; western **Ethiopia; Kenya; Uganda**; western, eastern and northeastern **Zaire; Tanzania**; western **Zambia; Angola** and **Malawi**. There are no records available from southern Tanzania or Mozambique, north of the Zambezi River.

*Southern African Subregion*

Recorded from the Okavango Delta in northern **Botswana**, in northeastern and southeastern **Zimbabwe** and from the Pafuri area of the Kruger National Park in the **Transvaal**.

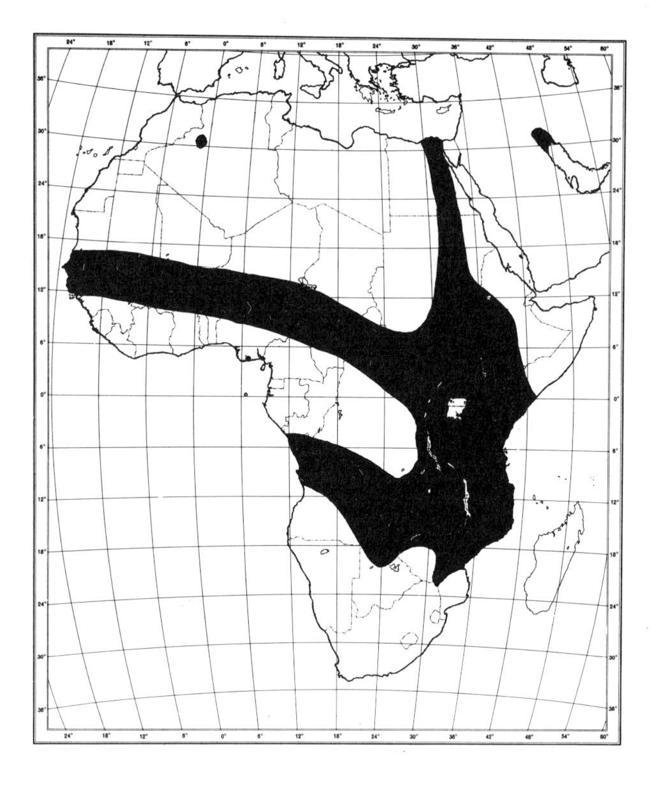

### Habitat

Throughout their range there is a very noticeable association of Rüppell's bats with riverine conditions. In the north they are associated with the Nile and its tributaries, in Zambia with the Zambezi and Kafue rivers, in Zimbabwe with tributaries of the Zambezi, and in the south with the Limpopo River. Their occurrence in the Okavango Delta with its associated swamps further confirms this association.

### Habits

Very little is known of the habits of this species from any part of their range and unfortunately all the specimens collected in the Subregion have either been shot or netted and we have therefore no knowledge of where they roost during the day. Judging from Roberts' (1951) collection of a series of specimens from the Okavango Delta at Maun, taken flitting over the Thamalakane River, they appear to congregate at least to feed. Allen, Lang & Chapin (1917) also observed this in Zaire.

### Food

Insectivorous.

### Reproduction

No information available.



## Genus *Chalinolobis* Peters, 1866

No. 77

## *Chalinolobis variegatus* (Tomes, 1861)

## Butterfly bat
## Vlindervlermuis

Plate 5

### Colloquial Name

The name may be derived from the dark reticulated pattern on the wings which has led to their being called leaf-winged bats. Although it is said that they resemble a large butterfly in flight, they are by no means butterfly-like in this respect as they are very high fliers and slow in their flight.

### Taxonomic Notes

Hayman & Hill (1971) listed two subspecies, *C. v. phalaena* Thomas, 1915 from the Sudan and *C. v. variegatus* from the remainder of the species' range and therefore the only subspecies to occur in the Subregion.

### Description

About 110 mm in total length, with a tail of 47 mm and a mass of 12,0 to 14,0 g (Table 77.1). Butterfly bats are among our most beautiful and more easily recognised species.

The characteristic feature of this species is the bold pattern of dark reticulations which contrast with the pale yellowish background colour of the wing and interfemoral membrane. The upper parts are yellowish, cream or light fawn in colour, the individual hairs lighter at their bases. The head, neck and upper parts of the shoulders are paler than the remainder of the upper parts. The throat is washed with grey, the remainder of the under parts off-white or washed with pale grey. The ears are small, pale brown in colour and rather squarish in shape with broadly rounded corners.

The ear tragus is very similar to that found in *Eptesicus* and *Pipistrellus*, its inner margin straight, the outer curved, the point rounded with a distinct basal lobe roughly triangular in shape.

The dental formula is

$I\frac{2}{3}\ C\frac{1}{1}\ P\frac{1}{2}\ M\frac{3}{3} = 32$

In the absence of the anterior upper premolar it more closely resembles *Eptesicus*. The inner upper incisors are long and pointed, sometimes bifid, sometimes plain, the outer incisors minute in comparison. The lower incisors are trifid. There is no sagittal crest and the supraoccipital crest is poorly developed.

**Table 77.1**

Measurements (mm) and mass (g) of butterfly bats, *C. variegatus*, from Zimbabwe (Smithers & Wilson, 1979)

| | Males | | | Females | | |
|---|---|---|---|---|---|---|
| | $\bar{x}$ | n | Range | $\bar{x}$ | n | Range |
| TL | 108 | 8 | 106–110 | 107,5 | 2 | 106–109 |
| T | 47 | 8 | 46–50 | 46 | 2 | 45–47 |
| Hf c/u | 10 | 8 | 9–10 | 9,5 | 2 | 9–10 |
| E | 14 | 8 | 14 | 14 | 2 | 14 |
| Mass | 12,3 | 8 | 12,0–14,0 | 14,0 | 1 | |

### Distribution

*South of the Sahara, excluding the Southern African Subregion*

They occur from **Ghana** in West Africa through **Nigeria** eastwards to the southern **Sudan** and western **Ethiopia** and southwards in **Uganda; Kenya; Tanzania**; in **Zaire** excluding the major part of the tropical forests, and in parts of the **Gabon**. They are recorded from **Angola; Zambia**, where Ansell (1978) believed that in time they will be shown to occur throughout, and in **Malawi**. While there are no records from Mozambique, north of the Zambezi River, the area remains zoologically little explored and probably they will be shown to occur in due course.

*Southern African Subregion*

Originally the species was described from a specimen from Otjoro, northern **Namibia**, and they occur east of this in the Grootfontein district. In **Botswana** they are recorded from the northwest of the country and in **Zimbabwe** have a wide distribution, but not apparently occurring on the central plateau. In **Mozambique**, south of the Zambezi River, they occur from the Beira District south to the Maputo District, extending southwards into Zululand. In the northern **Transvaal** they have been collected in the Soutpansberg, as well as Pafuri in the northern regions of the Kruger National Park.

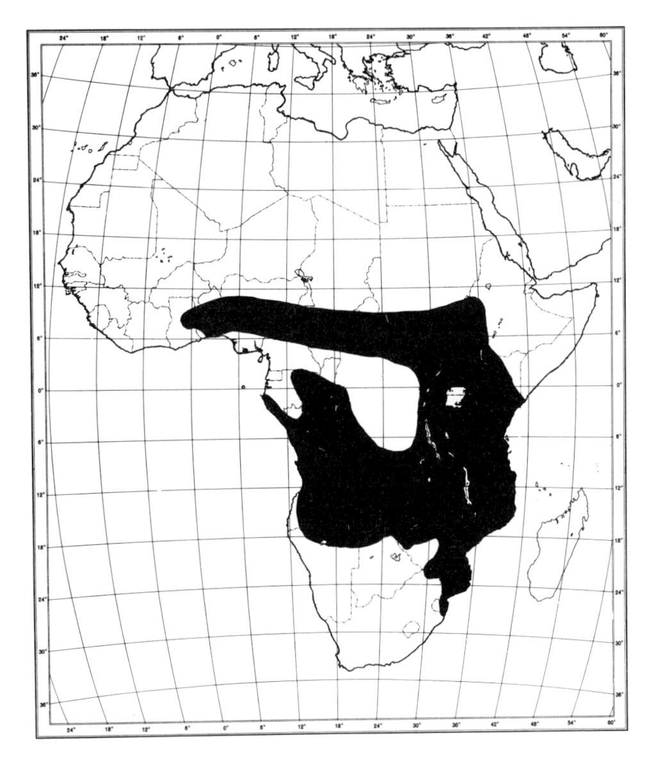

**Habitat**

A savanna woodland species, particularly associated with open woodland and not found in forest. Allen, Lang & Chapin (1917) recorded that in northeast Zaire they were restricted to the more open bush country outside the equatorial forest. In dry country, such as in parts of Zimbabwe, they are associated with riverine woodland.

**Habits**

Little is known about the habits of this species, except what was published by Allen, Lang & Chapin (1917) who recorded that they found over 10 huddled closely together hiding in the thatch of an abandoned hut. They stated that the bats appear to prefer to conceal themselves between suitable bunches of leaves, two or three together, leaving these roosting places as early as 17h00 in overcast weather. They fly high, about 18 m above the ground, fluttering along swiftly, then increasing their speed with spontaneous ease to catch their prey. While flying they utter a curious squeak.

**Food**

Insectivorous.

**Reproduction**

There is no information available from the Subregion.

## Genus *Laephotis* Thomas, 1901

Key to the species after Meester *et al.* (1986)

1. Larger, total skull length over 16 mm; ear length from meatus more than 21 mm; tragus with notch near base of outside edge; dorsal colour light drab
   ... *namibensis*

   Smaller, total skull length under 15 mm; ear length no more than 18 mm; tragus without notch near base of outside edge; dorsal colour buffy-brown
   ... *botswanae*

No. 78

## *Laephotis namibensis* Setzer, 1971

## Namib long-eared bat
## Namib-langoorvlermuis

Originally collected at the Namib Desert Research Station, Gobabeb, **Namibia**, the two specimens taken remain the only representatives of this species. They were netted over a waterhole in the bed of the Kuiseb River. Nothing is known of their life history. Rautenbach (pers. comm.) believes that the specimen from the Cedarberg, western **Cape Province** included in the first edition as *L. wintoni* Thomas, 1901 is placed more appropriately in this species.

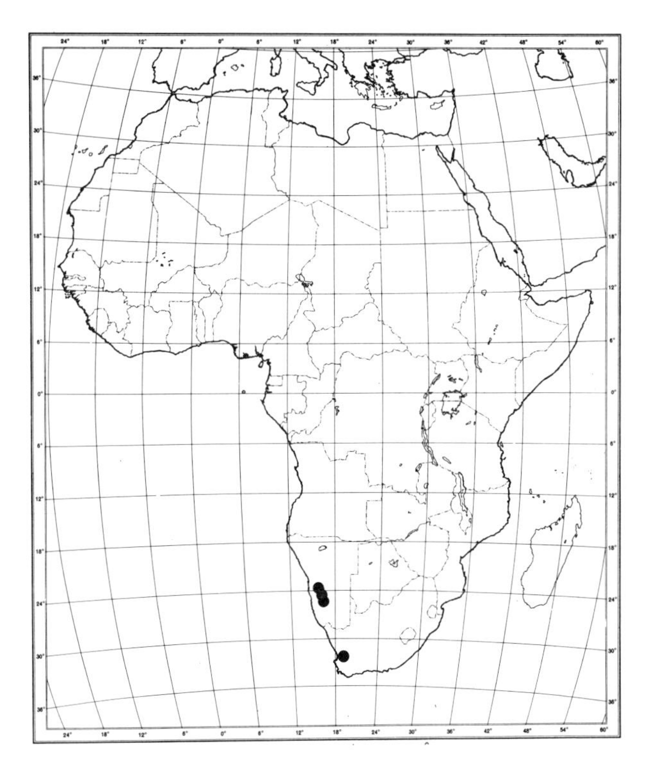

**Description**

This species is slightly larger than *L. botswanae*, with a total length of about 105 mm and a slightly longer forearm (Table 78.1). They are in addition lighter in colour, the upper parts a light buffy-brown, the wing membranes olive-brown. The individual hairs on the upper parts are annulated similarly to those of *L. botswanae*, but the tips are whiter. Their ears are similar in shape to those of *L. botswanae*, but larger (Fig. 78.1.b), the ear tragus much larger and with a distinct notch on the lower side of the outer edge (Fig. 78.1.c).

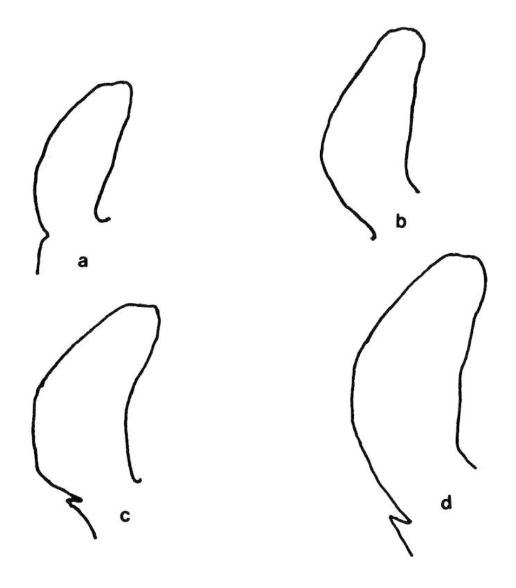


Fig. 78.1 Ear tragus of *Laephotis*:
(a) *L. angolensis* (extralimital) (b) *L. botswanae*
(c) *L. namibensis* after Setzer (1971).

**Table 78.1**

Measurements (mm) of the holotype and a paratype of the Namib long-eared bat, *L. namibensis* Setzer, 1971

**Females** (n=2)

| TL | T | Hf c/u | E | F/a |
|---|---|---|---|---|
| 106 | 47 | 8 | 25 | 38,2 |
| 104 | 46 | 8 | 24 | 38,6 |

No. 79

## *Laephotis botswanae* Setzer, 1971

## Botswana long-eared bat
## Botswana-langoorvlermuis

### Colloquial Name

The name is derived from the fact that the original specimen from which the species was described originated from near Shakawe in northwestern Botswana.

### Taxonomic Notes

No subspecies have been described. Peterson (1973) suggested that this species may prove to be a larger southern subspecies of *L. angolensis* Monard, 1935.

### Description

Botswana long-eared bats have a total length of 90 to 95 mm and a mass of about 6,0 g (Table 79.1). The upper parts are buffy-brown in colour, the wing membranes light brown, the under parts slightly paler than the upper parts. The individual hairs on the upper parts are black at the base, with a narrow band of pale buffy and tipped with buffy-brown.

The ears are noticeably large, reaching an average length of 21 mm, are rounded at the tips and have a characteristically shaped ear tragus with a plain outer edge, lacking the indentation seen in *L. angolensis* and *L. namibensis* (Fig. 78.1). The tragus is intermediate in size between that of *L. angolensis* which is smaller and *L. namibensis* which is considerably larger (Fig. 78.1).

**Table 79.1**

Measurements (mm) and mass (g) of Botswana long-eared bats, *L. botswanae*, from Zimbabwe (Smithers & Wilson, 1979)

| | Irrespective of sex | | |
|---|---|---|---|
| | $\bar{x}$ | n | Range |
| TL | 92 | 7 | 89–100 |
| T | 42 | 7 | 38–46 |
| Hf c/u | 8 | 7 | 6–8 |
| E | 21 | 7 | 20–22 |
| F/a | 36 | 7 | 33–37 |
| Mass | 5,8 | 7 | 4,5–6,8 |

### Distribution

So far only known from northwestern **Botswana**; western **Zambia**; southeastern **Zaire** and northwestern **Zimbabwe**, Punda Maria (Kruger National Park) and Vaalwater in the northwestern Transvaal.

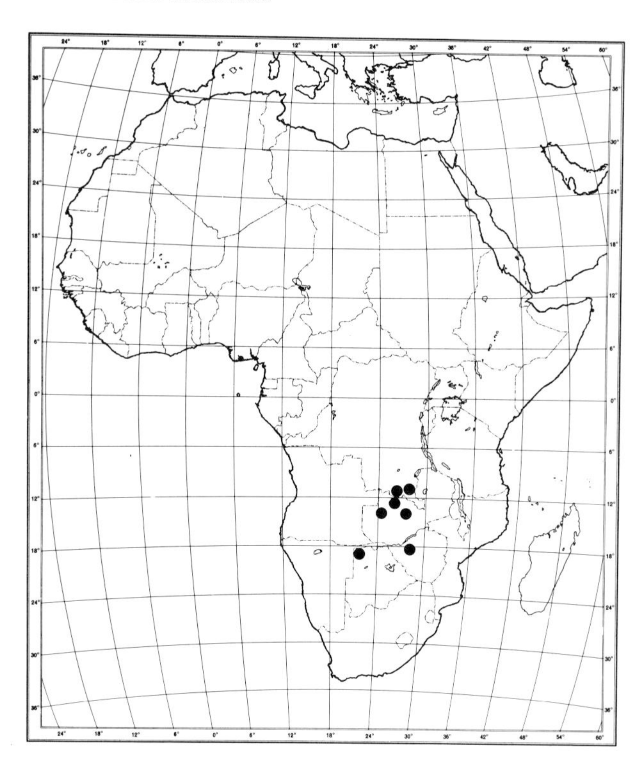

### Habitat

All the records so far available lie within savanna woodland and are from the vicinity of rivers. All the specimens were shot or netted and therefore no knowledge is available of where they roost during the day.

### Habits and Reproduction

No information available.

### Food

Insectivorous. In Zimbabwe, Fenton (1975) from his observations and from the size of the ears in this species, suggested that they may be found to take their prey off the leaves and twigs on which they are sitting, rather than in the air.

**WITHDRAWN**

No. 80

## *Laephotis wintoni* Thomas, 1901

## De Winton's long-eared bat
## De Winton se langoorvlermuis

Included in the first edition on the basis of a single specimen from the Algeria Forest Station, southwestern Cape Province. Further investigations in progress by Rautenbach and Schlitter reveal that this specimen is placed more appropriately with *L. namibensis* (Rautenbach, pers. comm.), with which it is provisionally included.

## Genus *Eptesicus* Rafinesque, 1820

Key to the species after Meester *et al.* (1986)

1. Wing membranes white or translucent
... *rendalli*

Wing membranes dark
... 2

2. Size larger, forearm more than 40 mm; inner upper incisors unicuspid
... *hottentotus*

Size smaller, forearm less than 40 mm; inner upper incisors bicuspid
... 3

3. Forearm 34,5–38 mm
... *melckorum*

Forearm 35 mm or less
... 4

4. Dorsal colour paler; wing membranes edged with white; dorsal fur up to 8 mm long; forearm 30–32 mm; condylobasal length usually less than 11,9 mm; skull lacking posterior occipital 'helmet'
... *somalicus*

Dorsal colour darker; wing membranes not edged with white; dorsal fur not more than 5 mm long; forearm 29–35 mm; condylobasal length more than 11,9 mm; skull with posterior occipital 'helmet'
... *capensis*

No. 81

## *Eptesicus rendalli* (Thomas, 1889)

## Rendall's serotine bat
## Rendall se dakvlermuis

### Colloquial Name
The original specimen was taken at Bathurst, Gambia, and was named after a Dr Percy Rendall.

### Taxonomic Notes
No subspecies are recognised by Hayman & Hill (1971).

### Description
There is insufficient material from the Subregion from which to judge the consistency in the size of this species. Rosevear (1965) showed that in West Africa they have a total length of about 85 to 90 mm including a tail of 36 to 40 mm and a forearm of 34,5 to 38 mm. In colour the upper parts are fawny-brown or sometimes reddish-brown, the individual hairs dark chocolate-brown at their bases with fawny-brown or reddish-brown tips. The under parts are very pale grey, pure white in the anal region and on the flanks.

The characteristic feature of the species, however, and one which distinguishes them from other members of the genus, is the white wing membranes. The interfemoral membrane is white, the ears pale brown. The ear tragus is short and broad and evenly curved on its outer edge with a distinct projection near the base of this edge.

The inner upper incisors have small hook-like projections about half way up their posterior faces, the outer incisors smaller than the inner.

### Distribution
While records are few and scattered, they indicate a wide distribution from Gambia in West Africa to the northern parts of the Subregion.

*South of the Sahara, excluding the Southern African Subregion*

Recorded from **Gambia; Nigeria**; southeastern **Sudan**; southwestern **Ethiopia; Somalia; Kenya**; northeastern and southern **Zaire; Zambia**; the Southern Province of **Malawi**, and northeastern **Mozambique**. There are no published records from Angola where they might well occur.

*Southern African Subregion*

Recorded from northern **Botswana** and the Tete District of **Mozambique**, south of the Zambezi River.

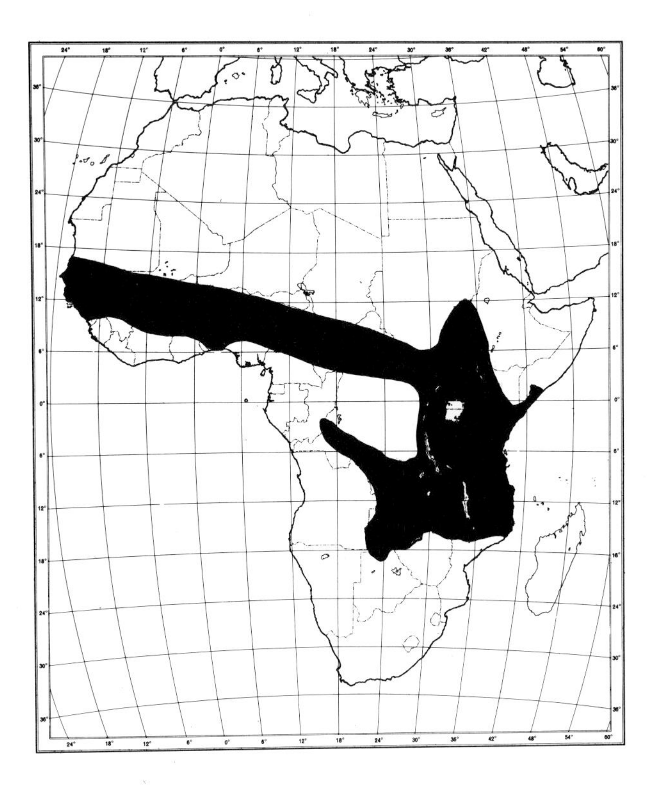

### Habitat
A savanna woodland species which appears to be associated with well-watered terrain.

### Habits
They appear to be solitary in habits, although in northeastern Zaire, Allen, Lang & Chapin (1917) found up to six together. There they apparently roost during the day in dense clusters of foliage of low trees or bushes. When roosting in dwellings they either cling to the brick walls or the roof rafters of the houses or hang from the thatch of huts, preferring the more secluded, darker places (Allen, Lang & Chapin, 1917). If they were disturbed in these situations, they clambered into secluded crevices. They fly low, not more than 2 m from the ground. The specimens collected in the Subregion have been netted and there is therefore no record of their roosting places.

### Food
Insectivorous.

### Reproduction
No information available from the Subregion.

No. 82

## *Eptesicus hottentotus* (A. Smith, 1833)

## Long-tailed serotine bat
## Langstert-dakvlermuis

### Colloquial Name

This species has a longer tail than any other *Eptesicus*.

### Taxonomic Notes

Meester *et al.* (1986) recognised three subspecies: the nominate *E. h. hottentotus* from the southern and southwestern Cape Province; *E. h. pallidior* Shortridge, 1942 from the northwestern Cape Province and Namibia, and *E. h. bensoni* Roberts, 1946 from the Natal Drakensberg, the northeastern parts of the Kruger National Park, Transvaal, Bophuthatswana, northeastern Cape Province, Zimbabwe and the Tete Province of Mozambique.

### Description

This is the largest species of *Eptesicus* that occurs in the Subregion with an average total length of about 115 mm and a tail of 47 mm and a mass of 16,6 g (Table 82.1). The upper parts vary in colour depending on the area from which they originate, those from the more arid western parts of the Subregion being fawn on the upper parts, those from the east much darker, some a dark brown, nearly black. The individual hairs are black at the base, broadly tipped with either fawn or dark brown. The under parts are lighter in colour and distinctly greyer, the dark bases of the hairs showing through and giving the under parts an uneven colour. The wing and interfemoral membranes, even in the lighter coloured specimens, are dark brown. The ears are dark brown and proportionately larger than in *E. capensis* and have rounded, upstanding tips. The ear tragus is knife-shaped with a rounded point (Fig. 82.1.b).

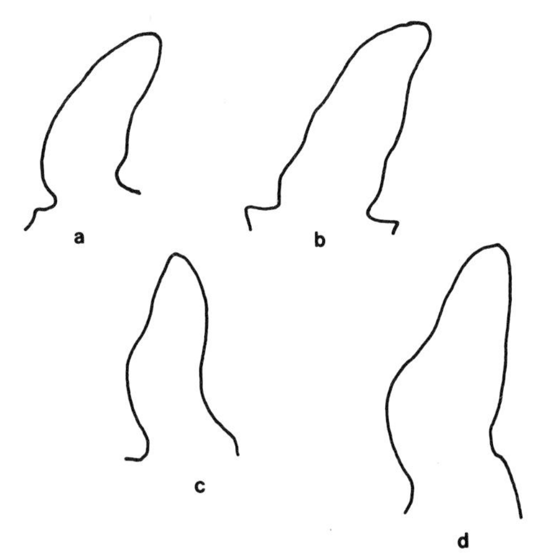


Fig. 82.1. Ear tragus of *Eptesicus* spp
(a) *E. capensis* (b) *E. hottentotus* (c) *E. somalicus*. (d) *E. melckorum*

### Table 82.1

Measurements (mm) and mass (g) of long-tailed serotine bats, *E. hottentotus*, from Zimbabwe (Smithers & Wilson, 1979)

| | Irrespective of sex | | |
|---|---|---|---|
| | $\bar{x}$ | n | Range |
| TL | 115 | 7 | 105–125 |
| T | 47 | 7 | 45–50 |
| Hf c/u | 11 | 7 | 10–11 |
| E | 17 | 7 | 16–18 |
| F/a | 47 | 7 | 46–48 |
| Mass | 16,6 | 6 | 10,8–20,0 |

### Distribution

Except for their occurrence in Malawi, long-tailed serotine bats are confined in their distribution to within the limits of the Subregion. They are nowhere common and records are few and scattered.

*South of the Sahara, excluding the Southern African Subregion*

They are recorded from the Central and Southern Provinces of **Malawi** and although *E. h. bensoni* (*E. megalurus*) was originally listed by Ansell (1960a) on the basis of a specimen purported to be in the Kaffrarian Museum, King William's Town, from the eastern sector of Zambia, the specimen cannot be traced. Ansell (1978) therefore deleted them from the Zambian list, although they may well occur owing to their occurrence in adjacent parts of Malawi.

*Southern African Subregion*

Recorded from the Mashonaland plateau and from Fort Victoria in **Zimbabwe** and from the Zambezi Valley northwest of Tete in **Mozambique**; the northeastern **Transvaal; Natal**; the **Cape Province** from parts of the southern mountainous areas west to the Cape Peninsula, northwards to Goodhouse on the Orange River, with an isolated record from Taung in **Bophuthatswana** (Herselman & Norton, 1985), and in **Namibia** the furthest north published record is from Omaruru.

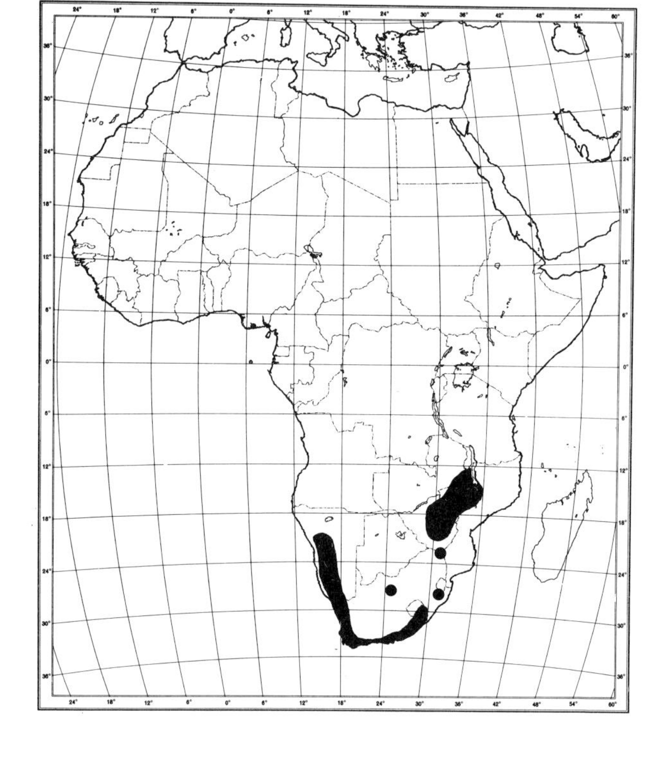

### Habitat

Too little information is available to assess the habitat requirements of this species. Six of the localities from which they were taken are in either broken or mountainous country, but they have also been taken in riverine forest.

### Habits

Long-tailed serotine bats occur in small numbers, never more than three or four together. They roost during the day in caves, in one case in a very wet cave, in others in dry caves, hanging up on the walls in a very loose formation. A single specimen was taken in Zimbabwe hanging on the outside of the wall of a building. Herselman (1980) took them from a small hollow in rocks at the entrance of an old mine tunnel.

### Food
Insectivorous.

### Reproduction
No data available.

---

No. 83

## *Eptesicus melckorum* Roberts, 1919

## Melck's serotine bat
## Melck se dakvlermuis

---

### Colloquial Name
Named after R. Melck of Kersfontein, Berg River, Cape Province, on whose property the original specimen was taken.

### Taxonomic Notes
The status of this species has been questioned by Koopman (in Honacki, Kinman & Koeppl, 1982) who suggested that it has not been distinguished clearly from *E. capensis*. This is under investigation by I.L. Rautenbach and D.A. Schlitter and until their findings are published it is retained as a full species in accordance with the treatment afforded it by Meester *et al.* (1986).

### Description
The essential difference between this species and *E. capensis* is that the colour of this species is a rich brown, the base of the individual hairs on the upper parts dark brown, not black as in *E. capensis*. There is some overlap in the length of the forearm in this species which ranges from 34,5 mm to 38 mm as against 29 mm to 36 mm in *E. capensis*, but when viewed against a series of *E. capensis*, with which they occur, they appear slightly larger. The ear tragus has a distinct bulge on its exterior edge (Fig. 82.1.d).

### Distribution
Roberts (1951) restricted the distribution of Melck's serotine bats to the winter rainfall areas of the southwestern Cape Province. They have been taken subsequently in Zambia and adjacent countries with no records to date between the two areas of occurrence and they have a somewhat wider distribution in the southwestern Cape Province than was thought by Roberts (1951).

*South of the Sahara, excluding the Southern African Subregion*

Recorded from Liwale in southeastern **Tanzania** and in southern **Zambia**. Ansell (*in litt.*) and Happold, Happold & Hill (1987) recorded the species from several localities in **Malawi**.

*Southern African Subregion*

Confined to the southwestern parts of the **Cape Province** from Namaqualand in the northwest to the Knysna area and inland to Three Sisters and Graaff Reinet.

### Habitat
Too little information is available to allow for a meaningful assessment of their habitat requirements. The northern populations generally occur in savanna woodland, the southern in the Macchia associations in the winter rainfall area with extensions northward and northeastward into dry terrain.

### Habits
Melck's serotine bats occur in small numbers, never more than up to about six. They roost during the day in crevices in the roofs of houses. Roberts (1951) recorded "fair" numbers between the outer walls and inner woodwork, and Herselman & Norton (1985) under the eaves of buildings and the bark of trees. These observations suggest that, like the Cape serotine bat, *E. capensis*, they tend to conceal themselves, well hidden, in crevices.

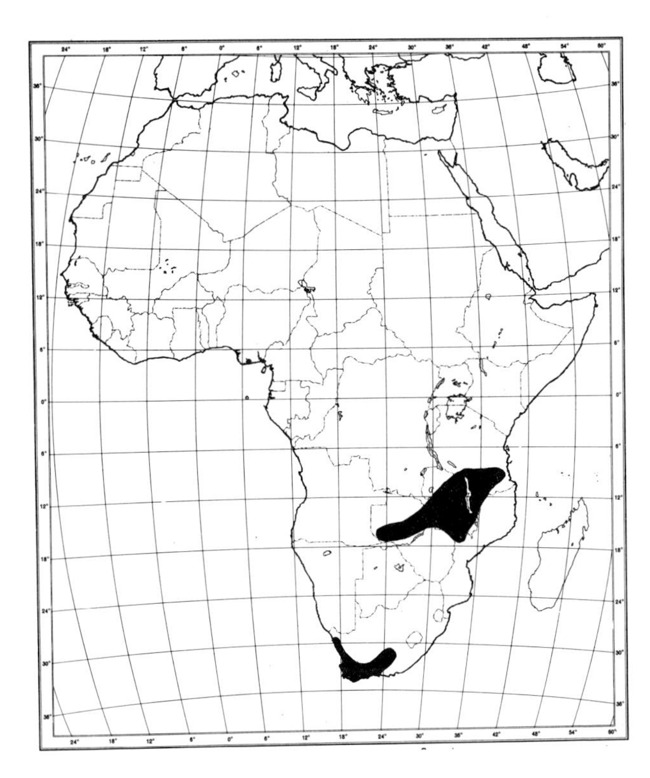

### Food
Insectivorous.

### Reproduction
Herselman (1980) recorded pregnant females, two with twin foetuses, in late October in the northwest Cape Province.

**WITHDRAWN**

---

No. 84

## *Eptesicus zuluensis* Roberts, 1924

## Aloe serotine bat
## Aalwyndakvlermuis

---

Included in the first edition, it is now considered to be conspecific with No. 85 *E. somalicus* (Thomas, 1901).

---

No. 85

## *Eptesicus somalicus* (Thomas, 1901)

## Somali serotine bat
## Somali-dakvlermuis

---

### Colloquial Name
The designation Somali is retained, as the original specimen from which the species was described came from Hargeisa, Somalia.

### Taxonomic Notes
Koopman (1975) discussed the relationship of *E. zuluensis* Roberts, 1924 to this species and came to the conclusion that it was probably conspecific with *E. somalicus*, a conclusion with which Meester *et al.* (1986) are in agreement and is now followed. Koopman's (1975) conclusion left a break in the distribution of the species in central Tanzania but he felt that

specimens from this sector identified as *E. pusillus* (Leconte, 1857) were actually *E. somalicus*. These are accordingly mapped as *E. somalicus*. Hayman & Hill (1971) regarded *E. zuluensis vansoni* (=*Neoromicia vansoni* Roberts, 1932) from northern Botswana as a synonym of *E. z. zuluensis* and records of this subspecies are included with those of *E. somalicus*.

### Description

This species is similar in colour to *E. capensis* with a tendency to be slightly paler on the upper parts. The skull is slightly smaller, the braincase slightly more elevated in relation to the rostrum and the skull lacks the distinct posterior "helmet" characteristic of the skull of *E. capensis* (Fig. 85.1). In measurements there is an overlap, *E. capensis* tending to be slightly larger, the forearm in male *E. somalicus*, for example, being 26 to 29 mm, in females 27 to 30 mm, whereas in *E. capensis* males it is 31 to 33 mm, in females 28 to 30 mm. Thomas (1901) in his original description of *E. somalicus* noted that the hair on the upper parts was longer at 6 mm than in *E. capensis* at 5 mm, while Rosevear (1965) stated that in *E. somalicus* it reaches a length of 8 mm. He noted also that the ear tragus of *E. somalicus* was more slender than in *E. capensis* and it has a distinct bulge on its exterior edge (Fig. 82.1.c).

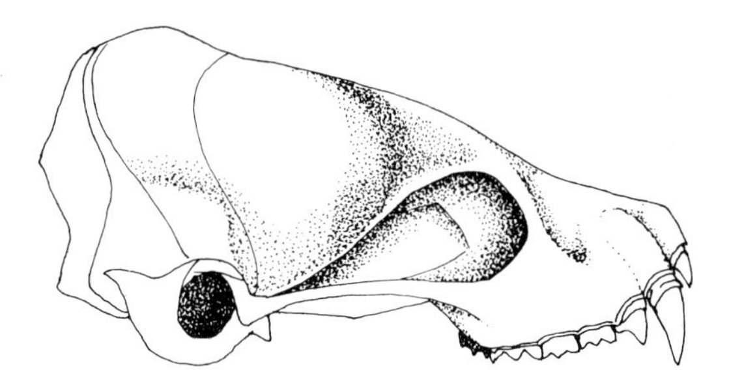

Fig. 85.1. Skull of *Eptesicus somalicus*

### Distribution

If it is accepted that the allied species *E. guineensis* (Bocage, 1889); *E. pusillus* (Leconte, 1857); *E. minuta* Temminck, 1840 and others are conspecific, then *E. somalicus* has a very wide, albeit scattered, distribution from Portuguese Guinea in West Africa eastwards to Somalia and southwards to northern Natal.

*South of the Sahara, excluding the Southern African Subregion*

There are records from **Guinea Bissau; Burkina Faso; Togo; Central African Republic; Uganda; Kenya; Sudan; Ethiopia; Somalia; Tanzania; Angola; Zaire** and **Zambia**.

*Southern African Subregion*

Recorded from northern **Namibia**; northern **Botswana**; western and northeastern **Zimbabwe**; eastern and northern **Transvaal** and northern **Natal**.

### Habitat

A savanna woodland species, which, in the drier parts of its distributional range, is associated with the availability of water.

### Habits

They occur in close company with the Cape serotine bat, *E. capensis* which is always by far the commoner species. Their daylight roosting places have not been discovered so far, although in Botswana it was thought that they were using the cover of loose bark of dead trees. Their flight is similar to that of *E. capensis* and is characterised by the

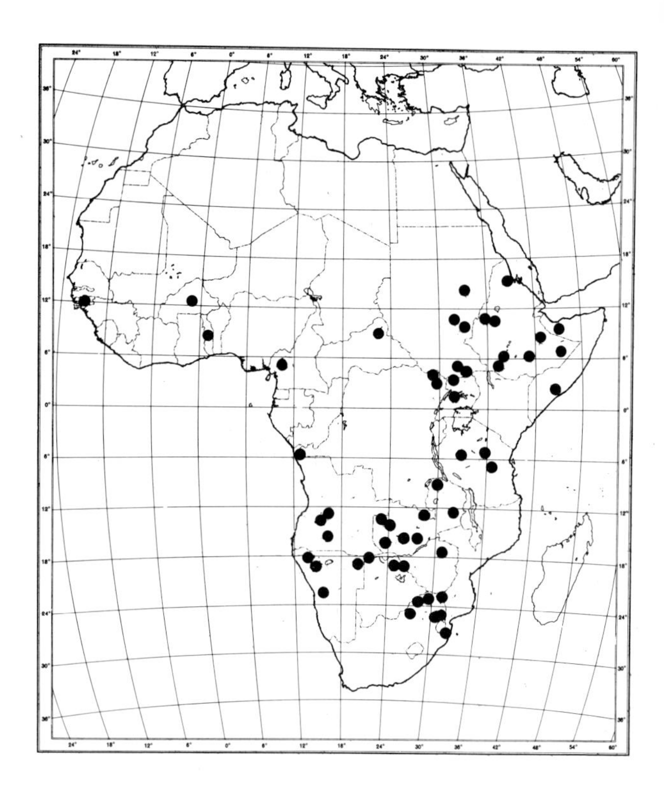

same jinking and turning and the use of set flight paths at a height of 10 m to 15 m above the ground.

### Food

Insectivorous.

### Reproduction

Young are born towards the end of November and the first half of December in the Subregion.

---

No. 86

## *Eptesicus capensis* (A. Smith, 1829)

## Cape serotine bat
## Kaapse dakvlermuis

Plate 4

---

### Colloquial Name

The name serotine is derived from the Latin *serotinus*, late in the evening (*serus* = late).

### Taxonomic Notes

There is such a close relationship between the genus *Eptesicus* and *Pipistrellus*, the difference hinging on the presence in *Pipistrellus* of a minute upper premolar and its absence in *Eptesicus*, that some workers have suggested that they should be combined in the genus *Vespertilio*. This difference is in fact not uniform, for sometimes specimens of *Eptesicus* possess these teeth. Hayman & Hill (1971) recognised this and preferred to deal with the two genera separately, a treatment which is followed here. Hayman & Hill (1971) listed 13 species of the genus that occur in Africa, listing, but not necessarily accepting, the 10 subspecies of *Eptesicus capensis* that have been described, and which for purposes of this work can be disregarded. Hayman & Hill (1971) listed *E. notius* which is only known from a single specimen from Cape Town. Re-examination of this specimen by Koopman (1975) has shown that it is a synonym of *E. capensis*. The granulated appearance of the wings, which was a character distinguishing it from *E. capensis*, was thought to be due to the presence of nematode parasites.

**Description**

Even within the Subregion there is such a wide range of variability both in size and colour that there is no typical Cape serotine bat. The females are larger than the males, the males with a total length of about 80 mm, the females 90 mm, with tails of about 30 mm and 35 mm respectively. The sexual dimorphism shows better in their mass where males average in series 5,9 g, females 7,3 g (Table 86.1).

The colour of the upper parts is a yellowish-brown, in darker and lighter shades, the individual hairs black at the base with narrow tips of various shades of yellowish-brown. The under parts are yellowish-white or white, the black bases of the hairs showing through and imparting to them an uneven colour. The wing and interfemoral membranes are blackish-brown. The ears have rounded points, their inner margins rising straight up from the head, then abruptly outward to the points, the outer edges concave. Within the species the significance of the shape of the ear tragus in relation to the variety of colour and sizes that exist is not at the moment resolved (Fig. 82.1.a).

The posterior end of the skull curves upward to a "helmet" formed by the supraoccipital and sagittal crests. No other *Eptesicus* has this feature developed to the same extent (Fig. 86.1).

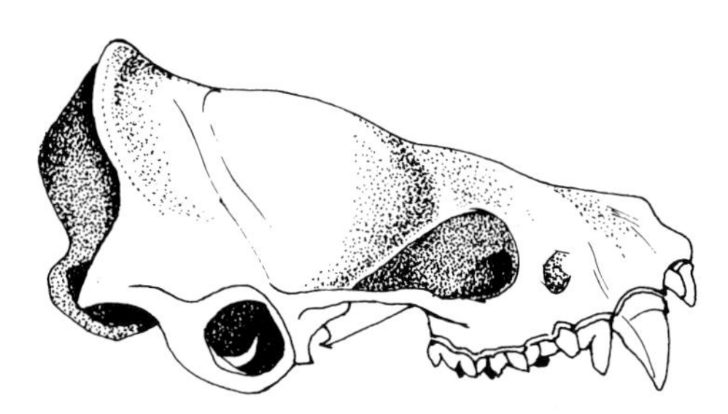

Fig. 86.1. Skull of *Eptesicus capensis*

**Table 86.1**

Measurements (mm) and mass (g) of Cape serotine bats, *E. capensis*, from the Transvaal (Rautenbach, 1982)

| | Males | | | Females | | |
|---|---|---|---|---|---|---|
| | $\bar{x}$ | n | Range | $\bar{x}$ | n | Range |
| TL | 82 | 41 | 69–97 | 90 | 51 | 70–115 |
| T | 31 | 40 | 23–38 | 34 | 51 | 25–46 |
| Hf c/u | 7 | 41 | 4–9 | 8 | 50 | 5–9 |
| E | 12 | 41 | 9–14 | 14 | 50 | 8–15 |
| F/a | 32 | 29 | 29–35 | 34 | 33 | 31–39 |
| Mass | 5,9 | 30 | 4,0–10,0 | 7,3 | 35 | 4,0–10,0 |

**Distribution**

Rosevear (1965) pointed out that the taxonomic situation as far as the Cape serotine bat, *Eptesicus capensis*, is concerned, is exceptionally obscure, as new names were added in the past to ostensibly different forms, as valid species or subspecies, the latter attributed first to one and then to another of originally ill-defined species. The situation remains in this unsatisfactory state, making it difficult to define distributional limits. He believed, however, that the species might be expected to occur throughout West Africa, more commonly in the Forest and Guinea Savanna Zones, although perhaps not at all in the Sahara. In other parts of the continent, judging from records from literature attributed by authors to *E. capensis*, they have a wide range throughout, although there remain vast areas from which no information is available at present.

*Extralimital to the continent*

**Madagascar**.

*South of the Sahara, excluding the Southern African Subregion*

Recorded from **Guinea** in West Africa eastwards to **Ethiopia** and parts of **Somalia** southward to the northern borders of the Subregion. Although recorded from **Zanzibar Island**, Swynnerton & Hayman (1950) did not list *E. capensis* from Tanzania and so far they have not been recorded from northeastern Mozambique, but occur in **Malawi**.

*Southern African Subregion*

They occur in **Namibia**, excluding the Namib Desert, but are recorded coastally in the south at Oranjemund on the Orange River; in **Botswana; Zimbabwe**; in at least the western parts of **Mozambique**, south of the Zambezi River; in the **Transvaal; Orange Free State** and **Natal**. In the **Cape Province** they occur widely throughout.

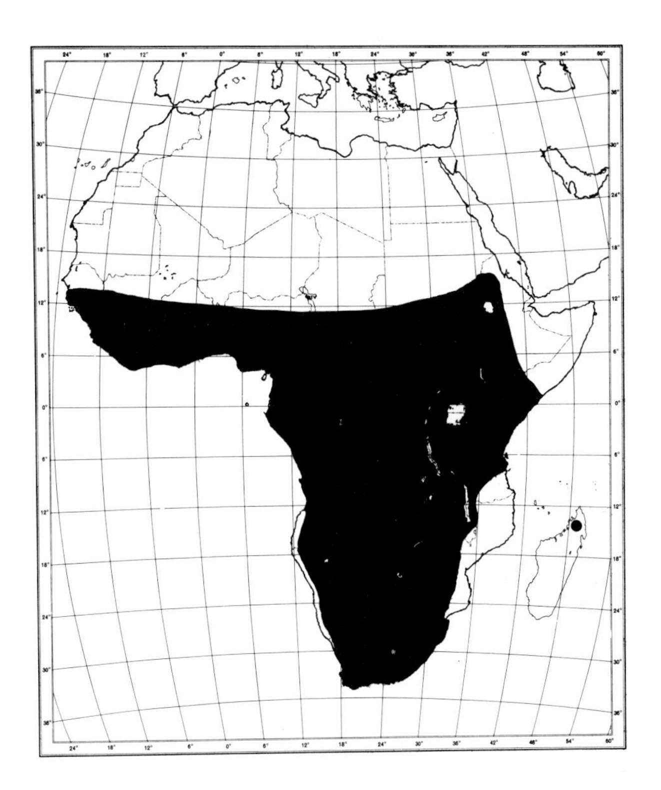

**Habitat**

Owing to the uncertain taxonomic status of the Cape serotine bat, *E. capensis*, which eventually may be shown to be comprised of a number of species, it is impossible to review their habitat requirements with any degree of certainty. Rosevear (1965) recorded them both from forest and savanna and believed that they may be absent from the desert regions. In the Subregion they occur widely in savanna and in the South West Arid Zone; there are no records from the western coastal desert.

**Habits**

They occur in small numbers, being commonly found in twos and threes roosting during the day, huddled closely together under the bark of trees, at the base of aloe leaves, and quite commonly in the roofs of houses, tucked away between overlapping sheets of corrugated iron or between this and the rafters. The fact that there are so few records of their daylight roosting places is certainly due to their being overlooked, as they so readily are, being hidden away in these narrow crevices.

They emerge before it is dark, their fluttering flight then being slow and sluggish. In Zimbabwe, Smithers (1983) saw a pied crow, *Corvus albus*, pick them one by one out of the air with its beak, swallowing them whole after returning to its perch on the top of a high cypress tree. Once they have limbered up they fly quite fast, generally holding to a prescribed route around the canopy of the trees some 10 to 15 m above the ground, jinking and turning, presumably in catching insect food. They come readily to lights at night and commonly enter houses.

### Food

Insectivorous.

### Reproduction

In Zimbabwe gravid females were taken in January, the average number of foetuses being carried by females being 1,6 with a normal range of one or two. A female taken near Harare carried three foetuses. In the Transvaal, Rautenbach (1982) recorded gravid females in October and November with one or two foetuses and a solitary female with three. He also took lactating females in September, November and December. In the northern parts of the Subregion these data indicate that the young are born during the warm, wet summer months.

## Genus *Scotophilus* Leach, 1821

The ear tragus of members of this genus is characteristically long and fine-pointed, the outer margin convex with a lobe towards its base. In the posterior molars the usual W pattern on their crowns is reduced to two legs, only half the teeth being present. *S. dinganii* and *S. borbonicus* are both quite common in the Subregion, the latter tending to be confined to lower altitudes, the former common in the roofs of houses and recognisable from the yellow or yellowish-orange colour of the under parts. The giant yellow house bat, *S. nigrita*, on the other hand is rare in the Subregion, only two specimens having been taken to date.

The dental formula is

$I\frac{1}{3}\ C\frac{1}{1}\ P\frac{1}{2}\ M\frac{3}{3} = 30$

They have a single pair of upper incisors (Fig. 88.2), the anterior lower premolar much smaller than the posterior and tightly packed between it and the canine in the toothrow.

Key to the species after Meester *et al.* (1986)
(Measurements in mm)

1. Size large, forearm 75–80; total length skull over 30 ... *nigrita*

   Size smaller, forearm 43–65; total length skull 16–23 ... 2

2. Forearm 50–65; total length skull 20–23 ... *dinganii*

   Forearm 43–50; total length skull 16–19 ... *borbonicus*

---

No. 87

## *Scotophilus nigrita* (Schreber, 1774)

## Giant yellow house bat
## Groot geel dakvlermuis

---

### Colloquial Name

This is the largest of the three yellow house bats which occur in the Subregion.

### Taxonomic Notes

Robbins (1978) showed that Dobson (1875) when describing *S. gigas* was in fact redescribing *S. nigrita* and that since 1800 the name *S. nigrita* has been applied to the wrong taxon. As a result *S. nigrita* becomes the senior synonym of *S. gigas*; the next available name for the taxon previously known as *S. nigrita* is *S. dinganii*. This leaves three species which occur in the Subregion, *S. nigrita*, the largest; *S. dinganii*, a medium-sized species, and *S. borbonicus*, the smallest. Only the subspecies *S. n. alvenslebeni* Dalquest, 1965 occurs in the Subregion.

### Description

As the name suggests this is a large *Scotophilus*, the total length about 170 to 180 mm as against that of *S. dinganii* at 130 mm and *S. borbonicus* at 110 to 120 mm (Table 87.1). In the Mozambique specimen the upper parts were dark sooty-brown in colour, the ears and wing and interfemoral membranes black. There appears, however, to be considerable variation in colour, for Rosevear (1965) stated that three specimens from Malawi ranged from darkish red-brown to yellowish-greyish-brown on the upper parts, the under parts varying from pale straw colour to white. Among our insectivorous bats they rank second in size after Commerson's leaf-nosed bats, *Hipposideros commersoni*.

The ear has a strongly rounded inner margin, the ear tragus typical of members of the genus with its evenly curved inner margin, long tapering shape ending in a fine point (Fig. 88.1.a). The sagittal crest on top of the skull is well developed and ends posteriorly in a rounded "helmet".

### Table 87.1

Measurements (mm) of giant yellow house bats, *S. nigrita* (Dalquest, 1965; Rosevear, 1965)

**Male from Zinave, Save River, Mozambique (Dalquest, 1965)**

| TL | T | Hfc/u | E | F/a |
|---|---|---|---|---|
| 175 | 77 | 14 | 20 | 77 |

Range of measurements as given by Rosevear (1965)

| HB | T | F/a |
|---|---|---|
| 112–117 | 68–78 | 70–80 |

### Distribution

There are very few specimens of this, the largest of the members of the genus *Scotophilus* which occur on the continent. These were taken in a scatter of localities from Senegal to the Sudan and south to the Save River in Mozambique. It is impossible at the moment to attempt to assess their limits of distribution and only the localities from which they have been taken are mapped.

*South of the Sahara, excluding the Southern African Subregion*

Recorded from **Senegal; Ghana; Nigeria**; the **Sudan; Kenya**; eastern **Zaire** and southern **Malawi**. Some doubt remains as to the authenticity of the record from Ghana (Rosevear, 1965).

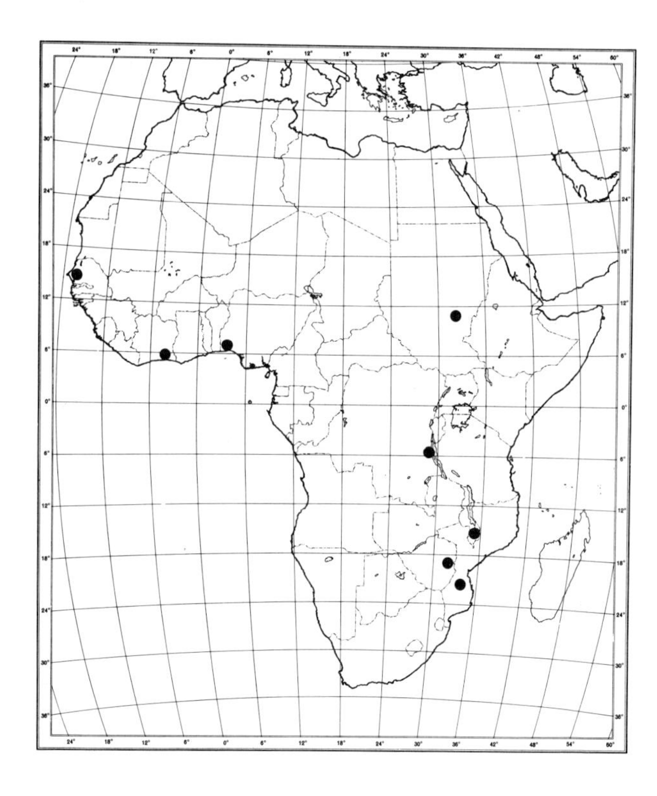

*Southern African Subregion*

Represented by two specimens, one from Odzi, near Mutare, **Zimbabwe**, the other from the Zinave National Park on the Save River in **Mozambique**.

### Habitat

Too little is known about giant yellow house bats to understand their habitat requirements. The type specimen came from rain forest in Nigeria, but another from the arid Sudan savanna (Rosevear, 1965). The two specimens taken in the Subregion were collected in the vicinity of major rivers lying within savanna woodland.

### Food

Insectivorous.

### Habits and Reproduction

No information available.

No. 88

## *Scotophilus dinganii* (A. Smith, 1833)

## Yellow house bat
## Geel dakvlermuis

Plate 5

### Colloquial Name

This is the only member of the genus which occurs in the subregion in which the adults have yellow coloured under parts. The juveniles are not so clearly coloured, but usually show some suffusion of this colour.

### Taxonomic Notes

Meester *et al.* (1986) recognised three subspecies as occurring in the Subregion: *S. d. dinganii* from Natal, Transvaal, Mozambique, Zimbabwe and eastern and northern Botswana; *S. d. pondoensis* Roberts, 1946 from the eastern Cape Province and Transkei, and *S. d. herero* Thomas, 1906 from northern Zambia.

### Description

Yellow house bats are of medium size, the total length being about 130 mm, with tails of 50 mm long and a mass of about 27 g (Table 88.1). The colour of the upper parts is variable, ranging from a light olive-brown or a greyish-olive to a rich reddish-brown. The under parts may be bright yellow, ochre-yellow or much paler, almost off-white, with or without yellow on the flanks. The hair of the under parts continues broadly on to the wing membranes between the elbow and the thighs. The hair is soft and woolly with a distinct sheen. There is variation in the colour of both the upper and under parts even in a series from the same colony. The wing and interfemoral membranes are a dark translucent brown. The ears are relatively small, the inner edges strongly curved, the tips bluntly pointed. The ear tragus is characteristic in shape (Fig. 88.1.a). They have a single upper incisor on either side (Fig. 88.2).

**Table 88.1**

Measurements (mm) and mass (g) of yellow house bats, *S. dinganii*, from Zimbabwe (Smithers & Wilson, 1979)

| | Males | | | Females | | |
|---|---|---|---|---|---|---|
| | $\bar{x}$ | n | Range | $\bar{x}$ | n | Range |
| TL | 130 | 15 | 113–137 | 131 | 14 | 123–141 |
| T | 52 | 15 | 46–55 | 54 | 14 | 50–57 |
| Hf c/u | 12 | 15 | 11–14 | 12 | 14 | 11–15 |
| E | 16 | 15 | 12–18 | 17 | 14 | 15–19 |
| F/a | 55 | 15 | 53–56 | 55 | 14 | 52–57 |
| Mass | 27,1 | 14 | 21,3–36,0 | 27,3 | 14 | 21,9–37,9 |

### Distribution

*Extralimital to the continent*

Recorded from the extreme southwestern parts of **Arabia** and from the islands of **Madagascar, Mauritius** and **Reunion**, if *S. robustus* Milne-Edwards, 1881 is conspecific.

*South of the Sahara, excluding the Southern African Subregion*

Recorded from **Senegal; Niger; Nigeria; Chad** eastwards to **Ethiopia** and **Somalia** and southward in **Uganda; Kenya; Tanzania; Zaire** excluding the forest; **Congo Republic; Angola; Zambia** and **Malawi**. Not at present recorded from Mozambique, north of the Zambezi River, but likely to occur.

*Southern African Subregion*

Recorded from northern **Namibia** as far south as Windhoek; from northern and eastern **Botswana; Zimbabwe**; parts of the **Transvaal; Mozambique**, south of the Zambezi River; **Natal** and the eastern **Cape Province** where they occur along the south coast westwards to about 26 °E. There is an isolated record from the Kalahari Gemsbok National Park (Erasmus & Rautenbach, 1984) which suggests that they may have a wider distribution in this sector than formerly supposed. So far they have not been found in the northeastern Transvaal and adjacent parts of Zimbabwe and Mozambique.

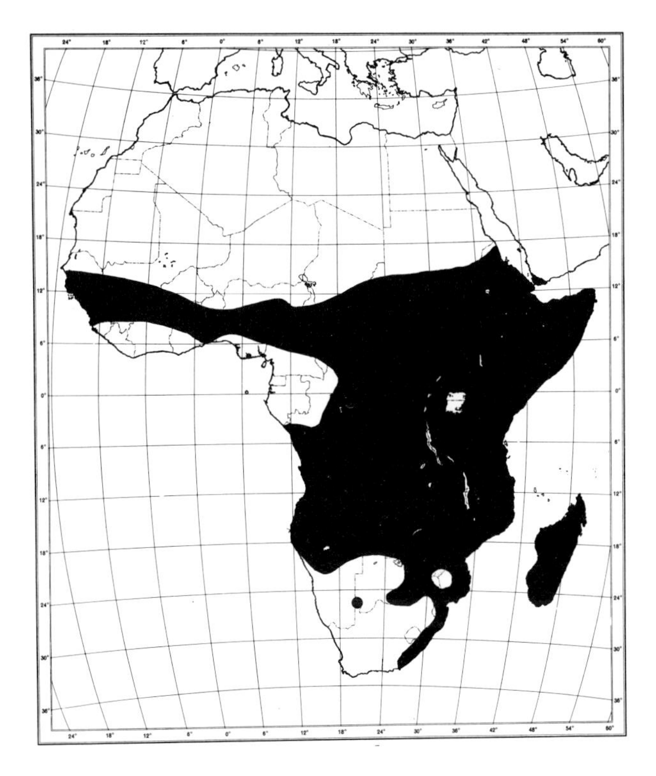

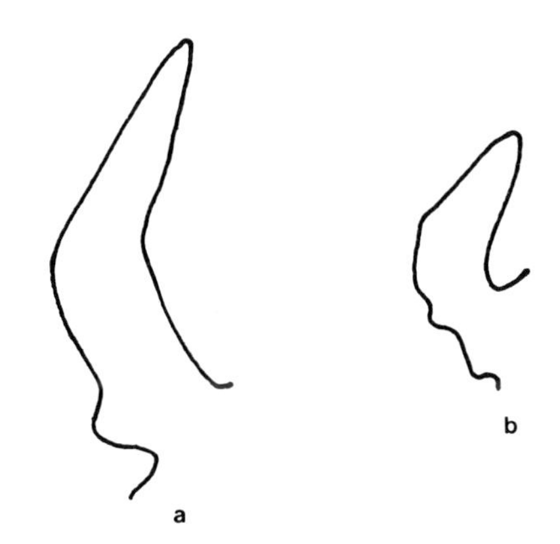


Fig. 88.1. Ear tragus:
(a) *Scotophilus dinganii* (b) *Nycticeius schlieffenii*

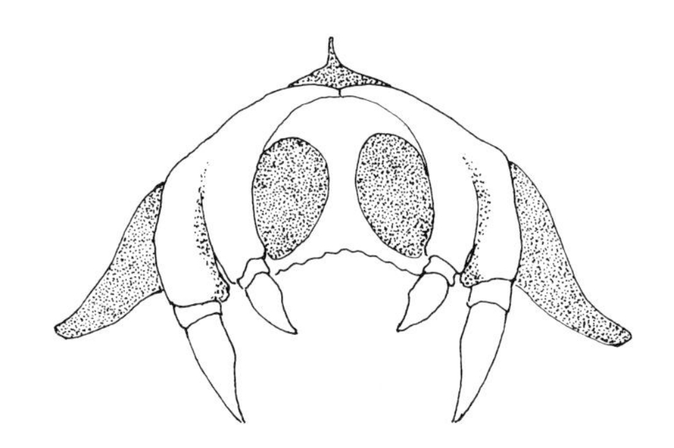

Fig. 88.2 Front view of the skull of *Scotophilus dinganii* to show the single upper incisor on either side and the canines.

**Habitat**

This is a savanna woodland species which is absent from desert areas and forest, although it occurs on forest fringes.

**Habits**

They are gregarious, but occur in small numbers of up to about a dozen together. They roost during the day tucked together into narrow crevices in the brickwork under the roofs of houses, or between the overlapping corrugated iron sheets. Numbers of these small clusters may be found under a single roof, the total numbers present amounting to dozens. They will also use hollow trees and have been taken tucked into crevices in the thatch inside disused rondavels. They have a tendency to be associated with built-up areas, occurring even in the peri-urban and urban surroundings of cities or in farm buildings. They quite often enter houses at night in foraging or fly around lights at night catching insects. They are fast fliers and are inclined to fly low over the ground. In Zimbabwe it was noticeable that they were absent from the plateau (1 200–1 500 m) during the colder months of the year from June to August, yet were present at lower altitudes (600 m) in the southeast of the country.

**Food**

Insectivorous.

**Reproduction**

In Zimbabwe gravid females were taken in September and October, and lactating and females with young clinging to them in November and December. Out of a sample of seven gravid females they were carrying twin foetuses in every case. In the Transvaal, Rautenbach (1982) reported that out of four gravid females taken in October, three carried twin foetuses, one triplets. These observations of parturition during early summer and the birth of twins have been confirmed by Penzhorn, Rautenbach & van der Merwe, N.J. (unpubl.).

No. 89

## *Scotophilus borbonicus* (E. Geoffroy, 1803)

## Lesser yellow house bat
## Klein geel dakvlermuis

**Colloquial Name**

This is the smallest yellow house bat occurring in the Subregion.

**Taxonomic Notes**

Meester *et al.* (1986) recognised two subspecies as occurring in the Subregion: *S. b. damarensis* Thomas, 1906 from northeastern Namibia and *S. b. viridis* (Peters, 1852) from the remainder of the species range, *S. b. borbonicus* being extralimital.

**Description**

As the name implies the lesser yellow house bat is smaller than its near relative, the yellow house bat.

The species has a total length of about 120 mm, with a tail of 46 mm and a mass of about 16 g (Table 89.1). The difference in size between the two species shows best in the length of the forearm which in this species ranges from 46–50 mm, in the yellow house bat from 52–57 mm. The colour of the upper parts varies from a light to a dark yellowish-brown, the under parts in the lighter coloured specimens being white, in the darker a greyish-white. In some specimens the under parts may be tinged yellow or there may be traces of yellow on the flanks. Because of the variation in colour the best criterion for distinguishing the two species is from their sizes.

**Table 89.1**

Measurements (mm) and mass (g) of lesser yellow house bats, *S. borbonicus*, from Zimbabwe (Smithers & Wilson, 1979)

| | Irrespective of sex | | |
|---|---|---|---|
| | $\bar{x}$ | n | Range |
| TL | 115 | 10 | 111–125 |
| T | 46 | 10 | 40–52 |
| Hf c/u | 11 | 10 | 10–15 |
| E | 14 | 10 | 10–16 |
| F/a | 48 | 6 | 46–50 |
| Mass | 15,7 | 7 | 13,0–18,0 |

**Distribution**

The nominate *S. b. borbonicus* was described for **Reunion Island** and also occurs on **Madagascar**.

*South of the Sahara, excluding the Southern African Subregion*

Recorded from the **Sudan; Kenya**; southeastern **Tanzania; Mozambique**, north of the Zambezi River; **Malawi** and **Zambia**. While there are no records at the moment from Angola or Zaire, it seems likely, owing to their occurrence in adjacent parts of Zambia, that in time they will be found to occur.

*Southern African Subregion*

Recorded in northeastern **Namibia**; in **Zimbabwe**, excluding most of the central plateau; in **Mozambique**, south of the Zambezi River; northern **Botswana**, in parts of the **Transvaal** and in Zululand.

**Plate 5**

40. Wahlberg's epauletted fruit bat, *Epomophorus wahlbergi*
    Wahlberg se witkolvrugtevlermuis
49. Tomb bat, *Taphozous mauritianus*
    Witlyfvlermuis
63. Egyptian free-tailed bat, *Tadarida (Tadarida) aegyptiaca*
    Egiptiese losstertvlermuis
68. Welwitsch's hairy bat, *Myotis welwitschii*
    Welwitsch se langhaarvlermuis
77. Butterfly bat, *Chalinolobis variegatus*
    Vlindervlermuis
88. Yellow house bat, *Scotophilus dinganii*
    Geel dakvlermuis
98. Common slit-faced bat, *Nycteris thebaica*
    Gewone spleetneusvlermuis
100. Hildebrandt's horseshoe bat, *Rhinolophus hildebrandtii*
    Hildebrandt se saalneusvlermuis
110. Commerson's leaf-nosed bat, *Hipposideros commersoni*
    Commerson se bladneusvlermuis

PLATE 5
40
49
63
77
68
88
98
100
110
Dick Findlay.

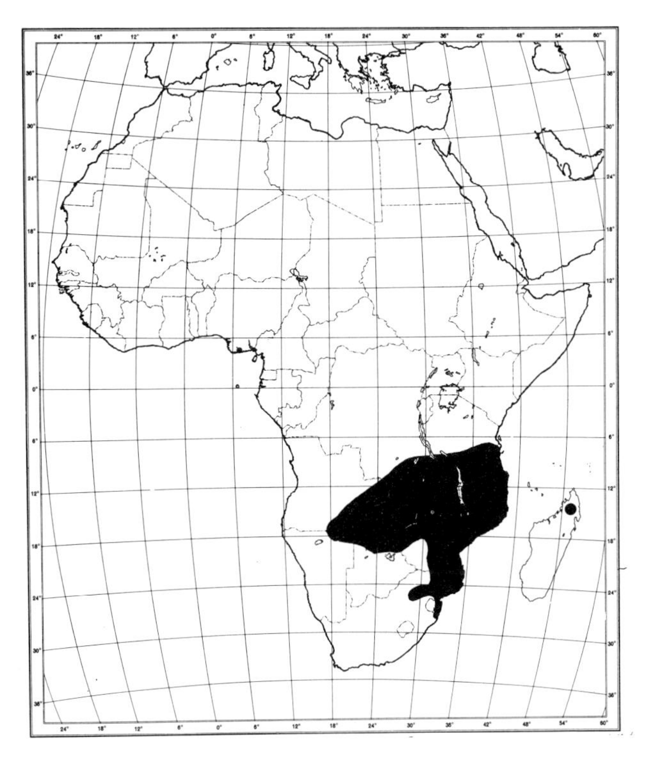

## Genus *Nycticeius* Rafinesque, 1819

No. 90

## *Nycticeius schlieffenii* (Peters, 1859)

## Schlieffen's bat
## Schlieffen se vlermuis

Plate 4

**Colloquial Name**

Named after the collector Count Wilhelm von Schlieffen-Schlieffenburg.

**Taxonomic Notes**

Meester *et al.* (1986) listed two subspecies from the Subregion, *N. s. australis* (Thomas & Wroughton, 1908) from Zululand; southern Mozambique; the eastern and northern Transvaal and Zimbabwe; and *N. s. fitzsimonsi* (Roberts, 1932) from northern Botswana and northern Namibia.

**Description**

Schlieffen's bats have a total length of about 75 mm, with tails 30 mm in length and a mean mass of 4,6 g (Table 90.1).

The upper parts are light fawn, the individual hairs unicolour or only slightly lighter in shade at their bases, the under parts slightly paler. In contrast to the body colour, the wing and interfemoral membranes are dark brown and tend to show a series of dark, roughly parallel striations across them. The ears are strongly convex on their inner edges, concave on the outer, the tips rounded. The ear tragus is of characteristic shape (Fig. 88.1.b).

The dental formula is

$I\frac{1}{3}\ C\frac{1}{1}\ P\frac{1}{2}\ M\frac{3}{3} = 30$

The single premolar in the upper jaw is sharply pointed and about three-quarters the height of the canine. The anterior lower premolar is half the size of the posterior one and tightly packed between it and the canine.

**Table 90.1**

Measurements (mm) and mass (g) of Schlieffen's bats, *N. s. australis*, from Zimbabwe (Smithers & Wilson, 1979), and *N. s. fitzsimonsi* from Botswana (Smithers, 1971)

| | Irrespective of sex | | | | | |
|---|---|---|---|---|---|---|
| | *N. s. australis* | | | *N. s. fitzsimonsi* | | |
| | $\bar{x}$ | n | Range | $\bar{x}$ | n | Range |
| TL | 75 | 12 | 69–80 | 71 | 10 | 64–78 |
| T | 30 | 12 | 28–31 | 29 | 10 | 24–30 |
| Hf c/u | 7 | 12 | 6–8 | 7 | 10 | 5–9 |
| E | 10 | 12 | 9–11 | 11 | 10 | 10–13 |
| F/a | 30 | 12 | 29–31 | 29 | 10 | 28–30 |
| Mass | 4,6 | 9 | 3,7–5,0 | | | |

**Distribution**

Schlieffen's bats have a wide distribution on the continent from Egypt southwards to Ethiopia and Somalia and westwards to Mali and south of this to northern Namibia and Zululand.

*Extralimital to the continent*

Recorded from the southwestern parts of **Arabia**.

*North of the Sahara*

Occurs along the western borders of the Red Sea and the Gulf of Suez to the delta of the Nile in **Egypt**.

*South of the Sahara, excluding the southern African Subregion*

Recorded from **Mali**; the northern parts of **Ghana**; southern **Mauritania**; northern **Nigeria; Niger**; **Chad**; northeastern and southern **Sudan; Ethiopia; Somalia**; parts of **Uganda; Kenya**; northeastern and southern **Zaire; Tanzania; Angola; Zambia** and **Malawi**. So far not recorded from the northeast-

**Habitat**

A savanna woodland species, in Zimbabwe restricted to altitudes of below about 1 000 m above sea level, although in the Transvaal this does not hold. They appear to be associated with riverine conditions or to areas with a mean annual rainfall in excess of 500 mm.

**Habits**

Little is known about the habits of this species except that they roost in small colonies in Zimbabwe in hollow trees. Cotterill & Giddings (1987) in netting at Tashinga in the Matusadona National Park, Zimbabwe, on the shores of Lake Kariba, found that they were active from 19h00 to 21h00, the peak of the male activity being 21h00 to 22h00, and of the females from 19h00 to 21h00. As the majority of the females were lactating, which involves added energy demands, and as insect abundance tends to be the greatest immediately after sundown, it was presumed that the females were benefitting by feeding early.

In Zimbabwe, where they were using holes in trees, they changed roost trees from one day to the next and frequently moved between night and day roosts, usually staying, however, within a relatively small area of woodland (Fenton 1983; Fenton, Brigham, Mills & Rautenbach, 1985; Fenton & Rautenbach, 1986). Individuals feed from about an hour following sunset, after which they return to their day-time roosts. Very little activity occurs during the rest of the night. They commute over considerable distances to favourable feeding sites.

**Food**

Insectivorous.

**Reproduction**

Of 18 females collected in Zimbabwe in November, nine were gravid, each carrying two foetuses. Cotterill & Giddings (1987) recorded that a high percentage of 46 females taken at Lake Kariba were lactating in December. Van der Merwe, Rautenbach & Penzhorn (1988) recorded parturition during November/December, with a high incidence of twins delivered.

ern parts of Mozambique, but little collecting has taken place there and they probably have been overlooked.

*Southern African Subregion*

They occur in northern **Namibia**; in the northern and northeastern parts of **Botswana**; in **Zimbabwe** and in **Mozambique**, south of the Zambezi River. In the **Transvaal** they occur in the north and east and southwards to the northern parts of Zululand.

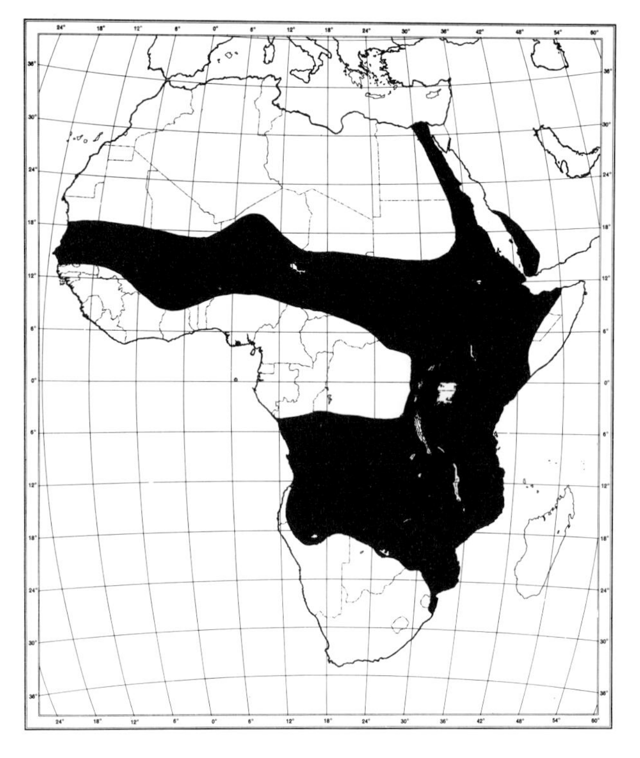

### Habitat

In West Africa they are absent from the High Forest Zone and parts of the Guinea savanna, tending to be associated with the more arid Sudan and Sahel savannas. In the more southerly parts of their distributional range they are associated with savanna woodland, but do not occur in the more arid open parts of the South West Arid Zone, nor locally in forest. In the eastern parts of the Subregion they are commoner at altitudes of less than 1 200 m.

### Habits

A solitary species which roosts during the day in houses, huts and cellars (Rosevear, 1965) and has been taken in narrow crevices in branches of trees (Verschuren, 1957). Numbers occasionally congregate to forage. Roberts (1951) recorded that they emerge from their roosting places before dusk and have an erratic flight. They occasionally enter houses while foraging. Most of the material from the Subregion was netted or shot and therefore there is no record of their habits.

### Food

Insectivorous.

### Reproduction

Van der Merwe & Rautenbach (1986, 1987) recorded that, in the Transvaal, mating takes place during the winter months, predominantly in June. Spermatogenesis extends over a 10-month period with the first signs of spermatozoa in the epididymides by the end of April. Spermatozoa were present in the epididymides from the end of April until the beginning of September. Copulation begins during June (early winter) and the females have spermatozoa in the uterine horns from then until the end of August (late winter) when ovulation occurs. These bats are seasonally monoestrus with the great majority of births occurring during November. The number of conceptuses varied; a maximum of 5 pre-implanted embryos was recorded, but the maximum number of foetuses observed was 3.

## Genus *Scotoecus* Thomas, 1901

No. 91

## *Scotoecus albofuscus* (Thomas, 1890)

## Thomas' house bat
## Thomas se vlermuis

### Colloquial Name

Named after O. Thomas who described the species.

### Taxonomic Notes

Meester *et al.* (1986) listed one subspecies, *S. a. woodii* Thomas, 1917 from the Subregion. The genus is subject to variability in its dental formula. Some individuals retain the tiny upper premolars that lie immediately behind the canines, in others they are missing. When they are present these tiny teeth are tucked away internal to the toothrow. In this species the broad rostrum, the shape of the ear tragus, and long bony penis, which reaches a length of a quarter of that of the head and body, mark them as clearly different from Schlieffen's bats, *Nycticeius schlieffenii*. *S. a. albofuscus* occurs in West Africa.

### Description

Thomas' bats have a total length of some 70 mm, a mass of about 4,5 g and forearms of 30–31 mm. The colour of the upper parts is a light fawn-brown, the under parts paler and lighter still in colour on the chest. The wing membranes are white, brownish towards the edges, the interfemoral membrane brown. The ears are oval with broad rounded points, the tragus short and rounded.

The dental formula is

$I\frac{1}{3}\,C\frac{1}{1}\,P\frac{1}{2}\,M\frac{3}{3} = 30$

or when the anterior upper premolar is present

$I\frac{1}{3}\,C\frac{1}{1}\,P\frac{2}{2}\,M\frac{3}{3} = 32$

### Distribution

At the moment there are only very few, scattered records from the continent and so little is known about this species that it is impossible to show its limits of distribution with accuracy.

*South of the Sahara, excluding the Southern African Subregion*

There are records from **Senegal; Gambia; Nigeria; Kenya** and the Southern Province of **Malawi**.

*Southern African Subregion*

So far recorded only from the Zinave National Park on the Save River in southern **Mozambique**.

### Habitat, Habits, Food and Reproduction

Unknown.

## Subfamily KERIVOULINAE

## Genus *Kerivoula* Gray, 1842

All members of this genus are characterised by their long, soft, woolly fur which stands erect from the body, the tips of the individual hairs curled and often paler than the general colour, giving the body a grizzled appearance. In the skull the high, rounded braincase rises steeply from the long rostrum which is characteristic of members of this genus (Fig. 93.1).

The dental formula is

$I\frac{2}{3}\,C\frac{1}{1}\,P\frac{3}{3}\,M\frac{3}{3} = 38$

and is therefore the same as *Myotis* spp with three premolars on each side above and below. The two anterior upper

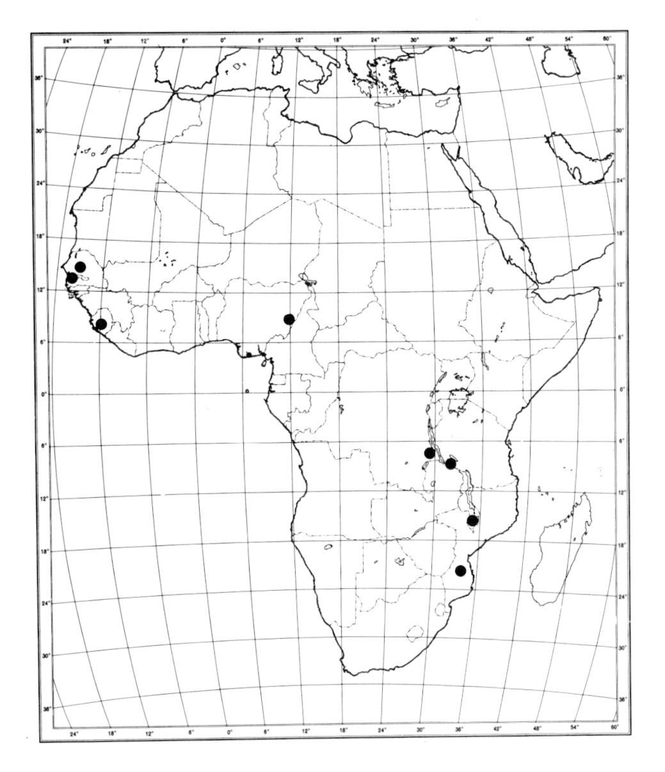

premolars are smaller than the third (Fig. 93.1) and the lower are the same size. The inner two lower incisors are trilobed, the outer conical.

Key to the species, after Meester *et al.* (1986)
(Measurements in mm)

1. Size larger, forearm 34–39; total length of skull 15 or more; colour of upper parts reddish-chestnut, under parts either whitish or white tinged buffy
   ... *argentata*

   Size smaller, forearm 30–36; total length of skull 13,5 or less; colour brownish, greyish-brown, sometimes lightly grizzled with greyish-white or white, the under parts brown to greyish-brown to greyish-white to white
   ... *lanosa*

No. 92

## *Kerivoula argentata* Tomes, 1861

## Damara woolly bat
## Damara-wolhaarvlermuis

### Colloquial Name

Originally described from a specimen from Damaraland, Namibia; the soft, curly, woolly hair is characteristic of members of this genus.

### Taxonomic Notes

Meester *et al.* (1986) listed three subspecies from the Subregion: *K. a. argentata* from northern Namibia, *K. a. nidicola* (Kirk, 1865) from central Mozambique and *K. a. zuluensis* Roberts, 1924 from northern Natal and Zululand. The paucity of material has rendered it difficult for authorities to determine the relationships of a number of species of this genus.

### Description

The Damara woolly bat is the larger of the two species of *Kerivoula* that occurs in the Subregion. About 95 mm in total length, including the tail of about 47 mm in length, they have a mass of between 6,0 and 9,0 g (Table 92.1). The colour of the upper parts is a rich brown, many of the soft woolly hairs with silvery tips giving an overall grizzled appearance to the pelage. The individual hairs are dark grey at their bases, then broadly buffy with brown tips. The under parts are greyish-brown, tending to be lighter in colour towards the anus and on the sides of the belly. The wing and interfemoral membranes are brown, the latter lighter brown than the wing membranes. There is a sparse covering of hair on the interfemoral membranes, but a very distinct fringe of hair on their hind margins. The fringe near the point of the tail is comprised of stiff hair hooked inwards towards the tips. The ear tragus is long, thin and tapers to a point (Fig. 92.1.a).

**Table 92.1**

Measurements (mm) and mass (g) of six Damara woolly bats, *K. argentata*, from Zimbabwe (Smithers & Wilson, 1979)

| | Irrespective of sex | | |
|---|---|---|---|
| | $\bar{x}$ | n | Range |
| TL | 93 | 6 | 83–100 |
| T | 47 | 6 | 42–50 |
| Hf c/u | 10 | 6 | 10–11 |
| E | 14 | 6 | 13–15 |
| F/a | 37 | 6 | 36–41 |
| Mass | 7,6 | 6 | 6,0–9,0 |

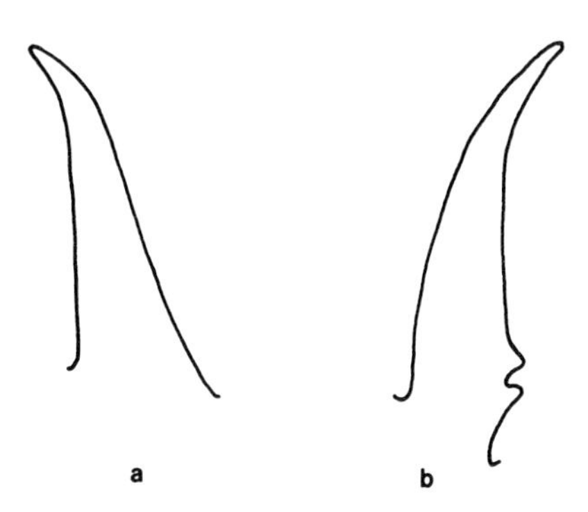


Fig. 92.1. Ear tragus of *Kerivoula* spp
(a) *K. argentata* (b) *K. lanosa*

### Distribution

Throughout their distributional range the records are scattered which makes it difficult at the moment to assess the limits of their distribution.

*South of the Sahara, excluding the Southern African Subregion*

They are recorded from central **Angola**; parts of **Zambia**, and **Malawi**. There are only two records from **Mozambique**, north of the Zambezi River, these from the lower Zambezi River in the southern Zambezi District. Northwards there is a single record from central **Tanzania** and others from southern **Kenya** and southern **Zaire**.

*Southern African Subregion*

Originally the species was described from a specimen from Otjoro, Ovamboland, **Namibia**, and they occur in the eastern half of **Zimbabwe** and **Mozambique**, south of the Zambezi river, south to the Maputo District. They have been taken in Zululand and in **Natal** south to the White Umfolozi River, and in the Pafuri region of the Kruger National Park.

### Habitat

A savanna woodland species with a tendency in the Subregion to be confined to well-watered areas or riverine associations in dry country.

### Habits

Damara woolly bats are solitary or may occur in small groups numbering up to about six. Their habits have not been studied in detail and there are only casual observations on record. Shortridge (1934) stated that they roost singly or in pairs in exposed situations among clusters of dead leaves, on the rough bark of trees or in deserted birds nests. He recorded that in Zambia four were found clinging

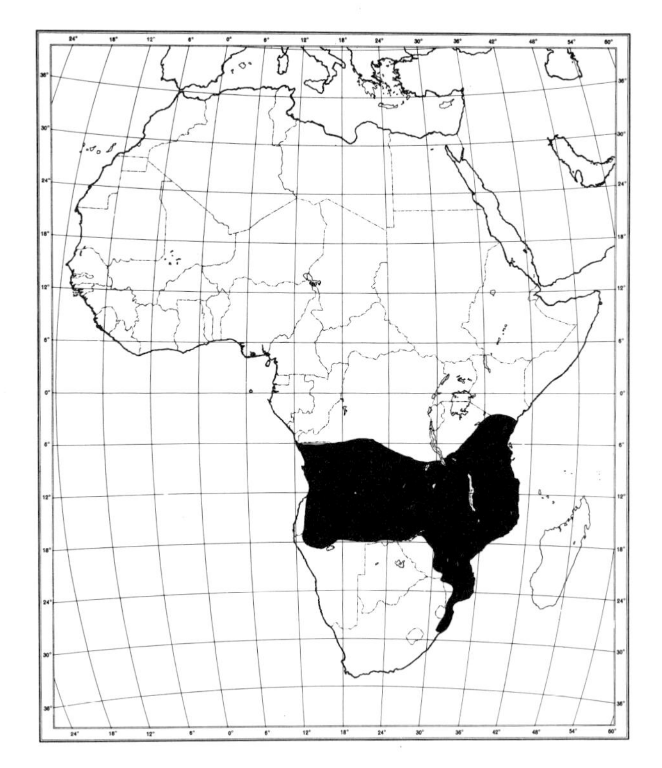

so closely together under the eaves of a rondavel that they looked like the mud nest of a wasp. In Zimbabwe 12 of the total number of specimens numbering 15 were taken in the disused nests of masked weavers, *Ploceus velatus*, and Roberts (1951) recorded them in Zululand from the nests of spectacled weavers, *Ploceus ocularis*. In two cases in Zimbabwe there were three tightly packed in such a nest (Smithers & Wilson, 1979). Wright (*in litt.*) in Fort Victoria, Zimbabwe, collected five, all females, from a tight cluster on the outside wall of a rondavel, sheltered by the overhanging eaves. They have a slow fluttering flight and when foraging fly within two or three metres of the ground.

### Food

Insectivorous.

### Reproduction

There is no information available from the Subregion.

---

No. 93

## *Kerivoula lanosa* (A. Smith, 1847)

## Lesser woolly bat
## Klein wolhaarvlermuis

Plate 4

---

### Colloquial Name

As can be seen from a comparison of the measurements and masses of *K. argentata* and this species, *K. lanosa* is all round smaller and less in mass.

### Taxonomic Notes

Meester *et al.* (1986) recognised two subspecies in the Subregion: *K. l. lanosa* from the southern and eastern coastal regions of the Cape Province extending eastwards to the Ciskei and *K. l. lucia* Hinton, 1920 from northern Natal and Zululand, the Transvaal, eastern Zimbabwe and adjacent parts of Mozambique and northern Botswana.

### Description

The lesser woolly bat is the smaller of the two species that occur in the Subregion. They have a total length of about 80 mm including a tail some 36 mm long and a mass of 6,0–8,0 g (Table 93.1). The upper parts are a dull buffy colour, the hair long, springy and curled which makes it stand out from the body. The bases of the individual hairs are dark in colour, the tips broadly paler and closely curled, giving the upper parts a grizzled appearance. The ears are very broad, the inner and outer edges curling inwards to give them a funnel shape, the ear tragus long and thin (Fig. 92.1.b).

The under parts are either white on the chest and belly or a lighter shade of buff, the throat the same colour as the upper parts. The wing and interfemoral membranes are brown, the curly hair extending sparsely along the forearm and fringes of the wing, on the tail and fringes of the interfemoral membrane. There is a very noticeable fringe of hairs on the hind edge of the interfemoral membrane, these hairs curving inwards like hooks. This fringe is a characteristic feature of bats of this genus.

The ankle spur or calcaneum that supports the outer fringes of the interfemoral membrane is at least as long as the length of the tibia and foot, the membrane extending far beyond the feet.

The shape of the skull is characteristic of members of this genus (Fig. 93.1).

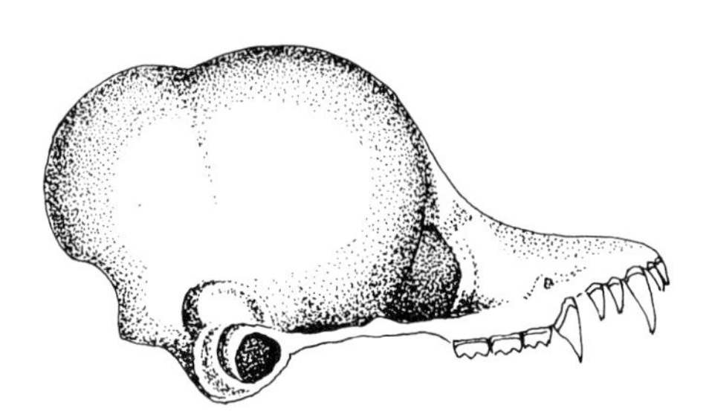

Fig. 93.1. Skull of *Kerivoula lanosa*

**Table 93.1**

Measurements (mm) and mass (g) of lesser woolly bats, *K. lanosa*, from Botswana (Smithers, 1971)

| | TL | T | Hfc/u | E | Length ear tragus | Mass |
|---|---|---|---|---|---|---|
| Male | 77 | 37 | 7 | 13 | 9 | 6,0 |
| Female | 80 | 39 | 7 | 13 | 9 | 7,0 |
| Female | 78 | 37 | 8 | 14 | 9 | 6,0 |
| Female | 78 | 35 | 8 | 13 | 8 | 8,0 |

### Distribution

So few scattered records from the southern parts of the distributional range of the lesser woolly bat are available that it is impossible at this stage to present their limits of occurrence. Kingdon (1974) showed that they are distributed widely in East Africa, but Swynnerton & Hayman (1950) only listed *K. africana* Dobson, 1878 which occurs in the extreme northeast of Tanzania.

*South of the Sahara, excluding the Southern African Subregion*

Recorded from **Liberia; Ivory Coast; Ghana; Gabon; Cameroun; Central African Republic; Ethiopia; Kenya; Tanzania;** eastern and southern **Zaire**; southern **Malawi** and **Zambia**. Their occurrence on the Okavango River in northwestern Botswana suggests that in time they may be shown to occur in southeastern Angola in riverine situations.

*Southern African Subregion*

They occur in the riverine woodland of the Okavango River in the extreme northwestern parts of **Botswana** and have been taken at Sepopa on the western fringe of the Okavango Delta and near Molepolole in the southeast of the country. In **Zimbabwe** they occur on the Mozambique border east of Mutare. In the **Transvaal** recorded from the Njelele River, Soutpansberg as well as from Pafuri, in Zululand from

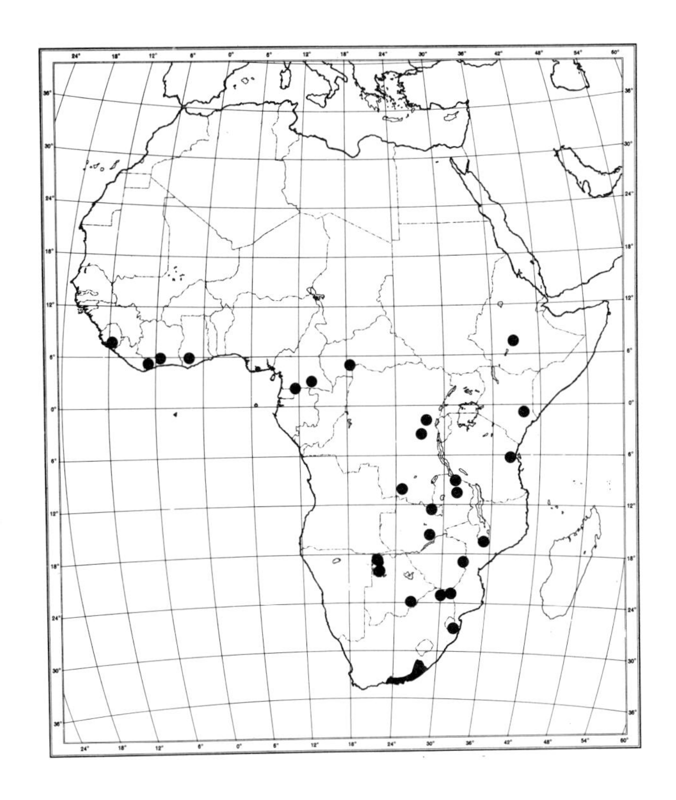

Ingwavuma and in the **Cape Province** from the Pirie Forest, King William's Town and Knysna.

### Habitat

There is a distinct tendency for this species to be associated with riverine associations in dry country as well as occurring in well-watered areas. Roberts (1951) reported that a specimen from Zululand was taken in a forest, as was the King William's Town specimen which was collected in the Pirie Forest.

### Habits

Little is known about the habits of this species. They have a slow fluttering flight like *K. argentata* and the same habit of using disused birds' nests to roost in during daylight hours. In northwestern Botswana a male and two females were taken from the nest of a masked weaver, *Ploceus velatus*, and a single female from the nest of a scarlet chested sunbird, *Nectarinia senegalensis*. In Zululand, Roberts (1951) collected specimens from the nests of spectacled weavers, *Ploceus ocularis*, three in one nest, two in the other.

### Food

Insectivorous.

### Reproduction

No information available from the Subregion.

# IX. Family NYCTERIDAE

## Slit-faced bats

The Family gets its name from the Greek name for a bat *nycteris*. Members of the Family all have a slit from the nostrils to above the eyes, which overlies a concavity in the skull enclosing the complicated noseleaves which, unlike those in the Rhinolophidae, are only visible when the slit is open (Fig. IX.1). These noseleaves serve in echolocation, the emissions in members of this Family being through the nostrils and not through the mouth. A characteristic feature of all members is the large ears which make them easily identifiable (Fig. IX.1). In the common slit-faced bat, *Nycteris thebaica*, which is common throughout the Subregion, the ears reach a length of up to 37 mm. They have rounded ends and when the sides are bent forward the ears are nearly parallel-sided. The shape of the ear tragus is a useful character in the recognition of the species. They all have a small rounded protuberance on the lower lip, with a raised ridge on either side, the ridges converging but not meeting posteriorly. They have long tails, the whole of which is contained within the interfemoral membrane, the last vertebra bifurcating at its joint in a Y with broad open ends which help support the fringe of the membrane. This membrane is further supported by long calcanea arising from the ankles of the hind feet (Fig. IX.2).

All members of the Family have long, soft fur, reddish-brown or greyish-brown in colour, and a bright orange phase is known to occur. The wings are broad and rounded at the ends.

The skull is elongated and characterised by the deep concave depression in front which houses the noseleaves (Fig. IX.3).

The dental formula is

$I\frac{2}{3}\ C\frac{1}{1}\ P\frac{1}{2}\ M\frac{3}{3} = 32.$

The single upper premolar is well developed, the relative size of the posterior lower premolar in relation to the molar next to it is a useful character in separating the groups of species.

Slit-faced bats are distributed widely throughout Africa and occur beyond the borders of the continent to Madagascar, Arabia, southeastern Asia and Malaya, being most abundant in the tropics. They are expert fliers and their powers of echolocation must be well developed as they are adept at avoiding being caught in mist nets, swinging away from them and over the top whereas other species fly directly into them.

After having caught their prey they hang on temporary feeding perches where their prey is eaten, the unpalatable portions accumulating below them, forming useful indications of what they are eating.

The Family is represented in the Subregion by a single genus and six species.

Fig. IX.1. Head of a Nycteridae: *Nycteris thebaica*

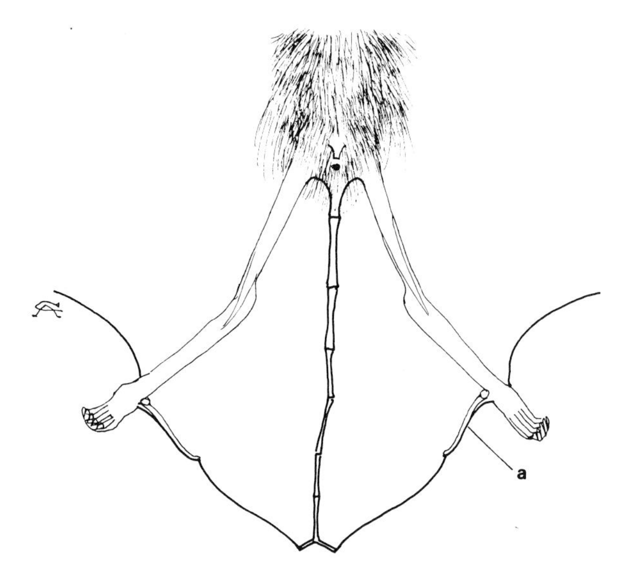


Fig. IX.2. Tail of a *Nycteris thebaica* (a) calcaneum.

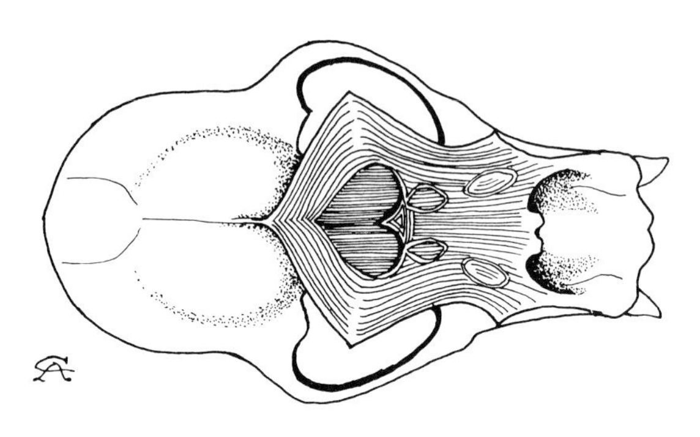

Fig. IX.3. Dorsal view of skull of *Nycteris* sp.

## Genus *Nycteris* G. Cuvier & E. Geoffroy, 1795

Key to the species after Meester *et al.* (1986)
(Measurements in mm)

1. Upper incisors trifid (Fig. 94.1)
   ... 2

   Upper incisors bifid
   ... 3

2. Forearm 36–45, ear 18–25; condylocanine length less than 18
   ... *hispida*

   Forearm 57–66, ear 28–35; condylocanine length more than 18
   ... *grandis*

3. Ear tragus semi-lunate, base of its posterior margin not notched (*aethiopica* group)
   ... 4

   Ear tragus pyriform, base of its posterior margin shallowly notched (*thebaica* group)
   ... 5

4. General colour greyish; forearm 37–42, ear 29–34
   ... *woodi*

   General colour brownish; forearm 45–50, ear over 21
   ... *macrotis*

5. Size smaller, forearm, 42–52, ears 28–37; skull less massive, breadth of supraorbital flanges about 6,8
   ... *thebaica*

   Size larger, forearm over 50, ears about 22; skull massive, rostrum 20% heavier than in *N. thebaica*, breadth of supraorbital flanges about 9,0
   ... *vinsoni*

Smithers (1983) noted that the ear length of *N. vinsoni* should be treated with caution as the ears of the type specimen were singed by fire (see Dalquest 1965)

## Hispida group

No. 94

### *Nycteris hispida* (Schreber, 1774)

### Hairy slit-faced bat
### Harige spleetneusvlermuis

**Colloquial Name**

This species is no more hairy than any other of the slit-faced bats, the name having applied to it as a translation of the specific name *hispida* which is from the Latin *hispidus*, hairy or bristly, referring to the bristly hair lying around the facial slit.

**Taxonomic Notes**

The nominate *N. h. hispida* originally described from Senegal occurs throughout the northern parts of the species range, being replaced in the Subregion by *N. h. villosa* Peters, 1852.

**Description**

Hairy slit-faced bats have a total length of about 90 mm and a wingspan of about 280 mm (Table 94.1). The upper parts are sepia-brown, the under parts much paler than the upper parts and usually greyer. They and the large slit-faced bat, *N. grandis*, are the only two members of the Nycteridae in which the upper incisors have three lobes on their cutting edges (Fig. 94.1). The ear tragus, which is blunter than in the large slit-faced bat, is similar in that the outer edge is smooth. The ears and membranes on the wings are dark blackish-brown, the ears and tail long but not as long as in the common slit-faced bat, *N. thebaica*.

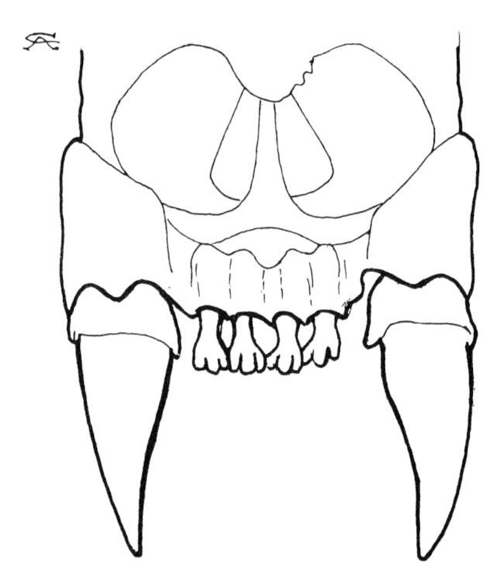

Fig. 94.1. Trifid upper incisors of *Nycteris hispida*

**Table 94.1**

Measurements (mm) of hairy slit-faced bats, *N. hispida* (Rosevear, 1965)

| HB | T | E | F/a |
|---|---|---|---|
| 40–54 | 43–52 | 18–25 | 36–45 |

**Distribution**

In the northern parts of their distributional range hairy slit-faced bats are one of the most commonly collected species and have one of the widest ranges. They occur from Senegal in West Africa eastwards to Ethiopia and south to the Subregion. Roberts (1951) listed two specimens from the "Cape of Good Hope" collected by Andrew Smith, but queried this locality as, at the time of publication of his work, there were no other records from southern Africa except those from Inhambane, Mozambique. He thought they might have been taken by A. Smith during his expedition to Zululand in 1831 for they do not occur anywhere near the Cape. In the southern parts of their range they are not common.

*South of the Sahara, excluding the Southern African Subregion*

Hairy slit-faced bats occur from **Senegal** eastwards to **Ethiopia** and **Somalia** and southwards in **Uganda; Kenya; Tanzania; Zaire; Cameroun; Gabon** and in parts of **Angola**. They occur in the central and southwestern parts of **Zambia** and in the northwest and, while there are no records at the moment from the eastern parts, Ansell (1978) believed that they do occur, as they are found in the Southern Province of **Malawi**. They occur in the Tete District of **Mozambique**, north of the Zambezi River.

*Southern African Subregion*

While there are no records from Namibia, their occurrence in Angola as far southwest as Mossamedes suggests that in time they will be found to occur there. In **Zimbabwe** they are recorded from the Zambezi Valley in the northwest and in the Eastern Districts. They have been taken in **Mozambique**, south of the Zambezi River, from the Tete, Vila Pery and Inhambane districts.

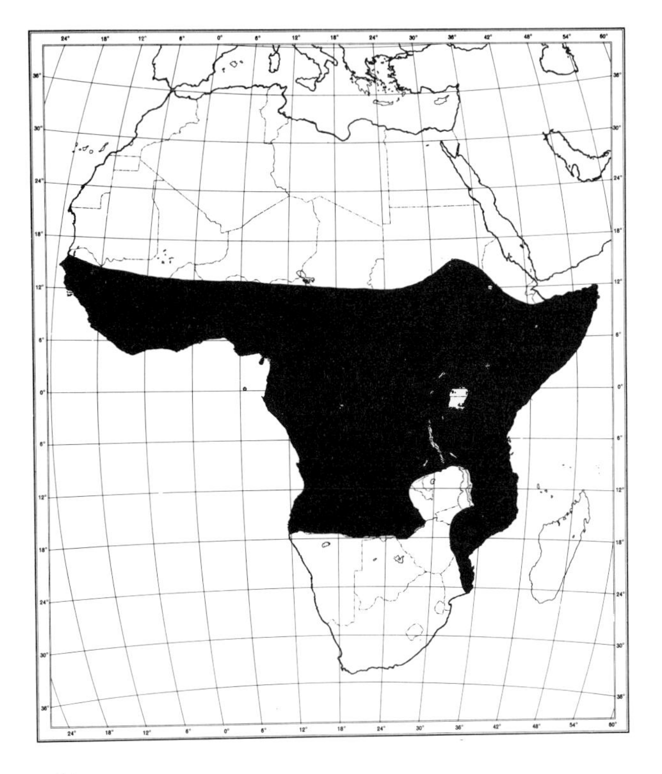

### Habitat

Hairy slit-faced bats are catholic in their habitat requirements, occurring in the High Forests of West Africa and Zaire as well as in relatively dry savanna woodland, as in Mozambique. Rosevear (1965) recorded their wide tolerance to a diverse range of vegetational associations and their habits show that they can use as diverse a range of shelters, not being restricted to any special type which in other species restricts their occurrence. Their distribution suggests that they avoid arid country.

### Habits

Hairy slit-faced bats are predominantly solitary, but have been observed in small colonies numbering up to about 20 (Rosevear, 1965). They roost during the day in the shelter of dense, low bushes, hanging from the finer twigs, but are also found in thatched African huts, hanging from the thatch or thinner projections of the roofing timbers. Kingdon (1974) recorded that, in East Africa, they also use aardvark holes, holes in termitaria, hollow trees and papyrus crowns. In Mozambique two were taken in a cave in granite with a wet, muddy floor (Smithers & Wilson, 1979). They come to lights at night to hawk insects and frequently enter houses when foraging. Allen, Lang & Chapin (1917) in their endeavours to catch individuals in a room appreciated the agility with which they evaded capture in a butterfly net, calling it a "warm and exhilarating sport". Like the common slit-faced bat, *N. thebaica*, they are adept at avoiding capture in bird nets, swinging vertically up the face of the net at the last minute and escaping over the top. Although like other nycterids they are slow fliers, they appear to have very acutely tuned echolocation systems, and have the ability to jink and turn which enables them to penetrate deep into thick bush either in seeking roosting sites or in feeding in forest underbrush.

Kingdon (1974) recorded that they become attracted to a roost and when disturbed from it return later to the exact same spot. They remain alert during the day and if disturbed, will flit around nearby bushes before returning to settle.

### Food

Insectivorous.

### Reproduction

There is no information from the Subregion.

---

No. 95

## *Nycteris grandis* Peters, 1865

## Large slit-faced bat
## Groot spleetneusvlermuis

---

### Colloquial Name

This is the largest member of the Family, all of which have a slit on top of the muzzle, from the nostrils to the base of the ears, under which lies the complicated noseleaves accommodated in a cup-like depression on the front of the skull.

### Taxonomic Notes

The nominate *N. g. grandis* was described from Guinea, West Africa; only *N. g. marica* Kershaw, 1923 occurs in the southern parts of the species' range.

### Description

The greater slit-faced bat is, as the name implies, the largest of the Nycteridae, adult males having a total length of about 160 mm and a mass of about 40 g (Table 95.1). They are light reddish-brown in colour, the under parts lighter in colour than the upper parts with a grey wash. The fur is long and soft, the wing membranes dark brown or nearly black and criss-crossed with fine parallel lines or dots. Their wings are broad and rounded at the ends, their ears broad and measuring up to 30 mm long.

In common with *N. hispida* the upper incisors have three small lobes on their cutting edge (Fig. 94.1); the outer margins of the ear tragi are smooth. Although not so far seen in the Subregion, bright orange-coloured phases of this species are known.

**Table 95.1**

Measurements (mm) and mass (g) of two male and one female large slit-faced bats, *N. grandis*, from Zimbabwe

| | | | | | |
|---|---|---|---|---|---|
| **Males** | | | | | |
| TL | T | Hfc/u | E | F/a | Mass |
| 164 | 84 | 15 | 31 | 64 | 35,7 |
| 157 | 70 | 15 | 31 | 64 | 42,5 |
| **Female** | | | | | |
| 145 | 64 | 15 | 31 | 63 | — |

### Distribution

In the southern parts of their range they probably occur more widely than present records indicate, as they probably do in Tanzania where at the moment there are no records between the northwestern parts of the country, Dar-es-Salaam and the offshore islands.

*South of the Sahara, excluding the Southern African Subregion*

Recorded from **Guinea** eastward in most of the West African countries to **Cameroun; Zaire**, except in the southeast; **Uganda**; northeastern **Tanzania** and in the Dar-es-Salaam area and the offshore islands of Zanzibar and Pemba. In **Zambia** there is a record from the southern sector of the Luangwa Valley, and they occur in **Malawi**.

*Southern African Subregion*

In **Mozambique**, south of the Zambezi River, they are recorded from the western parts of the Vila Pery District adjacent to the border with Zimbabwe and may well occur in the Dondo and Amatongas forests in this sector. In **Zimbabwe** they occur in the Zambezi Valley east of Lake Kariba.

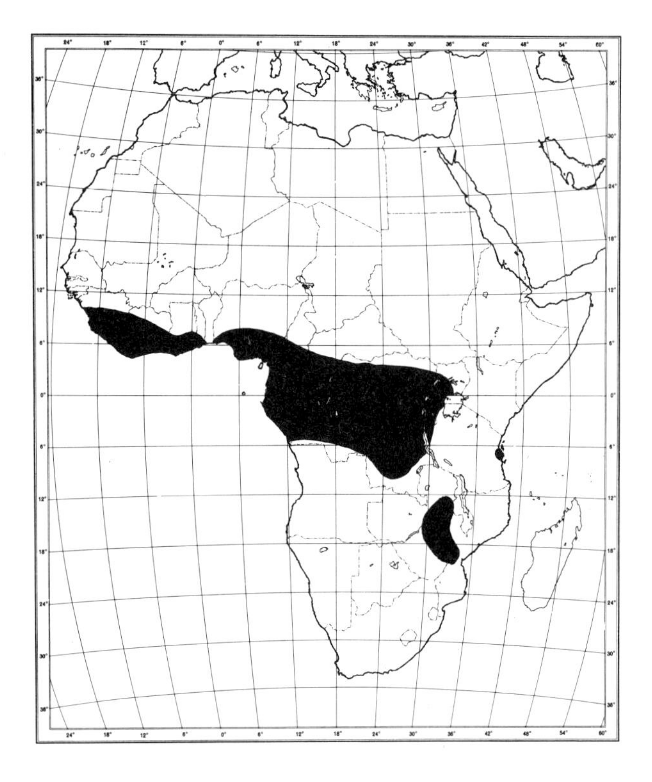

### Habitat

The greater slit-faced bat in the northern parts of its distributional range occurs in forest and the indications from the Mozambique specimens are that they are similarly associated. In Zimbabwe and Zambia, however, they are found in the well-developed evergreen riverine forests of the Luangwa and Zambezi rivers and should be looked for in other areas with this type of habitat in the southern parts of their range.

### Habits

They occur in small colonies of up to about six individuals. Ansell (1978) mentioned that the Luangwa Valley specimens were taken from a colony, not recording the numbers. They roost during the day in hollow trees, one of the Zimbabwe specimens being taken from the hollow trunk of a dead tree lying on the ground, a situation from which they have been collected in other parts of their range (Liberia; Allen & Coolidge, 1930). They have also been taken in culverts and shallow caverns in rocks (Rosevear, 1965). Fenton, Cumming, Hutton & Swanepoel (1987) recorded a colony of five roosting in a water tower in Mana Pools National Park, Zimbabwe. They return to the same feeding site to consume their food. At Mana Pools, Zimbabwe one regularly returned to hang up in the office of the Department of National Parks, scattering the discarded remains of its food below the feeding site.

### Food

Predominantly insectivorous, but with some carnivorous tendencies. In Zimbabwe, the discarded remains of food included much insect material, but also the remains of small fish and frogs, *Rana* sp. It was thought that the fish were being taken from pools cut off from the river and then drying up. They used two types of perches, the hunting perch from which they took off to fly low over the shallow fringes of water, and the feeding perch to which they returned to consume the prey (Fenton *et al.*, 1987).

### Reproduction

Fenton *et al.* (1987) recorded females each with a single clinging young in December in the Zambezi Valley at Mana Pools National Park, Zimbabwe.

---

No. 96

## *Nycteris woodi* K. Andersen, 1914

## Wood's slit-faced bat
## Wood se spleetneusvlermuis

---

### Colloquial Name

Named after Rodney C. Wood, a well-known naturalist and collector, who collected the original specimens at Chilanga, near Lusaka, Zambia.

### Taxonomic Notes

Meester *et al.* (1986) listed two subspecies, *N. w. woodi* from Zambia and *N. w. sabiensis* Roberts, 1946 from Zimbabwe.

### Description

A slightly smaller species than the common slit-faced bat, *N. thebaica*, this species is about 90 mm in total length with ears slightly shorter in series than *N. thebaica* (Table 96.1). The upper parts of the body are dark brown, the individual hairs grey towards their bases and about 10 mm long. The under parts are whitish tinged grey. The skull is typical of the genus with the concave depression in front which houses the noseleaves (Fig. IX.3).

**Table 96.1**

Measurements (mm) of Wood's slit-faced bats, *N. woodi*, from Zimbabwe (Smithers & Wilson, 1979)

| | Males | | | Females | | |
|---|---|---|---|---|---|---|
| | $\bar{x}$ | n | Range | $\bar{x}$ | n | Range |
| TL | 91 | 7 | 88–93 | 91 | 5 | 88–96 |
| T | 43 | 7 | 41–46 | 46 | 5 | 44–49 |
| Hf c/u | 9 | 7 | 8–10 | 9 | 5 | 8–10 |
| E | 31 | 7 | 29–33 | 33 | 5 | 31–35 |
| F/a | 38 | 7 | 37–39 | 39 | 5 | 38–40 |

### Distribution

Wood's slit-faced bats are confined in their distribution to central and eastern **Zambia**; to northeastern and southeastern **Zimbabwe** and to the Limpopo River valley and the northern parts of the Kruger National Park in the **Transvaal**.

### Habitat

A savanna woodland species.

### Habits

The Zimbabwe specimens were all netted and consequently there is no information on their daylight roosting places. In eastern Zambia they were roosting in rock fissures in a large rocky outcrop and one was taken in a building (Ansell, 1967a).

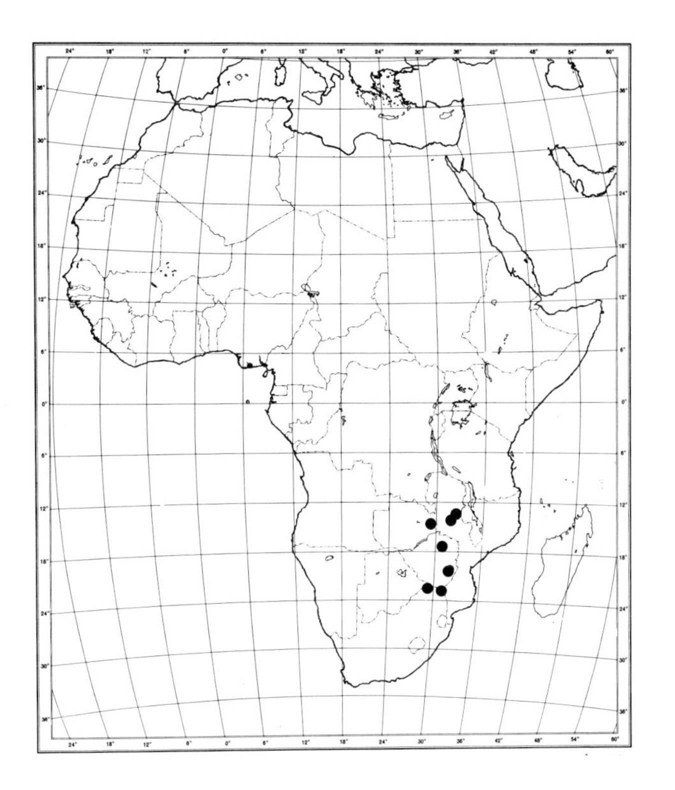

### Food

Insectivorous.

### Reproduction

No information is available.

No. 97

## *Nycteris macrotis* Dobson, 1876

## Greater slit-faced bat
## Groter spleetneusvlermuis

### Colloquial Name

Although the specific name *macrotis* is derived from the Greek *makros* and *otis* meaning large eared, their ears are in fact smaller than in species such as *N. thebaica.*

### Taxonomic Notes

The nominate *N. m. macrotis* was described from Guinea, West Africa; only *N. m. oriana* Kershaw, 1922 occurs in the Subregion and then only marginally in northeastern Zimbabwe.

### Description

Greater slit-faced bats have a total length of about 100 mm (Table 97.1). The upper parts are warm reddish-sepia in colour, the under parts greyer. Like the common slit-faced bat *N. thebaica* the upper incisors have two lobes on their cutting edges, but the ear tragus is broader at the end and not so rounded and lacks the indentation on the lower part of the outer edge seen in *N. thebaica.*

**Table 97.1**

Measurements (mm) of greater slit-faced bats, *N. macrotis,* from West Africa (Rosevear, 1965)

| | | | |
|---|---|---|---|
| HB | 52–70 | E | 28–30 |
| T | 40–60 | F/a | 45–50 |

### Distribution

*South of the Sahara, excluding the Southern African Subregion*

Recorded from **Gambia** eastwards to **Nigeria**; southern **Sudan**; western **Ethiopia; Uganda; Kenya** and **Tanzania**. They occur in northeastern **Angola**, in the central and parts of eastern **Zambia** and in **Malawi**. There are no records at the moment from northeastern Mozambique.

*Southern African Subregion*

So far recorded only from the Zambezi Valley in the northeast at the confluence of the Chewore and Zambezi Rivers and in the Matusadona National Park, Lake Kariba, in **Zimbabwe**.

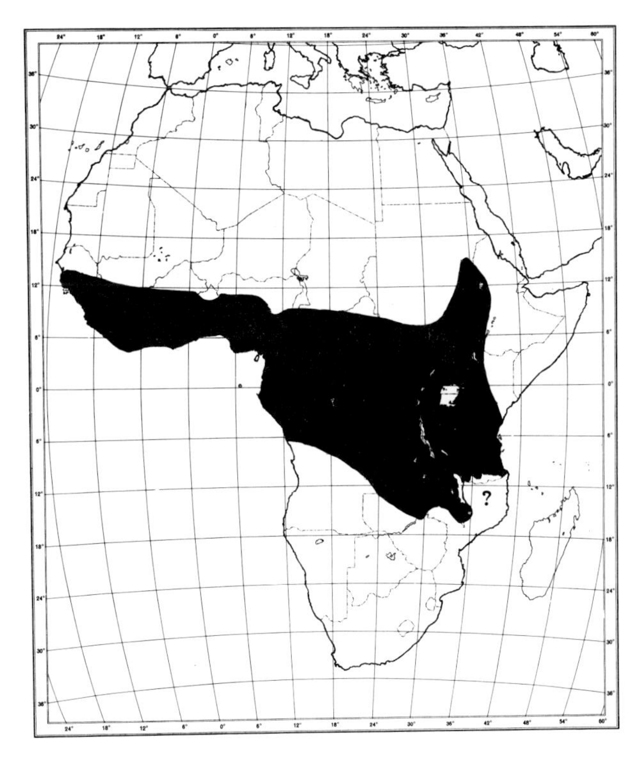


### Habitat

The specimens from the Subregion were netted in the riverine forest of the Zambezi River. In other parts of Africa they occur both in forest and in savanna woodland.

### Habits

In other parts of Africa they have been taken roosting in caves, culverts and dark cellars. They will also hang up in rondavels. Rosevear (1965) believed that they may also roost hanging in bushes or under rocks like *N. hispida.*

### Food

Insectivorous.

### Reproduction

There is no information available from the southern parts of their distributional range.

No. 98

## *Nycteris thebaica* E. Geoffroy, 1813

## Common slit-faced bat
## Gewone spleetneusvlermuis

Plate 5

### Colloquial Name

This is one of the commonest and most widespread small insectivorous bats found in the Subregion.

### Taxonomic Notes

Numbers of subspecies have been described, but their validity remains uncertain. Meester *et al.* (1986) recognised two subspecies from the Subregion: *N. t. capensis* A. Smith, 1829 from the Cape Province eastwards to southern Mozambique, the Transvaal and Zimbabwe, and *N. t. damarensis* Peters, 1871 from the western parts of the species' range including northern Botswana.

### Description

The conspicuous long ears make this species one of the more easily recognisable species that occur in the Subregion. Adult males have a total length of about 100 mm and a mean mass of 10,5 g, females, in series, slightly larger and heavier (Table 98.1).

The upper parts of the body are buffy-brown, the base of the hair slate-grey, the hairs on the sides of the neck and head with buffy bases. The under parts of the body are buffy or off-white. The long ears and the wing membranes are light brown. The hair is long and soft and on both the upper and under parts extends onto the bases of the forearms and on the under parts onto the wing membranes near the body. The light-coloured hair of the under parts extends upward onto the sides of the neck. Occasionally a rufous-coloured phase is encountered in the eastern parts of their distributional range. Specimens from Namibia are noticeably paler above and whiter below and have been considered as worthy of subspecific rank as *N. t. damarensis*. Unlike *N. grandis* and *N. hispida* the upper incisors of *N. thebaica* have only two lobes on their cutting edge as against three in the other two species. The ear tragus is pear-shaped with an indentation on the lower part of its outer edge.

**Table 98.1**

Measurements (mm) and mass (g) of the common slit-faced bat, *N. thebaica*, from the northern parts of the Subregion (Smithers & Wilson, 1979)

| | Males | | | Females | | |
|---|---|---|---|---|---|---|
| | $\bar{x}$ | n | Range | $\bar{x}$ | n | Range |
| TL | 102 | 14 | 92–110 | 110 | 7 | 98–120 |
| T | 53 | 14 | 46–57 | 55 | 7 | 50–59 |
| Hf c/u | 11 | 12 | 10–12 | 12 | 5 | 11–14 |
| E | 33 | 14 | 30–35 | 34 | 7 | 30–37 |
| Mass | 10,5 | 14 | 9,0–11,5 | 11,4 | 4 | 10,0–13,7 |

### Distribution

The common slit-faced bat has a wide distribution on the continent from parts of North Africa to the Cape Province. They also occur in Europe, having been recorded on the Island of Corfu, off the west coast of Greece, and in the Middle East. There are areas within the Subregion from which to date they have not been found to occur. As they range widely, this may be due to their having been overlooked; on the other hand they prefer woodland and some of these areas such as southern Botswana and the grassland areas of the Transvaal may be too open for them. They occur throughout their range in association with buildings, yet examination of scattered stone buildings in southern Botswana did not reveal their presence.

*North Africa*

They occur coastally in **Morocco; Algeria; Tunisia** and **Egypt** and in **Libya** have been taken at Zuara in the Tibetsi Massif deep into the Sahara.

*South of the Sahara, excluding the Southern African Subregion*

They occur from **Senegal** eastwards to the **Sudan; Ethiopia** and parts of **Somalia** and northwards to **Egypt** and southwards in at least parts of all the countries to the borders of the Subregion, excluding areas of tropical forest.

*Southern African Subregion*

Recorded as occurring widely in **Namibia** but in **Botswana** confined to the northern and eastern sectors and not so far recorded from the semi-desert central and southern parts of the country. Widespread in **Zimbabwe; Mozambique**, south of the Zambezi River, and **Malawi**. In the **Transvaal** not recorded to date from the grassland areas in the south, but are otherwise widespread. Recorded from the **Orange Free State; Natal** and the **Cape Province**.

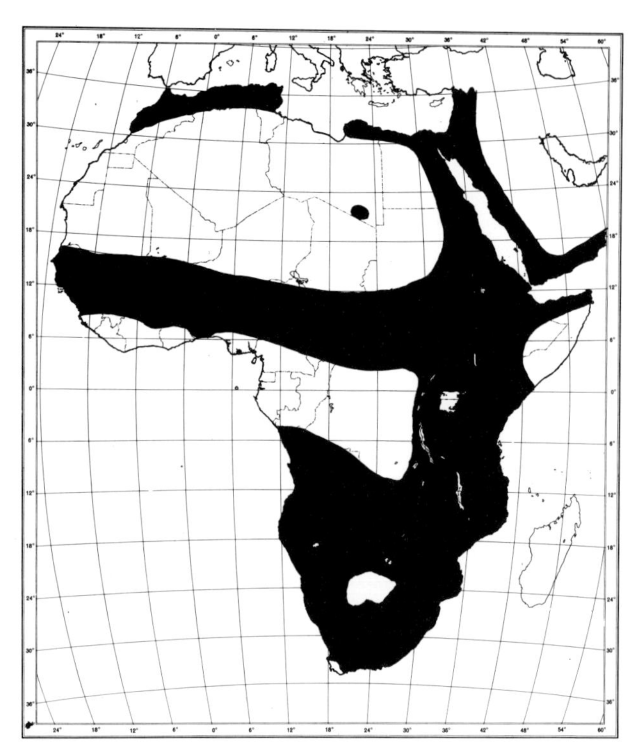

### Habitat

The common slit-faced bat is, throughout its range, associated with open savanna woodland although it has been taken on rare occasions in forests (Rosevear, 1965) and is found in oases in desert regions (Tibetsi, Libya; Hufnagl, 1972) and in isolated areas in the Sinai Peninsula and in Arabia, where there are scattered trees (Harrison, 1964). To some extent at least they have a wide habitat tolerance. In the Subregion they occur from sea level to over 1 500 m and in areas where the mean annual rainfall is as low as 100 mm and as high as 1 200 to 1 400 mm.

### Habits

The common slit-faced bat is a gregarious species, occurring in small to medium-sized colonies of up to hundreds. They roost during the day in the substantial cover of caves, culverts under roads, in mine adits, in hollow trees (baobab, *Adansonia digitata*), in rock fissures and disused antbear holes (Temby, 1977) and are common occupants of the shelter under the roofs of houses or thatched rondavels. In these situations they hang from the ceilings, clinging on to ridge poles of huts or the thatch and, in situations such as culverts, to the small irregularities in the cement. They roost either in half light or in the darkest parts of the interior of these shelters, having a preference for the latter. They tend to roost in scattered groups, not closely packed together as do other species.

In Drotsky's caves in Botswana, the colony was estimated to number 600, the individuals hanging from the 13 m high roof in total darkness, 270 m from the entrance. The atmosphere was humid with temperatures between 30 °C and 32 °C. They are late movers from their daylight roosting places, leaving well after sundown, usually about 20h30 to 21h00, and returning well before first light. On leaving they tend to scatter into small groups which break up, and the individuals forage separately. They are relatively slow fliers, but have great powers of jinking and twisting in flight. In foraging they may fly within a metre of the ground.

### Food

Insectivorous, the food, as indicated by the discarded remains picked up under their feeding sites, includes a high proportion of moths and long-horned and short-horned grasshoppers. Felton (1956) recorded that in Namibia they ate scorpions, including *Opisthophthalmus wahlbergi* and they will also take sun spiders, Solifugae. LaVal & LaVal (1980) provided a list of insects taken by the species in Natal, noting that many of the insects were taken while stationary rather than in flight.

Once prey is secured they fly to established feeding sites, which they will use over prolonged periods, as is shown by the accumulations of discarded remains beneath them. Fenton (1975) showed, from the examination of the remains of insects collected at a feeding site, that Orthoptera remains accounted for 54% of the prey, Lepidoptera 45%. The Lepidoptera included 29 species of moths, one species, a sphingid, *Polytychus compar*, accounted for 32% of the remains, the next most common species 3,5%. This shows a remarkable selectivity on the part of the bat and compared with the details of the food of Lander's horseshoe bat, *Rhinolophus landeri*, suggests that there is a sharing of the food resources available between different species of bats.

**Reproduction**

In the Etosha National Park, Namibia it was found that after a brief period of courtship, copulation occurs in flight with both bats hovering. Copulation is of short duration and is repeated up to three times (Lindeque, 1987).

In Natal, Bernard (1982a) found that ovarian and vaginal activity took place in two peaks, the first between April and early June, culminating in oestrus, the second between July and August during pregnancy. Copulation and fertilisation took place in early June, the young being born after a five month period of gestation in early November. Lactation lasted two months, followed by a period of anoestrus until the onset of pro-oestrus in April.

In Zimbabwe, Smithers & Wilson (1979) found that they were seasonal breeders, gravid females commonly being taken during the months of August to October and not at other times of the year. Females with tiny young clinging to them were taken from October to December, the early part of the warm wet months of the year. A single young is produced at birth and is carried around by the mother attached to one of her nipples and clinging to her with the wings and feet.

No. 99

## *Nycteris vinsoni* Dalquest, 1965

## Vinson's slit-faced bat
## Vinson se spleetneusvlermuis

**Colloquial Name**

Named after J. Vinson who sponsored an expedition to Mozambique during which the first specimens were taken (Dalquest, 1965).

**Taxonomic Notes**

Hayman & Hill (1971) stated that this species is more probably a member of the *aethiopica* group. Until its relationships are better known, however, it is considered to be a valid species. Only two specimens were collected; the species was described from an adult female.

**Description**

Dalquest (1965) in his description stated that it is a very large *Nycteris*, similar in proportions to *N. thebaica* but larger and stouter and with much shorter ears. One of the two specimens collected was in the orange phase, the other greyer like *N. thebaica*. *N. vinsoni* differs principally from *N. thebaica* in the features already mentioned and in its more massive skull and heavier teeth. The rostrum is 20% heavier than in *N. thebaica* and the supraorbital flanges overhang the eye orbits to a much greater degree, the breadth across the flanges being 6,8 mm in *N. thebaica* and 9,0 mm in *N. vinsoni*.

The type specimen had the following measurements (mm):

| TL | T | Hfc/u | E |
|---|---|---|---|
| 125 | 55 | 13 | 22 |

The ear measurement given by Dalquest (1965) should be treated with caution as it had been singed in the fire lit to move them from the hollow tree—"although some allowance was made for this".

**Distribution**

So far only known from the south bank of the Save River in **Mozambique** at about 34 °E.

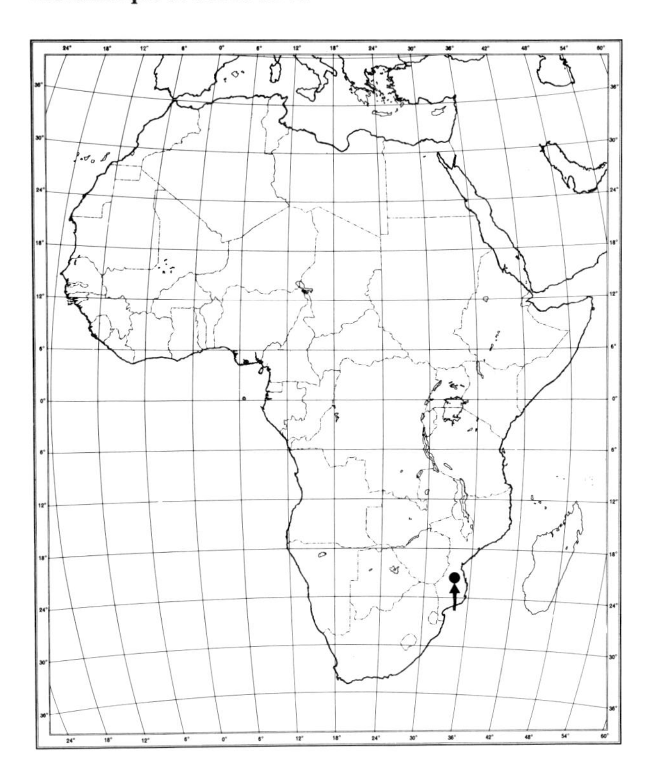

**Habitat**

Dry savanna woodland.

**Habits**

Two were taken from a small hollow at the base of a baobab, *Adansonia digitata*.

**Food**

Insectivorous.

**Reproduction**

Unknown.

# X. Family RHINOLOPHIDAE
## Horseshoe bats

Members of this Family, all of which are of small to medium size, are found throughout the world, with the exception of the American Continent. It contains only one genus *Rhinolophus*, of which 30 species have been described from Africa, 10 occurring in the Subregion.

They are called horseshoe bats from the shape of the anterior noseleaf, which is shaped like a horseshoe (Fig. X.1).

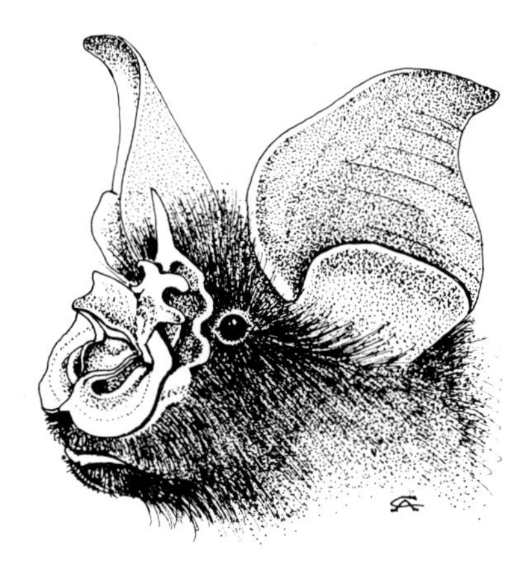

Fig. X.1. Head of a Rhinolophidae, *Rhinolophus* sp.

The generic name *Rhinolophus* is derived from the Greek *rhinos* a nose and *lophos* a crest, referring to the crest of noseleaves. The noseleaf is a highly complicated organ and includes the nostrils which are situated centrally just behind the posterior fringe of the anterior noseleaf (Fig. X.2). The shape of the various parts of the noseleaves is useful in distinguishing between the species but they tend to distort in dried specimens and are appreciated more accurately in pickled specimens or better still in fresh material. Möhres (1953) found that the noseleaves in the genus act as transmitters of echolocation impulses, the impulses being emitted through the nostrils. It is the function of the noseleaves to channel and focus the emissions so that they achieve a maximum intensity at a point of focus ahead of the flying bat. They also shield the ears from the direct reception of the impulses, only the echoes being appreciated by them.

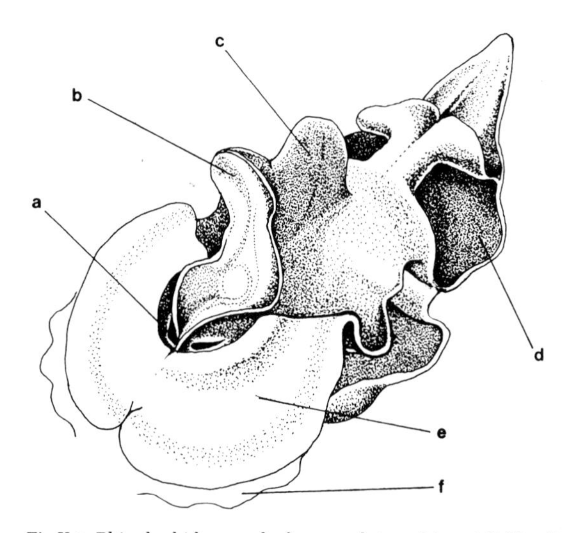


Fig.X.2. Rhinolophidae noseleaf nomenclature: (a) nostril (b) sella (c) connecting process (d) posterior noseleaf (e) anterior noseleaf (f) secondary leaflet

The ears are separated widely and are large and are capable of independent movement but lack ear tragi. The antitragi, however, are much enlarged and fold across the open base of the ears.

The wings are short and rounded, the second finger consisting of the metacarpal only, without phalanges, the third, fourth and fifth fingers with two phalanges each which, when the bat is at rest, fold under the wing.

The vertebrae of the tail end at the posterior fringe of the interfemoral membrane which is supported on either side by curved calcanea arising from the ankles. When at rest the tail and interfemoral membrane fold upwards.

The fur is long and soft and while in general they are greyish-brown in colour, a reddish-brown colour phase is not uncommon.

The females have a pair of false nipples situated low down on the abdomen just anterior to the genital orifice which may serve as alternative clinging points for the young.

In the skull the characteristic feature is the dome situated just above the nasal aperture (Fig. X.3). The two upper incisors are mounted in a projection of the palatine bone, which is partly cartilaginous and is often lost in preparation; these teeth are set well forward of the canines. On either side of this projection the skull is deeply emarginate.

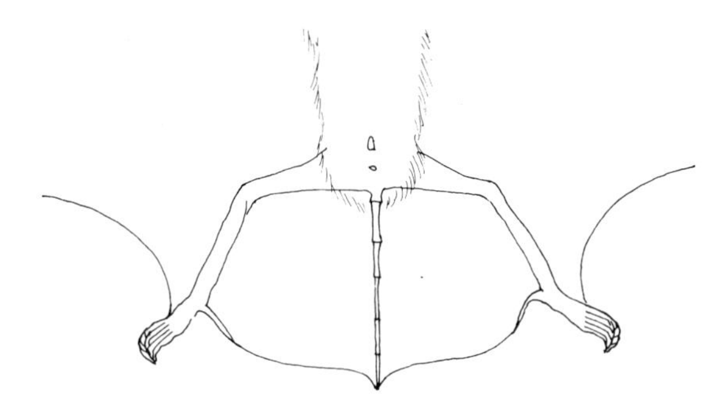

Fig. X.3. Skull of the Rhinolophidae, *Rhinolophus fumigatus*

The dental formula is

$I\frac{1}{2}\ C\frac{1}{1}\ P\frac{1-2}{2-3}\ M\frac{3}{3} = 28–32$

The lower incisors are trifid. The anterior upper premolar is small and may be missing on both or either side. Its position, within or external to the toothrow, is important in the grouping of the species (Fig. X.4).

## Genus *Rhinolophus* Lacépède, 1799

Key to the species after Meester *et al.* (1986)

1. Face and/or lateral margins of sella liberally furnished with long hairs; connecting process low, rounded; greatest width of horseshoe over 9 mm ... 2

   Sella naked; connecting process rounded or pointed; greatest width of horseshoe less than 9 mm ... 3

2. Forearm 62–67 mm ... *hildebrandtii*

   Forearm 50–60 mm ... *fumigatus*

3. Anterior upper premolar, when present, external to toothrow; canine and fourth upper premolar in contact; connecting process bluntly pointed ... 4

   Anterior upper premolar in toothrow; canine and fourth upper premolar not in contact; connecting process blunt or sharply pointed ... 5

4. Forearm 50–57 mm ... *clivosus*

   Forearm 45–50 mm ... *darlingi*

5. Connecting process rises to an erect point; interpterygoid groove usually shallow, not clearly defined by bordering ridges; anterior upper premolar usually not crowded between canine and fourth upper premolar, longer than wide ... 6

   Connecting process with a low bluntly pointed tip; interpterygoid groove deep and clearly defined by bordering ridges; anterior upper premolar usually more or less crowded between canine and fourth upper premolar, at least as wide as it is long

... 7

6. First phalanx of fourth finger notably shortened in relation to metacarpal length; connecting process pointed; molar width less than half width of palate between molars

... *landeri*

First phalanx of fourth finger not notably shortened in relation to metacarpal length; connecting process rises to a high narrow horn; molar width more than half width of palate between molars

... *blasii*

7. Larger, forearm 47–51 mm, skull 20 mm or more

... *capensis*

Smaller, forearm 40–46 mm, skull 18,7 mm or less

... 8

8. Sella broader; ears longer, 20–22 mm; condylocanine length more than 15,5 mm

... *simulator*

Sella narrower; ears shorter, 18–20 mm; condylocanine length less than 15,5 mm

... 9

9. Front edge of connecting process almost concave; lancet with sides almost convex; fur whitish at base

... *denti*

Front edge of connecting process convex; lancet with sides concave, tip pointed; fur nearly unicoloured

... *swinnyi*

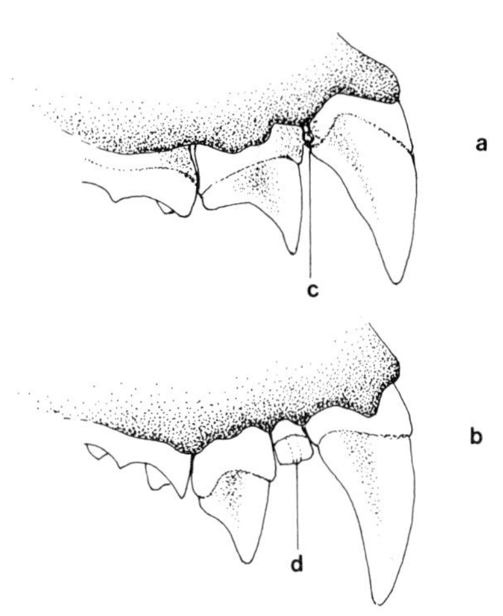


Fig. X.4. Teeth (a) *Rhinolophus darlingi*, with the minute anterior premolar (c) situated external to toothrow (b) *R. denti* with the anterior upper premolar (d) situated in the toothrow.

No. 100

## *Rhinolophus hildebrandtii* Peters, 1878

## Hildebrandt's horseshoe bat
## Hildebrandt se saalneusvlermuis

Plate 5

### Taxonomic Notes

No subspecies are listed by Hayman & Hill (1971).

### Description

Hildebrandt's horseshoe bats are the largest members of the genus that occur in the Subregion. Adult males have a total length of about 110 mm and a mass of about 27 g, the females slightly larger and heavier (Table 100.1). They are greyish-brown on the upper parts, the under parts about the same colour or very slightly lighter. The ears are conspicuously large and pointed at the tips, strongly convex on their inner edges and concave on the outer. The wing and interfemoral membranes are a translucent dark brown. The hair on the upper parts is unicoloured and is long and soft.

**Table 100.1**

Measurements (mm) and mass (g) of Hildebrandt's horseshoe bats, *R. hildebrandtii*, from Zimbabwe (Smithers & Wilson, 1979)

| | Males | | | Females | | |
|---|---|---|---|---|---|---|
| | $\bar{x}$ | n | Range | $\bar{x}$ | n | Range |
| TL | 114 | 15 | 108–121 | 116 | 15 | 109–125 |
| T | 38 | 15 | 32–40 | 39 | 15 | 31–43 |
| Hf c/u | 15 | 15 | 13–16 | 15 | 15 | 14–16 |
| E | 32 | 15 | 30–33 | 31 | 15 | 28–34 |
| F/a | 63 | 11 | 62–66 | 66 | 9 | 64–67 |
| Mass | 26,9 | 12 | 22,8–32,2 | 31,3 | 8 | 26,0–34,0 |

### Distribution

Confined to the eastern parts of the continent from the Transvaal north to southern Ethiopia and the Sudan. The most westerly records are from near Kabompo in Zambia.

*South of the Sahara, excluding the Southern African Subregion*

They occur in southern **Ethiopia; Sudan**; southern **Somalia**; in **Kenya; Uganda** and the extreme northeastern and southeastern parts of **Zaire** and in **Rwanda**. In **Tanzania** there are records from the eastern parts of the country, but their occurrence in Rwanda suggests that they have a wider distribution in this sector. There are records from **Malawi**, and in **Zambia** they are widespread except in the southwest. In **Mozambique**, north of the Zambezi River, they occur in the Tete District. While there are no records at the moment from the extreme northeastern parts of Mozambique, this area is little known and their occurrence in adjacent territories suggests that in time they will be shown to be present.

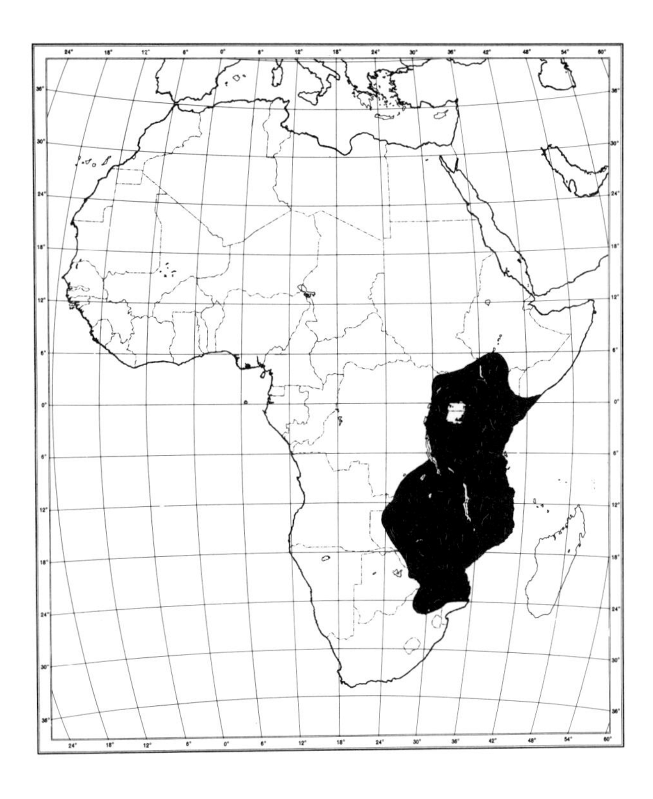

*Southern African Subregion*

They are widely distributed in **Zimbabwe** except in the northwest and occur across the border into **Botswana** in the Francistown district. They are recorded from **Mozambique**, south of the Zambezi River, as far south as the western parts of the Gaza District. In the **Transvaal** they occur in the northern, central and eastern parts of the province.

### Habitat

Hildebrandt's horseshoe bat is a savanna woodland species whose occurrence is dependent on the availability of suitable roosting sites (see **Habits**) and is therefore generally absent from open grassland.

### Habits

They are a gregarious species, occurring in their daylight roosting places in hundreds. While there are two records of individuals hanging in trees, this is atypical and they favour the more substantial shelter of caves, mine adits, fissures or cavities in rocks, piles of boulders, hollow trees such as baobab, *Adansonia digitata*, and mopane, *Colophospermum mopane*, disused antbear holes and occasionally in the roofs of houses. They hang in these, usually from the roof, but also from the walls in small clusters, numbering up to 50 individuals, evenly separated from one another and usually in total darkness. They are attracted to the insects flying around lights at night and quite frequently enter buildings in search of prey. Their flight is weak and fluttering. Fenton & Rautenbach (1986) found this species to hunt on the wing during the early part of the night, after which they adapt the fly-catcher mode of hunting. This species was found to concentrate its hunting activities in cluttered environments such as riverine forests, which correlates with observations on its manoeuvrability (Aldridge & Rautenbach, 1987).

### Food

Insectivorous.

### Reproduction

In the northern parts of the Subregion gravid females have been taken in October, suggesting that the single young is born during the early part of the warm, wet summer months from about October to December.

No. 101

## *Rhinolophus fumigatus* Rüppell, 1842

## Rüppell's horseshoe bat
## Rüppell se saalneusvlermuis

### Colloquial Name

Named after the describer of the species.

### Taxonomic Notes

Meester *et al.* (1986) stated that only the subspecies *R. f. aethiops* Peters, 1869 occurs in the Subregion; the nominate and other subspecies in the northern parts of the species range occur north of Zambia

### Description

The two closely related species *R. hildebrandtii* and *R. fumigatus* have a number of features in common. Among these the antitragus of the ear is not as well developed as in the other species of the genus, and the horseshoe is large, generally over 9 mm in breadth (Fig. 101.1.a). *R. hildebrandtii*, the larger of the two, has a forearm length of 62–67 mm, in *R. fumigatus* it is 50–60 mm (Table 101.1). In body size and mass the disparity between the two is equally marked, adult male *R. fumigatus* having a total length of about 100 mm and a mass of about 14,0 g (Rautenbach, 1982), against the figures given for *R. hildebrandtii* of 110 mm and 27,0 g. As in the case of *R. hildebrandtii* the females of *R. fumigatus* are slightly larger and heavier than the males.

The colour of the upper parts in Rüppell's horseshoe bat is very similar to that of Hildebrandt's, a greyish-brown, but tends to be slightly browner. The under parts are lighter in colour, a light grey, the hairs on the chest and belly with

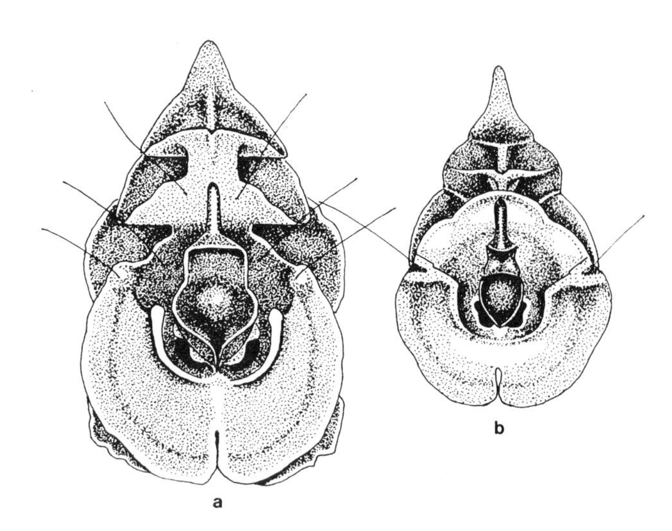


Fig. 101.1. Noseleaves: (a) *Rhinolophus fumigatus* (b) *R. landeri*

lighter tips. The wing and interfemoral membranes are a translucent greyish-brown, the hair of the under parts extending on to the wing membranes near the body.

The anterior upper premolars are so small that it is difficult to find them even with the aid of a lens. In some specimens they are lacking, in others absent on one side. When they are present they lie external to the toothrow (Fig. X.4).

**Table 101.1**

Measurements (mm) and mass (g) of Rüppell's horseshoe bats, *R. fumigatus*, from the northern parts of the Subregion

**Male** (Rautenbach, 1982)

| TL | T | Hfc/u | E | F/a | Mass |
|---|---|---|---|---|---|
| 105 | 29 | 10 | 25 | 53 | 14,0 |

**Irrespective of sex** (Smithers & Wilson, 1979)

| | $\bar{x}$ | n | Range |
|---|---|---|---|
| TL | 92 | 6 | 82–105 |
| T | 32 | 6 | 31–35 |
| Hf c/u | 13 | 8 | 11–15 |
| E | 25 | 8 | 24–26 |
| F/a | 50 | 8 | 48–51 |
| Mass | 16,0 | 5 | 12,4–20,0 |

### Distribution

Rüppell's horseshoe bat is distributed widely on the continent from the northwestern Cape Province to Ethiopia and westwards to Senegal, excluding the desert and semi-desert areas and tropical forest.

*South of the Sahara, excluding the Southern African Subregion*

Recorded from **Senegal** and **Sierra Leone** eastwards to **Nigeria; Cameroun; Central African Republic; Sudan** and eastern **Ethiopia** and southwards in the northeastern and southwestern parts of **Zaire**; in **Uganda; Kenya; Rwanda; Tanzania; Zambia; Malawi** and **Angola**. Except for some of the more northerly countries there is a paucity of records, as for example, in Zambia where all existing specimens are from the east. However, Ansell (1978) believed that eventually they will be shown to occur throughout. The same remarks were applied to Angola by Hill & Carter (1941), here with the reservation that they probably did not occur in the forested areas in the north. There are no records from northeastern Mozambique. Their occurrence in southeastern Tanzania suggests that eventually they will be shown to be present.

*Southern African Subregion*

They occur in the central parts of **Namibia** from the Cunene River to the Orange River in the south, extending southwards into the extreme northwestern parts of the **Cape Province**. They are not recorded from Botswana and in **Zimbabwe** are absent from the dry west and eastwards on the plateau to east of Harare. They occur in **Mozambique**, south of the Zambezi River, in the Tete and Vila Pery districts, south to about 19°50′S and in the extreme north-eastern corner of the **Transvaal**.

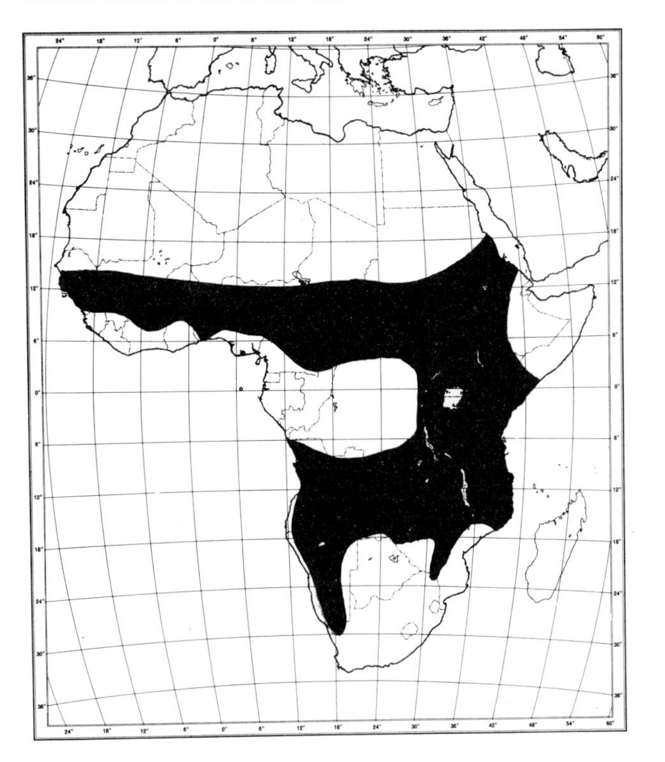

### Habitat

Rüppell's horseshoe bats occur in open savanna woodland and are absent from desert and semi-desert areas, and in forested areas are absent from within these, although they may occur on the fringes.

### Habits

They are a gregarious species but never occur in greater numbers than about a dozen together. They roost in caves, mine adits, piles of boulders or cavities in rocks, packed tightly together, hanging from the roof. When hanging they fold their tails and interfemoral membranes up the lower parts of their backs, the wings tightly folded around their bodies (Aellen, 1952).

### Food

Insectivorous.

### Reproduction

In the northern parts of the Subregion gravid females have been taken in September and October, which suggests that the young are born early in the warm, wet summer months from about October to December. All gravid females so far taken contained one foetus each.

No. 102

## *Rhinolophus clivosus* Cretzschmar, 1828

## Geoffroy's horseshoe bat
## Geoffroy se saalneusvlermuis

Plate 4

### Colloquial Name

Named after E. Geoffroy who collected bats in Egypt during the early part of the 19th century.

### Taxonomic Notes

Meester *et al.* (1986) listed two subspecies from the Subregion: *R.c. augur* K. Andersen, 1904 from the western Cape Province, Namibia, southwestern Angola and the Transvaal, and *R. c. zuluensis* K. Andersen, 1904 from the eastern Cape Province, Natal, Orange Free State, eastern Transvaal, Mozambique, Zimbabwe and extending northwards to Tanzania and Uganda. The nominate *R. c. clivosus* Cretzschmar, 1828 was described from the Red Sea coast in Arabia.

### Description

This species ranks close to *R. fumigatus* as the second largest of the rhinolophid bats occurring in the Subregion. They have a mean forearm length of about 54 mm, and females with forearm lengths of up to 57 mm are recorded (Table 102.1). The colour of the upper parts of the body is greyish or reddish-brown, the individual hairs pale buffy with brown tips. In some specimens the brown tips are darker on some parts of the body than on other parts, giving the upper parts a blotched appearance. The under parts are paler, the individual hairs a uniform pale greyish-brown. The ears are large and pointed as in other members of the genus. The wing and interfemoral membranes are dark.

The skull has a sagittal crest on the anterior part of the braincase which extends posteriorly over the top of the braincase to tail out on the back. The small anterior upper premolars lie external to the toothrow. The premaxillary bones carrying the pair of upper incisors are attached to the skull by a fine stalk and are often lost in preparation.

**Table 102.1**

Measurements (mm) and mass (g) of Geoffroy's horseshoe bats, *R. clivosus*, from the Transvaal (Rautenbach, 1982)

| | Males | | | Females | | |
|---|---|---|---|---|---|---|
| | $\bar{x}$ | n | Range | $\bar{x}$ | n | Range |
| TL | 96 | 63 | 80–112 | 97 | 75 | 85–110 |
| T | 32 | 63 | 27–38 | 32 | 75 | 27–38 |
| Hf c/u | 11 | 57 | 9–13 | 11 | 74 | 8–14 |
| E | 21 | 63 | 18–24 | 21 | 75 | 18–24 |
| F/a | 53 | 32 | 52–56 | 54 | 28 | 51–57 |
| Mass | 16,2 | 20 | 13,0–20,0 | 17,0 | 24 | 12,0–25,0 |

### Distribution

Geoffroy's horseshoe bats have a wide distribution on the continent from the Cape Province to North Africa. Extralimitally Harrison (1964) showed that they occur in the Sinai and Arabia and north to Israel, and Aellen (1959) found that, by the inclusion of *R. bocharicus* as a subspecies, they occur eastwards to Afghanistan and northwards to Uzbekistan and Turkmenistan.

*North Africa*

They occur in **Cameroun** and **Morocco; Algeria; Tunisia; Libya**, where they penetrate deeply into the southwestern parts of the country, and in **Egypt**, to the coast of the Mediterranean.

*South of the Sahara, excluding the Southern African Subregion*

They occur in the eastern parts of **Sudan**; in **Ethiopia; Somalia; Kenya; Uganda** and **Tanzania**. In **Zambia** they occur in the north of the central parts of the country and, in the east, to the borders of **Malawi**. There are no records from Mozambique, north of the Zambezi River, but their occurrence southwards and in Tanzania suggests that they will be shown to occur there in time. In **Angola** they occur in the southwest and in **Zaire** in the southeast, northeast and east. There is a single record from Mount Cameroun, in West Africa.

*Southern African Subregion*

They are widespread in **Zimbabwe**, excluding the dry western areas and have been recorded in the western parts of the Tete and Vila Pery districts of **Mozambique** south of the Zambezi River. In the **Transvaal** they occur widely except in the west. They are reported to occur in northeastern **Natal** and have been taken in the **Orange Free State**. The species originally was described from Kuruman in the northern **Cape Province** (*R. augur* K. Andersen, 1904) and there are numerous later records from the west, south and east of the province and they most probably occur throughout, except in the extreme north. To date they have not been recorded in Botswana. They are confined to the western and southern parts of **Namibia**.

### Habitat

Predominantly a savanna woodland species, but occurs on forest fringes and even in deserts. Their absence in areas such as the semi-desert parts of Botswana may be due to the absence of the right type of daylight roosting places (see **Habits**).

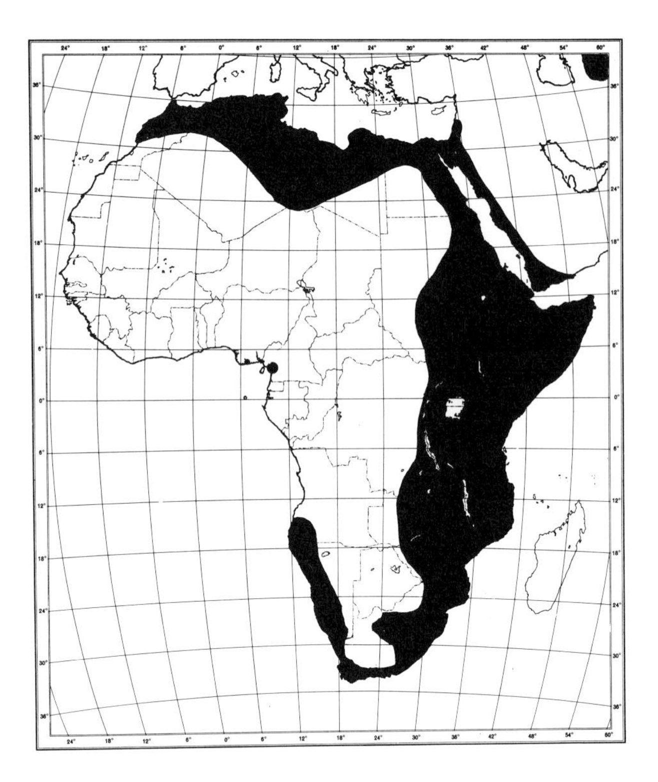

### Habits

They are gregarious, occurring in the Cape Province in colonies numbering up to 10 000 (Herselman, 1980). They roost during the day in caves, rock crevices and mine adits, hanging on the roofs or walls in small clusters, the individuals slightly separated from one another. They leave these shelters about half an hour after sunset to forage and return to them before first light. During the night they establish feeding sites, hanging from branches of trees or even entering the verandahs of houses to hang up and eat. These feeding sites are marked by the accumulations of discarded portions of the food on the ground underneath them. Occasionally they are found in cellars beneath houses (Herselman, 1980). When foraging, they fly below tree top level and are subject to local movements of up to about 10 km (Herselman, 1980).

### Food

Insectivorous. Rautenbach (1982) recorded the remains of moths and small beetles.

### Reproduction

Bernard (1983) showed that in Natal copulation took place in May, the sperm being stored in the oviducts and uterine horns of the females and remained there over the period of winter hibernation. Ovulation and fertilisation took place in August, parturition in December. Females become sexually mature during their first year, males in their second year.

In the Cape Province, Herselman (1980) stated that a single young is born about the middle of December.

In the Transvaal, Rautenbach (1982) took gravid females with a single foetus in November. These data suggest that they have their young during the warm summer months.

---

No. 103

## *Rhinolophus darlingi* K. Andersen, 1905

## Darling's horseshoe bat
## Darling se saalneusvlermuis

---

### Colloquial Name

Named after J. ff. Darling, a mining engineer, who first collected this species in Mazoe, Zimbabwe, and others in mine adits (*R. simulator*) in the early part of this century.

### Taxonomic Notes

Meester *et al.* (1986) listed two subspecies from the Subregion: the nominate *R. d. darlingi* from the Transvaal, Zimbabwe, western Mozambique, eastern and northern Botswana and extralimitally from Malawi and Tanzania and *R. d. damarensis* Roberts, 1946 from the Cape Province and Namibia and extralimitally from Angola.

### Description

A small species with a total length of about 85 mm and a mass of about 9,0 g (Table 103.1). There is some variation in the colour of the upper parts, the majority of specimens being drab grey, but others slightly browner. The colour of the under parts follows the colour of the upper parts, but is much lighter in colour, a light dove-grey. Specimens from Namibia, *R. d. damarensis*, are larger and lighter in colour than those from the east of the Subregion, although there is some overlap as far as size is concerned when series from west and east are compared. The wing and interfemoral membranes are light grey-brown, the ears, which have pointed tips, a translucent light brown. The anterior upper premolars are minute and lie external to the toothrow (Fig. X.4.a).

**Table 103.1**

Measurements (mm) and mass (g) of Darling's horseshoe bats, *R. darlingi*, from the northern parts of the Subregion (Smithers & Wilson, 1979)

| | Males | | | Females | | |
|---|---|---|---|---|---|---|
| | $\bar{x}$ | n | Range | $\bar{x}$ | n | Range |
| TL | 84 | 12 | 80–87 | 85 | 11 | 80–90 |
| T | 28 | 12 | 25–33 | 31 | 11 | 28–34 |
| Hf c/u | 10 | 12 | 9–10 | 10 | 11 | 9–11 |
| E | 22 | 12 | 20–30 | 21 | 11 | 21–22 |
| F/a | 45 | 12 | 43–48 | 46 | 11 | 43–48 |
| Mass | 8,7 | 12 | 8,1–10,0 | 8,6 | 10 | 8,0–10,0 |

### Distribution

While this species is common in Zimbabwe and in parts of the surrounding territories to the west, south and east, it has not been taken so far in Zambia in spite of the fact that it occurs along the Zambezi River within Zimbabwe limits. There are isolated records from Benguela, Angola (Andersen, 1912) and from Banagi, southeast of Lake Victoria, Tanzania (Swynnerton & Hayman, 1950) which suggest that it has a far wider distribution than it is possible to accurately show on a map at the present.

*South of the Sahara, excluding the Southern African Subregion*

As they occur in the Zambezi Valley in the Tete District, **Mozambique**, and in the Southern Province of **Malawi**, they are likely to be found to occur in the intervening area. At the moment there are no records from the northern Provinces of Mozambique but they are recorded as occurring in **Angola** and **Tanzania**.

*Southern African Subregion*

They occur in **Namibia** and in northeastern **Botswana** in the eastern sector of the country from Francistown south to Gaborone, and are distributed widely in **Zimbabwe**, except in parts of the dry west. They occur widely in the **Transvaal** and in parts of the northwestern, northern and southeastern **Cape Province**. In **Mozambique**, south of the Zambezi River, they occur at Zumbo on the Zambezi River and narrowly southwards along the Zimbabwe and Transvaal borders to the western parts of the Maputo District.

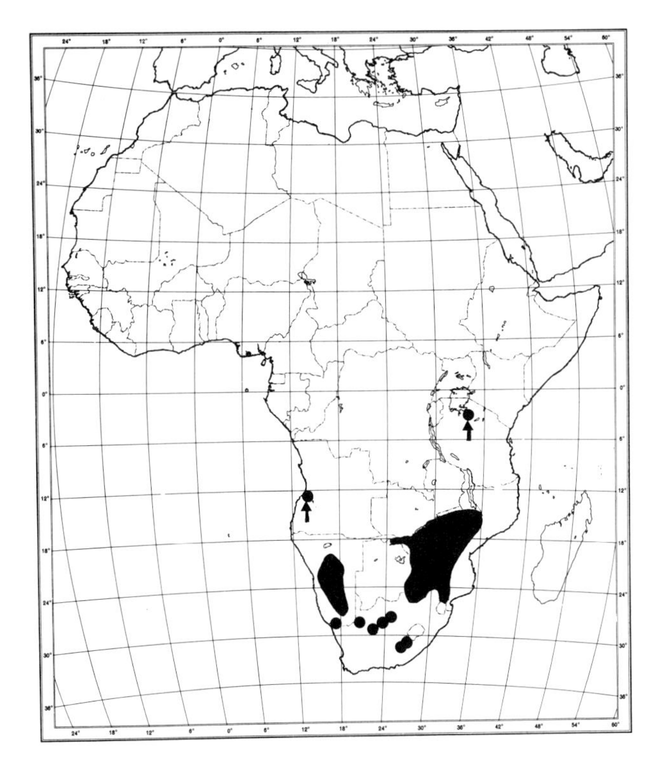

## Habitat

A savanna woodland species requiring the substantial cover of caves or mine adits to roost in during the day. They are more dependent on the availability of this type of cover than the type of vegetational association (see **Habits**). In the northern parts of the Subregion they are associated particularly with broken, rocky terrain.

## Habits

Darling's horseshoe bats are gregarious, occurring in colonies numbering dozens of individuals. During the day they roost hanging from the ceilings of caves, mine adits, cavities and fissures in rock or in piles of boulders and frequently they are found hanging from the ceilings of buildings where they are not subject to disturbance. Shortridge (1934) took them from outbuildings and stables. In roosting in these situations they tend to form clusters with individuals slightly separated from their neighbours.

## Food

Insectivorous.

## Reproduction

Rautenbach (1982) took a gravid female in October and Smithers & Wilson (1979) recorded gravid females in December, and females carrying young in October. These meagre data suggest that the young are born during the early part of the warm, wet summer months from about September to December. A gravid female from Zimbabwe carried twin foetuses.

No. 104

# *Rhinolophus landeri* Martin, 1838

# Lander's horseshoe bat
# Lander se saalneusvlermuis

## Colloquial Name

Named by Martin after an early West African explorer, Richard Lander (Rosevear, 1965).

## Taxonomic Notes

Meester *et al.* (1986) listed only *R. l. lobatus* Peters, 1852 from the Subregion.

## Description

Lander's horseshoe bats have a total length of about 80 mm with tails about 30 mm in length and a mean mass of 6,0 g (Table 104.1). The upper parts are buffy-brown or grey-brown, the under parts lighter in colour. In other parts of Africa a bright reddish-brown phase has been recorded, as they have been in Zimbabwe (Wright, pers. comm.). The wing and interfemoral membranes are dark brown. The greatest breadth of the horseshoe is under 9 mm (Fig. 101.1.b).

The anterior upper premolars lie in the toothrow separating the canines from the posterior premolars. In the lower jaw the anterior premolar is about half to three quarters the height of the posterior one, the middle posterior teeth external to the toothrow.

**Table 104.1**

Measurements (mm) and mass (g) of female Lander's horseshoe bats, *R. landeri*, from Zimbabwe

| | Females | | |
|---|---|---|---|
| | $\bar{x}$ | n | Range |
| TL | 76 | 18 | 74–78 |
| T | 23 | 18 | 20–25 |
| Hf c/u | 9 | 18 | 9 |
| E | 18 | 18 | 16–19 |
| F/a | 42 | 18 | 41–43 |
| Mass | 6,8 | 18 | 5,6–9,2 |

## Distribution

They occur from Gambia in West Africa eastwards to Ethiopia and Somalia and southwards to the Transvaal and adjacent parts of Mozambique. In the southern parts of their distributional range they are represented poorly in collections. For example, there is only one specimen from Angola and five from the Transvaal.

*South of the Sahara, excluding the Southern African Subregion*

They are recorded from **Gambia; Sierre Leone; Nigeria** and **Cameroun** from the High Forest Zone and parts of the Guinea savanna eastwards to southern and southeastern **Sudan** and the highlands of **Ethiopia**. They are listed by Funaioli & Simonetta (1966) from **Somalia** and although the number of localities from which they have been recorded in East Africa is small, there are records from **Uganda; Kenya** and **Tanzania** and from parts of **Zaire**. Recorded from the northwestern parts of **Zambia** near the Angola border and in the southeast of the country. Ansell (1978) believed that eventually they may be shown to be more widespread, except in the southwest. They occur in central and southern **Malawi** and while, at the moment, they are only known from the Tete District in **Mozambique**, north of the Zambezi River, they probably will be taken in time in other parts of northern Mozambique.

*Southern African Subregion*

Widespread in **Zimbabwe**, except in the dry areas; they occur in **Mozambique**, south of the Zambezi River, in the central parts of the country and in the western areas in the south, as far as about 24 °S. In the **Transvaal** they occur in the north and east, southwards to about 24 °S.

### Habitat

In West Africa, Lander's horseshoe bats are associated predominantly with forest but, in the southern parts of their distributional range, are a savanna woodland species, and are associated particularly within this to riverine woodland and to well-watered areas. The presence of substantial shelters to roost in during the day is probably a more important habitat requirement than the vegetational association in which they are found.

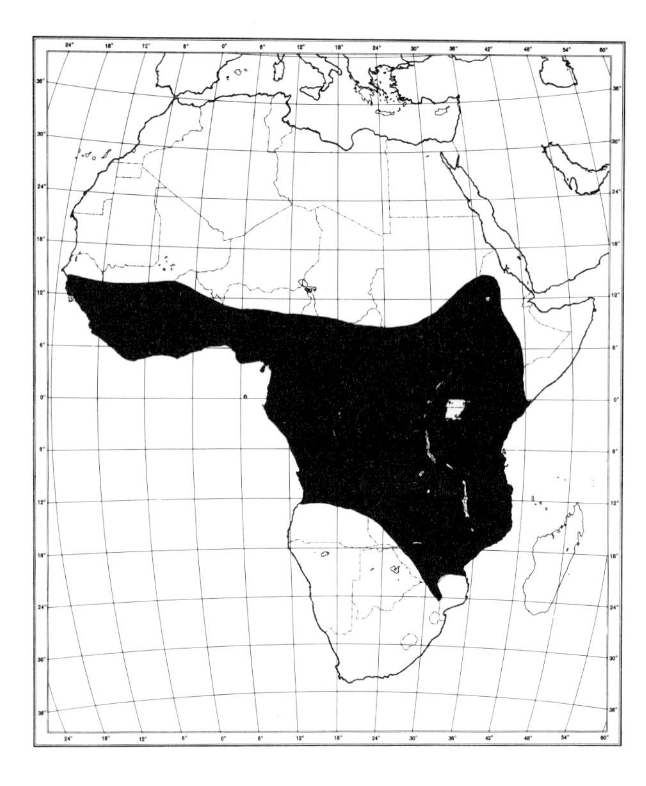

### Habits

Lander's horseshoe bats are gregarious, but only occur in the Subregion in small numbers, never over a dozen and, quite often, one or two only. They roost during the day in caves, mine adits, piles of boulders and hollow baobab trees, *Adansonia digitata*. They will visit lights at night to hawk insects and have been known to enter houses (Jones, 1971). In roosting they hang from the ceiling in clusters, the individuals well separated from one another.

### Food

Insectivorous. Fenton (1975), from the examination of insect remains under a feeding site, showed that 92% of the food consists of Lepidoptera, the remainder Orthoptera. Among the Lepidoptera there was a single butterfly, *Charaxes varanes*, but most of the remains consisted of noctuid moths. Of these 59% consisted of *Anua tirhaca*, 12% each of *Ophisma lienardi* and *Sphingomorpha cholorea*, 5% of *Achaea illustrata* and 3% of *Ophisma* sp. This shows a remarkable selectiveness on the part of the bat for certain moth species. If this is compared with details of the food given for the common slit-faced bat, *Nycteris thebaica*, there is the suggestion that different species of bats appear to feed selectively on available food resources.

### Reproduction

One gravid female was taken in Zimbabwe in October with a single foetus.



---

No. 105

## *Rhinolophus blasii* Peters, 1867

## Peak-saddle horseshoe bat
## Spitssaalneusvlermuis

---

### Colloquial Name

The name peak-saddle refers to the configuration of the noseleaves, the connecting process rising to a high point.

### Taxonomic Notes

The nominate *R. b. blasii* Peters, 1867 was described from Italy; only the subspecies *R. b. empusa* K. Andersen, 1904 occurs in the Subregion.

### Description

Peak-saddle horseshoe bats have a total length of about 80 mm, with tails of 30 mm and a mass of about 4,0 g (Table 105.1). The hair on the upper parts is long, soft and woolly, the bases of the hair cream-coloured. From the shoulders to the base of the tail it is tipped with dark brown, the hairs on the back of the neck showing very little tipping and giving the appearance of a lighter band over the top of the body in this region. The under parts are lighter in colour, in some white, in others creamy. The wing and interfemoral membranes are brown. The ears, which rise to pointed tips, are translucent light brown.

**Table 105.1**

Measurements (mm) and mass (g) of peak-saddle horseshoe bats, *R. blasii*, from the Transvaal (Rautenbach, 1982)

| | Males | | | Females | | |
|---|---|---|---|---|---|---|
| | $\bar{x}$ | n | Range | $\bar{x}$ | n | Range |
| TL | 76 | 18 | 70–100 | 75 | 14 | 63–89 |
| T | 26 | 18 | 21–30 | 26 | 14 | 21–30 |
| Hf c/u | 9 | 18 | 7–10 | 9 | 14 | 7–10 |
| E | 18 | 18 | 15–21 | 18 | 14 | 15–20 |
| F/a | 45 | 18 | 41–47 | 46 | 14 | 43–47 |
| Mass | 4,2 | 13 | 2,1–7,5 | 2,6 | 12 | 2,1–3,0 |

### Distribution

Extralimitally to the continent this species occurs in southern Europe and in southwestern Asia. Originally the species was described from a specimen from Europe; Ellerman, Morrison-Scott & Hayman (1953) fixed the type locality as Italy. They recorded their presence in Greece, Yugoslavia, Cyprus, Palestine, southwestern Arabia, southeastern Iran, Transcaucasia and Turkmenia. African records are scattered and there are very large areas from which there are no records. At this time it is not possible to indicate the distributional limits of the species as so few records are available and therefore scattered indications of the areas in which they have been collected only are given.

*North Africa*

Recorded from **Morocco; Algeria** and **Tunisia**.

*South of the Sahara, excluding the Southern African Subregion*

There are records from northern and southeastern **Ethiopia**, but so far the species has not been recorded from East Africa, the record southward being from eastern **Zaire** on the western fringe of Lake Tanzania. In **Zambia** they have been taken in the south and in the extreme northeast in the upper Luangwa Valley, and in **Malawi** in the Northern and Southern Provinces, the type locality of *K. empusa* (= *K. b. empusa*) being Zomba.

*Southern African Subregion*

Recorded from the Masvingo area and in the Eastern Districts of **Zimbabwe** and in adjacent parts of **Mozambique**, south of the Zambezi River. In the **Transvaal** they occur in the south central parts of the province, from the Pafuri area

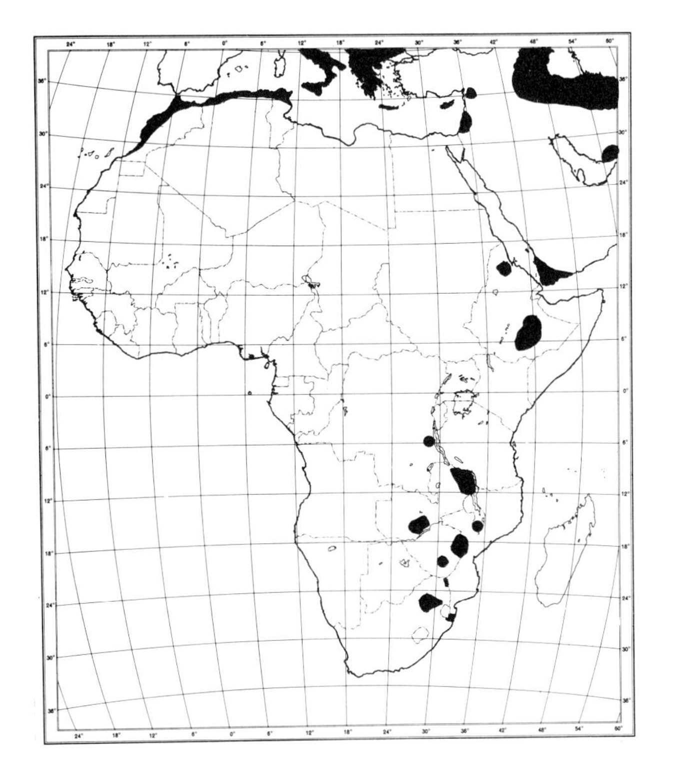

of the Kruger National Park in the northeast and from the **Natal** midlands and in the north of the province.

**Habitat**

A savanna woodland species dependent on the availability of substantial daylight roosting places in the form of caves or mine adits.

**Habits**

Peak-saddle horseshoe bats occur in small numbers, in the Subregion never more than three or four together. They roost during the day in caves, mine adits or piles of boulders, hanging from the ceiling in a cluster, the individuals separated from one another (Rautenbach, 1982). In regular visits to dolomite caves Rautenbach (1982) stated that they were not always present, suggesting that they were to some extent migratory.

**Food**

Insectivorous.

**Reproduction**

No data available from the Subregion.

---

No. 106

## *Rhinolophus capensis* Lichtenstein, 1823

## Cape horseshoe bat
## Kaapse saalneusvlermuis

---

**Colloquial Name**

Associated in their distribution with the southwestern parts of the Cape Province, the name Cape is retained for convenience to differentiate them from other horseshoe bats.

**Taxonomic Notes**

No subspecies have been described.

**Description**

This species is very similar in colour to Geoffroy's horseshoe bat, *R. clivosus*, but is smaller, the best indication of which is given by the comparative lengths of the forearm which in this species range from 46–51,8 mm. Cape horseshoe bats have a total length of about 90 mm with tails of about 30 mm (Table 106.1). It also has a skull with a total length of 20 mm or more. While the ears in the two species show an overlap in length, they are broader in *R. capensis* than in *R. clivosus*. The upper parts are dark brown in colour, the individual hairs cream-coloured at their bases; this lighter colour shows through and gives the upper parts an uneven colour. The under parts are lighter in colour, a light fawn-grey. The wing and interfemoral membranes are dark brown and show some reticulation of fine black lines, especially near the body. The ears are noticeably broad and rise to blunt tips.

The anterior upper premolar lies in the toothrow, the anterior lower premolar barely half the height of the posterior premolar; the middle premolar is external to the toothrow. The lower incisors are trifid. *R. capensis* is larger than *R. simulator*, which is very similar in colour.

**Table 106.1**

Measurements (mm) of a series of male Cape horseshoe bats, *R. capensis* from the Cape Province.

| | Males | | |
|---|---|---|---|
| | $\bar{x}$ | n | Range |
| TL | 88 | 9 | 84–90 |
| HB | 60 | 9 | 58–62 |
| T | 28 | 9 | 24–32 |
| Hf c/u | 10 | 9 | 9–12 |
| E | 23 | 9 | 21–25 |
| F/a | 49 | 9 | 48–52 |

**Distribution**

Although there are records in literature of the occurrence of this species in Zambia (Ansell, 1978); Malawi (Thomas, 1894), and Zimbabwe (Smithers & Wilson, 1979), Hill (*in litt.*) in re-examining the specimens from Zambia and Malawi, stated that they are not *R. capensis* and it appears that the Zimbabwe material has been similarly misidentified. There is a specimen from Prieska (Stuart, Lloyd & Herselman, 1980) and another from Natal (Cowles, 1936) which also require re-examination, as they appear to be out of the known distributional range of this species.

*Southern African Subregion*

Confined to the coastal belt of the western and southern **Cape Province** as far east as about East London.

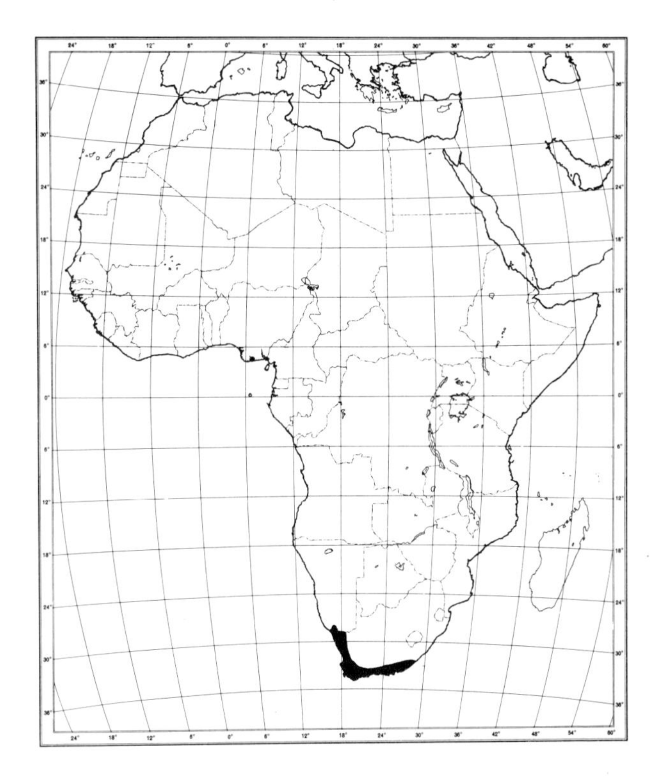

**Habitat**

They are a typical cave dwelling species and their occurrence is probably influenced as much by the availability of this type of shelter and a plentiful food supply as by any other considerations. They are abundant in parts of the southern Cape Province where there are many records from coastal caves.

### Habits

A gregarious species, occurring in the Cape Province in colonies numbering thousands. They roost during the day in caves and mine adits, hanging from the ceiling in clusters, often in company with Geoffroy's horseshoe bats, *R. clivosus*; the two species cluster separately (Herselman, 1980).

### Food

Insectivorous.

### Reproduction

Bernard (1985) found that in this species the storage of the sperm devolves upon the male. Spermatogenesis takes place between October and May in the Cape Province, the sperm being released to the cauda epididymis in April and May. At this time the females are in oestrus but copulation and ovulation are delayed until August/September after the winter hibernation. Parturition occurs in November and December after a three to four month period of gestation.

Herselman (1980) stated that in the Cape Province the young are born from the middle of December onwards, the females producing a single young at birth. He reported that the young cling to their mothers during the day, leaving them in the cave when they fly to forage at night.

---

No. 107

## *Rhinolophus simulator* K. Andersen, 1904

## Bushveld horseshoe bat
## Bosveldsaalneusvlermuis

---

### Colloquial Name

Named bushveld horseshoe bat as, in the Subregion, they occur in savanna woodland.

### Taxonomic Notes

Meester *et al.* (1986) did not recognise any subspecies.

### Description

A small rhinolophid with a forearm length of 40–46 mm and a skull with a total length of 18,7 mm or less. Bushveld horseshoe bats have a total length of about 80 mm with tails of about 30 mm (Table 107.1). The upper parts of the body are dark brown in colour, the individual hairs lighter brown towards their bases, the under parts greyish-white, tinged brown on the flanks. The wing and interfemoral membranes are dark brown. The anterior upper premolar lies in the toothrow, the lower anterior premolar about half the height of the posterior premolar, the middle premolar small and squeezed out externally to the toothrow.

### Table 107.1

Measurements (mm) of bushveld horseshoe bats, *R. simulator*, from the Transvaal.

| | Males | | | Females | | |
|---|---|---|---|---|---|---|
| | $\bar{x}$ | n | Range | $\bar{x}$ | n | Range |
| TL | 83 | 8 | 78–86 | 80 | 14 | 71–88 |
| HB | 57 | 8 | 50–63 | 55 | 14 | 48–58 |
| T | 26 | 8 | 21–30 | 25 | 14 | 23–30 |
| Hf c/u | 10 | 8 | 9–12 | 7 | 14 | 5–10 |
| E | 22 | 8 | 20–23 | 22 | 14 | 21–24 |
| F/a | 46 | 8 | 45–47 | 47 | 14 | 45–48 |

### Distribution

The bushveld horseshoe bat is poorly represented in collections and it is not possible to assess the limits of its distribution on the continent. All that can be done at this stage is to indicate the areas from which it has been collected. These suggest that they are confined to the eastern parts of the continent from Ethiopia to Natal.

*South of the Sahara, excluding the Southern African Subregion*

Recorded from the southern **Sudan** and from several localities in the southern highlands of **Ethiopia**; from the *Brachystegia* woodlands of eastern **Kenya**; from southern **Tanzania**, northern **Malawi** and western **Zambia**.

*Southern African Subregion*

Recorded from northeastern and parts of eastern **Zimbabwe** and from central and southern **Mozambique**. In the **Transvaal** they occur in the central parts of the province and westwards to the Botswana border. While there are no records at the moment from the eastern Transvaal, as they occur in the Limpopo Valley in southern Mozambique, they may have been overlooked. They are recorded from **Natal** and the only records from **Botswana** are from caves in the Molepolole district.

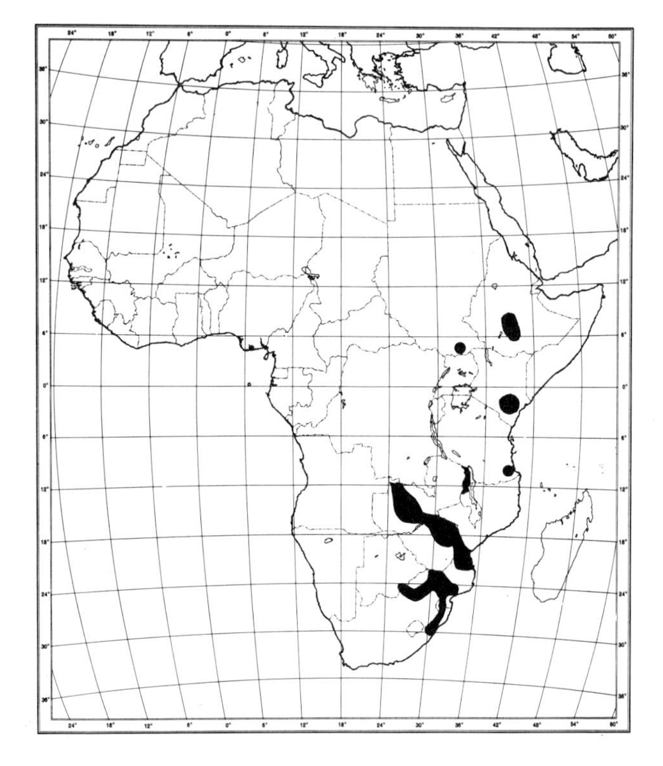

### Habitat

A savanna woodland species, dependent on the availability of substantial shelter in the form of caves and mine shafts. In Zimbabwe (Smithers & Wilson, 1979) they are associated particularly with *Brachystegia* woodland.

### Habits

In Zimbabwe they have been recorded from caves, the colonies numbering up to dozens. They hang from the ceiling, tending to form large clusters, each individual slightly separated from its neighbours. In the Transvaal, Rautenbach (1982) recorded colonies numbering up to 300 from both wet and dry caves. They will take insects at lights at night and enter houses.

### Food

Insectivorous.

### Reproduction

Rautenbach (1982) recorded that in January the females were in the final stages of lactation; the young, then roosting away from their mothers, were nearly fully grown. This colony appeared to be a maternity colony. He also recorded another colony located in September, showing a high incidence of pregnancy. From this the young appear to be born during the early part of the warm, wet summer months, about October/November.

No. 108

## *Rhinolophus denti* Thomas, 1904

# Dent's horseshoe bat
# Dent se saalneusvlermuis

### Colloquial Name

Called after R.E. Dent.

### Taxonomic Notes

Hayman & Hill (1971) listed two subspecies, *R. d. knorri* Eisentraut, 1960 from Guinea, West Africa and *R. d. denti* from the remainder of the species' range. *R. d. knorri* is slightly smaller than *R. d. denti*, the size of the forearm in the former 37,5 to 40,5 mm as against 41,5 to 43,0 mm in the latter; the total length and lengths of tail and ears are correspondingly smaller but with some overlap (Rosevear, 1965). Until *R. d. knorri* was described by M. Eisentraut (1960), the species was known only from southern Africa.

### Description

A very small species with a total length of 70 mm, a tail of 20 mm and a mass of about 6,0 g (Table 108.1). The colour of the upper parts is a pale grey, pale brown or pale cream, the individual hairs about 7 mm long and very soft and fine and broadly white at their bases with pale grey or pale cream tips. The under parts are off-white. The wing and interfemoral membranes are a pale translucent brown edged with white. The ears are sharply pointed.

The anterior upper premolars lie in the toothrow (Fig. X.4.b).

### Table 108.1

Measurements (mm) and mass (g) of a series of Dent's horseshoe bats, *R. denti*, from Drotsky's caves, Botswana (Smithers, 1971)

| | Males | | | Females | | |
|---|---|---|---|---|---|---|
| | $\bar{x}$ | n | Range | $\bar{x}$ | n | Range |
| TL | 70 | 8 | 68–76 | 69 | 8 | 66–76 |
| T | 21 | 8 | 20–21 | 21 | 8 | 19–23 |
| Hf c/u | 9 | 8 | 9–10 | 9 | 8 | 9–10 |
| E | 19 | 8 | 18–21 | 18 | 8 | 18–20 |
| F/a | 42 | 8 | 40–42 | 42 | 8 | 40–44 |
| Mass | 5,7 | 35 | Bulk sample | 6,6 | 35 | Bulk sample |

### Distribution

Apart from Eisentraut's (1960) record of *R. d. knorri* from Guinea, West Africa, Dent's horseshoe bat is confined in its distribution to the southwestern parts of the continent within the Southwest Arid Zone. Shortridge (1934) took specimens from the Ruacana Falls on the Cunene River and therefore they ought to occur in southwestern Angola, but Hill & Carter (1941) did not record them from this country. At present, therefore, they are presumed to be restricted to within the borders of the Subregion. Roberts (1951) questioned the identification of the material from Wakkerstroom, Transvaal, and Rautenbach (1982) did not include the species for the Transvaal. Similarly the three records from northeastern Zimbabwe are misidentifications (Smithers & Wilson, 1979).

*South of the Sahara, excluding the Southern African Subregion*

Recorded from **Guinea**, West Africa.

*Southern African Subregion*

Recorded from **Namibia** and occurring southwards to the northern **Cape Province** at Louisvale on the Orange River and in northwestern **Botswana**.

### Habitat

Dent's horseshoe bats occur widely in the more arid western parts of the Subregion. They apparently require substantial

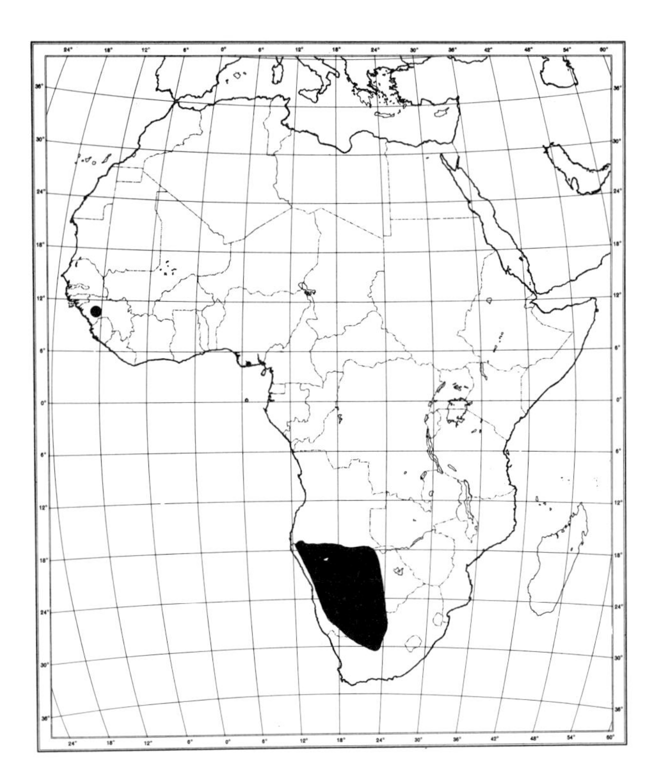

shelters in the form of caves or rock crevices in which to roost during the day and are probably dependent on their availability rather than on the type of vegetational association.

### Habits

In Drotsky's Caves in northwestern Botswana, which they used throughout the year, they were found clinging to the sides of stalactites in dozens, hanging freely from the sides in open clusters. They were taken both in semi-darkness 90 m from the entrance and from total darkness deep in the cave. At the Tsodilo Hills north of this there were no caves, but there was ample shelter available in the form of semi-dark crevices and caverns in the sandstone formation. The specimens taken there were netted and there was no evidence that they were using these, but it was thought that they were suitable. At Khuis on the Molopo River there are no koppies and the only available shelter appeared to be crevices in the calcareous outcrops exposed through erosion. In the Kaokoveld, Shortridge (1934) found two roosting under the thatched roof inside a rondavel.

### Food

Insectivorous.

### Reproduction

No data available from the Subregion.

No. 109

## *Rhinolophus swinnyi* Gough, 1908

# Swinny's horseshoe bat
# Swinny se saalneusvlermuis

### Colloquial Name

Named after H.H. Swinny who collected the original specimens from which the species was described from the Ngqueleni district, western Pondoland, Transkei.

### Taxonomic Notes

Hayman & Hill (1971) suggested that this species eventually may be shown to be a synonym of the older named *R. denti* Thomas 1904 but, until this issue is resolved, it is considered a valid species. No subspecies are recognised by Meester *et al.* (1986).

### Description

Swinny's horseshoe bats are very small, comparable in size to *R. denti.* They have a total length of about 70 mm, a mass of about 7,6 g and a forearm length of 43–44 mm (Table 109.1). The upper parts of the body vary in colour from a pale drab grey to a pale brown, the white or pale creamy bases of the individual hairs showing through to accentuate the general pale colour. The under parts are off-white or cream, tinged brown or grey. A bright orange phase is known. The ears are pale grey or pale brown, the tips pointed. The wing and interfemoral membranes in the pale brown individuals are pale brown, in the pale grey individuals pale grey.

The skull has a total length of about 17,5 mm. The anterior upper premolars lie in the toothrow, the canines and posterior premolar separated by them. The anterior lower premolar is barely half the height of the posterior, the middle premolar minute and lying external to the toothrow.

### Table 109.1

Measurements (mm) and mass (g) of five Swinny's horseshoe bats, *R. swinnyi*, from the Cape Province

| | Irrespective of sex | | |
|---|---|---|---|
| | $\bar{x}$ | n | Range |
| TL | 70 | 5 | 68–73 |
| T | 21 | 5 | 19–24 |
| Hf c/u | 9 | 5 | 9 |
| E | 19 | 5 | 19–20 |
| F/a | 43 | 5 | 43–44 |
| Mass | 7,6 | 5 | 7,4–7,7 |

### Distribution

Too few records of this small rhinolophid bat are available to assess the limits of its distribution. The greatest number of records are from north of the plateau in Zimbabwe, the scatter of records being from the eastern parts of the Cape Province to Zanzibar Island in the north and western Zaire.

*South of the Sahara, excluding the Southern African Subregion*

Recorded from **Zanzibar Island**; western **Zaire** near the mouth of the Congo River and from caves south of Lusaka, **Zambia**, which lie between this and the Kafue River. Taken at Missale Gold Mine in the northern Tete District of **Mozambique**, north of the Zambezi River.

*Southern African Subregion*

Recorded from north of the plateau in **Zimbabwe** and in the southeast of the country from the Bezwe River; from the western Vila Pery District of **Mozambique**, south of the Zambezi River. In the eastern **Cape Province** they have been collected in the King William's Town district and at Port St. Johns.

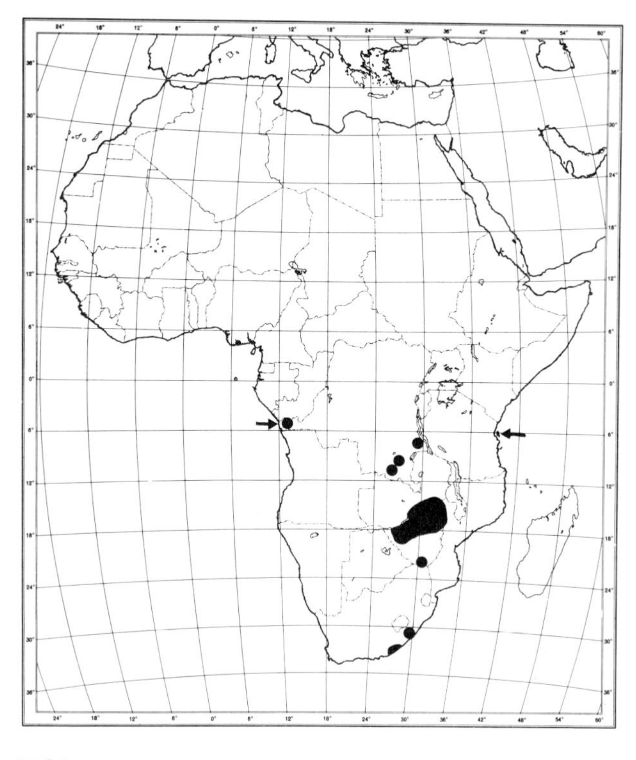

### Habitat

While Swinny's horseshoe bats are probably more dependent on the availability of substantial shelter in which to roost during the day than on the vegetational associations, they have been taken in savanna woodland in Zambia, Zimbabwe and in the northern Tete District of Mozambique. Roberts (1951), however, recorded a specimen from the Pirie Forest area in the eastern Cape Province, but made no mention of whether it was associated with the forest.

### Habits

In Zimbabwe they roost during the day hanging from the ceiling of caves, in ones or twos scattered throughout the shelter and so far are not found in greater numbers than five in the one cave. They hang in totally dark parts of the shelter.

### Food

Insectivorous.

### Reproduction

No data available from the Subregion.

# XI. Family HIPPOSIDERIDAE

## Trident and leaf-nosed bats

Members of this Family, which is represented in the Subregion by three genera and four species, occur in the Old World, in Africa, Asia, Australia and on islands in the Pacific Ocean, mainly within the tropics. At one time the Family was considered a Subfamily of the Rhinolophidae, but they differ in skeletal structure, in the form of the teeth, the feet and the noseleaves, which, while of the same general construction as those of the Rhinolophidae, show constant differences. Their noseleaves, for example, lack the single upstanding triangular process on the posterior part of the noseleaf characteristic of the rhinolophids (Fig. XI.1). In the genus *Triaenops* there are three upstanding processes, which give members of this genus their name "trident bats". Their large ears are well separated and are often as broad as they are long. They have a minute tragus and an antitragus, an upward fold of the ear on its outer margin, although it is not quite so large as in the rhinolophids. Their wings are similar to those of the rhinolophids but the fourth and fifth fingers are about the same length giving the wing a parallel-sided appearance. At rest the tip of the wing folds underneath. The vertebrae of the tail are enclosed within the interfemoral membrane which is supported on either side by calcanea arising from the ankles. In all members of this Family the toes are comprised of two joints only, in the Rhinolophidae they have three joints, except in the hallux.

There are many colour phases, especially in members of the genus *Hipposideros*, with ginger, deep chestnut-red, rich red-brown and orange phases being quite common; the individuals in these phases occur alongside those of the more general greyish-brown colour. Commerson's leaf-nosed bat, *H. commersoni*, is the largest member of the Family that occurs in the Subregion, with a forearm measuring up to 105 mm and wingspan of up to 600 mm and as such is among the largest of our insect-eating species.

Fig. XI.1 Head of a Hipposideridae: *Hipposideros commersoni*

The skull is very similar to that of the Rhinolophidae. In *H. commersoni* the sagittal crest is developed very well (Fig. 110.1).

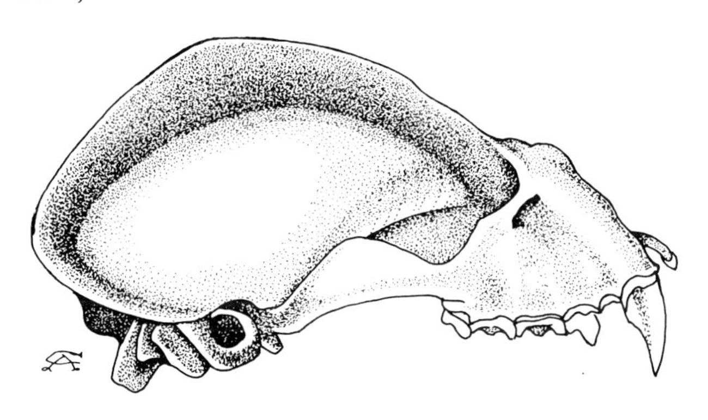

Fig. 110.1 Skull of *Hipposideros commersoni*

The dental formula is

$I\frac{1}{2}\ C\frac{1}{1}\ P\frac{2}{2}\ M\frac{3}{3} = 30$

The upper incisors are separated widely, the canines particularly well developed. The first upper premolar is tiny and is squeezed to the outside of the toothrow. The lower incisors are trifid, the lower anterior premolar well developed but only half the height of the posterior one.

Key to the genera after Hayman & Hill (1971)
(Measurements in mm)

1. Posterior leaflet on noseleaf simple in outline, elliptical or rounded, not tridentate; ears either separate or united by a low band; rostrum at least half as long as the braincase; small upper premolar present; forearm 40–110
... *Hipposideros*

Posterior leaflet of noseleaf tridentate; ears separate; small upper premolar present or absent; rostrum sometimes less than half as long as braincase; forearm 30–40
... 2

2. Size very small, forearm 31–35; ears very low, rounded, rim-like, length 8; noseleaf small and inconspicuous; thumbs minute, rostrum less than half length of braincase
... *Cloeotis*

Size larger, forearm 50–54; ears short, 10–14, pointed; noseleaf conspicuous; thumbs normal; rostrum more than half the length of the braincase; upper incisors bifid
... *Triaenops*

## Genus *Hipposideros* Gray, 1831

Key to the species after Meester *et al.* (1986)
(Measurements in mm)

1. Size larger, forearm 90–110; ears narrow and pointed; longitudinal frontal sac in both sexes
... *commersoni*

Size smaller, forearm 40–50; ears broader
... *caffer*

---

No. 110

## *Hipposideros commersoni* (E. Geoffroy, 1813)

## Commerson's leaf-nosed bat
## Commerson se bladneusvlermuis

Plate 5

---

**Colloquial Name**

Geoffroy's description was based on drawings and notes found among Commerson's papers, after whom Geoffroy named this species.

**Taxonomic Notes**

Hayman & Hill (1971) listed four subspecies, of which only one, *H. c. marungensis* (Noack, 1887), occurs in the Subregion and has a wide distribution from there north to East Africa and westwards to Zaire.

**Description**

Commerson's leaf-nosed bat is the largest of the insect-eating bats that occur in the Subregion. They are about 150 mm in total length with a tail of about 40 mm and a mass of between 117 and 130 g (Table 110.1). The largest specimens have wingspans of just under 600 mm. The upper parts are a pale fawn colour, lighter on the head and neck, which are cream-coloured. The hair is short and adpressed to the body and is sparse on the rump, thighs and flanks, the latter nearly naked. The under parts are light tawny, the hair on the flanks white. The wing membranes are pale brown, tending to be darker towards the tips of the wings, the interfemoral membrane translucent and lighter in shade than the wings. The lower part of the hind limbs including the feet are black. The ears are widely spaced on the head and rise to sharp points.

The skull is characterised by the great development of the sagittal crest that dominates the cranium, rising from it like a knife edge (Fig. 110.1). The upper canines are developed very well and are powerful and grooved on their anterior faces.

**Table 110.1**

Measurements (mm) and mass (g) of Commerson's leaf-nosed bats, *H. commersoni*, from Zimbabwe (Smithers & Wilson, 1979)

| | Males | | | Females | | |
|---|---|---|---|---|---|---|
| | $\bar{x}$ | n | Range | $\bar{x}$ | n | Range |
| TL | 149 | 8 | 140–167 | 133 | 6 | 130–136 |
| T | 41 | 8 | 31–45 | | | |
| Hf c/u | 25 | 8 | 23–28 | 23 | 6 | 23–24 |
| E | 30 | 8 | 27–32 | 28 | 6 | 26–31 |
| F/a | 101 | 5 | 93–105 | 95 | 6 | 93–102 |
| Mass | 2 only 116,5 and 114,7 | | | 2 only 132,0 and 120,0 | | |

**Distribution**

*Extralimital to the continent*

**Madagascar.**

*South of the Sahara, excluding the Southern African Subregion*

Recorded from **Senegal; Liberia; Gambia; Nigeria** predominantly in the Guinea Savanna Zone and eastwards to the highlands of **Ethiopia** and in **Somalia**. Southwards they have been taken in **Cameroun; Equatorial Guinea**; the **Congo Republic** and in northeastern and southeastern **Zaire**. They occur in **Uganda; Kenya** and in central and northeastern **Tanzania**, and on **Pemba** and **Zanzibar** islands. There remain areas in **Zambia** from which they have not been collected so far, but Ansell (1978) believed that they occur throughout. They are known from the southern Province of **Malawi** and from the northern parts of the Tete District in **Mozambique**, north of the Zambezi River, and while there are no records from the inland part of the northeast, there are coastal records from the Cabo Delgado District. There are a number of records from central **Angola**.

*Southern African Subregion*

They occur in northern **Namibia** south to about 21°S, in northern **Botswana** and in **Zimbabwe** except in the drier western and southern parts of the country. In **Mozambique**, south of the Zambezi River, they have been taken in a number of localities south to the northern parts of the Gaza and Inhambane districts and are known from the Pafuri area of the Kruger National Park, **Transvaal**.

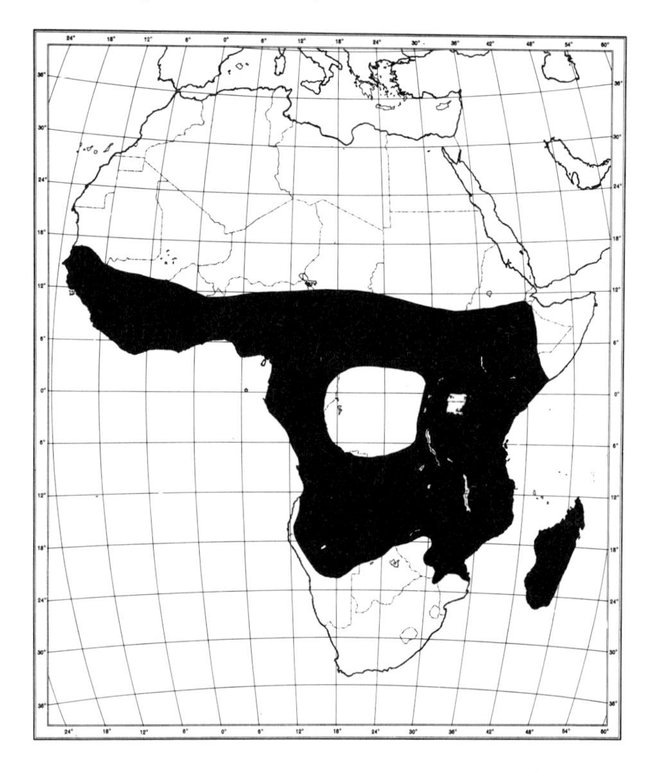

**Habitat**

Commerson's leaf-nosed bat is predominantly a savanna woodland species although in West Africa they occur in the High Forest Zone in Liberia (Kuhn, 1965) and in Cameroun and Equatorial Guinea (Rosevear, 1965).

**Habits**

They are a gregarious species, occurring locally in very large numbers. In Drotsky's Caves in northwestern Botswana a colony was estimated to consist of several hundred. They had used the caves for a very long period judging from the immense accumulation of their bones and skulls in the deep layer of guano on the floor. They roosted hanging from the ceilings of two large caverns 12 m high, some 270 m from the entrance in total darkness, each individual slightly separated from its neighbours. They are not always present in these caves for, while they were there during visits in January, April, May, July and September, they were absent during a June visit.

They are sensitive to the beams of light from torches and when some are disturbed in this manner a large part of the colony takes to the wing, flying around in the darkness with a roar of wings (Smithers, 1971). They share the use of these caves with Dent's horseshoe bats, *R. denti*, and Egyptian slit-faced bats, *Nycteris thebaica*, which occur in smaller numbers. They leave the caves just after sundown and apparently scatter to feed, as solitary individuals have been taken at night hanging in trees. At Nokaneng some 70 km east of the caves on the fringe of the Okavango Swamp an individual hung in a tree, flying off temporarily and then returning from time to time, apparently using this as a temporary resting site during nightly foraging. The colonies are noisy, individuals uttering piercing whistles as they jostle and flap with their wings to secure adequate spacing from their neighbours. Although they most frequently use caves for roosting in, in West Africa they have occasionally been taken from hollow trees (Rosevear, 1965).

**Food**

Insectivorous. Allen, Lang & Chapin (1917) stated that a specimen taken in northeastern Zaire had gorged itself with termite alates, the remains of which were stored in its capacious cheeks.

**Reproduction**

Males taken in April from Drotsky's Caves, Botswana, had enlarged testes and a fat layer several mm thick on the inner lining of the stomach and on the internal organs (Smithers, 1971). No other data are presently available from the Subregion.

---

No. 111

## *Hipposideros caffer* (Sundevall, 1846)

## Sundevall's leaf-nosed bat
## Sundevall se bladneusvlermuis

---

**Taxonomic Notes**

Meester *et al.* (1986) listed two subspecies from the Subregion. *H. c. caffer* occurs in the eastern and southern parts of the Subregion and *H. c. angolensis* (Seabra, 1898) in the western. They pointed out the close relationship with *H. ruber* which has been considered a synonym of *H. caffer*. *H. ruber* Noack, 1893 is larger and browner than *H. caffer* and its more colourful phase is rufous. *H. caffer* is smaller and greyer and in its colour phase orange. In addition Lawrence (1964) showed that there are characters in the skull by which the two may be distinguished. So far only *H. caffer* has been recorded from the Subregion.

**Description**

A small species, the total length is about 80 mm with a tail of about 30 mm and a mass of 7,6 g (Table 111.1). The colour of the upper parts is extremely variable, ranging from a dark greyish-brown to colour phases that in the extreme are a rich yellowish-golden; every intermediate shade being met. The fur on the upper parts is long and woolly, the individual hairs light-coloured at the base, tipped with greyish-brown or various shades between this and golden. In the rich yellowish-golden phase the entire length of the individual hairs are this colour. In specimens from Namibia some individuals look white overall, the tipping of the individual hairs being so meagre that the colour is imparted to the whole of the upper parts from the light-coloured bases to the hair. The under parts are similar in colour to the upper parts, but are usually slightly lighter in shade. Their ears are broadly rounded with pointed tips.

The position of the anterior upper premolars in relation to the line of the toothrow varies. In some they are clearly in the toothrow separating the canines from the anterior premolar, in others only just doing so. The lower incisors are trilobed, the anterior lower premolar about half the height of the posterior; there are only two premolars on each side of the upper and lower jaws.

Like members of the Family Rhinolophidae the females in the Hipposideridae have a pair of false nipples, the right hand one better developed than the left, situated in the anal region (Fig. 111.1). In the males the false nipples are vestigial.

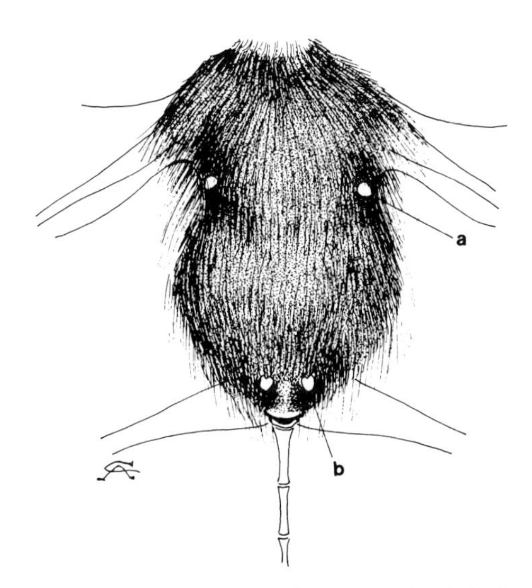


Fig. 111.1 *Hipposideros caffer*: (a) Functional nipples (b) False nipples

**Table 111.1**

Measurements (mm) and mass (g) of Sundevall's leaf-nosed bats, *H. caffer*, from Zimbabwe (Smithers & Wilson, 1979)

| | Males | | | Females | | |
|---|---|---|---|---|---|---|
| | x̄ | n | Range | x̄ | n | Range |
| TL | 83 | 19 | 78–89 | 86 | 14 | 83–92 |
| T | 33 | 20 | 27–35 | 34 | 14 | 31–37 |
| Hf c/u | 8 | 19 | 8–9 | 9 | 14 | 8–10 |
| E | 16 | 19 | 15–17 | 15 | 14 | 13–18 |
| F/a | 48 | 20 | 45–50 | 47 | 12 | 42–50 |
| Mass | 7,6 | 19 | 6,6–8,9 | 7,8 | 13 | 6,5–9,0 |

## Distribution

The species, as understood here, includes the subspecies *caffer, angolensis, tephrus* and *nanus*, which are inhabitants of savanna woodland, being replaced in forest by *H. ruber*. This is perhaps an oversimplification of a complex issue, for Aellen (1952) recorded *H. c. caffer* from forests in Cameroun. Rosevear (1965) commented that the issue is taxonomically controversial and the species is in need of revision.

*Extralimital to the continent*

Recorded from **Aden** and **Yemen** in the extreme southwestern parts of Arabia.

*North Africa*

Recorded on the littoral of **Morocco**.

*South of the Sahara, excluding the Southern African Subregion*

In West Africa they occur from **Senegal** to **Nigeria; Cameroun;** eastwards to parts of the **Sudan** and **Ethiopia** and southwards in **Uganda; Kenya; Tanzania**; northeastern, eastern and southeastern **Zaire; Angola; Zambia** and **Malawi**. They are recorded from the Tete District of **Mozambique**, north of the Zambezi River, but not from the northeastern sector, where little collecting has been carried out, their occurrence in adjacent parts of Malawi suggesting that in time they will be found to occur there.

*Southern African Subregion*

Recorded from the southwest and northern parts of **Namibia**, in the extreme northeastern parts of **Botswana** and, in the southeast, at Molepolole. Widespread in **Zimbabwe** except in the dry western areas. They occur in parts of the **Transvaal; Natal; Transkei,** and in the coastal areas of the **Cape Province**, with an isolated record from the extreme northwestern parts of the province, and another from Leelystaat on the Orange River (Erasmus & Rautenbach, 1984).

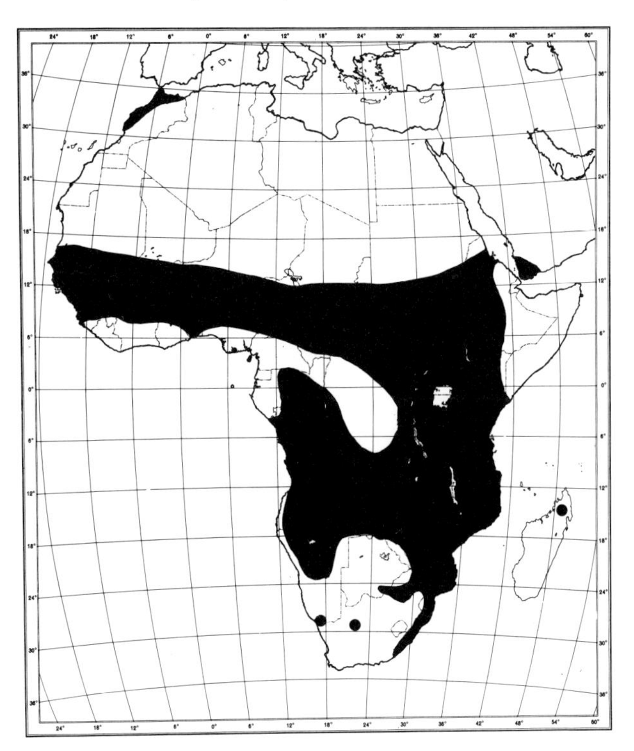

## Habitat

Generally associated with savanna woodland, their occurrence within this suggesting that the availability of surface water is an essential habitat requirement. The Cape Province records suggest that they may have a wider habitat tolerance than presently thought.

## Habits

Sundevall's leaf-nosed bat is predominantly a gregarious species occurring in colonies numbering in hundreds. Quite frequently they occur in much smaller colonies of up to a dozen, and twos and threes and even single individuals are found. They roost during the day in caves, mine adits, culverts under roads, in disused buildings, in wells, in the roofs of houses, in small rock cavities and fissures or in any substantial cover of this nature that offers seclusion from disturbance. They roost hanging from the ceilings of these shelters or from the rafters of houses and often enter houses at night while foraging. They can become a major pest in the roofs of occupied houses on account of the unpleasant smell of the guano. They roost hanging separated from one another in clusters.

While in flight they manoeuvre skilfully but fly relatively slowly and quite often are killed by vehicles at night on main roads. In dry country the frequency with which they are netted over dams and pools in rivers, sipping water in flight, suggests a dependence on this resource.

## Food

Insectivorous.

## Reproduction

Copulation and ovulation took place in April (early winter), development from fertilisation to implantation being normal, but embryonic development was retarded during winter, parturition only occurring in early December. Bernard & Meester (1982) found that in Natal the gestation period was about 100 days longer (about 220 days) than that recorded for the same species from the tropics. During gestation the period of embryonic diapause exceeded that of foetal development resulting in a long gestation period. Parturition was followed by a period of lactation and anoestrus of about 60 days. This is the first report of retarded embryonic development in the genus and only the third in the Chiroptera.

In Zimbabwe (Smithers & Wilson, 1979) and the Transvaal (Rautenbach, 1982) gravid females have been taken in September and October, and Rautenbach (1982) recorded lactating females in the Transvaal in January. This suggests that the young are born early in the warm, wet summer months from about October to December. The females all carried one foetus. In the early part of their lives the young attach themselves firmly to the females' nipples and cling to them as they forage. The pair of functional nipples in the females is situated on the chest and in addition they have a pair of false nipples situated closely together, one on each side, just in front of the anus (Fig. 111.1).

## Genus *Cloeotis* Thomas, 1901

No. 112

## *Cloeotis percivali* Thomas, 1901

## Short-eared trident bat
## Drietand-bladneusvlermuis

Plate 4

### Colloquial Name

So named from the three-pronged process at the top of the noseleaves and the noticeably short ears.

### Taxonomic Notes

Meester *et al.* (1986) listed two subspecies, only one of which, *C. p. australis* Roberts, 1917, occurs in the Subregion; the other, *C. p. percivali*, occurs in East Africa.

### Description

The smallest member of the Family Hipposideridae, the short-eared trident bat has a total length of about 70 mm, a short tail about 30 mm in length and a mean mass of about 4,0 g (Table 112.1).

Only this species and the Persian leaf-nosed bat, *Triaenops persicus*, possess the three-pronged, trident-like process on top of the noseleaves.

The colour of the upper parts is slate-grey, but some specimens from the Transvaal and in particular from Swaziland are buffy-brown. The hair is soft, silky and unicoloured and up to 9 mm long. The face is yellowish-white. The under parts are white tinged yellow, the individual hairs light slate-grey at their bases with yellowish-white tips, giving a general appearance of greyish under parts. The tiny ears are rounded, showing no sign of tips and lie close to the head, almost obscured by the long fur.

The anterior upper premolar lies in the toothrow separating the canines and the posterior premolar, but lies to the external side of the mid-line of the toothrow; the anterior of the two premolars in the lower jaw is about half the height of the posterior.

### Table 112.1

Measurements (mm) and mass (g) of short-eared trident bats, *C. percivali*, from Zimbabwe (Smithers & Wilson, 1979)

| | Males | | | Females | | |
|---|---|---|---|---|---|---|
| | $\bar{x}$ | n | Range | $\bar{x}$ | n | Range |
| TL | 69 | 8 | 64–76 | 67 | 11 | 63–74 |
| T | 29 | 8 | 27–30 | 29 | 11 | 26–33 |
| Hf c/u | 6 | 9 | 6–7 | 6 | 10 | 6–7 |
| E | 10 | 9 | 9–11 | 10 | 10 | 9–11 |
| F/a | 35 | 8 | 34–39 | 35 | 10 | 34–38 |
| Mass | 4,2 | 8 | 3,5–4,8 | 3,9 | 10 | 3,4–4,3 |

### Distribution

Too few records of this species are available to assess the limits of its distribution properly. Originally the species was described in 1901 from a specimen from Takaunga just north of Mombasa in coastal Kenya where it was taken from a coral cave; Kingdon (1974) reported that since then only one specimen has been taken in the area. Roberts (1951) reported that in a cave near Pretoria, Transvaal, where he originally had found them to occur in large numbers, they were not found on a subsequent visit.

*South of the Sahara, excluding the Southern African Subregion*

In East Africa they are only known from coastal **Kenya**. Not recorded from Tanzania. Recorded from southeastern **Zaire** and although at present known only from two localities in **Zambia**, Ansell (1978) believed that they might be more widespread in the eastern parts of the country. In **Mozambique**, north of the Zambezi River, they are only known from Missale Mine in the northeastern Tete District.

*Southern African Subregion*

In **Zimbabwe** they are known from six localities from the Kariba Dam in the north to Mutare in the east and westwards to Gwanda. In the **Transvaal** they are recorded from three localities in the Pretoria, Rustenburg sector and at Komatipoort in the east; from **Swaziland** and **Botswana** in the Kanye and Molopolole areas in the southeast.

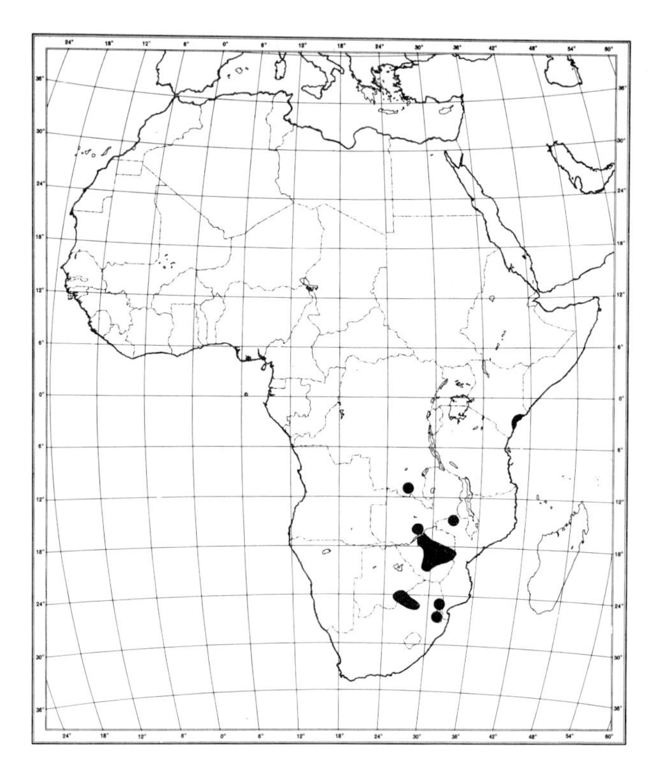

### Habitat

There are insufficient data available at the moment to assess their habitat requirements. The presence of substantial shelter in the form of caves or mine adits appears to be an essential habitat requirement.

### Habits

Short-eared trident bats are gregarious, occurring in colonies numbering hundreds. They roost during the day in caves and mine adits, hanging from the roof in tight clusters, far back into these shelters in total darkness. In Zimbabwe a very small colony of about 12 lived in an underground irrigation tunnel.

### Food

Insectivorous.

### Reproduction

In Zimbabwe gravid females each with a single foetus were taken in October, which suggests that the young are born during the warm, wet summer months from about October to December.

## Genus *Triaenops* Dobson, 1871

No. 113

## *Triaenops persicus* Dobson, 1871

## Persian leaf-nosed bat
## Persiese bladneusvlermuis

### Colloquial Name

Originally the species was described from a specimen from Shipaz, Persia (Iran) but subsequently has been found to occur in Arabia and on the continent of Africa. It is appropriately called the Persian trident bat because, like the short-eared trident bat, *Cloeotis percivali*, it has a three-pronged trident at the top of the noseleaves.

### Taxonomic Notes

Hayman & Hill (1971) listed two subspecies from the continent, *T. p. majusculus* Aellen & Brosset, 1968 from the Congo Republic and *T. p. afer* from the eastern part of the continent south to within the limits of the Subregion.

### Description

The Persian leaf-nosed bat is about 140 mm in total length with a tail of about 40 mm long. The upper parts are yellowish-brown tinged with orange, the sides of the face yellow, the under parts lighter in colour than the upper parts, a shade browner on the throat. The hair is soft and silky, the bases of the individual hairs yellowish-brown, slightly browner towards the tips. The wing and interfemoral membranes are dark brown. The ears, which are characteristic in shape, are a translucent light brown. This bat is much larger in size than the short-eared trident bat, *Cloeotis percivali*, which is the only other species in the Subregion that possesses the three-pronged, trident-like, processes at the top of the noseleaves.

The anterior upper premolar lies in the toothrow separating the canines and the posterior premolar, but lies to the external side of the mid-line of the toothrow; the anterior of the two premolars in the lower jaw is about half the height of the posterior.

### Distribution

*Extralimital to the continent*

Occurs in **Iran**, on the coast of the Persian gulf and in **Arabia** at an oasis in Oman in the east and Aden in the southwest, eastwards to **Pakistan**, and on **Madagascar**.

*South of the Sahara, excluding the Southern African Subregion*

Recorded from **Uganda** and a number of localities in **Ethiopia**, west in the valley of the Blue Nile to near the Sudan border; in western, northern and central **Somalia**; **Ethiopia; Congo Republic**; coastal **Kenya** and in two areas in the southeast of the country and coastal **Tanzania**. There are no records at the moment from the northeastern parts of **Mozambique**, but they occur in the Tete District, north of the Zambezi River.

*Southern African Subregion*

Recorded from the Mutare District in eastern **Zimbabwe** and in **Mozambique**, south of the Zambezi River, in the Tete and Inhambane districts.

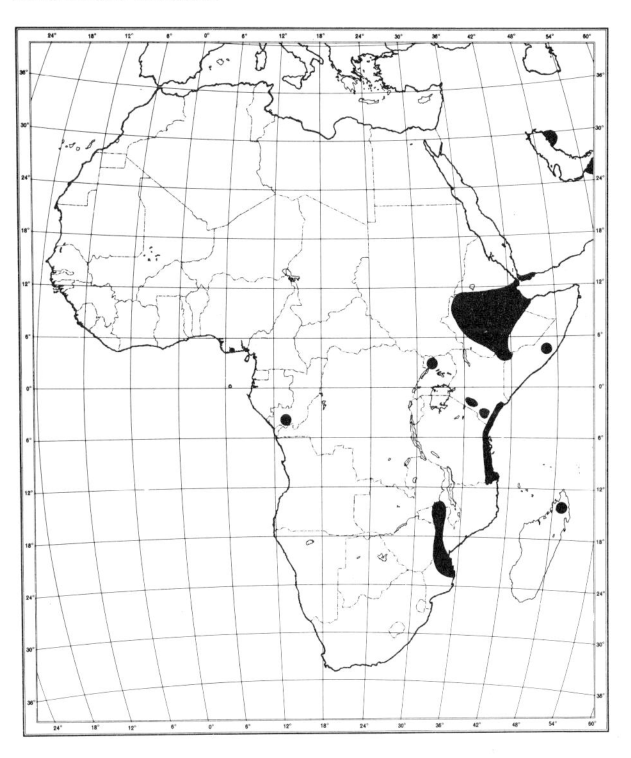

### Habitat

There are insufficient data available at the moment to assess their habitat requirements, but these include the availability of substantial shelter in the form of caves or mine adits. Hayman & Hill (1971) believed that they rarely occur inland, but since then they have been taken far inland including in Zimbabwe (Smithers & Wilson, 1979). In a coastal cave in the Inhambane District, Mozambique they occurred in hundreds, but only a single specimen was taken in a cave near Mutare, Zimbabwe.

### Habits

Persian leaf-nosed bats are gregarious. Where they occur in large numbers they hang from the ceiling of the caves in large clusters, slightly separated from one another.

### Food

Insectivorous.

### Reproduction

No information available from the Subregion.

# Order PRIMATES

## Bushbabies, baboons and monkeys

The higher classification adopted here follows that used by Meester *et al.* (1986) and is loosely based on that of Szalay & Delson (1979) who placed the living members of this Order in the Suborders Strepsirhini and Haplorhini. This is a departure from Simpson (1945) who divided the Order into the Suborders Prosimii and Anthropoidea, which in the past have been used widely.

Key to the Suborders after Meester *et al.* (1986)

1. Postorbital bar not forming a bony plate between the orbit and the temporal fossa
   ... *Strepsirhini*

   Postorbital bar separates the orbit from the temporal fossa
   ... *Haplorhini*

The fascinating story of the search for and study of the fossil material which is the evidence of Primate evolution and which leads up to the emergence of man, *Homo sapiens*, as we know him today, has exercised the attention of palaeontologists for over 150 years, and is beyond the scope of this book. The story opened 65 million years ago (Szalay & Delson, 1979) at which time there lived in what is now western North America a small primitive Primate named *Purgatorius unio* Van Valen & Sloan, 1965. Abundant fossil remains of this species were recovered from the late Cretaceous to early Palaeocene deposits which showed that they were about the size of small rats. Here the controversies start, for other authors (Cartmill, 1972; Martin, 1972) advocated the exclusion of the arboreal Plesiadapiformes, the Suborder to which *Purgatorius unio* belongs, from the Primates.

As far as the Hominidae are concerned, the recognition by Dart (1925a,b) of a skull from the Buxton limeworks near Taung in the northern Cape Province as a primitive hominid which he named *Australopithecus africanus*, stimulated a search for and study of hominid material and placed scientists from the Republic of South Africa and this country as a source of fossil remains of the Hominidae in the forefront of this important field. It also raised controversies which continue to be the subject of debate. The origin of *Homo sapiens sapiens* remains uncertain. The earliest more definite allocations are fossils from sub-Saharan Africa, a region not usually considered a source for this taxon (Szalay & Delson, 1979).

# Suborder STREPSIRHINI

## XII. Family LORISIDAE

### Bushbabies

### Subfamily GALAGINAE

Meester *et al.* (1986) listed three species from the Subregion: *Otolemur crassicaudatus* (E. Geoffroy, 1812); *Galago moholi* A. Smith, 1836 and *Galagoides zanzibaricus* (Matschie, 1893).

Galagos are dwarf to medium-sized nocturnal species which are active leapers in their arboreal habitat and use a quadrupedal or bipedal posture when moving on the ground. The three species are semi-social in habits, and familiar individuals sleep together during the day in groups. They maintain a dispersed social network by means of chemical and vocal communication signals. Bearder & Doyle (1974) recorded that males and maturing offspring would sleep alone often, while females and youngsters slept together. They found that, in the thick-tailed bushbaby, the size, shape and number of home ranges changed during the year, the young males, as they matured, tending to separate from their parents and they are tolerated by breeding males until they establish control areas.

The index finger on the hand is separated more widely from the other fingers than these are from each other; the first digit is opposable to the other digits, an adaptation to grasping branches. They have huge eyes, with eyeballs that are almost incapable of movement within the sockets. To compensate for this the head can be turned through 180°, allowing them to look directly backwards over the spine. Galagos have limited powers of facial expression, being unable to grimace or wrinkle their brows. They drink by lapping, not by dipping their hands and licking as do some lemurs. The females usually have two pairs of mammae, a pair inguinal and a pair pectoral.

The dental formula is

$I\frac{2}{2}\ C\frac{1}{1}\ P\frac{3}{3}\ M\frac{3}{3} = 36$

Key to the genera after Meester *et al.* (1986)

1. Larger, head and body length more than 230 mm; hind foot length more than 80 mm; greatest skull length more than 55 mm; body weight more than 500 g; pronounced postorbital constriction; foramen magnum directed backwards; muzzle long and robust
   ... *Otolemur*

   Smaller, head and body length less than 230 mm; hind foot length less than 80 mm; greatest skull length less than 55 mm; postorbital constriction slight; foramen magnum directed downwards; muzzle either short or elongated and pointed
   ... 2

2. Dorsal colour predominantly grey, sometimes with a slight yellowish wash; tail dark towards the tip or similar in colour to dorsal colour; muzzle shorter, upper toothrow length 13,3–14,4 mm; width of toothrow across outer surface of $M^3$ 12,5–13,0 mm; preorbital length of face 73 percent or less of transverse diameter of orbit
   ... *Galago*

Dorsal colour drab brown or yellowish-brown; tail black or blackish-brown for terminal two-fifths of its length; muzzle longer, upper toothrow length 14,5–16,1 mm; width of toothrow across outer surface of $M^3$ 13,2–13,9 mm; preorbital length of face 81 percent or more of transverse diameter of orbit

... *Galagoides*

## Genus *Otolemur* Coquerel, 1859

No. 114

## *Otolemur crassicaudatus* E. Geoffroy, 1812

## Thick-tailed bushbaby
## Bosnagaap

Plate 6

### Colloquial Name

Although the colloquial names bushbaby for this species and night ape for the smaller species are commonly used in the Subregion, two of the three species have acquired internationally accepted names in English, which it seems preferable to adopt. These are the thick-tailed bushbaby (or galago), *O. crassicaudatus*, and the South African lesser bushbaby, *G. moholi*. *O. crassicaudatus* has also been referred to as the greater galago. To distinguish the third species, *Galagoides zanzibaricus granti*, Grants' bushbaby seems appropriate, being named after the original collector, Capt. C.H.B. Grant. The name Zanzibar bushbaby is also used.

### Taxonomic Notes

Meester *et al.* (1986) listed two subspecies from the Subregion: *O. c. crassicaudatus* from the eastern Transvaal and adjacent parts of Mozambique southwards to eastern Natal as far as Port Shepstone; and *O. c. monteiri* (Gray, 1863), which intergrades with *O. c. crassicaudatus* in central Mozambique, and occurs in Zimbabwe, Malawi and ranges into Zambia, Angola, the western lake sectors of Tanzania, Zaire, Rwanda and Burundi. See Masters & Dunn (1988), Masters & Lubinsky (1988), Masters (1986, 1988) and Masters, Stanyon & Romagno (1987) for a review of speciation in the greater galagines. See also Nash *et al.* (1989) for a full listing of bushbaby species.

### Description

The thick-tailed bushbaby is the largest of the three species of galago that occur in the Subregion. There is a distinct size dimorphism between the sexes (Masters, 1988). Adult males have a total length of about 0,75 m, with tails longer than the length of the head and body and masses of about 1,25 kg. The females are slightly smaller and lighter (Table 114.1).

Their heads are small for the size of their bodies and are rounded, with huge eyes and extremely large, labile, sensitive ears. The rhinarium, which encloses the nostrils, extends downward narrowly to meet the median point of the upper lip forming a philtrum which divides the upper lip, a character common to all the Strepsirhini.

They are extremely variable in colour, but shades of grey predominate, tinged with buff or brown. Northern Transvaal animals tend to be very dark grey—hence the term "shadowy galagos". In the eastern Transvaal and Zululand, the animals have a predominantly brown coloration. In Zambia and Zimbabwe, the palest pelages are found (Masters, pers. comm.). The upper parts may be pencilled with black where the black tips of the guard hairs happen to lie in juxtaposition. The tail is usually a lighter and buffier colour than the upper parts and may or may not be suffused with black or brown towards the tip. The under parts are lighter in colour than the upper parts, the hair grey at the base, and broadly white or white-tinged-buffy towards the tip. The front limbs are similar in colour to the upper parts or tinged with buff or rufous-buff, and are lighter in colour below. The head is the same colour as the upper parts, but darker around the eyes and lighter on top of the muzzle. Depending on the subspecies involved the upper surfaces of the hands and feet are the same colour as the body or darker.

The fur is long, fine and soft. The individual hairs of the guard coat on the mid-back are dark grey at the base, with an annulation of buffy-grey or brown towards their black tips. They are about 25 mm long and up to 40 mm long on the rump. Profusely scattered through the guard coat on the shoulders and mid-back there are longer, broadly black-tipped hairs. The hair on the fluffy tail is about 30 mm long. The broad, rounded ears are naked inside, and on the outside, towards their tips, are dark greyish in colour.

There are five digits on the hands and feet. On the hands the first digit is opposable and can be bent across the palm; the second digit is separated widely from the first and the third digits. The remaining digits, three to five, are long and thin, the fourth being the longest of all. They have soft swollen pads at the tips and at the bases of each of these digits and on the palms of the hands. Each digit is equipped with a nail, the end of which is concave, unlike that of the sister species, *Otolemur garnettii*, in which it is convex (Hayman, 1937). The feet are similar to the hands, except that they are larger and more robustly built and the second digit is equipped with a claw instead of a nail, a feature of all strepsirhines. This claw which is broadly pointed and sharp-edged, may reach a length of 7 mm across the curve, and is used for scratching. On both the hands and feet the thumb and big toe respectively are broad and more robustly built than the remainder of the digits and are adapted for grasping branches.

The eye orbits in the skull are very large and are directed forwards. The braincase is broadest at the back and narrows forward to the post-orbital constriction.

In the upper jaw there are two incisor teeth on each side and a well developed canine tooth, which is exceptionally heavily built and sharply pointed. The incisor teeth in the lower jaw are long and thin and lie in a forwardly directed plane. Their function is the grooming of the long fur. The canine-like teeth in the lower jaw are the enlarged first premolar teeth which have taken on this function, and the canines have become incisor-like and lie in the incisor row (Fig. 114.1). This tooth comb is also a feature of all Strepsirhini (Cuvier & St. Hilaire, 1825).

**Table 114.1**

Measurements (mm) and mass (kg) of adult thick-tailed bushbabies, *O. crassicaudatus*, from Zimbabwe (Smithers & Wilson, 1979)

| | Males | | | Females | | |
|---|---|---|---|---|---|---|
| | $\bar{x}$ | n | Range | $\bar{x}$ | n | Range |
| TL | 739 | 23 | 685–798 | 727 | 12 | 685–780 |
| T | 416 | 23 | 360–450 | 407 | 12 | 355–450 |
| Hf c/u | 96 | 23 | 90–101 | 91 | 13 | 84–100 |
| E | 60 | 23 | 54–65 | 59 | 13 | 53–65 |
| Mass | 1,22 | 24 | 0,94–1,64 | 1,13 | 13 | 0,99–1,46 |

### Distribution

The thick-tailed bushbaby has a wide distribution in Africa from East Africa south to Natal and westwards to parts of coastal Angola. They only occur, however, within the limits shown on the map where there is suitable habitat.

*South of the Sahara, excluding the Southern African Subregion*

They occur in southeastern **Zaire** and westwards through central **Angola** to the coast. In **Zambia** they occur widely, except in the southwest and in the montane areas in the northeast. They are widespread in **Tanzania, Malawi** and in **Mozambique**, north of the Zambezi River.

*Southern African Subregion*

In **Botswana** they have been observed in the Limpopo riverine bush in the northeastern Tuli Block and must certainly occur eastwards along the Limpopo.

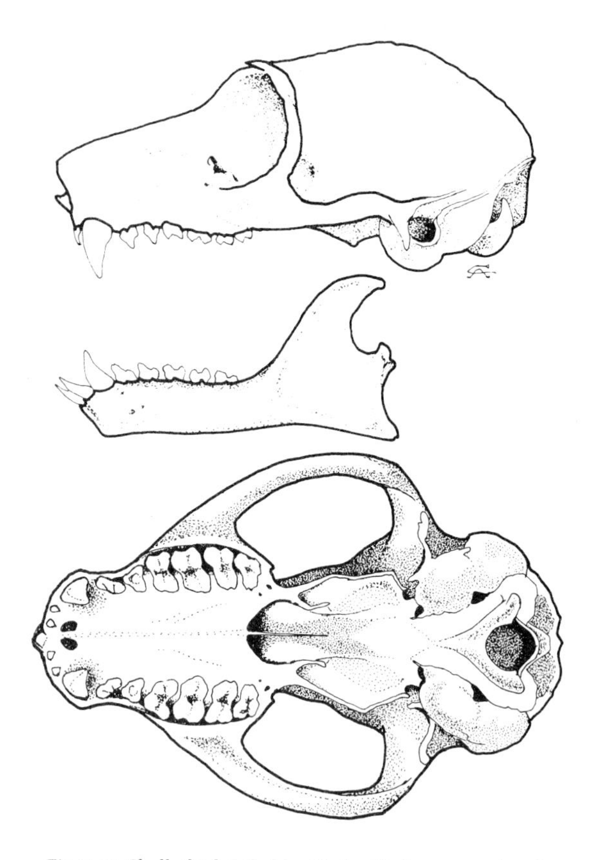

Fig.114.1 Skull: thick-tailed bushbaby, *Otolemur crassicaudatus* TL Skull 73 mm.

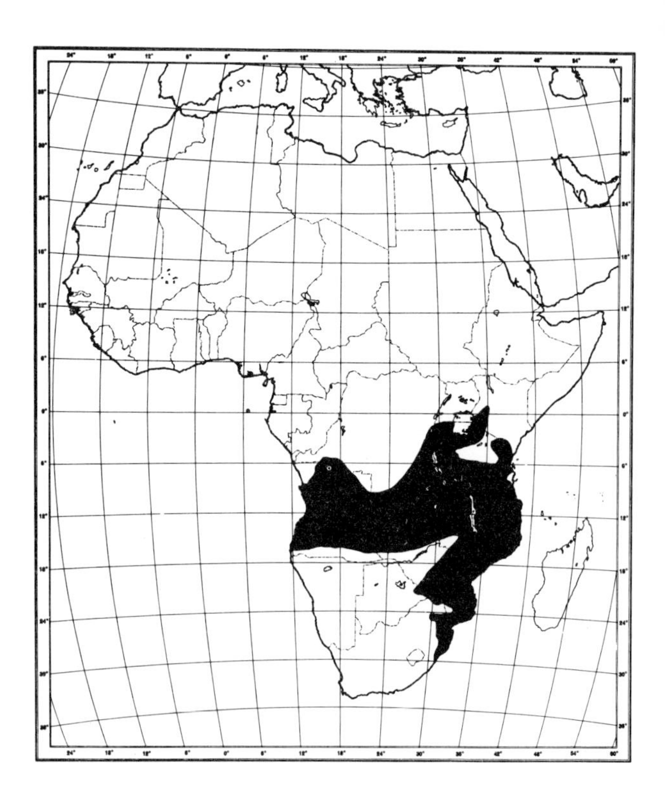

In **Zimbabwe** they occur in the eastern parts of the country and westwards, south of the plateau, to the Matopo Hills and to the Umguza Valley northwest of Bulawayo, but do not occur otherwise in the dry western areas, except as mentioned above. They are widespread in **Mozambique**, south of the Zambezi River, except in the more arid parts of the southwest, in the vicinity of the Banhine Flats.

In the **Transvaal** they are confined to the eastern parts of the province, but penetrate westward in riverine and montane forest to Louis Trichardt and Potgietersrus. They occur in the eastern parts of **Swaziland**, have adapted to wattle forests in western Swaziland, and are found around Mbabane. They occur southwards through eastern **Natal** to Port Shepstone, which marks their most southerly limits in the Subregion.

### Habitat

Thick-tailed bushbabies are associated with forests, thickets and well developed woodland in the eastern, higher rainfall parts of the Subregion. However, they do penetrate far into otherwise dry terrain in avenues of riverine forest or woodland, as they do in the western parts of Zimbabwe and in the Transvaal. In Zimbabwe they occur in *Brachystegia* woodland adjacent to river valleys and have adapted themselves to the use of *Eucalyptus* spp and *Pinus* spp plantations in which to rest. They are not uncommon in urban and peri-urban gardens where there is sufficient tree growth to afford them shelter and where there are orchards of tropical and semi-tropical fruits to provide food. They occur in these types of habitat from sea level in Mozambique and Natal to over 1 800 m in eastern Zimbabwe.

### Habits

Thick-tailed bushbabies are nocturnal, moving from their daylight resting places at about sunset and remaining sporadically active throughout the night. They appear to have active periods followed by long periods of relative inactivity and to be most active between about sunset and midnight, and least active around midnight. Their first action on emerging from the resting places at night is to groom themselves, using the tooth comb, long thin tongue and the long, sharp, broadly pointed claws on the second toes of the hind feet.

They form relatively stable groups throughout the year, sleeping alone or in groups of two to six during the day and generally dispersing solitarily or in small groups at night to forage (Bearder & Doyle, 1974). These groups may consist of an adult male and female and her offspring, or females with infants and males with older offspring. Females and their offspring remain together most of the time but the male may sleep with his group or sometimes in an adjacent resting place. Resting places are located usually up to about 12 m above the ground among the thick foliage of trees, particularly where this foliage is thickened up by the presence of creepers. Groups may have up to 12 resting places within their home ranges.

Bearder & Doyle (1974) found that the home range of a female group was about 7 ha, the home ranges of adjacent groups overlapping to a small extent. The males had home ranges overlapping those of one to several female groups. The movements of the thick-tailed bushbaby within the home range followed established pathways, but they would carry out extensive explorations of the home range in the search for fruit-bearing trees. The size and shape of home ranges change gradually through the year. As the young males mature their home ranges become increasingly separate from those of their parents. Pair bonds are established with females, which also show territorial behaviour, the larger and stronger males eventually establishing their home ranges over those of one or several females (Bearder & Doyle, 1974; Bearder, 1987).

They walk or run along branches, with short jumps where necessary. Longer jumps were made usually in a downward direction. On the ground they move quadrupedally, with the hindquarters and tail held high, galloping with both fore and hindquarters making contact with the ground, or will hop bipedally (Charles-Dominique & Bearder, 1979).

Olfactory communication in the thick-tailed bushbaby, in common with most other lorisids, includes urine-washing. In this action, which is a relatively leisurely one, the hand and foot on one side are raised, almost or quite simultaneously, and passed under the genital region where the hand is urinated upon. The foot is grasped one or more times with the hand during the process. The action is then usually repeated on the other side. The feet may be rubbed on the substrate following urine-washing, an action also observed after ordinary micturition. Urine-washing is common in galagos, while the individual gazes at a strange distant object. Under these circumstances it may be accompanied by lateral swaying of head and body. It occurs in *O. crassicaudatus* under any circumstances when they feel less secure, or excited. They also exhibit rhythmic micturition, the anogenital region repeatedly touched on the substrate as they move in exploration of a strange area (Andrew & Klopman, 1974).

Both sexes have chest glands, which can be seen as a longitudinal patch in the middle of the chest, and which are larger and more conspicuous in the males than in the females. They will rub these glands on branches and mark conspecifics by chest-rubbing. Tandy (1976) found that the closely related Garnett's bushbaby engaged in a number of scent-marking displays which involved rubbing parts of the body against the substrate. Chest-rubbing was one of the most important of these. Katsir & Crewe (1980) found that the secretion of the chest gland of *Otolemur crassicaudatus* contained three major volatile components, each with a different rate of evaporation. Applied to the arboreal routes frequented by the galagos, these supply time cues to recipients. All three components applied together induced pronounced sniffing behaviour which may be important to the recipient in passing on further information such as that of the identity of the marker. Applied singly the components failed to elicit a sniffing response.

Although normally silent, thick-tailed bushbabies can be very noisy, vocalising with a very loud, harsh wailing which can be heard over considerable distances. The call may be answered by others from a distance when it is thus possible to mark the presence of several individuals in the neighbourhood. Kingdon (1971) believed calling to be connected with territorial behaviour. When two individuals are near each other they will chatter and when alarmed emit a variety of shrill calls, often for long periods. The young chitter when in the nest or when handled.

### Food

Thick-tailed bushbabies live on 50% fruit and vegetable matter and 50% insects and other invertebrates (Masters, Lumsden & Young, 1988), and occasionally reptiles and birds (Hladik, 1979). Gum exuded from *Acacia* trees is only important in the less tropical parts of their distribution, where softer fruits are less available (Masters, pers. comm.).

### Reproduction

Thick-tailed bushbabies are seasonal breeders, the bulk of conceptions in the northern Transvaal taking place about June/July, with births about November (Bearder 1975a). In eastern Zimbabwe (Smithers & Wilson, 1979) and Zambia (Ansell, 1960a) the young are born in August/September. In the wild the females conceive only once during the year, although there are records from zoological gardens of bimodal breeding (Eaglen & Simons, 1980; van Horn & Eaton, 1979). In some cases in captivity they have been known to breed throughout the year (Buettner-Janusch, 1964).

The gestation period is 132,8 days (S.D. 2,6 days) (Bearder, 1975a). Of 20 pregnancies in captivity, six (30%) were singletons and 14 (70%) resulted in multiple births, two of which were triplets and 12 twins (Masters, 1988). The young are born in nests which, at other times, are used as resting places. Just before the litter is born the female relines the nest with fresh green leaves and twigs. At birth the young are covered with a coating of fur of a uniform greyish colour. Their eyes are open and they can crawl around within 30 minutes of birth. During the early part of their lives the mother may carry the young in her mouth, holding them by a fold of skin on their flanks or by their backs. If they stray too far from the nest she will carry them back to it in this manner. From about eight days old they also cling to their mother's back. At the age of about three days the young vocalise by squeaking and at nine days emit clicks and crackles. Bearder (1975a) found that in the wild the young travel with the mother from about 25 days old, either following her or being carried. Suckling and carrying cease after about 10 weeks and the young move independently after 17 weeks.

---

No. 115

## *Galago moholi* A. Smith, 1836

## South African lesser bushbaby
## Nagapie

Plate 6

---

### Colloquial Name

There has never been complete consensus in the use of a colloquial name for this species, as night ape, lesser galago and bushbaby have all been used. Internationally it has acquired the name lesser bushbaby, and it seems appropriate to use South African lesser bushbaby to distinguish it from the Senegal lesser bushbaby. The generic name *Galago* was the name applied to the species by the African people of Senegal and was adopted by E. Geoffroy who originally described the species from this country, by using the name "Galago du Senegal".

### Taxonomic Notes

In the first edition *G. moholi* was considered to be a subspecies of *G. senegalensis*. Subsequently it has been shown (Nash *et al.*, 1989) that the two species are sympatric in northeastern Tanzania. In addition, Zimmermann, Bearder, Doyle & Andersson (1988) provided strong support on the basis of differences in vocalisation for the separation of the two forms into distinct species. Two subspecies of *G. moholi* are listed from the Subregion by Meester *et al.* (1986): *G. m. moholi* in the eastern part of the species' range and *G. m. bradfieldi* Roberts, 1931 from northern Namibia, extending into Angola, eastwards in Botswana to the Makgadikgadi Pan, and occurring in western Zambia.

### Description

Lesser bushbabies rank among our most attractive small mammals, with their soft furry bodies, long tails, huge eyes and extremely mobile, membranous ears.

Adult males measure about 370 mm overall, with tails that are well over half this length, and masses of about 150 g. The females are slightly smaller than the males (Table 115.1). There are no particular features that serve to differentiate between the two sexes in the field.

They have small, rounded heads with short muzzles, very large round eyes with vertical pupils and large, naked, membranous ears which can be folded back against the sides of their heads. They have a thick pelage of soft, light grey or grey-brown fur on the upper parts of the body. The hair of the upper parts is about 12 to 15 mm long and is slate-grey at the base and greyish-buffy or brownish towards the tips. Their tails are usually the same colour as the upper parts of the body, often darker towards the tip where they are slate-grey or tinged with brown. The under parts are lighter in colour than the upper parts, the hair being slate-grey at the base and white towards the tips, often yellower on the inside of the limbs and on the chest. Their heads are greyer than the upper parts of the body, with diffused black markings around the eyes. Their foreheads are diffused with white which continues as a narrow white stripe down the centre of the muzzle to the rhinarium.

There are patches of long vibrissae just above the inside edges of the eyes and a few on the lower edges which no doubt serve to alert them to the proximity of objects that might damage their eyes during their nightly movements.

They have five digits on each of the feet, with soft, enlarged pads under the tips of each digit. The thumbs and big toes are opposable and are built more heavily than the remainder of the digits. Except on the second digit of the hind foot, which is armed with a curved grooming claw, each digit has a small nail with a convex edge; the fourth digit on each foot is the longest. At the base of each long, slender digit there is a soft pad and the whole palm of the forefoot and sole of the hind foot are similarly padded. The main function of the opposable thumb, which is set far back from the first digit, is to capture insect prey and to grip the branches on which they move. The whole structure of the hands and feet is adapted to these related functions.

The rhinarium, which encloses the crescent-shaped nostrils, extends downwards as a narrow groove, the philtrum, which divides the upper lip.

Unlike the braincase of the thick-tailed bushbaby, *O. crassicaudatus*, which is broadest at the back, the braincase of the lesser bushbaby is broadest towards the front, at the level of the insertion of the zygomatic arches. The postorbital constriction is nearly as broad as the broadest part of the braincase. The rostrum is short and the forwardly directed eye orbits are very large, their diameter about 35% of the total length of the skull.

The dental formula is:

$$I\frac{2}{2}\ C\frac{1}{1}\ P\frac{3}{3}\ M\frac{3}{3} = 36$$

As in other strepsirhines, the canines in the lower jaw form a procumbent grooming and scraping mechanism, comprised of the two incisor teeth on either side flanked by the incisiform canines. All these teeth are thin and elongated. The first premolar is developed into a canine-like tooth. In the upper jaw the canine tooth is slightly curved and very sharp, and occludes against the canine-like first premolar in the lower jaw.

The two incisors on either side of the upper jaw, which are separated by a space in the middle, are thin and small and it has been suggested that they are functionless. Lowther (1940) did not agree with this, and pointed out that when she was bitten by her captive lesser bushbabies, the upper incisors invariably left clear imprints of tooth marks. They may have a function, therefore, at least in defence.

The posterior parts of the ear bullae are so well developed that they can be seen, when viewed from above the skull, jutting out on either side of the back of the skull (Fig. 115.1).

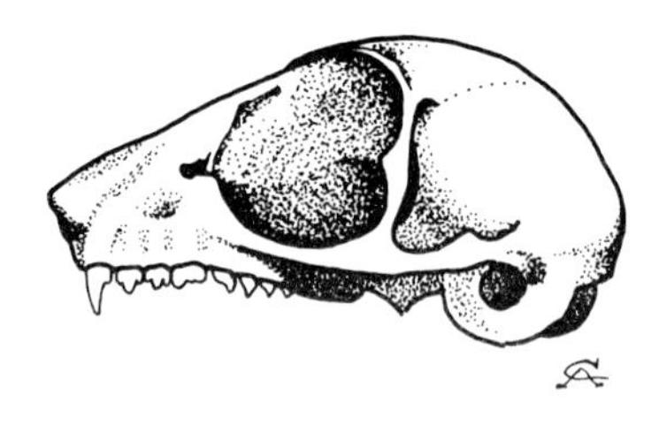

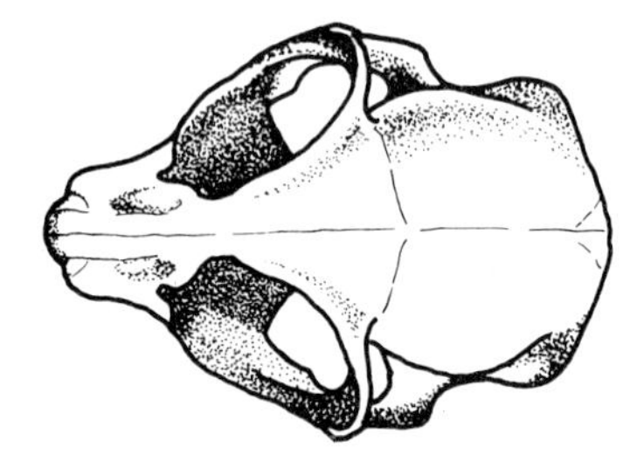

Fig.115.1. Skull: lesser bushbaby, G. *moholi*
TL Skull 39 mm

**Table 115.1**

Measurements (mm) and mass (g) of adult lesser bushbabies, *G. moholi*, from Botswana (Smithers, 1971) and the Transvaal (Rautenbach, 1978)

**Botswana**

| | Males | | | Females | | |
|---|---|---|---|---|---|---|
| | x̄ | n | Range | x̄ | n | Range |
| TL | 370 | 48 | 304–409 | 363 | 42 | 326–395 |
| T | 227 | 45 | 206–258 | 223 | 37 | 200–245 |
| Hf s/u | 57 | 48 | 51–62 | 56 | 43 | 51–62 |
| E | 38 | 44 | 32–41 | 35 | 41 | 31–41 |
| Mass | 155,5 | 33 | 124,8–189,6 | 150,7 | 30 | 132,1–176,7 |

**Transvaal**

| | Males | | | Females | | |
|---|---|---|---|---|---|---|
| | x̄ | n | Range | x̄ | n | Range |
| TL | 381 | 51 | 330–420 | 375 | 8 | 350–400 |
| T | 221 | 51 | 186–246 | 226 | 8 | 190–227 |
| Hf s/u | 59 | 51 | 50–66 | 58 | 7 | 50–63 |
| E | 38 | 51 | 30–46 | 37 | 8 | 35–39 |
| Mass | 177,0 | 26 | 145,0–212,0 | 155,0 | 4 | 126,0–176,0 |

## Distribution

Although they have a wide distribution in savanna woodland throughout most of southern Africa, within the range shown on the map they are absent locally from open grassland areas and forest, and are uncommon in some associations such as *Baikiaea* woodland. They penetrate deep into arid open country up avenues of riverine woodland. In the Kalahari, in Botswana, they are found deep into scrub associations in *Acacia* woodland fringing dry, fossil water courses.

*South of the Sahara, excluding the Southern African Subregion*

They occur in parts of **Zaire**; western and southern **Tanzania; Zambia** and westwards in the central and southern parts of **Angola**, excluding the coastal desert. They occur in **Malawi** and in **Mozambique**, north of the Zambezi River. From Tanzania to the north they are replaced by *G. senegalensis*.

*Southern African Subregion*

In northern **Namibia** they occur as far south as about the Waterberg and in the Grootfontein and northeastern parts of the country. In **Botswana** they are confined to the northern and eastern sectors, but penetrate deep into the semi-desert areas in the riverine *Acacia* woodland of dry watercourses. They occur widely in **Zimbabwe** and in **Mozambique**, south of the Zambezi River. In the **Transvaal** they occur in the west, north and east.

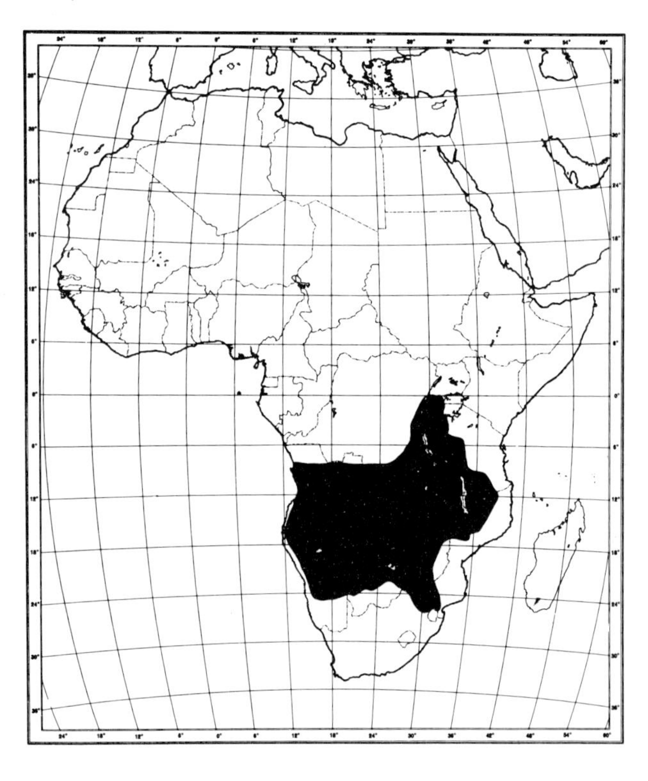

## Habitat

The South African lesser bushbaby is a savanna woodland species, particularly associated with *Acacia* woodland, and is less common in *Baikiaea* and *Brachystegia* associations. In the more arid parts of their range they are confined almost entirely to *Acacia* woodland, especially where this association fringes seasonally dry water courses. They also occur in mopane, *Colophospermum mopane*, and in various mixed-types of vegetational associations such as *Burkea*

—*Terminalia*; *Terminalia*—*Acacia*; and *Terminalia* —*Combretum*. In these mixed associations, however, they are less in evidence.

*Acacia* woodland is rich in insect life and a source of the gum which forms an important item of their diet, which probably accounts for their prevalence in this association. Both *Acacia* and mopane trees provide an abundance of holes and the latter often have deeply hollowed out trunks which are used by the lesser bushbaby as resting and breeding sites. They are independent of water, obtaining their moisture requirements from their food.

Although they occur on forest fringes, they generally are not found within them. In Zimbabwe and Mozambique they are replaced in forest at altitudes of less than 200 m by *Galagoides zanzibaricus granti*.

**Habits**

Lesser bushbabies are nocturnal and arboreal and rest in small groups of two to seven, dispersing solitarily to forage. In the wild they may construct open-topped, platform-like nests or will use disused birds' nests or naturally occurring dense clumps of foliage or debris held among the branches of trees. In western Zimbabwe and Botswana they more frequently used holes in *Acacia* spp or mopane, *C. mopane*, trees. It appears that the construction of their own nests takes place in areas where tree holes are not so freely available. They sleep curled up on their sides and their tails curled over the heads. When a number are occupying a nest they sleep in diverse positions, even upside down. When sleeping, the ears fold back against their heads. If woken up during the day they appear lethargic, slowly opening their eyes and taking a moment or two before becoming active and under these circumstances may be captured by hand. When aroused they fold back their ears, show their teeth and may bite. They emerge from their resting places about sunset, and are circumspect in leaving their shelter. Sitting adjacent to the entrance, they will stretch themselves, yawn and may groom their soft hairy coats with their comb of incisor and canine teeth or may scratch themselves with the long claw on the second digit of their hind feet (Doyle, 1974b).

They are active particularly in the first two or three hours after emergence from the resting place, are less active in the hours around midnight and active again before sunrise, after which they return to rest. They appear to alternate between periods of high activity, sleep, rest, exploratory feeding, toilet activities and social activities, without any pattern or rhythm (Doyle, 1974b). In Botswana they were noticeably sensitive to adverse weather conditions when they tended to remain in shelter (Smithers, 1983).

Lesser bushbabies urine-wash (see **Reproduction**) and frequently do so after genital smelling or grooming others, particularly females, or after smelling a spot where a female has urinated. There is an increase in the frequency of male urine-washing when a female comes into oestrus, and much of the urine is deposited directly on to the female. After genital smelling the male may vigorously chest-rub along the flank and back of the female, bringing the chest glands into play and may accompany this with urine-washing. Urine washing is most frequent in dominant males and this and chest-rubbing decreases as dominance is lost and increases in the female as she becomes more dominant (Doyle, 1974b). Scent-marking reinforces territorial attachment but does not appear to act as a deterrent to rival conspecifics. Bearder (1969) produced evidence to show that it plays little or no role in establishing olfactory trails in the wild.

Andersson (1969) recorded 25 different vocalisations in the species of which 10 or 11 were discrete basic sounds. Faint grunts are emitted when eating, clicks and crackles are elicted by strange objects, and a low moan as a warning. Two males may start to call in a long-lasting series of increasingly penetrating "tchak-tchak" sounds and females may join the males. This may rise under stress to a noisy chattering. They softly twitter among themselves. Zimmermann *et al.* (1988) tabulated and compared their vocalisations in detail, using these as an aid in taxonomic classification.

Naso-nasal contact is a common form of greeting and is especially common between unacquainted individuals. The two individuals approach each other with the head stretched forward, ears back and body held low. When there is a tendency to attack offensively the ears are held upright, the eyes rounded, the mouth open, the tongue and upper canine teeth showing. In defensive threat the open mouth becomes rounded, the teeth remain covered and the head is raised. As the threatening source approaches, the ears are flattened. When cornered they rise to a bipedal stance, the arms on either side of the head with the fists ready to deliver a cuff. Vicious fighting can occur between adult strangers of the same sex as they spring at each other, grappling, falling to the ground, and biting at each other. This can lead to the death of opponents (Doyle, 1974b).

Like thick-tailed bushbabies, *O. crassicaudatus*, the eyes of lesser bushbabies shine very brightly with a reddish glow if caught in the beam of a dazzling light at night. The reflection can be mistaken for a genet, as the distance between their eyes is very similar. Their reactions under these circumstances, however, are different as lesser bushbabies will turn away suddenly and leap to another branch or jump from tree to tree to avoid the glare, the eyes bobbing up and down, disappearing and reappearing frequently as they turn towards the light source. If isolated in a solitary tree they sometimes will refrain from looking at the light source.

Lesser bushbabies are renowned for their spectacular leaping abilities. Even on horizontal branches they prefer to hop, and leaping is their predominant locomotor mode. Quadrupedal progression is used only at slow speed. On the ground they move by hopping bipedally, the forelimbs making no contact with the ground (Walker, 1979). Being small and light, they can clamber freely amongst the finer outermost twigs, but are as equally at home on the thicker branches (Doyle, 1974b).

Bearder (1987) recorded that the home ranges of female *G. moholi* were 4,4–11,7 ha and those of males were 9,5–22,9 ha. Natural boundaries were formed by open spaces, roads *etc.* and there was considerable overlap of home ranges. Doyle (1974b) noted that they appeared to have a thorough knowledge of their environment.

Social contacts in the wild are typically brief, although they always sleep in close contact even when there is ample space. Contact includes regular periods of grooming, in addition to courtship, mating, aggression and sometimes play (Doyle, 1974b; Bearder, 1987). After waking and before leaving the nesting area they go through a sequence of yawning, stretching and self grooming with the tooth comb.

**Food**

Lesser bushbabies live on an exclusive diet of insects and gum, which exudes from certain species of trees, principally *Acacia* spp. The gum exudes from trees whose bark and cambium are damaged either by the activities of wood-boring arthropods or through other causes. Gum exuding onto the surface is collected nightly by bushbabies using the tooth-scraper (procumbent incisors) in the lower jaw to scoop it off. Gums consist predominantly of carbohydrates and water, with small quantities of protein and minerals. Although primarily a source of carbohydrate, special mechanisms must exist to enable the bushbabies to digest the polymerised pentose and hexose sugars, while the one percent calcium is probably important in offsetting the low calcium content in arthropod prey. Feeding on gum increases during the winter months, when insect numbers decline, but gums are an important year-round food resource (Bearder & Martin, 1980).

Charles-Dominique & Bearder (1979) observed that, in early summer before the rains, an average time of 12 minutes per hour (n=76) was spent feeding. At this time of the year 15 minutes per hour was spent foraging on the ground. After the onset of the rains there was a marked decrease in the time spent feeding and they seldom foraged on the ground. Gum-licking was carried out for much shorter periods and there was an increase of more nutritious foods such as insects. Available fruits were never eaten and they showed no interest in birds or their eggs.

The insect food is masticated very finely which makes specific identification difficult, but moths, grasshoppers, termites, spiders and small beetles have been recognised in stomach contents (Smithers, 1983). The lesser bushbaby catches live insect prey in its hands, shutting its eyes at the moment of impact and pulling its ears back as a protection against the flapping wings and kicking legs. Once the fingers have closed around the prey its head is bitten and then the bushbaby opens its eyes and raises its ears. Food too large to be picked up in one hand is held in or down with both hands, while in biting and shearing the food the canines and premolars are used (Doyle, 1974b). In the wild they appear to be independent of drinking water, obtaining their moisture from their food (Charles-Dominique & Bearder, 1979). In captivity they will drink occasionally by lapping water with their long narrow tongues.

### Reproduction

Males test the reproductive status of females by approaching them from behind and examining their genitalia; this action is accompanied or followed by urine-washing. If the female is not receptive the male rarely will continue the testing or try to mount. If a female is in oestrus the male may continue to approach her a number of times and urine-washing occurs at a much higher rate than when the female is quiescent. Urine-washing in the lesser bushbaby takes the form of depositing urine in the cupped hand held under the urethra and then wiping this hand on the sole of the foot on the same side. Generally, this process is repeated on the other side. Urine-washing is engaged in by both sexes, but males display a higher incidence.

If other males are present in the vicinity of a female in oestrus, the dominant male and sometimes the oestrous female will drive them away. The female in oestrus may at first reject the advances of the male by leaping away, but the male will follow, making at the same time a series of low "clucking" vocalisations. The male eventually approaches the female from behind, grasping her lower waist with his forearms. During mounting the male vocalises with a loud call which ends on a whistle (van Horn & Eaton, 1979). If it happens that a male tries to court a pregnant female she may become aggressive towards him, slapping him on the sides of the face with her hands.

The gestation period is given by Doyle, Anderson & Bearder (1971) as 123,5 days (121–124 days). The average number of foetuses is 1,8 (n=30), with an observed range of one to two; the mass at birth varies from about 9,3 g to 9,6 g (Smithers, 1971). In captivity 97 pregnancies produced 39 (40,2%) singletons and 58 (59,8%) multiple births—two triplets and 56 twins (Masters, 1988).

Field studies of the lesser bushbaby show that both in the northern and southern parts of their distributional range they have two restricted periods of mating and two pregnancies per year (van Horn & Eaton, 1979). In Botswana, Smithers (1971) collected gravid females in all months of the year, except during the dry season months of April to June. Bearder (1969) observed a bimodal cycle of reproductive activity in the northern Transvaal, females giving birth in October and early November and again in late January to early February, with a much higher proportion of births in the second season (Doyle *et al.*, 1971).

The young are born in the shelter of the nest which the female may reline with leaves prior to giving birth. Tree hollows may also be used. Females with young tend to change the site of the nests every 10 or 14 days (Doyle, 1974b). At birth the young are covered with uniform grey-coloured fur and their eyes are open. They crawl around in the nest half an hour after birth.

When foraging the mother will carry the young from the nest and leave them clinging to a branch, a phenomenon known as "parking" and one that is common in African lorisines (Doyle, 1974b). She returns them to the nest before dawn.

Bearder (1969) noted that the young leave the nest for the first time at about 10 to 11 days old. During their first excursions the young are watched carefully by the mothers and if they emit a distress call, *zee-zee-zee*, she will pick them up by a fold of skin on the flank and put them back in the nest. When being carried in this way the young relax completely, appearing like pieces of rag (Sauer & Sauer, 1963). The incisor teeth begin to erupt at two to three weeks old (Butler, 1964). By about four weeks the young show some resistance to being carried back to the nest and the females may have to roll them around until they relax and can be picked up.

Urine-washing following ano-genital smelling and grooming is seen at three weeks old. They start to eat solid food at this age. They catch their own insects at four weeks old, but are still dependent on their mothers. The young in twin infants play-wrestle from about six days old, the behavioural elements of fighting seen in play-kicking, pushing and pulling. Wrestling bouts take place and the individuals sometimes hang upside down from a branch suspended by their feet, cuffing and wrestling with the hands (Doyle, 1974b).

Lesser bushbabies have two pairs of mammae, one pair pectoral, in line with the inner border of the forearm, the other pair inguinal.

---

No. 116

## *Galagoides zanzibaricus* (Matschie, 1893)

## Grant's or Zanzibar bushbaby
## Grant se nagapie

Plate 6

---

### Colloquial Name

The southern form is named after Capt. C.H.B. Grant who collected widely in southern Africa (see Thomas & Wroughton, 1907–1908).

### Taxonomic Notes

Roberts (1951), Ellerman *et al.* (1953), Hill & Meester (1974) and other authors included *granti* as a subspecies of *Galago senegalensis*, while Smithers & Wilson (1979) and Groves in Honacki, Kinman & Koeppl (1982) considered it as a full species. Olson (1979) and Meester *et al.* (1986) concluded that *granti* is a subspecies of the East African *Galagoides zanzibaricus* (Matschie, 1893), a treatment which is followed here. *Galago granti* Thomas & Wroughton, 1907 was first collected by Capt. Grant at Coguno, Inhambane district, southern Mozambique.

### Description

The upper parts of the body are pale brown, the limbs lighter in colour than the upper parts; in some specimens the upper parts of the limbs have a yellowish tinge. The basal one-third of the tail is the same colour as the upper parts of the body, thereafter darkening towards the dark brown tip; the proportion of the dark brown colour on the tail is variable. The forehead is greyer than the top of the head. The sides of the face have a darkening around the eyes, and the white band on the top of the snout from the forehead to the nostrils is very conspicuous. The rounded ears are very large. The fur on the dorsal surface of the body is soft and woolly, the individual hairs broadly dark grey at the base with buffy brown tips. The under parts of the body are washed with yellow, the individual hairs, which are longer than those on the upper parts, being pale grey at the base with broad yellowish-white tips.

Harcourt (1984) showed that in East Africa there is a small but significant sexual difference in mass but not in size in *Galagoides zanzibaricus zanzibaricus*. In East Africa, *G. zanzibaricus* is slightly smaller overall than *Galago moholi*.

### Table 116

Measurements (mm) and mass (g) of Grant's bushbaby, *G. zanzibaricus granti*, from eastern Zimbabwe (Smithers & Wilson, 1979)

| | Irrespective of sex | | |
|---|---|---|---|
| | x̄ | n | Range |
| TL | 394 | 10 | (370–418) |
| (HB | 162) | | |
| T | 232 | 10 | (214–254) |
| Hf s/u | 62 | 10 | (59–63) |
| E | 40 | 9 | (38–41) |
| Mass | 165,0 | 6 | (139–178) |

### Distribution

*South of the Sahara, excluding the Southern African Subregion*

The Zanzibar bushbaby occurs from the eastern parts of **Kenya** southwards through eastern **Tanzania** to the north-eastern parts of **Mozambique**, north of the Zambezi River. It also occurs in **Malawi**.

*Southern African Subregion*

Grant's bushbaby occurs in the eastern parts of **Mozambique**, south of the Zambezi River, extending westwards narrowly into **Zimbabwe** in the Haroni Lusitu confluence area (200 m a.s.l) and southwards to the southern parts of the Imhambane District in Mozambique.

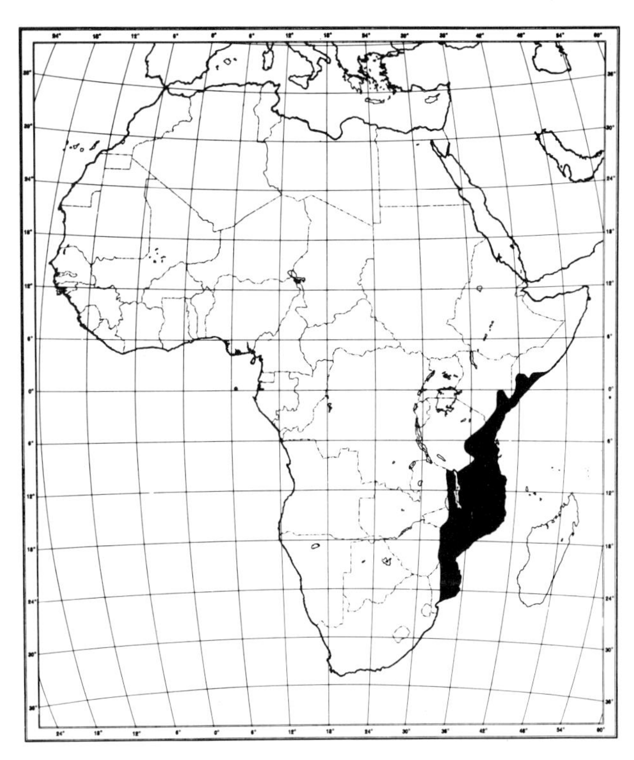

### Habitat

They are closely confined to evergreen forest at low altitudes (under 300 m) where they have a preference for the denser parts of the understorey from 6 m to 20 m.

### Habits

Grant's/Zanzibar bushbabies are nocturnal and rest during the day in holes in trees. They live in family groups consisting of a male with females and juveniles. Harcourt (1984) found that in East Africa they occupied relatively small home ranges, which in males ranged from 1,9–2,9 ha, in females 1,6–2,6 ha; the home ranges of the males coincided with those of the females. Related females may share a home range and may sleep together with their offspring. The males share a territory with one or two females and, unlike *G. moholi*, normally sleep with them (Harcourt, 1984).

Both in East Africa and in the Subregion they are more gregarious than the other galagos and their vocalisations are clearly recognisable from those of the other species. The call of this species is noticeably loud for such a small animal and is heard most commonly around sundown and just before sunrise, with some calling continuing throughout the night. Charles-Dominique (1977) considered that calling before dawn is a means of finding each other so that they can sleep together. The difference in the calls of *G. moholi* and *G. zanzibaricus* is seen clearly from the sonograms and reflects the differences that can be detected by ear.

### Food

Their diet consists of insects, spiders, termites and wild fruits. Unlike *G. moholi* little or no gum is consumed. Both in East Africa (Harcourt, 1984) and in the Subregion they were recorded eating small birds. In eastern Zimbabwe they were a persistent nuisance when small birds were being netted in the forest in the early evening, as several individuals congregated at the net to chew the heads off birds caught in them (Smithers, 1983).

### Reproduction

Information from the Subregion is meagre, but females carrying two foetuses have been recorded in December and it seems likely that they will have their young during the warm wet summer months from about November to February. Whether females will produce more than one litter in a season is not known. In East Africa, Harcourt (1984) found that this species has one young at a birth.

# Suborder HAPLORHINI

## XIII. Family CERCOPITHECIDAE

## Monkeys and baboons

Linnaeus (1758) attempted to divide the Simia, the tailed species of Primates, into three subordinate groups using the development of the tail as a criterion. He used the name *Cercopitheci* for the long-tailed forms. This was not a new name, for Brisson (1756) had used it in the singular, *Cercopithecus*, before Linnaeus, for all the long-tailed monkeys. However, as Brisson's names were published before 1758 they may not be used, and Linnaeus' name, *Cercopitheci*, as it was used in the plural, was rejected (Palmer, 1904), a quite correct procedure in line with international rules. However, the generic name *Cercopithecus* had been used for some 150 years by zoologists and to save confusion the International Commission for Zoological Nomenclature ruled in 1950 (*Bull. Zool. Nomencl.* 4: 311) that the use of the name *Cercopithecus* should stand and be credited to Linnaeus, 1758.

In the Subregion the Subfamily Cercopithecinae is represented by two species of monkeys: the vervet monkey, *Cercopithecus aethiops*, and the samango monkey, *C. mitis*; and the chacma baboon, *Papio ursinus*. The vervet monkey is a woodland species. The samango monkey is confined to forested areas and therefore has a more restricted distribution. The chacma baboon is distributed widely throughout the Subregion. Members of the Subfamily Cercopithecinae all have human-like shapes, but their fore and hind limbs are subequal in length, compared with man in which the legs are longer than the arms. They have five digits on the fore and hind feet, and rounded heads, with moderately long muzzles. The chacma baboons are exceptional as they have well developed muzzles.

Baboons have ischial callosities on the rump, one on each side of the anus, and the two species that occur in the Subregion have long non-prehensile tails. The noses of the monkeys are flattened. In Old World monkeys the comma-shaped nostrils are separated by a narrow septum, in New World monkeys the round nostrils are separated by a broad septum. The ears of the Infraorder Platarrhini, which include the baboon of the genus *Papio*, are oval and in the genus *Papio* tend to be pointed at the tips. The hands and feet are narrow and elongated, the thumb and big toe fully opposable, the palms and soles naked. Locomotion is quadrupedal. The body is held horizontally and when walking the limbs alternate in progression.

In a study of habitat utilisation by the two species of *Cercopithecus*, *aethiops* and *mitis*, and the yellow baboon, *Papio cynocephalus*, in Kenya, Moreno-Black & Maples (1977) found there was little overlap in their patterns of space and resource utilisation where they occurred sympatrically. The baboons and vervets had wider ranges of exploitative means than the samangos, but all three showed a trend towards a high degree of diversity of items eaten. Baboons and vervets, the more terrestrial forms, have increasingly adapted to unstable, heterogeneous microhabitats requiring the ability to respond to daily and seasonal fluctuations.

In the Subregion both monkeys and the baboons can become problem animals, their depredations not being confined solely to the raiding of crops. Encouraged by members of the public who toss them food items from vehicles, a practice prevalent in National Parks and reserves, they very quickly become exceedingly venturesome and are then an unmitigated nuisance. They associate vehicles with food and will raid these if they are unattended. They will enter houses, when the occupants are away, and cause extensive damage. The end result of this misguided kindness to these animals leads to their having to be destroyed.

Monkeys and baboons are exceedingly astute and, if fired on, thereafter recognise men carrying guns and make off. They recognise women, providing they are wearing dresses, and are less quick to move off. At the Victoria Falls in Zimbabwe, rangers involved in baboon control tried dressing up in skirts which worked for a short time, but the baboons soon recognised the ruse.

Monkeys and baboons are intensely social by nature. Sociality in these species has evolved to enable collective defence of resources and as a consequence of predation pressure. All the species are "female-bonded" (Wrangham, 1980): females live in their natal troops, while males leave them at adulthood, thereafter moving periodically from troop to troop in search of mating opportunities.

## Subfamily CERCOPITHECINAE

Key to the genera after Dandelot (1974)

1. Face elongated, terminal nostrils; ischial callosities broad; tail shorter than head and body

   ... *Papio*

   Face shorter, non-terminal nostrils; ischial callosities small and rounded; tail as long as or longer than head and body

   ... *Cercopithecus*

---

No.117

## *Papio ursinus* (Kerr, 1792)

## Chacma baboon
## Kaapse bobbejaan

Plate 6

---

### Colloquial Name

The name chacma was first used as a colloquial name in French by F. Cuvier in 1819 (Hill, 1970) and has remained associated with this species and is now well entrenched. Originally described from the Cape of Good Hope, the nominate subspecies is associated particularly with the Cape Province, hence the Afrikaans name *Kaapse bobbejaan*.

### Taxonomic Notes

Meester *et al.* (1986) listed six subspecies from the Subregion: *P. u. ursinus* from about the Orange River in the northwest to the Grahamstown district of the Cape Province; *P. u. griseipes* Pocock, 1911 from Zimbabwe, central Mozambique, northern Transvaal, northern Botswana and the Caprivi Strip, extending into Zambia; *P. u. occidentalis* Goldblatt, 1926 from the western Transvaal and southern Botswana; *P. u. orientalis* Goldblatt, 1926 from the Grahamstown area of the Cape Province, Natal, Swaziland, the eastern Transvaal and southern Mozambique; *P. u. chobiensis* Roberts, 1932 from northern Botswana and the Caprivi Strip, extending into southwestern Zambia, and *P.u. ruacana* Shortridge, 1942 from northern Namibia and southwestern Angola.

### Description

There is a wide range of variation in colour of individuals within troops, which depends on sex and age, and between corresponding age classes of individuals from different geographical areas. Adult males from the Cape Peninsula are dark brown with a tinge of yellow, especially on the forehead, the hairs dark brown at the base, in most cases with a subterminal band of yellow. Specimens from southeastern Botswana on the other hand are darker, with a profuse admixture of black hairs on the upper parts of the body, the hands, feet and tail. In the eastern Cape Province, Shortridge (1942) described the colour of old males as grizzled greyish-buff. Roberts (1951) described the colour of a specimen from northern Namibia as grizzled yellowish-brown with a blackish band along the back, on the crown of the head and on the neck. The upper parts of the limbs are yellowish, the hands blackish. The tail is dark brown from the base to the tip, partly tinged with yellow. Hall (1962a) pointed out that, in troops on the Cape Peninsula, after the dark phase of infancy has passed, the subadults are usually lighter brown in colour than the fully grown males; the adult females are intermediate in colour between the subadults and the old males. Stevenson-Hamilton (1947) stated that, in the eastern Transvaal, old males tended to be greyish.

The length of the tail is about the same length as that of the head and body. Characteristically the tail is carried with the proximal third of its length held upwards, the distal two-thirds drooping downwards. The limbs are long, the hind foot about twice the length of the forefoot, the digits, particularly the first digit, short and thickened.

An important character distinguishing the sexes is the formation of the ischial callosities, the horny epidermal thickenings on the rump. In the females these are separated in the middle by a wide space, their inner edges lying on either side of the vulva. In the males these callosities fuse across the middle below the anus (Pocock, 1925).

**Plate 6**

114. Thick-tailed bushbaby, *Otolemur crassicaudatus*
Bosnagaap
115. Lesser bushbaby, *Galago moholi*
Nagapie
116. Grant's lesser bushbaby, *Galagoides zanzibaricus*
Grant se nagapie
117. Chacma baboon, *Papio ursinus*
Kaapse bobbejaan
119. Vervet monkey, *Cercopithecus aethiops*
Blouaap
120. Samango monkey, *Cercopithecus mitis*
Samango-aap

PLATE 6
114
116
115
117
119
120
Dick Findlay.

In the chacma baboon, *P. ursinus*, the apex of the pinna of the ear which is slightly elongated, is directed backwards and upwards.

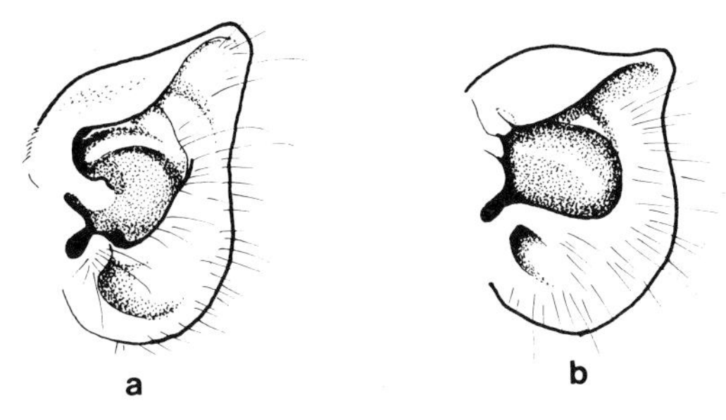


Fig.117.1. Ear pinna: (a) yellow baboon, *P. cynocephalus* (b) Chacma baboon, *P. ursinus* (after Hill, 1970).

Among the various subspecies occurring in the Subregion, *P. u. griseipes* is the largest of all, old males reaching a head and body length of 1,0–1,1 m, with tails of over 0,7 m (Haagner, 1920). The males have a mean mass of about 32,0 kg, females 15,4 kg. In all the subspecies the adult males are considerably larger than the adult females, whose muzzles never reach the elongation seen in the adult males, and the females lack the mane of long hair on the back of the neck and shoulders possessed by the adult males.

**Table 117.1**

Measurements (mm) and mass (kg) of chacma baboons, *P. ursinus*, from Botswana (Smithers, 1971)

| | Males | | | Females | | |
|---|---|---|---|---|---|---|
| | $\bar{x}$ | n | Range | $\bar{x}$ | n | Range |
| TL | 1451 | 9 | 1320–1570 | 1187 | 5 | 1075–1155 |
| T | 725 | 9 | 598–840 | 585 | 5 | 556–610 |
| Hf s/u | 223 | 9 | 217–236 | 184 | 5 | 176–194 |
| E | 58 | 8 | 54–65 | 50 | 5 | 44–52 |
| Mass | 31,75 | 9 | 27,22–43,54 | 15,42 | 5 | 14,06–17,24 |

**Skull** (Fig. 117.2)

A conspicuous feature of the skull is the enormous development of the rostrum in adult males. This is developed more conspicuously than in the yellow baboon, *P. cynocephalus*, or in the females of this species. This rostrum is roughly quadrangular in section and is variable in size and shape according to age and sex and to some extent individually. It is roughened or pitted and, at its posterior end on either side, there are forwardly directed foramina, more in number than in any other cercopithecid skull (Hill, 1970). The lateral surfaces of the rostrum are depressed deeply on either side; the upper anterior part of the muzzle slopes strongly forward and downward from the back of the nasal openings to the front of the skull.

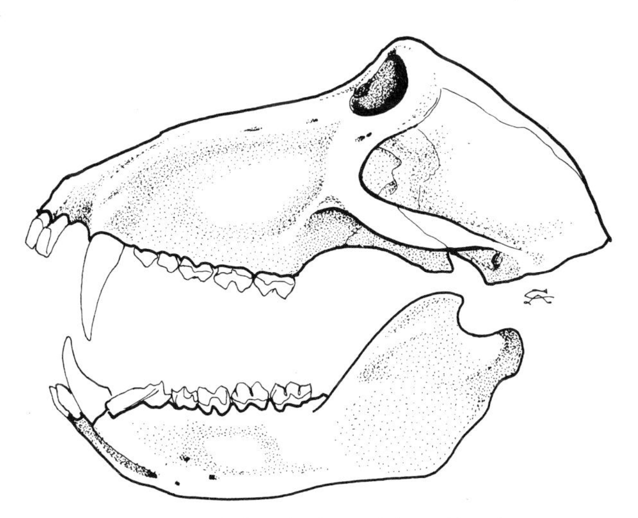

Fig.117.2. Skull: male chacma baboon, *P. ursinus* TL Skull 240 mm

The braincase is ovoid in shape, broader posteriorly than at the level of the postorbital constriction. The supraorbital ridges are well developed and more conspicuous in adult males than females; in the latter they are smoother and less rugose. The tori of these ridges, which are separated by a median depression, project forward over the eye sockets and, on their inner margins on either side, extend downwards in short bony processes. The eye sockets are separated by a broad bony septum and the lachrymal bones lie on their lower inner margins, enclosing the large oval lachrymal foramina. At the back of the skull there is a short sagittal crest which extends anteriorly for a short distance over the braincase to divide into low ridges which continue forward to the postorbital bars. The occipital foramen is flanked on either side anteriorly by the condyles which are separated in front by a broad notch. The zygomatic arches are developed well and stand out widely from the sides of the braincase.

The anterior lower premolars present the characteristic features of the Superfamily at its greatest development. These teeth are elongated in the line of the cheekteeth, their forward extremities reaching about halfway along the outer side of the base of the lower canines. These teeth through occlusion with the upper canines wear to sharp elongated occlusal surfaces and in doing so keep the edges on the posterior faces of the upper canines sharp. They have two roots, one lying just behind and to the outside of the canine, the other at the back of the tooth. All the molar teeth have two roots, but a third is sometimes present on the third lower molar. In the adult females the canine teeth are less strongly developed than in the males. The incisor teeth have broad spatulate crowns. The inner incisors in both jaws are larger than the outer. There is a broad diastema between the outer incisors and the canines in the upper jaw to accommodate the well developed lower canine. The upper canines are strongly developed, may reach a length of 50–60 mm in old males and have a deep groove running down the length of their anterior faces.

The glenoid fossa has a broad bony process on its posterior side and between this process and the equally projecting mastoid there is a deep hollow in which the bony auditory meatus lies.

The palate is parallel-sided and elongated, the anterior palatal foramina very large, the posterior oblique with two bony spicules projecting forwards over their openings.

In adults the cranial capacity of the skull is 175–213 cc (n=7) (Hill, 1970).

The mandible is massively built, the two halves fused and the symphysis strengthened by two broad bony processes on the outside.

The dental formula of the deciduous teeth is:

$I\frac{2}{2}\ C\frac{1}{1}\ M\frac{2}{2} = 20$

and the permanent teeth:

$I\frac{2}{2}\ C\frac{1}{1}\ P\frac{2}{2}\ M\frac{3}{3} = 32$

In the New World monkeys of the Infraorder Platyrrhini, the adults have three premolar teeth on each side of the upper and lower jaws. In *Papio*, which is an Old World monkey of the Infraorder Catyrrhini, one premolar is lost, and this is usually considered to be the second of the set.

**Distribution**

*South of the Sahara, excluding the Southern African Subregion*

They occur in southern **Angola** and widely in the southern parts of **Zambia**, being replaced in the northern parts of the country by the yellow baboon, *P. cynocephalus*. In eastern Zambia and **Malawi** the small subspecies *P. u. jubilaeus* occurs widely, its distribution extending marginally into **Mozambique**, north of the Zambezi River.

*Southern African Subregion*

They occur widely in the **Subregion**, but in the greater part of the South West Arid Zone they occur only where local conditions are suitable.

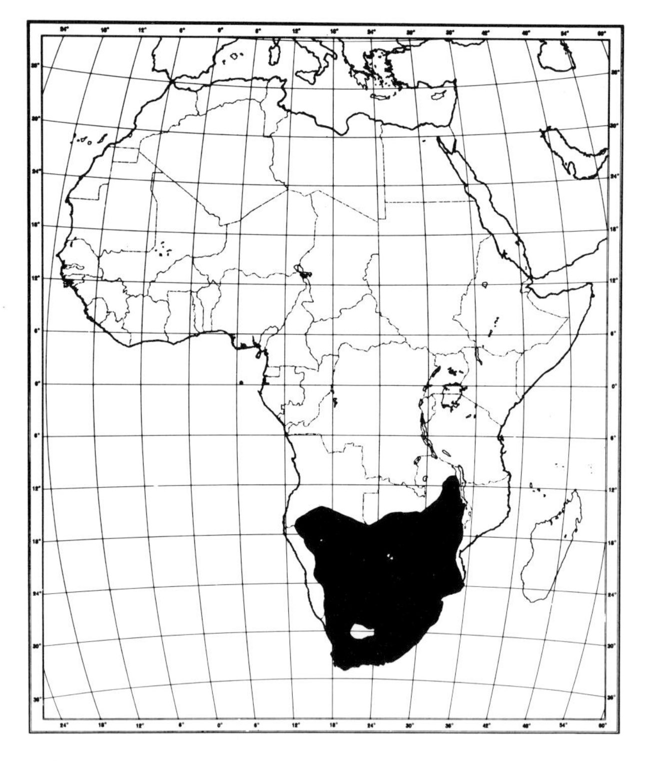

## Habits

Chacma baboons are gregarious and live in troops which may number up to 130 individuals in exceptional cases under optimum conditions. The numbers in individual troops vary through births, deaths and male migration.

In the Cape Point Reserve, De Vore & Hall (1965) found home range sizes for three troops of 20, 35 and 80 baboons to be 9,1, 14,8 and 33,7 km$^2$ respectively, home range size being related to numbers of individuals in the troops. On the other hand, Stoltz & Saayman (1970) found in the northern Transvaal that the size of the home ranges was determined largely by the availability of water, and the seasonal variation in the location of water brought about irregular movements of troops into unfamiliar terrain. Troops had overlapping home ranges, but on the common ground tended to avoid contact. Home ranges varied in size from 13 km$^2$ to 23 km$^2$. The largest troop, numbering 72 individuals, had a smaller home range than two other smaller troops. More recently, Anderson (1982), in a study at the Suikerbosrand Nature Reserve in the Transvaal Highveld, found a mean home range size of 24,6 km$^2$ for a troop size averaging 78 individuals. This lower density is possibly necessary for the greater energy requirements in a temperate region. This was also true for Drakensberg baboons which have smaller troop sizes ($\bar{x}$ = 26) and home range size varying from 18,9 km$^2$ at high altitudes to 10,0 km$^2$ at low altitudes, for seven and 13 animals respectively, which gives the lowest population densities known for savanna baboons (Whiten, Byrne & Henzi, 1987). Density of baboon troops in the Kuiseb Canyon in the Namib Desert was also low. Because of their restriction to the canyon, home ranges were highly linear in size, being 9,4 and 4,0 km$^2$ for two troops of 35 and 33 baboons respectively (Hamilton, Buskirk & Buskirk, 1976), whereas density in the Okavango swamp was six times as great, the home range being 4,7, 6,5, 2,1 and 4,8 km$^2$ for troops of 108, 109, 39 and 71 respectively. Hamilton *et al.* (1976) ascribed these differences to variations in water supply as well as to food abundance. In the Suikerbosrand Nature Reserve, baboon troops subdivided frequently during the dry winter, but rarely during the wet summer. Anderson (1981b, 1983) ascribed this to adaptation to the combination of scarce food and low temperatures (down to −11 °C).

In the Suikerbosrand Nature Reserve encounters between troops are rare and non-aggressive (Anderson, 1981a), but fierce fighting may take place. Facing-off is the most time-consuming activity in intertroop encounters. Baboons sit on an elevated perch facing the other troop, often leaning forward and shaking the branches of trees in which they sit. Branch-shaking is also a typical response to hyaenas and lions (Hamilton, Buskirk & Buskirk, 1975). Saayman (1971c) recorded that, in the Kruger National Park, most encounters took place at the sleeping sites, but in 76% of encounters there was no fighting. Some troops intermingled to the extent that they appeared as a single troop, but this caused a state of tension, the adult males barking and screaming, chasing and herding females to the rear of the troop, eventually leading to the troops segregating and moving off in separate directions (Stoltz & Saayman, 1970). On the other hand, in the Okavango with a population density of 24 baboons/km$^2$, this high density and territorial defence are exceptional among chacma baboons studied to date (Hamilton *et al.*, 1975). Saayman (1971c) noted that troops which were normally hostile would gang up against lions.

The number of adult males in troops can vary from a solitary individual in the smaller troops to up to 12 in some of the very large ones. Dominant males travel towards the front of the troop whereas subordinate males travel towards the rear. Dominant males tend to be young, physically in their prime, more confident and less cautious individuals; they also tend to be recent immigrants (Busse, 1984). Saayman (1971a) recorded that adult males in troops were in the forefront when their own troop was threatened. Aggression in males was demonstrated by direct staring and threat gestures such as chasing, seizing and biting. Aggressive encounters between two or three individuals often ignited large-scale fighting throughout the troop, the role of attacker and attacked often changing when others intervened. There was less aggression between adult males than between them and other troop members. Males would enlist the help of other males in taking action against stronger males by screaming, retracting the lips, showing the teeth and gums, and holding the tail upright. While intensive aggression was rare, some adults became deeply scarred by the canine teeth of opponents. Juveniles and females in the menstrual cycle were attacked more frequently than was expected, subadult males and lactating females much less, and pregnant females were never attacked. Cheney (1977) found that, when threatened, immature animals formed aggressive alliances with members of high ranking matrilines, whereas adult females formed alliances with related individuals of adjacent rank.

Those on the look-out warn the troop by barking at the approach of danger. When the troop is on the move, certain males tend to be located in peripheral positions. Some males will even spend prolonged periods living solitarily (Hamilton & Tilson, 1982). Low ranking females are located on the perimeter of the troop. High ranking females, which are more likely to have infants, are likely to be found toward the centre of the group (Busse, 1984).

The troops may start to move to the resting sites quite early in the afternoon, from 15h30 onwards, depending on food availability. Troops sleep at night on high krantzes but, in the same area, other troops use the shelter of trees with thick foliage. Stoltz & Saayman (1970) found that, in the northern Transvaal, the majority of the troops they observed used rocky krantzes as sleeping sites, others used tall trees such as thorn trees, *Acacia* spp; fig trees, *Ficus* spp and fever berry trees, *Croton megalobotrys*. In Zimbabwe in areas where rocky shelters and large trees were available, such as in the Matopo Hills and the Fort Victoria area, both types of resting site were used, often by the same troop on different nights (Smithers, 1983). While some troops use the same sleeping sites over lengthy periods, others will use different sites at different times and these sites may be used by one or more troops at different times. Saayman (1971a) recorded that a troop in the Kruger National Park used one site on 50 nights, another on five nights, in a series of 55 nights. The sleeping sites have a distinct smell, are marked by accumulations of dung, and are urine-stained. During the night adult males may bark if disturbed, the approach of large predators causing persistent barking and squealing until the danger has passed. As a general rule the troop is reluctant to leave the sleeping site but occasionally will move to higher, more inaccessible parts of the krantzes if seriously disturbed. Members of the troops may sleep widely dispersed. Often, however, two or more may huddle together and adult males often sleep in the vicinity of the receptive females in whose company they have spent the day (Stoltz & Saayman, 1970).

In the morning there is usually some predawn activity in the resting sites, the troops usually leaving the sites at first light. The mature males and juveniles tend to become active first, descending from the shelter of the resting sites, and the troop congregates at a specific point before moving off. In cold, windy weather the troop may move only a short distance and remain sitting, out of the wind, in sheltered corners sunning themselves; the adult males often sit with their backs to the morning sun before moving to forage (Stoltz & Saayman, 1970).

Hall (1962a) who studied baboon troops in the Cape Peninsula, found that troops moved shorter distances on hotter days, while in the northern Transvaal, Stoltz & Saayman (1970) showed that individual troops travelled daily for distances of 2,4 km to 14,4 km, usually resting after a few kilometres, particularly during the hotter times of the day. Distances travelled declined in relation to increasing temperatures. Foraging activity declined around the midday rest periods and as they approached the resting sites in the afternoon.

In most studies it has been found that regular access to drinking water is essential to their survival and they drink daily. However, recently Brain (1988) has found that a troop in the Kuiseb Canyon, Namib Desert, has balanced its water requirements by securing a source of moisture from nearby plants and conserving water by resting and sleeping during the hottest part of the day. Through this adaptation to their arid environment they have overcome restrictions imposed by the need for regular drinking.

Where there is a scarcity of water sources, troops frequently meet at watering places. Adult males of troops approaching water may climb trees and scan the area for other troops in the vicinity. If this is the case they may wait for up to two hours before the troop in occupation moves off. At other times troops may share a watering point without aggression.

Chacma baboons are tolerant of grazing and browsing mammals. They will forage close to herds of elephants, buffalo and antelope, but on occasion are chased by them and will take to trees for safety. In National Parks and reserved areas they soon become indifferent to vehicles and man. There is a commensal association between baboons and browsing species and even small carnivores. When feeding high in trees, baboons dislodge wild fruits which then become available to other species that can obtain them only if they are on the ground. This association has been observed with species such as kudu, *Tragelaphus strepsiceros*, bushbuck, *T. scriptus*, and with small carnivores such as civets, *Civettictis civetta*, and side-striped jackals, *Canis adustus* (Smithers, 1983).

The bisyllabic bark of the large males, which is repeated intermittently, is the most striking vocalisation. It is stimulated on the approach of danger and is often given from vantage points. Large males will interpose themselves between their troop and observers, slowly retreating from vantage point to vantage point as the troop withdraws. They may jerk their heads up and down, exhibiting the pale coloured skin around the eyes, as they bounce stiff-legged, side-on to the observer. They may throw sand around with one hand (Stoltz & Saayman, 1970). Females will bark and threaten observers and often juveniles will approach them in curiosity, threaten and then run off. Old adult females are frequently the most persistently vigilant individuals and, in general, vigilance in baboon troops is a process shared among the members of the troop.

The establishment of dominance among the males does not necessarily involve physical contact. The direct provocative gait of a male towards another is often sufficient to cause the submissive one to move off. This may be followed by screaming and chasing. Infrequently contact is established and blood may be drawn. All males, from subadults, are dominant over females and females are easily ranked. Females and males may form friendships that persist, but whether this affects the relationship between male dominance and mating opportunities has not been established (Henzi, pers. comm.).

Visual and auditory cues were used to establish contact within troops which tend to disperse when foraging. Individuals would climb trees to scan the terrain, and the grunting of old males, and the squealing and screaming during the frequent aggressive encounters provided clues as to the whereabouts of the main body of the troop. Scent probably plays a part as well.

Stoltz & Saayman (1970) found that the discharge of firearms would send troops running off, with the dominant males leading. On the other hand the dominant males would interpose themselves between the troops and attacking dogs which are killed often in the process.

Saayman (1970) noted that "presenting", the act of turning the vulval regions towards other individuals, has a sexual connotation in receptive females. It is also a social greeting and generally signifies appeasement, regardless of sex or age.

Mutual grooming is an important form of social behaviour and occurs in a variety of contexts. Saayman (1971e) studied this in relation to the menstrual and reproductive cycle in free-ranging baboons and found that adult males and cycling females were more active as groomers than other classes. Adult males only groomed adult females in the turgescent phase where their sexual skin around the vagina was inflated and swollen. Females with flat sexual skin in the late menstrual cycle would groom other cycling females and non-consorting adult males. Infants did not groom and pregnant females only groomed at a very low level and then groomed adult males proportionately more than other classes.

**Food**

Hall (1962a) stated that chacma baboons at the Cape fed continuously throughout the day. They are omnivorous, feeding primarily on fruit and leaves, while invertebrates are used throughout the year (Moolman & Breytenbach, 1976). De Vore & Hall (1965), for instance, stated that it is simpler to list the items not eaten by baboons than to describe the items which they do. Hall (1963), listed 94 different plant species utilised by them in the Cape Peninsula, including shellfish gathered along the coast. Grasses, seeds, roots, bulbs, leaves, flowers, bark and *Acacia* and other gums exuding from trees, mushrooms, wild fruits, pods and shoots have all been recorded in their diet. Of these the single most important item appears to be grass. De Vore & Washburn (1963) recorded that no day passed without grass being eaten and, during the dry season, might comprise up to 90% of the food ingested. The thicker basal end of grass stems or succulent rhizomes located just below the ground surface, and bulbs and tubers are sought after. These enable them to supplement their moisture requirements, particularly in the dry season when other vegetation has dried up. They will pull up or dig out clumps of grass and shake off the soil before eating, and are adept at noticing a tiny green shoot from an underground bulb or tuber and painstakingly will dig it up from depths of up to 350 mm below the ground surface (De Vore & Washburn, 1963). Wild fruits and pods are sought after and even the hard fruits of the sausage tree, *Kigelia africana*, with which monkeys are unable to deal, are chewed open and the pulp and pips eaten. The fruits of various species of the introduced prickly pear, *Opuntia* spp, are sought after. Agricultural crops such as maize, sorghum and peanuts and orchard crops such as pawpaws and bananas are all the objects of their raiding.

In their study in the Drakensberg on troops living at two altitudes, Whiten *et al.* (1987) grouped the foods eaten into six types and two major categories, each having different behavioural implications. Most of the above-ground items such as leaves, flowers, seeds and fruit required little processing other than tearing off the components to be discarded. On the other hand, bulbs and corms required time-consuming excavation and cleaning before eating. Although baboons elsewhere use subterranean resources, in the Okavango swamps and Kuiseb Canyon (Namib Desert), feeding on underground plant parts constituted less than 6%, whereas in mountain baboons these constituted 42,4 and 64,3% of the low and high group's diet respectively (Whiten *et al.*, 1987). Apparently, this ability to exploit underground resources at high altitudes, particularly during the winter nutritional bottleneck, enables the baboons to utilise this habitat.

It is characteristic of areas where chacma baboons have

been feeding to find that every stone had been turned over in their search for insects, spiders, scorpions, ants and even slugs. Cambefort (1981) found that juvenile baboons discover new food and, after the discovery, propagation within the troop is instantaneous.

Dart (1963) first described the hunting behaviour of *P. ursinus*, mentioning how they took reptiles, birds and mammals. Moreover, cannibalism following infanticide has been reported for the chacma baboon (Saayman, 1971d), but this is presumably not to obtain nutrients but to improve one's own inclusive fitness through improved opportunity to reproduce. To place hunting by baboons in perspective, Butynski (1982a) stated that during tens of thousands of hours of observations on primates, fewer than 450 sightings of vertebrate hunting and/or feeding have been reported and well over 80% of these are attributable to baboons. He gave the percentage meat from mammals in baboon diet as less than 1%. In a sample of 54 stomach contents, Moolman & Breytenbach (1976) found the remains of only one bird. In addition, hunting of mammals by baboons is predominantly a male activity (Altmann & Altmann, 1970). Baboons seldom kill wild mammals weighing more than 6 kg and, although they may stalk and hunt prey co-operatively and share the meat, such behaviours are infrequent and poorly developed in baboons (Butynski, 1982). Nevertheless, there are records in the literature of their killing and eating the young of the mini ungulates. Infant impala, *A. melampus*, weighing 5–8 kg are the largest wild prey captured by baboons (Strum, 1981). In a study of two troops in the Moremi Game Reserve, Botswana, each averaging 69 members, Hamilton & Busse (1982) observed over a four-year period that they consumed 28 vertebrate prey items including four neonate impala, five juvenile vervet monkeys, *C. aethiops*, nine adult bush squirrels, *P. cepapi*, four unidentified rodents, three francolins, *Francolinus* spp, and four unidentified birds. All known captors of monkeys and impala were adult males. Baboons have also been known to raid free-ranging domestic stock, taking poultry, lambs and young goats (Hall, 1962a; Stoltz, 1977; Stoltz & Keith, 1973), but will not take carrion.

### Reproduction

Herding involves high-ranking adult males which are also the individuals which copulate most often (Stoltz & Saayman, 1970). Lactating females are rarely herded and Kummer (1968) has suggested that herding is a means of maintaining a male's access to oestrous females over time. Adult males, particularly the alpha male which accounted for the largest single proportion of copulations and fertilized six of eight females who became pregnant in the Mountain Zebra National Park, were most likely to herd females with whom they had the closest long-term social bonds (Cheney, 1977). The alpha male's choice of particular females for herding had two main consequences. First, it served to increase his reproductive success by isolating females about to ovulate from other males and secondly these females were those in which he would invest the greatest direct social support in future.

In a study of a troop of 72 baboons along the Boro River in the Okavango Swamp, Hamilton & Arrowood (1978) found that in every mating with vaginal penetration, females vocalised; the call is a series of staccato grunts. Both male and female vocalisations erupted as thrusting ceased and the pair separated, but it has been suggested that only dominant males vocalise when copulating. Notes from the female are emitted in rapid regular rhythm which diminish at the end of the sequence. Mutual grooming often follows copulation. Female baboons may mate 100 times or more with different males during the course of an oestrous cycle, on occasion by two or three males in as many minutes. However, the oestrous swelling is the cue for timing of ovulation and, as this approaches, the rank of attending males increases. Vocalising during copulation reveals mating attempts and, together with the elaborate sex skin cycle, enhances the probability of mating by dominant males.

The mean length of the menstrual cycle in the chacma baboon is 35,6 days, with a range of 29–42 days. The size and colour of the sexual skin around the ischial callosities varies in relation to the phases of the cycle. During the gestation period it is an intense scarlet and during lactation the skin is quiescent. The skin swells with the onset of the menstrual cycle and becomes deflated and flat towards the end of the cycle. The mean length of the turgescent phase when the skin is inflating and swollen is 19,45 days, the deturgescent phase when the skin is deflating and flat and which is preceded two to three days by ovulation, lasts 16,07 days. Females approaching males prior to presenting may display "eyeface" in which the facial skin is taut, the ears flattened back and the eyebrows raised to show the white pigmented eyelids. This may be displayed at a distance of up to 25 m. "Eyeface" is accompanied often by lip-smacking, and may be exchanged between females as well as between male and female. From two to four oestrous cycles may precede that with fertilization (Altmann, Altmann & Hausfater, 1978).

The gestation period is six months. A single young is born at a birth, which occurs at any time throughout the year (Bielert & Busse, 1983), and lactation continues for about eight months. In the Amboseli National Park, Kenya, Altmann, Altmann & Hausfater (1978) found the range of postpartum amenorrhea in *P. cynocephalus* was 6–17 months, with a mean of 12 months, but females resumed cycles approximately three weeks after infant death regardless of the age at death. Where infants died two oestrous periods occurred before the dam became pregnant, whereas females with surviving infants took four oestrous periods before becoming pregnant after cycling recommenced. One consequence of more rapid conception after loss of an infant is that it enables rapid recovery from periods of high infant mortality. In addition, it enables rapid introduction of new genetic material in cases such as infanticide. Data are not available for *P. ursinus* on this aspect, but Gilbert & Gillman (1951) recorded that the shortest interval between two births by the same female was 14,5 months.

At parturition a female usually retreats to cover, and other females often gather in the vicinity to watch the birth. The newly born young is entirely black and from the time it is born is capable of clinging to its mother. Young can be aged up to about seven months on the basis of ear and muzzle colour which becomes progressively lighter (Whitehead, Henzi & Piper, 1990). There is a close bond between mother and young. Up to the age of six or eight weeks she grooms it and carries it about wherever she goes. In the early stages the infant clings under its mother but later clambers on to her back, clinging transversely across it. By the time it is ready to walk it will sit jockey-fashion on the mother's rump near the base of her tail, often leaning back against its upturned base. If she runs, the young will cling on with its hands. Mothers do not permit other females to pick up infants until they are walking.

Up to the age of about one year the young tend to associate with members of their own age group. Stoltz & Saayman (1970) noted that adult males in the troop would approach females with infants, grunting, and then carry off the infants clasped to their bellies, often sitting down and grooming them. When harassed by dominant males, an adult male would seize an infant from any female and the harassment would then cease.

Puberty is reached between the fourth and sixth year of life and physical growth continues up to the age of seven or eight years (Hall, 1962b). These ages may vary depending on local conditions and figures published, based on experience in zoological gardens, may have little relation to those pertaining in the wild (Bourlière, 1953).

The females have a pair of pectoral mammae.



No. 118

## *Papio cynocephalus* Linnaeus, 1766

## Yellow baboon
## Geelbobbejaan

This species was included in the first edition (see Smithers, 1983) as it was thought that the distribution of the species in Mozambique extended south of the Zambezi River. As this does not appear to happen, the species is withdrawn from the Subregion list.

## Genus *Cercopithecus* Linnaeus, 1758

Key to the species after Meester *et al.* (1986)

1. Face pure black; upper parts greyish grizzled; tail the same colour as the body or slightly darker, the tip blackish; patch of reddish hair under the root of the tail in adult males; hands and feet predominantly black, outer surface of the arms not black
 ... *aethiops*
2. Face brownish; upper parts darker on the shoulders, then posteriorly reddish-brown, the colour intensifying towards the base of the tail which is ringed with reddish hair; outer surface of limbs black
 ... *mitis*

---

No. 119

## *Cercopithecus aethiops* (Linnaeus, 1758)

## Vervet monkey
## Blouaap

Plate 6

---

### Colloquial Name

The name vervet is borrowed from the French vernacular name of this species, *cercopithèque vervet*.

### Taxonomic Notes

Meester *et al.* (1986) listed six subspecies from the Subregion: *C. a. pygerythrus* (F. Cuvier, 1821) from the southern and eastern Cape Province and Natal; *C. a. rufoviridis* I. Geoffroy, 1843 occurs in northern Mozambique, Malawi and southern Tanzania, extending marginally into the Subregion in the Tete district of northwestern Mozambique; *C. a. helvescens* Thomas, 1926 from northern Namibia, extreme northwestern Botswana and southwestern Zambia; *C. a. cloetei* Roberts, 1931 from northern Natal, KwaZulu and the western Transvaal; *C. a. ngamiensis* from northern and northeastern Botswana, and *C. a. marjoriae* Bradfield, 1936 from southern Botswana.

### Description

In individuals from the southern Cape Province, *C. a. pygerythrus*, the upper parts of the body, from the forehead to the base of the tail, are grizzled greyish; the long, coarse hairs are grey at the base with alternate bands of black and pale yellow or white. The lateral surfaces of the limbs are greyish, the hairs uniformly annulated black and pale yellow. The flanks of the body are brighter in tone than the upper parts. The face is covered with short black hair and the forehead has a transverse band of pure white hair. The hair of the side whiskers is long, white in front and speckled grey towards the back where it sweeps back from the cheeks to nearly cover the ears. The hair on the lower part of the cheeks is dirty white and lacks black tips. The hands are black with a scattering of greyish hairs on their upper surfaces and the distal parts of the feet including the toes are black. The tail is proximally the same colour as the upper parts and tends to darken towards the tip. The under parts are whitish, the white extending on to the inner side of the limbs. Around the anus and extending narrowly on to the under side of the base of the tail there is a patch of rufous hair. The scrotum of the adult males has been described variously as bright blue, turquoise blue, cobalt blue and turquoise green and is very conspicuous.

There is some variation in colour within the various subspecies that occur in the Subregion. *C. a. helvescens* of northern Namibia is much yellower down the mid-back than *C. a. pygerythrus* and has pale-coloured limbs and white hands and feet. The hairs are yellow, tipped with black, and are clear yellow on the flanks. In *C. a. rufoviridis* of the northeastern part of the Subregion the back is distinctly reddish, darker towards the base of the tail. In *C. a. ngamiensis* the tail tends to be darker, especially towards the tip, than in the other subspecies and the back is distinctly tinged yellow like *C. a. helvescens*.

Adult males have a vivid genital colouration—a red penis and perianus and powder-blue scrotum which they emphasize in a number of ways. The normal, abducted state of the scrotum allows for identification of the adult male (Henzi, 1981, 1985). Retraction of the scrotum during submission may have communicatory status. Price *et al.* (1976) confirmed that a deep dermal deposition of melanin in melanocytes accounts for the blue colouration. Changes in scrotal colour are unlikely to be due to changes in melanin synthesis or degradation, as synthesis is too slow and cutaneous melanin too stable. Price *et al.* (1976) suggested that the colour is controlled by the quantity or quality of dermal interstitial fluid above and between the melanocytes. It is not yet clear how this hydration is regulated. (See also **Habits**).

**Table 119.1**

Measurements (mm) and mass (kg) of vervet monkeys, *C. a. ngamiensis* Roberts, 1932, from northern Botswana (Smithers, 1971)

| | Males | | | Females | | |
|---|---|---|---|---|---|---|
| | $\bar{x}$ | n | Range | $\bar{x}$ | n | Range |
| TL | 1142 | 30 | 1045–1295 | 1021 | 30 | 971–1111 |
| T | 652 | 30 | 600–750 | 575 | 30 | 485–653 |
| Hf s/u | 144 | 30 | 133–170 | 125 | 30 | 115–137 |
| E | 38 | 30 | 31–42 | 35 | 30 | 30–40 |
| Mass | 5,51 | 29 | 3,86–8,00 | 4,09 | 30 | 3,41–5,22 |

### Skull (Fig. 119.1)

The rostrum, while conspicuous, is not elongated to the extent seen in the genus *Papio* and slopes evenly forward from the top of the eye sockets to the front of the skull. The eye sockets tend to be flattened on their upper margins, rounded on their lower, and are separated by a bony septum which broadens out slightly to the top of the nasal openings. The zygomatic arches are lightly built and only swing out slightly from the braincase, which is rounded. There is no sagittal crest and the supraorbital crest is represented by a barely perceptible ridge.

The palate is broadest at the level of the first molars. The anterior palatal foramen is large, the posterior considerably smaller.

The dental formula in the deciduous set is:

$I\frac{2}{2}\ C\frac{1}{1}\ M\frac{2}{2} = 20$

and in the permanent set:

$I\frac{2}{2}\ C\frac{1}{1}\ P\frac{2}{2}\ M\frac{3}{3} = 32$

The inner incisors, especially in the upper jaw, are considerably larger than the outer which tend to be rounded and peg-like. There is a diastema between the upper outer incisors and the canines which accommodates the lower canine when the jaw is closed. The canines are sharp-pointed and the upper has a sharp edge on the posterior surface which is kept sharp by occlusion on the elongated first premolar in the lower jaw. The lower first premolar has a high crown, the elongated anterior part of the tooth sloping forward and downward to end outside the canine. The elongated anterior part of this tooth occludes on the inside of the upper canine, keeping its posterior edge sharp.

### Distribution

The vervet monkey has a wide distribution in Africa, from southern Ethiopia and Somalia to the Cape Province. It is replaced in other parts of Ethiopia, in the Sudan and in West Africa by the grivet monkey, *C. aethiops*, which occurs as far

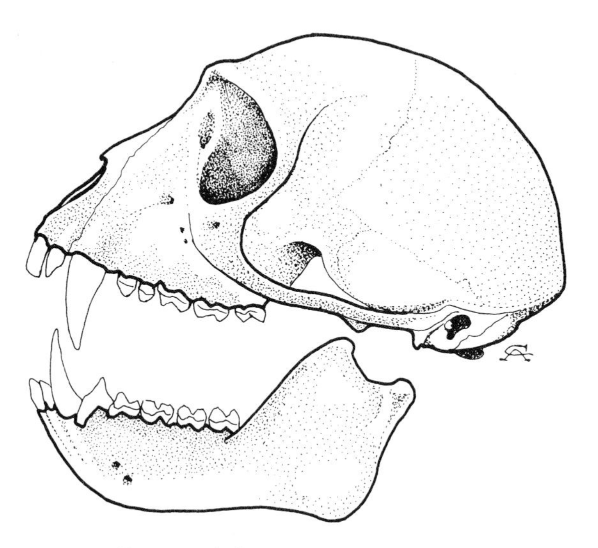

Fig.119.1. Skull: vervet monkey, *C. aethiops*
TL Skull 105 mm

west as Ghana, and by the green monkey, *C. sabaeus*, which occurs westwards of this as far as Senegal.

*South of the Sahara, excluding the Southern African Subregion*

They are recorded from **Senegal** and **Mauritania** eastwards to southern **Ethiopia** and **Somalia**; southern **Uganda; Kenya; Tanzania;** parts of eastern and southern **Zaire**; the **Congo Republic; Gabon; Angola; Zambia; Malawi** and **Mozambique**, north of the Zambezi River.

*Southern African Subregion*

They occur in northern, northeastern and southern **Namibia**; in northern, eastern and in parts of southeastern **Botswana**; the **Transvaal; Swaziland; Mozambique**, south of the Zambezi River; **Natal**; the western **Orange Free State**; in the eastern, southern and along the Orange and Vaal rivers in the **Cape Province**, where they occur coastally about as far west as the George and Knysna districts.

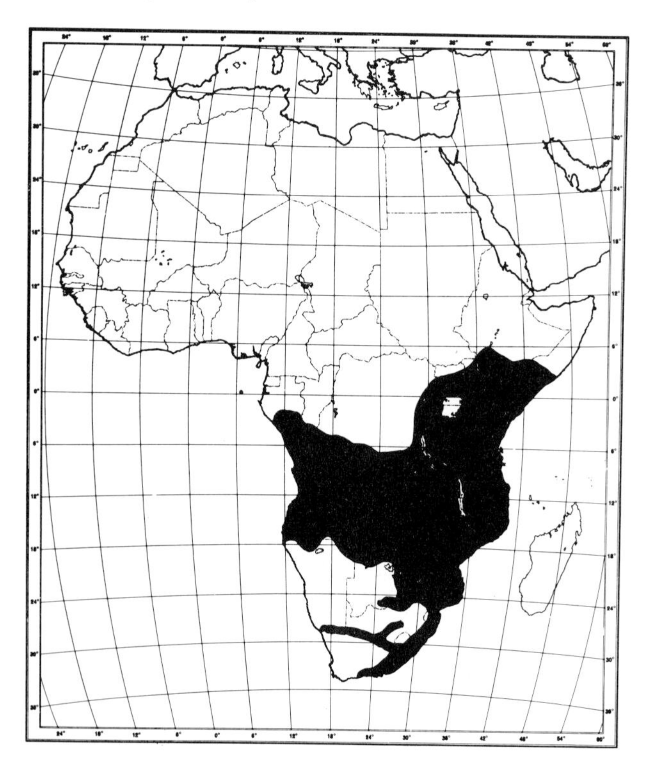

## Habitat

Vervet monkeys have a drier habitat than other members of this genus and are most abundant in and near riparian vegetation of savannas, being generally absent from open grassland and open scrub, except marginally. They will penetrate deep into otherwise totally unsuitable terrain along rivers and streams and will settle there if the riverine woodland is sufficiently developed to provide fruit-bearing trees and cover. This is demonstrated by their occurrence in the dry interior of the Cape Province where they are common in parts of the riverine woodland of the Orange River and in parts of the Vaal River, but where they do not occur in the surrounding country, except marginally. The same applies in Botswana where they occur widely in the Okavango delta and in parts of the eastern sector that are well watered, but not in the arid scrub associations of the Kalahari which cover the larger part of the country. Shortridge (1934) noted their occurrence in rocky hills in the Grootfontein and Tsumeb districts of Namibia where they depend on the occurrence of permanent springs, but are not found in the surrounding terrain. The troops will wander far from permanent water during times of the year when wild fruits are available, returning to the better-watered country as the food supply diminishes.

The vervet monkey has a wider habitat tolerance than the samango monkey, *C. mitis* whose distribution is discontinuous because of its more rigid attachment to forested areas.

## Habits

Vervet monkeys are diurnal and gregarious, occurring in small multimale troops of up to 38, with more than one unrelated male in a troop (Henzi, 1988). Within the troops there is a clear order of dominance. Rank-order within the troop is maintained by threat and aggression. Eyelid display as a threat gesture is widespread among cercopithecines. The skin of the eyelids and area immediately above them are light-coloured, contrasting with the dark face. By retracting the brow these areas are exposed and, when accompanied by a stare, this functions as a threat (Fig 119.2a). In vervets the function of this gesture seems highly dependent on the posture assumed by the displayer (Struhsaker, 1967). When crouching it functions as a defensive threat, whereas in the upright position it functions as an aggressive threat. Head-bobbing or jerking is another aggressive gesture and vervets demonstrate variations of this pattern representing a continuum from staring to attack when the recipient is grabbed and bitten. When a subordinate member of the troop is threatened or bitten, it redirects its own anger to the member next down the scale from it. In the course of status aggression, subordinates were bitten most often on the base of the tail (Brain, 1965).

Genital signals are associated with intermale agonism. An interesting form of behaviour is the penile display made by adult and subadult male vervets to one another and which lasts for two to five seconds. Although variations occur, usually one male approaches another which is seated, stands bipedally in front of him with his inguinal region directed toward, and close to, the seated male's face; although in Kenya the male then placed his hands on the seated male's head, shoulders or back, this was not observed in studies in Natal (Henzi, 1985). Sometimes the displayer has a penile erection throughout the encounter. Occasionally this display is followed by grooming. Only dominant vervets display this behaviour and its significance is not clearly understood (Struhsaker, 1967).

Another interesting behaviour described by Struhsaker (1967) is the "red, white and blue" display which also occurs between adult and subadult males (Fig. 119.1b). The dominant male holds his tail erect while pacing back and forth in front of a seated monkey, displaying his red peri-anus, his blue scrotum and the white medial strip of fur extending between the peri-anus and the scrotum. The subordinate male responds to this display by sitting hunched or crouching and uttering a series of specific grunts and screams.

The desire to groom and to be groomed is an important factor in troop cohesion. Grooming usually took place in mid-morning after the first feeding session when individuals were satiated and resting in the sun. High rates of grooming were significantly correlated with high rates of alliance formation. High ranking females received more grooming than others (Seyfarth, 1980), was practised more often by

Fig. 119.2 a. Eyelid display; b. Red, white and blue display

females than by males, and some males never took part in grooming at all. The presence of an infant in a troop appeared to strengthen the cohesion within it.

Brain (1965) classified the vocalisations of vervet monkeys into three categories: wanting, alarm and aggression. Infants attracted their mothers with a medium intensity, long drawn gargle with pursed lips. Hunger or pain induced a high-pitched squeal of distress, produced with the mouth open and the lips pursed, which had considerable troop significance. Low intensity aggression as a result of irritation or high intensity aggression when angry, elicited chattering. Seyfarth, Cheney & Marler (1980) found that adult vervets gave acoustically different alarm calls to leopards, *Panthera pardus*, martial eagles, *Polemaetus bellicosus* and pythons, *Python sebae*. Infants could only distinguish between general predator classes, for example between a territorial mammal and a flying bird. Leopard alarms were short tonal calls, eagle alarms low-pitched staccato grunts and snake alarms high-pitched "chutters".

Male vervet monkeys disperse non-randomly in the company of their brothers from their natal groups at sexual maturity, migrating to neighbouring groups, this activity peaking during the mating season (Henzi & Lucas, 1980; Cheney & Seyfarth, 1983). This benefits young males by minimizing the risk of predation or reducing the probability of attack by resident males and females. Older males transfer randomly and alone to more distant groups. This appears to have important genetic consequences for the population as a whole, avoiding the negative effects of excessive endogamy.

Brain (1965) found that at night individuals of the higher dominance status would sleep together, while other lower members formed a separate sleeping group. While a single member of a troop might remain separated from its troop during the day, it would show particular signs of distress if it could not join up with other members at night.

In the wild the troops may sleep either in rocky shelters or more commonly in the higher branches of large trees, in such a position that they are hidden from sight among the foliage. Activity starts at dawn, usually a little later during cold weather, and foraging continues actively until about mid-morning, when the troop may find a sheltered area in the sun in which to rest. In hot weather they may remain resting until early in the afternoon, when foraging recommences. The troop returns to the sleeping places well before sunset. Vervet monkeys are equally at home foraging in trees or on the ground.

Vervet monkeys are preyed upon by four types of predators, namely mammalian carnivores, eagles, baboons and snakes. Adult males who gave most alarm calls in response to possible predation were more likely to have fathered the group's juveniles and infants (Cheney & Seyfarth, 1983). Over a 3,5 year period, deaths due to illness in one group, which accounted for 27% of all cases of mortality, were concentrated among low-ranking individuals and resulted in part from the limited availability of food and water during winter. On the other hand, 50% of all deaths were due to predation, and high-ranking individuals were more likely to be preyed upon (Cheney, Lee & Seyfarth, 1981).

**Food**

Vervet monkeys are predominantly vegetarians living on wild fruits, flowers, leaves, seeds and seed pods. In Botswana the food included the fruit of the wild fig, *Ficus* spp; jackal berry, *Diospyros mespiliformis*; bird plum, *Berchemia discolor*; marula, *Sclerocarya birrea*; buffalo thorn, *Ziziphus mucronata*; the African mangosteen, *Garcinia livingstonei*; large sour plum, *Ximenia caffra*, and the raisin bush, *Grewia* spp. The seeds and seed pods of *Acacia* spp and in particular the camel thorn, *A. erioloba*, were sought after. The seeds of the mopane, *Colophospermum mopane*, are also eaten (Brain, 1965). In KwaZulu, van der Zee & Skinner (1977) listed 12 food plants of which either the buds, flowers, seeds or shoots are eaten, some common to the above list, but also including the white stinkwood, *Celtis africana*; white ironwood, *Vepris undulata*; coast red milkwood, *Mimusops caffra*; white milkwood, *Sideroxylon inerme*; flat-crown, *Albizia adianthifolia*; creepers and cucumbers and the gum of *Acacia* spp. They also eat insects, and grasshoppers and termites have been recognised in stomach contents. In agriculturally developed areas they can become problem animals, raiding beans, peas, young tobacco plants, vegetables, fruit and various grain crops.

In addition they are carnivorous. Skinner & Skinner (1974) recorded their raiding cattle egret, *Bubulcus ibis*, and weaver bird, *Ploceus* spp, colonies and eating the eggs and chicks.

**Reproduction**

There are not the same external signs of the menstrual cycle in female vervet monkeys as in baboons and consequently the elaborate social behaviour associated with these signs is not as apparent. The gestation period is 150–160 days (Henzi, pers. comm.).

Evidence from the Subregion suggests that the young may be born at any time throughout the year (Shortridge, 1934; Smithers, 1971). Birth mass is about 300,0 to 400,0 g. Usually a single young is produced at a birth, rarely twins (Shortridge, 1934).

The females have one pair of pectoral mammae.

---

No. 120

## *Cercopithecus mitis* Wolf, 1822

## Samango monkey
## Samango-aap

Plate 6

---

### Colloquial Name

The name samango is borrowed from the Zulu name for the species, *iNsimango*.

### Taxonomic Notes

Meester *et al.* (1986) listed two subspecies from the Subregion: *C. m. labiatus* I. Geoffroy, 1843 and *C. m. erythrarchus* Peters, 1852.

### Description

Samango monkeys, which are much darker in colour than vervets, have dark brown faces. The long hair on the throat is pure white and extends upwards on either side like a white collar which does not close on the nape of the neck. The hair on the head and shoulders is black, annulated with white or pale buff. The tail is dark above to the tip, the basal one-third buffy-white below. The under parts are whitish or buffy-white and this colour extends on to the inside of the limbs. The flanks and upper part of the limbs are paler than the shoulders. The lower parts of the limbs are black and contrast with the general colour of the body. The subspecies can be distinguished easily on the basis of colour. *C. m. labiatus* has no reddish tinge anywhere and it is generally darker on the shoulders and on the saddle, which is sooty grey, than *C. m. erythrarchus*. The ischial and anal regions are suffused with yellow and the underside of the distal third of the tail may be cream or white (Lawes, pers. comm.). In *C. m. erythrarchus* the saddle region is suffused with yellow and the ischial and anal regions are reddish-brown. Specimens from eastern Zimbabwe tend to be yellower on the upper parts and greyer on the under parts.

The adult males are larger and considerably heavier than the adult females (Table 120.1).

The East African representatives of *C. mitis* are generally larger than those from the Subregion.

### Table 120.1

Measurements (mm) and mass (kg) of samango monkeys, *C. m. erythrarchus*, from a. eastern Zimbabwe (Smithers & Wilson, 1979); b. Cape Vidal, Natal (Lawes, unpubl.) and c. mass of *C. m. labiatus* from Karkloof, Natal (McMahon, 1977)

a.

| | Males | | | Females | | |
|---|---|---|---|---|---|---|
| | x̄ | n | Range | x̄ | n | Range |
| TL | 1383 | 9 | 1323–1445 | 1182 | 7 | 1110–1220 |
| T | 806 | 9 | 783–866 | 697 | 7 | 660–742 |
| Hf s/u | 167 | 9 | 153–178 | 145 | 7 | 138–160 |
| E | 40 | 9 | 35–45 | 38 | 7 | 35–43 |
| Mass | 9,31 | 6 | 8,23–9,99 | 4,91 | 6 | 4,54–5,19 |

b.

| | Males | | | Females | |
|---|---|---|---|---|---|
| | x̄ | n | Range | x̄ | n |
| HB | 595 | 5 | 564–616 | 468 | 2 |
| T | 707 | 5 | 680–730 | 591 | 2 |
| Hf s/u | 153 | 5 | 147–156 | 123 | 2 |
| Mass | 7,16 | 5 | 6,2–7,8 | 4,45 | 2 |

c.

| | Males | | | Females | | |
|---|---|---|---|---|---|---|
| | x̄ | n | Range | x̄ | n | Range |
| Mass | 7,13 | 3 | 6,82–7,73 | 4,62 | 9 | 3,64–5,69 |

### Skull (Figure 120.1.)

Compared with the skull of the vervet monkey, *C. pygerythrus*, the skull in this species is narrower, the cranium less rounded, the rostrum less elongated and prominent and the palate is broader.

### Distribution

Throughout its range from the northeastern parts of Africa to the Cape Province the samango monkey is confined to areas of forest and therefore its distribution is discontinuous within the limits shown on the map.

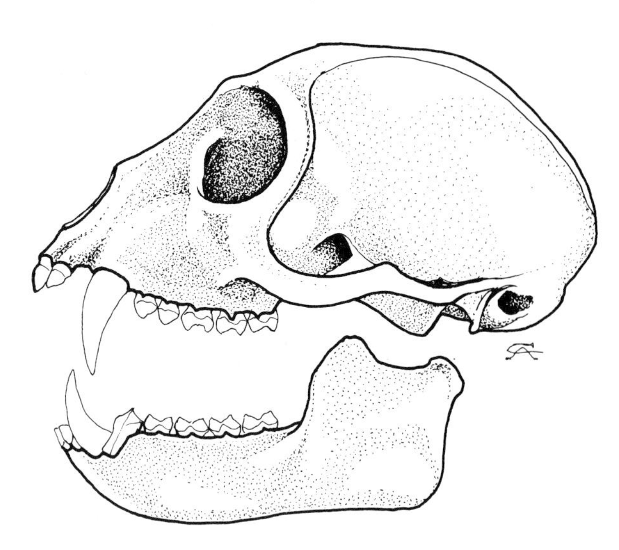

Fig.120.1. Skull: samango monkey, *C. mitis*
TL Skull 105 mm

*South of the Sahara, excluding the Southern African Subregion*

They occur in **Mozambique**, north of the Zambezi River; in **Malawi, Zambia, Tanzania, Kenya**, southern **Somalia**, southern **Ethiopia, Uganda**, and in parts of **Zaire** and northern **Angola**.

*Southern African Subregion*

*C. m. labiatus* occurs from the eastern **Cape Province** northeastwards to the **Natal** midlands. *C. m. erythrarchus* occurs from northern Zululand to the eastern and northeastern **Transvaal**; in the Lubombo mountains from the Mbuluzi River southwards to south of Siteki in **Swaziland**; in eastern **Zimbabwe**, and **Mozambique**, along the Zambezi River, as far as the Mpata Gorge.

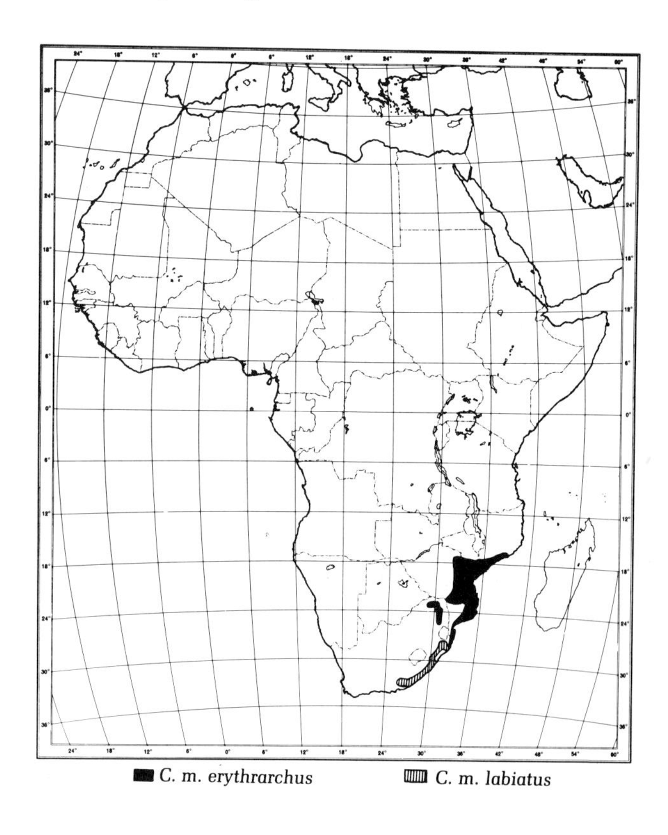


### Habitat

Throughout their distributional range samango monkeys are closely confined to a forest habitat, seldom straying from this except temporarily in transit or when foraging.

## Habits

Samango monkeys are diurnal and gregarious, living in troops which vary in number from four to over 30. Smithers & Wilson (1979) found that in eastern Zimbabwe troops numbered up to 20. Scorer (1980) noted that in the northeastern Transvaal troops numbered from four to 34, with an average of 13,6 (n=5); the size of two troops studied at Ngoye in Natal was 16 and 21, and at Cape Vidal it varied from 28 to 35 individuals (n=3) (Lawes, Henzi & Perrin, 1990). Where counts were made of the numbers in individual troops over a five-month period, the numbers remained constant. Troops invariably have a single adult male, although Scorer (1980) and Aldrich-Blake (1970) recorded more adult males in larger troops. Home range varied from 19,7 ha in the Transvaal to 15,0 ha at Cape Vidal, with a concomitant density of 1,45 *cf.* 1,98/ha respectively.

The troops rest at night in trees, the individuals or small groups of individuals sleeping together. Activity starts in the morning at or just before sunrise, the troops settling for a time sunning themselves at higher altitudes before moving off to feed. In the Natal midlands, MacMahon (1978) recorded that this sunning period could last up to one and a half hours. Scorer (1980) found that, in the northeastern Transvaal, there were seasonal differences in activity periods during the day. In summer troops were inactive 51,8% of the time *cf.* 38,6% in winter. This he ascribed to the greater availability of food and longer days in summer. At Cape Vidal troops feed in the morning and evening, with a midday rest period (Lawes, pers. comm.), with little difference between summer and winter activity periods. They fed for 38,6% of the time when food was abundant, *cf.* 33,2% when food was scarce. Food was abundant when days were short. These differences between the Natal and Transvaal troops' activity patterns may be due to differences in day length and tree-fruiting patterns. Both Scorer (1980) and Lawes (pers. comm.) noted differences in diurnal activity between the various age classes in the troops, males being the most inactive class as they have to be vigilant, but whereas Scorer found adult females to be the most active, Lawes found them next in inactivity. Both in summer and winter troops were inactive during the hottest time of the day, resting up exposed in the tops of the trees in winter and in the shade of the canopy in summer.

As visual communication is difficult in a forest habitat, vocal communication becomes important. Brown & Waser (1984) indicated that the calls of the closely related blue monkeys, *C. mitis stuhlmanni*, in Kenya are pitched in the 100–1000 Hz frequency band, thus being relatively unimpeded by background noises. Their hearing was superior to that of humans for tones below 800 Hz and above 8 kHz in frequency. They exhibited phonatory specialisations for vocal production in the relatively unused low-frequency band of 125–200 Hz. These specialisations for low-frequency vocal production and low frequency hearing collectively act to increase the effective distance of long-range acoustic communication in the forest canopy (Brown & Waser, 1984). Samango monkeys emit a variety of sounds, some of which Scorer (1980) could distinguish as calls, others he classed as grades of the same call. The adult males emit a low-pitched growl during inter-troop encounters, which usually caused the second troop to move off. The loud repeated "pyow" call is only used by adult males. It appears to be a response to potential danger such as the appearance of observers, motor cars or loud noises. "Ka-trains" often follow "pyow" calls. During male-male conflict they emit a dry rasping "ke-ke-ke". Lawes (pers. comm.) found the most distinctive call of the male's repertoire is the "boom" call which is a low frequency hollow boom sound which carries very well in forest but is difficult to locate by an observer. All classes except adult males emit high-pitched contact chirps and clicks to express alarm; they also emit a "rill" which is a reassurance call in response to clicks or boom calls. All classes chirp when one individual approached another or when an individual moved off after a period of inactivity. Females and infants in trouble squeal or scream (Henzi, pers. comm.). When settled they emit a soft contact growl "grr" (Lawes, pers. comm.).

Troop movement showed certain characteristic features. When the troop moved the adult male would move to a position of high visibility in mid canopy where he would sit, watching and listening. If members of the troop lost contact, the adult male would emit the "boom" call. Where accompanied by infants the females would shepherd them over difficult stretches.

Aggression between members of the troop is rare. Head-bobbing is very much part of the threat display by both sexes and is usually sufficient to cause the submissive individual to move off. Home range boundary disputes are settled by the females who group to face the females of the opposing troop. Each troop makes short rushes at the other until one troop yields. Males take little or no part in this activity. On the other hand males will defend their status in the troop from other intruding males by fighting fiercely on occasion, inflicting severe wounds mostly in the head and shoulder region (Henzi & Lawes, 1987, 1989). Henzi & Lawes (1987) found that the density of lone males declined with the onset of the mating season and recorded a concomitant increase in males associated with troops.

Butynski (1982b) described male replacement in a group of 17 to 20 individuals of *C. m. stuhlmanni* in the Kibale Forest of western Uganda. In this group there were at least six replacements of the harem male in 21 months, length of tenure averaging 2,2 months. One particular male, on assuming the alpha rank, was observed to kill a six-month old infant and there was strong indirect evidence that he killed a three-month old and a five-month old infant, the number of infants in the group declining from five to two. No further cases of infanticide during male replacement were observed, although one male made 13 unsuccessful attempts at infanticide during his first two days with the group.

The infanticidal male would move suddenly and rapidly, taking a direct route to the mother-infant pair. As the male began to move, the mother with infant would take refuge in the densest foliage. As many as two other females generally interposed themselves between the charging male and the mother-infant pair. Infanticide has not been observed in *C. mitis* in the Subregion.

In her review of infanticide Hrdy (1979) offered five hypotheses, four of which suggested that the perpetrator thereby increases his inclusive fitness. Data were too few to draw definite conclusions in this instance. Butynski (1982b) suggested that the data indirectly support the hypothesis that infanticide is part of a flexible, adaptive reproductive strategy of new harem males. Length of male tenure is probably a critical determinant of inclusive fitness, not only for males but also for females. Through their long tenures the "best" harem males contribute stability to the group, thereby minimizing the frequency of infanticide.

## Food

Scorer (1980) found that in the northeastern Transvaal Drakensberg samango monkeys utilised one or other part of a large percentage of plant species growing in the area. Ripe wild fruits were the commonest food item, 79 species out of the available 83 being taken. This was followed by flowers, where 28 out of 83 species were eaten, together with the leaves of 10 species. Mature leaves were taken in winter as well as the gum of *Acacia karroo*. Among the 83 plant species that provided food, Scorer (1980) listed 21 species which he considered of major importance. Of these the fruits, dry and green leaves, flowers, pods and shoots were eaten, in some cases only at specific times of the year. Insects were also eaten and caterpillars sought after. They would raid orchard fruits such as guavas, mangoes and bananas and wild-living mulberries and grenadillas were also taken. Usually small berries were plucked with the teeth from the branch, but larger fruits were plucked with the hands and conveyed to the mouth, the skin and pips of some fruits being discarded. In the Soutpansberg, following stomach analyses, Breytenbach (1988) confirmed that fruit and leaves were the most important items eaten.

Near Lake Sibayi in Natal, van der Zee & Skinner (1977) showed that the fruit, seeds, buds, flowers, leaves and shoots of a list of food plants were eaten, particularly wild figs, *Ficus natalensis*; white stinkwood, *Celtis africana*;

*Acacia karroo*; and creepers (Papilionaceae). In his study in the Cape Vidal dune forest further south in Natal, Lawes (pers. comm.) confirmed that samango monkeys in the Subregion are frugivorous, a limited number of food species dominating the diet at any one time. Indeed, over a 12 month period, four out of the 20 top species made up 49,4% of utilisation, namely *Isoglossa woodii*, coastal red milkwood, *Mimusops caffra*, sweet thorn, *Acacia karroo* and cross-berry, *Grewia occidentalis*. Lawes *et al.* (1990) found that samango monkeys in the Ngoye forest concentrated their attention on items of greater energy value during periods of food abundance, but were less selective during periods of food scarcity. The diets of samangos differ somewhat from vervet monkeys, with samangos being more frugivorous and including more leaf material in their diet. This is reflected in the volume of the samango hindgut (caecum and colon) which greatly exceeds that of vervets. Bruorton & Perrin (1988) suggested that the hindgut, with its many folds to increase surface area, slows down the passage rate of food and that an active fermentation process occurs, ensuring maximal energy returns from the foliar and undigested fruit component of the diet from the time it enters the hindgut.

Samango monkeys are known to strip bark from exotic trees in the Soutpansberg, causing considerable damage in some instances (Droomer, 1985; von dem Bussche & van der Zee, 1985). However, Beeson (1987) found this feeding behaviour to be extremely rare and is therefore not undertaken as a response to a deficient diet. Moreover, he observed that, after stripping, the monkeys only lick the inner bark and do not eat it. The reason for bark-stripping is unknown, but it is thought to result from disturbance by man, forcing the monkeys into plantations where stripping begins as an aberrant behaviour and they acquire a taste for sap. It has been suggested that this type of damage is caused by lone males, but Breytenbach (1988) could find no evidence for this, nor that phloem from *Pinus* sp was present in the stomach contents of 56 monkeys, with one exception.

Butynski (1982c) described two cases of predation on galagos (possibly *G. senegalensis*) by *C. m. stuhlmanni*. In one instance a female chased the galago and caught it, in the second a female was seen carrying a dead galago. The galagos were devoured totally and the meat was not shared with other members of the group. At least nine times, while feeding on the galagos, the two monkeys grabbed mature leaves of *Uvariopsis* and chewed them with pieces of skin, fur, viscera and flesh. This was the only time mature leaves from this tree were seen to be eaten, and appeared to be selected simply because they were the nearest available. Intermixing of leaves with portions of galago and other vertebrate prey has been observed in the chimpanzee, *Pan troglodytes* (van Lawick-Goodall, 1968), where it is referred to as "wadging". Whereas the chimpanzees often discard chewing-wads, blue monkeys swallow them. "Wadging" appears to prolong mastication of animal matter. No evidence of predation on galagos is available for the Subregion, but Breytenbach (1988) found meat and feathers in the stomachs of four monkeys.

**Reproduction**

Some information is available on the time of the year at which the young are born, indicating that they are seasonal breeders, the young being born during the warm, wet months of the year from October to December at Cape Vidal, Natal (Henzi & Lawes, 1987), January to April in the north-eastern Transvaal (Scorer, 1980) and, in eastern Zimbabwe, Smithers & Wilson (1979) recorded gravid females from August to February. Measured birth intervals for *C. m. stuhlmanni* for females in the wild whose first offspring survived, varied from 24–54 months (median 47, n=10) (Cords & Rowell, 1987). No information is available for the species in the Subregion.

The gestation period is 140 days (Cords, 1987). Usually a single young is produced at a birth, but a female from eastern Zimbabwe carried well developed twin foetuses.

At birth the pelage lacks the grizzling seen on the hairs of the adult coat and the infant is dark grey or nearly black in colour and has white eartips. The infant remains with its mother for about two months before becoming independent.

The females have a pair of pectoral mammae.

# Order PHOLIDOTA

## The pangolin

# XIV. Family MANIDAE

This Order is represented in Africa by one Family, the Manidae, and four species: the pangolin, sometimes called Temminck's ground pangolin, *Manis temminckii* Smuts, 1832, the only species which occurs in the Subregion; the giant pangolin, *M. gigantea* Illiger, 1815, which occurs in West Africa eastwards to Uganda and southwards to Angola, and as the name implies is considerably larger, and the rows of scales on the body and tail are more numerous; the long-tailed pangolin, *M. tetradactylus* Linnaeus, 1766, which has a similar distribution to *M. gigantea*, and the tree pangolin, *M. tricuspis* Rafinesque, 1820, which occurs in West Africa and eastwards to East Africa and south to the forested areas of northwestern Zambia.

In the past, authors have subdivided the Family Manidae to which they all belong into four Subgenera: *Smutsia*, for the pangolin which occurs in the Subregion, *M. temminckii*, and the giant pangolin, *M. gigantea; Phataginus* for the tree pangolin; *Uromanis* for the long-tailed pangolin (Pocock, 1924; Allen, 1939), and *Paramanis* for the Javan pangolin, *M. javanica*. Meester (1972a) in his review recognised these three genera as subgenera.

No fossil remains of pangolins were known from Africa until Klein (1972) recorded material which he questionably referred to the extant *M. temminckii*, from the late Pleistocene beds at Nelson Bay, Cape Province. This was followed by the discovery of post-cranial bones from Pliocene deposits at Langebaanweg, Cape Province by Hendey (1974). Patterson (1978) suggested that the reason for their scarcity as fossils is that the bones of species dying in burrows are particularly liable to destruction by the action of plant roots and percolating rain water. Also pangolins have no teeth, which is so often the only factual evidence that remains of mammals in fossil deposits.

Other genera of pangolins are known from the Pleistocene and the much earlier Eocene/Oligocene beds of Eurasia dating back to over 40 million years ago. Views differ on the origin of pangolins. Patterson (1978) believed that pangolins reached Africa from Eurasia late in the Oligocene Epoch about 22 million years ago, together with Orders such as the Carnivora and Perissodactyla.

## Genus *Manis* Linnaeus, 1758
## Subgenus *Smutsia* Gray, 1865

---

No. 121

## *Manis temminckii* Smuts, 1832

## Pangolin
## Ietermagog

Plate 8

---

### Colloquial Name

This is derived from the Malay *peng-goling*, meaning the roller, from their habit of rolling themselves into a ball as a defence mechanism.

### Taxonomic Notes

Only *M. temminckii* occurs in the Subregion.

### Description

The pangolin is unmistakable among mammals as it is covered with an armour of heavy, brown scales. Pangolins reach an overall length of over a metre and a mass of up to about 18 kg (Table 121.1). The head is small, the muzzle pointed and covered with small scales which continue forward of the eyes. The sides of the face to the back of the large, vertical, elongated ear openings are naked. The eyelids have a few fringing hairs, the ear openings have fluffy, soft hair inside and there are scattered curly hairs on the skin of the under parts. The small eyes are set in soft bulbous outgrowths on the sides of the head.

The body is widest at the level of the hind limbs, gradually tapering off to the broad tail tip and forward to the back of the head, then abruptly to the muzzle. The under parts and sides of the face are devoid of scales and the black or dark grey skin is tough and pliable. The under side of the tail, which is rounded on top and concave underneath to fit the rounded body when rolled up, is covered with scales to its tip. The limbs are covered with small scales which extend downwards to the top of the feet. The scales on the upper parts are thick and heavy, the mass of the skin plus the scales representing about a third of the total mass of the individual.

There are five digits on the front feet, the first with a small nail, the central three with long, strongly curved claws, the third, the longest, measuring up to about 45 mm over the curve. They have five digits on the hind feet, each with a short nail-like claw, and four of the nails normally mark in the spoor. The soles of the hind feet are rounded in front and taper off slightly behind (Fig. 121.2). Pangolins have anal glands which secrete a waxy fluid having a heavy, foul smell.

**Table 121.1**

A. Measurements (mm) and mass (kg) of pangolins, *M. temminckii*, from Zimbabwe (Smithers & Wilson, 1979) and B. mass (kg) of pangolins captured in the Transvaal (van Aarde & Richardson, pers. comm.)

| A. | Irrespective of sex | | |
|---|---|---|---|
| | $\bar{x}$ | n | Range |
| TL | 809 | 11 | 702–1 049 |
| T(to mid anus) | 388 | 11 | 310–440 |
| Hf c/u | 60 | 11 | 52–70 |
| Mass | 7,18 | 11 | 4,54–14,53 |

| B. | | | |
|---|---|---|---|
| | $\bar{x}$ | n | Range |
| Mass | 10,88 ±4,05 | 8 | 7,1–18,0 |

**Skull** (Fig. 121.1)

The skull of the pangolin is simple in outline. Viewed from above it is pear-shaped, the broadest part being just behind the ear openings, tapering off evenly forward to the nasals and more abruptly behind to the occiput. There is no interorbital constriction. The zygomatic arches are represented by short processes at either end which never join, and it lacks any sign of postorbital bars. The ear bullae are rounded. Pangolins have no teeth, but in the position of the toothrows there are narrow raised ridges of bone on the upper jaw. The mandible consists of a simple thin bony structure, joined in front, with two small bony processes one on either side extending outwards near the junction. The condyles are simple flattened sections of the bone structure which hinge on the internal faces of the hind process of the zygoma, to which they are attached by cartilage. The mandible is so fragile that it can play little part in mastication, this function being taken over by a special adaptation of the stomach (see **Food**).

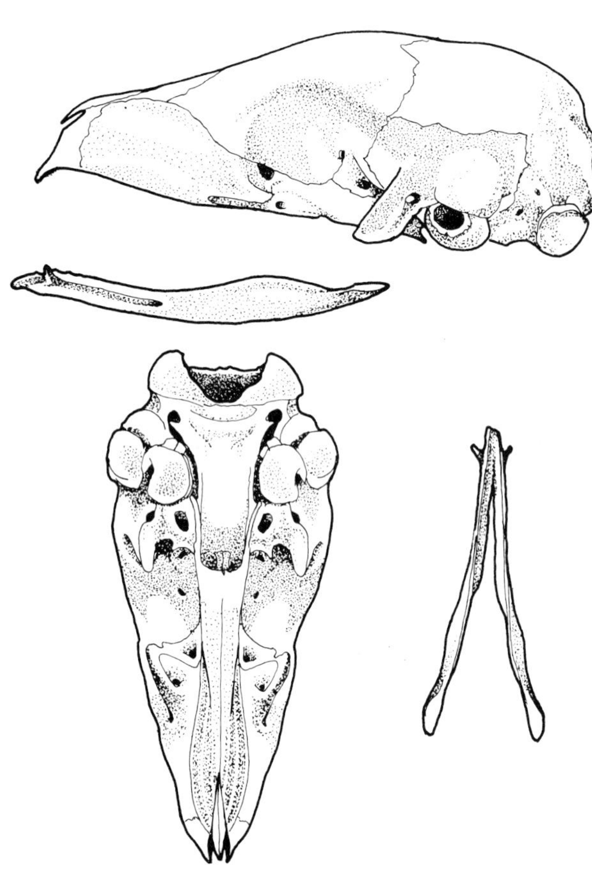

Fig.121.1. Skull: pangolin, *M. temminckii*.
TL skull 79 mm

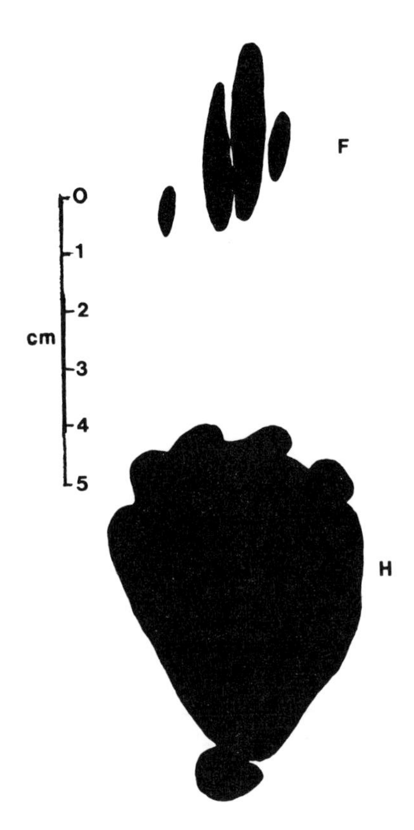


Fig.121.2. Spoor: pangolin, *M. temminckii*.
Note: Front claws only occasionally touch the ground.

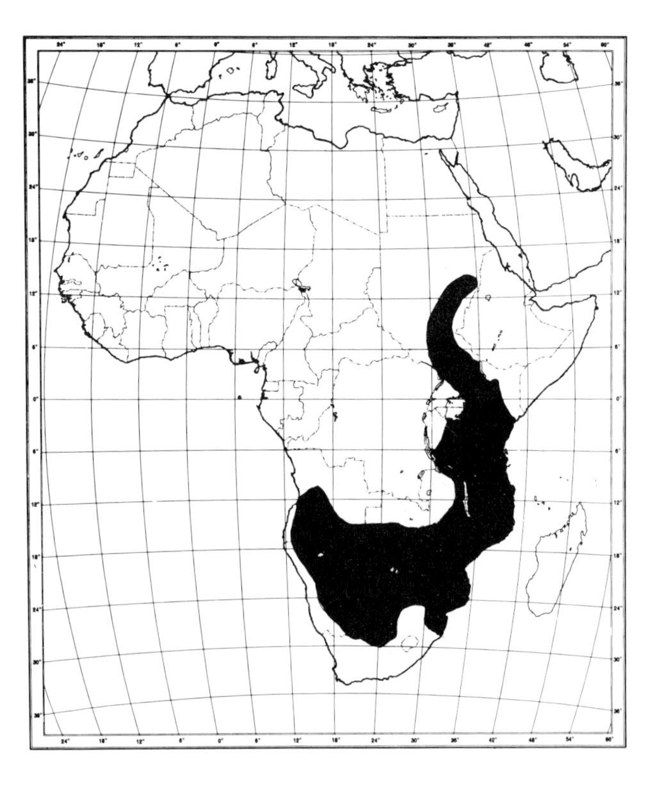

**Distribution**

At the northern limits of their distributional range, some authors extend their limits westward to the Central African Republic (Dorst & Dandelot, 1970), but there may be confusion here with *M. gigantea* and, until further information is available, these records are not incorporated. Funaioli & Simonetta (1966) stated that it is doubtful if they occur in Somalia and there do not appear to be any records from Ethiopia. In parts of Uganda the pangolin, *M. temminckii*, is sympatric with the giant pangolin, *M. gigantea*, but is replaced by it southwest of the Victoria Nile. There is a record from Mossamedes, in southwestern Angola, but as this lies in the coastal desert and as pangolins do not occur in this type of biome, the record is not plotted. The specimen probably came from an inland locality where they do occur. Throughout their range pangolins are not common and this, coupled with their secretive habits, makes them difficult to contact and records are few and scattered.

*South of the Sahara, excluding the Southern African Subregion*

They are recorded from the southern **Sudan**; western **Kenya**; eastern **Uganda; Rwanda; Tanzania; Zambia;** central and southern **Angola** and **Malawi**. There are no records to date from Mozambique, north of the Zambezi River, but they may well occur as they are known in other parts of this country and from surrounding countries.

*Southern African Subregion*

Pangolins occur widely in **Namibia**, except in the southern parts of the country and in the coastal desert. In **Botswana** they are widespread, but more frequently contacted in the northern and eastern sectors, with a few scattered records from the more arid central and southern areas. They occur widely in **Zimbabwe** and are not uncommon in parts of Mashonaland, in the vicinity of Harare. In **Mozambique**, south of the Zambezi River, they occur in the central parts of the Vila Pery and Beira districts and southwards throughout the remainder of the country. They are recorded from the northern **Cape Province**; the western, northern and eastern parts of the **Transvaal**; the central and southern parts of the **Orange Free State** and northeastern **Natal**.

## Habitat

The pangolin, *M. temminckii*, is a savanna species, not occurring in forests or in desert. Within this broad category, however, they are catholic in their requirements, occurring in scrub, in areas of low rainfall (250 mm per year), as well as in those with a much higher rainfall of up to 1 400 mm per year, in various types of savanna woodland. They have also been taken on floodplain grassland, in rocky hills, as well as on sandveld.

They require shelter to rest in during the day. This may be provided by holes in the ground, rock crevices or sufficient ground debris in which they can hide, which is available in any of the habitats mentioned. While they will drink water in captivity, they occur in areas where it is only available seasonally.

## Habits

Pangolins are solitary foragers and predominantly nocturnal, with some diurnal activity. In Zimbabwe they were quite frequently brought into the Queen Victoria Museum, Harare, after being picked up crossing roads during daylight hours, and in Botswana they were observed moving between 11h30 and 16h00. Pangolins radio-tracked in the Transvaal were active predominantly between sunset and 01h30, with a well defined peak in activity between 21h30 and 22h30. The total distances moved during a night varied from 0 to 6,2 km, with a mean of 3,8 ± 1,53 (S.D.) for 10 nights when activity did occur (van Aarde, pers. comm.).

When moving in dry grass or under bush, pangolins can be quite noisy, but they are shy, and at the least sign of danger, will "freeze", standing motionless, when they are overlooked easily. Their brown colour blends well with the background, making them difficult to see under these conditions. When walking the body is balanced on the hind feet, the forefeet and tail held clear off the ground. They may allow the tail to scrape the ground momentarily or swing forward, taking the weight onto the front edge of either set of claws of the front feet in a manner unsynchronised with the hind feet. The hind feet are round in front, tapering slightly towards the back, with cushioned pads. Characteristic of their spoor are the marks of the rounded pads of the hind feet with the five nails, intermittently the occasional scrape of the tail and the mark of the front edges of the long, curved, front claws.

Normally they are slow movers and can be followed at a walk. Under stress they can move at a smart pace raised high on the back legs and they will try and locate danger by pausing and raising the body into a near vertical position on the back legs, balancing on the broad tail, to sniff the wind. If touched or put under stress they will curl themselves into a tight ball with the head inside, the broad tough scales affording effective protection to the head and soft under parts. In this position it is difficult to prize them open. When this is attempted the broad tail, which is clamped securely around the outside of the ball, slides from side to side over it and a hand or finger caught between the sharp edges of its scales and those on the body can be severely cut.

It has been stated that pangolins excavate their own holes, but this has not been observed. Individuals that have been found have been taken either walking around or from disused antbear or springhaas burrows or buried in piles of debris in a shady situation. The Indian pangolin, *M. crassicaudata*, on the other hand, can claw a hole in loose soil with almost incredible speed, disappearing in a few moments, and closing the hole behind it with its tail. In the Subregion captive individuals that were allowed free movement in the bush never showed signs of excavating a hiding place for themselves, preferring rather to try and hide away under tree roots or in debris.

Normally terrestrial, pangolins climb over fallen logs or other obstructions with ease, and will surmount netting fences a metre in height. They are capable of forcing themselves through surprisingly small apertures. A 6 kg individual made its way out of the 100 mm × 80 mm interstices of a trap in which it was being held temporarily, repeating the perfomance under observation later.

Pangolins occupy definable home ranges, these ranging from 1,3 to 7,9 km$^2$ in extent for animals radio-tracked in the northern and eastern Transvaal. They apparently have a limited home range for a period of one to two months, after which they move to adjacent areas of similar size. Individual home ranges do overlap, but initial indications suggest that individuals remain temporarily separated (van Aarde, pers. comm.).

The tongue is long and rounded and is attached by muscles to a free-floating cartilaginous structure, which in turn is actuated by a series of muscles running the length of the body around the lower part of the abdomen to near the kidneys. This allows for an enormous extension of the tongue which, with its accessory muscle structure, is longer than the head and body. In addition they have a throat pouch into which part of the tongue folds when not extended.

## Food

The pangolin feeds predominantly on formicid ants. In a sample of nine stomachs the principal content was ants, termites appearing in only two, although in one case they predominated over ants in the proportion of 75% to 25%. The ants consisted of a large proportion of larvae and pupal stages.

Two individuals in captivity, allowed free movement, both excavated into the underground nests of *Camponotus thales* which were not apparent to the human observer on the surface. After locating the nests, which they appeared to do by scent, they opened them up with the curved front claws, inserted the head into the excavation, and lay there for a time. While it was impossible to observe exactly what transpired, it appeared that they were inserting their long, sticky tongues up the internal tunnels and withdrawing them covered with ants, pupae and larvae. On completion of this operation one individual licked up larvae and pupae from the surface of the excavation. In the process of feeding, considerable quantities of soil and debris are also ingested. Pangolins have no teeth and the food is ground up in muscular regions of the stomach where the ingested grit may well assist in the process. Kingdon (1971) rated pangolins as selective feeders and Sweeney (1956) recorded that one under observation ignored the mounds of termites, *Trinervitermes* sp and *Macrotermes bellicosus*. *M. bellicosus* mounds were readily available to the two individuals in captivity mentioned above and likewise were ignored in favour of formicid ants. Other species of formicids taken included *Anoplolepis custodiens* and *Paltothyreus tarsatus*.

## Reproduction

Few records are available from the Subregion on the time at which the young are born. Gravid females have been taken in July and a captive birth recorded in this month. Ansell (1960a) listed a 450 mm juvenile taken in July in Zambia. These records suggest that the time of birth may be during the colder, drier months of the year. One young only is produced at a birth.

The scales on a foetus are longer than on the juveniles, and have soft, transparent edges. The claws of the front feet have soft cartilaginous covers and the nails on the hind feet are curved under the soles.

In the very young stages, when under stress, a juvenile will take refuge underneath the female who curls up around it. As it grows up and becomes too large to be completely enclosed, its head and shoulders are enveloped, its tail firmly clasped across the body of the female. By this means the heads of both the female and the juvenile are afforded protection. When separated from the mother the juvenile, under stress, will curl up on its own from an early age.

Apparently the young accompany the females for a considerable time, for an 11,95 kg female was found accompanied by a 2,98 kg juvenile. This juvenile travelled on its mother's back, the long front claws firmly clamped under the scales of the female's flanks, its tail clasped tightly across the base of the tail of the female.

Females have one pair of pectoral mammae.

# Order LAGOMORPHA

## Hares and rabbits

# XV. Family LEPORIDAE

## Hares, rock rabbits, rabbits

This Family is represented in the Subregion by three genera: *Lepus* Linneaus, 1758, *Pronolagus* Lyon, 1904 and *Bunolagus* Thomas, 1929, and one introduced genus, *Oryctolagus* Lilljeborg, 1874. The number of species assigned to the first three named genera has been the subject of controversy over the years. Allen (1939) recognised 30 different species of *Lepus* as occurring on the continent, two of which, *L. saxatilis* F. Cuvier, 1823 and *L. capensis* Linnaeus, 1758, he listed as occurring in the Subregion. Roberts (1951) followed Allen (1939), but Petter (1959; 1972) using the variation in the enamel invagination of the principal upper incisor teeth, recognised that a third species occurred in the Subregion, *L. crawshayi* de Winton, 1899. With the collecting of more adequate material Smithers (1971) believed, however, that there is some evidence of clinal variation in both ear length and total length of skull from the southwestern Cape Province northeastwards to Botswana and Zimbabwe and only recognised *L. saxatilis* and *L. capensis* as occurring in this area. Rautenbach (1978) criticised the diagnostic characters proposed by Petter (1972) for *L. crawshayi* and treated it as a subspecies of *L. saxatilis*.

A similar type of disagreement prevailed over the species assigned to the genus *Pronolagus*. Roberts (1951) recognised six species, Ellerman *et al.* (1953) only three: *P. crassicaudatus*, *P. randensis* and *P. rupestris*, based primarily on occipitonasal length and length of the ear bullae. The latter, because of the configuration of the bullae, is a difficult measurement to arrive at with accuracy. Lundholm (1955a) considered *P. crassicaudatus* and *P. randensis* as inseparable. Peddie (1975) took the matter further and concluded by suggesting that only one species, *P. crassicaudatus*, occurs in the Subregion. It was not unexpected, therefore, that Petter (1972) in his review stated that this genus was in need of revision.

At the generic level the status of *Bunolagus* was also the subject of controversy. Originally it was described as *Lepus monticularis* Thomas, 1903, but generic differences between it and representatives of *Lepus* were later recognised (Thomas, 1929), and it was given the generic name *Bunolagus*. Nevertheless, Ellerman & Morrison-Scott (1951) regarded *Bunolagus* as a synonym of *Lepus* and this was accepted by Ellerman *et al.* (1953) and Meester, Davis & Coetzee (1964). Petter (1972), however, reverted to the treatment afforded to the genus by Thomas (1929) in the use of the name *Bunolagus monticularis*, a species which remains one of the rarest and most interesting of the mammals that occur in the Subregion.

With the uncertainties raised by these controversies it was apparent that a complete revision was required, bringing to bear on the problems not only traditional taxonomic methods, but in addition a number of modern techniques including univariate and multivariate morphometric analysis, karyology, sperm morphology, electrophoretic analysis of serum proteins and red blood cell enzymes. This challenge was accepted by Robinson (1981a) with the following results which do much to clarify the generic and specific relationships of the members of the Family in the Southern African Subregion.

The results of Robinson's (1981a) investigation on the indigenous genera support the recognition of *Lepus*, *Pronolagus* and *Bunolagus*. While morphometric analyses clearly show that, on cranial characters, *Pronolagus* is distinct from the others, the differences between *Lepus* and *Bunolagus* are not clear cut. Their skull morphology is similar, although in series *Lepus* has, on the average, larger skulls. Studies of their chromosomes, however, show that all three genera can be identified both by their diploid number: *Lepus* 2n=48; *Pronolagus* 2n=42 and *Bunolagus* 2n=44 and by the unique morphology of several of their chromosomes. This latter criterion provides unusually strong support for the generic

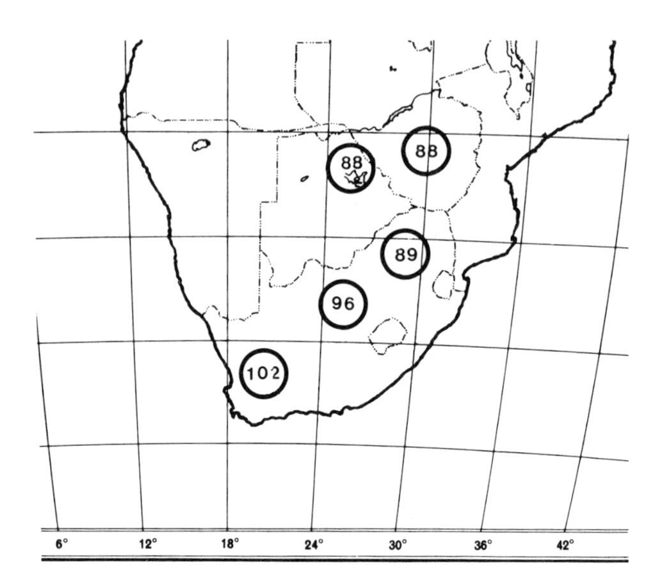


Fig. XV.1. Average total length of the skull (mm), *L. saxatilis*, from five localities in the Subregion (Smithers, 1971).

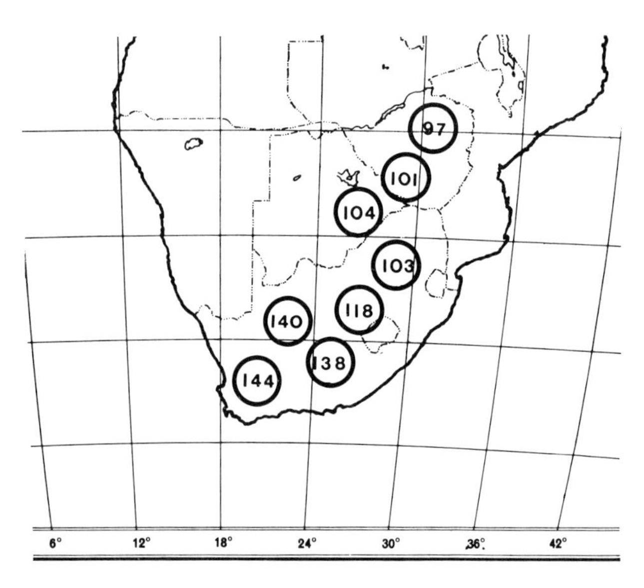


Fig. XV.2. Average ear length (mm), *L. saxatilis*, from eight localities in the Subregion (Robinson, pers. comm.).

status of *Bunolagus* as distinct from *Lepus*, the genus to which it has been assigned in the past.

In addition the shape of the incisor teeth in cross-section (see later text), the morphology of the sperm, and external phenotypic characters all serve to show that three discrete groups occur within the Family, these corresponding to the three genera, *Lepus*, *Pronolagus* and *Bunolagus*.

Morphometric analyses of members of the genus *Lepus* give a clear indication of two phenetically distinct species: *L. saxatilis* and *L. capensis* and do not substantiate the occurrence of the third species, *L. crawshayi*, as suggested by Petter (1972). An analysis of geographic variation in ear and skull length indicates that *L. saxatilis* varies clinally from the larger form found in the southwestern Cape Province in a northeasterly direction to at least Zimbabwe (Fig. XV. 1 & 2). Possibly when specimens of *L. whytei* Thomas, 1894 from Malawi, which is a small species, are re-examined the results may show an extension of the cline even further in a northeasterly direction. Ellerman *et al.*'s (1953) treatment of *L. saxatilis* as a synonym of the older named *L. europaeus* Pallas, 1778 is not borne out by Robinson (1981a) who showed that the configuration of the principal incisor teeth in the two species is markedly different.

Robinson's (1981a) conclusions support the recognition of the three species of *Pronolagus: P. crassicaudatus*, *P. rupestris* and *P. randensis*, particularly on the basis of morphometric analyses and pelage characteristics, as well as the unique characters of the monotypic *Bunolagus monticularis*.

Many people still persist in referring to the two members of the genus *Lepus* that occur in the Subregion, the scrub hare, *Lepus saxatilis*, and the Cape hare, *Lepus capensis*, as rabbits and to members of the genus *Pronolagus* as hares. Curiously enough few of the very early writers made this mistake. In 1605 Sir Edward Michelbourne (Raven-Hart, 1967 p.32) and Van Riebeeck in 1652 (Thom, 1952, 1: 61) correctly identified the small lagomorphs that they saw on the Cape Peninsula as hares (Skead, 1980). Mentzel (1787) was correct when, taking the matter still further, he recognised two hares "one that was a little bigger, the other a little smaller", which were presumably the scrub hare, *L. saxatilis*, and the Cape hare, *L. capensis*, but was incorrect in referring to a third as the "mountain hare", for this was presumably Smith's red rock rabbit, *Pronolagus rupestris*.

Confusion in the use of the colloquial names hare and rabbit is not confined to southern Africa. The North American jack "rabbits", to take an example, are members of the genus *Lepus* and therefore should be called hares. Colloquial names tend to become entrenched so deeply that it is almost impossible to change them, but it is felt that the time has come to refer to members both of the genus *Pronolagus* and the single species of *Bunolagus* as rabbits. One of the most pertinent arguments in favour of this is that while all members of the genus *Lepus* examined to date, both from the Subregion and many other parts of the world, have a chromosome compliment of 2n=48, *Pronolagus* has 2n=42 and *Bunolagus* 2n=44 (Robinson, 1980; Robinson, 1981a; Robinson, Elder & Lopez-Forment, 1981). In addition, while the hind limbs of both hares and rabbits are longer than the forelimbs, the difference is less marked in the rabbit, and in this respect both *Pronolagus* and *Bunolagus* fit better into the rabbit category. The mesopterygoid space in the skull of hares is broader and the palate shorter than in rabbits, except for the riverine rabbit, *Bunolagus monticularis*, in which they are similar to *Lepus* (Fig. XV.3). These differences may well be related to the different methods used to escape from predators. Hares which live in open spaces escape by running with frequent changes of direction, whereas rabbits seek cover. The riverine rabbit is somewhat intermediate.

Members of the genus *Lepus* rest in forms in clumps of grass or under bushes and the young are born in these forms which afford them little protection either from the weather or from predation. To improve their chances of survival they are precocial, being born fully furred with their eyes open and are capable from birth of moving around on their own. Young hares, if disturbed in the forms, are adept at making off and hiding themselves in nearby cover where their cryptic coloration makes them very difficult to find. On the other hand rabbits have their young in the security of their underground burrows and they are born altricial, almost naked and with their eyes closed, and do not leave the security of these burrows until they are grown up enough to look after themselves.

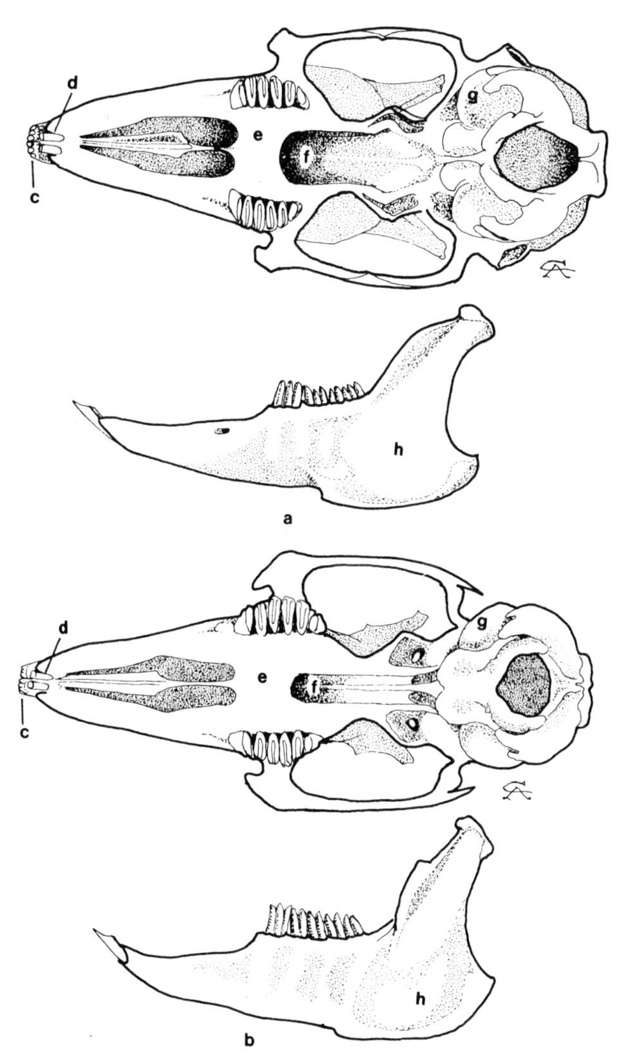


Fig. XV.3. Skulls: Leporidae
(a) *Lepus saxatilis*
(b) *Pronolagus crassicaudatus*
(c) principal upper incisor teeth
(d) secondary peg-like upper incisor teeth
(e) hard palate
(f) mesopterygoid space
(g) ear bulla
(h) mandible

The young of *Pronolagus rupestris* (Pepler, pers. comm.) and *Bunolagus monticularis* (Duthie, 1989) are born altricial. The latter are protected in a short, fur-lined burrow as neonates. This fact confirms the rabbit status of *Bunolagus* which originally was consigned to the genus *Lepus*.

A foetus of *Pronolagus randensis* in the collection of the National Museum, Zimbabwe, had a crown/rump length of 100 mm, a hind foot c/u of 24 mm and a mass of 73,7 g and was judged to be close to full-term. Its eyes and ears were closed and its body was naked except for a very sparse covering of fine hairs.

## Genus *Lepus*

*Morphology of the principal upper incisor teeth*

Forsyth Major (1898) noted the differences in the enamel pattern of certain species of *Lepus* and these differences were developed by Petter (1959; 1961; 1963a) and Petter & Genest (1965).

Robinson (1981a) investigated this character in the genera *Lepus*, *Pronolagus* and *Bunolagus* from the Subregion and found that the shape of these teeth in section, their measurements across the face and the presence or absence of cement in the invagination of the enamel layer on the anterior face of the teeth, afforded useful and reliable criteria for distinguishing the genera and species.

*Lepus capensis* (Fig. XV.4)

In this species the enamel fold is consistently relatively shallow, always of simple configuration and, without exception, is characterised by the presence of cement. In cross-section the teeth are more squarish compared to the more elongated teeth of *L. saxatilis*.

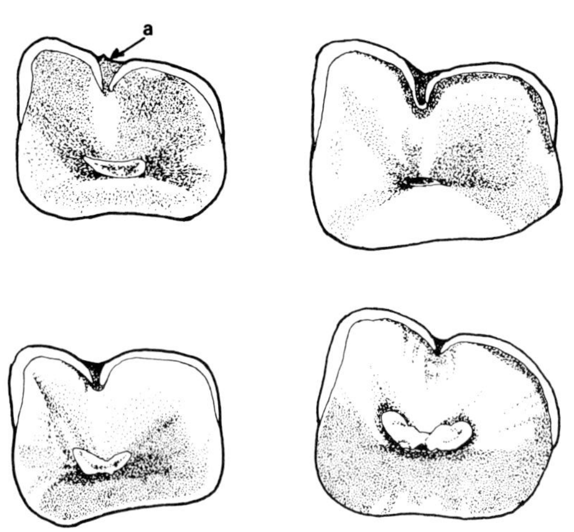


Fig. XV.4. Variation in the cross-section through a principal upper incisor in four specimens of the Cape hare, *Lepus capensis*. (a) cement.

*Lepus saxatilis* (Fig. XV.5)

In this species, in spite of the fact that there is more intra-population variation in the shape of the cement-filled enamel fold than in *L. capensis*, it nevertheless provides a reliable means of distinguishing this species from *L. capensis*. A range of shapes from specimens from the central Cape Province is shown in Fig. XV.5. Robinson (1981a) showed that there appeared to be a tendency towards increasing complexity of the shape of the fold from the southwestern Cape Province in a northeastern direction. In the southwestern Cape Province the fold was relatively simple and did not extend deeply into the tooth (Fig. XV.5.a). In material from further northeastward the fold tended to become more convoluted, with pronounced bifurcations of the fold (Fig. XV.5.b).

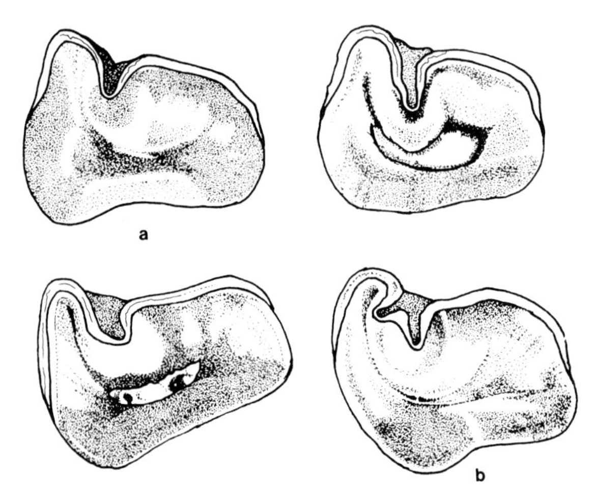


Fig. XV.5. Variation in cross-section through a principal upper incisor in four specimens of the scrub hare, *Lepus saxatilis*, from the central Cape Province.

The incisors are noticeably more robust in *L. saxatilis* and broader, the measurements being *L. saxatilis*: $\bar{x}$=3,1 mm (2,6–3,6 mm), compared with *L. capensis*: $\bar{x}$=2,5 mm (2,3–2,8 mm).

## Genus *Pronolagus*

The most striking difference between members of this genus and those of *Lepus* is that in *Pronolagus* there is a complete absence of cement in the enamel fold. At the species level the variation lies in the shape of the cross-section of the teeth and not on the enamel folding.

Distinct differences exist between the shape in *P. crassicaudatus* and *P. rupestris* (Fig. XV.6.a.b and c.d), although the shape in *P. crassicaudatus* and *P. randensis* is more similar in respect of this character.

The disparity in cross-section between *P. crassicaudatus* and *P. randensis*, and *P. rupestris*, lies in the elongation of the teeth lateral to the enamel fold. The incisor breadth in the three species is: *P. crassicaudatus* $\bar{x}$=3,2 mm (2,9–3,6 mm); *P. randensis* $\bar{x}$=3,0 mm (2,6–3,4 mm) and *P. rupestris* $\bar{x}$=2,5 mm (2,3–2,8 mm).

The width and shape of the cross-section of the teeth in *P. crassicaudatus* and *P. randensis* tend to be similar, but the incisors tend to be flatter anterio-posteriorly in *P. crassicaudatus* than in *P. randensis*, although the difference is slight. As far as the incisor teeth are concerned Robinson (1981a) felt that using this criterion alone would be insufficient to separate these two species. There remain, however, other characters by which they can be separated (see Key to the species).

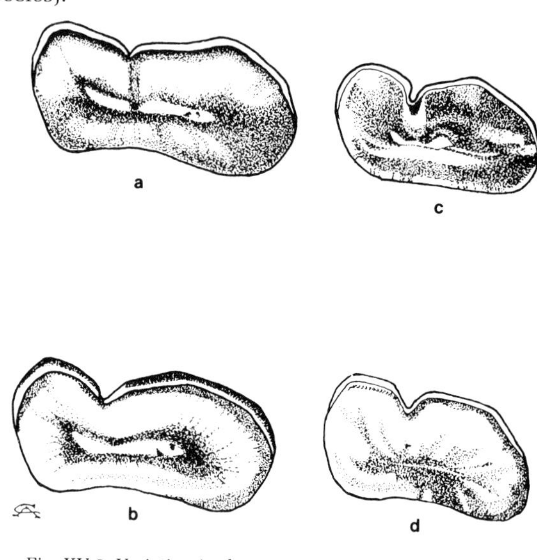


Fig. XV.6. Variation in the cross-section through a principal upper incisor of: (a) and (b) Natal red rock rabbit, *Pronolagus crassicaudatus*; (c) and (d) Smith's red rock rabbit, *P. rupestris*. Note elongation of tooth in *P. crassicaudatus* and absence of cement in both species.

## Genus *Bunolagus*

In the riverine rabbit, *B. monticularis*, the principal upper incisor teeth are much more rounded than in either *Lepus* or *Pronolagus* and lack cement in the enamel fold (Fig. XV.7).

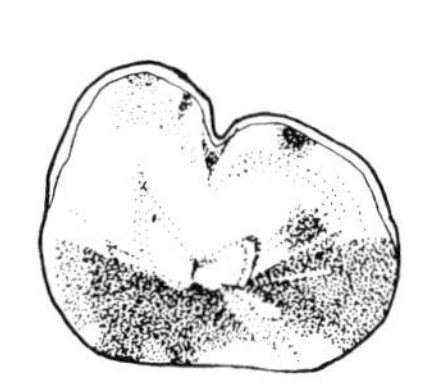

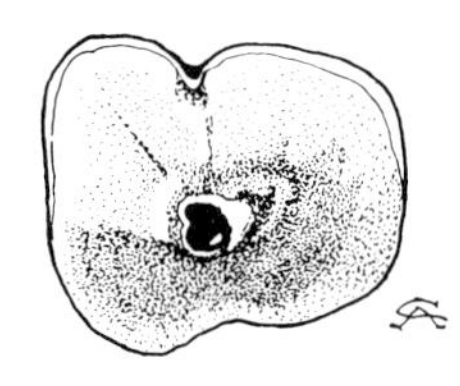

Fig. XV.7. Cross-section through a principal upper incisor of two specimens of the riverine rabbit, *Bunolagus monticularis*. Note roundness of tooth and absence of cement in the enamel fold.

Key to the genera after Robinson (1981a)

1. Tail white below, black above; groove on anterior face of the principal upper incisor invariably filled with cement (Fig. XV.4 & XV.5); chromosomal complement 2n=48; spermatozoa characterised by cap-like acrosome, not pronounced anteriorly

. . . *Lepus*

Tail not as above; groove on anterior surface of the principal upper incisor never filled with cement (Fig. XV.6 & XV.7); chromosomal complement never 2n=48; spermatozoa characterised by relatively large acrosome, pronounced anteriorly

... 2

2. Ears short (63 mm–106 mm); no evidence of a dark brown stripe extending along the lower margin of the jaw towards the base of the ear; mesopterygoid space always narrower than the minimal length of the hard palate (38,6% to 87,7% of the length of the hard palate) (Fig. XV.3.b), no interparietal bone present in adults; chromosomal complement 2n=42; occurs in rocky habitat

... *Pronolagus*

Ears long (109 mm–124 mm); dark brown stripe extending along lower margin of the jaw towards the base of the ear; mesopterygoid space always wider than the minimal length of the hard palate (124,9% to 180,5% of the length of the hard palate), well defined interparietal bone in adults; chromosomal complement 2n=44; occurs in riverine scrub

... *Bunolagus*

## Genus *Lepus* Linnaeus, 1758

Key to the species after Robinson (1981a)

1. Smaller, total length of adult skull 81,5 mm–91,1 mm; upper principal incisor narrow across the face, 2,3 mm–2,8 mm, squarish in cross-section with a simple enamel groove on the front face filled with cement (Fig. XV.4), chest and abdomen either totally pinkish-buff or white medially with diffuse ochraceous-buffy bands laterally between the white of the under parts and the colour of the upper parts; silver-stained spermatozoa with two or more argentophilic granules visible in the equatorial segment (Fig. XV.8.B); no detectable anodal erythrocytic carbonic anhydrase system using starch-gel electrophoresis (see Glossary: carbonic anhydrase)

... *capensis*

Larger, total length of adult skull 85,6 mm–107,7 mm; upper principal incisor robust and broad across the face, 2,7 mm–3,6 mm, appearing elongated in cross-section with enamel fold variable in shape and filled with cement (Fig. XV.5); under parts white, without ochraceous-buffy bands separating the white of the under parts and greyish of the upper parts; silver-stained spermatozoa without argentophilic granules visible in equatorial segment (Fig. XV.8.A); with a single monomorphic, anodal, erythrocytic carbonic anhydrase system visible using starch-gel electrophoresis

... *saxatilis*

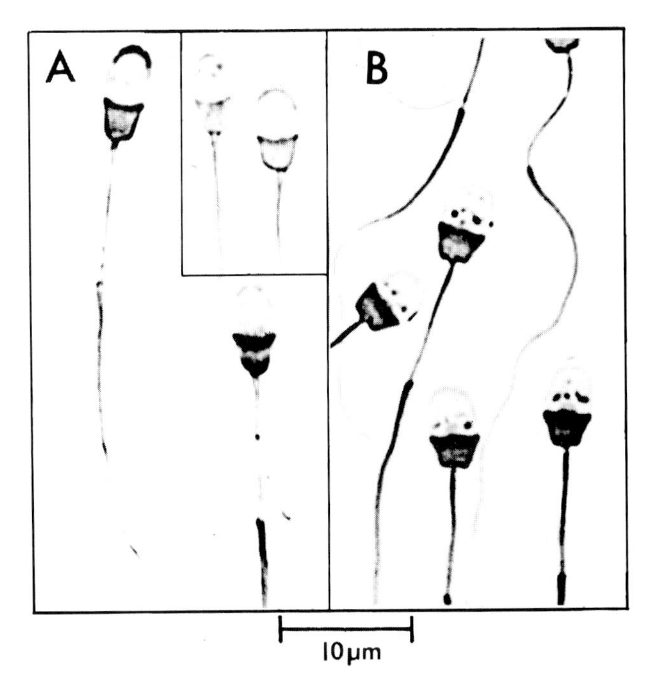


Fig. XV.8. Spermatozoa: *Lepus* spp
A. *L. saxatilis* B. *L. capensis*
to show absence of argentophilic granules in *L. saxatilis* and presence in *L. capensis* (photograph Robinson, 1981).

No. 122

## *Lepus capensis* Linnaeus, 1758

## Cape hare
## Vlakhaas

Plate 7

### Colloquial Name

Apart from the fact that the original specimen, which was used by Linnaeus to describe the species, came from the Cape of Good Hope, the Cape hare is by no means associated particularly with this part of Africa. They are distributed widely on the African Continent and occur in many parts of the Middle East and throughout Asia as far east as Mongolia and China. However, the name is well entrenched and warrants retention as a means of distinguishing them from the other species of hares which occur.

The Afrikaans *vlakhaas* is most appropriate as it indicates this species' preference for more open habitat than that which is required by the other species.

### Taxonomic Notes

Petter (1972) listed no less than 35 subspecies from the continent, of which Meester *et al.* (1986) listed 15 from the Subregion. Those occurring in the desert and semi-desert regions tend to be smaller and lighter in colour than those from the grassland areas with a higher mean annual rainfall. There is a lack of knowledge on the variation in colour within populations and how the moult alters the general pattern and colour. Except in certain areas, there are too few specimens available to compare size properly. There is little doubt that, in the course of time, it may be shown that colour and size have clinal implications. This appears to be the case with the colour of the under parts. Specimens from the southwestern Cape Province have ochraceous-buffy under parts, with some white on their abdomens. Further north the ochraceous-buff is restricted to the junction between the greyish colour of the upper parts and the white of the under parts and further north still in some localities it is barely discernible.

The semi-desert populations are much greyer, almost white on the upper parts, and totally lack any sign of ochraceous-buff on the under parts. Similarly the nuchal patches of specimens from the southwestern Cape Province are brownish-pink, contrasting with the greyish colour of the upper parts, whereas in semi-desert specimens they are very light grey to off-white.

Eventually it may be shown that many of the presently listed subspecies are invalid. The best way to distinguish this species from the scrub hare, *L. saxatilis*, when the two are available together for comparison, is by examining the incisor teeth. The upper incisors of the Cape hare (Fig. XV.4) are much narrower and lighter in build than those of the scrub hare (Fig. XV.5).

### Description

In the Cape hare, *L. capensis*, adult males measure about 490 mm and have a mass of some 1,6 kg, while in the scrub hare they are over 530 mm long and have a mass of 2,3 kg. The females are larger and heavier than the males, but not significantly so (Robinson, 1981a) (Table 122.1).

There is such a wide range of variation in colour and size of Cape hares from various parts of the Subregion that it is impossible to provide a description that fits all these variations, except within the broadest terms. The extremes are illustrated when a series from the southwestern parts of the Cape Province is compared with a series from their northern extension of distribution in the Makgadikgadi Pan area of Botswana. In the southwestern Cape Province the Cape hare is light buffy in colour, the upper parts grizzled with black ticking where the black tips of the guard hairs lie in juxtaposition. The sides of the nose and cheeks are yellowish. The nuchal patch, which lies on the nape of the neck, is brownish-pink, contrasting with the colour of the upper parts. The under parts are ochraceous-buffy and the abdomen white. Botswana specimens on the other hand are much lighter in colour, the upper parts whitish-grey with greyish ticking. The sides of the nose and cheeks and the nuchal patch are light grey, not contrasting with the colour of the upper parts. The under parts are pure white with either no sign, or, at most, a faint indication of ochraceous-buff at the junction of the white under parts and the grey of the upper parts. In the northern Cape Province and in southern Botswana, the ochraceous-buffy band on the fringes of the white under parts is more pronounced and develops in intensity further southwestwards. The overall colour is governed largely by the colour of the penultimate brighter coloured bands on the hair of the guard coat, each hair of which is black-tipped. The overall colour is grey or off-white in the lighter coloured individuals and various shades of buffy in the darker ones. The coarse, grizzled appearance of the upper parts is caused by the black tips of the hairs either lying in juxtaposition or separately. Within any population the wide range of general colour may be influenced by the moult, which so far has not been studied in detail. The lower parts of the limbs of specimens from the southwestern Cape Province are a pale buffy-yellow, those from southern Botswana paler still, and those from Makgadikgadi Pan white or a very pale grey.

The ears are long and rounded at the tips and are fringed with short black hair. Along the lateral edges of the ears there are narrow fringes of short, buffy-coloured hair. The eyes are ringed with short, pale buffy hair and immediately above these there are elongated brownish spots.

The under side of the buffy tail is pure white. In the darker coloured individuals the tail is jet black above, in the lighter ones the black is less intense.

**Table 122.1**

Measurements (mm) and mass (kg) of adult Cape hares, *L. capensis* from the western Cape Province (Robinson, 1981a) and Makgadikgadi Pan, Botswana (Smithers, 1971)

**Western Cape Province**

| | Irrespective of sex | | |
|---|---|---|---|
| | $\bar{x}$ | n | Range |
| TL | 595 | 19 | 555–615 |
| HB | 478 | 19 | 445–550 |
| T | 117 | 19 | 100–145 |
| Hf c/u | 119 | 19 | 110–138 |
| E | 124 | 19 | 110–140 |
| Mass | 2,04 | 19 | 1,70–2,45 |
| TL skull | 87 | 17 | 89–91 |

**Makgadikgadi Pan area, Botswana**

| | Males | | | Females | | |
|---|---|---|---|---|---|---|
| | $\bar{x}$ | n | Range | $\bar{x}$ | n | Range |
| TL | 483 | 21 | 460–540 | 471 | 19 | 440–515 |
| T | 87 | 21 | 70–107 | 90 | 14 | 80–110 |
| Hf c/u | 109 | 26 | 95–120 | 107 | 15 | 101–112 |
| E | 105 | 24 | 99–120 | 104 | 15 | 95–110 |
| Mass | 1,59 | 23 | 1,36–1,84 | 1,70 | 15 | 1,45–2,33 |

## Distribution

Outside the continent the Cape hare, *L. capensis*, has a wide distribution, occurring throughout the **Middle East** south of the Caspian Sea and eastwards of this in **Asia** as far as **China**.

*North and northwestern Africa*

They are recorded from **Senegal** northwards, at least coastally, to **Morocco** and **Algeria**, where they are also recorded from the vicinity of the Ahaggar Massif deep in the Sahara in the southwest; **Tunisia; Libya** and along the Mediterranean coast to **Egypt**, and southwards along the Red Sea to the eastern parts of the **Sudan** and **Ethiopia**.

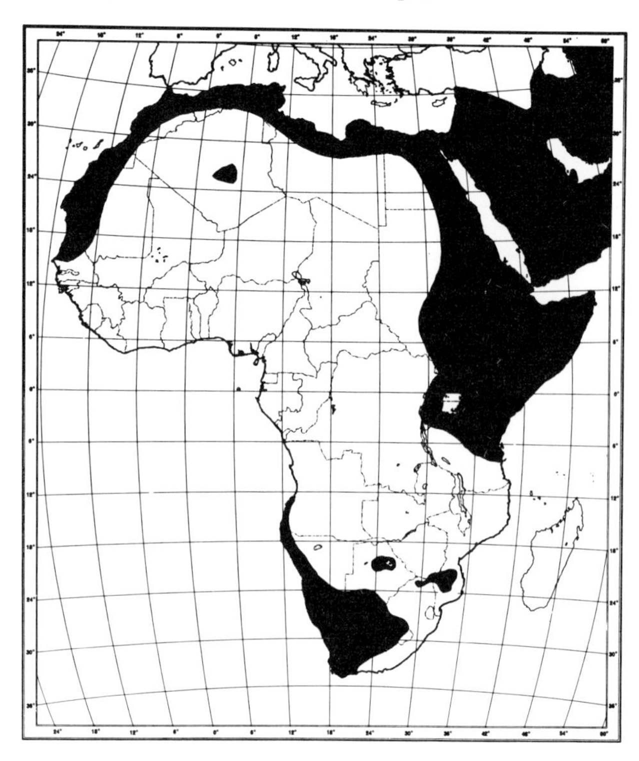

*South of the Sahara, excluding the Southern African Subregion*

They are recorded from **Somalia; Kenya; Uganda** and the northern parts of **Tanzania.** Southwards there is a break in their distribution, but they reoccur in Namibia; Botswana; Zimbabwe and in Mozambique, south of the Zambezi River. In **Angola** they occur narrowly along the coast from the Cunene River to Benguela.

*Southern African Subregion*

In **Namibia** they occur from the Cunene River, in the north, narrowly southwards along the coast and throughout the southern parts of the country. In **Botswana** they occur commonly on the open grasslands surrounding the Makgadikgadi Pan in the northeast, which appears to be an island of occurrence as there are no records southwards until about 24 °S where they again occur widely in the southern and southwestern parts of the country. In **Zimbabwe** they occur only in a very limited area in the southeast of the country and in **Mozambique**, south of the Zambezi River, from the vicinity of the Save River southwards to the dry, open Banhine Flats. In the **Transvaal** they occur in the southwest and there is a single record from the north, but they do not occur elsewhere in the province. They occur throughout most of the **Orange Free State** and in western **Lesotho** and widely throughout the **Cape Province** except in the southern sector.

## Habitat

Throughout their wide distributional range on the continent there are marked differences between the habitat requirements of the Cape hare as compared with the scrub hare, *L. saxatilis*, although their limits of distribution overlap in parts of their range. In broad terms their present distribution illustrates these differences quite dramatically. In North Africa the Cape hare occurs widely, even penetrating into the Sahara. In the Subregion they occur in the western coastal desert. Both these areas are too arid and open to support the scrub hare. Like some other mammalian species associated with arid, open country such as the black-backed jackal, *Canis mesomelas*, and the bat-eared fox, *Otocyon megalotis*, to mention but two species, there is a break in their distribution between Zimbabwe and Tanzania. During some former time when the rainfall in the intervening sector was less than it is today and, as a consequence the terrain more open and arid, there is little doubt that the distribution of the Cape hare was continuous from the Subregion through to East Africa. These factors highlight the preference of the Cape hare for dry, open habitat. On a regional basis this preference is illustrated no better than in parts of Botswana where on the vast open grassland plains fringing the Makgadikgadi Pan the Cape hare occurs, to the almost total exclusion of the scrub hare. The scrub hare on the other hand occurs in the fringing scrub and woodland that surround this grassland. Occasionally the two occur together in the ecotone of woodland and grassland, where there is an open scattering of scrub bush not sufficient to support the scrub hare permanently or dense enough to exclude the Cape hare. In the Subregion the Cape hare occurs where more open arid conditions are found. These conditions are found widely in the South West Arid Zone, in the dry grassland areas of the Transvaal and in parts of southern Mozambique (see **Habitat**, *Lepus saxatilis*).

Cape hares browse or graze and their habitat should provide palatable bush and grass and at the same time cover in which they can lie up during daylight hours. Even open grassland, where the grass is either naturally short or is retained this way by the grazing of stock or wild grazing species, has within it standing clumps of slightly taller grasses and bush to provide cover. They appear to be independent of water, occurring in areas, as for example in southern Botswana, where free water is only available seasonally. They probably rely on their food and dew to provide for their moisture requirements.

### Habits

Cape hares are predominantly nocturnal, but during overcast weather they may be seen foraging occasionally during the day. In cold weather they are less in evidence and during rain remain in cover.

They lie up during the day in forms, which are situated in a grass clump or under a small bush, with their ears folded flat on their shoulders, always on the alert and ready to run off if danger threatens. The form is not lined but may be scraped out with the forefeet to form a shallow hollow, otherwise it is simply the imprint of their bodies on the grass and the substrate. They lie up very tightly in these forms and can be approached closely if this is done slowly and quietly. Under these circumstances they draw the fur tightly to their bodies, their ears lying flat against their bodies, crouching low and relying on their cryptic coloration to avoid detection. Once flushed they run off with the ears held erect, pursuing a zig-zag course. Under extreme stress they run at full speed, with the body held low to the ground, with their ears flat on the shoulders and can make extremely tight turns at high speed. They can also leap sideways to escape from dogs. Once on the move they traverse great distances before slowing up and seeking a new resting site. Under stress they will use the cover of antbear, springhaas or other holes in the ground, behaviour not observed in the scrub hare.

They emerge from the forms just after sundown to feed and continue to forage far into the night, resettling in cover again before sunrise. If they remain undisturbed they may use the same form on several successive days, but if they have been flushed from them, usually seek a new site.

They are normally solitary but, when a female is in oestrus, several males may be in attendance. During this time fights between males frequently occur. When fighting they rear up on their hind legs, slashing at each other with the claws on the front feet. In close encounters they will kick with the hind feet. A great deal of fur is lost by contestants during these encounters.

Their senses are keen, their eyesight and hearing particularly acute. If disturbed at night they will sit up on their haunches, with ears erect, seeking the origin of the disturbance.

In captivity they grind their teeth and this may have some value in communication when they are at close quarters. They also stamp their hind feet and drum with their forefeet. Except for a high-pitched scream, uttered when they are handled or caught in traps, and a barely audible grunting, they are silent.

Wessels (1978) in the Orange Free State found that the home range of the male Cape hare was 6,49 ha, that of the female 8,25 ha, with overlap on the borders of the individual ranges, and that certain parts of their home ranges were defended.

### Food

Cape hares will graze or browse, depending on the availability of either grass or bush in their habitat, and have a preference for areas of short grass. No detailed investigation appears to have been carried out in the Subregion on the species of grasses which they eat. In East Africa, Stewart (1971) listed five genera and two species which were identified from their pellets. All these genera or species of grasses also occur widely in southern Africa and they may well utilise them in the Subregion. He showed that *Digitaria* sp and *Eragrostis* sp ranked high on the list, which included, in smaller percentages, *Aristida* sp, *Chloris* sp and *Hyparrhenia* sp, as well as couch grass, *Cynodon dactylon* and red grass, *Themeda triandra*. They have a preference for green grass and, when feeding on the higher standing species, forage around the bases in search of fresh green shoots to which they are attracted as they sprout after fire or where they have been utilised heavily or trampled by domestic stock or wild grazing species. Like the scrub hare they are seen frequently on the degraded ground around kraals or human habitations where the grass is kept short by stock.

While coprophagy, the eating of faecal pellets, is well known in lagomorphs, in a sample of 550 stomachs of the Cape hare from the Orange Free State, Wessels (1978) found pellets in only two stomachs, which can be attributed to accidental intake. He concluded that either this only occurs during the day when they are not hunted, his sample being collected after dark, or that, unlike other hares, they do not engage in this pursuit, which is most unlikely. Duthie (pers. comm.) observed coprophagy during the day by captive Cape hares.

### Reproduction

In Botswana there are records of gravid females from the warm, wet summer months as well as from the cold, dry winter months which suggest that they breed throughout the year (Smithers, 1979). In this sample of 121 females there was an indication of a peak in the birth of young during the warm, wet summer months from about October to February. In the Orange Free State, Wessels (1978) collected gravid females throughout the year, but found that 77% of the annual pregnancies occurred between July and December. The gestation period is about 42 days.

In 59 gravid females in the Botswana sample where details of the number of foetuses were known, there were six examples of triplets, 23 of twins and 30 single foetuses, the mean number of foetuses per female being 1,6 (n=62), with a range of one to three (Smithers, 1971). While two of the sets of triplets were taken in January 1965 before the break in a four-year drought, the remaining four were taken in April 1965 and February 1966 after copious rains had fallen. Reproduction certainly continues even under adverse conditions, although it was noticeable that of a series of seven adult females taken at Lechana, an area particularly heavily hit by the drought and where there was almost a total absence of grass, only one was gravid with one foetus. However, there were 42 pregnancies in 121 females, all taken before the break of the drought, to support that breeding does continue even under adverse conditions. The availability of food no doubt has an influence on the number of young that the females can successfully rear. Wessels (1978) showed that in the Orange Free State the females could produce up to four litters per year, three of these during the main breeding season from July to December.

The young are precocial, being born fully haired with their eyes open, in a form in a clump of grass or under a bush. Soon after birth they move around on their own in the vicinity of the form. They develop very quickly, and are weaned and independent at about a month old. Leverets are difficult to find and are adept at concealing themselves.

Their small size and cryptic coloration are advantageous to their concealment. In the early stages of life they do not appear to have a body scent as do the adults, as they are passed over by dogs.

---

No. 123

## *Lepus saxatilis* F. Cuvier, 1823

## Scrub hare
## Kolhaas

Plate 7

---

### Colloquial Name

Scrub refers to their association with this type of habitat as compared with the Cape hare, *L. capensis*, which prefers a much more open habitat, and the rock rabbits, *Pronolagus* spp, that live mainly among rocks. The Afrikaans *kolhaas* refers to the small spot on their foreheads present in the majority, although not in every individual. In the southwestern Cape Province, the white spot may be seen on the foreheads of some Cape hares, *L. capensis*, and it is frequently present on specimens from the northwest of the province.

### Taxonomic Notes

Although many subspecies have been described, there is a cline in bodily size and in the total length of the skull and the ears from the southwestern Cape Province to Zimbabwe.

### Description

Scrub hares vary in size, from the large individuals which occur in the southwestern Cape Province, where adult males have an overall length of over 600 mm, ears of 140 mm and a mass of over 3 kg, to those in Zimbabwe which are smaller, averaging just over 500 mm, with correspondingly smaller ears, about 100 mm, and average masses of 2 kg (Table 123.1) (Fig. XV.1 & 2). The females are larger and heavier than the males, but not significantly so (Robinson, 1981a). The nape of the neck varies in colour from a dark russet to an orange-buff and most of them have a distinct white spot on the forehead just above the eyes.

The upper parts are grizzled greyish or buffy. The general colour of the upper parts is imparted to them by the colour of the penultimate band of grey or buffy on the hairs of the guard coat. The grizzling is caused by the variation in length of the black tips on the same hairs and the way these lie in relation to each other. The forehead conforms in colour to that of the upper parts. The sides of the face and around the eyes are lighter in colour than the upper parts and are in some whitish, in others off-white or buffy. There is a distinct collar on the lower part of the neck which is of the same colour as the upper parts, or slighty lighter. This grades forward to the white chin and back to the white of the under parts which continues on to the inner parts of the limbs. The upper parts of the feet are lighter in colour than the body, the hind feet usually lighter than the fore in varying shades of buffy or buffy-tinged yellow. The fluffy tail is jet black above and pure white below, the black tapering off towards the tip.

**Table 123.1**

Measurements (mm) and mass (kg) of scrub hares, *L. saxatilis*, from three areas within the Subregion.

**Mountainous areas, southwestern Cape Province** (Robinson, 1981a)

| | Males | | | Females | | |
|---|---|---|---|---|---|---|
| | $\bar{x}$ | n | Range | $\bar{x}$ | n | Range |
| TL | 558 | 8 | 545–595 | 585 | 3 | 570–615 |
| T | 135 | 8 | 110–160 | 163 | 3 | 150–175 |
| Hf c/u | 145 | 8 | 138–155 | 153 | 3 | 150–155 |
| E | 140 | 8 | 130–150 | 140 | 3 | 130–150 |
| Mass | 3,19 | 8 | 2,70–3,75 | 4,00 | 3 | 3,65–4,5 |

**Transvaal** (Rautenbach, 1978)

| | Males | | | Females | | |
|---|---|---|---|---|---|---|
| | $\bar{x}$ | n | Range | $\bar{x}$ | n | Range |
| TL | 554 | 50 | 450–640 | 582 | 70 | 490–628 |
| T | 91 | 50 | 70–119 | 95 | 70 | 75–122 |
| Hf c/u | 112 | 50 | 100–127 | 114 | 70 | 99–128 |
| E | 109 | 50 | 95–148 | 112 | 70 | 97–143 |
| Mass | 2,2 | 50 | 1,4–2,9 | 2,6 | 70 | 1,6–3,5 |

**Zimbabwe** (Smithers & Wilson, 1979)

| | Males | | | Females | | |
|---|---|---|---|---|---|---|
| | $\bar{x}$ | n | Range | $\bar{x}$ | n | Range |
| TL | 529 | 20 | 400–564 | 539 | 30 | 480–587 |
| T | 92 | 20 | 80–107 | 90 | 30 | 80–111 |
| Hf c/u | 109 | 20 | 100–115 | 110 | 30 | 102–177 |
| E | 99 | 20 | 92–108 | 98 | 30 | 92–110 |
| Mass | 2,04 | 20 | 1,50–2,50 | 2,41 | 30 | 1,93–3,18 |

### Distribution

*South of the Sahara, excluding the Southern African Subregion*

The scrub hare, *L. saxatilis*, occurs from southwestern **Mauritania** and **Senegal** eastwards in most of the countries in West Africa to **Nigeria**, in parts of the Sahel, Sudan and Guinea savannas. They are recorded from northern **Chad;** the northeastern parts of the **Central African Republic;** southern **Sudan**; southeastern **Ethiopia; Uganda; Kenya**, excluding the northeastern parts of the country; **Tanzania;** the extreme northern and southeastern parts of **Zaire;** throughout most of **Angola**, excluding the coastal desert in the southwest; throughout **Zambia; Malawi**, and **Mozambique**, north of the Zambezi River.

*Southern African Subregion*

They occur throughout the **Subregion** except in forested areas, in the coastal desert of Namibia and in the arid country bordering the Orange River east to about 20 °E and in the northwestern parts of the Cape Province.

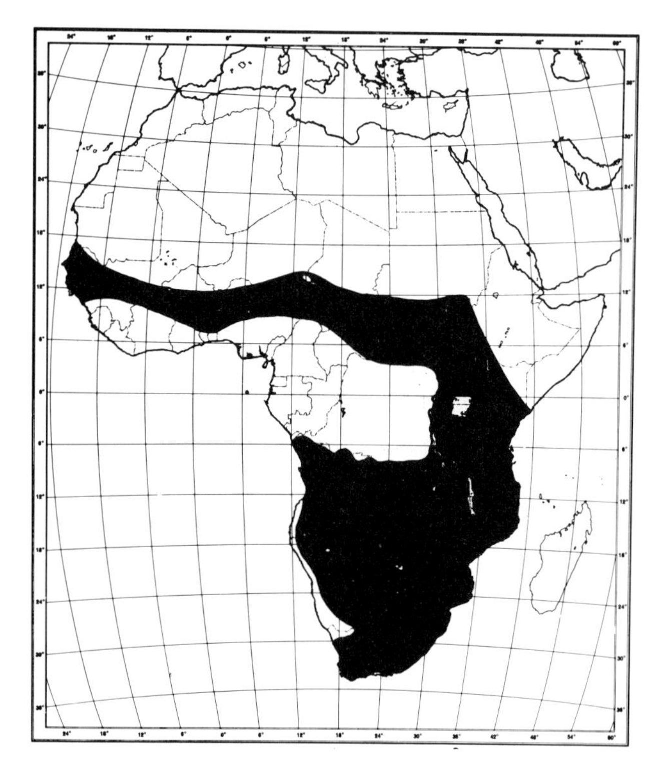

### Habitat

Scrub hares occur in savanna woodland and in scrub, where there is grass cover, but are absent from forest, desert and open grassland. They are common in agriculturally developed areas, concentrating in the vicinity of growing crops or in fallowed or derelict lands where there is bush regeneration. The analyses of the habitat in which 265 *L. saxatilis* and 66 *L. capensis* occurred in Botswana (Smithers, 1971) highlight the differences in the habitat requirements of the two species. Dividing the type of habitat in which these were collected into three broad categories: cultivation, scrub or woodland, and open grassland, the percentage occurrence of the two species was as follows:

| *L. saxatilis* (n=265) | No. taken | Percentage occurrence |
|---|---|---|
| Cultivation | 14 | 5,2% |
| Scrub or woodland | 214 | 80,8% |
| Open grassland | 37 | 14,0% |
| *L. capensis* (n=66) | | |
| Cultivation | 1 | 1,5% |
| Scrub* | 10 | 15,1% |
| Open grassland | 55 | 83,4% |

*No *L. capensis* were taken in woodland, the scrub here listed being either *Acacia* or mopane.

In the case of the anomalies, where 14,0% of *L. saxatilis* were taken in open grassland and 15,1% of *L. capensis* in scrub, investigation of the circumstances is revealing. Of the 37 *L. saxatilis* taken on open grassland, 27 were taken on grassland fringing pans. Here a scrub or woodland association fringes the grassland and the scrub hare wanders out at night marginally to forage in the open. A further five were taken on ground cleared for an airstrip in woodland and a further five in vleis which had been burnt and where the flush of green grass had attracted them into the open. In none of these 37 cases were the open conditions extensive enough to take them far from their preferred habitat of scrub or woodland. In the areas where the bulk of the 265 specimens was taken there was little cultivation, consequently this figure is low compared with conditions in Zimbabwe, where they were common in and around cultivated lands. Conversely no specimens of *L. capensis* were taken in woodland and the 10 taken in scrub were taken where it thinned out on the fringes of the pans.

During the day, *L. saxatilis* was flushed frequently from its forms under bushes in scrub or woodland, *L. capensis* only from forms in the barest of cover in open grassland. It appears that *L. saxatilis* requires a more adequately vegetated habitat than *L. capensis*.

### Habits

Scrub hares are nocturnal, emerging to feed at sundown. Apparently they are sensitive to weather conditions, being more in evidence on warm evenings than on cold and not moving during rain. In overcast weather they will feed during the morning. They lie up in forms under bushes, where there is some grass cover to afford additional shelter and concealment. They may return to the same form over a period of days, but if disturbed, will move to new cover. The forms are characteristic in shape, the grass flattened by the broader fore and hind portions of the individual as it crouches in the cover. When they lie up in the forms they do so with the ears folded back flat on to their shoulders, the head pulled into the body. In this position the drab colour of their bodies blends into the background, affording them effective concealment. They lie up in the forms very tightly and only flush when approached closely. When they do flush they run off with the ears back, jinking on an irregular course. Normally they occur singly, although when a female is in oestrus she may be accompanied by one or more males. Until recently, scrub hares, like other Leporidae, were thought to vocalize only when distressed. However, McKenzie (pers. comm.) has heard this species regularly emit a loud chirping call at night when disturbed. The call is emitted while the animal is in an erect position in open habitat. No seasonality in the incidence of calls was recorded, and it is unknown whether one or both sexes emit the vocalizations. If wounded or under stress they will squeal loudly, kick savagely with the back feet and bite if handled. A high proportion of specimens lacks the last few tail vertebrae, suggesting that intraspecific fighting may be more common than observed.

### Food

Scrub hares live on the leaves, stems and rhizomes of dry and green grass, but have a preference for green grass.

### Reproduction

Smithers (1971) and Smithers & Wilson (1979), in Botswana and Zimbabwe respectively, recorded gravid females throughout the year, with an indication of a peak during the warm, wet summer months from September to February. Both in Botswana and Zimbabwe the average number of foetuses per female was 1,6 (Botswana n=62; Zimbabwe n=24), with a range in both cases of one to three. In Botswana it was noticeable that triplets were more in evidence after a good rainy season. Like the Cape hare, they breed even under the most adverse conditions such as during the latter stages of a four-year drought that beset Botswana during the years 1962–1966. Like all members of the genus *Lepus*, the young are born in the forms and are precocial, being born fully haired with the eyes open and capable of moving around shortly after birth.

## Genus *Pronolagus* Lyon, 1904

All three species of *Pronolagus* appear to have similar habitat requirements and habits. They are confined closely to areas which offer substantial shelter in the form of rocks, occurring on krantzes, rocky hillsides, boulder-strewn koppies, in rocky ravines and even among piles of rocks in dry river beds. The type of geological formation appears to be immaterial for they are found in areas of sandstone, basalt or granite, the last-named appearing to offer particularly suitable habitat, and in parts of their range, such as in the Matopo Hills, Zimbabwe, this carries very large populations. In this habitat they lie up during the day in forms under rock ledges or boulders, their cryptic coloration making them difficult to see. They also shelter deep in the crevices between boulders, far out of sight. Their close confinement to such habitat, which is discontinuous in occurrence, means that their distribution is patchy and discontinuous and there are vast tracts of country, between areas where they occur, that are unsuitable for them. These rocky areas in which they live must also provide palatable grasses and also some cover, if only sparse, of scrub bushes.

All three species are predominantly nocturnal, moving from their shelters to feed at sundown. Occasionally, however, they may be seen during daylight hours but this is atypical and may be a result of their being disturbed. They never move far from their rocky habitat, although they will forage around the base of the koppies in which they live in search of fresh sprouting grasses. If they are disturbed, their immediate reaction is to seek the shelter of their rocky habitat and they have a remarkable proficiency in turning and doubling and making maximum use of the cover of boulders to escape. Shortridge (1934) remarked on their ability to "vanish like shadows behind rocks or down rock crevices on the slightest alarm". When lying in their forms under rock ledges or boulders, however, they lie up very tightly and if carefully approached can be caught by hand.

Their flesh is palatable, but can be highly aromatic with the rank odour of donkey urine (Mintoor, pers. comm.) This may result from their eating aromatic herbs that grow in their rocky habitat. All three species use latrines located in a flat area between the rocks, but there is also a considerable scattering of their characteristically-shaped flattened pellets throughout their home ranges.

In captivity red rock rabbits are not gregarious (Pepler, pers. comm.). They forage solitarily, but on preferred feeding grounds numbers may congregate together and, in the breeding season, a female in oestrus may be accompanied by more than one male.

While the resting forms are clean, the nests in which the young are born are lined with vegetable debris, with a central soft nest made of the fur of the female which she plucks from her pelage for this purpose.

Key to the species after Robinson (1981a)

1. Smaller, total length of adult skull 77,4 mm–87,5 mm; upper principal incisor narrow across the face, 2,2 mm–2,8 mm (Fig. XV.6.c. & d.); ear bulla robust and broad, 6,4mm–9,2 mm, bulla breadth expressed as a percentage of the total length of the skull 7,4%–11,4%, bulla breadth expressed as a percentage of the mandibular height 16,5%–25,1%

   . . . *rupestris*

   Larger, total length of adult skull 85,5 mm–96,3 mm, with upper principal incisor broad across the face 2,6 mm–3,7 mm (Fig. XV.6a. & b); ear bulla narrow, 5,1 mm–7,2 mm, bulla breadth expressed as a percentage of the total length of the skull 5,6%–8,0%, bulla breadth expressed as a percentage of the mandibular height 11,6%–16,7%

   . . . 2

2. Chin white to grey, this colour extending in a broad band along the lower jaw to approach the inferior margins of the nape patch; pelage coarse; cheeks dark grey, not contrasting with the sides and upper parts; ratio maxillary premolar length × 100/frontal length 19,9%–32,5%; ratio mesopterygoid space × 100/frontal length 11,7%–19,9%

   . . . *crassicaudatus*

   Chin white to grey but localised, never extending in a broad band along the lower jaw towards the nape patch; pelage soft; cheeks strikingly light grey contrasting with the colour of the sides and upper parts; ratio maxillary premolar length × 100/frontal length 16,9%–22,9%; ratio mesopterygoid space × 100/frontal length 9,4%–14,7%

   . . . *randensis*

No.124

# *Pronolagus rupestris* (A. Smith, 1834)

## Smith's red rock rabbit
## Smith se rooiklipkonyn

Plate 7

### Colloquial Name

Named after Andrew Smith who originally described the species.

### Taxonomic Notes

Meester *et al.* (1986) listed seven subspecies from the Subregion: *P. r. rupestris* from the Upington district, Cape Province; *P. r. melanurus* (Rüppell, 1842) from the northwestern Cape Province; *P. r. curryi* (Thomas, 1902) from the western Orange Free State; *P. r. saundersiae* Hewitt, 1927 from the Albany district, Cape Province; *P. r. australis* Roberts, 1933 from the southwestern Cape Province; *P. r. fitzsimonsi* Roberts, 1938 from the fringes of the escarpment in Namibia north to about 23 °N, and *P. r. barretti* Roberts, 1949 from the Ladysmith district, Natal northwards to the southeastern Transvaal.

### Description

This is the smallest of the three species of *Pronolagus*, with an average head and body length of about 450 mm (Table 124.1). The colour varies depending on the areas from which the specimens originate, but they are generally rufous-brown on the upper parts of the body with a distinct black grizzling, caused by the black tips of the guard hairs lying in juxtaposition. The rump and the back of the hind legs are brighter rufous in colour. The cheeks are greyish-buff but not in marked contrast to the colour of the upper parts of the body. The forehead and top of the muzzle have a brownish wash. The under parts are pinkish-buff, the abdomen with some white in the mid-line. The gular collar is similar in colour to that of the upper parts. The tail is bushy, the distal two-thirds dark brown to rusty-brown, the tip black. The nuchal patch is rufous.

**Table 124.1**

Measurements (mm) and mass (kg) of Smith's red rock rabbits, *P. rupestris*, from the Cape Province (Robinson, 1981a)

| | Irrespective of sex | | |
|---|---|---|---|
| | $\bar{x}$ | n | Range |
| (TL | 533) | | |
| HB | 447 | 15 | 380–535 |
| T | 86 | 15 | 50–115 |
| Hf c/u | 92 | 15 | 85–100 |
| E | 94 | 15 | 85–105 |
| Mass | 1,62 | 18 | 1,35–2,05 |
| TL skull | 82,4 | 13 | 78,4–87,8 |
| Width bullae | 7,8 | 13 | 6,6–9,4 |
| Width principal incisor | 2,6 | 15 | 2,4–2,9 |

### Distribution

Smith's red rock rabbits occur in two discrete areas on the continent, the northern area extending from Kenya southwards to eastern Zambia, the southern area in the southern parts of the Subregion.

Throughout their distributional range their occurrence is dependent on the availability of rocky habitat.

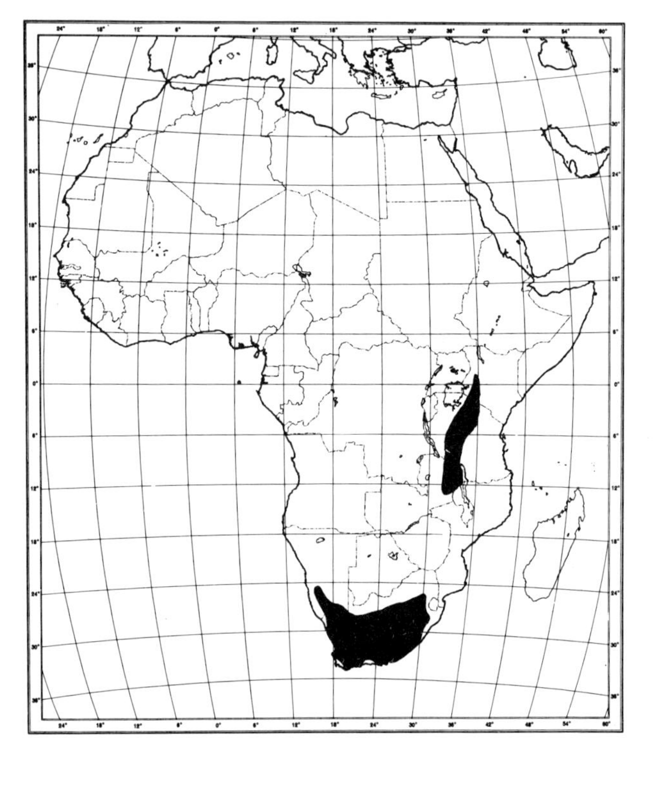

*South of the Sahara, excluding the Southern African Subregion*

They are recorded from southwestern **Kenya**; central **Tanzania**; eastern **Zambia** and northern **Malawi**. Southwards there is a break in their distribution, the next records being from the southern parts of the Transvaal.

*Southern African Subregion*

They are recorded from the southern and southeastern parts of the **Transvaal**; from the central and southern **Orange Free State;** central and southern **Natal** and widely in the **Cape Province**, excluding the coastal forested areas and the extreme northern parts of the province.

### Habitat

Like other species of the genus they are confined closely to areas of krantzes, rocky hillsides, boulder-strewn koppies and rocky ravines. These areas have accessible horizons which can be used as cover and the vegetation is shorter and less dense which suits *Pronolagus* feeding habits (Pepler, pers. comm.).

### Habits

They are nocturnal, emerging from the daylight shelters among the rocks to forage at sundown and never moving far from the vicinity of their rocky habitat. Fleeing rabbits use vertical surfaces or rocks as springboards to change direction sharply and zig-zag to a known hiding place when flushed. They excavate nests in the open at the base of a shrub. Their runs can be very long, up to 300 m, but tend to be shorter in denser vegetation like fynbos (Pepler, pers. comm.).

Vocalisations elicited from *P. rupestris* include a piercing scream from young under four months when handled, an alarm *tu . . . tu* (a sharp exhalation) when rabbits are disturbed when approached at night, or a loud grunt by adults when disturbed before sunrise (Pepler, pers. comm.); a cornered juvenile made a churring sound (Duthie, pers. comm.).

### Food

They are grazers, partial to areas where the grass is sprouting after fire.

### Reproduction

Shortridge (1934) published a photograph of a nest containing two young. The cup-shaped nest was located at the base of a hollow tree. Maternity nests are constructed on the night of birth, a small oval excavation about 100x150 mm in size and 40–80 mm deep being made. The nest has an inner lining of fur from the female's belly and flanks, a middle layer of fine grass and sticks, an outer layer of sticks and an entrance hole plugged with fur (Pepler, pers. comm.).

*P. rupestris* breeds from September to February. A female may produce three to four litters per season, consisting of one or two altricial young per litter, each weighing 40 to 50 g, after a gestation period of 35–40 days. At birth the young are blind, with a sparse hair covering and with ears plugged. The eyes open at nine to 11 days, and they leave the nest at three weeks, weighing 180–200 g (Pepler, pers. comm.).

---

No.125

## *Pronolagus crassicaudatus* (I. Geoffroy, 1823)

## Natal red rock rabbit
## Natalse rooiklipkonyn

Plate 7

---

### Colloquial Name

This is the largest of the three species of red rock rabbits which occur in the Subregion. The name indicates its distribution, which lies predominantly in Natal, with only marginal extensions into adjacent provinces.

### Taxonomic Notes

Meester *et al.* (1986) listed five subspecies: *P. c. crassicaudatus* was collected originally at Port Natal (=Durban), but the limits within which it occurs and the area of integration with adjoining subspecies is not known. *P. c. ruddi* Thomas & Schwann, 1905 occurs in northern Natal northwards to the southeastern Transvaal; *P. c. kariegae* Hewitt, 1927 in the eastern Cape Province; *P.c. bowkeri* Hewitt, 1927 in the Amatola Mountains, eastern Cape Province, and *P. c. lebombo* Roberts, 1936 in southern Mozambique.

### Description

Natal red rock rabbits have a head and body length of about 500 mm and have short, robust limbs and short, sparsely furred ears. They are slightly larger than *P. randensis* and noticeably larger than *P. rupestris*. This size difference is reflected in the mean total length of skulls which in *P. crassicaudatus* is 91,3 mm (n=27), in *P. randensis* 90,0 mm (n=14) and in *P.rupestris* 82,4 mm (n=13).

The pelage is dense and rather harsh, the upper parts and flanks grizzled rufous-brown with a blackish wash. The rump and back of the hind limbs are brighter rufous, attributable to the brighter underfur and diminution of the number of black-tipped hairs. The underfur is grey at the base with broad rufous-brown tips. The chin is greyish-white, this colour extending laterally in a broad band along the borders of the lower jaw to near the lower margins of the nape patch, a feature that is characteristic of this species and clearly identifies it from the other two species. They have a broad gular patch of the same colour as the upper parts of the body. The chest, abdomen, anal region and the insides of the limbs are rufous-buff; the outside of the limbs and lateral borders of the under parts are darker rufous than the rest of the under parts. The forehead and sides of the face are grey with a brownish wash, more tawny above the muzzle. The tail is short, not bushy, and is uniformly ochraceous-brown (Robinson, 1981a). The nape patch varies in colour geographically from brown to grey, a feature which is of taxonomic value at the subspecific level (Pringle, 1974).

**Table 125.1**

Measurements (mm) of Natal red rock rabbits, *P. crassicaudatus*, from Natal (Robinson, 1981a)

| | Irrespective of sex | | |
|---|---|---|---|
| | $\bar{x}$ | n | Range |
| (TL | 573) | | |
| HB | 508 | 28 | 460–560 |
| T | 65 | 26 | 35–110 |
| Hf c/u | 112 | 12 | 100–125 |
| E | 74 | 12 | 60–80 |
| Mass | 2,60 | 13 | 2,40–3,05 |
| TL skull | 91,3 | 27 | 85,3–94,8 |
| Width bullae | 6,1 | 27 | 5,1–7,0 |
| Width principal incisor | 3,2 | 27 | 2,9–3,6 |

### Distribution

Natal red rock rabbits are confined in their distribution to within the limits of the Subregion, occurring within the range shown on the map only where there is suitable habitat.

*Southern African Subregion*

They are recorded from the eastern parts of the **Cape Province;** from eastern **Lesotho;** from **Natal,** excluding the coastal plain in the north; from the extreme southeastern parts of the **Transvaal;** from the Lubombos in **Swaziland** as far north as the Mbuluzi river gorge through these mountains, and from the southwestern parts of the Maputo District of **Mozambique,** south of the Zambezi River, as far north as Estatuene.

Pringle (1974) recorded that in Natal the lower reaches of the Tugela River separate the northern subspecies, *P. c. ruddi*, from *P. c. crassicaudatus*. The former, however, occurs south of the river in its upper reaches.

### Habitat

They occur in rocky areas on steep, boulder-strewn hillsides which have a grass cover. In Natal they are recorded from sea level to altitudes of 1 550 m (Pringle, 1974).

### Habits

They are terrestrial and predominantly nocturnal. They occur in small colonies often consisting of only a few individuals. They lie up during the day in rock crevices, but sometimes are found resting in densely grassed areas from which they are difficult to flush. In undisturbed areas, Pringle (1974) noted that they may emerge from the resting places late in the afternoon, usually moving uphill to feed. They use latrines which usually are far removed from their resting places.

### Food

A grazing species.

### Reproduction

No data are available.

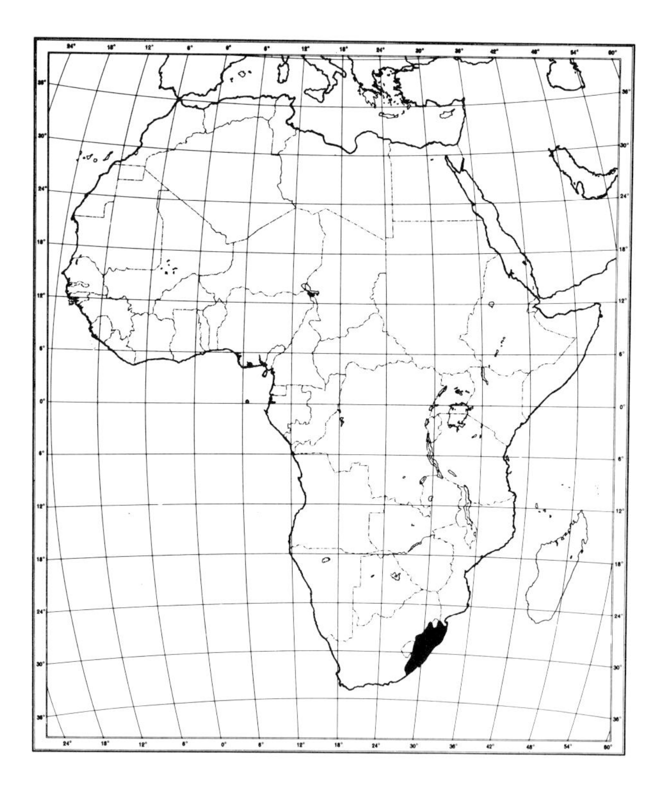

No. 126

## *Pronolagus randensis* Jameson, 1907

# Jameson's red rock rabbit
# Jameson se rooiklipkonyn

Plate 7

### Colloquial Name

Named after the describer of the species.

### Taxonomic Notes

Meester *et al.* (1986) speculated that eventually when more material is available for study, only the western subspecies *P. r. caucinus* Thomas, 1929 from Namibia and the eastern *P. r. randensis* will be recognised. They nevertheless listed nine subspecies from the Subregion: *P. r. randensis* from the southern and southwestern Transvaal; *P. r. powelli* Roberts, 1924 from the western Transvaal and eastern Botswana; *P. r. makapani* Roberts, 1924 from the Pietersburg district, northern Transvaal; *P. r. capricornis* Roberts, 1928 from the top of the Soutpansberg, northern Transvaal; *P. r. caucinus* from central Namibia; *P. r. kobosensis* Roberts, 1938, one known from the Rehoboth district, Namibia; *P. r. whitei* Roberts, 1938 from Zimbabwe and adjacent parts of central Mozambique; *P. r. kaokoensis* Roberts, 1946 from northern Namibia, and *P.r. waterbergensis* Hoesch & Von Lehmann, 1956, known only from the Waterberg, Namibia.

### Description

Jameson's red rock rabbits are slightly smaller in size than the Natal red rock rabbits, *P. crassicaudatus*. They have a mean head and body length of 460 mm. The size difference is shown in the mean total length of the skulls in adults which in this species is 90,0 mm compared with 91,3 mm in *P. crassicaudatus*. The pelage is fine and silky. The upper parts and flanks are grizzled rufous-brown. The rump and back of the limbs are lighter in colour than the upper parts of the body, with less grizzling. The underfur is rufous-brown, lighter in colour towards the base. The chin is whitish. The cheeks, sides of the neck and lower jaw are characteristically a light grey with some brown flecking which contrasts markedly with the colour of the body. They have a distinct gular patch of the same colour as the upper parts. The under parts of the body are pinkish-buff. The ears are sparsely haired and sometimes are tipped with black. The nape patch is rufous, the forehead with a slight rufous wash. The tail is large and bushy and a uniform ochraceous-brown colour with a black tip.

**Table 126.1**

Measurements (mm) and mass (kg) of Jameson's red-rock rabbit, *P. randensis* (Robinson, 1981a) from Zimbabwe (Smithers & Wilson, 1979)

| | Irrespective of sex | | |
|---|---|---|---|
| | $\bar{x}$ | n | Range |
| HB | 463 | 13 | 420–500 |
| T | 98 | 13 | 60–135 |
| Hf c/u | 100 | 13 | 87–110 |
| E | 84 | 13 | 80–100 |
| Mass | 2,3 | 43 | 1,82–2,95 |
| TL skull | 90,0 | 14 | 86,1–92,9 |
| Width bullae | 6,3 | 14 | 5,5–7,0 |
| Width principal incisor | 3,0 | 14 | 2,7–3,3 |

### Distribution

This species occurs in two discrete areas in the Subregion, with a marginal distribution into southwestern Angola. Within these distribution ranges their occurrence is patchy and discontinuous owing to their habitat requirements.

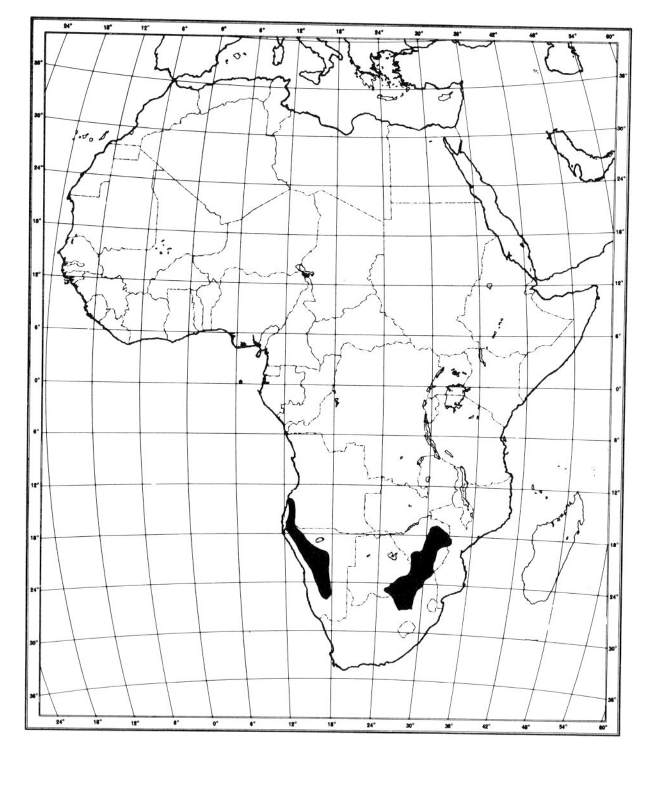

*South of the Sahara, excluding the Southern African Subregion*

They are recorded from the extreme southwestern parts of **Angola**.

*Southern African Subregion*

They occur from the Cunene River in northwestern **Namibia** southwards along the inland escarpment to about 26 °S. There is a break in their distribution from this sector to southeastern **Botswana** and the western **Transvaal,** in which province they have a central and western distribution from the border with the **Orange Free State** northwards to the Limpopo River. In **Zimbabwe** they occur from the southwestern parts of the country, south of the plateau, eastwards to Masvingo and north to the Harare District and eastwards to Mutare, occurring over the **Mozambique** border in the western parts of the Vila Pery District.

### Habitat

They are confined closely to areas of rocky koppies, krantzes, boulder-strewn hillsides, rocky kloofs and gorges. In the granite formations of the Matopo Hills in Zimbabwe and the sandstone formations of eastern Botswana they are very common. In eastern Botswana this species has been found to occur in isolated koppies up to 22 km from the nearest block of similar rocky terrain. Therefore they must be able to traverse what appears to be unsuitable habitat to reach and settle in such situations.

### Habits

Although predominantly nocturnal, they occasionally are seen feeding in the late afternoon or sunning themselves on the rocks in the early morning. They are generally solitary, but fairly often parties of a female with her young or one or more males accompanying a female in oestrus have been observed. They lie up during the day in rock crevices, under the shelter of boulders or in the cover of thick patches of grass in the rocky areas. In the last two named types of resting places, where they can be seen, they lie up very tightly and can be approached closely. When startled out of these resting places, they are adept at disappearing behind rocks as they run off, keeping the rocks between themselves and the observer. They are agile in leaping from rock to rock and will surmount steep faces to gain access to rock crevices. Through lying up in the resting places they create forms on the substrate like other species of lagomorphs. Their reaction upon being caught out in the open after sundown is always to make for rocky shelter.

They use latrines which can grow to a size of 1 m in diameter, with a deposit of droppings up to 80 or 100 mm deep, but they also defecate at random throughout the area they utilise. The pellets are characteristic in shape, being round and flattened on the top and bottom, and are unlike those of *Lepus* spp which are not flattened to the same extent. Roberts (1951) recorded that, when disturbed on the feeding grounds at night, they will utter a series of loud startling screams as they race for cover and that they will use boulders as observation posts. These statements are both questionable. They certainly scream when wounded but are silent as they make for cover and do not expose themselves on observation boulders as do dassies when they sun themselves.

### Food

They are grazers and, if the rocky habitat in which they live does not provide palatable grasses, they will move at night on to flat areas adjacent to and surrounding the rocky habitat to feed. They are partial to flushing green grass after a burn and several may congregate to feed in preferred areas.

### Reproduction

The young are born in secluded resting places. There is insufficient information available at the moment to confirm whether they are seasonal or all-the-year-round breeders, but information from the Transvaal, Zimbabwe and Namibia suggests that the young may be born throughout the year. Rautenbach (1978) recorded a gravid female in May in the Transvaal; Smithers & Wilson (1979) gravid females in July, August and January, and Shortridge (1934) a gravid female in January. In Zimbabwe the average number of foetuses per female was 1,1 (n=8), with a range of one or two.

## Genus *Bunolagus*

The cross-section of the incisor teeth, showing the absence of cement in the enamel fold, shows a rounder form than in any of the genera found in the Subregion (Fig. XV.7).

## Genus *Bunolagus* Thomas, 1929

No. 127

## *Bunolagus monticularis* (Thomas, 1903)

## Riverine rabbit
## Oewerkonyn

Plate 7

The riverine rabbit ranks among the rarest and most historically interesting of our southern African mammals and today is included in the International Union for the Conservation of Nature and Natural Resources *Red Data Book* and in the *South African Red Data Book: terrestrial mammals* (Smithers, 1986) as an endangered species.

The species was first discovered near Deelfontein in the Karoo, Cape Province, by Trooper (later Capt.) C.H.B. Grant of the British Army, who was stationed there in 1901 during the Boer War, and who brought it to the attention of authorities by sending a specimen to the British Museum (Natural History), London. Dr Oldfield Thomas, then keeper of the Department of Mammals, recognised the unique nature of the specimen and described it as a new species, *Lepus monticularis* in 1903. At the time of its description it is notable, in the light of subsequent findings, that Thomas remarked that at first sight it appeared to be allied to *Oryctolagus (Pronolagus) crassicaudatus*, the Cape red-tailed rabbit, his use of the term rabbit indicating his appreciation of the fact that *Pronolagus* and *Bunolagus* both had rabbit-like characters not apparent in members of the genus *Lepus*.

His choice of the specific name *monticularis*, which indicates rocky or mountainous terrain, was unfortunate for it misled those subsequently engaged in a search for it. As he had mentioned *Pronolagus* in his original description and as he had indicated that he thought *Bunolagus* was allied to members of this genus, which are associated with rocky, hilly terrain, he must have thought that *Bunolagus* was similar in its habitat requirements which, as will be seen, is far from the case.

Between 1901 and 1929 two other specimens turned up and in 1929 Thomas, in re-examining specimens, realised that they differed more markedly than originally thought from members of the genus *Lepus* in having short, heavily furred limbs, a bushy, unicoloured, pom-pom-like tail and in certain skull characters not possessed by *Lepus*. Therefore, he created the genus *Bunolagus* to accommodate it (Thomas, 1929). Capt. G.C. Shortridge, Curator of the Kaffrarian Museum, King William's Town, a prolific collector of zoological material, took up the search for this elusive species, offering a reward of one pound sterling for the capture of a specimen, which led to the species becoming known as the "pondhaas". He spent the best part of 20 years in his search, being misled by the original indication, entrenched in the name *monticularis*, that it lived in mountainous country. It was not until 1947 that residents of Calvinia, Cape Province, pointed out that he was looking in the wrong sort of terrain and that he should look for it on the alluvium fringing dry river beds. Searching the Karroid scrub along the seasonal Fish and Rhinoceros rivers in the vicinity, he was immediately successful, collecting four specimens. This rediscovery was reported in the *Cape Argus* (18th October 1947) as a highlight in Shortridge's career. It was the first indication that the habitat indicated by Thomas (1903) was incorrect. Now alerted to this, Shortridge returned the following year (1948) and collected further specimens along the Fish River, some 100 km south of Calvinia. After this rediscovery there seemed to be a lack of further interest in the species and although a series of specimens was available for taxonomic study, nothing was known about its life history. In 1978 a research project on southern African leporids was initiated by the Mammal Research Institute of the University of Pretoria. During the initial search for *Bunolagus* along the Fish and Rhinoceros rivers, it became apparent that most of the riverine habitat had been ploughed under. Further investigation resulted in the eventual capture of a specimen on a farm in the Victoria West district. In view of this alarming decrease in its habitat and the absence of any knowledge pertaining to its life history, the species was placed on the endangered list and a study of its ecology instituted.

### Colloquial Name

The species is also known as the *vleihaas* or *doekvoetjie*, the latter referring to the feet which have a dense covering of hair giving them a thickened appearance, more like the feet of red rock rabbits, *Pronolagus* spp, and in contrast to the rather slim feet of hares of the genus *Lepus*. Other names such as the Deelfontein hare and river hare have fallen out of use, although the last-named is appropriate in so far as the association with riverine condition is concerned. Robinson (1981a) has shown that the species is allied more closely to rabbits than to hares and any reference to hare or *haas* in colloquial names is inappropriate.

### Taxonomic Notes

No subspecies have been described. Robinson (1981a), using refined cytogenetic techniques, has shown that the riverine rabbit, *B. monticularis*, is a unique species more closely allied to rabbits than to hares, which have, regardless of where they come from, a uniform chromosomal complement (see Family Leporidae).

### Description

Adult riverine rabbits are about 430 mm in total length and have noticeably long ears of between 107 mm and 124 mm (Table 127.1). A characteristic feature of the species not possessed by any other member of the Family in the Subregion is the diffused dark brown band along the sides of the lower jaw which broadens out posteriorly and tails out upwards towards the base of the ears.

The colour of the upper parts is a grizzled drab-grey, the grizzling caused by the penultimate black bands on the hairs of the guard coat lying together or dispersed irregularly throughout the coat. The flanks are a slightly darker drab-grey, with a tinge of rufous, where they blend into the under parts. The individual hairs of the guard coat, which are about 23 mm long on the shoulders, have dark bases with a light buffy band, then a black penultimate band and end in buffy-coloured tips. The hair of the dense underfur is grey at the base with buffy tips. The whole coat is softer and silkier than that of hares of the genus *Lepus* and more akin in texture to that of Smith's red rock rabbit, *Pronolagus rupestris*. The under parts vary in colour. The chin is white centrally, the sides tinged yellow, the bases of the individual hairs grey. The throat is grizzled grey, the chest pinkish-buff or yellowish, the lower parts of the belly white. The anal region and inside of the hind legs are a darker pinkish-buff than the chest. The soles of the feet are grey. The top of the head is slightly darker than the upper parts. The eyes are encircled with distinct white rings, rather broader in front than behind, and immediately above these white rings are elongated dark patches. The long ears have fringes of short white hair on their inner margins and fringes of short, buffy hair on the outer. The tips are fringed with short black hair. The hair on the nuchal patch on the nape of the neck is slightly shorter than that on the shoulders and is a rich rufous colour. The fluffy tail is round and pale grey with a tinge of rufous and with a tinge of black towards the tip.

### Table 127.1

Measurements (mm) and mass (kg) of riverine rabbits, *B. monticularis*, (Robinson, 1981a)

| | Irrespective of sex | | |
|---|---|---|---|
| | $\bar{x}$ | n | Range |
| HB | 429 | 14 | 337–470 |
| T | 92 | 13 | 70–108 |
| Hf c/u | 104 | 15 | 90–120 |
| E | 116 | 15 | 107–124 |
| TL skull | 80,9 | 15 | 78,9–85,0 |

| | Males | | | Females | | |
|---|---|---|---|---|---|---|
| | $\bar{x}$ | n | Range | $\bar{x}$ | n | Range |
| Mass | 1,45±0,18 | 2 | 1,4–1,5 | 1,7±0,15 | 6 | 1,5–1,9 |

### Distribution

This species is endemic to the central Karoo region in the Cape Province. Museum specimens are known from the following localities: east of Calvinia (31°32′S, 20°32′E and 31°27′S, 19°50′E); Deelfontein (30°59′S, 23°48′E); Middelpos (31°55′S, 20°13′E); Nelspoort (32°07′S, 23°00′E); north of Sutherland (32°12′S, 20°42′E) and Victoria West (31°26′S, 23°07′E) (Robinson, 1981a).

Owing to habitat destruction in the Calvinia and Sutherland districts, the species currently survives in only the Victoria West, Fraserburg and Beaufort West districts; this area is half its original range (Duthie *et al.*, 1989).

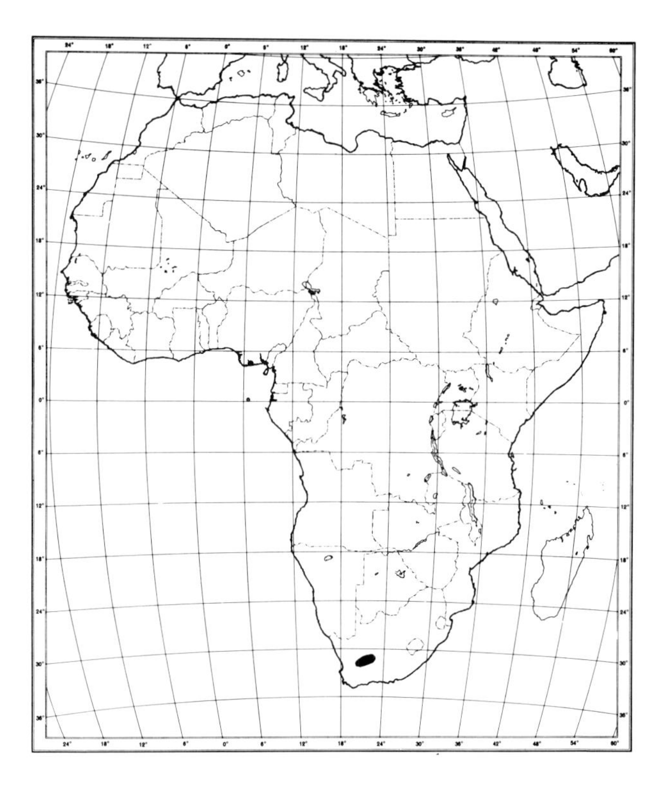

### Plate 7

122. Cape hare, *Lepus capensis*
Vlakhaas
123. Scrub hare, *Lepus saxatilis*
Kolhaas
124. Smith's red rock rabbit, *Pronolagus rupestris*
Smith se rooiklipkonyn
125. Natal red rock rabbit, *Pronolagus crassicaudatus*
Natalse rooiklipkonyn
126. Jameson's red rock rabbit, *Pronolagus randensis*
Jameson se rooiklipkonyn
a. *Pronolagus r. caucinus* (western distribution)
b. *Pronolagus r. randensis* (eastern distribution)
127. Riverine rabbit, *Bunolagus monticularis*
Oewerkonyn

PLATE 7
122
123
124
125
126a
126b
127
Dick Findlay.

**Habitat**

Riverine rabbits occur in riverine bush on the narrow alluvial fringe of seasonally dry watercourses in the central Karoo. This dense and discontinuous riverine bush consists of shrubs 50–100 m in height. *Salsola glabrescens* (11,8%) and *Lycium* spp. (6,5%) comprise most of the vegetation cover. Ephemeral grasses, abundant in the wet season, are represented poorly in the dry season, comprising only 5% of vegetation cover compared to 30% for dicotyledons (Duthie *et al.*, 1989).

**Habits**

They are nocturnal and solitary. Females have home ranges of 12,88±1,3 ha and males, home ranges of 20,2±1,44 ha. These overlap relatively little intrasexually (Duthie, 1989).

Adult male-female and adult female-juvenile couples form for short periods for mating and rearing of young, respectively (Duthie, 1989). They lie up during the day in forms under the cover of bushes. When flushed from cover they are as fleet-footed as any of the other African lagomorphs and not "slow and clumsy" as Shortridge remarked in his field notes (Robinson, 1981b).

Compared with the Cape and scrub hares which sometimes occupy the same habitat, they can be recognized as being different. They look darker in colour and run with less of a bobbing motion, their backs parallel to the ground. Their most unique characteristic, however, is the pompom-like grey tail which does not show the white-black of the tails of the hares.

**Food**

Riverine rabbits are predominantly browsers but also select grasses during the wet growing season when the green flush of new growth is available (Duthie, 1989). Favoured browse is *Pteronia erythrochaetha, Kochia pubescens, Salsola glabrescens* and Mesembryanthemaceae. The latter may be important in satisfying the species' water requirements (Duthie, 1989).

**Reproduction**

One, possibly two, altricial young are born from August to May. These young weigh 40 g at birth and are placed in a fur and grass-lined breeding stop. This burrow is 200–300 mm long and broadens from the entrance, 90–105 mm wide, into a chamber 120–170 mm wide. The entrance is plugged with soil and twigs when occupied by young (Duthie, 1989). Limited observations suggest the existence of post partum oestrus, breeding synchrony and a gestation period of 35–36 days.

## INTRODUCED

No. 128

## *Oryctolagus cuniculus* (Linnaeus, 1758)

### Rabbit
### Konyn

Skead (1980) reported that Leibbrandt (1: 1900) quoted a letter dated 13th May 1652 from Van Riebeeck to the Headquarters of the Dutch East India Company in Amsterdam advocating the introduction of "... some rabbits to breed from in the downs so suitable for them". Thus within a month of arriving in the Cape, Van Riebeeck had the idea of establishing rabbits as a source of meat for the garrison as well as for passing ships. In view of the fact that all current reports stated that the countryside teemed with game and waterfowl this idea seems somewhat incongruous. In sending the first consignment, the Council of the Company apparently issued instructions that they were not to be released on the mainland, for Leibbrandt (2: 1900) recorded that Van Riebeeck in a letter dated 5th March 1657 stated "... according to your orders we keep none here on the continent lest they damage the gardens and crops".

On the arrival of the first consignment of rabbits, nine were sent to Robben Island, with an instruction, dated 3rd April 1654 to Corporal Marcus Robbeljaert, that they were to be released in the sheep pen. They did not thrive and by December 1654 only one was left. Another consignment was released on the Island in 1656 and a further seven in March 1657, but four months later only three females had survived. In March 1658 two males, one female and three young were released and in April 1658 another male. The first births on the Island took place in June 1658 and by January 1659 it was reported that there were 50 and by March 1659 Van Riebeeck (3.30) reported that they were "... in abundance everywhere". (Thom, 1958).

Introductions to other offshore islands took place. Van Riebeeck did not think that Dassen Island was suitable for stocking "... on account of the stench of dead seals" (Leibbrandt, 2: 1900), but later left instructions that his successor, Commander Z. Wagenaar, should introduce them, which was done between 1662 and 1668. According to later reports (Mentzel, 2: 1787) they thrived, although they were thinned out by sealers who visited and used the island as a base on which to recover oil from their catches. There is no record of when they were introduced to Schaapen Island in Saldanha Bay, where they still live, but Francois le Vaillant (1: 1790) in 1781 found "a prodigious number of rabbits ... which were an excellent resource for our seamen". There is apparently no record of the first introductions to Jutten, Marcus or Vondeling islands. Layard (1861) recorded the introduction of a few pairs to an island in the Keurbooms River, Plettenberg Bay, in 1859, an introduction which failed. Brooke & Cooper (*in litt.*) stated that they probably were introduced to Possession Island sometime after 1850, but, as the island is sparsely vegetated, they only survive because they are fed by the staff working on the guano deposits. The same was the case on Malagas Island where they died out with the killing of the last survivor in 1976 and on Marcus Island with the withdrawal of the guano staff in the 1960's. Marcus Island was stocked in 1950, but by 1976 none were left. Rabbits are still found on Possession, Jutten, Vondeling, Schaapen, Dassen, Robben, Seal (Algoa Bay) and Bird islands (Algoa Bay) (Map 128.1).

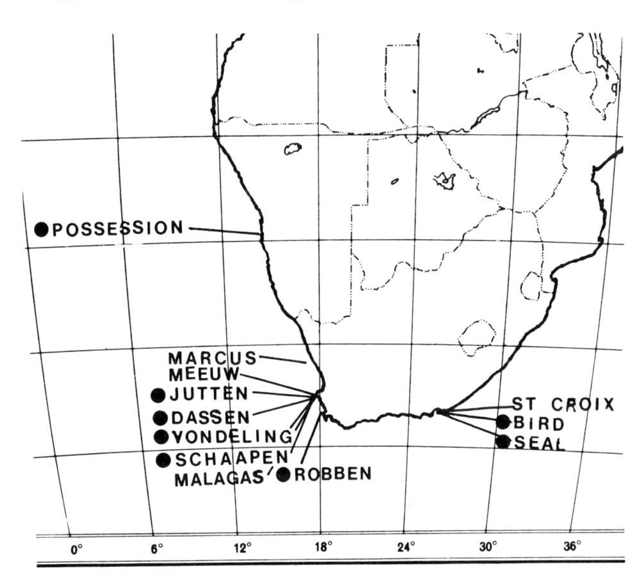


Map 128.1 Subregion offshore islands to which rabbits have been introduced. On those prefixed by ● they still occur.

As far as is known the introductions to islands have all been of domestic strains of rabbits, there being mention in the early records of white, grey and black rabbits on Robben Island (Thom, 1954. Journal of Van Riebeeck Vol. 2). Where islands have sufficient vegetation to support a rabbit population they have flourished, on others they have died out, as they did on Schaapen, new introductions taking place within more modern times (1950, Brooke & Cooper, *in litt.*).

Although deliberate or accidental introductions to the mainland may or may not have taken place since historical times, as rabbits are widely kept as pets, escapees have certainly had the opportunity of settling and becoming feral. However, predation pressures are high on the African Continent, from a wide range both of mammalian and avian species, and it appears that escapees do not survive as they do on the offshore islands where there are no predators. In Zimbabwe rabbits are commonly kept as a source of meat by indigenous people in country areas, from where they escape from time to time. In the Umzingwane Reserve near Bulawayo, Zimbabwe, during bird shoots over a two year period, at least four domestic rabbits were shot. This included one male and three females. The potential, therefore, for becoming feral is present. In the following years, however, no further individuals were seen.

# Order RODENTIA

## The rodents

The fossil record of the Rodentia is obscure. Romer (1971) presumed that they arose from an insectivorous, placental stock but transitional forms between this and *Paramys*, known from the Palaeocene Epoch and which was already a true rodent, are unknown. From this time they have proved themselves to be a highly successful group which have flourished since the Eocene (Colbert, 1969).

The name of the Order is derived from the Latin verb *rodere*, to gnaw. Their external morphology can vary greatly, from the furry pygmy mouse to the quilled porcupine, but there is a remarkable uniformity in the structure of their skulls and teeth. They all have a pair of ever-growing incisor teeth situated on the anterior part of the upper and lower jaws. The canine teeth and anterior premolar teeth are missing, leaving a toothless area between the incisors and the row of cheekteeth known as the diastema, which can be closed by a fold of skin on the upper lips. When the individual is gnawing on indigestible material the detritus arising from this action is allowed to fall out of the sides of the mouth and does not enter the buccal cavity. When feeding, the diastema is closed by this fold of skin and the food is then directed backwards to be masticated by the molar teeth. In gnawing, the tips of the lower and upper incisors occlude against each other, keeping the outer hard enamel layer on the front of the teeth honed to a chisel-like sharpness.

The cheekteeth, which lie posterior to the diastema, are usually three or four in number, occasionally five, and form an unbroken series. They consist of dentine ringed by an outer layer of hard enamel which may form a simple irregular ring or have a complicated series of re-entrant folds forming a pattern on the occlusal surface, which is of diagnostic importance. In some species these molar teeth have open roots and grow throughout life, in others the roots are closed and they eventually cease to grow.

As chewing is important to rodents, the external pterygoid, temporalis and masseter muscles are well developed. The lower jaws are adapted to this purpose, being capable of moving backwards and forwards or in a rotary motion, so as to thoroughly masticate the food between the molar teeth.

Romer (1971) stated that rodents are, without question, the most successful of all living mammals. Vaughan (1972) listed no less than 34 Families, 354 genera and about 1 685 species. They are the most numerous of all mammals, representing more than half of all the living species known. Only absent from Antarctica and some oceanic islands, they are well represented on a cosmopolitan basis. Within this great distributional range they have adapted themselves successfully to almost any type of habitat, some, such as the house mouse, *Mus musculus*, living as a commensal with man. Their habits are as varied; some spend their entire lives underground, such as the molerats, others are purely terrestrial and some are almost entirely arboreal.

There is no absolute agreement among authorities on the classification of rodents, especially above the Family level. It is, however, generally accepted that the squirrels, the rats and mice, and the porcupines are representatives of three distinct Suborders: the Sciuromorpha, the Myomorpha and the Hystricomorpha. The genera and species assigned to them, however, remain controversial. While on the one hand the porcupine-like Hystricomorpha and on the other the mouse and rat-like Myomorpha are reasonably important terminal groups, the Sciuromorpha have become a dumping ground of primitive and specialised small groups (de Graaff, 1981).

In the front of the skull in rodents there is a foramen which lies in front of the eye orbit known as the infraorbital foramen or, better, the antorbital foramen because of its position in relation to the eye orbit. It is this structure which has been the main component of taxonomic studies on rodents (Meester *et al.*, 1986). In many rodents this foramen is small, through which pass nerve and blood vessels. In other rodents, however, it is greatly enlarged and in addition to nerves and blood vessels, portions of the masseter muscle also pass through it. The masseter muscle is comprised of three sections: 1. A superficial section, the *masseter superficialis*, which arises on the side of the face, being attached to the maxillary bone, and runs backwards and downwards, inserting on the angular portion of the lower jaw. 2. A middle section, the *masseter lateralis*, which arises from the under edge of the zygomatic arch and inserts on the lower margin of the lower jaw. 3. A deep layer, the *masseter medialis*, which also arises from the under edge of the zygomatic arch as well as from the side of the rostrum. In the Myomorpha and Hystricomorpha this muscle passes through the enlarged infraorbital foramen to insert high up on the outer surface of the lower jaw, while in the Sciuromorpha the arrangement is different.

In the Sciuromorpha the foramen is too small to allow muscle tissue to pass through it and only nerves and blood vessels do so. In this Suborder the maxillary process forms a plate to which the *masseter lateralis* is attached.

In the Myomorpha, the rats and mice, the infraorbital foramen is enlarged to allow part of the *masseter medialis* muscle to pass through it, whilst in the Hystricomorpha most of the *masseter medialis* muscle passes through a greatly enlarged infraorbital foramen (Fig. 134.2).

The molerats of the Family Bathyergidae have always presented a special problem to workers on the Order for they do not fit exactly into the definition of any of the three Suborders. In all genera except adult *Cryptomys hottentotus* (Maier & Schrenk, 1987), the infraorbital foramen is too small to allow muscle tissue to pass through it (Fig. XVI.1), but there is no zygomatic plate. However, Maier & Schrenk (1987) have shown embryonic relics of infraorbital muscle in foetal bathyergids. The *masseter medialis* muscle is unlike members of any of the other groups and is highly complex, part of it arising from the wall of the eye orbit, while part of the *masseter lateralis* muscle is attached to the anterior face of the zygomatic arch (Wood, 1955). Roberts (1951), because of this, created two new Suborders, the Bathyergomorpha to accommodate the molerats and the Dipodomorpha, the dormice, but these Suborders have not found general acceptance. Meester *et al.* (1986) followed Anderson (1967), whose classification is in broad agreement with that of Simpson (1945), although they remained doubtful of its validity. This includes in the Hystricomorpha: the molerats, porcupine, canerats and the dassierat, in the Sciuromorpha: the squirrels and springhaas, and in the Myomorpha: the dormice and rats and mice.

Further information on these interesting taxonomic problems is provided by Meester *et al.* (1986) in their review of the Order. Some of the Families and genera comprising it are dealt with by authorities such as: Amtmann (1975) on the Sciuridae; Petter (1975) on the Gerbillinae; Davis (1975a) on the genera *Tatera* and *Gerbillurus*; Setzer (1975) on *Acomys*; Davis (1975b) on *Aethomys*; Petter (1975) on *Leggada*, and Coetzee (1977) on *Steatomys*. In addition, recent dramatic developments in the field of rodent molecular genetics have not been included as studies are presently in progress and will have to wait for the next edition.

Key to the Suborders and Families after Meester *et al.* (1986)

1. Lower jaw with angular process distorted outwards by a limb of lateral superficial masseter muscle ('SUBORDER HYSTRICOMORPHA')
 ... 2

 Lower jaw with angular process not so distorted
 ... 5

2. Infraorbital foramen small, not transmitting muscle except in foetus and in adult *Cryptomys*; fibula reduced and fused with tibia; cheekteeth 4/4, occlusal surfaces simple, without enamel infoldings or islands; eyes suppressed; ear pinnae absent; pelage soft; animals adapted to subterranean life
 ... *Bathyergidae*

 Infraorbital foramen much enlarged for muscle transmission, wider below than above; fibula well developed, not fused with tibia; cheekteeth 4/4, occlusal surfaces with infoldings and islands of enamel; eyes well developed; ear pinnae present; pelage modified to quills, bristles or springy hairs
 ... 3

3. Size large (head and body >600 mm); body covered with long spines; skull with dorsal profile oval, orbits placed far back, nasals very broad; cheekteeth 4/4, with wavy enamel patterning, occlusal surfaces flat; upper incisors smooth, ungrooved
 ... *Hystricidae*

 Size smaller (HB <600 mm); body without spines
 ... 4

4. HB 300–600 mm; hair bristly, also on tail which is less than half of HB length; body compact, legs short; cheekteeth 4/4, with enamel infoldings; upper incisors with two grooves on anterior surface
 ... *Thryonomyidae*

 HB <200 mm; tail about the same length, covered with scattered long hairs, not close-set as in squirrels; skull flattened; cheekteeth 4/4, with deep lingual and buccal enamel infoldings which virtually divide the crown into anterior and posterior halves; upper incisors not grooved
 ... *Petromuridae*

5. Infraorbital foramen not, or scarcely, transmitting muscle; zygomatic plate tilted upwards; jugal bone long, usually extending to the lachrymal; skull with postorbital processes; cheekteeth cuspidate, upper molars typically with a series of transverse ridges with cusps at corners; cheekteeth 4/4 or 5/4; tail bushy; fibula not fused with tibia ('SUBORDER SCIUROMORPHA', part)
 ... *Sciuridae*

 Infraorbital foramen enlarged for muscle transmission; skull without postorbital processes
 ... 6

6. Zygomatic plate narrow, situated below much enlarged infraorbital foramen; skull with mastoids inflated, frontals wide and zygoma thickened; cheekteeth 4/4, rootless, premolars normally as large as molars; molars with simplified occlusal pattern; body modified for bipedal and saltatorial way of life, with long hind limbs and tail ('SUBORDER SCIUROMORPHA', part)
 ... *Pedetidae*

 Zygomatic plate broadened; infraorbital foramen well developed; cheekteeth rooted and complex, either 3/3 or 4/4, premolars tend to be smaller than molars; fibula fused with tibia; hind feet with 5 toes (except in *Malacothrix*) ('SUBORDER MYOMORPHA')
 ... 7

7. Zygomatic plate not tilted upwards, infraorbital foramen not very large; cheekteeth 4/4; bullae large; jugal usually long; tail densely furred, bushy
 ... *Gliridae*

 Infraorbital foramen flattened by zygomatic plate, the latter tilted upwards to a greater or lesser degree; cheekteeth not exceeding 3/3; jugal usually short; tail usually not bushy
 ... *Muridae*

# XVI. Family BATHYERGIDAE

## Molerats

The name of the Family is derived from the Greek, *bathys*, deep, and *ergo*, to work, a reference to their subterranean life.

The colloquial name of members is unfortunate for they are neither moles, which are insectivores, nor rats, which are murids, but the name has become entrenched in literature and in usage. The Family is of doubtful relationship. Ellerman *et al.* (1953) set out the higher categories, within the Order Rodentia, to which authorities have relegated it from the time of Tullberg (1899) to Roberts (1951). Wherever they have been placed, all authorities consider them a Family on their own.

The general consensus of opinion is that the molerats are related more closely to the porcupines than to any other mammals, although there is not the slightest indication in their external appearance to suggest this. However, the powerful build of the lower jaws, in particular the well developed mandible with its posterior section out-curved to provide a broad base of attachment for the extra large masseter muscle, is a feature shared with the porcupines. Their molar teeth too, resemble the teeth of porcupines more closely than those of any other group of mammals, but they differ from the porcupines in their small infraorbital foramen.

The Family is endemic to the African Continent, members occurring from the Cape Province to north of the equator and westwards to Ghana in West Africa. All its members are subterranean and have reduced eyes and ear pinnae, short legs and tails (except in *Heterocephalus*) and a pair of large, stoutly built, ever-growing incisor teeth in both jaws which

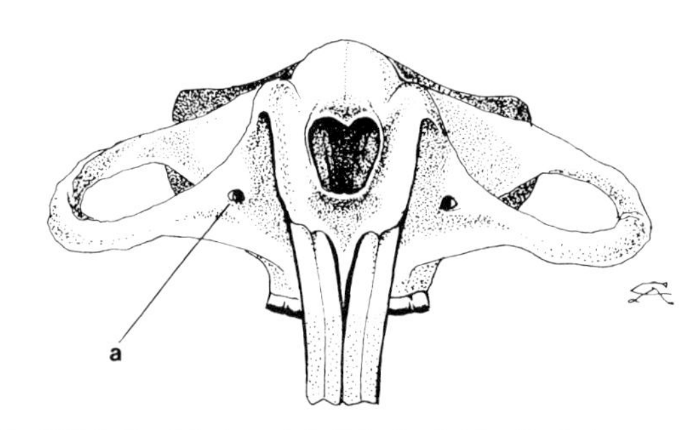


Fig. XVI.1. Frontal view of skull in the Subfamily Bathyerginae: *Bathyergus suillus* to show their grooved upper incisor teeth. (a) infraorbital foramen.

project from the mouth. They usually have four cheekteeth in each side of the upper and lower jaws, the homology of which is uncertain because of the absence of pertinent embryological data. Thomas (1909) suggested that in the southern African genera the four teeth consist of two premolars and two molars. They have five digits on the fore and hind feet, the hind claws shorter than those on the forefeet, and naked soles to the feet. The outer borders of the hind feet bear a fringe of stiff hairs. Their bodies are cylindrical in shape, the eyes very small and there is no external shell to the ear which opens as a hole in the surface of the skin and is obscured by the hair. The tail of the South African genome is very short and bears a fringe of stiff hairs. The head is blunt and strong. The prominent incisor teeth are used (except in *Bathyergus*) in burrowing (Fig. XVI.2). The claws on the front feet, except in *Bathyergus*, are not particularly well adapted to digging but are used in moving the soil loosened by the incisors. The lips meet behind the incisors and the mouth opening is small.

Fig. XVI.2 Incisor teeth are used in burrowing, the lips being pursed together behind the teeth for this purpose.

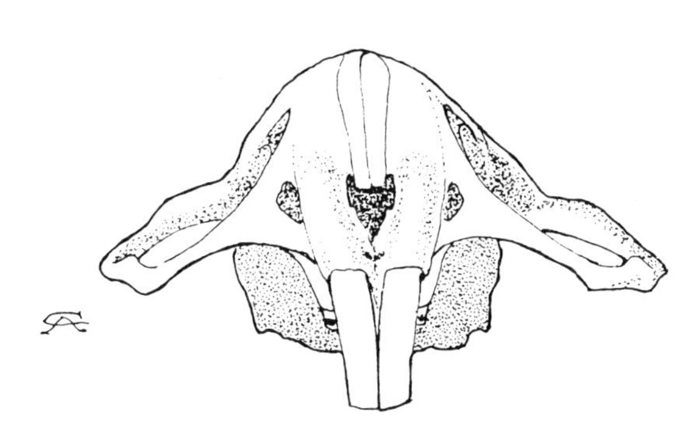

Fig. XVI.3. Frontal view of skull in the Subfamily Georychinae: *Georychus capensis* to show ungrooved upper incisor teeth.

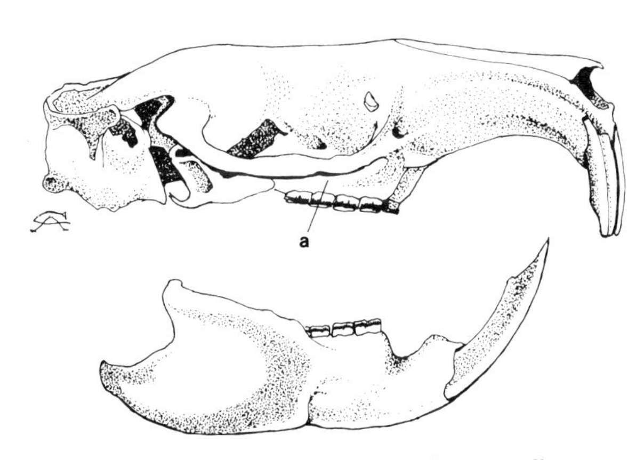


Fig. XVI.4. Skull: Bathyerginae, *Bathyergus suillus*
(a) position of the root of the incisor teeth situated above the toothrow.

Roberts (1951) divided the genera that occur in the Subregion into two Subfamilies: the Bathyerginae, to accommodate members of the genus *Bathyergus*, which have grooved upper incisors (Fig. XVI.1), and the Georychinae with the genera *Georychus* and *Cryptomys* which have plain upper incisors (Fig. XVI.3). In the Bathyerginae the roots of the upper incisors lie above the molar teeth (Fig. XVI.4), whereas in the Georychinae they lie far behind the molars in the pterygoid region (Fig. XVI.5). Ellerman *et al.* (1953) were in favour of Roberts' (1951) Subfamilies, but pointed out that if they were used, then another Subfamily would have to be created to accommodate the naked molerat, *Heterocephalus* sp, of East Africa. Studies on the five genera of the Bathyergidae, utilising karyotype and allozyme differentiation (Nevo *et al.*, 1986, 1987) and mitochondrial DNA variation (Honeycutt *et al.*, 1987) distinguish two sister groups (*Georychus/Heliophobius*; *Cryptomys/Heterocephalus*), with the genus *Bathyergus* very divergent from both but associated with either the *Georychus/Heliophobius* group or representing a more basal lineage.

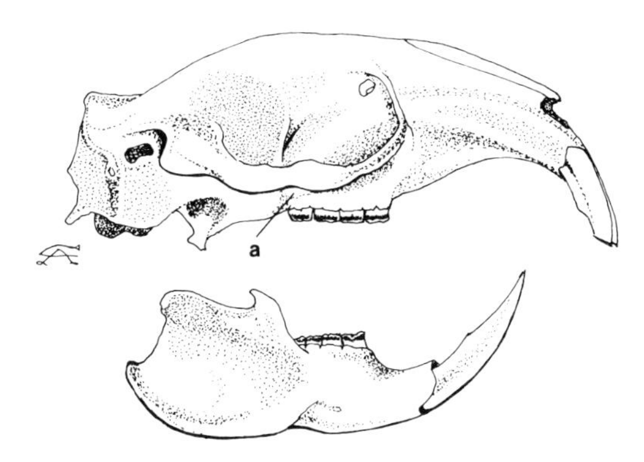


Fig. XVI.5. Skull: Georychinae, *Georychus capensis*
(a) position of the root of the incisor tooth behind the toothrow.

Key to the Subfamilies after Ellerman *et al.* (1953)

1. Upper incisor teeth heavily grooved (Fig. XVI.1), their roots lying above the molar teeth (Fig. XVI.4); foreclaws much enlarged; angular process of the mandible much drawn backwards
   ... *Bathyerginae*

   Upper incisor teeth not heavily grooved (Fig. XVI.3), their roots lying well behind the molar teeth in the pterygoid region (Fig. XVI.5); foreclaws not much enlarged; angular process of the mandible not much drawn backwards
   ... *Georychinae*

Key to the genera after Meester *et al.* (1986)

1. Upper incisors not extending behind toothrow, reaching only infraorbital foramen, and heavily grooved; foreclaws much enlarged, adapted to digging; angular portion of mandible produced considerably backwards, beyond occipital condyles
   ... *Bathyergus*

   Upper incisors extending behind toothrows to back of palate, frequently into pterygoids, not grooved; foreclaws not enlarged; angular portion of mandible hardly produced backwards beyond occipital condyles
   ... 2

2. Cheekteeth simple, ring-shaped in adults; posterior tooth erupts early in life; jugal fitting into a long groove on zygoma; face not contrastingly marked
   ... *Cryptomys*

   Cheekteeth retaining one inner, one outer fold to old age; posterior tooth erupts late in life (*ca.* 9–12 months —Taylor *et al.*, 1985); jugal fitting dove-tail fashion into zygoma; face contrastingly marked, black cap on head, white ring around ear, cheeks black, nose white
   ... *Georychus*

## Subfamily BATHYERGINAE

### Genus *Bathyergus* Illiger, 1811

Key to the species after Meester *et al.* (1986)

1. Body colour cinnamon, pale brown or tawny, no distinct dorsal band; size larger; head and body 204–360 mm
   ... *suillus*

   Body colour silvery-grey, with a distinct dark dorsal band from the nape of the neck to the hindquarters; size smaller, head and body 170–305 mm
   ... *janetta*

No. 129

## *Bathyergus suillus* (Schreber, 1782)

## Cape dune molerat
## Kaapse duinmol

Plate 8

### Colloquial Name

They are called the Cape dune molerat as they are confined in their distribution to the Cape Province. However, they are not associated solely with sand dunes, as they are common, in places, in sandy loam.

### Taxonomic Notes

Numbers of subspecies have been described, predominantly on colour and size. Those from the west coast are paler than those from the Knysna area, which may be correlated with humidity, as the Knysna area has a much higher mean annual rainfall (800–1 000 mm) than the west coast (200–300 mm). Meester *et al.* (1986) regarded the species as monotypic. The chromosome diploid number is 2n=56 (n=1) (Nevo *et al.*, 1986).

### Description

The Cape dune molerat is the largest of all the bathyergids and the largest known completely subterranean rodent in the world. Adults reach a head and body length in males of 330 mm, with a tail of 70 mm and a mean mass of some 896 g ± 362 (n = 208), but can exceed 1800 g; in females 300 mm, with a tail of 65 mm and a mean mass of some 670 g ± 193 (n = 257) (Jarvis, *in litt.*).

**Table 129.1**

Measurements (mm) and mass (g) of Cape dune molerats, *B. suillus*, from the Cape Province (de Graaff, 1981; Jarvis, pers. comm.)

| | Male | | | Females | | |
|---|---|---|---|---|---|---|
| | $\bar{x}$ | n | Range | $\bar{x}$ | n | Range |
| TL | 288 | 50 | 228–373 | 252 | 50 | 222–327 (Jarvis) |
| S.D. | 45,28 | | | 39,57 | | |
| HB | 281 | 39 | 240–330 | 256 | 45 | 204–300 |
| Hf c/u | 51 | 37 | 45–65 | 46 | 43 | 42–55 |
| Mass | 896 | 208 | | 670 | 257 | |
| S.D. | 362 | | | 193 | | |

The colour of the upper parts of the body is cinnamon, very pale brown or tawny; in some individuals the dark grey bases of the hairs show through the coat, giving the upper parts an uneven colour. Individuals may have a dark brown, mid-dorsal longitudinal band. The flanks are paler, the under parts greyish. They have a pale buffy or white patch around the eyes, and the chin and the muzzle are whitish. Both sexes may have a white patch on their foreheads (de Graaff, 1965). The individual hairs on the upper parts of the body are black at the base, then slate-grey and cinnamon, pale brown or tawny at the tips, those on the dark dorsal band with dark brown tips. Longer, sinusoidal (tactile) hairs occur on the body and stand higher than the rest of the pelage.

### Skull

The skull is heavily built and conspicuously flat on the upper surface, but curves downwards slightly to the nasals. Sexual dimorphism is apparent and adult moles have prominent sagittal and nuchal crests (Jarvis, pers. comm.) (Fig. XVI.4). The rostrum is elongated, with a wide diastema between the incisor teeth and the first teeth in the row of cheekteeth. The zygomatic arches swing out widely from the sides of the skull (Fig. XVI.1). The upper incisors are heavily grooved (one groove), the lower ungrooved (Fig. XVI.1). They have four cheekteeth on either side which Thomas (1909) stated were premolars numbers three and four and molars one and two, but which de Graaff (1979) suggested were more likely to be premolar number four, with three following molars. The cheekteeth are oval in shape, the longest diameter lying at right angles to the line of the teeth. In juveniles their teeth have re-entrant folds on the sides which, through wear, are generally lost in the adults. The mandible is heavily built, the two parts loosely joined at the symphysis.

### Distribution

*Southern African Subregion*

They are confined in their distribution to the coastal area of the southwestern Cape Province, from Lamberts Bay and Klaver in the northwest, to Knysna on the south coast, penetrating inland some 80 km from the coast in the northwest. All the localities from which they have been taken so far lie at an altitude below 300 m above sea level (de Graaff, 1981). Over part of their range, they occur sympatrically with either one or both of *Cryptomys h. hottentotus* or *Georychus capensis* (Davies & Jarvis, 1986; Lovegrove & Jarvis, 1986).

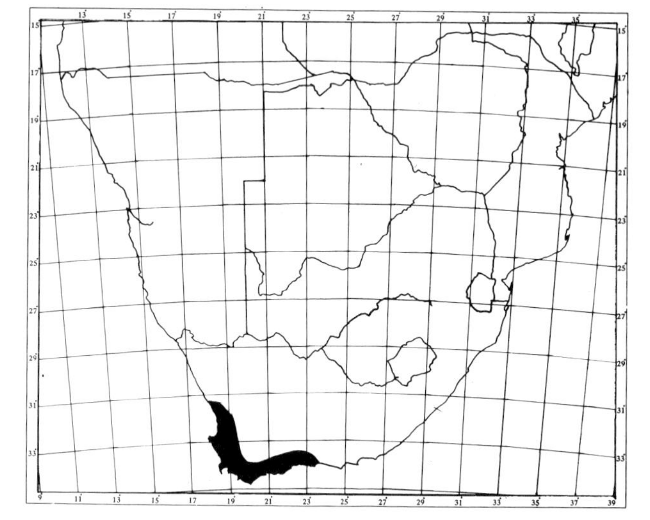

### Habitat

They occur only where there is a sandy substrate, in parts in coastal sand dunes, on sandy flats or in alluvial sand along river systems.

### Habits

A single individual occupies a burrow. Eloff (1952) stated that digging and tunnelling is instinctive but does not commence until the young are about six weeks old. If, for any reason, the burrow system is opened, the damage is quickly plugged and the plugs are often up to a metre in length. They are apparently sensitive to air currents and may detect that the burrows are open to the surface, by the air disturbance caused.

New mounds can be recognised as the soil pushed out is moist and often still retains the cylindrical form of the burrow. Where the areas in which they live are subject to seasonal flooding, as on the Cape Flats, the mounds occasionally have open holes in them through which the individuals may have left, to seek new and drier burrow sites or through which the molerats have been taken by predators. De Graaff (1964) stated that instances are known where molerats will walk around on the surface of the soil in daylight. The reason for this behaviour is not known. Many farmers claim that molerats come above ground a day or so before it rains. Davies & Jarvis (1986) excavated the burrow system of a male, whose tunnels were flanked on either side by the burrow systems of two females. The male system had a total length of 264 m. The burrow system of one of the females, which was accompanied by a juvenile, was 420 m, and that of the other, a single female, was 287 m. These lengths included the many side branches. The diameter of the tunnels ranged from 150 to 220 mm, the majority running 400 to 650 mm below the surface of the ground. Four out of six burrows had a longer (72 m), blind-ending "bolt hole". The burrow systems were changing constantly, the loose soil either thrown up to form surface mounds or packed into disused sections of the burrow system underground. The average monthly extensions of the systems ranged in one site between 15 and 101 m, in another up to 21 m, but in some cases no extension was recorded, whilst individuals could burrow up to 3,4 m per day. The level of burrowing activity was highest when the moisture content of the substrate was highest, in winter and also during the breeding season. The average home range was 0,27 ha (0,14 to 0,35 ha). The home range of adjacent individuals was bordered by corridors in which there was no activity.

At least two nesting chambers were located in a single burrow system near the centre, 0,4 to 0,9 m below ground level. Nesting chambers were lined with grass and leaves and soft vegetable debris. They had a single entrance from the main burrow which contained uneaten portions of food. Toilet chambers were located in blind-ending side branches of the burrow system or in some cases in the main burrow, sealing off the system into two sections.

Their eyesight is poor or may be lacking altogether, the eyelids may even be fused, but they have a keen sense of hearing and react immediately to nearby noises. They are sensitive to vibrations and will not attempt to plug open parts of their burrows while observers are walking around near them. They grunt loudly when captured and may drum on the ground with their hind feet when alarmed or when in close proximity to conspecifics (Jarvis, pers. comm.). The drumming consists of bouts of two closely spaced beats followed by a brief pause, and another two beats *etc.* and both hind feet are used simultaneously during drumming.

### Food

Cape dune molerats are vegetarian, living on roots, bulbs and green vegetable matter (Davies & Jarvis, 1986). On the Cape Flats they were also found to eat the underground stolons of grasses, the burrows rising close to the surface to gain access to these (Smithers, 1983). They are independent of water, obtaining their moisture requirements from their food. Feeding sites can be recognised by patches of loosened and lifted soil, severed pieces of vegetation and very shallow burrows (Jarvis, pers. comm.).

### Reproduction

In captivity, at the onset of the breeding season, both sexes drum with their hind feet and will apparently drum in response to the signals of the opposite sex. On meeting, the female raises her tail, vocalises and moves forward, with the male following her (Jarvis, pers. comm.). In the southwestern Cape Province females with foetuses are found from July to October, the greater proportion being in August (Jarvis, 1969). At least some of the population is dioestrus (Jarvis, pers. comm.), with a gestation period estimated to be two to two and a half months. The average number of foetuses is 2,4, with a range of one to four (Jarvis, 1969; De Graaff, 1981). Body mass at birth is 25,27 g (n = 2), eyes open when seven days old, solids are eaten when 15 days old, sparring (play-fight) with litter mates begins when 12 days old, and in captivity this play-fighting escalates into fighting and the young disperse at about 60–65 days old (Jarvis, pers. comm.).

### General

The flesh of this species is regarded as a delicacy by some people. In parts of their range de Graaff (1981) recorded that four or five were caught weekly by some families, this being their only source of protein apart from fish. Cape dune molerats present problems on golf courses, bowling greens and tennis courts and in the wheat growing areas, where their mounds cause heavy wear on reaping machine blades. Extensive burrowing under highways and railway tracks causes sagging of the roads and lines.

---

No. 130

## *Bathyergus janetta* Thomas & Schwann, 1904

## Namaqua dune molerat
## Namakwa-duinmol

Plate 8

---

### Colloquial Name

They are so called for, as far as is presently known, they are largely confined to Namaqualand.

### Taxonomic Notes

Ellerman, Morrison-Scott & Hayman (1953) regarded this species as being only subspecifically distinct from the Cape dune molerat, *B. suillus*. De Graaff (1981) believed it to be a monotypic species, worthy of specific rank, a view followed by Meester *et al.* (1986), Nevo *et al.* (1986, 1987) & Honeycutt *et al.* (1987).

In the skull the bullae are more swollen than in *B. suillus* and the palate does not extend as far posterior to the cheekteeth as it does in *B. suillus*. The chromosome diploid number is 2n=54 (n=1) (Nevo, Capanna, Corti, Jarvis & Hickman, 1986).

### Description

Namaqua dune molerats are slightly smaller in size than Cape dune molerats: adult males reach a total length of about 305 mm, with a tail of 47 mm; females 275 mm, with tails of 44 mm (Table 130.1). However, body size is regionally variable. Thus adult males in the Kamiesberg had body masses of up to 710 g, compared to ones captured near Hondeklip Bay and in the areas north of the Orange River with masses of up to 450 g (Jarvis, pers. comm.). The colour of the body varies from drab grey to silvery-grey, depending on the area from which they originate, with a dark band about 15 mm broad from the nape of the neck to the rump. The head is black, or dark brown in some individuals, with a white or light grey stripe on top of the muzzle, from the rhinarium to between the eyes or restricted to the vicinity of the rhinarium, and a white or light silvery-grey patch around the external ear opening and on the chin. The limbs are the same colour as the under parts proximally, the hands and feet off-white or light brown. The tail is pink above, white below and is fringed with stiff white hairs 20 mm long. The under parts are black or dark grey, with a silvery sheen. The claws on digits two to five of the front feet are long and curved, that on the pollux or first digit short. The second digit is longest of all and has a claw up to 10 mm across its curve. Digits three to five are progressively shorter, with shorter claws. The claws on the hind feet are slightly shorter than those on the forefeet, the third digit longest of all, with a claw about 6 mm across the curve. The hallux is short with a short claw. The digits on both the front and hind feet are fringed with short, stiff hairs. The hair on the upper parts of the body is about 10 mm long and is dark grey at the base, dark brown or black-tipped on the dorsal band and grey or silvery-grey on the flanks. Longer tactile hairs extend beyond the rest of the body pelage (Jarvis, pers. comm.).

### Table 130.1

Measurements (mm) and mass (g) of Namaqua dune molerats, *B. janetta*, from the northwestern Cape Province (*de Graaff, 1981; **Jarvis, pers. comm.)

| | Males | | | Females | | |
|---|---|---|---|---|---|---|
| | $\bar{x}$ | n | Range | $\bar{x}$ | n | Range |
| HB* | 205 | 10 | 170–235 | 190 | 13 | 170–230 |
| TL** | 270 | 4 | 223–315 | 233 | 9 | 205–260 |
| T** | 35 | 4 | 32–38 | 32 | 9 | 26–37 |
| Hf s/u** | 43 | 4 | 38–46 | 39 | 9 | 34–44 |
| Hf c/u** | 47 | 4 | 40–51 | 43 | 9 | 36–48 |
| Mass** | 468 | 8 | 242–710 | 338 | 19 | 195–540 |

### Distribution

They are confined to the northwestern parts of the **Cape Province** in coastal sand dunes as far north as Oranjemund and northwards into **Namibia**, Boegoeberg and Boesmanberg to about 90 km north of the Orange River (Jarvis & Griffin, pers. comm.). In the southern parts of their range they occur in the vicinity of Springbok and as far inland as Ezelfontein, in the Kamiesberg, at an altitude of 1 350 m. Over much of their range in Namaqualand, they occur sympatrically with *C. h. hottentotus* (Jarvis, pers. comm.).

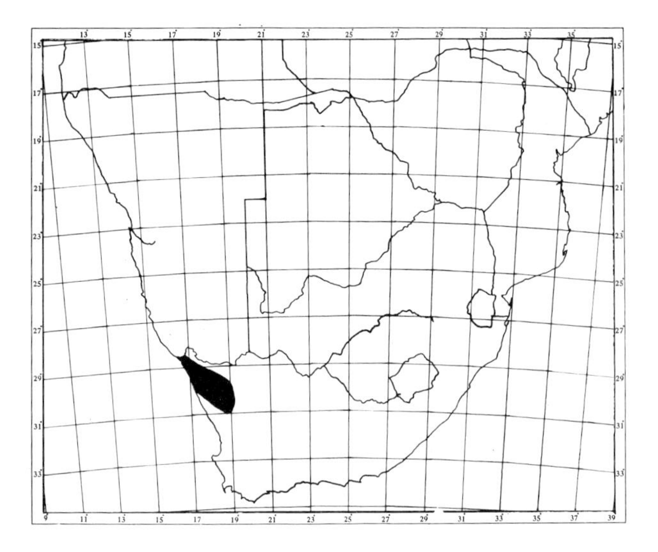

### Habitat

Coastally they occur in sand dunes and inland in a substrate of sandy alluvium in regions where there are geophytes. In Namibia they are associated with water seeps where there are small geophytes (Jarvis, *in litt.*).

### Habits

Like Cape dune molerats, Namaqua dune molerats live solitarily in burrow systems and throw up mounds at intervals along the main burrow line. One partly excavated burrow at Boesmanberg, Namibia, had a length exceeding 300 m (Jarvis & Griffin, pers. comm.).

### Food

Jarvis (*in litt.*) found that they will eat bulbs and roots and will pull above-ground vegetation such as daisies into the burrows to be consumed there.

### Reproduction

The females have one pair of pectoral and two pairs of inguinal mammae. Litter size is 2–7 (n=13). The young are born about September-November (Jarvis, pers. comm.) and pups have a newborn mass of 15,4 ± 5 g (n=8). Their eyes open 14 days after birth, they begin to eat solids at 10 days, begin to play-fight with their litter mates at 51 days and (in captivity) have to be separated from each other when 60 days old (Jarvis, pers. comm.). In the Kamiesberg area mating occurs in July and is the only time when two adults were found sharing a burrow (Jarvis, pers. comm.).

## Subfamily GEORYCHINAE

Key to the genera after Meester *et al.* (1986)

1. Cheekteeth simplified, ring-shaped in adults, hindmost molar cut earlier; face not contrastingly coloured

   ... *Cryptomys*

   Cheekteeth with one fold on each side in the upper jaw, hindmost molar cut late in life (*ca.* 10–12 months; Taylor *et al.*, 1985); black cap on the head, white ring around the ear openings, cheeks black, nose white

   ... *Georychus*

### WITHDRAWN

No. 131 The silvery molerat, *Heliophobius argentocinereus*, Peters, 1846, was included in the first edition on the evidence of specimens from the Tete District, Mozambique. It transpires that all these were taken north of the Zambezi River and the species therefore does not qualify for inclusion.

## Genus *Cryptomys hottentotus* Gray, 1864

No. 132

## *Cryptomys hottentotus* (Lesson, 1826)

## Common molerat
## Vaalmol

Plate 8

### Colloquial Name

This species is one of the most widely distributed and common molerats in the Subregion.

### Taxonomic Notes

As this species varies widely in many characters throughout the Subregion, many species have been described since Lesson described *C. hottentotus* in 1826, most of which are now recognised to represent, at best, subspecies. Meester *et al.* (1986) recognised five subspecies: the nominate *C. h. hottentotus* from the western to the eastern Cape Province, the Orange Free State, parts of the Transvaal, Zimbabwe and eastern Botswana; *C. h. darlingi* (Thomas, 1895) from parts of western, northeastern and eastern Zimbabwe and Mozambique, and *C. h. natalensis* (Roberts, 1913) from the southern, central and eastern Transvaal, Natal, southern Mozambique and Transkei. They also included *C. h. damarensis* (Ogilby, 1838) which occurs in the northwestern Cape Province, Botswana except the eastern sector, western Zimbabwe and Namibia (which is here afforded specific rank —see 132A *C. damarensis* (Ogilby, 1838)); and *C. h. bocagei* (De Winton, 1897) from northern Namibia and Angola, which Hill & Carter (1941) believed may be a subspecies of *C. damarensis* and for this reason is included with that species. The chromosome diploid number is 2n=54 (n=5) (Nevo *et al.*, 1986). Studies on karyotypes (Nevo *et al.*, 1986), allozymes (Nevo, *et al.*, 1987) and mitochondrial DNA (Honeycutt *et al.*, 1987) all indicate that the taxonomy of this genus needs revision. Thus, *C. h. hottentotus* and *C. h. natalensis* are as different from one another in magnitude of nucleotide sequence divergence as are *Georychus*, *Heliophobius* and *Bathyergus*.

North of the Subregion other subspecies have been described from Zambia and Zaire.

**Plate 8**

121. Pangolin, *Manis temminckii*
     Ietermagog
129. Cape dune molerat, *Bathyergus suillus*
     Kaapse duinmol
130. Namaqua dune molerat, *Bathyergus janetta*
     Namakwa-duinmol
132. Common molerat, *Cryptomys hottentotus*
     Vaalmol

132A Damara molerat, *Cryptomys damarensis*
     Damarase vaalmol

133. Cape molerat, *Georychus capensis*
     Kaapse blesmol

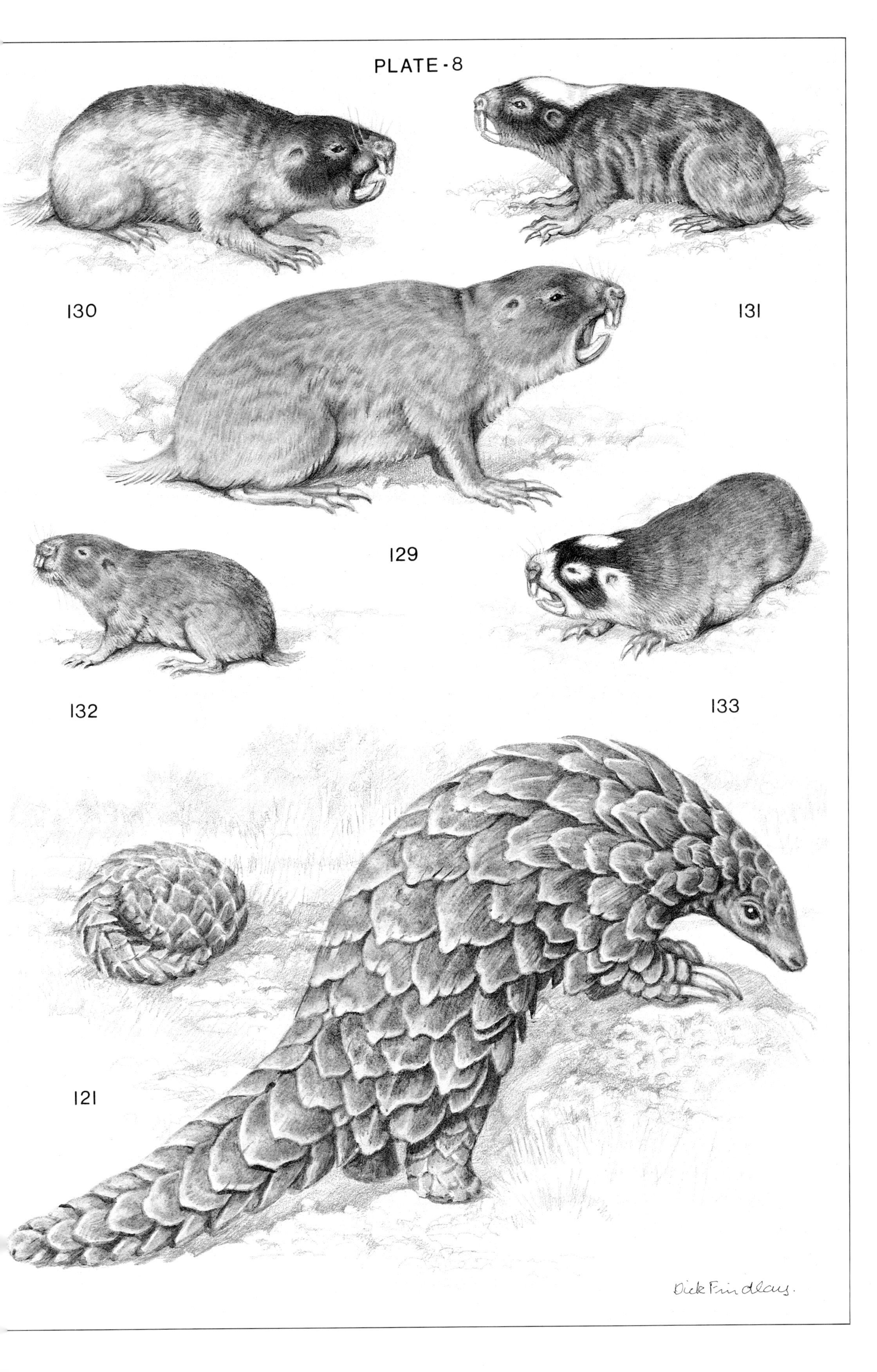
PLATE - 8
130
131
129
132
133
121
Dick Findlay.

### Description

Geographically, within populations and even within colonies they vary in size and colour. Bennett (1988) believed that the variation in size may be due to the status of the individual within the colony, dominant females having masses exceeding those of many males. Subordinate males and females remain small for years in this species as well as in *C. damarensis* (Bennett, 1989; Jacobs *et al.*, in review). If specimens of all the subspecies are considered together, adult males reach a head and body length of about 180 mm and have a mass of up to 145 g, females up to 160 mm, with a mass of up to 153 g (Table 132.1). However *C. h. hottentotus* from the southwestern Cape are considerably smaller (Table 132.1a). The colour of the upper parts varies from cinnamon-buff to clay-coloured, the under parts in all of them lighter in colour than the upper. In the southern populations the white patch on the forehead is usually absent. In those from the northern Cape Province it is more frequently present and in *C. h. darlingi* from the eastern part of Zimbabwe, even in individuals trapped in the same burrow system, some possess it, in others it is lacking and, where it is present, it varies in intensity. Occasionally albino specimens and buffy-yellow coloured individuals turn up within normally coloured colonies. The fur is short, soft and silky, the juveniles tending to be darker than the adults. Cranial measurements of *C.h. hottentotus* show no sexual dimorphism (Bennett, Jarvis & Wallace, in press).

### Table 132.1a

(a) Measurements (mm) and mass (g) of common molerats, *C. hottentotus*, from the Subregion (de Graaff, 1981)
(b) Body mass of three colonies *C. h. hottentotus* from the southwestern Cape (Bennett, 1989).

**(a)**

| | Males | | | Females | | |
|---|---|---|---|---|---|---|
| | $\bar{x}$ | n | Range | $\bar{x}$ | n | Range |
| HB | 133 | 271 | 105–185 | 129 | 248 | 100–164 |
| Hf c/u | 23 | 238 | 12–33 | 22 | 246 | 12–38 |
| Mass | 134 | 21 | 112–145 | 119 | 26 | 98–153 |

**Note**: Tail length in this species is not given as it is subject to too wide a range of interpretation.

**(b)**

| | Males | | | Females | | |
|---|---|---|---|---|---|---|
| No. in colony | Mass | n | S.D. | Mass | n | S.D. |
| 11 | 79,4 | 5 | ±33 | 41,1 | 6 | ±14 |
| 13 | 56,9 | 8 | ±18 | 54,3 | 5 | ±16 |
| 12 | 61,25 | 4 | ±22 | 45,3 | 8 | ±13,5 |

### Skull

The upper surface of the skull is very slightly convex, the bullae well developed. The two sections of the mandible are not firmly ossified at the symphysis and tend to come apart in cleaning. The upper and lower incisors are ungrooved. The cheekteeth are slightly broader than long, with a central portion of dentine surrounded by a ring of enamel and, unless very heavily worn, the posterior three show indications of re-entrant folds on their outer fringes (Fig. XVI.6) The infraorbital foramen is large enough for the passage of a small muscle.

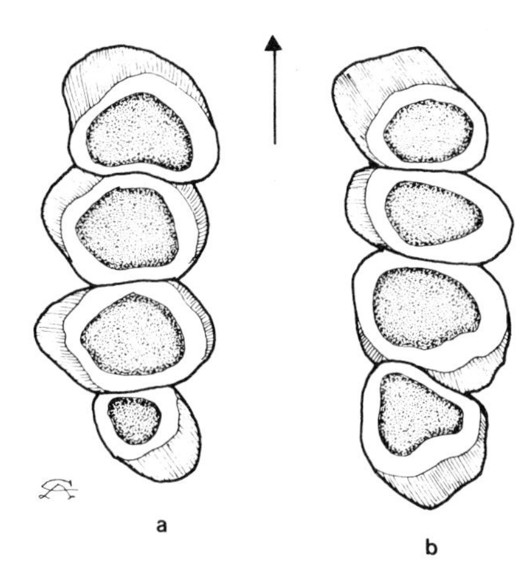


Fig. XVI.6. Cheekteeth: *Cryptomys* sp heavily worn: (a) right upper (b) right lower.

### Distribution

*South of the Sahara, excluding the Southern African Subregion*

They occur in parts of **Zambia** and in the Katanga Province of **Zaire**.

*Southern African Subregion*

They occur widely in **Mozambique**, south of the Zambezi River; in **Zimbabwe**, excluding parts of the western sector; in eastern **Botswana**; the **Transvaal**; the **Orange Free State**;

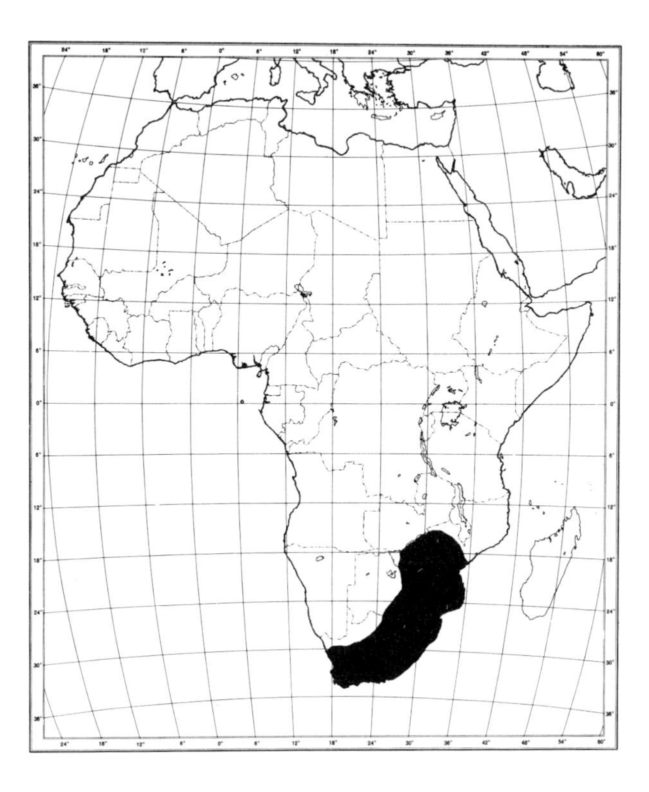

**Natal**, and in the **Cape Province**, excluding the northern and northwestern sectors.

### Habitat

Common molerats are capable of using a wide diversity of substrates, from sandy soils to heavier compacted types such as decomposed schists and stony soils. However, they cannot utilise heavy red clay soils or the hard soils associated with mopane woodland. They are much commoner in granite sand and other types of sandy soil including sandy alluvium along river systems. Over part of their range, in the southwestern Cape Province, they occur sympatrically with *Georychus capensis, Bathyergus suillus* or *B. janetta* (Jarvis, pers. comm.).

### Habits

They live in small colonies, up to 14 having been taken from a single system (Smithers, 1971; Davies & Jarvis, 1986). Like other molerats they throw up mounds along the main burrow to get rid of surplus soil loosened in excavation. They are particularly active after rain in expanding these burrows, as can be seen by the extending line of fresh mounds thrown up. The fresh mounds are recognised easily as the damp soil pushed out retains the shape of the burrow, only breaking down into a loose pile as it dries.

The main burrows run at a depth of about 150 to 300 mm underground, with many side tunnels and a nesting chamber. Especially during the summer months mounds are found with an open hole in their side through which the burrow occupants have dispersed, perhaps to seek more favourable feeding areas. Some of these are closed, having been blocked by burrow occupants that have left the burrow temporarily to move on the surface and have returned. Others remain open to the burrow system underneath, indicating that all the occupants have left, otherwise it would have been closed. De Graaff (1981) stated that they move on the surface at night as is evident by the fact that their skulls and bones are often found in barn owl, *Tyto alba*, casts. After heavy rain they are sometimes found on the surface during daylight hours. De Graaff (1981) stated that they use their incisor teeth in burrowing, while they certainly use them in cutting through roots and other woody obstructions underground as can be seen when the burrows are opened. Davies & Jarvis (1986) excavated a burrow occupied by an adult male, a pregnant female and a juvenile male that had a total length of 387 m including the blocked tunnels. The minimum home range was 1 582 $m^2$, the average depth 250 to 300 mm, the diameter of the tunnels 50 to 70 mm and the depth of the "bolt hole" 580 mm. In addition, Jarvis & Lovegrove (pers. comm.) excavated a 1 km system containing 14 individuals.

Their eyesight is poor and their sense of smell well developed. They are extremely sensitive to vibrations and the long vibrissae and bristle-like hairs on the fore and hind feet may serve a tactile function. They are extremely aggressive and quick to demonstrate with their heads thrown back, their mouths open and formidable incisor teeth ready to bite, grunting and squeaking as they face the danger.

If the burrows are opened they are quick to investigate the damage and, turning around, will push soil backwards and close up the tunnel. They do this more quickly if the observer moves well back from the burrow, as their sensitivity to vibrations is such that the slightest movement on the surface sends them deep into the burrow system. This burrow-sealing behaviour makes them easy to catch, as a trap inserted through the opening will hold them as they push the first load of soil towards the opening, being caught almost invariably with their hindquarters towards the opening.

Davies & Jarvis (1986) did not find defecation sites in the burrow systems, but stated that they may have been overlooked.

The molerat has adapted to life in a subterranean environment characterised by hypoxic conditions, a poor and periodic food supply and an atmosphere usually saturated with moisture (Haim & Fairall, 1986).

They fall prey to mole snakes, *Pseudaspis cana*, which can enter the burrows, and Davies & Jarvis (1986) believed that the blocking of the burrows was used as a defence mechanism against this type of predation.

**Food**

Common molerats are vegetarians, living on fleshy roots, bulbs, tubers and the succulent underground stolons of grasses, including couch grass, *Cynodon dactylon* (Smithers, 1971). De Graaff (1981) included among their food the rhizomes of the blue iris, *Moraea* sp; *Homeria* sp; the cucumber, *Citrullus* sp; *Pseudogaltonia* sp; the bulbs of *Gladiolus* sp and occasionally the leaves of certain species of aloes. In gardens they can be a problem, eating the bulbs of many garden plants and in vegetable gardens will eat root crops such as potatoes and carrots. Davies & Jarvis (1986), du Toit *et al.* (1985) and Lovegrove & Jarvis (1986) showed that they store food in deep, blind-ending burrows near the nest. This food consisted of tubers, corms and bulbs of *Othanna* sp, *Oxalis* sp, *Homeria* sp, *Micrauthus junceus*, *Ornithogalum thyrsoidas*, *Cyanella hyacinthoides*, *Hexaglottis virgata* and the root stock of *Wachendorfia paniculata*. Many of these geophytes are toxic to other mammals, and Lovegrove & Jarvis (1986) suggested that some of the Iridaceae have co-evolved with molerats—in ways that facilitate dispersal of the corms. Molerats have been shown to transport corms and bulbs for distances of over 60 m.

**Reproduction**

Molerats in established captive groups have been reported to copulate very rarely. Mating took place when a male encountered a strange female or when a male and female were placed in a strange environment (Hickman, 1982; Burda, 1989). However, once a pairing was effected and started to breed, this continued, whilst mating in younger animals was suppressed by the presence of older animals. Bennett & Jarvis (1988a, in press a) also found that only a single pair within a colony breeds. Most animals vocalised intensively during courtship and copulation (Burda, 1989) and many females kept on soliciting until mated. Mounts were short (5–15s) and a bruised vagina, evident vaginal opening or vaginal bleeding were evidence of oestrus or intromission. These symptoms persisted for three to seven days. Postpartum conception occurred at 78,4 days (S.D.=9,1; range 70–91; n=6). Pregnant females spent most of their time in the nest, where they were supplied with food by partner males and adolescent males, and left the nest only to excrete. Davies & Jarvis (1986) noted that the nesting chambers in the wild were lined with vegetable material of subterranean origin and included the bases and husks of corms, fleshy roots and root bark, with a small percentage of aerial plant material. Pregnant females' body mass increased by 20–35% from the fifth week of pregnancy, inguinal teats became prominent, and from 12 weeks the pectoral teats increased in size. Gestation lasted 98 days (S.D.=9.2; range 84–112; n=9) and average litter size was 2,0 (S.D.=0,75; range 1–3; n=9), with a sex ratio of 1:1. Newborn pups weighed 7,9 g (S.D. 0,5) (Burda, 1989). In the wild in the Transvaal, Rautenbach (1978) gave the mean number of foetuses in *C. h. natalensis* as 1,75 (n=8); in Zimbabwe, Smithers & Wilson (1979) gave the mean as 2,6 (n=5), with a range of 1–3.

In spite of the fact that several hundred specimens were examined from the Harare district in Zimbabwe, only five records of gravid females were obtained, two in July and three in August. The samples are small, but the indications are that the young may be born at any time throughout the summer. *Cryptomys h. hottentotus* pups are altricial at birth, their eyes open when 13–50 days old, they begin to eat solids by day 8–10, and are fully weaned when 72–105 days old. Growth rate was slow, 0,36 g/day from birth to weaning. When related to body mass, *C. hottentotus* develops and reproduces at a lower rate than other rodents which is similar to hystricomorphs. Reduced reproduction and development of a caste of helpers may be energy saving in response to the long gestation period (Burda, 1989). Weaning and newly weaned pups spar with each other and with adults, but levels of aggression are low and the pups are incorporated into the colony, which is probably an extended family (Bennett, 1989).

---

No. 132A

## *Cryptomys damarensis* (Ogilby, 1838)

## Damara molerat

## Damarase vaalmol

Plate 8

---

**Colloquial Name**

So named as the original specimen on which the species is based came from Damaraland, Namibia.

**Taxonomic Notes**

Formerly considered as a subspecies of *C. hottentotus* and dealt with in the first edition in this manner, Nevo *et al.* (1986) showed that whereas *C. h. hottentotus* and *C. h. natalensis* have a diploid chromosome number of 2n=54, *C. damarensis* has a number of 2n=74 and 78. Allozyme and mitochondrial DNA studies (Nevo *et al.*, 1987; Honeycutt *et al.*, 1987) confirmed that *C. damarensis* is a distinct species and not a subspecies of *C. hottentotus*. In Botswana

*C. damarensis* is associated with Kalahari sand and unconsolidated alluvial sand, whereas *C. hottentotus* is associated with a harder and more consolidated substrate of granite sand, schists and other compacted soils of various origins. These associations are repeated in Zimbabwe with a situation some 65 km north of Bulawayo at the abrupt southern fringe of the Kalahari sand which rises sharply from harder ground, where *C. hottentotus* is found in the latter and the darker *C. damarensis* in the former. In this situation, as in Botswana, the larger, darker coloured *C. damarensis* is clearly distinguishable from the smaller and paler coloured *C. hottentotus*.

*C. bocagei* (De Winton 1897) of Angola is described as being pale grey-drab, almost silvery-grey. Hill & Carter (1941) stated that the specimens they allocated from Angola to *C. bocagei* might be placed as a subspecies of *C. damarensis*, although the series exhibited a considerable range of colour variation. This material is presently included in this species.

### Description

Adults attain a mean total length of about 170 mm, with a hind foot length of 28 mm and a mean mass of about 100 g. Two colour morphs may occur in the same colony (de Graaff, 1981; Bennett & Jarvis, 1988a). Some colony members are buff-coloured and others black or very dark brown. They all have a broad, irregularly shaped white patch on the forehead, and sometimes a white band on the nape of the neck, which may continue down the mid-back to the base of the tail. They have a white patch on the throat and occasionally a white line down the middle of the abdomen.

The claw on the tiny first digit of the front foot barely reaches the base of the second digit. The second and third digits are the longest and are armed with long hollowed out claws. The claw of the fourth digit barely reaches the base of the claw on the third, and the fifth is shorter than the fourth. On the hind feet the third and fourth digits are the longest; the first is tiny. The digits are connected by narrow webs. Sexual dimorphism is apparent, with males being significantly smaller than females (Bennett, pers. comm.). The threat posture in *C. damarensis* differs from *C.h. hottentotus* in that the former rolls on its back with body slightly curled and mouth agape, whereas *C.h. hottentotus* remains standing with its head thrown back and mouth agape (Bennett & Jarvis, 1988a; Bennett, in press).

### Table 132A.1

Measurements (mm) and mass (g) of Damara molerats, *C. damarensis* (a) from Botswana (Smithers, 1971) and body masses of 6 complete colonies captured in Namibia and the Kalahari Gemsbok National Park (Bennett & Jarvis, 1988a; Bennett, 1988).

**(a)**

| | Males | | | Females | | |
|---|---|---|---|---|---|---|
| | $\bar{x}$ | n | Range | $\bar{x}$ | n | Range |
| TL | 166 | 32 | 150–196 | 169 | 29 | 153–176 |
| T | 18 | 32 | 11–27 | 19 | 29 | 15–33 |
| Hf c/u | 23 | 32 | 27–30 | 28 | 29 | 24–31 |
| Mass | 99 | 8 | 86–131 | 103 | 8 | 96–110 |

**(b)**

| | Males | | | Females | | |
|---|---|---|---|---|---|---|
| No. in colony | Mass | n | S.D. | Mass | n | S.D. |
| 22 | 103,8 | 15 | 103,8 | 88,4 | 7 | 14,6 |
| 12 | 130,0 | 5 | 130,0 | 101,1 | 7 | 31,4 |
| 25 | 185,5 | 11 | 185,5 | 132,2 | 14 | 32,6 |
| 17 | 117,3 | 6 | 117,3 | 102,4 | 11 | 40,6 |
| 16 | 202,1 | 7 | 202,1 | 145,5 | 9 | 39,7 |
| 15 | 146,2 | 8 | 146,2 | 129,2 | 7 | 54,5 |
| 107 | | 52 | | | 55 | |

Combined mean body mass 131,2 ± 54 g.

### Distribution

*South of the Sahara, excluding the Southern African Subregion*

They occur in the extreme western parts of **Zambia**, and if *C. bocagei* is included as a subspecies, then also widely in **Angola**.

*Southern African Subregion*

They occur in western **Zimbabwe**; in **Botswana**, excluding the eastern sector; in the **Caprivi Strip**; in parts of **Namibia** and in the northern and northwestern **Cape Province**.

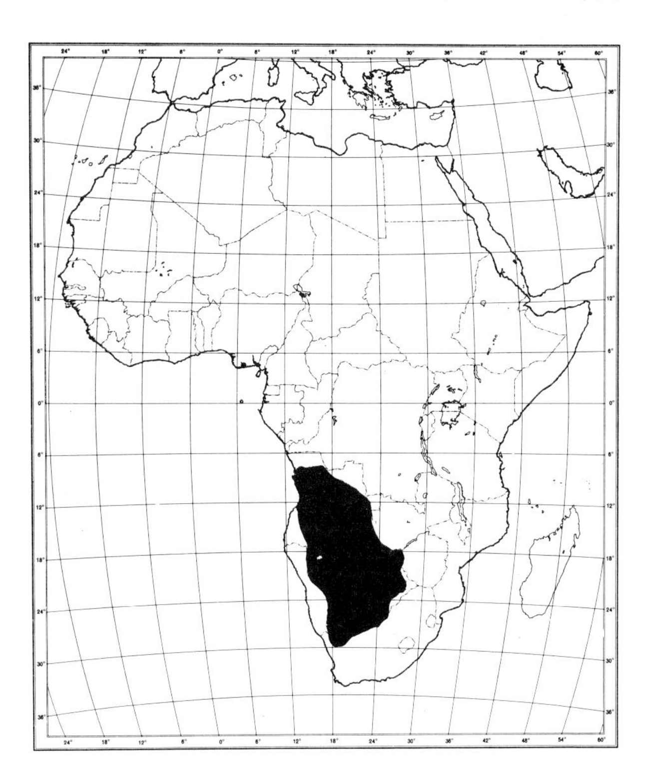

### Habitat

They occur predominantly in Kalahari sand and in loose unconsolidated alluvial sand, avoiding areas of more consolidated substrate.

### Habits

They live in colonies numbering up to 25 individuals (Bennett & Jarvis, 1988a). In the Kalahari Gemsbok National Park, Lovegrove & Painting (1987) recorded that they throw up two types of mounds. The first type is composed of soil thrown up in opening the main burrow. The second and larger mound, or a series of two or three mounds close together, are associated with the spiral burrow surrounding a large underground tuber on which they are feeding and which may extend to over a metre below the surface. The burrows have a diameter of up to about 70 mm, and have side tunnels running at right angles from the main tunnel, with many dead-end branches. During the winter the side tunnels are solidly blocked, whereas during the summer many remain open or are partially closed. A "bolt hole" burrow runs from the main burrow at an angle downwards to a depth estimated to be over 3 m. The main burrow has a deep (>3m) nesting chamber which contains nesting material, and close to this a toilet chamber loosely filled with sand and faeces, and sometimes a food store (Jarvis & Bennett, pers. comm.).

### Food

In the Kalahari Gemsbok National Park, Lovegrove & Painting (1987) and Bennett (1988) found that they fed almost exclusively on the succulent, underground organs of plants, in particular the tubers of the gemsbok cucumber, *Acanthosicyos naudinianus*, and the bulbs of *Dipcadi gracillium*. Only the outer bark of the older tubers was eaten; the young tubers were totally consumed.

### Reproduction

Smithers (1971) recorded two gravid females, one with five foetuses in February and another with three in July, and juveniles with a mass of up to 45 g in January, February, July, August and November. Despite the small sample there is evidence that they breed throughout the year, but in captivity do not have more than two litters a year (Bennett, pers. comm.). The oestrous female solicits the male prior to mating, and within each colony there is only one reproductive pair; the remaining females are non-reproductive. Gestation length is about 78 days (Bennett & Jarvis, 1988a). All males have functional gonads. The non-reproductive molerats in the colony can be assigned to frequent and infrequent worker castes (based on the amount of work they perform and on body mass). Some individuals within the colony show age polyethism, others appear to remain within the worker caste. Non-reproductive females will breed if removed from the colony and paired with a male. Pups are 8–9 g at birth, precocial in that they are mobile and begin to eat solids when about 8 days old. After weaning they spar with each other and adults, but do not fight and are incorporated into the colony, and, in common with *C. hottentotus*, this is believed to be an extended family (Bennett & Jarvis, 1988a).

---

No. 133

## *Georychus capensis* (Pallas, 1778)

## Cape molerat
## Kaapse blesmol

Plate 8

---

### Colloquial Name

The species was described originally from the Cape, hence the association of their name with this area. The Afrikaans *blesmol* refers to the conspicuous white frontal patch on the head which, in this species, is invariably present. The chromosome diploid number is 2n=54 (n=1) (Nevo *et al.*, 1986).

### Taxonomic Notes

Meester *et al.* (1986) did not recognise any subspecies. However populations from Natal have different allozyme and mitochondrial DNA differentiation and may prove to be species (Nevo *et al.*, 1987; Honeycutt *et al.*, 1987).

### Description

Cape molerats reach a head and body length in males of 200 mm, in females just over 200 mm. Records of mass that are available show that the males can reach 360,0 g, the females 326,0 g (Table 133.1).

**Table 133.1**

Measurements (mm) and mass (g) of Cape molerats, *G. capensis* (Taylor, Jarvis, Crowe & Davies, 1985)

| | Males | | | Females | | |
|---|---|---|---|---|---|---|
| | x̄ | n | S.D. | x̄ | n | S.D. |
| (TL | 179) | | | (177) | | |
| HB | 158 | 52 | 23,2 | 156 | 38 | 25,0 |
| T | 21 | 52 | 2,5 | 21 | 38 | 3,4 |
| Hf s/u | 28 | 52 | 3,0 | 28 | 38 | 3,3 |
| Mass | 181,8 | 51 | 73,3 | 180,0 | 37 | 92,3 |

The colour of their bodies is buffy to buffy-orange, and some of the hairs on the upper parts tipped with brown. The forefeet, hind feet and tail are white. The characteristic feature of the species is the marking on the head: the muzzle and the area around the eyes and ears are white on a background of black and they have a conspicuous frontal patch of white, which is invariably present but very variable in size. The pelage is thick and woolly. Albino individuals are known and others in which the colour of the body is light grey or creamy-orange. There is also some size and colour variation geographically: individuals from the Knysna area are drab while those from the Port Elizabeth area are more brightly coloured (de Graaff, 1981). Specimens from the Cape Peninsula are smaller than those from inland.

### Skull

The upper surface of the skull is distinctly arched, and old individuals exhibit a distinct sagittal crest (Fig. XVI.5). The bullae are well developed, the zygomatic arches swinging widely outwards from the skull (Fig. XVI.3). Taylor *et al.* (1985) found no sexual dimorphism in the skull. The infraorbital foramen is small. The upper and lower incisors are ungrooved. The upper and lower cheekteeth have inner and outer re-entrant folds in the enamel which persist in the upper even when the teeth are heavily worn, whilst the inner fold in the lower tends to disappear with tooth wear.

### Distribution

*Southern African Subregion*

The Cape molerat occurs in the **Cape Province** from the Cape Peninsula northwards to Nieuwoudtville, inland to Tulbagh and Worcester and eastwards narrowly along the coast to **Transkei**. There are no records between this and southwestern **Natal** near the Lesotho border or between this and Belfast and Ermelo in the **Transvaal** which may be due to their having been overlooked in the intermediate areas. In the southwestern Cape they may occur sympatrically with *C.h. hottentotus* and/or *B. suillus* (Jarvis, unpubl.).

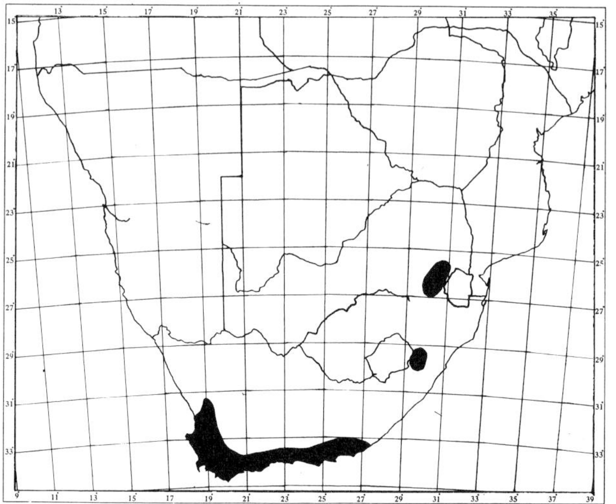

### Habitat

They occur in sandy soils, in coastal sand dunes and sandy alluvium along river systems and in the montane regions of the southwestern Cape Province.

### Habits

They are solitary and burrow shallowly, about 200 mm under the surface, throwing up mounds. There are blind tunnels in the burrow system and they may store food in underground chambers (de Graaff, 1981). Du Toit, Jarvis & Louw (1985) excavated a burrow system at Darling, Cape Province which had a total length of 130 m, a burrow diameter of 100 mm and a food store containing 528 g of geophytes. As with *C. h. hottentotus*, these molerats transport geophytes as much as 60 m to their food store.

### Food

De Graaff (1981) stated that they eat wild bulbs, roots and tubers. They can be a problem in gardens and vegetable gardens, eating potatoes, sweet potatoes, carrots, onions, lettuce and even carnations. Du Toit *et al.* (1985) noted that they would undermine the roots of plants from below and pull the entire plant into the burrow, and they found that stomach contents contained 6% of aerial plant material. Food storage chambers contained sufficient food to sustain the molerat for an estimated 84 days.

### Reproduction

The juveniles are slate-grey dorsally. The females have two pairs of pectoral and one pair of inguinal mammae. These solitary molerats signal to conspecifics through the soil, by drumming whith their hind feet. The signal consists of long bursts (up to two minutes) of very rapid drums. Drumming also occurs during courtship, while the male appears to drum with a different frequency and length to the female (Bennett & Jarvis, 1988b). Taylor *et al.* (1985) stated that the young are born on the Cape Peninsula during the summer months of September to December. The mean litter size is 5,9 and the number in a litter varies from one to 10. Females can have up to two litters in a season (Bennett & Jarvis, 1988b). At birth one cheektooth is erupted, the second tooth appearing at three weeks old. The fourth cheektooth does not erupt until they are about 9 to 10 months old (Taylor *et al.*, 1985).

# XVII. Family HYSTRICIDAE
## Porcupines

The Family Hystricidae consists of two Subfamilies: the Atherurinae, the brush-tailed porcupines, and the Hystricinae, the crested porcupines. Brush-tailed porcupines are very different in appearance from the porcupine we see in the Subregion, being clothed in a covering of short, chocolate-coloured, flattish, sharp-pointed bristles, with only a few long quills. They have long, slender tails with a pure white terminal tuft of long, stiff hairs expanded at intervals along their length like a string of flat beads. The expanded portions are hollow and when the tail is shaken give out a rustling sound. They are forest dwellers, *A. africanus* occurring in the tropical forests of West and East Africa and *A. macrourus* occurring in Asia and the Far East.

The second Subfamily, the Hystricinae, the crested porcupines, are represented widely in Africa by two species and occur also in subtropical Asia and in the East Indian islands.

## Genus *Hystrix* Linnaeus, 1758

Two genera of porcupines occur in Africa: the brush-tailed porcupine, *Atherurus africanus*, a small species with a mass of up to about 4,0 kg which occurs in the forests of West Africa and Zaire, and two species of the second genus *Hystrix*. The crested porcupine, *H. cristata*, occurs in East Africa and northwards to the coast of the Mediterranean and the Cape porcupine, *H. africaeaustralis*, in the more southerly parts of the continent. In central and eastern Africa *H. cristata* and *H. africaeaustralis* occur alongside each other, but apparently do not interbreed.

The crested porcupine, *H. cristata*, differs from the Cape porcupine, *H. africaeaustralis*, in the rattle quills and certain skull characters. It has short, slender rattle quills under 50 mm long; the mid-line of the rump is black or mottled. The rattle quills of the Cape porcupine are over 60 mm long and are thick; the mid-line of the rump is white. In the crested porcupine, *H. cristata*, the nasal bones are shorter than the frontals, whereas in *H. africaeaustralis* they are very large and much longer than the frontal bones.

---

No. 134

## *Hystrix africaeaustralis* Peters, 1852

## Cape porcupine
## Kaapse ystervark

Plate 11

---

### Colloquial Name

The generic name *Hystrix* is the Greek for porcupine; the specific name *africaeaustralis* indicates that they occur in the more southerly parts of Africa.

### Taxonomic Notes

Three subspecies have been described, but none of them is accepted by Meester *et al.* (1986).

### Description

Porcupines are the largest rodents that occur in the Subregion. They attain a mass of 12 to 19 kg when adult, and males and females are of similar size (Table 134.1).

**Table 134.1**

Age (months) and sex-specific mean body mass (kg), shoulder height, body length (mm), for Cape porcupines collected on the Tussen-die-Riviere Game Farm between September 1981 and July 1982 (van Aarde, 1987a).

| | Males | | | Females | | |
|---|---|---|---|---|---|---|
| | $\bar{x}$ | n | S.D. | $\bar{x}$ | n | S.D. |
| Age < 5 | | | | | | |
| TL | 512 | 7 | 47,3 | 516 | 5 | 73,2 |
| Sh.ht | 189 | 7 | 22,3 | 208 | 5 | 27,8 |
| Mass | 4,4 | 7 | 1,11 | 4,2 | 5 | 1,33 |
| Age 5,1–8 | | | | | | |
| TL | 622 | 14 | 40,8 | 618 | 13 | 68,7 |
| Sh.ht | 238 | 14 | 14,9 | 228 | 13 | 20,3 |
| Mass | 7,7 | 14 | 1,36 | 6,9 | 13 | 1,38 |
| Age 8,1–18 | | | | | | |
| TL | 683 | 9 | 36,0 | 715 | 4 | 30,9 |
| Sh.ht | 256 | 9 | 15,3 | 267 | 4 | 19,1 |
| Mass | 9,4 | 9 | 1,40 | 10,7 | 4 | 2,08 |
| Age 18,1–23 | | | | | | |
| TL | 665 | 2 | 21,2 | 729 | 4 | 48,0 |
| Sh.ht | 258 | 2 | 03,5 | 264 | 4 | 16,1 |
| Mass | 9,5 | 2 | 0,85 | 12,0 | 4 | 2,06 |
| Age 23,1–30 | | | | | | |
| TL | 725 | 6 | 22,6 | 780 | 5 | 33,9 |
| Sh.ht | 270 | 6 | 09,8 | 290 | 5 | 14,1 |
| Mass | 11,5 | 6 | 0,75 | 13,7 | 5 | 0,93 |
| Age > 30 | | | | | | |
| TL | 724 | 7 | 32,0 | 744 | 11 | 27,6 |
| Sh.ht | 279 | 7 | 19,0 | 273 | 11 | 14,9 |
| Mass | 11,7 | 7 | 0,91 | 12,6 | 11 | 1,45 |

**Table 134.2**

Age (weeks) and sex-specific mean body mass (kg) for Cape porcupines born in captivity (van Aarde, 1987a).

| | Males | | | Females | | |
|---|---|---|---|---|---|---|
| | $\bar{x}$ | n | S.D. | $\bar{x}$ | n | S.D. |
| Age 5 | | | | | | |
| Mass | 1,80 | 8 | 0,5 | 1,58 | 8 | 0,50 |
| Age 10 | | | | | | |
| Mass | 3,90 | 6 | 1,11 | 3,37 | 8 | 0,56 |
| Age 15 | | | | | | |
| Mass | 4,98 | 6 | 0,34 | 5,18 | 6 | 1,08 |
| Age 20 | | | | | | |
| Mass | 6,40 | 6 | 0,61 | 6,06 | 8 | 0,86 |
| Age 25 | | | | | | |
| Mass | 7,26 | 6 | 0,73 | 7,84 | 8 | 1,25 |
| Age 30 | | | | | | |
| Mass | 7,28 | 6 | 1,11 | 8,12 | 6 | 0,08 |
| Age 35 | | | | | | |
| Mass | 8,75 | 6 | 0,49 | 8,73 | 6 | 0,64 |
| Age 40 | | | | | | |
| Mass | 9,50 | 5 | 0,69 | 10,22 | 5 | 0,86 |
| Age 45 | | | | | | |
| Mass | 9,65 | 5 | 0,64 | 10,05 | 5 | 0,60 |
| Age 50 | | | | | | |
| Mass | 10,87 | 5 | 1,02 | 10,90 | 5 | 0,90 |
| Age 60 | | | | | | |
| Mass | 11,15 | 5 | 1,77 | 11,68 | 5 | 1,09 |

They are unique among southern African mammals in that their bodies are armed with long, pliable spines, stout, sharp quills and flattened bristly hairs. The spines and quills cover the posterior two-thirds of the upper parts and the flanks of the body. Both the spines and quills are white with black annulations, the black annulations declining in length towards their bases (Findlay, 1977).

Findlay (1977) believed that the formation of the alternate banding on the quills and spines is controlled by the intrinsic behaviour of a set of melanocytes supplying the individually growing quills or spines. When melanin is supplied to the growing quills or spines this results in a black annulation and when not being secreted the quill or spine remains white.

The spines are up to 500 mm in length, the quills up to 300 mm. The remainder of the body, except for the nose, lips and rounded ears, is covered with coarse, black, flattened hair, which in some older individuals may fox to a brownish colour. On the top of the head and along the neck they have an erectile crest of coarse hair about 500 mm in length; the hairs are black at their bases with broad white tips. On either side of the neck they may have white elongated patches which are more obvious in some individuals than in others. Their whiskers are particularly long, usually black and are exceedingly mobile. Their heads are blunt, broad across the nostrils, and their small eyes are set far back on the sides.

The spines, quills and crest are erectile at will, which appear to double the size of the individual and at the same time present a formidable fence of sharp spikes over most of the body which acts as a deterrent to predators and other tormentors.

The rump is covered with short, flat bristles on its upper and under surfaces, the spines lying flat against the skin. The end of the tail is armed with a rattle of hollow-ended quills with narrow, stalk-like bases. The hollow part of these quills is over 60 mm long and about 6 mm in diameter. In days gone by these were used by indigenous people as receptacles for alluvial gold dust, and were then used as articles of trade.

**Skull**

The skull is lightly built for its size, the bone structure thin. It is smooth and rounded on the upper surface. At the back of the posterior insertion of the zygomatic arches the skull narrows sharply and has a well developed supraoccipital crest to augment the area to which the neck muscles are attached. From this crest there extends forward, in the mid-line, a short sagittal crest which divides into two arms, fading out on the back of the braincase.

The infraorbital foramen is very large to allow the passage of most of the *masseter medialis* muscle which, arising from the lower edge of the lower jaw, attaches to the side of the rostrum, a feature of the hystricomorph rodents (Fig. 134.2). The eye orbits are relatively small, the diastema between the incisor teeth and the first tooth in the cheekrow about 30% of the total length of the skull. The incisor teeth are heavy, the enamel layer on the front of the teeth in both jaws a pale yellow; the upper incisors have very faint signs of grooving on their anterior faces (Figs 134.1 and 2).

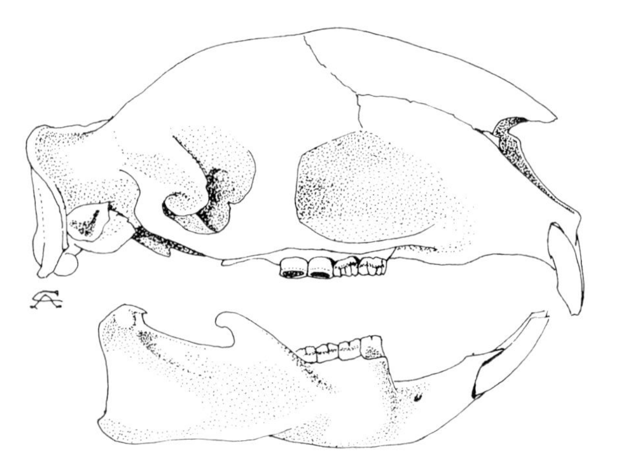

Fig. 134.1. Skull: porcupine, *H. africaeaustralis*, lateral view.

The dental formula is:

$I\frac{1}{1}\ C\frac{0}{0}\ P\frac{1}{1}\ M\frac{3}{3} = 20$

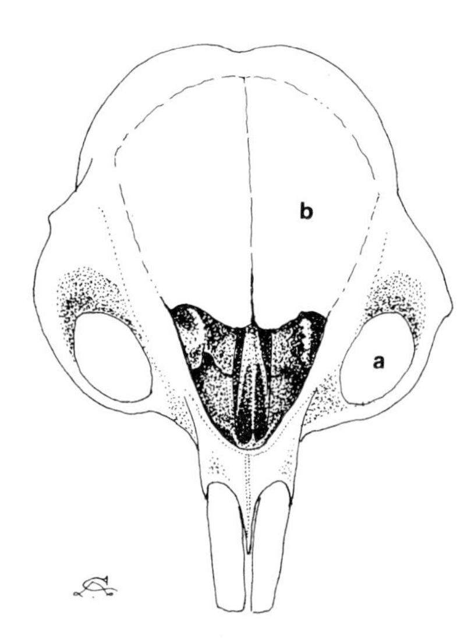


Fig. 134.2. Skull: porcupine, *H. africaeaustralis*, front view (a) infraorbital foramen (b) nasal bone.

Incisors are fully erupted at birth and deciduous premolars start erupting at the age of about 14 days. The first maxilla molar erupts at an age of 2 to 3 months and the second when they are 5 to 6 months old. The third molar erupts at an age of 11 months and the permanent premolars are fully erupted by the time they are about two years old (van Aarde, 1985a).

The unworn molars and premolars have a complicated, infolding system of the enamel layer. Wear on the teeth in the upper jaw leaves them with a single infold on the inside of the teeth and a pattern of ovals of enamel within them. In the lower jaw the infold in the worn teeth shows on the outside of the teeth.

The mandible is broad at the back where the lower edge has an infolding for muscle attachment. The loose hinging of the mandible allows for a considerable degree of backward, forward and rotary movements.

**Distribution**

In Tanzania the Cape porcupine, *H. africaeaustralis*, and the crested porcupine, *H. cristatus*, occur sympatrically.

*South of the Sahara, excluding the Southern African Subregion*

The Cape porcupine occurs in southwestern **Uganda**; southeastern **Kenya; Rwanda**; in most of **Tanzania**; on Zanzibar Island, and all other countries south of this to the borders of the Subregion. Although widely distributed in **Angola**, there are no records from the coastal desert in the southwest, but their occurrence in this type of terrain in Namibia suggests that they have been overlooked.

*Southern African Subregion*

They are distributed widely throughout the whole of the **Subregion**.

**Habitat**

Porcupines are catholic in their habitat requirements, occurring in most of the types of vegetational association encountered in the Subregion and from sea level to over 2 000 m. They have, however, a marked preference for broken country with rocky hills and outcrops. They are generally absent from forest, except marginally. They have been recorded recently in the coastal parts of the Namib Desert in Namibia, south of Luderitz.

Shelter in which to lie up during the day may take the form of crevices in rocks, caves and abandoned aardvark holes or other types of holes in the ground. Shelters often contain accumulations of bones carried in by the porcupines. In the Subregion they modify holes to their own requirements, by excavation with the front claws, and may dig their own burrows as they do in East Africa (Kingdon, 1974).

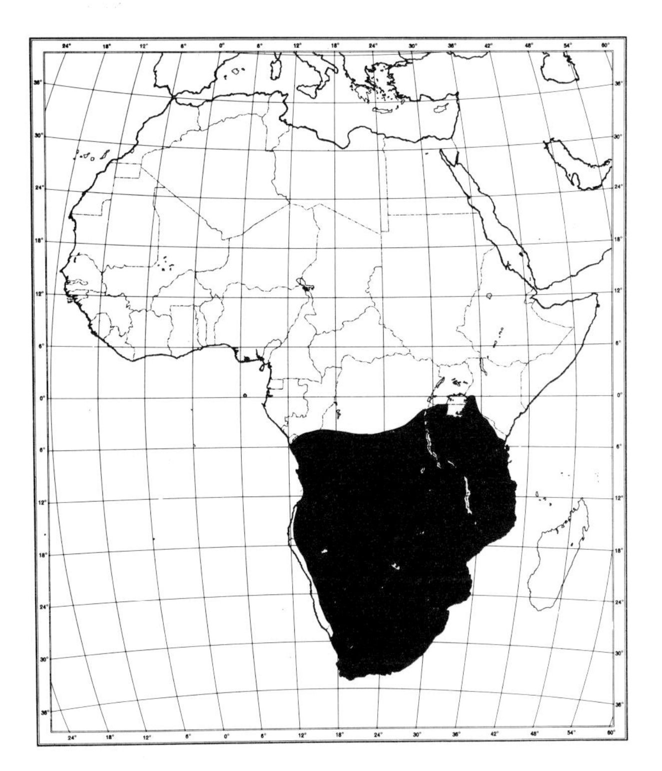

Porcupines have benefitted from agricultural development and are a problem in some farming areas, especially where root crops and maize are grown.

**Habits**

Cape porcupines live in extended family groups, each group comprising an adult male, adult female and variable numbers of offspring of consecutive litters (van Aarde, 1987b). They usually forage alone but 40 (29%) of the 138 porcupines encountered by van Aarde (1987c) at night were active in groups of two or three. Groups either comprised of an adult pair, an adult pair and their offspring, or an adult male and young of the year. Young porcupines start foraging alone when approximately five months old (van Aarde, 1987b). Porcupines are almost exclusively nocturnal, but occasionally may be found sunbathing close to the entrances of their shelters. They have the capacity to increase their heat loss in summer and in winter to increase heat production which, together with a low metabolic rate on the one hand and reducing heat loss on the other, are important mechanisms in winter acclimatization by Cape porcupines which enable them to have a wide ecological tolerance (Haim, van Aarde & Skinner, 1990a,b).

They have a ponderous gait, but under stress can run very quickly. Their hearing is apparently acute and often, when disturbed, they will "freeze", standing motionless, when they can be approached quite closely. This characteristic reaction allows them to remain undetected.

Porcupines, like so many other mammals, have the habit of using tracks to travel along. They are noisy animals and proceed with much snuffling and grunting accompanied by the noise of their quills and spines rasping against obstacles. They are also noisy eaters and their chewing can be heard several metres away.

If cornered they can become aggressive, stamping their feet, grunting, erecting their quills and rattling the hollow quills on their tails. When defending themselves they may run backwards or sideways on to their tormentors so quickly that fast evasive action is required. The quills are very sharp and may penetrate the skin deeply, and predators such as lions and leopards sometimes carry them embedded around their mouths and in their paws, causing septic wounds which can be fatal. This aggressive behaviour may also occur in intra-specific encounters.

They have five digits on both the front and hind feet, armed with claws. The first digit on the front foot is set far back from the other four and is reduced to a stump without a claw. The four claws of the front feet and five on the hind mark in the spoor. The spoor of the hind feet is rounded and often marks as far as the heels (Fig. 134.3).

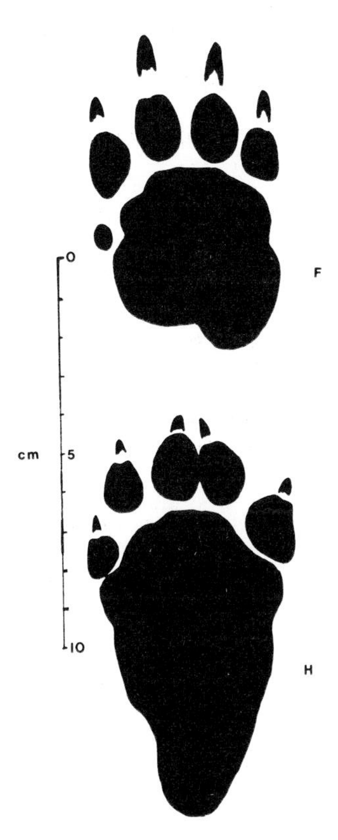


Fig. 134.3. Spoor: porcupine:
F. Forefoot H. Hind foot.

**Food**

The porcupine digestive tract is well suited for coping with their catholic dietary habits, as it consists of a muscular stomach and an enlarged caecum for the efficient digestion of both proteins and fibrous foods (van Jaarsveld, 1983; van Jaarsveld & Knight, 1984). Porcupines are predominantly vegetarian. Their food includes bulbs, tubers and roots which they dig up and, in an area where they have been feeding, their excavations to obtain these are often clearly marked by the characteristic rounded spoor of their hind feet in the loose excavated soil. They are fond of fallen wild fruits, such as those of the wild fig, *Ficus* spp; mahobohobo, *Uapaca kirkiana*; mobola plum, *Parinari curatellifolia*; marula, *Sclerocarya birrea*, and the sausage tree, *Kigelia africana*.

They gnaw on bones which they accumulate in the den as a source of calcium and phosphates. Duthie & Skinner (1986) showed that osteophagia by captive porcupines maintained on a diet with low calcium and phosphate levels was twice that of porcupines on a diet containing high levels of these minerals. Porcupines also gnaw on the bark of trees. Their habit of ringbarking selected species of trees resulted in Yeaton (1988) concluding that the role of porcupines in maintaining cyclical successions in savanna ecosystems has been underestimated. Trees such as *Dombeya rotundifolia* and *Burkea* ringbarked and thus injured by porcupines are susceptible to fire and their felling through fire opens sites for the establishment of other species. As a consequence closed-forest stands may develop in savannas when porcupine populations are reduced (Yeaton, 1988).

In farming areas they can be a problem in crops such as groundnuts, potatoes, pumpkins, root vegetables and maize which they cut at the base of the stalk to reach the cob. They eat beetroot, carrots and onions, and they will take young plants of cotton, beans and peas. They are destructive feeders, often damaging far more than they can actually eat. The food is manipulated with the front feet while eating, being held between them against the ground to allow effective use of the incisor teeth.

## Reproduction

Cape porcupines are monogamous (Morris & van Aarde, 1985) and sexual behaviour leading to copulation is initiated by the female (van Aarde, pers. comm.). Sexual behaviour such as mounting occurs daily throughout the year and physical contact between males and females is required to maintain cyclic ovarian activity, whilst females kept isolated from males do not experience oestrus (van Aarde, 1985b). A female in oestrus presents herself to a male by raising her tail vertically while standing close to him or by moving backwards towards him. This is usually followed by the male mounting the female by standing on his hind feet and resting his front feet on her back (Morris & van Aarde, 1985).

Copulation lasts less than two minutes and is terminated either by the female moving away or the male dismounting (van Aarde, pers. comm.). Paired males and females react aggressively towards the advances of intruders of either sex.

Captive porcupines produce litters throughout the year, but most litters (78,7%; n=165) are born between August and March (van Aarde, 1985b). Females subjected to seasonal climatic changes in the Karoo reproduce seasonally, young being born during the relatively wet and warm summer months from August to March, with a peak in January (van Aarde, 1987b). This is in agreement with data on porcupines from Namibia (Shortridge, 1934), Botswana (Smithers, 1971) and Zimbabwe (Smithers & Wilson, 1979).

Females typically conceive only once a year and the interval between litters is about one year (van Aarde, 1985b). Captive females may produce two litters per year, but young born at intervals of less than 200 days have not survived. Death of the young was due to interference from members of the preceding litter who actively prevented the newborn from suckling (van Aarde, 1987b). Females are pregnant for 93–94 days and lactation lasts 101 ± 37,8 (S.D.) days (van Aarde, 1985b). Females do not experience oestrus while lactating and normal cyclic ovarian activity commences 2–42 days after the cessation of lactation. The length of the oestrous cycle varies from 23 to 42 days (mean 34 ± 6,6 days) (van Aarde, 1985c) and females experience three to seven "sterile" cycles before conceiving (van Aarde, 1987b).

Litter size varies from one to three (mean 1,5 ± 0,66; n=165) and the young weigh 300 to 440 g (mean 351 ± 47,4 g; n=19) at birth (van Aarde, 1985b). The young are well developed at birth; they are born with their eyes open, parts of their bodies clothed with short spines and their incisor teeth erupted. Foot-stamping and other components of defensive and aggressive behaviour are in evidence at a very early age. They start taking solids at an age of four weeks and growth during the first 20 weeks of life is nearly linear (van Aarde, 1987a). Growth rate for males and females is similar (see Table 134.2) and adult body mass is attained at an age of about 60 weeks (van Aarde, 1987a). Males attain sexual maturity at an age of 8–18 months (van Aarde & Skinner, 1986a) and females experience their first oestrus when 9–18 months of age (van Aarde, 1985b). However, females do not conceive while living in their family groups and dispersal is a prerequisite for successful reproduction (van Aarde, 1987b). Age at first reproduction is affected by density and porcupine numbers are apparently regulated through social factors affecting reproduction (van Aarde, 1987c).

# XVIII. Family PEDETIDAE

## Springhaas

The Family Pedetidae is represented by the single species *Pedetes capensis* whose relationship has been debated widely since the species was described by Forster (1778). Ellerman (1940) concluded that he could find no alternative but to classify *Pedetes* in a Superfamily distinct from all other living Rodentia. Simpson (1945) placed the species in the Superfamily Anomaluroidea *incertae sedis*. Following Meester *et al.* (1986) they are included in the Sciuromorpha. Wood (1974a,b) stated that springhaas are neither related ancestrally nor collaterally to other rodents and that their pre-Miocene history is a mystery.

## Genus *Pedetes* Illiger, 1811

---

No. 135

## *Pedetes capensis* (Forster, 1778)

## Springhaas

## Springhaas

Plate 9

---

### Colloquial Name

This is derived from one of its characteristic forms of locomotion which consists of bounds and hops on the powerful hind legs, which propel it forward in a kangaroo-type manner, the long tail acting as a balancing organ. The name *springhaas* was first applied by the early Dutch settlers and has been translated into English as springhare which is unfortunate as hares belong to another Family, the Leporidae. The name springhare in English is deeply entrenched, although there is little doubt that the Dutch/Afrikaans name springhaas antedated it in usage.

### Taxonomic Notes

Misonne (1974) considered the East African *P. surdaster* Thomas, 1902 to be a subspecies of *P. capensis*. Numerous subspecies have been described, including five from the Subregion, but none of the five was recognised by Meester *et al.* (1986).

### Description

Springhaas are large saltatorial-bipedal rodents which, in build, resemble small kangaroos, with short front legs, long, very powerful hind legs and a long tail. They have short, round heads with noticeably large eyes and conspicuously long and narrow, upright ears. The development of their large orbits and acoustic apparatus is accompanied by a strong reduction of most bony elements of the postorbital part of the skull, differing from that of more primitive rodents. The muscles of the zygomasseteric complex are of the hystricomorphous type and show extremely strong development composing 87,5% of the total muscle mass (Offermans & De Free, 1989). In series the sexes are similar in measurements and mass, the adults having an overall length of up to 0,9 m, with a tail about half this length and an average mass of about 3,1 kg (Table 135.1).

**Table 135.1**

Measurements (mm) and mass (kg) of a series of adult springhaas, *P. capensis*, from Botswana (Smithers, 1971) and Nylsvley Nature Reserve, Transvaal (Temby, 1977)

**Botswana**

| | Males | | | Females | | |
|---|---|---|---|---|---|---|
| | x̄ | n | Range | x̄ | n | Range |
| TL | 813 | 23 | 770–858 | 801 | 21 | 758–860 |
| (HB | 378) | | | (375) | | |
| T | 435 | 23 | 400–463 | 426 | 20 | 405–451 |
| Hf c/u | 153 | 23 | 145–160 | 153 | 22 | 145–160 |
| E | 72 | 23 | 67–76 | 71 | 22 | 69–75 |
| Mass | 3,13 | 24 | 2,95–3,63 | 2,83 | 24 | 2,90–3,86 |

**Nylsvley Nature Reserve**

| | Males | | | Females | | |
|---|---|---|---|---|---|---|
| | x̄ | n | Range | x̄ | n | Range |
| (TL | 801 | 30) | | (794 | 35) | |
| HB | 390 | 31 | 335–421 | 391 | 36 | 367–420 |
| T | 411 | 28 | 350–449 | 403 | 34 | 365–440 |
| Hf c/u | 154 | 32 | 143–160 | 154 | 36 | 150–160 |
| E | 72 | 32 | 65–77 | 72 | 35 | 67–77 |
| Mass | 3,13 | 37 | 2,47–3,63 | 3,18 | 40 | 2,40–3,76 |

While the colour of the coat varies from one area to another, in general it is cinnamon-buff, slightly darker on the head, the tail with a broad jet-black tip. The under parts are whitish, faintly washed with yellow, the chin white, while the upper surface of the tail from the base to the black tip is usually a darker red than the body. The under surface of the tail is lighter in colour, except near the base where it is of similar colour to the upper parts of the body. In specimens from some areas the lighter colour of the under surface of the tail encircles the tail, forming a light band anterior to the black tip, and at the extremity of their distributional range, in northeastern Zimbabwe, the whole under surface of the tail is black.

The hair on the upper parts of the body is straight, long and soft. The hairs of the guard coat lengthen from the head, where they measure about 20–25 mm, towards the hindquarters, where they are about 45–50 mm long. The hair on the tail is of similar length to that on the hindquarters but lengthens towards the tip where it reaches 60 mm on the black tip. Many of the hairs of the guard coat have dark tips which give the coat a faintly grizzled appearance when seen close up. During the moult, which proceeds from the head backwards towards the tail, the dark tips of the guard hairs, lying in juxtaposition, show as a broad transverse band, defining the level of the moult. Butynski (1982d) recorded a juvenile moult, 13% of individuals moulting between 1,7 and 2,1 kg body mass and 90% between 2 and 2,5 kg; a first adult moult occurred between 2,7 and 2,9 kg. Peak moult for adults occurred in mid-summer and no springhaas were in adult moult in mid-winter.

Underlying the guard coat is an underfur of shorter hair. The individual hairs on the back are grey at their bases, those on the hindquarters and under parts yellowish-buffy. The hair on the upper parts of the feet is short, the sides with fringes of longer hair which continue along the feet and on to the outer digits.

The ears have well developed antitragi and can be folded back, thereby occluding the ear holes, preventing the entry of sand and dust. The nostrils, which are situated in a small rhinarium, can be closed for the same purpose. The eyes are large and they have long black eyelashes above and below, with a patch of long black sensory bristles just above their front edges, which assist them in avoiding obstructions which might injure their eyes.

The whiskers are black and particularly long. These, together with long, black, sensory hairs interspersed throughout the guard coat, help the individual to orientate itself when it is inside the burrow system.

There are five digits on the front feet, armed with narrow, sharp, strongly curved claws, which reach a length of 18–20 mm over the curve. Underlying these is a pad with a hard outer edge, and a semi-circular flap of tough skin, fringed with short bristly hair, which assist the claws in manipulating the food (Fig. 135.1). There are four digits on the hind feet, the first digit being absent. The third, fourth and fifth are elongated, the fourth the longest of all. The tips of the claws of the third and fifth digits barely reach the base of the claw on the fourth. The second, the shortest claw of all, does not mark in the spoor (Fig. 135.2). The claw of the fourth toe is broad and triangular, with sharp edges and tapers to a sharp point, measuring about 25 mm in length and 9 mm at its broadest part. The claws are slightly concave underneath.

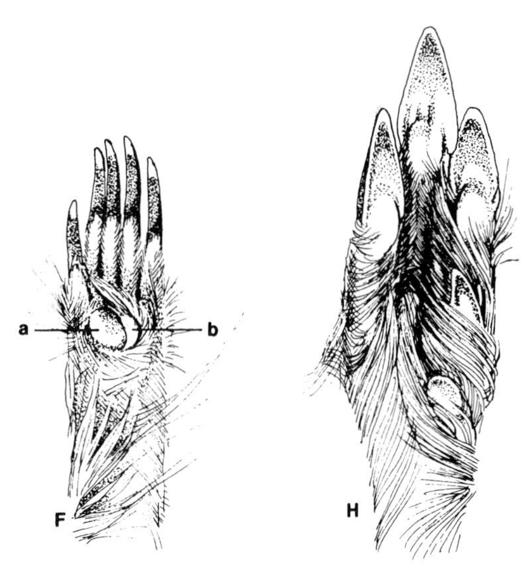


Fig. 135.1. Feet, springhaas: F. Forefoot, to show (a) plantar pad and (b) accessory pad with its fringe of long white hair. H. Hind foot.

The front feet with their curved claws are adapted to digging and loosening soil, and the hind feet with claws which are broad and sharp-edged, are for throwing the loosened soil clear of the excavations, making the springhaas a species which is highly adapted to burrowing. Live springhaas have to be handled very carefully for the hind claws can inflict deep cuts.

Both sexes have a pair of perineal glands lying in a slit between the penis or clitoris and the anus. When extruded these glands are 10 mm long and 6 mm in diameter, the orifice of the gland furnished with a group of stiff bristles coated with a thick yellowish exudate to which soil is usually found adhering. Captive springhaas anal-drag, probably as a means of using these glands in marking, but as they can also be extruded by newly born individuals, they may also serve a social function within the family (Coe, 1969).

**Skull**

In profile, the skull of the springhaas is relatively flat on top, the mastoids so greatly swollen that they show conspicuously at the posterior corners of the braincase (Fig. 135.3). Viewed from above the braincase is roughly rectangular, broadening out at the back where it accommodates the upward extension of the swollen mastoids. The rostrum is only slightly narrower in front than behind, the nasals curving downward to form side walls to the nasal passage. The infraorbital foramen is greatly enlarged. The zygomatic arches, which are thin at the back, broaden forwards as thin bony plates which are concave on the inside, to accommodate the greatly enlarged eyes. The diameter of the eye socket is about 70% of the distance from the front of the eye to the end of the nasals.

A conspicuous feature of the skull is the two broad ever-growing, ungrooved, incisor teeth in the upper and lower jaws. The long roots of the evenly curved upper pair are often discernible under the thin bony covering, curving back and arising just above the row of cheekteeth. Both pairs remain very sharp at the tips through occlusion against each other, and the enamel layer on the front of the teeth is pale yellow in colour.

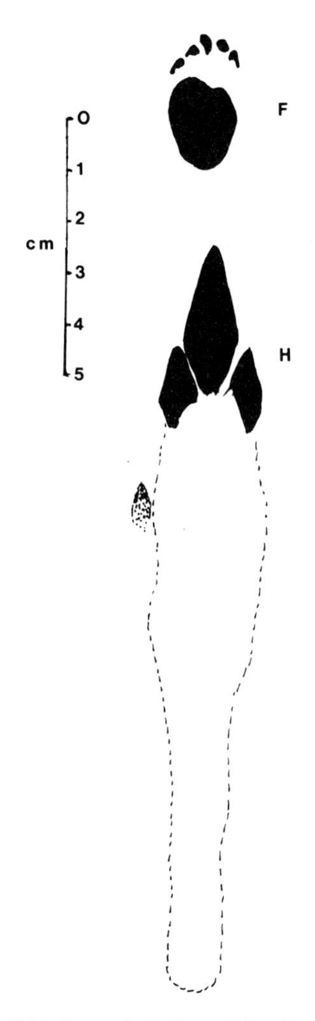


Fig. 135.2. Spoor: Springhaas: F. Forefoot, (rarely seen). H. Hind foot, when sitting on soft sand the whole of the foot back to the ankle may mark.

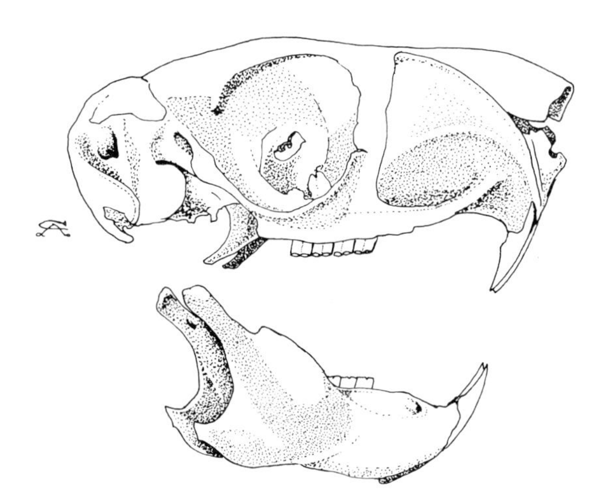

Fig. 135.3 Skull: springhaas, *Pedetes capensis*.

The dental formula is
$I\frac{1}{1}\ C\frac{0}{0}\ P\frac{1}{1}\ M\frac{3}{3} = 20$

The simple two-lobed cheekteeth are all of fairly even size and have flat surfaces for grinding up the soft food and, like the incisors, are ever-growing. The palate is short, extending posteriorly to about the anterior edge of the second upper molar teeth. The upper cheekteeth have a strong re-entrant fold of the enamel on their outside edges. In the lower jaw the re-entrant folds lie on the buccal side of the teeth.

The lower jaw is thick and massive, the coronoid process narrow at the top with a broad thin flange of bone in front and low down at the back. The loose articulation allows for an extensive movement of the lower jaw both backwards, forwards and sideways.

**Distribution**

Throughout their wide distributional range their occurrence is patchy and discontinuous, as they are unable to burrow in hard substrates and prefer lighter sandy soils. The distribution map represents the limits within which they occur, but they only do so where the substrate is suitable. In past geological ages, when the rainfall was less than it is today, there is little doubt that their distribution was continuous between the two areas of present day occurrence.

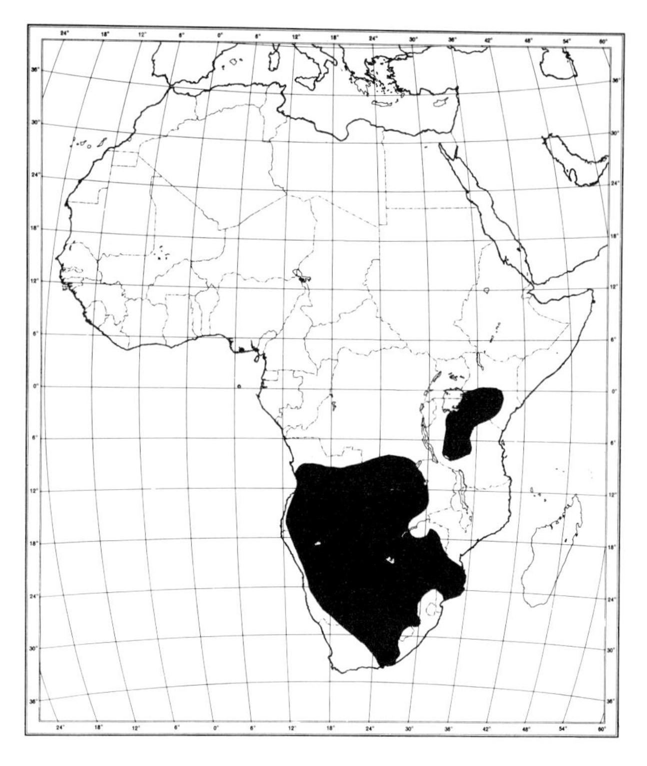

*South of the Sahara, excluding the Southern African Subregion*

They are of limited distribution in central and southern **Kenya** and occur throughout northeastern **Tanzania** south to about 8 °S. They occur in **Angola**, and are confined to the western parts of **Zambia**, not occurring east of about 28 °E; they extend marginally into southeastern **Zaire** in the vicinity of Sakania.

*Southern African Subregion*

They occur widely in **Namibia** and **Botswana**, while in **Zimbabwe** they are common throughout the western parts of the country, but they do not occur further east than the Harare District on the plateau or in the northeast of the country. In **Mozambique**, south of the Zambezi River, they are found only from the Save River southwards to about 25 °S, but not south of this. They occur in the northern and western **Transvaal**, but are absent in the southwest; they occur widely in the **Orange Free State**; marginally in northwestern **Natal**; and are common in the northern, northeastern and eastern parts of the **Cape Province**.

**Habitat**

An important habitat requirement is a substrate of compacted sandy soil in which to dig their burrows. They generally avoid hard ground, as is found in mopane woodland, or heavy clay soils, but occur in these areas where there are intrusions of sandy alluvium, such as that along rivers, or in patches of sandy soil overlaying the hard ground. As a consequence their distribution locally can be patchy and discontinuous. They occur widely on open sandy ground or sandy scrub, on overgrazed grassland, on the fringes of vleis and dry river beds, on floodplain grassland, cultivated areas or open scrub. They are not common where there is a heavy cover of tall grasses. In Botswana this habitat preference is clearly shown in their occurrence on the open grass fringes of pans in the south of the country, which have a short grass cover, heavily grazed by herbivores, and where, on the raised perimeter, they find suitable ground in which to excavate their burrows. Under these conditions they are absent from the tall grass areas which surround the pans.

## Habits

Springhaas are nocturnal, not emerging from their burrows until well after dark. They appear circumspect in emerging, first poking their noses out to test the air, and then their heads, with ears raised, to ensure there is no danger around. They will then pause for a few moments on the sandy pile at the burrow entrance before finally moving off to feed.

They excavate their burrows in well-drained, hard-packed sandy soils, generally associated with an abundant short-grass food resource and flat open terrain; this excavation is usually done during the wet season.

A newly opened burrow has a crescent-shaped mound of loose excavated soil at the entrance, up to 2 m across and 1,5 m wide, which is thrown out during excavation. The soil is loosened with the curved claws of the front feet, pushed under the body and thrown clear with the hind feet, roots or other obstructions being cut through with the aid of the incisor teeth (Butynski & Mattingly, 1979). The burrows enter the ground at an angle of some 40° and extend to a mean depth of 780 mm, when they level out to a mean length of 42 m. The mean number of entrances is 9,3 and the maximum depth is 1,22 m (n=3). Tunnels varied from 120 to 250 mm high and 100 to 230 mm wide. At the far end a vertical escape hole is cut through to the surface. This hole does not have a mound of soil at the entrance as it is excavated from inside the burrow. In the three burrows excavated (Butynski & Mattingly, 1979), mound holes outnumbered clean holes three to one. Short temporary earthen plugs formed from inside the burrow often were found just inside mound holes and probably discouraged predators. Much longer, permanent earthen plugs were found in each of the three burrows excavated. These filled entire tunnel branches and varied from 0,5 to 3,0 m in length. The long plugs may function as an alteration of burrow design, for removal of faecal material or for predator avoidance. In the course of time, a simple burrow may be extended to include other side burrows and can have several entrances and escape holes so that eventually the system may cover an area of anything up to 15 × 10 m. However, the tunnels contain no chambers or bedding material. This burrow system is occupied by a single springhaas and is used by the female when she gives birth to her young (Smithers, 1971). Since they are excavated often in close proximity to each other it is possible that some burrow systems may have underground connections between them, but individuals make every effort to return to their own holes when disturbed, even when these are some distance away and there are other holes nearby. They enter and leave the burrow system by both types of entrance holes and these may be plugged with soil during daylight hours when the animals are inside resting.

If the burrow system is in use the loose soil of the mound outside the entrance may show the characteristic spoor of the hind feet, with their long pointed triangular claws, and the two adjoining and much shorter toes, their claws normally imprinting less clearly towards the base of the central toe. In compacted soil the marks of the front claws, used in excavation, show clearly on the sides of the burrow, but seldom show in the spoor as most movement proceeds on the hind feet. When the individual rests momentarily, sitting up, the whole of the hind feet may show in the spoor (Fig. 135.2).

Locomotion proceeds in a series of short hops on the back feet, the front legs held close to the body. When chased they can move very fast in long leaps of up to 2 m, with a jinking movement, the tail with its long black tip flung from side to side to maintain balance and perhaps to confuse pursuers. When feeding the body is held low, the weight taken on the front feet and then the hind feet move forward, in rabbit-like fashion.

When caught in the beam of a dazzling light they tend to crouch close to the ground, the ears lowered, but they do not remain in this position for long, returning to the sitting stance or raising themselves on the hind feet to examine the source of the disturbance, with their ears raised. In a beam of light only one bright eye shows, which tends to bob up and down; the single eye and bobbing motion distinguishes them from other nocturnal species. Springhaas exhibit no territorial behaviour and when feeding tend to congregate in open groups, sometimes, as in parts of Botswana, in "dozens", the group resembling "city lights" when caught in a light beam.

Springhaas may remain in their burrows during heavy rain or very cold weather. They seldom feed further than about 400 m from their burrows, the feeding sites being characterised by shallow, crescent-shaped diggings and the discarded stems and other parts of grasses, where the individual has remained in one place and dug around for underground succulent rhizomes.

Springhaas fall prey to a wide range of predators, and the plugging of the burrows may be a defence against those small enough to enter. They are of considerable value as a source of protein, and Butynski (1975) estimated that in Botswana 2,5 million springhaas are cropped annually for food by the indigenous peoples, representing some four springhaas per person. The San secure them by hooking them out of their burrows using a 4 m pole with a 100 mm barb on the tip, as do the Ndebele in Zimbabwe using a burred seedpod lashed to the end of a pole which is screwed into the fur so tightly that the springhaas can be withdrawn. The San consume the whole springhaas, gaining some 2 kg of "meat" from each adult, whilst the skins are softened to make water and food containers, mats or karosses, and the best thread is made from the tail sinews. Butynski (1975) also recorded the use by the San of springhaas dung mixed with the tar and nicotine from a pipe as a smoking mixture.

Their burrows provide shelter for a wide range of small species of wildlife including pangolins, polecats, several species of mongoose, mice and reptiles. In addition, Ant-eating chats, *Myrmecocichla formicivora*, use springhaas burrows, nesting in excavations in the roof (Smithers, 1971).

Butynski (1982e) found that most springhaas in the Kalahari were infested with the stomach nematode *Physaloptera capensis*. Infestation increased with age, and lactating females showed the highest infestations.

## Food

Springhaas are grazers, living almost entirely on grass. Butynski (1975) showed that, in Botswana, they feed on the seeds of grasses during the months from January to March and at other times on green grass stems, leaves, corms, roots and rhizomes. They are highly selective feeders and will nip chosen sections from the plant with their teeth and discard the remainder. The food is manipulated with the front feet and directed into the mouth to be ground up finely with the cheekteeth to the extent that it becomes unrecognisable macroscopically. The manipulation with the front feet is made possible by the nail-like edges of the pad underlying the long curved claws which, impinging on the inside of the claws, act like a pair of pincers. The adjacent flap of skin with its hairy fringe no doubt assists in this process (Fig. 135.1). Direct observation of their diggings for underground roots and rhizomes suggests that couch grass, *Cynodon dactylon*, is heavily utilised, both the leaves and rhizomes being eaten. On the fringes of pans in Botswana the rhizomes of *Odyssea paucinervis* are eaten, the hard leaves and stems with their salt encrustation being discarded. Temby (1977) listed among their food the leaf bases of *Brachiaria* spp and *Eragrostis* spp, as well as the corms of *Gladiolus* sp and the roots of certain legumes.

They do not drink water, but meet their moisture requirements from rain and dew drops, free water in food eaten and oxidation of food (Butynski & Mattingly, 1979).

In agriculturally developed areas they can become a problem, and Butynski (1973) believed that between 10% and 15% of maize, sorghum, beans and groundnuts grown in Botswana are destroyed by springhaas.

### Reproduction

Young may be born at any time of the year in the Subregion, although Van der Merwe *et al.* (1980), judging from testicular histology and estimated conception dates of individuals from the Orange Free State (following Huggett & Widdas, 1951), noted a peak in breeding in July/August. More recently, Kofron (1987) ascribed a seasonal reproductive pattern in southeastern Zimbabwe, where the majority of pregnancies and births occurred during the wet season, to climatic seasonality. In contrast, the spread of births throughout the year in the Kalahari (Smithers, 1971; Butynski, 1978) may be due to the fact that the underground rhizomes and surface stolons of couch grasses, which form their staple diet, are available to them at any time.

Females normally carry a single foetus, but although rare, twin foetuses have been found by Butynski (1979—one set, whose death had apparently preceded that of the dam, in 152 pregnancies) and Smithers (1983—one in 104).

The gestation period is somewhere between 72–82 days (Rosenthal & Meritt, 1973b; Velte, 1978; Kofron, 1987), but there is insufficient data at the moment to set this with more accuracy. The pregnancy rate is high: in Botswana, while 46% of a total of 227 females were pregnant (Smithers, 1971), Butynski (1978) gave a figure of 76% and of those females not pregnant, 79% were lactating. In the Orange Free State van der Merwe *et al.* (1980) recorded a pregnancy rate of 58,4%.

Butynski (1979) found that the mean interval between conceptions was 101 days, the mean interval between parturition and conception 24 days, and that a female could be expected to undertake an average of 3,6 pregnancies per year. Kofron (1987) also found evidence for more than one pregnancy per year.

New-born pups have a mass of 280–300 g. They are born in the burrows fully furred, their eyes opening within two or three days. They remain in the burrows for the first six or seven weeks of their life, where they are suckled by their mothers, only emerging when they have a mass of about 1,25 kg and rapidly wean on to a diet of grass. This is the reason why one does not see small springhaas, for by the time they first leave the burrows, they are not obviously smaller than adults: on average they have hind feet and ears that are 97% and 93% of the adult size respectively, and they are just as active. Once the young start to feed above ground the amount of milk in their stomachs drops drastically, suggesting a rapid transition from total dependence upon, to complete independence from, the mother's milk (Butynski, 1979).

In the males, once spermatogenesis is established at a body mass of about 2,5 kg, it continues throughout the year. The scrotal testes slip easily up the inguinal canal, which has resulted in misleading naturalists to believe that the springhaas is a testicond or a species with abdominal testes.

The females have a pair of pectoral mammae, the teats situated on the flanks of the chest behind the forelimbs. Their position facilitates suckling as the female crouches in the burrow.

# XIX. Family GLIRIDAE

## Dormice

Both Allen (1939) and Ellerman (1940–41) used the Family name Muscardinidae for the dormice and it remained in general use until Simpson (1945) advanced arguments for the return to the name Gliridae given by Thomas (1897). Representatives of the Family are found over much of Africa as well as in Palaearctic regions and southeastwards to India and Malaya and in southern China. The Family is represented in the Subregion by four species, which have certain external features in common that render them easily distinguishable from small murids, in particular by their possession of bushy tails. Because of these bushy tails they often are mistaken for small squirrels, but most of our squirrels are considerably larger and none of them are plain grey in body colour like our dormice. The fur on the body of our dormice is soft and very dense, the head rounded with a short muzzle and small ears. The feet are broad and strong. The forefeet have four digits, lacking a thumb; the hind feet have five digits, the first digit very short and barely reaching the base of the second, the remainder subequal in length. The claws are curved and sharp and flattened from side to side.

The dental formula is:

$I\frac{1}{1}\, C\frac{0}{0}\, P\frac{1}{1}\, M\frac{3}{3} = 20$

and therefore they have four cheekteeth on either side in the upper and lower jaws, as compared with murids which have only three. Each of these teeth is basin-shaped, with an enamel perimeter which is connected across the basin by low, transverse, enamel ridges. The outer margin of each tooth bifurcates indistinctly to suggest a division of the tooth into two cusps, but there is nothing to suggest the multiple cuspidation seen in the teeth of most rats and mice. Sometimes the single premolar tooth is absent, having been shed.

The name dormouse has its origin in the Latin *dormitorium*, a sleeping place, from their habit, in the colder regions of the world, of hibernating. There is evidence of hibernation in the Subregion where they appear to enter a temporary state of torpidity in cold weather or at least to show signs of lethargy at such times.

The genus *Graphiurus* was split into a number of genera by Thomas & Hinton (1925). Misonne (1974) retained the subgenus *Graphiurus* for the spectacled dormouse, *G. ocularis*, which has very small premolar teeth, and the subgenus *Claviglis* for the other species in which they are not much reduced, a treatment which is followed here.

Misonne (1974) in his review provisionally included all the smaller forms in a *G. (C.) murinus* group, recognising that this was probably unjustified. Genest-Villard (1978) recognised among these smaller forms *G. (C.) murinus* and *G. (C.) parvus* distinguished predominantly on size, as set out in the following table:

| | HB | T | TL skull | Breadth inter-oribital con-striction | Length cheek-teeth row |
|---|---|---|---|---|---|
| *parvus* | 75–87 | 14–16 | 21,5–24,5 | 3,5–4,0 | 2,6–3,0 |
| *murinus* | 84–117 | 16–18,5 | 25,0–30,8 | 3,7–5,0 | 2,7–3,7 |
| *platyops* | 105–130 | 21–23 | 29,5–32,5 | 4,8–5,3 | 3,2–3,5 |
| *ocularis* | 133–145 | 23–25 | 34,0–37,5 | 5,0–5,7 | 3,1–3,4 |

In his key he further distinguished *G. (C.) murinus* from *G. (C.) parvus* by the fact that the hind foot in the former is over 16 mm, in the latter under 16 mm.

Key to the subgenera and species after Meester *et al.* (1986)

1. $P^1$ distinctly smaller than other teeth in the molar row (Subgenus *Graphiurus*)

 ... *ocularis*

 $P^1$ scarcely smaller than other teeth in the molar row (Subgenus *Claviglis*)

 ... 2

2. Head and body length less than 87 mm; hind foot length less than 16 mm; greatest skull length less than 24,5 mm

 ... *parvus*

 Head and body length equal to or more than 87 mm; hind foot length more than 16 mm; greatest skull length more than 24,5 mm

 ... 3

3. Hind foot length less than 21 mm; interorbital width less than 5 mm; head and body length usually less than 105 mm; greatest skull length usually less than 30,5 mm
. . . *murinus*

Hind foot length more than 21 mm; interorbital width more than 5 mm; head and body length usually more than 105 mm; greatest skull length usually more than 30,5 mm
. . . *platyops*

## Subgenus *Graphiurus* Smuts, 1832

## Genus *Graphiurus* Smuts, 1832

---

No. 136

# *Graphiurus (Graphiurus) ocularis* (A. Smith, 1829)

## Spectacled dormouse
## Gemsbokmuis

Plate 9

---

### Colloquial Name

The name stems from the characteristic black markings around the eyes which give the appearance of a pair of spectacles. The Afrikaans name *gemsbokmuis* is given as the black and white markings on the face are reminiscent of the facial markings of a gemsbok, *Oryx gazella*. In the Cedarberg, Cape Province it is called the namtap, which has a Nama origin referring to its ability to disappear rapidly from sight (Channing, 1984).

### Taxonomic Notes

No subspecies of this comparatively uncommon dormouse have been described.

### Table 136.1

Measurements (mm) and mass (g) of spectacled dormice, *G. (G.) ocularis*, from the Cape Province and the Transvaal (de Graaff, 1981)

| | Males | | | Females | | |
|---|---|---|---|---|---|---|
| | $\bar{x}$ | n | Range | $\bar{x}$ | n | Range |
| (TL | 245) | | | (227) | | |
| HB | 133 | 7 | 120–148 | 124 | 2 | 121–128 |
| T | 112 | 6 | 103–125 | 103 | 2 | 100–106 |
| Hf c/u | 25 | 7 | 23–26 | 20 | 2 | 20 |
| E | 20 | 7 | 15–25 | 18 | 2 | 18 |
| Mass | 83 | 2 | 81–85 | — | | |

### Description

This is the largest of the four species of dormice that occur in the Subregion. Adults reach a total length of up to about 250 mm and have bushy tails that are about 80% of the length of the head and body (Table 136.1). The upper parts of the body are grey with a silvery sheen; the individual hairs are dark grey with whitish or silvery tips. The facial pattern is a characteristic feature. The top of the muzzle, just posterior to the rhinarium, is sparsely covered with short, white hair which blends into the light grey hair between the eyes and on the forehead. On the sides of the face a black diffused band runs from the upper lip, broadening out in front of the eyes and enclosing them. It continues downward in front of and under the base of the ears where it narrows and becomes rather indistinct as it crosses the top of the head in front of the ears. The cheeks are pure white, contrasting markedly with the black band in front of the ears; there are patches of pure white hair above the ears. In front of the shoulders and rising high on to the flanks at the level of the belly the hair is broadly white-tipped, contrasting with the grey flanks. On the under parts the hair is grey at the base with broad white tips, the grey showing through to give an overall greyish appearance to the whole. The hair on the shoulders is about 12 mm long and is soft and fluffy. The hair on the upper parts and sides of the tail is much longer than that on the body, reaching a length of 40 mm towards the tip and is black at the base with broad white tips, giving a whitish appearance to the tail when seen from above. On the under surface the hair is shorter and black overall. The upper arm is black above and whitish below; the hands are white. The upper parts of the hind limbs are grey and the feet are white. Like other species of dormice the chin, throat and upper parts of the forelimbs tend to be heavily stained brown, probably through eating some type of insect. *G. ocularis* is adapted morphologically to living in rock cracks and climbing sheer faces, the hands and feet possessing well developed plantar tubercles and the digits possessing sharp claws.

### Distribution

*Southern African Subregion*

The spectacled dormouse is confined in its distribution to within the limits of the Subregion, occurring widely in the **Cape Province**, with a single record from the southwestern **Transvaal**.

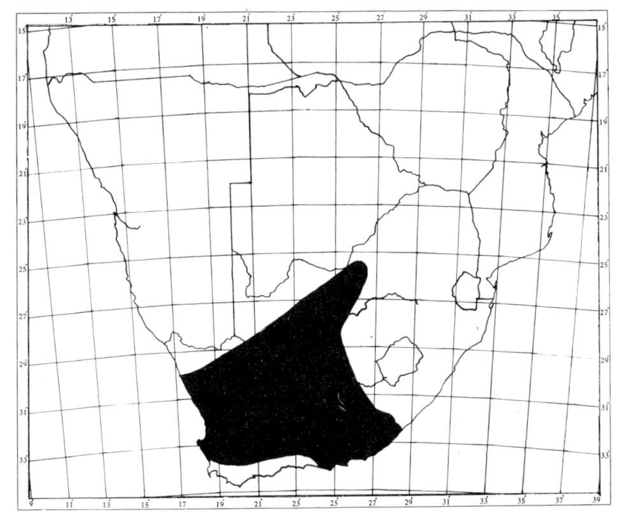

### Habitat

The species is associated with the sandstones of the Cape folded mountains which have many vertical and horizontal cracks and crevices which serve as habitat, in the drier parts of the Cape Province (Channing, 1984). In particular they use areas providing shelter in the form of horizontal and vertical cracks. They will cross sandy areas to move between isolated rocky areas. In the Cedarberg, Channing (1984) captured Namaqua rock rats, *Aethomys namaquensis* and elephant shrews, *Elephantulus edwardii* at the same site. In contrast, the original specimen used by A. Smith (1829) from which to describe the species was taken in a tree.

### Habits

They are nocturnal and terrestrial, moving rapidly on rocks including vertical faces, and they are also to some extent arboreal. Males, while occupying the same areas as females, also make occasional excursions into other areas. Females use smaller ranges (1,1 and 2,3 ha; n=2) than males (2,1–3,8 ha; n=4). It would appear that spectacled dormice maintain territories which are occupied by individuals or pairs, tenancy apparently giving the male access to a resident female (van Hensbergen & Channing, 1989). They are aggressive towards conspecifics, displaying intimidatingly with a loud call, open mouth, raised claws and bushy tail. The average distance between captures was larger for males than females, 127 *cf.* 81 m on a straight line; however, due to the nature of the three-dimentional habitat, these distances were much longer.

Van Hensbergen & Channing (1989) suggested that the main social unit consists of an adult pair with the young of the year and such social units occupy the most favourable habitat. The remaining dormice are unable to maintain a territory and occupy less favourable areas. These are mainly young which have left the natal group. Channing (1984) suggested that they live for at least four years in the wild, one captive animal living for six years.

Channing (1984) found that, provided sufficient food is available, they are active throughout the year. On the other hand, if food is withheld or if air temperature drops suddenly they become torpid for three or four days at a time and a combination of these factors will cause them to hibernate for a month or more.

### Food

Channing (1984), using faecal analysis, found that they are mainly insectivorous. Amongst the insects taken, ants (Hymenoptera: Formicidae) are numerically dominant (50%), followed by Coleoptera (11%) and Orthoptera (7%). The Hymenoptera are commonly seen at night, particularly around protea flowers. Vertebrates made up the largest volume of food taken in Channing's (1984) study, but only three animals, a Cape bunting, *Fringillaria capensis*, and two lizards, *Agama atra* and *Mabuya homalocephala*, comprised this sample. They also took millipedes, spiders, scorpions and honeybees, including one record of their eating larvae from a beehive. He suggested that honey could be a natural food item.

### Reproduction

Young are born from spring throughout summer, four to six young being produced in a litter, which in turn are produced six to eight weeks apart.

## Subgenus *Claviglis* Jentink, 1888

## Genus *Graphiurus* Smuts, 1832

No. 137

## *Graphiurus (Claviglis) platyops* Thomas, 1897

## Rock dormouse
## Klipwaaierstertmuis

Plate 9

### Colloquial Name

This species is associated particularly with a rocky habitat.

### Taxonomic Notes

Meester *et al.* (1986) listed two subspecies from the Subregion, the nominate *G. p. platyops* from the Transvaal, Zimbabwe, central Mozambique and eastern Botswana, and *G. p. rupicola* (Thomas & Hinton, 1925) from the northwestern Cape Province and the central plateau of Namibia.

### Description

Rock dormice are the second largest species that occur in the Subregion. Adults reach a total length of about 190 mm, with tails that are about 60% the length of the head and body and a mass of about 50,0 g (Table 137.1). The upper parts are dark grey, the cheeks white and they have a dark suffusion from the base of the whiskers running towards and surrounding the eyes and continuing back to the ears. The hair on the under parts is dark grey at the base with broad white tips, the grey showing through, giving the whole a dark grey appearance with an irregular white wash. The chin is white, the bushy tail is pale grey with a distinct white tip, the hairs on the upper surface longer than those on the body and reaching a length of about 30 mm towards the tip. The individual hairs have pale grey bases and whitish tips, the white tipping much broader on the hairs towards the end of the tail. The under surface is pale grey, the white tipping to the hairs narrower than on the upper surface. The ears are broad at the base and rounded.

### Skull

In this species the skull is flattened, an adaptation to its life in narrow rock crevices (Fig. 137.1.a). The palate ends at the posterior edge of the third upper molar, and the palatal foramina are situated along the length of the cheekteeth row in front of the first upper premolar.

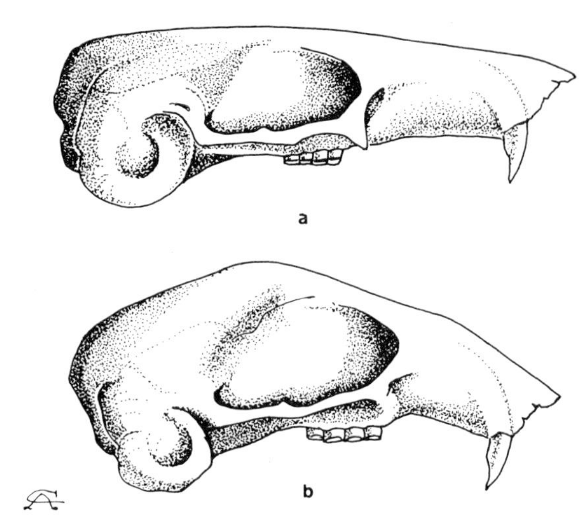


Fig. 137.1. Lateral view skulls:
(a) *G. platyops* (b) *G. murinus*.

**Table 137.1**

Measurements (mm) and mass (g) of rock dormice, *G. (C.) platyops*, from the Subregion (de Graaff, 1981)

| | Males | | | Females | | |
|---|---|---|---|---|---|---|
| | $\bar{x}$ | n | Range | $\bar{x}$ | n | Range |
| (TL | 185) | | | (180) | | |
| HB | 115 | 11 | 105–130 | 105 | 16 | 19–117 |
| T | 70 | 11 | 60–80 | 75 | 16 | 60–98 |
| Hf c/u | 20 | 11 | 18–23 | 20 | 19 | 17–22 |
| E | 16 | 11 | 14–18 | 15 | 17 | 13–18 |
| Mass | 43,6 | 3 | 39,0–52,0 | 48,6 | 3 | 40,0–65,0 |

### Distribution

*South of the Sahara, excluding the Southern African Subregion*

This species has a discontinuous distribution and occurs north of the limits of the Subregion in eastern **Angola; Zambia; Malawi**; and the Katanga Province of **Zaire**. Throughout their distributional range their occurrence is in the main governed by the availability of rocky terrain.

*Southern African Subregion*

They are recorded from the central plateau in **Namibia**, from Kaokoland in the northwest to the Orange River in the south; from eastern **Botswana**; widely from **Zimbabwe**; with two records from central **Mozambique**, south of the Zambezi River: one in the western Vila Pery District, the other from the Zinave National Park on the Save River. They occur widely in the **Transvaal**, excluding the western and eastern sectors.

### Habitat

They are generally confined to rocky terrain, and live in rock crevices, under the exfoliation on granite bosses, and in piles of boulders. In parts of their distributional range, where there is no available rocky habitat, they live in trees (Zambia, Ansell, 1960a; Mozambique, Smithers & Tello, 1976). Occasionally they are found in buildings.

### Habits

They are nocturnal, predominantly terrestrial, but to some extent arboreal, and generally solitary.

### Food

Stomach contents from Zimbabwe and Botswana contained the remains of well masticated small seeds, traces of green

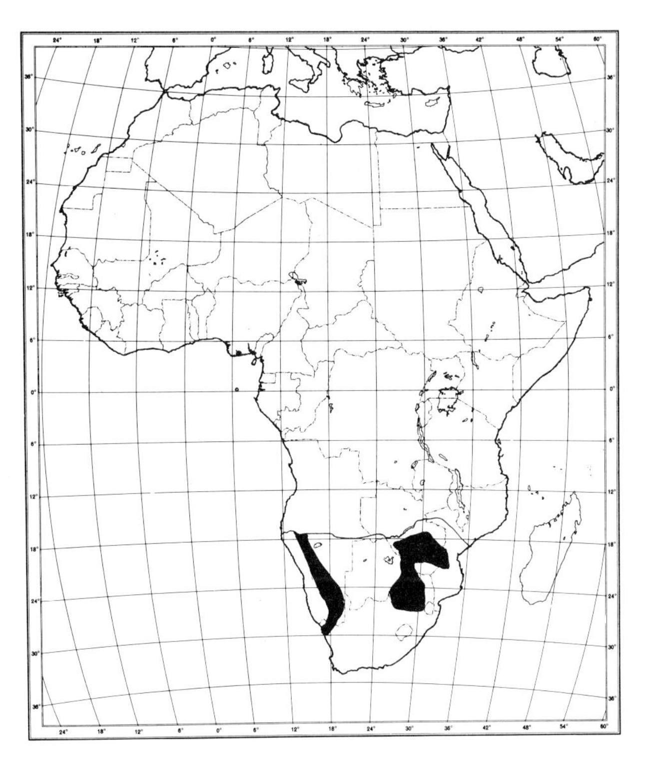

Southern African Subregion distribution only.

vegetable matter and the chitinous remains of insects, including moths. The forelimbs, chin and throat are often characteristically stained with a reddish-plum colour, thought to be caused by their eating some type of insects.

**Reproduction**

In Zambia, Ansell (1960a) recorded a female with six foetuses in February and juveniles in November and December and a subadult in April. No data are available from the Subregion.

No. 138

## *Graphiurus (Claviglis) murinus* (Desmarest, 1822)

## Woodland dormouse
## Boswaaierstertmuis

Plate 9

**Colloquial Name**

Throughout their wide distributional range they are associated with woodland.

**Taxonomic Notes**

Meester *et al.* (1986) listed three subspecies, the nominate *G. m. murinus* from the southern and eastern Cape Province and Natal; *G. m. microtis* (Noack, 1887) from the Transvaal, Zimbabwe and Mozambique, and *G. m. griselda* Schwann, 1906 from the northern Cape Province, Botswana and Namibia. Dippenaar, Meester, Rautenbach & Wolhuter (1983) found three diploid chromosome types in species from southern Africa, indicating that a review is necessary.

**Description**

This is the larger of the two small species of dormice that are recorded from the Subregion. Adults have a range of head and body lengths of from 84 mm to 117 mm, and skulls of 28,6 mm to 30,8 mm and are, therefore, larger than the lesser savanna dormouse, *G. (C.) parvus* (Genest-Villard, 1978) (Table 138.1).

The colour of the upper parts of the body is a uniform grey or a buffy-grey, the hair short, about 6 mm long on the shoulders, and is soft and woolly. The under parts are buffy-white, the individual hairs dark slate at the base with buffy-white tips. The bushy tail is shorter than the length of the head and body, whilst the hair on the upper surface graduates in length from the base, where it is the same length as on the upper parts of the body, to about 18 mm long towards the tip. The colour of the upper surface is faintly browner than the body colour, and the long hair towards the tip of the tail broadly white-tipped. On the under surface of the tail the hair is shorter and slightly paler in colour than the hair on the upper surface, and the hands and feet are white. The cheeks are buffy-white and they have a dark suffusion from the base of the whiskers which extends to and broadens out under the eyes.

**Skull**

In the skull the braincase is squarish and domed, the interorbital constriction marked. The rostrum is squat, tapering only slightly towards the tip, the nasal bones broad in front and swinging downwards at the sides towards the incisor teeth. The palate is broad, only tapering slightly posteriorly. The incisor teeth swing inwards towards each other, with the result that, with wear, the outsides of the cutting edges form into sharp points (Fig. 138.1 and 2).

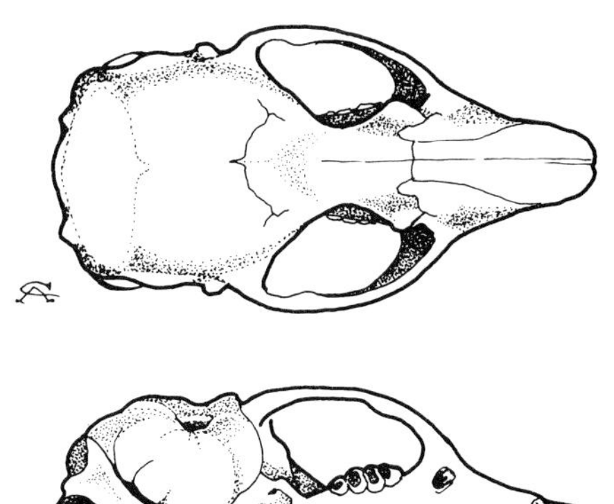

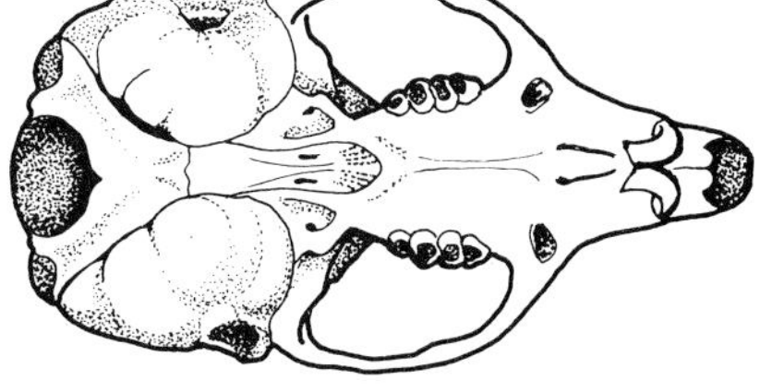

Fig. 138.1. Skull: *Graphiurus (C.) murinus* above, dorsal view; below, ventral view.

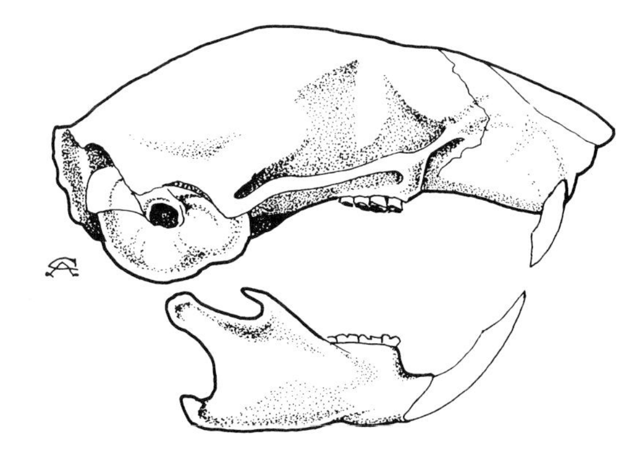

Fig. 138.2. Skull: *Graphiurus (C.) murinus* lateral view.

**Table 138.1**

Measurements (mm) and mass (g) of woodland dormice, *G. (C.) murinus*, from the Subregion (de Graaff, 1981)

| | Males | | | Females | | |
|---|---|---|---|---|---|---|
| | x̄ | n | Range | x̄ | n | Range |
| (TL | 166) | | | (171) | | |
| HB | 93 | 27 | 82–113 | 95 | 31 | 78–110 |
| T | 73 | 26 | 58–92 | 76 | 27 | 62–94 |
| Hf c/u | 17 | 27 | 15–20 | 17 | 28 | 15–20 |
| E | 15 | 27 | 10–19 | 16 | 27 | 13–20 |
| Mass | 27,9 | 10 | 24,0–34,0 | 27,6 | 13 | 23,0–34,0 |

### Distribution

*South of the Sahara, excluding the Southern African Subregion*

They occur in **Guinea Bissau** and throughout most of the countries in West Africa eastwards to **Kenya; Uganda; Cameroun; Gabon,** and **Zaire**. They occur widely in **Zambia** and have been recorded in southern **Angola**.

*Southern African Subregion*

The material from the Subregion requires re-examination, as in the past these small dormice were all considered to be *G. (C.) murinus*, and with Genest-Villard's (1978) separation of *G. (C.) parvus* we cannot be certain of the exact limits of the distribution of the two species. Genest-Villard (1978) gave the distribution of *G. (C.) murinus* as "South Africa, eastern littoral zone, Zululand and Caffraria". This indication of a western distribution for *G. (C.) parvus* does not appear to conform to the information presently available, for a series from Botswana (Smithers, 1971) is large with a head and body and tail length which conforms more closely to his *G. (C.) murinus*. Until the Subregion material is re-examined, the two species are mapped together as the "*G. (C.) murinus* group" which is the treatment provisionally used by Misonne (1974).

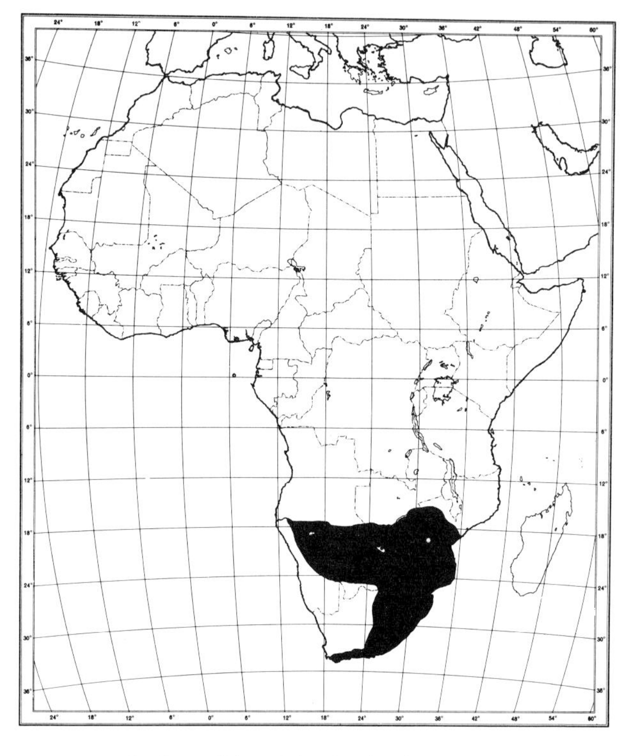

Southern African Subregion distribution only.

### Habitat

They are found in woodland, amongst rocks and trees (particularly *Acacia* spp), where they use holes in trees or crevices in which to rest during daylight hours. They commonly use the shelter of the roofs of houses, outbuildings or thatched huts and often nest in beehives or in switch boxes, water pumps and transformers where they can be a nuisance, causing short circuits in electrical supplies. They have also been taken in piles of debris deposited by high floods near seasonally dry rivers.

### Habits

They are nocturnal and arboreal, but to a lesser extent terrestrial. At night they forage singly on the trees in search of insects and other food items.

Although Eisentraut (1962) reported that *G. murinus* from Cameroun in West Africa could not enter torpor following cold exposure, Ellison & Skinner (1990) recently described prolonged bouts of torpor in *G. murinus* collected in the Transvaal. Following acclimation to 15 °C and 10 °C in the laboratory, these dormice all entered hibernation, characterised by a fall in body temperature to within 1 °C of ambient, whilst the dormice sustained a fall in body weight during hibernation similar to that described for temperate species of dormice (Ellison & Skinner, 1990).

### Food

In Botswana the dry outside skins of buffalo thorn fruits, *Ziziphus mucronata*, were recognised in stomachs, which invariably contained the unidentifiable remains of insects; one individual visiting a camp site lamp at night, taking large moths and rose beetles (Smithers, 1971). In the Drakensberg a sample of 11 stomachs all contained insect remains, but 82% also contained grass seeds (Rowe-Rowe, 1986).

### Reproduction

In Zimbabwe a gravid female was taken in February; schoolboys in western Zimbabwe who keep them as pets know that the young are usually available during late summer from February to March.

---

No. 139

## *Graphiurus (Claviglis) parvus* (True, 1893)

## Lesser savanna dormouse
## Klein savanne-waaierstertmuis

Plate 9

---

### Colloquial Name

The colloquial name indicates that they are the smallest species of dormouse occurring in the Subregion.

### Taxonomic Notes

Only the nominate *G. parvus* occurs in the Subregion.

### Description

They are smaller in size than *G. (C.) murinus*. Adults have a head and body length of 75–87 mm, a hind foot length of 14–16 mm and a skull length of 21,5–24,5 mm (Genest-Villard, 1978). The colour of the upper parts of the body is a uniform grey or grey with a trace of sandy colour. The hair is short, soft and woolly and except for size are otherwise similar to *G. (C.) murinus*.

### Distribution

*South of the Sahara, excluding the Southern African Subregion*

The species is recorded from **Mali; Niger; Sierra Leone; Ivory Coast; Ghana** and **Nigeria**. Originally it was described from **Kenya**, and occurs also in **Ethiopia; Somalia; Tanzania; Zambia** and **Malawi**.

**Plate 9**

135. Springhaas, *Pedetes capensis*
 Springhaas
136. Spectacled dormouse, *Graphiurus (Graphiurus) ocularis*
 Gemsbokmuis
137. Rock dormouse, *Graphiurus (Claviglis) platyops*
 Klipwaaierstertmuis
138. Woodland dormouse, *Graphiurus (Claviglis) murinus*
 Boswaaierstertmuis
139. Lesser savanna dormouse, *Graphiurus (Claviglis) parvus*
 Klein savanne-waaierstertmuis
150. Brants' whistling rat, *Parotomys brantsii*
 Brants se fluitrot
153. Angoni vlei rat, *Otomys angoniensis*
 Angoni-vleirot
157. Sloggett's rat, *Otomys sloggetti*
 Sloggett se rot

PLATE·9
136
139
138
137
150
157
153
135
Dick Findlay

*Southern African Subregion*

Genest-Villard (1978) recorded the species from two areas in **Zimbabwe**, Mazoe and near Gwero, but for the reasons given under **Distribution**—*G. (C.) murinus*—no attempt is made at the moment to map the distribution of the species and it is included in the map of the "*G. (C.) murinus* group".

**Habitat, Habits, Food and Reproduction**

In the past this species was not recognised as separate from *G. (C.) murinus*, and nothing is on record on these aspects of its life history in the Subregion.

# XX. Family SCIURIDAE

## Squirrels

The Family name is derived from the Greek *skiouros* meaning shady tail, which refers to the characteristic habit of some members of holding their tails swung up over their backs and heads. It is one of five Families of terrestrial mammals which have representatives in Africa, Europe and Asia as well as in North and South America. The others are the Mustelidae, with 29 genera, the Canidae with 12, the Leporidae with nine and the Felidae with three, compared with the Sciuridae which have 42 (Simpson, 1945). The squirrels, being diurnal, are among the easier mammals to collect and observe. Very large collections are therefore available, which have made possible detailed studies of their skull characters (Moore, 1959), although little is known of the social organisation and other aspects of the life histories of some species.

The Family Sciuridae is divided into two subfamilies, the Sciurinae, the typical squirrels, and the Petauristinae, the flying squirrels. The Petauristinae are not represented in Africa and should not be confused with the African flying squirrels, the Anomaluridae, from which they are markedly different. Members of the Sciurinae are recognised easily by their long and bushy tails. Although this is a character shared by dormice, the smallest squirrel in the Subregion, the striped tree squirrel, *Funisciurus congicus*, is distinguishable from the largest dormouse, *Graphiurus ocularis*, by longitudinal stripes along its flank.

Squirrels occur throughout Africa, except in association with deserts. Even so, ground squirrels, *Xerus* spp, occur in semi-desert areas with a mean annual rainfall as low as 100 mm, but are also distributed in areas north of the Orange Free State that receive up to 750 mm.

Kingdon (1974) treated the genus *Paraxerus* as a subgenus of *Funisciurus* as he believed that the characters used to separate the two genera are untenable, but in this work the distinction has been retained (Meester *et al.*, 1964; Amtmann, 1975).

Key to the genera after Meester *et al.* (1986)

1. Fur bristly; ears small; third finger of the hand normally longest; four upper cheekteeth; lachrymal enlarged; palate well over half of occipito-nasal length
   ... *Xerus*

   Fur not bristly; ears conspicuous; fourth finger of hand normally longest; four to five upper cheekteeth; lachrymal not enlarged; palate normally clearly less than half of occipito-nasal length
   ... 2

2. Four upper cheekteeth, with essentially normal occlusal pattern; three pairs of mammae; no lateral body stripe
   ... *Heliosciurus*

   Five upper cheekteeth, flat-crowned with isolated deep re-entrant folds in adults; females with two or three pairs of mammae
   ... 3

3. Cheekteeth of both upper and lower jaws more specialized, more or less flat-crowned in adults; lateral white and dark stripes along body; two pairs of mammae
   ... *Funisciurus*

4. Cheekteeth less specialized, those in lower jaw cuspidate in adults, while upper ones are flat-crowned; without lateral stripes; normally three pairs of mammae
   ... *Paraxerus*

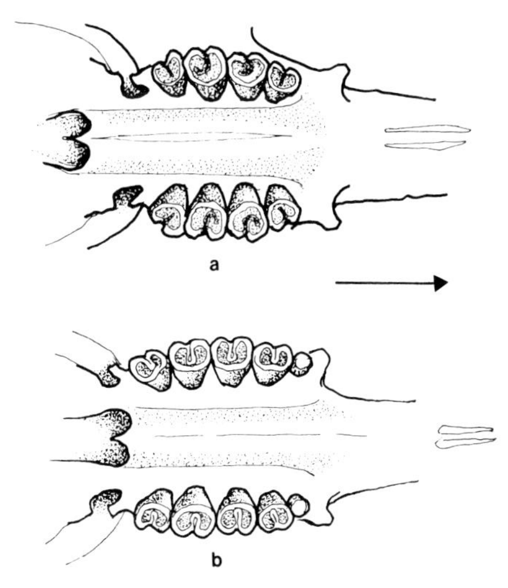


Fig. XX.1. Pattern of upper cheekteeth (a) *Xerus inauris* (b) *Paraxerus palliatus*.

## Genus *Xerus* Ehrenberg, 1833

Key to the species after Meester *et al.* (1986), with modifications (Herzig-Straschil, pers. comm.)

1. Incisor teeth white; tail hairs black at base, with another black band adjoining white tip; nasalia strongly broadening anteriorly
   ... *inauris*

   Incisor teeth yellow-orange; tail hairs with three blackish bands (at least on basal half of tail); nasalia not distinctly broadening anteriorly
   ... *princeps*

---

No. 140

## *Xerus inauris* (Zimmermann, 1780)

### Cape ground squirrel
### Waaierstertgrondeekhoring

Plate 10

---

**Colloquial Name**

This species, unlike its close relative the mountain ground squirrel, *Xerus princeps*, has no arboreal tendencies and is purely a ground living species; it was first found "100 miles north of the Cape of Good Hope". *Waaierstert*, fan-tailed, applies to the characteristic long-haired tail which, swung up along the back and back of the head with the hair laterally flattening out, presents a fan-like appearance.

### Taxonomic Notes

Several species of the genus occur on the continent: *X. rutilus* (Cretzchmar, 1826) in East Africa; *X. erythropus* (E. Geoffroy, 1803) in West Africa eastwards to the Sudan and in parts of East Africa; *X. princeps* (Thomas, 1929) in Namibia and southwestern Angola, and *X. inauris* which is confined to within the limits of the Subregion. Although the recognition of these two as different species was accepted with reservation by de Graaff (1981), it is justified by the results of a recent cytogenetical study of the two species (Robinson *et al.*, 1986) and by the analysis of morphological and morphometrical characters of the skulls (Herzig-Straschil *et al.*, in press). No subspecies of *X. inauris* are recognised.

### Description

The ground squirrel is a purely terrestrial species. It is about 450 mm in overall length, with a tail about half this length, and an average mass of about 600 g, although individuals of up to 1000 g are known (Table 140.1).

### Table 140.1

Measurements (mm) and mass (g) of a series of ground squirrels, *X. inauris*, from Botswana (Smithers, 1971)

| | Males | | | Females | | |
|---|---|---|---|---|---|---|
| | $\bar{x}$ | n | Range | $\bar{x}$ | n | Range |
| (HB | 243) | | | (239) | | |
| TL | 454 | 76 | 412–508 | 446 | 124 | 410–487 |
| T | 211 | 73 | 187–245 | 207 | 114 | 180–245 |
| Hf c/u | 68 | 78 | 61–74 | 66 | 125 | 60–73 |
| Mass | 649 | 40 | 511–1022 | 600 | 89 | 511–795 |

The upper parts are cinnamon in colour, but individuals show some variation in shade; some are darker, some lighter. The lower parts of the limbs, the under parts and sides of the neck are white, usually tinged buffy on the belly and on the inner sides of the thighs. Characteristic features are the white lateral stripes, one on either side of the body, which extend from the shoulders to the thighs, the white rings around the eyes and the fan-like tail with its long hair, which is broadly banded black at the base, then white, then black with broad white tips. The ears lack pinnae, which are represented by a fold of skin on the posterior fringe of the slit-like ear opening.

They have four digits on the front feet, the thumb being at most pad-like without a claw and five digits on the hind feet. The digits on the feet are armed with long, sharp, slightly curved claws about 10 mm long. These claws are much straighter and less curved than those of the arboreal squirrels and better adapted to digging. The body is covered with short bristly hair, with little or no underfur, the hair lying tightly adpressed to the body and measuring a bare 4 mm in length on the shoulders and 7 mm on the rump. This is in contrast to the long hair on the tail which measures up to 60 mm in length and has two blackish bands. The dorsal, ventral fur and tail hairs are significantly shorter during summer than winter. Straschil (1974) recorded the occurrence of three albinos inhabiting a burrow with normally coloured individuals in the western Orange Free State. According to de Graaff (1981) the number of albinos has increased since then.

The rhinarium, which encloses the slit-like nostrils, which can be closed at will, is small and the upper lip partially split. The nasals are robust and broaden anteriorly. The incisors are white.

### Distribution

They are confined to within the limits of the Subregion.

*Southern African Subregion*

They are distributed widely in **Namibia**, except where replaced by *X. princeps* in the northwest, but are absent from the coastal areas and in parts of the southwest and northeast. In **Botswana** they are confined to the semi-desert Kalahari associations in the central and southwest and, in the **Transvaal**, to the extreme southwestern parts of the province. They are widely distributed in the **Orange Free State** east to 30 °E and in western **Lesotho**. In the **Cape Province** they are confined to the northern and northeastern parts of the province and southwards to the Graaff Reinet district, which marks their most southerly limits of distribution.

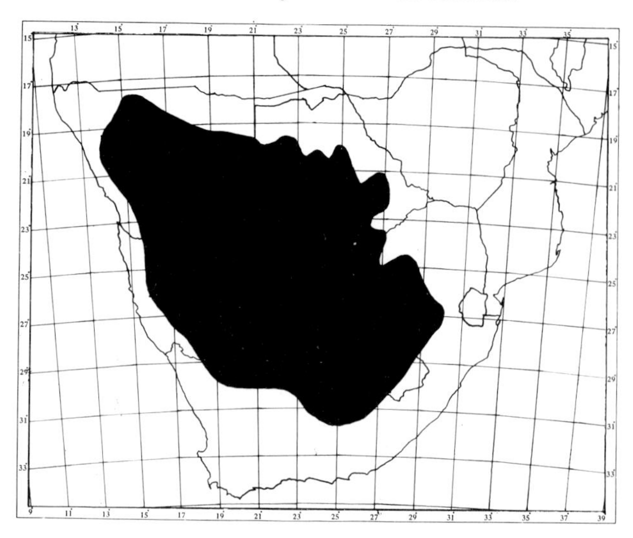

### Habitat

The ground squirrel occurs widely throughout the more arid parts of the Subregion, the greater part of its distributional range lying within the limits of the South West Arid Zone in areas with a mean annual rainfall of 100 to 500 mm. They extend eastwards, however, north of the Orange Free State to near the Natal border into areas with a mean annual rainfall of up to 750 mm.

They have a preference for open terrain with a sparse bush cover and a hard substrate. In southern Botswana, where they are particularly common, they tend to occur on open calcareous ground on the fringes of the many dry pans which are characteristic of the area. The substrate here is hard, consisting of consolidated sand with calcareous pebbles. While the surface appears sandy, the stony nature of the subsurface layers is revealed in the detritus which they dig out of the burrows. They avoid loose sandy areas for making their burrows but do occur in the dunes of the Kalahari. They excavate burrows in dune streets, pans and brackish areas. They occur also on the fringes of dry water courses, or floodplain, on open overgrazed ground, and in open grassland or karroid areas, providing the substrate is consolidated and hard.

Ground squirrels inhabit areas where night temperatures fall well below freezing point and rise during the day to over 30 °C. It has been shown, however, that the temperature inside the burrow system fluctuates very little and remains between about 11 °C and 14 °C in winter (Herzig-Straschil, 1979) and between 27,2 °C and 29,4 °C in summer (van Heerden & Dauth, 1987).

### Habits

Ground squirrels are diurnal, gregarious and colonial, living in coteries of up to about 30 in warrens with many entrances. The continuing excavation of the burrows eventually raises the warren system above the general ground level, forming distinct low mounds. Occasionally single burrows are found occupied by up to four individuals, which may be a family party.

The warrens consist of a complicated system of burrows, many of these disused and with their entrances closed by the occupants. Zumpt (1970) found that some of the burrows reached a depth of 1,5 m, but the majority lie at a depth of 0,7 to 0,9 m. New burrows are excavated continually and new tunnels opened up to join them from the surface. These and others in use are characterised by the crater-shaped mound of freshly excavated soil at the entrances. The tunnels are obliquely oval in section, with an average width of 140 mm and height of 110 mm (Herzig-Straschil, 1978). Ground squirrels are avid diggers, cutting through roots with their sharp incisor teeth and carrying these roots to the surface to be discarded. Loose soil is removed from the tunnels by pushing it back with the aid of the hind legs, the forefeet used in unison, causing the soil to be piled up in front of the hole and forming the characteristic crescent-shaped mounds. Chambers in the tunnel system are lined with grass in which they rest. This they do with their tails curled over their bodies and head. Ground squirrels are poor climbers and rarely clamber on to anything higher than low termitaria to gain a wider view of the terrain around them. However, they do feed on *Grewia flava* and *Boscia albitrunca* berries, and climb right up into the bushes to retrieve them.

The social organisation appears to be based on a group which may consist of several females with their offspring. When a female is in oestrus her group will accept a male (or males) as a member of the group for some weeks.

The dominant female in a group vigorously defends a territory around the tunnel opening against strangers from neighbouring groups, often chasing them back to their own burrows. Other female members of the group will also do so, but with less enthusiasm. Members of a group, including any males which have been accepted, live in harmony, except during feeding when the dominant female may chase off other members from preferred feeding areas by a demonstration, which involves facing them with the mouth open. This invariably causes them to move off and fighting or chasing between members of the same group is of rare occurrence. Play is regularly indulged in by sub-adults and juveniles who will chase each other around and play-fight. Members of a group identify each other by nose-touching which is used as a greeting ceremony (Herzig-Straschil, 1978).

They have several different calls. When alarmed they emit a high-pitched whistling call which can rise to a scream when seriously alarmed. During aggressive encounters they growl and, during play, the young rush around calling to each other with a *tschip-tschip*. The very young in the nest vocalise with a soft *mouk-mouk* call or a protesting squeak (Herzig-Straschil, 1978).

Ground squirrels only emerge from their burrows in the morning about an hour after sunrise and retire about 30 minutes before sunset. In cold overcast weather they are less in evidence and remain in the burrows during rain. On emerging from the burrows in the morning they have a characteristic habit of choosing a point near the entrance, scraping a small, shallow hole and either urinating in it or pressing the anal region into it, which Herzig-Straschil (1978) believed to be a marking behaviour. They also rub their snouts on stones near the burrow which probably has a similar function.

They will bask in the sun, lying on their bellies with the fore and hind limbs stretched out or, in very hot weather, will choose a shady spot and lie in the same position, as a means of cooling off. They also sand-bathe in this position, scratching the sand over their bodies until they are nearly covered, then lie there for a few moments, get up and shake themselves, repeating the process several times. Apparently this behaviour is not related to the presence of ectoparasites as these mainly locate themselves on the throat which is not dusted in the process (Herzig-Straschil, 1978), and for this reason the function of sand-bathing may be related to thermoregulation. Allogrooming and self-grooming are practised regularly by members of the group. Allogrooming is mainly directed towards the back and the throat, followed by the sides of the body and the head. Self-grooming includes attention to the tail which is nibbled along its whole length and combed with the forefeet.

In moving they walk over short distances or run over longer. When pursued or alarmed they run very fast with their bodies close to the ground and their tails stretched out horizontally behind them, making for the shelter of their own burrows. They seldom use other burrows even when these may be in their flight path.

Even when relaxed they remain acutely on the alert to the possibility of danger from the ground or the air above them. They will sit up on their haunches to gain a wider view of the surrounding terrain. They are sensitive to the alarm calls of certain birds, such as the blacksmith plover, *Vanellus armatus*, and crowned plover, *V. coronatus*, but ignore others. Large birds of prey such as the martial eagle, *Polemaetus bellicosus*, flying over send them scurrying for the burrows.

While feeding, the tail is carried bent over the back, which has a sheltering effect from the sun's rays. When alarmed they may wave the tail up and down as they give the alarm call, the tail-waving being a visual signal of danger to other members of the group. Frequently they share the warren system with suricates, *Suricata suricatta*, and yellow mongoose, *Cynictis penicillata*. Ground squirrels and suricates normally ignore each other. If part of the warren is occupied temporarily by suricates, the ground squirrel will use another part and when the suricates leave, will re-occupy the section previously used by them. When a pack of suricates moves into a ground squirrel burrow, they seem to prefer the part already in use by the ground squirrels (Lynch, 1979). Yellow mongoose may share a warren with the ground squirrels for lengthy periods, even occupying the same part of it. They appear to live in harmony, often sunning themselves within a short distance of each other, although the yellow mongoose will kill and eat sick or injured ground squirrels (Zumpt, 1970).

Herzig-Straschil (1978) obtained some data on home range from marked individuals which showed that the adult males were more mobile than the adult females, their home ranges being some 3 000 m$^2$ in extent, compared with the adult females' of some 1 600 m$^2$. Subadult males were more mobile than subadult females, with home ranges of some 1 600 m$^2$ compared with those of the subadult females of 900 m$^2$. In the Kalahari, home range size of bachelor males can be up to 2,5 km$^2$, whereas females and subadults have home ranges of 52 000 m$^2$. Defecation does not appear to have any significance as far as marking is concerned and may be performed anywhere the individual happens to be.

**Food**

Ground squirrels are predominantly vegetarians, but their diet includes a small proportion of insect food as well. Their main food consists of the leaves and stems of grasses, seeds, bulbs, roots and plant stems.

Herzig-Straschil (1978) listed couch grass, *Cynodon dactylon*, *Enneapogon brachystachys* and *Aristida obtusa* as among the most important species of grasses of which the stems and leaves are eaten in the western Transvaal, as well as the leaves and stems of the shepherd's tree, *Boscia foetida*, a small shrub common in the area. The seeds of herbs including *Leucas* sp, *Sophora* sp and *Tribulus terrestris*, and seed of the grass *Urochloa panicoides* were also taken, together with bulbs and tubers. Among the insect food the remains of termites, beetles, grasshoppers and caterpillars were recognised in stomach contents, in one case termites constituting half the contents of a full stomach.

In Botswana the succulent leaves and fine stems of karroid bushes and the fruits of wild cucumbers are eaten. Grasses that are preferred in the Kalahari are *Stipagrostis obtusa*, *Schmidtia kalahariensis*, *Centropodia glaucum* and *Eragrostis lehmanniana*. Annuals like *Limeum* sp, *Tribulus terrestris* and *Helichrysum* sp are consumed during the summer. Ground squirrels also take *Grewia flava* and *Boscia albitrunca* berries. While feeding they dig avidly for the bulbs and underground stems of grasses and will pull down the stems of tall grasses or low shrubs to get at the seeds or leaves. They use the forefeet to manipulate the food when eating. Ground squirrels have been blamed for depredations in maize lands, but Zumpt (1970) believed that this has been over-emphasised. He showed that of a normal loss of 0,2%, a maximum of 0,04% can be attributed to the ground squirrel.

**Reproduction**

Ground squirrels have their young at any time throughout the year, with indications that there may be peaks around May and again in August/September, but further information is required to substantiate this. The gestation period is not known, but Zumpt (1970) believed it might be between 42 and 49 days. Females have a single litter once a year which may consist of one to three young, with an average birth mass of some 20 g each.

The young are altricial and are born blind and naked, the eyes not opening until they are about 35 days old. The mothers remain with the young for the first three days, thereafter leaving for short periods, which gradually lengthen until, after about three weeks, she returns to feed them only twice a day (Zumpt, 1970). The first signs of hair appear when they are seven days old and they are completely covered by the time they are 14 days old (Herzig-Straschil, 1978). They make short excursions from the burrows at about 40 days old and start weaning at 50 days. Females have two pairs of inguinal mammae.

No. 141

## *Xerus princeps* (Thomas, 1929)

## Mountain ground squirrel
## Bergwaaierstertgrondeekhoring

Plate 10

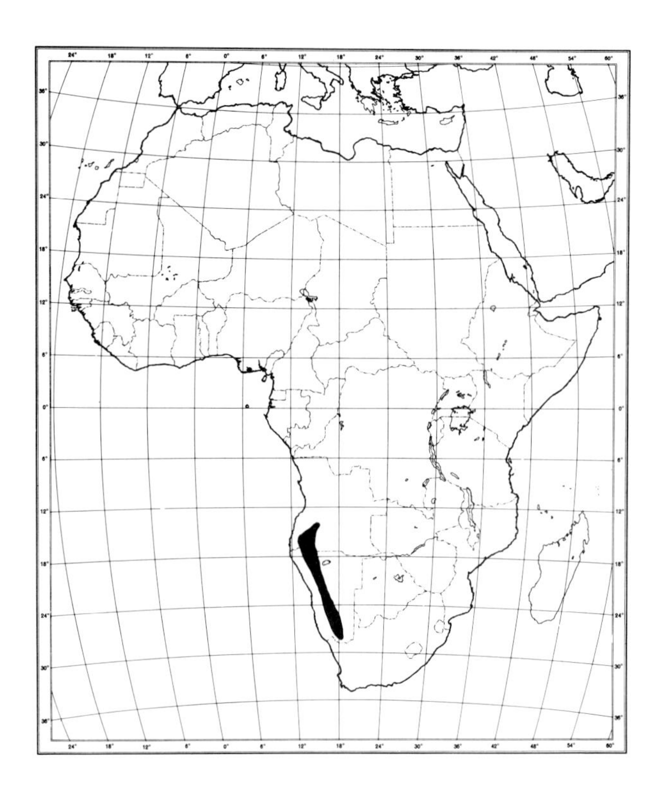

### Colloquial Name

The species is associated particularly with the mountains of the western escarpment in Namibia, although in parts they occur on the flats, but are less associated with this type of terrain than the ground squirrel, *X. inauris*.

### Taxonomic Notes

The species identity of *X. princeps*, sometimes regarded as doubtful (de Graaff, 1981), has since been proved by results of cytogenetic (Robinson *et al.*, 1987), morphological and morphometrical (Herzig-Straschil *et al.*, in press) studies. No subspecies have been described.

### Description

They differ from *X. inauris* mainly in having three black bands instead of two on the long tail hairs (at least on the basal half of the tail) and yellow to orange incisor teeth instead of white ones. Their nasalia are also narrower and not distinctly broadening anteriorly. In other respects they are very similar in general appearance to the ground squirrel, *X. inauris*, but slightly lighter in overall colour in individuals from the extreme northern parts of their distributional range, whilst the hind foot and tail are longer on average than *X. inauris*. It is difficult to distinguish between the two species in the field, although usually the longer and more bushy tail does give them a visibly different appearance from *X. inauris* (Herzig-Straschil & Herzig, 1989).

### Table 141.1

Measurements (mm) of a series of mountain ground squirrels, *X. princeps*, from Namibia (Shortridge, 1934)

| | Males | | | Females | | |
|---|---|---|---|---|---|---|
| | x̄ | n | Range | x̄ | n | Range |
| (TL | 485) | | | (478) | | |
| HB | 244 | 15 | 230–280 | 239 | 13 | 235–290 |
| T | 241 | 15 | 220–260 | 239 | 13 | 205–282 |
| Hf c/u | 70 | 15 | 65–75 | 71 | 13 | 68–73 |
| E | 13 | 15 | 12,5–14 | 14 | 13 | 13–15 |
| Mass | 528 & 665 g (two males; Herzig-Straschil, pers. comm.). | | | | | |

### Distribution

*South of the Sahara, excluding the Southern African Subregion*

They are confined to the southwestern part of **Angola** as far north as Mucungu (14°10′S 16°0′E) (Hill & Carter, 1941).

*Southern African Subregion*

They occur from the Fish River Canyon near Holoog (27°22′S) in the south of **Namibia** northwards following the western escarpment to Kaokoland (Herzig-Straschil & Herzig, 1989).

### Habitat

The range of *X. princeps* is confined to parts of the South West Arid Zone where the average annual rainfall varies from below 125 mm to just above 250 mm. They occur on mountains and among koppies and hills with sparse vegetation, but rarely on flats. Shortridge (1934) referred to this species as a rock-dwelling ground squirrel. Their warrens are found usually among rocky outcrops, sometimes on gravel plains and only exceptionally in more sandy soil. Burrow entrances are situated frequently under stones or rocks (Herzig-Straschil & Herzig, 1989).

### Habits

Like the previous species, the squirrels are diurnal, but live in rather simple warrens. One excavated burrow had one nestchamber at a depth of 0,67 m and two tunnels to the surface. Other burrows had up to five entrance holes, but generally were simple in their construction. Usually there is a small mound of excavated material in front of the holes.

In contrast to the Cape ground squirrel, mountain ground squirrels do not associate in colonies but live singly, in pairs or in a group consisting of a female and her offspring; no social contacts like allogrooming or playing are carried out between a female and her subadult offspring above ground.

In summer they leave their burrow well after sunrise and retire to it before sunset. Soon after emergence from the burrow they move away from it to feed. During the heat of the day they use their tail as a parasol, as frequently described for *X. inauris* (Smithers, 1971 and others). They keep to the shade of vegetation or rocks or even seek shelter in the burrow during the heat of the day where air temperature is up to 12°C cooler than in the sunshine (measurements in December; Herzig-Straschil & Herzig, 1989).

When alarmed during their daily activity they take shelter under boulders (Shortridge, 1934) or bushes and will run further only when forced to do so by a pursuer. Unlike Cape ground squirrels they usually do not directly enter their burrow as a means of escape, although this might be a result of their very large home range.

### Food

They are mainly vegetarian, but were also observed feeding on plant lice, *Copaifera mopane*, on mopane bushes (Herzig-Straschil & Herzig, 1989). In their search for food, mountain ground squirrels will climb bushes up to a height of about

2 m above ground and thus cannot be regarded as purely terrestrial.

### Reproduction

The gestation period in the mountain ground squirrel is about 48 days and they have one to three young per litter. No specimens younger than about eight weeks were observed during December/January, thus indicating a reproductive season during the winter months (Herzig-Straschil & Herzig, 1989).

## Genus *Heliosciurus* Trouessart, 1880

---

No. 142

## *Heliosciurus mutabilis* (Peters, 1852)

## Sun squirrel
## Soneekhoring

Plate 10

---

### Colloquial Name

The name may stem from their habit of sunning themselves on exposed branches of trees or simply from the generic name *Heliosciurus* which is derived from the Greek *helios*, the sun, and *skiouros*, shady tail.

### Taxonomic Notes

Too little material is available to allow for a proper assessment of the validity of the subspecies or their limits of occurrence within the Subregion. Meester *et al.* (1986) listed five subspecies from the Subregion: *H. m. shirensis* (Gray, 1867) from eastern Zimbabwe and adjacent parts of Mozambique; *H. m. beirae* Roberts, 1913 from eastern and central Mozambique; *H. m. chirindensis* Roberts, 1913 from eastern Zimbabwe, in the Melsetter and Inyanga Districts; *H. m. vumbae* Roberts, 1937 from the Mutare District, eastern Zimbabwe and adjacent parts of Mozambique, and *H. m. smithersi* Lundholm, 1955 from southeastern Zimbabwe. This species differs from *H. gambianus* of West Africa in being slightly larger and lacking the white ring around the eyes. The nominate *H. m. mutabilis* occurs in the Zambezia District of Mozambique, north of the Zambezi River. Too many subspecies have been described and a review is necessary.

### Description

Sun squirrels are the largest of the arboreal squirrels found in the Subregion. Adults measure about 500 mm overall, with a tail just over half this length and have an average mass of some 400 g (Table 142.1).

**Table 142.1**

Measurements (mm) and mass (g) of adult sun squirrels, *H. mutabilis*, from eastern Zimbabwe (Smithers & Wilson, 1979)

| | Males | | | Females | | |
|---|---|---|---|---|---|---|
| | $\bar{x}$ | n | Range | $\bar{x}$ | n | Range |
| TL | 495 | 15 | 410–528 | 502 | 15 | 462–557 |
| (HB | 225) | | | (232) | | |
| T | 270 | 15 | 230–294 | 270 | 15 | 210–304 |
| Hf c/u | 59 | 15 | 54–65 | 57 | 15 | 51–63 |
| E | 17 | 15 | 14–20 | 18 | 15 | 16–20 |
| Mass | 383,1 | 15 | 330,0–470,2 | 360,0 | 15 | 276,0–482,4 |

| | Irrespective of sex | | |
|---|---|---|---|
| | $\bar{x}$ | n | Range |
| TL skull | 55 | 10 | 53–58 |

The colour of the upper parts of the body is grizzled light brown, the grizzling caused by the broad, buffy annulations of the hairs of the guard coat which show clearly. The forehead is usually greyer than the remainder of the body. The upper parts of the limbs are similar in colour to the body. One cannot generalise, for the colour varies within the isolated populations which occur and, in some cases, extreme divergence is found even within these. In *H. m. smithersi* from the low country of the Sabi/Lundi confluence, for example, the upper parts are whitish as the hair annulations are pure white, whereas in *H. m. chirindensis* they are brown, imparting an overall brownish colour. In *H. m. vumbae* they are darker brown and in *H. m. mutabilis* yellow. Within populations of these subspecies, however, individuals vary in this character, the most extreme variation being found in *H. m. vumbae* from the Stapleford Forest Reserve, Zimbabwe, where there are individuals which have black upper parts without the grizzling, which only appears on the flanks.

This confused picture becomes even more so with the occurrence of the moult. Specimens in moult occur widely throughout the year and individuals can be seen in which the foreparts of the body are covered with new hair, the remainder "foxed" to a plain reddish colour so that the original colour and annulations are lost in the process. The contrast is most noticeable in the dark individuals and, as the moult proceeds from the head backwards, there is a distinct line of division between the new hair and the "foxed" hair.

The colour of the under parts runs more evenly to a geographical pattern. In *H. m. smithersi* this is pure white, in *H. m. chirindensis* yellowish-white, or in some specimens the chest is white, the remainder yellowish-white; in *H. m. vumbae* the under parts are brown or brownish-grey and in *H. m. mutabilis* they are yellowish. It is possible to place material into the four groups on the basis of this character.

The tails show a series of narrower light and broader dark bands, the colour of these bands following the general colour of the body. The tails of sun squirrels are banded much more distinctly than any of the other squirrels occurring in the Subregion. The guard hairs on the shoulders are about 20 mm in length, those on the rump 25 mm, those on the tail 40 mm, and are longest on the top of the tail, measuring 60 mm. They have four digits on the front feet and five on the hind feet, each equipped with a strong, curved claw, adapted to their arboreal life.

The dental formula is:

$$I\frac{1}{1}\ C\frac{0}{0}\ P\frac{1}{1}\ M\frac{3}{3} = 20$$

The upper incisors are faintly grooved longitudinally, broad and powerful and bright orange in colour.

### Distribution

*South of the Sahara, excluding the Southern African Subregion*

They occur in **Mozambique**, north of the Zambezi River; in **Malawi**; southern and eastern **Zambia** and in southern **Tanzania**.

*Southern African Subregion*

They occur in eastern **Zimbabwe** and in **Mozambique**, south of the Zambezi River, as far south as the relic forest patches in the southeastern Inhambane District, which mark their furthest south occurrence on the continent.

### Habitat

In the Subregion, sun squirrels are associated primarily with lowland or montane evergreen forest, but they also occur in riverine forest and thickets within the *Brachystegia/Julbernardia* woodland association. In riverine associations they occur in areas, such as on the northern bank of Lake Kariba in Zambia, with a mean annual rainfall of about 600 mm, the forests in the east lying predominantly in the higher rainfall areas of 1 000 mm and upwards. In the Subregion they occur from sea level to altitudes of about 900 m in the Mount Selinda Forest, and to over 1 500 m in the Inyanga district in Zimbabwe. In Mozambique the removal of forest to make way for agricultural development has reduced the habitat available to them, although in parts, such as in the

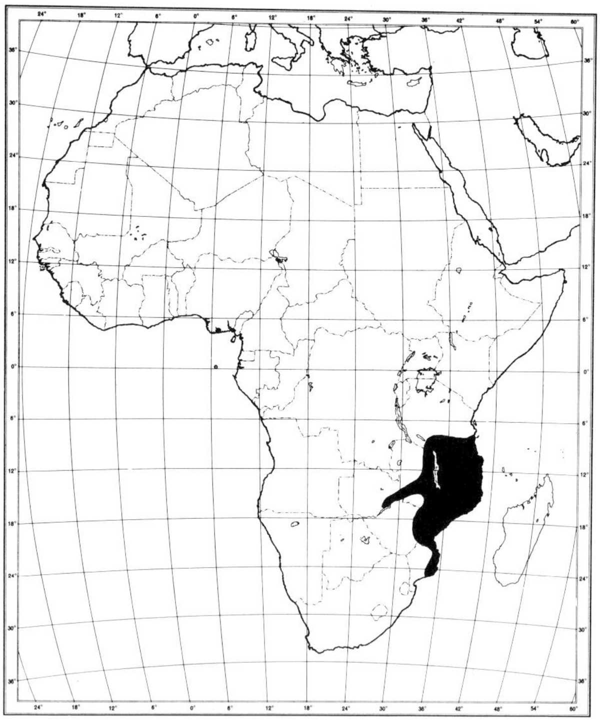

Inhambane, Vila Pery and Beira districts they are still to be found even in the relic forest patches.

**Habits**

Sun squirrels occur singly or in pairs. They are most active in the late morning and in the afternoon up to about 17h00 after which, during the colder times of the year, they retire to their resting places, although they remain active later during warmer weather. They use holes in trees or secluded, sheltered places in dense clumps of creepers high in forest trees in which to rest, and have their young. The holes are lined with fresh leaves and other detritus. When resting among the creepers they use a bed of naturally occurring fallen leaves and other debris caught in the twigs, where this has a sheltering roof of the same material.

When disturbed they have a tendency to make for the highest parts of the forest canopy, hiding themselves in the foliage or lying flat on branches where they are difficult to see. They are sun lovers and will bask on high branches, lying prone on their bellies with their feet stretched out and tail flat along the branch.

In forest areas, where they are found together with the red squirrel, *Paraxerus palliatus*, they tend to use the higher parts of the canopy, and the red squirrel the lower strata. Under these circumstances they are rarely found foraging on the ground. However, in thickets and riverine vegetation, where there are no red squirrels, they forage regularly in the lower underbush and on the ground. When disturbed, they cluck loudly, flicking their tails as they do so.

**Food**

Sun squirrels are predominantly vegetarian, but the diet includes a small proportion of insects, some of which are grasshoppers and termites. Flowers, leaves, buds, wild fruits, berries and nuts form the bulk of their diet and these are eaten *in situ*, with no signs of hoarding. The food is ground up very finely, making identification in stomach contents difficult.

**Reproduction**

In the Subregion there is a singular lack of information on the times of the year when the young are born. From eastern Zimbabwe, Smithers & Wilson (1979) recorded a single gravid female taken in August with four foetuses. Local reports from this area state that they have their young in holes high up in the forest trees.



## Genus *Funisciurus* Trouessart, 1880

No. 143

### *Funisciurus congicus* (Kuhl, 1820)

### Striped tree squirrel
### Gestreepte boomeekhoring

Plate 10

**Colloquial Name**

The species is predominantly arboreal and the only striped arboreal squirrel occurring in the Subregion.

**Taxonomic Notes**

Nine species of *Funisciurus* occur on the continent: seven in West Africa, one in East Africa, and one, *F. congicus* in the Subregion, where it occurs only marginally. No subspecies of *F. congicus* are recognised by Meester *et al.* (1986).

**Description**

Striped tree squirrels are the smallest species of squirrel occurring in the Subregion. Adults are about 300 mm in total length, with a mass of about 110 g (Table 143.1). The tail is slightly longer than the length of the head and body. The hair on the tail is shorter than in the tree squirrel, *P. cepapi*, and banded with annulations of yellow, black and buffy-yellow.

**Table 143.1**

Approximate average measurements (mm) and mass (g) of striped tree squirrels, *F. congicus*, compiled from Viljoen (1978), Roberts (1951) and Shortridge (1934)

| | Irrespective of sex | | |
|---|---|---|---|
| | $\bar{x}$ | n | Range |
| (TL | 315) | | |
| HB | 150 | 63 | 147–156 |
| T | 165 | 63 | 160–170 |
| Hf c/u | 40 | 63 | 38–40 |
| E | 16 | 63 | 15–17 |
| Mass | 111 | 63 | 108,2–113,0 |

The colour of the upper parts of the body between the white stripes is dark buffy-yellow, darker on the mid-back, lighter on the head where it is tinged rusty. The whole of the lower part of the back and thighs is distinctly suffused with a rusty colour. The shoulders and upper surfaces of the front limbs are lighter in colour than the upper parts of the body and are tinged rusty-yellow. The lateral white stripes are distinct at mid-body level, tailing out on the shoulders and towards the rump and barely discernible near the base of the tail. Just below these white stripes there is a dark band extending from the shoulders to the thighs. The under parts are whitish, tinged yellow towards the anus. The lower parts of the flanks are tinged grey, the sides of the face below the eyes whitish, with a distinct crescent of white hair above the eyes. The hair of the guard coat on the shoulders is about 7 mm long, up to about 8 to 10 mm on the rump, the hair on the tail up to about 20 mm long. The four digits on the front feet and five on the hind are armed with short, sharp, curved claws, which are an adaptation to their arboreal life. In proportion to their size the eyes and ears are larger than in the tree squirrel, *P. cepapi*. The lateral longitudinal white stripes on the body are a characteristic feature of this small squirrel.

**Distribution**

Throughout their range their distribution is patchy and discontinuous.

*South of the Sahara, excluding the Southern African Subregion*

They occur widely in the central and eastern parts of **Zaire**, east of the Congo River, their distribution extending only marginally west of the river. In **Angola** they are widespread in the north and northeast of the country, extending southwards to the Namibian border in the southwest.

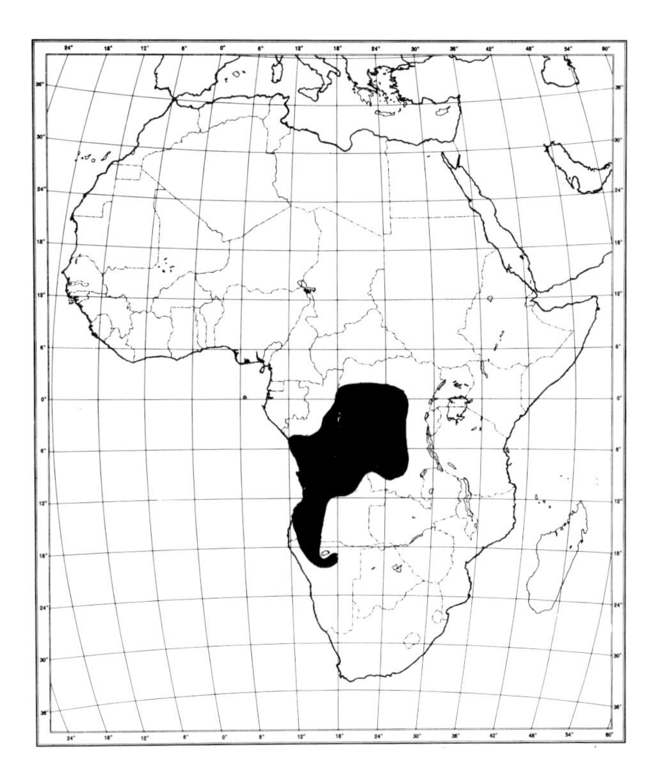

*Southern African Subregion*

They occur in the northwestern parts of **Namibia** southwards to about 20 °S and east to the Grootfontein District.

## Habitat

Striped tree squirrels, like their near relatives tree squirrels, *P. cepapi*, are associated with woodland. However, they are confined more closely to the denser types, where the trees attain a larger size with more luxuriant canopies, as they do along water courses and on rocky outcrops (Shortridge, 1934). In parts of their range they occur in palm scrub and palm groves (Walker *et al.*, 1964) and in forest up to altitudes over 2000 m. Tinley (1971) associated them with the vegetation on granite outcrops, not with the thinner woodland of the more open areas in which the tree squirrel, *P. cepapi*, occurs. He was of the opinion that there is some movement towards the riverine woodland fringes of water courses during the dry season.

## Habits

Striped tree squirrels are diurnal and arboreal, but spend almost as much time foraging on the ground as they do in the trees. Viljoen (1978) estimated that this takes up to 39% of their active period, the balance being spent in the subcanopy of the trees; 42% of their time is spent in the trees up to 2,5 m high and 18% in trees over 2,5 m. They live in small family parties of up to four, and while no grouping has been observed, as is found in the tree squirrel, *P. cepapi*, their social organisation has not yet been studied in great detail.

They are most active in the early mornings, returning to their resting places well before sunset, usually in the late afternoon. They rest in holes in trees lined with leaves and grass or in dreys which they construct in the forks of branches made of twigs, leaves and grass, which they roof over with the same materials. The construction of dreys is a unique feature of striped tree squirrels not found in any of the other species of squirrels occurring in the Subregion. Viljoen (1975, 1985) suggested that they use dreys during the warm summer months and holes in trees during the winter. It has been shown in other species of squirrels that they are sensitive to cold and the intense activity of striped tree squirrels early on chilly mornings may be a means of generating body warmth by movement. They are great sun baskers and will sit motionless on sheltered branches in sunny situations. They retreat to the shelter of their resting places well before sunset and this again suggests that they are sensitive to cold.

Unlike tree squirrels, *P. cepapi*, which carry their tails trailing loosely behind them, striped tree squirrels carry them in the form of a questionmark over their backs. The light colour on the under parts of the tail in this position presents a light-coloured reflecting surface to the sun and this assists in thermoregulation, the tail itself shading the back and head (Viljoen, 1978, 1985). The tail is used in the same way by the ground squirrel, *Xerus inauris*, and by Abert's squirrel, *Sciurus aberti* (Golightly, 1976).

Compared with other squirrels, striped tree squirrels are less prone to take fright when approached. Viljoen (1978) recorded instances where individuals moved off only when approached within two to three metres. When disturbed they flee to the nearest trees where, sitting motionless, they blend into the background and are difficult to see. Contact within the family party is maintained by vocalisation in a series of bird-like high-pitched chirps which sometimes develop into a duet (Viljoen, 1983c). Other vocalisations include a sporadic chattering indulged in by males, which may be continued for longer than 10 minutes. The alarm vocalisation may take the form of a bird-like chirping with much tail flicking or a high-pitched chattering which sounds like a whistle. This latter call will cause individuals in the vicinity to "freeze" instantly. The juveniles in the nests may answer a female's chirping by barking. Females in oestrus communicate this state of affairs vocally (Viljoen, 1980b). Recognition between individuals appears to be by scent and the family party probably maintains its own individual scent by the close contact established between members in the resting place and by the fact that allogrooming is a common feature in the species. Viljoen (1978) recorded that striped tree squirrels, unlike other squirrels, have a rat-like smell. Self-grooming is widely indulged in.

Striped tree squirrels, like tree squirrels, *P. cepapi*, will mob potential predators. Viljoen (1978) observed them mobbing a snake, peering down from safe vantage points on nearby trees and vocalising loudly, with much tail flicking. They also whistle loudly at the approach of birds of prey. Because of their small size and agility they can move around among the smallest of twigs in trees. They are agile jumpers and will move freely between trees, jumping considerable distances between branches.

## Food

Striped tree squirrels are predominantly vegetarians; however, they have been observed to eat insects and mopane caterpillars (Viljoen, 1978), but how important the latter are in the diet has not been assessed. Viljoen (1978, 1983b) recorded them eating the seeds or fruits of the mopane, *Colophospermum mopane*; the velvet commiphora, *Commiphora mollis*; the bastard raisin bush, *Grewia bicolor*; the rough-leaved raisin bush, *Grewia flavescens*; the bird plum, *Berchemia discolor*, and wild cucumbers, *Cucumis anguria*. They also eat the shoots and stems of *Commelina* sp, the leaves and shoots of *Justicia anselliana* and the galls on trees. They have been observed to bury dry mopane seeds (Viljoen, 1978) and therefore, like the tree squirrel, *P. cepapi*, most probably scatter-hoard hard food as a routine.

## Reproduction

From the meagre data available Viljoen (1978) suggested that the striped tree squirrel might have two peaks of breeding during the year, births taking place about October and again in March, the first just before the onset of the rains and the second towards the end of the wet season, but additional information is required. The average number per litter is two (n=8), and the young are born either in tree holes or in dreys (Viljoen, 1980). Females have two pairs of inguinal mammae.

## Genus *Paraxerus* Forsyth Major, 1893

Key to the species after Meester *et al.* (1986)

1. Ventral surface red or orange, the head rufous, the tail deep red to orange or a combination of these; skull length in adults 45 to 52 mm

   ... *palliatus*

   Ventral surface whitish, head dull grey, not rufous, tail neither deep red or deep orange, nor a combination of these; skull length in adults 39 to 45 mm

   ... *cepapi*

No. 144

# *Paraxerus palliatus* (Peters, 1852)

## Red squirrel
## Rooi eekhoring

Plate 10

### Colloquial Name

They are so named as most of the forms are reddish or auburn on the under parts and tail.

### Taxonomic Notes

Meester *et al.* (1986) listed six subspecies from the Subregion: *P. p. ornatus* (Gray, 1864) from the Ngoye Forest, KwaZulu; *S. p. sponsus* (Thomas & Wroughton, 1907) from the Inhambane District of Mozambique; *P. p. swynnertoni* (Wroughton, 1908) from the Melsetter District, Zimbabwe; *P. p. bridgemani* Dollman, 1914 from Panda, Inhambane District, Mozambique; *P. p. auriventris* Roberts, 1926 from the lower Limpopo River, Mozambique, and *P. p. tongensis* Roberts, 1931 from the Manguzi Forest, KwaZulu. Amtmann (1975) noted that probably too many subspecies are recognised.

These subspecies have been erected predominantly on colour, size and the number of dark bands on the tail hairs. Viljoen (1980) noted that *P. p. palliatus* and *P. p. sponsus* are dark forms and that *P. p. bridgemani, P. p. auriventris* and *P. p. tongensis* might be grouped together.

### Description

Red squirrels are predominantly arboreal and small in size, about 400 mm overall, having tails about half this length and a mass of some 300 g. In the Subregion there is a wide degree of variation in the colour of the body, the tail and the upper parts of the limbs, depending on the localities in which they are found and whether they occur in drier or moister habitats. Those from the drier habitats tend to be lighter in colour than those from moister habitats: the population in the Mount Selinda Forest, Melsetter, Zimbabwe which lies within the isohyet of 1000 mm of mean annual rainfall, is darker in colour than any others. The population in the Sabi/Lundi confluence area, which has a mean annual rainfall of a bare 400 mm and lies 100 km south of Mount Selinda, is distinctly lighter in colour. Those from the moister habitats also tend to be larger; those from the Ngoye Forest, Kwazulu (*P. p. ornatus*), which has a mean annual rainfall of about 1900 mm, are the largest of all.

**Table 144.1**

Measurements (mm) and mass (g) of adult individuals of subspecies of red squirrels, *P. palliatus* (Viljoen, 1980, 1989) (to nearest mm)

| | A. *sponsus** | | B. *ornatus* | | C. *swynnertoni** | | D. *auriventris** | | E. *tongensis* | |
|---|---|---|---|---|---|---|---|---|---|---|
| | Males | | | | | | Males | | | |
| | x̄ | n | x̄ | n | x̄ | n | x̄ | n | x̄ | n |
| HB | 202 | 23 | 219 | 18 | 201 | 9 | 193 | 4 | 184 | 5 |
| T | 204 | 23 | 204 | 53 | 205 | 9 | 173 | 4 | 176 | 13 |
| Hf c/u | 50 | 23 | 52 | 61 | 52 | 9 | 43 | 4 | 44 | 18 |
| E | 21 | 23 | 20 | 43 | 20 | 9 | — | — | 20 | 16 |
| Mass | 275,1 | 14 | 360,9 | 62 | 291,5 | 9 | — | — | 207,5 | 29 |
| | | | Females | | | | | | Females | |
| HB | | | 225 | 12 | | | | | 191 | 6 |
| T | | | 205 | 24 | | | | | 176 | 15 |
| E | | | 21 | 32 | | | | | 19 | 16 |
| Mass | | | 378,9 | 42 | | | | | 210,6 | 31 |

*Irrespective of sex

In the more dispersed populations, such as occur along the Save River in Mozambique and which extend from within Zimbabwe nearly to the coast, there is considerable individual variation in colour as opposed to those isolated populations which are found in forests such as Ngoye and Mount Selinda. In spite of the differences in colour and size found in the various subspecies of the red squirrel, *Paraxerus palliatus*, they are unmistakable in the field among the five species of squirrels which occur in the Subregion. The redder or yellower colour of the tail, the limbs, flanks and under parts of the body are distinguishing characters.

At close quarters the upper parts of the body are seen to be grizzled owing to the lighter coloured bands on the hairs of the guard coat. These may be buffy, reddish or yellowish and contrast with the darker background colour. Their foreheads, faces and limbs, in contrast to the colour of the upper parts, are yellower or redder. Their tails vary from a dark auburn, as they are in specimens from the Mount Selinda Forest, to a reddish-yellow in those from the Save River. In common with other arboreal squirrels they have four digits on the front feet and five on the hind, each equipped with a sharp curved claw as an adaptation to their arboreal way of life. The ears are rounded and inconspicuous.

The hairs of the guard coat are dark at the base, about 10 mm long on the shoulders, 20 mm on the rump and have alternate bands of black and buffy, reddish-yellow or yellow and end in black tips. Interspersed liberally among the hairs of the guard coat are much longer black hairs which may have a tactile function. The hairs of the under coat are soft and wavy and buffy in colour. The hair on the tail is longest of all, the individual hairs on the middle of the tail about 40 mm long, 50 mm on the tip. They are light-coloured at the base, with two or more black bands and broad tips of reddish-yellow or auburn which impart to the tail its characteristic pattern of banding and colour.

### Distribution

They are confined in their distribution to the eastern and, in parts, the coastal areas from southern Somalia southwards to

**Plate 10**

140. Ground squirrel, *Xerus inauris*
     Waaierstertgrondeekhoring
141. Mountain ground squirrel, *Xerus princeps*
     Bergwaaierstertgrondeekhoring
142. Sun squirrel, *Heliosciurus mutabilis*
     Soneekhoring
143. Striped tree squirrel, *Funisciurus congicus*
     Gestreepte boomeekhoring
144. Red squirrel, *Paraxerus palliatus*
     Rooi eekhoring
     a. dark form
     b. light form
145. Tree squirrel, *Paraxerus cepapi*
     Boomeekhoring
146. Grey squirrel, *Sciurus carolinensis*
     Gryseekhoring

PLATE 10
145
146
144a
144b
143
142
140
141
Dick Findlay

northeastern Natal (Viljoen, 1989). Within this range their occurrence is patchy and discontinuous on account of their habitat requirements. In parts of Mozambique the clearing of forest to make way for agricultural developments renders the areas unsuitable for them, although where logging is followed by coppice regeneration this provides suitable habitat.

*South of the Sahara, excluding the Southern African Subregion*

They occur coastally in the riverine associations of the Uebi Scebeli and inland up the Juba River in **Somalia**, southwards coastally to **Kenya** and eastern **Tanzania**. While at the moment there are only coastal records from **Mozambique**, north of the Zambezi River, they may well occur inland in this sector as they do in southern Tanzania. They occur in the Central and Southern Provinces of **Malawi**, and *P. vincenti* Hayman, 1950, known only from Namuli Mountain, Mozambique, north of the Zambezi River, is considered by Amtmann (1975) to be a valid species.

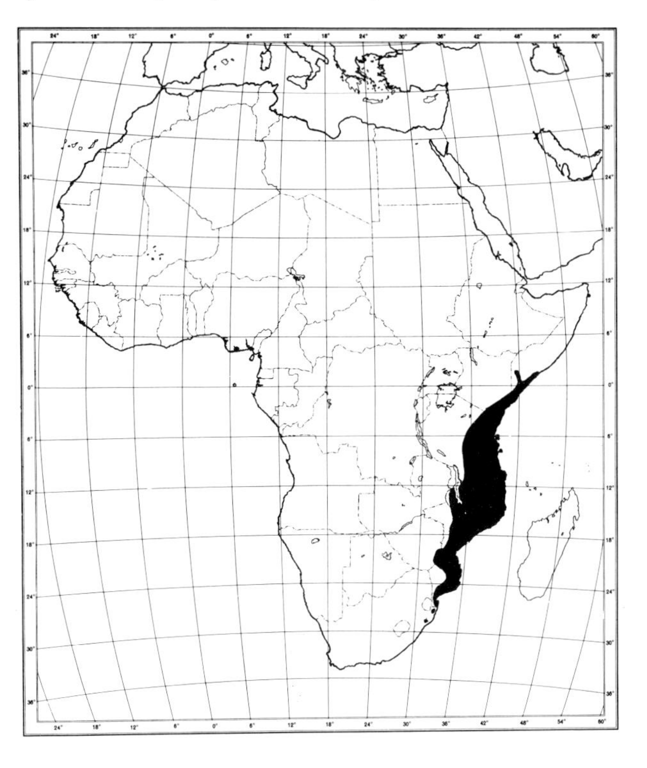

*Southern African Subregion*

They are widespread in suitable habitat in central and southern **Mozambique**. There is an isolated population in the Mount Selinda Forest in eastern **Zimbabwe** and they occur marginally in the southeast. In northeastern **Natal** they occur as far south along the coast as Lake St Lucia, with an isolated population in the Ngoye Forest, the latter marking the southern limits of their distribution on the continent.

## Habitat

Red squirrels occur in the eastern parts of the Subregion in either dry or moist evergreen forests, in woodlands, or in riverine or other thickets, where these have a shady understorey of leafy vegetation. In the Mount Selinda Forest they are associated particularly with the areas within it or around its fringes where there is sufficient light to support a dense understorey of shrubs, young trees and climbing plants.

Their habitat contrasts markedly with that of the bush squirrel, *Paraxerus cepapi*, which prefers a more open savanna habitat. In parts of their distributional range the two species overlap, but where they do they are clearly separated by their habitat requirements. In the extreme southeast of Zimbabwe the red squirrel occurs in the riverine and subriverine associations of the Sabi, Lundi, Chefu and Nuanetsi Rivers, in mountain acacia, *Brachystegia glaucescens*, and Lebombo ironwood, *Androstachys johnstonii*, woodland associations, but they do so only where these have an understorey of dense shrubs. The bush squirrel, *P. cepapi*, on the other hand, lives in the mopane, *Colophospermum mopane*, woodland and in the more open associations that adjoin the mopane (Sherry, 1977).

In the Mount Selinda Forest they have a marked tendency to use the forest floor and the lower parts of the forest stratum. This may be due to competition from the sun squirrel, *Heliosciurus mutabilis*, which is common in the forest, for where the sun squirrel is absent, they range widely to the highest parts of the canopy. In captivity, red squirrels drink water regularly and do so under natural conditions when it is available. Under forest conditions they may obtain their moisture requirements from the fleshy fruits which they eat, from dripping water on leaves or branches, or from water trapped in holes in trees.

## Habits

Red squirrels are diurnal, in the summer time leaving the shelter of their nests early in the morning, usually about 06h00 and retiring for the night in the late afternoon or early evening up to 18h00. In the winter months they emerge later, usually at about 08h00 and retire earlier at about 16h00. They are generally solitary, but a female may be accompanied by her young during the early stages of their excursions from the nest. Temporary associations of a male or males and a female occur while she is in oestrus. Despite this, their social organisation is based on a group system comprising a male, a female, and at least during the earlier part of their lives, her young. On becoming subadult the young are driven from the group by the parents. The female is the focal point of the group whose males may change from time to time. For a time after the young are born the female drives the male from the vicinity of the nest and, while she has very young offspring, will vigorously defend an area in the vicinity of the nest from trespassers (Viljoen, 1980a). Of the two subspecies, *P. p. tongensis* and *P. p. ornatus*, the former is the more aggressive (Viljoen, pers. comm.).

The home ranges of the females are smaller than those of the males, but both may overlap with those of other groups, especially when a good food source becomes available. Viljoen (1980) studied the home range of males and females both in the Ngoye and Mkwakwa forests in KwaZulu and found that in the Ngoye Forest the males had a home range of about 3,2 ha, the females 2,2 ha; in the Mkwakwa Forest the males roamed over 4,2 ha, the females over 1,2 ha. The males obviously roam far wider than the females, for the maximum distance that they moved in the Ngoye Forest was 1 065 m, in the Mkwakwa Forest 1 142 m, compared to movements of the females in the two areas of 699 m and 685 m respectively.

Within these home ranges Viljoen (1980a, 1983a) found that there are "foci of activity" in the form of fruit-bearing trees to which they are attracted, while this food is available. In forests, food resources are dispersed and the individuals, especially the males, range widely in order to locate these or test for their availability.

There is a greater intensity of tail-fluffing and flicking in red squirrels than in the more open habitat species such as the bush squirrel, *P. cepapi*. In forest habitat the tail movement is a means of advertising the presence of the individual, an action which might prove dangerous to the bush squirrel in its more exposed habitat, making them more prone to predation. Indeed, Viljoen (1980) found that in the denser habitat in the Mkwakwa Forest tail-flicking is more frequent than in the Ngoye Forest where the habitat is more open. Footstamping is noted occasionally.

Vocalisation takes a number of forms. Murmuring is stimulated by the desire for contact with another individual. A female with young will call them to her by murmuring and the male uses it in chasing a female at the time of mating, when it may serve as a trigger, bringing her into oestrus. A dominant male murmurs on seeing another individual, presumably to seek contact and assess its status. At a low level of stress they may hiss, at higher levels growl. During intraspecific chases following encounters at feeding sites, or during mating, the individual chased may grunt or growl in an attempt to inhibit contact. Clicking is a sign of alertness and rises in intensity with the degree of alertness, in

*P. cepapi* to a rattle and in *P. palliatus* to a trill or warble. Trilling is used in a spacing context and also in "mobbing" intruders. Young in the nest "tick" when they seek contact with the female, and when sudden close danger threatens, they give a deep bark.

Olfactory signalling takes the form of urine-dribbling or anal-dragging; in the latter the anal glands are brought into contact with the surface to be marked and dragged across it.

The normal reaction of the red squirrel on being disturbed is to make for the nearest thick cover in which it will hide itself or to make for their nest, if this is nearby. In the Mount Selinda Forest they often make for the shelter of hollow logs lying on the forest floor or take cover under fallen trees. Even if they are disturbed in the lower forest substrate their reaction is downwards to the forest floor rather than upwards.

**Food**

The main diet of red squirrels is nuts, berries and wild fruits, together with a small percentage of roots, leaf and flower buds, bark and lichens. Insect remains, including termites, can be recognised in most stomach contents. They have been reported to eat birds' eggs and fledglings, but this is unconfirmed.

They are wasteful feeders and half-consumed food is discarded frequently. They will either feed *in situ* or carry the food to vantage points on branches, a fallen log or a rock, where small accumulations of discarded debris mark these as chosen feeding sites. Surplus food is scatter-hoarded in small excavations at the base of a tree, under a fallen log, in a hole in a tree or even wedged between two branches. Only the larger and harder seeds are hoarded and, in the case of those with a fleshy outside layer, this is removed before it is hoarded. Red squirrels never amass the enormous collections of stored food as do some temperate squirrels. Regular chases can be witnessed as individuals try to steal from others and hoarding is carried out rarely if other individuals are within sight. If ripe fruits are not available they will take them while still green.

While they may, at certain times, feed almost exclusively on a single food resource, they tend to move widely within their home range, even when food is plentiful nearer to their nesting sites. By this means they familiarise themselves with other food which is or will become available later.

Viljoen (1980a) reported that in captivity they display hunting behaviour, following ants and moths and, in the field, they scratch in bark in search of insects. Viljoen (1980a, 1983b) listed 24 species of plants, the fruits of which are eaten by the Ngoye red squirrel, *P. p. ornatus*, and 25 species by the red squirrel, *P. p. tongensis*, in the Mkwakwa Forest. In nine species eaten by *P. p. ornatus*, both the fleshy layer and the kernel are eaten, in the remainder only the kernel. In 21 species eaten by *P. p. tongensis* both the fleshy layer and the kernel are eaten, in four the kernel alone. They gnaw the food by pressing it against their upper incisor teeth and chopping with the lower, usually opening the germination pore to gain access to the kernel. Viljoen (1980a, 1983b) recorded that it would take over 15 minutes to cut into the kernel of hard seeds such as those of *Landolphia kirkii*, and some seeds such as those of the vegetable ivory palm, *Hyphaene ventricosa*, remain too hard to open. With heavy fruits such as wild oranges, *Strychnos* spp, a small hole is cut in the hard outer skin so that it can be gripped and it is then carried to a feeding site, where the fleshy fruit and part of the seeds are eaten. Where available the fruits of the African mangosteen, *Garcinia* spp, are sought after and the nuts hoarded. Particularly aromatic fruits such as those of the Natal cherry orange, *Teclea natalensis*, and sticky fruits are avoided, and if they try to feed on these, the fruit is soon discarded and signs of distaste in the form of much mouth-wiping follows. Viljoen (1980a) recorded that they will recover and eat nuts from baboon droppings. Red squirrels play an important role in the regeneration of forest by seed dispersal and more especially by their habit of food hoarding by burying seed.

**Reproduction**

The young are born, after a gestation period of 60 to 65 days (Viljoen, 1980a,b), during the warm, wet months of the year between August and March. The females have their litters in holes in trees lined with leaves which they keep scrupulously clean, and the number of young in a litter is one or two. Corresponding with the slightly larger size of the adults, the birth mass of the young of *P. p. ornatus* from the Ngoye Forest was about 14,0 g as against those of *P. p. tongensis* at 13,0 g from the Mkwakwa Forest (Viljoen, 1980a,b).

While in captivity red squirrels may produce several litters in a season, in the wild, as far as is known, they only have a single litter per year. At birth the head, back, tail and limbs of the young are covered with fine hair, but they only have a sparse covering on the under parts. They are born blind, the eyes opening between the seventh and tenth day after birth. The first moult starts at about 40 to 60 days after birth and is completed at about 110 to 140 days, when they closely resemble the adults. They first move from the shelter of the nest at about 18 days old, at first remaining near its vicinity, and gradually, under the guidance of the female, increasing this distance. They are weaned by about 40 days of age (Viljoen, 1980), and during the early stages of their lives, while still in the nest or within its precincts, the females keep in close contact with them. She will actively drive the male away from the nest and is aggressive to trespassers in the vicinity. With the onset of the winter months the young are expelled from the family group to forage on their own.

---

No. 145

## *Paraxerus cepapi* (A. Smith, 1836)

## Tree squirrel
## Boomeekhoring

Plate 10

---

**Colloquial Name**

They are so named for their association with woodland and their use of holes in trees as resting places.

Alternative names: bush squirrel, yellow-footed squirrel.

**Taxonomic Notes**

Meester *et al.* (1986) listed nine subspecies from the Subregion: the nominate *P. c. cepapi* from the Transvaal, southern Mozambique, Zimbabwe, excluding the western sector, and southeastern Botswana; *P. c. sindi* (Thomas & Wroughton, 1908) from the eastern parts of the Tete District, Mozambique; *P. c. phalaena* Thomas, 1926 from northern Namibia; *P. c. chobiensis* Roberts, 1932 from northeastern Botswana; *P. c. maunensis* Roberts, 1932 from eastern Ngamiland, Botswana, eastwards to the western parts of Zimbabwe; *P. c. kalaharicus* Roberts, 1932 from western Ngamiland south to Lake Ngami, Botswana; *P. c. tsumebensis* Roberts, 1938 from the western parts of the Tete District of Mozambique; *P. c. cepapoides* Roberts, 1946 from the Beira and Vila Pery districts of Mozambique, and *P. c. carpi* Lundholm, 1955 from the western parts of the Tete District, Mozambique. In the main these subspecies are differentiated on colour and size and their limits are not known. Probably too many subspecies are recognised.

**Description**

Tree squirrels vary greatly in colour and size throughout their distributional range in the Subregion. Colour in particular is very variable. In general, specimens from the western parts of their range, as for example from northern Namibia, have an overall pale grey colour as opposed to those from more eastern localities which are darker, more buffy or in some cases more rusty in colour. The same remarks apply to the colour of the under parts, which vary from white to yellowish or buffy or white on the chest and yellowish or buffy on the remainder of the under parts. The colour of the head may be the same as the remainder of the upper parts or may contrast with these in various shades of rusty-yellow. In the lighter, greyer specimens the upper parts of the limbs are similar in colour to the body, but in the Transvaal they are distinctly rusty coloured and contrast with the general colour of the body. The hairs of the tail may have two or three black annulations, the lighter annulations varying in colour to a considerable degree. Without a full description of the wide variations met within the 10 subspecies presently recognised, one has to rely on generalisations.

Tree squirrels, as the name implies, are a woodland species with an overall length of some 350 mm and a tail about half this length. Adult males are slightly heavier than females, with an average mass in series of about 200 g in the western Transvaal. As an example of the variation in mass, a series from northwestern Botswana averaged only 170 g (Table 145.1).

**Table 145.1**

Measurements (mm) and mass (g) of tree squirrels, *P. cepapi*, from (a) the Transvaal (Rautenbach, 1978), (b) the Okavango Swamps, Botswana and (c) northwestern Botswana (Smithers, 1971)

(a) *P. c. cepapi*

| | Males | | | Females | | |
|---|---|---|---|---|---|---|
| | $\bar{x}$ | n | Range | $\bar{x}$ | n | Range |
| TL | 360 | 67 | 277–578 | 351 | 61 | 290–425 |
| (HB | 191) | | | (182) | | |
| T | 169 | 65 | 115–210 | 169 | 61 | 116–215 |
| Hf c/u | 43 | 67 | 26–49 | 43 | 61 | 38–49 |
| E | 19 | 66 | 15–40 | 20 | 61 | 13–22 |
| Mass | 190 | 28 | 76–242 | 195 | 24 | 130–265 |

(b) *P. c. maunensis*

| | Males | | | Females | | |
|---|---|---|---|---|---|---|
| | $\bar{x}$ | n | Range | $\bar{x}$ | n | Range |
| TL | 345 | 13 | 328–360 | 343 | 13 | 320–365 |
| (HB | 176) | | | (181) | | |
| T | 169 | 13 | 150–180 | 162 | 13 | 149–174 |
| Hf c/u | 45 | 13 | 43–48 | 44 | 13 | 42–47 |
| E | 19 | 12 | 17–20 | 19 | 14 | 14–24 |

*P. c. kalaharicus*

| | Males | | | Females | | |
|---|---|---|---|---|---|---|
| | $\bar{x}$ | n | Range | $\bar{x}$ | n | Range |
| TL | 329 | 10 | 305–355 | 329 | 12 | 315–355 |
| (HB | 167) | | | (166) | | |
| T | 162 | 10 | 130–180 | 163 | 12 | 135–181 |
| Hf c/u | 44 | 11 | 36–47 | 44 | 12 | 40–47 |
| E | 20 | 11 | 19–21 | 19 | 10 | 16–22 |
| Mass | 170 | 7 | 117–200 | 147 | 10 | 108–200 |

The upper parts of the body are grizzled owing to the lighter and darker annulations on the hairs showing, the flanks and upper parts of the limbs less so, the lower parts of the limbs even in colour. The lower part of the face and chin is usually lighter in colour than the rest of the body, and is often white. The inside and fringes of the ears have short, light-coloured hair. The hair on the head is short and closely adpressed to it. The hairs of the guard coat at the shoulder are about 10 mm long, on the rump 15 mm; the hair on the tail being longest, up to 40 mm. The black whiskers are conspicuous and up to 50 mm long. They have four digits on the front feet and five on the hind, each digit equipped with short, sharp, curved claws adapted to their arboreal life.

Viljoen (1975, 1986a) recorded the sequence of the moult, which takes place twice a year, the spring moult commencing in September and the autumn moult in January. Individuals in moult show a dark line across the body where the old hair is being shed. The dark line is caused by the loss of hair on one side which, through the removal of the overlying lighter coloured bands, reveals the darker bands on the fresh hair. The tail moults only once during the year, usually around March. In juveniles their first moult commences when they are about 40 days old and continues up to about 120 days. During this process they lose the woolly coat characteristic of this period of their lives and assume the rather coarser coat of the adults.

**Distribution**

The tree squirrel is confined in its distribution to the southern part of the continent, from southwestern Tanzania to southern Mozambique and westwards to southeastern Angola. They are absent from the South West Arid Zone, the southern part of the Southern Savannas and from the eastern forest patches.

*South of the Sahara, excluding the Southern African Subregion*

They occur marginally in a narrow sector in southwest **Tanzania** from Tabora to the southern end of Lake Tanzania. They occur in southeastern **Zaire** and in parts of southern and southwestern **Angola**. They are widespread in **Zambia** and **Malawi**, and they occur in the Tete and Zambezia provinces of **Mozambique**, north of the Zambezi River, and may be found in other parts of northeastern Mozambique adjacent to the Malawi border, from where at the moment there are no records.

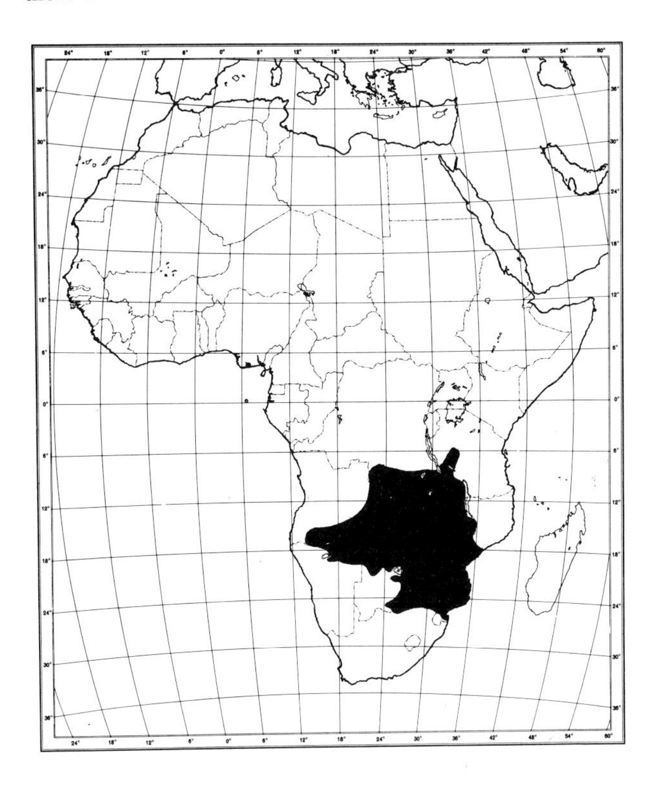

*Southern African Subregion*

They are recorded from the extreme northeastern parts of **Namibia**. They occur in the northern, northeastern and eastern parts of **Botswana**, and in **Zimbabwe** and **Mozambique**, south of the Zambezi River, excluding the extreme southern parts of the country. In the **Transvaal** they are found in the northern parts of the province, from the Zeerust district in the west to the northern border of **Swaziland** in the east.

**Habitat**

As the colloquial name implies, the tree squirrel, *P. cepapi*, is a savanna woodland species. Their occurrence is not dependent on any particular type of woodland and they are found in a wide variety of types, including in particular mopane, *Acacia* and mixed associations such as *Acacia/Terminalia*, *Acacia/Combretum* and others. They occur, but are far less common, in *Brachystegia/Julbernardia* and *Baikiaea* woodland and the reason may be that these do not provide the abundance of tree holes necessary for use as resting and breeding sites, which are a feature of the other associations. Older mopane trees, *Colophospermum mopane*, and various species of *Acacia* in particular are favoured as the trunks and branches are often hollow and riddled with holes. Their frequent association with mopane in some parts has led them to be known as "mopane squirrels". They avoid forest, where they are replaced by other species, and the arid and open grassland areas do not provide the tree and bush growth necessary to provide shelter and food.

### Habits

While the tree squirrel is observed to be generally solitary, pairs or small family parties of a female with two or three young may be seen. Viljoen (1978) found that, in the Transvaal, they live in groups. These consist of one or two adult males or females accompanied by subadults or, at the height of the breeding season, up to seven young. The average size of the groups over a period of one year was five. Members of a group recognise each other by their smell, acquired through occupation of the same nest, by mutual grooming or by marking each other by dragging the anal glands over each other's bodies, which is a common practice. It is quite common in the field to see an individual which is about to enter a nesting hole, being confronted by the occupant, with nose to nose mutual sniffing. Only if it is a member of the same group will the visiting individual be allowed to enter, otherwise it will be actively chased off. When the group is feeding, strangers will be chased from the vicinity.

When alarmed by a predator the whole group may join in mobbing it, all members vocalising with loud clicking calls accompanied by much tail flicking as they sit on safe vantage points. As the display increases in intensity the vocalisation may rise in tone from clicking to a harsh rattle, with corresponding increase in the degree of tail flicking. Individuals on their own may also react in this manner to danger. When extremely alarmed they vocalise with a high-pitched whistle.

Tree squirrels have to rely on their alertness for their safety, for much of their foraging is carried out on open ground. Their first reaction to danger is to run for the safety of the nesting hole or, if this is far removed, to the nearest tree. Climbing swiftly to high branches, they will leap (up to 2 m) from tree to tree until they reach the shelter of their hole or, alternatively, will hide among foliage or lie along a branch spreadeagled and motionless until they are satisfied that the danger is passed. They have a characteristic habit of keeping the trunk or the branch of the tree between themselves and the source of disturbance.

They are very cautious when on the ground and, if suspicious, may move in jerky, halting movements, hesitating and looking around every few steps, with the tail erect and twitching. When fleeing on the ground they move very quickly. Tree squirrels are both arboreal and terrestrial, a great deal of their time being spent foraging on the ground. They are diurnal, being most active in the morning and late afternoon and less so during the hottest hours of the day. In cool weather they remain active throughout the day, but are little in evidence during rain. They bask in the sun, especially on first emerging from the nest during the winter months, when they may spend up to two hours on branches basking and grooming, before descending to forage. Grooming is an important aspect of their behaviour. This involves licking, combing, nibbling and scratching and they are assiduous in this activity. The young are forcibly groomed by the mothers who hold them down with the front legs while performing this task.

The groups establish territories which are defended by the adult males. Viljoen (1975) found that in the Transvaal the average size of a territory was about 4 300 $m^2$. While the groups tended to remain in their territory, individuals occasionally roamed out of it. The territory is marked by mouth-wiping, urination and anal-dragging, the latter more frequently by the females. Marking is carried out as a routine, but appears to be stimulated by the presence of strangers (Viljoen, 1975).

The high percentage of specimens with torn ears and damaged tails indicates aggressiveness, but usually intruders to a territory are chased off by the male without contact. There is a clear hierarchy within groups, which are dominated usually by a male. This is evident during feeding when submissives are wary in approaching dominants.

The nests, which are either natural holes in trees or those made by barbets or woodpeckers, are lined with leaves or grass to form a nest. These may be cleaned out occasionally by the occupants and relined with fresh material, which may be a means of reducing the population of parasites.

Tree squirrels have an acute sense of hearing and the slightest rustling will alert them. Their eyesight is good and they will notice the presence of strange objects quickly, even if these are stationary.

Tree squirrels vocalise with a long, drawn out *chuck-chuck-chuck* which increases in intensity, the interval between the individual syllables decreasing until it becomes a rattle. This call is repeated over periods of up to five to 10 minutes as they sit in a prominent position and is accompanied by tail twitching and interspersed with croaking noises and single *chucks*.

### Food

Tree squirrels are predominantly vegetarians, although insects are an important secondary component of their diet during certain times of the year. Vegetable matter consists of the flowers, leaves, seeds, berries, fruits and bark of a wide variety of plants and grasses. Viljoen (1975, 1983b) listed over 30 species recognised in stomach contents, showing the months in which they were utilised. She included in the list for the Transvaal the flowers of *Acacia* spp; *Justicia* spp; *Portulaca* sp; *Commelina* sp; tamboti, *Spirostachys africana; Aloe* spp; *Senecio* spp and *Loranthus* sp. The seeds of *Acacia* spp, which they strip from the pods, are an important part of the diet, as well as *Aloe* spp seeds and the seeds of grasses such as *Urochloa* spp and *Panicum maximum* and the violet-tree, *Securidaca longepedunculata*. The fruits of the Transvaal red milkwood, *Mimusops zeyheri*, the red syringa, *Burkea africana*, jackal berries, *Diospyros* spp, buffalo thorn, *Ziziphus mucronata*, and puzzle bush, *Ehretia rigida*, are eaten. *Acacia* gum and lichens are also eaten, as well as the leaves of a wide variety of plants.

In Botswana they were seen to feed on the fruits of wild fig, *Ficus* spp, the seeds of mopane, *Colophospermum mopane*, the green shoots of *Acacia* spp, and couch grass, *Cynodon dactylon*. Insect food included termites, ants and aphids.

In feeding, tree squirrels display great agility, hanging by their feet to reach food and moving out among the outermost twigs of branches to get at it. When eating an individual sits down and manipulates the food with the front feet, turning a nut around until a grip can be secured on it with the teeth and access gained to the kernel. Often they will choose an elevated site on which to sit and feed, so that a better watch may be kept for possible danger. Accumulations of the discarded inedible remains of food mark these sites which may be on the top of a boulder or fallen tree trunk.

Both sexes bury hard food such as seeds and nuts. Scraping a hole with the front feet, they place the food in it, then cover it with the feet and pack the soil back with the nose. The sites are chosen carefully where the buried food is protected and they will not bury in the presence of other members of the group, preferring to do this when not under observation. In spite of this, food stealing does take place by other group members. The burying sites are scattered, with no large accumulations in any one place as is seen in some European squirrels.

### Reproduction

The mating behaviour of tree squirrels involves much vocalisation, chasing and mounting. A female in oestrus may be followed by several males, some being strangers from other groups. The onset of oestrus is heralded by a characteristic and highly excited version of the normal alarm vocalisation by the female, which may continue for up to 15 minutes at a time and may continue for an entire morning (Viljoen, 1977, 1980b). As the males follow the female, they vocalise with a soft murmur (which probably prevents fighting, Viljoen, pers. comm.), while flicking their tails. During the chase males may break away to chase other males and the female may chase males approaching too close. The vocalisation of the female in oestrus appears to have the effect of stimulating oestrus in other nearby females, resulting in a measure of synchronisation (Viljoen, 1977). When the female is receptive and prepared to stand, the male will groom her rump prior to mounting. The act of copulation is followed by self-grooming by both partners.

The young may be born at any time throughout the year, but a far higher percentage is born during the warm, wet summer months from October to April. The gestation period is 53 to 57 days (Viljoen, 1975). The young are born in holes in trees and litters number one to three, with an average of two. At birth the young are altricial, having a mass of about 10 g, are sparsely haired and the eyes are closed, not opening until about the eighth day. They leave the nest for the first time at about 20 days old, remaining on the trunk and branches near the entrance hole and staying close to the adult female until they are about five weeks old. They are weaned at about this age.

The females are very attentive to the needs of their young. For the first two or three days after their birth the mother remains in the nest with them, only emerging for short periods, and on her return to the nest, will groom them assiduously. Should the nest require to be relined she will move the young temporarily, carrying them by the hind leg as they cling to her neck with limbs and tail. She will also reshuffle them in the nest from time to time, manipulating them with her front feet as she would food or nesting material (Viljoen, 1975). The male remains with the family group during this period, advertising his arrival at the entrance to the nest by vocalising before entering. While the female is aggressive to disturbance right up to the time the young are weaned, the male is not, although he will chase off intruders from the vicinity of the nest, often following them for considerable distances. Both the male and female parents will groom the young, but only the female carries them. Once the young become fully mobile they follow the adults around and remain with them until they are about 10 months old, when they become sexually mature.

Food brought back to the nest by the parents is reserved for themselves, and they actually push the young away from it if they attempt to feed. From the time they are weaned, the young, as they follow the adults, have to find solid food for themselves. This they learn by watching the feeding habits of the adults. Viljoen (1975) recorded excessive parental anxiety at the time of the first emergence of the young from the nest, the parents being particularly alert and vocal.

Females have three pairs of mammae, one pair pectoral, one abdominal, and one inguinal.

## INTRODUCED

## Genus *Sciurus* Linnaeus, 1758

No. 146

## *Sciurus carolinensis* Gmelin, 1788

## Grey squirrel
## Gryseekhoring

Plate 10

### Colloquial Name

Alternative names: American grey squirrel, northeastern grey squirrel.

### Taxonomic Notes

Shorten (1951) noted that the feral populations in Great Britain, from whence the Subregion stock originated, were introduced from various places in the United States and are probably therefore hybrids between *S. c. carolinensis* and *S. c. pennsylvanicus* (Millar, 1980). She noted, however, that in the Subregion individuals have ear tufts in winter and measurements that are almost identical with those of *S. c. pennsylvanicus* (Table 146.1). Unlike the populations in Great Britain, where melanism is fairly common, no melanistic forms have been reported from the Subregion, although albinos and partially white individuals are known (Millar, 1980).

### Description

Grey squirrels are about 500 mm in total length and have a tail about half this (Table 146.1). They are therefore about the same size, but considerably heavier, than the largest of our indigenous squirrels, the sun squirrel, *Heliosciurus mutabilis*.

### Table 146.1

Measurements (mm) and mass (g) of adult Carolina grey squirrels, *S. c. carolinensis*, and northeastern grey squirrels, *S. c. pennsylvanicus*, from the United States of America (Barkalow & Shorten, 1973) and adult grey squirrels, *S. carolinensis*, from the Cape Province (Millar, 1980)

**United States of America**

| | Irrespective of sex | | | | | |
|---|---|---|---|---|---|---|
| | *S. c. carolinensis* | | | *S. c. pennsylvanicus* | | |
| | x̄ | n | Range | x̄ | n | Range |
| TL | 460 | 28 | 440–490 | 484 | 7 | 440–520 |
| (HB | 253) | | | (262) | | |
| T | 207 | 28 | 192–238 | 222 | 7 | 190–240 |
| Hf s/u | 65 | 36 | 60–67 | 69 | 6 | 61–76 |
| Mass | 474 | 34 | 300–590 | 579 | 373 | 413–750 |

**Cape Province**

| | Irrespective of sex | | |
|---|---|---|---|
| | x̄ | n | Range |
| TL | 498 | 250 | 413–572 |
| T | 216 | 250 | 115–269 |
| Hf s/u | 60 | 179 | 51–67 |
| Mass | 579,8 | 256 | 434–750 |

Millar (1980) showed that there is a marked difference between the summer and winter pelage of adults of the species. In summer the coat is smoother and a yellowish-brown colour, with a rufous streak along the flanks and on the upper surfaces of the feet. The tail hair is sparser than in the winter coat, the outer white band of hair less noticeable; the ear tufts are lost and the soles of the feet are completely naked. In the juveniles, where the hair on the tail is even sparser, the bare tail shaft can be seen. At this time of the year they look less attractive than they do in winter, looking almost rat-like.

In the winter coat the pelage is dense and silvery-grey, with a yellowish-brown dorsal stripe and is rufous in colour on the upper surfaces of the feet. White or yellowish-white tufts develop on the tips of the ears with the winter coat of most individuals and the soles of the feet are hairy. The tail is dark grey with a white fringe, and the under parts are pure white.

Spring-born juveniles and lactating females retain their winter coats longer than adult males and non-lactating females. The white under parts are off-white and, particularly in the lactating females, the under parts are stained a dirty brownish-white in colour.

In winter the hair of the guard coat on the upper parts is about 10 mm long, the individual hairs annulated with buffy, black and either rufous-brown or white tips, which tend to give the upper parts a grizzled appearance. The guard coat is freely interspersed with many longer, black hairs, which may have a tactile function.

The hair on the tail is much longer than on the body, reaching a length of about 45 mm at the tip. The individual hairs have rufous-buffy bases, followed by a suffused black annulation, another rufous-buffy annulation, a broad, distinctly black annulation and broad white tips. When the tail is fanned out flat the white tips to the hairs show conspicuously as a white fringe.

Millar (1980) found that in the Cape Province they have two body moults, one in spring (August/September), the other in autumn (March/April), while the tail moults only once, in late summer or early autumn (February/March). In spring the moult progresses from head and shoulders to hips, in autumn from hips to head and feet.

### Distribution

This arboreal species was introduced into South Africa by Cecil John Rhodes about the turn of the century and was released on Groote Schuur Estate, Cape Town. Millar (1980) instituted an enquiry in an endeavour to trace the actual date of the introduction, but was unable to find any records relating to this event. Bigalke (1937) put it at soon after 1900, Rosenthal (1961) at 1890 and Van der Westhuizen (1974) at the end of the 19th century.

Haagner (1920) recorded that by that year they had overrun the Cape Peninsula and extended their range across the Cape Flats. They established themselves in the Paarl and Stellenbosch districts, at Suider Paarl, Simondium, Groot Drakenstein, Pniel and Jonkershoek and by 1930 had reached the foothills of the Franschhoek and Hottentots Holland mountains. They had crossed the latter and reached Elgin by 1933 (Davis, 1950).

Millar (1980) reported on a questionnaire survey carried out in 1971, which showed that they were considerably more widespread than shown by Davis (1950). They had reached Koelenhof by 1925, Muldersvlei by 1941, Kuils River by 1943 and Firgrove and Faure by 1930. There had also been artificial introductions to Swellendam in 1957 and to Ceres in 1968. In the latter the colony was established by the introduction of a pair from Stellenbosch, in the former by seven from Paarl, which were released on the Swellendam Forestry Plantation. At that time Swellendam was the furthest point from Cape Town where they had established themselves.

On the other hand, within their known limits of occurrence there had been local shrinkages in their distribution in some areas due to the removal of pine plantations to make way for urbanisation. In others, there had been an extension in their distribution due to planting of new pine plantations and the development of new vineyards and orchards of deciduous fruits, with accompanying wind-breaks of pines.

Their further spread is governed by their primary habitat requirements which include the presence of food-tree species (see **Food**) and other trees, including indigenous species, which provide adequate cover for the construction of their dreys. The availability of water is also an important requirement.

Within the limits shown on the map their occurrence is patchy and discontinuous on account of their habitat requirements. The potential exists for an extension of this distributional range to forest plantations in other parts of the southwestern Cape Province, which are at present buffered by areas of fynbos, which these squirrels cannot utilise. Their spread to these plantations is unlikely unless by introduction (Millar, 1980).

## Habitat

In their ancestral home in the United States of America they are principally a squirrel of hardwood forests, with a preference for mixed associations, only occurring marginally in pine forests (Burt & Grossenheider, 1961). They are, however, highly adaptable and occur in other associations such as oak, oak-hickory and beech-maple forests in parts of their American range.

In the Subregion their habitat requirements include the presence in sufficient quantity of one or more of their staple food-trees. These are the oak, *Quercus robur*, and in particular, three species of pines, *Pinus pinea*, *P. pinaster* and *P. canariensis*. In addition they require adequate cover from the elements in which to build their nests, which is provided by these pines as well as by other introduced species such as *Eucalyptus* spp, willow, *Populus canescens*, and indigenous species such as thorn trees, *Acacia* spp. They do not occur as permanent populations in pure or single-species plantations of pines, such as *P. radiata*, nor any other species of pine, other than those mentioned as staple food-trees, in evergreen indigenous forest nor in open fynbos associations. They may make temporary use of such habitats at certain times of the year. They will use isolated plantations of oaks, and pine tree wind-breaks fringing orchards, as well as city parks and suburban estates where these trees are present.

## Habits

Grey squirrels usually occur solitarily or a female may be accompanied by her weaning young. Although they may be seen at any time throughout the day, they are most active in the early morning and late afternoon and much less so during the hotter hours of the day. Activity counts during March, April, August and September 1969 showed that least activity takes place between 10h00 and 14h00 (Millar, 1971).

Wind, then heat, around midday or on hot summer days, are the two factors most limiting their activity. Rain does not limit activity unless heavy and combined with cold and wind. In contrast cloud with light rain may stimulate or cause activity throughout the day or extend the duration of such activity (Millar, 1971).

They rest up in holes in trees lined with leaves and other soft debris, but more commonly construct dreys about the size of a soccer ball, at an average height of about 7 m (n=35; 4,6–11,5 m) in the branches of trees. Oak and pine trees are preferred, but they will also use bluegum, wattle, poplar or wild olive (Millar, 1971). They rest in these dreys during the night, sometimes adults in the same shelter, and the females also use them in which to have their young. The dreys are constructed of twigs, shredded bark, leaves and any other soft debris which may be available, such as rags, sacking, string or paper and they are lined with leaves or other soft material.

While these dreys may be used for considerable periods, they eventually disintegrate and new ones are constructed. When food becomes scarce locally, they may be abandoned and the squirrels move to a new location. In America whole populations move when food becomes scarce, these movements involving hundreds of individuals (MacClintock & Ferguson, 1970).

Under stress individuals flatten themselves along branches and remain motionless and have the characteristic habit, like our bush squirrel, *Paraxerus cepapi*, of keeping to the far side of tree trunks out of sight of the observer. The alarm call is a rapid, scolding *kuk-kuk-kuk*.

## Food

Millar (1980) reported in detail on the food of the grey squirrel as reflected from the results of a questionnaire survey, initiated in 1971. This indicated that, among the 30 food items listed, acorns had the highest relative importance rating, followed by pine seeds, vegetables and a range of deciduous fruits, including grapes, almonds and plums. Other items included birds' eggs, garden plants and grain crops. In terms of damage done, almonds ranked the highest, followed by peaches and grapes.

Although they do damage young trees, Millar (1980) believed that in forestry plantations this is minimal and that they do little damage upon grain-growing areas due to the scarcity of trees and the inability of relatively small populations of squirrels to exert a significant impact. Their feeding habits have the greatest impact on smallholdings in localised areas where the ratio of squirrel habitat and therefore density of squirrels to crop is much higher. They are considered a problem animal in areas where vegetables, fruit or grapes are grown. Between the years 1918 and 1958, when bounties were paid in the Cape Province, at least 32 953 such bounties were paid (Millar, 1980).

From the examination of 72 stomach contents, Millar (1980) found that they are dependent principally on a supply of nuts and pine tree seeds, which made up 70% of their annual diet. Their intake of the various food items varied seasonally: when the supply of acorns and pine seeds becomes scarce, during the spring and summer months, they turn to other secondary foods such as fungi, pollen, grass seeds, insects, birds eggs and fledgings, fruit, bark, leaves and grass, buds and twigs, stems and flowers.

In the United States of America the grey squirrel lives in areas where up to 36 species of nut-bearing trees occur, as against the three to four that are available to them in the Cape Province (Millar, 1980). Most of our indigenous trees bear drupes, berries or small fruits and do not provide suitable food requirements.

Millar (1980) showed that while acorns were low in protein (3,9%) and fat (5%), they had a very high carbohydrate content (84,5%). Pine seeds (*P. pinea*), on the other hand, had a very high protein (31,1%) and fat (47,4%) content, but were relatively low in carbohydrates (11,6%). A combination of these two items thus balances their diet. Possibly as a result of this, adult squirrels (n=135) from the protein-rich pine habitats had a significantly greater mass than those from protein-poor oak habitats (n=127), averaging 36,0 g heavier (Millar, 1980).

Grey squirrels scatter-hoard acorns, pine and other hard seeds, either hiding them in hollow trees or scraping a depression 20–30 mm deep in the ground, inserting the seed and then carefully covering it up. This latter action is beneficial in disseminating tree seed, which may germinate, but any benefits accruing are offset by the loss of seed in areas where it is required for commercial purposes (Davis, 1950).

**Reproduction**

In the Cape Province, Millar (1980) recorded two periods of mating, in July/August and November/December, with peaks in July and December respectively. He found a strong correlation between the spring mating season and increasing day lengths. Some mating, however, takes place outside these periods, May being the only month in which it was not observed. In the United States the gestation period is 44 days (Shorten, 1951; Smith, 1967). The young are born in the Cape Province during two main periods, August/November and December/February, the peaks falling in August and January. This is seasonally equivalent, but at opposite calendar months to the time of parturition in the Northern Hemisphere. In the Cape Province the spring litters are born just before the spring flush in September, when precipitation is frequent. The summer litters are born at the hottest and driest times of the year during the main fruit season and just before the pine seeds and acorns ripen, which are most abundant from March to June (Millar, 1980). Females may have up to two litters in a year (Smith, 1967) and the number in litters based on embryos varies from one to four, with an average of 2,5. Birth mass varies from 14,5 g to 16,0 g and in the litters of four there tend to be one or two runts which do not survive (Millar, 1980).

Millar (1980) showed that prenatal mortality resulting in resorption of the embryos amounted to 5,6%, and that the mortality between the litter size at implantation and the weaned juveniles amounted to 18,7%, which was of the same order as that in the United States of 27%. Millar (1980) found that in a sample of 126 adult females, 75,4% had mated, 84,5% of these producing two to three young and 15,5% producing litters of either one or four. Using embryo counts, summer litters are significantly larger 2,6 (n=16) than spring litters 2,2 (n=11), but litter size is lower in the Cape Province than in the United States or Great Britain. Based on studies in the United States the males usually breed in the second or third mating season after their birth, at an age of about 16 to 17 months; females breed in the second season, at about 11 months of age (Millar, 1980). The young wean at about 10 weeks old, but are recorded as taking solid food at seven weeks (Uhlig, 1955).

# XXI. Family THRYONOMYIDAE

## Canerats

The Family name is derived from the Greek *thryon*, a reed, and *mys*, a mouse, which refers to their common association with reed beds. In the Subregion the Family is represented by a single genus, *Thryonomys*, and two species, *T. swinderianus* and *T. gregorianus*. The former is associated more closely with a damp habitat, the latter being capable of utilising drier areas.

The incisor teeth are broad and powerfully built and have three grooves on their anterior faces; the position of these grooves differs in the two species (Fig. 147.1). The upper molar teeth have a deep inner and two outer infolds of the enamel layer which almost meet in the centre of the teeth. In the lower jaw this situation is reversed and they have two inner infolds and one outer. The upper premolar is slightly smaller than the three molars (Fig. XXI.1).

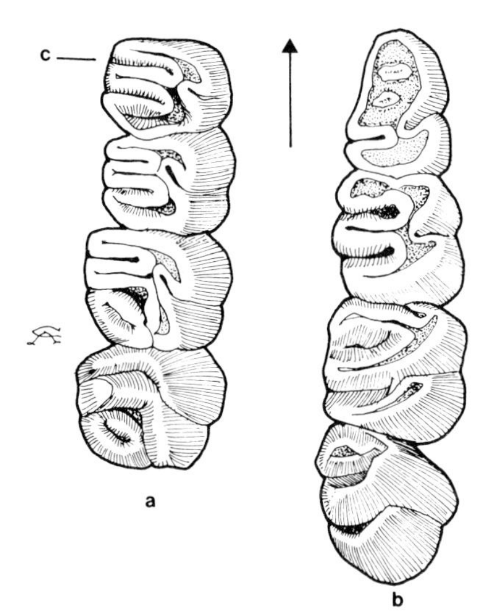


Fig. XXI.1. Cheekteeth: *Thryonomys swinderianus* (a) upper right (b) lower right (c) first premolar (after Rosevear, 1969)

## Genus *Thryonomys* Fitzinger, 1867

Key to the species after Meester *et al.* (1986)

1. Frontal region of skull arched anteriorly; outermost of three grooves in upper incisor teeth on mid-line of tooth ... *swinderianus*

   Frontal region of skull more or less flat; outermost groove in upper incisor teeth nearer to outer surface of the teeth rather than on the mid-line ... *gregorianus*

---

No. 147

## *Thryonomys swinderianus* (Temminck, 1827)

### Greater canerat
### Groot rietrot

Plate 11

---

**Colloquial Name**

They take their name from their association with areas of dense grass with reed or cane-like stems. This species is the larger of the two canerats known. In the northern Transvaal they are known in Afrikaans as *rietmuise*.

**Taxonomic Notes**

The species was named after Professor van Swinderen of Groningen and Thomas (1894) noted that the specific name therefore should be spelt *swinderenianus* which, however, has not been used (Rosevear, 1969).

No subspecies are recognised (Ellerman *et al.*, 1953; Meester *et al.*, 1986).

### Description

The greater canerat is the second largest rodent found in the Subregion, only being surpassed in size and mass by the porcupine, *Hystrix africaeaustralis*. Adult greater canerats are short-bodied, bulky animals, with a head and body length of about 500 mm and a tail about a third of this length (Table 147.1). Adult males have an average mass of some 4,5 kg, females some 3,6 kg, but males with a mass of over 7 kg have been recorded from the Subregion, these with correspondingly larger body measurements, but such a mass is exceptional.

**Table 147.1**

Measurements (mm) and mass (kg) of adult greater canerats, *T. swinderianus*, from Zimbabwe (Smithers & Wilson, 1979)

| | Males | | | Females | | |
|---|---|---|---|---|---|---|
| | x̄ | n | Range | x̄ | n | Range |
| TL | 715 | 5 | 670–792 | 666 | 3 | 654–670 |
| (HB | 527) | | | (483) | | |
| T | 188 | 6 | 180–192 | 183 | 3 | 165–195 |
| Hf c/u | 94 | 6 | 80–100 | 89 | 3 | 88–90 |
| E | 33 | 6 | 30–35 | 35 | 3 | 34–35 |
| Mass | 4,54 | 6 | 3,18–5,22 | 3,58 | 3 | 3,41–3,8 |

In East Africa, Kingdon (1974) recorded total lengths of over 800 mm and masses of up to 8,8 kg which indicate that they are larger and heavier than any so far recorded from the Subregion.

The colour of the body is a speckled dark brown, the speckling caused by the yellow or buffy-yellow subterminal bands on the spiny hairs of the coat. Some individuals are distinctly rusty-tinged around the base of the tail. The under parts are greyish-white or whitish, the lips, chin and throat white. The tapering tail is brown above and buffy-white below and is covered with short, bristly hairs. The rounded ears are broader than they are high and are obscured almost totally by the hair.

The first and fifth digits on the fore and hind feet are reduced to stumps, the remainder armed with slightly curved claws measuring up to 20 mm on the front and 30 mm on the back feet. The individual spiny hairs of the coat are sharply pointed and pliable, and profusely scattered among these on the dorsal surface are slightly longer, thicker gutter hairs up to 30 to 35 mm in length. The spiny hairs arise from parallel lines of pores in the skin, three to five to a pore.

A feature of the species is the extension of the muzzle which overhangs the nostrils and juts out in front of them. This acts as a pad when they aggressively butt each other. The chisel-like incisor teeth are very broad, heavily built and deeply grooved. This grooving is different in the two species. In the greater canerat, *T. swinderianus*, the grooves are situated nearer the inside of the teeth, leaving a broad smooth face on the outside (Fig. 147.1.a). In the lesser canerat, *T. gregorianus*, they are spaced more evenly on the teeth and there is consequently no broader smooth face on their outer edges, the smooth sections of the teeth being subequal in breadth (Fig. 147.1.b). The enamel layer on the front of the teeth is orange-yellow in colour.

In adult greater canerats the skull is arched and convex in profile, the highest point lying between the eye sockets. In the lesser canerat the skull is flatter. This has been used as a means of distinguishing the two species but does not entirely hold true, as in female and juvenile greater canerats, the convexity is less developed.

The comparatively longer tail in the greater canerat, as opposed to the lesser, has been used as a feature in distinguishing the two species. In East Africa, Kingdon (1974) stated that the length of the tail in *T. gregorianus* is 100 mm, in *T. swinderianus* over twice this length. While in the Subregion the tail of *T. gregorianus* is shorter than that of *T. swinderianus*, there is not the same disparity in length and this feature cannot be used as a distinguishing character (Table 147.1).

### Distribution

Owing to the specialised habitat requirements of greater canerats they only occur within the limits shown on the map where the habitat is suitable for them. As a consequence their distribution is patchy and discontinuous and there are very large tracts of country in which they are not found. The exact limits of distribution, in parts of the continent north of the Subregion, remain imperfectly known.

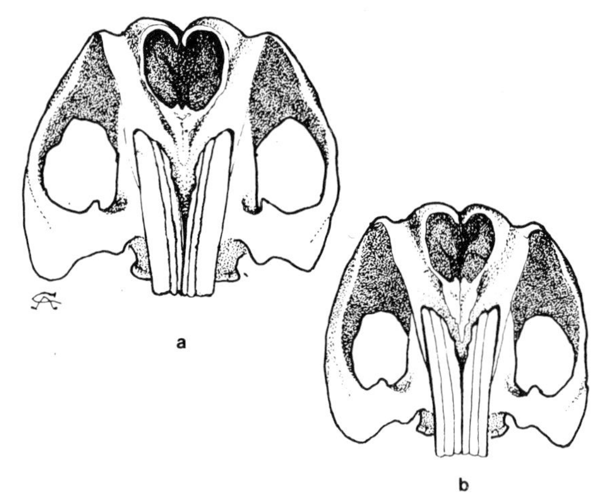


Fig. 147.1. Incisor teeth:
(a) *Thryonomys swinderianus* (b) *T. gregorianus*

*South of the Sahara, excluding the Southern African Subregion*

Originally the nominate form *T. s. swinderianus* was described from **Sierra Leone** and they occur in West Africa from **Gambia** to adjacent parts of **Cameroun**; and in parts of the **Central African Republic**; southern **Sudan; Uganda**; western **Kenya**; throughout **Tanzania; Zambia; Malawi**; and **Mozambique**, north of the Zambezi River. They are widespread in **Angola**, excluding the coastal desert.

*Southern African Subregion*

They occur on the Cunene River upstream of the Ruacana Falls in Angola and may, therefore, occur on the south bank in **Namibia**. The only other part of this territory in which they are found is in the extreme northeast in the vicinity of the Okavango River. In **Botswana** they are confined to the Okavango Delta and along the Chobe River in the northeast and, while there are no records at the moment, they may occur along the top reaches of the Limpopo River in the border area with the Transvaal. In **Zimbabwe** they are widespread, except in the more arid areas along the Botswana border in the west, and are recorded widely in **Mozambique**, south of the Zambezi River. In the **Transvaal** they are widespread, except in the southern parts of the province, their distribution extending southwards into northern **Natal** and narrowly into the eastern **Cape Province** to the Grahamstown district.

### Habitat

Greater canerats are specialised in their habitat requirements and are found in reedbeds or in areas of dense, tall grass of types with thick reed or cane-like stems. In the Subregion such associations occur in the vicinity of rivers, lakes and swamps and greater canerats are never found far from water. Observations recorded in literature, e.g. Shortridge (1934), of canerats occurring on "rocky hillsides" most likely should refer to the lesser canerat, *T. gregorianus*, which can utilise drier habitat than can the greater. In West Africa they occur in the High Forest Zone, but only where there are clearings within the forest, with a grassland invasion of species such as elephant grass, *Pennisetum purpureum*, or *Panicum maximum* (Asibey, 1974a). Throughout their range they are absent from desert and semi-arid areas.

In the Subregion, agricultural development in the growing of crops such as maize, sugar-cane and pineapples has greatly improved the habitat for the greater canerat and in these parts they can be a problem. In other parts of Africa they damage cassava and eggplant crops (West Africa; Asibey, 1974a).

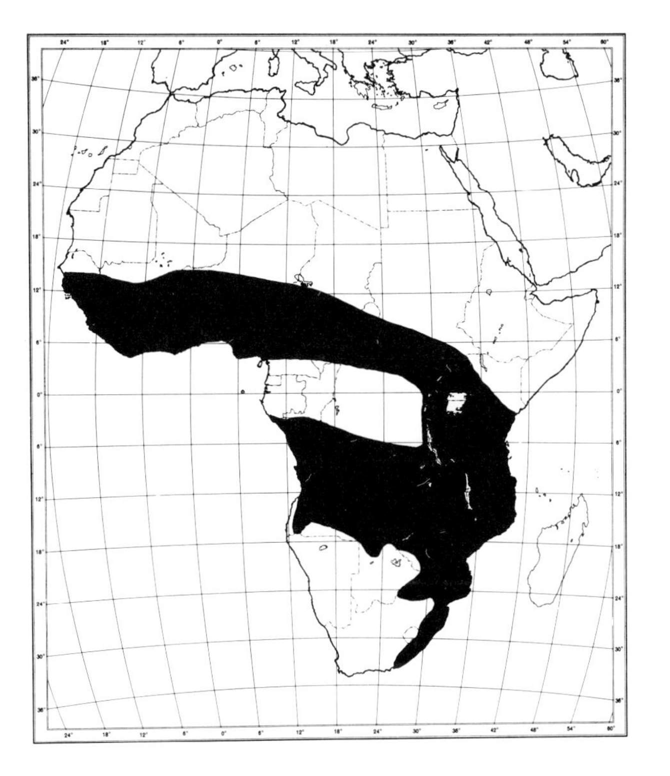

## Habits

Greater canerats are generally reported to be solitary animals, but small groups of up to eight to 10 may live in restricted areas of reedbed. In the Okavango Swamp 10 regularly appeared from an area of reedbed and matted semi-aquatic grass, some 150 $m^2$ in extent, to feed on vegetable scraps laid out for them. The party consisted of six adults with four young. How close their association was within the reedbed could not be ascertained, but it was quite common in "drives" to flush several adults that appeared to be living in close association. The furthest from the water that they were observed in the Okavango Swamp was 50 m and in other parts of the Subregion it was generally considerably less than this.

They are predominantly nocturnal but exhibit some crepuscular activity, being active up to about 07h00 and from 17h00 until around sunset. Distinct runs are formed in the reedbeds and among the matted grass along which they can move without being seen. These are marked by small piles of the cut stems of grasses and reeds discarded in feeding and by small scattered piles of faeces, where they have settled to feed. Resting places are usually in the densest part of the reedbed, where piles of debris or the broken down stems of the reeds provide good overhead cover and bedding on which to lie. They will also use the cover of matted tussock grasses. Where there is a lack of sufficient cover they will use holes in stream banks or cover under the root system of trees where the soil has been washed away, providing these are adjacent to cover of grass or reeds. Fitzsimons (1919) stated that, in areas where there is insufficient cover, they burrow, but this is atypical and normally they use existing holes, which they may adjust to their own requirements.

If they are disturbed in their runs, they have a habit of running along them for some distance, then "freezing" until they are closely approached, when they will repeat the process. Even with numerous beaters in "drives" they are difficult to dislodge from cover, and despite their heavy build they can run very fast. Greater canerats are excellent swimmers and freely cross narrow stretches of water to reach their feeding grounds. Their runs are frequently shallowly inundated, the resting places situated on slightly higher ground or among tussock grass so that they remain dry. When suddenly disturbed they have the habit of thumping the ground with their hind feet and whistling loudly. When a group is feeding they grunt softly. While their eyesight appears to be poor, their hearing is acute and the slightest rustling among the grass, where they are feeding, sends them scurrying off or will cause them to cease chewing and remain motionless until they feel that the danger has passed.

Greater canerats are much sought after by the indigenous people in Africa. Their flesh is very palatable and they are hunted widely with dogs or caught in fall-traps. In parts of West Africa they are a regular feature in native markets. Asibey (1974a) estimated that 13 restaurants in Accra annually purchased some 177 tons of greater canerats, their meat being in great demand, in spite of the fact that it was more expensive than beef, mutton or pork.

Apart from predation by man they also fall prey to leopards, baboons and pythons. For this reason, in sugar-cane growing areas, pythons are afforded special protection.

## Food

Greater canerats are vegetarians, living on the roots, shoots and stems of grasses and reeds that grow in damp places. In the northern parts of the Subregion they feed on the growing shoots of the reed, *Phragmites communis*, leaving the stems as they harden up in growth. The stems of Rhodes grass, *Chloris gayana*; couch grass, *Cynodon dactylon*; swamp couch, *Hemarthria altissima*; antelope grass, *Echinochloa pyramidalis*; Napier fodder (elephant grass), *Pennisetum purpureum*, and guinea grass, *Panicum maximum*, are included in their food. The grass stems are cut near the base with the broad, sharp incisor teeth, then into short lengths convenient for eating, being manipulated with the front feet during this process. The drier sections and leaves are usually discarded and mark the location of the feeding sites. While grasses are their principal food, they are raiders of agricultural crops when these grow in close proximity to their habitat. Maize, millet, sorghums, wheat and sugar-cane are all dealt with in the same manner as grasses. They will scratch the soil aside to get at potatoes and groundnuts in the same way as they do in exposing the succulent underground stems of couch grass, *Cynodon dactylon*, and the roots of other grasses which are part of their diet. Kingdon (1974) recorded that, in East Africa, they eat nuts and fallen fruit and will debark shrubs and trees. They favour the stems of grasses such as *Echinochloa* spp while they are green during the rains, but turn to the roots during the dry season.

Asibey (1974a) noted that in Ghana, where they are very common in the coastal areas, their numbers, if unchecked, could pose a threat to the economy owing to their depredations on agricultural crops.

## Reproduction

Greater canerats produce their litters in the resting places deep in the reedbeds or in holes adjacent to their habitat. Where holes are used these have a bed of grass or the leaves of reeds which are brought into them by the females.

There is a scarcity of information from the Subregion on reproduction. Shortridge (1934) recorded neonates in the Okavango Swamp between June and August, while in Zimbabwe juveniles were taken in August and November and a gravid female with three foetuses in November (Smithers, 1983). Stevenson-Hamilton (1947) gave spring and early summer as time of parturition in the eastern Transvaal. This indicates that they may be seasonal breeders, pupping just before and during the warm, wet, summer months. Further north, in Zambia, Ansell (1960a) recorded gravid females in January and March and near the equator throughout the year (Asibey, 1974b).

Asibey (1974b) gave the gestation period as 137 to 172 days, and more recently this was estimated at 152 days (Schröder & Mensah, 1987). The average birth mass was 128,5 g, but varied greatly in individual litters (range 79–190 g), whilst the mean litter size was four (range 1–8). The precocial young are born fully haired, with their eyes open, and are capable of following their mother an hour after birth. Females may have their first litter when about a year old and they may have two litters a year (Asibey, 1974b). The female eats the afterbirth of each individual in a litter before the next is born.

At birth the hair is soft, quite unlike the stiff textured, bristly hair of the adults. The young grow very fast. The females have three pairs of mammae situated on the sides of the body, like porcupines, and suckle the young standing or lying on their bellies. The young wean at about a month old.

Hall (1986) has made a preliminary study of the growth of this species, but the data are too erratic and do not follow an asymptotic curve.

No. 148

## *Thryonomys gregorianus* (Thomas, 1894)

## Lesser canerat
## Klein rietrot

Plate 11

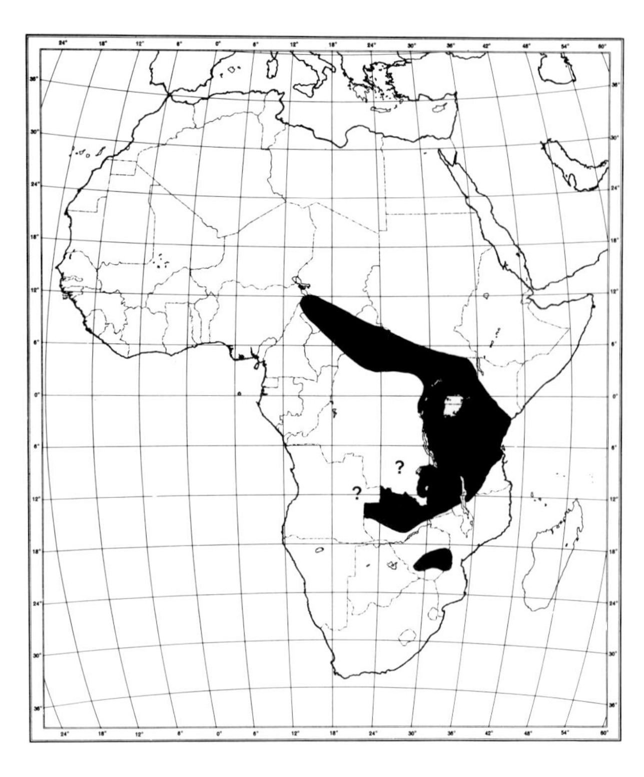

### Colloquial Name
So named as they are the smaller of the two species of canerats known.

### Taxonomic Notes
Meester *et al.* (1986) noted that they could not comment on the validity of the subspecies, and listed only *T. g. sclateri* Thomas, 1897 which originally was described from the Nyika Plateau, Malawi. When more adequate material becomes available, this subspecies may be shown to be the one occurring in the Subregion.

### Description
The lesser canerat, *T. gregorianus*, is very similar in external features to the greater, *T. swinderianus*, but can be distinguished most readily by the grooving on the incisor teeth which serves to distinguish the two species (see **Description** of the greater canerat, *T. swinderianus*). They are smaller overall and not as heavy as the greater (Table 148.1).

**Table 148.1**

Measurements (mm) and mass (kg) of a series of adult lesser canerats, *T. gregorianus*, from Zimbabwe (Smithers & Wilson, 1979)

| | Males | | | Females | | |
|---|---|---|---|---|---|---|
| | $\bar{x}$ | n | Range | $\bar{x}$ | n | Range |
| TL | 519 | 7 | 410–575 | 518 | 3 | 495–540 |
| (HB | 375) | | | (386) | | |
| T | 144 | 7 | 110–175 | 132 | 3 | 125–140 |
| Hf c/u | 60 | 7 | 55–90 | 72 | 3 | 70–75 |
| E | 29 | 7 | 27–30 | 29 | 3 | 25–31 |
| Mass | 1,87 | 7 | 1,42–2,38 | 1,88 | 3 | 1,76–1,90 |

### Distribution
While the distribution of the lesser canerat can be plotted with some accuracy in parts of its range, as for example in East Africa (Kingdon, 1974), in other parts information is meagre. While there are no records from Angola, their occurrence in adjacent parts of Zambia (Ansell, 1960a) points to the probability of at least a marginal occurrence in the east of the country.

In the Subregion they appear to occur as an island population in Zimbabwe and adjacent parts of Mozambique, but this is probably due to a lack of collecting or possibly a confusion with the young stages of the greater canerat, *T. swinderianus*, to which *T. gregorianus* specimens have been assigned. Therefore the present distribution as shown on the map must be treated as tentative.

*South of the Sahara, excluding the Southern African Subregion*

They have been recorded from northern **Cameroun**, on the borders of Chad, from the southern **Sudan** and from the northern parts of **Zaire**. They are widespread in East Africa, excluding the drier eastern and northeastern parts of **Kenya** and southeastern **Tanzania**, but including the whole of **Uganda**. They are widespread in **Zambia**, except in the southwest, and in the northern parts of **Malawi**.

*Southern African Subregion*

At present they are only known from scattered records in **Zimbabwe**, from the Matopo Hills eastwards to the eastern districts, and in adjacent parts of **Mozambique**, south of the Zambezi River.

### Habitat
While there is some common use made of damp areas with reedbeds and semi-aquatic grasses by both the greater canerat, *T. swinderianus*, and lesser canerat, *T. gregorianus*, only the lesser is able to utilise dry terrain. There has been some confusion in literature between the two species, but when the habitat of canerats is stated to be "rocky hillsides" and the like, then it can be assumed with confidence that the lesser canerat is referred to.

In the northern parts of the Subregion the greater canerat occurs along the more permanent lower reaches of rivers, the lesser canerat among koppies where the top reaches or rivers are tiny, dry rivulets, which only flow with the annual run-off from the surrounding hills. In this habitat they inhabit areas where there are stands of tall grasses, or thick mats of tussock grass, which provide cover and food.

In other parts of Africa the lesser canerat is shown to tolerate much higher altitudes than the greater canerat and has been taken on Mt Ruwenzori up to 2 600 m above sea level.

### Habits
Like the greater canerat, the lesser canerat, *T. gregorianus*, is predominantly nocturnal, with some diurnal activity as well. They are solitary animals, but small parties of up to a dozen will live in a restricted area with a good grass cover, although their association within these groups is not clear.

**Plate 11**

134. Porcupine, *Hystrix africaeaustralis*
Ystervark

147. Greater canerat, *Thryonomys swinderianus*
Groot rietrot

148. Lesser canerat, *Thryonomys gregorianus*
Klein rietrot

149. Dassie rat, *Petromus typicus*
Dassierot

PLATE·11
147
149
148
134
Dick Findlay.

They choose resting places at the base of clumps of grass where the grass overhangs, providing a hidden retreat from aerial predators and if the grass gets burnt the whole party will move to another area. Where the grass does not provide safe hiding places they will shelter in rock crevices, under rocks or in disused holes of antbears or springhaas. Kingdon (1974) stated that, in East Africa, they will excavate their own shallow burrows, but this has not been observed in the Subregion.

Through constant movement from resting to feeding areas distinct runs are formed, the feeding areas being marked by little accumulations of cut grass stem sections and scattered faeces.

**Reproduction**

There is a paucity of information on the time of the year at which the young are born, and there is no information on the young of this species. There are two records of gravid females, both from eastern Zimbabwe. One female, taken in May, carried two foetuses implanted in one uterine horn, and the other female, taken in November, carried three foetuses, two implanted in the right hand horn, one in the left.

As the lesser canerat usually lies up under the cover of matted grasses, it is probable that the litter is born in this type of resting place, as is the case in the greater canerat.

# XXII. Family PETROMURIDAE

## Dassie rat

This Family is comprised of a single species, *Petromus typicus*, which is confined in its occurrence to the western parts of the Subregion, with an extension into southwestern Angola. It is a rock-dwelling species and the skull is broad and flattened to allow their use of rock crevices, a feature similar to that seen in the rock dormouse, *Graphiurus platyops*. The enamel layer on the front of the ungrooved incisor teeth is yellow, the ear bullae well developed, and the anterior palatal foramina extends posteriorly to the anterior edge of the first upper molar teeth.

The dental formula is:

$I\frac{1}{1}\ C\frac{0}{0}\ P\frac{1}{1}\ M\frac{3}{3} = 20$

The upper cheekteeth have such deep infoldings of the enamel lying obliquely to the length of the row on the inside of the teeth that the teeth appear laminate, or that each tooth is composed of two transverse sections. In the lower jaw the infoldings are from the outside of the individual teeth.

The flattened infraorbital foramen is large for the size of the skull to allow for the passage of a portion of the masseter muscle, as in other hystricomorph rodents.

### Genus *Petromus* A. Smith, 1831

No. 149

### *Petromus typicus* A. Smith, 1831

### Dassie rat
### Dassierot

Plate 11

**Colloquial Name**

Dassie rats have acquired their colloquial name because, like dassies of the Family Procaviidae, they are closely confined to a rocky habitat and have habits that are reminiscent of dassies. The generic name *Petromus* is derived from the Greek *petro*, a rock, and *mys*, a mouse; the specific name *typicus* from *typikos*, typical; hence a mouse that lives typically in a rocky habitat. Although colloquially well entrenched, both this and the generic name are unfortunate as they are neither rats nor mice, the presence of the premolar teeth giving them a row of four cheekteeth, compared with three in rats and mice.

**Taxonomic Notes**

No less than 14 subspecies have been described, many more than are justified in a species with such a restricted distributional range. A wide variation in colour, coupled with size differences, led to the listing by Roberts (1951) of 10 subspecies and a further species, *P. cunealis*, which is now considered a subspecies by Meester *et al.* (1986).

**Description**

Adult dassie rats have a total length of about 300 mm, with tails slightly less than half this length (Table 149.1). Too few records of their mass are available to arrive at a mean assessment, but it appears to be about 220 g.

**Table 149.1**

Measurements (mm) and mass (g) of dassie rats, *P. typicus*, from the Cape Province and Namibia (de Graaff, 1981)

| | Males | | | Females | | |
|---|---|---|---|---|---|---|
| | $\bar{x}$ | n | Range | $\bar{x}$ | n | Range |
| (TL | 311) | | | (290) | | |
| HB | 171 | 14 | 154–210 | 150 | 9 | 137–190 |
| T | 140 | 9 | 125–150 | 140 | 7 | 116–168 |
| Hf c/u | 30 | 13 | 28–35 | 33 | 9 | 31–36 |
| E | 13 | 13 | 11–15 | 14 | 9 | 11–16 |
| Mass | Two only 170,0; 212,0 g | | | Two only 251,0; 262,0g | | |

They are squirrel-like in appearance without bushy tails, only having a scattered cover of long hairs over the terminal three-quarters of their tail, which do not fan out as they do in squirrels. The colour of the upper parts varies from a pale grizzled grey to a dark chocolate, some populations nearly black in colour, the rump and hind legs a dull chestnut. The under parts are paler than the upper parts and are similarly variable in colour, ranging from dirty white to yellow.

As in other hystricomorph rodents (e.g. canerats, *Thryonomys* spp) the hair grows in clusters of three to five and not evenly over the skin surface. The base of the hairs on the upper parts varies from pale ashy-grey to slate-grey. They have no underfur.

They have four digits on the forefeet, the thumb rudimentary, and five digits on the hind feet armed with short curved claws. The under surface of both the fore and hind feet is naked and has well developed pads, an adaptation to moving on a rocky substrate.

**Distribution**

Dassie rats are confined in their distribution to the South West Arid Zone where there is suitable habitat of rocky terrain.

*South of the Sahara, excluding the Southern African Subregion*

They are confined to the southwestern parts of **Angola**, as far north as Benguela.

*Southern African Subregion*

They occur in the northwestern parts of the **Cape Province**, northwards through the central and western parts of

**Namibia**, including the most xeric rocky areas, to the northwestern border with Angola.

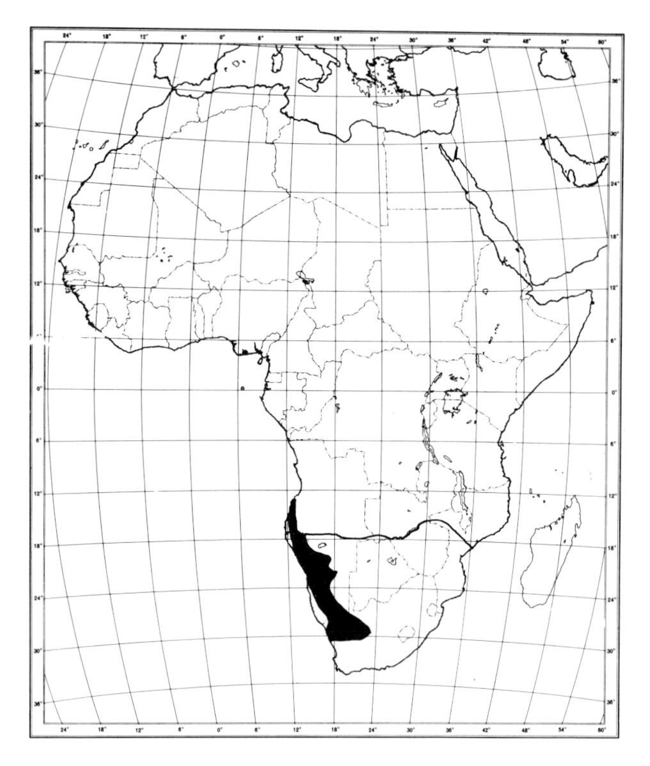

### Habitat

*Petromus* is the oldest rodent inhabitant of the Namib Desert (Meester, 1965). They are closely confined to rocky outcrops, living in crevices in these or under piles of boulders. *Petromus* may be scattered through different types of vegetation, but their location is determined by the availability of shelter rather than vegetation type (George & Crowther, 1981). *Petromus* inhabits rock shelters that *Procavia* (dassies) cannot enter in the Augrabies Falls National Park, where they compete with dassies. In the Namib Desert *Petromus* may be seen in slots with entrances up to 700 mm in height, but in the Augrabies Falls National Park minimum slot height was 44,2 ± 2,3 (n=54) *cf.* a maximum of 69,4 ± 3,1, and *cf.* a minimum of 15,1 ± 4,6 (n=69) for dassies.

### Habits

A crevice in their rocky habitat is occupied by pairs or a family. A suitable crevice must have adequate look-out points and sunbathing platforms and be linked to suitable feeding grounds by staging posts and bolt holes. They are diurnal, being most active in the early morning or late afternoon. When not foraging they will sun themselves in sheltered corners and, when disturbed, will run for the shelter of the crevices with great speed, their tails trailing behind them, being very fleet-footed and agile when jumping from rock to rock. They dust-bath in semi-sheltered places. The nests are lined with dry leaves and twigs. They tend to urinate in latrines, the rocks becoming stained with their whitish urine, especially below ledges on which they sun themselves, but they will defecate anywhere within their home ranges

They have low water and energy requirements and a kidney highly adapted for urine concentrating ability. However, in captivity, on a diet of air-dried seed they could not survive water deprivation for more than three weeks (Withers *et al.*, 1980). Most probably in the Namib Desert they assimilate water from advective fog and eating succulent plants.

### Food

*Petromus* have a simple stomach and moderately large caecum. They prefer grass and their obliquely ridged hypsodont cheekteeth, large infraorbital canal and deep zygomatic arch for masseter muscle attachment are adaptations for chewing lignified grasses. The greater part (69%–90% at three sites) of the diet in the dry season in the Augrabies Falls National Park consisted of monocotyledons, effectively the grasses *Enneapogon scaber*, *Cenchrus ciliarus* and *Triraphis ramossissima* (George, 1981). Dicotyledons (10–35%) comprised the leaves of *Schotia afra* and *Hermannia stricta*, with small amounts of *Cucumis dinteri* and *Lycium austrinum* (George, 1981). She found that 75% of grasses were cropped at the base of the clumps where the water content was three times as high as in the higher parts of the stems; moreover, the water content of dicotyledon leaves was much higher than that of monocotyledons, 57,6% $H_2O$ *cf.* 18,2% and 75,5% respectively (George, 1981). In the Namib Desert, the preferred grass was *Anthephora pubescens* and they also took *Stipagrostris* spp, which were unpopular elsewhere (George, pers. comm.). They relish the fleshy fruits of the wild cucumber, *Cucumis dinteri*, and Coetzee (1983) included the leaves of the thorny creeper, *Tribulus* sp. in their diet.

Dassie rats climb trees when foraging, plucking leaves and then scampering for cover to eat them. Coetzee (1983) recorded that when they crop grass, they also may carry them to the shelter of rocks to be eaten or used for nest-building. They may regurgitate food by bending the head until it nearly touches the abdomen in a quick jack-knife movement which forces the contents of the stomach back to the mouth where it is then masticated and reswallowed, a practice unique among non-artiodactyls. They also practise coprophagy, bending to take a faecal pellet from the anus, which is then eaten or thrown away with a quick jerk of the head to distances of up to a metre.

Faecal analysis of the rock dassie and the dassie rat from the Augrabies Falls National Park showed that *Schotia afra* formed 80% of the rock dassie droppings and grasses only 20%, whereas the dassie rat droppings consisted predominantly of grass. De Graaff (1981) noted that the flowers of Compositae are a preferred food when they are available.

### Reproduction

In Namibia gravid females have been taken in September and November (de Graaff, 1981) and Shortridge (1934) stated that they have their young during the warm, wet summer months. The young are born fully haired in rocky crevices lined with dry leaves. The females have two pairs of mammae situated on the sides of the body just behind the shoulders and a third pair further back on the body.

# XXIII. Family MURIDAE

## Rats and mice

A number of different arrangements of the Families comprising the Order Rodentia have been suggested since that proposed by Oldfield Thomas (1896). Ellerman (1940) used what he believed to be the best features of the five classifications of murids which had appeared up to that time: Thomas (1896); Tullberg (1899); Weber (1904); Miller & Gidley (1918) and Winger (1924). Misonne (1974) considered the Cricetidae as worthy of Familial rank and dealt with the Cricetidae and Muridae together as the status of some of the Subfamilies was not clear. He indicated that the only good character separating these two Families was the shape of the molar teeth. More recently Carleton & Musser (1984) included all the known muroid Subfamilies in the Family Muridae, basing this on convenience rather than conviction. Meester *et al.* (1986) used their proposals and approach which is followed in the present monograph.

In this the Family Muridae is divided into a series of seven Subfamilies, the genera comprising these being as follows:

| Subfamily | | |
|---|---|---|
| | 1. Otomyinae | *Otomys* |
| | | *Parotomys* |
| | 2. Murinae | *Pelomys* |
| | | *Acomys* |
| | | *Lemniscomys* |
| | | *Rhabdomys* |
| | | *Zelotomys* |
| | | *Dasymys* |
| | | *Grammomys* |
| | | *Mus* |
| | | *Uranomys* |
| | | *Mastomys* |
| | | *Myomyscus* |
| | | *Thallomys* |
| | | *Aethomys* |
| | | *Rattus* |
| | 3. Gerbillinae | *Desmodillus* |
| | | *Gerbillurus* |
| | | *Tatera* |
| | 4. Cricetinae | *Mystromys* |
| | 5. Cricetomyinae | *Cricetomys* |
| | | *Saccostomus* |
| | 6. Dendromurinae | *Dendromys* |
| | | *Malacothrix* |
| | | *Steatomys* |
| | 7. Petromyscinae | *Petromyscus* |

Key to the Subfamilies (Meester *et al.*, 1986)

1. The third upper molar the largest tooth; cheekteeth compactly laminate
   ... OTOMYINAE

   The first upper molar the largest tooth; cheekteeth not compactly laminate
   ... 2

2. The first upper molar tooth with three cusps in anterior row
   ... MURINAE

   The first upper molar tooth with only two cusps in anterior row (except in *Cricetomys*, which is distinguished by its large size)
   ... 3

3. Bullae much enlarged, at least 25 per cent of greatest skull length; upper cheekteeth with cusps in two longitudinal rows, weakly laminate when worn
   ... GERBILLINAE

   Bullae less enlarged, less than 25 per cent of greatest skull length
   ... 4

4. Soles of hind feet partly haired; upper cheekteeth with cusps in two longitudinal rows, weakly laminate when worn
   ... CRICETINAE

   Soles of hind feet naked (except in *Malacothrix*, distinguished by having only four toes on hind foot); upper cheekteeth with cusps in three longitudinal rows
   ... 5

5. With cheek pouches; upper incisors ungrooved; head and body length more than 110 mm, and may be much greater
   ... CRICETOMYINAE

   Without cheek pouches; upper incisors grooved or ungrooved; head and body length less than 110 mm
   ... 6

6. Upper incisors grooved
   ... DENDROMURINAE

   Upper incisors ungrooved
   ... PETROMYSCINAE

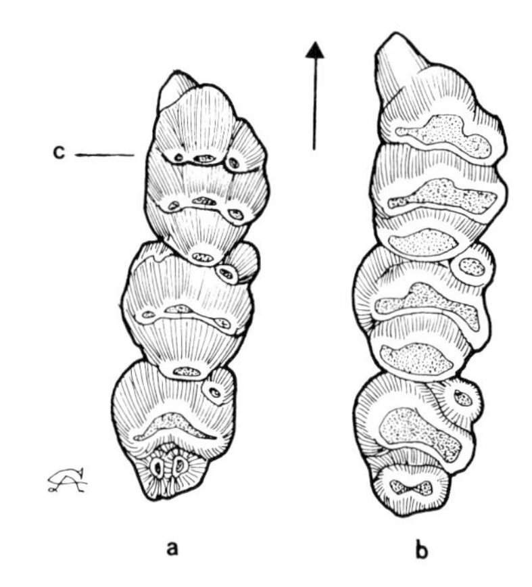


Fig. XXIII.1. Cheekteeth: Murinae
(a) upper right, juvenile unworn (b) upper right, adult worn
(c) first upper molar with three cusps in the first row.

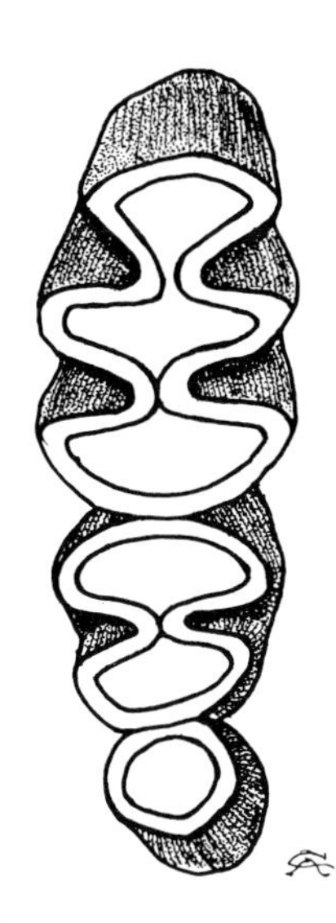

Fig. XXIII.2. Worn upper cheekteeth pattern: Gerbillinae
(after Ellerman, 1941).

In her significant contribution to the identification of cricetids and murids, Keogh (1985) showed that many species can be identified using hair characters and, in particular, cuticular scale pattern (Fig. XXIII.3) and groove characteristics which lend themselves to the formation of keys. Where only hair remains, as for example in stomach contents, then such keys can be vital aids to identification and have been dealt with under each species here.

## Subfamily OTOMYINAE

The name of the Subfamily is derived from the Greek *ous, otis*, an ear, and *mys*, a mouse, referring to their large, rounded ears. They are short-bodied, stocky-looking mice with stout bodies, blunt faces, well-haired ears and long, shaggy hair. They have short tails, less than half the length of the head and body, a feature by which they can be distinguished from the water rat, *Dasymys incomtus*, which also has a shaggy coat and looks somewhat similar, but has a noticeably longer tail. In members of the genus *Otomys* the upper incisors are grooved, in *Dasymys* ungrooved.

The skull is heavily built, the rostrum noticeably short and broad at the base, narrowing anteriorly. The cheekteeth are laminate (Fig. 156.1), the third upper molar teeth enlarged; these characters actuated Misonne (1974) to include them with the Cricetidae rather than the Muridae. The first upper molar has three laminae, the second two, the third with three to nine. In the lower jaw the first molar has four to seven laminae, the second two and the third two. The third upper molar and the first lower molar are therefore always the largest of the cheekteeth. The individual cheek-

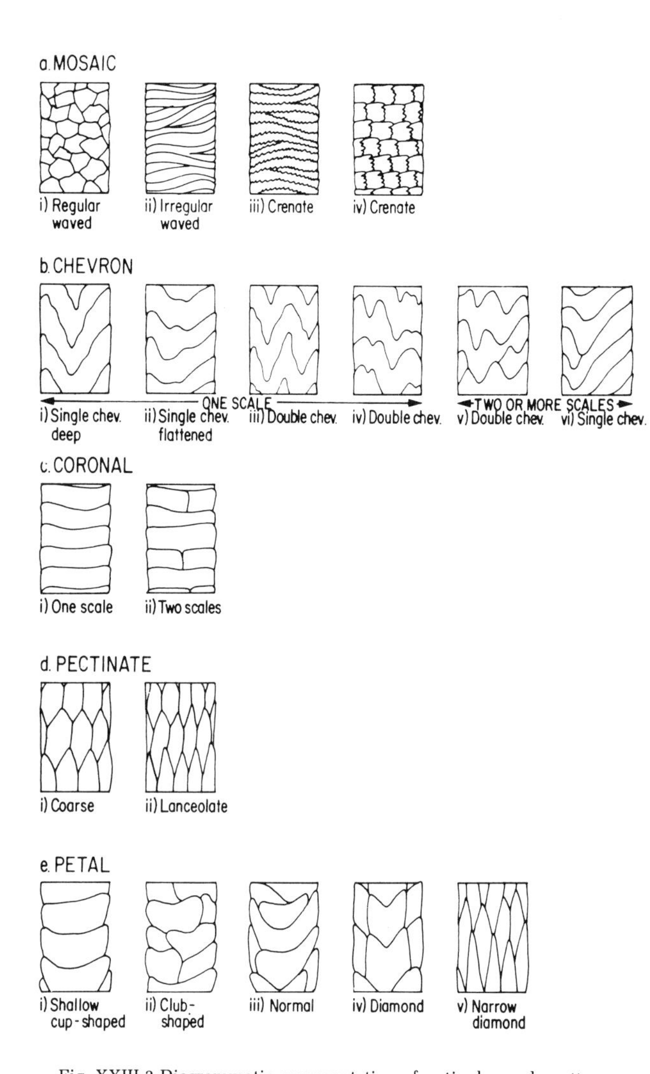


Fig. XXIII.3 Diagrammatic representation of cuticular scale patterns of some southern African cricetids and murids (Keogh, 1985)

teeth lie so closely together that they give the impression of a single, uniform laminate tooth. Each of the cheekteeth consists of a differing but more or less constant number of laminae, the division of the Subfamily largely depending on this character.

In *Parotomys brantsii* the upper incisors are grooved, in *P. littledalei* ungrooved. In the Subregion the Subfamily is represented by two genera, *Otomys* and *Parotomys*, with seven species of the former and two of the latter. Interspecific relationships within *Otomys* are complex, with the status of some of the species within the Subregion being doubtful (Robinson & Elder, 1987).

Key to the genera (Meester *et al.*, 1986)

1. Bullae much enlarged, minimum length of the bullae in adults 10,8 mm

   ... *Parotomys*

   Bullae little or not much enlarged, maximum length of the bullae in adults 9,5 mm

   ... *Otomys*

## Genus *Parotomys* Thomas, 1918

This genus is distinguished from *Otomys* Cuvier, 1823 by their noticeably inflated ear bullae, their meatus having a distinctly thickened process on the anterior edge.

Key to the species (Misonne, 1974)

1. Upper incisors grooved

   ... *brantsii*

   Upper incisors plain

   ... *littledalei*

No. 150

## *Parotomys brantsii* (A. Smith, 1834)

## Brants' whistling rat
## Brants se fluitrot

Plate 9

### Colloquial Name

So called from their habit, when sensing danger, of sitting up on their back legs and vocalising with a sharp, piercing whistle.

### Taxonomic Notes

Meester *et al.* (1986) listed three subspecies: the nominate *P. b. brantsii* from the northwestern Cape Province, *P. b. rufifrons* (Wagner, 1843) from the central Cape Province and *P. b. deserti* Roberts, 1933 from the northern Cape Province and southwestern Botswana.

### Description

The males have a total length of about 240 mm, with tails about 90 mm and a mass of up to 165 g; the females have the same total length and tail length, with a mass of up to 155 g (Table 150.1). The hairs have a pectinate pattern with a broad shallow groove (Fig. XXIII.3) (Keogh, 1985). The upper parts of the body and the flanks vary in colour geographically. *P. b. deserti* from the southern Kalahari is the most pallid form, the upper parts a pale, slightly rusty-yellow, with paler flanks and white under parts; *P. b. brantsii* is pale brownish-yellow streaked with blackish or dark brown, the flanks greyish-white streaked with brown, the under parts greyish-white. In the darker form, *P. b. brantsii*, the chin and throat are greyish-white like the under parts, the sides of the head and neck greyish-white streaked with brown. The nose and the proximal upper half of the tail are reddish-orange, the distal half reddish-brown. The individual hairs on the upper surface of the body are slate at the base, annulated with a band of colour in varying shades of brownish-yellow and with blackish-brown tips.

### Table 150.1

Measurements (mm) and mass (g) of adult Brants' whistling rats, *P. brantsii*, from southwestern Botswana (Smithers, 1971)

| | Males | | | Females | | |
|---|---|---|---|---|---|---|
| | $\bar{x}$ | n | Range | $\bar{x}$ | n | Range |
| TL | 239 | 4 | 220–263 | 246 | 18 | 227–274 |
| (HB | 146) | | | (153) | | |
| T | 93 | 4 | 85–100 | 93 | 18 | 80–110 |
| Hf c/u | 32 | 4 | 29–34 | 32 | 17 | 27–34 |
| E | 18 | 3 | 17–19 | 17 | 17 | 15–18 |
| Mass | Two only 130 and 145 | | | 121 | 8 | 89–155 |

### Distribution

They are confined to within the limits of the Subregion, occurring in the central, northern and northwestern parts of the **Cape Province**, and extending marginally into southern and southeastern **Namibia** and southwestern **Botswana**.

### Habitat

They are associated predominantly with a dry sandy substrate in the more arid parts of the Subregion within the South West Arid Zone, with a marginal extension into the Cape Macchia. Du Plessis (1989) reported that this species selects deep sands with coarse to medium particle size. Their occurrence falls roughly within areas which have a mean annual rainfall of less than 300 mm. In southwestern Botswana they are associated with dune slopes and troughs and the dry bed of the Molopo River and its adjacent sandy banks.

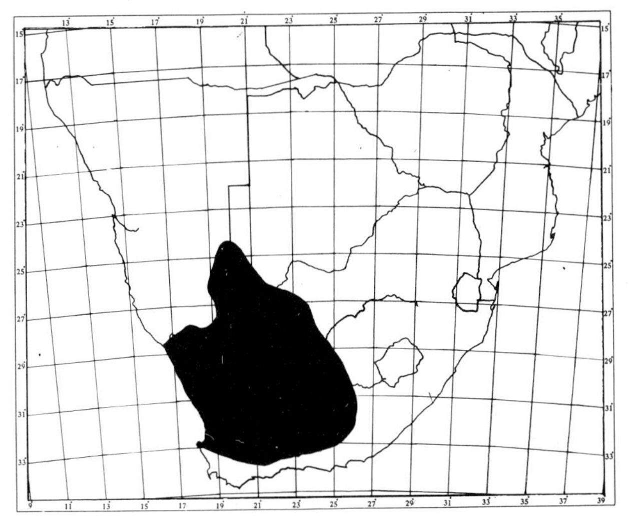

## Habits

Brants' whistling rat is predominantly diurnal in its habits, although Nel & Rautenbach (1974) found that, on moonlight nights, they were active and would whistle some hours after sunset, while Du Plessis (1989) found them to be transitional between crepuscular and nocturnal in captivity. They are most active in the morning around 08h00 and in the late afternoon about 18h30, with some activity throughout the day. Nel & Rautenbach (1974) recorded that they spend an average of about four hours during daylight hours above ground, most of the time (47%) being taken up in feeding; 35% in resting or in the alert position; 16% in digging, and 2% in grooming. In resting they sit or lie in shade near the entrance of the burrow. In the alert position they sit up on their back feet with their front feet extended horizontally or folded against the body, when they occasionally may indulge in head bobbing. In digging, the soil is scratched with the front feet in unison, pushed under the belly and kicked out with the hind feet, also operating in unison.

They live in isolated burrow systems or in warrens with many entrances, the burrows excavated in consolidated sandy ground between sand dunes or in dry river beds. When alarmed they vocalise with a loud, sharp, piercing whistle and stamp their back feet before diving for the shelter of the burrow. If a recording of this whistle is played back to them in captivity, individuals will immediately sit up and look around and then dive for cover. Under captive conditions domed shelters are constructed from fine vegetable debris, with a single entrance in which they rest with their noses protruding from the entrance hole. De Graaff (1981) found that in the wild the nests are chambers in the burrow system. He recorded that, in the Kalahari Gemsbok National Park, a single nest excavated from a chamber in a burrow had a mass of 190 g and was loosely constructed of vegetable debris which had been finely shredded. The chamber from which it was recovered was about 250 mm in diameter. Situated in the burrow system, it had a number of tunnels radiating from it, one running directly to the surface.

De Graaff & Nel (1965) noted that the burrow systems vary greatly in size and may extend over an area of about 4 m by 6 m and may have up to 21 entrances, which open either on to open ground or under bushes. The tunnels are more or less circular with an average diameter of 80 mm, wider in certain sections. Blind tunnels lead off the main tunnels, the purpose of which is unknown. Some, however, are used for defecation. The depth of the tunnels below the surface varies considerably but some reach up to about 0,75 m. Du Plessis (1989) measured more moderate temperatures and higher vapour pressures within the burrows compared to outside and postulated that the use of such refuges is critical for a species portraying few physiological adaptations to a semi-arid environment.

## Food

Brants' whistling rats are generalist herbivores (du Plessis, 1989), living on the succulent stems and leaves of xerophytic shrubs, on grasses, grass and other seeds, and annual plants. Nel & Rautenbach (1974) listed 15 species of grasses and plants on which they have been observed to feed, whilst the time of day affects their foraging activities. During early morning and in late afternoon they feed near burrow entrances, ranging further afield later, but during the hottest hours they would feed in the shade near the entrances. When foraging widely from their burrows, they would cut off short lengths of vegetation with succulent leaves and drag them back to near the burrow entrances, where they would be stripped of their edible portions, the area around the entrances becoming littered with discarded remains. Nel & Rautenbach (1974) recorded that they will climb into low shrubs, biting off tender shoots and dropping them to the ground to be collected later. They will dig up leafy plants, nipping them off from the root, and carry the whole plant back to be eaten. They will also stretch up to bite off parts of grass from clumps, whilst Du Plessis (1989) suggested that their dietary patterns merely reflect food availability within their microhabitat.

They sit on their haunches when eating, manipulating the food with the front feet. Seeding grasses are fed through the side of the mouth until the seeding portions are reached, when they are swung around forwards to be fed into the front of the mouth. In foraging, individuals tend to operate independently.

## Reproduction

Gravid females have been taken in southwestern Botswana in February, suggesting that the young are born during the latter part of the summer. The average number of foetuses is 2,1 (n=9), with an observed range of from one to three (Smithers, 1971). The females have two pairs of inguinal mammae and the young nipple-cling during the early part of their lives, being dragged along by the females even when they are foraging.

---

No. 151

# *Parotomys littledalei* Thomas, 1918

# Littledale's whistling rat
# Littledale se fluitrot

---

## Colloquial Name

Named after Major H.A.P. Littledale who collected the original specimen from which the species is described at Kenhardt, Cape Province, in 1911.

## Taxonomic Notes

Three subspecies are listed by Meester *et al.* (1986): *P. l. littledalei* from the central northern parts of the Cape Province and parts of southern Namibia; *P. l. molopensis* Roberts, 1933 known only from Hakskeen Pan near the southern end of the Kalahari Gemsbok National Park, and *P. l. namibensis* Roberts, 1933 from the Swakopmund District, Namibia.

## Description

Males and females are about the same size, with a total length of about 250 mm and tails that average about 77% of the length of the head and body. No masses of males are available, but females have a mass of up to about 145,0 g (Table 151.1). The hairs have a broad, shallow groove with a pectinate pattern (Fig. XXIII.3) (Keogh, 1985). In colour they are somewhat similar to *P. brantsii*, but slightly darker, the upper parts cinnamon-buff, the sides and belly paler buff. *P. b. namibensis* is deep tawny in colour and buffy below, especially on the throat which is a rich buffy colour. *P. l. molopensis* is paler than *P. l. littledalei*, the flanks and limbs greyer. The upper surfaces of the feet are white, compared with *P. l. littledalei* in which they are buffy-white. In this species the tail is longer than in *P. brantsii* and in *P. l. littledalei* is well-haired, dark buffy on its upper surface, a variable portion of the terminal part black or brown. In *P. l. molopensis* the tail has a black line on top for its whole length and in *P. l. namibensis* it is tawny-buff, browner above towards the tip.

### Distribution

This species is confined in its distribution to within the limits of the Subregion. The distribution pattern corresponds remarkably with that of *Gerbillurus vallinus*, occurring from coastal **Namibia** (at about 21 °S) and in the inland southern parts of the country to the northwestern and central parts of the **Cape Province**.

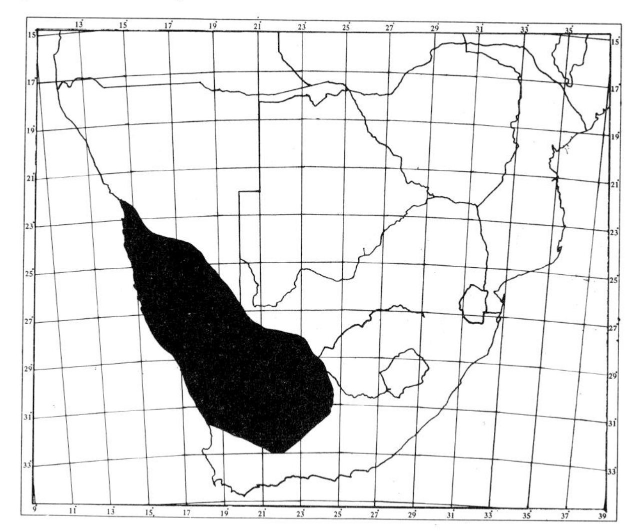

### Table 151.1

Measurements (mm) and mass (g) of Littledale's whistling rats, *P. littledalei*, from Namibia and the Cape Province (de Graaff, 1981)

| | Males | | | Females | | |
|---|---|---|---|---|---|---|
| | $\bar{x}$ | n | Range | $\bar{x}$ | n | Range |
| (T | 253) | | | (251) | | |
| HB | 150 | 6 | 135–170 | 146 | 9 | 130–161 |
| T | 103 | 5 | 93–122 | 105 | 9 | 92–117 |
| Hf c/u | 27 | 6 | 27–28 | 26 | 9 | 24–28 |
| E | 19 | 6 | 18–20 | 18 | 9 | 17–20 |
| Mass | No data | | | 127 | 2 | 110–145 |

### Habitat

Coetzee (1969) recorded that this species occurs in coastal hummocks, sand dunes and in the gravel plains of the Namib Desert, Namibia and in riverine associations. However, it is absent from the main dune systems. Their occurrence appears to be linked with the coastal hummocks which are covered with a low growth of *gannabos, Salsola* sp, *inkbos, Suaeda plumosa*, or *potloodplant, Arthraerua leubnitziae*. In the riverine association of the Swakop River they occur close to its mouth in the higher sandy parts of the river bed away from the damp, brackish bed. In the northwestern or central parts of the Cape Province they occur in the more arid areas with a mean annual rainfall of less than 200 mm.

### Habits

Littledale's whistling rats are more solitary in their habits than Brants'. Coetzee (1969) recorded that usually one individual or at most a female with young or up to two subadults would live in a single *Salsola* sp covered hummock. De Graaff (1981) recorded that nests are constructed at the base of dense bushes, with burrows below them and numerous runways formed from the nesting sites to feeding areas (Coetzee, 1969).

### Food

They are vegetarians living on the succulent leaves of shrubs. Coetzee (1969) recorded that runways lead to succulent *Zygophyllum stapfii* bushes on which they feed. Apart from this observation there is no further information available on their diet.

### Reproduction

No information is available on this aspect of the life history.

## Genus *Otomys* F. Cuvier, 1824

Members of this genus have skulls characterised by narrow interorbital constrictions, well-developed supraorbital ridges, which are continued backwards across the braincase, and nasal bones conspicuously broadened towards the tip of the rostrum. The short, deep mandible is powerfully built. The upper incisors are noticeably heavy and deeply grooved in some species; the lower incisors have only a very faint groove or none at all. The laminated molar teeth have no cusps, their general configuration being the same as that described under the Subfamily. In the upper jaw the first molar has three laminations, the second two, the third from four to nine. In the lower jaw the first molar has four to seven laminations, the second and third two each. The third molar is always the largest tooth in the upper jaw. The first molar in the lower jaw and the number of laminations on the teeth are useful characters in separating the groups of species (Fig. 156.1).

Key to the species after Meester *et al.* (1986)

1. One deep outer and sometimes also one shallow groove on each lower incisor tooth
   ... 2
   
   Lower incisors ungrooved
   ... 5
2. 9–10 laminae on the third upper molar teeth, the first lower molar teeth with 6–7 laminae
   ... *laminatus*
   
   4–7 laminae on the third upper molar teeth, the first lower molar teeth with 4 laminae
   ... 3
3. Posterior petrotympanic foramen a slit only (Fig. 153.1.b)
   ... *angoniensis*
   
   Posterior petrotympanic foramen a round hole (Fig. 153.1.a)
   ... 4
4. Molar series shorter than 8,8 mm; nasal width 6,3 mm and less; hind foot length less than 25 mm; fur buffy
   ... *saundersiae*
   
   Molar series longer than 8,8 mm; nasal width 6,5 mm and more; hind foot length more than 25 mm; fur greyish
   ... *irroratus*
5. Tail short, usually less than half of head and body length; posterior petrotympanic foramen slit-like
   ... *sloggetti*
   
   Tail longer, usually more than 60 percent of head and body length; posterior petrotympanic foramen round
   ... *unisulcatus*

No. 152

## *Otomys laminatus* Thomas & Schwann, 1905

## Laminate vlei rat
## Bergvleirot

### Colloquial Name

Laminate refers to the laminations on the molar teeth, this species having a larger number of these on the third upper molar teeth than any other. The Afrikaans name *bergvleirot* is misleading as they are not confined strictly to a submontane habitat from which they have been taken.

### Taxonomic Notes

Meester *et al.* (1986) listed five subspecies: the nominate *O. l. laminatus* from northern Natal and KwaZulu; *O. l. silberbaueri* Roberts, 1919 from the southwestern Cape Province; *O. l. pondoensis* Roberts, 1924 from Transkei; *O. l.*

*mariepsi* Roberts, 1929 from the Lydenburg District, Transvaal, and *O. l. fannini* (Roberts, 1951) from central Natal.

### Description

Adult males have a mean total length of about 300 mm, with tails just over 100 mm and a mass of about 190 g, the tails being about half the length of the head and body (Table 152.1). The scale pattern on the hairs is lanceolate-pectinate, but not noticeably sharp-toothed (Fig. XXIII.3) (Keogh, 1985). The fur is soft, fine and shaggy. The individual hairs are about 20 mm in length, basally black or very dark slate, with a rufous annulation near the tip and narrow black tips. The under parts are dull yellowish, the base of the individual hairs grey. The ears are naked externally and the paws and feet are blackish-grey on their upper surfaces. The tail is thickly haired, blackish above and dull buffy below. The colour of the body varies geographically and is the basis on which the subspecies have been created. Their validity warrants further study.

The skull conforms to the general pattern of the Subfamily, the third upper molar tooth always having over nine laminae. The formula of the laminae in this toothrow is 3.2.9 (de Graaff, 1981).

### Table 152.1

Measurements (mm) and mass (g) of laminate vlei rats, *O. laminatus*, from the eastern parts of the Subregion (de Graaff, 1981)

| | Males | | | Females | | |
|---|---|---|---|---|---|---|
| | $\bar{x}$ | n | Range | $\bar{x}$ | n | Range |
| (TL | 308) | | | (285) | | |
| HB | 199 | 5 | 188–213 | 178 | 3 | 158–197 |
| T | 109 | 5 | 97–115 | 107 | 3 | 105–111 |
| Hf c/u | 30 | 5 | 22–34 | 30 | 3 | 30–31 |
| E | 21 | 5 | 17–26 | 24 | 3 | 22–26 |
| Mass | 190 | 1 | — | 140 | 1 | — |

### Distribution

The species has a discontinuous distribution on the Lowveld side of the Eastern Escarpment/Drakensberg Range, as well as in **Natal** and **Transkei**, with a relict population in the Paarl Valley in the southwestern **Cape Province**.

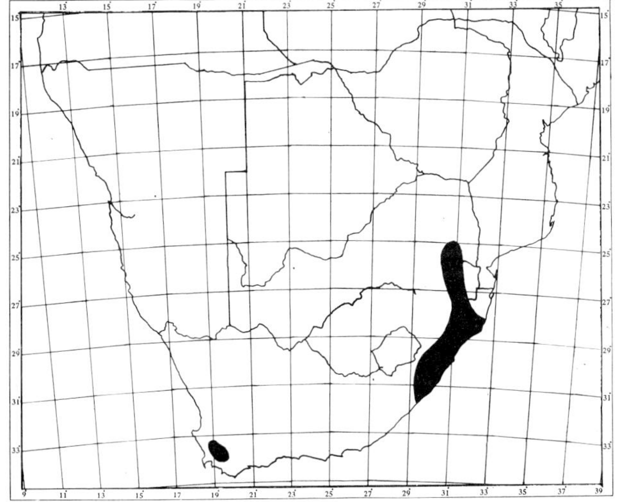

### Habitat

A grassland species, occurring in submontane as well as coastal areas.

### Habits

Apart from the fact that it is sympatric with *O. irroratus* and *O. angoniensis* in parts of its range, nothing is known of the habits of this species.

### Food

De Graaff (1981) recorded that they are vegetarian, their diet consisting of the shoots and stems of grasses and small shrubs.

### Reproduction

No information available.

No. 153

## *Otomys angoniensis* Wroughton, 1906

Angoni vlei rat
Angoni-vleirot
Plate 9

### Colloquial Name

So named as the original specimen from which the species was described came from M'Kombhiue, Angoniland, Malawi.

### Taxonomic Notes

Meester *et al.* (1986) listed three subspecies from the Subregion: *O. a. rowleyi* Thomas, 1918 from central and eastern Zimbabwe and Mozambique; *O. a. maximus* Roberts, 1924 from the Caprivi, northern Botswana and northeastern Namibia, and *O. a. tugelensis* Roberts, 1929 from the northeastern Cape Province, Natal, Lesotho, Swaziland, Transvaal and southeastern Botswana. The nominate *O. a. angoniensis* occurs in northern Malawi.

### Description

Adults reach a total length of about 300 mm, males with masses of about 100,0 g (Table 153.1). The hairs have a pectinate pattern, are relatively broad, with six or less than six scales across their width (Fig. XXIII.3) (Keogh, 1985). The upper parts vary in colour geographically from a pale buff to a dark buff; the individual hairs are slate-black at the base with an annulation of buffy towards the tip, and a black tip; some hairs lack the black tip. There are buffy-yellow patches around the eyes and on the throat. The tail is dark above and buffy-white below. The under parts are a dull dark grey. The best characters to separate this species from *O. irroratus* are the formation of the posterior petrotympanic foramen, which in this species is in the form of a slit (Fig. 153.1.b), and the ring of buffy-yellow around the eyes, which is absent in *O. irroratus*. The length of the hind foot in *O. angoniensis* is shorter than in *O. irroratus*, Davis (1973) giving this as 25–28 mm (n=15) in the former and 29–34 mm (n=159) in the latter. In Zimbabwe the range was slightly different although *O. irroratus* still has the longer hind foot, the ranges being: *O. angoniensis* 25–30 mm and *O. irroratus* 30–33 mm in a sample of 20 of each. *O. angoniensis* usually has seven laminae on the third upper molar teeth.

### Table 153.1

Measurements (mm) and mass (g) of Angoni vlei rats, *O. angoniensis* from the Transvaal (Rautenbach, 1978) and northern Botswana (Smithers & Wilson, 1979)

**Transvaal**

| | Males | | | Females | | |
|---|---|---|---|---|---|---|
| | $\bar{x}$ | n | Range | $\bar{x}$ | n | Range |
| (TL | 296) | | | (302) | | |
| HB | 217 | 91 | 140–279 | 223 | 97 | 143–272 |
| T | 79 | 91 | 43–102 | 79 | 97 | 44–125 |
| Hf c/u | 26 | 91 | 19–35 | 25 | 97 | 20–31 |
| E | 19 | 91 | 11–28 | 20 | 96 | 13–25 |
| Mass | 89,9 | 56 | 25,0–138,0 | 96,6 | 56 | 47,0–216,0 |

**Northern Botswana**

| | Males | | | Females | | |
|---|---|---|---|---|---|---|
| | $\bar{x}$ | n | Range | $\bar{x}$ | n | Range |
| TL | 296 | 14 | 259–330 | 283 | 6 | 217–317 |
| (HB | 405) | | | (403) | | |
| T | 109 | 13 | 95–122 | 120 | 6 | 100–150 |
| Hf c/u | 37 | 14 | 33–42 | 35 | 6 | 35–39 |
| E | 23 | 14 | 21–24 | 24 | 6 | 23–25 |
| Mass | 178,4 | 11 | 112,0–242,8 | 205,3 | 5 | 140,5–255,1 |

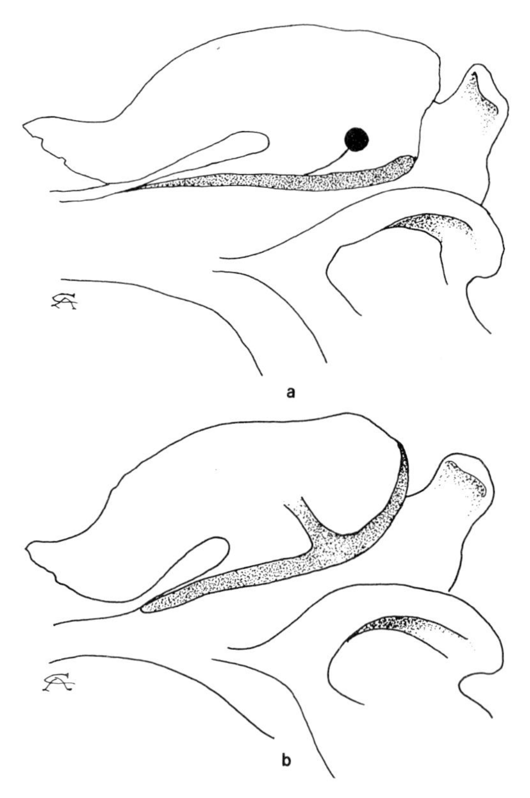


Fig. 153.1. Internal lateral view of bullae: *Otomys* spp
(a) Petrotympanic foramen a round hole: *O. irroratus*
(b) Petrotympanic foramen a slit: *O. angoniensis*.

## Distribution

*South of the Sahara, excluding the Southern African Subregion*

They are recorded from **Angola; Zaire; Zambia; Malawi; Mozambique**, north of the Zambezi River; **Tanzania** and **Kenya**.

*Southern African Subregion*

They occur in the northeastern and eastern parts of the **Cape Province**; in central and northern **Natal**; northeastern **Lesotho**; in northern **Botswana; Namibia**; and the **Caprivi Strip**; widely in the **Transvaal** and **Swaziland**; in the central and southern parts of **Mozambique**, south of the Zambezi River, and throughout central **Zimbabwe**.

## Habitat

They are associated particularly in the drier areas with wet vleis, swamps and swampy areas along rivers (Smithers & Wilson, 1979). De Graaff (1981) included savanna woodland and grasslands as suitable habitats.

## Habits

They are predominantly diurnal, with some nocturnal activity. They occur singly or in pairs or family parties. They build domed nests of shredded vegetation in clumps of tussock grass above water level or on raised ground, making well defined runs extending outwards from the nests to the feeding grounds. Small piles comprising short lengths of discarded grass stems mark these feeding grounds.

## Food

They are vegetarians, living on the succulent stems and rhizomes of grasses and fine reeds.

## Reproduction

Gravid females or juveniles have been taken from September to March, (Smithers & Wilson, 1979), suggesting that young are born during the warm, wet summer months. The average number of foetuses is 2,5 (n=10; range 2–5).

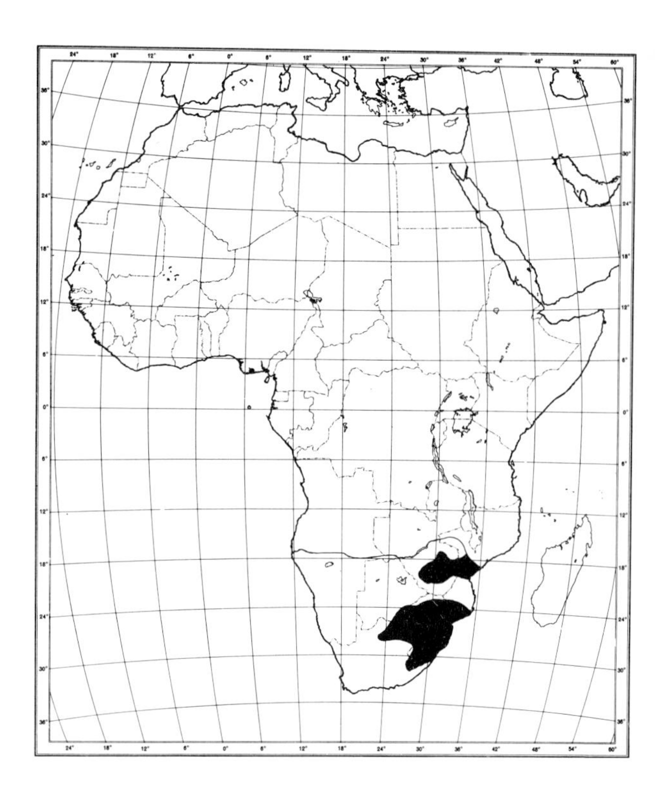

**WITHDRAWN**

No. 154

*Otomys maximus* Roberts, 1924, included in the first edition, is now considered to be a subspecies of *O. angoniensis*.

No. 155

# *Otomys saundersiae* Roberts, 1929

## Saunders' vlei rat
## Saunders se vleirot

## Colloquial Name

They are so called as the original specimens were brought to the notice of Roberts by a Miss Saunders of Grahamstown, who had made a study of the species.

## Taxonomic Notes

Originally described as *O. tugelensis saundersiae* by Roberts (1929) who later, in 1951 gave it full specific status as *O. saundersiae*.

## Description

Adult males have a mean total length of about 250 mm, the females 220 mm, with a mass of 111,0 g and 95,0 g respectively (Table 155.1). The hairs have a pectinate pattern, the scales obviously lanceolate-pectinate-sharply toothed (Fig. XXIII.3) (Keogh, 1985). The upper parts are light buffy in colour, grizzled with dark brown tipped hairs. The flanks are pale buffy and the under parts grey, the throat and distal parts of the limbs whiter. The under parts are buffy, the grey of the base of the hairs showing through to give them a greyish-buffy appearance. The tail is buffy-white on the upper surface, and buffy-grey on the under surface. The molar teeth have the same formula as *O. irroratus*; the laminae of the lower first molar are more curved. The upper and lower incisor teeth are deeply grooved towards their outer edges, as in *O. irroratus*.

**Table 155.1**

Measurements (mm) and mass (g) of Saunders' vlei rats, *O. saundersiae*, from the Cape Province and Orange Free State (de Graaff, 1981)

| | Males | | | Females | | |
|---|---|---|---|---|---|---|
| | x̄ | n | Range | x̄ | n | Range |
| (TL | 246) | | | (222) | | |
| HB | 151 | 13 | 133–17 | 210 | 14 | 124–165 |
| T | 95 | 12 | 79–111 | 82 | 11 | 74–92 |
| Hf c/u | 25 | 13 | 22–29 | 26 | 10 | 24–29 |
| E | 21 | 12 | 19–23 | 20 | 14 | 19–24 |
| Mass | 111 | 7 | 100–134 | 95 | 4 | 84–107 |

## Distribution

At present there are two discrete known areas of occurrence, one in the southwestern **Cape Province**, the other in the eastern parts of the province extending northwards to the southern boundary of the **Orange Free State** and the **Lesotho** border in the central-eastern Orange Free State sector.

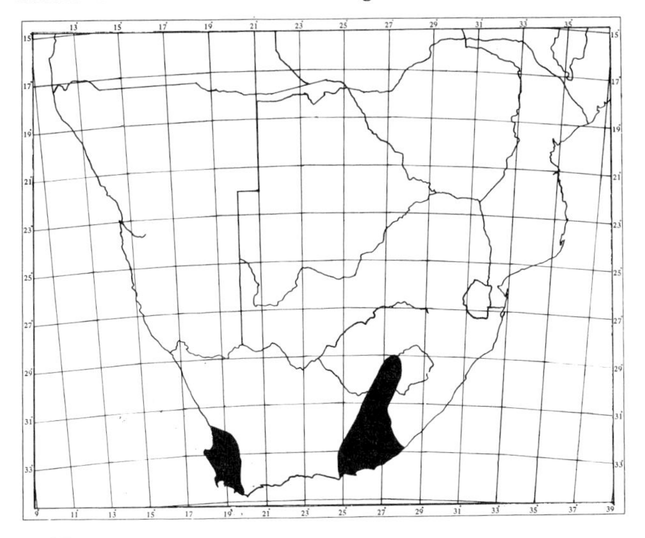

## Habitat

Shortridge (1934) stated that they have a preference for a mountainous habitat, occurring in belts of dry rushes in heath country on high mountain slopes.

## Habits

Shortridge (1934) stated that the species is diurnal, but apart from this nothing is known about this aspect of their life history.

## Food and Reproduction

No information available.

---

No. 156

# *Otomys irroratus* (Brants, 1827)

# Vlei rat
# Vleirot

---

## Colloquial Name

They are so called because of their association with damp vleis and wet grassland on the fringes of streams and swamps.

## Taxonomic Notes

Extensive changes in the *O. irroratus* genome (2n=28) have resulted in numerous structural rearrangements. Robinson & Elder (1987) have argued that this has resulted from their narrow habitat specificity and their susceptibility to climatic variation.

Meester *et al.* (1986) listed the following eight subspecies, noting that too many are recognised: *O. i. irroratus* (Brants, 1827) from the western and southern Cape Province east to Transkei; *O. i. auratus* Wroughton, 1906 from the northern Orange Free State; *O. i. cupreus* Wroughton, 1906 from the northern Transvaal; *O. i. coenosus* Thomas, 1918 from the northern Cape Province; *O. i. natalensis* Roberts, 1929 from central Natal to southeastern Transvaal; *O. i. randensis* Roberts, 1929 from Johannesburg, Transvaal; *O. i. cupreoides* Roberts, 1946 from the Soutpansberg, northern Transvaal, and *O. i. orientalis* Roberts, 1946 from northern Natal.

## Description

Vlei rats are of moderate to large size, with a total length of about 240 mm and a mass of about 122,0 g in males and 114,0 g in females (Table 156.1). They have stout bodies, blunt faces, large well-rounded ears and short tails which are about 60% of the length of the head and body. The coat is shaggy, the hair long and soft. The hairs have a pectinate scale pattern; they are relatively broad, with six or less than six scales across the width (Fig. XXIII.3) (Keogh, 1985). The colour of the upper parts varies geographically and is a grizzled dark slate-grey tinged with buff or brown. The individual hairs are dark slate at the base annulated with buffy towards the tips, which are black. The flanks and under parts are paler and greyer, the tail dark brown on the upper surface, buffy below, the feet dull dark grey. In the young the first moult starts at 14 days old and proceeds in a posterior direction until about the 42nd day. The subadult moult starts between the 56th and 70th day and is completed by about the 84th day. There does not appear to be a seasonal moult in the adults. Davis & Meester (1981) believed that this is a continuing process, the individual losing hair as the new hair develops. The ears are large and rounded and covered with hair. The forelimbs are short, the digits two to five well developed, the pollex rudimentary. The sides of the muzzle are buffy or rust-coloured, the cheeks and throat paler.

**Table 156.1**

Measurements (mm) and mass (g) of vlei rats, *O. irroratus*, from the Transvaal (Rautenbach, 1978)

| | Males | | | Females | | |
|---|---|---|---|---|---|---|
| | x̄ | n | Range | x̄ | n | Range |
| TL | 240 | 160 | 153–315 | 244 | 129 | 172–306 |
| (HB | 151) | | | (155) | | |
| T | 89 | 157 | 53–122 | 89 | 128 | 70–115 |
| Hf c/u | 30 | 171 | 23–53 | 29 | 133 | 26–35 |
| E | 20 | 171 | 14–25 | 21 | 136 | 17–27 |
| Mass | 122,0 | 121 | 59,0–178,0 | 114,0 | 108 | 71,0–238,0 |

## Skull

The skull is sturdily built, with a narrow interorbital constriction; the supraorbital ridges are pronounced. The palate is narrow, the palatal foramina long, reaching nearly to the level of the first upper molar. The mandible is heavily built, short, deep and heavily ridged.

The incisor teeth are large, yellow in colour and deeply grooved, the lower incisors with a deep outer and a shallower inner longitudinal groove. The molar teeth are laminated (Fig. 156.1); the first upper have three laminations, the second two, the number on the third varying, but usually being six. In the lower jaw the first molar is the largest tooth and has a variable number of laminae, usually four, the other two molars have two laminae each. The length of the row of cheekteeth in this species exceeds 8,8 mm; this distinguishes them from Saunders' vlei rat, *O. saundersiae*, in which it is less than 8,8 mm.

A characteristic feature of the skull which distinguishes this species from the Angoni vlei rat, *O. angoniensis*, which is similar in appearance, and which is sympatric in parts of its range, is the form of the petrotympanic foramen. In this species it is a large round hole (Fig. 153.1.a), in *O. angoniensis* the hole is tiny and lies in a slit-like depression on the inner face of the bulla (Fig. 153.1.b). Other features, useful in distinguishing the two species, are that in *O. irroratus* the length of the hind foot is 29–34 mm, in *O. angoniensis* 25–28 mm, and the conspicuous ring of orange-coloured hair around the eye in *O. angoniensis* is absent in *O. irroratus*. The degree of angular transition between the broad and narrow parts of the nasal bones is very distinct, less sudden in *O. angoniensis* (Fig. 156.2).

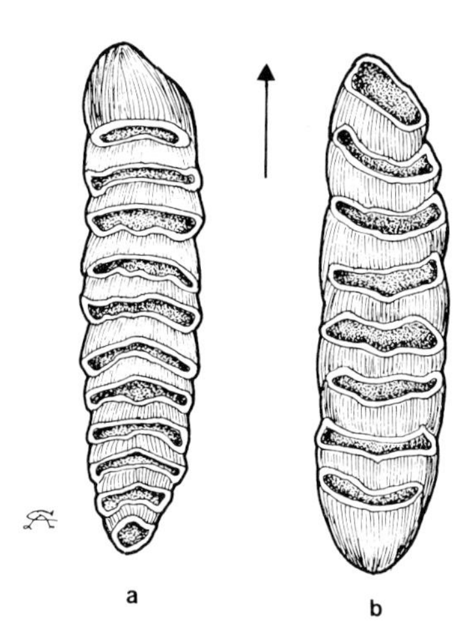


Fig. 156.1. Laminated cheekteeth: *Otomys irroratus* (a) upper right (b) lower right (after Rosevear, 1969).

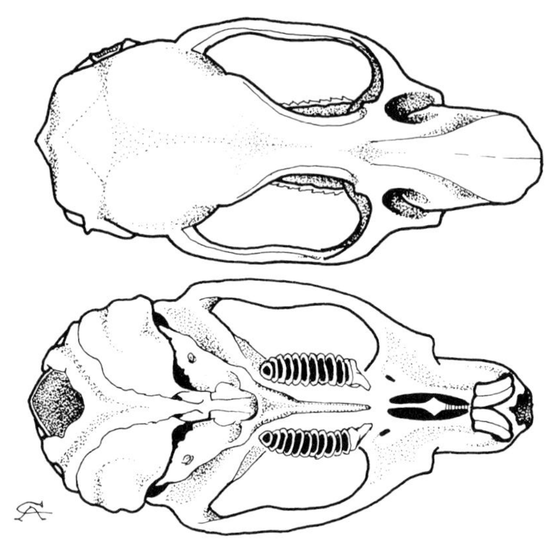

Fig. 156.2. Skull: *Otomys irroratus*, dorsal and ventral view.

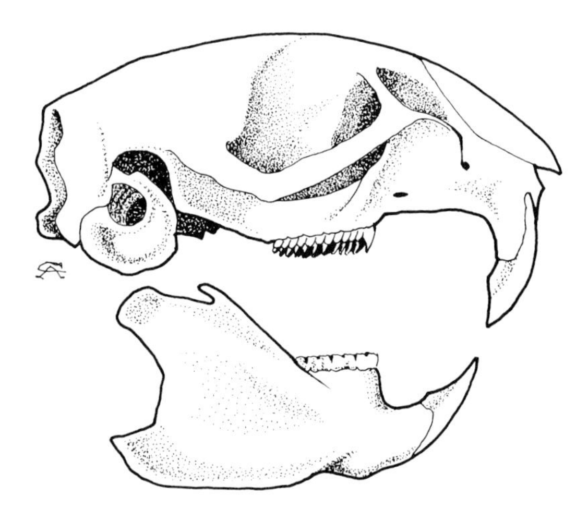

Fig. 156.3. Skull: *O. irroratus*, lateral view.

## Distribution

Until there is further evidence to show that *O. tropicalis* and *O. irroratus* are synonyms, they are each considered to be valid species. On this basis the vlei rat, *O. irroratus*, is confined in its distribution to within the limits of the Subregion.

*South of the Sahara, excluding the Southern African Subregion*

They are recorded from the eastern parts of **Zimbabwe** and adjacent parts of **Mozambique**, south of the Zambezi River. This appears as an isolated island of occurrence. Southwards they occur in the central and southern parts of the **Transvaal**; in **Natal**; the **Orange Free State** and widely throughout the **Cape Province**, except in the northwestern, northern and parts of the central sectors.

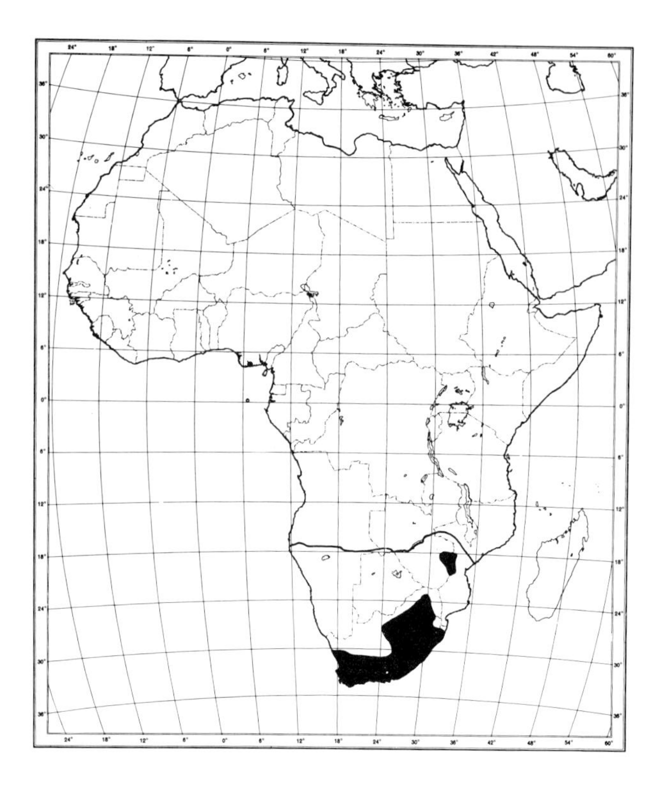

## Habitat

They have a wide distribution, occurring throughout grassland but are more abundant in moist habitats associated with damp soil in vleis, or along streams and rivers or on the fringes of swamp (Davis, 1973). In montane areas they occur on grass-covered hillsides and ridgetops, at considerable distances from water (Rowe-Rowe & Meester, 1982).

## Habits

Vlei rats are predominantly diurnal and terrestrial and to some extent semi-aquatic, but not to the extent seen in the Angoni vlei rat, *O. angoniensis*, and they seldom enter the water except when forced to do so. In suitable habitat they can be common and plentiful, but are generally solitary or found in pairs or family parties. They are probably territorial (Davis, 1973). They seldom if ever burrow but may use the burrows of other species where these are in dry ground. More commonly they construct their own saucer-shaped nests on rising dry ground or in clumps of grass. From these nests clearly marked runs lead to the feeding areas which are marked by the short lengths of grass stems discarded when feeding. Davis (1973) recorded two vocalisations, an alarm squeal when the individual is under stress, and a metallic "chit" directed at others as a threat as it sits upright on its haunches. The closer the intruder approaches, the more rapid and intense become the "chits".

Davis (1973) found that, in the Transvaal, the mean home range of the males is 1 730 $m^2$, that of the females 1 252 $m^2$. The size of the home range decreases in the winter months, but only slightly in relation to a doubling in the size of the population.

Vlei rats are preyed upon by small carnivores, diurnal birds of prey, snakes and in particular by the barn owl, *Tyto alba*, and the grass owl, *Tyto capensis*, the latter living in the same type of habitat as the vlei rat. They are considered a delicacy by some indigenous African people who trap them with nooses set in their runs, and assiduously search for their corpses after fires.

### Food

Vlei rats are wholly herbivorous and show advanced specialisation of the digestive tract. The teeth bear transverse lophs and the caecum is large and complex to enable efficient fibre digestion by microflora (Perrin & Curtis, 1980). Davis (1973) found that they will eat nearly all of the plant species that occur in their habitat: the succulent stems of grasses, young shoots of the reed *Phragmites* sp, forbs and even exotic plants such as the thistle, *Cirsium vulgare*, as well as grass and other seeds, have been recognised in stomach contents. Curtis & Perrin (1979) recorded that they eat grass in preference to other plant material or seeds. When feeding on grasses, the stems are bitten through near the ground and then picked up in the mouth and grasped on either side in the paws, and short 20–50 mm pieces cut off and chewed. If the grass is coarse the stem will be passed back and forth through the mouth to remove the unpalatable sections (Davis, 1973). Tell-tale piles of chopped sections of stem and other unpalatable parts are dropped and these mark the feeding areas. While feeding the individual sits on its haunches in a semi-upright position, the forelimbs rarely raised above the ground. Body fat content was seasonally stable indicating that this species has adapted its ingestion rate to an abundant and regular supply of green plant material (Perrin 1980a,b).

Coprophagy, the eating of faeces, is very common in the vlei rat. An adult individual will remove faeces from its anus with its teeth and eat it. They will also eat the fresh faeces of other individuals, which is an important habit in the weaning of young, supplying them with the proper microflora for the digestion of the food (Ewer, 1968).

### Reproduction

In the Transvaal, *O. irroratus* has an extended breeding season, young being born from August to early May with a peak in the warm wet summer months (Davis & Meester, 1981). The mean litter size is 2,33 (range 1–4; n=39). The females become sexually mature at a mass of 76,0 g when they are nine to 10 weeks old or exceptionally at 45,0 g and four weeks of age; males mature much later at a mass of about 96,0 g and 13 weeks of age. The estimated gestation period is 40 days and as they are polyoestrous up to seven litters may be produced during the protracted breeding season (usually four to five). On this basis a female may produce nine to 12 young in a season.

The young are precocial, having a generous covering of black underfur which on the upper parts is about 2 mm in length, with guard hairs up to 5 mm. Their eyes are either open or closed, the ears erect and the incisor teeth erupted. Davis & Meester (1981) gave the mass at birth as 12,5 g (9,6–15,5; n=28). The young nipple-cling for about the first 14 days of life and are seldom seen unattached, but when they are, they crawl around in an unco-ordinated manner. Davis (1973) suggested that the principal value of nipple-clinging in young is to reduce the risk of predation, which applies particularly to species with nests on the ground, which afford less protection to the young.

Davis & Meester (1981) found that growth of the young is rapid: under captive conditions the mass increases at the rate of 1,29 g per day up to the fifth day, and this is the same in the field; thereafter those in captivity have a growth rate 33% higher than those taken from the field.

The females have two pairs of inguinal mammae.

No. 157

## *Otomys sloggetti* Thomas, 1902

## Sloggett's rat
## Sloggett se rot

Plate 9

### Colloquial Name

They were named in recognition of the collections made at Deelfontein by Col. A.T. Sloggett in 1902. Alternative name: ice rat.

### Taxonomic Notes

Meester *et al.* (1986) listed five subspecies: *O. s. sloggetti* from the central Cape Province; *O. s. turneri* Wroughton, 1907 from the Orange Free State; *O. s. robertsi* Hewitt, 1927 from northeastern Lesotho; *O. s. jeppei* (Roberts, 1929) from the northeastern Cape Province, and *O. s. basuticus* (Roberts, 1929) from southern Lesotho.

### Description

Adults of both sexes are about the same size, with a total length of about 200 mm, their tails less than half the length of the head and body, and they have a mean mass of 137,0 g in males and 121,0 g in females (Table 157.1). The scales on the hairs have a lanceolate-pectinate pattern, but are not noticeably sharp-toothed (Fig. XXIII.3) (Keogh, 1985). The upper part of the body is vinaceous-brown, the flanks and under parts dull buffy, the individual hairs on the body having slate-coloured bases. The colour of the head is greyish-brown contrasting with the colour of the upper parts; the ears are of medium size with a dark fringe on the back. The upper surfaces of the hands and feet are buff in colour. The tail is short and thin with a narrow black line along the centre of the upper surface and dull buffy on its under surface. The fur is soft, fine and thick (de Graaff, 1981).

**Table 157.1**

Measurements (mm) and mass (g) of Sloggett's rats, *O. sloggetti*, from the Cape Province (de Graaff, 1981)

| | Males | | | Females | | |
|---|---|---|---|---|---|---|
| | $\bar{x}$ | n | Range | $\bar{x}$ | n | Range |
| (TL | 207) | | | (206) | | |
| HB | 144 | 6 | 130–153 | 143 | 6 | 135–150 |
| T | 63 | 6 | 55–71 | 63 | 6 | 58–70 |
| Hf c/u | 23 | 6 | 22–25 | 23 | 6 | 20–24 |
| E | 18 | 6 | 14–21 | 19 | 6 | 16–22 |
| Mass | 137,0 | 3 | 125,0–146,0 | 121,0 | 4 | 113,0–128,0 |

The upper incisor teeth have a single groove, more centrally placed than in other species; the single groove on the lower incisors is faint and barely perceptible. The upper third molar teeth have four distinct laminae and a fifth small rounded lamina at their posterior ends. The first lower molars have three transverse laminae and a fourth which is more rounded and shorter.

### Distribution

They occur in the eastern parts of the **Cape Province**, in **Lesotho** and parts of northwestern **Natal**. In Lesotho they occur at the highest altitudes found in South Africa, on the summit of Mont-aux-Sources in the Drakensberg at 3 282 m.

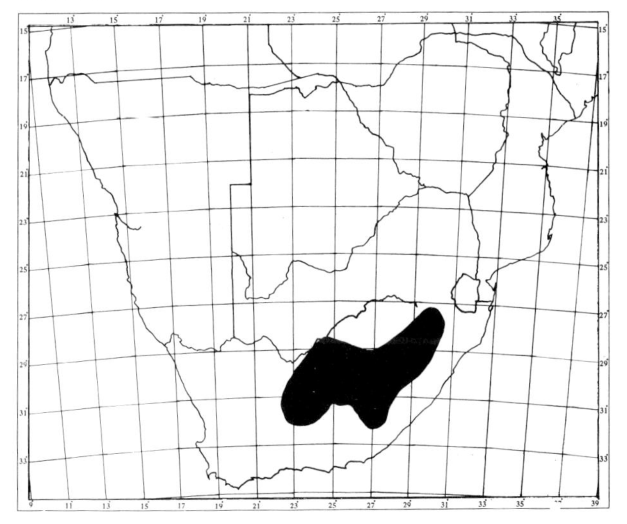

### Habitat

They occur at high altitudes, up to 2 700 m, amongst rocks and forbs, including the Karoo (Roberts, 1951; Rowe-Rowe & Meester, 1982).

### Habits

Diurnal and terrestrial, they live in crevices in rocks and in the shelter of piles of boulders. To the people in Lesotho they are known as ice rats as they have the habit of sunning themselves on rocks when there is snow on the ground.

### Food

Rowe-Rowe (1986) observed them eating leaves, young stems and flowers of *Helichrysum* plants on a number of occasions, suggesting that they are herbivorous.

### Reproduction

No information available.

---

No. 158

## *Otomys unisulcatus* F. Cuvier, 1829

## Karoo bush rat
## Karoose bosrot

---

### Colloquial Name

So named as they occur in drier bush habitat than other species of *Otomys*.

### Taxonomic Notes

Meester *et al.* (1986) listed five subspecies: *O. u. unisulcatus* from Matjiesfontein, Cape Province; *O. u. grantii* Thomas, 1902 from the central Cape Province; *O. u. bergensis* Roberts, 1929 from the western Cape Province; *O. u. albaniensis* Roberts, 1946 from the Albany District, Cape Province, and *O. u. broomi* Thomas, 1902 from the northwestern Cape Province.

### Description

Adult males have a mean total length of 240 mm; the females are about the same length. The males have a mean mass of 139,0 g, females about 110,0 g (de Graaff, 1981) (Table 158.1). The scales on the hairs have a lanceolate-pectinate pattern for half their length, changing rapidly to mosaic; there are never more than four scales across the hair (Fig. XXIII.3) (Keogh, 1985). The upper parts of the body are ashy-grey, the individual hairs broadly ashy-grey at the base; the remaining one-third is light buffy-yellow, the pelage interspersed with black hairs. The under parts are buffy-white, the hands and feet pale buffy. The tail has a black line along the upper surface and is dull white below. The upper incisor teeth are shallowly grooved towards the outer edge. The lower incisors in the majority of specimens are plain, some, however, have a faint shallow groove. The petrotympanic foramen appears as a round hole in the bullae (Fig. 153.1.a).

### Table 158.1

Measurements (mm) and mass (g) of karoo bush rats, *O. unisulcatus*, from the Cape Province (de Graaff, 1981)

| | Males | | | Females | | |
|---|---|---|---|---|---|---|
| | $\bar{x}$ | n | Range | $\bar{x}$ | n | Range |
| (TL | 244) | | | (239) | | |
| HB | 148 | 13 | 129–160 | 143 | 18 | 131–150 |
| T | 96 | 13 | 77–115 | 96 | 18 | 88–110 |
| Hf c/u | 26 | 13 | 23–28 | 26 | 18 | 24–29 |
| E | 24 | 14 | 17–29 | 23 | 17 | 20–28 |
| Mass | 139,0 | 11 | 125,0–156,0 | 110,0 | 12 | 101,0–135,0 |

### Distribution

They are confined in their distribution to within the limits of the Subregion.

*Southern African Subregion*

They are distributed widely in the **Cape Province**, from the northwest to the Albany District in the east, occurring in the Karoo and Little Karoo.

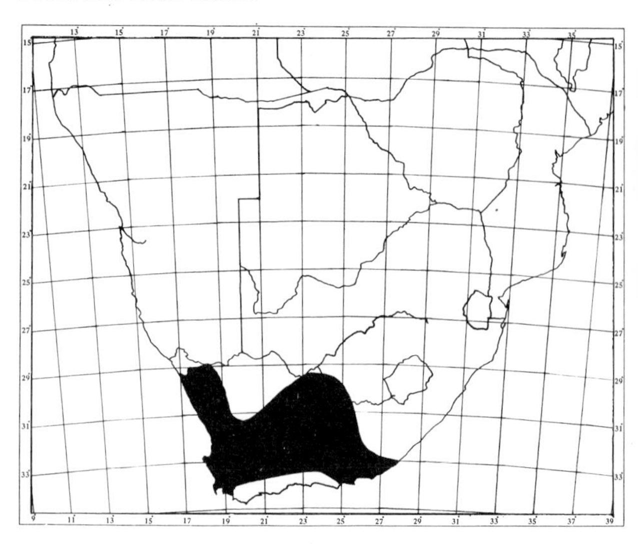

### Habitat

They occur in shrub and *fynbos* associations in parts where there are rocky outcrops, but also in coastal *fynbos*. They prefer a drier habitat than some of the other *Otomys* spp and tend to avoid damp situations. Du Plessis (1989) found that this species selected for high plant cover and foliage density.

### Habits

They are largely crepuscular, building huge shelters of sticks at the base of bushes. Vermeulen & Nel (1987) reported that in a western coastal area of the Cape Province the shelters are roughly parabolic in shape and are associated predominantly with *Exomis microphylla* bushes, being topped with a layer of sea shells near the coast. The mean size of these shelters is 1,45 m × 1,17 m with a mean depth of 0,38 m and they are constructed of sticks varying in size from 10 mm long to over 500 mm long. Within each shelter there are two nesting chambers lined with shredded grass and leaves, about 140 mm in diameter and 140 mm high, and two latrine chambers about the same size connected by tunnels. These tunnels lead to a run which surrounds the shelter and other runs lead from it either to other shelters, to areas where sticks for shelter building are available, or to feeding sites. Underneath the shelter there are also burrows in the substrate, in which Du Plessis (1989) has measured more constant temperatures and higher vapour pressures than those prevailing outside. It was estimated that shelters are constructed of up to 14 000 sticks and, to glean these, total distances of up to over 16 km must have been covered. Many of these shelters are occupied by a single individual, others by up to three males and one female.

### Food

They are generalist herbivores (Du Plessis, 1989) and feed on the leaves of green succulent karroid vegetation (de Graaff, 1981). Vermeulen & Nel (1987) gave a list of plants utilised, among which *E. microphylla*, *Zygophyllum flexuosum* and *Ruschia* spp figured prominently, although Du Plessis (1989) believed that the composition of their diet was ultimately determined by availability. They stated that stomach contents contained 70% leaves and 30% stems.

### Reproduction

The meagre information available suggests that the young are born as late as May.

## Subfamily MURINAE

Misonne (1974) remarked that the Murinae are taxonomically a difficult group. In his review he restricted the genus *Rattus* to the two introduced species, *R. rattus* and *R. norvegicus*, which differs from the approach of Ellerman *et al.* (1953) who included in this genus the following genera that occur in the Subregion: *Aethomys, Thallomys, Zelotomys* and *Praomys*. This view has not found general acceptance. Misonne (1974) regarded the genus *Leggada* as a synonym of *Mus*, although recent chromosome studies suggest that both may be valid genera. The species *Praomys natalensis* has also been shown to occur in two different chromosome numbers in the Subregion, 2n=32 and 2n=36, and another 2n=38 in West Africa (Matthey, 1966; Lyons, Gordon, Green & Walters, 1977). Meester *et al.'s* (1986) treatment of the Murinae is followed in this work.

Key to the genera, after Meester *et al.* (1986)

1. Upper incisors grooved
... *Pelomys*

Upper incisors ungrooved
... 2

2. Fur spiny
... *Acomys*

Fur not spiny
... 3

3. Longitudinal lines along mid-back
... 4

Back unlined
... 5

4. One dark line along mid-back
... *Lemniscomys*

More than one dark line along mid-back
... *Rhabdomys*

5. Tail white or whitish, with little hair
... *Zelotomys*

Tail not white or whitish
... 6

6. Strong interorbital constriction
... *Dasymys*

No strong interorbital constriction
... 7

7. T7 present on $M^1$ or at least represented by a strong ridge; head and body length 100–125 mm, tail long and slender, 145–195 mm
... *Grammomys*

T7 lacking on $M^1$
... 8

8. Rows of cusps on $M^1$ markedly distorted (Fig. XXIII.4.a)
... 9

Rows of cusps on $M^1$ not markedly distorted (Fig. XXIII.4.b)
... 12

9. Extreme distortion of cusps; size small, greatest skull length <24 mm
... *Mus*

Moderate distortion of cusps; size larger, greatest skull length in adults >25 mm
... 10

10. Incisors strongly proodont; mesopterygoid fossae far behind toothrows
... *Uranomys*

Incisors weakly or not at all proodont; mesopterygoid fossae reaching or nearly reaching toothrows; mastoid process narrow, directed backwards, leaving an opening in the skull behind it
... 11

11. Tail shorter than head and body, or subequal in length; molars wide, width of $M^1$ c. 1,55–1,70 mm
... *Mastomys*

Tail length at least 105 percent of head and body length; molars narrower, width of $M^1$ c. 1,40–1,50 mm
... *Myomyscus*

12. Dark markings ("spectacles") around eyes
... *Thallomys*

No dark markings around eyes
... 13

13. Incisive foramen extending between molar teeth; molars clearly cuspidate
... *Aethomys*

Incisive foramen not or only just extending between the molar teeth; molars clearly not cuspidate, with a tendency to become laminate
... *Rattus*

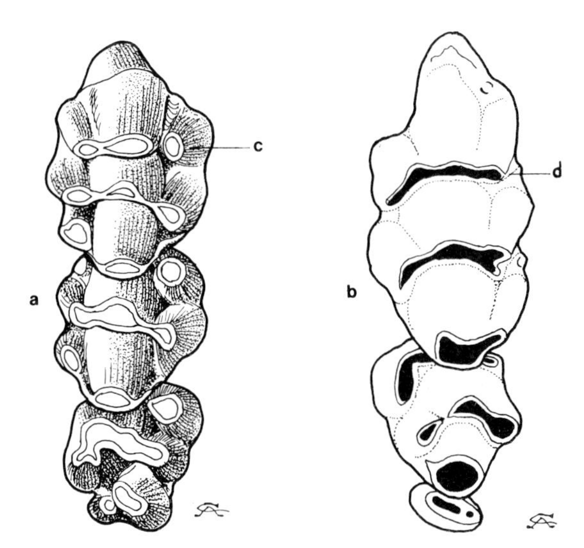


Fig. XXIII.4. Upper cheekteeth row:
(a) *Aethomys granti* with the anterior row of cusps (c) on the first upper molar not markedly distorted.
(b) *Mus* sp with the anterior row of cusps (d) on the first upper molar markedly distorted.

## Genus *Pelomys* Peters, 1852

Ellerman (1941) divided this genus into three subgenera: *Komemys; Desmomys* and *Pelomys*, of which only *Pelomys* occurs in the Subregion. Misonne (1974) stated that he regarded the status of *Pelomys* as unsatisfactory. It has affinities with the extralimital *Arvicanthus* and with *Lemniscomys*; one of the species, *Pelomys minor*, of Zambia and Zaire, is indistinguishable from *L. rosalia* on external characters.

The one species that occurs in the Subregion, *Pelomys fallax*, has deeply grooved incisors which immediately distinguish it from the single striped mouse, *L. rosalia*. The fifth digit on the forefoot in *P. fallax* is armed with a nail, not a claw.

The generic name *Pelomys* is derived from the Greek, *pelos*, dusky and *mys*, a mouse.

---

No. 159

## *Pelomys fallax* (Peters, 1852)

### Grooved-toothed mouse
### Groeftandmuis

Plate 12

---

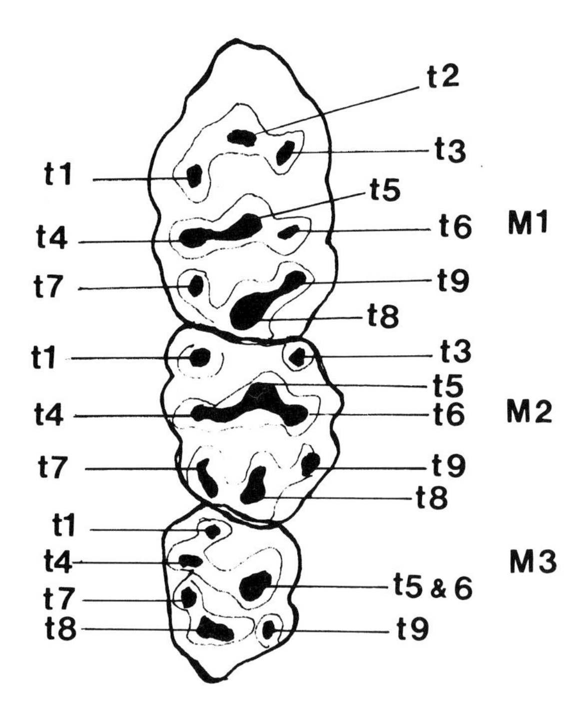


Fig. XXIII.5. Terminology of cusp pattern, cheekteeth; left upper toothrow.

## Colloquial Name

Neither of the colloquial names that have been applied to this species, creek rat or swamp rat, are appropriate as will be seen from their habitat requirements. Although the derivation of the generic name suggests that their coats are dusky, this is far from the case as the hair on the upper parts of the body has a blue-green sheen. As they are the only member of the Subfamily with grooved upper incisor teeth, grooved-toothed mouse seems more appropriate.

## Taxonomic Notes

In the Subregion this species can be recognised with reasonable certainty. In other parts of Africa, however, this is not so easy. In northeastern Africa it can be confused with two genera, *Komemys* and *Desmomys*, which do not occur in the Subregion. *Pelomys* has characters in common with *Lemniscomys*, one species of which occurs in the Subregion, *L. rosalia*, but this species has a very clearly defined line down its mid-back. In *Pelomys* this is indistinct and in some specimens can barely be discerned, so confusion of the two is unlikely anywhere south of the northern limits of the Subregion. Meester *et al.* (1986) listed three subspecies from the Subregion: *P. f. fallax* from the eastern parts of Mozambique; *P. f. rhodesiae* Roberts, 1929 from northern Botswana and northwestern Zimbabwe, and *P. f. vumbae* Roberts, 1946 from eastern Zimbabwe and adjacent parts of Mozambique.

## Description

Adults reach a total length of up to about 360 mm, with tails about the same length as the length of the head and body, and a mean mass of about 120,0 g (Table 159.1). There is some variation in colour geographically, ranging from a rusty-brown to a tawny-yellow on the upper parts of the body, intermixed with varying amounts of black-tipped hairs, which tend to give the pelage a grizzled appearance. Towards the rump the rusty or tawny colour intensifies and in some individuals towards the base of the tail shows in marked contrast to the colour of the upper parts. The dorsal dark stripe is barely perceptible in some specimens, but more distinct in others, its margins blurred and indistinct. It never reaches the clarity of definition seen in the dorsal stripe of *Lemniscomys rosalia*. A characteristic feature of the pelage is the green sheen that pervades the upper parts, which in some lights shows blue. The under parts of the body are off-white or light buffy-brown, the sides of the face, throat, flanks and upper parts of the limbs paler than the rest of the body. The tail is black on its upper surface and dirty-white or buffy below. The hair scales have a mosaic pattern with a very clearly defined broad groove, the scales on the sides of the groove being crenate margined in the distal half of the hair ( Fig. XXIII.3) (Keogh, 1985).

**Table 159.1**

Measurements (mm) and mass (g) of grooved-toothed mice, *P. fallax*, from northern Botswana (Smithers, 1971)

| | Males | | | Females | | |
|---|---|---|---|---|---|---|
| | $\bar{x}$ | n | Range | $\bar{x}$ | n | Range |
| TL | 292 | 20 | 220–365 | 287 | 30 | 239–330 |
| (HB | 147) | | | (141) | | |
| T | 145 | 19 | 114–183 | 146 | 29 | 131–175 |
| Hf c/u | 37 | 20 | 32–40 | 36 | 43 | 31–41 |
| E | 18 | 22 | 15–20 | 17 | 48 | 15–20 |
| Mass | 141,5 | 10 | 100,5–170,4 | 117,9 | 7 | 100,3–149,8 |

The fifth digit of the hand is armed with a nail, not a claw, and is short, not reaching the base of the fourth digit. Uniquely among the Murinae, the upper incisor teeth are deeply grooved.

## Distribution

*South of the Sahara, excluding the Southern African Subregion*

They are recorded from southern **Kenya**; southwestern **Uganda; Tanzania; Zaire; Angola** and **Mozambique**, north of the Zambezi River, and from **Malawi** and **Zambia**.

*Southern African Subregion*

They occur in northern **Botswana**, in the Okavango Delta and along the Chobe River in the northeast; in Mashonaland and in the eastern parts of **Zimbabwe**, as well as the extreme northwestern parts; and widely in **Mozambique**, south of the Zambezi River, south to the central parts of the Gaza District.

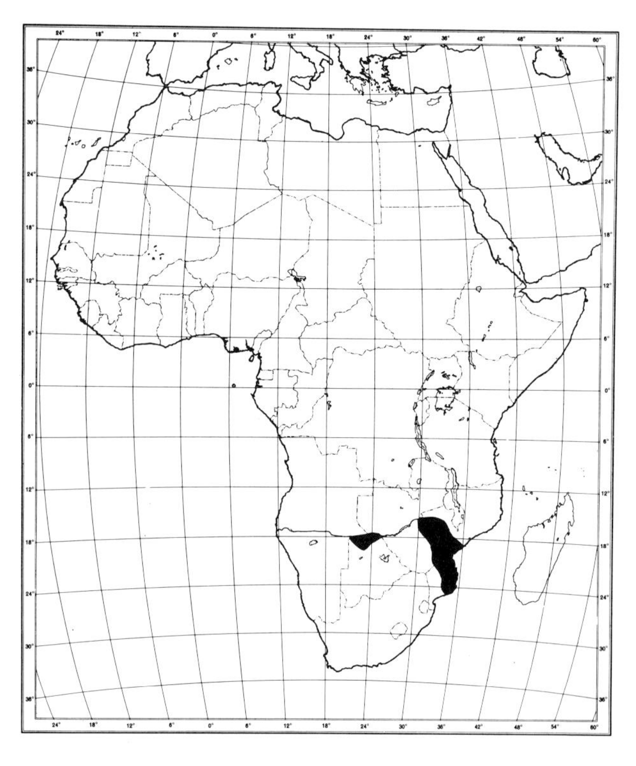

Southern African Subregion distribution only.

## Habitat

Grooved-toothed mice are associated generally with rivers, vleis, swamps and wet places which gives the impression that they live in a damp habitat, like some vlei rats, *Otomys* spp. However, they are not associated so closely with wet habitat as the vlei rats and, while they will forage in such places, they live on the ecotone of the wet areas and the dry hinterland. In Mashonaland, Zimbabwe they were most common in agricultural lands situated adjacent to river banks and the swampy reed beds associated with them, in which *Otomys* spp abounded. Along with multimammate mice, *Mastomys* spp, they were one of the species which was caught by hand by following the plough in maize lands adjacent to wet areas. They were trapped there regularly, albeit not easily, while the crop was standing.

### Habits

Grooved-toothed mice are predominantly nocturnal, with some diurnal activity. In the western Okavango, Botswana, specimens shot in the early morning were foraging on the fringe of the swamp. In Mashonaland, Zimbabwe, individuals may be trapped in the early morning and late evening, although the majority of the catches are at night. The regularity with which they are ploughed up during the day shows that they are then in the burrows (Smithers & Wilson, 1979). In contrast, Shortridge (1934) stated that the Okavango inhabitants say that *Pelomys* live above ground and do not burrow. This is believed to be a confusion with vlei rats, *Otomys* spp, for *Pelomys* excavate their own burrows in dry ground adjacent to wet places.

### Food

Grooved-toothed mice are predominantly vegetarian, living on the young shoots of reeds and semi-aquatic grasses which grow in wet places. They will eat grass seed as well as other types of seed.

### Reproduction

The meagre information that is available (Smithers, 1971; Smithers & Wilson, 1979) suggests that the young are born during the warm, wet summer months from about August to April.

## Genus *Acomys* I. Geoffroy, 1838

The name is derived from the Greek *akn*, a sharp point, and *mys*, a mouse, referring to their pelage of fine spines on the upper parts of the body.

Key to the species after Meester *et al.* (1986)

1. Teeth robust, maxillary toothrow 3,7–4,3 mm, mandibular molar toothrow 3,4–3,9 mm; ratio: maxillary toothrow/diastema length 54,7–71,3 percent; karyotype 2n=60, AA=68; four pairs metacentric, one pair submetacentric, 24 pairs acrocentric autosomal chromosomes ... *spinosissimus*

   Teeth small, maxillary toothrow 3,0–3,6 mm, mandibular molar toothrow 2,8–3,3 mm; ratio: maxillary toothrow/diastema length 42,2–54,0 percent; karyotype 2n=64, AA=70; two pairs metacentric, two pairs submetacentric, 27 pairs acrocentric autosomal chromosomes ... *subspinosus*

---

No. 160

## *Acomys spinosissimus* (Peters, 1852)

### Spiny mouse
### Stekelmuis

Plate 13

---

### Colloquial Name

They are aptly named as the hairs of the pelage are spiny, not soft as in other murids.

### Taxonomic Notes

No subspecies were recognised by Meester *et al.* (1986).

### Description

Adults have a total length of about 170 mm, with tails about the same length as that of the head and body and a mass of about 30 g (Table 160.1). They have wide, deeply grooved hairs with up to nine scales across the width of the groove (compared to up to 12 scales in the Cape spiny mouse) (Fig. XXIII.3) (Keogh, 1985) and the most characteristic feature of the species is the spiny coat, the nature of which is immediately apparent if the finger is run against the lie of the hairs. The moult is clearly marked: from December to April the upper parts are sepia-grey in colour, moulting in May to September from this colour to reddish. The junction between the two colours, while the moult proceeds, is clear cut, leaving one part of the body one colour and the other part the other colour. From October to December, at the conclusion of the moult, they are reddish on the upper parts and, at this stage, specimens from the western parts of their range can be seen to be much paler red than those from the eastern parts which are a much richer red. The under parts of the body are at all stages of the moult pure white, the tail sparsely bristled and darker above than below.

The braincase is rounded, the rostrum slightly longer than in *A. subspinosus*, the upper row of cheekteeth attaining a length of 3,7 mm or over, as compared with *A. subspinosus* in which the length is 3,5 mm or less.

**Table 160.1**

Measurements (mm) and mass (g) of spiny mice, *A. spinosissimus*, from Zimbabwe (Smithers & Wilson, 1979)

| | Males | | | Females | | |
|---|---|---|---|---|---|---|
| | $\bar{x}$ | n | Range | $\bar{x}$ | n | Range |
| TL | 173 | 13 | 149–190 | 173 | 15 | 140–185 |
| (HB | 85) | | | (90) | | |
| T | 88 | 11 | 85–97 | 83 | 15 | 72–92 |
| Hf c/u | 18 | 12 | 17–20 | 18 | 14 | 16–20 |
| E | 15 | 12 | 14–18 | 15 | 9 | 14–18 |
| Mass | 29,0 | 8 | 26,0–33,0 | 26,0 | 10 | 20,0–36,0 |

### Distribution

*South of the Sahara, excluding the Southern African Subregion*

This species occurs in **Zambia, Zaire** and northeastwards to the northern parts of **Tanzania**.

*Southern African Subregion*

They occur widely throughout **Zimbabwe**, where there is suitable habitat, and in **Mozambique**, south of the Zambezi River, as far south as the northern parts of the Gaza and Inhambane districts, with a single record from the coast at Massinga which marks their most southerly limits of occurrence in this country. They occur narrowly in eastern **Botswana** and in the northern and western parts of the **Transvaal**.

### Habitat

Generally associated with rocky terrain, they have been taken on sandy alluvium along rivers, in dry woodland and in thickets, where they use the cover of the roots of trees exposed by erosion or holes in termite mounds. These last-named shelters arc atypical of their more common habit of living under or among boulders in a rocky habitat. In areas where there are granite koppies, as in the Matopo Hills or in the Lundi River area in Zimbabwe, they live high up in these koppies in sheltered overhanging rocks, under exfoliated slabs and in other sheltered crannies.

### Habits

They are nocturnal and terrestrial. Some of the shelters in which they live may house numbers of spiny mice, up to nine having been taken from a single rock crevice. In others they occur solitarily or in pairs or family parties only. Usually their presence can be detected by the accumulation of their scats, which are cylindrical and slightly reddish in colour. Grass and other vegetable debris are dragged into the shelter to form a rough nest.

### Food

Their diet consists predominantly of grass and other seeds, but they also eat termites and other insects. Vesey-Fitzgerald

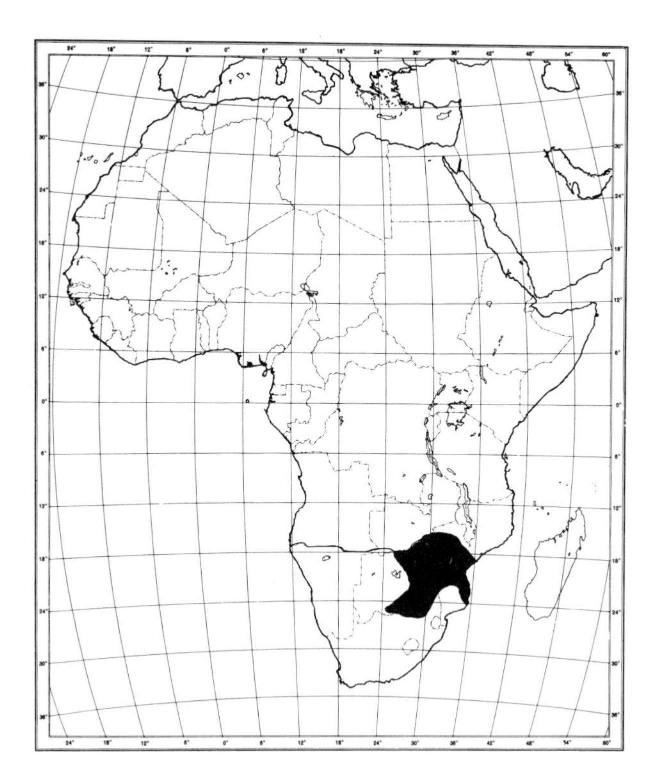

Southern African Subregion distribution only.

(1966) stated that they will eat millipedes, spiders and small snails, whilst Pienaar *et al.* (1980) observed them feeding on jackal berries, *Diospyros mespiliformis*, in the Kruger National Park.

### Reproduction

The young are born during the warm, wet summer months from about November to April, the average number in a litter being 3 (n=12), with a range of from two to five.

No. 161

## *Acomys subspinosus* (Waterhouse, 1838)

## Cape spiny mouse
## Kaapse stekelmuis

### Colloquial Name

This species has spines in place of fur, and is confined in its distribution to the Cape Province. The name Cape is applied to distinguish this species from the spiny mouse, *Acomys spinosissimus*, which occurs in the northeastern parts of the Subregion.

### Taxonomic Notes

Setzer (1975) listed 10 subspecies from the continent, two of which are found in the Subregion. Originally *A. s. subspinosus* was described from a specimen from Table Mountain, Cape Town, and *A. s. transvaalensis* Roberts, 1926 from the northern Transvaal, which is regarded here as a synonym of *A. spinosissimus*.

### Description

Adult male Cape spiny mice have a total length of about 170 mm and a mass of about 20,0 g; the females are slightly larger, with a mass of about 22,0 g (Table 161.1). Wide, deeply grooved hairs, with up to 12 scales across the groove (Fig. XXIII.3) (Keogh, 1985), cover the upper parts of the body which are dark greyish-brown in colour, the flanks lighter and tinged rusty. The chin, chest and lower part of the belly are white and the upper parts of the belly are light grey. Interspersed throughout the coat there are long black hairs, which may be tactile and a sprinkling of fine white hairs representing an underfur. The hair on the flanks and under parts is softer and shorter than on the rump. Compared with the spiny mouse, *A. spinosissimus*, the spiny gutter hairs of the coat in this species are longer, narrower and softer, especially on the shoulders. Those on the rump of this species are stiffer and more like those of the spiny mouse. The hands are white, the remainder of the forelimbs greyish. The feet are white and the remainder of the upper surface of the hind limbs is grey down the middle and white on the sides. The tail is dark above, lighter below and the black tip is sparsely covered with short, bristly hair. The tail is about the same length as the head and body or slightly shorter.

**Table 161.1**

Measurements (mm) and mass (g) of Cape spiny mice, *A. subspinosus*, from the Cape Province (de Graaff, 1981)

| | Males | | | Females | | |
|---|---|---|---|---|---|---|
| | $\bar{x}$ | n | Range | $\bar{x}$ | n | Range |
| (TL | 172) | | | (180) | | |
| HB | 88 | 16 | 81–97 | 93 | 17 | 82–98 |
| T | 84 | 16 | 75–98 | 87 | 17 | 81–96 |
| Hf c/u | 17 | 17 | 13–19 | 17 | 18 | 14–19 |
| E | 13 | 17 | 11–16 | 14 | 18 | 12–15 |
| Mass | 20,0 | 9 | 17,0–23,0 | 22,0 | 17 | 20,0–25,0 |

They have four digits on the front feet, five on the hind feet, and the digits are armed with claws. The ears are small and rounded and there is a bare patch just behind the lower part of the pinnae. The cheekteeth of this species are very small; the cheekteeth row is a bare 3,5 mm in length.

### Distribution

*South of the Sahara, excluding the Southern African Subregion*

This species occurs in the **Sudan; Uganda; Kenya** and **Somalia** as far south as central **Tanzania**, but is absent southwards, occurring again in the Cape Province. There remains doubt as to whether these northern records should be included in this species (Meester *et al.*, 1986).

*Southern African Subregion*

They are confined to the southwestern parts of the **Cape Province**, from Citrusdal in the west to Knysna in the east.

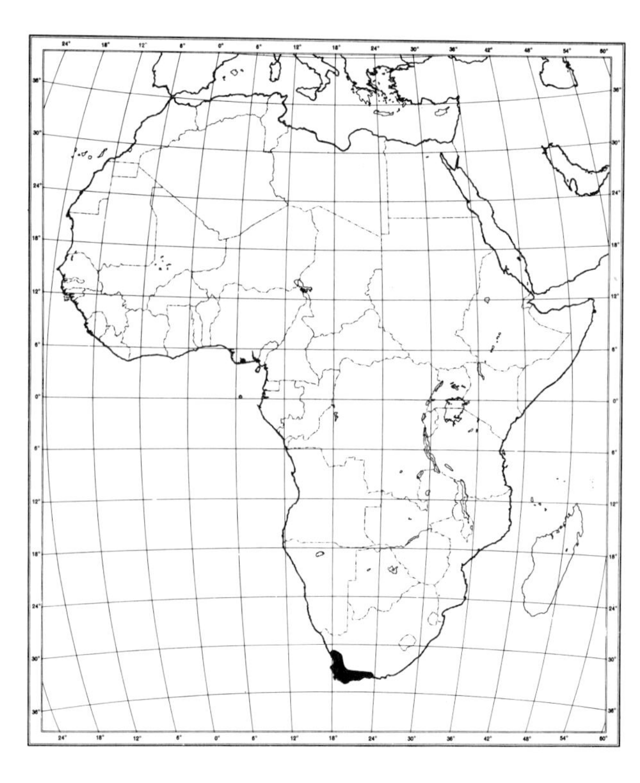

Southern African Subregion distribution only.

## Habitat

They are associated generally with rocky areas on mountain slopes, but do occur in other habitats as well and at reasonably high altitudes. They are a true *fynbos* endemic species (Breytenbach, 1982).

## Habits

They are nocturnal and terrestrial. At Swartberg, Breytenbach (1982) found that they nest in holes and not in cracks and crevices.

## Food

They feed extensively on nutlets of *Restio* spp.

## Reproduction

Nothing is on record regarding this aspect of their life history.

# Genus *Lemniscomys* Trouessart, 1881

The generic name is derived from the Greek *lemniscos*, a band, referring to the single dark stripe on the upper parts of their bodies, and *mys*, a mouse.

---

No. 162

# *Lemniscomys rosalia* (Thomas, 1904)

## Single-striped mouse
## Eenstreepmuis

Plate 12

---

## Colloquial Name

The colloquial name is appropriate as the conspicuous feature of the species is the single dark line down the mid-back.

## Taxonomic Notes

Meester *et al.* (1986) listed four subspecies from the Subregion: *L. r. calidior* (Thomas & Wroughton, 1908) from Mozambique and eastern Zimbabwe; *L. r. spinalis* Thomas, 1916 from eastern Natal, KwaZulu, eastern Swaziland, central and northern Transvaal and western Zimbabwe; *L. r. sabulatus* Thomas, 1927 from northern Namibia and north-western Botswana, and *L. r. fitzsimonsi* Roberts, 1932 from western central Botswana. The nominate *L. r. rosalia* occurs in Tanzania.

## Description

In a series from Zimbabwe the adults have a total length of about 270 mm, with tails slightly longer than the length of the head and body and a mass of about 58,0 g (Table 162.1). Hairs deeply grooved, scales "snakeskin"-like (Keogh, 1985). The upper parts vary in colour geographically. Specimens from the Tete Province of Mozambique, *L. r. spinalis*, are pale buffy to reddish-orange on the upper parts of the body. The sides of the head and limbs are grizzled with dark brown and the stripe on the mid-back is dark brown. The lips, chin and around the gape of the mouth, the throat, belly and inner surfaces of the limbs are a rusty-white. The feet are yellowish, the muzzle a rusty orange-yellow, the eyebrows and ears reddish-orange.

**Table 162.1**

Measurements (mm) and mass (g) of single-striped mice, *L. rosalia*, from Zimbabwe (Smithers & Wilson, 1979)

| | Males | | | Females | | |
|---|---|---|---|---|---|---|
| | $\bar{x}$ | n | Range | $\bar{x}$ | n | Range |
| TL | 269 | 10 | 265–300 | 269 | 18 | 240–295 |
| (HB | 122) | | | (125) | | |
| T | 147 | 10 | 135–165 | 144 | 18 | 132–156 |
| Hf c/u | 30 | 10 | 29–31 | 31 | 18 | 29–32 |
| E | 16 | 10 | 14–17 | 17 | 18 | 16–18 |
| Mass | 58,0 | 9 | 51,0–64,0 | 58,0 | 20 | 52,0–70,0 |

Specimens from the central Kalahari, *L. r. fitzsimonsi*, are a pale vinaceous-buffy on the upper parts, lighter on the flanks, with less dark grizzling on the pelage. The mid-dorsal stripe is black, the under parts pure white. The upper surface of the tail is rusty coloured with a thin dark line down the centre, the under surface pure white.

## Distribution

*South of the Sahara, excluding the Southern African Subregion*

They are recorded from **Mozambique**, north of the Zambezi River; **Malawi; Zambia; Angola; Tanzania** and southern **Kenya**.

*Southern African Subregion*

In the Subregion they occur in the northern parts of **Namibia**; central and northern **Botswana**; widely throughout **Zimbabwe**, except in the mopane belt of the Limpopo River valley; in **Mozambique**, south of the Zambezi River; in the central and northern parts of the **Transvaal**; eastern **Swaziland** and eastern **Natal**. So far they have not been recorded in southern Namibia, the Cape Province, the Orange Free State or Lesotho.

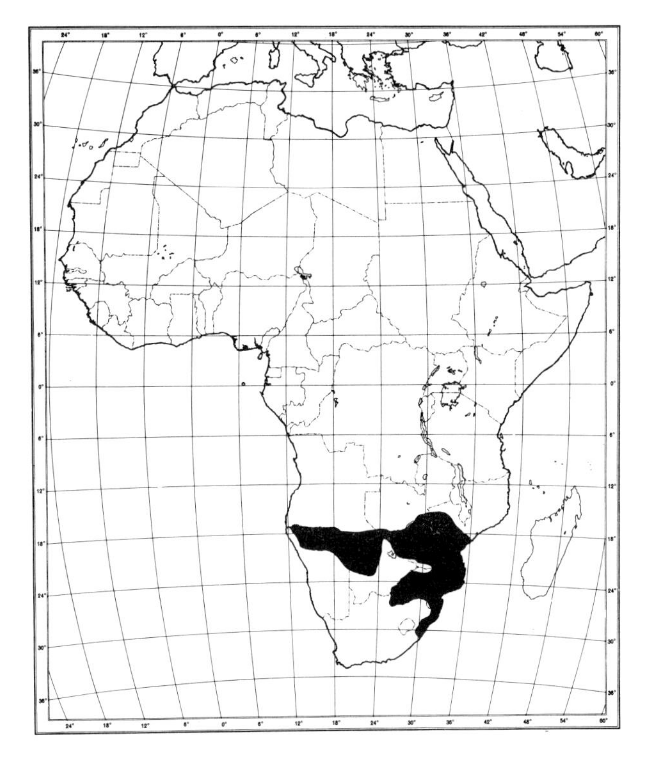

Southern African Subregion distribution only.

## Habitat

While they occur in a wide variety of different vegetational associations from savanna woodland to the dry open scrub of the Kalahari, the common factor is grassland areas within these diverse associations. They occur in dry grassland in the ecotone of vleis and woodland and in the stands of high grass surrounding agricultural lands, preferring areas where there is a good cover of grass and avoiding parts where the grass is short.

## Habits

They are diurnal and terrestrial. Burrows are occupied by a solitary individual, a pair or family parties, and are excavated where there is good overhead cover of tall or matted grasses. They form runs from the burrow entrances to feeding grounds. Swanepoel (1972) found that the home range of the males exceeds that of the females.

### Food

In a sample of 11 stomachs from *L. rosalia* taken in the wet season in the Kruger National Park, Watson (1987) found 50% seeds, 48% herbage and 2% insects.

### Reproduction

The young are born during the warm, wet summer months from September to March (Swanepoel, 1972; Kern, 1977; Scott & Meester, 1988). Foetuses from gravid females numbered two to five (Swanepoel, 1972; Smithers, 1983). In captivity mean litter size was 4,2 (range 2–6; n=5) and minimum interval between litters was 24 days (Scott & Meester, 1988). Mean mass at birth was 2,6 g. At birth pups are altricial, naked, with toes fused, eyes closed and ear flaps folded down, but development is rapid: toes loose by Day 4–5, eyes open by Day 9–11, ear flaps unfolded by Day 1–2 and young are fully furred by Day 18.

## Genus *Rhabdomys* Thomas, 1916

No. 163

## *Rhabdomys pumilio* (Sparrmann, 1784)

## Striped mouse
## Streepmuis

Plate 12

### Colloquial Name

They are so named from the four longitudinal black stripes on the back.

### Taxonomic Notes

Roberts (1951) listed 20 subspecies from the Subregion, of which Meester *et al.* (1986) retained seven: *R. p. pumilio* from the southwestern and southern Cape Province east to the southern Orange Free State; *R. p. bechuanae* (Thomas, 1893) from Namibia; *R. p. dilectus* (De Winton, 1897) from western Lesotho, northern Natal and eastern Zimbabwe; *R. p. cinereus* (Thomas & Schwann, 1904) from the northern and northwestern Cape Province; *R. p. griquae* (Wroughton, 1905) from parts of the northern Cape Province, central Botswana, southern Namibia, southwestern Transvaal; *R. p. intermedius* (Wroughton, 1905) from the central and eastern Cape Province, and *R. p. fourei* Roberts, 1946 from northern Namibia. The limits of distribution of these subspecies are poorly known.

### Description

There is a noticeable difference in size between series from different geographical areas and, depending on from where they come, the tails can be shorter or more or less the same length as the head and body (Coetzee, 1970). Specimens from the Cape Province can have maximum lengths of head and body of up to 132 mm and tails of 132 mm (Roberts, 1951), whereas the maximum length of head and body of specimens from the extreme northeastern parts of the Subregion only reach 100 mm and 85 mm respectively (Smithers & Wilson, 1979) (Table 163.1).

**Table 163.1**

Measurements (mm) and mass (g) of striped mice, *R. pumilio*, from two areas in the Subregion to illustrate difference in size and particularly length of the tail.

**Southwest Kalahari, Botswana** (Smithers, 1971)

| | Males | | | Females | | |
|---|---|---|---|---|---|---|
| | $\bar{x}$ | n | Range | $\bar{x}$ | n | Range |
| TL | 211 | 8 | 204–216 | 214 | 11 | 202–225 |
| (HB | 105) | | | (109) | | |
| T | 106 | 8 | 102–110 | 105 | 11 | 95–120 |
| Hf c/u | 24 | 12 | 22–27 | 24 | 14 | 23–26 |
| E | 12 | 13 | 11–14 | 12 | 13 | 11–15 |
| Mass | 42,2 | 5 | 32,0–55,0 | 45,7 | 9 | 37,0–54,0 |

**Eastern Zimbabwe** (Smithers & Wilson, 1979)

| | Males | | | Females | | |
|---|---|---|---|---|---|---|
| | $\bar{x}$ | n | Range | $\bar{x}$ | n | Range |
| TL | 185 | 23 | 170–200 | 184 | 19 | 171–196 |
| (HB | 100) | | | (101) | | |
| T | 85 | 21 | 79–92 | 83 | 23 | 80–90 |
| Hf c/u | 22 | 21 | 20–24 | 22 | 21 | 20–25 |
| E | 14 | 16 | 10–16 | 15 | 19 | 13–18 |

The pelage is made up of wide, deeply grooved hairs and the general appearance of the mosaic scale pattern is of horizontal lines (Fig. XXIII.3) (Keogh, 1985). The characteristic feature that makes them unmistakable among the murids that occur in the Subregion is the four stripes on the upper parts of the body, which extend from the back of the neck to the base of the tail. In the dark-coloured individuals from the east of the Subregion these stripes are black, in the lighter coloured individuals from the west they are reddish-brown or brown. In the dark-coloured individuals the background colour of the upper parts of the body is a dark grizzled greyish-buff, the flanks usually paler and the under parts white or off-white, the grey of the bases of the hair showing through. In specimens from Namibia the background colour is very pale, nearly white and grizzled. The four stripes are pale reddish-brown or brown, the under parts white, sometimes with a wash of pale yellow towards the flanks. The tail is always darker above than below, in the dark specimens black above and buffy below.

Characteristically the ears are reddish-brown and, in the darker specimens, they have a thin black line between the eyes extending back between the ears and in some specimens joining up with the central two dark stripes on the back. The upper parts of the feet are usually lighter in colour than the body.

### Distribution

Throughout their wide distributional range their occurrence tends to be patchy and discontinuous.

*South of the Sahara, excluding the Southern African Subregion*

They are recorded from central **Angola**; from the Nyika Plateau in northeastern **Zambia** and northern **Malawi**, where they also occur on the Mlanje Plateau in the Southern Province. There are no records from Mozambique, north of the Zambezi River. They occur in **Tanzania**; in western and central **Kenya**; in eastern **Uganda** and in parts of southern **Zaire**.

*Southern African Subregion*

They occur widely in **Namibia**, excluding the northeastern parts of the country; in the **Cape Province; Orange Free State; Natal**, and in most of the **Transvaal**, excluding the greater part of the northwestern and eastern parts of the province. In **Botswana** they have a discontinuous distribution, occurring in the south of the country south of about 23°45′S and in the southern parts of Ngamiland and eastwards to the Makgadikgadi Pan. In **Zimbabwe** they are confined to a sector east of Bulawayo on the plateau, eastwards to the Eastern Districts and extending narrowly into **Mozambique**, south of the Zambezi River, into the Vila Pery and western Beira districts.

### Habitat

The striped mouse is essentially a grassland species and occurs in a wide variety of habitats, only where there is good

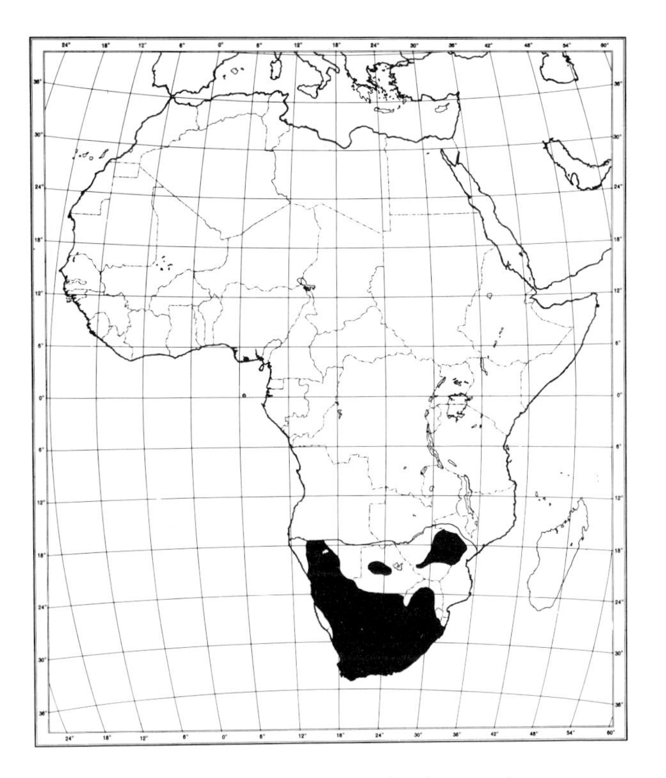

Southern African Subregion distribution only.

grass cover. In southwestern Botswana they are associated particularly with the verdant vegetation around the damp central sump drainage of pans. These sumps support a dense vegetation of buffalo thorn, *Ziziphus mucronata*, scrub bush and grass cover (Smithers, 1971). In Zimbabwe they are characteristically associated with stands of tall grasses such as *Hyparrhenia* spp and *Themeda* spp, in particular on the fringes of agricultural lands, where they can be very abundant (Smithers, 1983). In the Transvaal, Rautenbach (1978) noted their association with and preference for areas of short dense grass cover. The grass cover in the Drakensberg is good accounting for this rodent's even distribution in this region (Rowe-Rowe & Meester, 1982).

They occur from sea level in the Cape Province to altitudes of over 2 700 m in the Drakensberg and in areas with a mean annual rainfall of less than 100 mm in Namibia to over 1 200 mm in eastern Zimbabwe and western Mozambique.

### Habits

They are crepuscular, with peaks of activity in the early morning from about 05h00 to 08h30 and in the afternoon from 14h30 to 17h30. They excavate burrows with the entrances well hidden at the base of clumps of grass and, where they are numerous, their regular movements to feeding grounds eventually create narrow runs. Shortridge (1934) stated that they burrow into the ground at an angle, the burrows being excavated to a depth of 0,5 m below the ground surface. These have chambers in them lined with soft vegetable debris. In addition they will also use holes in termite mounds or construct round nests in clumps of grass near the ground. Brooks (1974) described these nests which are about 120 mm in horizontal diameter and 90 mm high, with a single entrance, and are made of grass stems cut 50 mm to 80 mm long.

### Food

The striped mouse is an opportunistic omnivore whose diet varies seasonally and the digestive tract is typically adapted to an omnivorous diet (Perrin, 1980c). Although Brooks (1974), Rowe-Rowe & Meester (1982) and Kerley (1989) found them to be predominantly granivorous, in Zimbabwe Churchfield (1985) found the bulk of the diet to be green plant material (54%) and seeds (45%), with Isoptera and other invertebrates making up the remainder. In the Drakensberg their diet varied seasonally, when the percentage green plant material and insects in stomachs was higher in the summer wet season (Rowe-Rowe, 1986). In Botswana they are recorded as eating the outside covering of the fruits of the buffalo thorn, *Ziziphus mucronata*, the raisin bush, *Grewia* spp, and the pods of *Acacia* spp (Smithers, 1971). Moreover, in the Cape Province, Rourke & Wiens (1977) noted that they feed on the succulent basal portions of the bracts and styles of flowers of Proteaceae flowering near ground level. In late winter the fleshy parts of the flowers are one of the best sources of soft vegetable matter. In feeding on these flowers there is good evidence that the rodents, by carrying pollen on their heads, play an important part in fertilisation of the flowers, a phenomenon also known for Australian Proteaceae.

### Reproduction

Brooks (1974) found that, in a captive colony in the Transvaal, breeding occurred in all months of the year, but in the wild in the Van Riebeeck Nature Reserve, Transvaal, the young were born during the summer months from September to April, similar to the situation in Zimbabwe (Smithers & Wilson, 1979) and on the Cape Flats (Henschel, David & Jarvis, 1982). However, this may vary geographically as gravid females were taken in June and July in southwestern Botswana (Smithers, 1971).

Brooks (1974) found that the mean gestation period is 25,4 days, with a minimum of 23 days. The mean litter size in the Transvaal is 5,9 (range 2–9). The altricial young are born in the nests either above ground or in chambers in the burrow system. At birth the young are greyish-pink and the four stripes appear as deeply pigmented lines extending from the base of the tail to the neck, the two central stripes joining and continuing as a fine line over the top of the head to between the eyes. They have a very fine, sparse covering of short black hairs on the pigmented areas and some longer, paler hairs on the rump. Their eyes are closed at birth, opening about the seventh day, in some cases not until the 10th day. The lower incisor teeth erupt on the fifth or sixth day and their tips are not adapted to nipple-clinging (Brooks, 1974).

Brooks (1974) stated that the age of sexual maturity, both in captivity and in the wild, is about two months, the breeding season being followed by a four-month period when the females are anoestrous. During the breeding season the adult females appear to be territorial and have a very limited home range, the adult males occupying larger home ranges which probably overlap those of the females.

## Genus *Zelotomys* Osgood, 1910

---

No. 164

## *Zelotomys woosnami* (Schwann, 1906)

## Woosnam's desert rat
## Woosnam se woestynrot

Plate 13

---

### Colloquial Name

This species was named after the original collector, R.B. Woosnam, who in 1911 with G. Legge, undertook an epic collecting expedition across the southwestern part of Botswana in an oxwagon (Ogilvie-Grant, 1912).

### Taxonomic Notes

No subspecies have been described.

### Description

Adult males have a total length of about 240 mm, with tails shorter than the length of the head and body and a mass of about 53 g. The females have the same total length, with tails in similar proportion and a mass of about 54 g (Table 164.1). The upper parts of the body are a pale smoke-grey pencilled with black; the flanks are paler, the under parts creamy-white, and the hairs have grey bases. The tail is white above and below, slightly darker towards the tip in specimens from the southern parts of their range, pure white in those from the northern parts. The upper parts of the feet are white. The fur is fine, soft and silky. The juveniles are darker in colour than the adults, their pelages lacking the dark pencilling seen in the adults.

Ellerman (1941) stated that the upper toothrow is 18% to 19% of the condylobasal length of the skull. From northern Botswana, in a series of six males with heavy and medium tooth wear, the mean percentage was 17,3%, and in a series of five females it was 13,2%.

The first upper molar teeth are very long, longer than the combined length of the second and third. The upper incisors are light orange in colour and ungrooved.

**Table 164.1**

Measurements (mm) and mass (g) of Woosnam's desert rats, *Z. woosnami*, from Botswana (Smithers, 1971)

| | Males | | | Females | | |
|---|---|---|---|---|---|---|
| | $\bar{x}$ | n | Range | $\bar{x}$ | n | Range |
| TL | 240 | 12 | 209–260 | 237 | 12 | 208–264 |
| (HB | 130) | | | (128) | | |
| T | 110 | 12 | 102–118 | 109 | 12 | 97–116 |
| Hf c/u | 27 | 12 | 25–28 | 26 | 12 | 24–27 |
| E | 19 | 12 | 17–20 | 19 | 12 | 16–20 |
| Mass | 53,7 | 3 | 50,0–57,0 | 54,5 | 4 | 48,0–62,0 |

## Distribution

This species is confined in its distribution to within the limits of the Subregion.

*Southern African Subregion*

They occur in western central **Namibia** adjacent to the Botswana border. In **Botswana** they occur in the northern and southwestern parts of the country and they are recorded from the northern parts of the **Cape Province**, in the Kalahari Gemsbok National Park and, east of this, in the vicinity of the Molopo River. They may well occur in central Botswana.

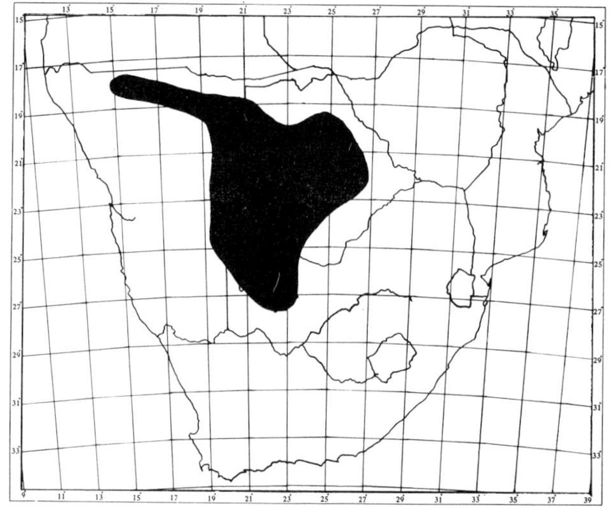

## Habitat

In Botswana they occur on Kalahari sand with a sparse vegetational cover of grass and thornbush, *Acacia* spp, raisin bush, *Grewia* spp, and cluster leaf, *Terminalia* spp, scrub, within the area with a mean annual rainfall of 200 mm to 500 mm. On the Botletle River in northern Botswana they were taken in riverine thornbush, *Acacia* spp, on sandy alluvium, from sandy areas fringing a dry riverbed and in open thornbush, *Acacia* spp, woodland.

## Habits

They appear to be a solitary species, occurring singly, in pairs or in family parties, and are not common in any part of their range. They are nocturnal and terrestrial, but are adept climbers, using their tails for balancing, and will jump from branch to branch. Birkenstock & Nel (1977) recorded a burrow system in the Kalahari Gemsbok National Park which ran 400 mm to 550 mm below ground level and had two chambers, one 140x100x100 mm, the other 140x160x150 mm, containing nesting material consisting of shredded grass, *Stipagrostis obtusa*. Shortridge (1934) stated that they live in the deserted or still occupied burrows of other murids, possibly gerbils, *Tatera* spp, and Woosnam (Roberts, 1951) found them inhabiting holes under thorn trees at Kuruman. It was very noticeable in Botswana that they were caught frequently when traps were set at the entrance to *Tatera* spp burrows and that, in the areas in which they were taken, these gerbils were particularly abundant.

## Food

Birkenstock & Nel (1977) recorded that stomachs contained 60% white vegetable matter, presumably the ground up remains of seeds; 20% insects (Coleoptera), and 20% nematode parasites. *Tatera* spp hair has been found in their stomachs (Smithers, 1971) and in captivity cannibalism has occurred (Ansell, 1960; Birkenstock & Nel, 1977), suggesting they might be carnivorous.

## Reproduction

Gravid females and juveniles have been taken from November to April, suggesting from meagre records that young are born during the warm, wet summer months (Shortridge, 1934; Smithers, 1971). Three females taken in February had five, five and 11 foetuses.

Birkenstock & Nel (1977) described the post-natal development of the species in captivity; the newly-born are altricial, naked and pink, the lips fused, with only a small orifice in the front to permit suckling, the eyes and ears closed. They show a slight grey tinge on the dorsal surface of the body, the hair first showing on the sixth day. The incisor teeth erupt between the 10th and 12th day, the lower incisors appearing in advance of the upper, and the young do not nipple-cling. The mouth can be opened almost fully by the 10th day, but remains fused at the corners, whilst the eyes open on the 16th or 17th day. The females have a post-partum oestrus, the minimum period between litters in captivity being 31 days. The females have three pairs of pectoral and two pairs of inguinal mammae.

# Genus *Dasymys* Peters, 1875

No. 165

## *Dasymys incomtus* (Sundevall, 1847)

## Water rat
## Waterrot

Plate 12

## Colloquial Name

The colloquial name reflects the type of habitat with which this species is associated.
Alternative name: shaggy rat.

## Taxonomic Notes

Meester *et al.* (1986) listed three subspecies from the Subregion: the nominate *D. i. incomtus* from Transkei, eastern and northern Natal, the Transvaal, and possibly Mozambique and eastern Zimbabwe; *D. i. nudipes* (Peters, 1870) from northeastern Namibia, northern Botswana and Zimbabwe, and *D. i. capensis* Roberts, 1936 from the southwestern Cape Province.

## Description

Water rats have a total length of about 330 mm, with tails that are about the same length as the length of the head and body (Table 165.1). The latter feature helps to distinguish them from vlei rats, *Otomys* spp, in which the tails are much shorter. In *O. angoniensis* and *O. irroratus*, two commoner species, the tails are about 58% of the length of the head and body.

**Table 165.1**

Measurements (mm) and mass (g) of water rats, *D. incomtus*, from northern Botswana (Smithers, 1971)

| | Males | | | Females | | |
|---|---|---|---|---|---|---|
| | $\bar{x}$ | n | Range | $\bar{x}$ | n | Range |
| TL | 325 | 11 | 301–350 | 329 | 8 | 309–352 |
| (HB | 161) | | | (166) | | |
| T | 164 | 11 | 146–178 | 163 | 7 | 152–180 |
| Hf c/u | 40 | 11 | 36–44 | 39 | 8 | 35–41 |
| E | 20 | 11 | 16–22 | 21 | 8 | 20–22 |
| Mass | 128,5 | 11 | 107,3–164,1 | 127,0 | 6 | 102,3–161,2 |

The hairs in water rats have a mosaic scale pattern, with lanceolate-pectinate scales present, proximal to the half-way mark (Fig. XXIII.3) (Keogh, 1985). The individual hairs are broadly slate-grey at the base, narrowly buffy towards the tips. The colour of the upper parts of the body is dark greyish-black. The top of the head is usually darker, almost black, the flanks and cheeks greyer. The hair on the under parts is slate-grey at the base, with broad off-white or buffy-white tips. The pelage on the upper parts of the body is soft and has a distinct sheen. The hair on the shoulders reaches a length of about 13 mm and up to about 15 mm on the rump. The underfur is dense, very fine and almost straight. The ears are rounded, almost naked on the back, and covered with short hair on the inside. The upper surface of the tail is dark, slightly paler on the under surface, the whole of the tail heavily scaled. The first fingers on the front feet are vestigial, the fifth well developed but only reaching the base of the fourth. The hind feet are heavy, the first and second toes short, the remaining three all about the same length. The claws are all whitish at the base with black tips.

**Skull**

The skull is heavily built, flattish on top, the rostrum short and broad, and the infraorbital foramina large. The ear bullae are small for the size of the skull, the anterior palatal foramina extending back to the level of the anterior edge of the first upper molar teeth. The molar teeth are large and heavily cusped when unworn, the central cusp on each tooth distinctly the largest. These teeth wear to flat faces. The upper incisor teeth are broad and ungrooved, the latter feature useful in distinguishing members of this genus from those of the genus *Otomys*, which they resemble and which have heavily grooved upper incisors. The enamel layer on the front of the upper incisors is orange in colour, on the lower yellower, and the lower incisors are more slender than the upper (Figs. 165.1 and 2).

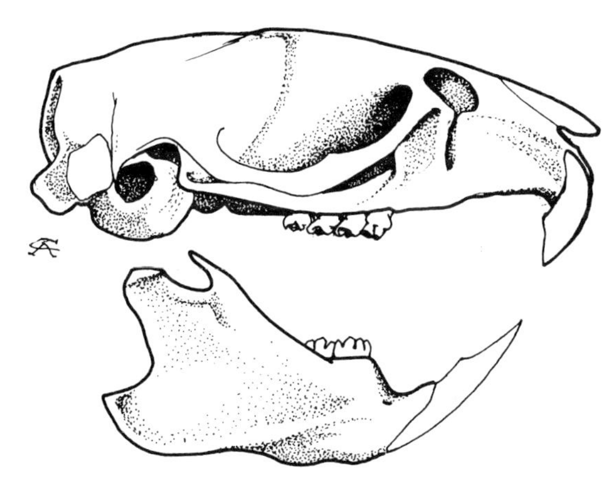

Fig. 165.1. Skull: *Dasymys incomtus*, lateral view.

**Distribution**

*South of the Sahara, excluding the Southern African Subregion*

Extralimitally to the Subregion the water rat has a wide distribution from **Sierra Leone** in West Africa eastwards to

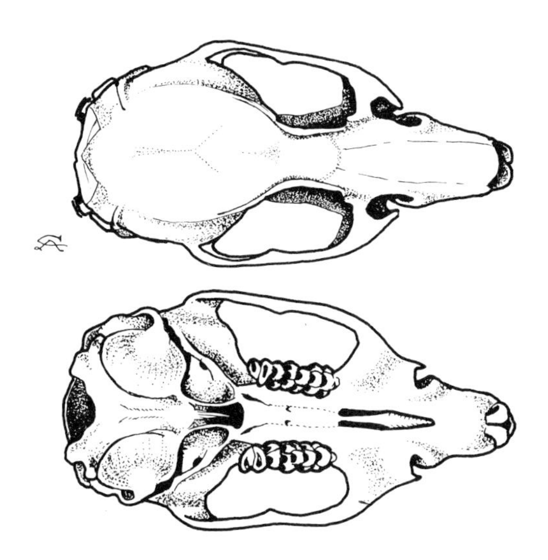

Fig. 165.2. Skull: *Dasymys incomtus*.

the **Sudan** and central **Kenya** and is recorded from most countries south of this to the borders of the Subregion.

*Southern African Subregion*

They are recorded from the extreme northeastern sector of **Namibia**, on the Okavango River; in the northern parts of the Okavango Swamp and along the Chobe River in northern **Botswana**; in restricted and isolated localities in western **Zimbabwe**, where they also occur in the Harare and Masvingo districts and widely throughout the eastern parts of the country. There are very few records from **Mozambique**, south of the Zambezi River, but they have been taken in the western Vila Pery District and at Beira in the central part of the country, with a single record from the Maputo District. They are widespread in the **Transvaal**, except in the dry western and southwestern parts of the province, and occur in the eastern and northern parts of **Natal**. They occur coastally in the eastern **Cape Province**, with a break in distribution westwards, reoccurring in the Humansdorp area and westwards in the southwestern parts of the province.

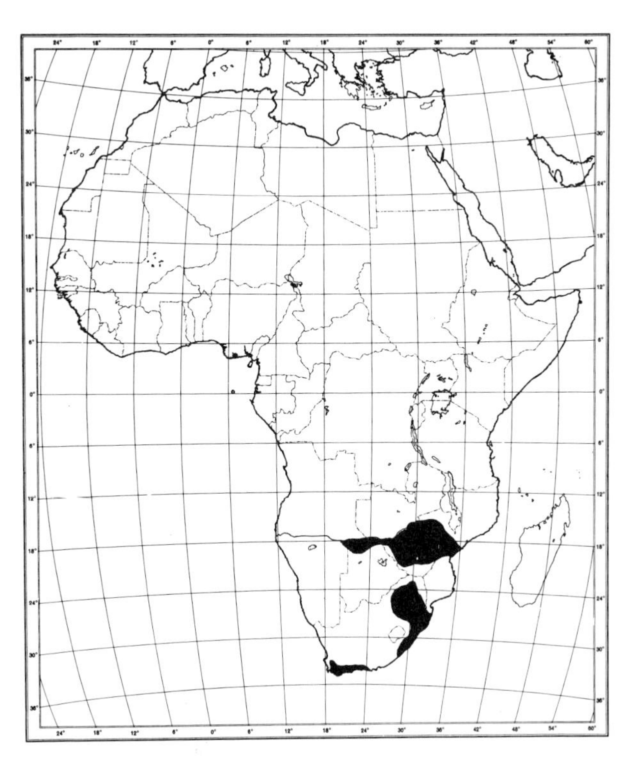

Southern African Subregion distribution only.

**Habitat**

As the colloquial name suggests, water rats are associated throughout their wide distributional range with a wet habitat. They occur in reed beds and among semi-aquatic grasses in swampy areas or along rivers and streams, in grassy or bracken-covered areas close to water. They share this habitat with vlei rats, *Otomys* spp. In the Subregion they occur from sea level to 1 800 m (eastern Zimbabwe).

### Habits

They are predominantly crepuscular, but also diurnal, being taken on the Chobe River as late as 11h00 in the morning and at 15h30 in the afternoon. Terrestrial and semi-aquatic, they move freely in their runs even when these are shallowly inundated and they swim well. Hanney (1975) excavated eight burrows in Malawi and found that they all conformed to a similar pattern. The nests are constructed in a depression on the sloping ground bordering the swampy edge of a river. They consisted of a double "bag", part on the ground surface, part in a depression. From the bottom of the depression a gradually declining burrow had been excavated either towards or parallel to the river. In two cases the ends were below water level, and from the burrow entrance well defined runs were traced. In Zimbabwe a domed nest, made out of grass, was constructed in a clump of tussock grass in a swamp some 150 mm above the water level. A short burrow led downwards through the clump and opened on the side at the water level, from which the characteristic runs led to feeding areas. The nest, which contained three young, had an entrance on its side within the tussock grass.

### Food

They are predominantly vegetarians, living on the succulent stems and fruiting heads of semi-aquatic grasses, reeds and other vegetation, but stomachs often contain insect remains (Smithers, 1971).

### Reproduction

In the northern parts of the Subregion gravid females or juveniles have been taken from August to December, the warm, wet summer months. The average number of foetuses per female was 5,3 (n=4; range 2–9). The females have one pair of pectoral and two pairs of inguinal mammae.

## Genus *Grammomys* Thomas, 1915

When Thomas (1907) created the genus *Thamnomys* he recognised that it could be subdivided into two groups on the basis of certain differences in the molar teeth. With more abundant material to work with later, he formally recognised this subdivision, creating the genus *Grammomys* for those specimens for which, in the first and second upper molar teeth, the postero-internal cusps are reduced to mere ridges, whereas in *Thamnomys* these cusps are well developed.

This grouping, although not recognised by Hollister (1919), was used by Roberts (1951) who described a further four species of *Thamnomys (Grammomys)*, one of which later turned out to be a synonym of *Thallomys, (T. (G.) ruddi)*, (Misonne, 1974). Ellerman *et al.* (1953) synonymised two of Roberts' (1951) species and considered all the material available from the Subregion as being referable to *Grammomys dolichurus* Smuts, 1832, with the following range of subspecies: *G. d. dolichurus* from the eastern Cape Province; *G. d. cometes* (Thomas & Wroughton, 1908) from southeastern Mozambique; *G. d. baliolus* (Osgood, 1910) from the northeastern Transvaal; *G. d. tongensis* Roberts, 1931 from northern Natal, and *G. d. silindensis* Roberts, 1938 from eastern Zimbabwe, later considered to be a subspecies of *T. (G.) cometes* (Misonne, 1974). Meester *et al.* (1986) recognised two species, *G. cometes* and *G. dolichurus*.

Key to the species of *Grammomys* after Meester *et al.* (1986)

1. Ears often but not always with subauricular tuft of white hairs; larger and greyer, with greatest skull length usually >31 mm

   ... *cometes*

   Ears without subauricular tuft; smaller, less grey, with greatest skull length usually <31 mm

   ... *dolichurus*

In Malawi, Hanney (1965), considering a series of specimens with a head and body length of over 94 mm, found that the difference in size between the two species was highly significant:

| | *G. dolichurus* | *G. cometes* |
|---|---|---|
| | **Males** | **Males** |
| HB | $\bar{x}$ = 107 (n=17) | $\bar{x}$ = 113 (n=12) |
| | **Females** | **Females** |
| HB | $\bar{x}$ = 104 (n=22) | $\bar{x}$ = 119 (n=13) |
| TL skull | $\bar{x}$ = 28,1 (n=15) | $\bar{x}$ = 30,3 (n=11) |

Hanney (1965) recorded that the two species in Malawi are similar in form and colour; the pelage on the upper parts in *G. cometes* is a richer brown than in *G. dolichurus* and never orange-tawny, the hair generally finer and longer.

The key does not entirely fit the situation in the Subregion, especially in eastern Zimbabwe and parts of Mozambique, except in so far as size is concerned. Some of the individuals which might be considered greyer, for example, are smaller in head and body size and in the total length of the skull than those that lack the grey and which are larger. Some of the smaller specimens have a subauricular tuft of white hairs, others have it on one side only or it is reduced to a few hairs only (Smithers & Tello, 1976). Size appears to be the only character which serves to distinguish the two species, but until a further revision is undertaken, Meester *et al.* (1986) are followed.

---

No. 166

## *Grammomys cometes* (Thomas & Wroughton, 1908)

## Mozambique woodland mouse
## Mosambiek-woudmuis

---

### Colloquial Name

They are associated predominantly with the more eastern parts of the Subregion and particularly within the Southern Savanna Woodland Zone in Mozambique.

### Taxonomic Notes

The nominate *G. c. cometes* occurs in northeastern Natal and Mozambique, *G. c. silindensis* Roberts, 1938 in eastern Zimbabwe.

### Description

Mozambique woodland mice, *G. cometes*, are slightly larger in size than woodland mice, *G. dolichurus*, with a head and body length in adults of about 120 mm and tails that are, on average, one and a half times the length of the head and body (Table 166.1). The condylobasal length of the skull shows the size difference, being on average 31,9 mm (n=4) in this species from the Ngoye Forest, KwaZulu (Panagis & Nel, 1981) and 31,4 (n=4) from eastern Zimbabwe and Mozambique, as against 28,3 mm (n=13) in *G. dolichurus* from eastern Zimbabwe. The colour of the upper parts is as variable as in the woodland mouse, some being greyish-brown, others tawny-grey in colour. The upper surfaces of the hands and feet are white. In some specimens there are tufts of white hair at the base of the ears, but these are not invariably present.

**Table 166.1**

Measurements (mm) of Mozambique woodland mice, *G. cometes*, from Mozambique and eastern Zimbabwe (Smithers, 1983)

| | Irrespective of sex | | |
|---|---|---|---|
| | $\bar{x}$ | n | Range |
| HB | 116 | 7 | 110–129 |
| TL skull | 31,4 | 4 | 31,0–32,0 |

**Distribution**

*South of the Sahara, excluding the Southern African Subregion*

Extralimitally to the Subregion the species occurs in **Mozambique; Zambia; Malawi; Tanzania; Kenya**; and the **Sudan**. They are not recorded from Mozambique, north of the Zambezi River, but their occurrence south of the river and in Tanzania suggests that they have been overlooked in this sector.

*Southern African Subregion*

They are recorded in the northern Beira, western and southern Vila Pery, southeastern Inhambane and Maputo districts of **Mozambique**, south of the Zambezi River; in the eastern parts of **Zimbabwe**, narrowly on the Mozambique border in the Mutare and Melsetter districts; in the southeastern **Transvaal**; northern and northeastern **Natal** and as far south as the Ngoye Forest which marks their most southerly limits of occurrence on the continent.

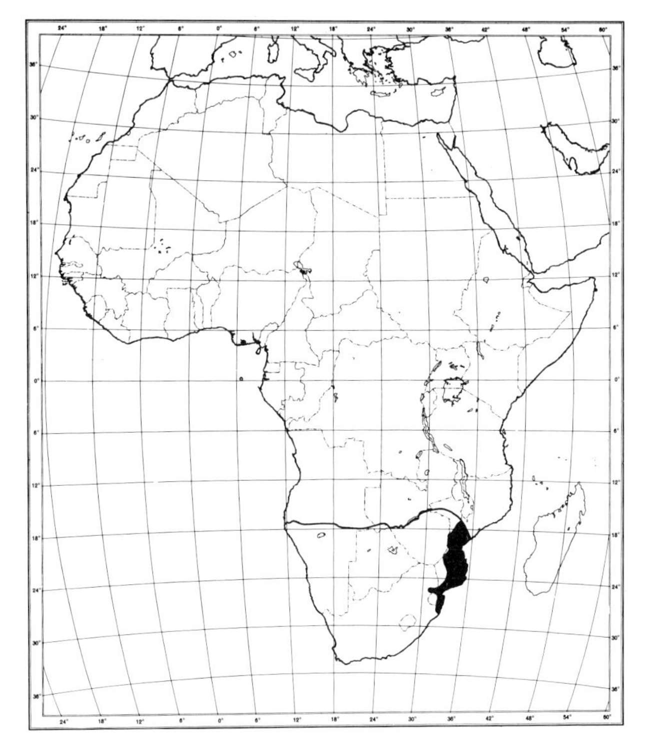

Southern African Subregion distribution only.

**Habitat**

In parts of its distributional range the Mozambique woodland mouse occurs on the same ground as the woodland mouse, *G. dolichurus*. They have a preference for thicker and better developed woodland or forest than *G. dolichurus* and consequently they are restricted in their range to the more easterly, higher rainfall areas. In Malawi, Hanney (1965) restricted them to within the 1 500 mm isohyet.

**Habits**

They are nocturnal and arboreal and probably have very similar habits to *G. dolichurus*, but these have not been studied in depth in the field. In captivity, Panagis (1979) found that they were capable of negotiating a 1,5 mm diameter wire strung horizontally, using the tail as a balancing organ which either hung below the wire or was held in a curve behind them.

**Food**

No data available.

**Reproduction**

Hanney (1965) in Malawi took gravid females in November, April and June. He stated that the peak of reproduction falls in the warm, wet season and that females can have up to three litters in a season. From the number of foetuses observed, litters number from two to five, with a mean of 2,9.

Panagis & Nel (1981) found that pairs in captivity which were identified as *G. cometes*, from their large body size, skull length and length of the cheekteeth row, had litters of one to four young, with a birth mass of 4,2 g (n=8). The newly-born pups are altricial, pinkish in colour and covered with fine greyish fur on the upper parts of the body and on the hind legs; the under parts and ears are covered with fine white hairs. The eyes are closed at birth and are fully opened by the 10th day. At birth the incisor teeth have erupted and have a central notch which assists in nipple-clinging, which can continue for a period of up to 26 days, although weaning usually takes place at about 19 days. The young emerge from the nest around the 15th day, but never move far and return to it immediately on threat of danger.

---

No. 167

## *Grammomys dolichurus* (Smuts, 1832)

## Woodland mouse
## Woudmuis

Plate 13

---

**Colloquial Name**

Named for their wide occurrence in the Southern Savanna Woodland Zone.

**Taxonomic Notes**

They differ only in size from *G. cometes*. Meester *et al.* (1986) listed four subspecies, the nominate *G. d. dolichurus* from the eastern Cape Province to parts of northern Natal; *G. d. surdaster* (Thomas & Wroughton, 1908) from the Limpopo River, northeastern Transvaal to eastern Zimbabwe and adjacent parts of Mozambique; *G. d. baliolus* (Osgood, 1910) from the northeastern Transvaal, and *G. d. tongensis* Roberts, 1931 from northern Natal. The status of these subspecies is questionable and a revision is necessary. Dippenaar *et al.* (1983) showed that there is geographic variation in the diploid chromosome number from 2n=44 at Woodbush, Transvaal to 2n=52 at Ngoye Forest, Natal, whilst in the northeastern parts of Africa chromosome numbers of 2n=54 and 2n=61 are known (Roche *et al.*, 1984).

**Description**

Adult woodland mice from the northern parts of the Subregion have an average total length of about 270 mm, with very long, thin tails well over half this length. In relation to the head and body the tail is usually about 160% to 170% of this length. The average mass is about 30,0 g (Table 167.1). There is a considerable variation in the colour of the upper parts of the body; the under parts in every case are pure white, this sharply demarcated from the colour of the upper parts. In eastern Zimbabwe the colour of the upper parts is tawny-reddish and much redder on the rump; in the northeastern Transvaal the upper parts are dark slate with a greyish tinge and a tinge of red on the rump. In northern Natal they are a dull tawny colour and in Transkei dark reddish with yellowish flanks. The individual hairs on the upper parts are dark grey at the base, the colour imparted by the tipping of the hairs. The hands and feet are usually white but may be tinged with rusty or buff.

**Table 167.1**

Measurements (mm) and mass (g) of a series of woodland mice, *G. dolichurus*, from eastern Zimbabwe (Smithers & Wilson, 1979)

| | Males | | | Females | | |
|---|---|---|---|---|---|---|
| | x̄ | n | Range | x̄ | n | Range |
| TL | 266 | 12 | 205–300 | 275 | 12 | 252–300 |
| HB | (98) | | | (103) | | |
| T | 168 | 12 | 140–198 | 172 | 12 | 159–190 |
| Hf c/u | 26 | 12 | 25–29 | 24 | 12 | 20–26 |
| E | 17 | 12 | 15–21 | 16 | 12 | 15–18 |
| Mass | 30,4 | 8 | 26,5–33,0 | 28,1 | 10 | 24,5–36,5 |

| | Irrespective of sex | | |
|---|---|---|---|
| | x̄ | n | Range |
| TL skull | 28,3 | 13 | 28,0–29,4 |

### Distribution

*South of the Sahara, excluding the Southern African Subregion*

The species has a wide distribution on the continent, from **Mali** in West Africa to the **Sudan** and from there southwards to the borders of the Subregion.

*Southern African Subregion*

They are recorded in **Zimbabwe** from the Harare District east to the Eastern Districts; from **Mozambique**, south of the Zambezi River, where they occur widely, south to the northern Gaza and Inhambane districts, with no records south of this at the moment. There seems a likelihood that, in time, they will be found to occur here as they are found in northeastern Natal. In the **Transvaal** they occur in the northeastern parts of the province; coastally in **Natal; Transkei** and the eastern parts of the **Cape Province** west to about the Port Elizabeth District.

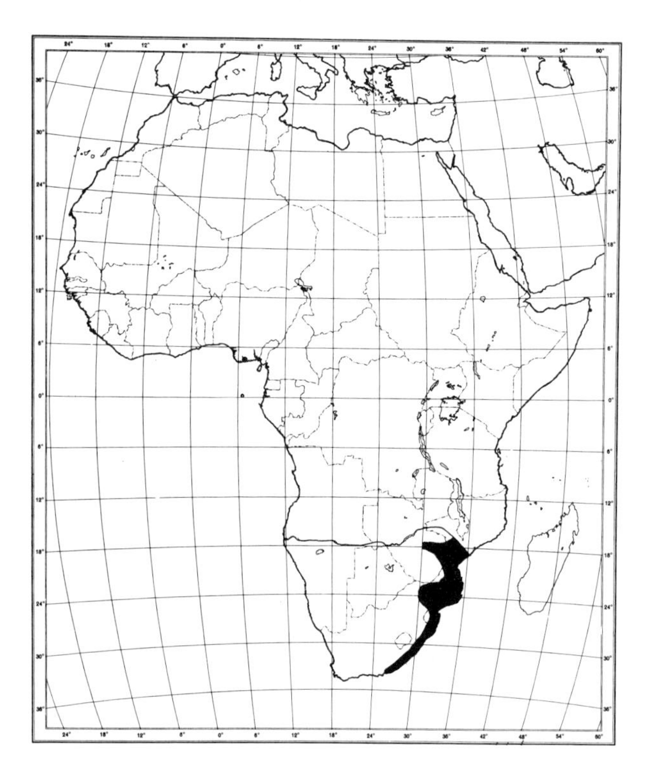

Southern African Subregion distribution only.

### Habitat

In the Subregion they are found in montane and other types of forest, including riverine forest and in thickets in woodland. However, they are not confined to these types of association, for in the Harare District in Zimbabwe they were found to be particularly common in *Phragmites* sp reed beds along the Mazoe River. Roberts (1951) believed that they were an evergreen forest species and this was the impression in Zimbabwe, where originally they were known as the forest mouse. In Malawi, Hanney (1965) gave the optimum habitat as damp, regenerating woodland.

### Habits

Woodland mice are nocturnal and predominantly arboreal. They construct nests of grass, leaves and other fine vegetable debris in the densest parts of thickets about half to two metres above the ground, which measure up to 200 mm in diameter. Hanney (1965) found them in the axils of banana and pineapple plants in Malawi. In Zimbabwe their nests were found in reed beds where these were thickened up with stands of asparagus or other shrubs or where the reed stems had fallen and were matted together. Roberts (1951) recorded that a nest was occupied by a family party consisting of adult, immature and juvenile young of two litters, and that they use holes in trees. Sclater (1901) mentioned their use of the holes excavated by barbets, and Hanney (1975) mentioned an individual that nested in the suspended nest of a golden weaver, *Ploceus xanthopterus*. When adapting weaver birds' nests in captivity, they use the single entrance, but are reported to furnish this with a similar screen (Hubbard, 1972). However, Smithers (1983) was unable to confirm this. In Tanzania, Hubbard (1972) reported that they build triangular-shaped nests with three escape entrances, well hidden in thick foliage. The walls are up to 25 mm thick and are made of woven grass, coarse on the outside, fine within. A fine grass screen is constructed about 25 mm inside the entrance, which opens to allow the individual to pass, closing after it.

### Food

No information is available from the Subregion, but, in Malawi, Hanney (1965) examined a series of 20 stomachs, and found that 90% contained green vegetable matter, including 10% wild fruit, 15% white plant material and 15% wood fibres. In captivity they disregarded insects, and he thus concluded that they are purely vegetarian, with a favourite diet of fruit and green bark.

### Reproduction

Very little information is available from the Subregion. In the Transvaal and Zimbabwe, pregnant females were taken in September and January (Rautenbach, 1978; Smithers & Wilson, 1979). In Malawi, pregnant females were recorded in February, April and May, and young were found in nests during February and July (Hanney, 1965), whilst in Zambia pregnant females were found from December to June. From this meagre information it appears that they have an extended breeding season, but probably, when further information is available, this may show a peak during the warm, wet summer months from around October to February.

Bland (1973) recorded that the gestation period in *T. surdaster* (= *T. dolichurus*) is 24 days, with intervals between litters of not less than 28 days.

## Genus *Mus* Linnaeus, 1758

Gray (1837), when examining the Indian species of the genus *Mus*, created the genus *Leggada* to accommodate those species which had taller molar teeth, with rather convex crowns, characters which are recognised now as having no diagnostic validity. Although Miller (1910) believed that it was impracticable to maintain the two genera, Thomas (1919) thought that there was a distinction, first in the comparative length of the rostra and secondly in the front edge of the zygomatic plate, which lies posterior to the mid-point of the anterior palatal foramina in *Leggada*, yet lies forward of this point in *Mus*. In doing so he recognised that not every specimen conformed to these criteria. Matthey (1958), working with *Mus minutoides* from Africa, showed that *Mus* and *Leggada* are separable on their chromosome formula, but left open the question as to whether the distinction is of generic or subgeneric order. Petter (1963b), however, believed that this cannot be accepted unreservedly, as it is not certain that the results apply to all species; furthermore he pointed out that it is impossible to draw up a diagnosis that will separate all reputed individuals of either genus. In reviewing the genus, Petter & Matthey

(1975) stated that it is impossible to present a key to all the African species. In some, examination of their chromosomal formulae and morphology allows a redefinition, but in others this is not possible. They retained the genus *Mus* for the African species. As an example of the difficulties arising from the present uncertainties, Petter & Matthey (1975) showed that it has not been possible to determine the relationship of the material from Zimbabwe (females: 2n=36; males: 2n=35) which is presently listed as *M. minutoides*, and which has a chromosome formulae of 2n=18–19. The Zimbabwe material has shorter tails than "typical" *M. minutoides* and differs in colour, but until further taxonomic studies are carried out must be considered as referable to this species.

In Botswana, Thomas (1910) described *Leggada bella induta* and *L. deserti*, both from the same locality, Molopo, Morokwen, in the south of the country, and Petter (1978) *M. setzeri* from near Mohembo in the extreme northwest. Petter & Matthey (1975) listed *M. deserti* as a synonym of *M. indutus*. *M. setzeri* is clearly different from the remainder of the Botswana material which, on present evidence, appears to be *M. indutus*, having long ears, a short tail and white under parts which extend upwards over the rump and high onto the face and muzzle. Owing to these uncertainties it is impossible to draw up the limits of distribution properly and the information that is given must be considered tentative.

Meester *et al.* (1986) included *M. sorella* Thomas, 1909 on the basis of records by Pocock (1974) from Zimbabwe and central Mozambique. These records are mapped, but it is possible that this species occurs more widely.

Key to the species (Meester *et al.*, 1986)

1. Size larger, head and body length >70 mm; ventral surface light buffy in colour
 ... *musculus*

 Size smaller, head and body length <70 mm; ventral surface white, off-white or grey
 ... 2

2. Ear length >13 mm
 ... *setzeri*

 Ear length <13 mm
 ... 3

3. Ventral surface grey
 ... *triton*

 Ventral surface white or off-white
 ... 4

4. Incisor teeth proodont; length of mandible and incisors usually >12 mm; $M_2$ two rooted
 ... *sorella*

 Incisor teeth opisthodont; length of mandible and incisors usually <12 mm; $M_2$ three rooted
 ... 5

5. Dorsal colour pale, pinkish grey or pinkish buff; dorsal surface of tail white or off-white; patch of white hair at the base of the ears; length of tail <80% of length of head and body; $M^1$ compact
 ... *indutus*

 Dorsal colour darker, brown, dark brown or nearly black; dorsal surface of tail darker, not white or off-white; length of tail >80% of length of head and body; $M^1$ slightly elongated
 ... *minutoides*

**INTRODUCED**

No. 168

## *Mus musculus* Linnaeus, 1758

## House mouse
## Huismuis

Plate 12

### Colloquial Name

Throughout its cosmopolitan distribution this species commonly occurs as a commensal with man.

### Taxonomic Notes

Several subspecies have been described. Ellerman & Morrison-Scott (1951) listed 15 from the Palearctic and Indian region. Meester *et al.* (1986) noted that it is not clear which subspecies provided the stock from which southern Africa was colonised, it being probable that more than one subspecies was involved.

### Description

Adults have a total length of about 160 mm, with tails that may be shorter or longer than the length of the head and body (Table 168.1). The hairs are short and wide with a slender base, a deep groove and single petal scales in the groove (Fig. XXIII.3) (Keogh, 1985). The upper parts of the body are buffy-brown, the flanks the same colour as the upper parts, and the under parts are a light buffy-brown. The tail is brown on the upper surface, lighter on the under. The hands and feet are light buffy-brown.

They can be distinguished from *M. minutoides* as they are larger, and on the colour of the under parts, which in *M. minutoides* is white. Albino and melanistic forms are known. The former are now important laboratory animals and are commonly sold in pet shops.

**Table 168.1**

Measurements (mm) and mass (g) of house mice, *M. musculus*, from the Subregion

**Zimbabwe** (Smithers & Wilson, 1979)

| | Irrespective of sex | | |
|---|---|---|---|
| | $\bar{x}$ | n | Range |
| TL | 161 | 14 | 151–185 |
| (HB | 75) | | |
| T | 86 | 12 | 80–100 |
| Hf c/u | 16 | 12 | 15–19 |
| E | 13 | 12 | 10–15 |

**Transvaal** (Rautenbach, 1978)

| | Males | | | Females | | |
|---|---|---|---|---|---|---|
| | $\bar{x}$ | n | Range | $\bar{x}$ | n | Range |
| Mass | 15,1 | 10 | 9,0–24,0 | 17,0 | 5 | 11,0–25,0 |

### Distribution

They are distributed widely in the populated parts of the Subregion. They are recorded from towns and settlements in central and southern **Namibia**; the **Cape Province; Orange Free State; Lesotho; Natal**; the **Transvaal** and **Zimbabwe**. Although there are no records from Mozambique, south of the Zambezi River, this is probably due to lack of collecting in built up areas such as Beira and Maputo, where they almost certainly occur. In **Botswana** they are absent from the greater part of the country, which is only sparsely settled, but occur on the line of rail at Francistown and therefore most probably are present at least in other settlements and towns served by the railway. The same applies in Zimbabwe where they are common in towns on the line of rail and settlements served by road transport agencies. They are common on Marion Island to which they were introduced, either through the activities of sealers who visited the island from the early part of the 19th century, or from shipwrecks. There is slight evidence that this population may have originated from Denmark (Berry, Peters & van Aarde, 1978).

The genetic complex known as the house mouse is thought to have originated on the dry steppes of southeastern Russia (Schwarz & Schwarz, 1943) and, having adapted to being a commensal with man, has been transported widely throughout the world. They occur as far north as Iceland (65 °N) and the Lofoten Islands (69 °N) (Bronson, 1979) and on most of the major land masses of the temperate and tropical zones of the world, excepting tropical Africa, and on many oceanic islands. The Subregion populations are probably the progeny of introductions from many parts of the world brought to the ports of the Subregion from the time of the earliest explorers and traders. Introductions have continued up to modern times.

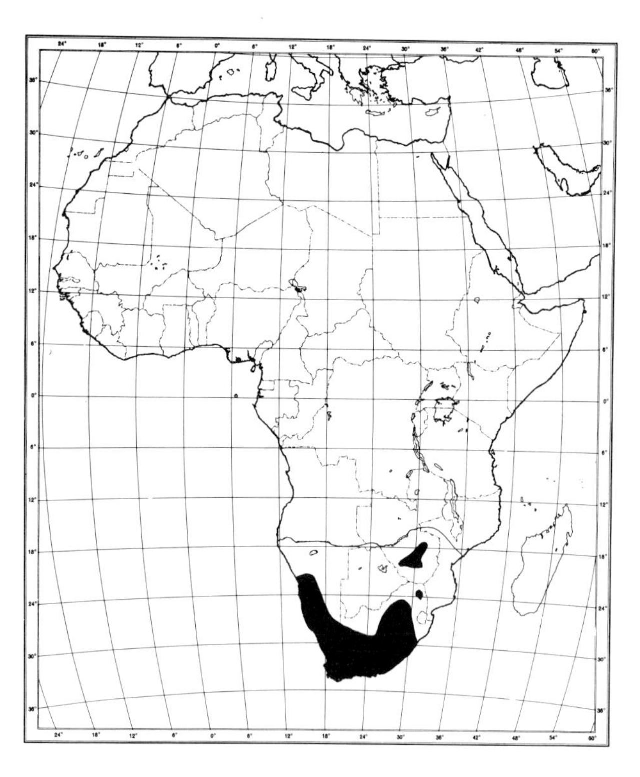

Southern African Subregion distribution only.

## Habitat

In the Subregion they are closely confined to dwelling houses, outbuildings, food stores, railway goods yards and to any other similar type of buildings, especially where foodstuffs are stored. Laurie (1945) recorded that in Great Britain the situation is similar, although they are known to live in hayricks and in other types of shelter in the field, where food and a certain amount of warmth and shelter are available. Temperature alone is not a restricting factor as they are known to live and breed in cold-storage rooms where the temperature may go down to at least −3 °C, but only if undisturbed and supplied with ample food and bedding material (Barnett, 1973).

In parts of their distributional range such as in southern Russia, in Australia and the United States where the climate is warm they take up residence in the field, but do not generally do so in the Subregion which may be due to the high level of competition from indigenous species. On Marion Island, where they are the only murid which occurs, they are not confined to dwellings and are common between the high tide mark and 400 m inland in the peat and particularly in the area of black lava, which provides ample shelter in the form of holes and cracks. They also burrow into the nests of the wandering albatross, *Diomedea exulans*, constructing nests which probably benefit from the warmth generated by the nesting birds (Gleeson, 1981).

## Habits

House mice are predominantly nocturnal, pairs constructing nests of paper, rags or any other soft household debris under the floors of houses, in sheltered crevices, in the thatch roofs of African huts or in any situation that offers cover and access to a source of food. In the Subregion they never occur in such numbers as to become a major problem, but they are nevertheless very destructive and cause considerable damage annually to stored food products. In other parts of the world they are subject to population explosions. Laurie (1945) recorded that in Australia in 1916–1917 it was estimated that one million Australian pounds worth of damage was done to stacked wheat during one of these explosions. In California, estimates of their numbers during such times reached the figure of over 80 000 individuals per acre.

Bronson (1979) reviewed the knowledge of the social organisation of the species under commensal conditions, showing that the males are territorial. Each territory is only a few square metres in extent and is defended by a single male. The boundaries are marked routinely by the use of urinary marking. Each territory includes several breeding females, usually less than 10, their offspring and a few subordinate males, all dominated by the single territorial male. There is a loose hierarchial ranking among the adult females but little aggressive behaviour between them, and pregnant females will assist the territorial male in the defence of the territory. Given good conditions several generations may be born and densities may approach 10 mice per m$^2$. While adult and young females may leave the territory and be accepted in another, the mortality among young males and adult subordinate males attempting to enter another territory is high.

In other parts of the world, where house mice live in the field, populations are usually, but not always, of low density, as little as one mouse per hectare. When populations explode, however, they are known to reach 100 mice per hectare. Field conditions seldom provide such adequate food supplies as are found under commensalism and their home ranges under field conditions, therefore, are usually much larger and may reach up to several thousand square metres. Little is known of their social organisation under field conditions.

## Food

Throughout their wide distributional range house mice are omnivorous. This applies to the populations now established on Marion Island where in the buildings of the Meteorological Station they are omnivorous, while in the field their principal food is the larvae and adults of a nocturnal flightless moth, *Pringleophaga marioni*. Other foods taken on the island include the larvae and adults of a second flightless moth, *Embryonopsis halticella*; weevils, including *Ectemnorrhinus similis*; spiders, *Myro paucispinosus*, *M. kerguelenensis*, *Erigone vagans* and *Porrhomma antarctica*. Occasionally they will take earthworms; snails, *Notodiscus hookeri*; adult and larval kelp flies; ticks; aphids; mites, and marine amphipods. During the summer months plant food in the form of seeds and shoots is eaten and they have also been known to scavenge on bird carcasses (Gleeson, 1981).

## Reproduction

Females can have their first litters when 40 days old (Hanney, 1965). The gestation period is 19 days and litter sizes in commensal populations vary between one and 13, with an average of about six (Laurie, 1945). The young are born in nests lined with any type of soft material including grass, leaves or household debris. Females breed throughout the year and communal nests are not uncommon.

Laurie (1945) found that populations living in cold-storage chambers in total darkness at temperatures of −10 °C to −21 °C produce significantly higher numbers of foetuses per female than those living in houses and food stores.

As opposed to the commensal populations, those living in the field are seasonal breeders (Bronson, 1979). On Marion Island, Gleeson (1981) stated that the young are born between August and April, the warmer summer months, and have mean litter sizes of 6,9 (n=30; range 5–9).

---

No. 169

# *Mus setzeri* Petter, 1978

# Setzer's pygmy mouse
# Setzer se dwergmuis

---

## Colloquial Name

They were named after Dr. H.W. Setzer, formerly Curator of Mammals at the United States National Museum, whose assistants T.N. Liversedge and W.S. Goussard collected the specimens, in northwestern Botswana, from which the species was described.

### Taxonomic Notes

This species has larger ears than *M. indutus*, in which the mean length is 11 mm (n=90) with a range of eight to 12 mm, compared with *M. setzeri* at 13,6 mm (n=11) with a range of 13 to 14 mm. The white of the under parts extends further up the flanks in *M. setzeri* and continues on to the upper parts on the rump and across the muzzle, posterior to the rhinarium. In *M. indutus* it is restricted to the under parts and flanks and does not extend over the rump or muzzle.

### Description

Slightly smaller than *M. indutus*, this species has a shorter tail and longer ears (Table 169.1). The colour of the upper parts is pinkish-clay, in some specimens darker on the forehead and between the ears, and they appear less grizzled on the back than *M. indutus*, as they have fewer black-tipped hairs scattered throughout the pelage. The flanks are pinkish-clay devoid of grizzling and are yellower under the ears and behind the eyes. The line of demarcation between the white of the under parts and the upper parts is distinct and the white is more extensive, extending upwards on to the cheeks and across the top of the muzzle posterior to the rhinarium and across the top of the rump anterior to the base of the tail. The upper surfaces of the hands and feet are white, the tail whitish, and they have a patch of white hair just below the ears. The individual hairs on the upper parts are pale grey at the base and broadly tipped with pinkish-clay and very few hairs are tipped with black.

**Table 169.1**

Measurements (mm) and mass (g) of Setzer's pygmy mice, *M. setzeri*, from Botswana (Smithers, 1971)

| | Irrespective of sex | | |
|---|---|---|---|
| | $\bar{x}$ | n | Range |
| TL | 90 | 9 | 82–97 |
| (HB | 54) | | |
| T | 36 | 9 | 31–48 |
| Hf c/u | 14 | 11 | 13–15 |
| E | 13,6 | 11 | 13–14 |
| Mass | 6,8 | 11 | 5,0–9,0 |

### Distribution

Petter (1978) listed five localities from which this species has been recognised: Numkaub in northeastern **Namibia**; two from the extreme northwestern parts of **Botswana**: 76 km east and 18 km south of Shakawe and 82 km east of Mohembo, both of these being settlements on the Okavango River; and a third from Sekhuma pan in the south of the country, indicating a wide distribution. The fifth locality is Balovale in southwestern **Zambia** near the Angola border.

### Habitat

*Mus setzeri* occurs alongside *M. indutus* and appears to have the same wide habitat tolerance. In southern Botswana both species have been taken on the fringes of pans in areas with a mean annual rainfall of 400 mm to 450 mm in arid terrain. They also occur on the fringes of the Okavango Swamp in well watered country in areas with a mean annual rainfall of up to 750 mm, and in Balovale, Zambia, in the range of from 900 mm to 1 000 mm.

### Habits, Food and Reproduction

These have not been studied so far and apart from the fact that they are nocturnal and terrestrial, nothing is presently known.

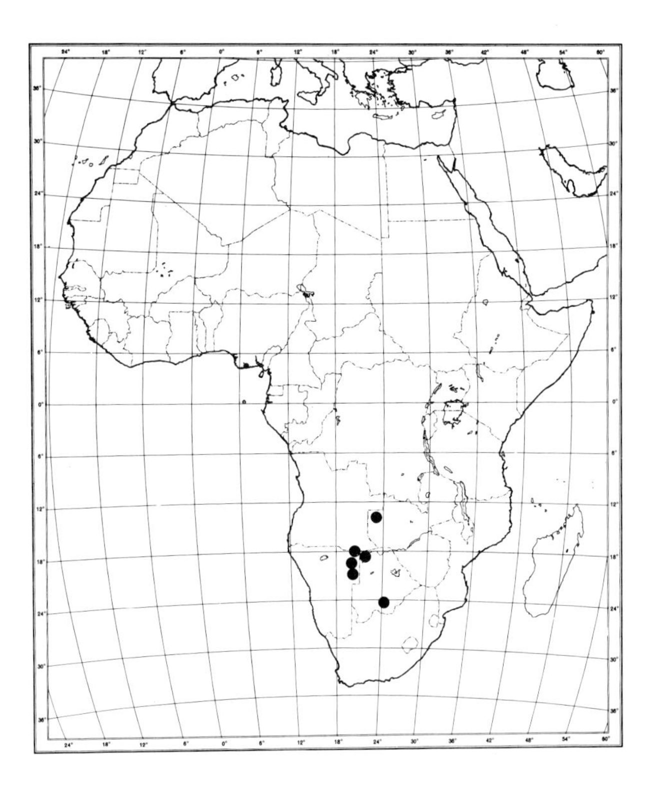

No. 170

## *Mus triton* (Thomas, 1909)

## Grey-bellied pygmy mouse
## Vaalpensdwergmuis

### Colloquial Name

So called as they are the only pygmy mice with grey under parts that occur in the Subregion.

### Taxonomic Notes

Ellerman *et al.* (1953) pointed out that the taxonomic status of this species is unsatisfactory. The diastema between the first molar teeth and the incisor teeth is short, as in *M. musculus*, and they cannot be distinguished at the moment from wild races of this species. Specimens from Angola have a longer diastema but then they become indistinguishable from *M. cervicolor* Hodgson, 1845 of India and its races which antedates the name *M. triton* by many years. A further complication arises from the fact that specimens at present considered as *M. triton* have different chromosome numbers in East Africa from those in Zaire, suggesting that two species may be involved (Petter, 1975a).

Until further study clarifies the situation, however, *M. triton* is considered as a valid species.

### Description

They have a mean head and body length of about 70 mm and tails of 50 mm. The upper parts of the body are dark brown, grizzled with buffy, the top of the head darker, the flanks paler and more buffy. The hair on the under parts is dark grey at the base with broad white tips, the grey of the hair bases showing through to impart a grey appearance to the under parts. The upper surfaces of the forefeet are brown, those of the hind feet much lighter and off-white or very pale brown. The chin is off-white, the tail dark brown above, off-white below. On the front feet, the pollex is very short, the third and fourth fingers the longest. On the hind feet the first and fifth toes are short, the remaining three much longer and all about the same length.

**Table 170.1**

Measurements (mm) and mass (g) of grey-bellied pygmy mice, *M. triton*, from the Tete District, Mozambique (Smithers & Tello, 1976).

| | Males | | | Females | | |
|---|---|---|---|---|---|---|
| | x̄ | n | Range | x̄ | n | Range |
| TL | 116 | 11 | 110–124 | 123 | 6 | 117–130 |
| HB | 63 | 11 | 56–69 | 70 | 6 | 65–77 |
| T | 53 | 11 | 45–59 | 53 | 6 | 51–55 |
| Hf c/u | 16 | 11 | 15–17Tc | 16 | 6 | 15–16 |
| E | 12 | 11 | 11–13 | 11 | 6 | 12–14 |
| Mass | 9,8 | 9 | 8,0–12,0 | 10,3 | 6 | 8,0–12,0 |

**Distribution**

*South of the Sahara, excluding the Southern African Subregion*

They are recorded from **Angola; Zaire; Zambia; Malawi; Mozambique**, north of the Zambezi River; **Tanzania; Kenya** and **Uganda**.

*Southern African Subregion*

They occur marginally into the Subregion in the Tete District of **Mozambique**.

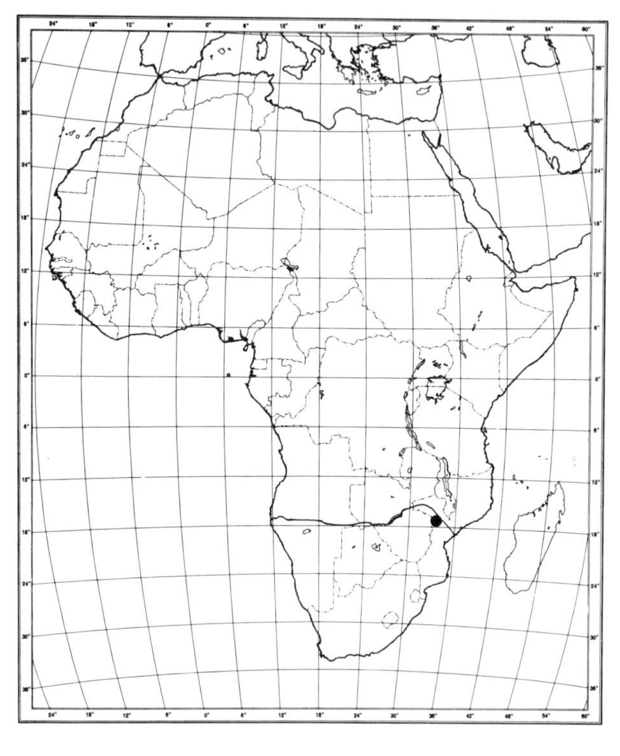

Southern African Subregion distribution only.

**Habitat**

The material taken in the southwestern sector of the Tete District occurred on the fringes of a swamp. Hanney (1965) recorded that in Malawi they prefer damp grassland situations, presumably where insects are most numerous. They were not found where the mean annual rainfall was below 965 mm.

**Habits**

They are predominantly nocturnal, but with some diurnal activity, and four out of 56 taken on the Zomba Plateau were taken in day traps (Hanney, 1965). In damp situations they will use *Otomys* spp runs and Hanney (1965) recorded that a male was dug out of a blind tunnel 0,61 m deep. Nests have not been found in the field, but in captivity they construct crude cup-shaped nests.

**Food**

Primarily insectivorous but also omnivorous, Hanney (1965) recorded in a sample of 36 stomachs, that 81% contained insect remains, mainly adult beetles, and 10% beetle larvae, while 8% contained remains of worms. One stomach was full of ant pupae and 28% of the sample contained vegetable matter, including slivers of wood, but no green plant cells.

**Reproduction**

Hanney (1965) found gravid females only between April and July in Malawi. Mean litter size was six (range 5–7). Newly born young had a mass of 1,3 g and were naked and pink, the first sparse covering of fine hair appearing at the age of four days.

---

No. 170A

## *Mus sorella* (Thomas, 1909)

## Thomas' pygmy mouse
## Thomas se dwergmuis

---

**Colloquial Name**

Named after Oldfield Thomas of the British Museum (Nat. Hist.) who originally named the species from a specimen from East Africa included in the C.D. Rudd collection.

**Taxonomic Notes**

Two subspecies are recognised: the nominate form from East Africa and *M. s. neavei* (Thomas, 1910) from Petauke (old Petauke), southeastern Zambia, which is the subspecies occurring in the Subregion.

**Description**

The measurements of the type were given by Thomas (1910) as HB 58 mm; T 39 mm; hind foot 13 mm, which are close to those of *M. indutus* (Thomas, 1910) and show that they have shorter tails than *M. minutoides* A. Smith, 1834. The colour of the upper parts of the body is a rich tawny, with a grizzling of black hairs on the mid-back; the under parts are white. This species can be distinguished from *M. indutus*, which has three rooted second lower molar teeth, as it has only two roots to these teeth, whilst the incisor teeth are more forwardly directed than in *M. indutus*.

**Distribution**

When a revision of the genus is undertaken it will be shown to have a wider occurrence. The records shown are taken from Pocock (1974), Ansell (1978), Petter (1981b), Meester et al. (1986) and from the type locality of *M. s. sorella* (Mt. Elgon, Kenya) and *M. s. neavei* (old Petauke, Zambia).

*South of the Sahara, excluding the Southern African Subregion*

Originally *M. s. sorella* was described from Mount Elgon, **Kenya** and this remains the only locality from which the species has been recognised among East African material.

**Plate 12**

159. Grooved-toothed mouse, *Pelomys fallax*
Groeftandmuis
162. Single-striped mouse, *Lemniscomys rosalia*
Eenstreepmuis
163. Striped mouse, *Rhabdomys pumilio*
Streepmuis
168. House mouse, *Mus musculus*
Huismuis
171. Desert pygmy mouse, *Mus indutus*
Woestyndwergmuis
172. Pygmy mouse, *Mus minutoides*
Dwergmuis
174. Natal multimammate mouse, *Mastomys natalensis*
Natalse vaalveldmuis
183. House rat, *Rattus rattus*
Huisrot

PLATE 12
168
183
174
172
162
163
171
165
159
Dick Findlay

*M. s. neavei* is recorded from eastern **Zambia** and from the Tete district of **Mozambique**, north of the Zambezi River.

*Southern African Subregion*

*M. s. neavei* occurs in **Zimbabwe** and in central and southern **Mozambique**. Apart from its occurrence in the Subregion nothing is known of its ecology here.

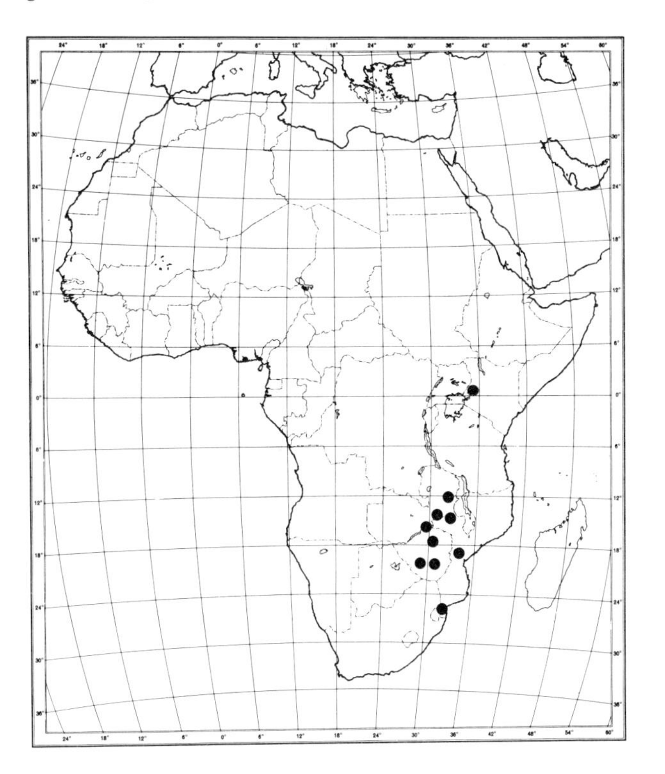

No. 171

## *Mus indutus* (Thomas, 1910)

## Desert pygmy mouse
## Woestyndwergmuis

Plate 12

### Colloquial Name

In a greater part of their known distributional range this species is associated with semi-desert terrain.

### Taxonomic Notes

Petter & Matthey (1975) treated *M. minutoides* and *M. indutus* as separate species, which is followed by Meester *et al.* (1986).

*Leggada bella induta* and *Leggada deserti* were both described by Thomas (1910) from the same locality, the Molopo River, west of Morokwen. The genus *Leggada* is now considered to be a synonym of *Mus*, whilst Meester *et al.* (1986) considered both these species to be synonyms of *M. indutus* (Thomas, 1910).

Until a detailed taxonomic revision of the genus is undertaken, the treatment afforded the species and subspecies by Meester *et al.* (1986) appears to be the best available. They recognised four subspecies: *M. i. indutus* from the northern Cape Province north to northern Botswana and western Zimbabwe; *M. i. sybilla* (Thomas, 1918) from Damaraland, Namibia; *M. i. valschensis* (Roberts, 1926) from the northern Orange Free State, and *M. i. pretoriae* (Roberts, 1926) from the southern, western and northern Transvaal.

### Description

Adults have a total length of about 100 mm, with tails that are shorter than the length of the head and body, and a mass of about 6,0 g (Table 171.1). The upper parts of the body are pinkish-buffy to pinkish-clay in colour, finely grizzled with black; the individual hairs are grey at the base with broad pinkish-buffy or pinkish-clay-coloured tips and some with black tips, which impart the grizzled appearance to the pelage. The flanks and rump lack the black-tipped hairs. The under parts are white, the white extending upwards to just below the eyes and along the flanks to the hind legs. The upper surfaces of the hands and feet are white. The tail is very pale pinkish-buff or pinkish-clay-coloured on its upper surface and white below. Below the base of the ears which are pale buffy they have a small patch of white hair. Some individuals have a darker suffusion on the forehead between the ears.

Matthey (1964) found that, in this species, the first upper molar tooth is less elongated than in *M. minutoides*, and while *M. minutoides* has a chromosomal formula of 2n=18, *M. indutus* has 2n=36.

**Table 171.1**

Measurements (mm) and mass (g) of desert pygmy mice, *M. indutus*, from Botswana (Smithers, 1971)

| | Males | | | Females | | |
|---|---|---|---|---|---|---|
| | $\bar{x}$ | n | Range | $\bar{x}$ | n | Range |
| TL | 96 | 90 | 76–118 | 100 | 46 | 87–116 |
| (HB | 54) | | | (57) | | |
| T | 42 | 90 | 30–52 | 43 | 46 | 31–49 |
| Hf c/u | 14 | 90 | 13–16 | 14 | 47 | 13–15 |
| E | 11 | 90 | 8–12 | 11 | 44 | 9–13 |
| Mass | 5,4 | 85 | 2,5–7,5 | 6,9 | 35 | 4,0–11,0 |

### Distribution

It is almost impossible at this juncture to be certain of the limits of distribution of this species. *M. indutus* is a pale-coloured species primarily associated with arid, semi-desert terrain and can be distinguished on external characters from material from south and east of its range. The question still remains, however, as to whether we are dealing with a single species presently designated *M. indutus.*

*Southern African Subregion*

Occurs throughout the semi-desert areas of **Botswana**, extending marginally eastwards into western **Zimbabwe** and the **Transvaal** and southwards into the northern parts of the **Cape Province**. In **Namibia** the species occurs throughout the central and northern parts of the territory.

### Habitat

They appear to have a wide habitat tolerance, occurring in the arid scrub savanna of southern Botswana to the better watered areas of the Okavango Swamp in the north of the country, in areas with a mean annual rainfall of about 200–700 mm.

### Habits

They are terrestrial and nocturnal. They lie up during the day in any fairly substantial cover such as crevices beneath stones, debris, fallen logs or the bark of trees, but will also excavate their own shallow burrows in sandy substrate or will use holes excavated by other species. They may also use the temporary cover of sacks, tarpaulins or sheets of corrugated iron left on the ground overnight. Specimens taken when moving camp have been found sheltering under the floor covering of tents and from ground bedding (Smithers, 1971). In more permanent shelter they construct ball-shaped nests of soft grass or other soft fibres, which pairs or pairs with their litter will occupy. Their populations explode at times of a plentiful food supply; numbers rise exponentially and crash as quickly to very low levels (Smithers, 1971 p. 301). They are very aggressive in captivity and are quick to kill each other, the survivor then eating the carcass. Under stress they exude a heavy musk smell.

### Food

The principal food appears to be grass seeds, *Acacia* spp seeds and the dry pods, as well as the dry exterior of fruits of trees such as buffalo thorn, *Ziziphus mucronata*. Most stomachs contain insect remains including Isoptera and

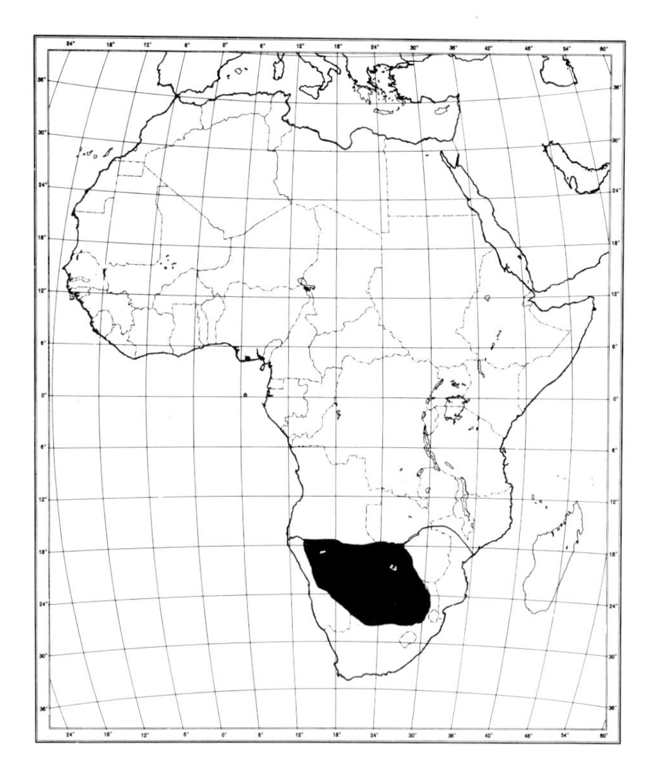

Southern African Subregion distribution only.

small beetles and at times they are cannibalistic. For this reason they probably should be designated as omnivorous.

### Reproduction

In Botswana, Smithers (1971) found that they breed at any time of the year. The mean number of foetuses from gravid females is 4,9 (range 2–8; n=17). The young are born in the ball-shaped grass nests and the parents remain with them until they are weaned.

---

No. 172

## *Mus minutoides* A. Smith, 1834

## Pygmy mouse
## Dwergmuis

Plate 12

---

### Colloquial Name

They are aptly named as they are among the smallest of the murids.

### Taxonomic Notes

The difficulties attending the relationship of members of this genus are mentioned under the text on the genus. *Leggada bella marica* Thomas, 1910 was described from Beira, Mozambique, a subspecies which Meester *et al*. (1986) included as a subspecies of *M. minutoides*. One of the characters of *M. minutoides* from the southwestern Cape Province (the type locality being Cape Town) is that it is a longer-tailed form, in series the length of the tail averaging 50 mm. For present purposes *M. minutoides* includes the material from the southeastern, southern and eastern parts of the Subregion, except for *M. triton* which has grey under parts and which occurs marginally in the Tete Province of Mozambique, south of the Zambezi River. It also excludes material from Botswana and westwards designated as *M. setzeri* and *M. indutus*, which are believed to have a wide distribution throughout the country.

Meester *et al*. (1986) listed four subspecies from the Subregion: *M. m. minutoides* from the western, southern and eastern Cape Province; *M. m. umbratus* (Thomas, 1910) from Swaziland north to the Pietersburg district, Transvaal; *M. m. marica* (Thomas, 1910) from the eastern Transvaal, Mozambique, extending into Malawi and Zambia, and *M. m. orangiae* (Roberts, 1926) from the Orange Free State and Lesotho.

Gordon (in prep.) has found that *Mus* from the southern and western Cape have a diploid chromosome number 2n=18, while specimens from Natal have 2n=34 (other specimens from the Transvaal which may represent *M. indutus* have 2n=34; yet other specimens from Namibia have 2n=32).

### Description

It is impossible to generalise in giving a description of this species owing to the uncertainty attending its taxonomic status. All that can be done at this stage is to give a description that fits the species in the Cape Province, from where the specimen on which the species was first described originated, and to comment at the same time on those from the northeastern areas.

In spite of this difficulty, pygmy mice from within the complex of species or subspecies are recognised easily. Hairs grooved wide and deep, scales cup-shaped (Keogh 1985). They have pure white under parts and are much smaller than any of the other species of murids, with the exception of the chestnut climbing mouse, *Dendromus mystacalis*, which is equally small but has a much longer tail and a dark stripe down its back. Only *M. triton* which is marginal in distribution in the northeastern parts of the Subregion, and *M. musculus*, the introduced house mouse, do not conform to these criteria, but the former have grey under parts, the latter buffy-brown under parts.

In the southwestern Cape Province pygmy mice have a total length of up to about 110 mm, with tails that are about 80% of the length of the head and body (Table 172.1). The upper parts of the body are brownish-buff. The brownish colour is imparted to the pelage by the presence of black-tipped hairs which become fewer on the flanks; these are orange-buffy in colour. The border between the colour of the flanks and the white of the under parts is sharply defined. The tail is brown above and buffy below, the ears brownish, the hands and feet buffy-white.

Specimens from Zimbabwe vary in colour; some are much more rufous on the upper parts of the body and flanks than those from the Cape Province, others are darker on the back with rufous flanks. They all have pure white under parts and are whitish on the upper surface of the hands and feet.

**Table 172.1**

Measurements (mm) and mass (g) of pygmy mice, *M. minutoides*

**Southwestern Cape Province**

| | Males | | | Females | | |
|---|---|---|---|---|---|---|
| | x̄ | n | Range | x̄ | n | Range |
| (TL | 108) | | | (112) | | |
| HB | 59 | 10 | 56–63 | 62 | 10 | 57–65 |
| T | 49 | 10 | 48–54 | 50 | 10 | 45–55 |
| Hf c/u | 15 | 10 | 14–15 | 15 | 10 | 14–15 |
| E | 10 | 10 | 8–10 | 10 | 10 | 8–11 |

**Transvaal** (Rautenbach, 1978)

| | Males | | | Females | | |
|---|---|---|---|---|---|---|
| | x̄ | n | Range | x̄ | n | Range |
| TL | 97 | 63 | 82–114 | 100 | 77 | 82–160 |
| (HB | 56) | | | (58) | | |
| T | 41 | 63 | 30–48 | 42 | 77 | 20–51 |
| Hf c/u | 13 | 63 | 8–15 | 13 | 77 | 8–14 |
| E | 10 | 62 | 7–14 | 10 | 75 | 8–14 |
| Mass | 5,5 | 49 | 2,0–12,0 | 6,2 | 56 | 3,0–10,0 |

**Zimbabwe** (Smithers & Wilson, 1979)

| | Males | | | Females | | |
|---|---|---|---|---|---|---|
| | x̄ | n | Range | x̄ | n | Range |
| TL | 95 | 20 | 39–111 | 99 | 17 | 87–115 |
| (HB | 51) | | | (56) | | |
| T | 44 | 20 | 40–46 | 43 | 17 | 40–50 |
| Hf c/u | 13 | 24 | 11–14 | 13 | 17 | 11–14 |
| E | 10 | 28 | 9–11 | 10 | 16 | 9–11 |
| Mass | 6,3 | 13 | 4,0–8,8 | 7,0 | 11 | 4,0–11,6 |

### Distribution

At the present state of our knowledge it is impossible to assess the limits of distribution of this species except within broad limits and this can be presented only on a provisional basis until a detailed review of the species occurring in the Subregion is undertaken.

*Southern African Subregion*

The situation appears to be that they occur in the **Cape Province**, excluding the northern sector; in the **Orange Free State; Lesotho; Natal**; eastern **Transvaal**; central and eastern **Zimbabwe; Swaziland** and in **Mozambique**, south of the Zambezi River.

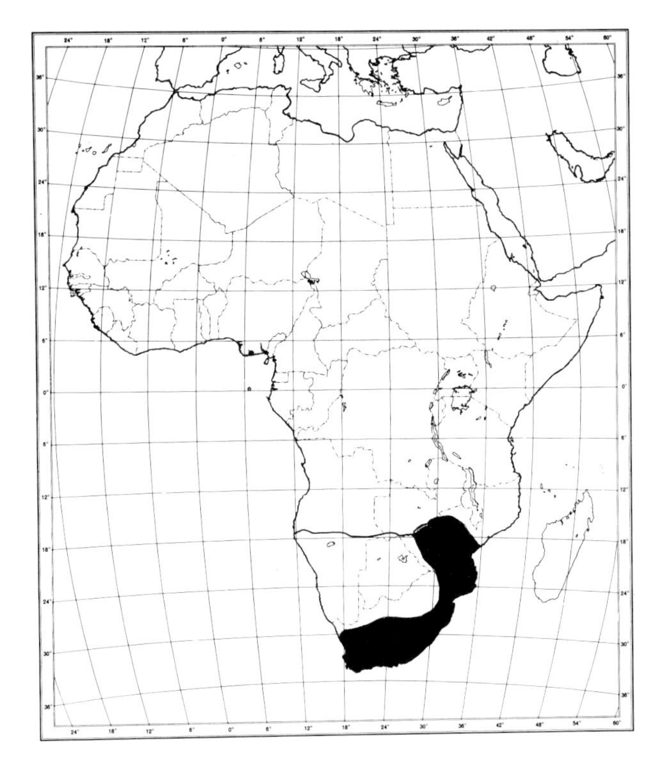

Southern African Subregion distribution only.

### Habitat

In addition to the "typical" *M. minutoides* from the Cape Province, the material from the more eastern and northeastern parts of the Subregion is tentatively included in this species which has a wide habitat tolerance, but it is unusual for them to enter human dwellings. They occur in the Cape Macchia Zone as well as in the savanna grassland and woodland areas to the east and northeast and in areas with a mean annual rainfall from about 100 mm in the southwest to 1 000 mm in the Drakensberg, and at altitudes up to 2 300 m. However, captive *M. minutoides* from mesic habitats are unable to survive water deprivation for 20 days when fed on a diet of air-dried seed (Withers, Louw & Henschel (1980).

### Habits

Pygmy mice are nocturnal and terrestrial. They are not a communal species, and the burrows or refuges are used only by a pair or a family party. In soft ground they construct shallow burrows, but much more commonly use existing shelter under fallen logs, piles of debris, boulders or holes in termite mounds. They apparently forage singly at night and may not be tied closely to a single shelter, as an effective way of catching them is to lay a tarpaulin or sheets of corrugated iron on the ground which they will use as temporary diurnal shelters. They are aggressive towards each other in captivity, males introduced to established females in cages being attacked. On the other hand when females are introduced to established males they are accepted freely.

### Food

The main diet is grass seed, insects and termites, Wilson (1975) recording the seeds of couch grass, *Cynodon dactylon*; golden Timothy, *Setaria sphacelata*, and blue grass, *Andropogon gayanus*, in stomachs in Zimbabwe. In the Drakensberg, Rowe-Rowe (1986) recorded grass seeds in all eight stomachs examined, while 25% contained green plant material and 38% Arthropoda. In contrast, specimens from the Karoo contained mostly foliage in their stomachs, although 40% of these had eaten a few insects (Kerley, 1989).

### Reproduction

Little information is available about reproduction in the wild. Litters have been found in December (five) and January (four), and a gravid female with eight foetuses was taken in February (Smithers & Wilson, 1979), which suggests that young are born during the summer.

In captivity, pairs captured in Natal bred freely (Willan & Meester, 1978). Litter size was 4,0 (range 1–7; n=27) and birth mass about 0,8 g. Courtship involves grooming of the female by the male. He nuzzles her neck and face as she sits in a hunched position with her face averted. Attempts to copulate may be rejected at first by the female kicking with her hind feet, but otherwise she shows no signs of aggression. The gestation period is 19 days. The female begins defending the nest by vocalising and biting from a few days before the young are born and while the litter is in the nest. The male occupies the nest with the female and her litter and takes part in the defence of the nest. The altricial young are bright pink at birth and their eyes are closed, while the skin is translucent, the abdominal viscera visible through it. Pigmentation of the skin on the shoulders is noticeable by the third or fourth day and by the fifth day the whole of the head, back and tail is pigmented. By the ninth day a fine brownish-buff pelage appears on the upper parts of the body extending on to the flanks and sparse white hairs appear on the under parts, and by the 14th day they resemble the adults. The incisor teeth erupt between the seventh and ninth day, the lower incisors a day ahead of the upper, and the eyes open between the 12th and 14th day. They are weaned by the 17th day. The first successful mating took place at about 42 days and the first birth at 62 days.

## Genus *Uranomys* Dollman, 1909

The generic name is derived from the Greek *ouranos*, a palate, and *mys*, a mouse, referring to the backward extension of the palatine bones in the roof of the mouth.

---

No. 173

## *Uranomys ruddi* Dollman, 1909

## Rudd's mouse
## Rudd se muis

Plate 13

---

### Colloquial Name

Named after C.D. Rudd, a colleague of Cecil John Rhodes, who obtained the Rudd Concession from Lobengula, Chief of the Matabele, which led to the European settlement of Rhodesia (Zimbabwe). He was a Director of De Beers Consolidated Mines, Kimberley, and financed expeditions to Mozambique and Rhodesia led by Capt. C.H.B. Grant.

### Taxonomic Notes

A number of species from the genus has been described, but today all these are considered as subspecies of *U. ruddi*

Dollman, 1909, which originally was described from a specimen from Mt Elgon, Kenya. Although too little material is available to judge the status of specimens from the Subregion, they are likely to be referable to *U. r. woodi* Hinton, 1921, described from Blantyre, Malawi, although Meester *et al.* (1986) stated that the relationship of this subspecies to *U. r. tenebrosus* Hinton, 1921 requires investigation.

### Description

Very few specimens of this very rare mouse have been collected from any part of its wide range in Africa. There are no specimens in collections in the Republic of South Africa and only three in the National Museum, Bulawayo, Zimbabwe. All other records are from skulls recovered from the casts of the barn owl, *Tyto alba*.

Their skins are very delicate and their tails difficult to prepare, and only one Subregion specimen is complete. They have a head and body length of about 150 mm, with tails about one-third of this length. In Uganda, Delany (1975) gave a head and body length in males of 100–102 mm, with a tail of 71 mm, and females 95–104 mm, with a tail of between 50 and 71 mm.

Specimens from the Subregion vary in colour from dark brown, tinged with light brown, to dark grey on the upper parts of the body, the flanks paler. The hair on the under parts is lighter in colour than on the upper parts, and some of the hairs have white tips. The hair is long and springy in texture, each hair like a long, fine bristle. The upper surfaces of the hands and feet are whitish tinged with buffy.

### Skull

The skull is rather flat, the rostrum narrow, the interorbital constriction distinct. The braincase is broad, the anterior palatal foramen long and broad and extending posteriorly to about the level of the back of the first upper molar. Daviş (*in litt.*), who examined skulls from the Subregion, remarked that the upper incisor teeth were markedly pro-odont. Rosevear (1969) drew attention to the broad palate which extends far back from the upper third molars, continuing onto a roof covering the mesopterygoid fossa, a feature shared only with *Acomys*.

### Distribution

As far as representation in museum collections is concerned, this species is the rarest African murid. They have been recorded from parts of **West** and **East Africa**, **Zaire**, and they occur southwards in the eastern parts of the continent to the Subregion. Their distribution appears to be scattered and discontinuous throughout their wide distributional range.

*Southern African Subregion*

Thus far the species is confined to the northeastern parts of the Subregion in **Zimbabwe**, from where there are three records, one each from Mutare, Mt Selinda and Chipinda Pools, Lundi River (21 31 B4), the last-named being a skull recovered from an owl pellet (Vernon in Smithers & Wilson, 1979). They also occur in the Vila Pery, Beira and Tete districts of **Mozambique**, south of the Zambezi River (Smithers & Tello, 1976).

### Habitat

In Mozambique they occur in seasonally inundated and dry grassland on alluvial soil in the vicinity of rivers and streams. Delany (1975) recorded their association in East Africa with wet grassland.

### Habits

They are nocturnal and terrestrial. In East Africa, Kingdon (1974) reported that in the Ivory Coast they are common, being caught in the hundreds in *Borassus* sp palm savanna. They excavate burrows which run up to 150 mm below the surface of the ground, with nesting chambers 100–150 mm in diameter. These burrows have two exits surrounded by piles of excavated soil and have a blind burrow penetrating to a depth of 300 to 400 mm. The nest is lined with finely cut grass and the burrows are inhabited by one or two individuals.

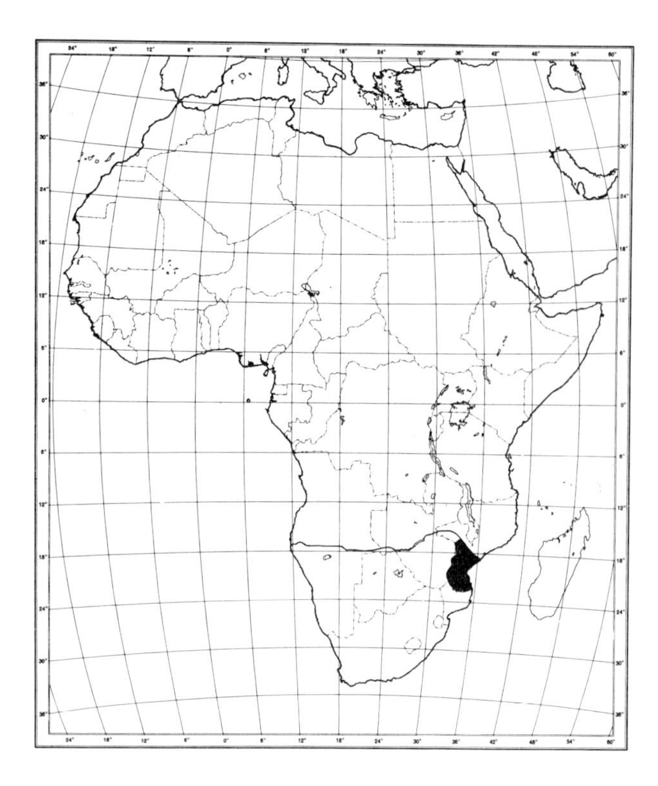

Southern African Subregion distribution only.

### Food

No information is available from the Subregion. Hanney (1965) recorded that stomachs examined from Malawi contained insect remains, dipterous larvae and ant pupae and noted that the pro-odont nature of the incisor teeth suggests that they are probably insectivorous.

### Reproduction

No information is available from the Subregion.

## Genus *Mastomys* Thomas, 1915

The taxonomy of the various genera and subgenera that have been established over the years to accommodate recognisable sections of the original genus *Mus* Linnaeus, 1758, which included all the then known "rats and mice", has been the subject of a wide diversity of treatment. Trouessart (1881) created the genus *Epimys* to include 140 forms of "rats", leaving *Mus* Linnaeus, 1758 to accommodate the remaining 27 species of "mice". In doing so he overlooked the fact that Fisher (1803) had already suggested the name *Rattus* for the very same purpose and as a consequence the generic name *Epimys* fell out of use. Thomas (1915) sought to clarify the unwieldy state of affairs by creating a number of genera for the huge assemblage of material then included in the genus *Rattus*, among which were *Aethomys* and *Mastomys* from the Subregion. He continued thereafter to further subdivide *Rattus* into other new genera, including *Thallomys* Thomas, 1920 and *Myomyscus* Thomas, 1942.

Thomas' genera were accepted widely until Ellerman (1940, 1941), using the cusp pattern on the cheekteeth, remarked that many groups were indistinguishable on valid generic characters and brought all the assemblage of genera together again under the genus *Rattus*. In general, this treatment has not been accepted because, in spite of their similarities in dentition, most people interesting themselves in murids have little difficulty in distinguishing between members of the various genera on external characters alone.

Matthey (1966), on the basis of chromosomal studies and morphology, removed the genus *Mastomys* from the *Rattus* complex and reinstated it and later, with the swing away from Ellerman's treatment, Davis (1965) classed *Mastomys* as a subgenus of *Praomys*.

While the known forms have been described under a great number of independent specific names, it was customary for many years to consider the multimammate mouse as Smith's *M. coucha*, until Roberts (1944) showed that *M. natalensis* was the prior name.

From this time the situation became more complicated when Matthey (1966) showed in West Africa, that there were no less than two chromosome types, 2n=32 and 38, and in South Africa another, 2n=36. Subsequently Lyons, Gordon, Green & Walters (1977) and Lyons, Gordon & Green (1980) recorded two chromosomal types in Zimbabwe, 2n=32 and 36. The type locality of *M. natalensis* (A. Smith, 1834), Port Natal (=Durban), has yielded only specimens with 2n=32; the type locality of *M. coucha* (A. Smith, 1836), Kuruman, Cape Province, has yielded only 2n=36. Gordon (1984) suggested that on this basis the name *M. natalensis* is valid for the genetical species 2n=32, *M. coucha* for the genetical species 2n=36. In sympatric populations of the two species, Gordon (1984) showed that distinct electrophoretic haemoglobin phenotypes were correlated with each diploid number, with no hybrids being detected. Unfortunately unlike the situation in West Africa where *M. huberti* (2n=32) and *M. erythroleucus* (2n=38) can be distinguished on external features, this is not possible with *M. natalensis* and *M. coucha* from the Subregion (Robbins & van der Straaten, 1989). Gordon (1984) was able to do this using multivariate morphometric analysis of skull characters and he also detected differences in the urethral lappet shape of the phallus and spermatozoa tail length of the two species (Gordon & Watson, 1986). Reproductive behaviour and ultrasonic vocalisations of the two species were also found to be distinct and preliminary investigation of their pheromones are also indicating differences (Apps *et al.*, 1990).

**Multimammate mice and human diseases**

Multimammate mice have been shown to be a reservoir host of a number of organisms which cause human diseases. Among these are: *Yersinia pestis*, which causes plague; Lassa fever virus, Banzi and Witwatersrand viruses, and pathogenic bacteria such as *Salmonella typhimurium*, *Escherichia coli* and *Pasteurella pneumotropica* (Keogh & Price, 1981). Although predominantly an indigenous veld rodent, multimammate mice have become a commensal with man and their close contact with him makes the transmission of diseases, of which they are a reservoir of the causative agent, more likely.

So far it has not been determined which of the two species *M. natalensis* or *M. coucha* is more prone to commensialism or whether there is a difference in this respect (Gordon, 1984). This has important medical implications for it has been found that *M. natalensis* (2n=32) is significantly more resistant to experimental plague infection than *M. coucha* (2n=36) and that the distribution of human plague in southern Africa corresponds closely to that of the latter, plague susceptible species (Keogh & Price, 1981).

While other diseases are carried by multimammate mice, it has not yet been determined if only one or both the biological species are involved in the transmission of these. Lassa virus was recovered from the tissues of *M. natalensis* (*M. huberti*) in West Africa (Monath, Newhouse, Kemp, Setzer & Cacciapuoti, 1974) and Wulff, Fabiyi & Monath (1975) isolated the virus from rodents in Nigeria. Banzi and Witwatersrand viruses have been isolated from multimammate mice, showing that wild rodents are the maintenance host of these (McIntosh, Dickinson, Meenehan & Dos Santos, 1976) and Zumpt (1959) showed that they were highly susceptible to experimental infection with *Borelia duttoni* which causes relapsing fever.

Plague is now endemic in the Subregion, rodents being reservoir hosts of the bacillus, *Yersinia pestis*, that causes the disease, and multimammate mice play an important role in its transmission to man. Originally the disease was introduced in "ship rats", *Rattus* sp, at our coastal ports. Infected fleas from these rats then transmitted the disease to our indigenous rodents, in particular to multimammate mice with which they would come into close contact in the warehouses of our coastal ports. Moving freely from houses and stores to their traditional home in the veld, infected multimammate mice, again through the agency of fleas, passed the disease on to gerbils, *Tatera* spp, and these gerbils are today one of the principal reservoir hosts of the disease in the Subregion.

Multimammate mice may abound in kraals, nesting in the thatched roofs of huts and in crevices in the walls, and freely enter houses, bringing the disease with them and the fleas to act as vectors.

Several species of fleas are involved as transmitters of the disease between rodents and from rodents to man, important among these being *Xenopsylla cheopis* (oriental rat flea), *Dinopsyllus lypusus* (African rodent flea) and *Leptopsylla segnis* (European mouse flea) (Duplaix, 1988).

Mitchell, Pirie & Ingram (1927) who documented the history of the disease in the Subregion were unable to find any record of the occurrence of plague before the early part of 1899. At that date it was endemic in India and had been carried by rats from ports in that country to several other countries including Madagascar. In November 1898 suspicious mortality among rats occurred in Lourenzo Marques (Maputo, Mozambique) and in January 1899 four cases of bubonic plague occurred in men inhabiting the same house. Two other cases followed after one of the victims had moved to Middelburg, Transvaal, and the other to Komatipoort. All of these six cases were bubonic plague and all died. This is the first record of the occurrence of the disease in the Subregion. Early in 1900 a family arrived from Mauritius and settled in Durban. All remained in good health for three weeks until one of the family unpacked a sea chest with clothing and then contracted the disease. It was presumed that infected fleas in the clothing had passed the disease on to him.

In March 1900 a steamer arrived in Table Bay with plague cases aboard, but of the five persons who developed the disease, all recovered. In the following February, 1901, there was an unusual mortality among rats in Cape Town docks which was found to be due to plague, infected rats carrying the disease to adjoining parts of the town. In April 1901 plague-infected rat carcasses were discovered in the harbour at Port Elizabeth, and human cases followed. Mossel Bay was subsequently infected by October 1901 and East London by February 1903.

The disease then spread rapidly inland and human cases were reported from Johannesburg in 1904. By 1931 it had reached the northern parts of Namibia where Fourie (1932) reported the presence of the disease in wild rodents. Following behind this spread, human cases were reported in Botswana in 1928 and a major outbreak occurred in Ngamiland in 1944 (Davis, 1946). This latter outbreak followed high floods in the Okavango Delta which stimulated rodent populations to reach high levels, a pattern which has repeated itself over subsequent years and leads, in this sector, to sporadic outbreaks of plague in man. By 1974 plague had spread eastwards into Zimbabwe, in the areas of Kalahari sand, reaching as far east as about St. Pauls Mission near Lupane, with human deaths resulting. By 1987 it was widespread in Owambo, northern Namibia (Duplaix, 1988). This wide spread of the disease, northwards from the coastal ports, has resulted in plague now being endemic in the Subregion.

Key to the species of *Mastomys* after Meester *et al.* (1986). It is recognised that the key provided is of limited use as it applies only to live caught material (Meester *et al.*, 1986)

1. Pterygoid fossae not especially narrow; females with 5 pairs of mammae; anterior palatal foramen does not reach inner root of first upper molar
   ... *shortridgei*

   Pterygoid fossae very narrow; females with 12 or more pairs of mammae; anterior palatal foramen extends beyond inner root of first upper molar
   ... 2

2. Karyotype 2n=32; 'slow' haemoglobin (Green *et al.*, 1980; 17–23)
   ... *natalensis*

   Karyotype 2n=36; 'fast' haemoglobin
   ... *coucha*

No. 174

## *Mastomys natalensis* (A. Smith, 1834)

## Natal multimammate mouse
## Natalse vaalveldmuis

Plate 12

### Colloquial Name

So called as the females have up to 12 pairs of mammae in two more or less continuous rows from the chest to the inguinal area. The possession of so many mammae is unique among the murids and is a useful character in the identification of the females.

### Taxonomic Notes

This species was first known to science from specimens described by A. Smith (1834) as *Mus natalensis* from "about Port Natal" (=Durban).

### Description

Gordon (1984), using series of *M. natalensis* (2n=32) and *M. coucha* (2n=36), could detect no significant differences in size between the two species, except that the ears in the former appeared to be slightly shorter than those of the latter, although an overlap in size occurs.

### Table 174.1

Measurements (mm) and mass (g) of a series of multimammate mice (a) with well-worn teeth from Zimbabwe (Smithers, 1983) and (b) from Mozambique (Gliwicz, 1985)

**a. Zimbabwe** (Smithers, 1983)

| | Males | | | Females | | |
|---|---|---|---|---|---|---|
| | $\bar{x}$ | n | Range | $\bar{x}$ | n | Range |
| TL | 244 | 11 | 218–269 | 237 | 11 | 221–275 |
| (HB | 125) | | | (126) | | |
| T | 119 | 11 | 101–138 | 111 | 11 | 99–137 |
| Hf c/u | 24 | 11 | 20–25 | 24 | 11 | 22–26 |
| E | 19 | 11 | 18–20 | 19 | 11 | 18–20 |
| Mass | 63,5 | 7 | 47,2–81,2 | 67,4 | 6 | 53,8–81,0 |

**b. Mozambique** (Gliwicz, 1985)

| | Irrespective of sex | | |
|---|---|---|---|
| | $\bar{x}$ | n | Range |
| HB | 111,0 | 7 | 100–120 |
| T | 98,7 | 7 | 85–113 |
| Hf c/u | 21,1 | 7 | 20–22 |
| Mass | 40,1 | 7 | 30–54 |

The following description applies equally to a range of *M. coucha*, as Gordon (1984) could not detect external differences between the two species.

They have slender hairs with knobbly scales on a longish base. Petal scales are seen clearly in the shaft which has a fairly narrow groove deepening in the distal half of the hair (Fig. XXIII.3) (Keogh, 1985).

There is a considerable range of colour variation which Roberts (1951) believed might be related to their habitat. The base of the hair on the upper parts is broadly pale grey to dark grey or nearly black, the hairs of the guard coat either very narrowly tipped with buffy-yellow, in which case the upper parts are dark in colour, or more broadly tipped, in which case they are paler in colour, giving an overall more buffy appearance to the individual. The flanks are paler in colour than the upper parts and tinged yellowish or fawn, often being clearly yellowish or buffy at the junction of the colour of the upper and under parts. The colour of the under parts is quite characteristic. The hair is dark or pale grey at the base with whitish tips, the greyish colour of the base of the hair showing through, giving the under parts a grey overall colour. In the adult females each mamma is surrounded by a sprinkling of whitish-tipped hair so that they stand out from the general greyish colour of the background. The upper surfaces of the narrow hands and feet are whitish or off-white. The tail is finely scaled and is very sparsely covered with very short bristly hair, darker on the upper surface, lighter in colour on the under. The fur is moderately long and soft to the touch.

Adult females are identified easily by the two rows of mammae, numbering up to 12 pairs, many more than possessed by any other mammal.

### Distribution

The limits of distribution of this species within the Subregion must be considered as provisional at this stage, as it has only been possible to investigate the genetical composition, haemoglobin electromorphs and other features of a relatively small number of specimens. The results that are available allow a provisional distribution which shows that this species and *M. coucha* No. 174A are sympatric in some areas and allopatric in others. Where single or very few specimens have been examined, the localities are marked by a solid circle (Gordon, 1978; Green *et al.*, 1980; Gordon & Watson, 1986; Gordon & Griffin, in prep.). On the map the overlay of light stippling shows the distribution of the genus *Mastomys*, the solid black areas and spots the known distribution of *M. natalensis* (2n=32) at present.

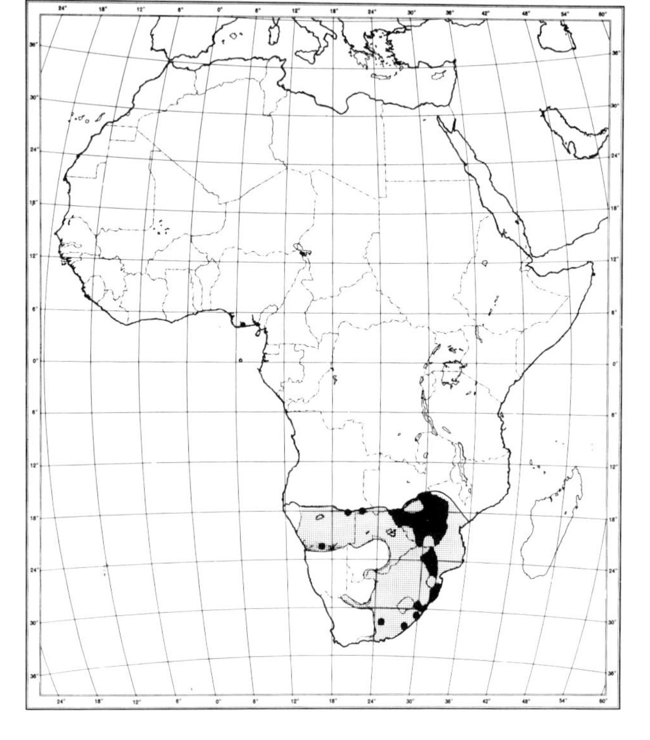

Southern African Subregion distribution only.
Stippled area: distribution of the genus *Mastomys*.
Solid black and spots: present known distribution of *M. natalensis*.

*Southern African Subregion*

They occur in the northern parts of **Namibia**; the **Caprivi Strip**; widely in **Zimbabwe**; in the eastern **Transvaal; Natal** and the eastern and southeastern parts of the **Cape Province**.

### Habitat

Multimammate mice have a wide habitat tolerance and, with the exception of areas with a mean annual rainfall of 400 mm or less, are one of the commonest murids in the Subregion. Even in the drier areas they occur in river valleys penetrating into otherwise unsuitable terrain. An example of this is their occurrence along and as far west as Goodhouse in the Orange River valley in the Cape Province. In the Subregion they are found from sea level to altitudes of about 1 800 m (Zimbabwe).

As they have become a commensal with man, they are well known to householders, finding an ample food and water supply in houses and food stores, and shelter in which to safely rear their young. In African kraals they occur in very large numbers, living in the fabric and thatch of pole and mud huts, and they also frequent grain storage bins.

They are less common in modern towns and cities, due perhaps to the types of construction used, which do not afford them the nooks and crannies and the wooden floors under which to nest. Generally they are not found in forest, although they do occur on forest fringes. Meester, Lloyd & Rowe-Rowe (1979) considered multimammate mice as pioneers, quick to colonise areas that are recovering from habitat destruction. As the succession proceeds they tend to be replaced by species that are more specialised and which are associated with more homogeneous vegetational communities, such as the striped mouse, *Rhabdomys pumilio*, a grassland specialist.

Multimammate mice are common on the fringes of and within agricultural lands where crops such as peanuts, maize, sorghum or other grains are grown. To some extent they are dependent on water, but occur in areas where this is only available seasonally.

**Habits**

They are nocturnal and predominantly terrestrial. In their association with man they use secluded corners in dwellings in which to construct their nests, cutting holes in the floors to gain access to warm shelter or using the interstices of brickwork. In the field they use shelters under the roots of trees or fallen logs, in piles of rocks or debris and cracks in the soil, or they will excavate their own burrows or use holes excavated by other species.

**Food**

Multimammate mice are omnivorous. Under field conditions they subsist mainly on the seeds of grass and other plants, the dried pods of *Acacia* spp and the dry pulpy exterior of wild fruits, augmented with a smaller proportion of insect material including termites, grasshoppers and Coleoptera. Wilson (1975) recorded their feeding on undigested seeds in elephant droppings and wild fruits and seeds lying on the ground. Watson (1987) determined diet from stomach contents of *P. natalensis* in the Kruger National Park during a period of high rainfall and found that they ate 5% insects, 32% vegetable matter and 63% seeds (n=12). At the height of population explosions, when food supplies are nearing exhaustion, they become cannibals and dried skins, feet and tails are commonly found in the vicinity of their burrows. As a commensal with man, they will eat any foodstuffs including bacon, butter and meat (Smithers, 1983).

**Reproduction**

Breeding activity in the Subregion peaks during the wet season, and densities increase markedly following rainfall (Watson, 1987). Although *M. natalensis* have their young at any time of the year, this declines during the colder, drier months of June and July. In a recent study in Natal it was found that the dry season decline in reproductive activity could be attributed to an anoestrous stage in females, complemented to a lesser degree by testicular regression in males (Bronner, Rautenbach & Meester, 1983). A high adult mortality at the onset of winter probably also contributed to the breeding depression. They concluded that this opportunistic breeder may not use seasonal environmental predictors to maximise reproductive success. Johnston & Oliff (1954) found that the gestation period is 23 days in captivity. The number in litters varies considerably, but when conditions are favourable, females in the field can carry as many as 22 foetuses. Oliff (1953) recorded a mean litter size over a four-year period in captivity of 7,3, while Meester (1960) found the average number was 8,5 (n=19), the average time between litters being 33,1 days (range 24–28; n=15), and a female having her first litter at 77 days old.

At birth the altricial young are naked, bright pink, with a tinge of grey on the back, marking the area where the fur on the upper parts later develops, and darker grey on the head and with their eyes closed. They are sparsely covered with black hair about 3 mm long on the upper parts and 2 mm long and white on the under parts, and they have an average mass of 2,2 g (Meester, 1960). Clumsy at birth, pups can move quite rapidly by the seventh day. The eyes open on Day 15–16, the young remaining in the nest until weaned.

Population explosions of multimammate mice are well known in the Subregion. They appear to be correlated with climatic conditions leading to an unprecedented increase in food supplies, although other factors, not presently recognised, may play a part in triggering off this phenomenon (Ellison, 1990). Smithers (1971) recorded the sequence of events leading up to such an explosion in northern Botswana. This occurred after an unprecedented four-year drought, during the latter part of which the percentage catch of murids per 100 traps in the northern sector remained at very low levels, once only reaching 7% in the case of multimammate mice, and more usually being 1% to 2%. In late 1965 copious rains fell in the Lake Ngami and western Makgadikgadi Pan sectors and by July 1966 populations in this sector were increasing, a high percentage of females being pregnant, with many juveniles in evidence. By the end of this year numbers were high and by April 1967 had reached explosive levels. By July 1967 it appeared that in the Botletle River sector the height of the explosion had been reached. Soon after dark they swarmed everywhere, even entering the tents and making it necessary to secure all foodstuffs in tin trunks or place them out of reach of the rodents. A dribble of maize meal from a sack placed on top of a 40 gallon water drum attracted numerous feeding mice from which 27 were killed from a single .410 dust shot. Attempts to set the 100 trap lines were unavailing, for after 15 or 20 traps had been laid, those at the start of the line were already being set off. On one occasion when 12 traps had been set, a return visit down the line produced seven multimammate mice. Often two mice per trap were taken. At this time cannibalism was rife and mice left in the traps from 18h00 until the late pick up at 22h00 were almost invariably eaten. This explosion of multimammate mice masked, in the trap lines, the fact that the explosion was not confined to this species. In moving around after dark in vehicles, gerbils, *Tatera* spp, were seen in large numbers as well as desert pygmy mice, *Mus indutus*. The latter, once they had fallen into the deep tracks left by vehicles in the sand, were unable to climb out and it was not unusual to see four or five together running along these tracks in front of the vehicles.

Scraps of skin and fur, feet and tails of multimammate mice lying outside burrows in August 1967 were further evidence of cannibalism, which is a feature of rodent population explosions after the peak is passed. Apart from cannibalism it was noted that many of the mice were diseased, with swollen lumps on their feet, on their intestines, scrotal sacs and uteri, which in some cases were grossly deformed.

---

No. 174A

## *Mastomys coucha* (A. Smith, 1836)

## Multimammate mouse
## Vaalveldmuis

---

**Taxonomic Notes**

Meester *et al.* (1986) accepted that there are two species within the complex listed in the first edition as *Praomys (Mastomys) natalensis* which has a diploid chromosome number of 2n=32 and *Mastomys coucha* 2n=36. Until a detailed investigation of the ecology of the two species is undertaken it is assumed that most of the information provided for *M. natalensis* is valid for *M. coucha*. Therefore reference is directed to the remarks under the various headings of *M. natalensis*.

**Distribution**

As in the case of *M. natalensis* the present information must be considered as provisional for the reasons given under **Distribution** No. 174 *M. natalensis*.

*Southern African Subregion*

They are recorded from Windhoek, **Namibia**, and occur widely in **Zimbabwe**; the **Transvaal** and **Orange Free State**, with a record from northern **Natal**. In the **Cape Province** they occur widely in the eastern parts of the province.

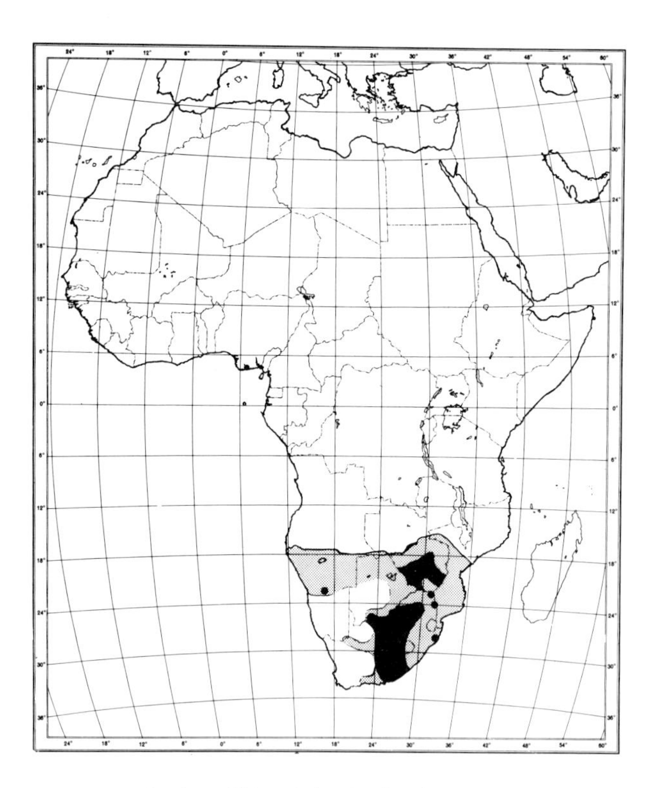

Southern African Subregion distribution only
Stippled area: distribution of the genus *Mastomys*.
Solid black and spots: present known distribution of *M. coucha*.

No. 175

## *Mastomys shortridgei* (St. Leger, 1933)

## Shortridge's mouse
## Shortridge se vaalveldmuis

### Colloquial Name

Named after Capt. G.C. Shortridge, at one time Director of the Kaffrarian Museum, King William's Town, Cape Province, and author of *The Mammals of South West Africa* (1934) and many papers on mammals.

### Taxonomic Notes

This species differs from the Natal multimammate mouse, *M. natalensis*, in possessing only five pairs of mammae arranged in a continuous row, without clear separation into pectoral and inguinal sets. In other respects it closely resembles the Natal multimammate mouse. Misonne (1974) recorded that this species and *M. angolensis* (Bocage, 1890) of southwestern Angola are very alike; in the latter, however, the mammae are often separated into three pectoral pairs and two inguinal pairs, although this separation is not clear-cut.

### Description

They are very similar to *M. natalensis*, from which they differ in that the females have only five pairs of mammae not clearly separated into pectoral and inguinal sets. In series they have shorter tails (Table 175.1) than *M. natalensis* and are much darker in general coloration; some individuals are smoke-grey, others nearly black on the upper parts, and the paler individuals usually darker down the mid-back. The individual hairs on the upper parts are iron-grey with narrow buffy tips; on the flanks the buffy tips of the individual hairs are broader. The under parts appear grey; the individual hairs are broadly white-tipped, the grey bases showing through. The upper parts of the hands and feet are white. Measurements and mass of a small series from northwestern Botswana are given in Table 175.1.

The palatal foramina (misinterpreted by de Graaff, 1981) extend to the back of the inner root of $M_1$ as determined for genetically identified material (Gordon, in press). Furthermore, Gordon (1984) found that they have the same diploid chromosome number (2n=36) as *M. coucha*, but there are differences between the species for an autosomal rearrangement, morphology of the sex chromosome and in the shape of the spermatozoa head.

**Table 175.1**

Measurements (mm) and mass (g) of a series of Shortridge's mice, *M. shortridgei*, taken at Shakawe, Botswana (Smithers, 1971)

| | Males | | | Females | | |
|---|---|---|---|---|---|---|
| | $\bar{x}$ | n | Range | $\bar{x}$ | n | Range |
| TL | 217 | 16 | 202–241 | 222 | 10 | 205–255 |
| (HB | 113) | | | (116) | | |
| T | 104 | 15 | 96–114 | 106 | 10 | 99–111 |
| Hf c/u | 27 | 15 | 25–28 | 26 | 9 | 24–27 |
| E | 18 | 14 | 17–19 | 19 | 9 | 17–20 |
| Mass | 45,0 | 15 | 35,0–67,0 | 48,0 | 10 | 36,0–74,0 |

### Distribution

*Southern African Subregion*

Only so far recorded from the extreme northwestern parts of **Botswana** and northeastern **Namibia** in the region of the confluence of the Okavango and Kwito rivers.

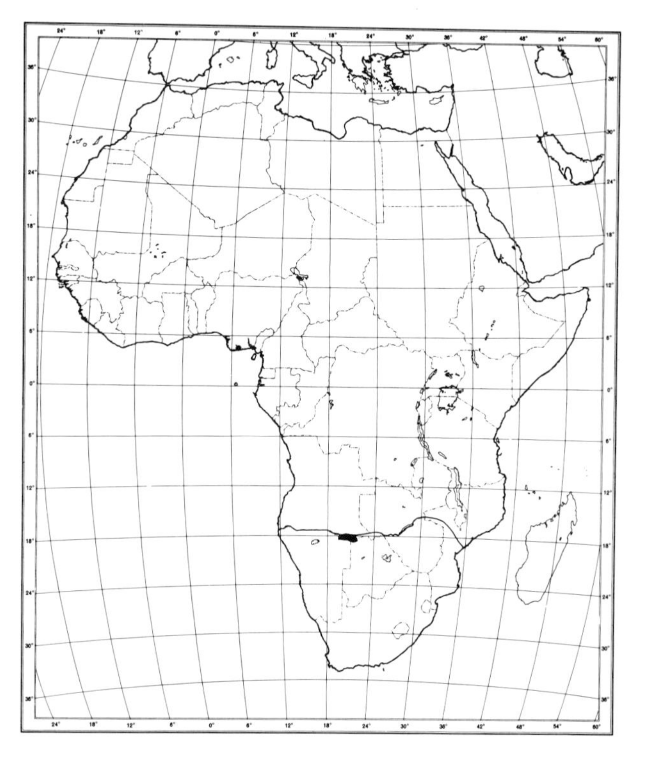

### Habitat

In northwestern Botswana they occur on the alluvium terraces bordering the Okavango River and in the gardens of houses on the river bank. Further west in Botswana they occur in the fringes of wet vleis on the Namibian border. In northeastern Namibia, Shortridge (1934) recorded their occurrence in reed beds and swamp grasses close to the Okavango River and in the bed of the Omuramba-Omatako to Ssannukannu, some 30 km south of the Okavango River. Shortridge (1934) associated the species with swampy terrain.

### Habits

Little is known about the habits of this species except that they are nocturnal. Unlike *M. natalensis* which was taken in the houses and outside stores at Shakawe, Botswana, *M. shortridgei* appears to live only outdoors, being trapped at burrow entrances and amongst piles of debris in the gardens. In Namibia, Shortridge (1934) stated that they are found in association with genera such as *Otomys* spp and

*Dasymys* spp which frequent swampy areas, and they do not appear to live in burrows.

### Food

In the Kruger National Park, Watson (1987) found, from stomach contents, that during a period of drought they ate 29% insects, 2% vegetable matter and 69% seeds (n=12), compared to 18% insects, 3% vegetable matter and 79% seeds (n=10) during a period of high rainfall.

### Reproduction

A tiny juvenile was taken at Shakawe in February, but none of the 18 females taken in April and May showed signs of breeding. Further than this nothing is known of this aspect of their life history.

## Subgenus *Myomyscus* Shortridge, 1942

No. 176

## *Myomyscus verreauxii* (A. Smith, 1834)

## Verreaux's mouse
## Verreaux se muis

Plate 13

### Colloquial Name

Pierre Jules Verreaux, after whom this species is named, was a naturalist and taxidermist. A number of birds including the black eagle, *Aquila verreauxi* (Lesson, 1830), were named after him. He lived in Cape Town from 1818–1830 and was acting Curator of the South African Museum during the absence of the Curator, Sir Andrew Smith.

### Taxonomic Notes

The genus *Myomyscus* was proposed by Shortridge (1942), with *Mus verreauxii* A. Smith, 1834 as the type.

### Description

About 110 mm in total length, Verreaux's mice have proportionately longer tails than multimammate mice and are smaller, with mean masses of about 40,0 g (Table 176.1). The colour of the upper parts is a dark buffy-grey and some individuals are blackish-grey due to the predominance of black-tipped hairs. They have a dark band extending from between the ears forward on top of the muzzle and tend to be dark around and particularly in front of the eyes. The flanks are paler than the upper parts and slightly more buffy; the under parts are whitish, the grey bases of the hairs showing through giving them a greyish appearance. The lighter colour of the under parts extends upwards on to the lower parts of the muzzle. The upper surfaces of the hands and feet are white. The tail is brownish above and white below and is finely scaled.

**Table 176.1**

Measurements (mm) and mass (g) of Verreaux's mouse, *M. verreauxii*, from the Cape Province (de Graaff, 1981)

| | Males | | | Females | | |
|---|---|---|---|---|---|---|
| | $\bar{x}$ | n | Range | $\bar{x}$ | n | Range |
| (TL | 249) | | | (253) | | |
| HB | 106 | 15 | 90–118 | 110 | 10 | 102–133 |
| T | 143 | 15 | 124–156 | 143 | 16 | 132–157 |
| Hf c/u | 24 | 15 | 20–28 | 24 | 16 | 22–26 |
| E | 18 | 11 | 17–20 | 10 | 14 | 16–21 |
| Mass | 44,0 | 4 | 41,0–54,0 | 38,0 | 5 | 36,0–42,0 |

The skull in this species is slightly broader than in *M. natalensis*, the palatal foramina only extending backwards to the level of about one-third of the length of the first upper molars from their front margins.

### Distribution

*Southern African Subregion*

They are confined to the southwestern parts of the Subregion in the **Cape Province**, from the Olifants River in the west to the Knysna district in the east.

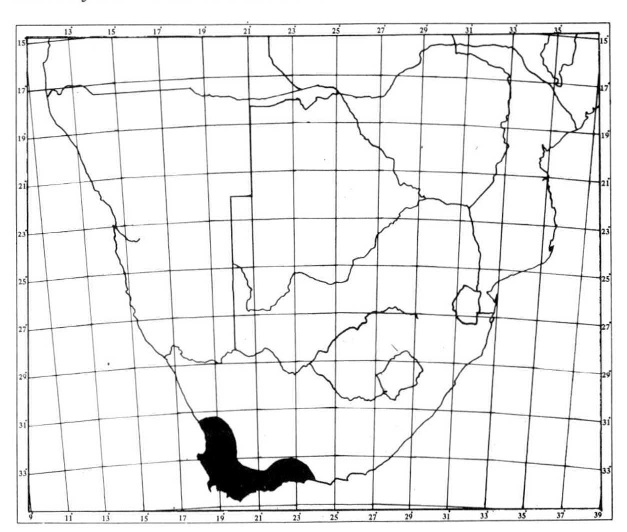

### Habitat

Rautenbach & Nel (1980) recorded this species as living in scrub on grassy hillsides and on forest margins, being particularly abundant in riverine forest. De Graaff (1981) stated that they occur in damp meadows, vleis with a grass cover, and in forest in the Knysna area, where they favour the shelter of fallen trees. David (1978) believes that this species is dependent on proteas for its existence, as some ground proteas depend on *M. verreauxii* for pollination, and he only captured them in protea stands. This has been confirmed by Breytenbach (1982) who only once captured *M. verreauxii* where proteas were present but not flowering. On the other hand, where *Leucodendron album* heathland had burnt and abundant seed was present the mice remained for at least a month following the fire and actually built up fat reserves.

### Habits

Nocturnal and terrestrial.

### Food

Breytenbach (1982) found that protea seeds form a substantial part of their diet and Rautenbach & Nel (1980) found 95% insect remains and 5% white plant material in two stomachs they examined.

### Reproduction

No information available.

## Genus *Thallomys* Thomas, 1920

The generic name is derived from the Greek *thallos*, a fine twig, and *mys*, a mouse, referring to their use of this type of material to line their nests and their habit of feeding on the fine young leaves and twigs of thornbush, *Acacia* spp.

Until the genus is studied in detail, two species are recognised: *T. paedulcus* (Sundevall, 1846) and *T. nigricauda* (Thomas, 1882), the former from the eastern parts of the Subregion, the latter from the western (Gordon, 1988).

*T. paedulcus* includes the subspecies *T. p. paedulcus* (Sundevall, 1846); *T. p. lebomboensis* Roberts, 1931; *T. p. acacia* (Roberts, 1915); *T. p. stevensoni* Roberts, 1933; *T. p. zambeziana* Lundholm, 1955 and *T. p. ruddi* (Thomas & Wroughton, 1908). The populations occurring east of the Cunene River in northern Namibia, in parts of northern Botswana and in the eastern Caprivi are at the moment more difficult to place, but appear to be more closely allied to *T. paedulcus* as the blackness of the tail is less distinct, the dark suffusion on the face is lacking or very indistinct, and the dorsal surface of the body and flanks is browner and less grey than in *T. nigricauda*. These include *T. p. herero* Thomas, 1926 and *T. p. leuconoe* Thomas, 1926.

Hill & Carter (1941) found that *T. nigricauda* includes the subspecies *T. n. damarensis* (de Winton, 1897) which occurs in the extreme northwestern parts of Namibia west of the Cunene River and into Angola; *T. n. bradfieldi* Roberts, 1933; *T. n. kalaharicus* (Dollman, 1911); *T. n. nigricauda* (Thomas, 1882) and *T. n. shortridgei* Thomas & Hinton, 1923.

Gordon (1988), investigating chromosome numbers, found 2n=43–46 from the eastern parts of the Subregion, and 2n=47–50 from the south-west arid zone. It may well be that with the application of additional modern taxonomic techniques some of the subspecies presently listed will be found to be worthy of specific rank.

---

No. 177

## *Thallomys paedulcus* (Sundevall, 1846)

## Tree rat
## Boomrot

Plate 13

---

### Colloquial Name

They are so called as they are an arboreal species.

### Taxonomic Notes

Specimens of *Thallomys* associated with the Southern Savanna Woodland biotic zone have chromosome numbers where 2n=43, 44, 45 and 46, with a species specific X chromosome (Bowland & Gordon, 1983; Gordon & Rautenbach, 1987; Gordon, 1988). This species with type locality Crocodile Drift, Brits, Transvaal (Davis, 1965), differs from *T. nigricauda* as the upper parts of the body are distinctly browner, the flanks much less grey, the dark suffusion around the eyes much less distinct, in some specimens barely discernible, the tail brown, not black as *T. nigricauda*, and about the same length as the head and body.

### Description

Hairs have wide clear petal scales (Keogh, 1985). The upper parts of the body are brown with a faint grizzling of yellow, the flanks paler with only a tinge of grey. The black facial markings are developed poorly, in some specimens barely noticeable or closely restricted to the area around the eyes. The tail is brown and almost the same length as that of the head and body. The under parts are white.

### Table 177.1

Measurements (mm) of tree rats, *Thallomys paedulcus*, from (a) the Transvaal (Smithers, 1983) and (b) a male and female specimen from Natal (Bowland & Gordon, 1983).

**a. Transvaal** (Smithers, 1983)

| | Males | | | Females | | |
|---|---|---|---|---|---|---|
| | x̄ | n | Range | x̄ | n | Range |
| (TL | 271) | | | (263) | | |
| HB | 135 | 10 | 107–144 | 127 | 13 | 110–143 |
| T | 136 | 10 | 117–151 | 136 | 13 | 124–150 |
| Hf s/u | 24 | 10 | 21–28 | 23 | 13 | 21–24 |
| E | 20 | 10 | 19–22 | 20 | 13 | 18–21 |

**b. Natal** (Bowland & Gordon, 1983)

| | Male | Female |
|---|---|---|
| | x̄ | x̄ |
| HB | 145 | 137 |
| T | — | 130 |
| Hf s/u | 21 | 25 |
| Mass | 71 | 57 |

### Distribution

*South of the Sahara, excluding the Southern African Subregion*

In **Zambia** and southern **Zaire**, and in all countries on the east of the continent northwards to the southern parts of **Ethiopia**.

*Southern African Subregion*

Occurs narrowly in the Caprivi Strip; **Namibia**; in northern and eastern **Botswana**; in **Zimbabwe**, excluding the northwestern sector; **Mozambique**, south of the Zambezi River; the **Transvaal; Swaziland** and **Natal**.

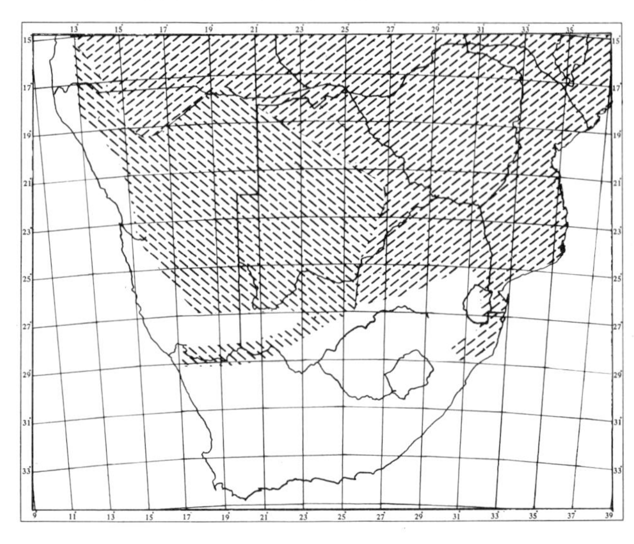

*Thallomys nigricauda*     *Thallomys paedulcus*

### Habitat

This is a savanna woodland species particularly associated with *Acacia* woodland, especially in riparian associations.

### Habits

The habits of this species are similar to those of the black-tailed tree rat, *T. nigricauda*. They are nocturnal and arboreal, and live in hollow trees or under the loose bark of trees, dragging into their shelters nesting material of grass, leaves and fine twigs. This material may overflow from the hole, accumulating over it and in time forming huge nests. Camelthorn trees, *Acacia erioloba*, so favoured by *T. nigricauda*, are absent in much of this species' range and they will then use any type of hollow tree providing it is adjacent to *Acacia* woodland.

### Food

Their diet is similar to that of the black-tailed tree rat, *T. nigricauda*.

**Plate 13**

160. Spiny mouse, *Acomys spinosissimus*
Stekelmuis
164. Woosnam's desert rat, *Zelotomys woosnami*
Woosnam se woestynrot
167. Woodland mouse, *Grammomys dolichurus*
Woudmuis
173. Rudd's mouse, *Uranomys ruddi*
Rudd se muis
176. Verreaux's mouse, *Myomyscus verreauxii*
Verreaux se muis
177. Tree rat, *Thallomys paedulcus*
Boomrot

177A Black-tailed tree rat, *Thallomys nigricauda*
Swartstert boomrot

179. Namaqua rock mouse, *Aethomys namaquensis*
Namakwalandse klipmuis
181. Red veld rat, *Aethomys chrysophilus*
Afrikaanse bosrot

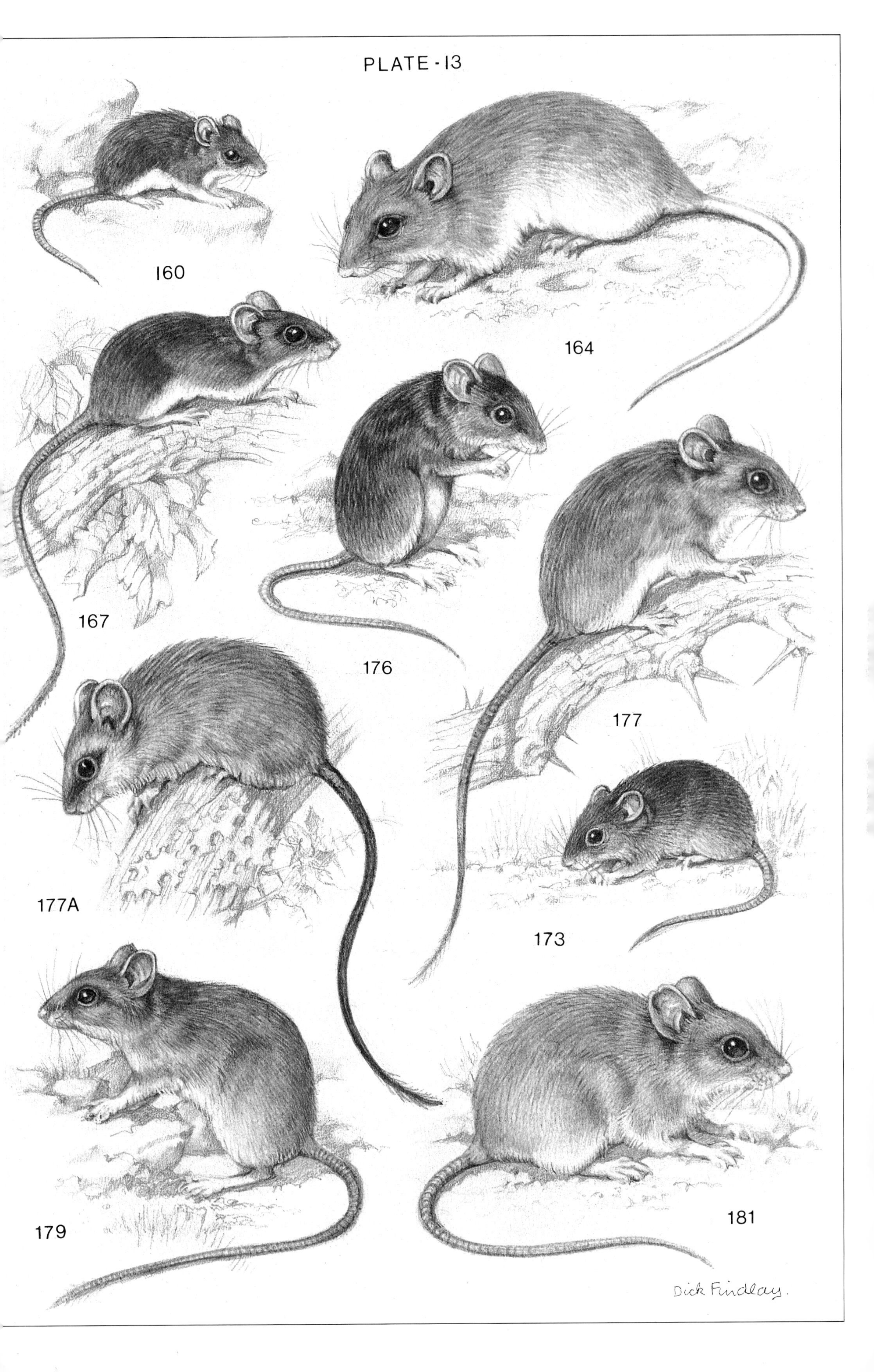
PLATE - 13
160
164
167
176
177
177A
173
179
181
Dick Findlay.

## Reproduction

Litters of two to five young are born in the nests during the summer months.

---

No. 177A

# *Thallomys nigricauda* (Thomas, 1882)

## Black-tailed tree rat
## Swartstert boomrot

Plate 13

---

### Colloquial Name

They are so called from their distinctive black tail and arboreal way of life.

### Taxonomic Notes

Specimens of *Thallomys nigricauda* associated with the South West Arid biotic zone have chromosome numbers where 2n=47, 48, 49 and 50 and they also have a distinctive X chromosome and chromosomal rearrangements which involve different chromosome pairs from that of *T. paedulcus* (Gordon, 1988). Moreover, they are separated relatively easily on external features (see **Description**). On this basis *T. nigricauda*, with a type locality of the Hountop (= Hudup or Hutop) River, west of Gibeon, Namibia appears to include the subspecies *T. n. damarensis* (de Winton, 1897); *T. n. bradfieldi* Roberts, 1933; *T. n. kalaharicus* (Dollman, 1911); *T. n. davisi* Lundholm, 1955 and *T. n. shortridgei* Thomas & Hinton, 1923.

Although Gordon (1988) found no areas of sympatry between the two species *T. nigricauda* and *T. paedulcus*, they may overlap marginally or join in the western Caprivi Strip; he suggested that a search within Botswana may establish their distributions as parapatric and correlated with the biotic zones.

### Description

The upper parts of the body from the nape of the neck to the base of the tail show a wash of yellow originating from the broad yellowish tips to the hairs of the guard coat. This hair is soft and woolly and reaches a length of 15 mm on the midback and 17 mm on the rump. Each hair is pale slate-grey at the base with a yellowish tip. Interspersed through the guard coat is a liberal sprinkling of long black hairs and the coat is underlaid with a sparse coat of fine grey underfur. The sides of the face, the flanks of the body and upper parts of the hind limbs are greyish, the under parts pure white. The top of the snout is greyish and they have a diffused black patch extending from the tip of the snout around the eyes which, in some specimens, continues as a narrow indistinct band back to near the base of the ears. The tail is longer than the length of the head and body and is black in colour, being covered in a liberal coating of jet black bristly hairs with which it is covered from its base to its tip. The upper parts of the feet are white.

The black tail, black facial patch, greyish flanks and yellowish wash to the upper parts of the body are characteristic features of the species.

### Table 177A

Measurements (mm) of black-tailed tree rats, *Thallomys nigricauda*, from central and southern Namibia.

| | Males | | | Females | | |
|---|---|---|---|---|---|---|
| | $\bar{x}$ | n | Range | $\bar{x}$ | n | Range |
| (TL | 310) | | | (299) | | |
| HB | 140 | 10 | 130–150 | 137 | 10 | 127–155 |
| T | 170 | 10 | 144–188 | 162 | 10 | 150–170 |
| Hf c/u | 26 | 10 | 24–27 | 25 | 10 | 23–26 |
| E | 23 | 10 | 20–28 | 23 | 10 | 21–25 |

### Distribution

*South of the Sahara, excluding the Southern African Subregion*

Occurs narrowly in the western parts of **Angola** as far north as about the Benguela district.

*Southern African Subregion*

Occurs in the **Cape Province**, north of the Orange River; in the southwestern and central parts of **Botswana**, and in southern, central and northwestern parts of **Namibia**, northwards to the Cunene River.

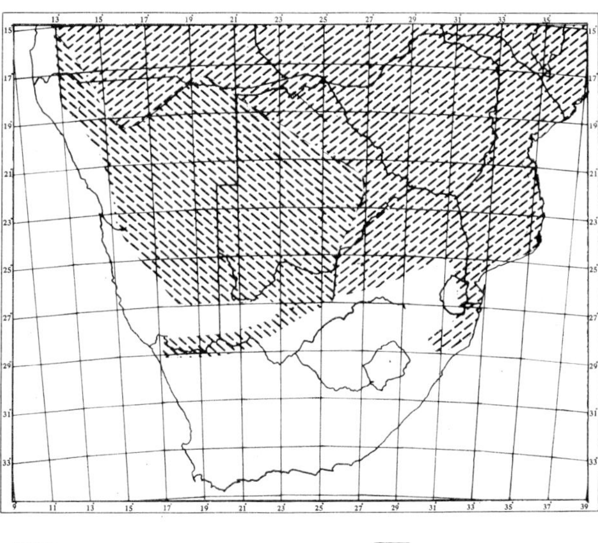


Southern African Subregion distribution only.

### Habitat

This species is associated with *Acacia* woodland, especially stands of camelthorn trees, *A. erioloba* in the South West Arid Zone.

### Habits

Tree rats are nocturnal and arboreal, living in hollow trunks and branches or under the loose bark of trees. Nesting material of grass, leaves and sticks is pulled into these hollows which may overflow the hole forming a large nest up to 300 mm deep, although sometimes there is no external accumulation of debris. Shortridge (1934) recorded that they build conspicuous nests in trees and (quoting Bradfield) these are similar to those of the buffalo weaver, *Bubalornis niger*. However, the tree rat nesting material is not as coarse and accumulates in the forks and hollows in trees rather than the outermost branches. The nests may be occupied by a pair and their offspring and up to eight adults have been seen leaving a single nest to forage at sundown (Smithers, 1983). On emerging at this time they run quickly up the trunks of the trees to the canopy and move from tree to tree to the preferred feeding area. Leadwood, *Combretum imberbe*, mopane, *Colophospermum mopane*, and other species of large trees are used, but they prefer to use camelthorn, *Acacia erioloba*, and other species of *Acacia* trees for nesting, as they feed on the fine shoots of these. They are seen easily using a spotlight as the light is reflected from their white bellies. They can be trapped while foraging on the ground as well as in the canopy of the trees and will enter refuse bins in search of food, from where they may be unable to escape.

Dollman (1911) stated that they are smoked out of their nests easily by setting fire to them, but this has not been confirmed as they appear reluctant to move and perish in the blaze rather than leave the nest.

### Food

They are predominantly vegetarian, feeding on the fine fresh leaflets of thornbush, *Acacia* spp, and the green outer coating of the seed pods. They also eat the young leaves of the shepherd's tree, *Boscia albitrunca*, and the green and dry outer coating of the seeds of the buffalo thorn, *Ziziphus mucronata*. They crop short lengths of the outermost, fine twigs of *Acacia* spp, sometimes with the green seed pods attached, and carry these back to the nest to be eaten; the discarded remains are then added to the nesting material. De Graaff (1981) included insects in their diet. They are independent of drinking water.

### Reproduction

They are seasonal breeders. In the northern parts of the Subregion the young are born during the warm summer months from August to April, the mean number in litters being 3,6 (range 2–5; n=5).

## Genus *Aethomys* Thomas, 1915

The name is derived from the Greek *aithos*, sunburnt, and *mys*, a mouse. Two subgenera are recognised by Davis (1975) and supported by Visser & Robinson (1986): *Micaelamys* which includes *A. namaquensis* and *A. granti*; the second subgenus, *Aethomys*, includes what Davis (1975) described as a mixed bag, namely *A. chrysophilus* which has a wide distribution in the Subregion; *A. nyikae*, so far only recorded in the Subregion from eastern Zimbabwe, and *A. silindensis*, known only from Mt Selinda and two other localities in eastern Zimbabwe. Davis (1975), in his review of the genus *Aethomys*, listed a number of described subspecies which he suggested are synonyms of *A. c. chrysophilus*, but removed *dollmani* and, following Ansell & Ansell (1973), regarded it as a subspecies of *A. nyikae*.

More recently, Visser & Robinson (1986) have found the karyotype for *A. namaquensis* is 2n=24, *A. granti* 2n=32, but for *A. chrysophilus* two distinct cytotypes 2n=44 and 2n=50. They suggest, as a result of the two distinct karyotypes of the latter, the absence of hybrids in the areas of sympatry, as well as marked differences in spermatozoan morphology (Gordon & Watson, 1986), that there is an absence of gene flow between the two cytotypes and they therefore deserve recognition as two species. Only the *A. chrysophilus* 2n=50 cytotype occurs at Mazoe, the type locality of this species (Gordon, in Visser & Robinson, 1986).

Key to the species after Meester *et al.* (1986) and for live caught material Visser & Robinson (1986)

1. Size larger, greatest skull length up to 43 mm
   ... *silindensis*

   Size smaller, greatest skull length not more than 39 mm
   ... 2

2. Size smaller, greatest skull length below 35 mm; $M^1$ with three cusps in anterior row
   ... 3

   Size larger, greatest skull length over 35 mm; $M^1$ with two cusps in anterior row
   ... 4

3. Tail *c.* 135% of head and body length; tail bristles paler, less dense or dark towards tip; ventral hairs white to roots, or grey-based, with greyish white or grey tips; incisors strongly opisthodont (greatest length minus condylobasal length *c.* 3,5 mm); karyotype 2n=24
   ... *namaquensis*

   Tail *c.* 115% of head and body length; tail bristles darker, becoming denser towards tip; ventral hairs grey-based, with greyish white or grey tips; incisors moderately opisthodont (greatest length minus condylobasal length *c.* 2,5 mm); karyotype 2n=32
   ... *granti*

4. Tail *c.* 120% of head and body length; width of $M^1$ 2,0 mm or less; incisors strongly opisthodont (greatest length minus condylobasal length *c.* 3,5 mm); karyotype 2n=44 or 2n=50
   ... *chrysophilus*

   Tail *c.* 95% of head and body length; width of $M^1$ 2,0–2,2 mm; incisors orthodont (greatest length minus condylobasal length *c.* 1,5 mm)
   ... *nyikae*

---

No. 178

## *Aethomys silindensis* Roberts, 1938

## Selinda rat
## Selinda-bosrot

---

In spite of diligent efforts to collect specimens, the original two males, collected by A.G. White of the Transvaal Museum at Mt Selinda, Melsetter District, Zimbabwe, in 1938 remained for 30 years the only specimens known. Roberts (1951), when he described the species, correctly predicted that eventually they might be found in other parts of eastern Zimbabwe, and they were collected at two other localities nearby in the late 1960's by the USA Smithsonian Institution mammal survey team. The species can be overlooked among the much commoner *Aethomys chrysophilus*, which they resemble and with which they are sympatric. Practically nothing is known about their ecology.

### Colloquial Name

They are named after the locality from which the original specimens were collected.

### Taxonomic Notes

Ellerman *et al.* (1953) regarded this species as a subspecies of *A. chrysophilus*; Davis (1975b) reinstated it as a valid species. Compared with *A. chrysophilus*, they are larger and more robust and the first upper molar teeth have five roots, whereas in *A. chrysophilus* these teeth are four-rooted.

### Description

Only two specimens are available in South Africa and character variation cannot be assessed. The hair differs from *A. chrysophilus* in being longer, with a deeper groove, and the scales are more rippled-crenate as the petal pattern changes to waved mosaic (Fig. XXIII.3) (Keogh, 1985). Roberts (1951) recorded that the upper parts of the body in the type specimen, a male, are buffy-brown, with a rusty-red tinge, the flanks paler, the under parts buffy-white, this extending upwards to the upper lips. The upper surface of the tail is light brown, the under surface paler. As in *A. chrysophilus*, the tail is heavily scaled and is only sparsely covered with short, bristly hairs. The upper surfaces of the hands and feet are buffy-white. The skull is stoutly built, the supraorbital ridges well developed and extending far back on to the cranium. The cheekteeth are large, the anterior cusp of the third upper molar well developed.

The measurements (mm) of the type specimen, a male, are given by Roberts (1951) as:
HB 160, T 194, Hf s/u 32, E 21.

### Distribution

They have been found only within the borders of the Subregion.

*Southern African Subregion*

They are known from three localities in eastern **Zimbabwe**: Mt Selinda and the Ngorima Reserve in the Melsetter District and Stapleford in the Mutare District. They may occur in the

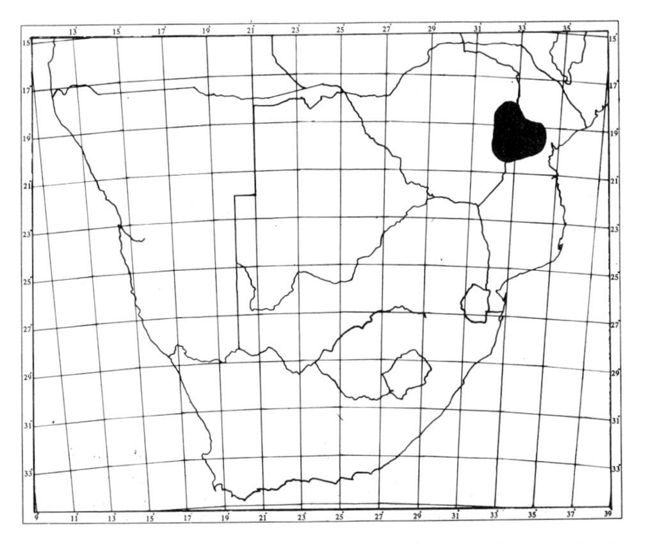

western areas of the Vila Pery District of Mozambique which are similar ecologically.

### Habitat

The three Stapleford specimens were taken at an altitude of about 700 m in the valley of the Nyamkwarara River in rank tangled vegetation in a rocky area. The two specimens from the Ngorima Reserve were taken in a similar association at about the same altitude. At Mt Selinda neither this species nor *A. chrysophilus* occurred within the forest itself. White (pers. comm.), who collected the original specimens, stated that they were not recognised at the time as different from *A. chrysophilus*. All the localities from which they have been taken lie in areas with a mean annual rainfall of from 1 200 mm to 1 400 mm.

### Habits, Food and Reproduction

No information is available on these aspects of their life history.

---

No. 179

## *Aethomys namaquensis* (A. Smith, 1834)

## Namaqua rock mouse
## Namakwalandse klipmuis

Plate 13

---

### Colloquial Name

The original specimen, from which Andrew Smith described the species, came from Little Namaqualand. "Rock" indicates the type of habitat with which they are associated in many parts of their range.

### Taxonomic Notes

Ellerman *et al.* (1953) listed 14 subspecies from the Subregion. Davis (1975b) regarded them all provisionally as synonyms of *A. n. namaquensis*, a treatment followed by Meester *et al.* (1986). The chromosome number in this species is 2n=24 (Matthey, 1964; Misonne, 1974; Visser & Robinson, 1986).

### Description

Namaqua rock mice vary in colour and in the length of their tails throughout their wide distributional range which has led to the description of many subspecies. In general, the upper parts of the body are reddish-brown to yellowish-brown, in some parts of their range with a profuse mixture of black-tipped hair. The hair on the under parts may be pure white or, particularly on the upper chest and flanks, the hairs may have grey bases imparting a greyish colour to these sections of the under parts.

They have broad hairs with a wide, shallow groove in the shaft and flattened cup-shaped petal scales in the groove (Fig. XXIII.3) (Keogh, 1985).

Populations from the more northern parts of the Subregion have proportionately long tails compared to the length of the head and body, the proportion being 140% for adults of both sexes. In more southerly populations the proportion may be between 125% and 133% and from parts of southeastern Botswana may fall as low as 125% for males and 133% for females (Table 179.1). However, from the southern coastal areas the tails are proportionately long. Shortridge (1934) noted the variation in tail length within their range in Namibia.

**Table 179.1**

Measurements (mm) and mass (g) of Namaqua rock mice, *A. namaquensis* from (a) Zimbabwe (Smithers & Wilson, 1979) and (b) Mozambique (Gliwicz, 1985); and tail as a proportion of head and body length in (c) southeastern Botswana (Smithers, 1971), (d) southwestern Botswana (Smithers, 1971) and (e) South Africa (de Graaff, 1981)

**a. Zimbabwe** (Smithers & Wilson, 1979)

| | Males | | | Females | | |
|---|---|---|---|---|---|---|
| | x̄ | n | Range | x̄ | n | Range |
| TL | 258 | 24 | 234–291 | 269 | 24 | 230–285 |
| (HB | 110) | | | (112) | | |
| T | 148 | 24 | 131–170 | 157 | 24 | 130–178 |
| Hf c/u | 26 | 24 | 25–28 | 26 | 24 | 24–29 |
| E | 18 | 24 | 16–20 | 18 | 24 | 16–20 |
| Mass | 47,2 | 24 | 33,0–57,9 | 47,7 | 24 | 35,0–54,4 |
| T/HB × 100 | 140,0% | | | 140,2% | | |

**b. Mozambique** (Gliwicz, 1985)

| | Irrespective of sex | | |
|---|---|---|---|
| | x̄ | n | Range |
| TL | 151 | 19 | 137–171 |
| HB | 111,3 | 19 | 103–125 |
| Hf c/u | 24,2 | 19 | 22–26 |
| E | 16,4 | 19 | 14–19 |
| Mass | 44,6 | 19 | 35–54 |
| T/HB × 100 | 133,3% | | |

**c. Southeastern Botswana** (Smithers, 1971)

| | Males | Females |
|---|---|---|
| | x̄ | x̄ |
| T/HB × 100 | 127,0% | 131,0% |

**d. Southwestern Botswana** (Smithers, 1971)

| | | |
|---|---|---|
| T/HB × 100 | 134,0% | 138,0% |

**e. South Africa** (de Graaff, 1981)

| | | |
|---|---|---|
| T/HB × 100 | 125,0% | 133,1% |

Although they superficially resemble the red veld rat, *A. chrysophilus*, they can be distinguished readily from this species. In Namaqua rock mice the tails are noticeably longer and thinner, the scaling finer and not as coarse as in the red veld rat. The best character to use in distinguishing the two is found in the first lower molar tooth. *A. chrysophilus* has two cusps in the first cusp row, *A. namaquensis* three, the anterior medium cusp small, but clearly visible in most stages, except in individuals with heavily worn teeth (Fig. 179.1). In *A. chrysophilus* there is sometimes a small cingulum situated on the anterior face of the tooth, but this always lies at a lower level than the two cusps, whereas in *A. namaquensis* the three cusps lie in the same plane. *A. namaquensis* has a more lightly built skull which lacks the clearly defined supraorbital ridges of *A. chrysophilus* (Smithers, 1983).

### Distribution

*South of the Sahara, excluding the Southern African Subregion*

They are recorded from **Angola**; the southern parts of **Zambia; Mozambique**, north of the Zambezi River and from **Malawi**.

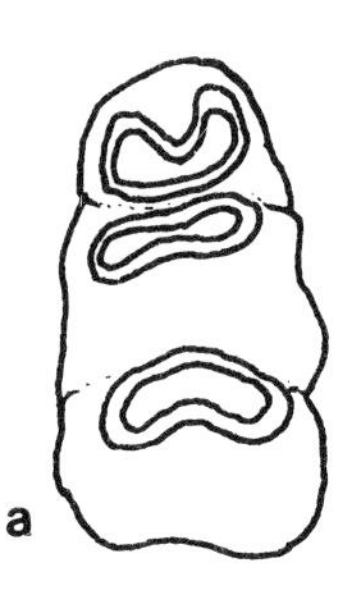


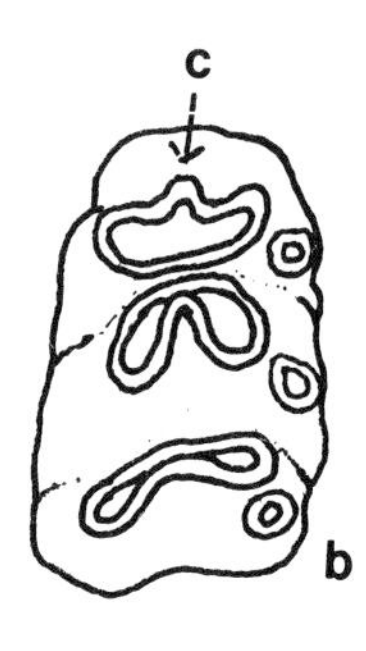


Fig. 179.1. First lower molar: (a) *A. chrysophilus* with two cusps in the first cusp row
(b) *A. namaquensis* with three cusps in the first cusp row
(c) Third cusp

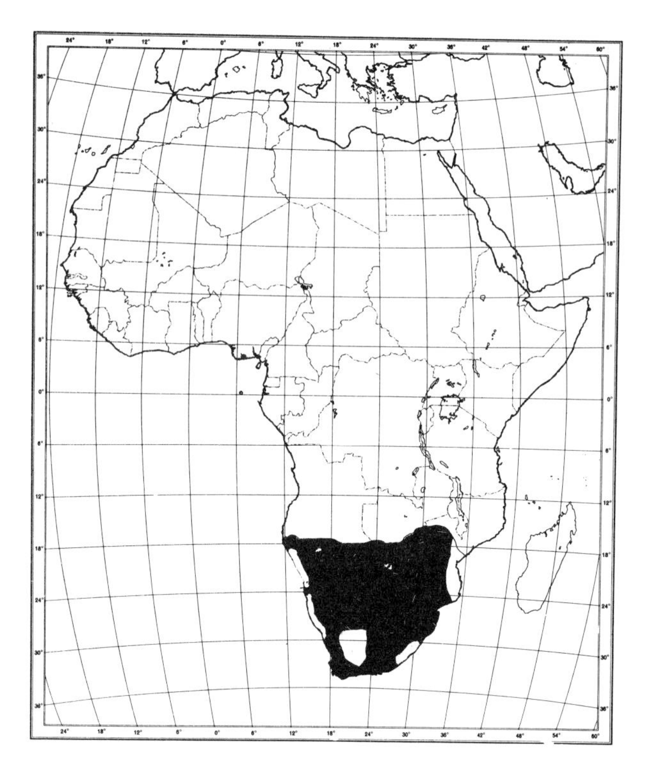

Southern African Subregion distribution only.

*Southern African Subregion*

They are distributed widely throughout the **Subregion**, except in parts of the central and northern parts of the Cape Province and coastal Natal.

### Habitat

They are catholic in their habitat requirements, but where there are rocky koppies, outcrops or boulder-strewn hillsides, they will use these in preference to other types of habitat. In the Swartberg of the southern Cape, Breytenbach (1982) found them only on low altitude sites on north-facing slopes with more than 30% and 50% of ground cover consisting of rocks less than 130 mm in diameter and total rock cover respectively and in areas of low total foliage cover. In the central Kalahari, where there are no such rocky areas, they occur in open scrub, open woodland, and on the fringes of pans where there are calcareous outcrops. In the Namib Desert *A. namaquensis*, the most recent invader (Meester, 1965), is the predominant rodent in the rocky outcrops along the eastern more mesic side (Coetzee, 1969; Stuart, 1975), but, unlike other rodents, utilises rock crevices as a shelter and does not burrow.

### Habits

They are nocturnal, communal, terrestrial, and to some extent arboreal. Small colonies live in rock crevices, holes in trees, in or under fallen logs or in piles of debris. They collect stems of grass, fine twigs and other debris (in the Swartberg sticks and *Restio* spp), eventually forming huge piles over the entrance to the shelters. Where there are no rocks these nests may be located in the forks of trees, covering a hole in the hollow interior. In the absence of trees, they make nests under scrub bushes, excavating a burrow in the soil underneath the grass pile. The grass piles are perforated by tunnels all leading to the burrow or to the holes underneath it. Where the grass nests are constructed in trees, they are seldom more than 3 m from the ground, and more usually at a height of 1–2 m from it. If these grass nests are set alight the occupants retreat to the safety of the burrows or holes under them. Buffenstein (1984) has shown that *A. namaquensis* is well adapted to life in hot arid environments, balancing its low basal metabolic rate with high pelage insulative properties. In the Namib Desert they aestivate during the hot, dry summer months as a water and energy conserving mechanism (Withers *et al.*, 1980).

### Food

They are omnivorous, with a large caecum (Perrin & Curtis, 1980; Woodall & Mackie, 1987) and eat seeds of grass and other plants. Bond & Breytenbach (1985) found they were proficient at recovering intact protea seeds even when buried, eating significant numbers of these seeds if they were not removed and buried by ants. Breytenbach (1982) found that they utilised *Restio* spp bearing nutlet-like fruits such as *Willdenowia teres* and *Hypodiscus* spp in the Swartberg.

### Reproduction

In a sample of 378 females from Botswana, taken throughout the year, gravid females were recorded from September to May, peaking in March/April (Smithers, 1971) and with no signs of breeding during the colder months, from June to August. In Botswana the average number of foetuses was 3,1 (range 2–7; n=42), in Zimbabwe 3,6 (range 1–5; n=11), and in the Transvaal 3,3 (range 1–5; n-43) (Rautenbach, 1978). They tend to have unstable population cycles associated with high mortality and high reproductive potential (Withers *et al.*, 1980). The females have one pair of pectoral and two pairs of inguinal mammae.

---

No. 180

## *Aethomys granti* (Wroughton, 1908)

## Grant's rock mouse
## Grant se klipmuis

---

### Colloquial Name

Named after the collector, Capt. C.H.B. Grant who, while attached to the British forces, collected the original specimen at Deelfontein, Cape Province, during the Boer War in February 1902. Capt. Grant later undertook collecting expeditions in Mozambique under the sponsorship of C.D. Rudd, a colleague of Cecil John Rhodes, and was co-author with C.W. Mackworth-Praed of books on African birds.

### Taxonomic Notes

The status of this species has in the past been the subject of speculation. At various times it has been placed in the genus *Myomys* (Allen, 1939); *Micaelamys* as a subgenus of *Rattus* (Ellerman, 1941); *Mastomys* (Roberts, 1951) and as of uncertain status (Ellerman *et al.*, 1953). Davis (1975b) placed it in the subgenus *Micaelamys* with *Aethomys namaquensis*, from which it differs in having a slightly shorter and greyer tail and greyish under parts. Karyotypes in analyses have shown that *A. granti* has 2n=32 (Matthey, 1964; Misonne, 1974; Visser & Robinson, 1986).

### Description

There appears to be little sexual dimorphism. Adults have a total length of about 21 mm, with tails that are from 110% to 115% longer than the length of the head and body. The upper parts of the body are dark brown grizzled with buff, the individual hairs with light slate- grey bases and either buffy- or black-tipped, with many totally black hairs especially on the mid-dorsal region, giving it a darker appearance than the flanks. The flanks are light buffy, in some specimens yellowish. The hair of the under parts is dark grey at the base with white tips, giving the under parts a dark grey appearance. The upper parts of the feet are white, the sides of the face, like the flanks, buffy and paler than the upper parts of the body. The tail is densely covered with black bristly hair which tends to form a tuft on the tip. Like *A. namaquensis* the first lower molar teeth have three cusps in the first row (Fig. 179.1).

**Table 180.1**

Measurements of Grant's rock mice, *A. granti* from the Cape Province compiled from the records of Dr D.H.S. Davis.

| | Males | | | Females | | |
|---|---|---|---|---|---|---|
| | x̄ | n | Range | x̄ | n | Range |
| (TL | 213) | | | (221) | | |
| HB | 101 | 12 | 90–120 | 103 | 17 | 85–120 |
| T | 112 | 12 | 96–130 | 118 | 15 | 105–130 |
| Hf c/u | 23 | 12 | 22–24 | 23 | 17 | 21–25 |
| E | 17 | 12 | 15–18 | 16 | 16 | 13–18 |
| **Skull** | | | | | | |
| Greatest length | 29,1 | 8 | 27,1–30,3 | 29,7 | 13 | 27,7–31,9 |
| Condylo-basal length | 26,2 | 8 | 24,3–27,1 | 29,0 | 13 | 25,1–28,9 |

Compared with *A. namaquensis*, with which they are sympatric in parts of their range, the following differences are useful in distinguishing them:

| | *A. granti* | *A. namaquensis* |
|---|---|---|
| Tail | Shorter in comparison to HB, hairier, the bristles denser, blacker and lengthening towards the tip. | Longer in comparison to HB, less hairy, the bristles sparser, paler and shorter. |
| Dorsal colour | Greyish ticked with black, the fur softer. | Yellowish-buff ticked with black, the fur crisper. |
| Ventral colour | Greyish. | Buffy white. |
| Anterior palatal foramen | Extends to root 2 of upper first molar tooth. | Extends to root 1 of upper first molar tooth. |

Live individuals in captivity viewed alongside *A. namaquensis* appeared to have heavier heads and the greyness of their bodies was a noticeable character.

**Distribution**

They are confined in their distribution to the south-central parts of the **Cape Province**.

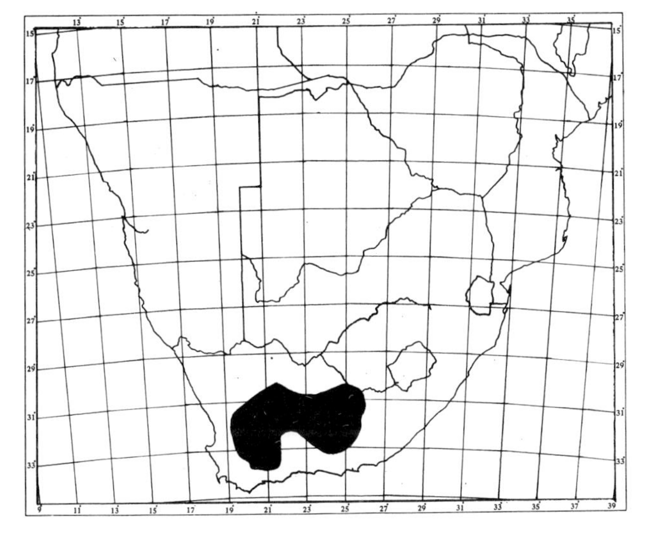

**Habitat**

They are associated with rocky terrain and in parts occur on the same ground as *A. namaquensis*.

**Habits, Food and Reproduction**

Nothing is known of these aspects of their life history.

No. 181

## *Aethomys chrysophilus* (de Winton, 1897)

Red veld rat
Afrikaanse bosrot

Plate 13

**Colloquial Name**

The colloquial name refers to the colour of the body which has a reddish tinge, often accentuated towards the rump. The specific name *chrysophilus* is derived from the Greek *chrysos*, gold, and *philos*, having an affinity to.

**Taxonomic Notes**

Davis (1975b) listed three subspecies. *A. c. chrysophilus*, is the subspecies that occurs in the Subregion. Within the Subregion, Visser & Robinson (1986) found that specimens have chromosome numbers where 2n=44 and 50, suggesting two distinct species, although, karyology apart, they appear to be indistinguishable using existing identification keys. The other two subspecies are extralimital, *A. c. singidae* (Kershaw, 1923) from central and northern Tanzania, and *A. c. voi* (Osgood, 1910) from northeastern Tanzania and southeastern Kenya.

**Description**

Red veld rats have a mean total length of about 280 mm, with tails that are longer than the length of the head and body (Table 181.1). They have broad hairs with a scooped-out appearance of the groove and flattened petal scales; in *A. namaquensis* the hair is broader and the scales closer together (Fig. XXIII.3) (Keogh, 1985). Within the range of subspecies originally listed by Roberts (1951), there is a considerable variation in the colour of the upper parts of the body, those from the drier areas in the west of the Subregion paler in colour than those from the east. Others are darker and greyer or yellower, some heavily pencilled with black on the upper parts, others less so. The typical form from Mashonaland, Zimbabwe, is reddish-fawn; the pelage has a sprinkling of black hairs; individual hairs on the upper parts are dark grey at the base and tipped with reddish-fawn. Some individuals are a darker reddish-fawn on the rump. The flanks are lighter in colour than the upper parts and the under parts are greyish, the individual hairs having grey bases and white tips. The upper parts of the hands and feet are covered with short, fine, whitish hair.

They are larger and more heavily built than the Namaqua rock rat, *A. namaquensis*, which they resemble quite closely. They can be distinguished from this species as their tails are thicker and not so long in proportion to the length of the head and body and are much more heavily scaled, especially towards their bases. The most useful feature distinguishing the two species is the formation of the anterior section of the first lower molar teeth. In *A. chrysophilus* there are two anterior cusps, in *A. namaquensis* three, the median cusp small in relation to the other two (Fig. 179.1). *A. chrysophilus* often has a small, centrally situated cingulum on the front of the tooth which, when the tooth is viewed from above, may appear to simulate a cusp. Its situation, however, on the front of the tooth and not on its uppermost face is sufficient to show that it is not a true cusp.

The heavier build of *A. chrysophilus* is reflected in the build of the skull in which the supraorbital ridges are prominent and well developed, a feature lacking in *A. namaquensis*. The molar teeth are heavy and broad, the upper third molar not much smaller than the second, whereas in *A. namaquensis* the upper third molar is clearly smaller than the second.

In *A. chrysophilus*, generally but not without exception, the under parts appear greyish, caused by the grey bases of the hairs showing through the white tipping of the individual hairs. The converse applies in the case of *A. namaquensis*, where the hair of the under parts is more usually pure white, but again in some areas the hairs are grey based, giving the whole a grey appearance, and this feature cannot be used in isolation to distinguish the two species.

### Table 181.1

Measurements (mm) and mass (g) of red veld rats, *A. chrysophilus*, from (a) the Transvaal (Rautenbach, 1978) and (b) Mozambique (Gliwicz, 1985)

**a**

| | Males | | | Females | | |
|---|---|---|---|---|---|---|
| | x̄ | n | Range | x̄ | n | Range |
| TL | 272 | 463 | 210–345 | 280 | 455 | 214–344 |
| (HB | 122) | | | (131) | | |
| T | 150 | 449 | 107–188 | 149 | 450 | 102–182 |
| Hf c/u | 28 | 459 | 22–32 | 27 | 477 | 20–33 |
| E | 20 | 450 | 16–23 | 21 | 471 | 16–24 |
| Mass | 76,7 | 331 | 38,0–112,0 | 68,1 | 344 | 26,0–125,0 |

**b**

| | Irrespective of sex | | |
|---|---|---|---|
| | x̄ | n | Range |
| TL | 284,0 | 4 | 279–296 |
| (HB | 132,2 | 4 | 128–143 |
| T | 152,0 | 4 | 151–153 |
| Hf c/u | 28,2 | 4 | 26–30 |
| E | 19,0 | 4 | 17–22 |
| Mass | 71,2 | 4 | 55,0–102,0 |

### Distribution

*South of the Sahara, excluding the Southern African subregion*

The species occurs in southeastern **Kenya; Tanzania; Zambia; Angola; Malawi** and in **Mozambique**, north of the Zambezi River.

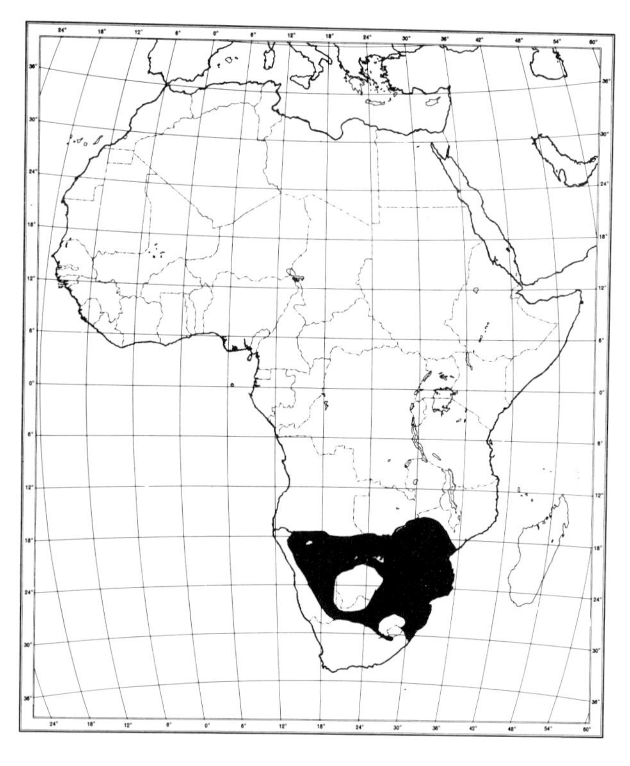

Southern African Subregion distribution only.

*Southern African Subregion*

They are recorded from **Namibia**, excluding the western desert regions; the **Caprivi Strip**; from northern and eastern **Botswana**; widely throughout **Zimbabwe; Mozambique**, south of the Zambezi River; the **Tranvaal** and **Natal**. In the **Orange Free State** they occur only in the extreme south, and in the **Cape Province** in parts of the northern sector, north of the Orange River.

### Habitat

Red veld rats are catholic in their habitat requirements, occurring both in grassland, with some scrub cover, and savanna woodland. They are associated especially with some form of cover in the form of rocky crevices, piles of boulders or debris, fallen trees or holes in termitaria, thick scrub or clumps of grass. In agriculturally developed areas they will use the cover of thorn fences, holes in stone walls or under farm outbuildings. While they do not generally become a commensal with man, occasionally they will enter houses.

### Habits

They are nocturnal and terrestrial. They excavate their burrows under the cover of bushes, but more commonly use more substantial cover. They are not gregarious and the shelters are used, at most, by a pair or a family party.

### Food

From a sample of 11 stomach contents in the wet season in the Kruger National Park, Watson (1987) found that they ate 21% insects, 32% vegetable matter and 47% seeds. Smithers (1983) found that they also ate the dry exocarp of berries, nut kernels, fruit and seeds of buffalo thorn, *Ziziphus mucronata*, and dry *Acacia* pods. Discarded remains of food may be found lying near the entrances to the shelters or at sites at which they eat. They will also raid grain crops such as maize and sorghum, and legumes such as peas and beans.

### Reproduction

Red veld rats breed throughout the year, the average number of foetuses being in: Zimbabwe 3,2 (range 2–5; n=15) (Smithers & Wilson, 1979); Botswana 3,6 (range 3–6; n=10) (Smithers, 1971), and in the Transvaal 3,3 (range 1–5; n=41) (Rautenbach, 1978). The young are born in nests within the shelters lined with vegetable debris or any other soft material available. They are born naked and pink, with their eyes closed, and are apparently not nipple-clingers. Females have one pair of pectoral and two pairs of inguinal mammae.

---

No. 182

## *Aethomys nyikae* (Thomas, 1897)

## Nyika veld rat
## Nyika-bosrot

---

### Colloquial Name

They are so named as the original specimen was collected on the Nyika Plateau in northern Malawi.

### Taxonomic Notes

Only the nominate *A. n. nyikae* occurs in the Subregion.

### Distribution

They are known to occur within the limits of the Subregion only in the eastern Ngorima Reserve in eastern **Zimbabwe**, and there only on the somewhat slender evidence of a single juvenile specimen identified by Davis (*in litt.*) in 1965. No further specimens have been taken in this reserve, where *A. chrysophilus* is quite common. Nothing is known of the ecology of the species in the Subregion, except that the Ngorima specimen was taken in woodland with a sparse grass cover. In view of the slender evidence available, Smithers & Wilson (1979) placed *A. n. nyikae* among a list of species that "may possibly" occur in Zimbabwe. Extralimitally they occur in Malawi, northeastern and northwestern Zambia.

### Habitat, Habits, Food and Reproduction

No data are available on these aspects of their biology within the Subregion.

## Genus *Rattus* Fischer, 1803

Linnaeus (1758) created the genus *Mus* to accommodate the rats and mice that were known then and it continued to be used for nearly 50 years for all other species discovered up to that time. Fischer (1803) created the genus *Rattus* to accommodate, from the many forms originally included in the genus *Mus*, the typical rats as distinct from the mice. These colloquial names, rats and mice, have little significance today and it is largely a matter of personal opinion whether a species is large and coarse enough to warrant its status as a rat, or small and dainty enough to warrant its status as a mouse.

In his monumental work on the rodents, Ellerman (1940/1949), using cheekteeth as his principal taxonomic character, came to the conclusion that many groups are indistinguishable as far as generic characters are concerned. This resulted in genera, which are represented in the Subregion (such as *Aethomys, Mastomys, Thallomys, Zelotomys* and others) being regarded as synonyms of *Rattus*. In spite of the fact that the configuration of teeth is of profound taxonomic significance, this has created what Rosevear (1969) described as a cumbersome jumble out of the convenience Linnaeus intended it to be. The genus *Rattus*, as designated by Ellerman, might be supposed to have some clearly marked characters which could render the association of some 550 forms throughout the world possible, but this is far from the case. Many of the characters used by Ellerman are subject to exception and today there is a swing away from his treatment, sound though it may be on the basis on which it was created. Anyone working with murids has no difficulty in immediately recognising members of any of the genera mentioned from members of the other genera, and *Rattus* in particular from any of them. With the growth of knowledge of the ecology of members of the genera, their habits, the habitat in which they live and general body structure, it becomes even more difficult to reconcile a single genus for all. Examination of the chromosomes of genera such as *Mastomys* and *Rattus* show that they are clearly different (Matthey, 1958), whilst Davis (1965), using more traditional methods, came to a similar conclusion. In short, it is convenient to regard the various genera as separate entities, a treatment that is followed in this monograph.

In the Subregion two species of *Rattus* occur: the brown rat, *R. norvegicus*, and the house rat, *R. rattus*, both of which have been introduced through man's agencies and both of which, by the same means, now have a cosmopolitan distribution. It is impossible to say just when either species was introduced to the Subregion, as the early historical records simply refer to "rats or mice" and do not make special mention of the species involved (Skead, 1980). It is likely, however, that rats came ashore with the earliest shipwrecks, but unless they did so near settlements it seems unlikely that they would have survived. The establishment of settlements on the coast of the Subregion by the middle of the 17th century, however, would have enhanced their chances of survival greatly, and there is little doubt that rats found their way ashore from sailing ships which were then infested with what were known as "ship rats". Most likely these were predominantly house rats, *R. rattus*, but could well have included the brown rat, *R. norvegicus*.

In the British Isles, Lawrence & Brown (1967) recorded that the house rat, *R. rattus*, had established itself 500 years before the introduction of the brown rat, *R. norvegicus*, which arrived there in the 18th century. With the latter's arrival the house rat appeared unable to compete and today is confined mainly to port towns, whereas the brown rat is distributed widely. The situation in the Subregion is reversed and, although the brown rat, *R. norvegicus*, remains the dominant species where the two occur together, it has not spread inland from the coastal ports, whereas the house rat, *R. rattus*, has done so. This is probably due to climatic factors, for the brown rat, *R. norvegicus*, originated in the temperate regions of Asia, possibly in Siberia or China, and therefore is not as attuned to the warmer climate of southern Africa. In contrast the house rat, *R. rattus*, which had its origins in the warmer climates of India and Burma (Rosevear, 1969), is more at home in the Subregion.

In the Subregion, the house rat, *R. rattus*, has penetrated inland, predominantly in the east, and has done so mainly along the railway systems into areas served by rail, motor or other services. It has not generally become a veld rodent except in restricted areas. The Carnegie Museum, Pittsburgh, has specimens of the house rat, *R. rattus*, collected in 1892 from the pioneer encampment on the site of what is today the city of Harare, Zimbabwe. Longden, who was in charge of the wagon train carrying supplies to this encampment from Kimberley (supplies which included bags of ground maize meal), reported in his diary (unpublished) that rats were found on the wagons. It seems likely that this may have been the means by which the house rats made their way to the early settlement. At the time of the building of the Kariba Dam on the Zambezi River in Zimbabwe and the erection of the power station, house rats arrived for the first time, having been transported there in the huge packing cases protecting heavy electrical machinery.

However, the brown rat, *R. norvegicus*, remains dominant and Rosevear (1969) showed that during an extermination campaign from 1954 to 1959 the percentage kill of the brown rat in Douala, Cameroun, rose from 60% to 98% of the total catch of the two species; in the last year 1 374 brown rats were killed against 24 house rats.

Both species are economic and medical pests of great importance. Both are omnivorous and no foodstuffs or stored grains are safe from their attack. Quite apart from what they eat, they soil and so destroy at least as much again, and by their gnawing they damage containers, building structures and fittings, including electric cables. It is impossible to estimate accurately the cost of such damage, but in the Subregion alone this probably runs into millions of Rands annually.

They contaminate food supplies with their droppings, thereby passing on to man bacteria such as *Salmonella* spp, which cause food poisoning, and they are reservoirs of diseases such as typhus and plague. One or other of the two species of *Rattus* was certainly responsible for the introduction of the bacillus *Yersinia pestis* to the African Continent, which causes plague in man, and for passing this on through the agency of fleas to our veld rodents so that today plague is an endemic disease.

The two species, *R. norvegicus* and *R. rattus*, exhibit a wide variety of shape, size and colour even within populations. The size of the ears, length of the tail and the colour of feet, however, are the best characters to use in distinguishing them. In both, the first digit on the forefoot is rudimentary and armed with a nail, the fifth digit reaching about halfway along the fourth which is slightly shorter than the third. The hind feet are heavily built, conspicuously so when compared with other murids. The three middle digits are the same length and much longer than the others, the first digit reaching the base of the second. The fifth reaches the first joint of the fourth digit.

Key to the species after Meester *et al.* (1986)

1. Size smaller, head and body length 150–200 mm, tail longer in proportion, 185–245 mm; greatest skull length 38–44 mm, width 18,5–21,5 mm; braincase wider; antero-external cusp of $M^1$ not reduced

   ... *rattus*

   Size larger, head and body length 210 mm and more, tail shorter, less than 210 mm; greatest skull length 45 mm and more, width 23–25 mm; braincase narrower; antero-external cusp of $M^1$ reduced

   ... *norvegicus*

No. 183

## *Rattus rattus* (Linnaeus, 1758)

## House rat
## Huisrot

Plate 12

### Colloquial Name

This species is associated closely with man's dwellings and storehouses.
Alternative names: Black rat, ship rat, roof rat.

### Taxonomic Notes

Very many subspecies have been described, but none specifically from the Subregion. The three colour phases listed in the **Description** at times have been considered valid subspecies.

### Description

The house rat has a total length of up to about 400 mm and a mass of up to about 180,0g. There is no difference in size between adults of the two sexes (Table 183.1). The pelage is harsh, the tail coarsely scaled and the hind feet noticeably large and heavily built in comparison with any indigenous species of murid. The tail is longer than the head and body and the large ears are more or less devoid of hair.

**Table 183.1**

Measurements (mm) and mass (g) of house rats, *R. rattus*, of the *alexandrinus* colour phase from Zimbabwe (Smithers & Wilson, 1979)

| | Males | | | Females | | |
|---|---|---|---|---|---|---|
| | $\bar{x}$ | n | Range | $\bar{x}$ | n | Range |
| TL | 371 | 10 | 340–395 | 371 | 10 | 355–392 |
| (HB | 175) | | | (175) | | |
| T | 196 | 10 | 180–215 | 196 | 10 | 190–205 |
| Hf c/u | 34 | 10 | 30–40 | 35 | 10 | 30–38 |
| E | 21 | 10 | 20–25 | 22 | 10 | 20–24 |
| Mass | 123,9 | 15 | 105,0–178,0 | 163,0 | 3 | 150,0–184,0 |

The large broad hairs have a mosaic pattern (Fig. XXIII.3) at the half-way mark made up of many scales across the width of the hairs (Keogh, 1985).

This species occurs in three colour phases:

*rattus*:

This was available to Linnaeus as his "type" specimen, being the darkest phase and occurring widely in Europe. It is a melanistic variant of the *alexandrinus* phase, the upper parts being black or dark blackish-brown, with dark slatey-grey or dark sepia-brown under parts.

*frugivorous*:

In this phase the under parts are white or yellowish, this colour sharply defined from the colour of the upper parts. It occurs alongside the *alexandrinus* phase in grain mills and railway yards in Zimbabwe, as well as in other parts of the Subregion, but apart from the colour of the under parts, is indistinguishable from the *alexandrinus* phase.

*alexandrinus*:

Originally this phase was described from Alexandria, Egypt. In the Subregion it is generally greyer on the upper parts than the other two phases, the upper parts greyish-brown, the flanks grey and the under parts dingy grey, with no clear demarcation between the colour of the flanks and the under parts. It occurs alongside the *frugivorous* phase in the Subregion where it was probably introduced through the eastern coastal ports.



### Distribution

Cosmopolitan

They are distributed widely in the Subregion, mainly in areas with a mean annual rainfall in excess of 500 mm, but where they occur in drier areas they are confined to urban centres.

*Southern African Subregion*

They are recorded in **Namibia** coastally at Swakopmund and from two localities inland of this. They occur widely in **Zimbabwe** on the plateau, from Bulawayo east to Harare, and widely in the eastern and northeastern parts of the country; in central and southern **Mozambique**, south of the Zambezi River; in the **Transvaal**, except in the dry western and in the northern and eastern parts of the province. They are distributed widely in the **Orange Free State; Natal** and in the eastern parts of the **Cape Province**, extending along the coast to Cape Town and to other localities in the southwest of the province. They occur predominantly as a commensal with man, but occasionally have settled in the veld where local conditions are suitable.

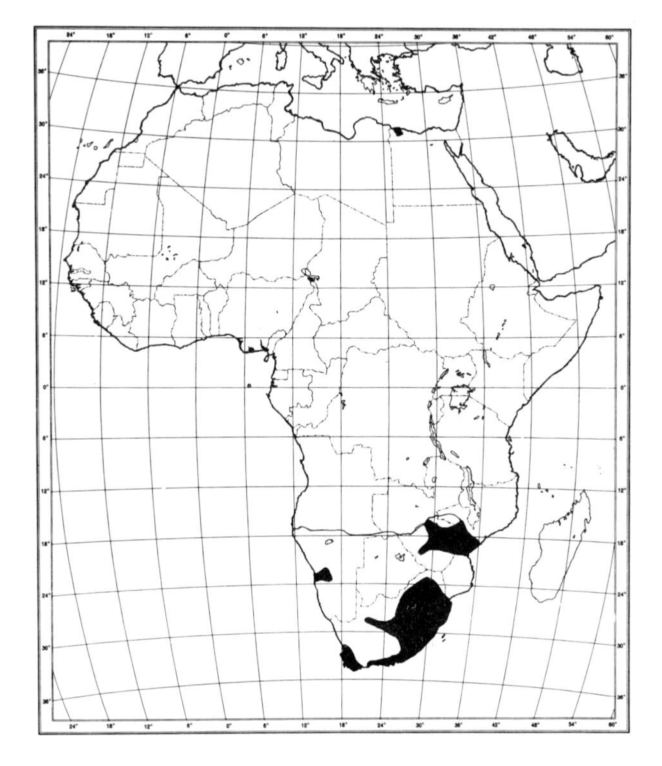

Southern African Subregion distribution only.

### Habitat

Shelter and food are essential habitat requirements of the house rat, *R. rattus*, and both are provided conveniently by man. Where they have established themselves in the veld, they have done so where there is thick underbush in thickets, forested areas or rocks in the vicinity of human habitations.

### Habits

They are nocturnal and predominantly terrestrial. They are accomplished climbers and can negotiate rough walls, climbing up the vertical surface with ease. They will run along narrow rafters and pipes. Regular runs are used between the nesting places and food supplies, which are marked by smears where difficult corners or obstacles have to be negotiated. These smears are caused by repeated contact with their greasy fur or feet. Their nests are well concealed under floors or in walls and are lined with any type of soft material which is available such as paper, rags, string or pieces of hessian bags. In the field they use vegetable debris for nest construction.

The normal gait is a run; in this species the tail trails touching the ground, whereas in the brown rat the tail is held free of the ground (Lawrence & Brown, 1967). They will gnaw on any material, causing substantial damage and are very destructive in opening runs, cutting through wooden obstacles, and will scratch and gnaw out excavations for nests in brickwork.

### Food

Omnivorous.

### Reproduction

The house rat is a prolific breeder and the young may be born throughout the year. A female may produce five or six litters within a year, litters numbering from five to 10 pups. Females have a post partum oestrus and thus breeding can be continuous. Females become sexually mature at about three months of age, the gestation period being between 21 and 30 days. The altricial young are born blind, pink and naked in well hidden nests. They are weaned at about 30 days. Occasionally a litter of young will get their tails so interlocked that they are unable to free themselves. Such a group is known as "king rats" and, as they are unable to forage, other rats will feed them, perhaps in some cases for the duration of their lives.

**INTRODUCED**

---

No. 184

## *Rattus norvegicus* (Berkenhout, 1769)

## Brown rat
## Bruinrot

---

### Colloquial Name

Also known as the Norway rat, which is the better name, as it was thought that the original described specimen, taken in Great Britain, had been introduced by way of Norway from Palaearctic Asia. However, the name brown rat is well entrenched in southern Africa.

### Taxonomic Notes

The brown rat is larger than *R. rattus*, has a stouter body, shorter ears, a shorter tail than the length of the head and body, and coarser fur. Ellerman & Morrison-Scott (1951) listed three subspecies; the nominate *R. n. norvegicus*; *R. n. caraco* (Pallas, 1779) from eastern Siberia, and *R. n. longicaudus* Mori, 1937 from Japan. Albino brown rats, *R. norvegicus*, are the "white rats" sold as pets to children and used in laboratories.

### Description

The brown rat has a bulkier body than the house rat and is shorter-tailed, with smaller ears. No record of mass is available for the brown rat from the Subregion, but a mass of up to 0,9 kg has been measured (Rosevear, 1969) which is much heavier than that of *R. rattus* in Zimbabwe (Table 183.1) or in the Transvaal (188,0 g—Rautenbach, 1978). The tail in *R. norvegicus* is, in series, 92% of the length of the head and body, compared to 117% in *R. rattus*. As they are indistinguishable by colour, these features are diagnostically important. They have large hairs with a mosaic pattern (Fig. XXIII.3) in the proximal part of the hair. Scales in the centre of the hair groove are smooth-margined, those on the sides ripple-crenate margined (Keogh, 1985). The brown rat is reddish-brown on the upper parts of the body, but this varies considerably. Individuals are known which have greyish-brown upper parts and are broadly black down the mid-back. The flanks are usually grey-brown or tinged with yellow; the under parts are paler than the flanks; the throat and chin are pale greyish. The upper surfaces of their feet are whitish, but they are also whitish in the *alexandrinus* phase of *R. rattus*. The tail in *R. norvegicus* is heavier than in *R. rattus* and has a generous covering of bristly hair which is black on the upper surface, whitish below.

**Table 184.1**

Comparison of skull measurements (mm) of the house rat, *R. rattus*, and the brown rat, *R. norvegicus*, from West Africa (Rosevear, 1969)

| | *R. rattus* Irrespective of sex | | | *R. norvegicus* Irrespective of sex | | |
|---|---|---|---|---|---|---|
| | $\bar{x}$ | n | Range | $\bar{x}$ | n | Range |
| TL skull | 42 | 10 | 39,5–45,3 | 48,5 | 5 | 43,3–54,5 |
| TL upper toothrow | 6,8 | 10 | 6,5–7,9 | 7,9 | 5 | 7,3–8,5 |
| Tail/HB % | 117% | | | 92% | | |

Rosevear (1969) recorded that the brown rat can have a mass of up to 2 lbs (0,9 kg), which is well over twice the mass of a mature house rat.

### Distribution

Its original home was Palaearctic Asia where, in the colder regions, it is a common species. From there it has attained a cosmopolitan distribution through the agency of man. They were first introduced to England about 1728 (Sclater, 1901) and to the United States in 1775 (Hanney, 1975). It is not known when they were introduced to southern Africa as most of the early records refer merely to "rats and mice", without specific identification. Significantly the first cases of plague in southern Africa occurred in 1898 in Maputo, Mozambique following a ship's visit from Madagascar where plague was then raging.

*Southern African Subregion*

In the Subregion they remain confined to the vicinity of coastal ports and towns.

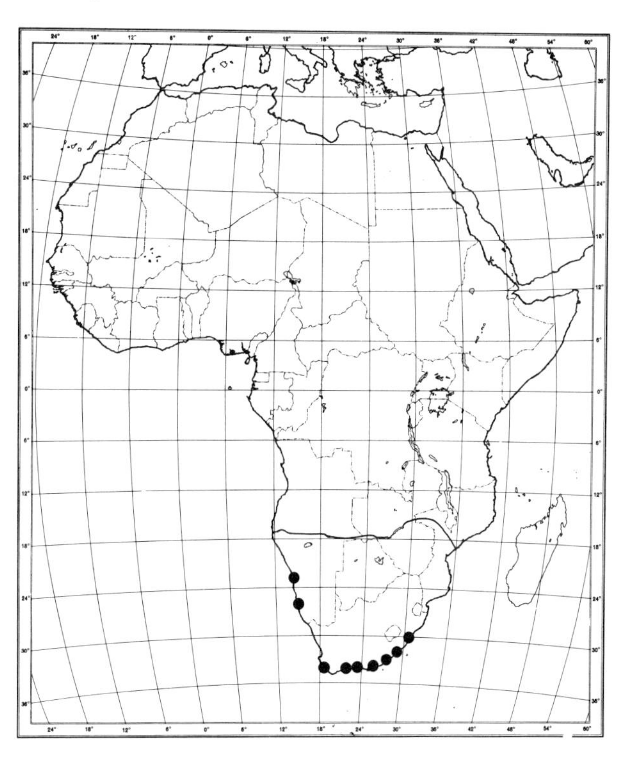

Southern African Subregion distribution only.

### Habitat

Brown rats originated in the colder parts of Asia and it has been suggested that the tropical, subtropical and possibly the temperate regions of the world are not optimal habitats for them. This may be the reason for their confinement to the points of entry into the Subregion.

In the coastal ports of the Subregion they have settled in warehouses, railway yards and dwelling houses, wherever there is a plentiful supply of any type of foodstuffs. So far they have not settled in the veld, but forage along beaches near settled areas (Hout Bay, Cape; Davis, 1974) and are more dependent on a water supply than the house rat, *R. rattus*.

### Habits

The brown rat is predominantly nocturnal and terrestrial. It is fiercer and much stronger than the house rat, *R. rattus*, and where the two come into contact the brown rat, *R. norvegicus*, is the dominant species. They are wary and suspicious of change and this makes them more difficult to trap than the house rat, although in other respects their habits are similar.

### Food
Omnivorous.

### Reproduction
De Graaff (1981) recorded that the number of young in litters varies from six to 12 and they are born at any time of the year, the gestation period being 20–26 days. The altricial young at birth are blind, naked and pink, the eyes opening between 14 and 17 days, and females become sexually mature at the age of three months.

## Subfamily GERBILLINAE

Members of this Subfamily are well characterised by their morphology and their habitat. All of them have tawny-coloured upper parts and white under parts, large eyes and well developed ear bullae. The hind legs are well developed, with a tendency to a saltatorial locomotion. The upper incisor teeth are slender and usually distinctly grooved. The molar teeth have two or three elongate, oval rings of enamel surrounding the central cement, and do not have rows of cusps as in the Murinae nor are they as distinctly laminated as those of the Otomyinae. Members of the Subfamily are adapted to life in desert or semi-desert habitats.

Key to the genera after Meester *et al.* (1986)

1. Bullae much enlarged, with prominent posterior mastoid portion clearly visible in dorsal view; anterior tympanic portion double the size of the mastoid bulla, and more than 12 mm in length; tail length much shorter than head and body length

   ... *Desmodillus*

   Bullae less enlarged, mastoid portion one-third or less of tympanic portion, which is shorter than 12 mm; tail length subequal to or greater than head and body length

   ... 2

2. Smaller, head and body length less than 120 mm; tail much longer than head and body; soles of hind feet partly or fully haired; zygomatic plate projecting less strongly forward

   ... *Gerbillurus*

   Larger, head and body length in adults usually greater than 120 mm; tail subequal in length to head and body; soles of hind feet naked; zygomatic plate projecting well forward

   ... *Tatera*

## Genus *Desmodillus* Thomas & Schwan, 1904

*Desmodillus* is a monotypic genus and, as far as is known, is confined in its distribution to within the limits of the Subregion. It seems quite possible, however, that eventually it will be shown to occur marginally in southern Angola.

The most conspicuous external features are the pure white spots behind and at the base of the ears and the relatively short tail which is up to about 80% of the length of the head and body. The greatly enlarged posterior section of the bullae is also characteristic (Fig. 185.1). The zygomatic plate is short and not as well developed as in the genus *Tatera*.

No. 185

## *Desmodillus auricularis* (A. Smith, 1834)

## Short-tailed gerbil
## Kortstertnagmuis

Plate 14

### Colloquial Name
They have shorter tails than other members of the Subfamily Gerbillinae.
Alternative name: Namaqua gerbil.

### Taxonomic Notes
No subspecies are recognised (see **Description**).

### Description
Short-tailed gerbils have a total length of about 200 mm and a mass of about 53,0 g (Table 185.1). Hairs have flattened chevron scale across width (Keogh, 1985). Where large series are available from the same locality, taken about the same time, it is seen that there is a wide variation in colour, except in the under parts which are always pure white. From Botswana, Smithers (1971) recorded a series of individuals that were brownish-buff, cinnamon-buff, grey-brown, and others with the rump and hindquarters grey-brown, the anterior parts lighter in colour, the upper parts tinged cinnamon. All these animals were taken in the same locality and on the same date. As the subspecies that have been described have been erected predominantly on colour, which is clearly variable, Misonne (1974) did not recognise any of them as valid.

The characteristic features of the species are the distinctive white patches behind the ears and the short length of the tail, which in series varies with locality, but is short compared with all other Gerbillinae, being only about 75% to 80% of the length of the head and body. The tail is the same colour as the upper parts of the body or slightly lighter; in the darker coloured specimens it is broadly dark-tipped.

### Skull
A characteristic feature of the skull is the greatly enlarged ear bullae, which show on top of the skull when it is viewed from above (Fig. 185.1). The upper molars are small; the first upper molar has three transverse laminae, the second two and the third only one. The middle lamina in the first upper molar is divided into two circular patterns of enamel. The incisor teeth are shallowly grooved.

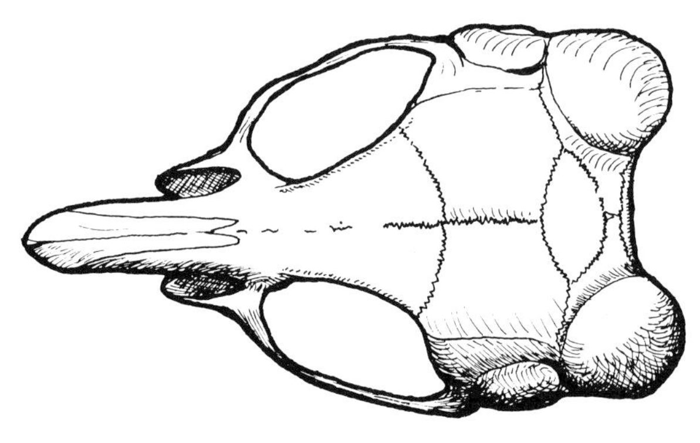

Fig. 185.1. Skull, dorsal view: *D. auricularis* to show enlarged ear bullae.

### Table 185.1
Measurements (mm) and mass (g) of short-tailed gerbils, *D. auricularis*, from southern Botswana (Smithers, 1971)

| | Males | | | Females | | |
|---|---|---|---|---|---|---|
| | $\bar{x}$ | n | Range | $\bar{x}$ | n | Range |
| TL | 200 | 18 | 186–221 | 204 | 19 | 190–214 |
| (HB | 110) | | | (113) | | |
| T | 90 | 18 | 84–99 | 91 | 19 | 81–100 |
| Hf c/u | 27 | 18 | 25–28 | 27 | 19 | 26–28 |
| E | 12 | 18 | 11–13 | 12 | 19 | 11–13 |
| Mass | 53,3 | 18 | 39,0–70,0 | 51,3 | 19 | 40,0–60,0 |

### Distribution
*Southern African Subregion*
This species is confined in its distribution to within the limits of the Subregion. They are distributed widely in **Namibia**, except in the northeast. In **Botswana** they occur north to about 20°S, being absent from the northern and parts of the eastern sector of the country. They occur in the southwestern parts of the **Transvaal** and widely in the **Cape**

**Province**, except in the southwestern and southern coastal areas and in the eastern parts of the province.

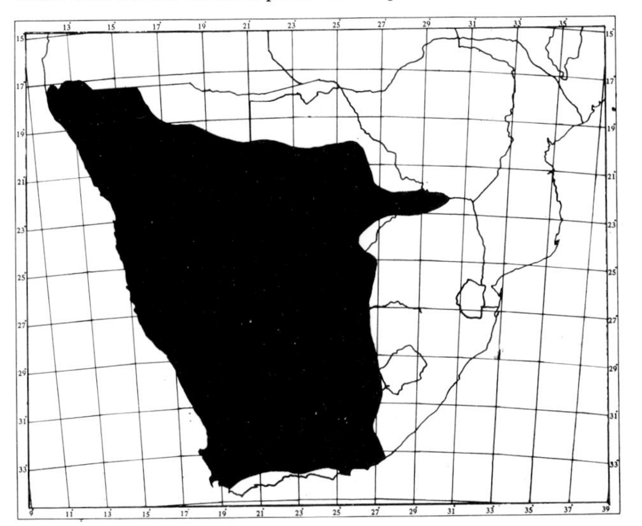

#### Habitat

Unlike other members of the Subfamily Gerbillinae, they tend to occur on hard ground with some cover of grass or karroid bush. In the southern parts of the Kalahari they are associated particularly with hard calcareous ground on the fringes of pans or on calcareous pans with some low cover of grass or karroid bush (Smithers, 1971).

#### Habits

They are nocturnal and terrestrial. The entrances to the burrows, which have a small ramp of loose soil at the lip, may open at the base of a clump of tussock grass or a low bush overhung by the vegetation, although they are also found in completely open ground. Another type of entrance to the burrow system is almost vertical to the surface and, as these have no ramp of loose soil, it appears that they are opened up from inside. Nel (1967) found that they excavate complicated and extensive burrow systems, the entrances to which are 53 mm in diameter, the burrow sloping steeply down and to an average depth of 300–600 mm. Rautenbach (1978) noted that there are well defined pathways between the burrow entrances. Blind alleys and storage chambers are common features. They do not have latrine chambers and the faeces are deposited at random throughout the system. Nel (1975) suggested that they may be an asocial species.

*D. auricularis* are very independent of free water intake, which could explain their aseasonal breeding habits (Christian, 1979) and Buffenstein, Campbell & Jarvis (1985) found that they do not lose weight on a diet of air-dried seed when deprived of water. They have very good renal concentrating abilities (Christian, 1978; Buffenstein *et al.*, 1985) and can produce urine concentrations as high as 5,5 $mOsm.kg^{-1}$ Wb (Buffenstein *et al.*, 1985). They also have remarkable thermoregulatory abilities and are able to maintain normal body temperatures of about 36 °C at ambient temperatures between 34 °C and -5 °C (Grobler, pers. comm.).

#### Food

They are predominantly granivorous and *dubbeltjie* seeds, *Tribulus terrestris*, are a common item in their diet (Nel, 1967). However, Kerley (1989) collected a single specimen from the Karoo whose stomach contained mostly green plant material, indicating a more omnivorous diet than previously thought. They have a simple stomach and caecum and fine villi lining the caecum may be concerned with water reabsorption (Perrin & Curtis, 1979). Judging from the accumulations of seed cases, calyxes of grass seed, husks of larger seeds, and the discarded stems of grass that have been stripped of seed, at least some of the food is carried back to the vicinity of a burrow entrance to be eaten or stored within. Similar accumulations are found inside the burrows, sometimes stored in blind tunnels, and non-sleeping chambers in preference to sleeping chambers (Christian *et al.*, 1977). No sexual differences were found in seed caching which is in contrast to many previous studies of small mammals which larder hoard.

#### Reproduction

Under favourable conditions they breed throughout the year, the average number of foetuses being 3,9 (range 1–7; n=13). They have a gestation period of 21 days and the mean mass at birth is 4,4 g (n=19). The white spots behind the ears become noticeable and they are covered with hair on day five, by day nine proper pelage covers the whole body, and their eyes open on day 10. No nipple-clinging occurs. The young start eating solid food on day 18 and appear to be fully weaned at day 21 (Keogh, 1973).

## Genus *Gerbillurus* Shortridge, 1942

The soles of the hind feet in members of this genus are covered with hair, the narrow central part naked. They are all small, with *Gerbillurus setzeri*, the largest, having a total length of about 230 mm. Two of the four species comprising the genus, *G. tytonis* and *G. setzeri*, to date have a restricted distributional range in the Namib Desert. On the other hand, *G. vallinus* and *G. paeba* are more widespread within the South West Arid Zone. All are nocturnal, with a preference for habitats with sandy substrates, their hairy feet being an adaptation to life on sandy ground.

Members of the genus have slender rostra which taper evenly forward; slender, grooved upper incisor teeth, in which the enamel layer on their anterior faces is yellow in colour, and molar teeth that tend to be laminate (Fig. 188.1).

The females have one pair of pectoral and two pairs of inguinal mammae.

Key to the species after Meester *et al.* (1986)

1. Bullae normally inflated, not extending behind occiput, up to *c.* 9 mm long; tail about 20 percent longer than head and body, tip slightly or moderately tufted; karyotype 2n=36, AA=68
   ... *paeba*

   Bullae more inflated, extending behind occiput, more than 9 mm long; tail with tip tasselled, normally about 40 percent longer than head and body (except in *setzeri*, which is distinguished from *paeba* by its large size, with head and body >100 mm, hind foot 30–35 mm, occipitonasal length 29,5–32,6 mm)
   ... 2

2. Bullae much inflated, *c.* 10–12 mm long; posterior palatal foramen long, almost as long as the molar toothrow
   ... 3

   Bullae less inflated, *c.* 9–10 mm long; posterior palatal foramen very short; occurs only in the Namib Naukluft National Park, Namibia
   ... *tytonis*

3. Tail longer, *c.* 40% longer than length of head and body
   ... *vallinus*

   Tail shorter, *c.* 20% longer than length of head and body
   ... *setzeri*

No. 186

## *Gerbillurus paeba* (A. Smith, 1836)

### Hairy-footed gerbil
### Haarpootnagmuis

Plate 14

#### Colloquial Name

All members of this genus that occur in the Subregion have hair on the soles of their feet.

*Gerbille* is French for a small mouse, the suffix *-urus* denotes belonging to. The specific name *paeba* is the Tswana name for a mouse.

### Taxonomic Notes

Meester *et al.* (1986) recognised four subspecies: *G. p. paeba* from the Cape Province to southwestern Angola; *G. p. exilis* (Shortridge & Carter, 1938) which has a restricted distribution from the Sundays River mouth to Port Elizabeth in the eastern Cape Province; *G. p. coombsi* (Roberts, 1929) from the Soutpansberg, northern Transvaal, and *G. p. infernus* (Lundholm, 1955) from the type locality Rocky Point, Skeleton Coast, Namibia.

### Description

Hairy-footed gerbils show no sexual dimorphism. In series both sexes have a mean head and body length of about 90 mm, with tails of 110 mm and a mass of about 27,0 g (Table 186.1).

They have fairly broad hairs, with a single chevron scale covering the width; scales are closely packed and hairs have a wide shallow groove (Fig. XXIII.3) (Keogh, 1985). Geographically and within populations there is considerable variation in the colour of the upper parts of the body, from reddish-orange to a greyish-red. The under parts, however, are invariably pure white. The tail is the same colour as the upper parts; in greyer specimens it is darker along the top.

The upper incisor teeth are distinctly grooved and orange in colour, the lower incisors ungrooved. The ear bullae are inflated, although not to the extent seen in *G. vallinus*.

### Table 186.1

Measurements (mm) and mass (g) of hairy-footed gerbils, *G. paeba*, from southwestern Botswana (Smithers, 1971)

| | Males | | | Females | | |
|---|---|---|---|---|---|---|
| | $\bar{x}$ | n | Range | $\bar{x}$ | n | Range |
| TL | 210 | 20 | 187–230 | 209 | 20 | 197–220 |
| (HB | 97) | | | (96) | | |
| T | 113 | 20 | 102–125 | 113 | 20 | 104–121 |
| Hf c/u | 27 | 20 | 26–29 | 27 | 20 | 26–28 |
| E | 17 | 20 | 17–19 | 17 | 21 | 16–18 |
| Mass | 25,6 | 20 | 21,0–37,0 | 25,2 | 21 | 20,0–30,0 |

### Distribution

*South of the Sahara, excluding the Southern African Subregion*

They occur in southwestern **Angola**.

*Southern African Subregion*

They occur widely throughout **Namibia**, except in the extreme northeastern parts of the country; widely throughout **Botswana**, except in parts of the northern and eastern areas; marginally in the western and southeastern parts of **Zimbabwe**; in the western and northern parts of the **Transvaal**, extending eastwards into the western parts of **Mozambique**, south of the Zambezi River. They occur in the southwestern **Orange Free State** and widely in the **Cape Province**, except in the northeast and eastern parts of the province and in the forested areas on the south coast.

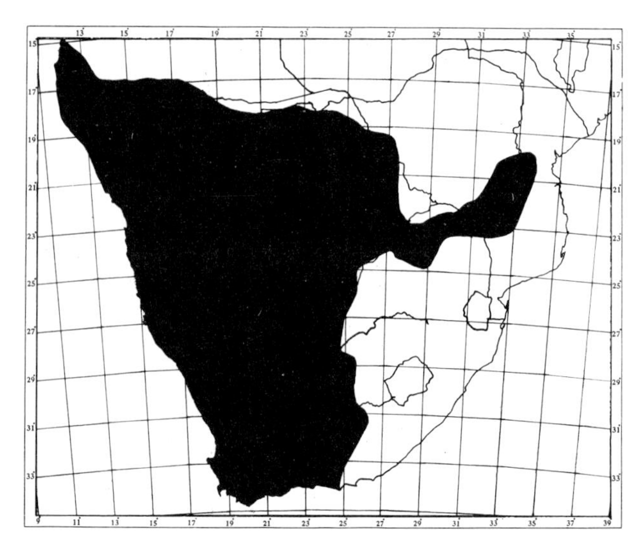

### Habitat

These gerbils are associated with the South West Arid Zone, only extending marginally into the southern savanna grasslands and the Cape Macchia. Throughout their distributional range they prefer sandy soil or sandy alluvium with a grass, scrub or light woodland cover in areas with a mean annual rainfall of 100 mm to 600 mm. They are very common on the Kalahari sand, particularly on dune slopes and crests, but are absent or scarce on calcrete riverbanks or pans where fine soil predominates (Nel & Rautenbach, 1975). In the northeastern sector of Botswana they do not occur on the more consolidated soils associated with mopane woodland. Their occurrence in northwestern Zimbabwe is within the eastwards extension of the Kalahari sand, and in southeastern Zimbabwe and adjacent areas of Mozambique within the areas of Mozambique sands. Further north in Mozambique they occur on the sandy alluvium of the Bubye River (Smithers, 1983).

### Habits

They are nocturnal, terrestrial and live in simple burrows, most of which have a single entrance, leading to a blind-ending tube occasionally broadened. In the Namib Desert, burrow temperatures remain constant at 22,9–24,4 °C, while surface temperatures range from 15,8–28,4 °C over 24 hours (Downs & Perrin, 1989). Burrows in use have a ramp of loose soil at the entrance, similar to those of the bushveld gerbil, *Tatera leucogaster*, but the diameter of the opening is smaller—30–40 mm in diameter. Usually the entrances are located at the base of perennial vegetation (such as *Acanthosicyos horrida*, *Stipagrostis sabulicola* and *Trianthema hereroensis*) and the burrows are up to 220 mm below the ground (de Graaff & Nel, 1965). In the Namib Desert they will exploit any possibility when burrowing, but Seely (1977) found that unconsolidated interdune valleys can be colonized successfully only under special conditions. However, sand patches can be solidified by gemsbok (*Oryx gazella*) urine, and in one sandy interdune valley, of 134 urine patches, 79% were used for gerbil burrow entrances. In the Sundays River area of the southern Cape Province, Ascaray (1986) noted the presence of two types of burrows: the first being a complex excavation including nesting and stored food chambers, and the second being a simple excavation used as a temporary safe refuge. In captivity, *G. paeba* will survive conditions of water deprivation on a diet of air-dried seeds indefinitely (Buffenstein, pers. comm.) and will increase evaporative water loss in the short term by salivation and panting (Buffenstein, 1984), but the latter would probably be less pronounced in the burrow.

Stutterheim & Skinner (1973) found that captive gerbils sleep during the day, either lying on their sides or sitting on their hind legs, tucking their heads under their bodies and curling their tails around their feet. Stretching was observed at the beginning of the period of activity. Scratching, face-washing, licking and tail-cleaning are indulged in regularly, as well as social grooming in which one individual lies down and the other stands over and grooms it. If provided with dry, loose sand they regularly sandbathe and after entering the nesting box to sleep, the entrance is blocked up with sand. Only the females collect and transport material for the construction of the nests which are open, cup-shaped structures.

### Food

Their diet consists of seeds, including those of the raisin bush, *Grewia* spp, and the fallen pods of thorn trees, *Acacia* spp, as well as insects. In the coastal Namib Desert, *Zygophyllum stapfi* fruit heads and seeds as well as twigs and chewed grass were found in burrows (Downs & Perrin, 1989). In the coastal area of the southern Cape Province, Ascaray (1986) has shown that, during the summer months, the principal foods were the seeds of *Arctotheca populifolia*, *Gazania rigens* and *Senecio inaequidens*, as well as insects, and during the winter the seeds and stems of these plants. In the Karoo, Kerley (1989) demonstrated that foliage consumption was highest in winter, but limited for the remainder of the year, while seeds dominated the diet during summer and autumn, and insects during the spring. Insects eaten included grasshoppers, beetles, earwigs and stink and assassin bugs, and Kerley (1989) suggested that the consumption of insects was related to their relative abundance.

### Reproduction

The spread of gravid females in a sample of over 300 specimens from Botswana indicates that young are born throughout the year. There is no clear sign of a peak in breeding at any time, the average number of foetuses per female in the wild being 3,7 (range 2–5; n=39) (Smithers, 1971). In captivity mean litter size was 4,6 (n=7) (Dempster & Perrin, 1989a).

Stutterheim & Skinner (1973) noted that a female in oestrus is very active, running up and down with her tail lifted off the ground, followed by the male who tests her condition by sniffing her genital region. Urination by a female in oestrus induces the male to smell the spot when he then becomes highly excited. Using vaginal smears Dempster & Perrin (1989b) suggested the oestrous cycle is 6,8 ± 1,7 days, and the gestation period is given by Ascaray (1986) as 21 days. A few days before parturition the female has an increased tendency to nest-build, covering the outside of the breeding box with sand. After the birth of the young the female becomes aggressive towards the male and remains in the nest, leaving it only to eat, drink, urinate and defecate. She closes the entrance with nesting material on leaving and when she returns, she broods the young with her hind legs widely spaced and forepaws stretched over the pups until they are 28–30 days old. She also grooms the young frequently, holding them in her forepaws when licking and nibbling them, and licking the anogenital region which stimulates urination and defecation (Dempster & Perrin, 1989a). Hair proliferation begins at 8–10 days and the whole body is covered with fur at 13–15 days. The young leave the nest for the first time on the 19th day when they are fully weaned (Stutterheim & Skinner, 1973).

No. 187

## *Gerbillurus tytonis* (Bauer & Niethammer, 1960)

## Dune hairy-footed gerbil
## Duinehaarpootnagmuis

### Colloquial Name

Dune refers to the association of this species with shifting sand dunes south of the Kuiseb River in Namibia, where specimens have been taken. The specific name *tytonis* has its origin from the fact that the species was first known from skulls found in the casts of the barn owl, *Tyto alba*.

### Taxonomic Notes

At first thought to be a subspecies of *G. vallinus*, they are accepted as a valid species (Schlitter, 1973).

### Description

Information on measurements and mass is only available for a small series of specimens, which shows that the males have a total length of about 220 mm, the females 230 mm, with a mean mass of about 27,6 g and 30,6 g respectively (Table 187.1).

The upper parts of the body are rich reddish-brown in colour, the under parts pure white. There is a sharp line of demarcation between the two colours, the white of the under parts extending well up the flanks. They have small white spots just above the eyes and behind the ears, and the hands and feet are white. The tail is the same colour as the upper parts of the body on the top, whiter underneath, with grey hairs on the tip. The ears are cinnamon-buff in colour.

The tail is proportionately longer in this species than in *G. paeba*, being approximately 120% of the length of the head and body, compared with *G. paeba* at about 115%.

The upper incisor teeth are grooved, the posterior palatal foramina noticeably shorter and the ear bullae smaller than in *G. vallinus*.

**Table 187.1**

Measurements (mm) and mass (g) of dune hairy-footed gerbils, *G. tytonis*, from the Namib Desert, Namibia (de Graaff, 1981)

| | Males | | | Females | | |
|---|---|---|---|---|---|---|
| | $\bar{x}$ | n | Range | $\bar{x}$ | n | Range |
| (TL | 220) | | | (229) | | |
| HB | 99 | 5 | 90–108 | 102 | 6 | 90–111 |
| T | 121 | 6 | 118–126 | 127 | 5 | 122–135 |
| Hf c/u | 317 | 7 | 27–33 | 31 | 8 | 30–33 |
| E | 14 | 7 | 12–15 | 14 | 7 | 13–16 |
| Mass | 27,6 | 5 | 24,0–30,0 | 30,6 | 5 | 29,0–33,0 |

### Distribution

*Southern African Subregion*

They are confined to a narrow sector of the high dune system from the Kuiseb River in the Namib-Naukluft National Park, **Namibia**, southwards to about 26 °S.

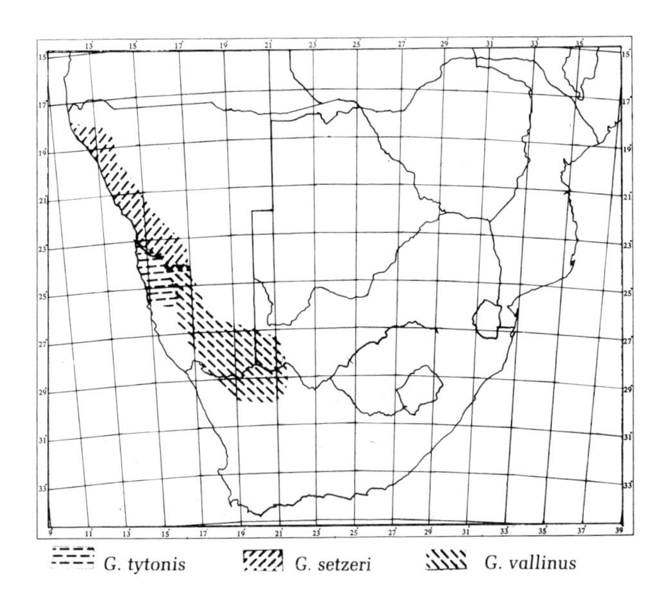


### Habitat

They occur in hot dry areas, on shifting red sand dunes south of the Kuiseb River, Namibia, with a mean annual temperature above 18 °C (Downs & Perrin, 1989). Most *G. tytonis* burrows occur on sand mounds stabilized by vegetation, either *Trianthema hereroensis* or *Stipagrostis sabulicola*. Most burrows are complex with a number of bends and more than one entrance, but deeper than those of *G. paeba*. However, at a depth of 200 mm burrow temperatures were higher at about 31 °C, while surface temperatures varied from 13–33 °C. In winter *G. paeba* co-exists on dune crests with *G. tytonis*, moving during the summer to the base of the dunes (Boyer, 1985).

### Habits

No information available.

### Food

*G. tytonis* burrows have been found to contain *Acanthosicyos horrida* seed husks, *Acacia erioloba* seeds, *Stipagrostis leutescens* stems and seed heads and exoskeleton remains of tenebrionid beetles (Downs & Perrin, 1989).

### Reproduction

From vaginal smears Dempster & Perrin (1989b) suggested an oestrous cycle of 6,2±1,2 days. Boyer (1985) noted that *G. tytonis* is a seasonal breeder, young being born during the summer months. Mean litter size is 4,4 (n=7) in captivity and cup-shaped nests are constructed of shredded grass or cotton waste (Dempster & Perrin, 1989a). They observed one birth, with the foetus being expelled while the female was in a quadrupedal posture. She then consumed the placenta and groomed the altricial neonate. Females suckle their pups in a position with their hind feet widely spaced and forepaws stretched over the young. They groom pups frequently, holding them in their forepaws while licking and nibbling them. In the anogenital region this activity stimulates urination and defecation and the mother will ingest both faeces and urine. *G. tytonis* neonates grow slower than *G. paeba*. Hair proliferation begins at 10–13 days and pups are fully furred at 16 days.

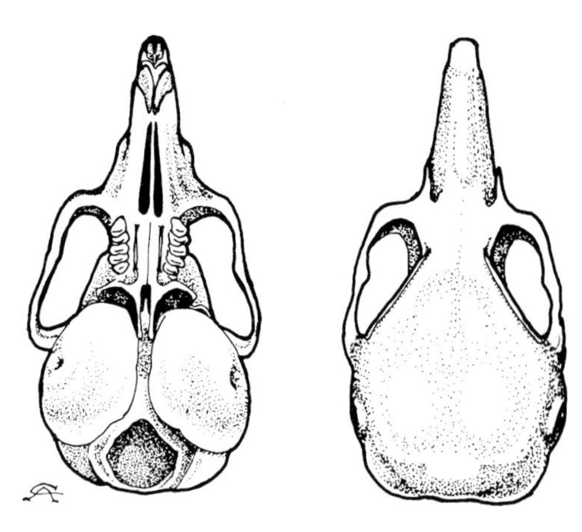

Fig. 188.1. Skull: *Gerbillurus vallinus*.

No. 188

## *Gerbillurus vallinus* (Thomas, 1918)

## Brush-tailed hairy-footed gerbil
## Borselsterthaarpootnagmuis

### Colloquial Name

So called from the tuft of long, dark grey hair on the end of the tail.

### Taxonomic Notes

Two subspecies have been described: *G. v. vallinus* from Kenhardt, Cape Province and the lower Orange River, and *G. v. seeheimi* Lundholm, 1955 from the Kuiseb River, Gobabeb area, in the Namib Desert, Namibia.

### Description

Judging from the few specimens for which measurements and mass have been recorded, males have a mean head and body length of about 80 mm, females 90 mm and a mean mass of 39,0 g and 31,5 g respectively (Table 188.1).

The upper parts of the body vary in colour from a reddish-brown to a dark greyish-brown; the under parts and forelimbs are white. The demarcation of the colour of the upper and under parts is very distinct, the white of the under parts rising high up on to the flanks between the fore and hind limbs. In the darker specimens the tail is dark on its upper surface, with a long tuft of dark grey hair at the tip. In some specimens these dark areas are black. The tail is very long, about 40% longer than the length of the head and body. The supraorbital white marking varies in intensity, in some individuals it is obvious, in others barely discernible. In most individuals there is a white or off-white patch at the base and behind the ears.

### Skull

In this species and in *G. setzeri* the ear bullae are enormously inflated and have a total length of between 10 mm and 12 mm. The posterior section of the bullae is not developed to the same extent as seen in the short-tailed gerbil, *Desmodillus auricularis*, but nevertheless shows when the skull is viewed from above, as two slight swellings, one on either side at the back of the braincase. The rostrum is slender and tapers evenly forward. The anterior and posterior palatal foraminae are elongated, the latter nearly the same length as the length of the row of cheekteeth (Fig. 188.1).

**Table 188.1**

Measurements (mm) and mass (g) of brush-tailed hairy-footed gerbils, *G. vallinus*, from Namibia and the northwestern Cape Province (de Graaff, 1981)

| | Males | | | Females | | |
|---|---|---|---|---|---|---|
| | $\bar{x}$ | n | Range | $\bar{x}$ | n | Range |
| (TL | 201) | | | (202) | | |
| HB | 81 | 8 | 58–95 | 91 | 8 | 89–109 |
| T | 120 | 8 | 80–145 | 111 | 8 | 70–131 |
| Hf c/u | 29 | 8 | 26–33 | 31 | 8 | 28–34 |
| E | 14 | 8 | 12–15 | — | — | — |
| Mass | 39,0 | 3 | 37,0–43,0 | 31,5 | 4 | 30,0–34,0 |

### Distribution

*Southern African Subregion*

They occur in the central part of the Namib Desert in **Namibia** as far south as Swakopmund and inland in the Brukaros-Karas Mountains, southeastwards to the Orange River and Kenhardt in the northwestern **Cape Province**.

Distribution map—see No. 187 *G. tytonis* Distribution

### Habitat

They are confined to the western sector of the South West Arid Zone, for the greater part to desert, particularly the gravel flats, and within the area of mean annual rainfall of under 150 mm. The range in surface temperature where they occur was greater (13,6–39,6 °C) than on the dunes, but the mean annual temperature is less than 18 °C.

### Habits

They are gregarious, terrestrial and nocturnal. This gerbil lives in burrows in sandy soils which penetrate to a depth of 1,5 m (Roberts, 1951). If these are excavated the gerbil closes the burrow behind it as it moves on, but if followed it may break surface and seek refuge in another set of burrows (Roberts, 1951). Downs & Perrin (1989) found burrows where mounds had formed under *Phaeoptilum spinosum* bushes; 75% of the burrows were complex with several side branches and a number of bends. At 200 mm burrow temperature was 25,5 °C.

### Food

Within burrows at Kenhardt, Downs & Perrin (1989) found insect exoskeletons, monocotyledon leaves and seeds.

### Reproduction

Roberts (1951) recorded that a female with five young was found in a chamber in the burrow system. The chamber was lined with dry vegetable debris.

No. 189

## *Gerbillurus setzeri* (Schlitter, 1973)

## Setzer's hairy-footed gerbil
## Setzer se haarpootnagmuis

### Colloquial Name

Named after Dr H.W. Setzer, formerly Curator of Mammals at the United States National Museum, who was interested particularly in desert rodents.

### Taxonomic Notes

This species is a member of the *vallinus* group of gerbils, with affinities both to *G. vallinus* and *G. tytonis*.

### Description

Too few records of measurements and mass are available to present a meaningful table but, from those currently available, males and females have a total length of about 230 mm; the mass of the males is about 38,0 g, the females 39,0g (Table 189.1). Schlitter (1973) gave the mean measurements (n=43) as TL 233, T 127, Hf c/u 32, E 14.

The upper parts of the body are light pinkish-cinnamon, with a slight mixture of grey hairs in some individuals. The areas around the mouth, the dorsal surface of the limbs and the under parts are white; the white supraorbital and post-auricular spots are clearly defined. The colours of the upper and under parts are sharply demarcated, the white of the under parts extending high up on to the flanks. The upper parts of the tail are the same colour as the upper parts of the body, the distal one-third tinged grey, with a tuft of long hair towards the tip, which is tinged grey. The under parts are white for the whole length of the tail and the hair on the inside of the ears is white.

The skull is large, the anterior palatal foraminae wide and short, the posterior pair long. The ear bullae are large and inflated; the mastoidal section projects beyond the occiput (Schlitter, 1973).

### Table 189.1

Measurements (mm) and mass (g) of Setzer's hairy-footed gerbils, *G. setzeri*, from Namibia (de Graaff, 1981)

| | Males | | | Females | | |
|---|---|---|---|---|---|---|
| | $\bar{x}$ | n | Range | $\bar{x}$ | n | Range |
| (TL | 228) | | | (234) | | |
| HB | 105 | 1 | — | 110 | 3 | 104–115 |
| T | 123 | 1 | — | 124 | 3 | 117–128 |
| Hf c/u | 32 | 1 | — | 32 | 3 | 32–33 |
| E | 14 | 1 | — | 13 | 3 | 9–17 |
| Mass | — | — | — | 38,6 | 3 | 33,0–48,0 |

### Distribution

*South of the Sahara, excluding the Southern African Subregion*

They occur in the Iona National Park in the extreme north-western Namib Desert in **Angola**.

*Southern African Subregion*

In **Namibia** the southern limits appear to be about the Kuiseb River and a little beyond in the Namib-Naukluft National Park, their distribution extending northwards, coastally, to the Cunene River.

Distribution map—see No. 187 *G. tytonis* Distribution

### Habitat

They are restricted to the feldspar and quartz gravel plains in the Namib Desert and in the adjacent red sand dunes where they occur on the same ground as *G. tytonis* and *G. paeba*.

Circles of vegetation in the Namib Desert were found to be 5,3 ± 1,5 m (S.D.) in diameter and mean nearest neighbour distance 11,2 ± 3,4 m (S.D.) and have been ascribed to burrowing activities of *G. setzeri* in the gravel plains of the Namib Desert (Cox, 1987). Their formation bears a close relationship to the calcareous gypsum soils with their underlying calcrete horizon. The gerbils mine the soil and deposit it in surface heaps tending to be oriented outward from the colony centre. The mined soils are porous and, together with the tunnels these favour water infiltration during rainy periods. Eventually the tunnels collapse forming a depression in which water accumulates for long periods and encourages colonisation by plants.

### Habits

The burrows of *G. setzeri* are found in dry river washes where the surface soil is loose and gravelly, below this it is compact, 90% of burrows being complex with several branches and bends and more than one opening. Downs & Perrin (1989) reported that the temperature at 200 mm was 27–29 °C, whilst the daily surface temperature ranged between 10–40 °C.

### Food

Downs & Perrin (1989) found remains of *Tetragonia reduplicata* (leaves, flower heads and dry fruit), *Blepharis grossa* (seeds, bracts, twigs and husks), *Acacia reficiens* (leaves, twigs and seedpods), sheaths of bulbs and insect elytras in excavated burrows.

### Reproduction

No information available.

## Genus *Tatera* Lataste, 1882

Davis (1975a) divided the species of this genus into two groups on the basis of the characters set out in the accompanying key. In doing so he noted that the characters used in distinguishing between the species unfortunately overlap to some extent. It is therefore necessary to have a small series at hand in order to be quite sure of the species involved. In the Subregion *T. leucogaster* can be picked out usually more easily than some of the other species as it has a distinct dark line down the upper surface of the tail, which is longer than the length of the head and body. Other characters include the dark-coloured under parts of the hind feet and the relatively narrow, lightly built molar teeth. In *T. brantsii* the pelage is softer and fluffier than in *T. leucogaster* and the tail is broadly white-tipped. The upper surface, proximally, has a band of colour similar to the colour of the upper body parts, not a dark band as in *T. leucogaster*, and they have broader molar teeth. *T. inclusa* is a very dark-coloured gerbil which only occurs in the extreme northeastern parts of the Subregion, in eastern Zimbabwe and northwestern Mozambique. *T. afra* has soft fluffy hair, long ears and a tail which is coloured evenly like the body throughout its length on the upper surface. They only occur in the extreme southwestern parts of the Cape Province.

All the members of the genus are nocturnal and terrestrial and, in suitable habitat, are among our commoner murids. They are of particular importance as they are the principal reservoir of the bacillus of plague, *Yersinia pestis*. Under normal conditions there is little contact between man and gerbils, as they are veld murids and normally do not become commensal with man. However, the disease is transmitted from them, through the intermediary of certain fleas, to other murids, in particular to multimammate mice, *Mastomys* spp, which are a major vector of this disease (see Text No. 174, *M. natalensis*).

In the Southern African Subregion the *afra* group is represented by *T. afra*, *T. brantsii* and *T. inclusa*; the *robusta* group by *T. leucogaster*. All the members have grooved upper incisor teeth.

Key to the species (Davis, 1975a)

1. Colour brighter, texture of fur sleek, silky; line of demarcation between flanks and belly sharp; belly pure white; mammary formula 2–2=8; tail longer than length of head and body, well-haired especially towards tip, never white-tipped; pads of hind feet normally dark; feet narrower; upper incisors grooved, moderately to strongly opisthodont; molars relatively narrow, lightly built (*robusta* group)

   . . . *leucogaster*

   Colour duller, texture of fur fluffy or somewhat harsh; line of demarcation between flanks and belly often indistinct; belly white, buffy or grey; mammary formula 1–2=6 or 2–2=8; tail longer, about equal to or shorter than length of head and body, fairly evenly haired throughout, with short hairs, sometimes white-tipped; pads of hind feet normally more light-coloured, feet broader; upper incisors grooved or plain, moderately opisthodont to orthodont; molars relatively broad, more heavily built (*afra* group)

   . . . 2

2. Ears long (averaging *c.* 24 mm); belly pure white; tail evenly coloured to tip; mammary formula 2–2=8; confined to western Cape Province

   . . . *afra*

   Ears shorter, averaging less than 24 mm; belly white, grey-buffy or white with greyish chest patch; tail evenly coloured above, paler below, but may be white-tipped; mammary formula 1–2=6 or 2–2=8

   . . . 3

3. Anterior palatal foramina reaching and normally extending beyond anterior margin of molar alveoli, fair proportion of individuals in any population with white-tipped tails

   . . . *brantsii*

   Anterior palatal foramina normally not extending to anterior margin of molar alveoli; tail very rarely white-tipped

   . . . *inclusa*

No. 190

## *Tatera leucogaster* (Peters, 1852)

## Bushveld gerbil
## Bosveldse nagmuis

Plate 14

### Colloquial Name

They are so called as they are commonly associated with savanna grassland and woodland.

### Taxonomic Notes

At least 17 subspecies have been described from the Subregion. There appears to be little discontinuity in distribution, and populations appear to integrate evenly throughout their range, making the determination of valid subspecies impossible (Davis, 1975a).

### Description

There is no sexual dimorphism in bushveld gerbils. Both sexes have a head and body length of about 130 mm, a tail slightly longer, about 150 mm, and a mass of about 70,0 g (Table 190.1).

The hairs are broad and long, with typical large chevron scales in a mosaic pattern (Fig. XXIII.3) (Keogh, 1985). The colour varies geographically: those from the drier, western parts of their distributional range are paler than those from the eastern parts. Generally they are reddish-brown to orange-buffy on the upper parts and pure white on the chin, throat, and the remainder of their under parts, with white hands and feet. In some areas they are slightly darker on the rump. The sides of their muzzles are white and they have a white mark above and behind the eyes, the ears being dark brown. The upper part of the tail has a distinct dark band down its entire length, sometimes with a poorly developed tuft of hair at the tip. The under parts are white. The hind legs are much longer than the forelegs, giving them an appearance reminiscent of a small kangaroo.

The upper incisors are grooved, the lower ungrooved, the ear bullae well developed (Fig. 190.1).

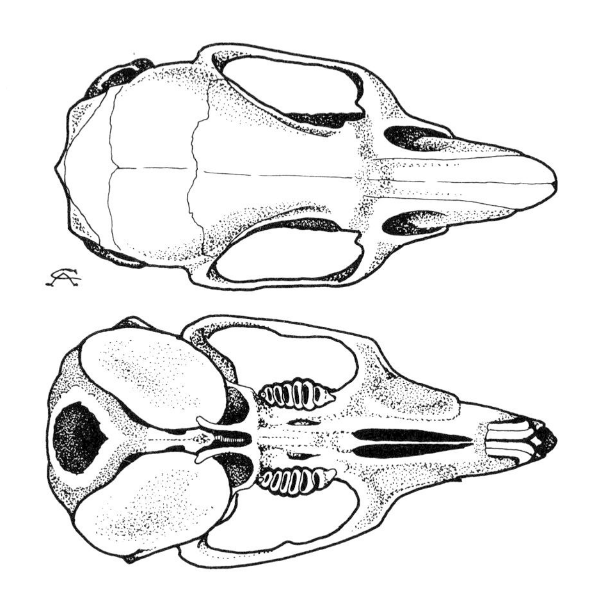

Fig. 190.1. Skull: *Tatera leucogaster*, showing grooved incisor teeth and well developed ear bullae.

**Table 190.1**

Measurements (mm) and mass (g) of bushveld gerbils, *T. leucogaster*, from the Transvaal (Rautenbach, 1978)

| | Males | | | Females | | |
|---|---|---|---|---|---|---|
| | $\bar{x}$ | n | Range | $\bar{x}$ | n | Range |
| TL | 276 | 482 | 210–321 | 278 | 541 | 225–330 |
| (HB | 128) | | | (129) | | |
| T | 148 | 493 | 121–173 | 149 | 531 | 120–175 |
| Hf c/u | 34 | 504 | 27–36 | 33 | 564 | 24–38 |
| E | 21 | 493 | 18–24 | 21 | 552 | 18–26 |
| Mass | 71,2 | 331 | 32,0–109,0 | 68,5 | 365 | 37,0–114,0 |

Comparison of these figures and others given by Smithers (1971) for Botswana, and Smithers & Wilson (1979) for Zimbabwe shows that at least between these three areas there is no noticeable difference in size and mass.

### Distribution

*South of the Sahara, excluding the Southern African Subregion*

This species occurs in southern **Angola; Zambia**; southern **Zaire**; southwestern **Tanzania; Malawi** and in **Mozambique**, north of the Zambezi River.

*Southern African Subregion*

They are distributed widely in northern and central **Namibia** and probably in parts of the southern sector of the country, although there are no records from this sector at the moment, except from the extreme south along the Orange River. They are common throughout **Botswana; Zimbabwe,** and **Mozambique**, south of the Zambezi River, extending eastwards into **Swaziland** and southwards into northeastern **Natal**. They are distributed widely in the **Tranvaal**, except in the southeast, and occur in the western and southern parts of the **Orange Free State** and in the **Cape Province** north of the Orange River.

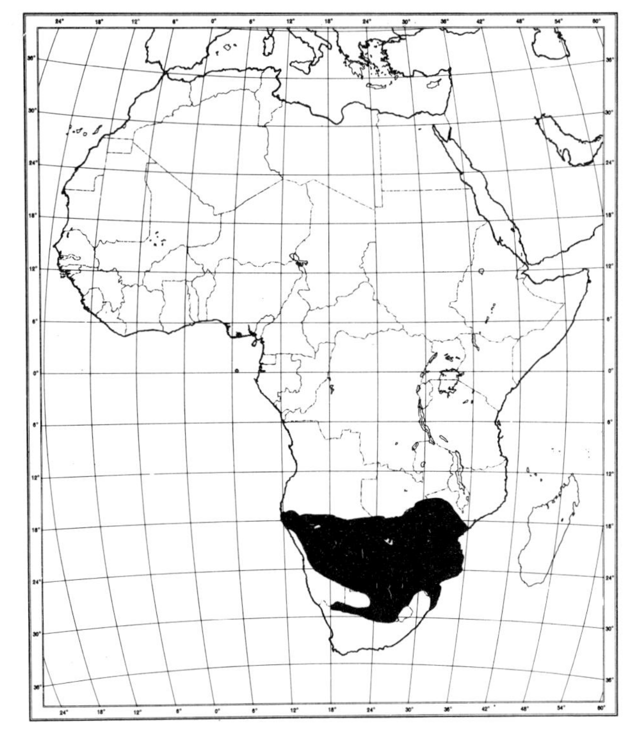

Southern African Subregion distribution only.

### Habitat

They are predominantly associated with light sandy soils or sandy alluvium, but are not confined entirely to this type of substrate as they have been taken on hard ground. They are absent from areas of heavy red clay soils, which may be due to their inability to excavate burrows in this substrate. Where they occur on hard ground, for example in mopane woodland, they use holes in termitaria or under tree roots and do not appear to excavate burrows for themselves. Apparently they are independent of any one type of vegetational association, as they have been taken in a wide variety of associations ranging from open grassland to savanna woodland. While they occur in northern Namibia in areas with a mean annual rainfall of less than 100 mm, they generally occur in areas of the Subregion with a mean annual rainfall of 250 mm and upwards and from sea level to over 1 600 m.

### Habits

They are nocturnal, terrestrial and they excavate burrows, about 40 mm to 45 mm in diameter in sandy soils, the entrances usually being at the base of small bushes or grass clumps. The burrows in use can be recognised by the fresh ramp of sand found at the entrances in the morning, on which their spoor may be seen. It appears that the burrows are cleaned up nightly. These are occupied by a pair, but warrens are found with many entrances which may interconnect underground. They have chambers lined with vegetable debris in which the gerbils presumably rest. In summer they may be parasitised by the blowfly *Cordylobia anthropophaga* (Korn & Braack, 1987).

### Food

Their gut morphology is typical of an omnivorous diet and there are no special adaptations. They are granivorous insectivores and Perrin & Swanepoel (1987), in a sample of 360 stomachs from the northern Transvaal, found they contained 41,4% insects, 26,4% seeds and 32,2% herbage, insects and seeds predominating in summer. In the Transvaal they show an annual cycle in weight, losing weight in winter when food is scarce (Korn, 1989).

### Reproduction

In Botswana, gravid females were taken in every month of the year, except September, with a peak late in the warm, wet summer months between February and March. The average number of foetuses was 4,5 (range 2–9; n=53) (Smithers, 1983). Rautenbach (1982) gave a summer breeding season for the Transvaal, with a litter size of 4,6 (range 3–7; n=21). In their study area, in the northern Transvaal, Perrin & Swanepoel (1987) also reported a distinct summer breeding season, with a bimodal peak in early and late summer closely related to rainfall, whilst the average number of foetuses was 4,4 (range 2–9; n=217). In Hwange National Park, Zimbabwe, Wilson (1975) gave the mean number of foetuses as 4,0 (range 2–7; n=2–8), with pregnancies in late summer and again during winter. The young are born altricial in grass-lined chambers within the burrow system.

---

No. 191

## *Tatera afra* (Gray, 1830)

## Cape gerbil
## Kaapse nagmuis

Plate 14

---

### Colloquial Name

They are associated particularly with the Cape Province, and are confined in their distribution to the southwestern sector.

### Taxonomic Notes

No subspecies are recognised.

### Description

Cape gerbils have a total length in males and females of about 300 mm, with a mean mass in males of 103,2 g and in females 91,0 g (Table 191.1). The fairly long, broad hairs have a chevron scale pattern (Fig. XXIII.3) (Keogh, 1985). The upper parts of the body, the flanks and outer surfaces of the limbs are reddish-orange or pale buffy, faintly grizzled with dark brown. The under parts are white and the line of demarcation between the colour of the upper and under parts is sharply defined. The individual hairs have grey bases tipped with the colour of the upper parts. The ears are a light flesh colour inside, brown outside and are long, measuring about 24 mm. The tail is the same colour as the upper parts or slightly lighter and is coloured evenly to the tip, lacking the dark band on the upper surface seen in the bushveld gerbil, *T. leucogaster*. The hind legs are much longer than the forelegs and the legs are white on the inside.

The upper incisor teeth are grooved on their front faces, the lower incisors plain; the molar teeth are broader and heavier than in *T. leucogaster*.

**Table 191.1**

Measurements (mm) and mass (g) of Cape gerbils, *T. afra*, from the Cape Province (de Graaff, 1981)

| | Males | | | Females | | |
|---|---|---|---|---|---|---|
| | x̄ | n | Range | x̄ | n | Range |
| (TL | 295) | | | (292) | | |
| HB | 147 | 21 | 130–157 | 136 | 23 | 124–152 |
| T | 148 | 21 | 141–175 | 156 | 23 | 133–168 |
| Hf c/u | 37 | 21 | 28–40 | 38 | 23 | 30–40 |
| E | 24 | 21 | 20–26 | 25 | 23 | 24–28 |
| Mass | 103,2 | 5 | 84,0–113,0 | 91,0 | 10 | 78,0–107,0 |

**Distribution**

*Southern African Subregion*

They are confined to within the limits of the Subregion, occurring in the Cape Macchia Zone in the southwestern **Cape Province**, from Niewoudtville in the west southwards to the Cape Peninsula and eastwards coastally to Herold's Bay, just east of Mossel Bay.

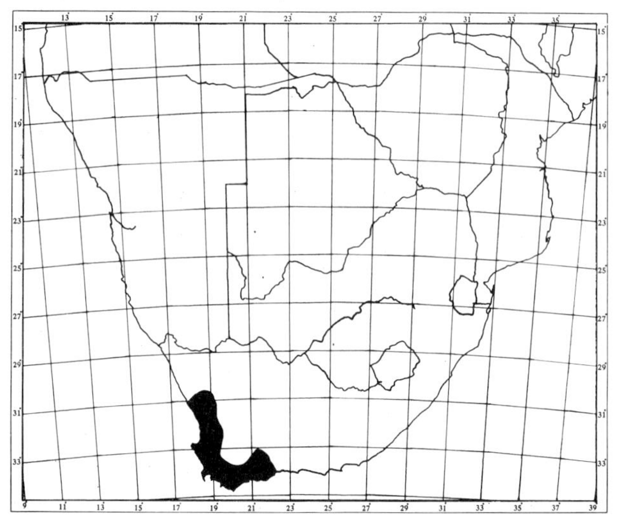

**Habitat**

They are confined to areas of loose, sandy soils or sandy alluvium and are common in cultivated lands.

**Habits**

They excavate extensive burrow systems in sandy soils. Adjacent burrow systems are often interconnected and have resting and breeding chambers, lined with soft vegetable debris. Like the bushveld gerbil, *T. leucogaster*, the entrances to these burrows are situated at the base of a clump of grass or in the shelter of a bush. Roberts (1951) noted some local movement, perhaps in response to depletion of food resources. When disturbed in their burrows, in common with other gerbils, they tend to move ahead of the disturbance, closing the burrows behind them.

**Food**

Roberts (1951) stated that they eat grass, bulbs and roots, as well as seeds.

**Reproduction**

*T. afra* breeds after the winter rains in the southwestern Cape Province (Measroch, 1954). The females usually have two pairs of pectoral and two pairs of abdominal mammae, but there is some variation.

---

No. 192

## *Tatera brantsii* (A. Smith, 1836)

## Highveld gerbil
## Hoëveldse nagmuis

---

**Colloquial Name**

They are associated with Highveld areas in a large part of their range, but are not confined to them.

**Taxonomic Notes**

A number of subspecies have been described, many of these synonymised by Davis (1975a) into three subspecies: *T. b. brantsii*, with synonyms *maccalinus, draco, milliaria* and *natalensis; T. b. griquae* Wroughton, 1906, with synonyms *perpallida, breyeri, namaquensis* and *joanae*; and *T. b. ruddi* Wroughton, 1906 with synonyms *tongensis* and *maputa*. Davis (1975a) stated that *T. b. namaquensis* (Shortridge & Carter, 1938) might eventually be shown to be a valid subspecies.

*T. b. brantsii*, which occurs in the eastern Cape Province, Lesotho and the Natal midlands, has buffy-grey patches on the chest and heavy molar teeth. *T. b. griquae* occurs in the Kalahari from the Orange River northwards to southern Angola and has pure white under parts and narrower molar teeth than *T. b. brantsii. T. b. ruddi* occurs from Richard's Bay northwards to southern Mozambique, and has buffy-grey under parts, relatively long tails and long hind feet. There is a wide range of intergradation between these three subspecies at the extremes of their distributional ranges, which at the moment are impossible to define adequately (Davis, 1975a).

**Description**

Highveld gerbils have a total length of about 270 mm, with tails slightly shorter or about equal to the length of the head and body, and a mass of about 80,0 g (Table 192.1). These measurements and mass and the description of the colour which follows, varies geographically, making it impossible to give a general description that fits the species throughout its wide distributional range. *T. brantsii* have long, broad hairs with a narrow base and a typical chevron pattern (Fig. XXIII.3) (Keogh, 1985). The colour of the upper parts varies from a pallid, light rufous-brown to a pale reddish colour, with a faint, uneven wash of brown. In central Botswana they are pallid, in the southwest distinctly reddish and in the southeast distinctly darker. The under parts may be pure white, as in *T. b. griquae*; buffy-grey as in *T. b. ruddi*, or may have buffy-grey patches on the chest as in *T. b. brantsii*.

Characters that are common throughout their distributional range are the soft, fluffy fur and the colour of the tail which, on the upper surface, is similar to the colour of the body or slightly darker for at least its proximal half, the remainder being white. It lacks the distinct dark line on the upper surface seen in *T. leucogaster*, and this and the white tip to the tail help to distinguish this species from *T. leucogaster*.

**Table 192.1**

Measurements (mm) and mass (g) of Highveld gerbils, *T. brantsii*, from the Transvaal (Rautenbach, 1978)

| | Males | | | Females | | |
|---|---|---|---|---|---|---|
| | x̄ | n | Range | x̄ | n | Range |
| TL | 273 | 114 | 202–315 | 282 | 123 | 200–350 |
| (HB | 133) | | | (136) | | |
| T | 140 | 114 | 103–174 | 146 | 123 | 104–186 |
| Hf c/u | 35 | 114 | 19–42 | 35 | 123 | 28–47 |
| E | 21 | 114 | 12–29 | 22 | 122 | 14–34 |
| Mass | 78,5 | 64 | 32,0–122,0 | 81,2 | 66 | 25,0–126,0 |

**Distribution**

*South of the Sahara, excluding the Southern African Subregion*

They are recorded as occurring marginally outside the Subregion in southern **Angola** and southwestern **Zambia**.

*Southern African Subregion*

They occur in the central and eastern parts of **Namibia**; throughout **Botswana** and marginally in western **Zimbabwe**. They are widespread in the **Transvaal**, except in the northern and eastern parts of the province; throughout the **Orange Free State**; in the northern and western parts of **Natal** and in

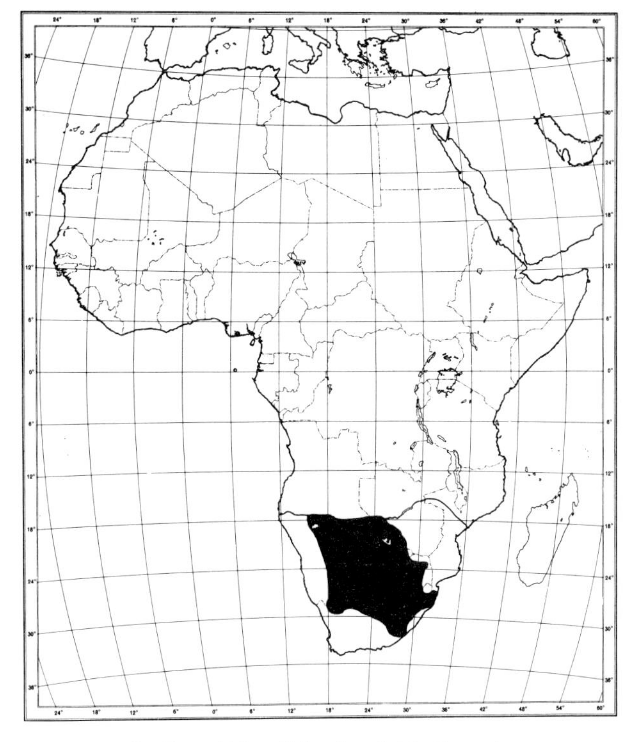

Southern African Subregion distribution only.

the northwestern, northern and eastern parts of the **Cape Province.**

## Habitat

They occur on sandy soils or sandy alluvium, with some cover of grass, scrub or open woodland. Normally they do not occur on heavy consolidated soils.

## Habits

Their habits are similar to those of the bushveld gerbil, *T. leucogaster*, with which, throughout a great part of their distributional range, they are sympatric. They can tolerate more arid conditions than the bushveld gerbil, occurring in areas where the mean annual rainfall is less than 200 mm. De Moor (1969) found that the home range of the males is 0,49 ha, the females 0,19 ha, but colony warrens may cover an area as great as 65–70 ha. Korn & Korn (1989) found that they have a significant effect on the habitat due to their habits of selective feeding and construction of soil mounds at burrow entrances. Within a recently vacated colony, total biomass of the standing crop of vegetation is drastically reduced. They found the climax grass *Eragrostis pallens* was reduced by 67% and together with *E. lehmanniana* (13%) and *Aristida* sp (6%) made up 86% of the total reduction of grass biomass. In contrast the biomass of dicotyledons increased from 16 g/m$^2$ to 28 g/m$^2$, with a resultant increase in plant diversity.

## Food

Adapted to an omnivorous diet, they have few trophic specialisations, and they eat grass, seeds, termites and small insects.

## Reproduction

Measroch (1954) recorded that in the Orange Free State, they breed throughout the year, except in the dry months, and, from a sample of 174 females, a similar situation exists in Botswana (Smithers, 1971), where the average number of foetuses was 3,3 (range 1–5; n=12). Measroch (1954) found that the gestation period is 22,5 days. The young are born in chambers in the burrows.

No. 193

# *Tatera inclusa* Thomas & Wroughton, 1908

## Gorongoza gerbil
## Gorongoza nagmuis

Plate 14

## Colloquial Name

They were described from material from the Gorongoza district of Mozambique, and originally were thought to be confined to a narrow sector in this district, but are now known to have a much wider distribution.

## Taxonomic Notes

Three subspecies have been described of which only one, *T. i. inclusa* Thomas & Wroughton, 1908, occurs in the Subregion.

## Description

This is a very large species, males having a total length of about 310 mm and a mean mass of 106,0 g, females about 330 mm, with a mean mass of 131,0 g (Smithers & Wilson, 1979) (Table 193.1). The upper parts of the body are darker in colour than any of the other species of *Tatera*, the flanks slightly lighter. Thomas & Wroughton (1908) described the colour as ochraceous-buff, washed with black, but the colour is very variable. In specimens from eastern Zimbabwe, the upper parts are very dark from the forehead to the base of the tail, the flanks dark ochraceous-buffy or reddish. These dark specimens have a black mark under the eyes which spreads out into the darker colour on the side of the muzzle. The under parts are white. The individual hairs on the back are dark slate at the base, with an annulation of ochraceous-buffy subterminally, and black tips. The ochraceous-buffy annulation is narrow or non-existent in the very dark specimens. The tail has a dark band along its upper surface, the under surface being white. The upper parts of the hands and feet are off-white. The upper incisor teeth are deeply grooved, the lower plain.

**Table 193.1**

Measurements (mm) and mass (g) of Gorongoza gerbils, *T. inclusa*, from eastern Zimbabwe (Smithers & Wilson, 1979)

| | Males | | | Females | | |
|---|---|---|---|---|---|---|
| | $\bar{x}$ | n | Range | $\bar{x}$ | n | Range |
| TL | 312 | 8 | 287–331 | 333 | 5 | 306–352 |
| (HB | 156) | | | (156) | | |
| T | 156 | 8 | 135–175 | 177 | 5 | 158–191 |
| Hf c/u | 42 | 8 | 40–44 | 40 | 5 | 39–43 |
| E | 25 | 8 | 23–26 | 25 | 5 | 21–29 |
| Mass | 106,0 | 8 | 99,0–122,0 | 131,0 | 5 | 113,0–154,0 |

## Distribution

*South of the Sahara, excluding the Southern African Subregion*

They occur in **Mozambique**, north of the Zambezi River, and in **Tanzania**.

*Southern African Subregion*

They are confined to the northeastern parts of the Subregion where they occur in the western Vila Pery and central Beira districts of **Mozambique** and narrowly into **Zimbabwe** in the eastern parts of the country.

## Habitat

In the Subregion they occur in the same type of habitat as the bushveld gerbil, *T. leucogaster*, but are confined to areas with a mean annual rainfall of not less than 800 mm, whilst

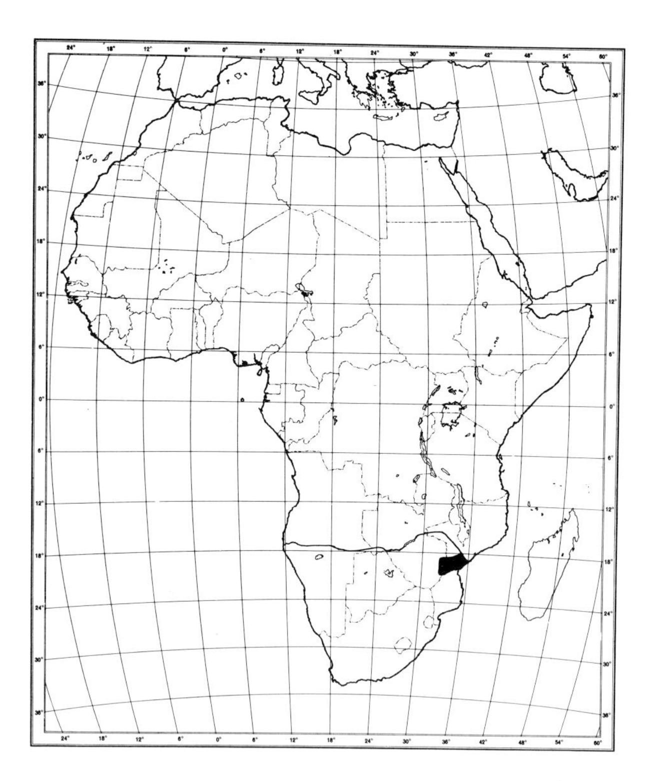

Southern African Subregion distribution only.

*T. leucogaster* occurs in much more arid environments than *T. inclusa*.

**Habits**

They are nocturnal and terrestrial. Their habits appear to be identical to those of *T. leucogaster*, with which they occur sympatrically, but always in smaller numbers. In some areas they are common on the fringes of and within cultivated lands, and on the fringes of forests, although not within these. However, they appear to be more solitary in habit than *T. leucogaster* and do not form warrens where burrow systems are occupied by a solitary individual, a pair or a female with young.

**Food**

Their association with agricultural lands suggests that they eat grain and other seeds, but judging from the green tinge of their stomach contents, they probably eat green vegetable matter as well.

**Reproduction**

No information is available.

## Subfamily CRICETINAE

This Subfamily is represented in the Subregion by a single species, the white-tailed mouse, *Mystromys albicaudatus*. In the Northern Hemisphere its nearest relatives, the hamsters, are also members of this Subfamily and have a wide distribution from central Europe to Asia. White-tailed mice have been referred to in the literature as South African hamsters. They are no less attractive, taking well to captivity, where they are prolific breeders, and if handled regularly from a young age, become tame.

White-tailed mice have thickset bodies, very soft fur, large ears and short tails. In *Mystromys* the first upper molar tooth has two deep infolds of the enamel on either side which closely approach each other in the middle, while the second upper molar has two on the outside, one on the inside, the latter tucked well forward on the tooth. The third upper molar is strongly reduced and the incisor teeth are ungrooved, the enamel layer on the front pale yellow. The bullae are only moderately large.

Their isolation from their nearest relatives in the Northern Hemisphere is puzzling. Ellerman (1941) noted the lack of clearly marked generic characters in *Mystromys*, making it difficult to place in a key. Misonne (1974) retained it with this Subfamily, as followed here.

## Genus *Mystromys* Wagner, 1841

Their cup-shaped nests may have led to the origin of the generic name, which is derived from the Greek *mystron*, a spoon, and *mys*, a mouse (Smithers, 1983).

No. 194

## *Mystromys albicaudatus* (A. Smith, 1834)

## White-tailed mouse
## Witstertmuis

Plate 14

**Colloquial Name**

The names in both languages are appropriate. South African hamster has also been used.

**Taxonomic Notes**

Ellerman (1941) noted that certain relationships of this genus make it difficult to place in a key. *M. albiceps* Wagner, 1841 and *Eurotis langinosa* Lichtenstein, 1842, both described from specimens from southern Africa, are synonyms of this species. No subspecies are recognised.

**Description**

Adult males have a total length of about 220 mm, and a mass of about 96,0 g; females 210 mm and a mass of about 78,0 g (Table 194.1). They are thickset in build, with large heads, and have soft, woolly pelages. Their tails are noticeably short, thinly haired and less than half the length of the head and body and, as the name implies, are pure white above and below. They have very narrow, shortish, ungrooved hair with coronal scales evenly spaced (Fig. XXIII.3) (Keogh, 1985). The upper parts of the body and the flanks are light grey or buffy-grey and some specimens have an irregular wash of black on the upper parts caused by some of the hairs being black-tipped. They have a band of darker colour extending posteriorly from between the eyes, which widens out between the ears, fading out on the top of the head. The sides of the face, around the nose, and the fore and hind limbs are paler than the upper parts, the upper surfaces of the feet being white. The under parts are greyish-white, the hairs white-tipped with grey bases. They have four toes on the front feet, five on the hind, each armed with sharp claws. The soles of the feet are naked, not partially haired as is sometimes stated.

**Plate 14**

185. Short-tailed gerbil, *Desmodillus auricularis* Kortstertnagmuis
186. Hairy-footed gerbil, *Gerbillurus paeba* Haarpootnagmuis
190. Bushveld gerbil, *Tatera leucogaster* Bosveldse nagmuis
191. Cape gerbil, *Tatera afra* Kaapse nagmuis
193. Gorongoza gerbil, *Tatera inclusa* Gorongoza nagmuis
194. White-tailed mouse, *Mystromys albicaudatus* Witstertmuis
195. Giant rat, *Cricetomys gambianus* Reuserot
196. Pouched mouse, *Saccostomus campestris* Wangsakmuis

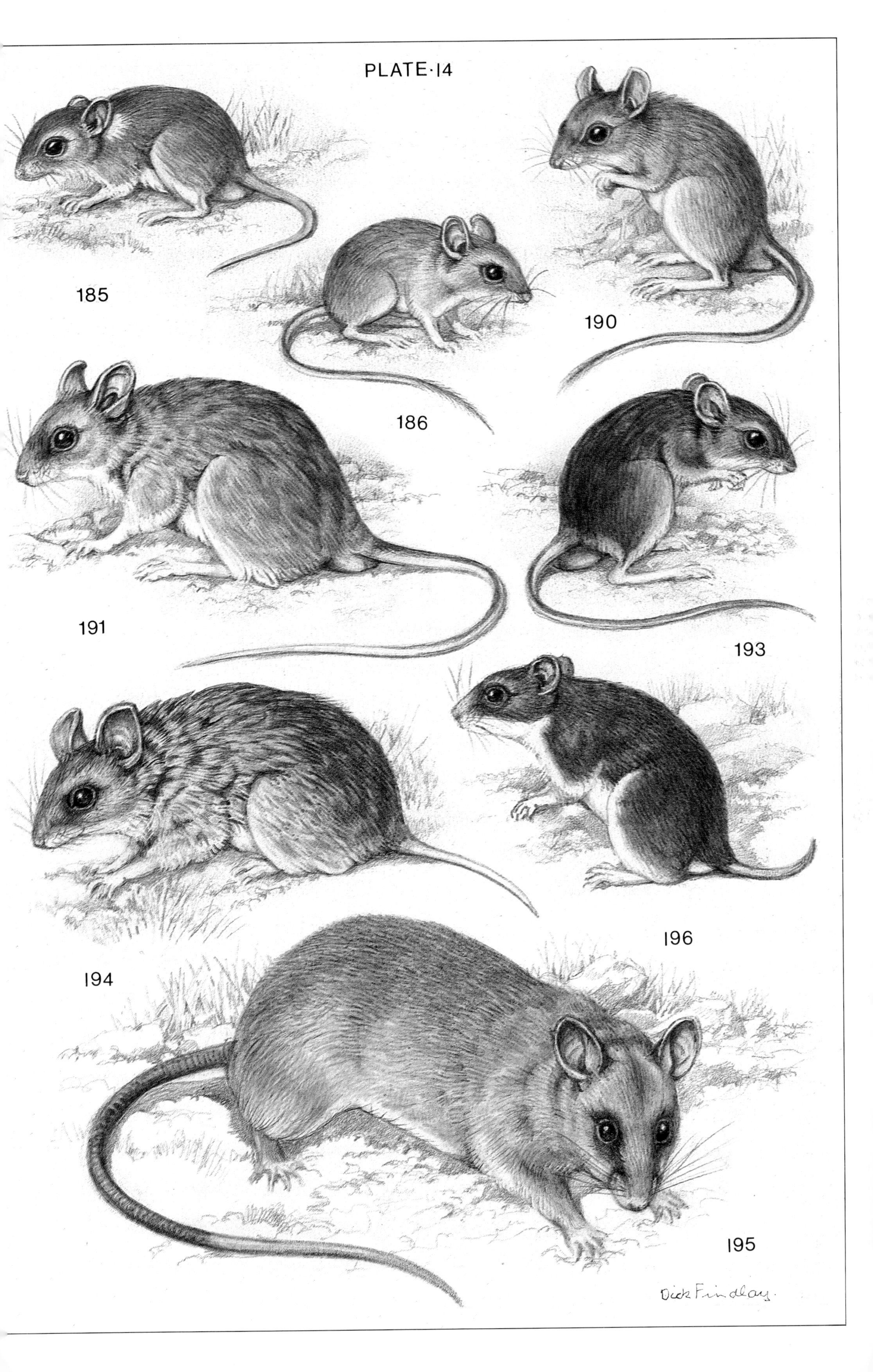
PLATE·14
185
186
190
191
193
194
196
195
Dick Findlay.

**Table 194.1**

Measurements (mm) and mass (g) of white-tailed mice, *M. albicaudatus*, from the Subregion (de Graaff, 1981)

| | Males | | | Females | | |
|---|---|---|---|---|---|---|
| | x̄ | n | Range | x̄ | n | Range |
| (TL | 221) | | | (207) | | |
| HB | 163 | 12 | 139–184 | 144 | 16 | 105–147 |
| T | 58 | 14 | 50–82 | 63 | 16 | 53–97 |
| Hf c/u | 27 | 14 | 24–30 | 26 | 16 | 24–28 |
| E | 26 | 14 | 20–28 | 24 | 16 | 20–27 |
| Mass | 95,7 | 2 | 78,0–111,0 | 78,0 | 2 | 75,0–81,0 |

## Distribution

*Southern African Subregion*

White-tailed mice are confined to within the limits of the Subregion. They occur in the western, southern, eastern and northeastern parts of the **Cape Province**; in **Natal**; the **Orange Free State**; the southwestern and southern parts of the **Transvaal** and in **Swaziland**.

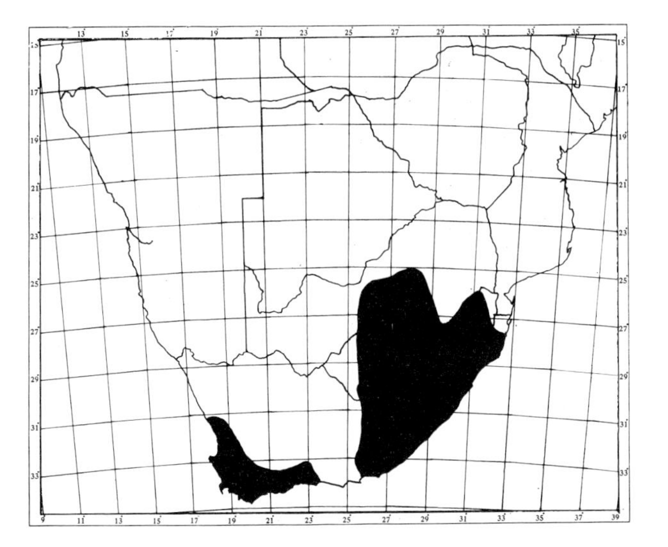

## Habitat

In the eastern parts of their distributional range they follow very closely the savanna grassland zone, but are not confined to this, occurring in the Karoo and, in the southwest, in the Cape Macchia Zone.

## Habits

They are nocturnal and terrestrial. They live in burrows or in cracks in the soil (de Graaff, 1981). When given soft paper for bedding in captivity, they shred this into fine, even strips and construct high-sided, cup-shaped nests, which look like Elizabethan neck ruffs. Young *M. albicaudatus* develop ringtail under low relative humidities in captivity (Stuhlman & Wagner, 1971) which suggests that the hairless tail performs a thermoregulatory function.

## Food

Their diet includes insects, seeds and green vegetable matter (Walker, 1975). Maddock (1981) studied their gastric morphology and found that *M. albicaudatus* have an abundance of symbiotic micro-organisms in their stomachs which may indicate a specialised herbivorous adaptation or a facility for extended amylase digestion, but the lengths of the small and large intestine are typical of an omnivore.

## Reproduction

Roberts (1951) stated that they breed throughout the year, but this remains to be confirmed under natural conditions. The gestation period is 37 days and mean litter size 2,9 (n=51), while the average mass at birth is 6,5 g (range 5,2–7,1 g). Hallett & Meester (1971) described their post-natal development in captivity: at birth they are altricial, pink and hairless, except for a few vibrissae 5 mm to 7 mm long and some short bristles about 1 mm long on the snout and chin. The eyes are closed and the ear pinnae folded over the external ear openings. By the fifth day the upper surface of the body shows a dark tinge and by the 16th day the whole back has become covered with light grey hair. By the fourth day the ear pinnae have loosened and the incisor teeth erupt between the third and seventh day, the lower usually before the upper. The eyes open between the 16th and 20th day.

The young attach to the nipples of the female shortly after birth and remain attached for a period of about three weeks, only occasionally becoming detached. Thereafter they detach from the nipples from time to time and start weaning. Some litters still attach up to 30 days (Smithers, 1983), with detachment and re-attachment continuing up to about 38 days after birth. By this stage they are fully weaned.

The minimum age of females at their first parturition is 146 days, the interval between litters being 36 days. The females have two pairs of inguinal mammae and when they have a litter of five, one will detach temporarily from a nipple so allowing the fifth to suckle. Even with a litter of four attached to her nipples, the female remains active, while in the nest both the parents huddle over the young.

# Subfamily CRICETOMYINAE

This Subfamily is comprised of two genera and two species, the giant rat, *Cricetomys gambianus*, and the pouched mouse, *Saccostomus campestris*, both of which have cheek pouches. Both species are burrowers, under certain conditions, or adjust existing holes or burrows excavated by other species, but *Cricetomys gambianus* has a greater tendency to use existing shelter such as is found under rocks, tree trunks, tree roots. Both species use holes in termitaria and both carry food back to their shelters in their cheek pouches, the discarded undigestible portions eventually forming a deep layer in the nesting chamber. While they share these features, their relationship has been the subject of controversy over the years. The argument hinges on the situation of the lingual cusps on the upper first and second molar teeth. Some associated these cusps with the front laminae and second laminae of the teeth and, therefore, considered them as members of the Subfamily Murinae. However, Petter (1966) clearly showed that the front cusp joins the second lamina of the teeth while the second cusp joins the third. He therefore argued that these species are essentially cricetid rather than murid (Rosevear, 1969) (Fig. 195.1).

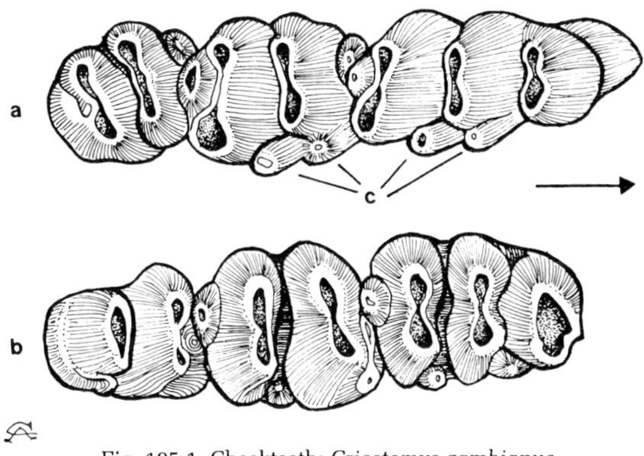


Fig. 195.1. Cheekteeth: *Cricetomys gambianus* (a) upper right (b) lower right (c) lingual cusps (after Rosevear, 1969).

Key to the genera after Meester *et al.* (1986)

1. Larger, length of head and body >300 mm ... *Cricetomys*

   Smaller, length of head and body <200 mm ... *Saccostomus*

## Genus *Cricetomys* Waterhouse, 1840

No. 195

## *Cricetomys gambianus* Waterhouse, 1840

Giant rat

Reuse rot

Plate 14

### Colloquial Name

The giant rat is so called as it is the largest murid species occurring in Africa. In the northern parts of its range it is known as the pouched rat.

### Taxonomic Notes

Opinions have differed as to the proper taxonomic treatment of members of this genus. Allen (1939) listed six species and 29 subspecies from the continent. Ellerman *et al.* (1953) recognised only one species, *C. gambianus*, with four subspecies occurring in the Subregion. Genest-Villard (1967) reviewed the genus and came to the conclusion that there were two species, *C. emini* and *C. gambianus*. While this division is not absolutely clear, *C. emini* is stated to be slenderly built, with sleek, short fur about 5–9 mm long and closely adpressed to the body, lacks a dark eye ring, and has a narrow face and white under parts clearly demarcated from the colour of the flanks. *C. gambianus* on the other hand is thick-set, with rough, loose fur about 10–15 mm long, has a dark ring around the eyes and a broad face; the whitish colour of the under parts blends into the colour of the flanks, with no clear line of demarcation. *C. emini* only occurs in forest and has a distribution from Sierra Leone in West Africa eastwards to Uganda, and is therefore of limited interest to us in the Subregion, where only *C. gambianus ansorgei* Thomas, 1904 occurs.

### Description

Giant rats have a total length of up to about 800 mm, with tails that are longer than the length of the head and body, and a mean mass in males of 1,31 kg, females 1,17 kg (Table 195.1). The most characteristic features of the species are the large size and the colour of the tail which, unlike the tails of other murids, is not scaled and is white for about 40% of its length towards the tip (Table 195.1). The large tail may be particularly important for thermoregulation.

The hairs are ungrooved, very long (16,7 mm, S.D. 1,42 mm) and broad, coronal scales on the hairs having a mosaic pattern (Fig. XXIII.3) (Keogh, 1985). The colour of the upper parts varies from pale grey to a buffy-grey and is usually darker down the mid-back; the flanks are paler and blend into the colour of the under parts which are white or off-white. They have distinct black or dark brown patches around the eyes and at the base of the long black whiskers. The ears are naked, upstanding and rounded at the ends. The eyes are very small for their size, which is unusual in a nocturnal species, and suggests that they may rely more on their senses of hearing and smell, which are acute. The upper surface of the hands is white, the digits pink-tinged and the soles of the feet naked and pink. The feet are white only on the upper surface of the digits. On the hands the first digit is rudimentary, with a small nail, the remainder of the digits having short claws. The fifth digit reaches about half way along the fourth, the third is the longest, and the second to the fifth are armed with short claws. They have five digits on the hind feet, each armed with a claw (Fig. 195.2).

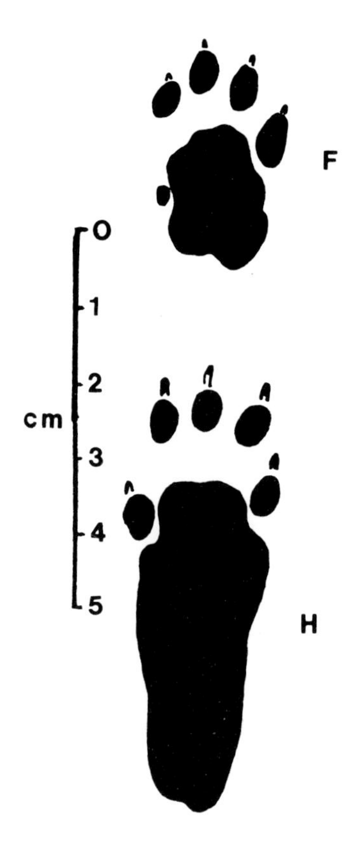

Fig. 195.2. Spoor: giant rat, *C. gambianus*
F. Forefoot H. Hind foot

### Skull

The skull is elongated and narrow, the upper surface nearly flat, the supraorbital ridges well developed, the rostrum long, the ear bullae relatively small. The orange-coloured incisor teeth are ungrooved. The third upper molar tooth is about the same size as the second (see also notes under the Subfamily). The palatal foraminae are short, not reaching the level of the anterior edge of the zygomatic arch.

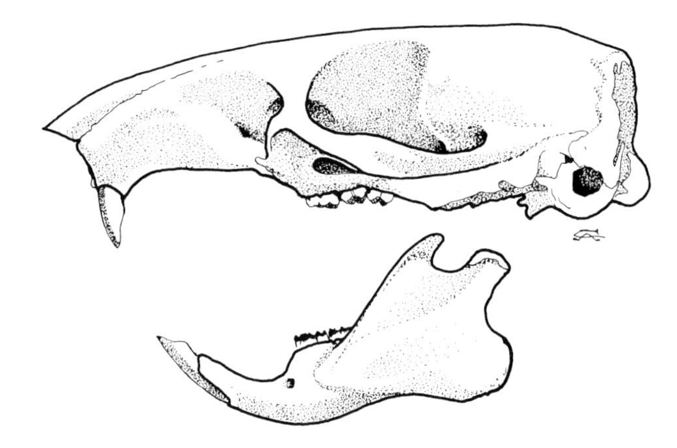
Fig. 195.3. Skull: giant rat, *C. gambianus*
TL Skull 70 mm

**Table 195.1**

Measurements (mm) and mass (kg) of giant rats, *C. gambianus*, from Zimbabwe (Smithers & Wilson, 1979) and proportionate length of white tail tip of specimens from the northern Transvaal (Knight, 1984)

**Zimbabwe**

| | Males | | | Females | | |
|---|---|---|---|---|---|---|
| | $\bar{x}$ | n | Range | $\bar{x}$ | n | Range |
| TL | 764 | 25 | 672–837 | 750 | 25 | 711–785 |
| (HB | 347) | | | (339) | | |
| T | 417 | 25 | 374–461 | 411 | 25 | 367–445 |
| Hf c/u | 74 | 25 | 69–78 | 71 | 25 | 67–75 |
| E | 41 | 25 | 39–49 | 41 | 25 | 38–45 |
| Mass | 1,31 | 25 | 1,00–2,80 | 1,17 | 25 | 0,96–1,39 |

**Northern Transvaal**

$\frac{\text{Length of white tail tip}}{\text{Length of tail}}\%$

| Males | | | Females | | |
|---|---|---|---|---|---|
| $\bar{x}$ | n | Range | $\bar{x}$ | n | Range |
| 41,0% | 12 | 36,9–46,2% | 38,5% | 8 | 30,9–45,3% |

**Distribution**

The giant rat, *C. gambianus*, has a wide distribution south of the Sahara. Within the limits of the Subregion they are confined to the eastern parts of the continent in areas with a mean annual rainfall in excess of about 800 mm.

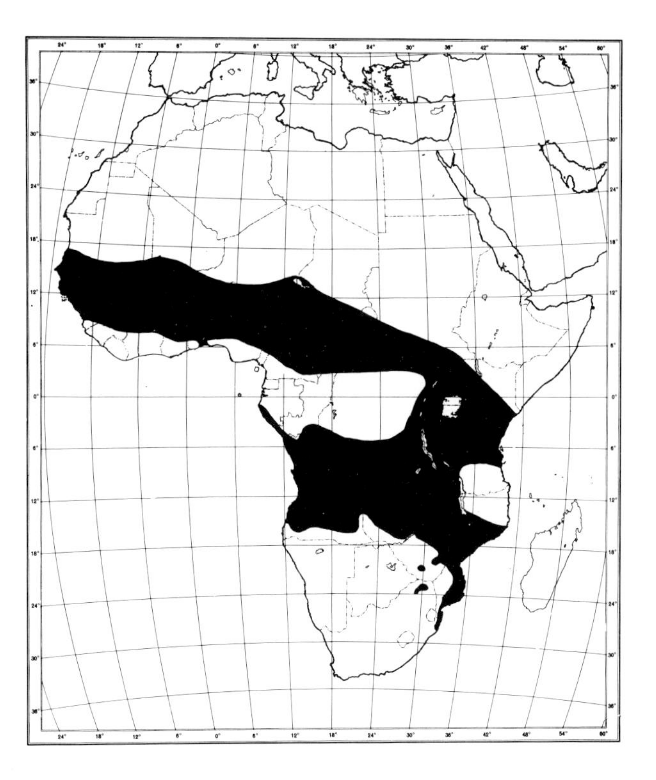

*South of the Sahara, excluding the Southern African Subregion*

They occur from **Senegal** eastwards to the southern **Sudan**; in **Uganda**; southwestern **Kenya**; northern and central **Tanzania; Zaire; Angola** and northwards coastally to **Gabon**. They are recorded widely in **Zambia**, excluding the southwest; in **Malawi** and in **Mozambique**, north of the Zambezi River, except in the northeast.

*Southern African Subregion*

They are recorded widely in **Mozambique**, south of the Zambezi River, excluding the more arid southwestern parts of the country; in northeastern and eastern **Zimbabwe**, with records from the Matopo Hills, an island of slightly higher rainfall in the west of the country; from the Soutpansberg in the northern **Transvaal** and **Natal**, which marks their most southerly limits on the continent.

**Habitat**

In the Subregion they occur in evergreen forest and in woodland in the higher rainfall areas (over about 800 mm of mean annual rainfall), where there is adequate undercover. They are very common in the urban and periurban areas of towns in the northeastern and eastern parts of Zimbabwe, using the cover of hedges and shrubberies. Urban development appears to have created particularly suitable habitat for the species, especially in its provision of a plentiful food supply.

**Habits**

Predominantly nocturnal, giant rats occasionally may be active in the late afternoon or early morning. They restrict their activity to short periods in areas with adequate vegetational cover (Knight, 1984), and this is permitted by consuming hoarded food within the burrow. They are terrestrial and, although they will climb trees in search of fruit if there is none available on the ground, climbing is unusual.

Their burrows are sometimes constructed in old termite mounds but are generally located in moist, shaded areas under boulders or at the bases of large trees (Knight, 1984). It has been suggested that their location is dependent upon soil texture (Ajayi & Tewe, 1978), but more probably these protect them from high ambient temperatures (Ajayi, 1977) as under experimental conditions Knight (1988) found they are unable to cope with temperatures above 34 °C. At the entrances to the burrows are piles of recently excavated soil which, characteristically, are in the form of small consolidated pellets, perhaps so shaped because the giant rats use their incisor teeth in burrowing, as their front claws are not well adapted to this purpose (Morris, 1963). Knight (1984) reported that the number of entrances vary from one to three, with a mean diameter of 196 ± 85,5 mm, and the main entrances are never sealed as found by Morris (1963). Their burrows invariably have a vertical shaft leading from the entrance, several chambers, one of which is a latrine and another, the nesting chamber, lined with sticks and leaves, amongst which is a store of food. Burrow tunnels average 136,7 ± 38,3 mm in diameter and the number of chambers vary from one to five, with only one of these used for nesting. The chambers have an average diameter and height of 454,6 ± 187,7 mm and 256,4 ± 98,2 mm respectively and are 727,1 ± 90,1 mm below the surface. Entrances to the nesting chamber are often sealed with rocks and sand, while a number of escape tunnels also exist in most burrows. Separate above-ground shelters outside the burrow are used for defecating and feeding, both types being protected on three sides and from above.

Knight (1988) found that burrow temperatures vary seasonally in forests in the Soutpansberg, northern Transvaal from 9,6 ± 2,1 °C at a depth of 700 mm in winter to 20,5 ± 2,6 °C in summer when respective forest temperatures (50 mm above ground) are 12,7 ± 1,9 °C and 18,6 ± 0,2 °C respectively.

In Zimbabwe many less complicated burrow systems are found which are used on a less permanent basis. These consist of a straight burrow, oval in section, about 100 mm to 140 mm in diameter, which leads under rocks, the roots of trees, or the floors of outhouses. Some penetrate not more than 1,5 m from the entrance, with a single chamber at the end and, in some cases, an additional latrine chamber. Nesting chambers are floored with the inedible parts of fruits and bulbs and a miscellaneous collection of all sorts of non-food items such as small stones, bones, nails, string, wire, and press caps off mineral water bottles. Indeed, giant rats seem to be prone to collecting any small, brightly coloured objects and carrying them back to the nest (Smithers, 1983).

Many of these burrow systems are occupied by a solitary individual. In Zimbabwe a gravid female accompanied by a male was dug out of one burrow, suggesting that the pair remain together when breeding. Ewer (1967) found no difficulty in keeping males and females together in captivity, even after the female had produced her litter and the female showed no signs of attempting to exclude the male from the nest. Giant rats are slow moving and docile when not alerted. Often, if caught in live traps, they will feed out of the hand immediately after being caught, but the females can be aggressive when they have a litter and will bite fiercely. They will turn on an aggressor if provoked, sit up on their haunches, blow up their cheek pouches and let out a noisy blast of air as a defence mechanism.

Of each nocturnal period, 67% is spent sedentary within the burrow, 9,5% active within the burrow and 23,4% active outside the burrow, the first and most active period lasting from 19h00 to 22h00 and then later from 01h00 to 05h00 (Knight, 1984). Home range size averages 4,95 ± 4,18 ha (range 2,23–11,10 ha), with males having larger home ranges than females, while females concentrate their activity closer to the burrow than males. Avoidance of predation is very important, and giant rats achieve this first by spending a limited time out of the burrow and secondly by spending this time predominantly within the forest scrub.

### Food

Giant rats have complex gut structures and slow passage rates, enabling them to utilise poor quality food (Knight & Knight-Eloff, 1987). They are omnivorous, their principal food being vegetable matter, together with a smaller amount of insects, such as termites. Coprophagy was noted by Ewer (1967) at 20 days of age, when the young eat the female's faeces, which suggests that giant rats also employ gut microbes to assist digestion. In the Transvaal, Knight (1984) recorded their preference for soft fleshy fruits. They are larder hoarders and carry back smaller food items in their cheek pouches and larger pieces in their teeth to be consumed or temporarily stored in the nesting chambers or outside feeding shelters. Knight (1984) recorded the recovery of 8,7 kg of pericarps of macadamia nuts from a single nesting chamber in the Transvaal. The inedible portions are amalgamated into the lining of the nesting chamber and these, together with stored food, indicate that a very wide variety of fruits, both wild and cultivated, grains, bulbs and tubers are eaten. In Zimbabwe, these include the fruits of mahobohobo, *Uapaca kirkiana*; marula, *Sclerocarya birrea*; mobola plum, *Parinari curatellifolia*; buffalo thorn, *Ziziphus mucronata*; large sourplum, *Ximenia caffra*; monkey orange, *Strychnos* spp, and bauhinia, *Bauhinia* spp when available. Cultivated fruits such as avocado pears, mangoes, pecan and macadamia nuts are much sought after and they will climb the trees to get at the fruits if these are not available on the ground. Many types of bulbs and tubers are taken, both wild and cultivated, as well as maize cobs, sorghums, wild and cultivated peas and beans, pumpkin and peanuts. Stomach contents show the remains of termites and other small but unidentifiable insects. They will drink water and appear to be dependent on its availability through direct use or from fleshy fruits.

Giant rats can become problem animals where vegetables are grown. Forty-two were taken off a 0,5 ha garden in Harare, Zimbabwe, where they were eating young plants of peas, lettuces and cabbages.

### Reproduction

Information on the times at which the young are born in the wild is lacking and no gravid females were found in a sample of 100 taken in all months of the year, in Harare (Smithers, 1983). One female taken in the Eastern Districts in August carried two foetuses (Smithers & Wilson, 1979), whilst in Malawi, Morris (1963) recorded young in September, January, March and May.

During courtship in captivity Ewer (1967) reported that the male approaches a female and attempts to copulate, but the female at first responds defensively, rearing up on her hind legs and pushing the male off with her paws. The two then both rise up on their hind legs and the male attempts to push the female backward, this process continuing over a distance of several metres. Neither make any attempt to bite, but if the female shows signs of moving away, the male catches her in his teeth and pulls her back. The male then grooms the female around the face, ears and nape of the neck, which has a calming effect on her. He then places his forelegs around the middle of her body, with the palms of his hands directed backwards so that the wrists are in contact with her sides, vibrating the forelegs backwards and forwards, in what Ewer (1967) interpreted as an assurance behaviour.

Ewer (1967) found that three pairs of females gave birth after cohabiting with males for 32, 32 and 31 days and because sexual behaviour was observed in these three pairs after five, four and three days, the gestation period appears to be between 27 and 28 days. In contrast Grassé (1955) and Morris (1963) gave this as 42 days. In the wild the young are born in the nests and after cleaning the young, the female eats the afterbirth. Birth masses range from 19,0 g to 33,4 g (Ajayi, 1975; Ewer, 1967). Litter size in captivity and in the wild varies from two to four (Knight, 1986). Ewer (1967) found that the altricial young are born naked, except for whiskers, the body unpigmented and the eyes closed. At two days of age mass of two pups averaged 27,43 g, increasing to 461,70 g by day 52 (Knight, 1984), with average growth rates of 3,8 g/day (Ajayi, 1975). At birth the tail is only 30% to 40% of the length of the body, but at 80 days it reaches the same length. Skin pigmentation starts to develop on the young at about four days after birth and by the fifth day the line demarcating the white tail tip develops. Fine hair develops on their bodies by the fifth day and after 10 days forms a silky covering. Pinnae only become free after seven days, and the eyes open at 28 days (Knight, 1986).

At the 11th or 12th day a behaviour pattern occurs in a number of litters in which the young engage in what Ewer described as "outbursts of insensate rage", fighting and biting each other. Peace is not restored until the mother returns to suckle them. The female remains with the young until they are about a week old and only then is prepared to leave them to forage.

She suckles them by crouching over them and in captivity the pups first attempt to eat solid food at the age of 17 days, taking it a day later. The eyes open at an age of 20 to 24 days when they first leave the nest to urinate, using the common latrine. In the wild, Knight (1986) only managed to catch two young during 411 trap nights over two years and he estimated these animals to be between 60 and 98 days old. He suggested they do not leave the burrow until a late stage of development. In captivity their first foraging journeys were undertaken between 43–52 days and they finally deserted the nest at 86 days when they were able to thermoregulate (Knight, 1986).

As giant rats tame easily, are cheap to feed, and reproduce well in captivity, schemes to introduce farming enterprises have been studied in West Africa where giant rat meat is considered a marketable proposition (Ajayi, 1975; Ajayi, Tewe & Faturoti, 1978).

## Genus *Saccostomus* Peters, 1846

The generic name *Saccostomus* is derived from the Greek *sakkos*, a sack, *stomatus*, a mouth, referring to their possession of cheek pouches, and the Latin, *mus*, a mouse. The specific name *campestris* is Latin for a plain.

No. 196

## *Saccostomus campestris* Peters, 1846

## Pouched mouse
## Wangsakmuis

Plate 14

### Colloquial Name

They are called pouched mice as they have cheek pouches like their close relative the giant rat, *Cricetomys gambianus*.

### Taxonomic Notes

Although numbers of subspecies have been described, it is accepted that the differences in size and colour are clinal and that no useful purpose is served by recognising subspecies. Gordon (1986) found a wide variation in the diploid number and chromosome structure of this species, and the taxonomic implications of this are presently under review (Ferreira & Robinson, unpubl.).

### Description

Adults have a total length of about 160 mm; the males have a mean mass of 48,5 g, the females 42,2 g (Table 196.1). In any large series of adults it is very noticeable that there is an even run of size, but with a small percentage of very large males or females, much larger than the mean size of the general series. While the larger male specimens may be in breeding condition, with enlarged scrotal testes and the females gravid with young, much smaller males are found to be in breeding condition and smaller females gravid.

Characteristic features are the robust body, thick-set head and noticeably short, pinkish tail, which is less than a third of the total length. In common with the white-tailed mouse, *Mystromys albicaudatus*, pouched mice tails may also serve a thermoregulatory function as they too suffer from ringtail at low relative humidities in captivity (Ellison & Westlin-van Aarde, 1990). The hairs have a steep chevron scale covering their width (Fig. XXIII.3) (Keogh, 1985). The colour of the upper body parts is grey, or grey tinged brown. Those from the western parts of their distributional range are lighter in colour than those from the higher rainfall, eastern areas. The under parts are white or off-white, the demarcation in colour between the upper and under parts being clearly defined. The fur is thick, soft and silky. The unscaled tail is thinly haired, slightly darker on top than underneath, and in the lighter coloured specimens the pink of the skin shows through the thin coat of hair.

The skull is elongated, albeit less so, in relation to its size, than in the giant rat, *C. gambianus*. The rostrum is relatively short and broad, and broader at the base than at the tip (Fig. 196.1). The palate is broad, the palatal foramina reaching the level of the anterior edge of the first upper molar teeth.

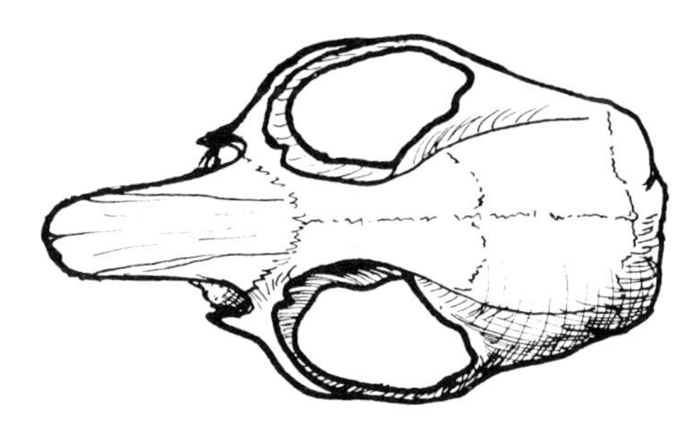

Fig. 196.1. Skull, dorsal view: *S. campestris*.

**Table 196.1**

Measurements (mm) and mass (g) of pouched mice, *S. campestris*, from Botswana (Smithers, 1971)

| | Males | | | Females | | |
|---|---|---|---|---|---|---|
| | $\bar{x}$ | n | Range | $\bar{x}$ | n | Range |
| TL | 156 | 20 | 138–178 | 155 | 20 | 134–174 |
| (HB | 112) | | | (109) | | |
| T | 44 | 20 | 37–55 | 46 | 20 | 34–54 |
| Hf c/u | 20 | 20 | 18–21 | 20 | 20 | 19–21 |
| E | 18 | 20 | 16–19 | 18 | 20 | 16–21 |
| Mass | 48,5 | 20 | 33,0–68,0 | 42,2 | 20 | 30,0–54,0 |

## Distribution

*South of the Sahara, excluding the Southern African Subregion*

They are recorded from parts of **Angola; Zambia; Malawi; Mozambique**, north of the Zambezi River, and southeastern **Zaire**.

*Southern African Subregion*

They are distributed widely in the Subregion, occurring in the central and northern parts of **Namibia**, but are absent from the coastal desert and from the southern parts of the country. They are distributed widely in **Botswana, Zimbabwe**, and **Mozambique**, south of the Zambezi River. They occur in the southeastern **Transvaal**; in the central and northern parts of the **Orange Free State**; in **Lesotho**; southern **Natal** and in the eastern and parts of the southern **Cape Province**.

## Habitat

Pouched mice are catholic in their habitat requirements, occurring in such diverse associations as the open short grass fringes of pans in the Kalahari, open *Acacia* spp bushveld in the Transvaal (Ellison, 1990), in rocky koppies, on the fringes of lowland forest (Mozambique), from sea level to altitudes of up to 1800 m (Zimbabwe) and in areas with a mean annual rainfall from about 250 mm to over 1200 mm. They are commoner, nevertheless, in areas where there is a sandy substrate with scrub bush or cover of open

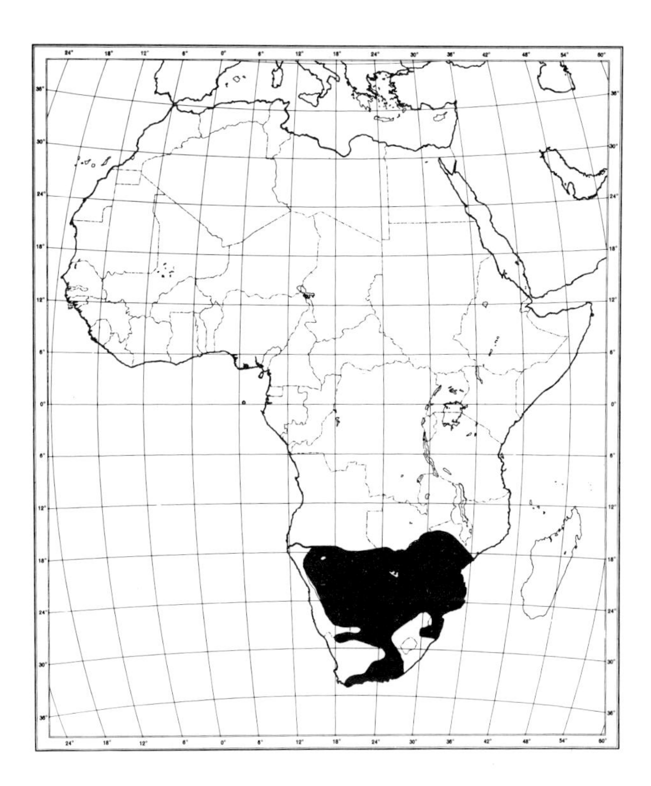

Southern African Subregion distribution only.

woodland. They are noticeably less common on hard ground and are rare on heavy red clay soils. In more mesic habitat such as *Acacia* woodland in Umfolozi Game Reserve, numbers tended to increase during droughts (Bowland, 1986).

## Habits

They are nocturnal and terrestrial and they will excavate their own burrows in sandy soils, but in hard ground use established holes such as those in termitaria or burrows opened by other species. They have been found occupying disused springhaas, *Pedetes capensis*, and aardvark, *Orycteropus afer*, burrows, as well as piles of rocks, holes under fallen logs and roots of trees exposed by erosion. Excavations of burrows from throughout South Africa suggest that there are two types of burrows: the first a simple, short (300–600 mm) burrow ending in a single nest chamber, the second large and complex containing more than one chamber and numerous tunnels and food stores (Ellison, pers. comm.). The depth of nests varies from 220–860 mm, although most nests are around 380 mm below the ground surface. As for *Mystromys albicaudatus*, a recurrent characteristic of burrows is the vertical entrance shafts, although these are not always present (Ellison, pers. comm.). In the Transvaal, during winter, soil surface temperatures vary between 0,2 °C and 30,7 °C, whilst within the nest (340 mm below ground) the temperature is remarkably constant between 15,0 °C and 16,2 °C throughout the day (Ellison, pers. comm.).

Pouched mice are solitary, with only a single occupant inhabiting each burrow, although during the breeding season a female will be found together with her young (Ellison, pers. comm.). Korn (1989) suggested that a decline in body weight of pouched mice during winter might reduce the overal energy requirements during the cold dry season in the Transvaal. Whether this phenomenon is a result of a reduction in body weight of adults or reflects a higher proportion of younger animals in the overwintering population remains unclear, but Ellison & Skinner (in press a) recorded significantly lower energy requirements for small, overwintering juveniles from the eastern Transvaal, whilst adults from throughout southern Africa display a small decline in body weight following acclimation to short days and cold temperatures in the laboratory (Ellison, pers. comm.). Recent studies have also shown that pouched mice from throughout southern Africa undergo short bouts of daily torpor in response to cold in the laboratory. Torpor is expressed in only 35–50% of any population and is characterised by a fall in body temperature to between 21 °C and 25 °C for 2–6 hours, with an associated decline in energy expenditure (Ellison & Skinner, in press b). They are slow movers and, judging from the frequency with which they are found in the stomachs of small carnivores, commonly fall prey to them. They wander widely from their burrows at night and have been followed for distances of up to 200 m from them on open ground (Smithers, 1971).

**Food**

*S. campestris* is a partially insectivorous granivore (Kerley, 1989) with bunodont molars having transverse lophs. The digestive system is adapted for a proteinaceous diet and because of their habit of collecting seeds and other types of food in their cheek pouches it is easier to give a proper identification of what they eat compared to other murids which masticate their food immediately after collection. Foraging widely from the burrow, they fill their cheek pouches with food, packing it into them with the forefeet, and then return to the entrance of the burrow or disappear into it to eat. The resting chamber in the burrow is littered with the remains of food items and there are even larger accumulations near the entrance where they sit and eat. This behaviour enhances their chances of survival for, if danger threatens while they are eating, they can dive down the burrow to safety.

Although grass seed is taken, it appears to form only a small percentage of the food which consists predominantly of the larger seeds of forbs, bushes and trees. Swanepoel (1972) recorded finding the seeds of umbrella thorn, *Acacia tortilis*; scented thorn, *A. nilotica*; and sweet thorn, *A. karroo*, in their cheek pouches. They store the seeds of torchwood, *Balanites maughamii*, in their burrows and also eat the fruits of the raisin bush, *Grewia monticola*. De Graaff (1981) recorded the seeds of nyala trees, *Xanthocercis zambesiaca*, and Smithers (1971) identified seeds of camelthorn, *Acacia erioloba*; raisin bush, *Grewia* spp; bush willow, *Combretum* spp; and mopane, *Colophospermum mopane*, in their cheek pouches. Pienaar, Rautenbach & de Graaff (1980) added sickle bush, *Dichrostachys cinerea*, and raisin bushes, *Grewia bicolor* and *G. flavescens* to this list and Jacobsen (1977) included the seeds of red syringa, *Burkea africana*; weeping wattle, *Peltophorum africanum*; and blue guarri, *Euclea crispa*. In the Kruger National Park, Watson (1987) found their diet varied seasonally when determined from stomach contents. In a drought period these contained 31% insects, 12% herbage and 57% seeds (n=14), compared to 9% insects, 12% herbage and 79% seeds during a period of rainfall.

**Reproduction**

In a sample of 143 females taken throughout the year in Botswana, gravid females occurred during the months of January to April (Smithers, 1971), in Zimbabwe from February to April (Smithers & Wilson, 1979), and in Natal from October and February (Swanepoel, 1972). The young are thus born during the warm, wet summer months within the nest chambers of their burrows.

They are spontaneous ovulators with a four-day cycle; there is no post-partum oestrus (Westlin-van Aarde, 1988), whilst they have a lactational anoestrus (Westlin-van Aarde, 1989b).

Earl (1978) gave the gestation period as 20 to 21 days and found that in captivity the females have their first litters at 96 days old and that the young are born fully haired with a mean mass at birth of 2,8 g. In Botswana the mean number in litters was 7,4 (range 5–10; n=8) (Smithers, 1971); in Zimbabwe 6,7 (range 1–10; n=7) (Smithers & Wilson, 1979). The eyes open at 20 days but are only fully functional at 24 days and pups are weaned at 25 days (Westlin-van Aarde, 1989c).

Earl (1977) recorded that the females pick up the young in their mouths up to the fourth day after birth, occasionally moving them into the cheek pouches to be transported. This behaviour is also known in the North American heteromyid rodent, *Liomys* sp. The females have three pairs of pectoral and two pairs of inguinal mammae.

## Subfamily DENDROMURINAE

The name of the Subfamily is derived from the Greek *dendron*, a tree, and the Latin *mus*, a mouse. However, none of the members of any of the genera, *Dendromus*, *Malacothrix* or *Steatomys*, occurring in the Subregion are associated with trees and the last two named are exclusively terrestrial. Members of the genus *Dendromus* certainly are climbers, but predominantly on low bushes or tall grass. Long after the use of the name was well established, Thomas (1916) created the genus *Poemys* for one of the species (*Dendromus melanotis*) which, derived from the Greek *poe*, grass, and *mys*, a mouse, would have been a better basis for the name of the Subfamily in the Subregion and more in accord with their habits.

All the species occurring in the Subregion have grooved upper incisor teeth, the groove lying nearer the outer margin of the tooth than the inner. The dental formula is:

$I\frac{1}{1}\ C\frac{0}{0}\ P\frac{0}{0}\ M\frac{3}{3} = 16$

Members of the Subfamily show considerable variety in form and have poorly marked characters which serve to distinguish them from the Murinae. These differences lie predominantly in the cuspidation of the teeth, which are not well marked and are subject to different interpretations. In the typical rats and mice the cusps on the molar teeth are arranged in three longitudinal rows (triserial). In the Dendromurinae it is argued that the cusps lie in two longitudinal rows (biserial), although the first and second upper molars have three cusps on the middle lamina, the anterior lamina of the second is missing or consists of one cusp and that the third molar is so reduced that it renders the arrangement indeterminable. Rosevear (1969) remarked that one is left with the impression that the Dendromurinae are a "rubbish heap" of forms with dental relationships subject to differing interpretations and are by no means clear cut.

Members of all three genera have external characters that mark them as among our most attractive small mice. *Dendromus* spp are dainty, with distinct dark bands down their backs and very long tails. Their agility in climbing is best appreciated as they climb among the stems of tall grass. *Malacothrix* is also an attractive species, with its body pattern of dark markings on a background of grey or buffy. *Steatomys* has a particularly shiny coat and they store fat under the skin which gives them their colloquial name, fatmice.

The long tail of *Dendromus* is also semi-prehensile, and as the tail twines around grass stems, it acts more as a steadying than a grasping aid.

Within the genus *Dendromus* the possession of a nail or a claw on the fifth toe of the hind foot is sometimes difficult to determine. Misonne (1974) pointed out this difficulty, but it is a character, nevertheless, used pending the determination of other characters to separate the species groups.

Key to the genera after Meester *et al.* (1986)

1. Tail length >90% of head and body length, semi-prehensile; three functional digits on forefeet; hallux lacks claw
   ... *Dendromus*

   Tail length <60% of head and body length; four functional digits on forefeet
   ... 2

2. Pterygoid fossa extends far behind toothrows; only four hind toes, hallux absent
   ... *Malacothrix*

   Pterygoid fossa does not extend behind toothrows; five hind toes, hallux present, with claw
   ... *Steatomys*

## Genus *Malacothrix* Wagner, 1843

The genus is endemic to southern Africa, and while they have teeth somewhat similar to those of *Dendromus* and

*Steatomys*, they can be distinguished from them by the characters set out in the key to the genera. Their palate is very broad, the toothrows extending far forward in the skull. The interorbital constriction is pronounced, and they have a narrow, straight-edged rostrum. The bullae are medium-sized and the palatal foramina long and large and extending posteriorly to about the middle of the first upper molar teeth.

No. 197

# *Malacothrix typica* (A. Smith, 1834)

## Large-eared mouse
## Bakoormuis

Plate 15

### Colloquial Name

This refers to the noticeably large ears of this small dendromurid.

### Taxonomic Notes

Meester *et al.* (1986) listed six subspecies; *M.t. typica* from the Graaff Reinet area; *M.t. fryi* Roberts, 1917 from the Transvaal; *M.t. molopensis* Roberts, 1933 from southeastern Botswana; *M.t. kalaharicus* Roberts, 1932 from southwestern Botswana; *M.t. damarensis* Roberts, 1932 from the Gobabis district of Namibia and *M.t. egregia* Thomas, 1926 from northern Namibia. The status of these subspecies warrants investigation.

### Description

Large-eared mice are small, with a total length of about 110 mm and short tails of about 36 mm. The males have a mass of about 16 g (Table 197.1). Narrow hairs have single coronal scale across width (Keogh, 1985). There is a wide variation in colour, from those that occur in the southwestern Cape Province to those from the north, in Namibia in the west and central Botswana. They are pale reddish-brown in the southern parts of their range, buffy-grey in eastern Botswana and reddish-buffy in the west. All have the characteristic dark pattern on the upper parts of the body which consists of a dark patch between the ears, a dark stripe down the mid-back and a dark patch on top of each hip (Fig. 197.1). There is a similar variation in the colour of the under parts. In the northern parts of their range the hairs of those from the eastern areas are grey at the base, those from the western areas pure white. The lighter colour of the under parts extends upwards to include the upper lip, the forelimbs and the front of the thighs.

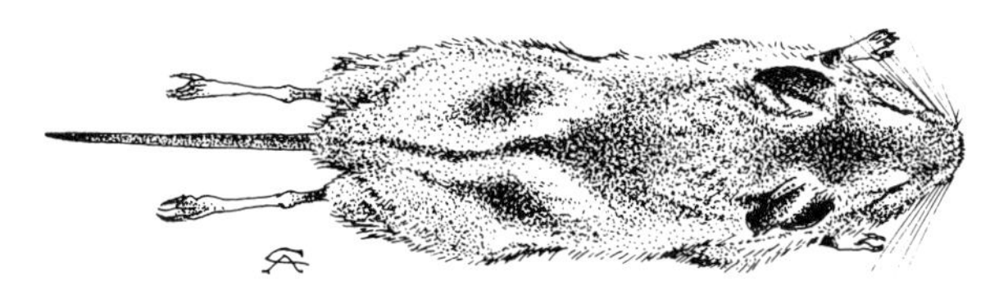

Fig.197.1. Body pattern: *Malacothrix typica*.

**Table 197.1**

Measurements (mm) and mass (g) of large-eared mice, *M. typica*, from southwestern Botswana (Smithers, 1971)

| | Males | | | Females | | |
|---|---|---|---|---|---|---|
| | $\bar{x}$ | n | Range | $\bar{x}$ | n | Range |
| TL | 112 | 8 | 104–120 | 107 | 6 | 102–116 |
| HB | 76) | | | (72) | | |
| T | 36 | 9 | 34–40 | 35 | 5 | 32–39 |
| Hf c/u | 19 | 8 | 18–20 | 18 | 5 | 18–19 |
| E | 20 | 9 | 19–20 | 20 | 5 | 18–22 |
| Mass | 16,4 | 9 | 12,0–20,0 | 10,4 | 5 | 7,0–13,0 |

### Distribution

*South of the Sahara, excluding the Southern African Subregion*

This species occurs marginally in southwestern **Angola**.

*Southern African Subregion*

Large-eared mice are not easy to trap and consequently records are scattered and there are large areas within their distributional range from which no specimens are available. The information available indicates that they occur widely in the **Cape Province,** except in the extreme eastern parts; in the **Orange Free State;** southwestern **Transvaal;** southern **Botswana** and in **Namibia.**

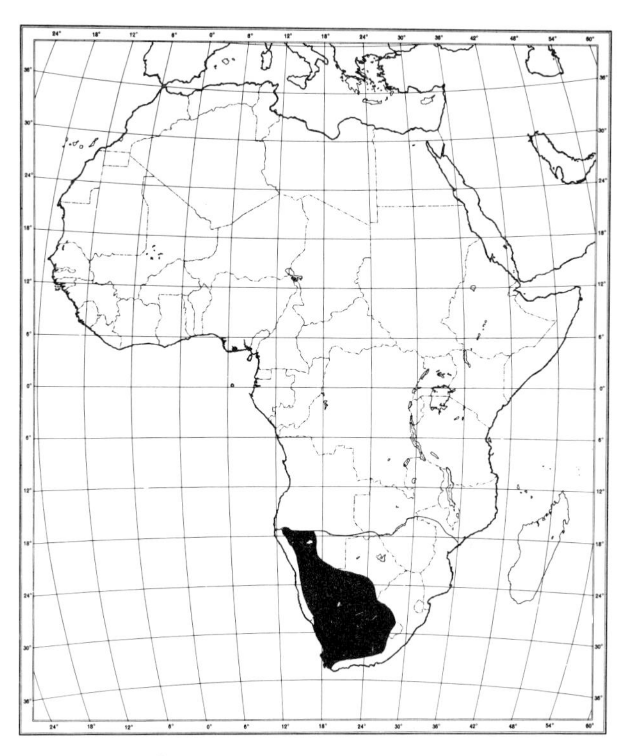

Southern African Subregion distribution only.

### Habitat

In the northern parts of their distributional range they are associated with areas of short grass on a hard substrate. In Botswana they are associated with the short grass areas on or fringing pans, where these have a cover of karroid bush. They occur in areas with a mean annual rainfall from about 150 mm up to about 500 mm, but are found predominantly within the South West Arid Zone.

### Habits

They are terrestrial and nocturnal, exhibiting the highest level of activity between 20h00 and 24h00 in captivity (Knight & Skinner, 1981). Roberts (1923) recorded that they excavate deep burrows leading to a nesting chamber; the entrances to these open to the surface of the ground, with no loose detritus at the burrow opening. The material excavated is used to fill the original burrow which remains closed, and on hard ground in southeastern Botswana the small open burrows, 20 mm to 25 mm in diameter, are nearly vertical (Smithers, 1971). They wander widely at night, individuals being chased for distances of up to 100 m before disappearing down holes. If they are found at night on open ground they can be caught by hand, with the aid of a dazzling light. They are handled easily and not prone to bite, but upon capture and under stress in captivity they vocalise with a loud *dzizz-dzizz*.

Individuals in captivity have lived up to two and a half years (Smithers, 1971). Their movements in the wild are relatively slow, a disadvantage overcome by having large ears and eyes well developed for predator detection. They practise freezing behaviour when in danger, whilst the pattern of body coloration has a cryptic function (Knight & Skinner, 1981).

### Food

The diet appears to consist predominantly of green vegetable matter, but they will also take grass seed. In captivity they do well on a diet of lettuce, fresh lucerne and finger millet seed (Smithers, 1971).

### Reproduction

From the occurrence of juveniles in February and from data from captive pairs, the young are born during the warm, wet months of the year from about August to March (Smithers, 1971). From observations in captivity females produce their first litter at about 51 days old and are capable of producing more than one litter during any one season. Knight & Skinner (1981) found that litter size in captivity was 4,0 (range 2–8; n=9). The mean gestation period for 11 litters conceived at post partum oestrus was 27,45 days and for 19 litters conceived during oestrus at other times 23,11 days. Knight & Skinner (1981) believed this was a result of a delay in implantation caused by incomplete uterus involution immediately post partum. The average birth mass was 1,1 g and increased rapidly up to the 18th day, thereafter slowing down to reach the adult mass of about 21,0 g after 90 days. The young are born naked and blind, but the ear pinnae become free after six days and the external auditory meatus opens on day 15. Weaning occurs at about 32 days, and the young became sexually active after 70 days. Two females had their first litters at 102 and 120 days old.

## Genus *Dendromus* A. Smith, 1829

Four species are recorded from the Subregion: *D. mesomelas*, the largest, with a wide distribution in the better-watered areas; *D. mystacalis*, with one record from the south coast of the Cape Province, otherwise with a predominantly eastern occurrence; *D. melanotis*, widely distributed, but restricted in Namibia to the northern sector, and *D. nyika*, at present known only from the Subregion from a few specimens from the eastern Transvaal and eastern Zimbabwe.

The name of the genus (see Subfamily Dendromurinae) implies a more arboreal habitat than they deserve, for their climbing is confined generally to heights of up to about 2 m only, in grass and on small bushes.

As a group they are most attractively coloured mice, with long tails and patterned bodies. They are agile climbers. Their long tails twine around the stems as they climb, helping to steady them, and are prehensile, but they cannot hang suspended from the tail as can some primates. The long slender centre digits on the forefeet, numbers two to four, are adapted to grasping the grass stems and twigs among which they forage for insects. The first and fifth digits on the forefeet are greatly reduced; in some the fifth is a tiny, barely perceptible stub. In *D. mesomelas* and *D. mystacalis* the fifth toe on the hind foot is armed with a tiny claw; in the other two species it takes the form of a tiny, broad nail. It is difficult in some cases to decide, even under a binocular microscope, whether it is a nail or a claw, in others it is fairly obvious and is useful then in identification of the species' group.

Their little ball-shaped nests are sturdy enough to last the few months required for the shelter of the litters, a new nest being built every year.

For their small size they are aggressive. Misonne (1963) noted that in captivity they dominate the equally small pygmy mice, *Mus minutoides*, and Roberts (1951) recorded similar behaviour with the large-eared mouse, *Malacothrix typica*. They adapt well to captivity providing they are given a plentiful supply of insects as well as grain.

In the skull the braincase is rounded and there are neither occipital nor supraorbital crests. The interorbital constriction is pronounced, the rostrum long and moderately narrow. The palate is broad between the anterior molars and tapers posteriorly, continuing to just behind the third upper molar. The large anterior palatal foraminae reach to about the middle of the first upper molar; the posterior pair are minute and lie in line with the second upper molar. The ear bullae are well developed (Fig. 199.1). The slender zygomatic arch curves upwards anteriorly (Fig. 199.2).

## Genus *Dendromus* A Smith, 1829

Key to the species after Meester *et al.* (1986)

1. Fifth hind toe with rounded nail; fifth forefinger present, vestigial; ears darker than back; general colour normally grey
 ... 2

 Fifth hind toe with pointed claw; fifth forefinger lacking; ears resemble back in colour; general colour normally brown
 ... 3

2. Larger, adult skull normally longer than 21 mm; ears relatively small, usually <20% of head and body
 ... *nyikae*

 Smaller, adult skull normally shorter than 21 mm; ears relatively larger, usually about 20% of head and body; black line sometimes present on back
 ... *melanotis*

3. Larger, adult skull longer than 22 mm; ventral hair usually slatey-based; black line invariably present on back
 ... *mesomelas*

 Smaller, adult skull <22 mm long; ventral hair white or ochraceous, not slatey
 ... *mystacalis*

---

No. 198

## *Dendromus nyikae* Wroughton, 1909

## Nyika climbing mouse
## Nyika-klimmuis

---

### Colloquial Name

They are so called as the species was described originally from a specimen from the Nyika Plateau in northern Malawi.

### Taxonomic Notes

Meester *et al.* (1986) listed two subspecies from the Subregion: *D. n. longicaudatus* Roberts, 1913 from the north-eastern Transvaal and *D. n. bernardi* Lundholm, 1953 from eastern Zimbabwe.

### Description

They are very similar in size and external appearance to grey climbing mice, *D. melanotis*, but in the Transvaal are brighter and redder in colour. In eastern Zimbabwe they are brownish-grey and have longer tails, and skulls about 22 mm in total length or slightly larger. The under parts are white. So few specimens are available that mean sizes cannot be provided. Specimens from eastern Zimbabwe measure 180 mm in total length, with tails about 104 mm long. A single male from the Transvaal measured TL 173; T 94; Hf c/u 20; E 15 and had a mass of 13,0 g (Rautenbach, 1978).

### Distribution

*South of the Sahara, excluding the Southern African Subregion*

They occur in **Malawi; Angola** and **Zambia**, in the latter on the Zaire and Angola border.

*Southern African Subregion*

So far they are recorded only from the Tzaneen district of the eastern **Transvaal** and the Inyanga district of eastern **Zimbabwe**; both of these are at altitudes of over 1 000 m.

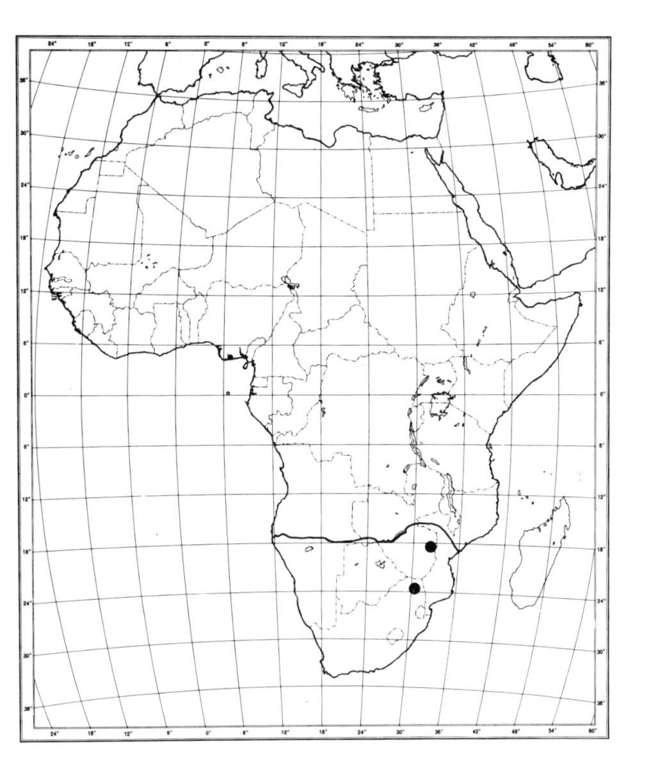

Southern African Subregion distribution only.

### Habitat

Rautenbach (1978) recorded that one of the eastern Transvaal specimens was taken in dense grass in mopane woodland. The Inyanga specimen was taken in montane grassland.

### Habits, Food and Reproduction

Nothing is known of these aspects of their life histories in the Subregion.

No. 199

## *Dendromus melanotis* A. Smith, 1834

## Grey climbing mouse
## Grysklimmuis

Plate 15

### Colloquial Name

This is the only member of the genus that has a grey body, compared with the browner or redder bodies of the other members of the genus.

### Taxonomic Notes

Meester *et al.* (1986) listed five subspecies from the Subregion: *D. m. melanotis* from the western, southern and eastern Cape Province; *D. m. vulturnus* Thomas, 1916 from northern Natal, Mozambique, eastern Transvaal and eastern Zimbabwe; *D. m. arenarius* Roberts, 1924 from the northern Cape Province and southern Botswana; *D. m. concinnus* Thomas, 1926 from northern Namibia, and *D. m. shortridgei* St. Leger, 1930 from northern Botswana and western Zimbabwe.

### Table 199.1

Measurements (mm) and mass (g) of grey climbing mice, *D. melanotis*, from Zimbabwe (Smithers & Wilson, 1979)

| | Males | | | Females | | |
|---|---|---|---|---|---|---|
| | x̄ | n | Range | x̄ | n | Range |
| TL | 156 | 4 | 140–163 | 148 | 5 | 127–167 |
| (HB | 66) | | | (60) | | |
| T | 90 | 4 | 80–98 | 88 | 5 | 80–95 |
| Hf c/u | 17 | 4 | 16–18 | 17 | 12 | 16–18 |
| E | 16 | 5 | 14–17 | 16 | 11 | 14–17 |
| Mass | 6,7 | 3 | 6,0–8,0 | 6,7 | 8 | 6,1–8,2 |

### Description

They are about the same size as chestnut climbing mice, *D. mystacalis*, with a total length of about 150 mm, a tail longer than the length of the head and body, and a mass of about 7,0 g. Constructions occur at random intervals along the length of the hairs which are covered with coronal scales typical of fluff-type hair (Fig. XXIII.3) (Keogh, 1985). The upper parts of the body are ashy-grey tinged with rufous, with a dark band on the mid-back extending from just in front of the shoulders to the base of the tail. Some individuals have a dark spot on the forehead. The under parts are greyish-white. The long tail is dark above and lighter in colour on the under surface. The ears are dark in colour with a white patch at the anterior base of the ear. There is a broad overall similarity between the skulls of *Dendromus* and *Steatomys* (see under genus *Dendromus* and Figs 199.1 and 199.2).

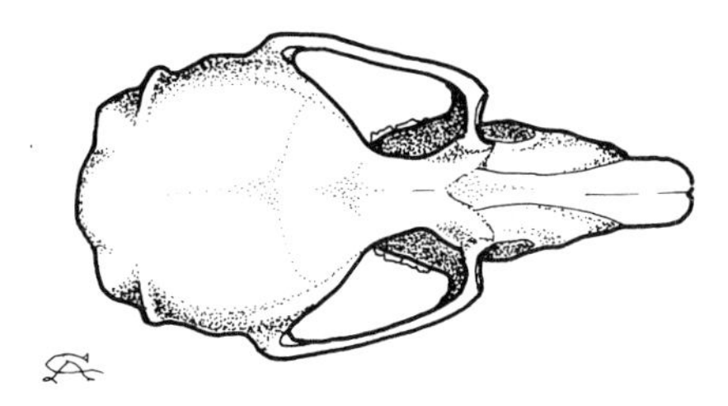

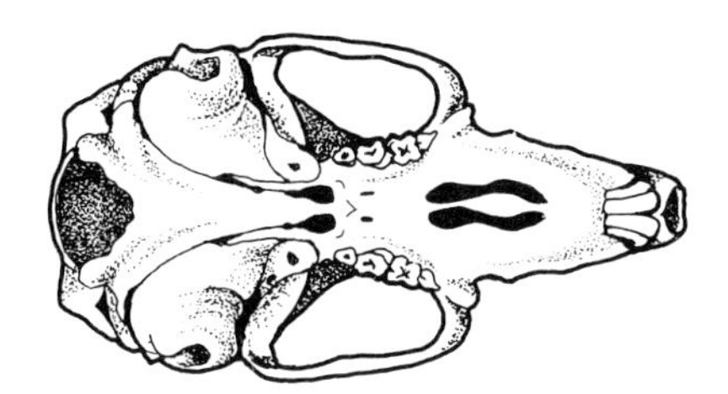

Fig. 199.1. Skull: *Dendromus melanotis* above, dorsal view; below, ventral view.

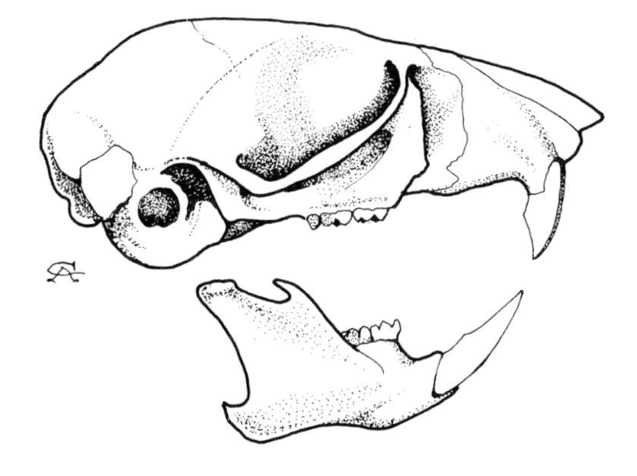

Fig. 199.2. Skull: *Dendromus melanotis* lateral view

### Distribution

*South of the Sahara, excluding the Southern African Subregion*

This species is recorded from **Angola; Zambia; Malawi; Zaire; Tanzania; Kenya; Ethiopia** and from parts of northern **Nigeria** and **Guinea**.

*Southern African Subregion*

Although records of the species are scattered, they are recorded from the western, southern, northern and eastern parts of the **Cape Province**; from **Lesotho; Natal; Orange Free State**; the **Transvaal**; the central and southern parts of **Mozambique**, south of the Zambezi River; **Zimbabwe**; widely in **Botswana**; the northern and northeastern parts of **Namibia** and from the **Caprivi Strip**.

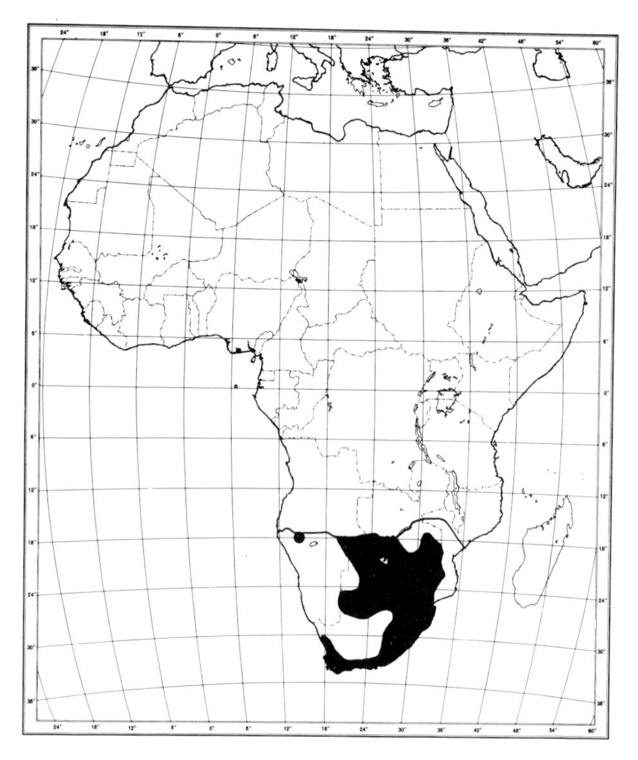

Southern African Subregion distribution only.

### Habitat

Often they are associated with stands of tall grass such as *Hyparrhenia* sp, especially where these are thickened up with bushes and other vegetation. On the other hand, Rowe-Rowe & Meester (1982) did not find them in tall grassland but in grassland up to 33 months after fire. Although they are associated in many parts of their distributional range with riverine conditions, they occur in the dry, often waterless scrub of the Kalahari where the mean annual rainfall is as low as 200 mm to the eastern parts of the Subregion with a mean annual rainfall of over 1 200 mm, and from sea level to 2 700 mm in the Drakensberg.

### Habits

Agile climbers, they are nocturnal and largely terrestrial, foraging in low bushes and in tall grass up to about 2 m above the ground. Like the chestnut tree mouse, *D. mystacalis*, the long tail is used in climbing, curling around the grass stems and twigs to steady them as they move. It is not known whether they excavate their own burrows, but they certainly use those of other species, and Jacobsen (1977) recorded their using holes made by large dung beetles.

During the early summer months they construct ball-shaped nests, 40–60 mm in diameter, with a single entrance, weaving them securely between several grass stems or the twigs of low bushes, up to a metre above the ground level. They use the shredded leaflets of high standing grass and other fine fibres in the construction of these nests. They litter down in these nests, the parent remaining with the young for some time after they are weaned. The nests are deserted by the onset of the winter months, about June, and new nests are constructed with the onset of the next rainy season.

### Food

They will eat seeds, but are predominantly insectivorous, taking a wide range of insects including termites, grasshoppers, crickets, moths and small beetles, but not stink-bugs (Hemiptera) or certain types of rose beetles (Smithers, 1983). In the Drakensberg, Rowe-Rowe (1986) found that grass seeds were present in all 14 stomachs examined, only 24% of which contained Arthropoda.

### Reproduction

A gravid female was taken in December with four foetuses (Smithers, 1971) and de Graaff (1981) recorded females with three foetuses in the Kruger National Park in February. Jacobsen (1977) gave the litter size as two to four, with a record of up to seven. The females have two pairs of pectoral and two pairs of inguinal mammae (de Graaff, 1981).

---

No. 200

## *Dendromus mesomelas* (Brants, 1827)

## Brants' climbing mouse
## Brants se klimmuis

Plate 15

---

### Colloquial Name

Named after the describer of the species.

### Taxonomic Notes

Meester *et al.* (1986) listed two subspecies: *D. m. mesomelas* which occurs in the western, southern and eastern Cape Province, Natal, the Transvaal and central Mozambique, and *D. m. major* St Leger, 1930 from northern Botswana, the Caprivi Strip and northeastern Namibia.

### Description

Adults of this species from the northern parts of their distributional range in the Subregion (*D. m. major*) reach a total length of 185 mm. The hairs have no constrictions along their length and the coronal scales (Fig. XXIII.3) covering the hairs are never more than two across the width of the shallow grooved hairs (Keogh, 1985). The upper parts of the body in the southern subspecies (*D. m. mesomelas*), which have a mean total length of 175 mm (Table 200.1), are brownish-pink with a blackish-brown admixture of darker tipped hairs on the back; the northern subspecies (*D. m. major*) are reddish-brown with the same darker tinge. Both have a black band on the middle of the back, extending from just anterior to the shoulders to the base of the tail. The flanks are paler in colour than the upper parts, the outside of the limbs paler than the flanks, the under parts off-white, the feet whitish. The tail is considerably longer than the length of the head and body and is about the same colour as the upper parts of the body on top and lighter in colour underneath. The black stripe on the back is variable in intensity and, with the exception of *D. melanotis*, may be absent (Roberts, 1913).

### Table 200.1

Measurements (mm) and mass (g) of Brants' climbing mice, *D. mesomelas*, from the Cape Province and the Transvaal (de Graaff, 1981)

| | Males | | | Females | | |
|---|---|---|---|---|---|---|
| | x̄ | n | Range | x̄ | n | Range |
| (TL | 175) | | | (177) | | |
| HB | 76 | 5 | 69–80 | 74 | 7 | 67–85 |
| T | 99 | 4 | 91–105 | 103 | 7 | 94–109 |
| Hf c/u | 20 | 4 | 19–21 | 20 | 7 | 18–22 |
| E | 18 | 3 | 15–21 | 14 | 7 | 12–17 |
| Mass | 12,0 | 4 | 11,0–13,0 | 10,6 | 5 | 9,0–14,5 |

The measurements (mm) of two males from the northern Okavango Delta, Botswana (Smithers, 1971)

| | x̄ | n | Range |
|---|---|---|---|
| TL | 174 | 2 | 165–183 |
| (HB | 76) | | |
| T | 98 | 2 | 91–105 |
| Hf c/u | 26 | 2 | 26 |
| E | 15 | 2 | 15 |

**Distribution**

*South of the Sahara, excluding the Southern African Subregion*

This species is recorded from **Angola; Zambia; Malawi; Tanzania; Zaire; Kenya; Ethiopia**; southern **Nigeria; Guinea** and **Cameroun**.

*Southern African Subregion*

They occur from the southwestern **Cape Province** eastwards coastally to **Natal**; to the central and eastern parts of the **Transvaal**. In **Mozambique**, south of the Zambezi River, they are recorded from Gorongoza Mountain. There then appears to be a break in their distribution, and they reoccur in the Okavango Swamps in northern **Botswana**, in the western **Caprivi Strip** and in the extreme northeastern parts of **Namibia**.

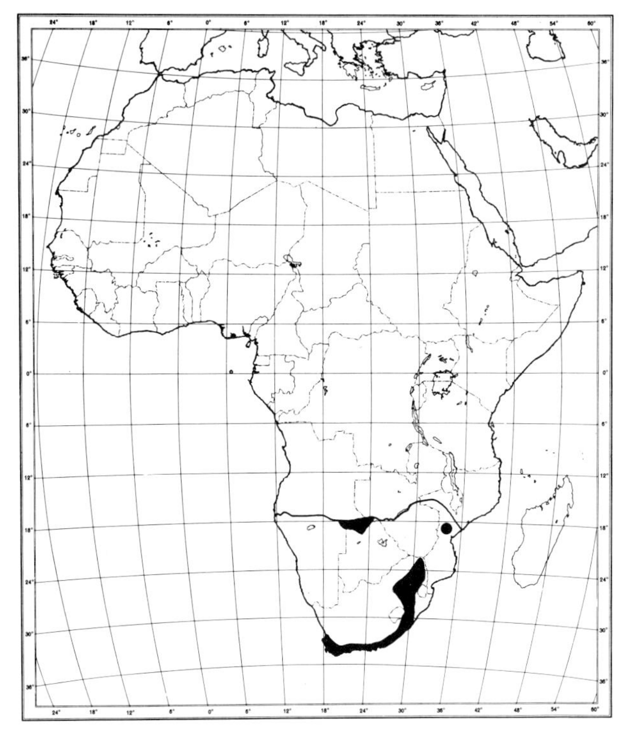

Southern African Subregion distribution only.

**Habitat**

Like other species of *Dendromus* they are associated with rank vegetation, especially tall grass with scrub. Rowe-Rowe & Meester (1982) found in the Drakensberg that the habitat of *D. mesomelas* did not overlap with that of *D. melanotis* which avoided tall grassland. They occurred at altitudes up to 2 400 m. In the northern parts of the Okavango Swamp in Botswana they were taken in thick clumps of tussock grass standing in flood water.

**Habits**

They are nocturnal and they are adept at climbing around in low vegetation, using their long tails to support and balance themselves.

**Food**

Stomachs of *D. m. major* from northern Botswana contained ground-up remains of largely insects and grass seed. In the Okavango Swamp area with no access to seed, their stomachs contained insect remains only (Smithers, 1971). In the Drakensberg stomachs all contained grass seeds and 75% insect remains (Rowe-Rowe, 1986).

**Reproduction**

No information is available from the Subregion.

No. 201

## *Dendromus mystacalis* Heuglin, 1863

## Chestnut climbing mouse
## Roeskleurklimmuis

Plate 15

**Colloquial Name**

The name refers to the rich chestnut colour of the upper parts of the body.

**Taxonomic Notes**

Meester *et al.* (1986) listed two subspecies from the Subregion: *D. m. jamesoni* Wroughton, 1909 from the southern and eastern Cape Province, Natal, Swaziland, Transvaal, Zimbabwe and southern Mozambique, and *D. m. whytei* Wroughton, 1909 from northeastern Botswana. It is thought that the northeastern Botswana material would be better placed with *D. m. jamesoni* as the type locality of *D. m. whytei* is Fort Hill, Malawi.

**Description**

This species is smaller than Brants' climbing mouse, *D. mesomelas*, and adults have a total length of about 150 mm, with tails over half this length (Table 201.1). The hairs are lined with single "chunky" coronal scales (Fig. XXIII.3) (Keogh, 1985). The colour of the upper parts is a bright chestnut, with a black band down the mid-back from just in front of the shoulders to the base of the tail. The under parts are white, while the top of the tail is similar in colour to the upper parts of the body; underneath it is lighter in colour. The fifth digit of the hind foot is armed with a claw, and they lack a fifth finger on the forefoot.

**Table 201.1**

Measurements (mm) and mass (g) of chestnut climbing mice, *D. mystacalis*, from Zimbabwe (Smithers & Wilson, 1979)

| | Males | | | Females | | |
|---|---|---|---|---|---|---|
| | x̄ | n | Range | x̄ | n | Range |
| TL | 151 | 6 | 136–156 | 142 | 8 | 138–157 |
| (HB | 65) | | | (62) | | |
| T | 86 | 6 | 79–90 | 80 | 8 | 77–85 |
| Hf c/u | 17 | 8 | 16–20 | 17 | 7 | 15–19 |
| E | 14 | 8 | 13–15 | 13 | 7 | 12–15 |
| Mass | 7,7 | 6 | 6,3–11,8 | 7,6 | 5 | 5,5–10,6 |

**Distribution**

*South of the Sahara, excluding the Southern African Subregion*

They are recorded from **Angola; Zambia; Malawi; Mozambique**, north of the Zambezi River; **Tanzania; Kenya; Zaire; Ethiopia**; eastern **Nigeria** and **Ghana**.

*Southern African Subregion*

Except for a single record from Knysna, on the south coast, they are confined to the eastern parts of the Subregion, from the extreme eastern parts of the **Cape Province** northwards, in parts of **Natal; Swaziland**; the central and eastern parts of the **Transvaal; Zimbabwe**; central and southern **Mozambique** and the extreme northeastern parts of **Botswana**. As they have been recorded extralimitally in Mozambique, north of the Zambezi River, in time they probably will be shown to be more widespread in this country.

**Habitat**

They are found in grassland, predominantly associated with rank vegetation, especially stands of high coarse grasses

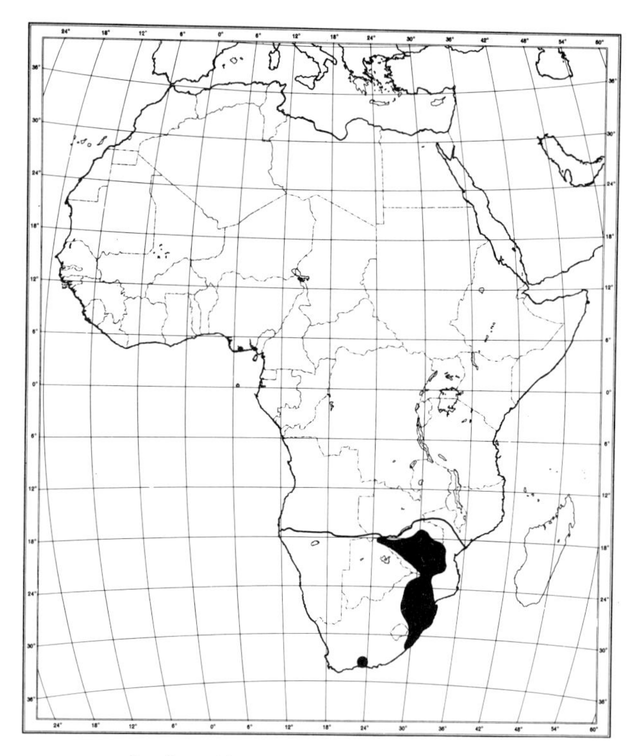

Southern African Subregion distribution only.

such as *Hyparrhenia* sp, 1–2 m in height, in which they climb around at night in search of food.

### Habits

They are nocturnal, terrestrial and to some extent arboreal, as they build their ball-shaped nests during the early part of the warm, wet season of the year in low bushes and in trees up to about 2 m from the ground in common with other *Dendromus* spp. The long tails may be loosely twined around grass stems or twigs to assist in steadying them when climbing. They have some subterranean activity, but it is not known whether they excavate their own burrows or use the burrows of other species. However, they have been dug out of dung beetle chambers about 450 mm underground (Boulton, pers. comm.). They use nests for resting in and in which to have their young, until about May or June when they vacate these, constructing fresh nests the following season. The nests, 80–100 mm in diameter, are woven into several stems of tall grass or bushes, and have a single side-entrance. They have been recorded as using disused weaver and bishop birds' nests (Jacobsen, 1977). They are used primarily for rearing their young and the whole family party uses them even after the young are weaned, and perhaps until the young disperse, before the onset of the cold weather.

### Food

Although the finely masticated, whitish stomach contents show that they consume seeds, insects constitute their principal food, at least during the warm summer months. These are taken during their nightly foraging on the tops of the grass stems, while in captivity they will take moths, cockroaches, grasshoppers, termites and small beetles.

### Reproduction

Litters have been observed in nests in Zimbabwe between the months of January and March, three to four constituting a litter. Rautenbach (1978) took a pregnant female with eight foetuses in March in the Transvaal.

## Genus *Steatomys* Peters, 1846

Members of the genus are small mice, with soft, shiny fur generally of a brownish-grey colour. They all have very short tails, half or less than half the length of the head and body, and pure white under parts. Their forefeet differ from *Dendromus*, having four well-developed digits on the front feet and five toes on the back feet, all armed with sharp claws. The muzzle is sharp-pointed, the ears large, with a white patch at the base of the outer margin. The number and positioning of the mammae varies in the different species.

Three species occur in the Subregion. The name of the genus is derived from the Greek *steatos*, fat, and *mys*, a mouse. The colloquial name fat mouse refers to the accumulation of fat in their tissues, particularly under the skin, which is a characteristic feature of members of the genus. This fat layer is built up during the warm, wet summer months and helps to tide them over the dry cold months when food is less plentiful and during which they lie up underground in a state of torpidity. One can still trap them during the cold, dry months, but during spells of very cold weather they remain underground. If they are dug out at this time and are picked up in the hand they will lie dormant for a few moments before becoming active, almost as if they were awakening from a very sound sleep. How long they remain in this state of torpidity is not known, but it could be for two or three weeks at a time. A few days of warmer weather brings them to the surface, but they return underground if the temperature falls. Specimens collected during the months of March to June have to be degreased, otherwise the fat slowly leaches out and mats the skin and stains the base of the storage drawers. Those taken late in the dry season from about September to early October have usually used up most of the accumulated fat and normally do not require such treatment. Because of this feature they are sought after as food by indigenous people. Skewered on a sharpened stick, the fur is burnt off in the flame and the stick is then inserted in the ground by the fire to grill them over the flames. When dealt with in this way they are considered a delicacy superior to other mice similarly treated.

It is difficult to distinguish the males of *S. pratensis* from *S. krebsii*, although the latter are slightly larger. *S. parvus* on the other hand, as the name implies, is considerably smaller than the other two species and has a pure white tail. The adult females of *S. pratensis* can be distinguished from the other two by the position and number of the mammae, a character which cannot be applied to juveniles or males, but no better character is known at the moment to separate them.

Key to the species after Meester *et al.* (1986)

1. Multimammate, mammae more than 2+2=8, usually 12, up to a maximum of 16, not necessarily arranged in pairs
   ... *pratensis*

   Mammae 2+2=8
   ... 2

2. Smaller, head and body length 63–80 mm, greatest skull length 19,5–23,0 mm; ear length subequal to or greater than hind foot length (s/u); tail white; dorsal colour reddish
   ... *parvus*

   Larger, head and body length 70–105 mm, greatest skull length 21,0–27,0 mm; ear length subequal to or less than hind foot length (s/u); tail brownish-grey above, white below; dorsal colour brown with a greyish tinge
   ... *krebsii*

---

No. 202

## *Steatomys pratensis* Peters, 1846

## Fat mouse
## Vetmuis

Plate 15

---

### Taxonomic Notes

Meester *et al.* (1986) listed three subspecies from the Subregion: *S. p. pratensis* from Mozambique, northeastern Zimbabwe, extralimitally from Malawi, Zambia and southwestern Tanzania; *S. p. natalensis* Roberts, 1929 from western

Natal, north to the eastern Transvaal, southeastern Zimbabwe and Mozambique, and S. p. *maunensis* from northern Botswana and Namibia and adjacent parts of Zimbabwe and Zambia.

### Description

Fat mice have a total length of about 130 mm, with short tails about 50 mm long and a mass of about 26,0 g (Table 202.1). They have comparatively short hair with a definite groove in the chevron pattern (Fig. XXIII.3) (Keogh, 1985). Their colour varies throughout their wide distributional range, being lighter or darker shades of rusty-brown on the upper parts of the body, brownish on the flanks. The under parts, hands and feet are white. The individual hairs on the upper parts have slatey bases and the pelage has a distinct sheen. The forefeet have four and the hind feet five clawed digits.

**Table 202.1**

Measurements (mm) and mass (g) of fat mice, *S. pratensis*, from the Transvaal (Rautenbach, 1978)

| | Males | | | Females | | |
|---|---|---|---|---|---|---|
| | $\bar{x}$ | n | Range | $\bar{x}$ | n | Range |
| TL | 130 | 39 | 117–157 | 135 | 39 | 110–162 |
| (HB | 87) | | | (91) | | |
| T | 43 | 39 | 32–55 | 44 | 39 | 33–53 |
| Hf c/u | 16 | 39 | 14–19 | 16 | 39 | 14–19 |
| E | 14 | 38 | 10–16 | 15 | 38 | 10–17 |
| Mass | 21,2 | 22 | 12,0–29,0 | 25,3 | 22 | 10,0–44,0 |

### Distribution

This species has a much wider distribution in Africa south of the Sahara, than either of the other two species of *Steatomys*.

*South of the Sahara, excluding the Southern African Subregion*

They occur from **Cameroun** eastwards to the southwestern **Sudan** and southwards in **Zaire; Angola; Zambia**; in the extreme northern parts of **Malawi**, near the Tanzanian border and in **Mozambique**, north of the Zambezi River.

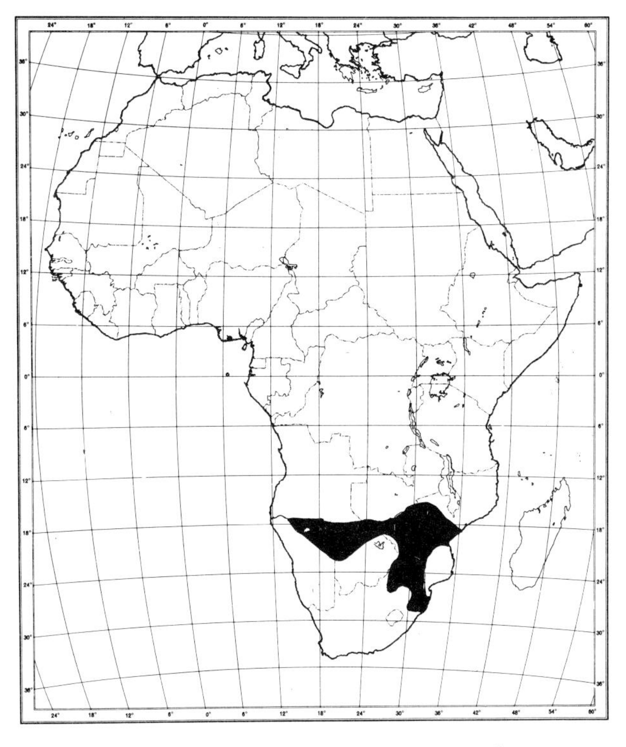

Southern African Subregion distribution only.

*Southern African Subregion*

They are recorded from the northern and northeastern parts of **Namibia**; in northern **Botswana**; widely throughout **Zimbabwe** and **Mozambique**, south of the Zambezi River; **Swaziland**; in central and northern **Natal**. They occur widely in the **Transvaal**, except in the southern and southwestern parts of the province.

### Habitat

Where the species occurs in generally arid terrain, they are associated with the fringes of rivers and swamps and, throughout their range, with a sandy substrate. In the Zambezi Valley they are particularly common in sandy alluvium on the flat valley floor in areas cultivated by the indigenous people, and in Botswana are found under similar conditions on the fringes of the Okavango River and Okavango Swamp where they are easily caught by hand with the aid of a spotlight. Their common occurrence in cultivated lands suggests that they prefer a loose, sandy substrate where a plentiful food supply is available.

### Habits

They are nocturnal and terrestrial, occurring singly or in pairs. They construct several burrows sloping downwards to a chamber about 250 mm below the surface, filled with shredded vegetation (de Graaff, 1981). In the state of hibernation during the cold, dry months of the year they dig themselves in, shallowly, under clumps of grass. Recent observations of *S. pratensis* in captivity reveal that they hoard food and enter prolonged bouts of torpor, with body temperatures falling to 16,5 °C at an ambient temperature of 15 °C (Ellison, pers. comm.).

### Food

In a sample of 11 stomachs from *S. pratensis* taken in the wet season in the Kruger National Park, Watson (1987) found their diet consisted of 83% seeds, 4% herbage and 13% insects, indicating that they are essentially omnivorous granivores.

### Reproduction

Kern (1977) recorded no reproductive activity in the Kruger National Park in either sex from April to November, when all individuals examined showed signs of activity. In northern Botswana, gravid females were taken in September, October and December (Smithers, 1971; Skinner, unpubl.) and in Zimbabwe, in addition to these months, in April and May as well (Smithers & Wilson, 1979). This suggests that the young are born during the warm, wet summer months from about October to May. The average number of foetuses per female is 3,2 (range 1–9; n=5). Females have up to 16 mammae arranged in two irregular rows from the pectoral to the inguinal region.

---

No. 203

## *Steatomys parvus* Rhoads, 1896

## Tiny fat mouse
## Dwergvetmuis

Plate 15

---

### Colloquial Name

They are so named as they are the smallest of the three species of fat mice occurring in the Subregion.

### Taxonomic Notes

Meester *et al.* (1986) listed three subspecies from the Subregion: *S. p. minutus* Thomas & Wroughton, 1905 from northern Namibia and extralimitally from Angola and Zambia; *S. p. tongensis* Roberts, 1931 from northern Natal and southern Mozambique, and *S. p. kalaharicus* Roberts, 1932 from central and northern Botswana and western Zimbabwe.

### Description

As the colloquial name suggests, this is a smaller species than *S. pratensis* or *S. krebsii*, adults being about 120 mm in total length, with tails about 40 mm and a mean mass of

13,3 g (Table 203.1). Their short hairs are covered with one broad, flattened, double chevron scale (Fig. XXIII.3) (Keogh, 1985). The colour is variable, those from Natal being buffy-brown on the upper parts, with tails that are brown above and white below, those from northern Botswana and the Kalahari being much paler, with white tails. In the latter form they are easily recognisable from the other two species, but not so easily in the former, except on the basis of size and the mammary formula of females. The pelage, like that of the other two species, has a distinct sheen.

**Table 203.1**

Measurements (mm) and mass (g) of tiny fat mice, *S. parvus* (de Graaff, 1981) and from Botswana (Smithers, 1971)

| | Males | | | Females | | |
|---|---|---|---|---|---|---|
| | $\bar{x}$ | n | Range | $\bar{x}$ | n | Range |
| (TL | 116) | | | | | |
| HB | 76 | 5 | 64–86 | | | |
| T | 40 | 5 | 36–50 | No data available | | |
| Hf c/u | 15 | 5 | 14–16 | | | |
| E | 14 | 5 | 13–14 | | | |

**Botswana** (Smithers, 1971)

| | Irrespective of sex | | |
|---|---|---|---|
| | $\bar{x}$ | n | Range |
| TL | 121 | 7 | 110–157 |
| (HB | 78) | | |
| T | 43 | 7 | 34–49 |
| Hf c/u | 16 | 7 | 14–17 |
| E | 15 | 7 | 12–18 |
| Mass | 13,3 | 3 | 11,1–15,0 |
| TL skull | 22,1 | 7 | 21,3–22,9 |

### Distribution

*South of the Sahara, excluding the Southern African Subregion*

They are recorded from **Angola; Zambia; Tanzania; Kenya; Uganda; Somalia** and the **Sudan**.

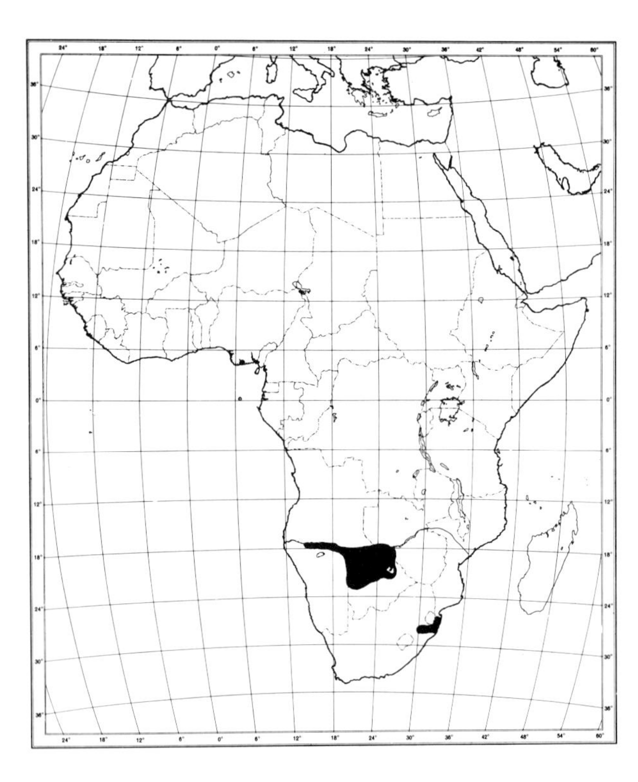

Southern African Subregion distribution only.

*Southern African Subregion*

They occur in northern **Namibia** in the eastern parts of the country as far south as about 23°S; in central and northern **Botswana** and the **Caprivi Strip** and marginally in north-western **Zimbabwe**. There is a break in distribution in a southeastern direction, the species reoccurring in northern **Natal** and southern **Mozambique**.

### Habitat

This species appears to have a wide habitat tolerance, but usually occurs on sandy ground. In northern Botswana they occur in scrub with a sandy substrate, in the Okavango Delta and on the Chobe and Botletle rivers in sandy alluvium, and in the central Kalahari on the fringes of pans in sandy soil. Coetzee (1977b) noted that they appear to prefer a drier habitat than *S. pratensis*.

### Habits

They are nocturnal and terrestrial, and occur singly or in pairs, often on the same ground as *S. pratensis* and *S. krebsii*.

### Food

Coetzee (1977b) stated that they eat the seeds of grass and other plants.

### Reproduction

Little is known about this aspect of their life history, although a lactating female was trapped during November in the central Kalahari. In line with other members of the genus, it is likely that the young are born during the warm, wet summer months. Females have two pairs of pectoral and two pairs of inguinal mammae.

---

No. 204

## *Steatomys krebsii* Peters, 1852

## Krebs's fat mouse
## Krebs se vetmuis

Plate 15

---

### Taxonomic Notes

Meester *et al.* (1986) listed four subspecies from the Subregion: *S. k. krebsii* from the eastern Cape Province; *S. k. pentonyx* (Sclater, 1899) from the southwestern and western Cape Province; *S. k. orangiae* Roberts, 1929 from the Orange Free State, northwestern Natal, Transvaal, northern Cape Province and southeastern Botswana, and *S. k. angolensis* Hill & Carter, 1941 from northeastern Botswana and the eastern Caprivi Strip.

**Plate 15**

197. Large-eared mouse, *Malacothrix typica*
Bakoormuis
a & b colour variations
199. Grey climbing mouse, *Dendromus melanotis*
Grysklimmuis
200. Brants' climbing mouse, *Dendromus mesomelas*
Brants se klimmuis
201. Chestnut climbing mouse, *Dendromus mystacalis*
Roeskleurklimmuis
202. Fat mouse, *Steatomys pratensis*
Vetmuis
203. Tiny fat mouse, *Steatomys parvus*
Dwergvetmuis
204. Krebs's fat mouse, *Steatomys krebsii*
Krebs se vetmuis
206. Pygmy rock mouse, *Petromyscus collinus*
Dwergklipmuis

206A. Barbour's rock mouse, *Petromyscus barbouri*
Barbour se klipmuis.

PLATE 15
199
200
201
206
206A
197a
197b
202
203
204
Dick Findlay.

### Description

Krebs's fat mouse is the about the same size as the fat mouse, *S. pratensis*, 130 mm in total length, with a tail just over half the length of the head and body and a mass of about 24,0 g (Table 204.1). Their relatively short hair has a steep chevron pattern across the width of the hair (Fig. XXIII.3) (Keogh, 1985). There is a wide range of colour within their distribution range. Those from the vicinity of the Orange River in the Cape Province are orange-buff on the upper parts; those from northern Botswana are much duller and greyer. Where this species and *S. pratensis* occur together, in the northern parts of their range, this species can be picked out on their greyer colour. The flanks are the same colour as the upper parts, while the under parts and front feet are white, and the hind feet are the same colour as the upper parts of the body. The individual hairs on the upper parts are grey at their bases.

**Table 204.1**

Measurements (mm) and mass (g) of Krebs's fat mice, *S. krebsii*, from Botswana (Smithers, 1971)

| | Males | | | Females | | |
|---|---|---|---|---|---|---|
| | x̄ | n | Range | x̄ | n | Range |
| TL | 130 | 9 | 118–146 | | | |
| (HB | 79) | | | | | |
| T | 51 | 9 | 44–61 | | | |
| Hf c/u | 17 | 9 | 14–19 | | | |
| E | 17 | 8 | 16–18 | | | |
| Mass | one only 24,0 | | | | | |
| TL skull | 23,9 | 9 | 22,9–24,9 | | | |

### Distribution

Krebs's fat mouse is not a common species in collections and at the moment its distribution seems discontinuous, which may be due to lack of collecting. So far there are no records north of 10°S on the continent (Coetzee, 1977b).

*South of the Sahara, excluding the Southern African Subregion*

They occur in **Angola** and in western **Zambia**.

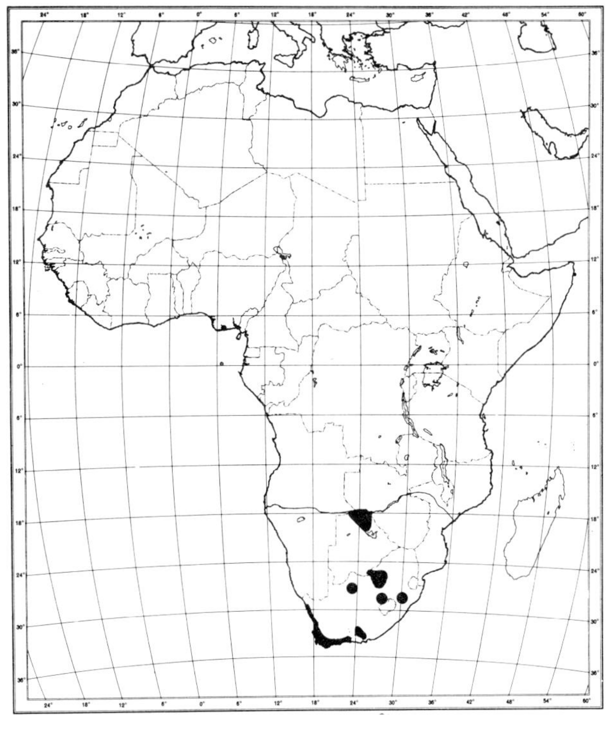

Southern African Subregion distribution only.

*Southern African Subregion*

They are recorded in the Subregion from the southwestern, northern and eastern **Cape Province**; from the southwestern **Transvaal**, northeastern **Orange Free State**, northern **Botswana** and the eastern Caprivi Strip, **Namibia**.

### Habitat

Like other species of *Steatomys* they prefer a sandy substrate, occurring in dry, sandy grassland and sandy alluvium, in some parts on the same ground as *S. pratensis* and *S. parvus*.

### Habits

Nocturnal and terrestrial, they occur solitarily or in pairs. Otherwise nothing is known of this aspect of their life history.

### Food

No information is available, but like other species of *Steatomys* their diet probably consists of both insects and seeds.

### Reproduction

No information is available. Females have two pairs of pectoral and two pairs of inguinal mammae.

## Subfamily PETROMYSCINAE

While members of the genus *Petromyscus* are retained by some authorities as members of the Subfamily Dendromurinae, their molar teeth are different in structure, having a zig-zag pattern of enamel and, in addition, the incisor teeth are not grooved, as they are in members of the Dendromurinae. It was on this basis that Roberts (1951) created this Subfamily as its members share features with both the Cricetidae on the one hand and the Muridae on the other.

## Genus *Petromyscus* Thomas, 1926

In members of this genus the skull is broad and flattened, the infraorbital foramen not enlarged and the palate broad. The posterior lamina of the upper first and second molar appears doubled or twisted around itself, while the third upper molar is small. The lower molars are reminiscent of the genus *Mystromys*.

Key to the species (Ellerman *et al.*, 1953)

1. Tail shorter than head and body; ear about 11–12 mm ... *monticularis*

   Tail averages longer than head and body; ear 13 mm or more ... *collinus*

---

No. 205

## *Petromyscus monticularis* (Thomas & Hinton, 1925)

## Brukkaros pygmy rock mouse
## Brukkaros-dwergklipmuis

---

### Colloquial Name

So named because the original specimen was taken on a small stony koppie near the base of Great Brukkaros Mountain in southern Namibia.

### Taxonomic Notes

No subspecies have been described.

### Description

This is a very small species, smaller than *P. collinus*. The upper parts are brownish-buff, the under parts grey. The bases of the hairs on the upper parts are slate-grey. The ears are short and dark brown in colour, the hands and feet white. The tail is short, shorter than the length of the head and body. Compared with the better known *P. collinus*, they have much narrower internal nares and shorter ears.

**Table 205.1**

Measurements (mm) of Brukkaros pygmy rock mice, *P. monticularis*, from the type locality (Shortridge, 1934)

| | HB | T | Hfc/u | E |
|---|---|---|---|---|
| Male | 77 | 72 | 15,5 | 12,5(TYPE) |
| Female | 74 | 64 | 15 | 11,5 |

**Distribution**

Known from the vicinity of Great Brukkaros Mountain in southern **Namibia**, Meester *et al.* (1986) noted the possibility that the species might have a much wider distribution, perhaps extending into the northern Cape Province.

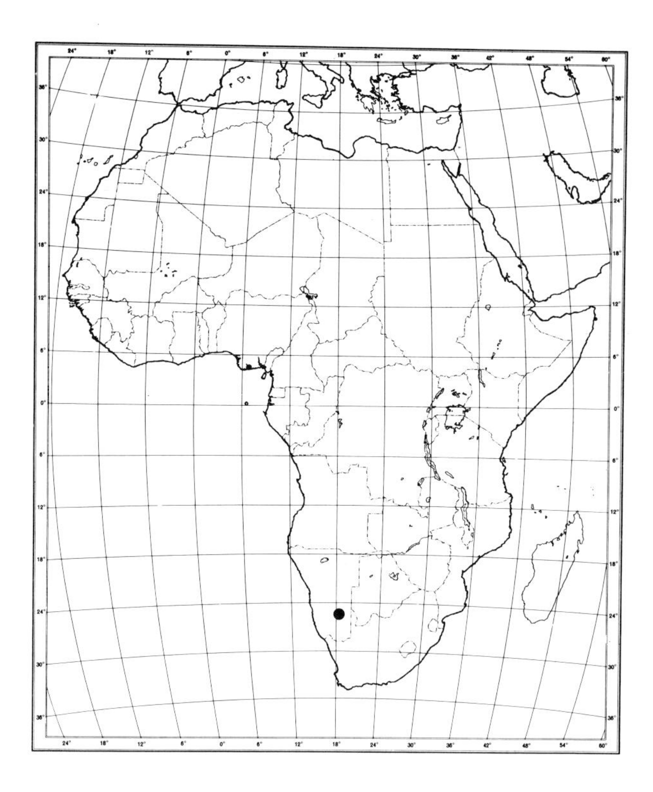

**Habitat, Habits, Food and Reproduction**

Unknown.

No. 206

## *Petromyscus collinus* (Thomas & Hinton, 1925)

### Pygmy rock mouse
### Dwergklipmuis

Plate 15

**Taxonomic Notes**

Meester *et al.* (1986) listed three subspecies: *P. c. collinus* from Great Namaqualand to Damaraland, Namibia; *P. c. shortridgei* Thomas, 1926 from the Kaokoveld, extending northwards into Angola; and *P. c. barbouri* Shortridge & Carter, 1938 from the northeastern Cape Province, which are afforded specific rank here (see 206A; 206B).

**Description**

The adults have a total length of about 190 mm and a mass of about 20,0 g. Their tails are longer than the length of the head and body and the heavy scaling is clearly visible through the sparse hair. Short narrow hairs with a single chevron scale covering width of hair (Fig. XXIII.3) (Keogh, 1985). The colour of the upper parts is buffy-yellow, the fur soft and silky. The under parts, hands and feet are greyish-white. It is a quadrupedal rodent, with the hind foot toes adapted for climbing rocks (de Graaff, 1981). The fifth toe of the hind foot is long, the hallux well developed and the ears are large. The juveniles are smoky-grey in colour (Shortridge, 1934).

**Distribution**

*South of the Sahara, excluding the Southern African Subregion*

They occur in southwestern **Angola**.

*Southern African Subregion*

In the Subregion they are confined to the South West Arid Zone, from the Swartberg in the southeast through central, western and northwestern **Cape Province** and ranging northwards through central and western **Namibia**, including parts of the Namib Desert.

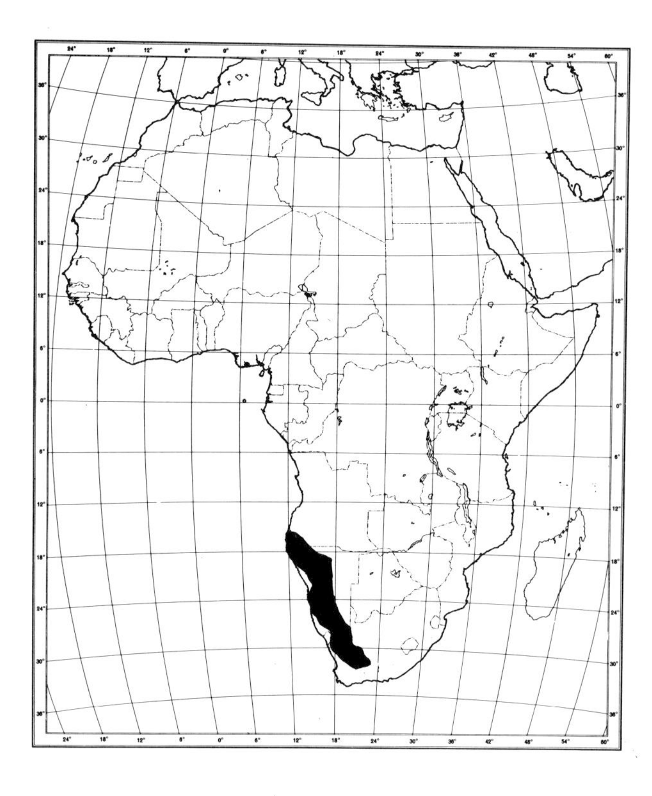

**Habitat**

They occur in arid areas on rocky outcrops or koppies, preferring areas with rocky overhangs, crannies, cracks and vegetation to provide hiding places (Withers, 1979). Breytenbach (1982) only found them in *Portulacaria afra* shrubland in the Swartberg where succulent vegetation is prominent..

**Habits**

They are nocturnal and terrestrial animals from arid regions and can survive for several weeks in captivity without water on a diet of air-dried seed (Withers *et al.*, 1980), whilst those from more mesic regions are more dependent on exogenous water. *Petromyscus* aestivate in the Namib Desert during the hot, dry summer months, lowering their body temperature as a water conservation measure (Withers *et al.*, 1980).

### Food

In the laboratory they are granivorous, which probably reflects their diet in the wild.

### Reproduction

Shortridge (1934) reported a pregnant female with two foetuses in September in southern Namibia and 12 with two or three foetuses in May in the north. In the Namib Desert it breeds seasonally, one litter of 2–3 pups being produced each summer (Withers, 1983). In captivity, they breed in December with a litter size of 2,8 (n=8). Following birth, pups are firmly attached to nipples in the nest. Pups weigh about 2,2 g at birth, the ear pinnae become free at 0–3 days, the toes at 2–4 days, hair appears at 0–4 days and the eyes open at 12–14 days (Dempster & Perrin, 1989b). They form stable populations with a high survival-rate, and display a demographic pattern derived from a low reproductive-potential (Withers *et al.*, 1980).

No. 206A

## *Petromyscus barbouri* Shortridge & Carter, 1938

## Barbour's rock mouse
## Barbour se klipmuis

Plate 15

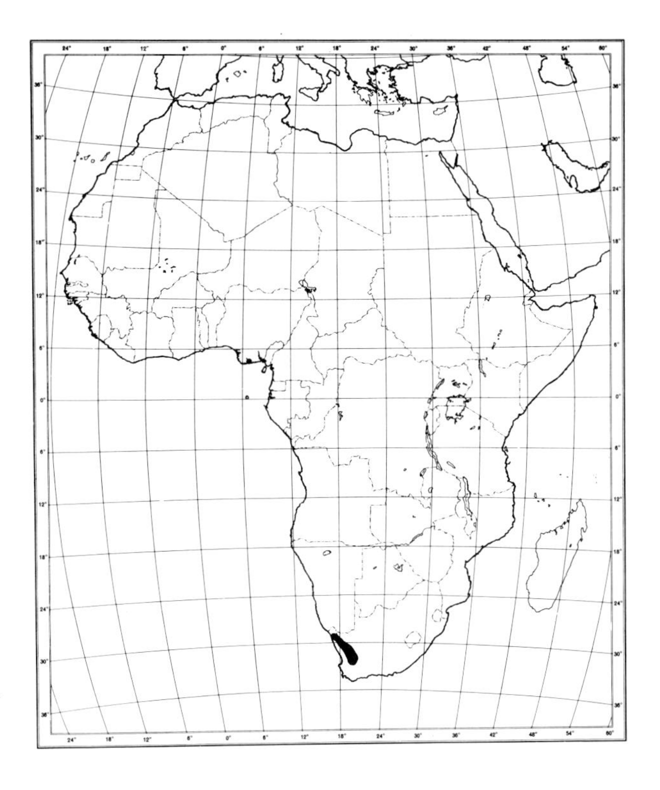

### Habits, Food and Reproduction

Except that they are known to be nocturnal and solitary, they have not been studied in detail and no further information is presently available.

### Colloquial Name

This species is named after Dr Thomas Barbour, formerly Director of the Museum of Comparative Zoology, Harvard University.

### Taxonomic Notes

Formerly this species was considered a subspecies of *P. collinus* by Shortridge & Carter (1938) who in describing it, featured its drab grey colour and its bicoloured tail.

### Description

The upper parts of the body and head are drab grey faintly grizzled with buff, the under parts whitish, and the pale grey bases of the hairs showing through to give the whole a greyish appearance. The sides of the face are tinged buffy, the upper parts of the feet white. The tail is darker above than below, is finely scaled and covered with bristly hair, especially towards the tip. The type specimen from Witwater (Kamiesberg), Little Namaqualand, had the following measurements: HB 78; T 80; Hf s/u 19; E 14. A series of four specimens from Springbok, Cape Province averaged as follows: HB 69; T 81; Hf s/u 18; E 14.

### Distribution

*Southern African Subregion*

They are confined to the northwestern Cape Province where so far they are recorded from five localities.

### Habitat

Associated with rocky areas.

No. 206B

## *Petromyscus shortridgei* Thomas, 1926

## Shortridge's rock mouse
## Shortridge se klipmuis

### Colloquial Name

Named after Capt. G.C. Shortridge, formerly Director of the Kaffrarian Museum, King William's Town, Cape Province.

### Taxonomic Notes

Meester *et al.* (1986) included this as a subspecies of *P. collinus*, but this dark-coloured, long-tailed species is recognisable in a collection of *P. collinus* and until a review of the genus is undertaken, it is here afforded the specific rank given to it originally by Thomas (1926).

### Description

It is a dark-coloured species, the upper parts of the body greyish tinged with buffy, the hairs with slate-grey bases and tipped with buff, giving a grizzled appearance. The sides of the face are lighter in colour than the upper parts of the body. The upper parts of the feet are white, the tail bicoloured and darker above than below. The under parts are grey, the hairs grey at the base with whitish tips, the throat white. The anterior palatal foramen barely reaches the front of the upper first molar tooth. The measurements of the type are HB 85; T 90; Hf 17; E 15.

**Table 206B.1**

Measurements (mm) of Shortridge's rock mice, *P. shortridgei*, from northern Namibia (Shortridge, 1934)

| | Males | | | Females | | |
|---|---|---|---|---|---|---|
| | $\bar{x}$ | n | Range | $\bar{x}$ | n | Range |
| (TL | 177) | | | (181) | | |
| HB | 86 | 14 | 80–94 | 86 | 13 | 80–92 |
| T | 91 | 14 | 83–98 | 95 | 13 | 82–103 |
| Hf c/u | 17 | 14 | 16–18 | 17 | 13 | 17–18 |
| E | 15 | 14 | 14–16 | 16 | 13 | 14–17 |

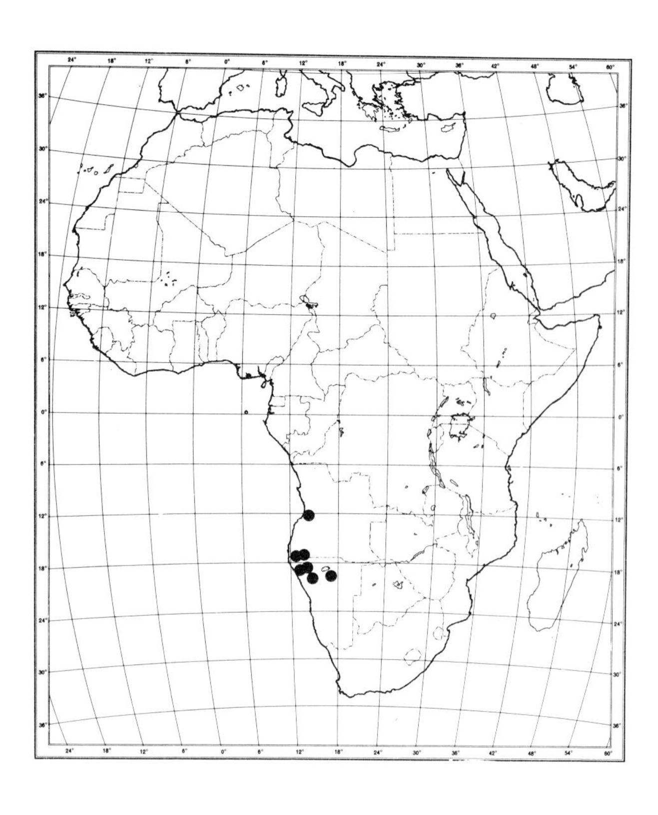

## Distribution

*South of the Sahara, excluding the Southern African Subregion*

Hill & Carter (1941) recorded the species from Caporolo, western **Angola** (1214 Ac).

*Southern African Subregion*

Occurs in the extreme northwestern parts of **Namibia**, the type locality being the Cunene (Ruacana) Falls on the Cunene River, the border with Angola.

## Habitat

They are associated with rocky areas, in common with other species of *Petromyscus*.

## Habits

Nocturnal and solitary.

## Food

Unknown.

## Reproduction

A dozen gravid females with 2–3 foetuses were taken by Shortridge (1934) in May. He noted that the number of mammae appeared to be variable; most have two pairs of inguinal mammae but about 10–15% have an additional pair of pectoral mammae.

# Order CETACEA

## Whales and dolphins

Grave concern has been expressed in recent years regarding the status of the great whales, some species of which have been depleted to the level that some scientists consider could put their very survival in jeopardy. The early 20th century witnessed the passing of the days when whaling was carried out in sailing ships and the harpooning from rowing boats. It is a popular misconception that the nature of the operation limited the catches, often made at the greatest risk to those taking part and the vessels from which they operated, and that their effect on the stocks was minimal. In fact whaling from the 17th to 19th centuries saw the severe depletion of most bowhead, right and gray whale stocks. These whalers, however, could not effectively exploit the bigger and faster rorquals (blue, fin and sei whales) that sank when killed. More sophisticated methods employing steam-driven vessels and harpoon guns, the harpoons later equipped with explosive charges, were needed to pursue, kill and secure these animals. This form of whaling, pioneered by Svend Foyn and others in the 1870's, commenced in the North Atlantic. Attention of whalers, however, soon turned to the search for new and more profitable whaling grounds and was directed to the southern oceans, now readily accessible to steam-driven vessels. Here the great rorquals congregate seasonally to feed on the vast concentrations of shrimp-like creatures, krill, which are their principal food. The mid 1920's saw the advent of factory ships with their fleet of fast catching vessels which allowed for the quick processing of the catch at sea. The resulting systematic slaughter then reached unprecedented proportions. By the 1960's the blue whale, *Balaenoptera musculus*, was estimated to have been reduced to about 6% of the numbers living before commercial whaling started, and the humpback whale, *Megaptera novaeangliae*, to 7% (Scheffer, 1976). Over-exploitation has reduced many populations to a stage from which, even with a moratorium on whaling, they will take decades to recover.

The attention of international conservation agencies is not, however, solely directed to the great whales. In 1948 the Survival Service Commission of the International Union for the Conservation of Nature and Natural Resources (SSC/IUCN) was established to conserve world genetic resources. At first concerned with the study and management of species considered to be in danger of extinction, in 1970 the Whale Specialist Group drew attention to the fact that while some progress had been made to improve conservation measures as far as the great whale fisheries were concerned, no international regulations existed which were directed to the smaller species of whales. Some of these smaller species have a history of exploitation which antedates the beginnings of modern whaling. Some of the methods used are indiscriminate, such as the driving ashore of whole schools of species such as long-finned pilot whales, *Globicephala melaena*, in Newfoundland and in other parts of the Northern Hemisphere. In 1956 the catches of this species reached nearly 10 000 annually in Newfoundland alone, the result being that in subsequent years the catches fell dramatically, so that by 1962 a bare 100 were taken. Mitchell (1975a) ascribed this decline to their over-exploitation.

Some of the biggest kills of small cetaceans, however, come from fisheries where they are not the target species. The most striking example is the mortality of dolphins (mostly spinner and spotted) in the purse-seine fishery for tuna in the eastern tropical Pacific. As tuna associate with schools of dolphins, nets are set around the dolphins with the intention of securing the tuna beneath. However, incidental mortality of the dolphins occurs before they can be released from the nets. In the 1960's the annual mortality in this fishery was as high as 200 000 to 500 000 dolphins per year, but this figure declined in the late 1970's to as little as 20 000 to 30 000 per year due to major improvements in gear and technology. More recent estimates indicate that the kill has increased again slightly, to about 100 000 a year.

The danger both with great and small cetaceans is that their utilisation has preceded our knowledge of what populations exist and what they can stand on a renewable resource basis. It was recognised that if their survival was to be assured, whaling would have to be controlled, especially in the case of the larger species, the baleen whales of the Family Balaenopteridae, the blue, Bryde, fin, humpback, minke and sei whales, and the single species of the toothed whales of the Family Physeteridae, the sperm whale. Starting in the 1930's, efforts were made to conserve remaining stocks through regulations agreed upon internationally. The last and most enduring of these attempts was the International Convention for the Regulation of Whaling, the final protocol of which was signed by 15 nations in 1946 (including South Africa). This established an International Whaling Commission (IWC) with the objective of *inter alia* regulating the industry "to provide for the conservation, development, and optimum utilisation of the whale resources".

Space does not permit a detailed review of the subsequent actions of the IWC. Suffice to say that through a combination of being formed too late and having some fatal flaws in its constitution, but mainly through a lack of political will by the majority of its members over a number of decades to limit catches to what might be termed "sustainable", the IWC failed to prevent the over-exploitation of humpback, blue, fin, sei and, to some extent, sperm whale stocks. Each of these species eventually had to be given total protection from commercial whaling. In 1982, reacting to overwhelming public pressure, and as a result of the accession to the Convention of a number of non-whaling nations, the IWC voted to adopt a pause in all commercial whaling from 1986. A comprehensive assessment of the effect of the pause on whale stocks was to be undertaken by 1990, but as worded the pause is indefinite unless the IWC votes for its partial or total revision. At this stage (1989) the duration and effectiveness of the pause are uncertain.

The Order Cetacea is divided into three Suborders: the Archaeoceti, the fossil members of the Order; the Odontoceti, the toothed whales, and the Mysticeti, the baleen whales. The archaeocetes had teeth differentiated into incisors, canines and grinding teeth, and nostrils situated near the tip of their snouts. The most primitive were members of the Family Protocetidae which had a total length of 2–9 m, long reptilian snouts and reduced hind limbs. Another Family, the Basilosauridae, had total lengths up to 21 m and were elongated and snake-like in shape. In members of the Subfamily Durodontidae, which had total lengths of up to 6 m, the teeth had accessory cusps on their anterior and posterior cutting edges. These archaeocetes probably evolved to fill the niche left vacant by the extinction of the great reptiles about the end of the Cretaceous period 65 million years ago. No undisputed archaeocetes remain after the Eocene. The primitive mysticete *Aetiocetus* from the late Oligocene is now believed to be a link between the Archaeoceti and the Mysticeti, while the *Agorophiidae*, also from the late Oligocene, are believed to occupy a similar position between the Archaeoceti and Odontoceti (Barnes, Domming & Ray, 1985).

Fossil deposits have yielded evidence from species which, during an Eocene epoch, lived in the ancient Tethys Sea which covered parts of North Africa and the Middle East. At the same time the Atlantic Ocean encroached into parts of West Africa and fossil remains have been recovered from what is today Senegal and Nigeria of species which lived in this part of the ocean during the middle Eocene. Post Eocene fossil remains are rare and have not been well studied, but have been found in the Oligocene deposits in Australia, New Zealand, Europe, Asia and North America. A few fossil remains have been found in Miocene deposits in Libya and Egypt and from Pliocene deposits in Libya and at Langebaanweg in the Cape Province (Hendey, 1970, 1973, 1974, 1976; Barnes & Mitchell, 1978).

The Cetacea are among the most highly modified and specialised of all mammals. They retain, nevertheless, all the attributes of mammals, breathing air and suckling their young. Although their skin appears to be devoid of hair, in some species a few scattered hairs are found on the chin and snout and hair occurs on the very young.

The flippers, which correspond to the forelimbs of terrestrial mammals, are adapted to their aquatic life. The digits or fingers, however, have no independent movement and are totally enclosed in skin inside which lie the elongated finger bones, connected to the skeletal structure by the bones of the forearm and a short upper arm bone. The whole of the forelimb in whales lies external to the body, rotating as one unit on the shoulder joint, whereas in seals only the hand, in the form of a flipper, lies in this position.

No trace of the hind limbs in whales is externally visible, but the degenerate remains of these may be found embedded in the flesh with no connection to the skeletal structure. In the preparation of whale skeletons in the field these loose bones are often difficult to find and are easily overlooked. In the oldest known fossil, *Protocetus atavus*, the sacral vertebrae have a definite facet for articulation and it is probable that it possessed some type of pelvic limbs (Barnes & Mitchell, 1978). Anomalous projecting rudimentary pelvic limbs have been reported in some dolphins (Ohsumi, 1965), a humpbacked whale (Andrews, 1921) and a sperm whale (Ogawa & Kamiya, 1957).

The skin or epidermis of Cetacea varies from 1–13 mm in thickness. This overlies a thinner dermis and a very thick, fat-rich hypodermal layer known as blubber. This blubber acts as a food store and is generally assumed to act as an insulator against the very cold water in which they spend most or all of their lives. Kanwisher & Sundnes (1966), however, questioned whether its primary function is insulation, for whales appear to be grossly over-insulated, and suggested that the blubber may play an important part in maintaining hydrostatic buoyancy. When a cetacean is out of the water the blubber can act as an insulator in the air, literally boiling the individual in its own metabolic heat (Gaskin, 1972).

Contrary to popular opinion, rather than keeping warm, their problem may be to keep cool. Tomilin (1967) stated that heat loss takes place through the thinner skin of the flippers, dorsal fin and flukes. In the vascular system there are a series of *retia mirabilia* which are assumed to have a function in diving such as regulating pulsations of pressure in the vascular system developing as a result of breath-holding in cetaceans. They may have the function of heat transfer, conserving the heat from the arterial blood before it passes to areas where heat loss occurs, such as the flippers and flukes. Whales have no sweat glands in their skin and when it becomes necessary to lose heat the arteries in the *retia mirabilia* dilate, closing off the surrounding veins and forcing the blood to return via the subsurface veins. These subsurface veins are very abundant in the flippers and tail flukes where the blubber is thin and allows for great transfer of heat from the body to the sea water (Scholander & Schevill, 1955).

Cetaceans, unlike man, are capable of diving very deeply without ill-effects. The pressures experienced in deep dives cause nitrogen to be transferred from the air in the lungs into the blood system and fatty tissues. Repeated dives to great depths can cause the nitrogen to be absorbed to such a degree that, on returning to the surface, where the pressure is less, it forms bubbles in the blood stream and causes a condition in man known as "the bends" which can have serious if not fatal consequences. The deepest man has been able to dive, with the aid of Scuba equipment, is about 500 m. If he remains for only four minutes at this depth, he has to spend 14 days decompressing in order to allow the nitrogen in his blood and fatty tissue to be released slowly enough to avoid an attack of "the bends" (McNairn, pers. comm.).

Cetaceans on the other hand have been recorded to dive to much greater depths and to do so repeatedly. The sperm whale, *Physeter macrocephalus*, has been recorded as diving to 1 134 m, the fin whale, *Balaenoptera physalus*, to 500 m and the bottlenosed dolphin, *Tursiops truncatus*, to 300 m. They do not have to wait to decompress on returning to the surface. Their ability to achieve this is brought about by a series of morphological adaptations and physiological processes. In cetaceans the diaphragm is set at an oblique angle so that under pressure the lungs empty into the non-respiratory air passages. The lungs are to all intents and purposes empty of air for the duration of the dive and therefore no nitrogen can be absorbed by the blood (Scholander, 1964). Also the endothelium of the lungs thickens to such a degree under compression that the rate of diffusion is slowed, which also prevents excess nitrogen uptake (Steen, 1971).

In man, when the chest is compressed under pressure to a volume smaller than the volume at full expiration, a partial collapse of the lungs may occur causing rupture of the pulmonary capillaries. A certain degree of acclimatisation can occur in professional divers, as much as a litre of blood being forced into the capillaries and blood vessels in the lungs, which tends to prevent the deleterious effects of this "thoracic squeeze". This is known as the "stiff lung". Cetaceans and seals do not have this problem as their lungs are able to collapse totally under pressure without damage.

The body requires oxygen during dives and this can be stored in two major areas: in the lungs as gas and in the blood and tissues in combination with haemoglobin and myoglobin respectively. Because of the fact that, in cetaceans, the lungs empty under pressure, the amount of free oxygen that is available is minimal. It has been shown that some cetaceans have 60% more blood in their systems than a man of equivalent mass. The haemoglobin in blood absorbs oxygen which is made available as required. A greater amount, however, is stored in the myoglobin in the muscle tissue. Cetacean muscle contains far more myoglobin per gram than the muscle in terrestrial mammals. It has 10 times more affinity for oxygen than haemoglobin. They also utilise anaerobic respiration during the course of an extended dive.

These adaptations, however, are not sufficient in themselves to allow for the body requirements in deep diving and others assist in the process. At the onset of a dive it has been shown that in some species of seals the heart rate drops dramatically from 140 beats per minute to 10 (Steen, 1971). In spite of this the arterial pressure remains constant, although the blood output decreases. This is due to the operation of a swelling in the main artery of the heart, the aorta, the swelling being known as the aortic bulb. In addition, in all the Pinnipedia, there is a muscular sphincter in the posterior *vena cava*, so that in diving, while the blood supply to the head remains unimpeded, the supply to the rest of the body is occluded. The muscles utilised in swimming then rely on an oxygen supply stored in the myoglobin.

There is also a decrease in the metabolic rate during the dive which enables cetaceans, in conjunction with the other adaptations, to regulate the oxygen supply making a sufficient supply available to tide them over the period of lengthy dives.

Unlike most terrestrial mammals the nostrils or blowhole open about the middle of the face, the form and elongation of the jaws making it appear that they open on top of the head. This positioning allows them to breathe with only the minimum of the upper surface of the head above water.

While all cetaceans have teeth at least during the foetal period, in the Suborder Odontoceti they are retained after birth, there being no milk teeth. The tooth shape and position of the teeth may differ between the sexes; the females sometimes have much smaller teeth than the males or have teeth which do not erupt above the gums.

In the Suborder Mysticeti, on the other hand, the teeth never erupt above the gums, even after birth, and are replaced by plates of baleen which grow from the palatine ridges on the roof of the mouth and serve as food collectors.

Baleen whales can be aged by ascertaining the number of annual layers formed in the keratinous earplug which lies at the inner end of the auditory meatus. This plug is thought to have a function in the transfer of sound waves from the water to the inner ear. The baleen plates, characteristic of members of the Family Balaenopteridae, the baleen whales, are composed of keratin. Before the discovery of plastics, baleen, or "whale bone" as it was called, was in demand for a multitude of purposes in everyday life, from brushware to the supports for stays and other women's articles of apparel, now long out of fashion. Transverse ridges in the baleen plates can also be used to determine the age of young individuals.

Age determination in toothed whales is achieved normally through the examination of longitudinal sections of the teeth, in which growth layers in the dentine or cementum can be counted.

Many of the smaller species adapt themselves very well to captivity and a great deal has been learnt about their behaviour under these conditions. Anyone who visits an oceanarium and sees a display by dolphins comes away convinced that they are intelligent animals. Unfortunately we cannot really define intelligence and it is very difficult to differentiate between behaviour which can be called intelligent and behaviour which is the result of training in response to visual and auditory stimuli. One cannot but admire, however, their capacity for learning and it has been shown that they can solve simple problems, although they do not score more highly in this respect than some terrestrial mammals.

Their grace of action and the co-ordination of the individuals in schools in their natural environment mark them as among the most appealing and interesting of our mammals. A great deal of research has been directed to their methods of communication and echolocation within recent years using modern sophisticated apparatus. Toothed whales generally make two types of sounds, pulsed and unpulsed. Some pulsed sounds ("clicks") are implicated in echolocation, others ("squawks, blats, groans, moans" *etc.*) may have a social function. Unpulsed sounds are most commonly "whistles", and appear to have no other function than communication. Some species, including sperm whales, porpoises and some dolphins (including our Heaviside's dolphin) appear not to make unpulsed sounds, so for these species communication must be via pulsed sounds only. In general such species are found in smaller groups than the whistling species. Since at least some of the latter animals can produce whistles and clicks simultaneously, it is possible that the unpulsed sounds have developed as a means of communicating within large herds while foraging using echolocation.

Baleen whale sounds are very different to those of toothed whales, generally being of lower frequency and longer duration. They can be classified into low frequency "moans", shorter grunt-like noises, chirps and cries (from humpback whales) and click-like sounds. It is not clear whether the latter are used for echolocation; the low frequency moans may be used in this way to locate large targets such as shoals of prey. The low frequency sounds typical of mysticetes can travel long distances under water, and many serve some purpose in maintaining social contact. The humpback whale has been studied particularly closely because of its habit of producing ordered themes of repeated phrases resembling a "song". Songs can last for eight to 20 or more minutes and may be repeated several times in succession. Generally they are sung by solitary animals (probably adult males) on the breeding grounds, and may be a communal acoustic display (Herman & Tavolga, 1980).

The stranding of cetaceans is a well-known but poorly understood phenomenon. It is a feature of nearly all species, but the mass stranding of a dozen to several hundred individuals usually involves deep-sea species only. Single strandings are believed to represent debilitated or injured animals, while the cause of mass strandings is more conjectural. Recently it has been proposed that, because mass strandings frequently take place where lines of geomagnetic force are perpendicular to the coast, these species are using the earth's geomagnetic field for navigation, moving along rather than across "contours" of the field. Local geomagnetic disturbances may cause the animals to become disorientated and make a "wrong turn", following the contours in to the coast (Klinowska, 1986). It is not yet clear why, as they near the shore and pick up other cues of their imminent danger, such animals do not realise their predicament and reverse their direction.

The taxonomy and biology of the majority of the cetaceans are poorly known compared with our knowledge of terrestrial mammals. Only in the case of those species which are hunted commercially and where, therefore, more adequate material has been available for study, has it been possible for workers to contribute substantially to our knowledge. Far less is known about the smaller cetaceans where, out of the 55 that occur in the oceans of the world, less than 10 stocks of fewer species can be considered as well known (Mitchell, 1975a). As there has been little or no exploitation of these smaller cetaceans in South African waters, a great deal of reliance has had to be placed on information gleaned from individuals that strand on our coasts, coupled with sightings at sea and observational data on captive individuals. In so far as food is concerned, the remains of food items in the stomachs of stranded specimens of species normally living in deep water do not always represent the normal food of the species, for they may well have spent time in inshore waters prior to stranding where different types of food are available.

Many of the smaller species of Cetacea are not well known and a great deal of valuable information can be gleaned from individuals which strand on our coasts. The public is urged to report the finding of any type of stranded whale as soon as possible to the nearest Museum, Nature Conservation or Fisheries officer, or to the Sea Fisheries Research Institute in Cape Town and to try to ensure that the specimen remains intact. In the past rare species have been destroyed before they could be examined, with the consequent loss of valuable information.

In illustrations in literature there is a considerable variation in the interpretation of the shape of the body, the markings and colour of the individual species. We have followed sketches kindly provided by Dr G.J.B. Ross of the Port Elizabeth Museum whose major work on the smaller cetaceans of the southeast coast of South Africa provides the most complete assessment to date (Ross, 1979a), and to Dr P.B. Best of the Mammal Research Institute, University of Pretoria for information and guidance, to whom our grateful thanks are due.

### Classification of the vertebral bones

The neck in the Cetacea is generally shortened, with varying degrees of fusion of the cervical (neck) vertebrae. In some species of Cetacea all seven cervical vertebrae remain unfused, in others all the bones fuse to form a single bony unit. The remainder of the vertebral column is modified by extension especially in the lumbar region, the total number of vertebrae being variable. The caudal (tail) vertebrae have chevron bones, each one of which articulates on two of the vertebrae. These provide a greater surface for the attachment of the caudal muscles, the movement of the tail being important as it is the primary organ of movement.

The vertebral formula is based on the number and degree of fusion of the vertebrae and is expressed as follows (Nishiwaki, 1972):

C. Cervical vertebrae

The first seven vertebrae posterior to the skull. Where these vertebrae are fused the individual vertebra can be recognised and counted by observing the number of nerve bundles arising from the spinal cord. Occasionally the cervical vertebrae are found to have attached but incomplete bones, the cervical ribs, which are not considered to be true ribs. Examples of the various fusions in Subregion species are as follows:—All seven free: fin whale, *Balaenoptera physalus*; two fused: common dolphin, *Delphinus delphis*; three fused: pygmy killer whale, *Feresa attenuata*; four fused: killer whale, *Orcinus orca*; six fused: long-finned pilot whale, *Globicephala melaena*; all seven fused: dwarf sperm whale, *Kogia simus*.

Five are fused in the finless porpoise, *Neophocaena phocaenoides*, a species which is purported to have come from the Cape of Good Hope, but is not included in the Subregion list.

T. Thoracic vertebrae

The vertebrae to which the true ribs are attached. One or more of the anterior ribs are generally attached to a sternum. The most posterior rib often floats free of the vertebrae (the "floating rib") and therefore can be lost in preparation of skeletons. The number of thoracic vertebrae is equivalent to the number of pairs of ribs.

L. Lumbar vertebrae

The vertebrae to which neither ribs nor chevron bones attach. They are identified easily by their transverse processes.

Cd. Caudal vertebrae

The vertebrae to which the chevron bones attach. Although the anterior chevrons are distinct and recognised easily, those attached to the most posterior of the caudal vertebrae are difficult to distinguish. Many of the most posterior of these vertebrae lack attachment to bony chevrons and therefore the number of caudal vertebrae and chevron bones are not equivalent.

Key to the Suborders (Best, 1971c)

1. Teeth present in the lower or both jaws; blowhole single; ribs articulated with centra of vertebrae; sternal ribs distinct, ossified or cartilaginous
   ... Odontoceti

   Baleen present in upper jaw; blowhole double; ribs only articulated with transverse processes of the vertebrae; no sternal ribs present
   ... Mysticeti

# Suborder ODONTOCETI

## Toothed whales

The Suborder Odontoceti, the toothed whales, is represented in the high seas and coastal waters of the Subregion by members of three Families, comprising 21 genera and 29 species. Watson (1981) included the genera *Sousa* and *Steno* in a fourth Family Stenidae, but we follow Ross (1981) and Meester *et al.* (1986) in including these genera in the Delphinidae. In all the odontocetes the blowhole, the outer opening of the nostrils, is single, the two nasal cavities joining together to form the blowhole. As the name suggests all have teeth, which vary in number from a single pair (sometimes unerupted in adult females) to over 60 pairs. The degree of fusion of the seven cervical vertebrae is variable and all have a large sternum.

Members of the Family Platanistidae, none of which occur in the Subregion, either live in large freshwater rivers such as the Ganges, Indus, Amazon and Yangtze Rivers or (in the case of the franciscana) in coastal waters of Brazil, Uruguay and Argentina. They contain some of the currently most endangered cetaceans (Perrin *et al.*, 1989).

Key to the Families after Best (1971c) and Meester *et al.* (1986)

1. Upper jaw prolonged into a narrow beak; usually one or two pairs of teeth in lower jaw, usually erupting only in adult males; no notch on rear edge of flukes, two grooves form a V-shaped groove on throat
   ... Ziphiidae

   Several pairs of teeth present, usually in both jaws; notch present on rear edge of flukes; throat grooves absent or of a varied pattern
   ... 2

2. From 8–28 pairs of erupted teeth present in lower jaw only; lower jaw shorter than upper; nasals raised as crest overhanging nares; sternal ribs cartilaginous
   ... Physeteridae

   Many pairs of teeth present in both jaws (except in *Grampus*, where 3–7 pairs present in lower jaw only); no nasal crests overhanging nares; sternal ribs ossified
   ... Delphinidae

# XXIV. Family ZIPHIIDAE

## Beaked whales

These are small to medium-sized whales, with total lengths in adults from about 4,3 m-12,8 m, with narrow protruding beaks, a pair of grooves on the throat converging, but not joining anteriorly, and no median notch in the trailing edge of the caudal flukes. The dorsal fin is always placed much nearer the tail than the head. All but one species (*Tasmacetus*) have one or two pairs of teeth in each half of the lower jaw, which (except in the case of *Berardius* and *Tasmacetus*) erupt in adult males only. *Tasmacetus* is unique amongst beaked whales in having a series of 17 to 30 pairs of teeth in both upper and lower jaws of both sexes, with a much larger apical pair in the mandible that may erupt only in adult males. In *Berardius* the apical pairs of mandibular teeth erupt in adults of both sexes. The crest of the skull usually is noticeably asymmetrical, particularly in so far as the nasal bones are concerned which lie posterior to the blowhole and which give the impression of being twisted to the right.

Key to the genera after Best (1971c) and Meester *et al.* (1986)

1. Two pairs of large teeth at tip of lower jaw (Fig.207.1), which projects considerably beyond upper; skull more or less symmetrical
   ... *Berardius*

   Single pair of large teeth; skull and in particular the nasal crest, asymmetrical
   ... 2

2. Teeth laterally compressed, usually near centre of lower jaw, but if at tip are noticeably flattened in cross-section; nasals sunk between upper ends of premaxillae
   ... *Mesoplodon*

   Teeth at extremity of lower jaw, circular or oval in cross-section
   ... 3

3. Tip of snout to blowhole 10–13% of body length; nasals arch over nares, separated from premaxillae by a notch ... *Ziphius*
   Tip of snout of blowhole 14–22% of body length; nasals sunk between upper ends of premaxillae; maxillary crests enormously enlarged in adult males ... *Hyperoodon*

## Genus *Berardius* Duvernoy, 1851

Members of this genus have two pairs of teeth in the lower jaw, the largest pair situated near the tip, the second and smaller pair slightly further back (Fig.207.1). The skull is bilaterally asymmetrical.

Two species of the genus *Berardius* are known, *B. arnuxii* of the southern oceans and *B. bairdi* of the northern Pacific Ocean. *B. bairdi* is larger than *B. arnuxii*, male specimens reaching a total length of 11,6 m and females 12,2 m as compared with a maximum of 9,75 m in *B. arnuxii* (Ross, 1984). Omura, Fujino & Kimura (1955) suggested that the apparent constant size difference is due to the foreshortening of the caudal region, due to the smaller caudal vertebrae in *B. arnuxii*. The only external difference between the two species appears to be size, which led McLachlan, Liversidge & Tietz (1966) to suggest that they were only separable at the subspecific level. Best (1971c), however, accorded them full specific status, a view which is followed here. Ross (1984) in reviewing the situation came to the conclusion that re-evaluation of the specific status of the two species required further material, and although there are consistent (but minor) differences in skull characters, on present evidence there is little to suggest that they are specifically distinct.

Very few specimens of *B. arnuxii* are known and there is very little information available on their life history.

---

No. 207

## *Berardius arnuxii* Duvernoy, 1851

# Arnoux's beaked whale
# Arnoux se snoetwalvis

---

### Colloquial Name

Named after the ship's surgeon Dr M. Arnoux of the French corvette *Rhin* which brought the skull back from New Zealand. The generic name *Berardius* was created to honour the ships captain Bérard. Alternative name: Southern four-toothed whale.

### Description

The single published record of Arnoux's beaked whale from the coast of South Africa, which stranded at the Kromme River mouth, near Port Elizabeth, had a total length of 9,3 m (McLachlan, Liversidge & Tietz, 1966). The type specimen from New Zealand measured 9,75 m, which is the maximum length recorded. According to Watson (1981), less than 50 specimens of this species have been recorded.

The body is robust, rounded anteriorly and becoming progressively compressed laterally in its posterior third. The melon is bulbous, its anterior face somewhat flattened and slopes steeply down to merge with the prominent rounded beak. The blowhole shape is unique to the genus, being crescent-shaped with the rounded side facing forwards (rather than backwards, as in other ziphiid genera). The protruding tip of the lower jaw carries the larger, anterior pair of the two pairs of teeth carried by this species, which erupt ahead of the tip of the upper jaw. This anterior pair of teeth is forwardly directed, conical and laterally compressed in shape. The upper parts of the body are black, the dorsal and lateral surfaces of the melon and small dorsal fin greyish-black (Ross, 1984). The colour of the under parts of the South African specimen is not recorded, but the New Zealand specimen had a narrow band of grey on the belly (McCann, 1975). Adult specimens, particularly males, may carry numerous linear white scars on the body, single or paired in nature, which are thought to be the consequence of intraspecific aggression (Fig. 207.1).

Fig. 207.1 Arnoux's beaked whale, *Berardius arnuxii*. Male at 9,30 m. Males reach a total length of up to 9,75 m, the females are slightly longer (after Ross, 1984).

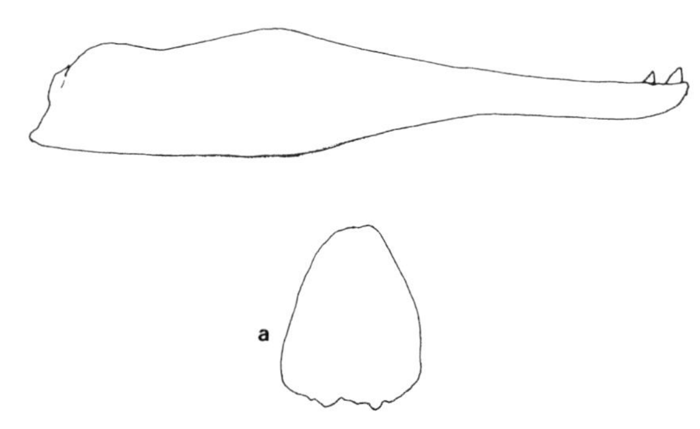


Fig. 207.2. Mandible and teeth, *Berardius arnuxii* (a) anterior tooth in male. After Ross (1984).

The vertebral formula is C7+T10–11+L12–13+Cd17–19 = 47–49 (True, 1910; Hale, 1962). It has been claimed that the number of ribs differs between *arnuxii* (10) and *bairdi* (11), but Ross (1984) stated that further material is required.

### Distribution

Arnoux's beaked whales have been observed or collected at scattered localities throughout the southern oceans, mostly from the New Zealand area, but including southern Australia; the Chatham Islands; Falkland Islands; South Shetland Islands; Argentina and Graham Land on the Antarctic Peninsula. Most of these records are south of latitude 40 °S, the South African records being amongst the furthest north (latitude 34 °S). Ross (1984) stated that they have a circumpolar distribution in the Southern ocean. In six years of systematic surveys for cetaceans in the Antarctic, only 5 schools of a total of 17 Arnoux's beaked whale were seen, most frequently within 60 nautical miles of the pack ice, and although large numbers of other, unidentified ziphiids were seen, the majority (perhaps 90%) of these were probably southern bottlenose whales (Kasamatsu, Hembree, Joyce, Tsunoda, Rowlett & Nakano, 1988). The species has been recorded trapped in the pack ice some 65 km from the open sea (Taylor, 1957).

### Food

Cephalopod beaks were recovered from a specimen which stranded in New Zealand. Nishiwaki & Oguro (1971) examined 383 stomachs of *B. bairdi* containing food, of which 40,7% contained deep sea fish, 28,9% squid and 23,0% fish such as mackerel, sardine, flat fish and other species, the balance of the stomachs being unidentified.

### Reproduction

No data are available.

## Genus *Mesoplodon* Gervais, 1850

Five species of this genus are known from South African waters, identifiable from the position of the teeth in the mandible and their form and orientation (in females or subadult males this will require the gum to be dissected away).

Key to the species after Meester *et al.* (1986)

1. Teeth are at or near tip of lower jaw ... 2

   Teeth at or posterior to posterior end of symphysis ... 3

2. Teeth 10–25 mm from tip of lower jaw; width of premaxillary crests equal to or less than premaxillary width at anterior border of nares ... *M. hectori*

   Teeth at extreme tip of lower jaw; premaxillary crests wider than premaxillary width at anterior border of nares ... *M. mirus*

3. Line of gape almost straight; dorsal margin of mandible approximately straight; teeth not directed anterodorsally ... 4

   Line of gape rises abruptly at about mid-length; dorsal margin of mandible strongly elevated at mid-length; teeth directed anterodorsally ... *M. densirostris*

4. Teeth directed posterodorsally; in dorsal view prominential notches present where maxillae widen to base of rostrum ... *M. layardii*

   Teeth directed dorsally; no prominential notches in dorsal view; 15–22 rudimentary teeth in upper jaw ... *M. grayi*

---

No. 208

## *Mesoplodon hectori* (Gray, 1871)

## Hector's beaked whale
## Hector se snoetwalvis

---

**Colloquial Name**

Named after Sir James Hector, Curator of the Colonial Museum in Wellington, New Zealand.
Alternative names: Skew beaked whale; New Zealand beaked whale.

Up to 1987 this species was only known from 21 specimens and two sightings at sea (Lichter, 1986; Mead & Baker, 1987). Adult males have the smallest skulls of any described *Mesoplodon* species, and presumably the adult animal is also relatively small: the largest known male was 3,90 m and the largest female 4,43 m long. Calves as small as 1,9 and 2,02 m have been recorded (Lichter, 1986). It is distinguished from all other species of *Mesoplodon* by having a single pair of triangular-shaped, flat teeth set a few millimetres back from the tip of the mandible (Fig. 208.1). It has been recorded from Tasmania, New Zealand, the Falkland Islands, Argentina and Chile, and up to 1975 was only known from the Southern Hemisphere. Remarkably, however, since that date there have been four strandings and two sightings at sea in California (Mead, 1981), so the species must occur in both hemispheres. Their latitudinal limits of distribution are unknown (Ross, 1984).

Two skulls of immature animals were picked up at the Lottering River mouth just west of Port Elizabeth in March 1967, and these remain the only records from South Africa.

**Food**

The very scanty stomach content data suggest that Hector's beaked whale feeds on pelagic species of squid (Mead, 1981).

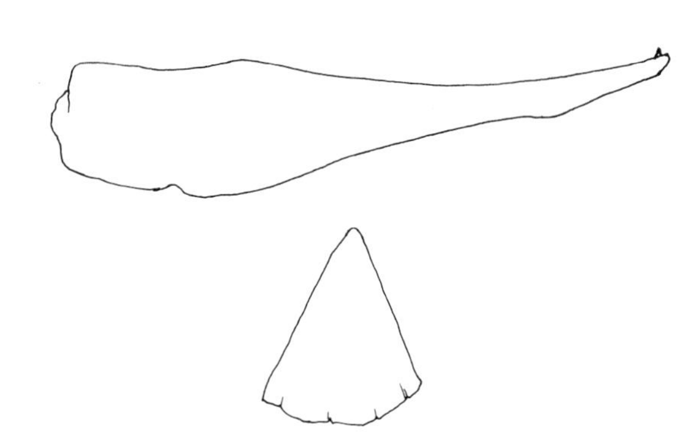

Fig.208.1. Mandible and tooth, *Mesoplodon hectori*. After Ross (1984).

---

No. 209

## *Mesoplodon mirus* True, 1913

## True's beaked whale
## True se snoetwalvis

---

**Colloquial Name**

Named after F.W. True of the United States National Museum who published several papers on cetaceans and originally described the species.
Alternative name: Wonderful beaked whale.

**Taxonomic Notes**

The available evidence suggests that the species has an anti-tropical distribution, there being no records between latitudes 30 °N and 30 °S (Ross, 1984) apart from one South African record at 28 °27′S that has been attributed to unusual oceanographic conditions (Ross, Cockcroft & Cliff, 1985). In a comparison of nine Northern Hemisphere and six Southern Hemisphere specimens, Ross (1984) reported that they differ in only one out of 47 standard cranial measurements, in one additional cranial measurement, and in one out of 25 descriptive characters of the cranium, but in none of 13 mandibular measurements. He concluded that if further material confirms these differences, the populations might warrant subspecific status.

**Description**

The body of True's beaked whale is robust, deep and laterally compressed. The melon is bulbous anterior to the blowhole and slopes relatively steeply and smoothly into the short beak (Ross, 1984).

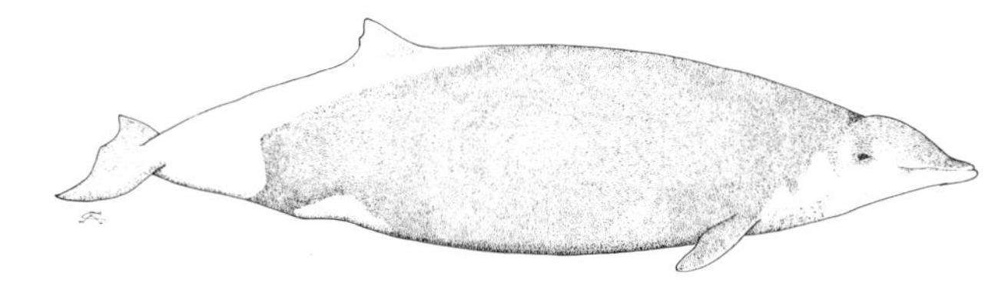

Fig. 209.1 True's beaked whale, *Mesoplodon mirus*. Adult female at 4,85 m. Greatest total length recorded in males and females 5,33 m (after Ross, 1984).

The species has a total length of about 4,8 m to 5,3 m. An adult female 5,1 m long weighed 1 533 kg, allowing for loss of body fluids during dissection (Ross, 1984). In a Southern Hemisphere adult the anterior half of the upper parts of the body, the flanks and under parts are dark blue-black. The underside of the jaw and the posterior portion of the body, the area enclosing the genital aperture, the dorsal fin and under surface of the tail flukes are whitish. True's original description mentions purple and yellow tints on the belly. The edges of the jaw and the throat are speckled with blue-black on a light grey background, and the rest of the body is dark blue-black (Ross, 1984). The flippers are small with rounded tips, dark in colour, and are situated low down on the sides of the body and fit into slight depressions in the body. The small, triangular or slightly hooked dorsal fin is situated about two-thirds of the total length of the body from the tip of the snout. The tail flukes are wide laterally but relatively narrow antero-posteriorly, and there is no central notch on their trailing edge. A stranded Southern Hemisphere calf was very different in coloration to the accompanying adult female (described above), being cloud-grey on the head, sides and belly, merging gradually into a dark blue-grey dorsally (Ross, 1984).

The species has a single pair of teeth embedded in a deep alveolus at the tip of the lower jaw. The teeth are conical in shape and laterally compressed (Fig. 209.2).

Ross (1984) gives the vertebral formula of a specimen from Plettenberg Bay, Cape Province as C7+T11+L13+Cd17(+1) = 48(+1), whereas northern hemisphere specimens have been recorded as C7+T10+L10–11+Cd18–19(+1 or 2) = 46 (+1 or 2).

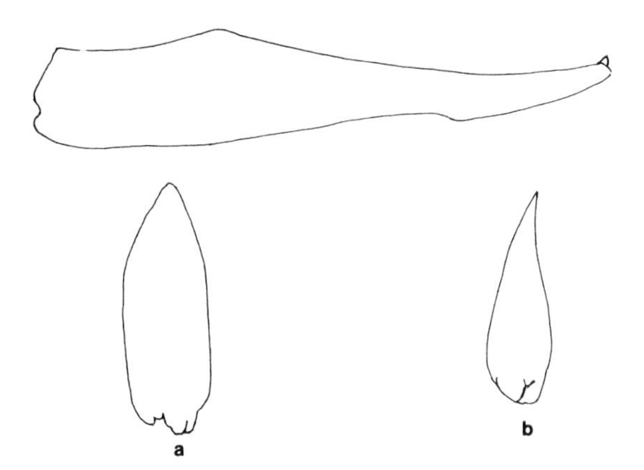


Fig. 209.2 Mandible and teeth of True's beaked whale, *Mesoplodon mirus* (a) Tooth of male (b) Tooth of female (after Ross, 1984)

### Distribution

Up to 1959 True's beaked whale was only known from 12 stranded specimens, all from the North Atlantic (either from the west coast of Ireland or the eastern seaboard of North America), and all north of 30 °N. In May 1959, however, an adult male beaked whale stranded at the Wilderness on the southern coast of South Africa and proved to be a specimen of *M. mirus* (McCann & Talbot, 1963). Initial scepticism over the existence of a separate southern population of the species was overcome when in January 1969 a pregnant female and its calf stranded at Maitland River mouth near Port Elizabeth, followed by an adult male at Jeffreys Bay in July 1969 and another female and calf at Plettenberg Bay in May 1971 (Ross, 1984). Subsequently the species has been recorded also from Australia (Baker, 1983). In the Southern African Subregion, apart from the "extralimital" record from Natal, strandings of True's beaked whale have now occurred from Saldanha Bay to Port Elizabeth (Meester *et al.*, 1986). Ross *et al.* (1985) concluded that the species typically occurs in the region of mixing cold and warm waters off the southern Cape coast. Moore (1966) in discussing the Northern Hemisphere information, suggested that they inhabit the deeper waters of the Continental Shelf off the middle Atlantic States of the United States of America, stragglers following the Gulf Stream northwards towards the British Isles.

### Food

Ross (1984) recorded that the stomach of one female from Port Elizabeth contained the beaks of the inshore squid, *Loligo reynaudi*.

### Reproduction

The Port Elizabeth female that stranded with a calf in January 1969 was pregnant as well as lactating, carrying a foetus 105 mm long. A near term foetus of 2,18 m has been recorded from the Northern Hemisphere (Brimley, 1943), while the neonate from Plettenberg Bay was 2,33 m long. Both were recorded in March, which would suggest (if northern and southern populations should have breeding seasons six months out of phase) that the calving season is extended rather than restricted. The 3,40 m male calf from Maitland River mouth was still nursing (Ross, 1984).

---

No. 210

## *Mesoplodon layardii* (Gray, 1865)

## Layard's beaked whale
## Layard se snoetwalvis

---

### Colloquial Name

Layard's name is associated with this species by Gray as he described it from notes provided by Dr E.L. Layard who was then Director of the South African Museum, Cape Town. He originally named it *Ziphius layardii* (*Proc. zool. Soc. Lond.* 1865: 358).

Alternative name: Straptoothed whale.

### Taxonomic Notes

No subspecies have been described.

### Description

Adult Layard's beaked whales reach a total length of at least 6 m, and may therefore be the largest *Mesoplodon* species (Moore, 1968). Ross (1984) recorded an adult female from Whangarei, New Zealand, that was 6,15 m in total length; adult males may be somewhat smaller. The head is small, the melon distinct, its anterior face slopes forward to the snout and rises to a distinct apex above the eyes. The snout is long and slender. The flippers are small, rounded at the ends, and placed low down on the body. The dorsal fin is small, hooked and situated about two-thirds of the total length of the body posteriorly from the tip of the snout. The flukes are broad and have no notch in the centre of the trailing edge.

Fig. 210.1 Layard's beaked whale, *Mesoplodon layardii*. Male at 5,28 m. Males recorded up to 5,84 m, females 6,15 m (after Ross, 1984).

In an adult animal the anterior portion of the snout, the throat, the band behind the eye and the genital region are white. The dorsal surface from the melon anterior to the blowhole to about the mid-length of the whale is pale grey. The remainder of the body surface is black (Ross, 1984), although the undersurface of the tips of the flukes may be tinged with white or grey. Characteristically, in fact, the tips of the flukes may be curled permanently upwards in adults. The colour pattern of immature animals may be quite different, being dark grey or bluish dorsally, lightening gradually on the side to a pale grey or pinkish colour ventrally (Ross, 1984). The characteristic feature of the adult males is the two long strap-like teeth, up to 65 mm in breadth and about 6 mm in thickness, which arise, one from each side of the middle of the lower jaws at the posterior end of the mandibular symphysis, and cross over the top of the snout to virtually meet in the mid-line anterior to the forehead (Fig. 210.2). This restricts the gape of the mouth to extremely narrow limits. These teeth are slightly twisted backwards and have distinct triangular enamel denticles mounted near their tips that project more or less perpendicular to the tooth (and the animal's) main axis. In the female these teeth are more or less triangular in shape and do not erupt through the gums. The incidence of linear scarring (sometimes paired) on the skin of adult males of this species may reflect the use of the teeth (and especially the denticles) as an aggressive weapon.

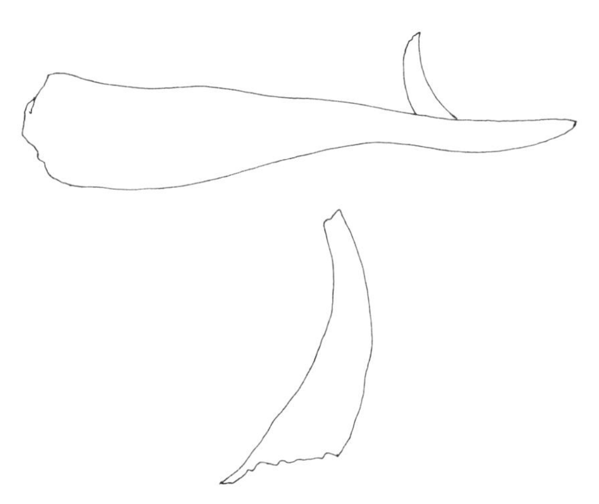

Fig. 210.2. Mandible and tooth of male *Mesoplodon layardii*. After Ross (1984).

A specimen from the coast of South Africa had a vertebral formula of C7+T10+L12+Cd16(+1) = 46. Other specimens have been recorded with counts of C7+T9–10+L10+Cd18–19 = 44–46 (Ross, 1984).

### Distribution

The type specimen of this species originated from the Cape of Good Hope and a number of individuals have over the years stranded on the coast of the Subregion between Walvis Bay, Namibia, and East London (Ross, 1984). Sclater (1901) recorded that the Challenger Expedition obtained parts of two skulls, one of an individual which was said to have stranded near Cape Point in 1865, the other stated to have been brought from Walvis Bay.

Elsewhere strandings of Layard's beaked whales have been recorded from Australia (including Tasmania); New Zealand (including the Chatham Islands); the Falkland Islands; Heard Island; Uruguay; Chile and Argentina (Ross, 1984; Lichter, 1986; Guiler, Burton & Gales, 1987). There is also an unpublished record of a stranding of five animals on Marion Island in March 1989 (Best, pers. comm.). If stranding records are considered reliable, the species appears to have a circumpolar distribution in southern seas between about 23 and 53 °S.

There is a marked seasonality to the stranding records, particularly north of 38 °S, where 19 of the 21 dated strandings occurred from January to April (Ross, 1984). This may indicate that the species undergoes definite migrations.

### Food

There is no published information on stomach contents for this species, but squid beaks have been found in animals stranded in the southwestern Cape (Best, pers. comm.). Fitzsimons (1920) recorded that, because of the curve of the strap-like teeth over the upper jaw, the mouth could only be opened some 110–130 mm. However, this measurement may have been made on the prepared skull; measurements in the flesh suggest a maximum opening (at the tip of the snout) of only 20–30 mm (Best, pers. comm.), raising interesting questions about the feeding habits of the species.

### Reproduction

Very little is published on this aspect of their life history. The smallest reported calf is 2,8 m and the largest foetus 0,76 m in length; Ross (1984) speculated that conception may occur in the first months of the year.

---

No. 211

## *Mesoplodon densirostris* (Blainville, 1817)

## Blainville's beaked whale
## Blainville se snoetwalvis

---

### Colloquial Name

Sometimes called the dense beaked whale as de Blainville found that the rostral bone was 34% denser than ivory and so the densest structure produced by a vertebrate animal (Watson, 1981). H.M. Ducrotay de Blainville was the successor of Cuvier in the chair of comparative anatomy at the Natural History Museum in Paris in 1817.

Alternative name: Dense beaked whale.

### Taxonomic Notes

No subspecies have been described.

### Description

The largest South African specimens had a total length for a male of 4,73 m, a female 4,71 m (Ross, 1984). An adult female 4,56 m long weighed 939,5 kg in pieces (Ross, 1984). This species has a robust, deep body, laterally compressed, particularly in the caudal region. In cross-section anterior to the dorsal fin the ventral surface appears rounded, but the dorsal region is markedly angular, especially in the midline. The melon is small and poorly defined, its anterior face descending evenly forward to the tip of the snout which is moderately long and partly concealed posteriorly, when viewed from the side, by the elevated portion of the lower jaw. In side view this gives the line of the lower jaw a shape characteristic of the species, being elevated from the gape to a point about two-thirds its distance forward, leaving only about one-third of the upper jaw projecting. The tip of the lower jaw extends slightly in front of the tip of the upper.

Fig. 211.1 Blainville's beaked whale, *Mesoplodon densirostris*. Adult male (Ross, *in litt.*). Males up to 4,73 m, females up to 4,71 m (Ross, 1984)

The single pair of conical, laterally compressed teeth is carried on the anterior corners of an elevated, pulpit-like section of the lower jaw, so that the tips (in adult males) emerge at the apex of the elevated portion of the mandible. The teeth in adult males are impressive structures measuring about 140 mm in length and 90 mm × 50 mm in width, and although only a fraction of this is exposed above the gum, the tips of the teeth are elevated by the jaw structure to as much as 40 mm above the dorsal surface of the upper jaw. Although this is the one beaked whale species in which the adult male tooth does not seem to possess a true denticle (Moore, 1968), its size and projection above the body surface must make it a formidable weapon, as is suggested by the deep linear scars on the skin that some individuals display (Best, pers. comm.). Female teeth are much smaller, achieving a maximum length only half that of the males, and do not erupt (Fig.211.2) (Ross, 1984).

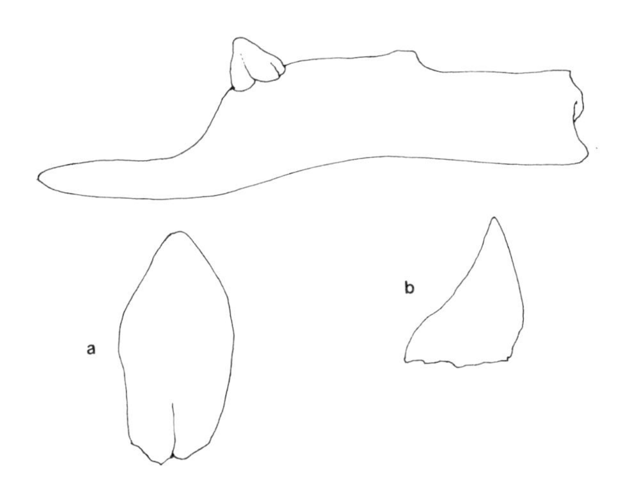


Fig. 211.2. Mandible and teeth, *Mesoplodon densirostris* (a) male tooth (b) female tooth. After Ross (1984).

The flippers are small for the size of the body, convex on both margins and taper to round points; they are placed low down on the body. The tail flukes have no notch on the mid-line of the trailing edge and are broad and tapered laterally. The dorsal fin is triangular or hooked in shape, situated at about two-thirds of the way back from the tip of the snout.

In the adult the colour of the upper parts of the body and flukes is very dark greyish-black, the under parts from the chin to beyond the anus light bluish-grey. The transition from the darker colour of the upper parts to the lighter colour of the under parts is rather abrupt, extending from the corner of the mouth to the anterior insertion of the flipper and along the side from the axilla of the flipper to about the midpoint of the caudal peduncle (Ross, 1984). The lighter coloration of the lower jaw means that the elevated section of the mandible forms a marked contrast with the darker pigmentation of the side of the head. The anterior portion of the ventral surface of the flukes is pale grey, the trailing edge dark grey. There is a dark patch around the eye and the outer surface of the flippers is black. In larger specimens the under surface of the body, particularly in the region of the genital aperture, may be covered with white oval scars that can become so dense as to obliterate the colour pattern (Ross, 1984). The origin of such scars is unknown but may result from the attentions of a small shark (Jones, 1971). From the colour of a near term foetus it appears as though juvenile *M. densirostris* may be differently pigmented to adults (Ross, 1984).

Ross (1984) noted that in a series of specimens the right tympanic bullae are consistently longer than the left, an asymmetry shown in Northern Hemisphere specimens by Besharse (1971).

There was variation in the vertebral formula of South African specimens from a total of 43 to 48: C7+T9–11+L10–12+Cd16(+1)-18(+1) (Ross, 1984). Variation was also found elsewhere: C7+T10–11+L8–11+Cd17–21 = 45–47 (Raven, 1942).

### Distribution

The species has a wide distribution in the tropical and temperate Atlantic, Pacific and Indian Oceans, frequently stranding on oceanic islands. In southern Africa strandings of Blainville's beaked whale have occurred between Port Alfred and St Helena Bay (Ross, 1984). In the North Atlantic the warm waters of the Gulf Stream have been suggested as a route by which sick individuals are carried from their deep sea, mid-oceanic range to the North American coast (Moore, 1966), and Ross (1984) suggested a similar situation for the southern African records, where the Agulhas Current either acts as an extension of tropical waters or creates a conduit by which the animals reach the coast from tropical waters.

### Food

While in other parts of their distributional range squid remains are recorded from their stomach contents, in one adult female from Schoenmakerskop, examined by Ross (1984), only fish otoliths were found, mostly of high-oceanic, mesopelagic lantern fish (*Lampanyctus*).

### Reproduction

What little is known about reproduction in this species comes mainly from information gleaned from animals stranded in South Africa. The largest recorded foetus is 1,9 m and the smallest calf 2,61 m long. The former was considered near term and could have been born around March or April (Ross, 1984). It is not known at what length females reach sexual maturity, but it may be very shortly before they attain physical maturity (Ross, 1984).

No. 212

## *Mesoplodon grayi* Von Haast, 1876

## Gray's beaked whale
## Gray se snoetwalvis

### Colloquial Name

Named after Edward Gray, a former Director of the British Museum (Nat. Hist.) who published widely on marine mammals and described many new species, one of his principal publications being a *Catalogue of Seals and Whales in the British Museum* (Nat. Hist.) 1866.

Alternative name: Scamperdown whale.

### Taxonomic Notes

No subspecies have been described.

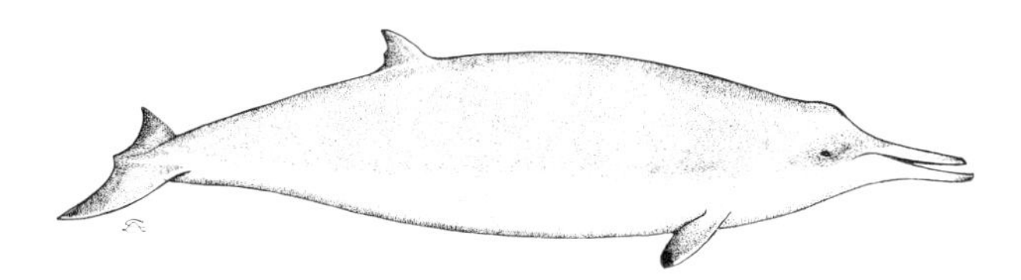

Fig. 212.1 Gray's beaked whale, *Mesoplodon grayi*. Adult female at 4,60 m. Males recorded up to 5,64 m, females 5,33 m (after Ross, 1984).

### Description

Gray's beaked whales reach a total length of 5,64 m and, from the few records presently available, there does not seem to be any sexual difference in size. Gambell, Best & Rice (1975) stated that the mass of an adult female weighed in pieces was 999,5 kg, excluding an allowance for loss of blood or body fluids.

Like *M. layardii*, the body of *M. grayi* is laterally compressed, being higher than it is wide. The melon bulges dorsally anterior to the blowhole, then slopes down anteriorly to merge smoothly into the long, slender beak. Therefore there is almost no apparent indication of a separate melon to the "forehead". The lower jaw projects slightly beyond the tip of the upper. The small dorsal fin is situated two-thirds of the way back from the tip of the snout and is triangular in shape, the rear edge slightly concave. The flippers are slightly wider than in other members of the genus but are short, slightly less than one-tenth of the total length, and are set low down on the body. The blowhole is wide and opens anterior to the level of the eyes and is situated slightly to the left of the mid-line.

The pair of relatively small, broad, roughly triangular, flattened teeth are situated about the middle of the lower jaw (Fig. 212.2), but erupt only in adult males. In addition they have a series of 15 to 22 (usually 17–19) tiny dolphin-like teeth, which may protrude 2 mm to 3 mm above the gums, set in a deep basirostral groove in the upper jaw behind the level of the mandibular teeth (Ross 1984). Some at least of these minor teeth may erupt in adult females as well as adult males.

Fig. 212.2. Mandible and male tooth, *Mesoplodon grayi*. After Ross (1984).

The upper parts of the body are black to slate-grey, shading to pale brownish-grey on the flanks, the under parts light grey tinged brown, darkening slightly in the mid-line from the flippers posteriorly.

The beak, the throat and around the navel and genital region are white. The white beak is a prominent field characteristic, as the species lifts it clear of the water before blowing (Best, pers. comm.).

The vertebral formula is C7+T9–11+L10–12+Cd19–20 = 47–48, although a South African specimen would have had a total of 49 vertebrae if (as suspected) three terminal caudal vertebrae were missing (Ross, 1984).

### Distribution

Although the species is said to have a circumpolar distribution in the Southern Hemisphere between 30 °S and 45 °S (Ross, 1984), records exist as far south as 53 °S (Lichter, 1986) and as far north as 21 °S on the Namibian coast (Best, pers. comm.). Amazingly enough, there is a solitary record for the Northern Hemisphere from the coast of Holland in 1927 (Boschma, 1950).

Strandings on the coast of South Africa have occurred between East London and Table Bay, with records from Namibia near Luderitz (Meester *et al.*, 1986) and Ugab River mouth (Best, pers. comm.). Ross (1984) recorded that of 20 dated records worldwide, 85% occurred between December and April, which suggests that the species may have definite migrations.

### Food

No published information available. An animal taken at sea in the southwestern Indian Ocean had been eating fish (Best, pers. comm.).

### Reproduction

A near-term foetus of 2,1 m is recorded from New Zealand in September, and calves about 2,4 m long have stranded there from January to April, suggesting that the calving season is in spring and summer (Baker, 1983).

### General

Most strandings are of single individuals, but 25 stranded together on the Chatham Islands and three in New Zealand (Ross, 1984), and Gambell *et al.* (1975) recorded four sightings in the southwest Indian Ocean of one, five, five and six individuals respectively, which suggests that they form small schools.

## Genus *Ziphius* G. Cuvier, 1823

This is a monotypic genus in which there are a pair of spindle-shaped teeth, circular in cross-section, set in alveoli one on each side of the apex of the mandible. These teeth do not erupt in the females and are smaller and more slender in cross-section (maximum diameter less than 40% *cf.* males more than 40% of maximum height of tooth).

No. 213

## *Ziphius cavirostris* G. Cuvier, 1823

## Cuvier's beaked whale
## Cuvier se snoetwalvis

### Colloquial Name

Originally described from a fossil skull by G. Cuvier, three years later an individual stranded in Italy, in 1850 another turned up from Corsica and in 1865 from South Africa. All of them were given different names, the South African specimen being called *Petrorhynchus capensis*. In 1872 Sir William Turner showed that they could all be ascribed to *Z. cavirostris*, Cuvier's name being retained in the colloquial name.

Alternative name: Goosebeak whale.

### Taxonomic Notes

In the past specimens of *Z. cavirostris* were described under no less than seven genera and 19 specific names, but today it is accepted as a single, widely distributed species with no subspecies (Ross, 1984).

### Description

The mean length of 123 sexually mature males longer than 5,5 m taken in Japanese waters was 6,07 m and that of 71 females 5,99 m, and the maximum length in both sexes was 7,0 m, which suggests that the sexes do not differ in size. The largest male recorded in South African waters is 5,97 m and the largest female 6,1 m (Ross, 1984). The mass of an adult male at 5,69 m was 2 450 kg. The colour has been recorded as variable, but Ross (1984) believed that adults of both sexes have a distinctive pattern. The snout, head and upper parts of the body, as far back as the dorsal fin and including it, are white, the remainder of the body dark bluish-grey or black. White oval scars are scattered over the body, but particularly ventrally around the genital region. Parallel, linear scars also appear on the skin of adults, particularly males, and these may be tooth marks incurred during intraspecific interactions. Juveniles may have a very different colour pattern, being light grey with a yellowish tinge dorsally and much lighter, almost white, ventrally. The flippers and dorsal fin are almost black, the tail flukes with a white patch ventrally. As the animal matures, the belly darkens, the head becomes greyish then white, and oval/linear scars start to accumulate.

The melon slopes gently anteriorly, merging imperceptibly into the beak which is short and broad at the base. This, together with the relatively short gape (5–7% of body length) which is slightly sigmoid in shape in lateral view, somehow combines to make the animal's snout reminiscent of a duck or goose's beak. The blowhole lies on top of the head, slightly in front of the level of the eyes. The small, pointed dorsal fin is located about two-thirds of the way back from the snout. The flippers are placed low down on the sides of the body and are relatively small. The males have two heavy spindle-shaped teeth situated one on each side of the front tip of the lower jaw, about 70 mm in length and 40 mm in maximum diameter. Because the lower jaw projects beyond

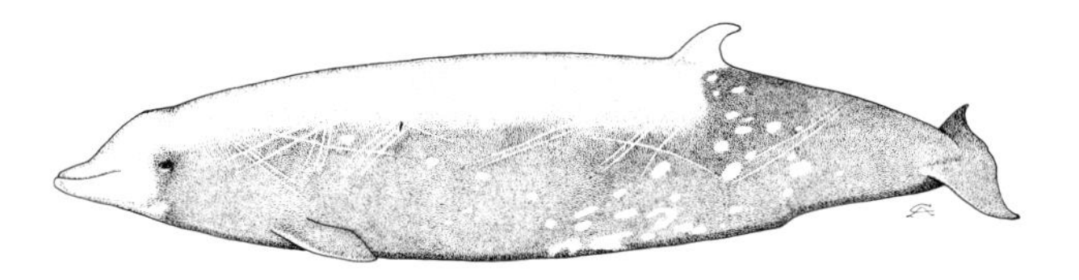

Fig. 213.1 Cuvier's beaked whale, *Ziphius cavirostris*. Adult male at 5,88m. Mean total length mature males 6,07 m, females 5,99 m (after Ross, 1984).

the upper, the teeth effectively project clear of the body surface and presumably form formidable weapons. In the females the teeth are smaller and much lighter and do not erupt above the gums. The gums of juveniles may contain 28–30 rudimentary teeth in both upper and lower jaws, which resorb with age, although Ross (1984) reported finding one erupted vestigial tooth in the upper jaw of an adult male (Fig. 213.2).

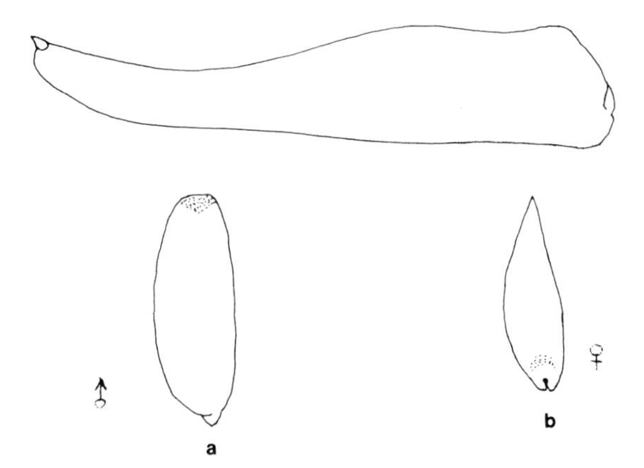


Fig. 213.2. Mandible and teeth, *Ziphius cavirostris* (a) male tooth (b) female tooth. After Ross (1984).

The vertebral formula is C7+T9–10+L9–11+Cd19–22 = 46–49 (Ross, 1984).

**Distribution**

Cuvier's beaked whale has a cosmopolitan distribution in temperate and tropical waters, occurring in all oceans with the exception of those parts of them that lie within high latitudes. In the Southern Hemisphere, however, strandings have been recorded as far as 55 °S (Lichter, 1986), and there are two sightings south of the Antarctic Convergence (Kasamatsu *et al.*, 1988).

Ross & Tietz (1972) listed seven records from the coast of the Subregion between Cape Cross, Namibia and East London. Three of these, from the Cape of Good Hope, are 19th century records from the British Museum (two specimens) and the Louvain Museum. One of the former was an individual that stranded on the shores of Table Bay during a storm in July 1846. It was grey in colour and "gave 500 bottles of very good oil". Later records listed by Ross & Tietz (1972) are of a bleached skull found near Cape Cross, Namibia, in 1964, and strandings near Port Elizabeth in 1966, near East London in 1967 and at Stilbaai, 80 km west of Mossel Bay, in 1969. Ross (1984) recorded three further specimens, a stranding from Fish River Point in 1976 and two specimens taken at sea by whale catchers from the Durban land station in 1973, one being found floating dead and the other harpooned. He also reported a sighting at sea 372 km almost due south of Cape St Blaize in 1975. The three at-sea records were all in water depths of 1000 m or more, indicating that this is a deep-sea species.

**Food**

Nishiwaki & Oguro (1972) recorded the species as feeding on deep-sea fish and squid, the former being found in the stomachs of animals caught in somewhat deeper water than those feeding on squid. Ross (1984) found the beaks of oceanic squid (mainly cranchiids, octopoteuthids and onychoteuthids) and fish otoliths (a deep-sea cod *Antimora*) in the stomach of a specimen from Port Elizabeth. Other objects in the same stomach included a plastic bottle top and cap, two pieces of pumice and a large seed!

**Reproduction**

Nishiwaki & Oguro (1972) suggested that both sexes are sexually mature at a total length of 5,5 m, while Omura *et al.* (1955) reported mean lengths at sexual maturity of 5,8 m for females and 5,5 m for males. The largest reported foetus is 2,67 m and the smallest calf 2,69 m; Mead (1984) concluded that the mean length at birth is 2,7 m. The wide range of foetal lengths recorded for any one month suggests that breeding and calving seasons may be spread over several months (Ross, 1984).

**General**

Up to the mid 1970's Cuvier's beaked whales were hunted commercially for oil and meat off the coasts of Japan and they are therefore better known from this region than from any other part of their distributional range. Mitchell (1975b) recorded that, although the level of hunting was high, there was no firm evidence that they were being over-utilised. Tomilin (1967) stated that stranded carcasses along the USSR coast are used as dog and fox food.

## Genus *Hyperoodon* Lacépède, 1804

Two species are known, *H. ampullatus* from the northern parts of the North Atlantic, and *H. planifrons* from the Southern Hemisphere. They are medium-sized whales with total lengths of up to 9,8 m. *H. planifrons* is apparently the smaller of the two, although much less information is available for it. Unlike other members of the Family Ziphidae, all seven cervical vertebrae are fused together in adults.

---

No. 214

## *Hyperoodon planifrons* Flower, 1882

## Southern bottlenose whale
## Suidelike stompneuswalvis

---

**Colloquial Name**

The development of the melon on the front part of the head and the way it overhangs the elongated snout give it the name bottlenose, although this might well be applied to other species with a similar configuration, such as Arnoux's beaked whale.

**Taxonomic Notes**

Apart from an overall difference in size, distinction between northern and southern bottlenose whales is based primarily on skull characters, principally the development of the maxillary crests which are greater in the northern species. No subspecies have been described.

Fig. 214.1 Southern bottlenose whale, *Hyperoodon planifrons*. Males recorded up to 7 m, females 7,45 m (after Nishiwaki, 1972)

**Description**

Southern bottlenose whales are recorded as reaching a total length in males of 7,0 m (Lichter, 1986), in females 7,45 m

(Gianuca & Castello, 1976). The largest examples from South Africa are a 6,43 m male (Ross, 1984) and a 6,55 m female (Best, pers. comm.). In a 6,9 m male described by Hale (1931), the upper parts of the body were bluish-black, the under parts creamy or grey. Tietz (1966) stated that in a specimen stranded near Port Elizabeth the upper parts were cloud-grey, paler along the flanks and belly and the underside of the flippers. From photographs of a specimen now in the South African Museum, Ross (1984) recorded that the upper parts appeared to have been entirely brownish-grey with pale grey or cream outlines to the genital, anal and mammary slits, and with a few oval and longitudinal scars on the flanks.

A juvenile male examined by Ross (1984) had dark bluish-black upper parts behind the blowhole, the flanks dark grey merging smoothly into the white of the under parts. Posterior to the eye a broad band of dark bluish-black extended to the anterior insertion of the flippers, becoming greyish-black as it did so. A band of bluish-black extended vertically from the blowhole to join with an intense black patch surrounding the eye. From the blowhole to the apex of the melon the skin was pigmented with dark grey in the midline. Most of the upper jaw and dorsal margin of the tip of the lower jaw were intensely black, contrasting with the white of the face, lower jaw and throat. The flippers were black externally, white internally. The dorsal fin had a whitish blaze enclosed by a dark grey-black posterior margin and anterior third of the dorsal fin. The posterior half of the caudal peduncle was dark grey above, streaked and flecked with dark and pale grey below. The flukes were black above; on their under surfaces the margins were bluish-black with fine grey streaks radiating across the white surface as far as the leading edge.

The blowhole of this species appears to be a transverse slit, curved slightly forwards on each side, rather than a crescent shape.

Southern bottlenose whales have only one prominent tooth on either side of the front of the lower jaw, as against two on either side in *B. arnuxii* (Fig.214.1). In adult males these teeth are conical or subconical in shape and about 59 mm in length and 37 mm in greatest diameter, although only about 20 mm might protrude (Hale, 1931). In adult females the teeth are smaller and more slender and do not erupt. Tiny vestigial teeth may be present in both upper and lower jaws, posterior to the level of the apical teeth and about 10–20 in number, some of which may erupt through the gum.

The vertebral formula is C7+T8–9+L10–12+Cd17–20 = 44–46, although a juvenile had 10 thoracic vertebrae (Ross, 1984). Unlike other ziphiids, all seven neck vertebrae in this species are fused together in the adult.

**Distribution**

They have a circumpolar distribution in the southern oceans. Although the type specimen was recorded at about 20 °S, most other stranding records are south of 30 °S.

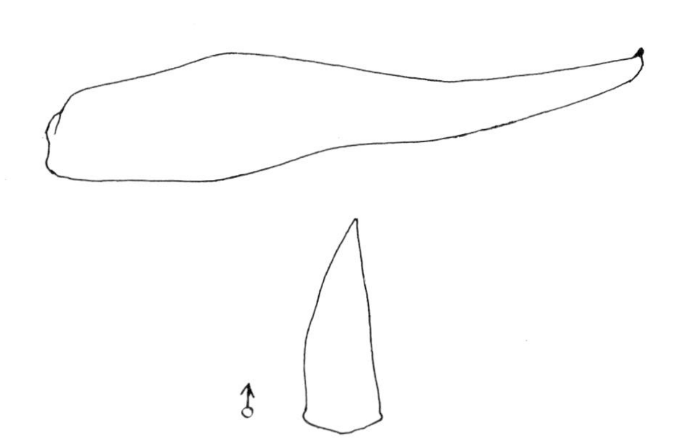

Fig. 214.2. Mandible and male tooth, *Hyperoodon planifrons*. After Ross (1984).

Sightings of an apparent *Hyperoodon* species in the equatorial Pacific, however, confuse the issue (Leatherwood *et al.*, 1988). The most southerly specimen records come from the South Shetland Islands, or about 65 °S, but the species has been seen frequently between 60 °S and the ice edge, where it has comprised about 90% of all sightings of identified ziphiids (Kasamatsu *et al.*, 1988). Although stranding records in South Africa are very few (Ross, 1984, lists only three), Gambell *et al.* (1975) recorded that they were the predominant ziphiids sighted between 35 °S and 40 °S in the southwestern Indian Ocean in summer. Ross (1984) stated that they appear to occur seasonally in South African waters, sightings attributable to the species being a consistent feature of whale-marking cruises off Natal and the Eastern Cape in summer, but being entirely absent on a winter cruise, a pattern also confirmed from the observations of the spotter aircraft attached to the Durban whaling station.

**Food**

Ross (1984) records that squid beaks were recovered from the intestine of one specimen off South Africa, while cephalopod beaks and eye lenses have been reported from the stomachs of specimens from South Australia and South Georgia.

**Reproduction**

Very little information is available, and caution should be exercised in attempting to extrapolate from the better known northern species. A female as small as 5,7 m in length was lactating and therefore sexually mature (Mead, 1984). The juvenile 2,91 m long examined by Ross (1984) was classified as "not more than a few weeks old" from the presence of birth creases visible on the sides of the animal. This animal was stranded in November, and observations of calves at sea estimated to be 3–3,5 m long in January led Ross (1984) to propose that the species calves in spring or early summer.

# XXV. Family PHYSETERIDAE

## Sperm whales

The Family is comprised of two Subfamilies, the Kogiinae, with one genus and two species, and the Physeterinae, with one genus and a single species. The Kogiinae are small whales with a total length of up to about 3,5 m. By contrast, the single representative of the Physeterinae, the sperm whale, *Physeter macrocephalus*, is the largest of the toothed whales, adult males reaching a total length of 19,0 m. It is the only one of the three species known to venture into colder polar waters.

All the members of the Family have functional teeth in a Y-shaped lower jaw in which the symphysis comprises about one-third of the length. Relatively tiny vestigial teeth occur in the gum of the upper jaw in *P. macrocephalus* and *K. simus*, some of which may erupt occasionally, but erupted maxillary teeth do not seem to occur in *K. breviceps*: it is unclear whether such teeth are present in the gum of *breviceps*. The head carries the large bulbous spermaceti organ, the anterior dorsal surface of the skull being cupped to support it. All seven cervical vertebrae are fused in the two *Kogia* species, but the atlas bone in the sperm whale is free.

The skull is asymmetrical, the blowhole (crescentic in shape in *Kogia*, sigmoid in *Physeter*) is situated to the left of the mid-line and at the tip of the snout in *Physeter*. In the sperm whale the dorsal fin is represented by an ill-defined hump, while in the other two members it is distinctly developed.

Key to the Subfamilies (after Best, 1971c)

1. Small, up to 3,5 m in length; 7 to 16 pairs of teeth in the lower jaw; head about one-sixth of the body length, blowhole on top of the head some distance from the tip of the snout
   ... Kogiinae

   Large, up to 19 m in length, 18 to 28 pairs of teeth in the lower jaw; head almost one-third of the body length; blowhole at the extreme left tip of the snout
   ... Physeterinae

## Subfamily KOGIINAE

## Genus *Kogia* Gray, 1846

These are small whales, attaining a length of 3,5 m in the case of *breviceps*, with slender, curved and sharply pointed teeth in the lower jaw. The spermaceti organ is bulbous and variable in shape with age (Ross, 1984), the blowhole crescentic with its convex margin facing forward and to the left. The rostrum of the skull is very short and broad, the cervical vertebrae fused. A characteristic of this genus, perhaps only shared with some phocoenids, is the extreme anterior position of the genital slit in males, lying only a short distance behind the umbilicus (Best, pers. comm.).

Key to the species (Best, 1971c)

1. Dorsal fin low and somewhat rounded; 12 to 16 (rarely 10 or 11) pairs of teeth in the lower jaw, of which the symphysis is long and keeled ventrally; dorsal sagittal crest on the skull 20 to 38 mm thick near the vertex
   ... *breviceps*

   Dorsal fin high and recurved; 7 to 12 (rarely 13) pairs of teeth in the lower jaw, of which the symphysis is short and plain ventrally; dorsal sagittal crest on the skull 6–14 mm thick near vertex
   ... *simus*

---

No. 215

## *Kogia breviceps* (Blainville, 1838)

## Pygmy sperm whale
## Dwergpotvis

---

### Colloquial Name

Sometimes referred to as the lesser cachalot or lesser sperm whale.

### Taxonomic Notes

No subspecies have been described.

### Description

Although lengths at physical maturity of 4,5 m for males and 4,0 m for females are on record (Bryden, 1972), Ross (1979b) threw doubt on the validity of these figures; of 19 accurately measured specimens from the South African coast the largest male was 3,25 m and the largest female 3,1 m long. As a 3,5 m female has been recorded elsewhere, there may not be much sexual dimorphism in this species. The weights of specimens 2,8 and 2,99 m long have been recorded as 342 kg (Carvalho, 1966) and 417 kg (Tomilin, 1967) respectively.

The upper parts of the body are charcoal or dark grey, fading to pale blue-grey laterally, with the under parts white tinged with pink or light grey. The light colour of the under parts extends on to the chin and the side of the head anterior to the eyes, which are surrounded by a ring of dark pigment. Behind the eye and running ventrally from the vicinity of the external ear opening there is a characteristic short, bracket-shaped, white marking which varies in shape individually and extends downwards to join the white of the under parts. The flippers and flukes are slate-grey above, white below, the flukes dark grey along their anterior and posterior margins on their under surfaces. A faint shoulder stripe runs antero-dorsally from the flipper insertion.

The head shape changes as the animal grows. Although in general "shark-like" in appearance, with a blunt snout projecting well forward past the tip of the much smaller, underslung lower jaw, with age the head becomes blunter and more rectangular in lateral view. The blowhole is situated further forward than the level of the eyes, slightly to the left of the mid-line, and is crescent-shaped and convex anteriorly. In *breviceps* it is characteristically more than 10% (*cf. simus* less than 10%) of the body length back from the tip of the snout. The girth of the body is greatest between the flippers and the small dorsal fin, the body laterally compressed, especially in the tail section. The flippers are moderate in size, convex on upper and lower margins tapering to a rounded tip. The dorsal fin is situated about the mid-part of the body, and is small, low and hooked. Its height in *breviceps* is less than 5% of the body length (*cf. simus* more than 5%).

The upper jaws are devoid of erupted teeth, while the lower jaw has 12 to 16 pairs of small, slender, recurved teeth which are longer and thicker (maximum 39,5 × 9,0 mm) than in *K. simus* (Ross, 1979b).

The length of the mandibular symphysis is 36,5 mm to 128 mm long and it is keeled ventrally (Ross, 1979b).

The vertebral formula is C7+T12–14+L9–12+Cd20–26 = 50–55 (Ross, 1984). The seven cervical vertebrae are all fused together (Nishiwaki, 1972).

Fig. 215.1 Pygmy sperm whale, *Kogia breviceps*. Adult female at 3,04 m. Both sexes recorded up to 3,5 m (after Ross, 1984)

### Distribution

The pygmy sperm whale occurs throughout the temperate, subtropical and tropical waters of the world. In South African waters up to 1976, Ross (1979b) listed 44 strandings representing 48 individuals, on the coast between Cape Cross in Namibia and Durban, Natal. The seasonal occurrence of these records does not suggest that the species is absent or more abundant in any particular season. Most of our knowledge of the species comes from stranded specimens, as there have been very few sightings at sea.

### Food

In the stomachs of stranded specimens from the South African coast squid predominated, about 75% of the species representing families that are almost entirely oceanic in distribution, suggesting that the species normally feeds beyond the edge of the continental shelf (Ross, 1979b). This conclusion was later amended to refer to adults only, the prey items of immatures, calves and accompanying females suggesting that these components of the population fed closer inshore (Ross, 1984). Prawns, crabs and deep-sea mysids also featured commonly in stomachs, and fish remains in 25% of the stomachs. One stomach contained the remains of eight tunicates (*Pyrosoma*) plus a paper bag and eight polythene bags of various colours (Ross, 1984)!

**Reproduction**

The mean length of females at sexual maturity is estimated to be 2,7–2,8 m, and males about 2,7–3,0 m (Ross, 1984). The gestation period is not known and records of foetuses and new-born calves are too scattered throughout the year to indicate the calving season. The length at birth is believed to be about 1,2 m, and solid food has been found in calves of 1,6 m or more in length, although calves up to 2,11 m have stranded in association with an adult female. Some females have been recorded as being simultaneously pregnant and accompanied by a calf, so that conceiving in successive breeding seasons is possible. A surprisingly high proportion (80%) of calves and foetuses are male (Ross, 1979b).

**General**

Both this species and *K. simus* have been killed in Japanese coastal cetacean fisheries, but never in large numbers (Mitchell, 1975b).

---

No. 216

## *Kogia simus* (Owen, 1866)

## Dwarf sperm whale
## Miniatuurpotvis

---

**Colloquial Name**

Sometimes referred to as Owen's pygmy sperm whale.

**Taxonomic Notes**

No subspecies have been described.

**Description**

Dwarf sperm whales reach a maximum length of about 2,7 m, or somewhat smaller than pygmy sperm whales. Ross (1979b) recorded a male which stranded on the coast of the Eastern Province that measured 2,61 m and a female of 2,64 m from Saldanha Bay. Other specimens have been estimated to be 2,68–2,7 m in length. A 2,35 m animal weighed 209,1 kg. In colour they closely resemble the pygmy sperm whale, *K. breviceps* (Ross, 1979b). The snout to blowhole distance is shorter than in the pygmy sperm whale (see above), and the head is therefore more pug-like in shape. The skull and lower jaw are smaller than in the pygmy sperm whale, and the mandibular symphysis measures only 23–51 mm in length, lacking a keel to the ventral surface. Seven to 12 pairs of teeth are carried in the lower jaw, fewer than in the pygmy sperm whale, and they are smaller (maximum length × width: 26 × 4,2 mm). Unlike the pygmy sperm whale, this species frequently has one to three pairs of teeth erupted in the upper jaw also. The dorsal fin is larger than in *K. breviceps* (see above), more erect and dolphin-like.

The vertebral formula of 10 specimens from southern Africa is C7+T12–13+L10–14+Cd22–26 = 53–56 (Ross, 1984). Specimens from Japan seem to have a slightly greater number of vertebrae. The seven cervical vertebrae are all fused together (Nishiwaki, 1972).

Fig. 216.1 Dwarf sperm whale, *Kogia simus*. Adult female at 2,35 m (after Ross, 1979a). Maximum total length 2,7 m (Handley, 1966).

**Distribution**

Like the pygmy sperm whale, *K. breviceps*, this species appears to occur widely in temperate and tropical seas. Ross (1979b) recorded 40 strandings of 42 animals up to 1976 on the coast of South Africa, ranging from Saldanha Bay to East London, Cape Province. A subsequent record from Natal is attributed to unusual oceanographic conditions (Ross *et al.*, 1985), and the general lack of records on the west coast north of Saldanha Bay and on the east coast north of East London led Ross (1984) to propose that the species may be associated with the mixed water region south of the continent formed by the interaction of the Agulhas and Benguela Current systems. There is no indication from the monthly distribution of stranding records that the species is more abundant in South African waters at any particular season.

**Habits**

Ross (1979b) suggested that they move in schools numbering up to 10, the females with calves grouping together, the immatures doing likewise and mature males and females occurring together in the same school. Kogiids in general may be found basking on the surface of the sea, when they are easy to approach (Yamada, 1954). When disturbed or threatened, however, they may release a cloud of reddish faeces, covering sometimes an area of 100 m$^2$, possibly for concealment (Scott & Cordaro, 1987).

**Food**

Ross (1979b) stated that cephalopods are the principal food of this species, but the proportions of oceanic forms are less than one-fifth of those recorded for pygmy sperm whales, while nearly 70% are cuttlefish, typically inhabitants of the continental shelf (seldom recorded in water deeper than 100 m in this area). Fish remains were only found in 20% of stomachs, mainly being light fishes and myctophids. Crustaceans were found in about half the stomachs. From a comparison of the species of squids eaten by adults and other classes, Ross (1984) concluded that juveniles and calves plus their accompanying mothers feed closer inshore than adults. The continental shelf or slope therefore may be an important "nursery area" for *Kogia*, especially *K. simus*.

**Reproduction**

Ross (1979b) stated that foetal records are too scanty to suggest distinct breeding and calving seasons or gestation periods. A foetus 960 mm long in December 1976 is thought to have been near term (Ross, 1984), the length at birth being previously estimated as around 1 m. Suckling continues until the calf is over 1,5 m long, although the smallest independent animal recorded is 1,89 m long. It is believed that both sexes become sexually mature at a total length of 2,1 m to 2,2 m. Simultaneously lactating and pregnant females are not uncommon, suggesting that some mature females may fall pregnant in successive seasons (Ross, 1979b).

## Subfamily PHYSETERINAE
## Genus *Physeter* Linnaeus, 1758

No. 217
## *Physeter macrocephalus* Linnaeus, 1758

## Sperm whale
## Potvis

### Colloquial Name
The blunt, squarish snout of this species houses a large reservoir of a glistening white waxy substance which, at body heat, is a clear viscous oil. The colloquial name arises from the fact that this substance originally was thought to be the whale's semen, or "spermaceti", (literally whale semen). Alternative names: cachalot; great sperm whale.

### Taxonomic Notes
The specific name has been the subject of much recent debate. Although many authors have used *catodon*, Husson & Holthuis (1974) concluded that *macrocephalus* and *catodon* are subjective synonyms and that the former should be given priority in terms of the "first reviser" principle. Schevill (1986) contested this, inter alia on the grounds that the description of *macrocephalus* does not fit the sperm whale, in particular the location of the blowhole in the neck region. Holthuis (1987) considered that Linnaeus copied his description of the location of the blowhole in *macrocephalus* from a description based on a "faulty" representation of a true sperm whale, an argument that Schevill (1987) did not accept, putting more weight on Linnaeus' own diagnoses that seem to suggest that only *catodon* (where the position of the blowhole is given correctly) could have been a sperm whale. As Schevill (1987) rightly said, "how can it be that taxonomists cannot agree on a name for the sperm whale, a most distinctive animal recognized worldwide ... as a single species?".

### Description
Sperm whales are by far the largest members of the Subfamily, males growing to a total length of 19 m and females 12 m. Gambell (1970) recorded that the mass of a 13,3 m male, weighed whole on a railway low loading truck in Durban, was 31 450 kg. Subsequently cut up and reweighed in parts it was found that there was a loss of 12% due to the loss of blood and body fluids.

At sea the sperm whale can be distinguished from other whales from the low, bushy blow directed anteriorly from the tip of the snout, and the small, triangular fleshy dorsal fin. A series of distinct smaller humps may be situated behind the dorsal fin. The dorsal fin of adult females bears a callus, or a distinct, roughened area of skin on the leading edge near the tip, somewhat paler in colour than the surrounding skin (Kasuya & Ohsumi, 1966).

Their blunt heads are enormous, accounting for about a third of the total length, with small eyes situated just above and behind the gape of the mouth. The skull is unique in that the bones grow out to form a depression which contains the spermaceti organ. The function of this organ is not known, but it has been suggested that it acts as an acoustic "lens" for focussing vocal emissions produced by the whale (Norris & Harvey, 1972), or as buoyancy regulator (Clarke, 1978). The nasal passages are asymmetrical; the left passage runs along the side of the head, while the much larger, flattened right passage runs through the middle of the spermaceti organ. The two join in a distal cavity at the front of the head, the left passage through a narrow slit-like opening known as the "museau de singe" (or monkey's face), before opening to the exterior through the single blowhole on the left side of the tip of the snout. The mandible is Y-shaped, terminating in a long narrow lower jaw; in a specimen 15 m long it is about 200 mm wide in front and 700 mm near the corner of the mouth (Nishiwaki, 1972). There are about 10 to 15 pairs of small, maxillary teeth embedded in the gum, of which some can erupt with age. The lower jaw, which is much shorter than the upper, has 18–28 pairs of heavily built, conical teeth, oval in section, and much larger than the maxillary teeth, measuring about 200–250 mm in length in adult males (although only about one-third to one-half may be exposed above the gum). The teeth in the lower jaw fit into sockets in the upper when the jaw is closed. Eruption of the mandibular teeth seems to be more correlated with attainment of sexual maturity than with weaning.

Females have relatively smaller heads than males, at least in adults, where the distance from the tip of the snout to the centre of the eye is about 19–20% in females compared to 22–26% in males. This difference is the result of a greater anterior extension of the melon in males (Nishiwaki, Ohsumi & Maeda, 1963).

For their great body size the flippers are noticeably small and rounded; the flukes on the other hand are very large (their span attaining one-quarter to one-third of the body length in adult males). The flippers play little part in propulsion and even individuals that have lost a flipper do not appear to be impeded (Gaskin, 1972).

The upper parts of the bodies of adult sperm whales are dark grey-blue or black, the under parts lighter in colour. Most have white patches and/or light grey streaks in the umbilical region. The front of the head may also carry a spiral whorl of light streaks. Upper and lower lips and palate are usually white, and the entire lower jaw may become white with age. Adult males carry numerous linear, parallel scars on the head, sometimes attributed to the suckers of their cephalopod prey, but from the spacing and conformation of the scars almost certainly are attributable to intraspecific interactions with other males. These and other scars may become so numerous in older animals that the front of the head becomes whitened. Although the legend of the albino Moby Dick is fictional, there is at least one record of the capture of a pure white sperm whale in Japanese waters (Ohsumi, 1958).

Their body surface posterior to the head is typically corrugated into a series of longitudinal ridges or ripples.

The vertebral formula is C7+T11+L8–9+Cd20–25 = 47–51 (Berzin, 1972). The first cervical vertebra is free and articulates on the mass formed by the fusion of the following six (Nishiwaki, 1972).

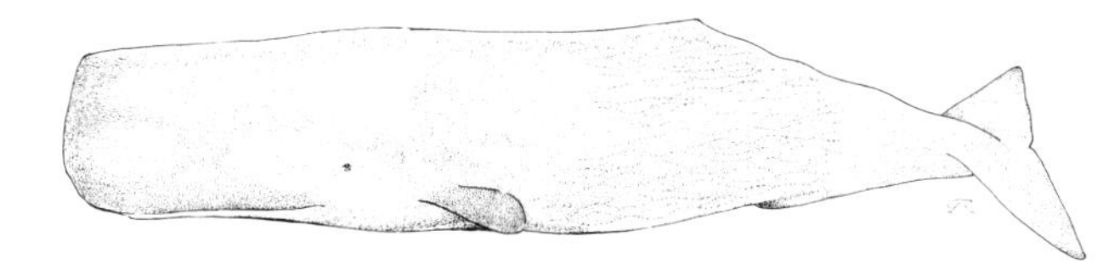

Fig. 217.1 Sperm whale, *Physeter macrocephalus* Male. Maximum lengths: males 19 m, females 12 m (after Ross, in litt.).

### Distribution
Sperm whales occur in all the major oceans of the world and have been recorded both in the Baltic and Mediterranean. It is essentially a deep-sea animal, rarely being found in water shallower than 300 m, and usually in much deeper seas.

Female sperm whales and their young rarely move out of the warmer waters between the latitudes of about 40 °N and 40 °S; adult males, however, migrate in summer as far as the latitudes of 70 ° north and south, with in general the larger males penetrating further north or south than the smaller. Such males return to temperate waters in mid-winter, when some large males at least reach tropical waters.

From tagging results it is known that some individuals can move very large distances, the record being a male tagged in 1961, in the North Atlantic at 21 °33′N by the Soviets, that was killed by whalers operating from the land station at

Saldanha Bay in 1966 at a latitude of 33°20'S, a straight-line distance of 7 400 km (Ivashin, 1967)! This is evidence of some mixing of northern and southern populations, although the breeding seasons are six months apart.

**Habits**

Both sexes of sperm whales exhibit migratory movements, there being a general movement towards the equator during the winter months. They are most numerous in the seas off the South African coast during the summer months.

Their movements in South African waters have been studied by Bannister & Gambell (1965), Gambell (1967) and Best (1969b). They found that the population density was least in the winter months of June to August, movement into the area taking place in September and the greatest density (in the eight-month whaling season) being in April and May. In past years when whaling occurred throughout the year off Durban, clear seasonal trends in the composition of the population could be seen. Females predominated between October and April, medium-sized (12,2 to 13,7 m) and large males (13,7 m or more in length) from May to August, while small males were least abundant and showed least signs of seasonality (Best, 1974). The occasional occurrence of large accumulations of sperm whales has been recorded since the days of open boat whaling. These occurrences are considered rare and may involve up to 4 000 individuals (Tomilin, 1936). Such a trek was reported off Durban, Natal in July 1972, when in two hours the spotter aircraft of the whaling company found 19 separate sightings of groups of sperm whales, some of over 50 individuals, extending over 40 nautical miles in a line parallel to the continental shelf. It was estimated that over 700 individuals were involved (Paterson, 1986).

Sperm whales are among the longest and deepest divers of all cetaceans so far investigated, being reported to remain submerged for periods up to 90 minutes (Caldwell *et al.*, 1966) and possibly up to 112 minutes (Clarke, 1976). The best substantiated depth achieved is a record of a sperm whale entangled in an undersea cable at a depth of 1 136 m (Heezen, 1957), while there is a tantalising account of a complete dive monitored on an acoustic array down to a depth of 2 250 m that has never been published directly because the identification of the whale concerned was made from its vocalisations rather than its external appearance (Whitney, in Norris & Harvey, 1972)! From monitoring asdic traces of the profiles of 931 dives during whaling operations off Durban, Lockyer (1977) has shown that there is a tendency for the depth and duration of dives to increase with increasing body size, and that at least under such conditions of stress dives below 800 m and for longer than 30 minutes formed less than 5% of all observed dives. Rates of ascent and descent were similar, averaging about 90 to 150 m per minute. The average depth and duration of dives for small sperm whales (9,5–10,9 m in length) tended to increase in the evening hours compared to the morning and middle of the day. During recovery times on the surface between dives, respiration rates varied with the size of the animal, the extremes being a calf blowing at 10 blows per minute and a large male at two blows per minute.

When angered they can become dangerous and there are many references to their ramming ships with their heads, flailing them with their tail flukes or attacking with their teeth. They have the reputation of being "dangerous at both ends". In days gone by, when harpooning was carried out from rowing boats, when attacked the whalers would throw a cask overboard in the hope that they would vent their rage on this instead of their boat (Caldwell *et al.*, 1966).

Group care is well developed in sperm whales; the reaction of a group to the "attacks" of a school of killer whales included sudden coalescing of school members and keeping their heads facing towards the killer whales have been recorded by Arnbom *et al.* (1987).

They have been reported to play with flotsam and to "breach" with almost all of their bodies out of the water, to "lobtail" vertically in the water with the flukes and part of the tail above the surface, swinging them from side to side. They will also investigate disturbances by swimming vertically in the water with their heads and eyes above the surface looking around, an action known as "pitch poling". Encounters between males are on record. The contestants lock jaws and wrestle, tearing out large chunks of flesh and blubber, and broken jaws may result (Caldwell *et al.*, 1966).

While the teeth are used in these encounters they do not pierce the gums until the individual reaches sexual maturity, yet during the interim period they must be able to feed successfully. Examinations of large squid in adult stomachs show no signs of tooth marks and it has been suggested that the presence of teeth are more a secondary sexual character than a mechanism for food capture (Nishiwaki, Hibiya & Ohsumi, 1958).

When alarmed, sperm whales react in various ways. They may either swim away rapidly, throw their flukes in the air and dive perpendicularly, or simply settle quietly on the surface of the water. They are very sensitive to noises and it was well known to the old whalers that the noise of an oar knocking on the boat was sufficient to put them to flight. Haas (1959) recorded that the click of an underwater camera causes them to change course. Once they have sounded after being alarmed they will swim long distances submerged (Caldwell *et al.*, 1966).

Sperm whales do not produce squeals, moans or whistles, only pulsed clicks at a variety of repetition rates (from less than one per second to more than 75 per second). Certain repetitive patterns ("codas") seem to occur in stereotyped sequences that are unique to an individual and presumably serve some communicatory purpose (Watkins, 1977). They are reported to communicate alarm over distances of up to 11 km, the recipients of the message either fleeing or coming to the assistance of the individual emitting them (Caldwell, Caldwell & Rice, 1966).

Ambergris, used in the perfumery trade, is a product of the sperm whale. It is formed in the rectum apparently as a concretion resulting from the irritating effect of squid beaks, which pass through the alimentary canal undigested. It is a sticky, blackish-brown substance when fresh, with a heavy unpleasant smell. When passed out in lumps and weathered it becomes light in colour and fibrous and will burn with a clear blue flame. Ambergris only occasionally gets washed up on beaches.

Age composition data (using counts of dentinal growth layers) for the commercial catches at Durban, in Western Australia and from the Antarctic indicate that while female sperm whales may live to 50–55 years, males may only achieve 40–45 years (Gambell, 1977). This result may be influenced by the greater historical exploitation of adult males, but it does agree with the contention of Ralls, Brownell & Ballou (1980) that male sperm whales have a higher adult natural mortality rate than females.

**Food**

Throughout their wide distributional range the principal food of the sperm whale is mid-water or deep-water squid, although in some areas bottom-dwelling fish may predominate (Roe, 1969). Although some very large individual squid may be eaten, (Clarke (1956) recorded a specimen of the giant squid *Architeuthis* 4,96 m in standard length and weighing 184 kg from the stomach of a sperm whale in the Azores), the average size of squid eaten is very much less, being about 0,5–0,6 kg in South African waters and about 7,0 kg in Antarctic waters. Males seem to favour larger species (and larger specimens of the same species) than females, possibly reflecting some difference in the vertical distribution of the prey rather than any direct selection (Clarke, 1980). Besides cephalopods, sperm whales at Durban were recorded with egg cases and remains of elasmobranchs, some bony fish remains and crustaceans, including the mysid *Gnathophausia* (Clarke, 1980), while Clarke (1976) reported two bottom-dwelling sharks in a sperm whale from the same locality. The latter whale had been swimming in water over 3 000 m deep, and this plus other evidence of the ingestion of bottom-dwelling fish and squid make it "difficult to avoid the conclusion that at least some of these whales dived more than 2 000 m to collect squids from the sea floor" (Clarke, 1980). Assuming that adult males consume 2% of their body weight per day, and females

3%, Clarke (1977) calculated average daily consumption as 300 kg for males and 150 kg for females.

**Reproduction**

There is a surprising similarity between the social organisation of the sperm whale and the African elephant. The basic social unit appears to be the mixed school of adult females plus their young, totalling about 20–25 individuals, of which the adult females may be in long-term association. Mature males may join these schools during the breeding season (which has its peak from October to December in the Southern Hemisphere), but the evidence suggests this is only a brief association, and the concept of a "harem" does not seem valid. From the similarity of foetal lengths within sperm whale schools at any one time it has been suggested that there is some synchronization of oestrus, possibly attributable to the arrival of the adult male. A single calf is born after a gestation period of 15–16 months at a length of 4,0 m. The length for which a calf is suckled may depend on the age of the mother, ranging from an average of one to two years in the youngest to three years or more in the oldest. Solid food is first taken before the calf is a year old, but some individuals still have traces of milk in the stomach at ages of 7,5 years in females and 13 years in males! It is possible that some communal suckling takes place in the school, with older females being more involved than younger. Females reach sexual maturity at 8,5 m and an age of nine years. While males may start producing spermatozoa at about the same age, their potential fertility is much lower than that of larger males, the minimum level of potential fertility (based on the density of spermatozoa produced) being attained at a mean length of 12,5 m and an age of about 20 years. Achievement of "breeding bull" status, however, normally may be even later (when maximum spermatozoa densities are produced), at a mean length of 13,7 m and an age of about 25 years (Best, Canham & MacLeod, 1984). Juvenile males may leave the mixed school from an age of four to five years to form bachelor schools of 1–50 animals. As these males become older the school size drops and the individual distance between members seems to increase, so that large bachelors may be found in groups of one to six animals spaced half a mile or more apart (Best, 1979).

# XXVI. Family DELPHINIDAE

## Dolphins, pilot whales, killer and false killer whales

The Family Delphinidae is a diverse group with members ranging in size from about 1,5 m to 9,5 m, in all of which the first two (and up to the first six) cervical vertebrae are fused together. Most of the smaller forms have a distinct beak, in the larger the head is globose. Adults of all but one species have erupted teeth in both jaws, varying from two to over 60 pairs, the exception being Risso's dolphin, *Grampus griseus*, which lacks teeth in the upper jaw. One member, the southern right whale dolphin, *Lissodelphis peronii*, lacks a dorsal fin, all the others having a more or less falcate dorsal fin, which varies in shape in different members. The tail flukes have a notch in the median line of the trailing edge.

True porpoises, or members of the Family Phocoenidae, can be distinguished from dolphins as small animals with blunt, beakless heads, a triangular or ridge-like dorsal fin, small moderately pointed flippers and spade-shaped teeth. There are no records of true porpoises in South African waters: the suggestion that *Neophocoena* might occur, based on a misallocation of a skull to the Cape of Good Hope (Allen, 1923) and a probable misidentification of a Cape fur seal at sea (Gibson Hill, 1950) has not been substantiated subsequently and is considered highly improbable.

The relationship of the various genera within the Family has not yet been settled satisfactorily and consequently no subfamilial divisions are used (see Ross, 1984).

Key to the genera (adapted from Meester *et al.*, 1986)

1. Permanent teeth in lower jaw only
   ... *Grampus*

   Permanent teeth in both upper and lower jaws
   ... 2

2. No more than 13 pairs of teeth in upper and lower jaws
   ... 3

   20 or more pairs of teeth in upper and lower jaws
   ... 6

3. Teeth confined to anterior half of rostrum; length of dorsal fin clearly greater than height
   ... *Globicephala*

   Teeth covering two-thirds or more of rostrum
   ... 4

4. Teeth flattened anteriorly and posteriorly, pterygoids separated but in close proximity
   ... *Orcinus*

   Teeth more or less circular in cross-section, pterygoids meeting in mid-line
   ... 5

5. Small, up to 2,4 m in length; teeth occupying two-thirds of rostrum; pre-maxillae expanded proximally
   ... *Feresa*

   Larger, up to 5,8 m in length, teeth occupying whole rostrum, premaxillae not expanded proximally
   ... *Pseudorca*

6. Beak present but not marked off from melon by transverse crease; teeth with crennulate crowns
   ... *Steno*

   Either beak present, marked off from melon by transverse crease, or no beak; teeth usually with more or less smooth crowns
   ... 7

7. Long-beaked dolphins with snout projecting beyond, and sharply demarcated from, remainder of head; rostral portion of premaxillae convex in lateral view
   ... 8

   Dolphins with beak very short, indistinct or absent; rostral portion of premaxillae flat in lateral view
   ... 11

8. Diameter of largest tooth 2–4 mm
   ... 9

   Diameter of largest tooth 5–9 mm
   ... 10

9. Palate deeply grooved; dark stripe running from flipper halfway along jaw or to tip of lower jaw
   ... *Delphinus*

   Palate ungrooved or grooves shallow; dark stripe, if present, running from flipper to eye or angle of mouth
   ... *Stenella*

10. Dorsal fin mounted on prominent ridge along back; symphysis of mandible about one-quarter to one-third of length of mandible
... *Sousa*

Dorsal fin not mounted on prominent ridge; symphysis of mandible less than one-quarter of length of mandible
... *Tursiops*

11. No dorsal fin
... *Lissodelphis*

Dorsal fin present
... 12

12. More than 35 pairs of teeth in upper and lower jaws
... *Lagenodelphis*

Fewer than 35 pairs of teeth in upper and lower jaws
... 13

13. Head melon-shaped, with no trace of beak; dorsal aspect of maxillary bones narrowing noticeably about one-third of distance anterior to base of rostrum
... *Peponocephala*

Head with beak which, even if indistinct, is marked off by lateral grooves; dorsal aspect of maxillary bones straight or slightly convex
... 14

14. Dorsal fin falcate; sides of rostrum more or less straight throughout length
... *Lagenorhynchus*

Dorsal fin triangular; sides of rostrum expanded laterally in mid-length
... *Cephalorhynchus*

## Genus *Grampus* Gray, 1828

These are large dolphins with total lengths of up to 4,0 m. The head is globose, the melon well developed and the head without a beak. They have two to seven pairs of teeth in the lower jaw only. The flippers are long and narrow, the dorsal fin high and erect, set at the mid-length of the body.

No. 218

## *Grampus griseus* (G. Cuvier, 1812)

## Risso's dolphin
## Risso se dolfyn

Plate 16

### Colloquial Name

Originally Risso's name was associated with the "Delphinus de Risso" of G. Cuvier (=*Grampus rissoanus* Gray, 1850), a species which lives in the Mediterranean which is now considered to be a synonym of *G. griseus*.
Alternative name: Grey dolphin.

### Taxonomic Notes

A skull from the South African Museum, sent to the British Museum (Natural History), was attributed to *G. richardsonii* (Gray, 1865), a species which was later shown by True (1889) to be within the normal range of variation for North Atlantic *G. griseus*.

### Description

Risso's dolphins seem to vary in size in different oceans. In the eastern North Atlantic, specimens reach 4,0 m in length, but in South African waters have only been recorded up to 3,41 m (Ross, 1984; Best, pers. comm.). The latter specimen weighed 485 kg. There is stated to be no sexual dimorphism in size (Ross, 1984).

The anterior part of the body is robust and slightly compressed laterally, while posterior to the dorsal fin the body is attenuate in profile and becomes increasingly compressed laterally towards the flukes. The animal thus gives the impression of being disproportionately "heavy" in front of the dorsal fin. The head is rounded, sloping steeply in front to the tip of the snout, which projects beyond the tip of the lower jaw. There is no beak, and the anterior face of the melon has a characteristic median vertical groove, a feature unique to this species. The dorsal fin is prominent, its height comprising 8–15% of the body length, erect, with a straight or slightly convex leading edge and a moderately concave trailing edge. It is set in the middle of the body. The flippers are long (17–20% of body length), narrow and curved.

Juveniles are a brownish-grey colour above, light grey on the sides and a pale cream colour below and on the melon anterior to the blowhole. There is an anchor-shaped whitish mark below on the chest between the flippers which extends back as a white band to the anus, broadening posteriorly. The overall body colour darkens with age early in life, but then a progressive loss of pigment occurs. This is associated with the development of a white lacing of elongate, linear scars, circular spots of varying size and oval scars on the body of adults. The origin of at least the linear scars (judging from their number and spacing) appears to be intraspecific interaction. These scars tend to be straighter from the dorsal fin forwards and more curved posterior to the dorsal fin. Fraser (1974) noted that this scarring is more intensive in older individuals and Mizue & Yoshida (1962) stated that the males are more scarred than the females. In the largest animals the anterior section of the body becomes almost completely white.

They usually have no teeth in the upper jaw and from two to seven large teeth on each side of the lower jaw, about 15 mm in diameter and projecting 25 to 30 mm from the gums.

The vertebral formula is C7+T12–13+L18–20+Cd31–32 = 68–70. The first six cervical vertebrae are fused together to form a mass, with the seventh a very thin vertebra (Nishiwaki, 1972).

### Distribution

Risso's dolphins occur throughout the tropical and temperate seas of the world, generally in water over 1 000 m deep, but frequently associated with the shelf edge (Kruse *et al.*, in press). On the coast of South Africa they have been recorded from off Natal, the eastern, southern and western Cape, usually in water more than 200 m deep but apparently associated with the shelf edge. They are also recorded as strandings from Namibia (Findlay, 1989).

### Food

Ross (1984) stated that they feed entirely on squid and in captivity they will only accept squid (Tsutsumi, Kamaimura & Mizue, 1954).

### Reproduction

Ross (1984) suggested from very limited data that sexual maturity in the female is attained at a total length of about 2,77 m, and that males begin maturing between 2,6 and 3,0 m. From the lengths of two foetuses and a young calf and, with a gestation period estimated to be one year, Ross (1984) concluded that the calves are born in the summer months between December and April. This agrees with information from Japanese waters (Mizue & Yoshida, 1962). Mitchell (1975a) stated that at birth the calves have a total length of about 1,5 m.

### General

In South African waters school size varies from one to 80 animals, with a mean of just over 11 (Findlay, 1989). Strandings and incidental sightings have been recorded throughout the year, and there is no evidence of seasonality in this area (Ross, 1984; Findlay, 1989).

Risso's dolphins are not exploited to any great extent, although in Japanese waters they have been taken by small harpoon boats and were one of the main species caught in the East China Sea (Mitchell, 1975b).

This species cannot be caught by driving schools ashore, as can the long-finned pilot whale, *G. melaena*, as they become much more excited and cannot be contained (Mitchell, 1975b).

The famous dolphin "Pelorus Jack", that escorted ships in New Zealand waters between 1888 and 1912, and that was protected by an Order in Council from the Colonial Governor in 1904, belonged to this species (Baker, 1974). That this dolphin rode the bows of vessels from time to time is unusual behaviour for the species, which normally is reluctant to bow-ride vessels of any size.

A hybrid between a captive male Risso's dolphin and a female bottlenosed dolphin (*Tursiops truncatus*) was recorded in Japan, the calf surviving at least 1 000 days (Nishiwaki & Tobayama, 1984). Hybridization between these two species may also take place in the wild (Fraser, 1940).

## Genus *Globicephala* Lesson, 1828

Two species of this genus have been recorded in South African waters, *G. macrorhynchus* and *G. melaena*, the former with seven to 10 pairs of teeth in the upper and lower jaws, the latter with nine to 12.

The melon is globular and projects forward to overhang beyond the short beak, especially in adult males. In *G. macrorhynchus* the flippers are shorter than in *G. melaena* .

Key to the species Meester *et al.* (1986)

1. Seven to 10 pairs of teeth in both upper and lower jaws; flipper length 14–19 percent of body length; premaxillae expanded in anterior half of rostrum to almost completely cover maxillae
   ... *G. macrorhynchus*

   Nine to 12 pairs of teeth in both upper and lower jaws; flipper length 18–27 percent of body length; premaxillae comparatively unexpanded in anterior half of rostrum, leaving maxillae clearly visible on either side
   ... *G. melaena*

No. 219

## *Globicephala macrorhynchus* Gray, 1846

## Short-finned pilot whale
## Kortvinloodswalvis

### Colloquial Name

So called to distinguish them from the closely related species, the long-finned pilot whale, *G. melaena*, which, as the name implies, has relatively longer flippers.
Alternative name: short-finned blackfish.

### Taxonomic Notes

A. Smith (1834) recognised two species of pilot whales from the seas off the South African coast, *Phocoena globiceps* (=*G. macrorhynchus* Gray, 1846) and *Phocoena edwardii* (=*G. melaena* (Traill, 1809)).

Fig.219.1 Short-finned pilot whale, *Globicephala macrorhynchus*. Adult male at 5,21 m. Males recorded up to 5,89 m, females 4,05 m (after Ross, 1984).

### Description

Male short-finned pilot whales from South African waters have been recorded as reaching a total length of 5,89 m and females 4,05 m: the species is strongly sexually dimorphic in size (Ross, 1984). They are almost entirely black in colour except for a dark grey anchor-shaped marking on the under parts between the flippers, the points extending to the base of the flippers on either side, the shaft extending posteriorly down the mid-line to the ano-genital region. The distinct greyish saddle posterior to the dorsal fin present in specimens from the North Pacific (Mitchell, 1975a) is not found in any Southern African specimens examined to date (Ross, 1984).

The head is large in relation to the size of the body, the melon bulbous, the mouth noticeably large. The dorsal fin, which is situated nearer the head than the tail, is extremely broad at the base, with the tip pointing backwards rather than upwards, and the trailing edge concave. The length of the sickle-shaped flippers comprises 14–19% of the body length, and the width of the tail flukes is about one-quarter of the body length. The front parts of the body anterior to the dorsal fin are stocky, tapering off posteriorly and becoming slender and laterally compressed towards the flukes.

There are seven to 10 pairs of teeth in both upper and lower jaws, although the most usual number in South African specimens is seven or eight pairs (Ross, 1984).

The vertebral formula from other localities is C7+T10–11+L11–12+Cd27–28 = 57. No post-cranial material from South African specimens has been collected (Ross, 1984).

This species can be distinguished externally from *G. melaena* by the absence of a grey saddle or post-ocular eye stripe, the smaller number of teeth and the relatively shorter flippers.

### Distribution

Short-finned pilot whales occur in the warmer waters of the North Atlantic, Pacific, and Indian oceans, though their limits of distribution are tentative in the tropical Atlantic and southern Pacific oceans (Ross, 1984). Van Bree, Best & Ross (1978) discussed all records of *Globicephala* from the South African coast up to 1971, almost all of which were strandings. *G. macrorhynchus* has only been recorded from the southeast Cape between East London and Jeffrey's Bay, although an unlabelled skull from the Mossel Bay Museum may indicate a westward extension as far as the Mossel Bay area. Sightings of pilot whales resembling *macrorhynchus* were also made off Durban, and Van Bree *et al.* concluded that this species appears to be confined to the tropical and subtropical waters of the east coast of South Africa, as opposed to *G. melaena* which is confined to the west coast, with an overlap in their distribution between (possibly) Mossel Bay and East London.

Findlay (1989) considered that pilot whales in South African waters (of either species) appear to be associated with the shelf edge or in waters of over 1000 m.

### Habits

Short-finned pilot whales are relatively slow swimmers and schools are recorded lying motionless on the surface of the water (Mitchell, 1975a). They occur in schools averaging about 29 whales, but these may occasionally accumulate into aggregations of over 200 animals (Kasuya & Marsh, 1984). During whale-marking operations off the Natal coast, Van Bree *et al.* (1978) recorded schools of two, 10 and 25 pilot whales attributable to this species. They frequently are associated with bottlenosed dolphins, *Tursiops truncatus*.

They have been hunted since the middle of the 19th century for their oil and are still exploited in Caribbean and Japanese waters (Mitchell, 1975b). Like *G. melaena* mass strandings are not uncommon.

### Food

Caldwell & Caldwell (1971) found that, in the Caribbean, fish and squid appear to be their principal food. Ross (1984) recorded cephalopod remains in the stomachs of four specimens which stranded near Port Elizabeth.

### Reproduction

There are very few data for South African waters. Females may become sexually mature at about 3,8 or 3,9 m (Ross, 1984). The species has been extensively studied, however, in drive and harpoon fisheries in Japan (Kasuya & Marsh, 1984). Breeding is seasonal but diffusely so; conceptions peak in spring (April/May) and births 14,9 months later in summer (July/August). The calf is born at an average length of 1,4 m and nursed for a minimum of two years; calves of older females may be nursed for considerably longer than this. Females mature at an average body length of 3,16 m and age of nine years. Male maturation is protracted, but animals are considered functionally mature at a mean length of 4,14 m and age of 16 years. Females are only reproductively active up to an age of about 40 years, by which time they will have produced four or five calves, though they may live for up to 63 years. Males on the other hand do not live so long (up to 46 years), but they remain reproductively active until death. This results in a surplus of reproductive females over males and a polygynous mating system. As suggested for sperm whales, females may remain in their mothers' schools for life, whereas males probably migrate between schools after weaning (bachelor schools are apparently unrecorded for pilot whales—Martin, Reynolds & Richardson, 1987).

No. 220

## *Globicephala melaena* (Traill, 1809)

## Long-finned pilot whale
## Langvinloodswalvis

### Colloquial Name

So called to distinguish them from the closely related *G. macrorhynchus* which has shorter flippers.
Alternative names: ca'aing whale; Atlantic blackfish; common pilot whale; pilot whale; pothead.

### Taxonomic Notes

The northern and southern populations of this species are separated geographically by a wide tropical belt, and sometimes have been accorded either specific or subspecific rank. Van Bree *et al.* (1978) pointed out that the differences between the northern and southern populations are small, but if the southern populations can be recognised as subspecifically different from the northern, then their name would be *G. m. edwardii* (A. Smith, 1834).

Fig. 220.1 Long-finned pilot whale, *Globicephala melaena*. Female at 4,5 m. Males recorded up to 6,3 m, females 5,46 m (after Ross, 1984).

### Description

In the Northern Hemisphere males reach a total length of 6,3 m, females smaller at about 5,46 m, but there may be some difference in the maximum sizes achieved in separate populations. Ross (1984) recorded the length of a female that stranded at the Sundays River mouth, Cape Province, as 4,5 m. In Southern Hemisphere specimens the upper parts of the body are black, except for a small greyish-white diagonal streak behind the eyes and a pale grey saddle-shaped marking behind the dorsal fin. These markings may intensify with the size of the animal, and may be faint or absent in neonates. Ventrally there is a greyish-white anchor mark on the throat and chest of a very similar shape to that in *G. macrorhynchus*, extending posteriorly as a median streak to the umbilicus, then broadening out into a lozenge-shaped marking between the umbilicus and the anus. The head has a bulbous melon that projects dorsally beyond the tip of the upper jaw, but which immediately above the mouth is concave in profile, forming a short, distinct beak. The body is robust and slightly compressed laterally anteriorly, but more slender and increasingly compressed towards the tail, where the caudal peduncle becomes distinctly keeled. The flippers are long (18–27% of the body in length) and sickle-shaped, and tend to curve sharply back from their mid-length. The dorsal fin is situated slightly forward of the mid-point of the back and is of a similar shape to that of *G. macrorhynchus*, being very broad at its base, the tip tending to curve backward.

There are nine to 12 pairs of teeth in both upper and lower jaws (Ross, 1984).

The vertebral formula is C7+T11+L13–14+Cd27–29 = 58–60 (True, 1889).

This species can be distinguished externally from *G. macrorhynchus* (in this Subregion) by the greyish-white post-ocular streak and saddle behind the dorsal fin, the longer flippers and the larger number of teeth.

### Distribution

The northern populations occur in the northern Atlantic Ocean from West Greenland and Iceland to Cape Hatteras on the west, and from the Barents Sea to the coast of northwestern Africa (including the North, Baltic and Mediterranean seas) on the east; the existence of *G. melaena* in the northern Pacific in recent times is doubtful (Kasuya, 1975). The southern populations are circumpolar from warm temperate waters to about as far south as 70 °S, and in the cold Humboldt, Falkland and Benguela currents. A discontinuity in summer distribution seems to occur between about 45 and 50 °S, but the significance of this is not clear (Kasamatsu *et al.*, 1988). Van Bree *et al.* (1978) listed eight records from the coast of South Africa up to 1971, from the Saldanha Bay area to East London, six of these as strandings. They stated that this species is predominantly confined to the colder waters on the west coast of South Africa, with an overlap in distribution with *G. macrorhynchus* between (possibly) Mossel Bay and the East London sector.

### Habits

A spotter aircraft, flying from Saldanha Bay during the 1963 and 1964 whaling seasons, reported 21 sightings of pilot whales, totalling about 2 800 individuals, some of which at least were *G. melaena* (van Bree *et al.* , 1978). Schools of the species are accompanied frequently by bottlenosed dolphins, *Tursiops truncatus*. In the northwest Atlantic the basic social unit seems to be 15–25 animals and rarely exceeds 100, but under some circumstances these can aggregate into larger groups of over 200 animals (Sergeant, 1962).

Their sound repertoire is extensive involving unpulsed (whistles) and pulsed (creaks) sounds. The whistle repertoire is a continuum or matrix with no mutually exclusive categories; differences in whistle contour use, mean whistle frequency and duration, and mean calling rate can in some cases be related to context and arousal state (Taruski, 1979).

### Food

Nothing is known locally. Sergeant (1962) listed squid as the principal food in inshore waters in the northern Atlantic Ocean, with Atlantic cod and other fish when squid is not available.

### Reproduction

Nothing is known locally. In the western North Alantic birth takes place at a length of 1,74 m (females) to 1,77 m (males), after a gestation period of 15,5–16 months. Females reach sexual maturity at 3,63 m and an age of six to seven years (Sergeant, 1962), while in males "breeding maturity" is reached at 12 years old, at a length of 4,6 m (Kasuya, Sergeant & Tanaka, 1988). Lactation may last 22 months, though calves start taking solid food at an age of six to nine months, and the complete reproductive cycle takes 39 to 40 months (Sergeant, 1962). The species seems to mature earlier and have a shorter life span than *G. macrorhynchus*, and neither the decline in pregnancy rate with age nor the existence of a significant number of post-reproductive females seen in *G. macrorhynchus* have been detected in this species. It is speculated that the cohesive matrilineal school structure and the long maternal care of *G. macrorhynchus* are not so pronounced in *G. melaena* (Kasuya *et al.*, 1988).

### General

In the Northern Hemisphere they are exploited for their oil, Mitchell (1975b) recording that over a 10 year period off Newfoundland (between 1951 and 1961) over 4 000 were killed annually, in some years up to 10 000 (Mitchell, 1975b). Since then catches have dropped dramatically which Mitchell (1975b) believed to have been due to overexploitation. In other areas, for example the Faeroe Islands, catches remained at a high level, indicating that there appeared to be local and discrete populations of the species. Exploitation in the Southern Hemisphere is low and sporadic.

## Genus *Orcinus* Fitzinger, 1860

No. 221

## *Orcinus orca* (Linnaeus, 1758)

## Killer whale
## Moordvis

Plate 17

### Colloquial Name

Aptly known as the killer from its predatory habits. The specific name *orca* in Latin means "sea monster", Roman writers referring to them as "formidabilissimus balaenarum hostis" (the most formidable enemy of the whales). Recently it has become fashionable to use "orca" as the colloquial name, reflecting a change in public reaction to the species from fear and hostility to affection and fascination.

### Taxonomic Notes

Mikhalev, Ivashin, Savusin & Zelenaya (1981) described the existence of a "dwarf" form of killer whale from the Antarctic for which they proposed the name *Orcinus nanus* Mikhalev and Ivashin; this was later pointed out to be a *nomen nudum* because it was not accompanied by a figure, diagnosis or designation of a holotype specimen (IWC, 1982). Subsequently Berzin & Vladimirov (1983) published a fuller description under the name *Orcinus glacialis*. This whale was smaller (maximum length 7,5 m in males and 6,5 m in females, compared to 9,0 m in males and 7,7 m in females), and *inter alia* had smaller tail flukes (40% less in area), smaller teeth (half the height and width and one-quarter the weight), and significant differences in skull measurements and configuration compared to other killer whales. The dwarf killer whale was found in large schools near the ice edge and among large, broken pack ice, was typically covered with diatoms, and fed almost exclusively on fish (compared to the marine mammals found in other killer whales). This form of killer whale has not been recorded yet from the Subregion.

### Description

The killer whale is the largest of the Delphinidae. Adult males reach a maximum length of about 9,1 m and adult females about 7,6 m in the Antarctic (IWC, 1982). From South African waters males are known up to 8,8 m and females up to 7,9 m (Best & Ross, 1977). Two males 4,82 m and 5,93 m long from the southwest Indian Ocean weighed 1 434 and 3 166 kg respectively (Gambell *et al.*, 1975), and the largest specimens have a mass of up to eight tonnes (Tomilin, 1967).

Most striking in appearance, the upper parts of the body are black with a lozenge-shaped white mark above and posterior to the eyes and an irregularly shaped white or greyish saddle just behind the dorsal fin. The black of the upper parts extends down over the flanks to encompass the flippers and the belly, but does not join along the mid-line of the under parts, which are wholly white from the chin to just behind the anus. A black spot is frequently associated with the position of the genital slit, and the shape of the pigmentation pattern in the ano-genital region is sexually dimorphic (Bigg, Ellis, Ford & Balcomb, 1987). The white of the under parts extends upwards in front of the anus onto the flanks, swinging backwards in an oval-shaped marking which extends beyond the anus on the flanks. The dorsal surface of the tail flukes is black while the ventral surface is white with a thin black trailing edge. While in broad terms the general pattern of white and black markings is constant, there is considerable individual variation (Evans, Yablokov & Bowles, 1982). Ross (1984) stated that off the southeast coast of South Africa the saddle behind the dorsal fin is usually grey or is absent in some individuals, whereas in populations from the Antarctic seas it is white, suggesting that the two populations are discrete.

A characteristic feature of the killer whale, apart from its distinctive black and white markings, is the striking sexual dimorphism in the size and shape of the dorsal fin. At birth the height of the dorsal fin is only about 7–9% of body length in both sexes, and in adult females it may reach 10–12% of body length, but in adult males the height of the fin reaches 18–25% of body length (reaching an actual height of 1,6–1,8 m). In such an attenuate structure without any skeletal support it is not surprising that the fin should tend to flop or curl over to one side in some adult males. The dorsal fin is not only of a different size in adult males and females, it also differs in shape, becoming much taller than broader in adult males, with both leading and trailing edges virtually straight to form a pointed isosceles triangle. In adult females the height of the fin is only just greater than its breadth, and remains (as in the calf) inclined backwards, with the front edge convex and the back edge concave (Fig.221.1).

The flippers are oval in shape and broadly rounded at the tips. Their relative length increases in both sexes from about 11% of body length in calves to 20% in adults, forming massive paddle-shaped structures. The tail flukes are broad, their total width increasing with body size only in males, where they grow from about 22% of body length in calves to 31–37% in adults; in females they retain juvenile proportions. The body reaches its maximum girth at the level of the dorsal fin, the tail section relatively slender. The mouth is very large, the eyes relatively small.

There are 10–13 pairs of robust teeth in both upper and lower jaws. The teeth are conical but compressed somewhat antero-posteriorly, and up to 130 mm long, of which about 40 mm to 50 mm protrude above the gums. They are curved inwards and slightly backwards at the tip. When the jaws close, the teeth interlock to form an efficient gripping mechanism. Tooth-wear can be considerable, apparently as a result of the grinding action permitted by the great freedom of movement of the jaws on the closely interlocked teeth (Caldwell & Brown, 1964).

The vertebral formula is most commonly C7+T11–12+L10–11+Cd21–24 = 50–52. The first three or four cervical vertebrae are fused together (Nishiwaki, 1972).

Fig. 221.1. Dorsal fins, *Orcinus orca*
(a) adult male (b) adult female (c) juvenile.

**Distribution**

Killer whales are perhaps the most cosmopolitan of all cetaceans, being distributed widely in all the oceans and seas of the world. Although they have been recorded in tropical waters, they tend to be commoner in the colder waters of the Arctic and Antarctic oceans. Some groups or communities are seen regularly in particular areas and appear more or less "resident", others are highly unpredictable in their occurrence and range, and seem to be "transient". It is thus difficult to generalize about distribution or migration in this species. In the Puget Sound area on the west coast of North America, residents travel in larger pods (5–50 vs 1–7), use more predictable travel routes, do not make such long dives, and feed mainly on fish (salmon) rather than the marine mammals that transients seem to seek. There are even morphological differences, the shape of the dorsal fin being generally different in the two races. It is against such a background that it is difficult to evaluate the validity of species such as *O. glacialis*!

The only locality in the Subregion where killer whales occur predictably is at Marion Island, where Condy, van Aarde & Bester (1978) have shown that although killer whales can be seen in all months of the year, there is a noticeable increase in numbers during the summer months, coincidental with the elephant seal, *Mirounga leonina*, breeding season. Two strandings are recorded from the island (Bester & Panagis, pers. comm.). On the southern African coast the species has been recorded from about 21 °S on the Namibian coast to Inhambane (23°51′S), Mozambique (Findlay, 1989; Ross, 1984). Rice & Saayman (1987) also listed incidental sightings from the Mozambique Channel (at 15°25′S) and Uniabs River mouth, Namibia (20°11′S).

They appear to occur off the South African coast throughout the year, although Findlay (1989) has detected a bimodality of occurrence offshore in the whaling grounds, one peak occurring around June but a larger peak in September/October. These coincided with seasonal migrations of rorquals, especially sei whales.

Elsewhere they have been known to enter rivers, Norman & Fraser (1949) reporting an individual 50 km from the sea in England, feeding on salmon, and Martinez & Klinghammer (1970) a female which travelled up the Columbia River for a distance of about 180 km.

**Habits**

Off Marion Island, Condy *et al.* (1978) recorded that the largest herd seen numbered 25, the mean number being 4,2 individuals. Where solitary individuals were seen they were usually adult males, groups of two consisting usually of an adult female and its calf, or pairs of subadults. Groups of three were either an adult male and subadults, or an adult male, a female and her calf. In southern African waters Findlay (1989) reported school sizes ranging (in three different data sets) from three to 11 (mean 5,3), one to 12 (mean 4,5) and one to 25 (mean 7,3). Rice & Saayman (1987) reported a range of one to about 50, but the latter seems an outlier, the next largest group being 10–15.

Research in the Puget Sound area of North America has established that in this area the resident pods (containing 5–50 individuals) each have their own "dialect" of five to 15 discrete calls, and that pods can be placed in "clans", with other pods that share some of the same calls. These dialects are so distinct that it is even possible to identify from which pod a captive animal was taken (Bigg *et al.*, 1987).

At Marion Island groups will rest in sheltered coves for periods of several hours. They may swim around leisurely or lie motionless, being moved backwards and forwards by the surge of the water. Some lie belly up, either at the surface or on the bottom (Condy *et al.*, 1978).

Care behaviour of injured companions is found in many cetaceans, and especially in the killer whale. Injured group members are not deserted and occasionally their companions may remain with them for some time (Martinez & Klinghammer, 1970). Caldwell & Caldwell (1966) recorded a female that remained in the vicinity after her calf had been killed.

Killer whales are fast swimmers and are capable of making leaps out of the water or of holding themselves vertically in the water with only their heads protruding. In leaping they may momentarily hold themselves out of the water in a vertical position with only their tail section submerged.

**Food**

Killer whales feed on just about any palatable marine organism of any size, including fish, squids, turtles, birds and marine mammals. They are well known for the vigour of their attacks and the co-ordination within the herds when hunting. Condy, van Aarde & Bester (1978) recorded seeing a group of three killer whales disposing of 20 king penguins, *Aptenodytes patagonica*, which appeared to be swallowed whole. Both Condy *et al.* (1978) and Martinez & Klinghammer (1970) recorded that killer whales will raise their heads out of the water in search of prey. In catching seals or penguins they have been known to rock or break up ice floes, so dumping their prey into the water. Perhaps the most remarkable behaviour is that of deliberate stranding in an attempt to catch elephant seals, *M. leonina*, or sea lions, *Otaria flavescens*, as observed on the Patagonian coast (Lopez & Lopez, 1985). In 365 attempts, killer whales were successful on about one-third of the occasions, holding their prey in their mouths and turning parallel to the beach so that subsequent waves could assist them in returning to sea. On six occasions an adult and a juvenile stranded together, and the adult would catch a sea lion and throw it towards the juvenile, even if the latter had caught one successfully itself. These and other interactions led the authors to postulate that the adult may be teaching the young to hunt in this manner, which appeared to have a higher success rate than hunting in water. Killer whales show a remarkable degree of group co-operation and division of labour when tackling large whales (Tarpy, 1979). Some group members will grab the lower jaw, others will attack the flippers and so immobilise it, while others will prize open its mouth and tear out the tongue (Martinez & Klinghammer, 1970). With large whales they appear to feed selectively on the tongues and blubber, and the prizing open of the mouth to get the tongue has been observed frequently (as well as attacks directed at the tongue when dead whales are being towed alongside whale-catchers). They have also been observed to strip skin and blubber off whales that have been killed and await collection.

Brown & Norris (1956) recorded that, when feeding on dolphins, a group of killer whales will surround them, gradually constricting the circle, until they are tightly crowded. One killer whale would then rush in and feed, then return to the circle, another taking its place. Martinez & Klinghammer (1970) could find no record of cannibalism or injury of killer whales to each other.

Condy *et al.* (1978) noted that, when feeding, groups of one or more would patrol the coast, surfacing at regular intervals. They moved reasonably fast, with their dorsal fins showing for much of the time. On reaching a cove with a beach they would submerge and move close to the surf zone, swimming submerged along it and only surfacing once past the beach. They are attracted to disturbances and will investigate when a stone is thrown into the water (Kerley, pers. comm.).

**Reproduction**

Little is known about this aspect of their life history in the southern oceans. In the Northern Hemisphere calves are born at a total length of about 2,1 m to 2,7 m. In North Atlantic killer whales the peak of conceptions occurs between September and January (Christensen, 1982). Data from captive animals suggest that gestation lasts 15–17 months (Bigg *et al.*, 1987), and calves begin mouthing solid food by three to four months and may be nutritionally independent by 11 months (Heyning, 1988), although in the wild calves may continue to associate with their mothers into adulthood (Bigg, 1982).

Females are believed to be sexually mature at 4,87 m, the males at 5,79 m (Bigg, 1982). Females may give birth for the first time at an age of 12 years but on average at an age of 14 years, while males may start maturing at 14 years but do not reach full size until they are 20 years old. Natural mortality seems very low in this species, and while bulls may live for at least 30 years, cows could survive much longer. Typically an adult female produces four to six offspring over a 25 year period and then stops breeding. Such post-reproductive females may live another 20 years or more, some perhaps reaching 80 years of age (Bigg *et al.*, 1987).

**General**

Martinez & Klinghammer (1970) could find no account of an attack by killer whales on man in the wild. Divers finding themselves among them have not been molested, although the killers show curiosity at their presence (see Rice & Saayman, 1987, for a local example). Incidents involving killer whales, their trainers and others have occurred in captivity, however, including at least one case of serious injury, but the whale's motivation in these cases is unclear.

Martinez & Klinghammer (1970) recorded an extraordinary relationship between killer whales and men which continued for over 50 years in Twofold Bay, Australia. It was claimed that one individual killer whale (a male, "Old Tom") was recognised by a damaged dorsal fin over the whole period. The group of killer whales would arrive each year in time for the whaling season, and would "assist" the whalers by harassing passing humpback (or right) whales until the whalers arrived. When a humpback whale was harpooned, the killer whales would swim under its head to prevent it diving. After the humpback was killed it would sink, and the killers would remain to eat the tongue and lips. The whalers would return the next day to recover the carcass, which was then floating on the surface, and the process was repeated. Mitchell & Baker (1980) reviewed the evidence for the duration of this association and especially for the reputed age of Old Tom.

Killer whales are not harvested currently to any great extent, although in Norway, Mitchell (1975b) recorded that 250 were taken in 1970 and Soviet whalers killed 916 in the Antarctic in 1979/80. Their live capture for oceanaria used to be carried out in western Canada and the United States of America, 65 being taken between 1962 and 1977 (Bigg, 1982). Subsequently capture attempts have centred around Iceland.

Killer whales can become a pest when dropline fishing is practised. Off Southern Tasmania in 1979–81 the extent to which they removed fish off hooks caused this type of fishing to be temporarily abandoned (Guiler, pers. comm.), and Sivasubramanian (1964) reported that around 4% of the catch in tuna long-lining operations in the Indian Ocean may have been lost to killer whales and sharks. Incidents of interaction between killer whales and sportfishermen for tuna off the Cape Peninsula have also been recorded (Best, pers. comm.).

## Genus *Feresa* Gray, 1871

No. 222

## *Feresa attenuata* Gray, 1874

## Pygmy killer whale
## Dwergmoordvis

**Colloquial Name**

In body-shape pygmy killer whales closely resemble false killer whales, *Pseudorca crassidens*, but they are much smaller.

**Taxonomic Notes**

The original date of the description of the species seems to have been 1874 (*Ann. Mag. nat. Hist.* (4) **14**: 238–239), not 1875 (*J. Mus. Godeffroy* **3**: 184) as usually cited, as pointed out by Caldwell & Caldwell (1971), following Best (1970a).

**Description**

Pygmy killer whales are rare and very little is known about their life histories. Maximum recorded lengths are 2,59 m for males and 2,45 m for females (Lichter, Fraga & Castello, 1990), but sexual dimorphism in size has not yet been demonstrated in this species (Best, 1970a). A male 2,33 m long weighed 166 kg (Best, pers. comm.).

The anterior half of the body is moderately robust and slightly laterally compressed, but posterior to the dorsal fin is noticeably slender (Ross, 1984). They have a narrow groove mid-ventrally, between the lower thoracic region and the genital aperture. The melon projects beyond the tip of the lower jaw and is well formed but not bulbous in lateral view, and tapers to a broadly rounded apex in dorsal view. The flippers are moderately long, about 15–23% of the total length of the body, broad at the base and tapering to rounded apices; their leading edges are convex, the central portion of the trailing edge concave (Fig.233.1). The dorsal fin, placed centrally, is relatively larger and more pointed than in the false killer whale, *Pseudorca crassidens*. The flukes are broad, tapering to points, their trailing edges, like those of the dorsal fin and flippers, often irregularly indented (Best, 1970a).

Fig. 222.1 Pygmy killer whale, *Feresa attenuata*. Female at 2,24 m. Males reach a total length of 2,59 m, females 2,45 m (after Ross, 1984).

The upper parts and most of the lateral and ventral surfaces are bluish-black. Ventrally there is a large, roughly oval-shaped patch of white around the genital and anal apertures which extends anteriorly either side of the mid-line, and there is an ill-defined area of greyish-white on the chest between the flippers, reminiscent of the anchor mark on Risso's dolphin, *Grampus griseus*. The upper and lower lips are edged with white, forming a node (or "goatee") at the tip of the lower jaw. In the living animal there is a pale grey area on the sides extending from just behind the eye to the caudal peduncle, and to the ventral surface posterior to the anal aperture. The upper margin of this is sharply defined from the dark dorsum. After death, however, this colour almost completely disappears (Best, 1970a).

There are 8–12 pairs of teeth in the upper jaw and 10–13 in the lower jaw (Best, 1970a).

The vertebral formula is C7+T12–13+L15–17+Cd32–34 = 67–70. The first three cervical vertebrae are fused together, and occasionally numbers 4 and 5 (Best, 1970a).

### Distribution

They are known from tropical and subtropical waters of the Pacific, Atlantic and Indian oceans. Apart from the type specimen from "the South Seas", pygmy killer whales were first recorded in the Southern Hemisphere in January 1968 when five stranded in the lagoon at Luderitz, Namibia (Best, 1970a). Subsequently they have been recorded in the Southern Hemisphere from Australia, west of the Seychelles bank, Indonesia, west of Ecuador, in the southern Mozambique Channel, in Argentina (Lichter *et al.*, 1990) the eastern tropical Pacific and Peru (Van Waerbeek & Reyes, 1988). Around southern Africa, Findlay (1989) recorded the species from 23 °S on the Namibian coast to Richards Bay (28 °36′S) on the Natal coast, with a lack of specimens between Cape Town and Port Elizabeth, which he attributed to the greater width of the continental shelf in this region.

The majority of records listed by Caldwell & Caldwell (1971) were from within the tropics. They concluded that this species normally inhabits tropical, subtropical and possibly warmer waters of warm temperature zones. On this basis the Luderitz, Namibia, record made in January is an anomaly, for Ross (1984) recorded that the water temperature near the coast in that month is 12 °C. However, they may have moved inshore from the warmer waters (18 °C) 200 km off the coast, the same applying to the Sea Point, Cape, record. Subsequently there are records from Walvis Bay (Findlay, 1989) and St Helena Bay (Best, pers. comm.), so the presence of the species off the west coast seems firmly established.

From the few records available there is some indication of a summer-autumn seasonality in the Subregion (Findlay, 1989).

### Food

Ross (1984) recorded that the stomach of a specimen stranded near Port Elizabeth contained the beaks of cephalopods (unidentified). The species has been implicated in attacks on dolphins, *Stenella* spp during purse-seine operations for tuna in the eastern tropical Pacific (Perryman & Foster, 1980). It accepted fish and squid in captivity (Pryor, Pryor & Norris (1965).

### Reproduction

Nishiwaki, Kasuya, Kamiya, Tobayama & Nakajima (1965) recorded two pregnant females at 2,21 and 2,27 m in length. Pryor, Pryor & Norris (1965) reported that a male at 2,16 m was sexually mature. Perrin & Hubbs (1969) described a newly born calf at 822 mm taken off Costa Rica in May 1967.

### General

For many years pygmy killer whales were known only from two skulls, one from the "South Seas" and another from an unknown locality. In 1952 a specimen was taken in the seas off Japan which provided the first information on their external appearance and post-cranial skeleton (Yamada, 1954). Further specimens were taken off Senegal (Cadenat, 1958) and Hawaii (Pryor *et al.*, 1965). In 1963, 14 were captured in Sagami Bay, Japan, and transported to an oceanarium where unfortunately they all died within a month (Nishiwaki *et al.*, 1965).

Pryor *et al.* (1965) recorded animals resting on the surface at sea, as well as "spyhopping" vertically with head out of water. Some "lobtailing" also occurred at the approach of a vessel. Nishiwaki *et al.* (1965) also reported "spyhopping" in semi-captive animals.

Pygmy killer whales are recorded as being aggressive, a recently captured animal snapping at humans (Pryor *et al.*, 1965), although the specimen stranded at Sea Point, Cape Town, in 1970 was transported to a tidal pool where for an hour it swam around among bathers without any signs of aggression towards them. However, after it was transported to a tank in which four dusky dolphins, *Lagenorhynchus obscurus*, were housed, the dolphins became agitated and kept to the opposite end of the tank. The pygmy killer whale subsequently killed one of them and savaged another (Best, 1970a). Aggressive behaviour of this sort towards other captive cetaceans is reported by Pryor *et al.* (1965), a pygmy killer whale killing a young pilot whale and aggressively chasing a dolphin around the tank.

## Genus *Pseudorca* Reinhardt, 1862

No. 223

## *Pseudorca crassidens* (Owen, 1846)

## False killer whale
## Valsmoordvis

### Colloquial Name

The specific name means "thick-toothed", but originally this was used in conjunction with the generic name *Phocoena*, or porpoise, where it is appropriate. In fact the teeth are by no means as thick or as large as those of the killer whale (Purves & Pilleri, 1978). Gray (1846) termed the species the "Lincolnshire killer whale", from the locality of the original specimen, until Reinhardt (1862) described the external appearance of the animal following a stranding in the Bay of Kiel in 1861.

### Taxonomic Notes

This species was described originally from the sub-fossil skeleton of a specimen recovered from the Lincolnshire Fens in England long before it was known in the flesh. No subspecies have been described.

### Description

False killer whales can be distinguished readily from killer whales, *Orcinus orca*, even at sea, because of their much smaller dorsal fins and their uniformly dark appearance above, as they lack the oval-shaped white marking behind the eye and the grey saddle behind the dorsal fin so characteristic of the killer whale. Adult male false killer whales may reach a total length of 5,8 m (Smithers, 1938); the females are smaller, on average by estimates ranging from 0,46–0,61 m to approximately 0,9 m, although the maximum size attained seems to be about 4,8 m (Purves & Pilleri, 1978). A 3,58 m male had a mass of 372 kg (Ross, 1984), and a 5,14 m male weighed 1 302,8 kg in pieces (Best, pers. comm.).

They are black or slate-grey overall. Some specimens at least carry a light grey blaze mark on the chest resembling the anchor-mark of Risso's dolphin, *Grampus griseus*, broadest at the flipper insertions but narrowing rapidly to a mid-ventral streak behind the flippers that connects posteriorly with an ill-defined greyish area around the ano-genital region. It is quite likely that this ventral pattern is a universal feature in the species which rapidly fades after death or exposure to the sun (Purves & Pilleri, 1978; Ross, 1984).

The head is small when compared with the body, the forehead more streamlined and less bulbous than in the pilot whale, and although it projects forward beyond the tip of the lower jaw, there is no beak. The flippers which are situated far forward on the body, comprise some 9,5–14,5% of the body in length. They are most characteristic in shape, being sharply pointed, and curving sharply backwards from about their mid-point, with the leading edge forming a distinct S-shape. The long-finned pilot whale is the only other cetacean in which this feature sometimes appears (Purves & Pilleri, 1978). The tail flukes have a total spread of about a fifth (19–25%) of the total length and are deeply notched in the mid-line. The dorsal fin is situated slightly in front of the mid-part of the back, increasingly so in larger animals. It is relatively small (height 6–10% of body length), the leading edge sloping backwards, the trailing edge concave, and the tip rounded. This fin never reaches the development seen in the killer whale.

There are 7–11 pairs of teeth in the upper jaw and 8–12 in the lower. They are conical in shape, not flattened antero-posteriorly as in the killer whale (Purves & Pilleri, 1978).

The vertebral formula is C7+T9–12+L9–11+Cd18–26 = 47–52 (Purves & Pilleri, 1978). All seven cervical vertebrae are fused into one in adults.

Fig. 223.1 False killer whale, *Pseudorca crassidens*. Male at 3,58 m. Males recorded up to 5,8 m, females about 5,0 m (after Ross, 1979a)

### Distribution

Judging from the records of strandings and specimens taken commercially or captured alive for oceanaria, false killer whales have a very wide distribution in all the oceans of the world. They occur generally in tropical and warm temperate waters, but exceptionally wander into colder waters (Mitchell, 1975b).

Around southern Africa the species has been recorded from the Luderitz area, Namibia, and between St Helena Bay on the west coast and the north coast of Natal (Findlay, 1989). As in other parts of the world, several of the strandings, particularly in the southwestern Cape between St Helena Bay and Cape Agulhas, have been mass strandings, including 120 animals at Kommetjie (1928), 200–300 near Mamre (1935), 58 in St Helena Bay (1936) and 65 at exactly the same locality in 1981. Findlay (1989) also illustrated seven sightings, six on the Durban whaling grounds in water depths exceeding 1 000 m and one off the Cape Peninsula in 100–200 m of water. This suggests that the species is primarily oceanic, but on occasion can come into continental shelf waters.

Bruyns (1969) stated that most of his observations of the species were "marine" to "quite coastal", usually in water temperatures over 25 °C but clearly over 20 °C, with isolated records down to 16 °C. He recorded an observation of six individuals off the South African coast at 29 °02′S, 32 °02′E.

### Habits

Bruyns (1969) stated that the normal school consists of 20 to 30 individuals subdivided in family groups of from four to six. Findlay (1989) gave the range of school sizes for whales observed in southern African waters as 1–50, with a mean of 16 animals, with one incidental sighting of about 68 animals. Ross (1984) pointed out the difference in size between groups seen at sea and most of the mass strandings; he suggested that the latter represent an amalgamation of several groups, possibly for exploitation of locally abundant cephalopods. They are attracted to ships but are slow movers, reaching a maximum speed of about 22 km/h. When breaching they jump out of the water in a low, flat arc, just clearing the surface. They blow at 12 to 15 second intervals, the calves at about eight second intervals (Bruyns, 1969).

### Food

One specimen taken at sea off Durban contained the beaks of 11 cephalopods, mostly Todarodes (Ross, 1984). It has been suggested that the species feeds mainly on cephalopods (Tomilin, 1967), but in some localities it has been observed feeding on large fish such as coryphaenids (dorado) and scombrids (tunas, mackerels, bonitos), and the stomachs of four out of five weaned animals killed in a drive fishery in Japan contained yellowtail, *Seriola quinqueradiata*, between 600 and 874 mm long (Kasuya, 1985). Two of these animals also contained squid beaks, as did the fifth stomach which also contained fish otoliths. The species has been implicated in attacks on dolphins, *Stenella* spp, during the purse-seine fishery for tuna in the tropical eastern Pacific (Perryman & Foster, 1980). In captivity they have been observed to prepare large fish by shaking them until the head and entrails break free and then to peel off and discard the skin before swallowing. They have been accused of causing much damage to the Japanese tuna long-line fishery (Mitchell, 1975b).

### Reproduction

Birth takes place at a length of 1,73–1,83 m, after a gestation period of 15,5–15,7 months (Purves & Pilleri, 1978; Kasuya, 1985). Birth may take place in summer (Purves & Pilleri, 1978), a conclusion supported by the presence of a number of calves 1,6 to 1,8 m long at the Mamre stranding in November 1936. Sexual maturity in the female is reached at a length of 3,66–4,27 m, and in the male at an estimated 3,96–4,57 m, when both sexes are between eight and 14 years old. The fecundity of this species seems extremely low; in 59 mature females examined from two strandings in the British Isles, only 13,6% were pregnant (Purves & Pilleri, 1978), and Kasuya (1985) estimated from animals taken in the drive fishery in Japan that the gross reproductive rate was only 5–6%.

### General

Several instances of hybridization in captivity between false killer whales and bottlenosed dolphins, *Tursiops truncatus*, have been recorded, only one of which was a live birth, surviving about nine months (Nishiwaki & Tobayama, 1982).

It has been rated as the most aggressive cetacean species in captivity, frequently displaying threat postures and sounds and attacking other cetaceans and apparatus (Defran & Pryor, 1980).

## Genus *Steno* Gray, 1846

No. 223A

## *Steno bredanensis* (Lesson, 1828)

## Rough-toothed dolphin
## Growwetand-dolfyn

### Colloquial Name

So called as the teeth are longitudinally ridged and furrowed.

### Taxonomic Notes

When Cuvier (1823) described the species *Delphinus frontatus* from a specimen stranded at Brest on the French coast, he mismatched the skull of the dolphin with the skin and other body parts of an Amazon River dolphin. This was later corrected by Lesson (1828), after seeing a colour painting of the Brest specimen by an artist Van Breda; hence the specific name *Delphinus bredanensis* (later to be included in the genus *Steno*).

### Description

Relatively little is known about this dolphin. The maximum length achieved is 2,75 m (Cadenat, 1949), and males seem to grow larger than females, the peak in size frequency being at 2,4 m for males and 2,25 m for females. A 2,5 m male weighed 145 kg (Miyazaki, 1980). The head is a very characteristic conical shape, there being a long slender beak sloping smoothly up into the melon without any hint of division between the two. The eyes tend to bulge from the sides of the head. The gape is long with a distinct "smile", which, with the long row of prominent teeth gives the head a distinctly reptilian look. The flippers are relatively large, 16,5–18% of the body in length and broad, and the spread of the flukes is wide, 20–28% of body length. The dorsal fin is prominent (height 9–12% of body length), the leading edge sloping back to form an obtuse angle with the back at its anterior insertion. The trailing edge is moderately concave. Coloration appears highly variable, even in adults (Miyazaki, 1980), but generally the animal is dark grey above, lighter below, but with the lower jaw, throat and anogenital region a pinkish-white speckled with grey (Cadenat, 1949, 1959). The dark dorsum may be distinctly marked off from the paler sides to form a "cape" running from above the eye mid-dorsally back to behind the dorsal fin (Leatherwood & Reeves, 1983). Frequently the abdominal region and flanks are marked with irregular star-shaped blotches of white tinged with pink, their number and position being highly variable, sometimes completely absent. Some individuals are very dark, almost black, without any white blotches or traces of light colour below or on the lower jaw. These may be young animals (Miyazaki, 1980). In others the sides and tip of the beak may also be white flecked with grey (Cadenat, 1949, 1959).

At sea rough-toothed dolphins can be recognised by the characteristic head shape and narrow dorsal "cape"; the white tip and sides to their beaks may also be visible.

They have 19–24 (most commonly 22) pairs of teeth in upper and lower jaws. The teeth carry minute ridges or furrows which impart a roughness to the crown of the teeth.

The vertebral formula is C7+T13+L15–16+Cd30–31 = 66 (Nishiwaki, 1963).

#### Distribution

They are widespread in all tropical and subtropical waters where they have a preference for deeper water. All sightings have been made in water temperatures of over 25 °C, and animals stranded in cold temperate waters are considered vagrants (Leatherwood & Reeves, 1983). They are included in the Subregion list on the basis of a female specimen which stranded 1 km north of Sheffield Beach (29°28′S, 31°16′E), Natal in February, 1984 (Ross, Cockcroft & Cliff, 1985) and a skull, whose exact provenance is unknown, found in a collection at Möwe Bay (19°20′S, 12°35′E), Namibia, in 1986 (Findlay, 1989). The validity of all previous records of this species from South African waters is in doubt (Ross *et al.*, 1985).

#### Habits

They live in schools of 50 or more which tend to be attracted to fast moving vessels. When travelling normally they break the water clearly with the top of the head and shark-like fin every seven to 10 seconds (Watson, 1981).

Open ocean tests with a trained rough-toothed dolphin showed that the animal could dive with ease to 30,5 m (in 18 seconds), and the impression was gained that the species is a proficient diver (Norris, Baldwin & Samson, 1965).

#### Food

In three stomachs examined in West Africa, all contained remains of decapod cephalopods and two also contained unidentifiable fish remains (Cadenat, 1959).

#### Reproduction

The average size at birth and length of gestation are unknown. In West African waters three pregnant females in May were carrying foetuses 602, 700 and 868 mm in length (Cadenat, 1949, 1959); in Japanese waters two foetuses 90 and 380 mm long were recovered in October (Miyazaki, 1980). Sexual maturity is attained at less than 2,25 m in both sexes (Miyazaki, 1980), the smallest known mature animals being a 2,16 m male and a 2,12 m female (Perrin & Reilly, 1984).

#### General

In captivity they have been described as being bolder and more investigative than the bottlenosed dolphin, highly trainable but volatile and aggressive. It is the only captive cetacean rated as frequently threatening humans or actually attacking them (Defran & Pryor, 1980).

In 1971 a hybrid calf was born in captivity in Hawaii to a female roughtoothed dolphin and a male bottlenosed dolphin, *Tursiops truncatus*; it survived for almost four years (Dohl, Norris & Kang, 1974; Shallenberger & Kang, 1977).

## Genus *Delphinus* Linnaeus, 1758

No. 224

### *Delphinus delphis* Linnaeus, 1758

### Common dolphin
### Gewone dolfyn

Plate 16

#### Colloquial Name

One of the commonest species throughout their wide distributional range.
Alternative names: saddleback or whitebelly dolphin.

#### Taxonomic Notes

Common dolphins appear to be highly variable in pigmentation and skeletal characters throughout their range, and this has led to some taxonomic confusion. In the North Pacific, for example, Evans (1982) showed that four stocks of *Delphinus* can be distinguished on the west coast of North America: a long-snouted, coastal form, and three short-snouted offshore forms differing from each other in other cranial proportions. Earlier, Banks & Brownell (1969) had recognised the distinction between the long- and short-snouted forms in the Eastern North Pacific as two distinct species, *D. bairdii* and *D. delphis* respectively, with the holotype of *D. capensis* (described from the Cape of Good Hope in 1828) associated with *D. bairdii*. Van Bree & Purves (1972), however, concluded that the species distinction was invalid, and that *D. bairdii*, and *D. capensis*, could not be distinguished from *D. delphis*.

A group of specimens from the northern Indian Ocean and South China Sea, however, have especially long snouts, the ratio of rostrum length to zygomatic width ranging in adult animals from 1,94–2,03, compared to 1,50–1,77 in other *Delphinus*. This, plus other differences in tooth counts and cranial dimensions, have caused it to be recognised as a separate species, *D. tropicalis* van Bree, 1971 (Pilleri & Gihr, 1972a; Van Bree & Gallagher, 1978). Ross (1984) considered that the southern African population should be considered conspecific with *D. delphis*.

#### Description

The species is sexually dimorphic in size, males achieving maximum lengths of 2,6 m and females 2,3 m (Perrin & Reilly, 1984), although Ross (1984) found maximum lengths of 2,54 m for males and 2,22 m for females in the Subregion. A 2,5 m male weighed 163,3 kg.

The body is streamlined, slightly compressed laterally anterior to the dorsal fin and strongly compressed towards the flukes. The head tapers evenly anteriorly, forming a long narrow beak which is 6,6%–7,9% of the total length of the body. The beak is sharply divided off from the melon at its base by lateral creases. The flippers are moderate-sized, their length about 14,0%–16,5% of body length in specimens over 1,5 m long, and taper to pointed apices. The dorsal fin is prominent with a straight back-sloping leading edge and a concave trailing edge, and in height ranges from 7,7 to 11,4% of body length. It is set at the mid-length of the body. The flukes are crescentic in dorsal view, tapering to rounded apices, with their span 18,5–24,5% of body length (Ross, 1984).

The characteristic colour pattern is complex, and has been described as criss-cross (Mitchell, 1970; Perrin, 1972), referring to the lateral view in which a figure of eight is formed by the buff or brownish-grey thoracic patch between the eye and the middle of the body, and the pale grey flank patch from the middle of the body over most of the caudal peduncle. Dorsal to the criss-cross pattern the back is dark brownish-black, and there is a dark ring around the eye and a streak therefrom running anteriorly to the apex of the melon. A dark grey or black flipper stripe extends from the flipper insertion to a point on the lower jaw about two-thirds the way from its tip. A primary body stripe extends from the angle of the gape along the flanks to the mid-ventral line behind the anus. The anterior two-thirds of this stripe is buff or buffish-grey in colour, the posterior third dark grey. Accessory stripes may be present; one dark grey in colour lies below the posterior half of the primary stripe, and a faint buff or buffy-grey stripe branches from the primary stripe between the eye and flipper insertion running posteriorly to about the level of the flipper tip. An antero-dorsal branch of the primary stripe may extend as an indistinct greyish streak into the posterior third of the thoracic patch. There may be a narrow greyish stripe running anteriorly ventral to the flipper stripe. The upper surfaces of the flippers and both surfaces of the flukes are black or greyish-black, but in some individuals the flippers may have a brownish hue. The dorsal fin is also dark but may carry a central blaze, roughly triangular in shape and grey or pale brown in colour (Ross, 1984). The under parts of the body may be white or white tinged with pink.

In specimens from South African waters there are 47–60 (average 51–52) pairs of teeth in the upper jaw and 47–57 (average 50–51) pairs in the lower jaw (Ross, 1984). The teeth are small, the largest about 3 mm in diameter in adults.

The vertebral formula is C7+T14–17+L18–23+Cd29–34 = 72–76 (Ross, 1984). The first two cervical vertebrae are normally fused together (Nishiwaki, 1963).

**Distribution**

Common dolphins are found throughout the warm temperate and tropical waters of the world, both inshore and offshore. In the New Zealand region they generally occur in water with a surface temperature of 14 °C or higher (Gaskin, 1968), although Evans (1982) considered that worldwide the species is distributed over the range of 10–28 °C. In the southern oceans their distribution in general lies north of the Subtropical Convergence. In the North Pacific it has been proposed that the species follows features of bottom topography in response to seasonally fluctuating water temperature (Dohl *et al.*, 1986), but the association with regions of high topographical relief may be coincidental with the presence of upwelling in such regions (Hui, 1979). In the Subregion, common dolphins have been recorded throughout the year from the area south of 32 °S (Lamberts Bay) on the west coast to longitude 27 °E (Port Alfred) on the south coast (Findlay, 1989). Ross (1984) suggested that the species migrates further up the east coast in winter, in association with the sardine run, a suggestion somewhat supported by the seasonality of catches of common dolphins in shark nets off Natal (Findlay, 1989). On the west coast north of 32 °S there is a marked absence of sightings of the species inshore, and only one sighting (made in winter) offshore in water 500–1 000 m deep. Strandings of common dolphins in the vicinity of Walvis Bay, Namibia (23 °S) and an incidental mortality at *ca* 18 °S, confirm that the species does occur on the west coast, but presumably offshore outside the main influence of the cold Benguela Current. The possibility of there being separate inshore/offshore stocks of common dolphins therefore cannot be discounted (Findlay, 1989).

**Habits**

The species generally is highly gregarious. In the Subregion, Findlay (1989) recorded 52 group sizes ranging from one to about 1000 (mean 267) animals from dedicated sightings, and 21 group sizes from incidental sightings, including the highest estimate of group size of 1 000–5 000 animals (Ross, 1984), with a mean of 174 animals. In New Zealand waters Gaskin (1972) recorded schools of up to 200 individuals, with aggregations up to 1 000 during the summer months. In the Black Sea where at one time as many as 120 000 were taken annually, Tomilin (1967) recorded aggregations of up to 300 000 individuals over concentrations of fish! Although they are a gregarious species, when they strand on the coast they do so singly rather than *en masse*.

In the Subregion schools of common dolphins are frequently associated with flocks of gannets or other seabirds, in a seemingly important association.

In the North Pacific, common dolphins fitted with radio-tags have been recorded diving to average depths of 73 m, and to a maximum depth of 258 m. Significant diurnal differences in respiration pattern and diving behaviour occurred, with the deep dives, below 18 m, only taking place between sunset and sunrise, when the acoustic deep scattering layer (a concentration of organisms that migrate vertically depending on ambient light conditions) rose towards the surface. The same study showed that schools of common dolphins might move as much as 120 km in a 24-hour period, following well-defined routes along coastal escarpments and other features of bottom topography. Some herds might thus move hundreds of kilometres in one direction, then work their way back again (Evans, 1974).

**Food**

Common dolphins feed predominantly on small schooling fish and cephalopods, but have also been recorded as taking larger fish such as cod and hake. In 16 stomachs from the southeast coast of South Africa, Ross (1984) showed that fish constituted the bulk of the prey (77% by number) and squid the remainder (23%). The fish consisted mainly of pilchards, *Sardinops ocellata*, and redeye herring, *Etrumeus teres*, with the common squid *Loligo* forming the bulk of the cephalopods eaten. The prey items eaten were generally small, occurred in schools or were locally concentrated.

**Reproduction**

Little is known locally. The calf is born at a length of 790–810 mm (Hui, 1977), or 900 mm (Collet, 1981), after a gestation period of about 11 months (Harrison, Boice & Brownell, 1969). Calving may take place over several months, with a peak in summer (Collet, 1981), a pattern that Ross (1984) thought might apply in the Subregion. Lactation may last 14—19 months. Females attain sexual maturity in South African waters at about 2,1 m to 2,2 m total length (Ross, 1984), compared to 1,9 m for females and 2,0 m for males estimated by Collet (1981) in the eastern North Atlantic. Males may be 5–7 years (Collet, 1981) or 7–12 years (Hui, 1977) old at sexual maturity, while females may be 6–7 years old (Collet, 1981). Calves may be born at intervals of 2–3 years (Perrin & Reilly, 1984). Judging by the incidence of tooth rakes on, and broken or missing teeth in, adult males compared to females there must be competition for access to females (Tomilin, 1967).

**General**

In many parts of their distributional range common dolphins are hunted for their meat, or become an incidental catch in fishing operations. Best & Ross (1977) recorded annual catches of up to 94 common dolphins in shark nets off Durban, and mentioned that the species is also taken incidentally in the purse-seine fishery for pelagic fish on the west coast, and occasionally by hand harpoon for meat. Numbers involved in the last two instances are unknown, but likely to be small (possibly a total of 100 dolphins a year of all species in either case). The more recent introduction of mid-water trawling may add another source of incidental mortality (Best, pers. comm.).

Common dolphins, of all species of dolphins, are probably the most compulsive bow-riders, rolling from side to side as they do so and often accompanying ships for considerable distances. In New Zealand waters, Gaskin (1972) recorded an instance where four accompanied a ship for about 100 km. They can swim at an estimated speed of up to 20 knots.

## Genus *Stenella* Gray, 1866

These are small to medium-sized dolphins attaining total lengths of up to 2,6 m. The taxonomy at the specific level has been confused, largely due to an inadequate series of specimens on which to establish properly limits of variation in most regions. Recently, however, order is appearing out of the chaos, largely due to the efforts of Dr William Perrin and colleagues.

The species can be divided into three groups: (a) the striped dolphins, with a single species, *S. coeruleoalba*; (b) the spotted dolphins, including a pantropical species, *S. attenuata*, and an Atlantic endemic species, *S. frontalis*; and (c) the spinner dolphins, including a tropical and warm temperate species, *S. longirostris*, and a tropical Atlantic species, *S. clymene*.

Three species of *Stenella* are recognised from South African waters, *S. coeruleoalba*, *S. attenuata* and *S. longirostris* (Ross, 1984).

Key to the species after Best (1971c) and Ross (1984)

1. Palate of skull with shallow longitudinal grooves; 44–64 pairs of teeth in both jaws

   ... *longirostris*

   Palate of skull ungrooved; 34 to 53 pairs of teeth in both jaws

   ... 2

2. 39 to 53 pairs of teeth in both jaws; with a narrow dark stripe from the eye to the vent and from the flipper to the eye

   ... *coeruleoalba*

   34 to 48 pairs of teeth in both jaws; no dark stripe on the side

   ... *attenuata*

No. 225

## *Stenella longirostris* (Gray, 1828)

## Spinner dolphin
## Toldolfyn

Plate 16

### Colloquial Name

Called the spinner dolphin or *toldolfyn* because of its characteristic habit of leaping out of the water and spinning around longitudinally in mid-air. The alternative names are also appropriate as they have much longer beaks than other members of the genus.
Alternative names: long-beaked dolphin; long-snouted dolphin.

### Taxonomic Notes

Recently a dwarf form of the spinner dolphin has been recorded from Thailand, with possibly similar animals off northern Australia, but its systematic status is uncertain (Perrin, Miyazaki & Kasuya, 1989).

### Description

Males attain a maximum size of 2,35 m, females 2,04 m, although there are regional differences (Perrin & Reilly, 1984). As there are a number of variations in markings and form within this species, and very little information available for the Subregion, it is impossible to describe a typical specimen. Ross (1984) based his description of the species on the eastern Pacific *S. longirostris* as given by Perrin (1972, 1975), stating that the body is slender and streamlined, the melon depressed dorsally, tapering anteriorly to an acute apex and meeting the beak abruptly. The dorsal fin is high, erect and hooked (in Hawaiian specimens), becoming triangular in the adult male of "whitebelly" spinners and canted forward in the adult male of "eastern" spinners. A prominent post-anal hump may develop on the ventral caudal peduncle of adult male "whitebelly" and "eastern" dolphins. In adults the entire dorsal surface of the body, the caudal peduncle posterior to the anus, the dorsal fin, flippers and flukes are dark grey. A broad dark band extends from the eye to the flipper insertion and a thin dark line from the eye to apex of the melon. In "eastern" spinners the dark dorsal field extends to the ventral midline, leaving white axillary and genital patches; in "whitebelly" spinners these patches run together but the dorsal field is extended ventrally as spots; in Hawaiian spinners the dorsal field only extends to the mid-depth of the body. A newborn calf from Natal resembled a Hawaiian dolphin figured by Perrin (1972); a dorsal cape was clearly visible, the anterior edge of the eye-flipper stripe contrasted strongly with the pale throat, and the ventral surface almost to half way up the sides was whitish (Ross, 1984). Photographs taken at sea near Sodwana Bay, Natal, in 1973 indicate that animals in this area also had colour patterns resembling that of the Hawaiian spinner dolphin (Ross, Cockcroft & Cliff, 1985).

There are 46–64 pairs of teeth in the upper jaw and 44–62 pairs in the lower jaw (Perrin *et al.*, 1989). The Natal juvenile had 51 teeth above and 48 below (Ross, 1984).

The vertebral formula of the calf from South African waters was C7+T15+L18+Cd32 = 72 (Ross, 1984). Perrin (1975) gave the ranges C7+T14–17+L15–20+Cd32–36 = 72–76, with Hawaiian animals possibly having fewer vertebrae (70–72).

### Distribution

Spinner dolphins occur in tropical, subtropical and occasionally warm temperate regions of the Atlantic, Pacific and Indian Oceans. They are primarily a pelagic species, although they do venture into shelf waters in some areas. In the Subregion the only authentic records (with accurate localities) are two incidental sightings in the vicinity of Sodwana Bay (27°46'S 32°o38'E), northern Natal (Ross *et al.*, 1985). The species has also been seen frequently off Cape Vidal (28°07'S 32°33'E) during shore watches for humpback whales (Best, pers. comm.). As pointed out by Findlay (1989), the absence of records further south from the very well covered Durban whaling grounds indicates that northern Natal may be the southernmost limit of the distribution of spinner dolphin in the western Indian Ocean. No sightings of the species were made in the southwest Indian Ocean during a two-month cruise between 20° and 42°S in summer (Gambell, Best & Rice, 1975), so the species may be limited to near-shore waters.

### Food

There is no local information. Fitch & Brownell (1968) and Perrin, Warner, Fiscus & Holts (1973) examined stomachs of the species in the North Pacific. Small mesopelagic fishes, mainly myctophids and gonostomatids, were the most important food items, though cephalopods were also taken. Fitch & Brownell (1968) considered that the contents indicate that the species had been feeding at 250 m or more below the surface, while Perrin *et al.* (1973) concluded that spinner dolphins feed deeper than spotted dolphins, *Stenella attenuata*, and at a different time of day.

### Reproduction

In the eastern tropical Pacific spinner dolphin calves are born at an average length of 770 mm (the newborn calf from Natal was somewhat larger, 825 mm—Ross, 1984). Gestation is estimated to last 10,6 months (Perrin, Holts & Miller, 1977). Seasonality of reproduction does occur but it differs by population and even within inshore/offshore areas of the same population (Barlow, 1984). Sexual maturity is reached at a body length of 1,6 to 1,7 m in both sexes, and at an average age of 6–9 years in males and 4–6 years in females;

there are very slight differences between populations (Perrin & Henderson, 1984). The average calving interval is about three years, of which lactation may occupy 15 to 19 months (Perrin & Reilly, 1984).

**General**

The species is gregarious, generally travelling in schools of up to several hundred individuals. It frequently bowrides ships and engages in spectacular gymnastic displays, of which the longitudinal spinning on its own axis is the most unusual. Because of its association (along with other delphinids) with tuna in the eastern tropical Pacific, it has been used as a cue for the presence of tuna, and thus purse-seine nets have been set on whole schools with the aim of securing the underlying fish (Perrin, 1969). Resultant incidental kill rates as a result of entanglement in the net were as high as 130 000 spinner dolphins in 1971 (Perrin, Smith & Sakagawa, 1982), but in recent years this mortality has declined from such high levels, to 16 000–18 000 in 1987 (Hall & Boyer, 1989). Although controversial, some estimates suggest that the "eastern" spinner population was so affected by this exploitation that it is now less than half (Perrin, 1989) and possibly nearer one-third (Buckland & Anganuzzi, 1988) of its original abundance in the eastern tropical Pacific. The species also made up 40% of the landed catch from an incidental mortality of an estimated 42 500 cetaceans in gill nets in Sri Lankan waters (Alling, 1985).

---

No. 226

## *Stenella coeruleoalba* (Meyen, 1833)

## Striped dolphin
## Streepdolfyn

Plate 16

---

**Colloquial Name**

Alternative names: blue-white dolphin; euphrosyne dolphin.

**Taxonomic Notes**

Despite a variety of species of striped dolphin described in the past, there is now believed to be only one valid species, *S. coeruleoalba* (Fraser & Noble, 1970; Mitchell, 1970).

**Description**

The species reaches a maximum length of 2,56 m in males and 2,44 m in females; maximum lengths recorded in the Subregion are 2,50 m for males and 2,28 m for females. A 2,4 m male weighed 156,1 kg (Ross, 1984). The body is slightly laterally compressed anterior to the dorsal fin but increasingly compressed towards the flukes. The melon tapers anteriorly to a distinct apex at the base of the beak. The beak is distinct, forming about 4–6% of body length. The hooked dorsal fin is located about the mid-point of the back, and its height ranges from 7,2 to 11,6% of the body length. The flippers are relatively small (11–16% of body length) and curve backwards to sharply pointed tips. The spread of the tail flukes is about 20–25% of the total length of the body.

The colour pattern of this species is variable but it must rate as one of the most attractive of all the delphinids. The upper parts of the body from the tip of the beak to midway between the dorsal fin and the flukes, the appendages, lower lips and tip of the lower jaw are dark bluish-grey. The lateral surfaces of the head from just in front of the eye are pale bluish-grey, and this colour extends posteriorly first as a narrow grey mid-lateral band, but at the level of the dorsal fin this widens dorsally to cover the whole upper half of the body from halfway between the dorsal fin and the flukes backwards. Beginning at about the level of the flipper insertion a branch of this lateral grey colour extends upwards in a diffuse band towards the dorsal fin, forming a spinal blaze that contrasts strongly with the rest of the dark back anteriorly. The under parts are white from the chin to the anus. Thin dark lines form a "bridle" from the apex of the melon to the blowhole and to the oval dark patch surrounding the eyes. Most characteristically there is a dark grey stripe of varying width along the flanks from the eyes to the anus, where it widens to cover the ventral surface of the peduncle. A second stripe from the eyes runs below the principal stripe, ending at the level of the anterior insertion of the flipper or slightly beyond. A dark grey stripe extends from the anterior corner of the eyes to the anterior insertions of the flippers and may be composed of one to three bands (Ross, 1984).

There are 40–53 pairs of teeth in the upper jaw and 39–52 in the lower jaw (Ross, 1984), the teeth heavily enamelled and about 3 mm in diameter.

The vertebral formula is C7+T13–16+L20–25+Cd31–37 = 75–80 (Ross, 1984). The first two cervical vertebrae are fused together and occasionally in old age the third and fourth are co-joined (Nishiwaki, 1972).

**Distribution**

The striped dolphin has a wide distribution in all tropical, subtropical and warm temperate seas and is seen frequently in the Mediterranean. In the Subregion, strandings have occurred along the entire coast from Tofo Beach (23°50′S), Mozambique (Ross, 1984) to the southwestern Cape (Yzerfontein), but there have been sightings of schools of this species only as far west as the longitude of Cape Agulhas (20°oE). All these sightings have been in water more than 500 m deep, confirming that the species is pelagic by nature. The absence of sighting records from the west coast therefore may reflect a lack of searching effort in this area, or the strandings in the western Cape may reflect individuals that temporarily invade the Benguela system, possibly in eddies of Agulhas Current water (Findlay, 1989). The fact that there have been no strandings from Namibia might support the latter hypothesis. South of the country the species has been recorded down to 38–39°S (Kasamatsu *et al.*, 1988), while on a two-month cruise in the southwest Indian Ocean between 20°S and 42°S, the species, with the spotted dolphin, was the commonest delphinid seen. Seventeen sightings were made, all of them north of 35°S, and in surface water temperatures of 22–28°C (Gambell *et al.*, 1975).

Although Ross (1984) suggested that stranding records might indicate some seasonality of occurrence in the eastern Cape, data for the whole coastline do not suggest any seasonality (Findlay, 1989).

**Habits**

Ross (1984) listed sizes of 16 schools off the South African coast, ranging from four or five to "several hundred"; Findlay (1989) analysed much of the same data to produce an average group size of 74,5 animals. Schools seen pelagically in the southwest Indian Ocean ranged from 20 to 500 in number, with an average of 122,6 animals (Gambell *et al.*, 1975). The size of 37 schools captured in the Japanese drive fishery was much higher, ranging from 25 to 1 832, with a mean of 389 (Miyazaki, 1977), but these may represent amalgamations of several groups.

**Food**

Ross (1984) examined 15 stomachs from stranded animals in this Subregion that contained food. Cephalopod remains occurred in more stomachs than fish remains, but numerically overall were far less important, forming 19,4% of all items consumed. Myctophids, especially *Symbolophorus* or *Hygophum*, formed 82,5% by number of all fish eaten. Some of the cephalopods eaten were neritic forms that were presumably taken immediately prior to stranding. The limited data available on depth distributions of the prey species suggest that some feeding may have occurred down to 200 m, although the majority of prey items belonged to genera known to move into surface waters at night, so the preferred feeding depth of the striped dolphin remained unknown. In an extensive study of feeding habits off Japan, with one exception all the food items taken were less than 300 mm in length and 74% of them had luminous organs (Miyazaki, Kusaka & Nishiwaki, 1973).

## Reproduction

In Japanese waters calves of the striped dolphin are born at about 1,0 m in length, after a gestation period of 13,4 months. There seem to be two peaks of conception per year, one in January (winter) and the other in June (summer). Lactation may last 16,5 months, and the average interval between calves just over three years (Miyazaki, 1984). Males reach sexual maturity at an average length of 2,19 m and females at 2,16 m (Miyazaki, 1977). In South African waters Ross (1984) estimated that females become sexually mature at about 2,1 m and males at 2,1–2,2 m in length. The average age at sexual maturity in females from Japanese waters was 9,7 years for animals born in 1956 but declined to 7,2 years for animals born in 1970, and the average interval between calves declined from 4,0 to 2,76 years from 1955 to 1977; these changes were apparently in response to very heavy exploitation of the stock by drive and harpoon fisheries (Kasuya, 1985).

## General

In Japanese waters they have been hunted in a drive or net fishery since the late 19th century. Between 1942 and 1953 at least 10 000 a year were taken, and in the late 1950's to early 1960's an estimated 14 000 a year were being killed (Kasuya & Miyazaki, 1982). Between 1961 and 1981, 3 600 to 16 000 a year were landed, and clear signs of a reduction in dolphin availability from 1961 to 1983 became apparent (Kasuya, 1985).

---

No. 227

# *Stenella attenuata* (Gray, 1846)

# Spotted dolphin
# Gevlekte dolfyn

Plate 16

---

## Colloquial Name

Appropriately named from the profuse spotting on the body in the adult.

Alternative names: narrow-snouted dolphin; bridled dolphin.

## Taxonomic Notes

*Steno capensis* Gray, 1865, from the Cape of Good Hope, is a synonym of this species (Fraser, 1950).

## Description

The species reaches a maximum length of 2,57 m in males and *ca* 2,42 m in females. In the Subregion the largest male measured has been 2,2 m and the largest female 2,15 m long; a 2,14 m female weighed 93 kg (Ross, 1984). The body is slender and streamlined. The melon tapers in front to a distinct sharp point at the base of the slender beak, which ranges from 4,5 to 5,7% of the body in length. The dorsal fin is hooked, placed about the middle of the body, and its height is about 6–9% of the body length. The flippers are short (their length about 11–13% of body length), recurved and pointed at the tip. A post-anal hump may develop on the ventral caudal peduncle of adult males (Ross, 1984).

In animals from the eastern tropical Pacific the colour pattern shows marked changes with size and age (Perrin, 1970). Five stages have been recognised in what is clearly a continuous development. In "newborn" animals the body is dark purplish-grey above and white below, the border between the two running from the side of the melon back above the eye before sweeping down to a mid-lateral position at the mid-length of the body and then up again to terminate on the dorsal peduncle half way between the dorsal fin and tail; the rest of the caudal peduncle is grey above, white below, and there are no spots on the body. In the "two-tone" stage the ventral colour becomes greyer and the head pattern develops; this includes a dark streak from flipper to gape and a dark ring around the eye running forward to the apex of the melon; there is still no spotting. In the "speckled" stage discrete, very dark grey spots appear on the ventral surface, and some light grey spots may appear on the dorsal surface. In the "mottled" stage the dark ventral spots start to converge and overlap, although the light grey colour still can be seen in places; discrete or merging light grey spots are present on upper surfaces. In the final "fused" stage, the ventral dark spots are completely confluent so that the belly gives the impression of a uniform, medium to dark grey surface. None of the first two stages contain sexually mature animals, whereas 4% of "speckled", 50% of "mottled" and 96% of "fused" animals are sexually mature; in fact colour phase may indicate sexual maturity more accurately than either age or length (Myrick, Hohn, Barlow & Sloan, 1986). Although not all the intermediate stages have been identified in animals from the Subregion, the "newborn", "mottled" and "fused" stages have all been recognised (Ross, 1984), and it can be assumed that a similar developmental process takes place. As in the eastern tropical Pacific, white tips to the beaks sometimes occur in adults of both sexes. An example of a "mottled" individual is illustrated (Plate 16).

There are 35–48 pairs of teeth in the upper jaw and 34–47 pairs in the lower jaw (Perrin *et al.*, 1987). Counts for the Subregion have ranged from 37–43 pairs for upper and 37–40 pairs for lower jaws (Ross, 1984).

The vertebral formula is C7+T13–17+L17–24+Cd32–42 = 74–84 (Perrin *et al.*, 1987). In a series of five South African specimens the vertebral formula was C7+T13–15+L22–24+Cd32–35 = 78–79 (Ross, 1984).

## Distribution

Spotted dolphins occur in tropical and occasionally in warm temperate waters circumglobally. In the Subregion the species has been recorded as strandings from 28°24'S to 29°50'S on the east coast (with two exceptions). Sightings have also been made on the Durban whaling grounds as far south as 32–33°S, all in waters over 200 m deep (Findlay, 1989). The species therefore seems to be confined to the east coast, east of about 29°E. One of the two exceptions was a live stranding near Gansbaai in the Western Cape (34°40'S 19°30'E), and the second an animal found dead 11,6 km north of Yserfontein (*ca* 33°15'S 18°07'E) in June 1985 (Findlay, 1989; Best, pers. comm.). These individuals, hundreds of kilometres from the nearest sighting, either represent individual strays from the east coast, as postulated for the striped dolphin, or they could indicate that the species occurs offshore on the west coast. The total lack of other records for the west coast tends to support the first hypothesis. In addition there have been 14 sightings in summer in the Southwest Indian Ocean, between 20°43'S and 35°30'S, in water temperatures from 20 to 28°C (Gambell *et al.*, 1975).

## Habits

Ross (1984) recorded that the number of individuals in seven schools sighted off the Natal coast ranged from 20 to 200–300, with an average number of about 100. In the southwest Indian Ocean 14 schools seen ranged from 25 to 200, with a mean of 57,5 animals (Gambell *et al.*, 1975).

## Food

Ross (1984) recorded squid beaks (mainly *Oregoniateuthis*) and fish otoliths (mainly the lantern fish, *Symbolophorus*) from the stomachs of three specimens in South African waters. In the eastern tropical Pacific, Fitch & Brownell (1968) and Perrin *et al.* (1973) concluded that spotted dolphins fed mainly on surface-dwelling organisms such as flying fish, *Oxyporhampus*, and frigate mackerel, *Auxis*, as well as mesopelagic organisms such as the myctophid *Benthosema* and ommastrephid squid which migrate to the surface at night. Fitch & Brownell (1968) concluded that, unlike the spinner dolphin, the species fed within 30 m of the surface, and probably even shallower. Bernard & Hohn (1989) showed that pregnant spotted dolphins consumed more squid by mass and proportion than lactating animals, and lactating animals consumed more fish by mass and proportion than pregnant females. There was also an indication that lactating females had greater stomach fills than pregnant females. These differences were related to the greater energetic demands of lactation.

### Reproduction

There is very little information available from the Subregion (Ross, 1984). In the eastern tropical Pacific, calves are born at a mean length of 825 mm, off Japan at 890 mm, after a gestation period of 11–12 months (Kasuya, Miyazaki & Dawbin, 1974; Perrin, Coe & Zweifel, 1976). Lactation may last on average 20 months (Myrick, Hohn, Barlow & Sloan, 1986) to two years (Kasuya, 1985). Sexual maturity is achieved at average lengths of 1,94 m in males and 1,82 m in females. Ages at sexual maturity have been estimated as 10,7–12,2 years for females (Myrick *et al.*, 1986) and 11,8 years in males (Kasuya, 1976). The average calving interval is about 3,0–3,3 years (Myrick *et al.*, 1986; Kasuya, 1985). Seasonality of reproduction is complicated in the eastern tropical Pacific by location; within one apparent stock, animals in the northern half showed very little evidence of seasonality, while those in the south showed a strong peak of births in spring (Barlow, 1984). Off Japan there were at least two peaks of conception, one in summer (July/August) and another in winter (January/February), and possibly a third in November (Kasuya *et al.*, 1974).

### General

In the eastern tropical Pacific the species has suffered severe exploitation as a result of incidental mortality in the tuna purse-seine fishery (see under spinner dolphin above). The number of spotted dolphins so killed in 1972 was estimated as 270 000 (Perrin, Smith & Sakagawa, 1982). This figure has fallen subsequently to 55 000–60 000 in 1987 (Hall & Boyer, 1989), due in part to gear modifications allowing a greater escapement. However, although controversial, it is believed that at least one of the stocks affected (the northern offshore spotted) may now be less than half (and possibly nearly a third) of its original size (Buckland & Anganuzzi, 1988). A drive fishery for the species also occurs in Japanese waters, and a peak catch of 4 184 spotted dolphins was made in 1978 (Miyazaki, 1983).

The swimming speed of this species has been investigated through training captive animals in a lagoon to chase a lure; they could reach a top speed of 21,4 knots (11,03 m/sec) in two seconds (Lang & Pryor, 1966).

## Genus *Sousa* Gray, 1866

Five nominal species of this genus have been recognised, although the lack of comparative material renders their evaluation difficult (Pilleri & Gihr, 1972a). More recent texts seem to favour reducing the number to two, the Indo-Pacific humpback dolphin, *S. chinensis*, and the Atlantic humpback dolphin, *S. teuszii* (Rice, 1977; Honacki, Kinman & Koeppl, 1982). Ross (1984), however, was not convinced that all Indo-Pacific humpback dolphins are conspecific, and favoured retaining *S. plumbea* for southern African forms. This view is shared by Zhou, Li, Qian & Yang (1979), who believed that there are probably two species of humpback dolphin in the Indo-Pacific region, the Pacific humpback dolphin, *S. chinensis* and the Indian humpback dolphin, *S. plumbea*, differing apparently in geographical distribution and dorsal fin shape. The genus includes a range of medium-sized dolphins with total length up to about 3,2 m, with long snouts and a low dorsal fin situated on an elongated ridge on the back.

No. 228

## *Sousa plumbea* (G. Cuvier, 1829)

## Humpback dolphin
## Boggelrugdolfyn

Plate 16

### Colloquial Name

Alternative names: Plumbeous dolphin; lead-coloured dolphin; Indian humpbacked dolphin.

### Taxonomic Notes

Ross (1984) considered that the Atlantic humpback dolphin, *S. teuszii*, known from Mauritania to northern Angola, might be a subspecies of *S. plumbea*, as it only differed in tooth counts (overlapping) and the length of the mandibular symphysis.

### Description

The humpback dolphin reaches a total length of 3,2 m in males and 2,44 m in females. In the Subregion specimens up to 2,79 m (male) and 2,44 m (female) in length have been measured, of which the male weighed 284 kg (Ross, 1984). The body is robust, slightly laterally compressed in front of the dorsal fin but increasingly so towards the tail flukes. Both upper and lower margins of the caudal peduncle are raised as elongate low ridges. The melon, moderate in size, in profile slopes gradually anteriorly to a distinct apex; laterally, however, the junction between melon and snout is indistinct. The beak is long (about 6,5–8% of the total length) and slender. In some animals the tip of the mandible is misaligned with the tip of the snout, giving a "crossbeak" appearance to the animal (Saayman & Tayler, 1979). The line of the gape is straight apart from a short downward curve at the back. The base of the dorsal fin is elongated and thickened (up to 80 mm in an adult), becoming thinner dorsally to form a small, hooked, centrally placed dorsal fin. The length of this fin base increases with the size of the animal (from about 25% of body length in neonates to 30–37% in adults). The total height of the dorsal fin varies from 6–9% of body length. The flippers are moderate in length (12–14% of body length), but broad and rounded at the tip (Ross, 1984).

In a small calf the dorsal surface was a dark lead-coloured grey, contrasting perceptibly with the pale grey on the lateral surfaces of the body and caudal peduncle, which in turn shaded gradually into the off-white colour of the belly anterior to the anus. An incomplete greyish flipper to eye stripe was present. The flukes were dark grey above, light grey below, and the ridges on the caudal peduncle were white (Ross, 1984). Saayman & Tayler (1979) reported some changes in coloration with size. Young calves were generally off-white in colour, deepening to grey when about half the size of their mother. "Juveniles" were a uniform grey, as were "graybacks", in which the uniform slate grey of back and sides sometimes had a purplish sheen, and was characteristically unblemished by scars. "Whitefins" were adults characterised by a remarkable girth and a whitening of the dorsal fin and adjacent areas, extending in some animals to a whitening of the tip of the rostrum and flukes; they often were scarred prominently, particularly behind the dorsal fin.

There are 30–38 pairs of teeth in the upper jaw and 30–37 pairs in the lower jaw; the teeth are stout, 7,0 mm diameter at the base, and usually expanded antero-posteriorly at the base (Ross, 1984).

In a series (n=7) of South African specimens the vertebral formula was C7+T11–12+L10–14+Cd19–22 = 48–51, with an outlier at 55 (Ross, 1984).

### Distribution

This species occurs in shallow nearshore waters (including estuaries in some areas) of the western and northern Indian Ocean from the Gulf of Siam to South Africa (although there are large stretches of coast in this range from which no specimens have been recorded—Ross, 1984). In the Subregion it has been recorded from northern Natal to False Bay, although the latter record (a skull collected in 1896) has been considered a vagrant (Ross, 1984). The next furthest west definite record is a sighting off De Hoop, at 20°13′E (Findlay, 1989), although there are unconfirmed sightings from False Bay (Best, pers. comm.). Observations at Algoa Bay and Plettenberg Bay indicate that they occur in these waters throughout the year. Ross (1984) stated that they appear to be restricted to a very narrow coastal belt, rarely occurring more than 1,0 km offshore or in water more than 20 m in depth. However, they do not enter estuaries in this sector.

### Food

A stomach examined by Ross (1984) from Mtunzini, Natal, contained the remains of fish species common in the coastal waters of Natal, including the spotted grunter, *Pomadasys commersonnii*, piggy, *P. olivaceum*, flathead mullet, *Mugil*, and southern mullet, *Liza*. They appear to feed on or close to reefs along rocky coastal areas in preference to areas with a sandy bottom (Saayman, Bower & Tayler, 1972), the preferred times of feeding being on a rising or at high tide (Saayman & Tayler, 1979).

### Reproduction

Two stranded neonates measured 0,97 m and 1,08 m, the first being dehydrated (Saayman and Tayler, 1979), so presumably the length at birth is about 1 m. There seems to be a distinct peak in births in summer, especially January and February, although precopulatory behaviour and mating was seen at all times of the year with no quantitative variation between seasons. Newborn calves constitute about 10% of the population (Saayman & Tayler, 1979).

### General

Ross (1984) observed 49 schools in eastern Cape waters, ranging from one to about 30 individuals, with a mean of 6,9 dolphins per school, which is almost identical to the range (1–25) and mean (6,5) given by Saayman & Tayler (1979) for 211 sightings at Plettenberg Bay.

The species has a characteristic way of surfacing, the long slender beak appearing first above water before the animal's melon breaks the surface and it exhales (Saayman & Tayler, 1979). It appears to be shy of boats (Pilleri & Gihr, 1972a).

Three individuals were held for less than three months in captivity in South Africa in 1963 (Best & Ross, 1984), one of which proved to be pregnant with a foetus *ca* 76 mm (not 0,75 m as reported by Ross, 1984) long when it died in about March (Best, pers. comm.).

## Genus *Tursiops* Gervais, 1855

Members of this genus attain lengths of up to about 3,8 m, have short snouts, up to about 6% of the total length of the body, and broad, moderately high dorsal fins. They are distributed widely in the cool temperate to tropical waters of all the oceans of the world. In all areas where the systematics of bottlenosed dolphins have been studied there appear to be two "forms", one coastal and one offshore. This Subregion is no exception, and Ross (1977a) has documented the existence of a larger form with a shorter beak and fewer teeth, believed to occur offshore on the southeast coast, and a smaller form with longer beak and more numerous teeth that is neritic in the same area. These he considered separate species, *T. truncatus* and *T. aduncus* respectively (see also Ross, 1984). Tomilin (1967) and other authorities (IWC, 1975; Honacki *et al.*, 1982), however, believed that there is a single cosmopolitan species, *T. truncatus*, and this is the position adopted here (which Ross *et al.*, 1989, seem tacitly to support).

---

No. 229

## *Tursiops truncatus* (Montagu, 1821)

## Bottlenosed dolphin
## Stompneusdolfyn

Plate 16

---

### Colloquial Name

Although many allied species have heads and snouts that are bottle-shaped, the name is well entrenched for this species (Ross, 1984).

### Taxonomic Notes

Ross (1984) listed 16 characters by which the *truncatus* and *aduncus* forms could be distinguished: these included the following

| | *truncatus* form | *aduncus* form |
|---|---|---|
| Total length (maximum) | 3,3 m | 2,6 m |
| Beak length (% body length) | | |
| Mean | 3,8% | 5,2% |
| Range | 3,1–4,7% | 4,4–6,0% |
| Mandibular teeth, number | | |
| Mean | 22,4 | 26,1 |
| Range | 21–24 | 23–29 |
| Vertebral count | 57–63 | 64– 65 |

In the following account references will be made to the *truncatus* and *aduncus* "forms" *sensu* Ross (1984) whenever differences between them have to be elucidated

### Description

Male bottlenosed dolphins reach a maximum length of 3,81 m, females 3,67 m. In the Subregion the *truncatus* form has been recorded up to 3,65 m (male) and 2,93 m (female)—Best (pers. comm.); the maximum lengths recorded for the *aduncus* form in this Subregion are 2,54 m (male) and 2,52 m (female)—Ross (1977a). A 3,40 m male *truncatus* form weighed 429 kg in pieces (Best, pers. comm.); a 2,54 m male *aduncus* form weighed 226,4 kg entire (Ross, 1977a).

The body is robust, rounded in cross-section anteriorly but becoming increasingly compressed towards the flukes. The melon is distinct, rounded and slightly depressed dorsally, in the vicinity of the blowhole. It slopes evenly down in profile to a definite apex at the base of the beak. The beak is short and stout, forming 3,1–4,7% of the body length in the *truncatus* form and 4,4–6,0% in the *aduncus* form. The line of the gape is almost straight except for the most posterior section which curves down. The dorsal fin is prominent (its height 8–10% of body length), hooked, with a broad base; it is situated at the midpoint of the body. The flippers are of moderate size (15–16% of the body in length), broad at the base and tapering to a rounded tip; the leading edge is strongly convex and the trailing edge concave. The flukes are broad and full (Ross, 1984).

The coloration pattern is subtle but complicated: it does not differ significantly between the two forms, although *truncatus* may be a little darker overall. The upper parts of the body are dark grey, including the beak, the tip of the lower jaw, an anchor-shaped mark (from the blowhole to the apex of the melon and then to the eyes) and the back from the blowhole to about halfway between the dorsal fin and

**Plate 16**

218. Risso's dolphin, *Grampus griseus*
Risso se dolfyn
224. Common dolphin, *Delphinus delphis*
Gewone dolfyn
225. Spinner dolphin, *Stenella longirostris*
Toldolfyn
226. Striped dolphin, *Stenella coeruleoalba*
Streepdolfyn
227. Spotted dolphin, *Stenella attenuata*
Gevlekte dolfyn
228. Humpback dolphin, *Sousa plumbea*
Boggelrugdolfyn
229. Bottlenosed dolphin, *Tursiops truncatus*
Stompneusdolfyn
234. Dusky dolphin, *Lagenorhynchus obscurus*
Vaaldolfyn
235. Heaviside's dolphin, *Cephalorhynchus heavisidii*
Heaviside se dolfyn.

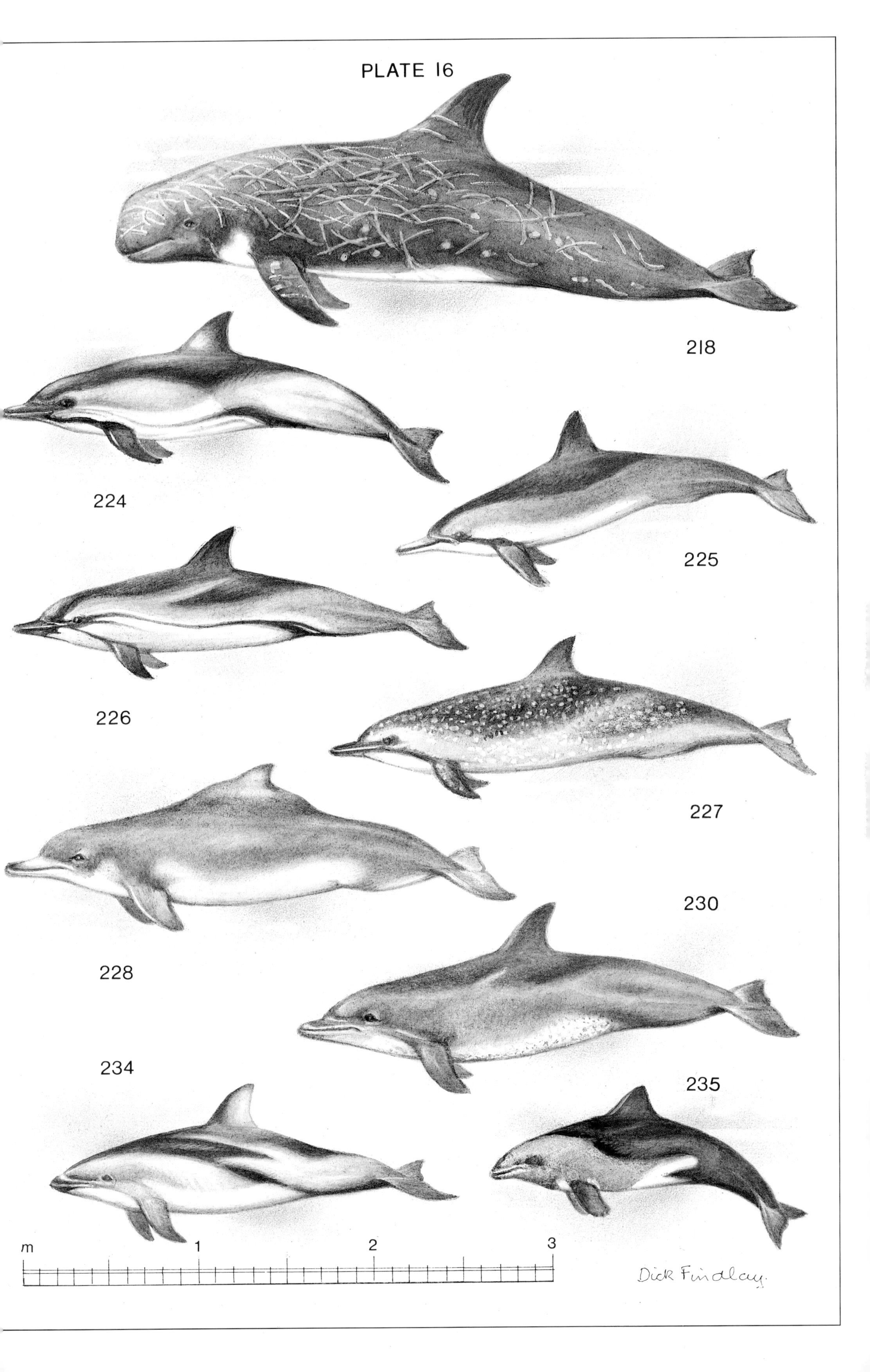
PLATE 16
218
224
225
226
227
230
228
234
235
m
1
2
3
Dick Findlay

the fluke insertion. This "cape" as it is called, is broadest at the level of the anterior insertion of the dorsal fin, where it extends about one-third of the way down the side. The dorsal fin, flukes and flippers are also dark grey. A paler grey overlay extends over the lateral surfaces of the body to about half way down the side. Behind the anus it covers the entire caudal peduncle. A broad dark stripe runs from the flipper to the eye (edged above by a thin white or pale grey line), and from there connects with the anchor mark on the head. The ventral surface from the throat to the anus is off-white or a very pale grey colour, sometimes pinkish. Dark spots appear on the belly of larger, sexually mature animals, particularly in the *aduncus* form from Natal, where such spots were large, dark and found over the whole ventral surface, except for a narrow strip enclosing the ano-genital aperture(s) (Ross, 1984).

There are 22–28 pairs of teeth in the upper jaw, 21–29 pairs in the lower jaw, with a separation between forms as given above (Ross, 1984). The teeth are stout, *ca* 6 mm in diameter at the gum.

Vertebral counts range in total from 57 to 63, with a separation between forms as given above. The formula for the *truncatus* form given by Ross (1984) is C7+T12–13+(L+Cd)44–46; that for the *aduncus* form is C7+T12–14+L13–18+Cd22–27.

**Distribution**

Bottlenosed dolphins are cosmopolitan in all seas apart from the highest latitudes. One form is found usually close inshore (inside the 20 m contour—Leatherwood & Reeves, 1983), including estuaries and sometimes ascending rivers (the type specimen is from 8,0 km up the river Dart in England!); the other is an open sea animal possibly associated with regions of high productivity such as shelf edges or sea mounts. In the Subregion the species has been recorded from *ca* 27 °S on the east coast to *ca* 18 °S on the west coast (Findlay, 1989). This statement masks a more complicated situation, however. Because it is almost impossible to distinguish between the two forms at sea (except from an assumption based on habitat), some inferences have to be drawn from a combination of strandings or live captures (where there is usually no problem with form recognition) and sightings at sea. The *aduncus* form occurs (usually in waters less than 20 m deep—Ross, Cockcroft & Butterworth, 1987) from northern Natal to False Bay, and is entirely absent from the west coast (Findlay, 1989). There is a single record from Mozambique, at 23°20′S, 35°25′E (Ross, 1984). The *truncatus* form is found in offshore waters on the south and southeast coasts in waters more than 200 m deep (Ross, 1984), and may have a continuous offshore distribution right around the whole coast: bottlenosed dolphins are certainly found offshore on the west coast but their form is only deduced from the lack of strandings of the *aduncus* form in the area. From about Walvis Bay northwards, bottlenosed dolphins again occur very close inshore, but animals taken from this coastal population belong to the *truncatus*, not the *aduncus* form. The relationship between the inshore and offshore *truncatus* populations on the west coast is unknown at this stage, as is the southern limit to the distribution of the inshore population on the west coast (Findlay, 1989). There is no indication of any seasonality in the occurrence of either form (Ross, 1984).

The *aduncus* form appears to be distributed non-uniformly along the Natal coast, and tends to occur more frequently in particular areas, comprising about 30–40 km of coastline. At least one of these areas seems to be the "home range" of a resident population (Ross, Cockcroft, Melton & Butterworth, 1989).

**Habits**

In the Subregion bottlenosed dolphins attributable to the *aduncus* form have been recorded as occurring in groups of from one to five to 300–1 000 animals, with an average functional group size of 20–50 animals (Ross, 1984). Saayman & Tayler (1973) estimated a mean group size of 140, but Ross (1984) commented that the functional group size in their data may be much less than this. For bottlenosed dolphins seen in water depth of more than 200 m (and therefore presumably referable to the *truncatus* form), school sizes ranged from three to about 100 animals, with a mean of about 22. In general it seems that the *truncatus* form tends to be found in smaller groupings than those described for the *aduncus* form above (Ross, 1989). Schools of bottlenosed dolphins seen offshore (and therefore presumably of the *truncatus* form) have been associated frequently with other species, in particular the long-finned pilot whale, *Globicephala melaena*, but also the false killer whale, *Pseudorca crassidens*; the significance of this association is unknown.

Observations of free-ranging bottlenosed dolphins in other parts of the world show that there is a discernible social organisation in the groups, adult males forming small bands that moved between female groups within the population's range, subadult males forming bachelor groups in another part of the range, occasionally accompanying female groups when they moved through the area. These association patterns are recurrent and long-lasting. Females with calves moved regularly through apparent nursery areas, and there may be long-term associations between mothers and their offspring, lasting three to six years or even more occasionally (Shane, Wells & Wursig, 1986).

Both wild and captive bottlenosed dolphins have been observed to come to the aid of injured individuals and, in the case of females whose calves were stillborn or died shortly after birth, to carry their dead young around for days or weeks (Caldwell & Caldwell, 1966).

Cooperative feeding behaviour within bottlenosed dolphin schools has been observed several times. This includes crowding of fish against shoals and shorelines, even driving them up a mudbank. In Plettenberg Bay, Tayler & Saayman (1972) recorded incidents involving a shoal of shad, *Pomatomus saltatrix*, trapped in a corner of the bay by the dolphins, and a shoal of pelagic fish trapped against the surface by dolphins below and around it: the former incident demonstrated a highly organised herding and capturing manoeuvre, in which individuals fed on the periphery of the shoal while others prevented the fish from dispersing.

Bottlenosed dolphins emit a wide range of sounds including those of an unpulsed nature (mainly whistles) or a pulsed nature (squeaks, squawks, yelps, grating sounds and echolocation bursts). Caldwell & Caldwell (1965) reported that each individual appears to have a "signature" whistle which others can recognise, but it is now known that individuals can imitate the signature whistle of another individual with which they have a strong social bond. Perhaps such imitations are used to maintain or initiate social interaction with a specific individual in the same school.

Open ocean tests with trained members of this species have shown that they can dive to a depth of 390–535 m successfully; at such depths collapse of the lungs and thorax (for which the dolphin is anatomically adapted) occurs, and thus the animal is protected from the "bends" (Ridgway & Harrison, 1986). Further open ocean tests with trained dolphins have revealed that the bottlenosed dolphin can maintain swimming speeds of 16,1 knots (29,9 km/hr) for 7,5 seconds and 11,8 knots (21,9 km/hr) for 50 seconds (Lang & Norris, 1966).

**Food**

Cockcroft & Ross (1990a) examined stomach contents of 127 animals of the *aduncus* form caught in shark nets off Natal. Four fish and two cephalopod species (all common inshore) accounted for about 60% by mass of the food eaten. Of the four fish species, two can be considered as benthic, the piggy, *Pomadasys olivaceum*, occurring over reefs and the red tjor-tjor, *Pagellus bellotti*, over sandy bottoms, while the other two, the mackerel, *Scomber japonicus*, and African maasbanker, *Trachurus delagoa*, are both pelagic shoaling fish. The two cephalopods, the squid, *Loligo* sp., and the cuttlefish, *Sepa officinalis*, are commonly seen around the shark nets. Although frequently considered primarily a benthic feeder, in these animals a wide variety of food resources, including both benthic and pelagic species, was eaten. Ross (1977a, 1984) also examined two stomachs of the *truncatus* form from the southeast Cape. The dominant food item was a squid, *Oregoniateuthis*, although buttersnoek, *Lepidopus caudatus*, and hake, *Merluccius capensis*, were also taken. The evidence suggested that the *truncatus* form feeds further offshore than the *aduncus* form, at least on the southeast Cape coast (Ross, 1984).

Feeding rates in captive animals ranged from 6,7% of body weight per day in a 1,93 m long, 83 kg animal to 3,87% per day for a 2,35 m, 156 kg female (Ross, 1984).

**Reproduction**

In the *aduncus* form from Natal, birth takes place at a mean length of 1,03 m and mass of 13,8 kg, after a gestation period of 12 months. Births seem to occur in most months of the year, but with a definite peak in summer (November to February). Lactation lasts approximately two years, although the calf can start taking solid food as early as six months, and the mother-calf association can last as long as three years. Sexual maturity is reached between nine and 11 years in females and about 14,5 years in males, at body lengths of about 2,30 m and 2,40 m respectively. The average calving interval is about three years. Life expectancy is similar for both sexes (maximum age about 43 years); there is no evidence of reproductive senescence in females (Cockcroft & Ross, in press a).

Much less is known about reproduction in the *truncatus* form in the Subregion. A neonate from Henties Bay, Namibia (presumably from the inshore *truncatus* population) measured 1,35 m and weighed 25,8 kg, substantially larger than the east coast *aduncus* form at birth (Best, pers. comm.). A female at 2,8 m in length was still sexually immature, and a 2,72 m long male was classified as maturing but not fully sexually active (Ross, 1984); both these are larger than the largest known *aduncus* form from the east coast! A 3,16 m female from the Namibian inshore population that died in captivity is estimated (from the number of growth layers in her teeth at death and the age of the calf that she produced in captivity) to have been 5,5 years old when she conceived. This is considerably younger than for the *aduncus* population from Natal (Peddemors, 1989).

Some observations on reproductive behaviour have been made on captive animals (Tavolga & Essapian, 1957) or captive and wild animals (Tayler & Saayman, 1972). During early spring an adult male actively seeks the company of a selected female, accompanying her at all times for periods of three to four days, sometimes up to several weeks. The male's courting behaviour includes posturing, stroking, rubbing, muzzling, jaw-clapping and yelping. In posturing he bends his body into an S-shape in front of the female, holding the posture for up to five seconds at a time. In stroking, both the male and female swim close to each other, stroking each other with their flippers. Between surfacing to breathe this continues for half an hour or more. They stroke each other's body with their heads, or the genital region of the other partner with the tip of the tail fluke. The male rubs his body vigorously against that of the female. He muzzles the female with his snout, or "mouths" her on various parts of her body. When another male interferes with his courtship he jaw-claps, the clapping being clearly audible outside the tank in which they lived. If this did not intimidate the intruder, he would lash him with his flukes or attack him with his teeth, inflicting severe gashes. During the more intense stages of the precopulatory behaviour the male vocalised with a high-pitched yelp, produced through the blowhole, not the mouth. At copulation the males approach the right side of the females as their penises, in erection, deviate to the left. Copulation takes place with the partners on their sides (Tavolga & Essapian, 1957). In captive bottlenosed dolphins at Port Elizabeth, South Africa, the full pattern of copulatory behaviour was seen throughout the year, but with the frequency of copulation increasing in spring and early summer (September to December), occupying a large proportion of the diurnal activities of the bulls. Peak mating activity occurred near midday, extending into early afternoon. Adult females seemed to have periods of greater receptivity in spring and early summer of two to 40 days, during which it is assumed ovulation occurred. The normal patterns of sexual activity seemed to be interrupted from about eight weeks prior to giving birth to six weeks after parturition (Tayler & Saayman, 1972).

Observations on the behaviour and development of a newborn calf of the *aduncus* form in captivity have also been made at the Port Elizabeth Oceanarium (Cockcroft & Ross, 1990b). Directly after birth the calf swam high up on his mother's flank, where he could obtain an assisted passage through hydronamic forces "pulling" him along, only having to beat his flukes occasionally and thus receiving an enormous energetic advantage. This behaviour started to change by day nine, the calf frequently adopting a position beneath the female. By day 16 he breathed alone more often, and after day 22 he swam about 700–1000 mm away from his mother, constantly moving his flukes. For the first four weeks all suckling was carried out with the female turning on her side, presumably to allow the calf easier access to the teats when its respiratory and swimming efficiencies are low. Thereafter the mother would also suckle the calf while in her normal vertical position. The daily intake of milk was estimated at about 4,3 litres.

**General**

Bottlenosed dolphins are by far the most popular cetacean species in oceanaria; in 1975 the population of captive *Tursiops* worldwide was estimated as 450 animals. Apart from being the species that seems to adapt best to captivity, it is rated, with the killer whale and false killer whale, as being the most manipulative, playful and curious species, and therefore potentially suitable for training. In a comparison of the ease of training of eight cetacean species, the bottlenosed dolphin scored equally or better in 16 out of 21 behaviours (Defran & Pryor, 1980). The species has been kept successfully at the Port Elizabeth Oceanarium (since 1961) and Sea World, Durban (since 1977); a number of calves have been born at both institutions.

In what seems like an extension of cooperative behaviours amongst dolphin schools, in some areas of the world a mutually beneficial relationship has developed between a school or schools of bottlenosed dolphins and human fishermen. Ranging from the Mediterranean to North Africa (Mauritania) to Brazil to Australia, the process is remarkably similar in each case. Fishermen on shore observe mullet travelling along the coast but too far out to encircle with nets from the shore. After attracting the attention of passing bottlenosed dolphins, the fish are herded within reach of the fishermen by the dolphins, which are then also able to prey on the fish (Pryor, Lindbergh, Lindbergh & Milano, 1990).

Large sharks are responsible for attacks on bottlenosed dolphins. About 10% of the dolphins caught in shark nets off Natal bear scars indicating they have survived shark attacks; from the incidence of dolphin remains in shark stomachs from the same source it is estimated that some 20 bottlenosed dolphins are taken by sharks annually in this region (Cockcroft, Cliff & Ross, 1989).

## Genus *Lissodelphis* Gloger, 1841

No. 231

## *Lissodelphis peronii* (Lacépède, 1804)

## Southern right whale dolphin
## Suidelike noordkaperdolfyn

**Colloquial Name**

This dolphin is so called to distinguish it from another species, the northern right whale dolphin, *L. borealis*, which occurs in the northern Pacific Ocean. The species is named after Francois Peron, a naturalist on a French expedition to Australia in 1800–1804 who gave Lacépède a manuscript report on the species. Specimens were not available until the middle of the 19th century. The name "right whale" dolphin

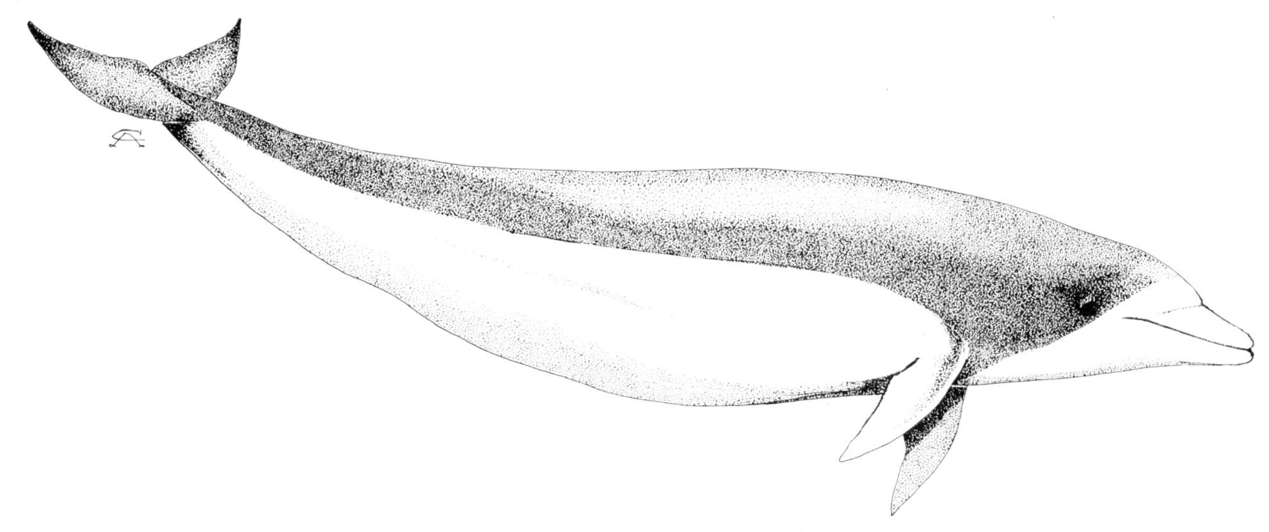

Fig. 231.1 Southern right whale dolphin, *Lissodelphis peronii*. Total length about 2,0 m (after Ross, *in litt.*).

arises simply from the fact that, like the right whales, these animals lack dorsal fins.

### Description

The lack of a dorsal fin and the striking colour pattern makes this species of dolphin more readily identifiable than most. Males up to 2,3 m and females up to 2,35 m in length have been measured, but if the species is similar to its northern congener, then males might be expected to exceed females in length, possibly up to 3,0 m in total length. The upper parts of the body are black, but the flanks, most of the dorsal aspect of the flippers and flukes, and the under parts from the chin to the under parts of the tail flukes are white, faintly tinged with pink. The dividing line between the dorsal and ventral coloration is sharp and extends from the blowhole down below the eye but above the flipper insertion, to rise again behind the flipper to above the mid-line of the body, before terminating at the insertion of the flukes. The trailing edge of flippers and flukes is tinged with black dorsally. Cruikshank & Brown (1981) noted that there were colour variations in separate herds. In some individuals there was a white dorsal patch on top of the melon, in others the white of the flanks extended dorsally to form a white saddle, and there appeared to be variation in the extent of pigment on the trailing edge of the flippers. They have 43 to 49 pairs of tiny pointed teeth in upper and lower jaws.

### Distribution

Southern right whale dolphins occur circumpolar in the southern oceans, mainly between the Subtropical and Antarctic Convergences. Their range does extend considerably beyond the Subtropical Convergence; however, where cold coastal currents flow northwards, for example in the cold Peru Current, in the seas off the coast of Chile, it extends to 19 °S.

Nishiwaki (1962) reported that *L. peronii* is abundant in Antarctic waters. They are a species of the high seas, rarely venturing close to shore. Within the Southern African Subregion the species has been recorded in the Benguela current only, as far north as 26 °S. It has also been recorded from the vicinity of Marion Island (Cruikshank & Brown, 1981).

### Habits

Gaskin (1968) stated that they have been seen in schools numbering from four to 20, in larger schools up to 200 and in huge aggregations of up to 1 000. Their reaction to ships is not consistent, sometimes apparent fear or excitement is displayed, at others indifference or mild agitation (Cruikshank & Brown, 1981). Southern right whale dolphins are seen frequently in the company of other cetaceans, such as (off Namibia) pilot whales and dusky dolphins (Cruikshank & Brown, 1981).

When they leap they may do so very high out of the water and can be recognised then from their lack of a dorsal fin, pure white under parts and beak. Cruikshank & Brown (1981) recorded swimming behaviour which consisted of slow swimming, exposing just the head and blowhole; rapid swimming just below the surface, surfacing briefly to breathe; fast surface swimming with low angle leaps, re-entering the water smoothly head first, or belly-flopping, side-slapping or lobtailing on re-entry; sounding for 10 to 75 seconds individually and up to 6,5 minutes for a herd, and bow-riding with frequent leaping. At high tempo and speed they gave the impression of hardly re-entering the water, bouncing along with well-timed flicks of the tailfin for distances of 8 to 10 km.

The northern species has been timed to swim at 15 knots for 26 minutes and 18 knots for 10 minutes, while *L. peronii* kept up with a ship moving at 12 knots for 20 minutes (Cruikshank & Brown, 1981).

### Food

Torres & Aguayo (1979) recorded otoliths of lantern fish, principally *Hygophum hanseni*, and squid beaks, principally *Gonatus antarcticus*, in a stomach from central Chile. Cruikshank & Brown (1981) identified the area of the sightings off Namibia as being one with a high abundance of lantern fish, and where euphausiids and small squid were also common.

## Genus *Lagenodelphis* Fraser, 1956

These are medium-sized dolphins with total lengths of up to 2,65 m and very short beaks about 1,0%-2,5% of the total length.

The dental formula is $\frac{38-44}{38-44}$ (Ross, 1979a).

---

No. 232

## *Lagenodelphis hosei* Fraser, 1956

## Fraser's dolphin
## Fraser se dolfyn

---

### Colloquial Name

Named after F.C. Fraser of the British Museum (Nat. Hist.) from a skeleton, collected prior to 1895, by E. Hose at Sarawak, in the South China Sea. Originally this was identified as *Sousa chinensis* by Lydekker and remained in the collection under this name until re-examined by Fraser 55 years later. Fraser recognised its distinctive nature, creating

Fig. 232.1 Fraser's dolphin, *Lagenodelphis hosei*.
Adult male at 2,64 m. Maximum lengths recorded for males and females 2,64 m (after Ross, 1979a).

the new genus *Lagenodelphis* for it and naming the species after its collector. This specimen remained the only representative of the species until 1971, when within the space of five months it was "rediscovered" in localities as separate as the eastern tropical Pacific, the southwestern Indian Ocean-off Durban and the coast of New South Wales, Australia (Perrin, Best, Dawbin, Balcomb, Gambell & Ross, 1973).

### Taxonomic Notes

Fraser (1956) gave the species the generic name *Lagenodelphis* as the skull had features both of *Lagenorhynchus* spp and *Delphinus delphis*, in particular the rostrum had a pair of deep palatal grooves similar to *Delphinus*.

### Description

An adult male from the seas off the South African coast had a total length of 2,64 m and a mass of 209 kg, this being the largest specimen from which there is information to date. A female taken in the same year had a total length of 2,36 m and a mass of 164 kg (Perrin *et al.*, 1973), while a female stranded at the Cefane River mouth in 1977 was also 2,64 m long (Ross, 1984).

The body is robust, slightly laterally compressed in front of the dorsal fin and becoming increasingly compressed towards the tail. There is a very short but distinct beak to the front of the head. The dorsal fin is small, 6,2–8,3% of the total length in height, is very weakly falcate (almost triangular) in shape, and set at the mid-point of the body. The flippers are short, their length being 8,4–12,2% of body length; the forward edges are evenly convex, the trailing edges slightly concave and they taper to sharp points. The flukes are moderate in width, 18,8–24,1% of the total length, and are narrow and crescentic, with a distinct caudal notch.

The upper parts of the body are greyish-blue, the pigmentation originating at the apex of the melon and covering the upper parts as far back as about three-quarters of the length of the body from the tip of the beak and curving downward on the flanks, reaching its broadest point just in front of the dorsal fin. A dark grey stripe originates on the upper part of the beak and extends backwards as a broad stripe to the anus, a branch of which extends from below the eyes to the flipper insertions. Between this stripe and the greyish-blue of the upper parts is an area of lighter bluish-grey which broadens posteriorly to cover the upper parts, the flanks and the under parts of the caudal peduncle. Thin dark stripes extend from the apex of the melon to the blowhole and to the dark patches around the eyes and a dark line from the tip of the upper jaw to the melon. The tips of both jaws are black. The under parts of the body from the chin to the anus are white suffused with pink in life. There is evidence that the above pattern is typical of adults, and that juveniles of the species are less strikingly coloured. In particular, the lateral stripe from eye to anus is much reduced and almost indiscernible in young animals, and the width and intensity of pigmentation of the stripe seems to be correlated roughly to the size of the animal.

The dental formula is $\frac{38-44}{38-44}$ (Ross, 1979a).

The vertebral formula is C7+T15+L21+Cd37 = 80 (correct within one or two) (Perrin *et al.*, 1973). In two South African specimens the total number was 78 and 78(+1) (Ross, 1979a).

### Distribution

The species was only known from a skeleton collected in 1895 until 1971 when for the first time a whole fresh specimen was examined. Details on the distribution of Fraser's dolphin at sea have therefore only become available since 1971. Ross (1984) recorded seven specimens and six sightings from southern African waters, all from Natal or the Eastern Cape. They have also been reported from the high seas off Japan and Taiwan (Tobayama, Nishiwaki & Tang, 1973), the tropical Pacific, off eastern Australia, and from the island of St Vincent in the tropical Atlantic. The species appears to be confined to tropical and subtropical seas in all three major ocean basins. Ross (1984) noted that sightings at sea off South Africa were all over water in excess of 1 000 m in depth and appeared to be associated with the warmer waters of the Agulhas current.

### Food

Tobayama *et al.* (1973) reported that, from examination of stomach contents, they feed on deep sea fishes and squid. Some of the fish consumed rarely rise to within 200 m of the surface, suggesting that the dolphin may dive to at least that depth. Ross (1984) recorded fish, squid and crustaceans in the stomachs of three specimens taken in the seas off the South African coast. One of these specimens was taken from a school which was seen feeding on the surface.

### Reproduction

This aspect of their life history does not appear to have been studied in any detail. The record of a pregnant female with a foetus 0,11 m long in February 1971 and the sighting of numerous calves, including one very small one, in February, suggest that calving and conception may occur in summer months (Ross, 1984). A calf 1,10 m long was collected in the eastern Pacific in January (Perrin *et al.*, 1973). Ross (1984) recorded that a female with a total length of 2,26 m was sexually immature, whereas another at 2,36 m was pregnant.

### General

Fraser's dolphins are not exploited commercially, but are caught occasionally in tuna nets in the eastern Pacific Ocean. Perrin *et al.* (1973) recorded an observation by Balcomb of a school of about 400 in the central Pacific Ocean, and in South African waters Ross (1984) recorded schools of from seven or eight up to 1 000. The species might be confused with the striped dolphin, *Stenella coeruleoalba*

Fig. 233.1 Melon-headed whale, *Peponocephala electra*. Male at 2,48 m. Recorded up to 2,73 m (Goodwin, 1945) (after Nishiwaki *et al.*, 1965; Best & Shaugnessy, 1981).

at sea, because both carry a lateral stripe, but Fraser's dolphin can be distinguished by the very short snout, small appendages, and great variation in the width and intensity of the stripe.

## Genus *Peponocephala* Nishiwaki & Norris, 1966

No. 233

## *Peponocephala electra* (Gray, 1846)

## Melon-headed whale
## Bolkopdolfyn

### Colloquial Name

Also known as the Hawaiian porpoise; little killer whale; many-toothed blackfish; broad-beaked dolphin or Electra. The Afrikaans name *bolkopdolfyn* was proposed by Best & Shaughnessy (1981).

### Taxonomic Notes

Formerly considered by Gray (1846) to belong to the genus *Lagenorhynchus*, the species had a new genus *Peponocephala* created for it by Nishiwaki & Norris (1966), on the basis of differences in external morphology and skeletal structure.

### Description

Melon-headed whales reach a total length of up to 2,73 m (Goodwin, 1945) and a mass of over 180 kg (Nishiwaki, 1972). The Hout Bay, Cape Peninsula, specimen recorded by Best & Shaughnessy (1981) had a total length of 2,48 m and a mass of 206 kg and is, therefore, the heaviest specimen examined to date. The upper parts of the body are bluish-black, the upper and lower jaws irregularly edged with white as far back as the angle of the gape. On the under parts there is a greyish-white blaze in the mid-line extending from the throat to the anal slit. On the throat it is roughly bracket-shaped, narrowing to a thin mid-ventral streak between the flippers but widening out to a lozenge-shaped mark from the umbilicus to the anus. The outer margins of this blaze are ill-defined except towards the posterior extremity. There is a well-defined pale band in the mid-line of the head from the snout to the blowhole, wider on the snout than posteriorly (Best & Shaughnessy, 1981).

Viewed from above, the head is distinctly triangular but without a definite beak; in profile the head resembles that of a false killer whale but with a sharper snout. The forehead is rounded and melon-shaped. The dorsal fin, which is situated about the middle of the back, is tall (about 250 mm high) and distinctly back-curved. The length of the flipper is about a fifth of the total length, and is relatively straight and pointed at the tip (Fig.233.2.b). The width across the flukes is about a quarter to a fifth of the total length of the individual.

Adult males may develop a pronounced protuberant hump or "keel" posterior to the anus, similar to that seen in the adult males of some other delphinid species (Best & Shaughnessy, 1981).

Best & Shaughnessy (1981) recorded that the teeth of the Hout Bay specimen showed extensive wear, the five largest in the upper and lower jaws having a mean maximum diameter of 6,3 mm and 6,6 mm respectively, while three relatively unworn teeth in the upper jaw had mean overall dimensions (length x maximum diameter) of 8,8 mm × 5,8 mm; 7,7 mm × 5,9 mm and 7,6 mm × 5,8 mm. The number of teeth in the upper jaw varies from 20 to 26 each side, and in the lower jaw 22 to 25 each side.

The species with which the melon-headed whale, *P. electra*, can be confused most easily, is the pygmy killer whale, *Feresa attenuata*, which has a relatively shorter head region, the flippers being less pointed and the trailing edges more curved. The teeth of the pygmy killer whale are larger, the mean length × maximum diameter of the five largest in the upper and lower jaw being 21,1 mm × 6,8 mm (upper) and 23,2 mm × 7,4 mm (lower) (Nishiwaki, Kasuya, Kamiya, Tobayama & Nakajima, 1965).

The vertebral formula is C7+T14+L17+Cd44 = 82. The anterior three cervical vertebrae are fused (Nishiwaki, 1972). Best & Shaughnessy (1981) gave the formula for the Hout Bay, Cape, specimen as C7+T14+L18+Cd42 = 81, with the first four cervical vertebrae fused.

### Distribution

They are distributed in tropical and subtropical waters worldwide. The first record of this species from the South Atlantic was a male that was stranded alive at Hout Bay, Cape Peninsula, in July 1976, and was considered by Best & Shaughnessy (1981) to be an animal at the probable extreme end of its range. This remains at the moment the only record from the seas off southern Africa.

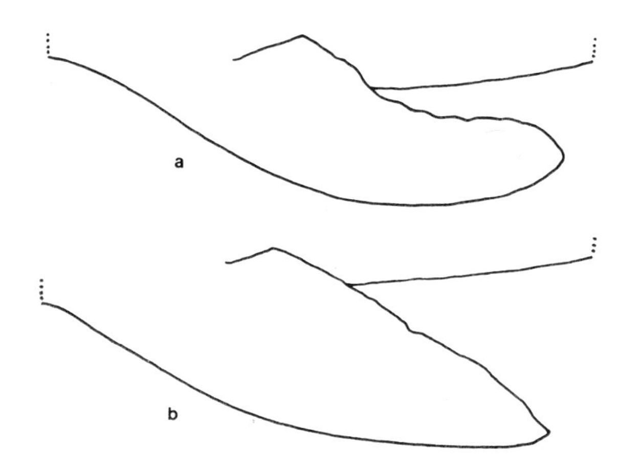


Fig.233.2. Outline of left flipper
(a) *Feresa attenuata* (b) *Peponocephala electra*
After Best & Shaughnessy (1981).

**Food**

Prior to the examination of the Hout Bay specimen there were no previously identified stomach contents of this species. Best & Shaughnessy (1981) recorded squid beaks and a squid pen, including *Loligo reynaudi*, and two fish otoliths of *Merluccius* sp. There are curious reports of melon-headed whales herding and possibly attacking dolphins of the genus *Stenella* as they escape from tuna purse-seine nets in the tropical Pacific.

**Reproduction**

From examination of a sample from a stranding of 53 on Moreton Island, southeastern Queensland, Bryden, Harrison & Lear (1977) concluded that females reach sexual maturity at between 2,25 and 2,57 m and males at about 2,60 m in length. Births may occur over a protracted period, estimated to be from August to December in the Southern Hemisphere, after a gestation period of approximately one year.

**General**

The original specimens (2 skulls) on which the species was created by Gray had no data on locality, and the external characteristics of the animal were unknown. The first whole specimens to be examined were an animal stranded in Japan in 1963 and a newborn calf stranded in Hawaii in 1964. Subsequently the species has been recorded from the west coast of Central America, the Marquesas and Tuamotus, the Philippine sea, Australia, the Maldive Islands, Seychelles, the Lesser Antilles, and the Gulf of Guinea. Like some other species such as the false killer whale, what had been considered a rare species formerly now suddenly appeared in abundance (Watson, 1981). From sightings at sea and mass strandings, the melon-headed whale appears to be a social species, living in schools of 100 to 500 individuals (Bryden *et al.*, 1977). It seems to be a deep-sea animal, not being seen often over the continental shelf, but apparently frequenting the vicinity of oceanic islands.

## Genus *Lagenorhynchus* Gray, 1846

No. 234

## *Lagenorhynchus obscurus* (Gray, 1828)

## Dusky dolphin
## Vaaldolfyn

Plate 16

**Colloquial Name**

Gray (1866) used the name "dusky dolphin" and it has become entrenched in literature.

**Taxonomic Notes**

Six species of *Lagenorhynchus* are recognised now, of which three are confined to the Southern Hemisphere. Of these, only the dusky dolphin occurs in South African waters. The original specimen on which the species was created by Gray (1828) came from the Cape of Good Hope.

**Description**

Adult dusky dolphins have a total length of up to about 2,1 m. The upper parts of the body, the flippers and tail flukes are black, the dorsal fin paler on its trailing edge. The flanks are greyish-white, with two black "brush" marks extending from the black of the upper parts downward and backwards on the flanks and directed towards the anus, one arising from just in front of the dorsal fin, the other between this brush mark and the head. A thin black line runs from the eye to the insertion of the leading edge of the flipper. The under parts are white, except near the extremity of the tail where the black of the upper parts extends around onto the under parts. The black tipped snout is short, the dorsal fin high and pointed.

The dental formula is $\frac{24-36}{24-36}$. Watson (1981) gave the vertebral formula as C7+T15+L23+Cd36 = 81.

**Distribution**

The species has an almost circumpolar distribution in warm temperate and cold temperate waters. It does not occur south of the Antarctic Convergence, and according to Gaskin (1972) is associated closely with the Subtropical Convergence in the New Zealand area, rapidly becoming rare north or south of it. In the cold Benguela and Humboldt currents, however, dusky dolphins can occur as far north as 12 °S. The species is essentially coastal in nature, so that the circumpolar distribution is almost certainly discontinuous. It has been recorded off South America, South Africa, Kerguelen Island, Campbell Island, the Falkland Islands, and New Zealand. Off South Africa, dusky dolphins are found from the vicinity of False Bay, around Cape Point and up the west coast of the Republic, Namibia, and into southern Angola, having been photographed in Lobito Bay. They occur from close inshore to out over the continental shelf edge. According to Wursig & Wursig (1980), dusky dolphins rest in shallow water and move into deeper water to feed.

**Habits**

In the seas off the New Zealand coast, Gaskin (1972) recorded schools of six to 20 in winter and of hundreds during the summer months. Wursig & Wursig (1980) also found a seasonal shift in group sizes, with groups of less than 20 animals being more common from May to September than at other times of the year. Dusky dolphins accompany ships quite freely, riding the bow waves. They indulge in spectacular aerial displays, and two or three together will leap out of the water, turning complete somersaults before falling back. Wursig & Wursig (1980) found that this behaviour was prevalent especially during bouts of surface feeding, and attributed it to attempts to herd the fish, or to recruit other dusky dolphins via the auditory (or visual) cues provided; alternatively it could serve a social facilitation function.

**Food**

Nishiwaki (1972) stated that in the seas around the Falkland Islands their principal food is squid. In South African waters the species eats a wide variety of fish and cephalopods, principal prey items being anchovy, lantern fish, *Lampanyctus*, hatchet fish, *Maurolicus*, hake, and squid, *Todarodes*. Off Argentina, surface feeding activity seemed to involve predation on anchovy exclusively (Wursig & Wursig, 1980).

**Reproduction**

Gaskin (1972) believed that off New Zealand mating takes place late in the summer when they still occur in large aggregations and are about to scatter for the winter. Off Argentina, Wursig & Wursig (1980) only saw small calves (equal to or less than one-third of their mother's length) from November through February, suggesting a summer calving peak. The seasonal occurrence of stranded neonates in South Africa agrees with this conclusion (Best, pers. comm.). Size at birth is about 0,85 m. Cows with calves may be found together in nursery groups on occasion, possibly when the remainder of the school is feeding actively.

**General**

This species is not hunted commercially, but small numbers are taken fortuitously in the course of net fishing throughout their distributional range. In South African waters mortalities have been recorded mostly from purse-seines and set nets—numbers taken are unknown, but believed to be less than 100 per annum (Best & Ross, 1977).

The species can be distinguished at sea from the grey flare to the posterior half of the dorsal fin, and its short, almost non-existent beak.

## Genus *Cephalorhynchus* Gray, 1846

No. 235

### *Cephalorhynchus heavisidii* (Gray, 1828)

### Heaviside's dolphin
### Heaviside se dolfyn

Plate 16

**Colloquial Name**

It seems Gray named this species after the wrong ship's captain. Captain Haviside of the East India Company transported the Villet collection of zoological material back to England in 1827, this collection including a skull and stuffed skin of this species. At the same time a collection of anatomical material belonging to a Captain Heaviside was sold, but this did not contain any cetacean material (Fraser, 1966). It appears that, in naming the species, Gray confused the two individuals and the species' name therefore should be spelt *C. havisidii*.

Alternative names: Tonine; Benguela dolphin.

**Taxonomic Notes**

No subspecies have been described.

**Description**

Best (1988), who examined 11 freshly caught specimens taken at sea as part of a research project aimed to provide biological information on the species, described the colour as a dark blue-black above with a grey "cape" over the head and thoracic region and with four well-defined, unpigmented areas ventrally.

The grey cape covers the melon, except round the blowhole and a roughly elliptical area around the eyes which are dark blue-black. The blue-black area around the blowhole is connected by a similarly coloured, posteriorly broadening band with the blue-black of the posterior half of the dorsal surface of the body. This band separates the grey "cape" of the left and right sides of the body. From a point halfway between the flipper and the dorsal fin the grey "cape" swings downwards on the flanks and tails off posteriorly to a point low down on the flank, about the level of the anus, being fringed below by a narrow unpigmented band, an upward extension of the white area on the under parts. On the under parts of the body there is a roughly diamond-shaped unpigmented patch anterior to the flippers, the lateral arms of which end at their leading insertion, and an ovoid unpigmented patch immediately behind the trailing insertion of the flippers. Centrally a broad unpigmented band starts just behind the trailing edge of the flippers, extending posteriorly as a narrow extension enclosing the anus and two lateral arms which sweep upward onto the flanks to fringe the posterior tailing-off section of the grey "cape", and ends at the level of the anus. This unpigmented area has a dark grey streak in the region of the umbilicus and a dark grey streak or streaks at the genital opening. The shape of the posterior extension of the unpigmented area on the under parts appears to be sexually dimorphic, the posterior unpigmented area tapering off in males behind the anus, in females terminating more abruptly and less regularly.

The head is cone-shaped, the melon sloping gradually to the top of the snout. The lower jaw projects slightly beyond the top of the snout, the eyes small, the blowhole slightly behind the level of the eye. The flippers are small and blunt-ended, the margins almost parallel for most of their length, the leading edge curving strongly back at the extremity. In some individuals (particularly mature males) the leading edges of the flippers are serrated naturally, especially near the tip, and this may indicate an importance in tactile communication during play or mating behaviour.

The dorsal fin is roughly triangular, the leading edge longer than the trailing, and is situated about the middle of the body. The tail is crescent-shaped in outline, the trailing edge forming an almost perfect curve, broken only by the central notch.

Colour variants are known, Best (1988a) recording individuals that were almost entirely white dorsally with dark tips to the snout, another with dark flukes and caudal peduncle. An individual seen on the west coast off Kleinsee had pale streaks on the upper parts.

The total length reached a maximum of 1,74 m in a male which was physically mature; only physically immature females were measured, the largest 1,68 m. The heaviest female (1,61 m long) had a mass of 74,4 kg, the heaviest male (1,69 m long) 70,8 kg (Best, 1988a).

The teeth are small and conical, the total number in 14 specimens examined being 93 to 111 with a mean of 100,1; the dental formula was $\frac{22-28}{22-28}$ (Best, 1988a). The vertebral formula varies as C7+T12–14+L16–20+Cd27–32 = 65–68 (Best, pers. comm.).

**Distribution**

The original specimen came from "the Cape of Good Hope". Best (1988) stated that there are now 120 sightings of 450 individuals. The species is confined to the seas off the west coast of southern Africa associated with the cold Benguela Current, being found from Cape Point to the Angolan border, and possibly beyond. Heaviside's dolphins have been seen from the breaker zone to 45 nautical miles offshore, but are most abundant inshore in water depths of less than 100 m (Best, pers. comm.).

**Food**

The species feeds on a mixture of bottom-dwelling organisms (octopods), demersal species (hake, kingklip) that may migrate off the bottom, and pelagic species (bearded goby) that can be found from the surface to near the sea floor on the continental shelf (Best, pers. comm.)

**Reproduction**

Young are about 850 mm in length at birth. Females can be simultaneously pregnant and lactating. There does not appear to be a strong seasonality of births (Best, pers. comm.).

**General**

Small numbers may be taken annually by hand harpoon. Incidental mortality in fishing nets, particularly gill nets set off Namibia, may be higher (Best, pers. comm.).

# Suborder MYSTICETI

## Baleen whales

The Suborder Mysticeti, the baleen whales, is represented in the high seas off the coast of the Subregion by members of three Families, the Balaenopteridae, Neobalaenidae and Balaenidae, comprising four genera and eight species. In all members the blowhole, the outer opening of the nostrils, is double, the two nasal cavities opening separately, although lying adjacent to each other.

While the foetuses have teeth in both the upper and lower jaws, they are degenerate and are absorbed by the time of birth, being replaced by 140 to 400 baleen plates on each side, which grow on the palatine ridges and hang from the roof of the mouth. These baleen plates are used to strain the food, which consists principally of tiny planktonic crustaceans, which occur in vast numbers in the waters of their feeding grounds. The shape and colour of the baleen plates vary according to the species. The skulls are greatly enlarged in some species, comprising one-third of the total length of the body. The cervical vertebrae are fused together in some species, separated in others.

Members of this Suborder have been the most harried and hunted of all the whale species, to the extent that some are considered endangered. At one time their baleen was prized as an article of commerce, but has been replaced largely by synthetic materials. Their oil and especially flesh remain in demand.

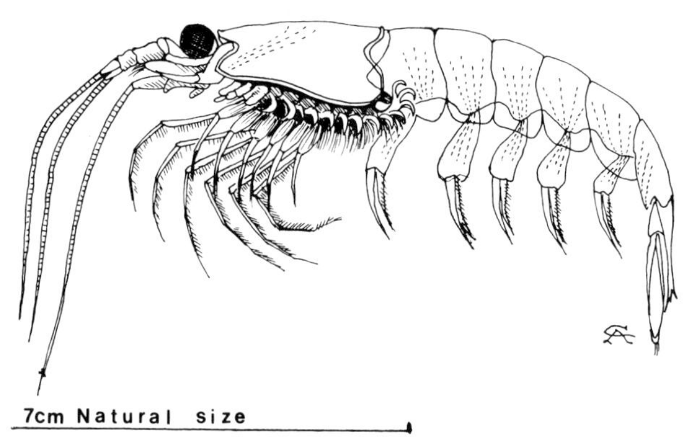


Fig.XXVII.1. Krill, *Euphausia superba*.

**Krill** (Fig.XXVII.1)

Krill is a Norwegian whaling term meaning "tiny fish", which in fact is a misnomer as they are crustaceans, not fish. In the southern oceans there are several commonly occurring species, *Euphausia superba*, *E. vallentini*, *E, triacantha*, *E. frigida*, *E. crystallarophias* and *Thysanoëssa macrura*. Of these *E. superba* is the largest, the adults reaching an overall length of about 70 mm. It is the most abundant species and is often referred to as Antarctic krill.

*E. superba* which has a circumpolar distribution south of the Antarctic Convergence, has the habit of forming dense aggregations between the Antarctic coastline and the Antarctic Convergence. Other species replace it from the Antarctic Convergence northwards to the Subtropical Convergence and two species, *E. lucens* and *E. similis*, still further north of this. At night their antennae light up, the swarms then becoming a mass of blue-green light.

Not all baleen whales feed exclusively on krill, taking squid and fish as well, but these in turn feed extensively on this food resource.

Antarctic krill, *E. superba*, is the principal food of five species of baleen whales, three species of seals, 20 species of fish, three known species of squid and many species of birds. The krill swarm during the summer months from about December to May and the baleen whales move south on their annual migration to feed on them.

Within recent times the shortage of protein for human consumption as well as for livestock has led to thoughts of exploiting krill, which is thought to have increased with the reduction in whale populations caused by over-utilisation. Estimates of the total amount of krill available have ranged from a few million to tens of millions of tonnes. These figures are pure estimates and a great deal remains to be learnt about Antarctic krill before it can be exploited on a sustained yield basis. Exploitation should take into account the effect on recovering baleen whale populations in particular. At the moment the effect that exploitation would have on other species in the food chain such as fish and cephalopods, and so the smaller cetaceans that feed on them, is unknown.

Experimental work is already proceeding with a view to investigating the technical process of recovery, preservation and transportation of krill to the world's markets.

Key to the Families (Best, 1971c, adapted)

1. No throat grooves or dorsal fin present; rostrum distinctly arched; baleen plates very long and tapered; all seven cervical vertebrae fused; mandible with no coronoid process
   ... Balaenidae

   No (or possibly one pair of) throat grooves; small dorsal fin present; 17–18 pairs of strongly flattened ribs
   ... Neobalaenidae

   Throat grooves present; rostrum nearly flat; baleen plates short and wide; cervical vertebrae unfused; coronoid process present on mandible
   ... Balaenopteridae

# XXVII. Family BALAENIDAE

## Right whales

This Family is represented in South African waters by a single genus and species, the right whale, *Balaena glacialis*, which reaches a total length of about 14 m.

Members of the Family have strongly arched mouths; the baleen plates are very long relative to the total length of the body. In the Greenland or bowhead whale, *Balaena mysticetus*, which is extralimital to our waters, these plates reach a length of about 4,0 m, in the right whale, *B. glacialis*, about 2,0 m. Unlike the Balaenopteridae they lack a dorsal fin, have no ventral grooves or creases in the skin of the throat, their heads are smaller, only about a quarter of the total length of the body, and all seven cervical vertebrae are fused together.

## Genus *Balaena* Linnaeus, 1758

No. 237

### *Balaena glacialis* (Müller, 1776)

### Southern right whale
### Suidelike noordkaper

Plate 17

#### Colloquial Name

In the early days of whaling they got their name from the fact that they were the right whales to catch because they floated after being killed, had long baleen plates and a very high oil yield.

Alternative name: black right whale.

#### Taxonomic Notes

Three species of right whales were recognised at one time: *B. japonica* Lacépède, 1818 for those occurring in the North Pacific Ocean; *B. glacialis* Müller, 1776 for the North Atlantic and *B. australis* Desmoulins, 1822 for the southern oceans. All these populations apparently are isolated and there is no mixing.

Best (1971c) included all three under the older name *B. glacialis*, noting that the northern right whale, *B. g. glacialis*, is sometimes separated from the southern, *B. g. australis*.

#### Description

Adult southern right whales reach a total length at maturity of about 14–16 m. Nishiwaki (1972) recorded the mass of a female from the North Pacific, which had a total length of 14,1 m, as about 47 tonnes (46 866 kg) and a male, 17,1 m in total length from the North Pacific, as about 67 tonnes (67 197 kg). Their bodies are round and fat and they have a high arched jaw and no dorsal fin.

Characteristic features are the wart-like areas, or "callosities", on the external skin of the upper and lower jaws and forehead. The largest, called "bonnet" in the parlance of the old whalers, is situated near the tip of the upper jaw, others are situated in the vicinity of the blowhole, above the eye, on the rostrum behind the bonnet, on the sides of the lower jaw and on its upper margin. These callosities are heavily convoluted skin, infested with parasites, and each may correspond to the position of a tactile hair or hairs. Best (1970b) showed that in the southern right whale the incidence of callosities on the upper edge of the lower jaw, is higher than in the northern right whale. The upper fringe of the lower jaw is scalloped.

Best (1970b) recorded that there is a wide variation in the colour of the upper parts, which are dark blue-black to light brown. Similarly the pattern and extent of the white areas, both on the upper and under parts, were also individually variable. Best (1970b) showed that in specimens of the southern right whale the incidence of white ventral markings is lower than in the northern right whale, and that none of the northern individuals had white markings on the upper parts whereas they are present in 10,3% of the southern. In the southern right whale the white markings on the upper parts vary from a small white spot on the mid-dorsal surface to irregular white markings over the whole of the back, giving the individual a spotted appearance. The head is large, about a quarter of the total length of the body. The span of the tail flukes is about one-third of the total length (Nishiwaki, 1972). The baleen plates are black and about 2,0 m long and 300 mm wide.

Studies in Argentina and South Africa have shown that the individual callosity patterns and white dorsal marks are consistent from year to year, so that individual whales can be recognised repeatedly over time. This has greatly assisted recent studies of their biology.

#### Food

Nishiwaki (1972) recorded that the species is a selective feeder on a range of small Copepods including *Calanus* spp; *Microcalanus* spp; *Pseudocalanus* spp; *Oithona* spp and *Metridia* spp.

#### Distribution

Southern right whales occur in the South Atlantic, South Pacific and Indian oceans and during seasonal movements they occur as far north as about 20°S and south to 50°S. They have been reported off Marion Island (Condy & Burger, 1975) and are seasonally common along the southern and eastern coasts of South Africa. Best (1970b) recorded that southern right whales spend the winter in latitudes of 20°S to 30°S, where most of the calving and mating takes place, moving south in time to arrive on the Antarctic feeding grounds between 40°S and 50°S in late summer and early autumn. The southerly movement in spring is more leisurely than the return northwards in the autumn.

They are a well known sight in sheltered bays around the South African coast between May and December, particularly along the south coast between Cape Town and Port Elizabeth. Some bays are apparently preferred by cows with calves as nursery areas, others by adults without calves for mating (Best, 1981; Donnelly, 1969).

During courtship the female tends to remain on the surface, the male or males driving and caressing her. The male will roll sideways under the female, belly to belly (Donnelly, 1969) and if she is unresponsive she will roll onto her side or lie on her back, making copulation impossible. He will try and re-orientate her by lifting her out of the water, these processes continuing until she becomes responsive. The gestation period is estimated to be 11 to 12 months. The females calve on average every three years (Best, 1981; Best, in press).

While the calves are normally coloured like the adults, Best (1970b, 1981) reported more or less completely white calves, comprising some 4% of all calves born. Such animals do not stay white, but gradually darken with age. Adults that are not black but overall greyish in colour with darker mottling are believed to have been white calves originally, and may be mostly males.

#### General

Southern right whales were quite common in Table and Saldanha bays at the time of the arrival of Van Riebeeck in 1652. Best (1970b) recorded that with the decline in coastal whaling along the eastern coasts of the United States of America, the whalers sought more profitable fields and from the latter years of the 18th century started to exploit, among other species, the southern right whale off the coasts of South Africa. Preferred areas for this exploitation were Walvis Bay, Angra Pequena (=Luderitz) and Saldanha Bay. Many of these whalers were able to take on full loads of oil within a matter of a few weeks and, at one time, were taking so many that they only recovered the heads with the baleen and were discarding the bodies. Several proclamations were issued forbidding foreign vessels from continuing this slaughter, but with little effect, and these activities continued until late in the 19th century.

In the meantime coastal whaling started in the Cape Colony about 1792. Best & Ross (1986) reviewed the catches of the species from shore-based stations in southern Africa over the years 1792–1975. By 1836 catches had declined drastically and by the 1850's or thereabouts it was recognised that the species had become seriously over-exploited. It was only in 1935, however, that right whales were afforded international protection.

This has led to a recovery in numbers in those in South African waters. An investigation including monitoring of the numbers of this species is under way by Dr P B Best under the Mammal Research Institute, University of Pretoria. This shows that the population in South African waters is recovering at the rate of 7% a year.

# XXVIIA. Family NEOBALAENIDAE

## Pygmy right whales

This family is represented by a single genus and species, the pygmy right whale, *Caperea marginata*. This, the smallest of the mysticetes, has been lumped frequently with the black right and bowhead whales in the Family Balaenidae. Although it has several features in common, namely an apparent lack of ventral grooves, all seven cervical vertebrae fused together, an arched lower jaw and long narrow baleen plates, the pygmy right whale also differs in many morphological characters from the balaenids. It has a dorsal fin, small flippers with four instead of five digits and a shorter humerus, its skull is markedly different in construction, and its ribs are unique amongst cetaceans in their number and extent of flattening. For the latter reasons it has been assigned more recently to its own family, Neobalaenidae (Barnes & McLeod, 1984). Genetic analysis using DNA has confirmed the distinctness of *Caperea* from the balaenids, and the species appears closer to the balaenopterids (Arnason & Best, in press).

## Genus *Caperea* Gray, 1864

---

No. 236

## *Caperea marginata* (Gray, 1846)

## Pygmy right whale
## Dwergnoordkaper

---

### Colloquial Name

Pygmy is applied to this species as they are very small in relation to all other members of the Suborder Mysticeti.

### Taxonomic Notes

Only one species of this genus is known and no subspecies have been described. The species was first known from three baleen plates from Western Australia. The baleen of this species is unique in colour and shape, being about eight times as long (510 mm) as it is broad at the base (630 mm), white or pale yellow in colour with a thin black edge on the outer edge (Gray, 1866).

### Description

Pygmy whales reach a total length of just over 6,0 m and a mean mass of about 4 500 kg. They are black on the upper parts, dirty white on the under parts. The skin is smooth and they lack the bonnet and callosities of the southern right whale, *B. glacialis*. The tongue and interior of the mouth are creamy-white, the baleen situated on the upper jaw is ivory or pale yellow in colour with dark outer margins. They have 230 baleen plates on either side of the upper jaw. Just above the baleen the gum shows as a white band. The jaw is arched as in the southern right whale but, unlike this species, they have a small dorsal fin situated about two-thirds of the total length posteriorly from the tip of the snout. They may have a pair of grooves on the throat which allows for an increase in the volume of water and food drain in when feeding. This feature remained obscured until the 1960's when underwater films of the living animal were taken for the first time in South African waters (Ross *et al.*, 1975). The flippers are small and balaenopterid in shape, the tail flukes distinctly notched in the mid-line and sharply pointed.

The ribs are a feature of this species. They have 17–18 pairs, which are more than any other whale; each rib is broad and flat and they are set so close together that they form an almost complete bony armature around the enclosed viscera. The last pair almost meet in the mid-ventral line near the anus. Each of these ribs is only loosely attached by ligaments to the transverse processes of the vertebrae. The function of these highly specialised ribs remains to be explained.

### Distribution

Pygmy right whales are confined to the Southern Hemisphere where they have a circumpolar distribution. The most southerly records are from the seas off the Falkland Islands at about 52 °S. They do not appear to be inhabitants of strictly Antarctic waters. The most northerly records of specimens are from Walvis Bay at 23 °S (Best, pers. comm.). Davies & Guiler (1957) noted the preponderance of occurrences in the seas off Australia and New Zealand, perhaps influenced by more efficient reporting than elsewhere or greater liability to stranding. They show that of the 35 records available to them, 30 are from Tasmania and all lie in warmer waters with summer temperatures in excess of 20 °C. They show no seasonal bias (Guiler, pers. comm.). Ross, Best & Donnelly (1975) listed nine, possibly 10, records of strandings, nettings or sightings of individuals on or close to the coast of South Africa. All these were recorded during the summer months of December to February and were made in the coastal sector from False Bay to Algoa Bay.

### Habits

Ross *et al.* (1975) noted that when inshore they are prone to use sheltered, shallow bays. All nine South African records were from large bays along the south and southeast coast. Davies & Guiler (1957) suggested that they spend long periods under water although not diving to great depths. Ivashin *et al.* (1972), however, stated that animals seen in a patch of plankton did not dive to depths of more than 2–3 m and only stayed under water for periods up to four minutes. Their blow is small and barely distinguishable, the intervals between blows being an average of 49 seconds (Ross *et al.*, 1975). When at the surface the dorsal fin often fails to show

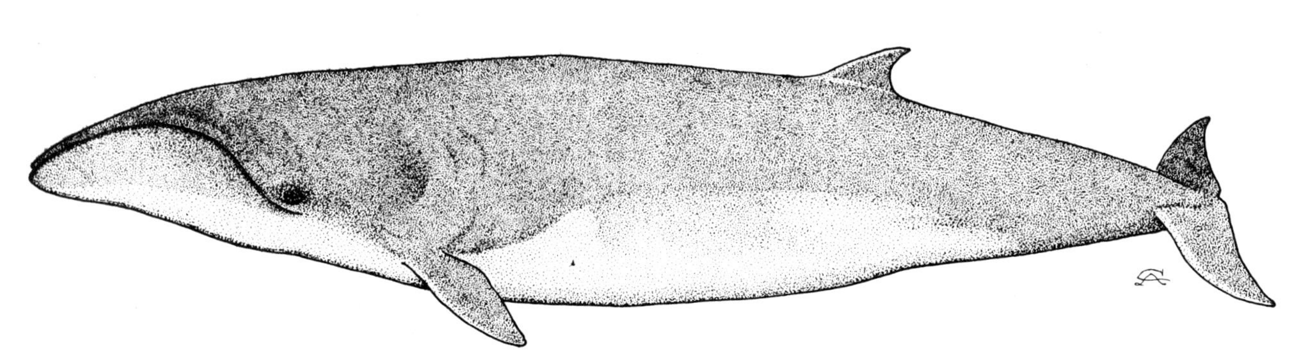

Fig. 236.1 Pygmy right whale, *Caperea marginata*.
Total length about 6,0 m (after Ross, *in litt.*).

and when the snout breaks surface the white flash of the gum is often visible. They are slow swimmers, the most striking action being the extensive flexing of their whole body in the process. In moderate or fast swimming the flippers are held close to the body (Ross *et al.*, 1975).

### Food

Two specimens taken by Russian whalers had been feeding on copepods (Ivashin, Shevchenko & Yukov, 1972).

### Reproduction

There is very little information on this aspect of their life history. Ross, Best & Donnelly (1975), by analogy with other baleen whales, gave the theoretical total lengths of pygmy right whales at birth as 1,6–2,2 m and at weaning as 3,2–3,8 m. They noted that nearly all of the specimens seen or caught inshore, as opposed to strandings, have been juveniles or subadults and the seven juveniles whose sizes are accurately known were all recorded from September to February. They suggested that their appearance inshore might represent a general dispersal of individuals after weaning. There are records of pregnant females taken in November and December (Ross *et al.*, 1975) and Guiler (1961) recorded that a female which stranded in Tasmania in June had a foetus 600 mm in total length. Ivashin *et al.* (1972) stated that from the information that is presently available they appear to have an extended mating and calving season.

### General

Pygmy right whales are accounted a rare species, data on only some 40 specimens being reported in literature from individuals captured or stranded in widely separated localities in the Southern Hemisphere. Ross *et al.* (1975) provided information on the nine South African records up to that date, the first being made in 1917 when an individual was harpooned in False Bay. Guiler (*in litt.*) reported the stranding of 28 on the Tasmanian coast.

There is a scarcity of sightings at sea and they do not figure in commercial whale catches, although Soviet whalers harpooned two in the South Atlantic in 1970 (Ivashin *et al.*, 1972). Davies & Guiler (1957) concluded that its habits render it difficult to observe but that it seems to be prone to stranding.

# XXVIII. Family BALAENOPTERIDAE

## The rorquals

This Family includes some of the largest mammals ever to exist on earth, some of them even larger than the biggest Dinosaurs. In Antarctic waters the blue whale, *Balaenoptera musculus*, has been known to reach a maximum total length of 32,64 m in a male and 33,58 m in a female (Gambell, 1979). Such enormous specimens cannot be weighed complete and estimates of their mass have to be arrived at by cutting them up and weighing individual parts of their bodies separately. In this way masses of up to 190 000 kg are on record for blue whales, but this excludes an allowance of 6% for the blood and body fluids lost in cutting them up (Lockyer, 1976).

Members of the Family Balaenopteridae have a dorsal fin and their seven cervical vertebrae are free. They have a series of characteristic ventral grooves running from the tip of the lower jaw to about the mid-length of the body, depending on the species. Relative to the total length of their bodies the baleen plates in their mouths are much shorter and broader than in members of the Families Balaenidae or Neobalaenidae, the right or pygmy right whales.

The Family Balaenopteridae is represented in the Southern Hemisphere by two genera and six species. The humpback whale, *Megaptera novaeangliae*, with its very long flippers and squat body, does not conform to the general pattern of the rorquals, which have short flippers and streamlined bodies, but is nevertheless a member of this Family.

Experienced whalers can recognise the different rorqual species from the shape and size of the blow, the frequency and manner of surfacing, and the shape of the dorsal fin, although the first two are influenced by the depth of the dive from which the whales are surfacing and the wind and other climatic conditions. They have difficulty in distinguishing between the blow of the sei and Bryde's whale which are very similar.

Key to the genera (Best, 1971c)

1. Flipper long, nearly one-third of the total length of the body ... *Megaptera*

   Flipper short, about one-fifth of the total length of the body ... *Balaenoptera*

## Genus *Megaptera* Gray, 1846

No. 238

### *Megaptera novaeangliae* (Borowski, 1781)

### Humpback whale
### Boggelrugwalvis

Plate 17

### Colloquial name

The name is derived from the characteristic shape as it breaches (see **Description**). The generic name is derived from the Greek, *megas*, great and *pteron*, a wing, referring to the enormous flippers.

### Taxonomic Notes

Populations that are more or less reproductively isolated occur in various parts of their distributional range, but no subspecies have been recognised.

### Description

The International Whaling Statistics record that the largest individuals ever taken were a male with a total length of 17,5 m and a female of 19,0 m. Heavily over-exploited in the past, fully grown females over 15,0 m have not been taken in recent times. Characteristic features are the enormous flippers, which may reach a length of one-third of the total length of the body. These are serrated and have conspicuous nodules on their leading edges and are notched on the trailing edges. They are generally black on their upper surfaces and white on their under surfaces; there is much variation in the colour of the upper surfaces, which in some individuals are whiter than in others, usually however, with varying degrees of black especially towards the flipper insertions. In some individuals in the Northern Hemisphere the whole of the body is black. Lillie (1915) recorded the presence in southern humpbacks of four main colour patterns ranging from those which are predominantly black to those which are whiter. Animals of all four main (and intermediate) colour groups are found in most populations, but it seems that there are relatively more dark individuals in the South Atlantic, including South Africa and more light-coloured ones in the southwestern Pacific (Matthews, 1937).

Their heads, chins, throat grooves, leading edges of the flippers and edges of the genital slit frequently carry large barnacles of the genus *Coronula* (Gaskin, 1972). Whale-lice or cyamids are also frequently present. The ventral grooves extend as far back as the umbilicus, and number 21 to 36, considerably fewer than in other balaenopterids.

The dorsal fin is small and set well back on the body, slightly behind the level of the anus. It is characteristic in shape, the leading edge being much longer than the trailing edge with usually a "bump" in the outline to give the appearance of a "hump"back. Posterior to it, there is often a series of humps on the top of the tail section. The sperm whale, *Physeter macrocephalus*, which is a toothed species and belongs to another Family, the Physeteridae, also has a similar series of humps, but its dorsal fin is much lower and fleshier.

The dorsal surface of the upper jaw, the chin and the mandibles bear a series of raised papillae each supporting a tactile hair. On each side of the roof of the mouth there are 350 to 370 grey to almost black baleen plates with white to greyish white fringes, the external edges of the individual plates up to 0,8 m long. Some anterior plates may be white.

The vertebral formula is C7+T14+L10+Cd21–22 = 52–53.

**Distribution**

Humpback whales occur in all the major oceans of the world. The populations inhabiting the seas in the vicinity of Africa migrate seasonally between the Antarctic and the coasts of Africa, wintering in latitudes near the Equator where calving and mating takes place, and moving south to the Antarctic feeding grounds during the summer months. There have been only two recoveries of marked humpbacks in our region; two individuals marked in the Antarctic south of Africa were recovered near Madagascar. At the time when the Saldanha Bay shore station was in operation, whales migrating north off the west coast were taken in July and again in September when moving southwards (Olsen, 1915).

**Habits**

The most intensive studies on the biology of the humpback have been carried out in Australian and New Zealand waters (see Gaskin, 1972). Dawbin (1966) found that there was definite social segregation within the migratory populations. On the northward leg of the movement from the Antarctic feeding grounds, sexually immature males and females and females just at the end of lactation pass the coast of New Zealand first, mature males and non-pregnant females follow, with near-term pregnant females at the end of the migrating stream. In general, those that reach the breeding grounds first leave to move southward first, lactating females with newborn calves being the last to leave for colder waters. On average only four to six weeks may be spent on the breeding grounds before moving southwards. In the Southern Hemisphere it is believed that although the populations on the breeding grounds are discrete, there is considerable mixing of populations on the feeding grounds. In the Southern Hemisphere, breeding grounds tend to be close to the shores of the continents. The migration routes followed are independent of the direction of ocean currents, the nature of the water masses or the topography of the ocean bottom (Dawbin, 1966). When land masses are encountered by chance, such as those of New Zealand, this produces large assemblages by a funneling effect near the shores (Dawbin, 1966).

Humpback whales are highly vocal on the breeding grounds, producing an incredible variety of sounds in a sequence of repeated themes that may last for a period of 8–20 minutes. The sequence is highly consistent between individuals at any one time on a particular breeding ground, but evolves in parallel over time within one season and between seasons. Such vocalisations have been described as "songs", and the principal singers appear to be adult males, advertising their presence.

**Food**

In Antarctic waters humpback whales congregate during the summer months to feed on krill, in particular *Euphausia superba*; in other parts of their range they feed on other species. Slijper (1962) recorded that an adult humpback eats about one tonne of krill per day. In some areas schooling fish may be actively preyed upon. While they may obtain a limited amount of food on migration northwards and on their return migration southwards, the main bulk of feeding takes place seasonally in the Antarctic, the food being converted into an energy reserve in the form of fat in the blubber. Chittleborough (1965) recorded that up to 55 barrels of oil could be expected from a northbound whale, while those of similar size taken on their southward migration to the feeding grounds only yielded about 45 barrels.

**Reproduction**

The males become sexually mature at a total length of about 11,5 m, the females at 12 m. They calve and mate in the Southern Hemisphere in tropical coastal waters with a temperature of about 25 °C (Dawbin, 1966) during the winter months. The gestation period is about 11,5 months, the mean total length at birth being about 4,3 m. Lactation lasts 10–11 months (Chittleborough, 1958), although Dawbin (1966) believed that the calves start to take solid food when only a few months old. The calves grow very rapidly and by the time of weaning, at about 10 months old, have reached a total length of about 8,8 m (Lockyer, 1984). Females may calve annually, but usually every two years.

**General**

Through over-exploitation humpback whales have been reduced to a remnant of their former numbers and although all stocks are now protected (since 1963 in the Southern Hemisphere), it will take many years before they recover to anything approaching their former numbers.

## Genus *Balaenoptera* Lacépède, 1804

Key to the species (Best, 1971c)

1. Throat grooves not extending as far back as umbilicus ... 2

   Throat grooves reach as far as, or beyond, umbilicus ... 3

2. Up to 10,0 m in length; forepart of head triangular in shape when viewed from above; baleen generally off-white, posterior ones with black outer border ... *acutorostrata*

   Up to 18,2 m in length; forepart of head sharply pointed; baleen generally black, sometimes with few anterior white plates ... *borealis*

**Plate 17**

221. Killer whale, *Orcinus orca*
     Moordvis
237. Southern right whale, *Balaena glacialis*
     Suidelike noordkaper
238. Humpback whale, *Megaptera novaeangliae*
     Boggelrugwalvis
239. Minke whale, *Balaenoptera acutorostrata*
     Minkewalvis
241. Bryde's whale, *Balaenoptera edeni*
     Bryde se walvis

PLATE 17

3. Up to 15,2 m in length; two longitudinal ridges on top of head, on either side of blowhole; baleen blue-black with few anterior white plates
   ... *edeni*

   Up to 29,0 m in length; no longitudinal ridges on top of head on either side of blowhole
   ... 4

4. Baleen jet black throughout; forepart of head with sides nearly parallel throughout most of their length
   ... *musculus*

   Baleen greyish with yellow and white streaks, anterior plates on right side white; forepart of head wedge-shaped, sides not nearly parallel
   ... *physalus*

No. 239

*Balaenoptera acutorostrata* Lacépède, 1804

## Minke whale
## Minkewalvis

Plate 17

**Colloquial Name**

Alternative names: little piked whale, a name derived from the old English *pic*, a sharp point, referring to the characteristic sharp-pointed snout of the species; lesser rorqual and little finner have also been used.

**Taxonomic Notes**

The taxonomic position of minke whales worldwide is unclear. The commonest Southern Hemisphere form of the species differs in several morphological characters from that found in the North Atlantic or North Pacific; it is larger, lacks the pure white flipper patch of the northern form and possesses a thick black band to the outer edge of the posterior half of the baleen series (Best, 1985; Williamson, 1961). There are also some differences in skull morphology (Omura, 1975). Animals with some of these characters have been assigned to a separate species, *B. bonaerensis* (Burmeister, 1867), but more latterly this has been regarded by some as a subspecies of *B. acutorostrata* (Meester *et al.*, 1986). The situation is further complicated by a second southern "form" recently described that is smaller than the *bonaerensis* form, has a distinct pure white flipper patch connected to a shoulder blaze, and carries baleen that is either all white in colour or with a thin black outer margin to some of the plates (Best, 1985; Arnold, Heinsohn & Marsh, 1987). This form appears to be sympatric to the *bonaerensis* form, but may be distributed closer inshore in winter, and it does not seem to penetrate to such high latitudes in summer. It differs in a number of skull characters from the *bonaerensis* form, and may be closer to *acutorostrata* from the Northern Hemisphere. At present it would seem safest to refer to all these forms as *B. acutorostrata*, recognising that later work may show that one or more forms should be given separate specific or subspecific status. The rest of this account will deal with the two southern "forms" exclusively.

**Description**

The *bonaerensis* form of the minke whale reaches a total length in males of 9,2 m and 9,8 m in females and a mass of up to 5 255 kg in an 8,0 m male, and 7 961 kg in a 9,3 female (Ohsumi, Masaki & Kawamura, 1970). The diminutive form is, naturally, somewhat smaller, attaining 7,62 m in males and 7,77 m in females.

The body is slender and spindle-shaped, the snout sharply pointed. The total spread of the tail flukes is almost one-quarter of the total length of the body. The dorsal fin is high and located at about two-thirds of the total length of the body from the tip of the snout. There are 44–76 ventral grooves between the flippers, extending posteriorly beyond the flipper insertions, but not as far back as the umbilicus. The flippers are small for the size of the body and rather sharply pointed.

The upper parts of the body are dark grey or bluish-grey, the under parts white. In the *bonaerensis* form the lower jaw is light grey and the throat white; in the diminutive form the lower jaw is also grey but this extends as a dark pigmented patch onto the throat in front of the flipper insertion. In the latter form the flippers are white at the base with a black tip, and the thorax around the flipper is white. In the *bonaerensis* form the flippers are single or two-tone grey, and the thorax in the region of the flipper insertion is also grey. Both forms have 215–310 baleen plates on each side. In the commoner *bonaerensis* form, the baleen plates are completely white anteriorly but with a black outer border (reaching one-third of the width of the largest plate in the series) posteriorly. There is asymmetry in the coloration, such that there are more pure white plates on the right side of the head. In the less common diminutive form, either all the baleen plates are completely white, or a proportion have a thin black outer margin (up to 10% of the width of the largest plate). In both forms the baleen fringes are all white.

The vertebral formula is C7+T11+L12+Cd17–19=47–49 (Nishiwaki, 1972).

**Distribution**

The *bonaerensis* form is found circumpolar in summer in the Antarctic, with highest densities occurring in the vicinity of the pack ice edge, especially in embayments in the ice. Individuals can penetrate the pack ice (especially in up to 30% ice cover—Condy, 1977a), and some have become entrapped in the fast ice during winter (Taylor, 1957). In winter, however, the majority of the population leaves for breeding grounds in lower latitudes, in some cases as far as equatorial regions (Williamson, 1975). The species is typified by extreme segregation by sex, size, reproductive status and possibly age. Within the Antarctic, larger animals, especially females, seem to be found farther south than smaller animals, and cows with calves are extremely rare near the pack ice. Off Durban, males outnumbered females by about two to one, and pregnant females were taken rarely. This segregation complicates investigation of the basic biology of the species. The diminutive form has been recorded from both east and west coasts of South Africa, east and west coasts of Australia, New Zealand, New Caledonia and Brazil, and from about 7 °S (Best, 1985) to 58 °S (Anon, 1989). Off Durban it seemed to occur closer inshore (mainly within 30 nautical miles of the coast) than the *bonaerensis* form.

**Habits**

Ohsumi *et al.* (1970) stated that in waters north of 50 °S lone individuals predominated, the number in schools increasing southward. In the Indian Ocean sector of Antarctica, Arsenyev (1960) recorded schools of from 10 to over 50. The species penetrates deeper into the pack ice than any other southern rorqual (except possibly the blue whale) and has been observed to extend its head vertically to breathe through holes and cracks in the ice. The blow reaches a height of about 2,0 m and they remain on the surface for a few seconds between the shallow dives which may last from five to seven minutes.

**Food**

In Antarctic waters euphausiids (krill) and copepods constitute their principal diet, with small fish up to 100 mm in length figuring so infrequently as to suggest that they are taken fortuitously (Ohsumi *et al.*, 1970). Although most whales feed early in the morning, Ohsumi *et al.* (1970) from examination of stomachs taken at varying times, came to the conclusion that minkes feed whenever food is available. Off Durban the incidence of food (exclusively euphausiids) in stomachs and the degree of stomach fill were much less than that in the Antarctic (Best, 1982). The feeding habits of the diminutive form are as yet unknown.

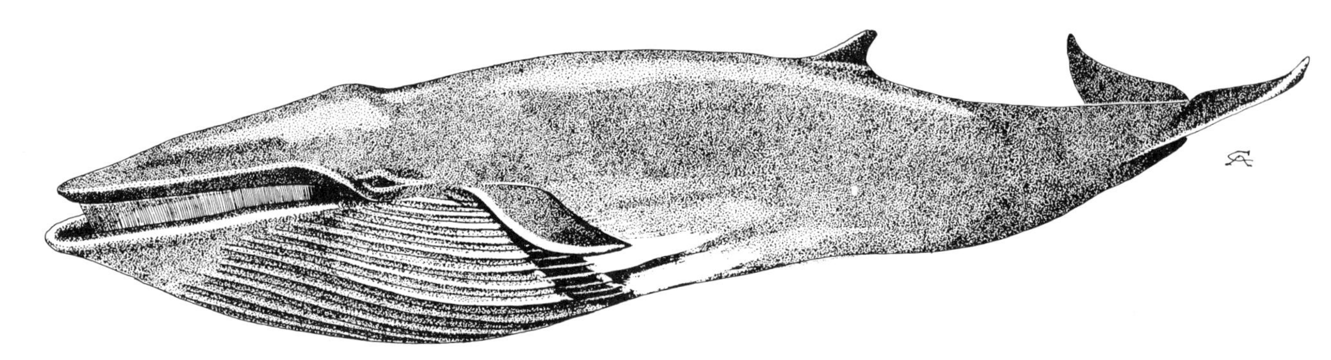

Fig. 240.1 Sei whale, *Balaenoptera borealis*.
Largest male ever recorded 18,3 m, female 20,0 m.
Maximum in recent years: male 15,0 m, female 16,0 m.

**Reproduction**

Males of the *bonaerensis* form achieve sexual maturity around 7,5 m and females around 8,1 m. Data collected at the Durban whaling station have shown that females regularly experience a post partum oestrus, the only baleen whale to do so. The average calving interval was correspondingly much shorter than other baleen species, estimated to be about 14 months (Best, 1982). Ohsumi *et al.* (1970) found that, in Antarctica, the pregnancy rate in 114 sexually mature females was just on 90%, this being similar to figures obtained in the Northern Hemisphere, and is the highest among the Balaenoptera. The calf is born at a length of 2,7–2,9 m, and lactation lasts about six months (Best, 1982). In the dimunitive form the calf is much smaller at birth, one newborn individual 1,92 m long being recorded, while lengths at sexual maturity are also obviously much less (Best, 1985).

**General**

They will approach stationary or slow-moving ships freely and therefore are seen more often than other members of the genus. They are fast swimmers and keep pace with ships travelling at 13–16 knots (24–30 k.p.h.) (Watson, 1981). Minke whales are by far the most abundant of the remaining balaenopterids in the Southern Hemisphere, there being an estimated 450 000 in the higher latitudes of the Antarctic in summer (Anon, 1989). The abundance of the diminutive form is unknown, but it is apparently not as common as the *bonaerensis* form.

---

No. 240

## *Balaenoptera borealis* Lesson, 1828

## Sei whale
## Seiwalvis

---

**Colloquial Name**

Alternative names: northern rorqual; pollack whale; sardine whale; Rudolphi's rorqual; Japan finner. They got their name sei because they appeared off the Norwegian coast at the same time as the *seje* or pollack fish, *Theragra* spp.

**Description**

The largest sei whales recorded in the International Whale Statistics are a male of 18,6 m in total length, and a female of 19,5 m, but these are exceptional animals and average sizes at physical maturity are about 14,5 m in males and 15,5 m in females. The heaviest sei whale recorded was a 16,4 m pregnant female of 37,75 tonnes, weighed whole at Durban in 1966 (Lockyer, 1972).

The upper parts of the body are a dark bluish-grey in colour, the flanks grey, this fading into the white of the under colour. The dorsal coloration characteristically extends further onto the throat grooves than in the minke or fin whale, leaving a highly irregular border ventrally. The inner surfaces of the flippers and underside of the tail flukes are grey. The sharply recurved dorsal fin is situated well behind the mid-point of the body and the flippers are small for the size of the body. The throat grooves, about 40 to 62 in number, do not extend back as far as the umbilicus, falling short by about 6,5% of the body length. The baleen plates, which vary in number from 300 to 400, are black with very fine, white fringes. A few anterior plates may be white. There are tactile hairs around the blowhole, on the outer surface of the upper jaw and on both sides and the tip of the lower jaw.

The vertebral formula is C7+T14+L13+Cd22–23 = 56–57.

**Distribution**

Sei whales occur worldwide in all waters apart from higher latitudes of the Arctic or Antarctic. In the Southern Hemisphere only the larger individuals go farther south than the Antarctic Convergence (at about 55 °S). It is also a species that tends to avoid shallow water over the continental shelf. Similar seasonal migrations to other balaenopterids are carried out, between winter breeding grounds in warmer waters and summer feeding grounds in the Subantarctic. In general, sei whales seem to prefer warmer water to blue, fin or minke whales, generally being found in waters of 8–18 °C in summer.

**Habits**

Sei whales move in small schools of three to eight. On feeding grounds these schools may join to form aggregations of over 100. There appears to be some segregation of sexes and ages during migration, Bannister & Gambell (1965) recording that of 32 taken in a period of a few days, 30 were females, harpoon gunner selection not accounting entirely for this phenomenon.

The blow of the sei whale is similar to but not so high or profuse as that of the fin whale. The two species can be distinguished also by (amongst other things) the more upright dorsal fin of the sei whale (Gambell, 1966). Sei whales are fast swimmers over short distances, speeds of up to 30 knots being recorded (Nishiwaki, 1972).

**Food**

Sei whales in the Southern Hemisphere feed mainly on euphausiids and copepods. Although they may take krill, *Euphausia superba*, in the Antarctic, their principal prey is believed to be copepods. Their baleen structure, with very fine fringes, seems to be adapted for consuming such small organisms, and it is believed that their feeding behaviour ("skimming" through the water with their mouths open rather than "swallowing" in gulps) permits them to exploit the dense surface swarms that are needed to supply their daily energy requirements. In South African waters sei whales take both euphausiids and copepods, but in very small quantities (Bannister & Baker, 1967; Best, 1967).

**Reproduction**

Pairing and calving in the Southern Hemisphere takes place between April and August, with a peak in June. The gestation period is about 12 months. At birth calves have a total length of about 4,5 m and by the time they are weaned six months later have reached a total length of about 8,0 m. Males are sexually mature at a length of 13,5 m and females at 13,8 m. Most females give birth at two-year intervals (Gambell, 1968; Lockyer, 1984).

### General

With the decline in numbers of blue whales, *B. musculus*, humpback whales, *M. novaeangliae*, and fin whales, *B. physalus*, in the early 1960's catches of sei whales rose sharply. In the 1962/63 season 5 503 sei whales were taken in the southern oceans, 20 380 in the 1964/65 season, after which catches declined. Quotas set by the IWC were not allocated on a species basis but rather in combination with quotas for fin whales, and were not subdivided geographically. This resulted in the most rapid collapse of any whale stock in modern times; sei whale abundance fell by about 80% from 1965 to 1967 at both the Durban and Donkergat whaling stations (Best, 1974; Gambell, 1974), and by 1968 sei whales were seen by the Durban spotter aircraft about as frequently as blue whales. Complete protection to southern sei whales was granted in 1979.

Sei whales in South African waters are generally on migration north from their feeding grounds, peaking about May/June, or moving south from their breeding grounds, peaking about August/October (Bannister & Gambell, 1965; Best, 1967).

---

No. 241

## *Balaenoptera edeni* Anderson, 1878

## Bryde's whale
## Bryde se walvis

Plate 17

---

### Colloquial Name

The scientific name of the species is called after Sir Ashley Eden, at one time Chief Commissioner in Burma. The colloquial name was chosen by the scientist (O. Olsen) who first described the external characters of the species from animals examined at Saldanha Bay and Durban in 1912. He named the whale in honour of the Norwegian entrepeneur, Johan Bryde, who sponsored his visit to South Africa. Alternative name: Tropical whale.

### Taxonomic Notes

Best (1977) recognised two morphologically distinct forms of Bryde's whale off South Africa. The first, a smaller, more or less non-migratory form, resident inshore, subsists on small pelagic schooling fish, has no restricted breeding season, is relatively unscarred and has baleen plates shaped like those of the sei whale. The second is a larger form that occurs in the seas off the Continental Shelf and seems to move seasonally between the tropics and more temperate waters, subsisting on krill and more mesopelagic schooling fish. It has a breeding season apparently restricted to the autumn, can become heavily scarred posteriorly, and has broader baleen plates than the sei whale.

### Description

Bryde's whale is very similar in the shape of the body to the sei whale, but can be distinguished by certain morphological characters. The most conspicuous of these, which can be seen when Bryde's whale surfaces, are the three ridges/grooves on the head. The median ridge runs from the tip of the snout to the level of the anterior ends of the blowholes and is flanked, one on either side, by similar ridges which rise behind the tip of the snout, diverging posteriorly to end at the level of the front of the blowholes, and continue posteriorly as grooves to about the level of the back of the blowholes. The proportion of ridge to groove varies considerably. In some individuals the ridges are entire throughout most of their length, in others they become grooves about the mid-point of the snout. The sei whale possesses only the median ridge. Other external features which can be used to distinguish the sei from Bryde's whale include the ventral grooves which in the sei whale fail to reach the umbilicus but which in Bryde's whale continue posteriorly to end at or behind the umbilicus. The bristles at the edge of the baleen plates in Bryde's whale are grey and coarse, whereas they are fine and white in colour in the sei. The palate between the baleen plates is much broader in Bryde's whale than in the sei (Omura, 1966).

Bryde's whales of the offshore stock reach a maximum length of about 13,6 m in males and 14,2–14,5 m in females, compared to 13 m for males and 13,6 m for females of the inshore form (Best, 1977). They are therefore slightly smaller than sei whales. The upper parts of the body are dark bluish-grey, the under parts white, the transition between the two colours less noticeable than in the sei whale, although otherwise the colours are very similar. Adults of the offshore form may become scarred so heavily from bites of a small pelagic shark that their flanks take on a pale, "galvanised" appearance. They have about 40–50 grooves between the flipper insertions, which extend from the chin to the umbilicus, and nearly all have a single median groove between umbilicus and genital aperture. They have 255–365 baleen plates on either side of the upper surface of the mouths, approximately 500 mm in length.

### Distribution

Bryde's whales occur in tropical and subtropical waters in the Pacific, Atlantic and Indian Oceans, usually in water over 15 °C. On the west coast of South Africa one inshore stock is resident in water where the surface temperature in winter falls to 12–13 °C and another favours water of 18–19 °C (Best, 1967).

While their distribution is generally confined to between 40 °N and 40 °S, Bryde's whales are found occasionally outside these limits; they have been taken by Japanese whalers in the North Pacific as far north as 41–43 °N.

### Food

Bryde's whale feeds on small pelagic shoaling fish, euphausiids or squid, depending on its locality and form (see **Taxonomic Notes**). In South African waters the inshore form feeds on anchovy, maasbanker and pilchards (Best, 1967), as well as occasionally the shoaling squid, *Lycoteuthis diadema*. The offshore form feeds on euphausiids and mesopelagic shoaling fish such as *Maurolicus* and *Lestidium*. Olsen (1913) reported on the ingestion of seabirds and sharks, but these were associated probably with the pelagic fish on which the whale was feeding, as Bryde's whale frequently feeds in association with other vertebrate predators (Best, Butterworth & Rickett, 1983). In Australian waters they are recorded as taking pilchards, herring and mackerel together with planktonic crustacea. Gaskin (1972) observed a small school feeding among a number of dense patches of surface shoaling fish, racing among them at speeds of eight to 12 knots with their snouts clear of the water, occasionally leaping out of the water vertically, so that the flippers were visible.

### Reproduction

In South African waters the apparent distinction in breeding seasons between the two forms has been mentioned already (see **Taxonomic Notes**). Being different in overall size, the two forms also mature sexually at different lengths (inshore form 11,8–12,2 m for males and 12,4 m for females, offshore form 12,7–13 m for males and 12,4 to 12,7 m for females) (Best, 1977). Ovulation rates also seem to differ between the two forms, but the calving intervals may be similar, about two years. The calf is about 4,0 m long at birth.

### General

Locally very little is known about the movements of Bryde's whales. Whales belonging to the inshore form may be more or less resident over the continental shelf, but the offshore form may be highly migratory. One whale marked off Saldanha Bay was killed 10 years and five months later almost on the equator. Although this whale was officially recorded as a sei whale at both marking and recovery, other evidence suggests that it might have been a Bryde's whale (Best, 1977). In the North Pacific large-scale movements from tropical regions to the latitudes of Japan have been documented. Nishiwaki (1972) stated that they often form dense schools with tens of individuals or sometimes over a hundred being observed at one sighting.

No. 242

## *Balaenoptera musculus* (Linnaeus, 1758)

## Blue whale
## Blouwalvis

### Colloquial Name

Aptly described, as in the water they appear a bluish grey. Alternative names: Sibbald's rorqual; sulphurbottom.

### Taxonomic Notes

Three subspecies have been described, the nominate *B. m. musculus* from the North Atlantic and North Pacific; *B. m. intermedia* Burmeister, 1821 from the Southern Hemisphere, which spends the summer in the Antarctic, and *B. m. brevicauda* Ichihara, 1966 from the southern Indian Ocean.

Ichihara (1966), in describing *B. m. brevicauda*, recognised 10 points of difference between them and blue whales, *B. m. musculus*. Important differences were that *brevicauda* (as its name implies) had a relatively shorter tail section to the body (average 25 to 27% of body length, compared to 29 to 30% in *musculus*), relatively broader baleen plates (average length:breadth ratio 1,48 compared to 1,79 for *musculus*) and was silvery-grey in colour as opposed to the steel-grey of the blue whale "proper". Pygmy blue whales cease to grow at mean lengths of 20,4–20,7 m in males and 21,6–21,9 m in females. The females become sexually mature at a mean total length of 19,2 m, against 23,7 m in the blue whale "proper". Pygmy blue whales were thought to have a restricted distribution between O° and 80°E in the summer months, migrating to the subtropical waters of the Indian Ocean in winter. However, they have been identified from the east coast (Gambell, 1964) and the west coast (Bannister & Grindley, 1966) of South Africa, from Chile and Western Australia, so that they occur more widely than was previously supposed.

Ichihara (1966) felt that as hybrids were not produced between them and blue whales, they were worthy of subspecific status.

The following account refers exclusively to the "true" rather than pygmy blue whale.

### Description

The blue whale is the largest mammal that has ever lived. Gambell (1979) recorded a female 33,58 m long landed at South Georgia, another female taken off the Falkland Islands that was 33,27 m long, and a 32,64 m male. The heaviest ever weighed was a 27,6 m female, caught in the Antarctic by the Soviet whaling fleet, *Slava*, in March 1947, which had a mass of 190 tonnes.

The upper parts of the body and flanks are bluish-grey, mottled with lighter spots especially on the back and flanks. The under parts are lighter in colour than the upper parts, and there are usually a number of white flecks scattered over the posterior end of the throat grooves. The under surface of the flippers has little and sometimes no pigment, while the under surface of the tail flukes is a rather paler blue than the upper surface, and has a radiant pattern of whitish striations running from front to back.

The whole body is streamlined, with the dorsal fin small and triangular to falcate in shape, set about three-quarters of the way back from the snout. The flippers are small and lancet-like. There are 70 to 116 throat grooves, the longest of which extends from the chin to the umbilicus. In life these grooves are held tightly into the throat so that the head looks narrow when viewed in profile. When viewed from above, however, the rostrum (area in front of the blowhole) is broad, flat and nearly U-shaped, with a central ridge running from just behind the tip to the blowhole.

The baleen plates, about 250 to 400 each side, are large and broad and dark bluish-black, with bristles of a similar colour.

The vertebral formula is C7+T15–16+L14–16+Cd26–27 = 64–65. The rudimentary pelvic bones lie in the muscle tissue above the anus and have no connection with the vertebrae. They are triangular in shape with a slightly concave base and, having lost their original function of supporting hind limbs, now act as a support for the reproductive organs. Occasionally small bones representing hind limbs are present, which also lie in the muscle tissue.

### Distribution

Blue whales occur in all the major oceans of the world. In the Southern Hemisphere in summer they migrate south to the fringes of the ice shelf, circumpolar, in the winter moving north to subtropical waters.

### Habits

Blue whales usually occur solitarily or in pairs, although small groups and aggregations of up to 40—50 have been seen together. By marking whales, by shooting stainless steel numbered darts into the muscle, it has been shown that blue whales exhibit regular migratory movements both in the Northern and Southern Hemisphere. In the Southern Hemisphere they concentrate in the Antarctic in summer to feed on the swarms of planktonic krill, moving northward to warmer subtropical waters to breed. Because the seasons are opposite in the two hemispheres, the northern and southern populations never meet in the subtropical part of their ranges. In the Antarctic the larger individuals tend to move southwards right up to the ice shelf and when the time comes to move northwards the older individuals and the pregnant females tend to move in advance of the remainder (Gambell, 1979).

### Food

In the Antarctic the planktonic krill, *Euphausia superba*, forms the bulk of the blue whale's diet; in other oceans of the world, other species of krill are eaten. The krill live in the upper 100 m of the sea so that at times the whale may have to dive for them. It is believed that the krill shoals may be located by an echolocation system (Gambell, 1979).

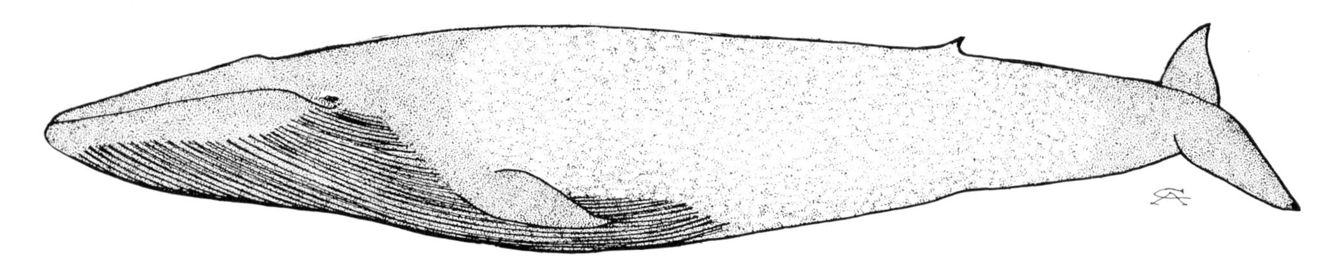

Fig. 242.1 Blue whale, *Balaenoptera musculus*.
Males recorded up to 32,64 m, females 33,58 m (after Nishiwaki, 1972).

As the blue whale only feeds for three or four months in the summer it requires to take in sufficient food during this short period to carry it through the remainder of the year. Gambell (1979) stated that 3,5–4,0 tonnes of krill a day may be consumed during the feeding period. The energy is stored in the form of fat in the blubber layer under the skin.

When feeding a mouthful of food and water is taken, and the water squeezed out through the baleen plates by tightening up the previously expanded grooves in the throat region and moving the bag-like tongue forwards, the krill being retained in the mouth by the baleen plates. It is believed that they will only feed in this way where the krill is particularly abundant. They may also swim through the water with the mouth partially open to catch the krill in the baleen (Gambell, 1979).

**Reproduction**

The main oestrous cycle in the female falls in the winter months when the majority conceive. Some females, however, ovulate at other times of the year, particularly after giving birth and at the end of lactation (Gambell, 1979). Sexual maturity is reached in females at an average length of 23,5 m, and in males at 22,6 m (at about five years of age).

The gestation period is 11 months and lactation lasts for six to seven months. The females then pass through a resting period of five to six months before mating again. While twin foetuses have been observed, there is no evidence that both reach full term and the energy demands in raising twins would probably be beyond the powers of the female. The young normally are born tail first, an adaptation to an aquatic life. This delays the need to breathe air until the newborn is completely free and can be assisted to the surface by its mother.

Some researchers believe that over the past 50 years there has been a significant decline in the calving interval of blue whales, the reproductive rate increasing in response to the increased availability of food resulting from the depletion of whale stocks. The whales that remained, being better fed, ovulated more frequently (Gambell, 1979), and so may have a greater rate of conception, thus breeding more rapidly.

In the Southern Hemisphere the main mating season is from April to late August, with a peak in conceptions in late May and June, calving taking place in the following year about mid-April. At birth the calves are about 7,0 m in total length and have a mass of 2,5 tonnes. By the time the calf is weaned at about seven months old, it has grown to a total length of 16,0 m and has a mass of about 23 tonnes (Gambell, 1979).

**General**

At least three geograpically isolated populations are recognised, one in the North Atlantic Ocean, another in the North Pacific Ocean and a third in the Southern Hemisphere, each probably made up of a number of more or less discrete stocks. In the Antarctic they appear to concentrate in five feeding grounds, but these are not totally separated from one another, whale marking recoveries indicating considerable latitudinal movements.

It was estimated that in the Southern Hemisphere there were originally some 200 000 blue whales, which from the 1930's onwards were severly depleted in numbers by gross over-exploitation before being afforded complete protection in 1965. Present populations are estimated to comprise 1% or less of their original numbers.

Blue whales in the Southern Hemisphere tend to be slightly larger than those in the Northern, physical maturity being reached in males at about 25 m and 26 m in females, as against those in the North Pacific at 18,6 m and 20,1 m respectively.

At sea, blue whales can be recognised by their mottled bluish-grey colour, the tiny dorsal fin set so far back that it only seems to appear just before the whale submerges completely, and from their habit of lifting their flukes above the water when diving (this being the sole balaenopterid to exhibit such behaviour).

---

No. 243

## *Balaenoptera physalus* (Linnaeus, 1758)

## Fin whale
## Vinwalvis

---

**Colloquial Name**

The characteristic shape of the dorsal fin which shows clearly above the surface of the water when they rise to blow, gave them their colloquial name (Fig.243.1).
Alternative names: finback; common rorqual; herring whale; razorback.

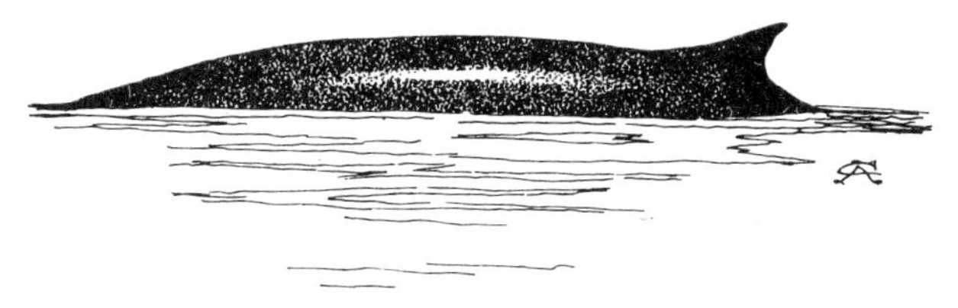

Fig.243.1. Characteristic outline of fin whale about to dive shallowly (after Gale in Gaskin (1972)).

**Taxonomic Notes**

While there are probably discrete stocks of fin whales which occupy different winter breeding areas, no subspecies have been described.

**Description**

Fin whales are the second longest of all the whales, in the Southern Hemisphere reaching maximum lengths of 25,0 m

Fig. 243.2 Fin whale, *Balaenoptera physalus*.
Largest male and female recorded 25 and 27 m respectively.

Fig. XXVIII.1 Map Antarctica: to show the localities mentioned in the texts of the Orders Cetacea and Pinnipedia; the location of the Antarctic Convergence; the mean summer and winter limits of the pack ice; the location of the Prince Edward Islands and the South African Antarctic Expedition (SANAE) base.

for males and 27,0 m for females (and about 3,0 m shorter in the Northern Hemisphere). Average lengths at physical maturity in southern fin whales are 19,9–20,9 m for males and 21,6–22,3 m for females (Lockyer, 1981a). The species is more slender than the blue whale, with a more streamlined head.

The upper parts of the body are dark bluish-grey, fading gradually into the white of the under parts. The undersides of the flippers and flukes are white, with a margin of pigmentation to the anterior and posterior borders of the flukes. The most remarkable feature of the fin whale's coloration is the striking asymmetry of pigmentation anteriorly. The outer ventral grooves, side of the head and shoulders, upper and lower jaws and baleen are all affected. The whole mass of pigmentation externally has shifted slightly to the left, so that pigmentation extends further ventrally on the left side of the ventral grooves, the left mandible is pigmented externally while the right is white, and the lefthand baleen series is almost all pigmented while at least the anterior third of the righthand baleen plates is white. The upper lips are pigmented according to the adjacent baleen plates, *i.e.* the anterior third of the right upper lip is white. A narrow pale streak runs backwards from the ear, and there is a V-shaped pale streak on the back with the apex in the middle of the back pointing anteriorly. Shortly behind the anus there is a narrow pigmented band which reaches downwards and forwards towards the anus. The dorsal fin is located about three-quarters of the way back from the tip of the snout, and is characteristic in shape, the leading edge making an obtuse angle with the back, so that the point of the moderately falcate fin points backwards rather than upwards. The flippers are short, about 10% of the total length of the body, and the width of the tail flukes less than one-fourth of the total length. The eyes are small. The two slit-like blowholes are situated on top of the snout a little in front of the level of the eyes, and from in front of the blowholes a median ridge runs to the tip of the snout. As in blue whales, tactile hairs are located on the chin, along the side of each mandible and on the dorsal surface of the rostrum. There are 68–114 throat grooves which extend back as far as the umbilicus.

Fin whales have 260–480 pairs of baleen plates. Those on the left hand side of the mouth are bluish-grey with vertical streaks of white or yellow, while the front one-half to one-third of the baleen plates on the right hand side are white. The bristles on the plates are uniformly yellowish-white.

The vertebral formula is C7+T15+L14–16+Cd25–27 = 60–63. Sometimes the first two cervical vertebrae are partly fused.

**Distribution**

Fin whales occur in all the oceans of the world including the Mediterranean. They are species of the high seas and are not usually found in coastal waters. Southern fin whales congregate in Antarctic waters during the summer months to feed, and at that time seem to have a circumpolar distribution. During the winter months they move to lower latitudes and were at one time included in the catches of whalers operating from shore factories at Saldanha Bay and Durban. Bannister & Gambell (1965) suggested from the pattern of seasonal abundance at Durban (a unimodal peak in July) that fin whales may not migrate much farther north than the Durban area, but at least some reach tropical waters, and the location of the breeding grounds of southern fin (and blue) whales remains the largest unsolved problem concerning their distribution (Mackintosh, 1966).

**Habits**

The curious asymmetry in colour of the lower jaw is purported to be associated with their habit, when feeding, of swimming tilted to the right so that the black side of the jaw is above the water, the white side below it. Watkins & Schevill (1979) found, however, that in feeding they tilt to either side. Fin whales only congregate in large aggregations on their feeding grounds or on migration, schools usually numbering up to five individuals. Cows and calves tend to segregate themselves from other animals (Nemoto, 1964). Vocalisations are typically simple and repetitive low frequency moans (usually at 20 Hz), and it has been speculated that such sounds could travel hundreds of kilometres underwater if the whales were at the right depth and under the right conditions (Payne & Webb, 1971). The function of such sounds could therefore be social rather than as some sort of broad-scale echolocation.

**Food**

In the Southern Hemisphere the principal food of fin whales is euphausid krill, the fish occasionally found in their stomachs probably taken fortuitously. In the North Pacific, however, they have been reported to feed on small shoaling fish such as mackerel, herring and even on squid. Stomachs examined at shore stations such as Durban, when they are moving into their wintering breeding range, contained very little food and it is not clear whether they totally rely on their blubber resources to tide them over this season or whether they actively seek enough food to try and help balance their energy output. They are undoubtedly thinner on reaching the Antarctic at the beginning of the summer than they are later (Mackintosh, 1966).

**Reproduction**

The young are born in temperate and subtropical waters during the winter months (peak from April to June), the single young at birth having a total length of about 6,4 m. Pregnancy lasts 11 to 12 months, and lactation about 7,0 months. Average calving interval is believed to be about two years. In the Southern Hemisphere sexual maturity is reached at a total length of 19,0 m in males and 20,0 m in females, those in the Northern Hemisphere maturing at shorter lengths (Ohsumi, Nishiwaki & Hibiya, 1958).

**General**

Fin whales are the fastest and most active of all the baleen whales and were seldom caught prior to the onset of modern whaling. Nishiwaki (1972) recorded how even modern catcher boats may have to follow them at 18 knots for periods of up to 30 minutes before they tire and can be brought within range. At their maximum speed Nishiwaki (1972) estimated fin whales can reach 20 knots. The species was the mainstay of the southern whaling industry after the end of World War II, and a record catch of 28 761 fin whales was taken in the Antarctic in 1960/61. In the process the species was reduced from a former estimated population of some 400 000 to about 84 000, and has been totally protected since 1976.

A mark shot into a southern fin whale in 1934 was recovered 37 years later (Brown, 1973), which indicates that they may live up to 40 years or more.

# Order CARNIVORA

This Order was named at a time when it was thought that the constituent members were flesh eaters, the name being derived from the Latin *caro*, flesh, and *voro*, to eat. However, not all the members eat flesh, some in fact such as the African civet, *Civettictis civetta*, are predominantly vegetarian and others insectivorous. It is also known that some mammals, not members of this Order, eat flesh. Carnivores are all, however, to a lesser or greater degree predators.

In the past the Order Carnivora was divided into two Suborders, the Fissipedia or terrestrial carnivores, and the Pinnipedia, the marine carnivores. The name Fissipedia is derived from the Latin *fissum*, to cut, and *pes*, a foot, indicating that the digits on the feet are independent of one another, and Pinnipedia from the Latin *pinna*, a feather, and *pes*, a foot, owing to the superficial resemblance of the flipper to the wing of a bird.

However, there has been some difference in opinion among authorities as to whether the Pinnipedia should be considered as a Suborder of the Order Carnivora or as a full Order. Neither Pocock (1941) nor Simpson (1945) gave the Pinnipedia ordinal rank, in fact the former regarded them as warranting less than subordinal rank. However, they were regarded as a distinct Order by Meller (1923), Ognev (1935), G.M. Allen (1938) and Bobrinskii (1944), and this treatment was followed by Ellerman & Morrison-Scott (1951). Rosevear (1974) believed this obscured the close relationship existing between the two Orders. Meester *et al.* (1986) considered it unavoidable to include the families Otariidae, the fur seals, and the Phociidae, the true seals, in the Order Carnivora, rather than the separate Order Pinnipedia, despite their distinctive way of life, in view of the reported polyphyletic origin of the Otariidae from the Ursidae, the bears, on the one hand, and the Phocidae from the Mustelidae on the other. This treatment is followed in this edition.

Simpson (1931) divided the terrestrial members of the Order into two Superfamilies: the Canoidea, the dog-like members, and the Feloidea, the cat-like members. In the Subregion the Canoidea is represented by the Families Canidae, Mustelidae, Otariidae and Phocidae. Extralimitally the Canoidea includes the Ursidae (the bears) and the Procyonidae (the racoons, coatis and other New World and east Asian mammals). The Feloidea includes the families Felidae, Viverridae, Protelidae and the Hyaenidae.

It is impossible to find characters that clearly separate the Canoidea from the Feloidea, but those that are useful lie predominantly in the skull. In the Canoidea the ear bullae have no septum dividing the anterior and posterior chambers; in the Feloidea a septum is present. Members of the Canoidea have a lengthened bony ear meatus; in the Feloidea it is little more than a ring. The paroccipital process in the Canoidea is independent of the ear bullae, except in *Ictonyx* and *Mellivora*, where it is similar to that in the Feloidea, being closely adpressed to the posterior face of the bullae over which it spreads and to which it fuses.

In the Subregion the Superfamily Canoidea is represented by four genera and five species of Canidae, five genera and five species of Mustelidae, one genus and three species of Otariidae and four genera and four species of Phocidae.

The Family Canidae is subdivided into three Subfamilies: the Caninae, the typical dogs, which in the Subregion is represented by two species of jackals and the Cape fox, and in other parts of the world by the wolves, coyotes and foxes. The Simocyoninae is represented in the Subregion by the wild dog which is related to the bush dog, *Speothos venaticus*, of South America and the red dog, *Cuon alpinus*, of Asia. The Otocyoninae has one representative, the bat-eared fox, which has more teeth, at its full development, than any other extant mammal.

The Mustelidae is subdivided into three Subfamilies: the Lutrinae, represented in the Subregion by two species of otters, the Mellivorinae by the honey badger, and the Mustelinae by the striped polecat and African weasel. The Otariidae includes three species of the genus *Arctocephalus*, and the Phocidae four genera and four species, all of the Subfamily Monachinae.

Superficially the Feloidea is a more homogenous group than the Canoidea and is represented in the Subregion by three Families: the Felidae, Hyaenidae, and Viverridae, an assemblage of 19 genera and 27 species.

The Hyaenidae are included because their fossil record shows a close relationship with the viverrids. Moreover, their auditory meatus, which internally extends to form a partial septum dividing the ear bullae, and the formation of their paroccipital process, demonstrate their feloidean associations.

The relationship of the aardwolf, *Proteles cristatus*, has been variously interpreted; some authorities feel it is worthy of a Family of its own, the Protelidae, others include it in a Subfamily, the Protelinae of the Family Hyaenidae. Following the treatment afforded to this species by Meester *et al.* (1986) and in view of the paucity of data from the fossil record, it is given familial rank in this revision.

The Family Felidae comprises a single Subfamily, the Felinae, which in the Subregion is represented by three genera and eight species. The cats are considered the most typical of the carnivores, with their lithe, muscular bodies, specialised claws for holding struggling prey, and teeth adapted to flesh-cutting. The Family Hyaenidae is represented in the Subregion by two species. The Family Viverridae comprises three Subfamilies: the Herpestinae, the mongooses, a heterogeneous assemblage comprising the less specialised residual members of the basic stock from which the cats and hyaenas originated; the Viverrinae, the genets and civet, and the Paradoxurinae, the tree civet, unique in that the ear bullae do not ossify.

Carnivores have adapted in various ways to secure their prey, kill it and reduce it to a form suitable for swallowing and their bodily form and teeth are adapted to these processes. A cheetah, *Acinonyx jubatus*, has long legs, for its method of catching its prey depends on its ability, after a stalk, to attain high speeds over short distances to enable it to close in for the kill. Another method employed involves a stalk and a pounce, as in the other cats. The African weasel, *Poecilogale albinucha*, has very short legs and a sinuous, snake-like body which allows it to enter rodent burrows in search of its prey. A water mongoose, *Atilax paludinosus*, has long sensitive digits on its front feet, which it uses to feel around in holes under water for crabs.

The process used in killing the prey is reflected in the configuration of the teeth, in particular the canine teeth. A kill may be effected by strangulation, by severing the spinal column, by biting the head or by violent shaking or by a combination of these processes. In an African wild cat, *Felis lybica*, the canine teeth are long and blade-like and, when pressed in between the vertebrae of the neck of the prey, sever the spinal column. The canines of a cheetah are round and not particularly long as they are used for gripping and strangulation. A civet, *Civettictis civetta*, immobilises its prey by violent shaking and if this does not kill it, repeated biting on various parts of the body or on the head eventually does so.

After killing the prey, various methods are used to reduce it to a size suitable for swallowing. This involves the configuration of the teeth, backed by the masseter and temporalis muscles that actuate the lower jaw. In species that eat tough food, such as the hyaenas, these muscles are well developed and the temporalis muscles are provided with an extra surface for firm attachment by the increase in size of the sagittal crest on the top of the braincase. A characteristic feature of carnivores that eat tough food is the adaptation of the cheekteeth to slicing; the grinding of the food is unnecessary. This reaches a high degree of development in the hyaenas, allowing them to slice the toughest skin and to crack the larger bones, and is brought about by the heavy cheekteeth having blade-like cutting surfaces. In particular the fourth upper premolar teeth and the first lower molar teeth are enlarged and occlude on the sides of each other, keeping their cutting edges honed to keen, blade-like edges. These teeth are known as carnassials or, in combination as the carnassial shear (Fig. XXXII.1). However, not all carnivores possess carnassial teeth, as these have adapted to the particular diet. In species which live predominantly on insects, for example, premolars are not enlarged and instead have high cusps on their faces for breaking up the hard chitinous exoskeletons of insects. In the aardwolf, for example, which feeds on soft-bodied termites, the cheekteeth have become vestigial and are peg-like in appearance, having no real function in mastication. As the teeth of the civet are not adapted specifically to slicing, other adaptations have taken place to reduce prey to a size suitable for swallowing. The prey, held down with the front feet, is torn into shreds and this overcomes this disability. Between the extremes of adaptation to slicing or crushing lie forms in which the cheekteeth can satisfactorily perform either function.

The eyes of carnivores are mostly of moderate size or sometimes relatively small. They are situated well to the front of the head, giving them binocular vision which permits them to judge distance accurately. Many of them hunt in poor light and these species have irises that are highly and rapidly responsive to changes in light intensity. This is achieved in the typical cats by having a pupil which, in response to lessening light intensity, changes from a vertical slit to a wide circular opening. The effect of this in dim light is augmented by the possession of a second means of increasing the efficacy of the light, an adaptation that is not unique to the carnivores, being possessed by other mammal species, including whales. This involves the possession of a subcircular area of tissue at the back of the eyes, situated immediately behind the retina and around the optic nerve called the *tapetum lucidum*. This augments the intensity of poor light by reflecting it back again through the receptive cells of the retina instead of it being absorbed in the posterior layers of the eyes. The eyes of species so equipped brightly reflect the beam of a dazzling light back to the observer, the eyes assuming a red, green or yellow luminosity.

Carnivores have an acute sense of smell and are highly skilled in stalking their prey, which they approach from downwind, thereby allowing their own scent to drift away from the prey. The Canidae are notable in their possession of a highly developed sense of smell which they generally rely on in preference to sight, while cats appear to be more dependent upon hearing as an auxiliary to vision.

The degree of sociability varies greatly among the carnivores. The banded mongoose, *Mungos mungo*, may live in packs of up to 50 or 60, while others, such as the African wild cat, *Felis lybica*, live solitary lives, except during the mating season.

Carnivores have their origins in a group of mongoose-like mammals, the Miacidae, which existed in Eurasia in Eocene times some 50 million to 40 million years ago. A group of these, the viverravine miacids, resemble early viverrids so closely that they are barely distinguishable from them. Gregory & Hellman (1939) suggested in fact that extant viverrids were nothing more than advanced miacids with which they could be grouped in a single Family. Miacids are unknown in Africa and the first incursions into Africa, probably in the early Miocene Epoch, were already indistinguishable from extant viverrids (Savage, 1978).

Only two Subfamilies have a fossil record in Africa, the Viverrinae (the genets and civets) and the Herpestinae (the mongooses). Fossil carnivores are rare compared with herbivores, the bulk of our knowledge coming from the Pliocene/Pleistocene beds of Africa. The material that has been recovered in the Subregion originates from these beds, with one from the Miocene. Notes on the fossil history of the various Families of Carnivora are given under the individual Families.

Figs. XXXI.2 and 3 which are based on a dorsal, lateral and ventral view of the skull of a black-backed jackal, *C. mesomelas*, provide keys to the nomenclature of the bones and teeth as used throughout the section on the Family Carnivora.

Rosevear (1974) provided keys both to the cranial and external characters of the Superfamilies of the Carnivora, the Canoidea and Feloidea, but noted that the distinctions are either shared partly by the two Superfamilies or differ in ways that make the characters incapable of clear definition.

Key to the Families after Meester *et al.* (1986)

1. Lower incisors 0, 1 or 2; cheekteeth essentially homodont and usually unicuspid; carnassials never present; limbs modified as flippers; tail short or absent
 ... 2

 Lower incisors 3; cheekteeth usually heterodont and multicuspid (except in Protelidae); dentition frequently sectorial and carnassials usually well developed; limbs not modified as flippers
 ... 3

2. With external ears; hind limbs capable of forward rotation; alisphenoid canal present
 ... OTARIIDAE

 Without external ears; hind limbs not capable of forward rotation; alisphenoid canal absent
 ... PHOCIDAE

3. All cheekteeth vestigial, peg-like and widely separated, although canines are normally developed; body striped, back maned
 ... PROTELIDAE

 Cheekteeth well developed, usually with clear defined cusp pattern
 ... 4

4. Upper carnassial ($P^4$) the dominant cheektooth; postero-internal to it is one small practically functionless molar, which may be shed
 ... 5

 At least one well developed functional upper molar
 ... 6

5. Face long; jaws very powerful; 32–34 teeth; skull with well developed sagittal crest forming a keel-like ridge; 4 fingers and toes
 ... HYAENIDAE

 Face relatively short, usually 28–30 teeth; skull with sagittal crest frequently well developed, but usually not keel-like; 5 fingers, 4 toes
 ... FELIDAE

6. Limbs usually rather short, not adapted for running; molars 2/2 or fewer
 ... 7

 Limbs elongated, adapted for running; 4–5 fingers, 4 toes, with pollex, when present, not reaching the ground; skull long; molars at least 2/3
 ... CANIDAE

7. Two upper molars; bullae either rudimentary or divided into two compartments; 4–5 fingers and toes
 ... VIVERRIDAE

 Only one upper molar; bullae not divided into two compartments; 5 fingers and toes; either clearly modified for aquatic life or with conspicuous black and white dorsal stripes
 ... MUSTELIDAE

# XXIX. Family PROTELIDAE

## Aardwolf

There remains some difference of opinion concerning the relationships of the single species, *Proteles cristatus*, which represents the Family, as its fossil history is relatively unknown. One school of thought is that they are descended from small hyaenas of the genus *Lycyaena* that existed alongside the huge hyaenas of the Pleistocene Epoch. As opposed to these huge hyaenas, with their massive teeth, *Lycyaena* had sectorial teeth, ill-adapted to breaking bones. Unfortunately they disappeared from the fossil record early in this Epoch. The reason suggested for their extinction was that they were unable to hold their own in competition with their larger relatives for carrion and, since they were not adapted so well to predation as the cats, they died out (Ewer, 1973).

An interesting fossil ancestor of the aardwolf, *P. transvaalensis* Hendey, 1974 was discovered in early Pleistocene deposits at Swartkrans, Transvaal. It was larger than the extant aardwolf and was dentally less degenerate (Brain, 1981).

## Genus *Proteles* I. Geoffroy, 1824

No. 244

### *Proteles cristatus* (Sparrman, 1783)

### Aardwolf
### Aardwolf

Plate 18

#### Colloquial Name

The English colloquial name has been borrowed from the Afrikaans which means earth-wolf, a reference to their living in holes in the ground. In Afrikaans *maanhaarjakkals* is sometimes used, referring to the mane of long hair on the upper parts of the body which can be erected at will, giving the individual a fearsome appearance.

#### Taxonomic Notes

Meester *et al.* (1986) recognised two subspecies: *P. c. cristatus* (Sparrman, 1783) from the southern parts of the species' distributional range, and *P. c. septentrionalis* W. Rothschild, 1902, from central and northeastern Africa.

#### Description

In outline the aardwolf is higher at the shoulders than at the hindquarters. This is accentuated by the long hair of the mane on the shoulders, which is erectile when the individual is under stress. Larger than a jackal, they stand about 0,47 m at the shoulder and measure some 0,9 m from the tip of the nose to the end of the tail (Table 244.1).

The background colour of the body varies from pale buffy to yellowish-white, some individuals showing more yellow than others. There are three vertical black stripes on the body, and one or two diagonal stripes across the fore and hindquarters. These stripes run from the mid-back and tail out towards the under parts. Irregular horizontal stripes run across the legs, which are darker towards the feet. Sometimes black spots or stripes are present on the neck. The hairs of the mane, which runs from the back of the head to the base of the tail, are broadly black-tipped and show as a broad black band down the mid-back. The muzzle is black. The upstanding, pointed ears are black behind, white in front. The tail is bushy and broadly black-tipped. Except on the rhinarium, the black muzzle and the chin are densely covered with very short, fine black bristles. The face is usually greyer than the remainder of the body. The hair is relatively short, not more than about 10–15 mm; the individual hairs are dark at the bases, then broadly white, with black tips.

The hair of the dorsal crest is long and wiry and up to 70 mm on the back of the head, increasing in length to up to 200 mm on the shoulders and decreasing to about 160 mm towards the base of the tail. The individual hairs have broad white bases, two buffy or off-white annulations and broad black tips. The hair of the guard coat, on the remainder of the body, is shorter than on the crest and is rather sparse. The coat is given body mainly by the dense, soft, crinkled underfur, the hairs of which are silvery-white at the bases, buffy or yellowish-white at the tips. Interspersed throughout the guard coat, especially on the forequarters, are long tactile hairs which are either entirely buffy or with black tips. The hair on the tail is long and wiry like that of the crest. The individual hairs are up to 150 mm long, broadly whitish at the bases for about two-thirds of their length, the remainder black.

There are five digits on the front feet, four on the hind. The presence of the first digit on the front feet is one of the characters in which they differ from the hyaenas. The claws on the first digits of the front feet are well developed and distinctly curved, the remaining four only slightly so. When viewed from above the claws are narrow, but in side view they are broad at the bases and strongly built and about 20 mm long over the curve. The claws on the hind feet are similar, but slightly more curved. The tips of the claws show clearly in the spoor (Fig. 244.1).

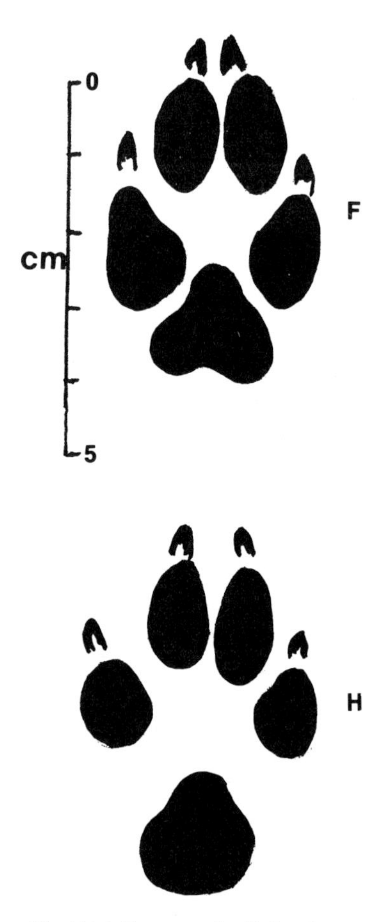


Fig. 244.1. Spoor: aardwolf, *P. cristatus*.
F. Right forefoot H. Right hind foot.

**Table 244.1**

Measurements (mm) and mass (kg) of aardwolf, *P. cristatus*, from Zimbabwe (Smithers & Wilson, 1979)

| | Males | | | Females | | |
|---|---|---|---|---|---|---|
| | $\bar{x}$ | n | Range | $\bar{x}$ | n | Range |
| TL | 909 | 10 | 840–990 | 924 | 5 | 900–970 |
| T | 240 | 10 | 190–260 | 245 | 5 | 223–280 |
| Hf c/u | 156 | 10 | 149–162 | 151 | 5 | 149–156 |
| E | 97 | 10 | 90–101 | 98 | 5 | 91–102 |
| Mass | 8,91 | 10 | 7,83–9,99 | 8,73 | 5 | 7,72–9,99 |

## Skull

(Fig. 244.2)

There are two characteristics which particularly mark the skull of the aardwolf from all other carnivores. The first is the extraordinary reduction of the cheekteeth, the second the great breadth of the palate.

They are equipped with a full set of incisor teeth and formidable canines, but the remainder of the teeth are poorly developed and, at maximum development, are peg-like.

The dental formula is:

$I\frac{3}{3}\ C\frac{1}{1}\ P\frac{3}{3}\ M\frac{1}{1} = 32$

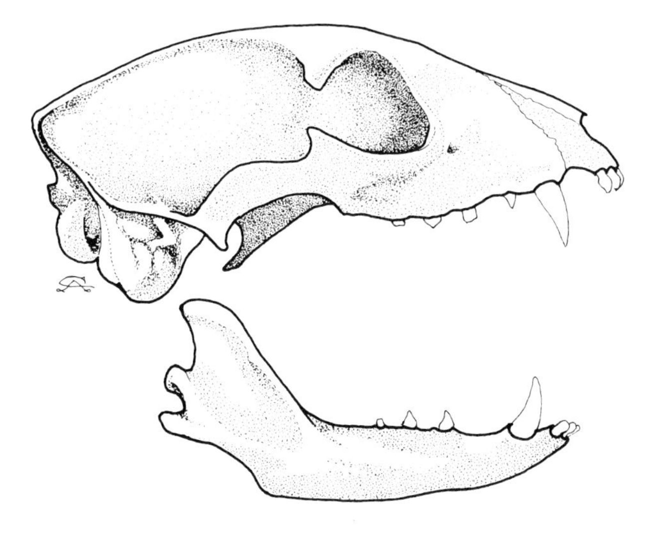

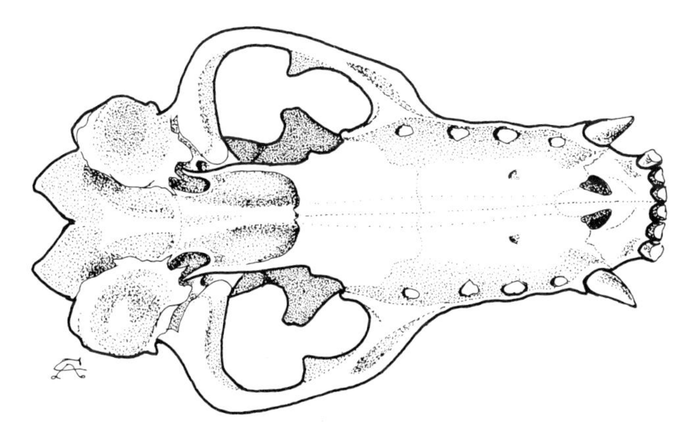

Fig. 244.2. Skull: *Proteles cristatus* to show peg-like cheekteeth, well developed canine, forwardly sloping lower incisors and broad palate to accommodate the large tongue.

The incisors are set in curved rows. The individual teeth are broad and set narrowly apart from one another in the upper jaw, closely together in the lower. The setting of the upper incisors allows for a broad, near parallel-sided palate, which continues well back from the upper molars. The upper canines are long, curved and very sharp, the lower canines more sharply recurved than the upper. The upper first premolars are set nearer to the canines than to the second, which are better developed than the other cheekteeth, but still only just protrude from the gums as tiny pegs. The upper first molar is barely 2 mm long and 1 mm broad. In the lower jaw the tiny first premolar is set nearer to the second than to the canine. The first molar is longer than its counterpart in the upper jaws, and is peg-like. When the jaw is closed with incisors occluding, the cheekteeth of the upper and lower jaws do not touch. The glenoid fossae are very open, not enclosing the process on the lower jaw.

In profile the skull from above the eye orbits to the back of the braincase is flat, then falls off rapidly to the supraoccipital crest. In front, however, it falls off abruptly in front of the eye orbits to flatten out towards the nasals.

The supraoccipital crest is well developed, rising 6 to 7 mm from the braincase and sloping back. It is heavily built and joined by a short sagittal crest at right angles, which tails out quickly on the back of the braincase. The zygomatic arches are broad and heavily built, suggesting well developed masseter muscles. Considering the food eaten by the aardwolf, powerful jaw action in feeding is unnecessary and this development is more likely for the purpose of giving the species a strong action of the canine teeth in defence. Even in old individuals the eye orbits are incomplete, albeit the two postorbital processes approach quite closely. The front chamber of the ear bulla is tiny compared with the hind chamber, which is elongated and swollen, rising high from the braincase when viewed from below. The broad parallel-sided palate is for the purpose of accommodating the broad tongue; the lower jaw, when viewed from above, is bowed out in front for the same reason.

It is noticeable that in the aardwolf and Meller's mongoose, *Rhynchogale melleri*, two species in which termites are the principal food, both have broad palates and bowed out lower jaws, although these characters are not as well developed in the latter as in the former.

## Distribution

The aardwolf occurs within two discrete distributional areas on the continent, one in east and northeastern Africa, the other in the Southern African Subregion, with narrow extensions beyond its borders into Angola and Zambia. There is little doubt that, at some past period in the Pleistocene Epoch, when the climate of the central part of Africa was drier than at present, their distribution would have been continuous between the two areas, now separated by about 1 500 km.

*South of the Sahara, excluding the Southern African Subregion*

They are recorded in the extreme southeastern coastal area of **Egypt**; in the **Sudan**, near Port Sudan on the Red Sea and Suakin, and narrowly southward along the coast to **Ethiopia** and inland to just east of Awash at low altitudes, under 1 500 m. They occur in **Somalia** and are recorded from a number of National Parks and Reserves in central and southeastern **Kenya**; and from northeastern **Uganda**, where they are not uncommon throughout the central plains and possibly up the lower slopes of the mountain masses. They occur in the central and northeastern parts of **Tanzania** as far south as about 8 °S, which is as far south as the species has been recorded in East Africa. They occur in **Zambia** and southern **Angola** as far north as about 14 °S.

*Southern African Subregion*

In **Namibia** they are widely distributed throughout, except on the Namib Desert coast, and they occur throughout **Botswana**. In **Zimbabwe** there are no records from the northeastern parts of the country, but otherwise they are widespread, although not common. Their occurrence on the eastern boundary of Zimbabwe with Mozambique suggests that they probably occur in Mozambique at this latitude, but there are no records so far north. However, they do occur in southwest and southern **Mozambique**. In the **Republic of South Africa** they occur throughout, except in the forested areas in the south along the coast.

## Habitat

Within certain limits aardwolves appear to be catholic in their habitat requirements. In the Southern African Sub-

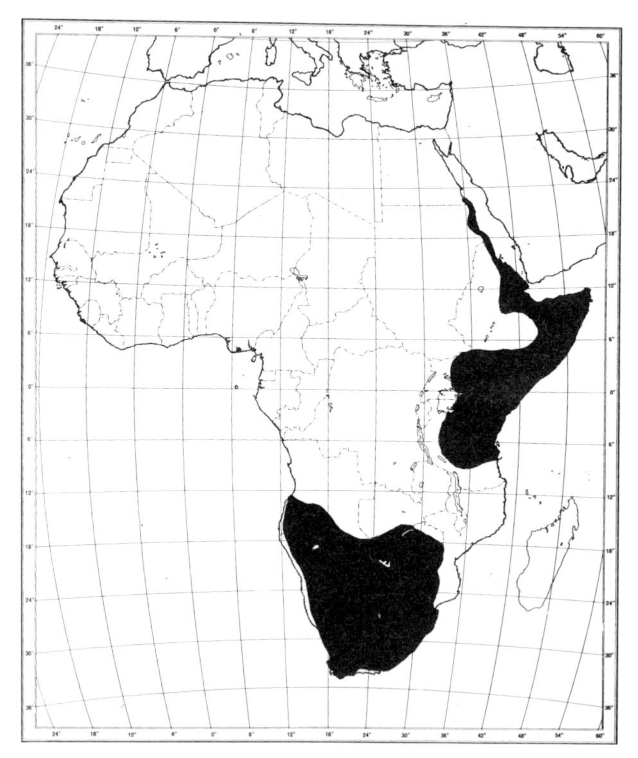

region, they occur in areas of mean annual rainfall of between about 100 mm and 800 mm, but are commoner in areas of between 100 mm and 600 mm than in the 600 mm to 800 mm range. They occur both in the South West Arid and the Southern Savanna zones and within this wide range are found in as diverse associations as the open karroid associations of the Cape Province, the grasslands and scrub of Botswana, the open savanna woodlands of Zimbabwe and the inland gravel plains of the Namib Desert in Namibia, north to the Iona National Park in southwestern Angola (Skinner, unpubl.). They avoid forested areas; so far they have not been recorded from *Baikiaea* woodland. Wherever they occur they are independent of water. In savanna woodland of the eastern parts of their distributional range, there is a tendency for them to be associated with the more open areas such as the broad, open and predominantly dry vleis and associated grasslands on drainage lines and the more open country in the vicinity of pans. Their occurrence anywhere is dependent on the availability of certain *Trinervitermes* species of termites which constitute their principal food (Cooper & Skinner, 1979; Richardson, 1987a,b, 1990).

## Habits

Aardwolves are primarily nocturnal, although they may be active during the late afternoon if termites are available at that time (Kruuk & Sands, 1972; Bothma & Nel, 1980; Richardson, 1987a). During summer in the northern Cape Province they generally become active 30–60 minutes after sunset, and remain active until an hour or two before sunrise. During the winter months, however, (May-August) they are often active an hour or two before sunset, then remain active for as long as termites are available. This is generally until the air temperature drops to about 9 °C (Richardson, 1987a). Aardwolves then retreat to their dens which provide a more equable climate, protecting them against the cold nights of winter and the daytime heat of summer.

Dens may be old aardvark or porcupine burrows, but are more often enlarged springhaas burrows (Richardson, 1985; 1986). Furthermore, aardwolves are avid diggers and there is evidence to suggest that, in the absence of existing holes, they may excavate their own. On Nxai Pan, Botswana, individuals chased at night took refuge in holes on the pan surface where there were no antbear or springhaas diggings. These burrows tended to originate in springbok middens, where the surface was broken and churned up, the burrows underlying the hard calcareous surface layer penetrating into the sandy soil underneath, shallowly, for a length of two to three metres. Most dens are oval-shaped, being about 320 mm high and 420 mm wide at the entrance, but rapidly narrowing down to about 200 × 300 mm inside the tunnel. One den excavated by Richardson (1985) was over 5 m long and had a small chamber (1000 mm long × 400 mm wide × 250 mm high) at the end. This den had been occupied simultaneously by two adults and a year-old cub. Dens are regularly occupied for six to eight weeks at a time before another den is used. A den may be re-occupied six to 18 months later (Richardson, 1985).

The location of these dens appears to be well known, for when aardwolves were pursued, they made directly for them from distances of over a kilometre. After they had disappeared down the holes and the holes were kept under observation, the aardwolves were seen to reappear later, and lie with their heads protruding, watching the pursuer. Aardwolves are prone to stand in a beam of light, appearing confused, unlike other species which quickly move off. This may be the reason why there are so many road-kills at night. Over 75% of the material in the collection of the National Museums, Zimbabwe, amounting to some 40 specimens, emanates from road kills.

Aardwolves are entirely solitary foragers, except when accompanying their young cubs (Bothma & Nel, 1980; Richardson, 1987a), but even cubs four months old will spend most of the night foraging alone (Richardson, 1985; Koehler & Richardson, 1989). During winter aardwolves from the same territory may very occasionally come together in a loose group, spread over 100 m or more, as they feed on the harvester termite, *Hodotermes mossambicus*, emerging from a single but very large colony (Richardson, pers. comm.). Generally, however, if another aardwolf from the same territory is encountered during a foraging bout, both individuals raise the mane of hair along the back as they slowly approach each other. Once the other individual is recognised the hair is lowered and they pass by each other without any further greeting. Occasionally, particularly in a greeting between a mother and her cubs, the two individuals may sniff each other's noses briefly before separating (Richardson, 1985; Koehler & Richardson, 1989).

Aardwolves are socially monogamous, a mated pair occupying a perennial territory with their most recent offspring. Territory maintenance is by means of overt aggression and scent-marking. When territorial intruders are detected the resident immediately raises its mane of hair and chases the intruder. If an intruder is caught, they fall to the ground and bite at each others' necks while resting on their carpals (Richardson, 1985; Koehler & Richardson 1989). Aardwolves occupy territories that vary between 1–4 km$^2$ depending on the density of termite mounds (Kruuk & Sands, 1972; Richardson, 1985; Skinner & Van Aarde, 1986).

When scent-marking, or pasting (Gorman & Mills, 1984), aardwolves straddle a grass stalk, then rapidly squat while everting the anal pouch and wiping a smear of secretion, approximately 6 mm in length, onto the grass (Kruuk & Sands, 1972; Richardson, 1985). The anal gland is situated immediately behind the anus, sharing a common external aperture, and consists of a T-shaped reversible pouch of sebaceous tissue (Flower, 1869a; Pocock, 1916a). A yellowish-orange secretion is produced which turns black with oxidation when exposed to the atmosphere (Richardson, 1985). The gland structure is very similar to that in striped and spotted hyaenas (Pocock, 1916a), but the gland of the brown hyaena is more complicated as it produces two separate secretions (Mills *et al.*, 1980). Although it is quite widely reported that the aardwolf ejects the contents of its anal gland as a form of defence when attacked (Roberts, 1951; Boitoni & Baretoli, 1983), this behaviour has not been confirmed. Scent-marking is observed from a very early age. An individual in captivity would not drink from its bottle until this had been well marked, which it did by straddling it and rubbing its anal region over it repeatedly (Smithers, 1983).

Both sexes scent-mark, although males mark more than females, pasting on average more than 2 times per 100 m travelled. Pastings are concentrated along the territory boundary and at dens and middens (Richardson, 1987b).

Richardson (1985, 1987b) believed this behaviour to be related to territoriality and mate acquisition. However, Nel & Bothma (1983) reported that in the Namib the aardwolf makes a second type of pasting in which a very small spot of secretion is deposited; apparently this is related to advertising areas that have been traversed while feeding. This form of pasting has not been recorded elsewhere (Kruuk & Sands, 1972; Richardson, 1987b).

The aardwolf is generally silent and is usually only heard when under stress. The lowest form of threat is a soft clucking sound apparently made by opening and closing the mouth (Richardson, pers. comm.). Under more stress, such as when captured and restrained, aardwolves may utter a deep-throated growl, and during fights or when suddenly surprised, they may give a surprisingly loud and explosive roar (Smithers, 1971; Koehler & Richardson, 1989). During fights and chases aardwolves always have the mane fully erected. However, if an aardwolf is only slightly disturbed, it just fluffs out the hairs of its tail. This is seen frequently in cubs when they are playing (Richardson, pers. comm.).

Although the cheekteeth are small and redundant, the canines are well developed and with a powerful jaw musculature the aardwolf is capable of inflicting a severe bite. These features have almost certainly been retained for fighting (Ewer, 1973), as aardwolves have very aggressive territorial disputes and frequently chase jackals from their breeding dens (Richardson, 1985; 1987b). The use of the canines for fighting is reflected clearly in their wear, as in old animals they are broken down to rounded stumps (Richardson, 1985; Koehler & Richardson, 1989).

Aardwolves defecate mostly at middens, although they sometimes defecate at random (Richardson, 1985; Koehler & Richardson, 1989). Middens are usually 1–2 m in diameter and often are made up of soft, bare sand from frequent digging by the aardwolves. There may be as many as 20 middens located throughout the territory, but those near the territory boundary seem to be used more frequently (Richardson, 1985; 1990). To defecate, a narrow trench is dug with alternating strokes of the forepaws, after which the animal turns around and squats over the trench. After defecating the equivalent of one-tenth of his body weight, he scratches the hole closed and moves off (Richardson, 1990). This will be the first defecation of the evening, as the subsequent two or three defecations are much smaller. After defecating, the aardwolf usually deposits a few scent marks before leaving (Richardson, 1985; Koehler & Richardson, 1989). The sand content of faeces may vary from negligible amounts to 40% in very sandy areas (Cooper & Skinner, 1979; Bothma & Nel, 1980), or when few termites are available (Richardson, 1985).

Aardwolves usually urinate into the same hole they use for defecating. However, when termites are abundant they may urinate five or six times a night, when on many occasions they simply stop where they are foraging, squat and urinate, and then continue foraging (Richardson, 1985; Koehler & Richardson, 1989).

## Food

The aardwolf's diet is the most thoroughly documented aspect of its biology. Throughout its distribution, it has been found to feed primarily on nasute harvester termites (genus *Trinervitermes*) and, in any particular region, mainly on one species. These are *T. bettonianus* in East Africa (Kruuk & Sands, 1972), *T. rhodesiensis* in Zimbabwe and Botswana (Table 244.2) and *T. trinervoides* in South Africa (Cooper & Skinner, 1979; Richardson, 1987a). These species appear to be ecological equivalents and share a number of common features. Throughout most of the year the termites forage in dense concentrations, completely exposed on the soil surface while browsing or collecting dry grass (Richardson, 1987a). These are the only termites that regularly forage on the soil surface. Most other African termites forage underground, under the protection of mud galleries, or are very irregular in their surface foraging (eg. *Hodotermes*) and therefore present a much less reliable food source (Kruuk & Sands, 1972).

**Table 244.2**

Genera and species of Isoptera identified from the contents of 40 stomachs of aardwolves, *P. cristatus*, from Zimbabwe and Botswana (Smithers, 1983)

| Isoptera | Number of occurrences |
|---|---|
| *Trinervitermes rhodesiensis* | 26 |
| *T. dispar* | 3 |
| *T. rapulum* | 3 |
| *Trinervitermes* sp | 7 |
| *Macrotermes falciger* | 4 |
| *Macrotermes* sp | 1 |
| *Hodotermes mossambicus* | 5 |
| *Odontotermes latericius* | 2 |
| *Odontotermes* sp | 5 |
| *Pseudacanthotermes militaris* | 3 |
| *Fulleritermes coatoni* | 3 |
| Undet. | 3 |

Like all other nasute termites (Nasutitermitinae), *Trinervitermes* possess a highly effective means of chemical defence. The soldiers have well developed frontal glands from which they can squirt threads of very sticky and noxious, terpene-based secretions (Prestwich, 1983; Braekman *et al.*, 1984). Kruuk & Sands (1972) suggested that the aardwolf's hairless muzzle prevents the defensive secretions of the termites from sticking to the same extent as it would if the muzzle was haired.

Termites emerge from small holes on the soil surface and form dense foraging parties. Some parties may contain up to 4 000 individuals, of which about 32% are soldiers; the soldiers protect the workers by lining the foraging path and facing outwards (Richardson, 1985; 1987b). The aardwolf appears to tolerate these soldiers' secretions and feeds on foraging parties by licking them off the soil surface (Kruuk & Sands, 1972; Richardson, 1987a). An aardwolf may consume as many as 300 000 termites per night (Richardson, 1987a). Aardwolves appear to locate termites primarily by scent and hearing as they typically turn short distances upwind in order to feed (Kruuk & Sands, 1972; Richardson, 1985).

Another feature about *T. trinervoides* (and probably most nasute termites), is that they are very poorly pigmented and consequently cannot tolerate direct sunlight (Hewitt *et al.*, 1972). They are therefore almost entirely nocturnal (Richardson, 1987a). By contrast, the larger harvester termites, *Hodotermes mossambicus*, are pigmented, and are mainly active by day and during winter (Nel & Hewitt, 1969; Hewitt *et al.*, 1972). This is fortuitous for the aardwolf, because during winter in southern Africa (May—August) it is frequently too cold for *T. trinervoides* to forage at night, so the aardwolf becomes more diurnal and frequently feeds on *Hodotermes* during the afternoon (Richardson, 1987a).

Richardson (1987a) estimated that an aardwolf in the northern Cape consumes about 105 million termites per year. Of these, *Trinervitermes* constitutes the vast majority, with *Hodotermes* being of limited importance during winter. Together these two species comprise essentially the entire diet, as only traces of other termites or insects were recorded in the faeces.

A second feature of the aardwolves' diet in the northern Cape, is that during midwinter (June/July) they consume only one-fifth the amount of termites per month that they do outside the winter months. This places great stress on the animals which lose up to 20% of their body weight during winter (Richardson, 1987a). It is also the period of highest mortality for the cubs (see below). This suggests that aardwolves are highly dependent on *Trinervitermes* and unable to feed successfully on alternative sources of food (Richardson, 1987a,b). The reports of the association of aardwolves with carcasses are probably the result of the presence of maggots and carrion insects which they will eat when other food is scarce (Cooper & Skinner, 1979).

Furthermore the cheekteeth are developed so poorly that it is doubtful if they could deal with flesh in any form.

Another result of the aardwolf's dependence on a food source that is nutritionally low (Redford & Dorea, 1984), filled with chemical poisons (Prestwich, 1983) and seasonally unavailable (Richardson, 1987a), is that the aardwolf has a basal metabolic rate that is only 70% of that expected from the allometric Kleiber curve (McNab, 1984). Territory sizes vary according to the density of *Trinervitermes* mounds, with each territory having approximately 3 000 mounds, each containing an average of 55 000 termites (Richardson, 1985). The standing crop of these mounds provides approximately half the annual consumption of a family of aardwolves, so it is presumed that these termites must have a high production/biomass ratio in order to accommodate this high predation rate (Richardson 1985; 1986; 1987a).

Aardwolves are generally independent of surface water as they get all their water requirements from termites. However, during prolonged cold spells during winter, when termites are not active, the aardwolves may walk long distances in search of water. This is the only time of year when they have been observed to drink (Richardson, 1985).

**Reproduction**

In the northern Cape Province females come into pro-oestrus during the last weeks of June. Mating usually takes place during the last days of June and the first two weeks of July. Copulation may last from one to four hours, with ejaculation, indicated by pelvic thrusting and tail bobbing, occurring after an hour and then at approximately hourly intervals. There is no copulatory tie as in canids. Females remain receptive for one to three days, but are normally not receptive after a copulation lasting more than three hours. A female will recycle if she is not fertilized (Richardson, 1985; 1987b).

The gestation period is approximately 90 days (Brady & Lyon, pers. comm.). Most litters consist of two to four young but litters of five have been recorded in zoological gardens (Van Ee, pers. comm.). In South Africa cubs are born from October through to December (Shortridge, 1934; Stuart, 1977; Richardson, 1985), although with the warmer winters further north in Botswana and Zimbabwe the breeding season may be less restricted, as gravid females were found in May and others were lactating in April (Smithers, 1983).

The cubs are born in dens, from which they first emerge after about a month. From four to six weeks of age they play around the den for short periods when the adults are present. From six to nine weeks they may play outside but usually remain within 30 m of the den. From nine to 12 weeks they may go foraging with an adult and start feeding on termites, but usually remain within about 100 m of the den. From 12 weeks to four months they may forage throughout the territory, but are usually accompanied by a parent. Cubs are weaned by the end of this period. Up to seven months of age the cubs may still occasionally be accompanied by a parent for a short period of the night, but thereafter they almost invariably forage entirely alone. At about a year old the cubs start making excursions into neighbouring territories and generally have left their natal territory by the time the next year's cubs have emerged from the den. Once they have finally left their territory, cubs seldom return but become transients in search of vacant territories elsewhere in the region (Richardson, 1985; 1987b). Bothma (1971b) collared an aardwolf which was found 35 km away three weeks later. If a parent dies a cub of the same sex usually remains in its natal territory (Richardson, 1985; 1987b).

Males help in rearing the young by guarding the den against jackals, which are probably their greatest natural enemy. Paternal care varies, but during the first two months some fathers may spend up to six hours a night guarding the cubs while the female is away foraging (Richardson, 1985; 1987b). Richardson (1987a) found that between 1981 and 1984 the survival rate of cubs up to the age of 12 months in the northern Cape was 68%. However, most of this mortality was during the height of a drought in 1984 when 55% of the cubs died during winter. The record lifespan for an aardwolf in captivity is 15 years in the East London Zoo (Von Ketelhodt, *in litt.*).

If taken at an early age the young are very difficult to hand-rear, but if taken halfgrown, they thrive in captivity.

# XXX. Family HYAENIDAE

## Hyaenas

The Hyaenidae is the second smallest Family of carnivores, being represented in Africa by two genera and three species: the spotted hyaena, *Crocuta crocuta*; the brown hyaena, *Hyaena brunnea*, and the striped hyaena, *H. hyaena*. The striped hyaena occurs outside the Subregion, from central Tanzania northwards, into North Africa and throughout the Middle East and eastwards to India.

Fossil hyaenids are known from late Miocene sites in North and East Africa and the fossil remains of *Hyaena* are known from the middle Miocene beds in Tunisia which, if they are indeed authentic, would mean that the genus *Hyaena* is one of the longest existing genera of Carnivora (Savage, 1978). Species of hyaenids peaked during the early Pleistocene in Africa when nine were extant (Ewer, 1973). Hyaenids developed powerful musculature to drive the jaws and teeth adapted for bone crushing and it is possible these evolved in the Pleistocene with its abundant artiodactyls and flesh-eating sabre-tooths. Hyaenids would have exploited the resultant food supply. Both the extant species, the brown hyaena, *H. brunnea*, and the spotted hyaena, *C. crocuta*, are recorded in the Subregion and in other parts of Africa from the early Pleistocene. Among early records Hendey (1974) described *H. australis* from Pliocene beds at Langebaanweg, Cape Province, which is the earliest record of the genus *Hyaena* from southern Africa. Randall (1981), working at Makapansgat in the northern Transvaal, has confirmed that *H. abronia* from Langebaanweg is the likely ancestor of *H. h. makapani*.

The Family Hyaenidae had its origins in the Viverridae of which *Progenetta* of Europe may be the earliest member known (Beaumont, 1967 in Savage, 1978). The genera *Hyaena* and *Crocuta* separated in the late Miocene (Thenius, 1966).

Key to the genera (Meester *et al.*, 1986)

1. Ears pointed; body not spotted; back heavily maned; upper molar less reduced, with largest measurement twice or more than that of first upper premolar ... *Hyaena*

   Ears rounded; body spotted; back not maned; upper molar much reduced, much smaller than first upper premolar, often shed in adults ... *Crocuta*

### Genus *Hyaena* Brisson, 1762

No. 245

### *Hyaena brunnea* Thunberg, 1820

### Brown hyaena
### Strandjut

Plate 18

### Colloquial Name

The English name is descriptive of the general dark brown colour. The Afrikaans *strandjut* or *strandwolf* refers to their characteristic habit in some areas, such as in Namibia, of frequenting beaches in search of carrion. Stories about the "mountain-wolf" persist to this day due to the brown hyaena's occurrence in mountainous areas.

### Taxonomic Notes

No subspecies are recognised.

### Description

The brown hyaena was first described by Thunberg in 1820; he did not provide details of a specimen examined, although the plate shows a stuffed specimen. Nor did he see a brown hyaena during his travels (Rookmaker, 1989). In profile the brown hyaena has the typical hyaena build, being higher at the shoulders than at the rump. The head, neck and shoulders are massive, the extra mass carried by the forelegs being shown in the size of the forefeet which are much larger than the hind, a feature which marks clearly in the spoor (Fig. 245.1). Adult males stand about 0,8 m at the shoulder, 0,74 m at the hindquarters, the males with average masses of 47 kg, females slightly less in shoulder height and lighter, at 42 kg (Table 245.1).

**Table 245.1**

Measurements (mm) and mass (kg) of brown hyaenas, *H. brunnea*, from (a) Zimbabwe and the Kalahari (Mills, *in litt.*), (b) total length and mass (±S.D.) from brown hyaenas in the Kalahari (Mills, 1990) and (c) mass and other measurements of mature hyaenas from the Transvaal (Skinner & Ilani, 1979)

**(a)**

| | Males | | | Females | | |
|---|---|---|---|---|---|---|
| | $\bar{x}$ | n | Range | $\bar{x}$ | n | Range |
| TL | 1462 | 10 | 1350–1609 | 1425 | 12 | 1260–1516 |
| T | 207 | 8 | 180–236 | 219 | 9 | 196–254 |
| Hf c/u | 224 | 8 | 204–234 | 214 | 9 | 204–225 |
| E | 151 | 7 | 138–161 | 143 | 9 | 135–167 |
| Sh.ht | 788 | 10 | 745–850 | 788 | 8 | 715–879 |
| Mass | 40,2 | 12 | 35,0–43,3 | 38,38 | 16 | 28,0–47,5 |

**(b)**

| | Males | Females |
|---|---|---|
| TL | 14466±78,7 | 1399±60,1 |
| Mass | 40,2±3,0 | 37,6±3,4 |

**(c)**

| | Males | | | Females | | |
|---|---|---|---|---|---|---|
| | $\bar{x}$ | n | Range | $\bar{x}$ | n | Range |
| Sh.ht | 790 | 8 | 740–880 | 740 | 4 | 640–770 |
| Mass | 47,1 | 8 | 43,0–49,5 | 42,0 | 4 | 37,0–45,5 |
| TL skull | 254,8 | 10 | 234,5–266,9 | 247,2 | 10 | 231,9–267,9 |
| Greatest zygomatic width | 163,4 | 10 | 143,8–173,2 | 152,9 | 10 | 135,0–175,2 |

The colour varies from dark brown to almost black. A feature of the pelage is the white mantle which extends well on to the shoulders and forward to the sides of the forehead. This stands out very clearly in contrast to the darker body. At close quarters, the body colour is uneven, there being darker patches or irregular bands caused by the broad black tips of the guard hairs lying in juxtaposition or unevenly. The upper parts of the limbs on the outside are distinctly cross-banded with broad off-white or tawny bands. The bushy tail is black or dark brown. The broad muzzle is black and naked, the rhinarium black, the whiskers long and jet-black. The forehead is lighter in colour than the body, often with an admixture of whitish hairs giving it a grizzled appearance. The under parts and insides of the limbs are light-coloured, tawny-white or dirty white. The ears which are about 140 mm long, are characteristic, being large and upstanding. They are narrower at the bases, then widen out and rise to narrow, rounded points. Unlike the spotted hyaena, the testes in males show clearly immediately below the anus.

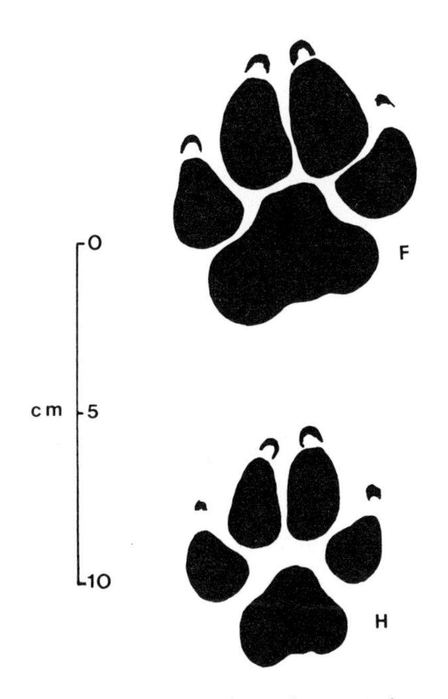


Fig. 245.1. Spoor: brown hyaena, *H. brunnea*. F. Right forefoot H. Right hind foot.

**Skull** (Fig. 245.2)

One of the characteristic features that marks the skull of the brown hyaena from that of the spotted hyaena is the shape of the braincase. In the brown it is much narrower, lacking the outwardly bulging pear-shape of the spotted (Skinner, 1976). In proportion to the size of the two species, the skull of the brown is smaller and the rostrum narrower than in the spotted hyaena.

In profile the skull of the brown hyaena is highest at about the level of the intertemporal constriction, sloping off very gradually backwards and abruptly forwards to the nasals. While the sagittal crest is well developed and extends backwards beyond the level of the occipital condyles, there is little or no sign of a supraoccipital crest. The zygomatic arches are broad, but less heavily built than in the spotted hyaena, being hollowed out inside, leaving a thin bone structure. They swing out broadly at the back, allowing ample room for the well developed masseter and temporalis muscles, the latter being provided with a broad face of attachment to the sides of the braincase and the extension of the sagittal crest. The postorbital bars are incomplete.

The dental formula is:

$$I\frac{3}{3}\, C\frac{1}{1}\, P\frac{4}{3}\, M\frac{1}{1} = 34$$

The upper outer incisors are much larger than the remainder, and are recurved and canine-like, adapted to assisting the canines in holding. The upper canines are relatively short, stout and rounded, with a cutting ridge on the back. The first upper premolars are small, the fourth sectorial, with well developed protocones on their inner sides. The first upper molars are elongated and set at right angles to the toothrow, which is also a distinctive characteristic. The elongation and development of the molar teeth are characteristic of the brown hyaena as opposed to the spotted, in which they are tiny, may be absent altogether or present on one side only. In the brown hyaena they occlude against the shelf at the back of the upper fourth premolar, performing a grinding function.

The lower canines are more recurved than the upper and have a cutting ridge on their inner backs. Adapted to tearing flesh and breaking bones, the dentition of the brown hyaena has the extra function not possessed by the spotted hyaena of a grinding ability provided by the occlusion of the upper first molar on a posterior shelf on the lower first molar. This reflects its greater utilisation of insects and other small invertebrates as well as vegetable matter.

### Distribution

Except for a marginal extension of their distributional range into the arid southwestern parts of Angola, they are confined

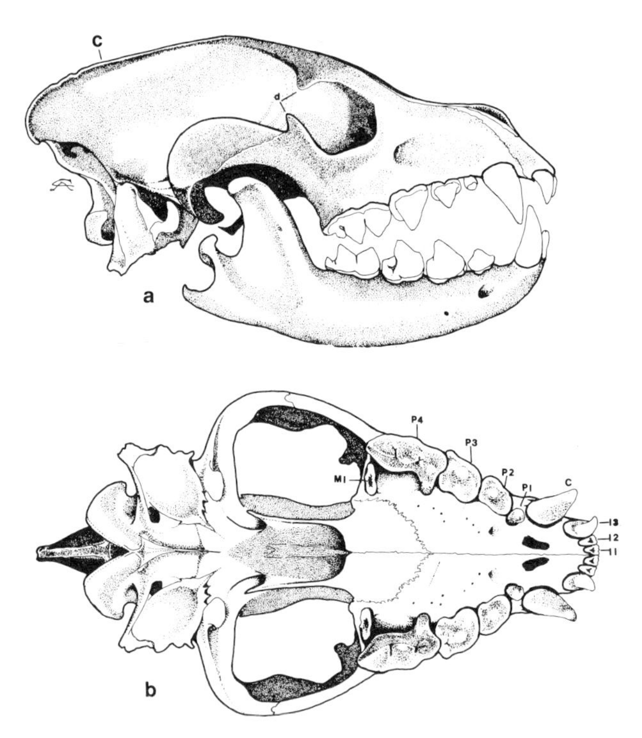


Fig. 245.2. Skull: brown hyaena, *H. brunnea*. TL skull 270 mm.

in their occurrence to the limits of the Southern African Subregion. There are very few detailed records from the historical record, but one may assume they once occurred throughout the Cape Province, and their distributional range has shrunk dramatically since the end of the 18th century when Sparrman (1786) recorded them from the shores of Table Bay.

*South of the Sahara, excluding the Southern African Subregion*

Hill & Carter (1941) did not obtain specimens in **Angola**, but Huntley (1974) recorded them from the arid southwest, in the Iona National Park.

*Southern African Subregion*

In **Namibia**, they occur in the central parts of the country as far north as the Etosha Pan and southwards throughout the coastal Namib Desert. They are widespread in **Botswana**, excluding the northern parts, and extend eastwards marginally into western and southwestern **Zimbabwe** and recently have been recorded for the first time in the extreme southeast of the country. In **Mozambique**, although there are no material records, they are persistently reported from the Banhine Flats, an arid area in the southwest. They are widely, although discontinuously, distributed in the **Transvaal**, as they are in the **Orange Free State**. In **Natal** they have been reintroduced to the eastern shores of Lake St Lucia and the Itala Game Reserve near Vryheid. Occasionally brown hyaenas make incursions into the northeastern Karoo in the **Cape Province**, but today they are only resident in the Richtersveld in the northwest and the Kalahari.

## Habitat

Brown hyaenas are associated particularly with the South West Arid Zone and the drier parts of the Southern Savannas. Within these they occur in desert, with a mean annual rainfall of less than 100 mm, semi-desert, open scrub and open woodland savanna with a maximum rainfall annually of up to about 650 mm. In central Botswana they occur in semi-desert scrub, while in the northern Transvaal, Skinner (1976) stated that they favour rocky, mountainous areas with a bush cover. In Namibia they occur particularly in the Namib Desert, scavenging along open beaches at night and taking refuge during the day.

Cover in which to lie up during the day is an essential requirement. Mills (1977) showed that during the hot summer months in the southwest Kalahari in Botswana they

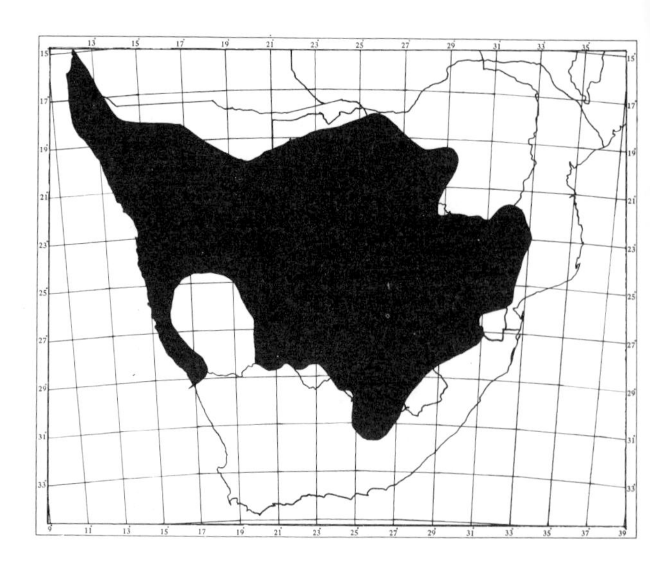

favour the deep shade provided by shepherd's bush, *Boscia albitrunca*, or they will use holes in the ground. During the cooler months a thick bush suffices, or, during cold periods, a patch of tall grass where they are warmed by the sun. Water is not a requirement, although they will drink when it is available. This gives them a selective advantage over the spotted hyaena, *C. crocuta*, which apparently is dependent on a water supply (Skinner, van Aarde & van Jaarsveld, 1984). They will make use of tsamma melons, *Citrullus lanatus*, and gemsbok cucumbers, *Acanthosicyos naudinianus*, for their water requirements. Moreover, their shaggy coats enable them to survive in the cold west coast region, which the spotted hyaena cannot tolerate.

## Habits

Brown hyaenas are nocturnal in the southwestern Kalahari. Mills (1977) showed that they are active from about 18h00 to 08h30 during the summer months and from about 16h30 to 06h00 during the winter months; and along the Namib Desert coast they are active from sunset to sunrise (Skinner, van Aarde & Goss, unpubl.).

They are solitary foragers, but most of them live in groups which occupy fixed territories which, in the southwestern Kalahari, averaged 308±39 km$^2$ (n=6) (Mills, 1990). Group size varies through the year, depending on births, mortality and emigration, numbers of adults not fluctuating to the same extent as subadults and cubs; one group had five members in January, rising to 14 in July, and falling to six in the following January (Mills, 1982). In the Namib Desert, territory size of two groups of eight and 12 individuals was 420 and 220 km$^2$ respectively (Skinner *et al.*, unpubl.). Mills (1981) recorded that the number in groups was positively correlated with the availability of food. In the Transvaal, Skinner & van Aarde (1987) estimated that the size of the home range occupied by an adult male was 18,83 km$^2$, which varied monthly from 13,35 km$^2$ to 23,63 km$^2$. This home range overlapped with that of at least one other individual. Radio-tracking showed that, at night, they visited rubbish dumps in the proximity of farm houses and kraals in the neighbourhood. They suggested that this constant source of food enables the brown hyaenas to obtain all their food requirements within a relatively small area.

In addition to the groups, Mills (1982) detected the presence of nomadic males which temporarily entered the territory of groups. The origin of these could not be traced and some were never resighted, but their behaviour was atypical of group-living males (Mills, 1990). He believes nomadic males account for 33% of the adult male segment of the population. Even territorial males will migrate over great distances; one dominant male left his group near Luderitz on the Namib Desert coast for no apparent reason and migrated south along the coast to the Olifants River mouth in the Cape Province—a distance of 650 km as the crow flies—where he was shot two years later (Skinner *et al.*, unpubl.). On another occasion a female released at Rustenburg in the Transvaal was shot six months later near the Verwoerd Dam.

Mills (1982) found that when two individuals from the same group met they would often engage in a meeting ceremony. This is a simple ceremony involving mutual sniffing at the head, back and anal regions. Muzzle-wrestling and allogrooming were also indulged in. Muzzle-wrestling usually takes place between subadults, and between subadults and adults, rarely between adults; allogrooming takes place between all the age classes in the groups (Mills, 1990).

When members of the same sex, but from different groups, meet they often will engage in ritualistic fighting. When individuals of different sexes, from different groups, meet, these meetings are often amicable and they may greet each other. Ritual fighting involves threat, with the erection of the mane. Owens & Owens (1978) described more serious encounters with neck-biting lasting up to 10 or 12 minutes, which drew blood. Within the group they observed a distinct social hierarchy maintained by neck-biting, muzzle-wrestling and chasing; the submissives, when approaching dominants, lower themselves to a crawl, with squealing and whining.

During the day, brown hyaenas lie up in rock crevices, in the shelter of bushes, clumps of tall grass or holes in the ground. Mills (1977) showed that these resting places may be situated near food supplies. They are often dug out to produce a hollow in which to lie, the undersurface sand occasionally being kicked up by the back legs onto the body to keep the individual cool. There may be very many of these resting sites scattered throughout their home range. In the Kalahari, Mills (1990) found that 94% of brown hyaena dens were located in the dunes, whereas 52% of spotted hyaena dens were in the river beds, and suggested this was due to competitive exclusion caused by spotted hyaena dominance where the two species co-exist.

Brown hyaenas are more secretive than spotted, and Skinner (1976) recorded specimens taken in the centre of Johannesburg and in urban Pretoria, the latter surviving by raiding dustbins.

Their senses are well developed, scent particularly so, for they will detect carcasses over considerable distances. Mills (1978) recorded how an individual detected the dry leg of a gemsbok from 1,8 km away and then moved upwind to it. The large upstanding ears are adapted to a keen sense of hearing and they quickly react to rustling in grass, the cry of a springhaas in distress or the high-pitched bark of black-backed jackals, which have detected leopards or other predators. Their night sight appears to be well developed (Mills, 1978).

Mills, Gorman & Mills (1980) showed that scent-marking, by pasting with secretions of the anal pouches, is carried out regularly throughout the territory, but mostly in the core, heavily used area. When they are moving near the border of their territory they increase the rate of pasting. By this means the whole territory becomes saturated with the smell of the resident group. Scent-marking may be carried out on grass stems, bushes or rocks. In marking a grass stem, the individual bends the stem by walking over it, extrudes its anal pouch and, with tail curved over its back and its back legs slightly bent, manoeuvres the anal pouch over the stem, depositing a paste mark. The paste consists of two components, a white paste with a strong odour, which can be detected by the human nose some 30 days after deposition, and a black paste whose smell is not as long-lasting. These pastes originate in different parts of the anal pouch, the black paste being applied higher up the grass stem than the white (Mills *et al.*, 1980). These authors suggest that this scent-marking serves two functions. It conveys information within the group. As the black paste loses its smell relatively quickly, it may be a means of transmitting information to others on the length of time that has elapsed since the individual passed that way. Secondly, scent-marking may also serve to pass information between the groups, showing that a territory is occupied and so serving to reduce its ritualised defence. Mills (1990) found the overall pasting frequency of seven hyaenas followed for 1 947 km was 2,64 pastings/km, with no difference between the sexes.

Brown hyaenas defecate in latrines which are scattered throughout their territory but tend to be concentrated around the territorial boundary. They visit the boundary latrines more frequently than those situated within the territory (Mills, 1982). These latrines have a characteristic saucer-shape, are about a metre in diameter and 150 mm deep. Hyaenas use them as marking posts, defecating a small stool in each as they move from one to the other (Skinner & van Aarde, unpubl.). Some of these latrines are used over a short period only, being situated near large carcasses which attract them over a period of several nights. Other latrines are used over a period of years. In Namibia, Skinner & van Aarde (1981) found that the number of faecal stools per latrine is far less than in the spotted hyaena, *C. crocuta*, numbering an average of 5,0 (n=10), as against 12,4 (n=5) in the spotted hyaena.

Owens & Owens (1978) recorded a number of vocalisations, in addition to the squeal or whine of a submissive in greeting a dominant. In muzzle-wrestling they growl or grunt; the cubs and subadults utter a soft growl, accompanied by panting, when muzzle-wrestling. They yell when confronted by lions or before fleeing, and submissive animals may scream when neck-biting with dominants, or squeak while crawling on being confronted by them. When adults in captivity confront one another, they will utter a continuous guttural growl or snort (Henschel, pers. comm.). In addition Mills (1982) recognised a harsh whine, uttered by the cubs prior to suckling, or by the adults when squabbling over food, and a soft whine by the cubs when being groomed. Adult males utter a very soft growl when calling cubs in the den. He also recorded a loud growl when they are frightened, a short deep growl when faced by a lion or when being chased by one, or in encounters with spotted hyaenas. The adults hoot and pilo-erect when approaching others on a kill. This expresses aggression and may be followed by attack. Brown hyaenas are on the whole quieter than spotted hyaenas and have no whooping call so characteristic of the spotted hyaena.

Apps (1982) recorded an encounter between a lion and a brown hyaena in the Kalahari Gemsbok National Park. When first seen the lion was carrying the hyaena by the throat. When it was released the hyaena lay motionless for some 10 minutes and then was rolled over and played with by one of the young lions. When it was thrown in the air, the hyaena rolled onto its feet, faced the lion and screamed, and then ran off to safety. It appeared that the hyaena was shamming death to avoid attracting further attention from the lions.

**Food**

Brown hyaenas are predominantly scavengers, although their diet includes a wide range of small mammals, birds, reptiles, fruit and insects. Although they are known to kill sheep, goats and calves, this is due to an individual or individuals which become adept at this practice and, if they are removed, the depredations usually cease. Skinner (1976) recorded that over a period of four months an individual killed sheep in the Machadodorp area. When it was destroyed, the predation on sheep ceased, although there were other brown hyaenas on the property. In another instance near Potgietersrus a female with five three-quarter grown cubs started attacking young calves. When these were removed by trapping there were no more instances of preying on calves, although hyaenas were still present. Similar instances are known, not only involving brown hyaenas, but other carnivores as well, where an individual only is responsible and not the species in general, to which this type of behaviour is atypical. The finding of a predator on a carcass too often leads to its being blamed for the killing. Skinner (1976) has a report of a calf being killed near Pretoria and a brown hyaena was found on the carcass. As it was the first ever seen on the property, the blame was apportioned to it. Investigation showed in fact that a litter had been raised in a den on the property and that the hyaenas must have been there for many months. In 8 kg of scats collected at this den no hair from domestic stock was found.

Brown hyaenas spend little time and energy hunting prey. Mills (1990) found they rarely hunt small mammals and only 4,7% of attempts were successful (n=128), when a hyaena caught a bat-eared fox, *Otocyon megalotis*, a springbok lamb, *Antidorcas marsupialis*, two springhaas, *Pedetes capensis*, a striped polecat, *Ictonyx striatus* and an unidentified rodent. Brown hyaenas never hunted large herbivores. Seven out of 28 hunting attempts on birds were successful.

They only look for prey on the rare occasions when they hunt. After a short chase and grab at their prey, they give up (Owens & Owens, 1978). Their success rate hunting springbok lambs is only 6% compared to the 31% success rate of spotted hyaenas hunting this prey (Mills, 1990).

Carrion, which constitutes a major part of their diet, consists of any vertebrate remains that they may locate. However, they have a preference for fresh meat. Much of their food consists of small pieces of bone and other scraps which are consumed alone. A brown hyaena has difficulty in breaking off and consuming large bones of species such as wildebeest or gemsbok, which they will crack up *in situ*; they tend to choose the rib cages and smaller bones and to carry off the larger bones for the attached scraps of flesh and gristle and the marrow, which is highly nutritious. The entire skeleton of a springbok, except for the head, was consumed in 1 hour 23 minutes. Eggs, including ostrich eggs, feature in the diet, as do wild melons and cucurbits which, apart from their high moisture content, have a food value as well. Sometimes several hyaenas congregate at a large carcass but, unless there is much meat on a carcass, only one feeds at a time (Mills, 1990).

Faecal analyses showed that 60,1% of adult faeces contained insect remains (mainly Coleoptera and Isoptera) and 19,8% reptile remains (Mills & Mills, 1977) which are under-represented in the diet as reflected in direct observations (Table 245.2). On the other hand scat analyses of hyaenas from the Namib Desert coast reflected prey abundance in the area.

**Table 245.2**

(a) Items observed being eaten by brown hyaenas, *H. brunnea*, in the Kalahari Gemsbok National Park (Mills, 1990) and (b) remains of food items found in scats from brown hyaenas from the central Namib Desert (Skinner & van Aarde, 1981)

**(a)**

| | Carcasses from kills and scavenging | |
|---|---|---|
| | No. | % |
| Mammalia | 329 | 41,4 |
| Aves | 29 | 3,7 |
| Reptilia | 7 | 0,9 |
| Insecta | 16 | 2,0 |
| Fruit | 183 | 23,0 |
| Miscellaneous | 25 | 3,1 |
| Unidentified | 205 | 25,8 |
| Total | 794 | |

**(b) n=68**

| | % occurrence |
|---|---|
| Mammalia | |
| *Arctocephalus pusillus* | 75,0 |
| *Canis mesomelas* | 7,4 |
| *Procavia capensis* | 2,9 |
| *Lepus capensis* | 1,4 |
| *Desmodillus auricularis* | 19,3 |
| Aves | 5,7 |
| Scorpionidae | 2,9 |

Mills (1990) also listed differences in the diet between hyaena adults and cubs in the Kalahari from scat analyses (Table 245.3)

**Table 245.3**

Comparison of the percentage occurrence of different food items in the scats of *H. brunnea* adults and cubs (Mills, 1990)

| Food item | Adults n=143 | Cubs n=240 |
|---|---|---|
| Mammalia | | |
| *Oryx gazella* | 51,7 | 20,4 |
| *Alcelaphus buselaphus* | 27,3 | 13,8 |
| *Connochaetes taurinus* | 15,4 | 5,4 |
| *Raphicerus campestris* | 8,4 | 29,2 |
| *Pedetes capensis* | 11,9 | 4,6 |
| *Lepus capensis* | 10,5 | 1,7 |
| Carnivora (small) | 30,8 | 41,3 |
| Aves | 15,4 | 14,2 |
| Reptilia | 23,1 | 17,9 |
| Insecta | | |
| Coleoptera | 35,0 | 62,9 |
| Fruit | 80,5 | 37,9 |

Cubs' milk diet is supplemented by adults bringing food to the den and by cubs foraging after nine months of age. Cubs eat more insects and fewer fruits. The difference in size of mammals is because adults tend to carry smaller mammals back to the den (Mills, 1990) where the cubs spend the first 15 months of their lives.

Whether hyaenas accumulate bones at den sites has been disputed for a long time. Recent studies (Skinner, 1976; Mills & Mills, 1977; Owens & Owens, 1978) have shown that brown hyaenas carry food to feed their young at the den. Both species of *Hyaena* do this (Skinner, Davis & Ilani, 1980) and the bones remaining at the den reflect the faunal composition of the area at that particular time (Skinner *et al.*, 1980; Skinner & van Aarde, in press). This has been an important discovery for palaeontological research.

Excess food may be cached under bushes, in stands of tall grass and sometimes down holes which, it has been suggested, is to lessen the chances of it being taken by other scavengers; on 10 occasions hyaenas retrieved the food item within 72 hours (Mills, 1990). Mills (1978) described how an individual, finding a nest with 26 ostrich eggs, stored those not eaten *in situ* in caches scattered 150 to 600 m from the nest.

Owens & Owens (1978) stated that, while brown hyaenas keep clear of lions or their kills, they easily appropriate the kills of cheetahs, and have been known to steal from leopards. They are wary of spotted hyaenas, and wild dogs will drive them off carcasses. Their greatest competitors for food are black-backed jackals which may trail them when foraging (Skinner & van Aarde, unpubl.). When confronted by a number of these on a carcass and being unable to chase them off, brown hyaenas will dismember a limb or other portion of a carcass and move off with it to where they are less disturbed.

Brown hyaenas forage alone, often over long distances of up to 50 km (Mills, 1977), but members of a group occupying the same home range will scavenge communally. Owens & Owens (1978) estimated that brown hyaenas when foraging could move 30 km in 12 hours, but that the movements of a female with cubs were restricted, as she might visit them twice a night. Although brown hyaenas will use paths freely and roads when foraging, their movements are more inclined to be erratic. Their keen sense of smell is used to locate food. Although they are not normally stalkers, this technique is used to secure small mammals or birds. They have been known to try and dig out springhaas. Brown hyaenas are much more leisurely feeders than spotted hyaenas, and consume 7,0 to 8,0 kg of meat at a feed, which is less than spotted hyaenas which have been recorded by Bearder (1977) as eating up to 18,0 kg of elephant meat at a feed and Kruuk (1972a) in East Africa as eating up to 14,5 kg. Brown hyaenas, however, cache food which spotted hyaenas do not.

## Reproduction

The oestrous period of the female lasts several days. In captive brown hyaenas Yost (1980) reported mating behaviour in a pair over a 15 day period. During mating the male may softly bite the neck of the female and in the wild during the period of the female's oestrus the male accompanies her as she moves around. Mills (1990) gave details of six mating bouts where the mean mating frequency is 0,13 mounts/min, the mean interval between mountings is 6,6 min and the mean duration of mounting is 42 min.

Reproduction appears to be aseasonal. In the Kalahari Gemsbok National Park, Mills (1977) gave birth dates from August. In the Transvaal, Skinner (1976) gave the time of birth of young in the wild from August to November, but in captivity at De Wildt Research Station females give birth from May-January (n=11). Females are polyoestrus, with a lactational anoestrus. Interval between litters is 16,5 months (n=4; Skinner, unpubl.) and when a litter is removed from a female (Schultz, 1966; Skinner, unpubl.) or dies, she will come into oestrus sooner and the interval between litters is reduced to 9–10 months.

Mills (1989) found in the Kalahari that most matings are carried out by nomadic males. These males visit the groups, mate with receptive females, and are usually tolerated by all members of the groups. Group males might show interest in females by anal sniffing, but do not court or mount them. Being nomadic involves no investment in cubs as group members care for them. However, lifetime reproductive success of nomads may be low as intervals between births are long and a female may mate with more than one nomad. The reproductive pattern avoids incest but nomads forego foraging advantages incumbent in a well known territory. Immigrant males may also mate and their chances are better when hyaena density is higher as in the central Kalahari (Owens & Owens, 1984).

Mean litter size is 2,3 (range 1–5; n=23) (Skinner, 1976 and unpubl.). Litters are larger in the wild, averaging three cubs (n=12), and just under two in captivity (n=11). Schultz (1966) recorded that cubs are born with their eyes closed, ear pinnae folded and their bodies covered with short hair of the same colour as the adults. The eyes begin to open on the eighth day and are fully open by the 14th day; ears become erect at 28 days. Cubs are born in dens, these often disused aardvark burrows which are adjusted by the female to suit her requirements and that of the young. Brown hyaenas are avid diggers and are perfectly capable of excavating their own dens. Entrances may be large but they narrow down to a size only large enough to admit cubs. As they grow, the cubs excavate as well. Skinner (1976) illustrated a maternity den excavated in the Transvaal which had three entrances and two underground chambers, but Mills (1990) found that 93% of dens in the Kalahari have a single entrance.

In the early stages of the cubs' lives, up to an age of about two months old, the mother may carry them to a new den. At the age of about six months the cubs may initiate the moves themselves. Mills (1990) found that dens were occupied for a mean period of 3,6 months. He suggested that this short period of occupancy may result from disturbance by man or from a build up of fleas.

Although usually a single litter is found in a den, Mills (1982) recorded a case where a female and her eldest daughter both had their litters in the same den, the mother's litter being six or eight months older than that of the daughter. Although the females showed a clear preference for their own cubs, they on occasion suckled the other female's cubs as well.

At least up to the age of about eight weeks the cubs rarely come out of the den, except when their mother or another adult is present. Up to about three months the mother regularly visits them to suckle them, calling them out of the inner burrows by putting her head into the hole and softly growling. She suckles them lying down, rarely standing up.

By the time they are four months old, her visits to the cubs decrease in frequency and she and other group members begin to bring food back for them. This food is left as far down the hole as the adult can reach. Later as they grow up they will come out of the hole and meet the carrier of the food who will drop it, and the cubs carry it back to the den.

By the time the cubs are 10 to 15 months old, the mother's visits are still further decreased and the cubs spend time away from the den during the day. They may still suckle up to about a year old, but are fully weaned at about 15 months, when they leave the den to forage alone (Mills, 1990).

The maternity dens are the focal point of social activities of the group. Even if they do not bring food, all members of the group visit the dens and in this way the cubs get to know the other members. Subadults will bring food for cubs from the age of 22 months old (Mills, 1982). Food for the cubs may be carried back from long distances; one individual carried 7,5 kg of a domestic cow calf to the den from a distance of 15 km (Mills, 1982).

## Genus *Crocuta* Kaup, 1828

No. 246

### *Crocuta crocuta* (Erxleben, 1777)

### Spotted hyaena
### Gevlekte hiëna

Plate 18

#### Colloquial Name

The spotting on the body distinguishes this species from the brown hyaena, *Hyaena brunnea*. In old, relatively unspotted individuals the rounded ears of the spotted hyaena, as opposed to the pointed ears of the brown, and their shorter, less shaggy coat, also distinguish the two species.

#### Taxonomic Notes

Although Allen (1939) listed six subspecies from the African Continent, Matthews (1939a) showed that there is a wide individual variation in the characters used to separate them. Meester *et al.* (1986) did not recognise any of the subspecies that have been described.

#### Description

Spotted hyaenas are massively built, with particularly heavy forequarters and sloping backs. The immense power of the muscles of the neck and forequarters is best appreciated when an individual is seen tearing pieces off a carcass or when carrying a heavy section of a carcass high off the ground. The powerful build of the forequarters reflects in the size of the front feet, which are much larger than the hind, a feature clearly marked in the spoor (Fig. 246.1). The head is broad and massive, with a short, bluntly pointed dark brown or nearly black muzzle and broad rounded ears. The ground colour of the body varies from off-white to dull grey-white, tinged with yellow, often yellower down the mid-back. With the exception of the head, neck and lower part of the limbs, the body is covered with dark brown or blackish, irregularly distributed spots. Juveniles are uniformly black to dark brown at birth, but soon develop pale fur with clear dark spotting, which is progressively lost with age and in old individuals may be apparent only on the legs.

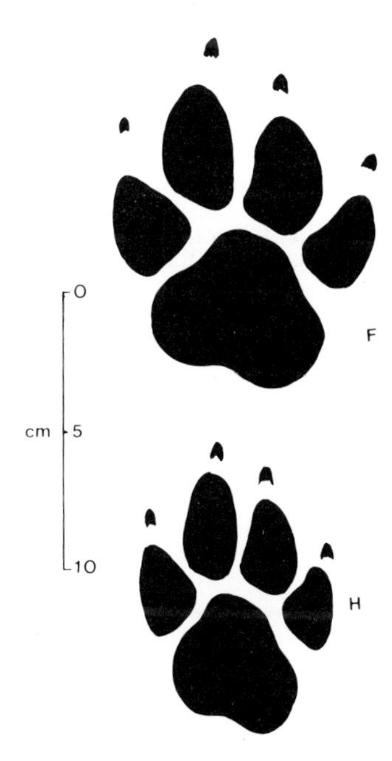


Fig. 246.1 Spoor, spotted hyaena, *C. crocuta*
F. Right forefoot H. Right hind foot

Standing about 0,8 m at the shoulder, adults have masses of up to about 81 kg. Despite overlap in size (Whateley, 1980), adult females are usually heavier and of stouter build than the males (Table 246.1), a trend that was also apparent in East Africa (Kruuk, 1972a; Hamilton, Tilson & Frank, 1985).

**Table 246.1**

Measurements (mm) and mass (kg) of spotted hyaenas, *C. crocuta*, from (a) Zimbabwe and the Transvaal (Rautenbach, 1978; Smithers, 1983); (b) Kruger National Park (Henschel, 1986); (c) Natal (Whateley, *in litt.*) and (d) Kalahari (Mills, 1990 and *in litt.*)

**(a)**

| | Males | | | Females | | |
|---|---|---|---|---|---|---|
| | $\bar{x}$ | n | Range | $\bar{x}$ | n | Range |
| TL | 1483 | 3 | 1455–1535 | 1562 | 5 | 1500–1600 |
| T | 254 | 3 | 241–275 | 256 | 5 | 240–270 |
| Hf c/u | 245 | 3 | 235–254 | 255 | 5 | 240–270 |
| E | 120 | 3 | 117–123 | 118 | 5 | 110–122 |
| Mass | 57,8 | 3 | 49,0–66,3 | 64,8 | 5 | 55,8–76,7 |
| TL Skull (Smuts, *in litt.*) | 22,47 | 3 | 21,0–25,54 | 22,60 | 5 | 21,42–24,38 |

**(b)**

| | Males | | | Females | | |
|---|---|---|---|---|---|---|
| | $\bar{x}$ | n | Range | $\bar{x}$ | n | Range |
| TL | 1587 | 9 | 1465–1735 | 1572 | 8 | 1440–1794 |
| T | 249 | 9 | 227–280 | 249 | 8 | 130–315 |
| Hf s/u | 230 | 9 | 220–245 | 228 | 5 | 215–250 |
| E | 112 | 8 | 100–125 | 114 | 7 | 110–120 |
| Sh.ht | 802 | 10 | 775–870 | 794 | 9 | 735–845 |
| Ht hq. | 669 | 9 | 605–720 | 648 | 8 | 575–680 |
| Mass | 62,5 | 11 | 54,0–70,0 | 68,2 | 9 | 55,0–81,0 |

**(c)**

| | Males | | | Females | | |
|---|---|---|---|---|---|---|
| | $\bar{x}$ | n | Range | $\bar{x}$ | n | Range |
| TL (on curve) | 1339 | 13 | 1250–1420 | 1327 | 13 | 1220–1440 |
| Hf c/u | 242 | 8 | 230–250 | 233 | 6 | 200–250 |
| E | 110 | 8 | 80–120 | 90 | 6 | 80–110 |
| Sh.ht | 796 | 8 | 700–830 | 822 | 6 | 760–840 |
| Mass | 66,6 | 8 | 55,0–79,0 | 70,0 | 6 | 56,0–80,0 |

**(d)**

| | Males | | | Females | | |
|---|---|---|---|---|---|---|
| | $\bar{x}$ | n | Range | $\bar{x}$ | n | Range |
| TL | 1585 | 7 | 1439–1670 | 1631 | 7 | 1505–1710 |
| T | 223 | 5 | 208–245 | 260 | 7 | 246–280 |
| Hf c/u | 258 | 4 | 240–270 | 256 | 6 | 250–260 |
| E | 123 | 6 | 116–138 | 124 | 7 | 119–127 |
| Sh.ht | 839 | 6 | 790–855 | 860 | 7 | 838–885 |
| Mass | 59,0 | 7 | 55,8–62,5 | 70,9 | 6 | 67,1–75,0 |

The hair is coarse, very short on the face and head and longer on the body. From the nape of the neck to just behind the shoulders there is an erectile crest of long hair down the mid-back which, on the neck, may reach a length of 70–80 mm. The hair of the guard coat on the shoulders is about 30 mm long, lengthens to about 50 mm behind the shoulders and tails off in length to about 30 mm on the hindquarters. The terminal two-thirds of the tail carries a prominent brush of long black hair, each up to 140 mm long.

There is a dense undercoat of silvery-buff wavy hair underlying the guard coat on the upper parts of the body. The hairs on the spots are wholly dark brown or blackish. The under parts of the chin and neck are lighter in colour than the body, the guard coat on the under parts of the chest consisting of long, whitish hair with a dark undercoat, giving the whole a dark appearance.

There are four digits on each foot armed with short, heavy dog-like claws up to 18 mm long.

**Skull** (Fig. 246.2)

The skull of the spotted hyaena is of massive build. That of an adult male, when cleaned, has a mass of over 3 kg. A characteristic feature is the high sagittal crest which extends backwards beyond the occipital condyles and overshadows the relatively small pear-shaped braincase.

In profile the highest point lies about the level of the middle of the braincase, gradually tapering off forwards to the nasals, then levelling out towards the nasal orifice and curving backwards to the end of the sagittal crest. These is no clear junction between the sides of the braincase and the sagittal crest which sweeps upwards as an extension of its sides. While in some skulls the supraoccipital crest is represented by a backward sloping narrow flange, in others it is absent or at most indicated by a low ridge. The backward extension of the sagittal crest is particularly heavy, in some skulls up to 10 mm thick. The rostrum is broad, its breadth over half the distance between the front of the eye orbits and the incisors. The zygomatic arches are very strong and sweep out towards the back to provide ample room for the well developed masseter and temporalis muscles that actuate the lower jaw. The postorbital ring is broadly incomplete.

The dental formula is:

$I\frac{3}{3}\ C\frac{1}{1}\ P\frac{4}{3}\ M\frac{1}{1} = 34$

The upper first molars are often absent or may occur irregularly on either side. When present they are tiny and hardly functional. This helps to distinguish spotted from brown hyaena skulls for, in the latter, the upper first molars are always present and are functional teeth.

The outer upper incisors are much larger than the remainder and are strongly recurved towards their points and are canine-like to assist the canines in tearing and holding.

The upper canines are heavy, sharp-pointed, rounded and slightly recurved, with a faint knife-like ridge on their backs. In cross-section they show dentine lines which indicate age (van Jaarsveld, Henschel & Skinner, 1987). The upper first premolars are small, the second and third rounded with high central cusps; the fourth have distinct protocones on their inner edges and are otherwise sectorial, their cutting edges kept sharp by occlusion on the first lower molar. Wear of the mandibular third premolar allows crude age estimation (Kruuk, 1972a; van Jaarsveld *et al.*, 1987).

The mandible is massively built. The lower canines are stout and recurved, the premolars massive, with strong, rounded central cusps; the first lower molar is sectorial. Although the first lower molar has a narrow flat shelf at the back, this has no grinding function as so often there is no upper first molar to occlude against it and even when these are present they are so situated as to be out of contact.

The outer lower incisors in the spotted hyaena are bifid, the outer cusp, however, greatly reduced. In the brown hyaena these teeth are normal, lacking bifurcations.

The whole skull is built to accommodate the powerful jaw muscles which lend the power to the bite of spotted hyaenas. The heavy canines, assisted by the upper outer incisors, have the power to hold and tear, the conical premolars the ability to break the heaviest bones and the heavy carnassial teeth are able to slice the thickest hide and gristle.

**Distribution**

Spotted hyaenas have a wide distribution on the continent south of the Sahara, but do not occur in forests. In most of the continent their distribution has been modified greatly by human influences and has shrunk considerably in historical times.

**Plate 18**

244. Aardwolf, *Proteles cristatus*
Aardwolf
245. Brown hyaena, *Hyaena brunnea*
Strandjut
246. Spotted hyaena, *Crocuta crocuta*
Gevlekte hiëna

PLATE 18
244
245
246
Dick Findlay.

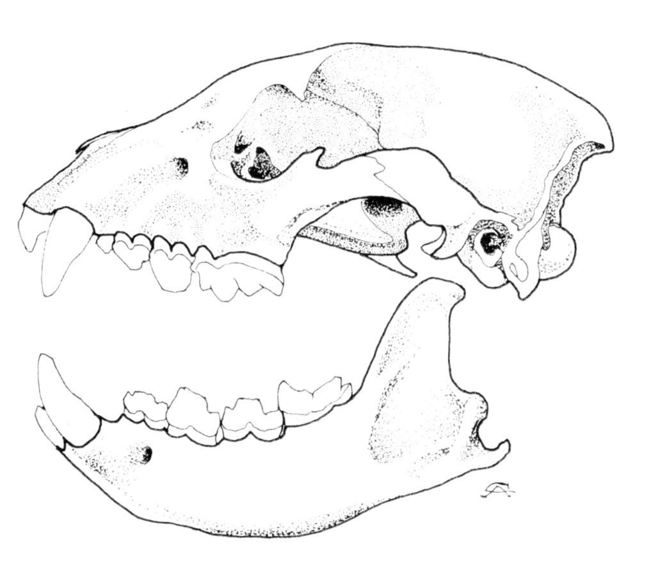

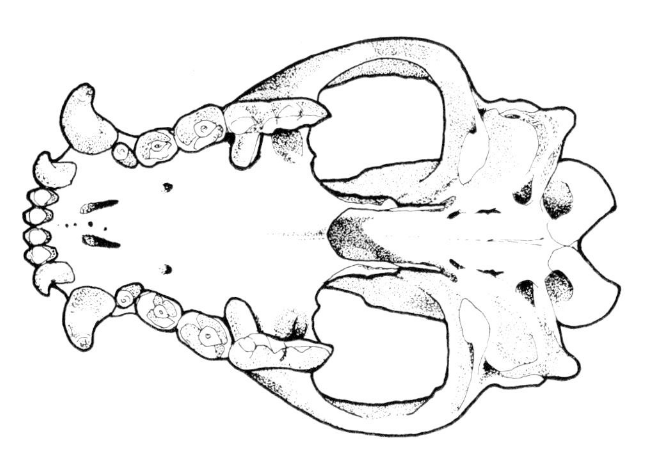

Fig. 246.2. Skull: spotted hyaena, *C. crocuta*.
TL Skull 280 mm.

*South of the Sahara, excluding the Southern African Subregion*

They still occur in **Senegal** and adjacent parts of southern **Mauritania**. They are abundant in **Guinea Bissau** and in the western parts of **Sierra Leone**. Eastwards of this they occur in the Sahel, Sudan and Guinea zones, through to the **Sudan; Ethiopia** and parts of **Somalia**. They occur commonly in **Kenya, Uganda** and **Tanzania**. They are absent in the forests of Zaire, but their distribution extends westwards in the south to **Gabon**. They occur in **Angola**, and there are many records of specimens from all parts of **Zambia**, excluding the intensely developed areas. They are listed as widespread in **Malawi** and in **Mozambique**.

*Southern African Subregion*

The historical situation in **Namibia** is obscure and it may be that they have had a restricted distribution for a long time, being replaced along the extremely dry west coast, where surface water is absent and temperatures are low, by the brown hyaena, *Hyaena brunnea* (Skinner & van Aarde, 1981). Today spotted hyaenas are confined narrowly to the central Namib Desert and to the north and northeast of the country, although there is probably some movement of vagrants westward into the country from Botswana as far south as 20°S. They are widespread in **Botswana**; there are no records along the Namibian border between 20°S and the Kalahari Gemsbok National Park in the southwest, but this is mostly waterless and unsuitable for this species.

They are common and widespread in **Zimbabwe**, except on the central plateau, and in the more highly developed areas. In **Mozambique**, south of the Zambezi River, they are found throughout, except in the eastern Inhambane District, where no doubt they occurred historically.

In the **Transvaal** they occur in game reserves and records from the west are probably those of vagrants from Botswana. They occur in game reserves in northern **Natal**. In the **Cape Province** distribution records from 1650–1790 show they were widely distributed along the well watered east coast, as far as Bergvallei and in the north along the Orange River (Rookmaker, 1989). Shortridge (1934) recorded that they were known at Riebeek East, in the Eastern Province as late as 1870. Today, apart from rare incursions into the Eastern Province they are confined to the Kalahari Gemsbok National Park and the larger Game Reserves in the Subregion, but they are prone to turn up from time to time, sometimes far outside their usual limits of distribution. Although we have no evidence at the moment, it may be that, like the brown hyaena, *H. brunnea*, (see Species 245, **Distribution**), individuals may have nomadic tendencies which may induce them to travel far out of their resident range. Subadult males are known to disperse at sexual maturity (Henschel & Skinner, 1987; Mills, 1990).

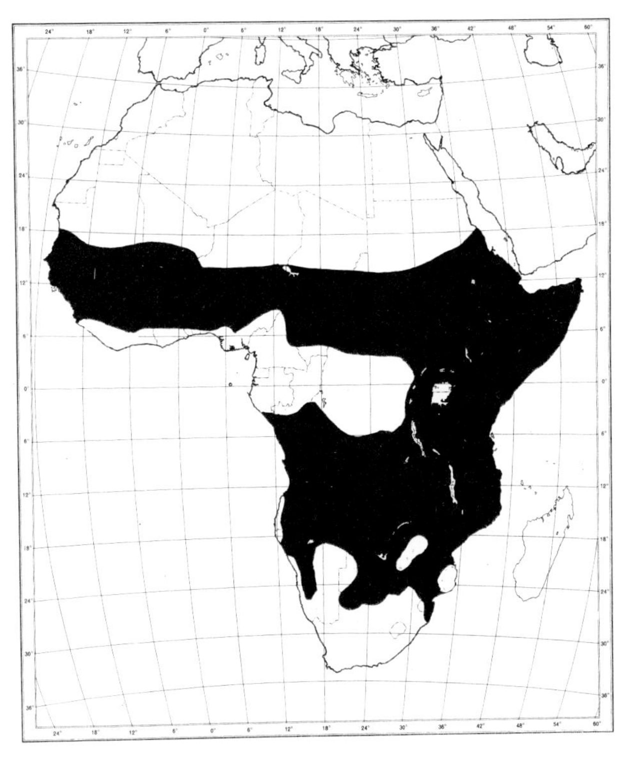

## Habitat

The spotted hyaena is a savanna species, associated in parts of its distributional range with open plains, in others with open woodland and semi-desert scrub. They occur from sea level up to high altitudes. Although they have the reputation of being scavengers, which is unquestionably true, they are also active predators. As such it is to their advantage to live in open country and throughout their wide distributional range they avoid forests or only use them marginally. A plentiful food supply is an essential requirement and they only occur in substantial numbers where there remain good populations of game species to supply this need. Their disappearance results from rigorous control, involving poisoning and shooting, in the face of which populations appear to have little resilience (Henschel, 1986). Throughout their distributional range they are associated often with human habitations and in parts are actively encouraged in this association.

Although periods of a week may elapse between drinking (Kruuk, 1972a), spotted hyaenas are dependent on the availability of water and will travel long distances to obtain it. Tilson & Henschel (1986) reported that a clan in the Namib Desert dispersed when the only waterhole in their range dried up.

## Habits

Kruuk (1972a) showed that spotted hyaena social organisation was based on a matriarchal system of clans. In the

Subregion, clans comprise four to 18 or more adults, with densities ranging from 0,005–0,46 hyaenas/km$^2$. In the Transvaal Lowveld, clans of 9–18 occupy clearly delineated territories of 25–130 km$^2$ (Bearder, 1977; Henschel, 1986) and density is estimated at 0,06–0,18/km$^2$ (Mills, 1985a). In the Etosha National Park density in three clans of 15 individuals each, mean territory size was 360 km$^2$ and density 5/100 km$^2$ (Gasaway, Mossestad & Stander, 1989). Large territory size in the woodland habitat was ascribed to adapting to patchy and temporarily variable distribution of food and widely scattered permanent water holes. Density and clan sizes decrease in arid areas. In the Kalahari and Namib Desert, some clans only have three or four adult members that roam over areas of 400–2000 km$^2$, but may only demarcate and defend the central region of that range (Mills, 1984a; Tilson & Henschel, 1986).

Henschel & Skinner (1987) studied a clan in the Kruger National Park over a period of 27 months. This clan comprised females, cubs and three social classes of males: resident natal males, peripheral immigrant males and central immigrant males with mating status. The clan had a territory size of 130 km$^2$ which all members defended against trespassers. The territory boundaries were marked by scent-marking, pasting, defecating and scratch-marking with interdigital glands. Pasting was carried out by eversion of the anal pouches and dragging these over stems of grass or other objects, the white secretion from these glands having a strong and persistent smell (Kruuk, 1972a). Members of the clan would move outside territorial boundaries on occasion. On being challenged, the females in particular speedily returned to their own territory. Physical contact was usually avoided, defence taking the form of calling, displaying and chasing, contestants occasionally being killed in territorial encounters (Kruuk, 1972a; Henschel, 1986).

The females form the social nucleus (or sisterhood—Goss, 1989) of the clan, which can be regarded as extended family groups (Ralls, 1976) or as harem groups of long duration (Crook, Ellis & Goss-Custard, 1976). Females, cubs and central immigrant males spend most of their time in small foraging groups. The peripheral immigrant males and resident natal males were usually solitary.

Where clans chase and kill prey within the territory of another clan, they usually are driven off, the prey being eaten by the owners of the territory. Territorial boundary patrols are carried out by members of the clans, at which time they show little interest in hunting. The meeting of patrols from neighbouring territories invariably leads to aggression, but seldom to bloodshed (Kruuk, 1972a).

In meetings between two hyaenas, the decision between aggression and non-aggression is made apparently before they actually get close to one another, as they recognize each other at a distance. One may walk in a wide circle to catch scent downwind, or if they recognise each other by sight, one of them will look away as the other approaches. When close contact is established, sniffing at the sides of the head and at the genitals takes place, one or both lifting the leg to expose these organs to the other. Signs of fear are often shown by the submissive individual, the ears held low, the tail between the legs. Within a clan, adult females are usually dominant, while natal clan members, including cubs, usually dominate immigrants. Further study is required to understand the mechanisms underlying this general rule, and its exceptions (Kruuk, 1972a; Frank, 1986; Henschel & Skinner, 1987).

Spotted hyaenas are often slow to colonize vacant or underpopulated areas, even if resources are plentiful. This is evidenced in the long time it takes hyaenas to recover their numbers in areas where they have been shot (Henschel, 1986). However, eventual repopulation can take place either from recruitment by surviving remnant clans, or by neighbouring clans expanding their territories, or when large clans elsewhere split and splinter groups occupy such vacant areas (Mills, 1985b; Henschel, 1986). In other areas, recolonization may not take place at all for no apparent reason (McKenzie, 1989).

Spotted hyaenas possess acute senses of sight, smell and hearing. Their night vision is very good and they have no difficulty in hunting during the hours of darkness. Bearder (1977) noted that they were frequently the first carnivores to detect a carcass and they were able to follow scent trails of meat or even old bones dragged three days previously. He also found that they reacted to sounds before an observer did so.

On balance they are predominantly nocturnal, but at times are also active during daylight hours. They rest in the shade of bushes or trees, among piles of boulders or in krantzes during the hotter parts of the day. Where this type of shelter is not available, as for example in semi-desert areas of Botswana, they will use holes in the ground, but on occasion may be found lying out in the full sun on the sides of termite mounds or on other raised ground. Their activity varies greatly depending on local conditions and season and is largely governed by the distribution and availability of prey. While Kruuk (1972a) found that in the Serengeti no less than 80% of their time was spent resting, with peaks in activity in the early morning and early evening, more recently in the adjoining Mara (Rainy & Rainy, 1989), 30 hyaena fatal attacks on topi, *Damaliscus korrigum*, were recorded between 10h00 and 15h00. It was found that topi graze actively in the early morning. As the temperature rises, topi activity declines, the animals eventually lying down with heads lowered and chins resting on the ground. The hyaenas then move in and lie down 50–100 m away. By about 11h00 hyaenas wander, seemingly aimlessly, among the resting topi, looking for animals deeply asleep. Most topi get up and move out of range, but not all. As a hyaena draws near to a potential victim, it stalks forward head held low in a deliberate walk and at 10 m breaks into an open-mouthed charge, biting and hanging on to any point of contact. Most intended victims escape, at which the hyaena resumes its walk; some do not wake in time and the bellows attract other hyaenas within a minute to the scene.

In another instance where spotted hyaenas adapted their methods of hunting to particular prey species, Wasson (1990) recently described in the Mara how a single adult hyaena attacked a male blue wildebeest, *C. taurinus*, after separating it from the herd. The wildebeest tried to escape by running in short, erratic circles. The hyaena kept attacking the hindquarter at the hip bone point until it obtained a firm grip just forward of the socket joint of the hip. The hyaena also, while dodging the sweeping horns, tore into the flank, making a large wound. The hyaena was dragged along but never let go and as the wildebeest tired, the hyaena tried to cut the muscle supporting the hip which it succeeded in doing and the wildebeest lost control of its right leg. At this point the hyaena started to rip the skin covering the flank. The wildebeest, now in a state of shock, was no match for the hyaena and fell to the ground repeatedly and died soon after being disembowelled.

Spotted hyaenas move widely. Eloff (1964) recorded distances of up to 80 km in the Kalahari Gemsbok National Park. Movement is at a walk of 4 km/h and at its fastest, a bouncing gallop. When walking they can cover very long distances. In chasing prey they can gallop at speeds of 40 to 50 km/hour for distances of up to five kilometres, after which, if no kill is made, they give up. Chases of medium-sized prey normally only cover distances of 300 to 400 m (Kruuk, 1972a; Mills, 1984a; Henschel, 1986).

The call of the spotted hyaena is one of the characteristic sounds of the African night, a series of long drawn out "whoops", each beginning low and rising high on the scale. It is very loud and may be heard at distances of several kilometres. Often it may end, as it tails away, in deep lowing. They also grunt, groan, giggle, yell and whine, the characteristic giggling often being heard when they congregate at a carcass. The cubs whine when following a female and individuals may groan or whine during greeting ceremonies. Under severe duress they snarl or yell, and when challenging other clans or lions as a group, they all simultaneously call loudly by fast whooping, squealing, lowing and giggling.

Kruuk (1972a) showed that the position in which the ears and tail is held indicates the attitude of the individual. In the fleeing attitude the tail is curled between the legs, the ears held flat as it runs off. In the attack the tail is held high, the ears cocked, and when excited the tail may arc forward over the back. Normally the tail droops straight down, the ears held upright. Spotted hyaenas are often playful, chasing each other, with their tails in the air, or playing with bones or sticks.

Where man has exterminated the game species which are their natural food, and introduced cattle, spotted hyaenas are considered problem animals and are subject to intensive campaigns of poisoning and shooting. Lions are responsible for more than 50% of hyaena mortalities in most regions where they coexist, although they sometimes gang up on the lions (Kruuk, 1972a; Moss, 1976; Henschel, 1986). Other deaths are from fighting between clans, man, starvation and disease. Pienaar (1969b) noted that spotted hyaenas fed on the carcasses of animals that had died of anthrax and foot-and-mouth disease, but did not contract the diseases. He believed that they might well be a factor in preventing the spread of these diseases. Rarely, hyaenas may catch rabies, which can decimate clans (Knight, 1989).

Spotted hyaenas scent-mark at latrines. In the Transvaal Lowveld, these are situated often on or near the boundaries of clan territories (Bearder & Randall, 1978; Henschel, 1986), but in the Kalahari and Namib Desert are located nearer the territory centre (Mills & Gorman, 1987). Latrines often bear a particular relationship to certain features of the environment, such as roads, pathways, streams, dens or water, and are spaced at fairly regular intervals. They are used over periods of months or years. They may have up to 144 stools spaced out over an area of 800 $m^2$, but some have only few stools and many pastings or scratch marks. Hyaenas also defecate away from latrines, while urination does not appear to be used for scent-marking.

Spotted hyaenas visit latrines more often than they use them and Bearder & Randall (1978) found that, even when the entire latrine was removed to a new site together with the topsoil and grasses and the old site sprinkled with disinfectant, they invariably used the old site and disregarded the transplant. Revisiting the sites without their being used indicates their signalling potential. They could convey information to a visiting member of the clan on the activities of other members and a reassurance of its position within its territory. Furthermore, they appear to signal territory ownership, which may affect the outcome of contests against intruders in favour of residents (Gorman & Mills, 1984a).

Skinner & van Aarde (1981) showed that there is a significant difference in size of individual stools between those of the spotted hyaena (160,92 g $\pm$ 21,65 g; n=36) and the brown hyaena (45,78 g $\pm$ 4,15 g; n=33). Part of the reason is that those of the brown hyaena contain a large percentage of hair. Spotted hyaenas characteristically regurgitate oral casts of hair and hoof, whereas in the brown hyaena, casts are rarely found.

## Food

The principal food of spotted hyaenas is dictated largely by what is available and, therefore, varies from locality to locality. Throughout their range, spotted hyaenas feed predominantly on large or medium-sized ungulates, although they can hunt or scavenge a wide variety of other items. In the Transvaal Lowveld, impala, *Aepyceros melampus*, an abundant species, were hunted often, while wildebeest, *Connochaetes taurinus*, zebra, *Equus burchelli*, and kudu, *Tragelaphus strepsiceros*, were hunted occasionally. Giraffe, *Giraffa camelopardalis*, and buffalo, *Syncerus caffer*, were scavenged often (Hirst, 1969; Pienaar, 1969b; Bearder, 1977; Henschel & Skinner, 1989). In the Kalahari Gemsbok National Park the order of priority was adult and young gemsbok, *Oryx gazella*, wildebeest, *C. taurinus*, springbok, *Antidorcas marsupialis*, eland, *Taurotragus oryx*, and red hartebeest, *Alcelaphus buselaphus*, calves (Eloff, 1975; Mills, 1984b). In the central Namib Desert in Namibia, gemsbok, *O. gazella*, made up more than 80% of the diet, but mountain zebra, *Equus zebra hartmannae*, were also eaten where they occurred (Tilson, von Blottnitz & Henschel, 1980; Skinner & van Aarde, 1981).

Prey species take little notice of hyaenas walking or lying down. If, however, one runs towards them, they are immediately alerted. Kruuk (1972a) showed that a male territorial wildebeest had a reaction distance of some 8 m to solitary hyaenas, female and non-territorial male wildebeest a reaction distance of 20 to 30 m, and herds a distance of 10 to 20 m. Wildebeest bulls often may stand up to and attack solitary hyaenas, but never press this home over more than a few metres. Often herds will chase them over short distances. With more than one hyaena the reaction distances are longer and herds will break into a run when running packs of hyaenas are 100 m or more away.

Killing is effected after initial biting on the soft under parts until the prey is slowed up, when it may be seized by other members of the pack by the neck or any other part of the body and pulled down to be torn apart. Kruuk (1972a) recorded mass killings of Thomson's gazelles, *Gazella thomsonii*, by a pack of 19 hyaenas, no less than 109 gazelles being either killed or so badly mauled that they were found lying in the vicinity. Once a hyaena has selected its victim and started to chase it, it is usually joined by others. In hunting zebra, hyaenas normally operate in packs, with the size of the pack being related to prey size (Kruuk, 1972a). The chase is much slower than with wildebeest and they may face attacks from the stallion, which hangs behind to protect the now tightly bunched herd of mares and foals. If one of these falls out of the formation, it is likely to become the chosen victim. This hunting behaviour explains why there is a selection for female zebra over males (Kruuk, 1972a; Tilson *et al.*, 1980). Hyaenas sometimes kill formidable prey, such as adult gemsbok, aged buffalo bulls or even hippopotamus, which they distract or disable by harassment, allowing others to attack the prey's vulnerable parts (Henschel, 1986).

Spotted hyaenas kill a substantial proportion of their food. In the Kalahari more than 61% of carcasses fed on were kills, providing 73% of the meat eaten (Mills, 1990) (Table 246.2). Mills (1990) found that they locate their prey by scent and then pull it down after a long and fast chase. In 82% of chases of gemsbok calves the hyaenas secured their prey, the distance of the chase increasing with age of gemsbok. Adult gemsbok in poor condition appear to be selected.

**Table 246.2**

Number of carcasses either killed or scavenged by spotted hyaenas, *C. crocuta*, from direct observations in the Kalahari (Mills, 1990).

| Species | Killed | Scavenged |
|---|---|---|
| Gemsbok adult | 14 | 14 |
| calf | 15 | 4 |
| Wildebeest adult | 18 | 18 |
| calf | 16 | 2 |
| Springbok adult | 2 | 24 |
| lamb | 8 | 2 |
| Hartebeest adult | 3 | 9 |
| Eland adult | 4 | 5 |
| calf | 7 | 0 |
| Ostrich | 3 | 2 |
| Total | 127 (61,4%) | 80 (36,6%) |

In Savuti, Botswana, hyaenas hunted primarily at night to avoid overheating, except in the cool months when they hunted warthogs. They hunt alone or in groups of two or four. It takes two hyaenas to catch adult tsessebe. They chased zebras significantly more often than other species. They hunted more frequently on dark nights and their main prey weighed less than 150 kg, largely juveniles (Cooper, 1990a).

Once a kill is made by individuals in a clan, it may be joined by other members of the clan. The females have priority of access to carcasses, so that they obtain a high proportion of the meat (Henschel & Skinner, 1987). This richer diet may explain why females are generally heavier than males. When many hyaenas congregate at a carcass, they simultaneously feed alongside each other. There may be frequent displays of intraspecific aggression, with much vocalisation and chasing, although they do not bite each other (Kruuk, 1972a). Large chunks are torn off the carcass which can be consumed in a remarkably short time. Kruuk (1972a) timed a pack of 21 hyaenas dismembering a yearling wildebeest of 100 kg which took 10 minutes, and 35 hyaenas clearing a site of all remains of a zebra (220 kg) and foal (150 kg), 36 minutes after killing them. A single hyaena can consume a gazelle fawn (2,5 kg) in about 2 minutes. In contrast, in areas where hyaena clans are small, carcass consumption proceeds in a slow and orderly fashion (Tilson & Hamilton, 1984; Henschel & Skinner, 1989). As a result of expression of dominance by a feeding female, usually only one or two feed at a time, with other group members waiting their opportunity to feed. Under such circumstances it may take hyaenas several nights to finish a zebra or gemsbok (Tilson & Henschel, 1985). However, at small carcasses, such as springbok, hyaenas abandon this orderly procedure and feed much faster (Tilson & Hamilton, 1984).

While ungulates are an important food, spotted hyaenas have been recorded as taking a wide range of other prey, including springhaas, birds, fish, reptiles, crabs, snails and termites as well as fruit. At one time it was thought that they relied entirely on carrion for food. Their predatory habits should not have been overlooked for so long, for Johnston as far back as 1884, pointed out that they were not entirely scavengers, being "more predatory than one generally imagines". Today there is ample evidence that they are active predators in their own right and even a solitary individual has been known to kill an adult wildebeest with a mass of twice its own (Deane, 1962). Not only can they, with their well adapted carnassial teeth, cut through the toughest hide, discarded by other predatory species as too tough to be dealt with, but with the aid of the heavily built teeth in the upper and lower jaws, they can splinter and break up the largest bones of their prey and, furthermore, can digest these completely. In the crushing process bone fragments are left which then become available to the vultures which swallow them and feed them to their chicks, which require a calcium-rich diet for which flesh alone may not suffice (Richardson, Mundy & Plug, 1986).

They are well known as scavengers of rubbish from settlements. In Ethiopia, Nesbitt (1934) and Kruuk (1972a) recorded their regular presence in and around settlements at night, where they were actively encouraged in this pursuit to the extent of being fed. In southern Angola they wandered freely through settlements and up to houses. They will feed on carcasses of other spotted hyaenas and are known to eat the carcasses of other predatory species. They are not averse to eating human corpses when the opportunity permits (Pitman, 1931a). The Masai lay out their dead for the hyaenas to dispose of. There are many records in the literature of their attacking human victims. This usually takes place at night when people are asleep. In Malawi, Balestra (1962) listed the deaths of no less than 27 persons through attacks by spotted hyaenas.

They are prone to try and steal food from other predators, and while they accomplish this with cheetah, prides of lions and large wild dog packs are normally a match for them and drive them off. Leopards will take evasive action by caching their prey in trees. While hyaenas will snap at vultures on kills, these are usually tolerated, as are jackals. Both, however, are wary in their relations with feeding hyaenas. Where hyaenas cannot see or smell a carcass they will react quickly to vultures descending onto it. Kruuk (1972a) remarked on the mutually beneficial relationship of the two species in this regard, a relationship which also involves competition.

Skinner & van Aarde (1981) questioned why spotted hyaenas in Namibia do not avail themselves of the abundant food supply in the form of seals and carrion on the beaches, although they occur inland only 70 km from the coast. They suggest that this may be due to the lack of fresh water, or the intense cold winds coming off the Benguela Current (Skinner, van Aarde & van Jaarsveld, 1984). They are unafraid of water and will lie up in it during the hotter parts of the day. Both Goodall (1970) and Kruuk (1972a) have seen them diving for submerged carcasses.

Assemblages of bones are characteristic of hyaena breeding dens. These are never so extensive in the case of the spotted hyaena as in the brown hyaena, *H. brunnea*, or the striped hyaena, *H. hyaena*, of northeastern Africa, as the spotted hyaena does not carry food back for the young as do the other two species. Sutcliffe (1970), Bearder (1977), Mills & Mills (1977), Henschel, Tilson & von Blottnitz (1979), Brain (1981) and Skinner, Henschel & van Jaarsveld (1986) examined bone assemblages at spotted hyaena dens and recorded a variety of animal remains, mostly associated with legs or heads of medium to large ungulates. Such an assemblage can be distinguished from other bone assemblages in caves by the type of bone damage such as splintering and gnawing (Brain, 1981). Large assemblages can be used to describe the ungulate fauna in an area (Skinner *et al.*, 1986).

Spotted hyaenas, when hungry, gorge their food, consuming very large quantities at a meal. Kruuk (1972a), Bearder (1977) and Henschel & Tilson (1988) measured hyaenas consuming extremes of 14,5, 18 and 17 kg respectively. This appears to be an important adaptation in building energy reserves for milk production. Females do not carry food back to cubs which exist on a milk-only diet in contrast to brown hyaenas which consume less than half this amount at a "sitting", but cache food which spotted hyaenas seldom do, and also carry food back to their cubs. Henschel & Tilson (1988) determined that on an annual basis, food consumption was 4,0 kg/hyaena/day in the Namib, a quantity that compared well with other estimates from the Subregion (Green, Anderson & Whateley, 1984; Henschel & Skinner, 1989). This quantity is what one would expect for a social carnivore of that size (Henschel & Tilson, 1988).

**Reproduction**

In the Subregion they have their young at any time throughout the year (Deane, 1962; Smithers, 1966a; Fairall, 1968; Pienaar, 1969b; Smithers, 1971; Eloff, 1975; Lindeque & Skinner, 1982a). There is a peak during the late summer which is to the advantage of the female and the litter, for this is the time when bovids and zebra have their young (Lindeque & Skinner, 1982a). They have a polygynous mating system.

Male spotted hyaenas become sexually mature at approximately two years of age (Matthews, 1939b), females at approximately three years. Females have an oestrous cycle of 14 days (Grimpe, 1916), recurrent (polyoestrous) with intermittent anoestrous periods of 14 days. The gestation period is about 110 days (Schneider, 1926). Parturition occurs in the open, with the dam squatting upright (Henschel & Skinner, in press). The average number of young in a litter is two, with a range of one to four (Kruuk, 1972a; Frank, 1986; Van Jaarsveld, Skinner & Lindeque, 1988). The birth mass is about 1,5 kg (Pournelle, 1965). They are born in an advanced stage, with their eyes open and covered with soft brownish-black hair. Should a female lose her litter through cub removal in captivity or natural mortality in the wild, she is capable of mating again after an interval of 14–45 days (Grimpe, 1916; Kruuk, 1972a; Henschel & Skinner, in press). Henschel (1986) reported that one female that lost five litters in succession, gave birth at intervals of 135±6 days. Lindeque (1981) found that in the Kruger National Park the average time between litters was 15,9–19,3 months. The central immigrant males are the only consorts of females in oestrus, the precarious social status of the peripheral males precluding them from approach and attempts at mating. Henschel & Skinner (1987) noted that, although several natal males were present when a central immigrant male mated, they showed no interest in the female.

Females in East Africa keep new-born cubs in isolated maternity dens for 11±4,28 days before bringing them to communal dens, the reason for this initial exclusive association between dam and cubs probably to ensure firm imprinting and mother-cub recognition—difficult at a communal den (Kruuk, 1972a; East, Hofer & Turk, 1989). This has not been recorded in the Kalahari (Mills, 1990) and may be related to the smaller clan sizes in the Subregion. Twin cubs are invariably a male and a female, and the female exerts dominance from birth, fighting the male cub which grows more slowly, probably due to only having second choice of teat and frequent disturbance by the more aggressive female cub (Frank & Glickman, 1989; Skinner & van Jaarsveld, unpubl.). Disused aardvark holes or small caves are often converted into dens. The cubs, which are assiduous diggers, extend these in a series of narrower tunnels which only they can enter. A den may have several wide oval-shaped entrances. These provide a safe refuge while the female is away hunting. The dens become the focal point for members of the clans to gather. A female with cubs tolerates only females, her older offspring and central immigrant males in the vicinity of the den, other members of the clan being chased off.

Siblicidal aggression is common among raptors (Gargett, 1990), but Frank & Glickman (1989) have shown that twin spotted hyaena neonates start fighting immediately after birth and when twins are of the same sex, one invariably dies. The precocial cubs are born with deciduous canines and incisors fully erupted and locomotion, orientation and aggressive behaviours are well developed. Aggression continues for several weeks, coincident with elevated androgen secretion in cubs of both sexes. When the mother has access she intervenes. Hofer & East (1989a) found that in the wild mass of cubs of the same cohort could vary by as much as 30–50%. They showed that a twin may benefit from siblicide due to increased growth rate and some mothers may bias their reproductive effort towards daughters.

Social rank of mothers resulted in differences in maternal care in two ways (Hofer & East, 1989b). Those from high ranking females received meat at an earlier age and the proportion of meat was greater for the former. Secondly, high ranking mothers spent less time away from their cubs, feeding on prey nearer the den and usually returning to it daily.

When more than two cubs are found in a den, they are usually the progeny of more than one female. Kruuk (1972a) counted up to 20. The adults seldom enter the dens, but may lie near the entrances, the females suckling their cubs in this situation. Spotted hyaena cubs are permitted to suckle from only their own mothers and attempts to do so from other females are usually repulsed. However, Knight, van Jaarsveld & Mills (unpubl.) recorded that mutual suckling occurred when an intense drought resulted in increased cub mortalities in the Kalahari. Investment in lactation is high in spotted hyaenas and the cubs are suckled for nine to 15 months, being dependent on the female for this period. Cubs have an amazing capacity to consume milk, one cub being observed to suckle for five hours in one bout (East, 1989). In the Serengeti where prey migrates, mothers may be away for up to five days during which time cubs receive no nourishment and no water. They rarely waste energy on play and on cold nights huddle to conserve energy. Under these conditions, mortality may be high and it is the male cub of a twin who dies first.

The average period of den occupancy averaged only 1,5 months in the Kalahari compared to over six months, even several years at a den in the Kruger National Park (Mills, 1990). Vacating a den seems to be related to infestation by fleas.

By the age of two months the cubs' heads are light grey and by about four months the spotting can be discerned on their flanks. The cubs are very playful, running and chasing each other and pestering the adults by climbing over them and biting. Scent-marking starts when the cubs are about four to six weeks old, although their scent glands are still inactive at this stage (Apps, unpubl. obs.). When the cubs are a few months old, they start to follow the mother for gradually increasing distances in the hunt. They do not actually join in the kill until they are nearly full grown.

The resemblance between the external genitalia of male and female spotted hyaenas has been the subject of discussion since the time of Aristotle (384–322 B.C.). Female spotted hyaenas mimic the males in the possession of a penis-like and highly erectile clitoris and a false scrotum and this has given rise to the erroneous supposition that they are hermaphrodites. This phenomenon is not restricted to spotted hyaenas, but is also seen in female spider monkeys, *Ateles* sp, and squirrel monkeys, *Saimiri* sp. Both adult male and female spotted hyaenas frequently fully erect their penis and clitoris respectively as it forms an integral part of the elaborate meeting ceremonies between pairs of natal clan members (Kruuk, 1972a; Hamilton, Tilson & Frank, 1985; Henschel & Skinner, 1987). Lindeque & Skinner (1982a) suggested that the masculinisation of the genital tubercle of female spotted hyaena foetuses results, as in the male, from an episode of androgen secretion by the foetal gonad. Adult males and females have similar androgen levels (Racey & Skinner, 1979; Lindeque, 1981) which seem to indicate that males have suppressed androgen levels (van Jaarsveld & Skinner, 1987). On the other hand, young females are exposed to high levels of androgens, a character usually associated with dominance and aggression. This probably explains the dominance of females over males (Glickman *et al.*, 1987). Females have one pair of abdominal mammae.

# XXXI. Family FELIDAE
## Cats

### Subfamily FELINAE

This family comprises a single Subfamily of living forms, the Felinae, and two or more Subfamilies of fossil genera. The Felinae is a well-defined and homogeneous group represented in the Subregion by three genera and eight species. This includes one introduced species, the domestic cat, *Felis catus*, which has become feral in many parts of the Subregion. They cross freely with the indigenous wild cat, *Felis lybica*.

Often cats are considered to be the most typical carnivores. All of them have a preference for flesh, although the smaller species can subsist on an insectivorous diet when flesh is not available. They are adept stalkers and killers, their teeth admirably adapted to delivering the killing bite and to slicing food into chunks of a size suitable for swallowing. Their sharp curved claws, sheathed in most species when not in use, hold struggling prey until the killing bite can be delivered. The claws are protractile rather than retractable, for their normal position, with the muscles at rest, is retracted within the sheaths, the action of the ligaments being to extend them when they are required (Fig. XXXI.1). The cheetah is the exception for, although the claws can be extended, they do not retract into sheaths and remain exposed.

Hallmarks of members of the Subfamily are the conspicuous upstanding ears, rounded head, well developed long vibrissae, large eyes, muscular, lithe bodies and the soft padded feet with hair between the pads. The tails vary in length in different members, but in all of them express their mood. All members have five digits on the front and four digits on the hind feet.

In the skull the zygomatic arches are bowed outwards to accommodate the powerful muscles which actuate the lower jaw and are heavily built for the anchoring of muscle.

The dental formula is:

$$I\frac{3}{3}\ C\frac{1}{1}\ P\frac{2-3}{2}\ M\frac{1}{1} = 30$$

The incisor teeth lie in a straight row. The fourth upper premolar, the carnassial, is the largest tooth; the first molar in the lower jaw, the second member of the carnassial shear, has a wide open V-shaped occlusal surface, the function of which is to help prevent tough food sliding out of the slicing apparatus. The cheekteeth are all laterally compressed and adapted to slicing rather than crushing. The upper molar tooth is always small, its long axis set at right angles to the

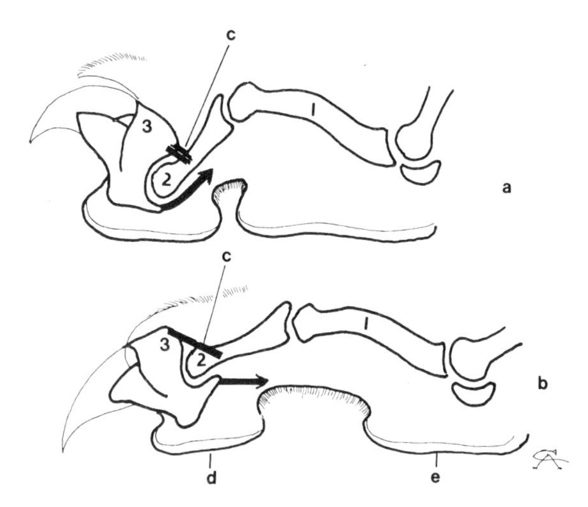


Fig. XXXI.1. Claw mechanism in Felidae
(a) at rest: claw in retracted position, whole digit flexed.
(b) claw in use: contraction of muscle in direction protracts the claw, whole digit extended.
(c) retractor ligament (d) digital pad (e) carpal pad
1, 2, 3 phalanges (after Ewer, 1973).

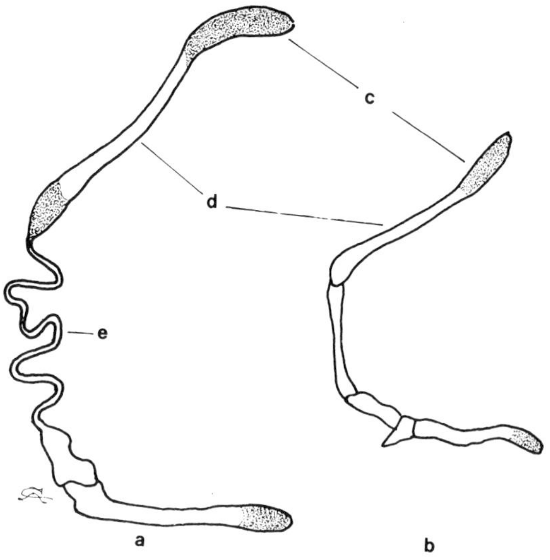

Fig. XXXI.2. Suspensorium (hyoidean apparatus): in members of the genus
(a) *Panthera* (b) *Felis* (c) cartilage (d) bone
(e) elastic cartilage (after Pocock, 1939)

toothrow. When in use it occludes on the posterior part of the lower molar.

Although the felids are not a large Family, they are well represented in the fossil record in Africa, although the most primitive forms are recorded from Europe. In Africa *Afrosimilis africanus* is recorded from early Miocene beds in East Africa. The true sabre-toothed cats of the Subfamily Machairodontinae occur in Pliocene and Pleistocene beds in Africa. Hendey (1974) recorded a good specimen from Langebaanweg, Cape Province, and other genera are recorded from this site, as well as Makapansgat and Kromdraai, in the Transvaal.

Among the extant species the lion, *Panthera leo*, is represented in early Pleistocene beds in the Subregion. The genus *Felis* is rare in these beds, but well represented in the middle and later Pleistocene Epoch. The cheetah, *Acinonyx jubatus*, is first known from fossil remains from Bulawayo, Zimbabwe in late Pleistocene beds dated about one million years old.

Key to the genera (Meester *et al*., 1986)

1. Claws not retractable into sheaths; body with solid black spots; black line from inner corner of eye, down side of nose to upper lip; face short; skull arched in profile, short and high, total skull length 146–203 mm; legs long ... *Acinonyx*

   Claws retract into sheaths; body unicoloured or with rosettes or bars as well as spots, or indistinctly marked bars and spots; no black line from inner corner of eye to upper lip; skull less arched in profile ... 2

2. Hyoid apparatus modified by conversion of median part of suspensorium into a long, elastic tendon; size large, total skull length in adults 175 mm or more ... *Panthera*

   Hyoid apparatus of normal mammalian type, suspensorium a chain of bones joined end to end; size smaller, total skull length in adults not exceeding 155 mm ... *Felis*

## Genus *Acinonyx* Brookes, 1828

Rosevear (1974) stated that the generic name *Acinonyx* is probably derived from the Greek *akaina*, a thorn, and *onyx*, a claw, referring to the foot with its unsheathed claws. It has been suggested that its origin lies in the Greek prefix *a*- signifying deprivation of, and *kineo*, to move, in reference to the commonly held, but mistaken, belief that the claws are incapable of retraction. The specific name *jubatus* is derived from the Latin, having a crest or mane, which refers to their nuchal crest of long hair.

The genus is monospecific, the cheetah, *A. jubatus*, now recognised as the only species occurring throughout its wide distributional range which extends from Africa to parts of the Middle East.

The fossil record shows that the giant cheetah, *Acinonyx pardinensis*, occurred in Europe during the Villafranchian period some 3,8 to 1,9 million years ago. During the early Pleistocene Epoch a smaller species, *A. intermedius*, had a distributional range that extended eastwards to China and by the late Pleistocene Epoch some 700 000 years ago fossil remains reveal that the cheetah then living was indistinguishable from the cheetah we know today.

The early historical records of the occurrence of cheetahs in the Cape Province are vague and unclear about their former distribution. Backhouse (1844) recorded their spoor at Goodhouse on the Orange River, which he visited in 1840, but never saw one himself although they were reported locally to be common (Skead, 1980). Nearly a century later, Shortridge (1942) did not see cheetahs in this area but it was reported to him that a few were to be found in the Bushmanland and Kenhardt districts and that possibly they might survive in the Richtersveld and along the Orange River opposite Goodhouse. In recent times, five were shot on the golf course at Oranjemund 3 km from the Orange River mouth in 1965 (Sweatman, pers. comm.).

Further to the southeast, Jackson (1919) reported on five cheetahs being killed in the Beaufort West district in the 1860's. The Zoological Society of London purchased from Mr Arthur Mosenthal a young live male aberrant cheetah which originated from the Beaufort West area, which lived in the Zoological Gardens for many years (Sclater, 1877). On its death the skin and skull were preserved and are now in the collection of the British Museum (Nat. Hist.), London. This was named the "woolly cheetah", *Felis lanea*, as its fur was more woolly and dense than the cheetah and it had shorter, stouter limbs. Its body was covered with fulvous blotches, not black as in the cheetah, and it had no characteristic black marking between the eye and the mouth.

Pocock (1927) described what he believed to be a unique African species from Zimbabwe, *A. rex*, in which many of the spots on the upper parts of the body and on the flanks had coalesced into bars (Fig. 247.1). Pocock (1939) subsequently stated that this was simply an individual aberration of the normal *A. jubatus*.

No. 247

*Acinonyx jubatus* (Schreber, 1775)

# Cheetah
# Jagluiperd

Plate 19

### Colloquial Name

The name cheetah is derived from the Hindu *chita*.

### Taxonomic Notes

Originally described from a specimen from southern Africa, Allen (1939) listed seven subspecies from the continent of which five generally are recognised (Smithers, 1975b). Only one occurs in the Subregion, *A. j. jubatus*. Following their biochemical analyses, O'Brien, Wildt & Bush (1986) concluded that the southern African cheetah population is genetically uniform (monomorphic), which makes them very susceptible to diseases. This, however, requires confirmation.

### Description

Cheetahs are famed as the fastest animals on earth over short distances. They have spotted coats and are tall and slender in form, with long tails. On account of its unique pattern of striped markings, the variant known as the "king cheetah", has attracted considerable attention and at first was known only from skins, and later a number of sightings, the most recent from Tshokwane in the Kruger National Park in 1989 (van Dyk, pers. comm.) and the northern Transvaal where two cubs were captured. All the skins and sightings came from a restricted area in eastern and southeastern Zimbabwe, the northern and eastern Transvaal and eastern Botswana (Hills & Smithers, 1980) (Fig. 247.2). However, between 1980 and 1989, 18 "king cheetahs" have been bred

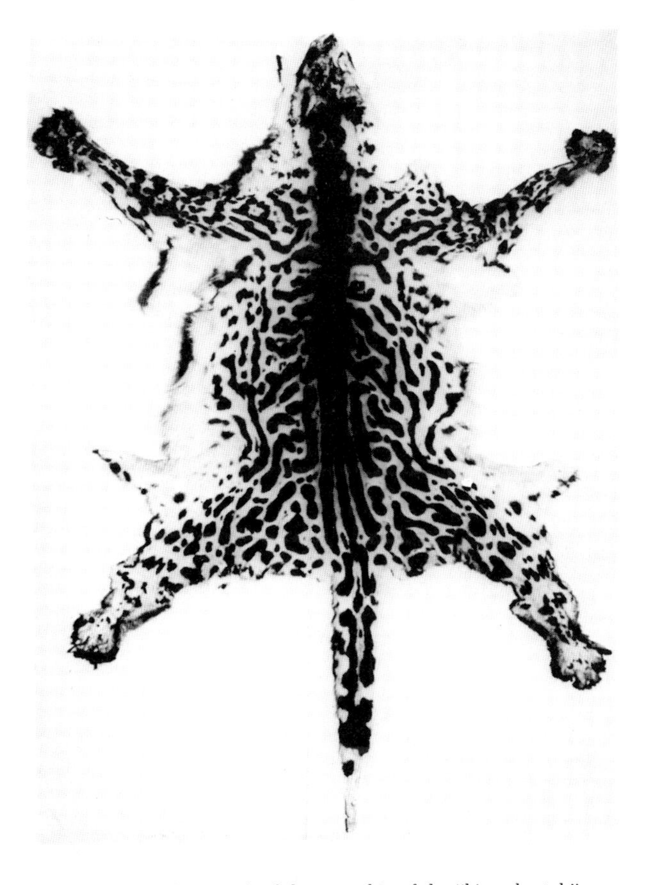

Fig. 247.1. Photograph of the type skin of the "king cheetah", *Acinonyx rex* Pocock, 1927 from Macheke, Zimbabwe. This skin no longer exists (Photo R.H.N. Smithers).

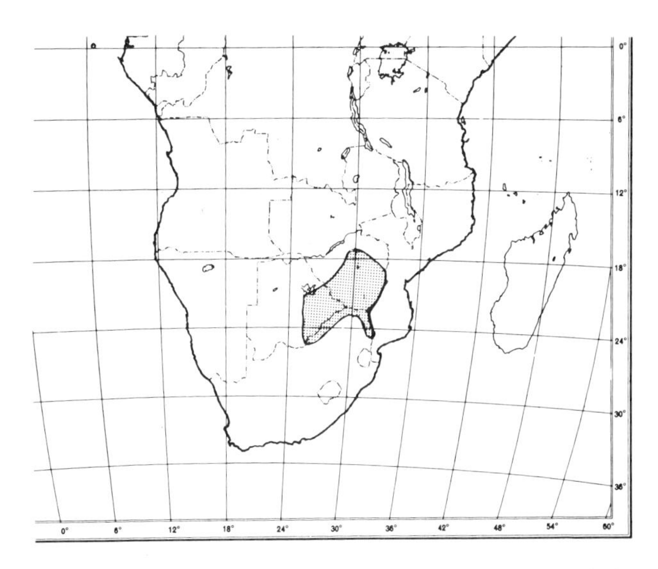

Fig. 247.2. Area within the Southern African Subregion within which there are material and visual records of the "king cheetah".

Fig. 247.3. Photograph of a "king cheetah" born at de Wildt Estates, Transvaal, from a male *A. jubatus* from Messina, Transvaal and a female from Acornhoek, Transvaal. Age 10 months (Photo J.D. Skinner).

at the De Wildt Cheetah Research Centre of the National Zoological Gardens, Pretoria (van Dyk, pers. comm.) and the family trees of nine of these have been reported on by van Aarde & van Dyk (1986) (see Fig.247.3). Their research confirmed that the "king cheetah" merely represents a colour variant of *A. jubatus* and that the "king" trait is inherited as an autosomal recessive allele which probably arose as a mutation at the tabby locus.

The body of the cheetah is slender and is held high off the ground on the long thin legs. Their heads are distinctly rounded, their muzzles very short, the relatively small, rounded ears set widely apart from each other. They have a total length, from the tip of the snout to the end of the tail, of about 2,0 m, the tail about half the length of the head and body, and a mass of between 40,0 kg and 60,0 kg (Table 247.1). They stand about 0,8 m at the shoulders, a height accentuated by the erectile crest of hair. The profile of the back is slightly concave, and the hindquarters are lower than the shoulders.

**Table 247.1**

Measurements (mm) and mass (kg) of adult cheetahs, *A. jubatus* from Namibia (Labuschagne, 1979)

| | Males | | | Females | | |
|---|---|---|---|---|---|---|
| | $\bar{x}$ | n | Range | $\bar{x}$ | n | Range |
| TL | 2060 | 7 | 1910–2210 | 1900 | 6 | 1840–1960 |
| T | 717 | 7 | 650–760 | 667 | 6 | 630–690 |
| E | 75 | 7 | 75 | 75 | 6 | 75 |
| Sh.ht | 881 | 7 | 830–940 | 847 | 6 | 790–940 |
| Mass | 53,9 | 7 | 39,0–59,0 | 43,0 | 6 | 36,0–48,0 |

The pelage is distinctive; the background of the upper parts and flanks is buffy-white, darker along the mid-back, and is covered with numerous jet black, round or slightly oval spots. The chin, throat and posterior parts of the belly are white, the chest and anterior part of the belly spotted. The distal parts of the tail are spotted, the spots tending to coalesce into black rings. Towards the tip of the tail, which is white, there are two or three black rings. The under surface of the tail is white, except where crossed by the black rings. The front limbs are spotted on the insides and outsides, the hind feet from the ankles to the toes devoid of spots. The top of the head and the cheeks are finely spotted and they have a characteristic black band or "tear mark" curving downwards from the inner corners of the eyes to the corners of the mouth, and white marks above and under the eyes. The pupils of the eyes are round.

The pelage is slightly harsh, the hair short. In the "king" form it is slightly longer and distinctly silkier. They have an erectile crest of greyish hair up to 70 mm long on the nape of the neck and shoulders, which in some individuals continues down the mid-back for varying distances. In some individuals it is hardly noticeable, being poorly developed. The underfur may be sparse in some individuals, abundant in others, in the latter case sometimes dominating the pelage, which may be a factor of age or season.

They have long legs and five digits on the front feet and four on the hind, the first digits on the front feet set well back from the other four and not marking in the spoor (Fig. 247.4).

**Skull** (Fig. 247.5)

The high domed skull of the cheetah is characteristic, reflecting the rounded head of the live individual. In profile it is highest at the level of the middle of the eye orbits, sloping abruptly both forward to the nasals and back to the supraoccipital crest. The braincase is rounded, the sagittal crest confined to its posterior part, where it rises abruptly from the surface of the braincase to a height, in old specimens, of up to about 10 mm, where it joins the well developed back-sloping supraoccipital crest. Forward across the top of the braincase the sagittal crest is less in evidence, dividing into two low ridges to end on the postorbital processes, which are incomplete. The top of the skull between the post-orbital processes is flat and very broad, the rostrum short and wide. The nasal openings are very large, facilitating the rapid intake of air required after extreme exertion. The zygomatic arches are broad in the front, narrower behind, relatively lightly built and widen out posteriorly. Unlike other felids, they are distinctly upcurved when viewed from the side. The mandible is relatively lightly built, the coronoid high and narrow.

The dental formula is:

$I\frac{3}{3}\ C\frac{1}{1}\ P\frac{3}{2}\ M\frac{1}{1} = 30$

The second upper premolar, the first in the series of those present, is missing in some individuals. The outer upper incisor is slightly enlarged, but all these teeth are small and poorly developed. The canines are short, sharp and rounded. In the fourth upper premolar, the upper section of the carnassial shear, the antero-internal cusp, which is well developed in other felids, is represented, at most, by a small knob which occludes between the fourth premolar and first molar of the mandible. Its reduction allows the jaws to close tightly. The cheekteeth are all adapted to slicing. The canines do not require to be long as their function in the killing bite is to hold the prey by the throat, while strangulation proceeds. Unlike some other felids, they do not use these for severing the spinal cord at the nape of the neck. It has been said that the cheetah's throat bite is designed to sever the jugular vein of its prey, but examination of kills does not confirm this.

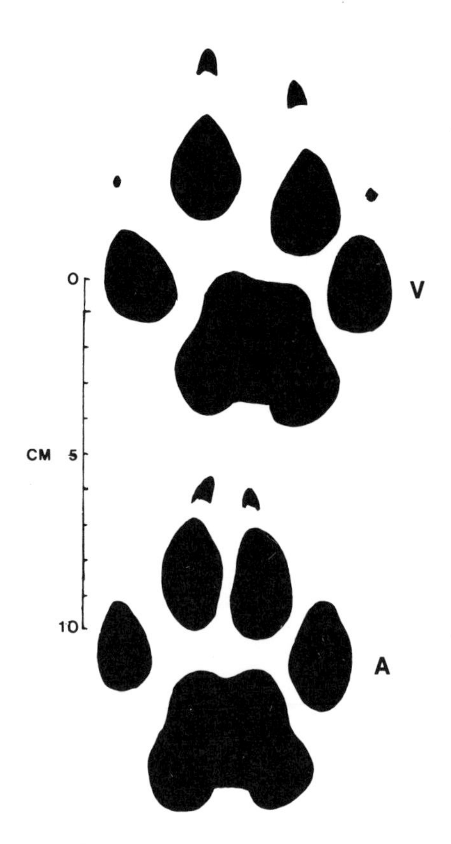


Fig. 247.4. Spoor: cheetah, *A. jubatus*.
F. Right forefoot H. Right hind foot.

**Distribution**

The distribution of the cheetah has been modified greatly over historical times by modern man's colonisation of the African Continent. The demand for skins and an over-emphasis on their predatory habits on domestic stock have led to a shrinking in their distributional range and their disappearance from very large areas of the continent. In addition, material records are few, as skins are traded rather than passing to museum collections.

Outside the continent they are still found in the northern parts of the Arabian Peninsula (Harrison, 1968), in Iraq, Iran and east of the Caspian Sea to Afghanistan and Baluchistan. At one time widespread in India, they became extinct by 1952, as they are in the countries immediately bordering the eastern Mediterranean.

*North Africa and the Sahara*

They are recorded from the following Saharan massifs: Ahaggar in southeastern **Algeria**; Adrar des Fores on the borders of Algeria with **Mali** and Aïr in northwestern **Niger**. In **Libya**, until 1969, they were still found sparsely throughout, except in the extreme south and southeast.

*South of the Sahara, excluding the Southern African Subregion*

In West Africa their optimum habitat is found in the Sahel and Sudan zones, with seasonal occurrences marginally into the Guinea Savanna during the dry season, after the grass is burnt. Although there are very few material records, it is likely that they occur from southwestern **Mauritania** through to **Chad**. In the central and southern parts of the **Sudan** there is a specimen from the El Duiem. They occur in **Ethiopia, Somalia** and in the extreme southeast of **Uganda**.

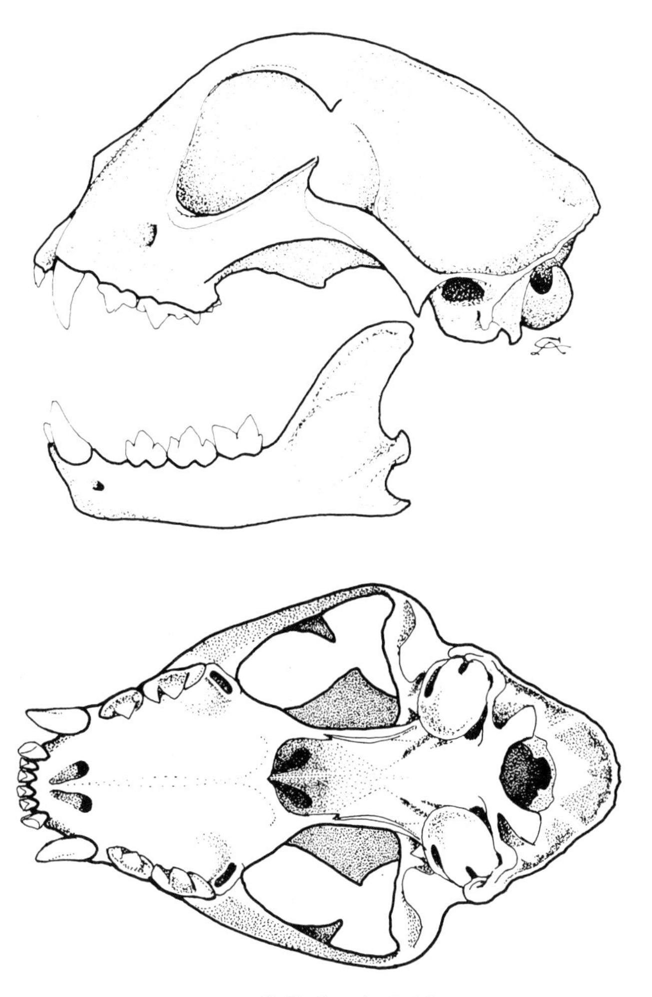

Fig. 247.5 Skull: cheetah, *A. jubatus*
TL skull 175 mm

They are distributed widely in **Kenya**, although absent in parts of the west and coastally. There are no records for northwestern **Tanzania**, although otherwise they have a wide distribution. They occur in southern and southeastern **Zaire**, and in the central and southern parts of **Angola**. They are widespread in **Zambia**, excluding the Zambezi Valley and parts of the Eastern Province. They occur in **Malawi** in reserves in the Central and Northern Provinces. There are scattered records from the central and eastern parts of **Mozambique**, north of the Zambezi River.

*Southern African Subregion*

In **Namibia** they occur widely but sparsely throughout, even occasionally as far south as the Orange River mouth. In **Botswana** they have a wide distribution, except in the extreme southeast. In **Zimbabwe** they are absent from the northeast, which corresponds with their absence in parts of the Tete District of Mozambique and southern Malawi. They occur in **Mozambique**, south of the Zambezi River, only being absent from the south and southeast. They occur sporadically in the northern parts of the **Cape Province**, in the Kalahari Gemsbok National Park and in parts of the northwestern, northern and eastern **Transvaal** to the southern border of the Kruger National Park. In **Natal** they were exterminated by the 1930's, but stock from Namibia was reintroduced to Hluhluwe, Umfolozi and Mkuze Game Reserves in 1965, and in 1978 to the eastern shores of Lake St. Lucia.

## Habitat

In general cheetahs are believed to be animals which frequent open plains, which is probably brought about by their being depicted so often in film or seen in this type of habitat. However, they are just as at home in savanna woodland, an association in which they occur throughout a great part of their distributional range. In the southern part of Africa in the past they occurred both in the South West Arid and the

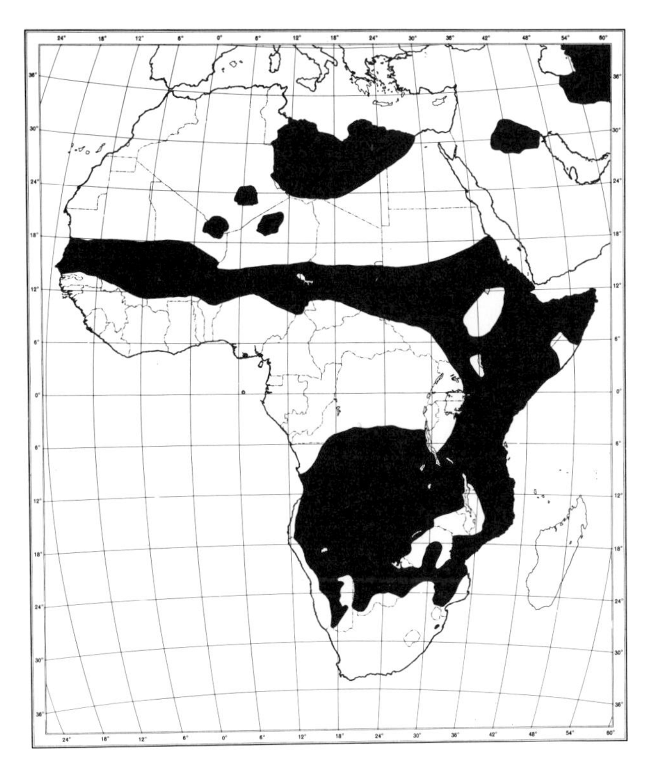

Southern Savanna zones in parts of which, in fact, they are still found. They can in addition utilise the fringes of desert, as can be seen by their occurrence in the pro-Namib of Namibia. They do not occur in forest or in woodland, with a thick underbush or tall grass cover, although they will use this for shelter.

While they will drink when water is available, its presence is not an essential habitat requirement. In southern Botswana it may be available to them only seasonally for limited periods. They rely on their prey for their moisture requirements.

## Habits

Cheetahs are predominantly diurnal, with peaks of activity around sunrise and sunset. Pettifer (1981b) noted that in cold weather they sun themselves in the early morning, moving later than in warm weather. During the hottest hours of the day they lie up in the shade, choosing an elevated resting place from which a clear view of the surrounding terrain is obtained.

In Botswana, Smithers (1971) recorded that over half his observations were of two's or family parties of three or four, with fewer solitary individuals. As the cubs remain with the female for almost a year, usually one is seeing a family party. However, males form bachelor groups of up to four or five, with strong cohesion between members. Pettifer (1981b) noted that, in a group of three males released in a natural area, when one got injured, the group remained together without food for a period of 11 days. Each member of this group took turns in leading the group and selecting the prey when hunting.

Where a female is accompanied by cubs these are always of one litter, for before she produces another litter, members of the former litter disperse, siblings often remaining together for a time thereafter. Males do not accompany these family groups, only joining the females when they are in oestrus.

Cheetahs have very large home ranges. In the eastern Transvaal, Pettifer (1981a) recorded a mean area of 76,6 $km^2$ (range 69,5–85,9) for three females and 48,8 $km^2$ for two males, excluding random excursions far outside these areas. In Namibia, Morsbach (in Stuart & Wilson, 1988) gave a mean of 1 500 $km^2$ for females and 800 $km^2$ for males. Their home ranges overlap to a considerable extent and within them they have a preferred area to which they will return. The selection of resting or sleeping sites within the home range is opportunistic, but these are chosen to offer a clear view of the surrounding area.

Males are apparently not territorial and may move over areas held by several females (Morsbach, in Stuart & Wilson, 1988), and Labuschagne (1979) also mentions nomads which ignore boundary markings of resident cheetahs. Pettifer (1981a) noted that, when he introduced three strange male cheetahs to a natural area where cheetahs were resident, aggressive encounters took place, suggesting territorial tendencies. On the other hand, cheetahs are assiduous urine and faecal markers, the urine-marking effective up to periods of about 24 hours, and is carried out only by the males. Male urine marks are examined assiduously by members of other groups and the area avoided. This mechanism allows another group, after about 24 hours, to use the same ground previously used by the other. The female urine has no territorial significance, although when they are in oestrus it attracts males. Where groups do contact each other, while there may be some threatening behaviour, with the ears drawn back, the head held low and the mouth open, usually nothing more serious develops. Males may fight over a female in oestrus, when deaths of combatants have been recorded. In such encounters individuals slap each other with a downward motion of one or both front paws and biting ensues.

Cheetahs are terrestrial and ill-adapted to climbing, but do make use of trees with stout sloping trunks or branches on which to rest, using them as observation posts. Their normal method of locomotion is a slow, stately walk from which, if disturbed, they may break into a fast gallop in which they do not exert themselves to the extent witnessed in the final spurt to catch prey. They are averse to swimming.

Cheetahs chirrup when excited or when they meet members of their own group. A female may also use this vocalization to contact scattered cubs. This call is bird-like and can be heard over several hundred metres and may be accompanied by a soft chirr (Schaller, 1972b). They purr loudly when content, and in threatening, may growl, snarl, hiss or cough. Schaller described how, when they are approached by another predator at a kill, they may moan, which he interpreted as a threat, and they will bleat when lost or pursued.

Cheetahs can attain a speed of 74 km per hour when fully extended (Bigalke, 1964). This is faster than the best greyhound and twice the speed attainable by man. Such speeds can be maintained only for short distances of up to 300 m and are employed only in the final sprint to catch prey, after which they tire and give up if unsuccessful. It has been known for a long time that, given the right terrain, a cheetah can be run down by a man on horseback, as it cannot maintain its speed over long distances.

**Food**

Pettifer (1981a) found that a group of three male captive-bred and reared cheetahs released in a natural area in the Transvaal, hunted as a group only when they were hunting large species such as giraffe and waterbuck, although simultaneous hunts of smaller species would take place, resulting in two cheetah killing two impala. Not all hunts are successful. Pettifer (1981a) recorded that of 97 hunting attempts on impala, only nine succeeded, although five out of 12 hunts on young giraffe were successful. The cheetahs usually ignored giraffe unless they were accompanied by calves, when one of the group would chase the giraffe group, the other two attacking a selected calf. One would hook its dew claws into the giraffe, while the other attacked it high up on the shoulder, bringing it to the ground. One or both would then take a strangle-hold on its throat. This behaviour has not been observed in wild cheetahs which apparently are not taught by their mothers to hunt giraffe.

In open country cheetahs may simply walk up to the prey, pausing motionless from time to time if the prey shows anxiety. In woodland or scrub country, cover may be used for concealment in stalking. Cheetahs prefer to attack stragglers around the fringes of the herd and, if the selected prey mingles with a large herd, they frequently abandon the chase. Cheetahs approach to about 100 m, and the chase after small bovids starts if the prey takes fright and runs off, whereupon cheetahs give chase, maintaining maximum speed for about 300–400 m. If they catch up with the prey, one of the cheetahs slaps it with one or both of the front limbs, using the dew claws to secure a hold and so throwing the prey off balance, when it is seized by the throat. The kill takes time to achieve, as it is a process of strangulation. After killing, the prey may either be eaten *in situ* or dragged to shelter to be consumed. Some time may elapse before the exhausted cheetah starts to feed. Cheetahs feed rapidly, keeping a careful watch, probably because other predators frequently drive them off their kills.

They usually eat the meat off the ventral surface first, then the liver and the heart, but most of the intestines are dragged out and discarded. Unless the prey is very small the bones and most of the skin are left at the end of the meal, an adult impala looking like a fully articulated skeleton with parts of the skin and most of the ribs remaining. However, with a 29,5 kg baboon the pattern was different, the whole vertebral column and ribs being eaten (Brain, 1981).

The principal prey consists of any medium-sized or small bovids or the young of larger bovids; prey with masses of up to about 60 kg are favoured. In addition they take a wide range of ground-living birds and small mammals including guineafowl, bustards, hares and porcupines. Pienaar (1969b) and Wrogemann (1975) included ostriches.

In the Transvaal Lowveld, impala and reedbuck are taken, together with waterbuck, kudu and tsessebe (Pienaar, 1969b, Pettifer, 1981a). In Botswana, in the drier areas, springbok and springhaas figure highly in their diet and, where impala replace springbok in the northeastern sector, they were the principal food (Smithers, 1971). Even with smaller species such as blesbok they prefer to tackle the smaller herds (Pettifer, 1981a). Cheetahs are injured often in their attempts to tackle large species such as wildebeest, zebra and buffalo (Pettifer, 1981b). Cheetahs will also scavenge on ungulate carcasses (Pienaar, 1969b; Richardson, 1980).

In common with lions and domestic cats, cheetahs may suffer from an essential fatty acid deficiency, which Davidson, Cantrill & Varaday (1986) found could be cured by augmenting their diet with natural oils.

**Reproduction**

In the wild cheetahs are not restricted to a breeding season (Labuschagne, 1979; Pettifer, 1981b) and young are born at any time throughout the year. If a female loses a litter it has been found she may mate again and successfully rear the next litter (Wrogemann, 1975). The courtship of cheetahs is a subtle and complex process. Although much still remains to be learnt, the pioneering work of Meltzer (1988), has contributed substantially to our knowledge. When the female is non-receptive, she is aggressive towards males that approach her, swatting at them, and uttering a stuttering call which may be answered by the males. Wrogemann (1975) provided a broad outline of the processes in operation around the time that the female comes into oestrus. In the wild, more often than not, this is the only time that the females associate with other adult cheetahs. During pro-oestrus, a male may approach her close enough to test her reproductive condition by smelling her vagina, and may, when thoroughly excited, mock charge the female which will reciprocate. At this stage copious urine spraying on the part of the male may occur, which also engages, more frequently than normally, in scraping up small mounds of earth with his back legs and urinating or defecating on top of them. After about seven to 14 days of this initial period, the female comes into oestrus and is receptive, and male inter-aggression reaches a peak. The female cheetah in oestrus induces copulation by lordosis and the male approaches her from behind. In the wild oestrus seldom lasts more than two days (Pettifer, 1981b).

It has been found that to stimulate breeding in captivity the males and females should be kept separate throughout the year and, when a female comes into oestrus, a male should be given access to her.

Pseudo pregnancies are known in captive cheetahs, the females after the 90–95 days of gestation period showing slight lateral swellings and discharge from the vagina and they may actually go into labour without being pregnant. Much remains to be learnt about this anomaly.

Cubs are born in the shelter of tall grass or in underbush and are hidden very cunningly. Litters number an average of four (range 3–6, n=8) (Pettifer, 1981b). Sixty-seven litters born in captivity had a mean of 3,43 cubs (S.D. 1,3; range 1–8). Of the 230 cubs in the litters, 99 were male and 94 female, the other 37 were not identified (Meltzer, pers. comm.). The female eats the afterbirth after removing the foetal membrane with her teeth. With a mass of 250 g to 300 g at birth, the cubs are altricial, born blind and defenceless. Their eyes open on about the 10th to 12th day and are initially dark gold in colour, clearing to light gold as they grow older. By the age of about three weeks they can walk around and at six weeks are capable of following their mother. During the early part of their lives the female frequently moves them to a new hiding place, carrying them one by one by the scruff of the neck. The upper and lower canine teeth erupt at about three weeks and cheetahs are unique among the felids in having three cusps (Broom, 1949). The full set of milk teeth has erupted by the time they are about six weeks old. The milk set is replaced by the permanent set from about eight months old and they are fully equipped with their permanent teeth at nine months old.

The cubs start to wean at about five or six weeks old, when the female allows them to tear at the carcass of her kill which she may drag back to them. They are fully weaned at about three months old. By the age of eight to 12 months old the cubs may initiate hunts and make kills on their own (Eaton, 1970a).

Up to the age of about three months the cub's back is covered with a mantle of long bluish-grey or smoky coloured hair, 70 to 80 mm in length, which conceals the tiny spots on the pelage underneath. This affords them a measure of camouflage in the early stages of their life when they are prone to predation.

When the cubs eventually leave the female they may remain together as a group or move off singly, the break-up of the family being an abrupt transition from family life to independence. The mother thereafter begins to raise another litter (Schaller, 1972b).

The young females do not become sexually mature until they are from 21 to 24 months old.

## Genus *Panthera* Oken, 1816

The name *Panthera* was first proposed by Oken (1816), but in 1956 the International Commission on Zoological Nomenclature rejected this name. However, mammalogists have continued to use it and now any other name would create confusion. Therefore, Morrison-Scott (1965) proposed the retention of *Panthera* which has led to differences of opinion amongst taxonomists, but it remains in use.

The two great African cats occurring in the Subregion, the lion, *Panthera leo*, and the leopard, *P. pardus*, differ from representatives of the genera *Felis* and *Acinonyx* in a character of the hyoidean apparatus. This apparatus consists of a chain of small bones, called collectively the suspensorium which passes from the ear bullae on either side to further small bones at the root of the tongue and encloses the top of the windpipe. In most cats the suspensorium, except at its cartilaginous extremities, is fully ossified and thus the larynx is held firmly to the base of the skull and limited in its movement. In *Panthera*, however, the suspensorium remains unossified and elastic, allowing the larynx freedom of movement. The result is that members of the genus *Panthera* can vocalise much more loudly than members of the other two genera (Fig. XXXI.2).

Key to the species (Meester *et al.*, 1986)

1. Body with distinct rosettes or spots; no tuft on end of tail; males without mane; smaller, total skull length about 175–260 mm; sagittal crest, mastoid process and paroccipital process not prominent ... *pardus*

   Body unicoloured, lacking spots or rosettes; end of tail tufted, males normally with mane on head and neck; larger, total skull length 250–460 mm; sagittal crest, mastoid process and paroccipital process prominent ... *leo*

No. 248

## *Panthera pardus* (Linnaeus, 1758)

## Leopard
## Luiperd

Plate 19

### Colloquial Name

The name is derived from the Greek name for a leopard, *panther*.

### Taxonomic Notes

Smithers (1971) listed 13 subspecies from the continent of Africa, only one, *P. p. melanotica* (Günther, 1885) occurring in the Subregion. Dobroruka (1966) regarded it as a melanistic mutation, not a subspecies. This is unfortunate as the type is a melanistic form which was collected in the Grahamstown district of the Cape Province. However, it antedates *P. p. shortridgei* Pocock, 1932 by some 14 years. The great variation in colour aberrations and markings of leopards has long been recognised. Sportsmen assert that the woodland leopard is small and dark compared with its larger counterpart from more open country, but it is difficult to judge the validity of these arguments, because size is affected by nutrition.

### Description

The largest spotted cat in Africa hardly requires description. Measurements of skins cannot be used as a criterion of size as they can be manipulated in processing to far exceed the size of the live individual. The largest leopard so far measured in the flesh was 2,92 m from tip of snout to tip of tail (Best & Best, 1977) and any individual over 2,3 m can be accounted as very large. The average mass for a fully grown male is about 60 kg, and for a female about 32 kg (Table 248.1).

No two leopards are alike, either in the markings or the ground colour, but in general they tend to have black spots on the limbs, flanks, hindquarters and head, with rosettes on the remainder of the body. These rosettes take an infinite variety of forms, but generally consist of a broken circle of irregular, roughly circular pattern of black, which may enclose a black spot or spots. An example of the variation that is found is illustrated by eight adult skins in Allen (1922–1925).

The tail, which is over half the length of the head and body, is spotted or rosetted on top and, corresponding with the lighter colour of the under parts of the body, lighter in colour underneath, usually white or off-white. The guard hair is shortest on the face and head where it is a bare 3–4 mm long, about 10 mm on the top of the shoulders and 15 mm on the hindquarters. Increasing in length on the flanks, it may reach a length of 25–30 mm on the under parts. On the back it has a harsh feel, but the hair on the under parts is silky and softer. The light-coloured hair on the under parts of the tail may reach a length of 30 mm and is particularly thick and woolly towards the black tip. The underfur is dense and slightly shorter than the guard hair; the individual hairs are fine and wavy.

Leopards, like all cats, have five digits on the front feet and four on the hind which are equipped with strong, very sharp, curved claws, protractile at will (Fig. XXXI.1) and which, in a medium-sized specimen, measure up to 30 mm across the curve. The claw of the first digit on the front feet, the dew claw, lies to the back of the plantar pad, and is put to good use in holding large prey. The claws and first digits on the front feet do not mark in the spoor (Fig. 248.1).

The rounded ears appear small for the size of the individual, the insides with a profuse covering of long, fine, light coloured hair. The white whiskers are particularly long and there are usually two or three extra long hairs in the

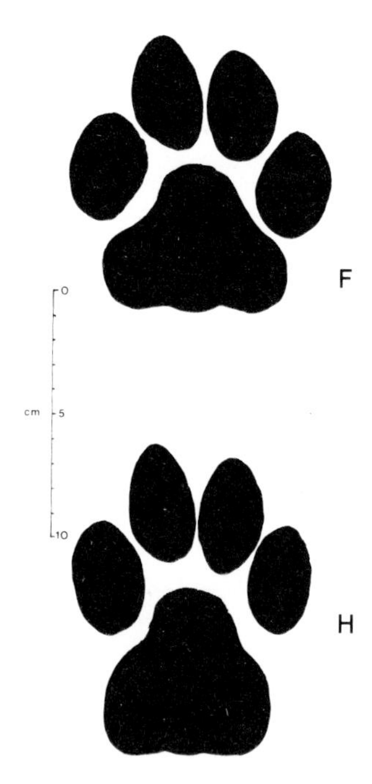


Fig. 248.1. Spoor: leopard, *P. pardus*.
F. Right forefoot H. Right hind foot.

eyebrows, both features serving to assist the individual in avoiding obstructions when moving in the darkness.

**Table 248.1**

Overall measurements (mm) and mass (kg) of leopards, *P. pardus*, (a) taken on safari hunts at Matetsi, Zimbabwe (P. Johnstone, *in litt.*), (b) captured during an ecological research project in the Waterberg, Transvaal (Grimbeek, pers. comm.) and (c) a series from the Cape Province (Stuart, 1981)

**(a)**

| | Males | | | Females | | |
|---|---|---|---|---|---|---|
| | $\bar{x}$ | n | Range | $\bar{x}$ | n | Range |
| TL | 2110 | 13 | 2010–2360 | 1850 | 7 | 1780–1880 |
| Mass | 59,7 | 13 | 51,8–71,3 | 31,5 | 7 | 28,2–34,9 |

**(b)**

| | | | | | | |
|---|---|---|---|---|---|---|
| Mass | 58,8 | 5 | 52,8–64,1 | 34,9 | 6 | 29,2–41,0 |

**(c)**

| | Males | | | Females | | |
|---|---|---|---|---|---|---|
| | $\bar{x}$ | n | Range | $\bar{x}$ | n | Range |
| TL | (1785) | | | (1707) | | |
| HB | 1107 | 21 | 920–1250 | 1030 | 8 | 950–1050 |
| T | 678 | 20 | 510–800 | 677 | 8 | 640–740 |
| Hf s/u | 219 | 20 | 190–252 | 206 | 7 | 190–220 |
| E | 73 | 20 | 65–100 | 70 | 7 | 65–72 |
| Mass | 30,9 | 27 | 20,0–45,0 | 21,2 | 9 | 17,0–26,0 |
| TL skull | 219 | 21 | 195–248 | 200 | 9 | 190–210 |

**Skull** (Fig. 248.2)

Males are generally bigger and heavier than the females and their skulls therefore are correspondingly larger. In addition male skulls have a distinct sagittal crest, represented in females at the maximum development by a low ridge. When viewed from above the postorbital constriction in males is narrower than the interorbital; in females this relationship is reversed.

The whole skull is massively built. The zygomatic arches are broad and heavy, to accommodate the powerful masseter muscles, and swing outward at the back, albeit to a lesser extent than in the smaller felids, to give room for the temporalis muscles which, together with the masseters, provide for the powerful action of the lower jaw. In profile the skull is highest just above the eye orbits, sloping off more sharply to the nasals than to the supraoccipital crest and being much less domed than in the cheetah. The lower jaw is heavily built with a broad high coronoid process giving an ample attachment for the temporalis muscles. The posterior end of the lower jaw is deeply excavated to allow a broad attachment of the masseters. The glenoid articulation allows just sufficient side-to-side action of the lower jaw to ensure the efficient cutting action of the carnassials.

The dental formula is:

$I\frac{3}{3}\ C\frac{1}{1}\ P\frac{3}{2}\ M\frac{1}{1} = 30$

The upper second premolars, which are absent in some of the smaller felids, are usually present in the leopard. The outer incisors are slightly larger than the remainder. The canines are sharp-pointed, heavily built and slightly flattened on the inner sides. The cheekteeth, which include the carnassials, are clearly adapted to slicing. The upper first molars are tiny and hardly functional.

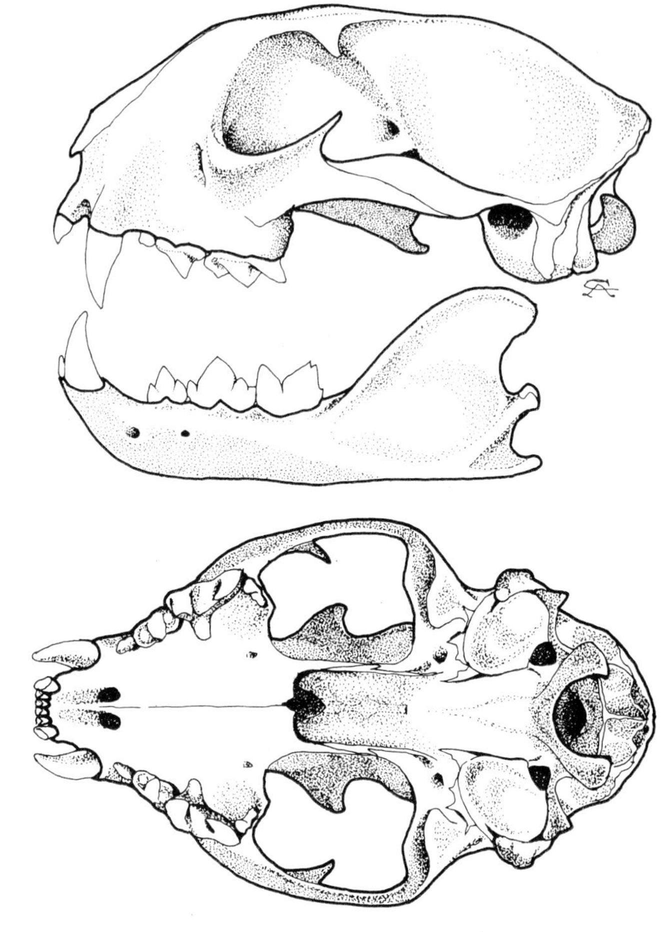

Fig. 248.2. Skull: leopard, *P. pardus*.
TL Skull 185 mm

**Distribution**

The leopard has a wider distributional range than any of the larger felids, occurring from the southern parts of the African continent through the Middle East to the Far East, northwards to Siberia and south to Sri Lanka and Malaysia.

*North Africa*

Leopards are rare in the Moyen and Haut Atlas Mountains in **Morocco** and their extension eastwards through **Algeria** to **Tunisia**. In Algeria they probably now occur only in the Akfadou National Park. They may occur on the Libyan plateau in northwestern **Egypt**, but there are no recent records from other parts of this country.

*South of the Sahara, excluding the Southern African Subregion*

Recorded from southwestern **Mauritania**, they occur widely throughout West Africa, although material records are few. They occur in **Senegal**, from where *P. p. leopardus* (Schreber 1777) was described; **Guinea Bissau; Sierra Leone; Liberia; Nigeria, Cameroun** and **Gabon**. Further east they are recorded from the southeastern and east central parts of the **Sudan**. They occur in **Ethiopia** and have a wide distribution in **Somalia**. They occur throughout **Uganda; Kenya; Tanzania; Zaire** and the **Congo Republic**. They are widespread in **Angola; Zambia; Malawi** and north of the Zambezi River in **Mozambique**.

*Southern African Subregion*

They are widespread in **Namibia**, except in the coastal desert. They extend eastwards throughout **Botswana**. The situation in **Zimbabwe** is disturbed by the intensive farming and ranching development of the central plateau from which they have been eradicated in many parts. They still occur locally, however, where there are extensive areas of broken terrain and throughout the remainder of the country. They are found south of the Zambezi River in **Mozambique**.

In **Natal** they occur in the northeast of the province, and reports have been received of sporadic sightings from the Drakensberg Mountains. In the **Transvaal** they are found throughout, except on the Highveld grassland areas of the southern part of the province. They occur sporadically in the **Orange Free State**. In the **Cape Province** they occur in the mountainous areas along the south coast from about the King William's Town district westwards, and in the northern and northwestern parts of the province.

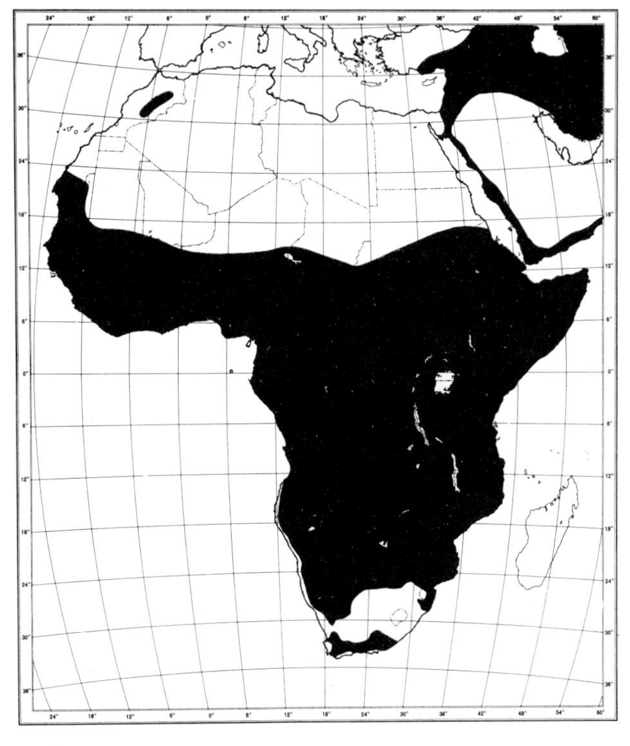

## Habitat

Leopards have a wide habitat tolerance and while generally associated with areas of rocky koppies, rocky hills, mountain ranges and forest, they also occur in semi-desert. In desert areas they utilise watercourses and rocky outcrops where sufficient prey animals occur. While they are independent of water supplies as they rely for their moisture requirements on their prey, they will drink regularly when water is available.

Cover to lie up in safely during daylight hours and from which to hunt is an important requirement. In areas of intense development, providing there is adjacent cover of rocky hills or forest, they manage to persist even in the face of intensive control. They are found from sea level to over 2 000 m and they occur in areas of mean annual rainfall of less than 100 mm to 1 200 mm.

## Habits

Leopards are solitary animals, except during the mating season or when a female is accompanied by juveniles. Primarily nocturnal, they may be seen moving during daylight hours, particularly in National Parks and in remote undisturbed areas. During the heat of the day they lie up in dense cover, in the shade of rocks, in caves or occasionally spreadeagled on the thick branches of trees, particularly those in which they have hoisted kills. In semi-desert areas such as the Kalahari, where shade is scarce, they use holes in the ground, such as disused aardvark burrows. In the early morning they have the habit of lying out in the sun on vantage points such as rocks and rocky ledges, which give a wide view of the surrounding terrain. While predominantly terrestrial, they are accomplished tree climbers and negotiate steep rocky areas with agility. They are expert swimmers and take to water readily. During the formation of Lake Kariba leopards remained on the small islands while a food supply was still available, then swam to others, over distances of up to 900 m (Child, 1968a).

Leopards are secretive animals and difficult to contact; moreover they normally are silent. Their most characteristic vocalisation is a hoarse rasping cough, repeated at intervals. Often it is answered if another individual is in the vicinity and may be repeated between them as they move. In encounters between territorial males, grunting and growling reach a high level of intensity. In captivity they may growl under stress, and purr loudly during or after feeding.

Both males and females scent-mark by spraying urine. Female home ranges tend to be segregated and smaller than those of the males which may overlap the range of more than one female. When overlapping occurs in male ranges they tend to confine their activities to the parts little used by the other (Moss, 1976).

Leopards are territorial in that both males and females defend territories against conspecifics of the same sex (Hamilton, 1976; Bertram, 1982). The former recorded a number of fights between territorial males resulting from accidental encounters and, in one case, deliberate interception. He pointed out, however, that fights only develop after normal avoidance behaviour has failed to prevent these encounters. Le Roux & Skinner (1989) reported the death of a female by throttling, in an encounter with a female conspecific.

In a study of leopards in the Stellenbosch mountains, Cape Province, Norton & Lawson (1985) found some ecological separation between leopards and caracals, *Felis caracal*; the leopards preferred the high mountain *fynbos* areas, whereas the caracals kept to the foothills. They found home ranges for an adult male and female leopard to be 388 and 487 $km^2$ respectively, which was of the same order as that given for leopards in the Kalahari Gemsbok National Park of about 400 $km^2$ by Bothma & le Riche (1984). On the other hand, in a study of three adult male leopards in the Cedarberg mountains, home range sizes were calculated as 40, 44 and 69 $km^2$, with varying amounts of overlap (Norton & Henley, 1987). Smith (1977) gave home ranges of 10 to 19 $km^2$ for Matobo Hills National Park, Zimbabwe. Le Roux & Skinner (1989), in an intensive study of a single female in the Sabi Sand Game Reserve, eastern Transvaal, found she had a home range of 33 $km^2$. The size may well depend on the type of terrain and the availability of food.

Leopards move at a slow, casual walk. If disturbed, they bound away in a bouncing gallop which soon gives way to a fast trot which carries them quickly out of sight as they make for the nearest cover. Unlike cheetahs, they are stalkers and pouncers, not chasers, and do not maintain fast movement except over limited distances. When stalking, the leopard crouches, the body held close to the ground, the tail horizontal, and while their acute night sight is used primarily to locate the prey, hearing also plays a part. All their senses are well developed, in particular their sight and hearing. The use of the former is demonstrated by their use of high vantage points on which to lie up during the early morning and sometimes in the late evening so that they can keep the surrounding terrain in clear view. Both Kruuk & Turner (1967) and Bothma (pers. comm.) have observed leopards, lying up in this way, sight reedbuck and springbok, and slink off to the stalk and make successful kills.

## Food

Leopards tend to prey on animals less than 70 kg in mass, but will take whatever is available within their home range. Kills occur after a painstaking stalk, a relatively short chase (less than 30 m) and throttling, although occasionally a bite is directed towards the back of the head. Thus in the Sabi Sand Game Reserve 23 species were taken (Table 248.2), with impala predominating while, in the adjacent more heterogeneous Kruger National Park, 31 species were taken, but impala (78%) still predominated (Pienaar, 1969b) as they did in the adjoining Timbavati Game Reserve (Hirst, 1969). Elsewhere, in the Matobo Hills, Zimbabwe, Grobler & Wilson (1972) showed from scat analyses that dassies among the smaller prey, and klipspringer among the larger, had the highest percentage occurrence. Norton *et al.* (1986) found similar results from scat analyses of leopards in the Cedarberg Mountains, Cape Province: their small antelope included klipspringers, vaalribbok and Cape grysbok, and a smaller number of records of steenbok and duiker. Feral pigs, *Sus scrofa*, ranked high in the Wemmershoek area, and birds, hares, rodents, reptiles, insects, plant material and baboon remains were traced in scats.

**Table 248.2**

Numbers of each prey species killed by leopards (n=127) at Sabi Sand Game Reserve (July 1982—July 1984) and from scat analayses (n=17) (November 1983—January 1984) (Le Roux & Skinner, 1989)

| Species | Scat analysis (%) | No. of kills recorded (%) |
|---|---|---|
| Warthog, *Phacochoerus aethiopicus* | | 5 |
| Grey duiker, *Sylvicapra grimmia* | 2(12) | 15(12) |
| Steenbok, *Raphicerus campestris* | | 2 |
| Impala, *Aepyceros melampus* | 12(70) | 65(51) |
| Kudu, *Tragelaphus strepsiceros* | | 4 |
| Bushbuck, *T. scriptus* | | 5 |
| Waterbuck, *Kobus ellipsiprymnus* | | 1 |
| Baboon, *Papio ursinus* | | 2 |
| Vervet monkey, *Cercopithecus pygerythrus* | | 7 |
| Pangolin, *Manis temminckii* | | 1 |
| Scrub hare, *Lepus saxatilis* | | 1 |
| Tree squirrel, *Paraxerus cepapi* | | 3 |
| Cane rat, *Thryonomys swinderianus* | 1 | – |
| Unidentified rodent | 1 | – |
| Civet, *Civettictis civetta* | | 2 |
| Genet, *Genetta genetta* | | 2 |
| Banded mongoose, *Mungos mungo* | | 1 |
| Dwarf mongoose, *Helogale parvula* | | 1 |
| Aardvark, *Orycteropus afer* | | 2 |
| Knob-billed duck, *Sarkidiornis melanotos* | | 1 |
| Francolin, *Pternistis afer* | | 1 |
| Tortoise, *Geochelone pardalis* | | 1 |
| Peter's spitting cobra, *Naja mossambica* | | 1 |
| Leguaan, *Varanus exanthematicus* | | 3 |

In the Transvaal Lowveld, a female leopard kills one animal (10 kg) every 12 days (Le Roux & Skinner, 1989). In Kenya, Hamilton (1976, 1981) recorded one kill every 13 days for both males and females. In the Kalahari, Bothma & le Riche (1982) found that males kill every three days and females with cubs twice as frequently. Only small to medium-sized prey are killed, mainly bat-eared foxes, duikers and gemsbok calves, and occasionally aardwolves and porcupines. The quills of the latter may pierce their internal organs or paws so that they are unable to hunt properly and become emaciated (Jobaert, 1960). Although larger ungulates are occasionally taken, these are the exception rather than the rule. For example, Schaller (1972b) found that of 11 wildebeest kills, 10 were calves and one a yearling.

They occasionally appear to have food preferences. Fey (1964) recorded an individual that specialised in bushpigs, even where other species were available, and Estes (1967) observed one which killed 11 jackals within three weeks. Leopards' liking for domestic dogs is well known and Estes (1967) suggested that small canids, where plentiful, may be preferred. Fey (1964) recorded a leopard, confined to a small island in Lake Kariba and with impala and duiker available, taking to a diet of fish, *Tilapia* sp., perhaps the same individual which, when translocated to the Kafue National Park, was observed taking catfish, *Clarias* sp (Mitchell *et al.*, 1965). Apart from mammals and fish, leopards take birds of any size from turtle doves to ostriches; francolin and guinea fowl are recorded regularly. They will also take reptiles (Grobler & Wilson, 1972), although these are not a common item in their diet. In the absence of their normal prey they become adept domestic livestock raiders, taking calves, sheep, goats and poultry, and as a consequence are subject to control measures to the level of their local extermination.

Turnbull-Kemp (1967) listed 28 records of leopards as man-eaters, the majority being adults in good condition, not aged or infirm, and still perfectly capable of taking their normal prey. Wounded, cornered or suddenly disturbed, leopards can become exceedingly dangerous and there are many cases, especially among hunters, of people being seriously hurt and sometimes being killed by leopards.

Both Estes (1967) and Bothma (pers. comm.) have watched them using watercourses or dunes to bring them close to prey. Kingdon (1977) recorded the use of vehicles or even dust-devils as screens in stalking.

Smaller prey such as mice and birds are killed by swatting with the paw and are eaten on the spot. Larger prey are held in the embrace, the claws extended, full use being made of the powerful dew claws. Jobaert (1960) stated that prey are disembowelled and they bury the entrails under the earth or leaves. With porcupines or dassies the stomach and entrails are not eaten but are not necessarily buried. These appear to be distasteful to leopards, perhaps owing to the aromatic properties of the herbs which the dassies eat or the astringent properties of the bulbs dug up by porcupines.

Leopards may kill more than they immediately require. Where they live in areas frequented by other large predators, food is stored in the branches of trees; where other large predators are absent, food is left on the ground (Brain, 1981). In both cases the leopard returns to eat later, even after they have become putrid. In semi-desert areas such as the Kalahari where trees are scarce they have been known to cache their prey in holes.

Kruuk (1972a) recorded spotted hyaenas appropriating leopard kills, but also a case where a leopard appropriated a carcass from a hyaena, which in turn had taken it from a cheetah. Kingdon (1977) recorded wild dogs unsuccessfully attempting to deprive a leopard of its kill. In both these cases the leopard avoided further dispute by taking its kill up a tree. Caching of a heavy carcass several metres up a tree requires great strength. Hamilton (1976) recorded this process with a young giraffe estimated to have a mass of nearly 100 kg. When moving carcasses the leopard first straddles them, lifting them with the powerful jaws and neck muscles, sometimes clear off the ground, then carries them off. Birds such as guinea fowl and small well-furred mammals will be assiduously plucked before eating. The leopard shows obvious distaste for fur or feathers which adhere to its mouth and gets rid of them by vigorous head-shaking.

Not all the hunts for prey are successful. An incident was witnessed in the Hwange Game Reserve where a leopard, lying up near a water hole, attempted to attack a young baboon in a troop that was drinking. It was mobbed immediately by the troop, from which it fled to take refuge high in a tree. The noise created by the troop was sufficient in itself to deter the predator from further aggression. While individual baboons climbed to threaten it in the tree, the remainder sat around on the ground, defying it to descend. It remained there for two hours and only came down after sunset when the troop had departed. Normally leopards will only attack stragglers in a troop of baboons, avoiding the main body (Smithers, 1983). Norton *et al.* (1986) found baboon hairs in only two percent of the leopard scats they examined from the mountain areas. Leopards will scavenge from carcasses where these are available.

## Reproduction

There is no evidence of seasonality in the reproductive pattern (Le Roux & Skinner, 1989). Leopards become sexually mature from about two and a half to four years old.

During courtship the pair remains in close association and copulation takes place about every 15 minutes through the night (Ilani, pers. comm.). Cubs are born after a gestation period of about 106 days (n=2) in caves, sheltered places among rocks, hollow trees or in holes in the ground, with an interval between births of 17 months (n=3). Le Roux & Skinner (1989) found that the mean number of cubs per litter was 2,2 (n=5). In the early stages of their lives the mother moves them to new shelters every two or three days. They are blind at birth and have a mass of 50 to 60 g; the eyes open on the sixth to 10th day. Although presented with meat at 65 days of age, they only start eating at 72 days and suckling ceases after 101 days. From then until 9,5 months the cubs are led to the kill, but after that age they accompany the mother on the hunt and, at 11 months, kill their first impala. They attain independence at about 12,5 months, siblings remaining together for a further 2–3 months. Turnbull-Kemp (1967) observed motherly tuition whereby the cubs are allowed to accompany her on a hunt but remain behind, in response to a vocal signal, as she moves in to the kill. Schaller (1972b) reported that, long after they have become independent, affectionate reunions between mother and offspring may take place. Van Lawick (1977) also observed similar reunions, as well as play between members of the litter. When moving with cubs the mother's tail is curved up towards the tip, revealing its white underside which may act as a guide to the young in tall grass (Bertram, 1978). Females have two pairs of abdominal mammae.

No. 249

## *Panthera leo* (Linnaeus, 1758)

## Lion

## Leeu

Plate 19

### Colloquial Name

The name lion originates from the Greek name for the species, *leon*.

### Taxonomic Notes

The lion was originally described by Linnaeus from a specimen from North Africa, a more precise locality, Constantine, Algeria, being later designated by Allen (1924). Over the intervening years well over 20 subspecies have been described from various parts of the continent. Some of these were based on specimens from zoological gardens, which have striking effects on skull shape (Hollister, 1917), rendering such specimens taxonomically valueless. Here the lion is considered to be a monotypic species, following Ellerman *et al.* (1953).

### Description

The lion is the largest of the African carnivores, males standing up to 1,25 m at the shoulder. Smuts (1982) weighed and measured 344 individuals of all ages over a four-year period in the Kruger National Park and found that the average mass was greater in these than in corresponding groups further north in Africa. They grow rapidly during the first three years of their lives, growth thereafter slowing down, the females now being almost adult. The mass of the largest male was 225 kg, the mean being about 190 kg, the largest female 152 kg, the mean about 126 kg. Males reach their maximum weight by about seven years old, females at about five to six years old, tending to decline in weight thereafter.

The colour of the body in adults is generally unicolour sandy or tawny on the upper parts and flanks and white on the under parts. Some adults retain the rosettes and spots that are characteristic of young lions to a lesser or greater degree, even into their later years. The backs of the rounded ears are black and contrast sharply with the colour of the body. The tail, which is just over half the length of the head and body, has a well developed tuft of long tawny, dark or sometimes black hair on the tip, which conceals a horny spur. In contrast to other species of Carnivora, for example the leopard, *P. pardus*, melanistic forms of the lion are extremely rare. On the other hand very pale-coloured individuals are known from Kaokoland in the western parts of the Subregion, as are some specimens from southwestern Botswana. Individuals from the Timbavati Private Game Reserve in the eastern Transvaal are nearly white and have earned the title of the "white lions of Timbavati" (McBride, 1981). Examples of these white lions, which are not albinos, are now housed in the National Zoological Gardens, Pretoria and the Johannesburg Zoological Gardens. They represent one of two possible mutations known as chinchilla or acromelanic albinism which, like albinism, are known to arise from the same gene locus in the individual's chromosomes. They are not as rare as formerly thought, Smuts (1982) recording several others from the Kruger National Park and from Timbavati.

The hair on the face, the upper parts of the body, the flanks and the tail, excluding the tip, is short, while that on the under parts is softer and longer. Just behind the shoulder on the upper parts of the body the stance of the hair changes direction, forming a whorl on either side and there is a similar reversal of direction of the hair on the upper parts in the lumbar region which, when it meets the backwards directed hair about the mid-dorsal region, forms a short transverse crest of upstanding hair.

Adult males have a mane of long hair, up to about 160 mm in length, on the sides of the face and top of the head which extends onto the shoulders, around the neck and for a short distance down the spine. In subadults this mane is sandy, yellowish or tawny, but in some, with advancing age, it becomes black. Black-maned adult lions are not uncommon in the Subregion and occur alongside adults with tawny manes. Close examination of the hair on these black-maned individuals shows that the bulk of the hair is a very dark brown, profusely mixed with black hairs, giving the mane a black appearance. In black-maned lions the fringe of hair surrounding the face is yellowish or tawny. A black mane gives these individuals a strikingly dignified appearance. Adult maneless males are known to occur but are not common. The mane serves as a sexual signal to the females and distinguishes them at great distances (Bertram, 1978). It also serves to protect the head and neck when fighting. In addition to the mane, some adult males have tufts of long hair on the elbows and an extension of the mane in the form of a band of long hair on the chest, extending to the anterior part of the abdomen.

Lions have long whitish whiskers arranged in parallel rows on the sides of the upper lip. Each whisker arises from a black spot, but the top row of spots have no accompanying whiskers. Rudnai (1973a) found that it was possible to recognise individuals by the arrangement of these spots, as in no two lions were they arranged in exactly the same way.

They have five digits on the front feet, four on the hind feet. Each digit is armed with an extremely sharp, highly curved, laterally compressed, retractile claw. The first digit on the front feet is set well back of the other four and does not mark in the spoor (Fig. 249.1).

### Skull (Fig. 249.2)

In profile the skull is comparatively flat on top compared with a leopard, the highest point being on the broad flat shelf between the postorbital process from where it slopes off very gradually forwards to the nasals and rather more abruptly back to the supraoccipital crest. In relation to the size of the skull the braincase is surprisingly small, lacking the pear-shaped outward bulge seen in the leopard. The bone structure is massive and a cleaned skull may have a mass of over 3 kg. The zygomatic arches are particularly broad and heavily built to provide a firm attachment for the masseter muscles and swing outward at the back to allow ample room for the massive temporalis muscles which together with the masseters actuate the powerful action of the lower jaw. The supraoccipital crest is more than just a flange, being reinforced ventrally to form a thick bony structure projecting far back from the occipital condyles. The high sagittal crest provides extra attachment for the temporalis muscles and may extend for a height of some 25–30 mm from the braincase, where it joins the supraoccipital crest. The postorbital processes are incomplete, the rostrum broad.

The massive lower jaw is deeply hollowed out posteriorly to provide for the attachment of the masseter muscles. The coronoid process is high and coarsely roughened towards the top to give firm attachment to the temporalis muscles.

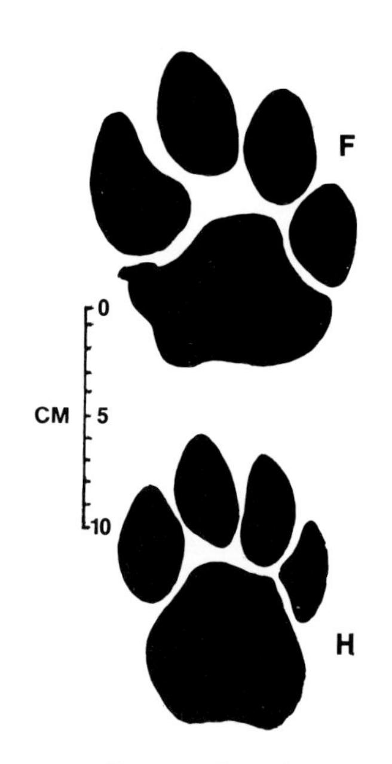


Fig. 249.1. Spoor: lion, *P. leo*.
F. Right forefoot H. Right hind foot.

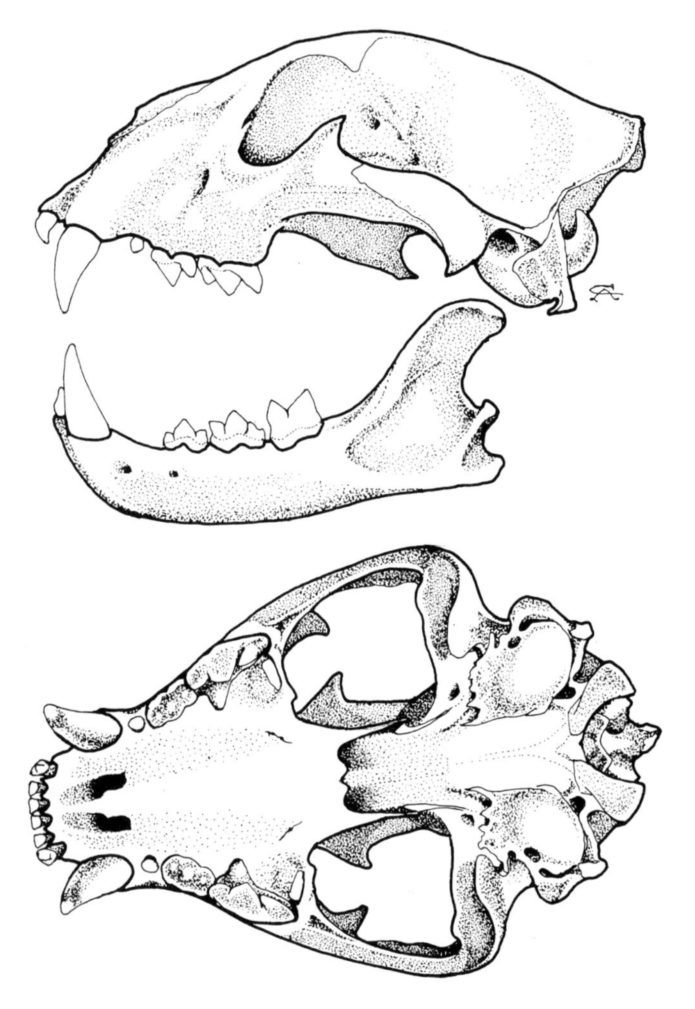

Fig. 249.2. Skull: lion, *P. leo*.
TL Skull 370 mm.

The dental formula is:

$I\frac{3}{3}\ C\frac{1}{1}\ P\frac{3}{2}\ M\frac{1}{1} = 30$

The upper outer incisors are considerably larger than the remainder. These are rounded, heavily built and recurved towards the points. The canines are heavy and sharp and slightly flattened on their inner sides. The second upper premolar is small and rounded and rises to a central point. The other two upper cheekteeth are adapted to cutting; the whole length of the upper fourth premolar has a sharp cutting edge and the first upper molar is tiny.

The outer incisors in the lower jaw are larger than the remainder, but do not reach the development of the upper. The canines are recurved. The cheekteeth are all adapted to cutting. The first lower molar has a sharp edge which, occluding on the back half of the fourth upper premolar, serves to keep the edges of these two teeth continually sharpened. The huge canines and canine-like upper outer incisors are adaptations to the holding of heavy prey and the delivery of the strangling, killing bite. The remainder of the teeth are adapted to slicing up the food. The small upper first molars, set at an angle to the cheekteeth, become worn on their front edges and while they may assist in keeping tough food from sliding backwards during the process of slicing, they have little or no grinding ability.

**Distribution**

There is probably no other species whose distributional range has shrunk over historical times to the extent shown by the lion. At one time they occurred widely in Europe, over much of Asia and the continent of Africa. Today extinct in Europe, the last remaining individuals were exterminated in Greece about AD 100 and they persisted in Palestine until about the 12th century. The Asian population is represented today by about 190 individuals living on the Gir Peninsula, in northwestern India. This population has declined from about 300 in 1953 to present levels, which were given by a census in 1970 (Red Data Book, IUCN).

The situation is similar on the Continent of Africa where they are now extinct in North Africa, disappearing from Tunisia and Algeria about 1891 and from Morocco in 1920. In the Southern African Subregion the shrinkage in their distributional range is well documented in the historical record. From the time of Kolb (1719), who stated that they were not uncommon near Cape Town, they gradually disappeared, in the face of man's encroachment, from most of the Cape Province during the 1860's and from the greater part of Natal, excluding the northeast, shortly thereafter. Today, apart from areas into which they have been reintroduced, they only occur in some National Parks and Game Reserves in the Republic of South Africa.

As lions are great wanderers they may be expected to turn up from time to time in areas where for many years they were unknown, often far from their present limits of distribution. There are many examples of this in the Subregion. Coetzee (*in litt.*) reported that every two or three years lions appear in the vicinity of Windhoek, Namibia, and vagrants still wander onto the Zimbabwe plateau, killing cattle and then vanishing, even though they were extirpated there many years ago. In 1965 a female and a juvenile penetrated to the outskirts of Gwelo and in 1971 at least two reached the periurban areas of Harare. They are not resident in the eastern parts of Zimbabwe, but nevertheless regularly cross over from Mozambique. They occasionally turn up near Louis Trichardt in the northern Transvaal and an individual turned up near Heidelberg, Transvaal, within recent years.

**Plate 19**

247. Cheetah, *Acinonyx jubatus*
Jagluiperd
248. Leopard, *Panthera pardus*
Luiperd
249. Lion, *Panthera leo*
Leeu

PLATE 19
247
248
249
Dick Findlay.

*South of the Sahara, excluding the Southern African Subregion*

They still occur along the Senegal River in **Senegal** and in **Mali** on the Niger River. They are found in the northern parts of **Sierra Leone** and eastwards of this in the Sahel and Sudan zones and in parts of the Guinea Savannas to **Ethiopia**. They are found throughout most of **Somalia**. They occur in northern, eastern and southern **Zaire**. They are widespread in **Uganda, Kenya** and **Tanzania**. The situation in **Angola** is not so clear, for there are few records, but it appears that they still occur throughout the country, even in the desert areas in the southwest. They occur widely in **Zambia** and north of the Zambezi River in **Mozambique**.

*Southern African Subregion*

In **Namibia** they are widespread in the northern and northeastern parts, including Etosha National Park, and are also found in Kaokoland and along the Namib Desert coast. They are widespread in **Botswana**, except in a narrow sector in the west and in the more highly developed parts of the east. In **Zimbabwe** they are absent from the central plateau except as vagrants, otherwise they occur widely throughout. In **Mozambique** south of the Zambezi River, they occur widely, except along the Zimbabwe border in the west, in the eastern Inhambane District and not south of about 24 °S except as vagrants from the Kruger National Park. In the **Transvaal** resident populations are confined to the larger conservation areas in the east, which include the Kruger National Park, with vagrants wandering in from time to time in the northern and northwestern parts of the province. Today the only resident population in the Cape Province is in the Kalahari Gemsbok National Park, from where, occasionally, wanderers make their way into adjacent parts of the province and Namibia. In 1958 a single wanderer made its way southward into the Umfolozi-Hluhluwe-Corridor area in **Natal** and with reintroduction of the species thereafter, there is now a flourishing population in this sector. This today marks their most southerly limits of distribution on the continent.

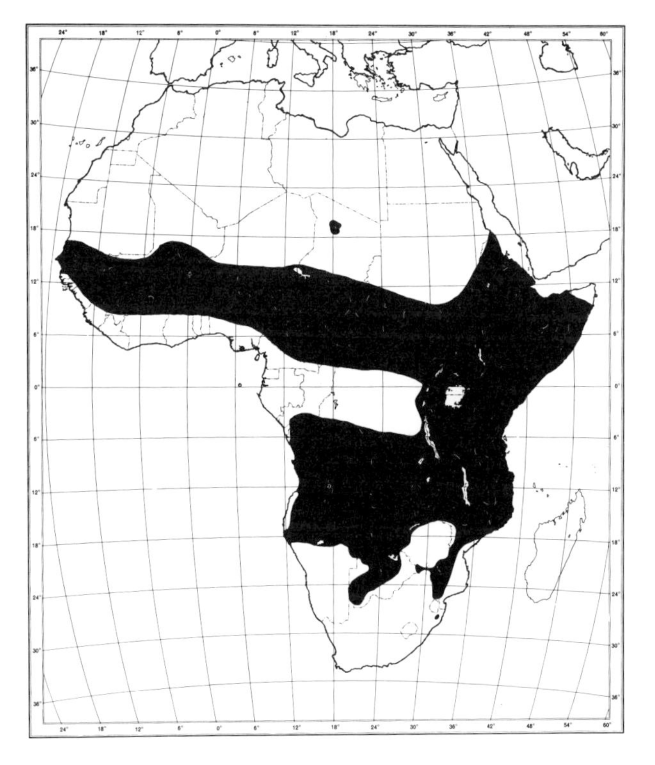

### Habitat

Lions have a wide habitat tolerance, the only association in which they generally are not found being forest. This is demonstrated by their absence from the forests of West Africa and the Congo basin in Zaire. They will penetrate deep into desert, where there are avenues of watercourses, and are common in semi-desert areas such as in parts of the Sahelian Zone of West Africa or the Kalahari in Botswana. Where water is available they will drink regularly, especially after feeding, but they are by no means dependent on this and they can subsist for long periods without it, getting their moisture requirements from their prey.

Probably the most important requirements are that their habitat should provide an ample supply of food in the form of medium and large-sized game animals, which form their principal food, some shade in which to lie up during the heat of the day and the barest of cover to facilitate stalking of prey.

### Habits

Lions are predominantly nocturnal, with a tendency to be active around sunrise and towards sunset, yet quite frequently they are observed moving or hunting during daylight hours. They are averse to exerting themselves during the heat of the day, when they loll about or sleep in the shade, usually in compact groups. Although they are a terrestrial species they are good climbers and during these resting periods will sometimes drape themselves along branches of trees to take advantage of cool breezes or perhaps to avoid flies (Fosbrooke, 1963), or dangerous animals (Makacha, 1969). Authorities who have studied lions have found them lethargic, their lives consisting of short periods of intense activity when hunting or exhibiting aggression, with longer periods of slow movement or relaxation. In spite of their apparent obliviousness to events around them during resting periods, they can become aggressive quickly if suddenly and unduly disturbed.

The social structure of lions has been the subject of close study by authorities such as Guggisberg (1961), Schaller (1968, 1969), Schaller & Lowther (1969), Bertram (1978) and others. They are the only felids that are distinctly social, living and hunting in prides, which may number from a few individuals to up to 30 or more. In the Kruger National Park, Smuts (1976, 1982) found that 12 was the mean number, with a maximum of 21. On average there were two adult males per pride, the range being one to five. Although Child (*in litt.*) in Botswana noted that the prides were smaller, never numbering over six, more recently Patterson (1988) in the Mashatu Game Reserve in eastern Botswana observed that under optimum conditions one pride increased to 16 individuals, with two resident males, but poaching and a reduction of large prey due to drought tended to suppress this number. Van Orsdol *et al.* (1985) concluded that food supply during the lean season was the major determinant of pride size.

Lions hunt in areas where prey is concentrated, and the cover poor, so it is to their advantage to co-operate in hunting. Prides occupy home ranges which may vary greatly in size depending on local conditions or the availability of food. Schaller (1972a), working in an area which covered both woodland and plains, found that there was an overlap in home ranges, whereas Bertram (1978), working in the woodland only, found that home ranges were largely exclusive and, as they were actively defended, merited the term territories. In Schaller's situation the explanation seemed to be that there was local movement of the prey species between the two associations, which was followed by the prides. Smuts (1982) found that the home range of a pride in the Kruger National Park averaged 25 $km^2$ and in the Mashatu Game Reserve, Patterson (1988) gave an area of 72 $km^2$. Van Orsdol *et al.* (1985) found that there is a strong negative correlation between home range size and the abundance of prey during the season of least abundance.

Lionesses form the nucleus of the society. Adults spend the whole of their lives within their home range and rarely move out of it. Prides may include several males, one of which is dominant, a role also adopted by one of the females. The members of a pride do not necessarily all move together within the territory, but individually or collectively they all make use of it. Prides may split up into subgroups which tend to operate in different parts of the territory, joining up amicably from time to time, but exhibiting hostility to encroachment by subgroups of other prides from adjacent territories. Like so many other situations in nature there are exceptions to these general rules. Bertram (1978), for example, recorded that an adult lioness with a radio collar, which had for two years occupied a territory with her companions, suddenly left it and was found some eight kilometres from its boundary. She returned from her wanderings the following day. Again some lions tend to be nomadic, not occupying established territories. These are confined to males ousted from prides, as well as subadult males and females. Smuts (1976), in the Kruger National Park, followed the movements of the females and young of a pride, which were following herds of zebra and wildebeest, for a distance of 45 km. He also recorded the movements of solitary subadult males and adult females, one of the latter up to 70 km. Bertram (1978) stated that fewer cubs from these nomadic prides reach maturity due to a lack of the security afforded by a territory. Nomadic lions are also in poor condition (Melton *et al.*, 1987). These prides tend to follow the movements of their prey and are more tolerant of strangers than members of prides holding territories. Lion territories are not defined precisely, zones between them being less intensively used than the remainder. Lions tend to avoid encounters where they can do so, relying on roaring, scent-marking and patrolling to demonstrate their right to the territory so as to warn others off it. Schaller (1972a) pointed out that if trespassers are discovered they usually flee back to the safety of their own territory on being threatened, the discoverer appearing reluctant to catch the intruders, preferring simply to see them off. Sometimes it may develop into a snarling, swatting match, but serious injury to either party is rare.

However, fights between rival males are much more serious and may result in the death of combatants. These take place when one or two groups of males attempt to take over a pride by ousting the male already in possession (Bertram, 1978). In these encounters the heavy mane assists in protecting the neck from the raking claws of the adversary. Between prides there is some interchange of males, the arrival of a new male or males having far-reaching effects on issues such as cub survival (see **Reproduction**). On occasion a single male can dominate two prides (Estes, 1967; Makacha, 1969; Patterson, 1988).

In the Etosha National Park, Orford, Perrin & Berry (1988) found an average emigration/mortality of pride lions to be 17% and the annual loss of lionesses from the three prides was 7%. The mean number of adults recorded in these prides was 1,5 males and 4,8 lionesses. Smuts *et al.* (1978) stated that the average tenure of males in a pride is two years, but Orford *et al.* (1988) found that, of 10 instances known to them, three died in their prides, while five were still in their prides after being there for a minimum of four years. This may be a result of the low density in Etosha.

Before the start of a hunt or when returning to rest after it, members of prides indulge in what Rudnai (1973a) called "contagious activities" such as yawning, grooming, defecating or urinating, which means that if indulged in by one member, the rest often follow suit. Communal roaring too may follow the start given by an individual member.

### Food

Lions feed on a wide range of mammals from mice to buffalo, birds up to the size of an ostrich, as well as reptiles and even insects. Pienaar (1969b) listed no less than 37 species of prey in the Kruger National Park. Smuts (1982) calculated that on the average edible weight of each prey animal and knowing the frequency at which they occurred in stomach contents, giraffe were supplying 43% of the food, wildebeest 23%, zebra 15%, impala 6%, buffalo 4%, waterbuck 4%, warthog 2%, kudu 2% and miscellaneous small mammals 1% each. An adult male lion was found to have 30 kg of impala meat, skin and bones in its stomach. In addition they are known on occasion to tackle young elephants and hippopotamus, and Pienaar (1969b) recorded the severe mauling, resulting in death, of an adult white rhinoceros. Their principal foods, however, depend on what is available, falling generally within a range of species with a mass of between 50 and 300 kg. In the Mashatu Game Reserve, Botswana, Patterson (1988) observed lions to feed on baby elephants, adult eland bulls as well as the grazers such as wildebeest and zebra and predominantly impala; on one occasion he saw a pride surround a troop of baboons, several juveniles of which were captured by the pride before the troop made its escape.

In the Chobe National Park, McBride (1982) recorded 120 kills, 89% of which were made during the hours of darkness. Buffalo comprised the major part of the kill sample (46,7%) of which three-quarters were of young or sub-adults. Wildebeest and zebra constituted 21,7% of their kills, half of which were young, and the remaining 30% of kills comprised giraffe, kudu, waterbuck, sable, impala, tsessebe, two baby elephants, six springhaas, an aardvark and two steenbok lambs.

In the Kalahari Gemsbok National Park, Eloff (1964) found that small animals and juvenile antelopes made up 50% of the diet, porcupines ranking high, together with gemsbok, red hartebeest and springbok.

Lions will take carrion even when it is putrid and they are not adverse to eating fish when these can be obtained easily in drying up pools. Pienaar (1969b) also listed termites and locusts as being taken on occasion and recorded the killing and eating of spotted hyaenas, leopards, cheetahs, jackals, civets, honey badgers, caracals and even crocodiles. In the Skeleton Coast Park, Namibia, Bridgeford (1985) recorded 14 instances of their eating Cape fur seals, *Arctocephalus pusillus*; carcasses were dragged on average 1 100 m from the beach—also a characteristic of these lions with gemsbok kills much further inland.

Lions hunt predominantly at night and are much more successful when a hunt is joined in by all members of a pride. There is a measure of disagreement among authorities who have studied lions in the field as to whether there is in fact a co-ordinated and deliberate plan of attack (Guggisberg, 1961; Schaller, 1972a) or whether each member is working on its own and taking maximum advantage from the developing situation (Kruuk & Turner, 1967). Whatever the answer may be, Schaller (1972a) noted that 30% of stalks were successful when members of the pride took part, against 17–19% when only a single individual was involved. Hunting behaviour has been shown to vary with cover availability, prey availability and prey body size (Van Orsdol, 1984). During nocturnal hunting the amount of moonlight affects hunting success independently of factors such as hunting group size—hunting success during moonlight hours is significantly less than when no moonlight is present (Van Orsdol, 1984). Lions are expert stalkers and will make use of the barest cover to close in on their prey. In stalking, the head and body are held low to the ground, their eyes fixed on the intended victim as they move towards it slowly and purposefully. If the prey shows signs of nervousness they will freeze motionless until it relaxes and continues feeding before they move forward again. Most chases are short, not over 100–200 m, the aim being to get as close to the prey as will allow for a spring onto its back, without having to make the final sprint. It has been estimated, however, that in the final short sprint to catch they may cover 100 m in six seconds. During the whole process of hunting, lions remain silent, although they may roar after the kill is made.

The attack may be delivered at the rump or shoulders of the prey, the sheer weight of the aggressor, in the case of medium-sized prey, bringing the prey to the ground, when it is seized by the throat and killed by strangulation. With larger prey the lion aims to land sideways on the shoulder or rump of its victim. In the former case sometimes one paw clutches the muzzle, forcing the head sideways, so that in falling the neck may be broken. As soon as the prey is down it is seized by the throat and sometimes by the muzzle to effect strangulation.

Lions will stun readily with the paw and eat small prey found fortuitously. They will deal with the young of small antelope hiding up in the grass in this manner. They also will dig out and eat adult warthogs from shallow burrows.

An interesting variation of the more normal method of killing large prey is recorded by Eloff (1964) where, in the Kalahari, they leap upon the hindquarters, their weight, together with an upward jerk of the victim's hindquarters, breaking the back at the junction of the last lumbar vertebrae.

Lions may take their meat at the site of the kill or they may drag it to the nearest cover. Normally the belly is ripped open and the stomach and intestines pulled out. These may be covered with sticks or grass (Bertram, 1978) or sand (Eloff,

1977), but often the intestines are eaten after being drawn through the incisor teeth so as to squeeze out the contents.

The males take little part in the hunt, leaving this to the females, but are quick to take part in feeding once the kill is made, lionesses having to wait until the pride male has eaten his fill. He may be more tolerant of cubs sharing his meal.

Lions are opportunists and a hungry pride will keep a watch for vultures descending to the kills of other predators and will readily follow this up rather than exert themselves to make their own kills. Spotted hyaenas are often robbed of their kills by lions. However, the presence of a male in the pride is an important factor in interaction with clans of spotted hyaenas, *Crocuta crocuta*. In the Chobe National Park prides of females lost 20% of their food to hyaenas and a further 17% to unrelated lions, although hyaenas had to outnumber lionesses by 3/4:1 to drive them off their kill. For hyaenas losses to lions were balanced by gains from lionesses (Cooper, 1990b). A solitary lion at a kill is at a disadvantage in this situation for if it leaves the kill, it is likely to be taken over by other predators.

During or after a meal lions will wander to the nearest water for a drink. Food passes through the stomach and intestine quickly and lions are able to take a second meal not long after gorging themselves.

In the absence of their normal prey, lions can become problem animals and can cause grave losses to cattle and small stock. They can become "man eaters" and the individuals involved are not always old and decrepit individuals. It is said (Goodwin, 1953) that they do not return to the remains of a human meal.

**Reproduction**

Smuts (1982) found that in the Kruger National Park male lions become sexually mature at 26 months old although they do not get the opportunity to mate until they are about five years old. The females become pregnant for the first time at about 43 months old and continue to breed until they are quite old, producing a litter every two years. Females may reproduce up to an age of about 15 years but usually not thereafter (Rudnai, 1973a). Although mating may take place at any time throughout the year, Smuts (1982) found that, in the Kruger National Park, a large proportion of the cubs was born between February and April which is related to the period during which the prey species have their young.

Courtship in lions may be initiated by either member of the pair, who remain in close association during this period, the male following the female at all times and resting with her. The female usually invites copulation by lordosis. Although at this time the proximity of other male members of the same pride may be tolerated, strange lions are driven off. In northern Botswana a mating pair was observed copulating about every 15 minutes over a period of several hours and in East Africa, Rudnai (1973a) recorded copulation every 17 minutes, the process continuing through the night. During periods between copulation members of the pair will lie down next to each other or walk together for short distances until the next mating, which may last up to about a minute. If the female does not respond to the facial demonstration of the male he may gently stroke her with his tongue on the shoulder, neck or back and the female may respond. Towards the end of the period of copulation the male may gently neckbite the female. During copulation the female may purr loudly. Unlike other carnivores there is very little aggressive behaviour during this period; the snarl which the male may emit is ritualised and the neckbite is symbolic. Rudnai (1973a) noted that the majority of matings do not result in pregnancy. Of 14 mating periods observed by her in the wild, only four appeared to result in fertilisation.

Rudnai (1973b) found that the level of nutrition of the female influences her fertility. Smuts (1976) believed that the number in litters was regulated by the availability of food.

Zuckerman (1953), from observations in captivity, gave the gestation period as 110 days.

Lionesses are polyoestrus, oestrus lasting from about four to 16 days, the period between oestruses varying from a few days to over a year. They have a post partum oestrus, but do not conceive if the litter survives, but if it is lost a new litter may be produced within four months (Rudnai, 1973a).

For purposes of parturition the females leave their pride and remain separated from it until the cubs are four to eight weeks old. Litters average 2,6 in number (n=19), with a range of one to four, but up to six have been recorded (Rudnai, 1973a; Patterson, 1988). The sex ratio at birth is parity, the mass at birth about 1,5 kg.

The female with her cubs rejoins the pride when the cubs are four to eight weeks old, but only if cubs already established with the pride are not more than three months old. The reason for this is that any female in milk will suckle cubs and members of the younger litter would suffer in competition with other cubs if they were much larger. The cubs suckle regularly for the first six to seven months of their lives, the frequency declining thereafter. They remain with their mothers for 21 to 24 months (Rudnai, 1973a); Schaller (1972b) gave this period as 30 months for cubs in Serengeti, East Africa.

Cub mortality is high. Stevenson-Hamilton (1934) gave a survival rate for the Kruger National Park of 50%, and 40% seems to apply to the Mashatu Game Reserve, Botswana (Patterson, 1988) and the Etosha National Park, Namibia (Orford *et al.*, 1988). In the Kruger National Park, Smuts (1982) noted that cub mortality increased when food was in short supply or when there was insufficient cover for the cubs to hide in while the females were out hunting. Moreover, prides without males in constant attendance failed to rear any cubs.

Eloff (1980) stated that in the Kalahari, with its harsh environment and where lions fed predominantly on small-sized prey, which was consumed largely by the adults, leaving little for the cubs, and where the adults have to travel long distances to secure food, cub mortality was very high. In this sector he stated that starvation is apparently the principal cause of cub mortality, followed by their abandonment, disease and predation.

## Genus *Felis* Linnaeus, 1758

This genus, in its widest sense, covers the majority of the living species of the subfamily Felinae, which includes the genera *Acinonyx*, *Panthera* and *Felis*.

The genus is represented in the Subregion by four indigenous species: the caracal, *F. caracal* Schreber, 1776; the African wild cat, *F. lybica* Forster, 1780; the small spotted cat, *F. nigripes* Burchell, 1824; the serval, *F. serval* Schreber, 1776 and a single introduced species, the domestic cat, *F. catus* Linnaeus, 1758.

There remains a difference of opinion regarding the status of the African wild cat, *Felis lybica*. Haltenorth (1953) suggested that it was conspecific with the older named European wild cat, *F. silvestris* Schreber, 1777 and, within recent years, there is a growing tendency among authors to accept this view. Ellerman *et al.* (1953), while admitting that African members of the species are very closely allied to *F. silvestris*, nevertheless retained the name *F. lybica* for the African wild cat. There is no conclusive evidence available to support either view and the treatment given to the problem depends largely on individual opinion. In this work for the reasons given under *Felis lybica* (**Taxonomic Notes**) they are considered to be separate species.

The Egyptians were certainly among the first people to domesticate the African wild cat, *F. lybica*, records of this going back to at least 2000 B.C. Some archaeologists hold that the domestication of this species dates from the First Dynasty, about 3000 B.C. (Zeuner, 1963). The cat became worshipped universally by the Egyptians to the extent that, when their cats died, the owners would go into mourning by shaving their eyebrows. The cats were mummified and buried in special consecrated places set aside for this purpose. If their owners were wealthy they had bronze mummy cases made for them and they were buried with them in their tombs. Herodotus related that when a house was on fire they were more anxious to save their cats than their property (Zeuner, 1963). It was a very serious offence to kill a cat, as Greek and Roman visitors to Egypt found out to their cost when they accidentally did so. From paintings and hieroglyphics, it appears that this cat was ginger-coloured, with long legs and ears, and a long, ringed tail. The numbers of mummified cats in cat cemetries were so enormous that, during the latter part of the 19th century and first few years of the 20th century, they were recovered and their remains sold as fertiliser, 19 tons of which were exported to England (Morrison-Scott, 1951).

The domestic cat, *Felis catus*, on which Linnaeus (1758) based his species, is now represented by a wide variety of forms, which originated from selection by man, and has a cosmopolitan distribution. They have accompanied their owners to the furthest corners of the earth to be disposed of to new owners or, of their own volition, chosen new ownership or become feral in new lands.

Domestic cats are catholic in their ecological demands and are versatile enough to settle and breed in the wild in a wide variety of environments, from the harsh conditions of sub-Antarctic islands to tropical and sub-tropical parts of the world. As a feral species they are established widely in the Southern African Subregion, including Marion Island.

By the beginning of the Christian era domesticated cats were kept regularly by the Romans and were carried by them to the outermost parts of their empire, including England.

The dental formula of the Felinae is:

$I\frac{3}{3}\ C\frac{1}{1}\ P\frac{3}{2}\ M\frac{1}{1} = 30$ or

$I\frac{3}{3}\ C\frac{1}{1}\ P\frac{2}{2}\ M\frac{1}{1} = 28$

The teeth are highly specialised to capturing, holding and killing live prey and to slicing up flesh. The canines are long and sharp and the outermost incisor teeth enlarged to assist the canines in holding. There is a gap between the canines and the cheekteeth, the post-canine gap, whose purpose is to free the canine teeth for deep penetration. The cheekteeth are all adapted to cutting, the upper fourth premolar tooth, with three cusps set in line, bearing on the first lower molar with its two blade-like cusps, forming a highly efficient carnassial shear for chopping up the food. In all members of the Subfamily there are occasional aberrations in the dental formula affecting the premolar teeth.

Key to the indigenous species (Meester *et al.*, 1986)

1. Ears elongate and tufted at tips with long black hair; body unicoloured, tawny or reddish; greatest skull length about 109–150 mm (Subgenus *Caracal*)

   ... *caracal*

   Ears not elongate nor heavily tufted; body colour spotted or barred

   ... 2

2. Ears large and broad, 82–99 mm long; larger, greatest skull length 101–135 mm; body distinctly spotted (Subgenus *Leptailurus*)

   ... *serval*

   Ears smaller, less than 80 mm long; smaller, greatest skull length normally less than 100 mm, occasionally up to 112 mm (Subgenus *Felis*)

   ... 3

3. Tail less than half of head and body length; bullae enlarged; body distinctly spotted; smaller, greatest skull length less than 87 mm

   ... *nigripes*

   Tail more than half of head and body length; bullae less enlarged; body spotting indistinct; larger, greatest skull length normally 81–100 mm, occasionally up to 112 mm

   ... *lybica*

No. 250

## *Felis caracal* (Schreber, 1776)

## Caracal
## Rooikat

Plate 20

### Colloquial Name

In published papers the caracal is persistently referred to as the lynx which is unfortunate, for European and New World lynxes are externally very different, being spotted and barred. The Turkish name for caracal is "garah-gulak" or "black ear" which presumably has become caracal in English, and its translation is singularly appropriate, for the characteristic features of the caracal are the black backs to the tufted ears, which contrast with the unicoloured body. The Afrikaans *rooikat* is descriptive.

### Taxonomic Notes

The caracal, *F. caracal*, although it has a wide distribution beyond the confines of the African Continent, was first officially known from a specimen illustrated and described by Schreber in 1776 from Table Mountain. Schreber's plate has the caption "*Felis caracal* Buff.", thus acknowledging Buffon's prior knowledge of the species, which he had illustrated, and to which he had applied the name caracal. However, Schreber did not accredit his illustration to Buffon, as he usually did when copying from his work, because in fact he was using as his model a specimen from "Vorgebirge", Cape of Good Hope.

Meester *et al.* (1986) recognised two subspecies from the Subregion: *F. c. damarensis* from Namibia, northern Cape Province, southern Botswana and southern and central Angola, and the nominate form, *F. c. caracal*, from the remainder of the species' range in the Subregion.

### Description

Caracals are built robustly and adult males have a mass of up to 17 kg, females 11,5 kg. Caracals are short in the limbs, and they stand some 0,4–0,45 m at the shoulder. Their tails are short, only some 27% of the total length or 36% of the length of the head and body (Table 250.1).

**Table 250.1**

Measurements (mm) and mass (kg) of caracals, *F. caracal*, from (a) Botswana and Zimbabwe (Smithers, 1983), and (b) & (c) the Cape Province (Stuart, 1977; Pringle & Pringle, 1979)

| | Males | | | Females | | |
|---|---|---|---|---|---|---|
| | $\bar{x}$ | n | Range | $\bar{x}$ | n | Range |
| **(a)** | | | | | | |
| TL | 1116 | 6 | 1065–1226 | 1062 | 3 | 1020–1110 |
| T | 298 | 6 | 255–320 | 288 | 3 | 275–305 |
| Hf s/u | 209 | 6 | 200–225 | 188 | 3 | 185–190 |
| E | 84 | 6 | 80–87 | 83 | 3 | 81–86 |
| Mass | 13,8 | 6 | 11,5–17,0 | 11,9 | 3 | 10,9–11,5 |
| **(b)** | | | | | | |
| TL | 868 | 97 | 750–1080 | 819 | 94 | 710–1029 |
| T | 264 | 99 | 210–340 | 252 | 101 | 180–315 |
| Hf s/u | 193 | 101 | 170 | 180 | 101 | 160–208 |
| E | 0 | 98 | 65–92 | 76 | 100 | 60–94 |
| Mass | 12,9 | 77 | 7,2–19,0 | 10,0 | 63 | 7,0–15,9 |
| **(c)** | | | | | | |
| TL | 1170 | 46 | 102–127 | 1093 | 32 | 99–119 |
| Mass | 14,53 | 46 | 8,6–20,0 | 10,98 | 32 | 8,6–14,5 |

The unicolour coat, which is usually grizzled with silvery-white, is thick and soft in the longer winter coat and is shorter and slightly harsher in the summer coat. The colour varies from a pale light reddish in specimens from arid semi-desert areas to sandy-brown or even brick-red in areas of higher rainfall. There is a tendency for material from the southern part of their range in the Subregion to have a greyer rather than a silvery appearance because of the more liberal admixture of guard hair with darker annulations. In all cases the colour is darker down the mid-back; the tip of the tail often has a higher admixture of black hairs, giving it a dark appearance. Below and between the eyes, around the mouth and on the chin the hair is white.

The hair of the guard coat which in winter skins is up to 30 mm long, in summer half this length, is pale in colour at the base, some of the hair with broad whitish annulations near the tips, others with dark brown or black tips. The preponderance of either of these types imparts either a silvery-white colour to the coat or a darker colour. There are indications of a distinct moult commencing with the onset of the hot weather about October/November. In the winter coat the underfur is thick, the individual hairs wavy and only slightly shorter than those of the guard coat, their colour is lighter than the overall colour of the coat. In the summer coat the underfur is sparse, in some specimens almost imperceptible.

Above and at the level of the inner side of the eyes and the base of the whiskers there is a darker patch on either side and the hair darkens in a line from the forehead to near the nostrils, with a black band between the inner edges of the eyes to the nostrils. The under parts are white from the chest to the belly, the chest spotted, the spots the same colour as the upper parts but lighter in colour. The pointed ears are black on the back with a sprinkling of white hairs, the hair inside the ears white. The long ear tufts are black with some long white hairs. The insides of the limbs are white with indistinct spotting or barring.

The paws are noticeably large, with five digits on the front and four on the back feet. The first digits on the forefeet, the "dew claws", are situated so far back from the other digits that they do not touch the ground and do not mark in the spoor, but are armed with particularly strong, heavily built claws (Fig. 250.1). The claws are creamy-white in colour. Those on the front feet are sharp, characteristically feline and about 24 mm over the curve; those on the back feet are not so sharply curved, more sectorial and about 36 mm across the curve. Both sets are fully protractible. Characteristic features are the unicolour pelage, the long tufts of hair on the tips of the ears which are black at the back, and the short tail.

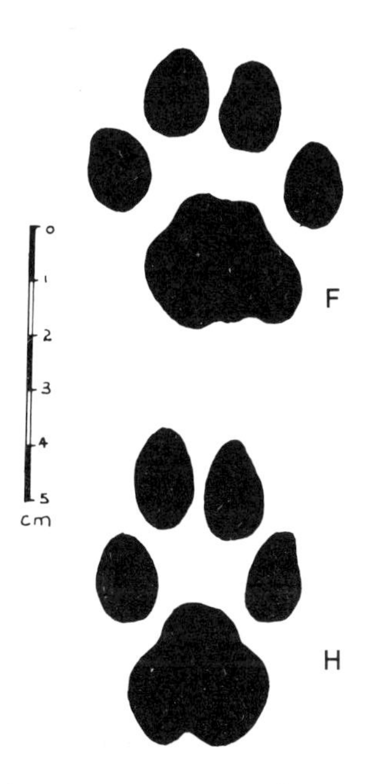


Fig. 250.1. Spoor: caracal, *F. caracal*.
F. Right forefoot H. Right hind foot.

**Skull** (Fig. 250.2)

In profile the skull is high and rounded, the highest point about the interorbital constriction from which, posteriorly, it falls away gradually to the supraoccipital crest and, anteriorly, sharply to the short blunt rostrum. The ear bullae are large, reflecting the keen sense of hearing of the species. The supraoccipital crest is well developed and, in older individuals, is joined at right angles by a sagittal crest which continues forward across the top of the cranium giving an extra surface of attachment for the temporalis muscles.

The lower jaw is stoutly built, the coronoid process tall and narrow, giving extra leverage to the temporalis muscles in closing the jaw, the process ridged to give additional hold to the muscle attachments.

The zygoma is thick and heavy, providing substantial attachment for the masseter muscles. The glenoid articulation is elongated transversely, giving a strong hinge joint which, however, allows for sufficient lateral movement to allow the blades of the carnassial shear to slide past each other accurately.

The dental formula is:

$I\frac{3}{3}\ C\frac{1}{1}\ P\frac{2}{2} = 24$

$I\frac{3}{3}\ C\frac{1}{1}\ P\frac{3}{2}\ M\frac{1}{1} = 30$

In a sample of 50 skulls $p^2$ was present in only 16%. Permanent dentition was complete at 10 months (Stuart, 1982a). The second upper premolar teeth are usually absent, unlike the serval in which they are usually present, albeit peg-like and poorly developed. The upper molar teeth are minute. The canine teeth are heavy and sharp, in an adult measuring up to 20 mm from the jawbone to the tip, and are well adapted, with their backing of powerful masseter and temporalis muscles, to deliver the killing bite. As is common in felids the teeth of the carnassial shear, consisting of the fourth premolar in the upper jaw and the first molar in the lower, are fully adapted to cutting. The teeth in the lower jaw show no adaptation to crushing, as is found in the canids. In common with other felids the food is sliced into pieces and swallowed without any degree of mastication.

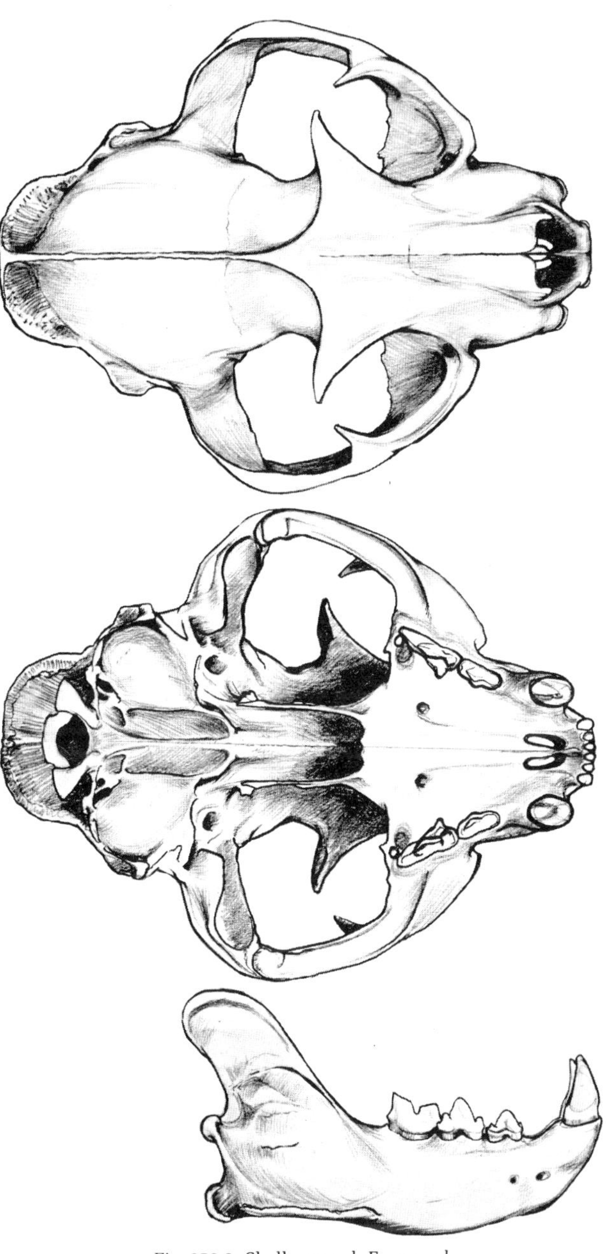

Fig. 250.2. Skull: caracal, *F. caracal*.
TL Skull 150 mm.

**Distribution**

In parts of their range (Cape Province) caracals are widespread and common and, as they have become problem animals, there are many records of their occurrence. Stuart (1982a) recorded that over the years 1931–1952 an average of 2 219 individuals per year were killed in control operations in the Karoo, Cape Province. In other parts, however, they are considered sparse but this may be on account of their being nocturnal and highly secretive.

*Extralimital*

They are recorded from the **Sinai Peninsula; Israel; Jordan; Syria**; southeastern **Turkey; Arabia; Aden**; the **Trucial States; Kuwait; Iraq; Iran; Turkmenskaya** (east of the Caspian Sea); **Afghanistan; Pakistan** and **India**.

*North Africa*

They occur in **Morocco** in the regions between the Anti Atlas and High Atlas Mountains and the coast, and south of the western end of the High Atlas in Ifni; eastward in the coastal area and foothills, in **Algeria** and **Tunisia; Libya** and **Egypt** and south to the **Sudan**.

*South of the Sahara, excluding the Southern African Subregion*

They occur from southern **Mauritania; Senegal; Guinea Bissau; Guinea** and eastwards to the **Sudan; Ethiopia** and **Somalia**; in the Sahel, Sudan and occasionally in parts of the Guinea savannas. South of this there are records from **Uganda, Kenya, Tanzania, Angola, Zambia**, and **Malawi**; and in **Mozambique** they occur in the northeastern sector, north of the Zambezi River.

*Southern African Subregion*

They occur widely in **Namibia, Botswana, Zimbabwe** and **Mozambique**, south of the Zambezi River, but appear to be absent from the southeast. They occur widely in the **Transvaal, Orange Free State** and southeastern parts of **Natal** along the Drakensberg escarpment. In Natal, Rowe-Rowe (1978a) recorded their introduction into the Itala Nature Reserve in 1976, where they have been re-sighted subsequently. They have a wide distribution in the **Cape Province**.

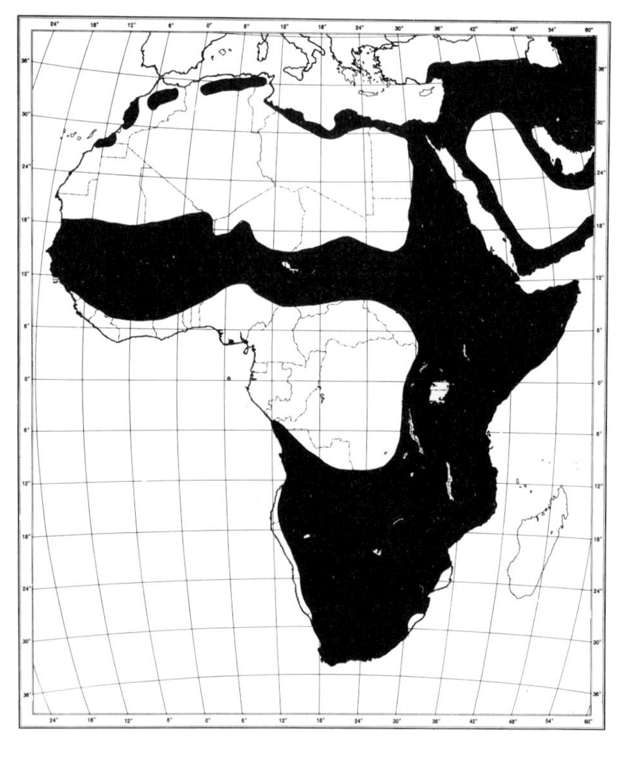

## Habitat

The caracal can tolerate arid conditions and occurs in the Subregion in semi-desert and karroid areas. They are associated with open country and open savanna woodland, more especially with open vleis and open grassland within this association, even where cover is minimal, consisting of widely scattered clumps of *Acacia* and solitary stands of high grass. They are absent from forested areas in the Subregion. They occur from sea-level to an altitude of 1 700 m.

## Habits

They are solitary and predominantly nocturnal, even in undisturbed areas. It is exceptional to find caracals moving during daylight hours. Stevenson-Hamilton (1912) recorded seeing an individual in the Transvaal at 08h00 and Skinner (unpubl.) observed one at 17h00 in summer after rain near Mara. Smithers (1971) saw individuals in Zimbabwe at 15h00 and 16h00 and in Botswana just after sundown at 18h30. Shortridge (1934) believed they hunt by day in cool or cloudy weather and other authors (Maberly, 1963; Williams, 1967) agree they are to some extent diurnal. Normally terrestrial, they are adept tree climbers, making full use of the powerful dew claws in this pursuit. When hunting, they are predominantly terrestrial. Individuals associate to mate, thereafter going their own ways. Of 40 sightings in the wild, all were of single individuals (Smithers, 1983). Moolman (1986a,b) showed that in the Cape Mountain Zebra National Park and its vicinity female home ranges overlapped slightly and varied in size from 3,9 km$^2$ to 6,5 km$^2$, those of the males, which were widely overlapping, from 5,1 km$^2$ to 30,6 km$^2$; male home ranges overlapped those of the females. In the eastern Karoo near Robertson, Stuart (1982a) found three females had slightly overlapping home ranges of 11,8 to 26,7 km$^2$, another in the coastal sandveld, a home range of 11,9 km$^2$. The only male he tracked in the Karoo had a home range of 48,0 km$^2$.

Because of their nocturnal and secretive habits, there is a paucity of field observations. Caught in a spotlight, they make off at speed for the nearest cover, not stopping to look back until they have put a substantial distance between themselves and the observer. Even in daylight their remarkable powers of concealing themselves in meagre cover leads to their being easily overlooked.

Smithers (1983) observed that a captive female's actions when playing are characteristic of the adults' when hunting, when given small birds tossing them in the air and leaping after them and catching them in mid-air. Their speed surpasses that of most cats (Pocock, 1939). In killing, prey are despatched either with preferably a throat bite or a bite in the nape of the neck (Grobler, 1981; Stuart, 1982a; Moolman, 1986). In killing hares, the captive caracal would bite them on the nape of the neck and if they still showed signs of life, she would throw herself on the ground and rake the prey with her back feet.

## Food

Most information on the prey of caracals emanates from the Cape Province (Table 250.2). The caracal is a hunter killer, generally averse to taking carrion, although they have been recorded doing so (Skinner, 1979; Stuart 1982a). They live predominantly on small and medium-sized prey including the young of larger antelopes, birds and small-sized mammals.

**Table 250.2**

Prey species of caracals, *Felis caracal*, in the Cape Province (from Stuart, 1982a)

| **Species** | **246 stomachs analysed (Karoo, Sandveld and Bedford)** | | **248 stomachs analysed (Karoo, Robertson)** | |
|---|---|---|---|---|
| | No. | % | No. | % |
| *Raphiceros melanotis* (Grysbok) | 34 | 10,5 | – | – |
| *Sylvicapra grimmia* (Common duiker) | 21 | 6,5 | 15 | 4,8 |
| *Raphiceros campestris* (Steenbok) | 8 | 2,5 | 8 | 2,6 |
| *Tragelaphus scriptus* (Bushbuck) | 7 | 2,1 | – | – |
| *Redunca fulvorufula* (Mountain reedbuck) | 4 | 1,2 | – | – |

| Species | 246 stomachs analysed (Karoo, Sandveld and Bedford) | | 248 stomachs analysed (Karoo, Robertson) | |
|---|---|---|---|---|
| | No. | % | No. | % |
| *Cephalophus monticola* (Blue duiker) | 4 | 1,2 | – | – |
| *Oreotragus oreotragus* (Klipspringer) | 1 | 0,3 | 7 | 2,3 |
| *Pelea capreolus* (Grey rhebok) | 1 | 0,3 | 4 | 1,3 |
| *Ovis aries* (Domestic sheep) | 68 | 21,0 | 28 | 9,0 |
| *Capra hircus* (Domestic goat) | 22 | 6,8 | 24 | 7,8 |
| Unidentified ungulate | 22 | 6,8 | – | – |
| *Rhabdomys pumilio* (Four-striped mouse) | 11 | 3,4 | 17 | 5,5 |
| *Aethomys namaquensis* (Namaqua rock rat) | 1 | 0,3 | 57 | 18,4 |
| *Pedetes capensis* (Springhaas) | 3 | 0,9 | 16 | 5,2 |
| *Cryptomys hottentotus* (Common mole rat) | 2 | 0,6 | 4 | 1,3 |
| *Bathyergus suillus* (Dune mole rat) | 2 | 0,6 | 1 | 0,3 |
| Unidentified rodent | 12 | 3,7 | 60 | 19,3 |
| *Procavia capensis* (Rock hyrax) | 22 | 6,8 | 28 | 9,0 |
| *Lepus* spp (Hares and rabbits) | 17 | 5,2 | 16 | 5,2 |
| *Chrysochloris asiatica* (Cape golden mole) | 1 | 0,3 | – | – |
| *Crocidura* spp (Shrews) | 2 | 0,6 | – | – |
| *Galerella pulverulenta* (Small grey mongoose) | 8 | 2,5 | 5 | 1,6 |
| *Ictonyx striatus* (Polecat) | 2 | 0,6 | – | – |
| *Cynictis penicillata* (Yellow mongoose) | 2 | 0,6 | – | – |
| *Atilax paludinosus* (Water mongoose) | 1 | 0,3 | 4 | 1,3 |
| *Genetta* spp (Genets) | 1 | 0,3 | – | – |
| *Felis caracal* (Caracal, kittens) | 3 | 0,9 | – | – |
| *Otomys unisulcatus* (Karoo rat) | – | – | 57 | 18,4 |
| *Otomys irroratus* (Vlei rat) | – | – | 16 | 5,2 |
| *Tatera afra* (Cape gerbil) | – | – | 4 | 1,3 |
| *Hystrix africae australis* (Porcupine) | – | – | 1 | 0,3 |
| Small birds (*Prinia* size) | 7 | 2,1 | 16 | 5,2 |
| Medium birds (Pigeon size) | 10 | 3,2 | 16 | 5,2 |
| Game birds | 7 | 2,1 | 16 | 5,2 |
| Fish | 1 | 0,3 | – | – |

Grobler's (1981) analysis of scats from the Mountain Zebra National Park showed that 93,8% of prey were mammals *cf.* Moolman's (1986) figure of 94,9% *cf.* Stuart's (1982a) figure from stomachs of 94,8%, the remaining 6,2%, 4,3% and 5,2% in each case being birds, while Grobler found reptile remains in two scats and Moolman reptiles in 0,8%. In adjacent Karoo farming areas, Moolman (1986b) found a similar picture, 96,9% mammals and 2,1% birds, but 22,9% of the mammals were domestic sheep and goats whose hair was not present in caracal scats from the adjacent National Park. Similarly in stomachs from caracals taken in farming areas, Stuart (1982a) found in the Karoo 27,8% and 16,8% contained hair of small domestic livestock (Table 250.3); Pringle & Pringle (1979) in the eastern Cape Province, 55% and Bester (1982) in the Orange Free State 43%. In half the stomachs Bester (1982) analysed, taken during predator control, remains of wild mammals only occurred, and these were dominated by springhaas, *P. capensis* (76%) and mountain reedbuck, *R. fulvorufula* (82%). Comparing scat analysis of caracals with those of *Felis lybica* and *Panthera pardus* from the eastern Robertson Karoo, Stuart (1982a) found 93% rodents, 3% shrews, 17% birds, 11% reptiles and 30% invertebrate remains in *F. lybica* scats and 68% antelope, 32% hyrax and 4% bird remains in *P. pardus* scats. Palmer & Fairall (1988) from scat analysis from caracals in the Karoo National Park, found that grey rhebok, *P. capreolus*, occurred in 28%, hyrax, *P. capensis* in 22%, Lagomorphs in 19% and rodents in 39%, with *Praomys natalensis* (13%) and *Aethomys namaquensis* (11%) being most prominent. Arthropoda remains were found in 17% of scats.

In nine stomach contents from Botswana (Smithers, 1971) mammals had a percentage occurrence of 89%, birds 33% and reptiles 11%. No vegetable matter of any sort was observed in the sample. The largest mammal was an impala, *A. melampus*, probably a juvenile, other species being springhaas, *Pedetes capensis*; hares, *Lepus* spp; and murids, including gerbils, *Tatera* spp, and the Namaqua gerbil, *Desmodillus auricularis*; pouched mice, *Saccostomus campestris*; pygmy mice, *Mus* spp; multimammate mice, *Mastomys* spp; and the remains of a goat, *Capra hircus*. Aves included a grey lourie, *Crinifer concolor*, a red-billed francolin, *Francolinus adspersus*, and a button quail, *Turnix sylvatica*. Reptiles were represented by a black-lined plated lizard, *Gerrhosaurus nigrolineatus*.

Skinner (1979) recorded mass killing by two caracals in the Cape Province. Overnight they killed 22 sheep, eating part of the buttock of one only. The sheep were killed by biting on the nape of the neck. Mass killings by the smaller cats is a rare occurrence, although it is recorded for leopards, *Panthera pardus* (Kruuk, 1972) and lions, *P. leo* (Schaller, 1972a).

Mean daily food intake for captive adult caracals has been estimated at 586 g by Grobler (1981) and 500 g for males and 316 g for females by Moolman (1986b).

**Reproduction**

Litters have been recorded in all months of the year, with births peaking between October and February (Stuart & Wilson, 1988). Spermatogenesis is aseasonal and mean length of the oestrous cycle is 14 days (n=15) (Bernard & Stuart, 1987), oestrus lasts 1,8 days (range 1–3; n=7) and copulation lasts 3,8 minutes (range 1,5–8; n=12). The mean gestation period is 79 days (range 78–81; n=5) (Stuart, 1982a). Stuart (1982a) found a mean of 2,2 foetuses (n=22) in gravid females.

Caracals appear to litter down in substantial cover, including in particular disused aardvark holes. The young are born blind, the eyes opening on the 9th or 10th day (Rosevear, 1974). Smithers (1983) found that in a captive female at the age of nine days the black facial markings were pronounced and at 11 days she first started to clean herself; the first sounds of the bird-like twittering were heard on the 12th day. Although the ears were not fully erected, the ear tufts were 10 mm long by the 21st day, the ears fully erected by the 30th day.

Bernard & Stuart (1987) found the youngest captive males to fertilise females were 12,5 and 14 months old and the youngest females to conceive were 14 and 15 months old. Longevity in captivity is recorded as just over 16 years.

No. 251

## *Felis lybica* Forster, 1780

## African wild cat
## Vaalboskat

Plate 20

**Colloquial Name**

The African wild cat, *F. lybica*, differs from the European wild cat, *F. silvestris*, but there is still some disagreement about the genetic basis for this.

### Taxonomic Notes

The African wild cat, *F. lybica*, interbreeds with the domestic cat, *Felis catus*, where they come into contact. Two features of the African wild cat, *F. lybica*, mark them as distinct from domestic cats, features which are at least partially lost in the progeny, when they interbreed. The first is the rich red colour of the back of the ears. In crosses this red colour may be totally lost, or it may remain to a much lesser degree towards the base of the ears. The second and more striking feature is in the length of the legs. The African wild cat, *F. lybica*, has long slender legs. When they sit upright, the long front legs raise the body into a near vertical position, a posture impossible to the domestic cat or the crosses. Today it is becoming increasingly difficult to find pure-bred African wild cats anywhere near settled areas. The process of hybridisation with domestic cats is a continuing one and, with the increasing human settlement, pure-bred African wild cats may no longer exist, rendering the species vulnerable (Smithers, 1986).

Meester *et al.* (1986) listed two subspecies for the Subregion: *Felis l. cafra* Desmarest, 1822 and *F. l. griselda* Thomas, 1926. Smithers (1971) gave the distribution of these two subspecies, which have a wide zone of intergradation: *F. l. cafra* occurring in the southern and eastern parts of the Republic of South Africa, north to eastern Zimbabwe and central and southern Mozambique; *F. l. griselda*, the remainder of the species' range in the Subregion. This is based on the general lighter, sandier colour of *F. l. griselda*, which is associated with the drier western part of the Subregion, as opposed to the darker colour of *F. l. cafra*, from the better watered southern and eastern areas, a colour cline often seen in other small mammals.

Within the two subspecies there is considerable variation in colour and markings locally and care must be exercised in assessing characters as, wherever there is contact with domestic cats, interbreeding occurs.

### Description

While there is a general similarity in the marking on the bodies and tails of the two subspecies which occur in the Southern African Subregion, in colour they are very different. The sandier coloured *F. l. griselda* blends well with the sandier coloured conditions ruling in the arid areas, thus gaining a selective advantage. The overall colour of *F. l. griselda* is light sandy, the forehead darker, with an indistinct darker band down the mid-back from the forehead to the base of the tail. The tail is darker than the body, owing to a more profuse admixture of black banded hairs; the upper part has four or five black bands, on a ground colour of greyish white, and a black tip. On the flanks, from the shoulder to the thighs, they have a series of about six indistinct, sometimes barely visible, reddish vertical bands which extend from the dark dorsal band to the under parts. The front legs are distinctly marked with a series of four or five broken black bands on the upper parts and normally two broad black bands on the lower, which contrast distinctly with the lighter colour of the under parts of these limbs. On the back legs there are a series of narrow black or reddish-black bands on the thighs, the remainder of the upper parts of these limbs being light sandy colour, lighter than the body colour. Both the fore and hind feet underneath are jet black.

The chin and throat are white; the chest is white, washed with pale rufous; the lower chest and belly are pale reddish, lighter or near white towards the anus. The throat has one or two encircling reddish bands; the back of the ears are rich reddish.

In *F. l. cafra* the colour is dark grey or iron-grey overall, the markings similar to *F. l. griselda*, but black or grey-black instead of red. The back of the ears and throat band are dark red. Males are normally larger and heavier than females (Table 251.1).

**Table 251.1**

Measurements (mm) and mass (kg) of a sample of African wild cats, *F. l. griselda*, from (a) Botswana (Smithers, 1971) and *F. l. cafra* from (b) the Cape Province (Stuart, 1981)

**(a)**

| | Males | | | Females | | |
|---|---|---|---|---|---|---|
| | $\bar{x}$ | n | Range | $\bar{x}$ | n | Range |
| TL | 920 | 32 | 850–1005 | 886 | 27 | 820–947 |
| T | 344 | 32 | 320–375 | 336 | 27 | 310–370 |
| Hf s/u | 153 | 34 | 135–170 | 147 | 27 | 138–158 |
| E | 70 | 34 | 64–79 | 68 | 27 | 62–73 |
| Mass | 5,1 | 32 | 3,8–6,4 | 4,2 | 26 | 3,2–5,5 |

**(b)**

| | Males | | | Females | | |
|---|---|---|---|---|---|---|
| | $\bar{x}$ | n | Range | $\bar{x}$ | n | Range |
| TL | (906) | | | (845) | | |
| HB | 601 | 21 | 545–665 | 550 | 15 | 460–620 |
| T | 305 | 21 | 275–360 | 295 | 16 | 250–355 |
| Hf s/u | 138 | 21 | 120–150 | 133 | 14 | 120–150 |
| E | 62 | 20 | 55–70 | 64 | 15 | 55–72 |
| Mass | 4,9 | 10 | 4,0–6,2 | 3,7 | 10 | 2,4–5,0 |

As with all subspecies there is a wide zone of intergradation of colour in the area where their distributional ranges approach each other, within which it is difficult, if not impossible, to assign the specimens to one subspecies or another.

Both subspecies have tails that are between 50% and 60% of the length of the head and body. The tails are ringed with black towards the tips, which are broadly black. The feet are hairy below, except on the pads, the hair black or very dark brown. They have five digits on the front feet and four on the back, the first digits on the front feet set far back from the other four and, therefore, not marking in the spoor (Fig. 251.1).

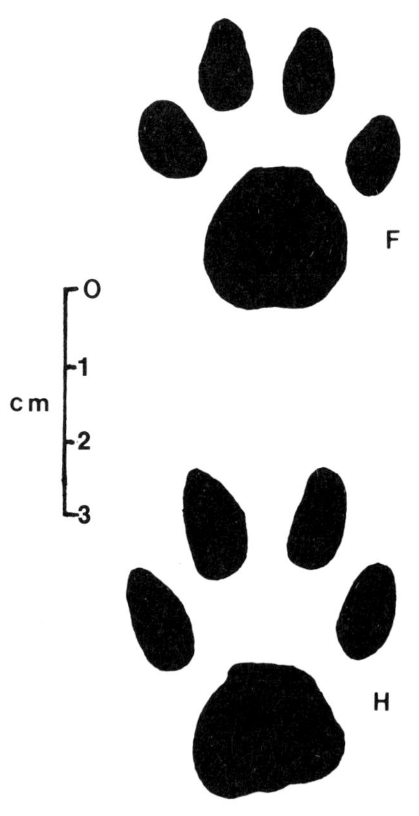


Fig. 251.1. Spoor: African wild cat, *F. lybica*.
F. Right forefoot H. Right hind foot.

**Skull** (Fig. 251.2)

The skull is high, arched and comparatively lightly built. In front it falls away sharply to the incisors, reflecting the short muzzle of the species. The zygoma is thick and heavily built, providing substantial attachments for the masseter muscles and, bowed out from the sides of the skull, gives ample space for the well developed temporalis muscles. The supraoccipital crest, which lies at the back of the skull, is wide and strong and from it a short sagittal crest runs at right angles over the back part of the braincase. In some felids, this sagittal crest continues forward over most of the braincase, giving additional anchorage for the fibres of attachment of the temporalis muscle which activates the closing of the lower jaw. The postorbital processes are well developed above and below but do not join, although there may be a cartilagenous junction, which is lost in the cleaned skull.

The dental formula is:

$I\frac{3}{3}\ C\frac{1}{1}\ P\frac{3}{2}\ M\frac{1}{1} = 30$

The presence of the second premolar in the upper jaw is not constant and, in a sample of 137 adult wild cat skulls of both sexes, in 5,1% they were absent and in a further 2,2% occurred on one side only. In all cases, where they are present, they are small and peg-like. The carnassial shear is adapted to cutting up the prey once it has been killed. Almost the whole of the upper fourth premolar and the lower first molar, which occlude one on another, are provided with sharp edges which act as cutting blades for chopping up the toughest of prey. In addition the cutting edges on the first lower molar lie at an angle to each other which prevents tough prey slipping away. The canines are flattened, long and sharp, adapted to performing the killing bite by entering between the neck vertebrae of their prey, forcing these apart and severing the spinal column.

The bullae are large, reflecting the keen sense of hearing of the species. Corresponding with the slightly larger size of males, the total length of their skulls is slightly larger than in females. The length of the toothrow, measured from the front of the canine, at the junction with the bone, to the back of the molar in the upper jaw, and the breadth of the back of the palate measured between the bases of the upper first molars on either side of the upper jaw ($M^1$-$M^1$) show, however, little sexual difference (Table 251.2).

**Table 251.2**

Average skull measurements (mm) of a series of African wild cats, *F. lybica* from (a) Zimbabwe (Smithers, 1983) and (b) the Cape Province (Stuart, 1981)

| | (a) | | | (b) | | |
|---|---|---|---|---|---|---|
| **Males** | | | | | | |
| | $\bar{x}$ | n | Range | $\bar{x}$ | n | Range |
| TL | 102,8 | 25 | 95,5–110,5 | 102,0 | 18 | 95,0–116,0 |
| Condylobasal length | 92,8 | 25 | 86,8–101,1 | | | |
| Length toothrow | 32,9 | 25 | 29,9–38,4 | | | |
| $M^1$-$M^1$ | 32,2 | 25 | 32,0–36,9 | | | |
| **Females** | | | | | | |
| TL | 98,5 | 28 | 93,6–107,2 | 96,0 | 7 | 90,0–103,0 |
| Condylobasal length | 88,4 | 28 | 83,3–96,6 | | | |
| Length toothrow | 31,6 | 28 | 28,9–33,9 | | | |
| $M^1$-$M^1$ | 33,0 | 28 | 30,0–36,0 | | | |

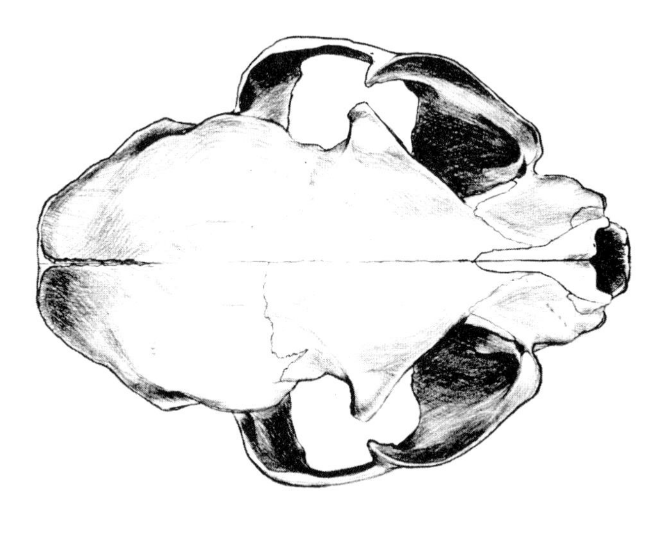

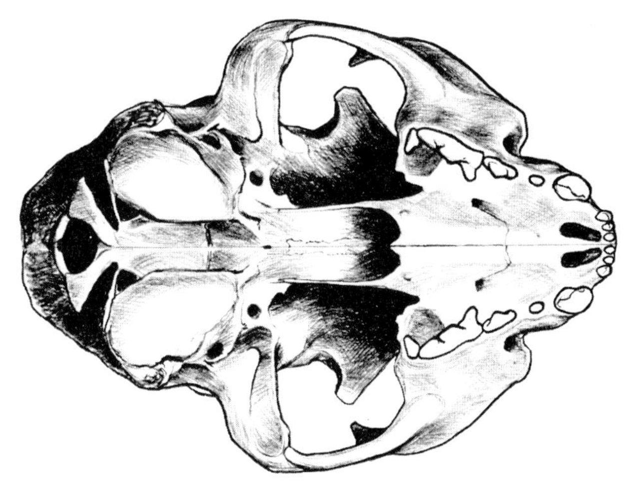

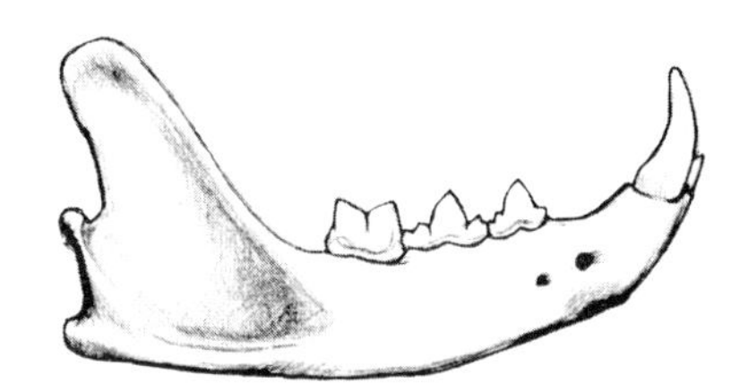

Fig. 251.2. Skull: African wild cat, *F. lybica*.
TL Skull 100 mm.

## Distribution

The African wild cat, *Felis lybica*, has a wide distribution on the continent, being absent only in tropical and montane forest. Extralimitally, their distribution extends to the Sinai Peninsula, Arabia and countries bordering the eastern Mediterranean, eastwards to the plains of India. In many parts of their range they are the commonest small carnivore occurring.

*North Africa*

Discontinuously distributed in **Western Sahara** and **Morocco**, they occur eastwards in **Algeria; Tunisia** and **Libya**; narrowly between the fringes of the Sahara and the Mediterranean coast, to **Egypt** and in northwestern **Niger** in the Aïr massif.

*South of the Sahara, excluding the Southern African Subregion*

They occur in the **Sudan**, excluding the southeastern extension of the Sahara; **Ethiopia; Somalia; Kenya; Uganda; Tanzania; Zaire**, excluding the forested areas of the Congo basin, and westwards in the Guinea and Sudan savannas and in part of the Sahel, to northern **Sierra Leone** and southern **Mauritania**. South of this they are recorded from **Angola; Zambia; Mozambique**, north of the Zambezi River and **Malawi**.

*Southern African Subregion*

In **Namibia** they occur widely, except in the coastal Namib Desert; throughout **Botswana; Zimbabwe** and **Mozambique**, south of the Zambezi River. In the **Transvaal** and **Orange Free State** they occur throughout. In **Natal** they occur widely, but appear to be absent from the low lying, coastal regions; they are found throughout the **Cape Province**.

## Habitat

The African wild cat has a wide habitat tolerance. In the Subregion they occur at altitudes of between sea level and about 1 600 m. Their distribution on a continental basis follows the isohyet of mean annual rainfall of 100 mm quite closely, below which they normally do not occur except where river courses act as avenues into otherwise drier terrain, or where isolated mountains catch a slightly higher rainfall than the surrounding country (Sahara).

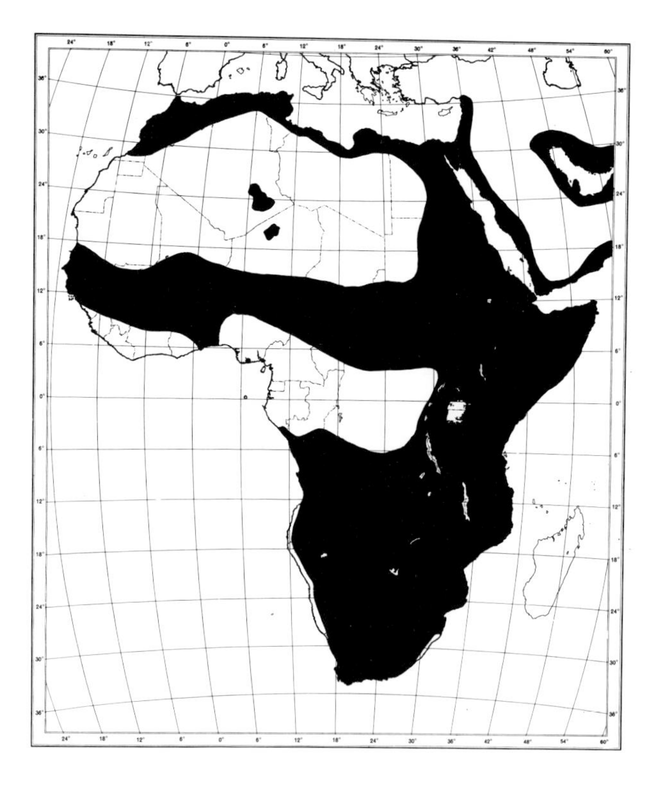

Throughout their range they require cover of some sort in the form of rocky hillsides, underbush, reedbeds or stands of tall grass in which to rest during the day. In open semi-desert country such as the Kalahari, they will use isolated stands of *Acacia* scrub or other bushes (Smithers, 1971). Where adequate cover of vegetation is not available in plains country, they will lie up in holes in the ground excavated by other species such as the antbear, *Orycteropus afer*, under the roots of trees, where the soil is eroded away, or in holes in termitaria. Riverine underbrush, thickly wooded kloofs, dense underbrush on termitaria, piles of rocks or debris thrown up by flooding have also been recorded, as well as agriculturally developed areas, where they use the shelter of standing crops such as maize and other high standing grain crops.

## Habits

They are almost entirely nocturnal, and usually move late after sundown. An oestrous female may be attended by several males, otherwise wild cats are a solitary species. They have terrestrial habits, although they are adept at climbing trees under stress or when hunting. They are secretive and cunning and are difficult to trap. They are highly territorial and the territories, which are marked both by the males and females, are defended by both sexes. With two hand-reared, free-ranging *F. lybica* females, territorial instincts only became apparent some time after each had produced a litter (Smithers, 1983). Territories are assiduously urine-marked, each over-marking various points marked by the other. They "caterwaul" loudly at each other before an attack develops.

## Food

Murids predominate in their diet as shown by analyses of the stomach contents of 58 specimens from Zimbabwe (Smithers & Wilson, 1979) and 80 from Botswana (Smithers, 1971) (Table 251.3); the eastern Robertson Karoo and Karoo National Park respectively (Stuart, 1982a; Palmer & Fairall, 1988). There are close similarities between the occurrence of the other items, except that birds are less well represented in the Botswana sample; hunting spiders, Solifugae, on the other hand, are better represented, reflecting their commoner occurrence in this semi-desert habitat as opposed to the higher rainfall areas in Zimbabwe.

**Table 251.3**

Percentage occurrence of food items in a sample of 58 stomach contents of African wild cats, *F. lybica*, from Zimbabwe and 80 from Botswana (Smithers, 1971; Smithers & Wilson, 1979)

| Item | Percentage occurrence Zimbabwe | Botswana |
|---|---|---|
| Muridae | 72 | 74 |
| Aves | 21 | 10 |
| Insecta | 19 | 19 |
| Reptilia | 10 | 13 |
| Mammalia | 9 | 6 |
| Solifugae | 7 | 18 |
| Amphibia | 2 | 1 |
| Araneae | 2 | 1 |
| Myriapoda | 2 | 1 |
| Scorpiones | — | 2 |
| Wild fruit | 2 | 1 |

**Table 251.4**

Percentage occurrence of species of murids occurring in a sample of 58 stomachs of African wild cats, *F. lybica*, from Zimbabwe and 80 from Botswana (Smithers, 1971; Smithers & Wilson, 1979)

| Species | Percentage occurrence Zimbabwe | Botswana |
|---|---|---|
| Multimammate mice, *Mastomys* spp | 31 | 8 |
| Angoni vlei rat, *Otomys angoniensis* | 14 | — |
| Bushveld gerbil, *Tatera leucogaster* | 12 | 40* |
| Pouched mouse, *Saccostomus campestris* | 3 | 8 |
| Fat mouse, *Steatomys pratensis* | 3 | 5 |
| Pygmy mouse, *Mus minutoides* | 3 | 15 |
| House rat, *Rattus rattus* | 2 | — |
| Creek rat, *Pelomys fallax* | 2 | — |
| Namaqua rock mouse, *Aethomys namaquensis* | 2 | 3* |
| Hairy-footed gerbil, *Gerbillurus paeba* | — | 6 |
| Grey pygmy climbing mouse, *Dendromus melanotis* | — | 1 |

*Involves species other than those on the Zimbabwe list.

Multimammate mice, *Mastomys* spp had by far the highest occurrence in Zimbabwe and were found in stomachs in every month of the year (Table 251.4). This reflects their wide habitat tolerance as the commonest murid species occurring in this savanna woodland habitat. As they do not occur in desert or semi-desert areas and as the latter association covers the largest part of Botswana, their occurrence in this sample is much lower. Angoni vlei rats, *Otomys angoniensis*, wander far from swampy areas to feed on the new flush of grasses, which constitute their main food, when they become available. All the occurrences of vlei rats in stomachs from Zimbabwe are from the months of March to July, indicating that the wild cats were catching these during the times when they were wandering out of their swampy habitat. The high occurrence of gerbils, *Tatera* spp, in the Botswana sample reflects their wide occurrence throughout. Two species, *T. leucogaster* and *T. brantsii* occur, but it was not at that time possible to specifically identify the material in stomachs. *T. brantsii* has a very limited distribution in Zimbabwe, the common and widespread species there being *T. leucogaster*. Both species are nocturnal and, therefore, available to the nocturnal wild cat. The house rat, *Rattus rattus*, is an introduced commensal and does not occur in the veld and, therefore, must be taken in the vicinity of homesteads, farm outbuildings and stores. So far it has not been shown to occur in Botswana but is well established in Zimbabwe. The wild cat is not averse to hunting close to human habitations as is shown by its predatory habits on poultry, at which times house rats become available to them.

The highest occurrence of birds in stomach contents in Zimbabwe was poultry in the form of ducks and chickens (Table 251.5). The largest wild bird in the two samples was a korhaan, *Laephotis* sp, but they are known to take species up to the size of a guineafowl, *Numida mitrata*.

**Table 251.5**

Breakdown of species of the Aves occurring in a sample of 58 stomachs of African wild cats, *F. lybica*, from Zimbabwe and 80 from Botswana, showing the percentage occurrence (Smithers, 1971; Smithers & Wilson, 1979)

| Species | Percentage occurrence Zimbabwe | Botswana |
|---|---|---|
| Poultry | 7 | — |
| Turtle dove, *Streptopelia capicola* | 3 | 3 |
| Button quail, *Turnix sylvatica* | 2 | 4 |
| Korhaan, *Laephotis* sp | 2 | 1 |
| Harlequin quail, *Coturnix delegorguei* | — | 1 |
| Quelea, *Quelea quelea* | 2 | 5 |
| Undet. weavers | 3 | — |

Most small carnivores eat reptiles and the wild cat is no exception. These are treated in the same way as murids and are chopped into sections without mastication, rendering their identification easier. The wide range of species represented is listed. They occur at 10% and 13% for the two areas (Table 251.6).

**Table 251.6**

Species of Reptilia occurring in a sample of 58 stomachs of the African wild cat, *F. lybica*, from Zimbabwe (Smithers & Wilson, 1979) and 80 from Botswana (Smithers, 1971)

| Species | Zimbabwe | Botswana |
|---|---|---|
| **Sauria** | | |
| Many lined plated-lizard, *Gerrhosaurus multilineatus* | + | − |
| Black lined plated-lizard, *G. nigrolineatus* | + | + |
| Striped scrub-lizard, *Nucras taeniolata* | + | − |
| Common striped skink, *Mabuya striata* | + | − |
| Variable skink, *M. varia* | − | + |
| Sundevall's writhing skink, *Lygosoma sundevallii* | + | + |
| Percival's limbless skink, *Acontias percivali* | − | + |
| Sand lizard, *Eremias* sp | − | + |
| Worm lizard, *Zygaspis quadrifrons* | − | + |
| Whistling gecko, *Ptenopus garrulus* | − | + |
| **Serpentes** | | |
| Black templed cat snake, *Crotaphopeltis hotamboeia* | + | − |
| Schlegel's blind snake, *Typhlops schlegelii* | + | − |
| Puff adder, *Bitis arietans* | − | + |
| Pygmy sand snake, *Psammophis angolensis* | + | − |

**Note:** The Mozambique writhing skink, *Lygosoma afer*, was recognised in a stomach from Mozambique.

Apart from the murids already listed, other mammals had occurrences of 9% and 6%. In the Zimbabwe sample the scrub hare, *Lepus saxatilis*, and the red rock rabbit, *Pronolagus* spp, were both recorded, as well as an elephant shrew, *Elephantulus* sp, an unusual food item for small carnivores. In one stomach there were the remains of a very young, perhaps newly-born, grysbok, *Raphicerus sharpei*, or steenbok, *R. campestris*. The taking of the young of small antelopes has been recorded by Watson (1950), Maberly (1963) and Dorst & Dandelot (1970). They are not capable of taking adults.

Amphibia were represented in both samples by the bullfrog, *Pyxicephalus adspersus*, and Myriapoda by the centipede, *Scolopendra morsitans*.

Insects in both samples consisted predominantly of grasshoppers and crickets, but included Isoptera and, in Botswana, Lepidoptera in the form of the convolvulus hawk moth, *Herse convolvuli*, from the stomachs of two specimens taken at the Makgadikgadi Pan during an unprecedented hatch of these moths.

Sunspiders, Solifugae, which were much commoner in the Botswana sample, were recorded mainly from the warm wet months of the year, October to March, when they move widely at night and were in evidence, especially around camp lights, searching for their insect prey.

In the Zimbabwe sample the fruits of the jackal-berry, *Diospyros mespiliformis*, were found in two stomachs; these are commonly eaten by small carnivores.

During the last two years of the four year drought of 1962/65 in Botswana, when murid populations were at an unprecedented low level (Smithers, 1971), contents of 16 wild cat stomachs consisted of invertebrates, fruit and birds only. They are capable of switching their food requirements to what is available.

Their hunting technique is typically felid: the stalk, the crouch, accompanied by a settling of the back feet to get a good grip on the ground, and then the rush in to the kill. Capture of small mammals is achieved by the use of the claws of the front feet, the killing bite delivered with the blade-like canines on the neck of the prey, the vertebrae being forced apart and the spinal cord severed. With larger prey the individual may throw itself on its side, raking the prey with its back claws, until the killing bite becomes effective.

### Reproduction

Litters of two to five, averaging three, are born during summer from September to March, with occasional records outside this period, in holes in the ground, excavated by other species such as the antbear, *Orycteropus afer*, or the springhaas, *Pedetes capensis*. They do not dig themselves. Other situations recorded include crevices in rocks, under thick underbush, in tall grass stands and in the shelter of standing maize. No bedding material is used, although a litter found in a maize land had been born on top of a pile of fallen leaves and other debris which effectively insulated the young from the soil. A captive free-ranging female *Felis lybica* produced litters as follows (the number of kittens in the litters indicated in parentheses) (Smithers, 1983):

| | | | | | | |
|---|---|---|---|---|---|---|
| 1966 | February | (1) | August | (2) | | |
| 1967 | June | (3) | October | (1) | | |
| 1968 | May | (3) | | | | |
| 1969 | February | (3) | June | (5) | October | (5) |

The male does not appear to assist in the rearing of the young, but when one female in captivity was rearing kittens, the other female would bring mice or birds to them when their mother was away. When the female with young was in the enclosure the "auntie" simply left the offering at the entrance gate.

A captive reared African wild cat crossed with a serval, *F. serval*, and produced several litters over a period of three years that reached maturity (Fig. 251.3). The kittens were in every case premature. The gestation period was 63 days as against 65 for the wild cat or 68–74 for the serval (Smithers, 1983).

Fig. 251.3. Hybrid *F. lybica* x *F. serval* bred by Mrs. M. Schmolke of Harare, Zimbabwe (Photo C.K. Brain).

No. 252

## *Felis nigripes* Burchell, 1824

### Small spotted cat
### Klein gekolde kat

Plate 20

### Colloquial Name

The colloquial name black-footed cat is entrenched throughout the Subregion, which is unfortunate. First, only the under parts of the feet are black, the upper parts are never black. Secondly, African wild cats, *F. lybica*, are in many cases also black under the feet which has led to confusion between the two species.

*Miershooptier* has been used in Afrikaans; this is applied because of their high degree of association with termite mounds.

### Taxonomic Notes

There are two subspecies *F. n. nigripes* from the Kalahari and *F. n. thomasi* from the Karoo. With Shortridge's (1931a) description of the reddish-fawn *F. n. thomasi* and the pale, almost tawny specimens from Botswana, north and northwest of Kuruman, we can see clearly that the two subspecies do differ, at least in colour.

### Description

The small spotted cat is the smallest of the felids occurring in the Subregion, to which it is confined (Table 252.1).

**Table 252.1**

Measurements (mm) and mass (kg) of a series of small spotted cats, *F. n. nigripes*, from Botswana (Smithers, 1971)

| | Males | | | Females | | |
|---|---|---|---|---|---|---|
| | $\bar{x}$ | n | Range | $\bar{x}$ | n | Range |
| TL | 579 | 5 | 540–631 | 513 | 3 | 495–530 |
| T | 177 | 5 | 164–198 | 153 | 3 | 126–170 |
| Hf s/u | 99 | 5 | 94–104 | 92 | 3 | 89–94 |
| E | 54 | 5 | 51–57 | 47 | 3 | 45–50 |
| Mass | 1,6 | 5 | 1,5–1,7 | 1,1 | 3 | 1,0–1,4 |

The body is marked with lines and spots, the background colour in the southern part of the range (*F. n. thomasi*) cinnamon-buff, in the northern (*F. n. nigripes*) lighter in colour, being tawny, in some specimens off-white. On the nape of the neck of those from the northern areas there are four black bands running on to the shoulder, these often broken into short lengths or spots. The outer two on either side swing over the shoulders and on to the flanks; the inner two break into spots or short bands down the middle of the back and continue to the base of the tail. In specimens from the south the four bands may be strongly developed and, originating on the forehead, the two central ones extend unbroken to the base of the tail.

In the southern subspecies, *F. n. thomasi*, the spots and bands are satiny black, and are defined more clearly; in the northern, *F. n. nigripes*, more washed out, less distinct and tinged rusty. In both, the limbs have a series of three broad transverse black bars on the upper parts and shorter narrow bars towards the feet, these sometimes taking the form of spots. The tail has the same background colour as the back and is indistinctly spotted to near the tip in both subspecies. The chin, chest and insides of the thighs are white in both subspecies; the remainder of the under parts is washed with buff in *F. n. thomasi*, pure white in *F. n. nigripes*, in both cases with black spots and bars.

A distinctive feature of *F. n. thomasi* is the three throat rings, which are black, narrowly edged with rufous; in *F. n. nigripes* they are reddish-brown or black, edged with reddish-brown or rufous. In some individuals only two rings are in evidence, the third ring indistinct or broken; in others it is barely distinguishable. The head is usually slightly darker than the remainder of the body, being suffused with dark, white-tipped hair. The hairs of the coat are about 25 mm to 30 mm long, grey at their bases and conform to the general colour of the upper parts throughout their length, except that some have white, others dark, subapical annulations and white or tawny tips. The hairs of the spots and bars are satiny black in *F. n. thomasi*, in *F. n. nigripes* brownish-black or tawny. The hairs of the dense underfur are fine, wavy and not as long as the guard hairs.

The tail is short, narrowly black-tipped and less than half the length of the body and head; the legs are relatively long. The backs of the ears are predominantly the same colour as the background of the upper parts, often darker. The undersides of all four feet are black, or very dark blackish-brown. The spoor is identical to that of *Felis lybica*, only about half the size (see Fig. 251.1).

### Skull (Fig. 252.1)

The skull of the small spotted cat is high and rounded, with a flatter section on top from the level of the eye orbits to the middle of the braincase, where it slopes off abruptly to the supraoccipital crest. In the front it slopes sharply from above the front of the eye orbits to the nasals, the rostrum being very short and broad. The zygomatic arches swing out widely at the back, their width at this point about 75% of the total length of the skull. The postorbital constriction is wide, about 40% of the total length of the skull. The postorbital bars are incomplete. The jugals, which form the anterior part of the zygomatic arch, are very broad in front and concave internally, where they support the very large eyeballs.

The dental formula is:

$I\frac{3}{3}\ C\frac{1}{1}\ P\frac{3}{2}\ M\frac{1}{1} = 30$

The outer, upper incisors are only very slightly larger than the remainder, the canines very sharp and flattened on their inner sides. The upper second premolars are tiny, the fourth sectorial. The molars are tiny. The canines in the lower jaw curve evenly from the bases and are long and sharp. The first molar, which functions as the lower part of the carnassial shear, has sharp edges, the cusps set in a wide open V which prevents tough food sliding out while being cut.

The bullae are large and swollen, their total length about 25% of the total length of the skull; their width, at the widest point, about 18%.

The pattern of the teeth follows the characteristic felid arrangement in their adaptation to the killing bite, with long, sharp, blade-like canines, and in the sectorial action of the other teeth in slicing the food into sections suitable for swallowing.

### Distribution

The small spotted cat is confined in its distribution to the central parts of the Subregion, within the South West Arid Zone, with an extension eastwards to eastern Lesotho.

*Southern African Subregion*

In **Botswana** they occur from just south of the Okavango Delta at about 20°S, throughout the southwestern parts of the country, but are not recorded in the eastern sector. In **Namibia** they are confined to the central and southern parts of the eastern areas of the country from about 20°S on the Botswana border, and narrowly southwards to where the Namibia border meets the Orange River, but not west of about 17°E. They may occur westwards of the present known limits in dry water courses which run in this direction from the escarpment, but no material exists at the moment to confirm this. They occur in the **Orange Free State**. There is a record from the eastern Injasuti Triplets peak in the Drakensberg in **Lesotho** at an altitude of 2 000 m on a snow covered ledge. They occur widely in the **Cape Province** from the west coast, near Bitterfontein, from several localities in the Calvinia and Ceres districts, and from Montagu, which suggests that they may occur over much of the interior, eastwards to the eastern parts of the Province. Surveys in the **Transvaal** (Rautenbach, 1978) show that they occur only marginally in the southwestern parts of the province, with a recent record of a roadkill from Marble Hall

**Plate 20**

250. Caracal, *Felis caracal*
Rooikat
251. African wild cat, *Felis lybica*
Vaalboskat
252. Small spotted cat, *Felis nigripes*
Klein gekolde kat
253. Serval, *Felis serval*
Tierboskat

PLATE 20
253
252
251
250

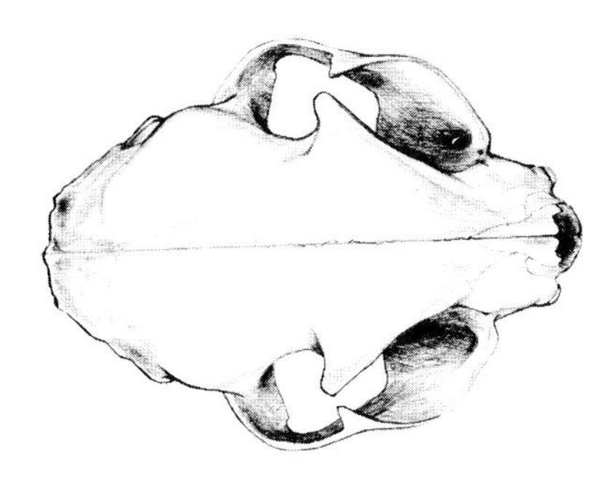

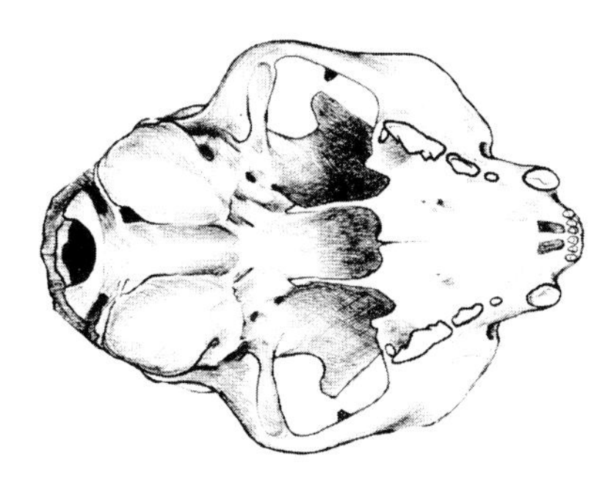

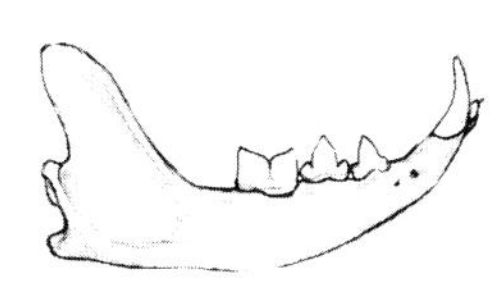

Fig. 252.1. Skull: small spotted cat, *F. nigripes*.
TL Skull 80 mm.

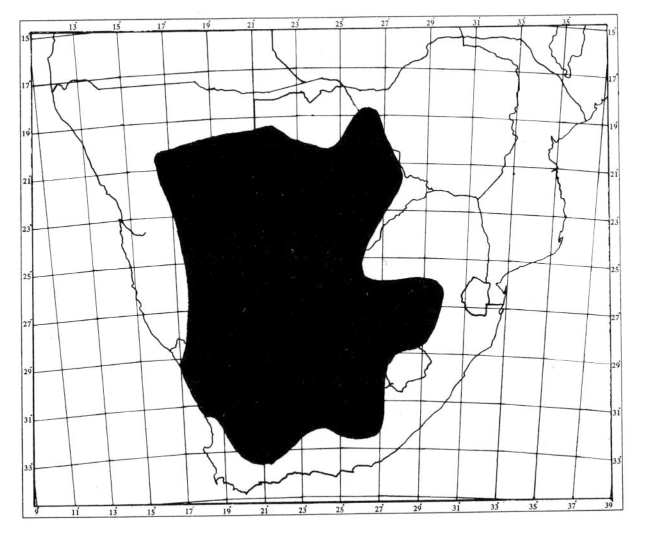

(Skinner, 1989, unpubl.), but no link as yet with the main population.

### Habitat

Throughout their range small spotted cats are associated with arid country with a mean annual rainfall of between about 100 to 500 mm, particularly with open habitat which provides some cover in the form of stands of tall grass or scrub bush to which they will retreat quickly if disturbed. They will also use disused springhaas or antbear holes or holes in termite mounds in which to lie up during daylight hours. They are independent of water but will drink occasionally when this is available.

### Habits

They are a nocturnal and highly secretive species, not being in evidence until some two hours after sunset. They are not common anywhere throughout their range, and very little has been published on their habits in the wild. If caught in the beam of dazzling lights at night their reaction is to slink off, only looking back to reveal their brightly shining eyes momentarily as they make for the nearest cover to hide. Most observations are of solitary individuals. For their size they are vicious and aggressive, intractable in captivity, quite unlike the African wild cat, which, reared under the same conditions, may show some independence, but lends itself more easily to domestication.

### Food

In a sample of seven stomach contents from Botswana (Table 252.2), murids had the highest percentage occurrence and included the grey pygmy climbing mouse, *Dendromus melanotis*; the pouched mouse, *Saccostomus campestris*; the Namaqua gerbil, *Gerbillurus paeba*, and gerbils, *Tatera* spp. Reptilia consisted of the remains of the spiny agama, *Agama hispida*. Arachnida consisted principally of hunting spiders, Solifugae, among which *Solpuga monteiroi* was well represented, together with the remains of small spiders, *Palystes* sp. Insects were principally small adult Coleoptera.

**Table 252.2**

The percentage occurrence of various food items in seven stomach contents of the small spotted cat, *F. nigripes* from Botswana (Smithers, 1971)

| Food item | Percentage occurrence |
|---|---|
| Muridae | 57 |
| Arachnida | 43 |
| Macroscelididae | 14 |
| Reptilia | 14 |
| Insecta | 14 |
| Aves | 14 |

### Reproduction

Rautenbach (1978) recorded a female with two foetuses in November from the Transvaal and Visser (1977) stated that the gestation period is 67 to 68 days, litters of one to three kittens with a mass of 66 to 80 g being born in November or December. The eyes open 3–9 days after birth.

---

No. 253

## *Felis serval* Schreber, 1776

## Serval
## Tierboskat

Plate 20

---

### Colloquial Name

The English colloquial name is derived from the Portuguese for the European lynx, "lobo-cerval" (Rosevear, 1974). Forster (1781) in his description of the species from the Cape used the name "*Tyger bosch katten*", applied to the species by Kolb (1719). The Afrikaans name is a literal translation of this and is still widely used.

### Taxonomic Notes

Allen (1939) listed 17 subspecies from the continent, three of the small spotted *F. brachyura* and 14 of *F. serval*. Ellerman *et al.* (1953) considered the small spotted forms as merely pattern phases or mutants of the normal *F. serval*. This view has not been accepted universally up to the present time (Ansell, 1978). It is well known, however, that spotted cats, in particular, are prone to produce aberrant forms. To date, no small spotted forms corresponding to the extreme, as exemplified by *F. brachyura*, have been taken in the Subregion. Meester *et al.* (1986) relegated all the material from the Subregion to *F. s. serval*.

### Description

The serval is an elegant species, with its long legs and neck, small head, large ears and beautifully spotted and barred coat. One feature of the serval is the long, slimly built limbs which give it a height at the shoulder of about 0,6 m. The serval's ears are particularly large, broad at the base with rounded tips, their size accentuated by the comparatively small head. The tail is short, about 40% of the length of the head and body (Table 253.1).

**Table 253.1**

Measurements (mm) and mass (kg) of servals, *F. serval*, from the Harare District, Zimbabwe (Smithers, 1978)

| | Males | | | Females | | |
|---|---|---|---|---|---|---|
| | $\bar{x}$ | n | Range | $\bar{x}$ | n | Range |
| TL | 1111 | 23 | 960–1205 | 1 097 | 23 | 970–1230 |
| T | 814 | 23 | 280–380 | 290 | 23 | 254–330 |
| Hf s/u | 193 | 23 | 180–205 | 182 | 23 | 165–194 |
| E | 91 | 23 | 83–97 | 86 | 23 | 80–97 |
| Mass | 11,13 | 20 | 8,63–13,53 | 9,67 | 23 | 8,63–11,80 |

The background colour of the upper parts varies greatly in individuals from a restricted area and may vary from off-white to a light golden-yellow, often with a broad darker band of yellow or golden-yellow down the mid-back, which sometimes is suffused with grey. The black bands and spots, which are so characteristic of the species, vary in width and size and there is a wide variety of combinations of marking and background colour within populations from relatively small areas. In spite of this the black markings of specimens from the Subregion conform to a recognisable pattern. Arising from between the ears a series of black bands extends down the neck, the outer two swinging outwards across the top of the shoulders on to the flanks. These two bands are usually distinct and unbroken on the neck, but tend to break up on the shoulders and flanks into short bars or spots. The inner two are usually less distinct, more broken up, and end behind the shoulders. Between them at shoulder level, a further two black bands arise, usually broken into short bars which continue to the base of the tail. The flanks are distinctly spotted, this continuing on to the upper parts of the limbs. The upper parts of the front limbs are encircled with two broad black bands; in some specimens the upper band in front breaks up into short bars or spots. The hind limbs are similarly banded, but only on their inner sides; these bands break into short bars or spots on the outer sides, in some individuals giving the impression of bands. The marking on the back of the ears is very characteristic, consisting of two black bands, one covering the tip, the other about half way down, with a pure white band between them; the front is covered with pure white hair.

The under parts are lighter in colour than the upper and in some specimens are pure white from the chin to the base of the tail, with a distinct black collar high up on the neck, black spotting lower down and black spots or bars on the chest and upper parts of the belly.

The tail has a series of black encircling bands or, in some specimens, irregular black markings that give the impression of bands. The tip is black, the ground colour similar to that of the upper parts.

The hair of the guard coat on the upper parts is soft and, while shorter on the head, about 10 mm, is fairly even in length over the remainder of the body at about 30 mm. The underfur is dense, wavy and shorter than the hairs of the guard coat and tends to have a tinge of grey at the base. Interspersed through the coat are numerous tactile hairs up to about 60 mm in length with pale bases and broad black tips. They have five digits on the front feet. The fifth digit, which carries the dew claw, is set far back from the other four and does not mark in the spoor. They have four digits on the hind feet (Fig. 253.1).

**Skull** (Fig. 253.2)

Compared with its close relative the caracal, the skull of the serval is lightly built, lacking the high sagittal crest and the flange-like supraoccipital crest which are features of the skull of the caracal. Typically feline in outline, the highest point is about the level of the postorbital bars. The front portion of the serval skull does not fall off so abruptly to the nasals as in the caracal, reflecting its more forward projecting muzzle. Even in old specimens with well worn teeth the sagittal crest only reaches the back of the braincase, continuing forward over the top of the skull as two low, barely

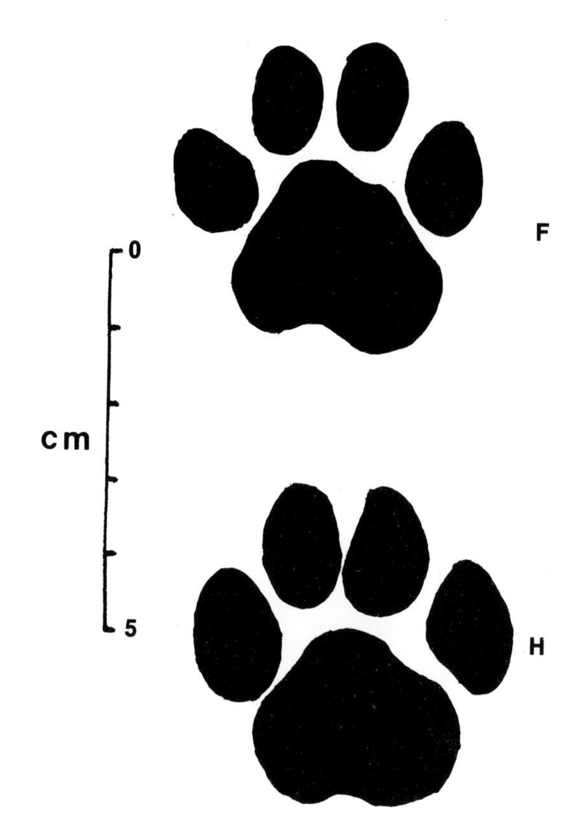


Fig. 253.1. Spoor: serval, *F. serval*.
F. Right forefoot H. Right hind foot.

discernible ridges, between which the bone is smooth and to a large extent devoid of muscle attachments. The braincase is broader and rounder than in the caracal; the zygomatic arches do not swing out so widely, their width about 60% of the total length of the skull as opposed to 75% in the case of the caracal. The postorbital constriction is broad, about 27% of the total length of the skull compared with 20% in the caracal. The postorbital bars are incomplete, even in old individuals.

The dental formula is:

$I\frac{3}{3}\ C\frac{1}{1}\ P\frac{3}{2}\ M\frac{1}{1} = 30$

The small second upper premolar, which is the first tooth behind the canine and normally absent in the caracal, was present in all specimens examined. The upper fourth premolar, which forms the upper section of the carnassial shear, is adapted to cutting; the molar is small but slightly better developed than in the caracal. The coronoid process of the lower jaw never reaches the height and development seen in the caracal, reflecting the lack of need in the serval for the extra powerful jaw action required by the caracal in tackling much larger vertebrate food. Only the third and fourth premolars are found in the lower jaw, together with the first molar which has two high cusps with cutting edges, set in a wide V and which forms the lower component of the carnassial shear.

The ear bullae are well developed, reflecting the keen hearing of the species; their total length is about 22% of the length of the skull.

Viewed from above, a forward projection of the jugal and maxillary bones forms a very distinct rounded ridge overhanging the infraorbital foramen which, although present, is smaller than in the caracal.

**Distribution**

The serval has a wide distribution on the continent south of the Sahara, with a relict population in the mountainous areas from Morocco to Tunisia.

*North and northwestern Africa*

The serval still exists in **Morocco** (Lambert, 1967). It is a relict species in the humid forests of northern **Algeria**. They are recorded from **Tunisia**.

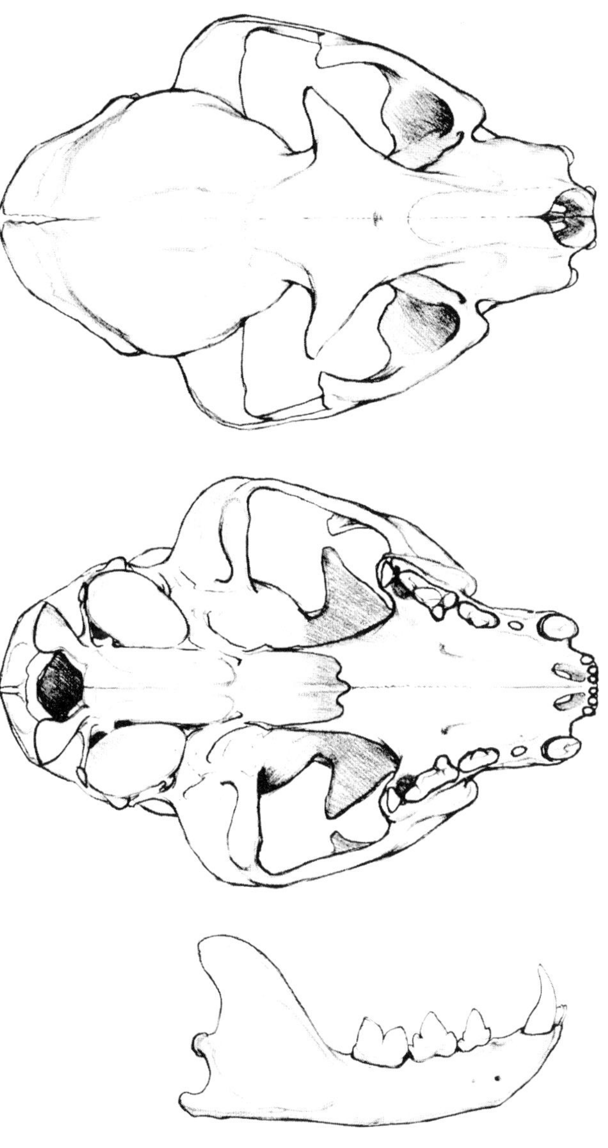

Fig. 253.2 Skull: serval, *F. serval*.
TL Skull 125 mm

*South of the Sahara, excluding the Southern African Subregion*

South of the Sahara they are much more widespread, being listed from most countries from Senegal in the west to Somalia in the east, and southwards to the Subregion. There are specimens in the British Museum (Nat. Hist.) from **Senegal** and they are recorded from **Mali, Guinea Bissau, Sierra Leone, Liberia, Ghana, Togo, Benin, Nigeria**, northern **Cameroun, Chad, Gabon** and the eastern sector of the **Central African Republic**. In the **Sudan** they are absent in the more arid parts of the country, but are found in the vicinity of the White and Blue Nile and in a number of other localities in the south of the country. They occur in **Ethiopia, Somalia, Uganda, Rwanda, Burundi**, northeastern **Zaire**, excluding the forested areas of the Congo basin; **Kenya**; widely in **Tanzania**; throughout **Mozambique**, north of the Zambezi river and in southern **Malawi**. They are widespread in **Zambia** and are recorded from a number of localities in **Angola** where they may occur throughout except in the desert areas.

*Southern African Subregion*

In **Namibia** they occur narrowly in the northeast; in **Botswana** throughout the Okavango Delta, northeastwards to the Chobe River and its associated swamp areas and southwards along the Zimbabwe border to about 20°S, reappearing again in the northern Tuli Block farming area. In **Zimbabwe** they occur widely throughout, except in the southwest. They are widespread and common in **Mozambique**, south of the Zambezi River. They are common in the eastern **Transvaal**, with fewer records westwards and none in the extreme southwestern parts of the province. They occur in the southern, western and northern parts of **Natal**, but not in the coastal areas. Three were released in the Tongaland Elephant Park in 1987 (Skinner, unpubl.). They are now accounted as rare in the **Cape Province**, where they at one time occurred at Port St Johns and near King William's Town, and a specimen was taken near East London and another near Aliwal North. Stuart (1977) recorded that two were trapped and released in the Tsitsikama National Park in that year. Their status is at present uncertain, but if they still occur it will be in a narrow coastal strip as far west as Tsitsikama, which is as far west as they are known to occur at present.

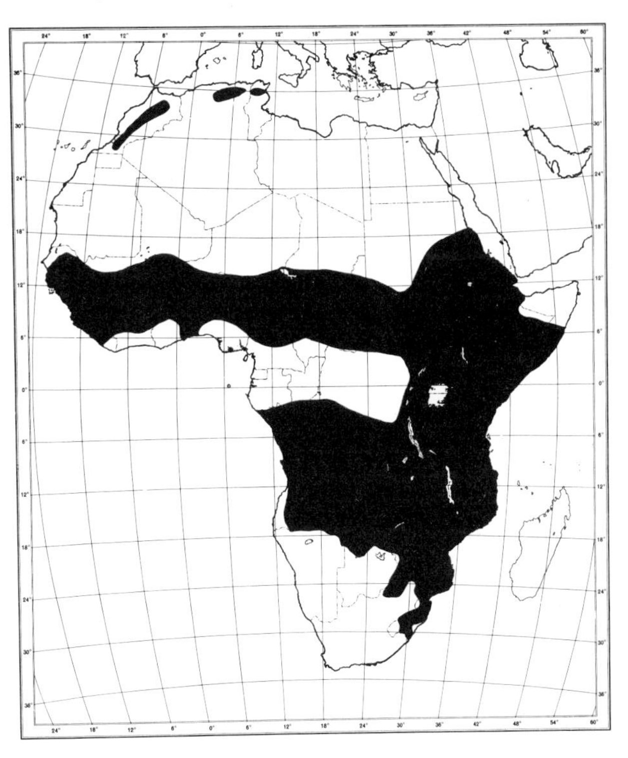

## Habitat

Within their wide distributional range, servals are restricted by their habitat requirements. They do not occur in the South West Arid Zone which covers a large part of the southwestern parts of the Subregion. In Botswana and western Zimbabwe they are confined to areas where there is permanent water, becoming more widespread and common eastwards in the higher rainfall areas, the same situation ruling in the Transvaal.

Proximity to water is an essential requirement, coupled with the availability of adequate cover, whether in the form of stands of tall grass, underbush or reed beds, in which they lie up during the day (van Aarde & Skinner, 1986c).

## Habits

Servals are predominantly nocturnal, with limited activity occurring during early mornings and late afternoons, but diurnal activity is unusual (van Aarde & Skinner, 1986c). Normally solitary, pairs move and hunt together and females accompanied by juveniles up to 3 kg have been recorded, suggesting that the female and her offspring remain together for a considerable time. The male is not in evidence during this time.

Van Aarde & Skinner (1986c) found that two male servals foraged over distances of zero to 205 m per hour during the day and 90 to 463 m per hour during the night. Home ranges of these males overlapped considerably and were 2,08 and 2,70 km$^2$ respectively. Like other small carnivores they tend to use established paths or roads to reach their hunting areas, often preferring to use these even if they entail a longer journey, rather than a more direct route through rough country. In their search for vlei rats, *Otomys* spp, they will hunt in swampy areas, sometimes among aquatic grasses where the water is 50–80 mm deep, conditions avoided by other species such as the African wild cat. On being disturbed servals will make for the nearest stands of tall grass or reed beds or take to adjacent hillsides where there is good cover of underbush or tall grass. Under stress they will climb trees. Their long legs enable them to run fast over short distances and they are difficult to follow at night. When caught in the beam of a dazzling light, they tend to move off quickly to a considerable distance before pausing to look around.

Servals drop their scats fortuitously along roads or paths, usually choosing a patch of short grass or a depression. Having defecated, they make little or no effort to cover the scats, making no more than a few quick scratches with the back feet, which may not even powder the scat. No attempt is made to use the front feet, this behaviour being different from the African wild cat which excavates a depression and carefully covers the scats by scraping with the front feet. Although the scats may vary with the size of the individual, and be up to 20 mm in diameter, they are quite characteristic when dry, being light grey in colour, bound together with the hair of the rodents it has eaten, with a light grey powdery admixture which may be caused by the end products of the digestion of bones. Most bones are digested but often teeth can be recovered (*Otomys* spp, *Tatera* spp), and these can give useful clues to the prey involved.

### Food

In a sample of 65 stomachs from Zimbabwe murids had the highest percentage occurrence, being found in 97% of the stomachs (Table 253.2).

**Table 253.2**

Percentage occurrence of various food items in a sample of 65 stomachs of the serval, *F. serval*, from Zimbabwe (Smithers & Wilson, 1979)

| Food item | Percentage occurrence |
|---|---|
| Muridae | 97 |
| Aves | 15 |
| Reptilia | 12 |
| Mammalia | 6 |
| Insecta | 5 |
| Soricidae | 5 |
| Amphibia | 1 |

Two species, the Angoni vlei rat, *Otomys angoniensis*, and multimammate mouse, *Mastomys* spp, which are widespread and common throughout the distributional range of the serval in the Subregion, predominated (Table 253.3). The vlei rat lives in damp places along rivers and in and on the fringes of swamp where there is a cover of semi-aquatic grasses, sedges or reed beds.

**Table 253.3**

Percentage occurrence of various species of Muridae in the stomachs of 65 servals, *F. serval*, from Zimbabwe (Smithers & Wilson, 1979)

| Species | Percentage occurrence |
|---|---|
| *Otomys angoniensis*, Angoni vlei rat | 42 |
| *Mastomys* spp, Multimammate mouse | 42 |
| *Tatera* sp, Gerbil | 6 |
| *Mus minutoides*, Pygmy mouse | 6 |
| *Saccostomus campestris*, Pouched mouse | 4 |
| *Steatomys pratensis*, Fat mouse | 3 |
| *Aethomys chrysophilus*, Red veld rat | 3 |
| *Dendromus* sp, Climbing mouse | 1,4 |
| *Dasymys incomtus*, Water rat | 1,4 |
| *Pelomys fallax*, Creek rat | 1,4 |
| *Rattus rattus*, House rat | 1,4 |
| *Rhabdomys pumilio*, Striped mouse | 1,4 |

Birds ranked next after murids, but at a lower percentage occurrence of 15%. They consisted of small birds, weavers, *Ploceus* spp; bishop and widow birds, *Euplectes* spp; waxbills, *Estrilda* spp, and quelea, *Quelea quelea*. The occurrence of weavers, waxbills and quelea, which roost in reed beds or in stands of tall grass in damp places, is again an indication of the type of terrain over which servals hunt. They are known to take domestic stock up to the size of peacocks (Smithers, 1983).

Reptiles ranked next at 12%, including three species of lizards and two of snakes (Table 253.4). In the stomach of a serval from Mozambique a yellow-throated plated lizard, *Gerrhosaurus flavigularis*, was recognised.

**Table 253.4**

Species of Reptilia found in a sample of 65 serval, *F. serval*, stomachs from Zimbabwe (Smithers & Wilson, 1979)

| Species | Number of occurrence |
|---|---|
| **Sauria** | |
| *Mabuya striata*, Common striped skink | 3 |
| *Chamaeleo dilepis*, Common flap-necked chameleon | 1 |
| *Lygosoma sundevallii*, Sundervall's writhing skink | 1 |
| **Serpentes** | |
| *Crotaphopeltis hotamboeia*, Herald snake | 2 |
| *Naja mossambica*, Mozambique spitting cobra | 1 |

Among miscellaneous mammals the scrub hare, *Lepus saxatilis*, occurred in two stomachs and the canerat, *Thryonomys swinderianus*, in one. Canerat quills were commonly observed in serval scats and it is thought that when analysis is carried out on a larger series of scats and stomach contents, they will be shown to be eaten more commonly than present information suggests, particularly as they occur in the type of habitat frequented by hunting servals. It is atypical for servals to take antelope.

Insects had a low occurrence at 5%, consisting mainly of grasshoppers and crickets, with an equal occurrence of shrews, *Crocidura* spp, an unusual food item for small carnivores, to which they are generally distasteful. Shrews also occur commonly in the damp habitat frequented by the serval and, therefore, are freely available to them. Amphibia in the form of the remains of a bull frog, *Pyxicephalus adspersus*, was found in one stomach. In killing mice they slap them with a downward blow of the front foot which effectively stuns or kills them.

### Reproduction

Of 20 litters born in captivity at the Zoological Gardens in Pretoria and Johannesberg, these were randomly distributed in eight months of the year (Van Dyk & Wilkinson, pers. comm.); litter size was 1,96 (S.D. 0,5), with a sex ratio not differing significantly from 1:1. Stevenson-Hamilton (1912) recorded young accompanying females in July, August and October in the eastern Transvaal.

In the wild gravid females have been taken from November to March, with a single record for July, indicating that the young are usually born during the middle or latter part of the warm, wet season. The gestation period is 68–72 days (Jones, 1952).

The mean number of foetuses is 2,5 (range 1–3; n=8); implantation is irregular. Foetuses are naked up to about 90 g, pigmentation of the skin clearly marking the location of the black spots and bars at about 150 g. When near full term the foetuses develop a covering of short, soft, woolly hair which shows the black markings, albeit indistinctly. The newborn young retain the soft, woolly coat. The background colour is greyer than in adults, the markings suffused and indistinct (Smithers, 1983).

The four records at present available show that the females litter down on the surface of the ground, either in thick clumps of high grass in open grassland, in underbush or in the cover of stands of maize (Smithers, 1983). If disturbed, females will carry off members of a litter one by one in their mouths. The juveniles certainly accompany the females for a considerable time for they have been collected from family parties at up to 3,4 kg. When a 3 kg juvenile was trapped, the female remained in attendance on it until closely approached.

Females have two pairs of abdominal and one pair of inguinal mammae.

No. 254

## *Felis catus* Linnaeus, 1758

## Domestic cat
## Huiskat

### Colloquial Name

From earliest historical times man has had an affinity for cats. Through man's commercial and exploratory activities in which domestic cats have accompanied him, they now have a cosmopolitan distribution. The seas of the world which act as barriers to most animals, are not barriers to domestic cats who have travelled with their owners by ship, to be sold or to adopt new owners in strange lands. Domestic animals have no place in a work of this type unless they break away from domestication to establish themselves in the wild as a breeding species. This the domestic cat has done in many parts of the world including the Southern African Subregion and so qualifies for inclusion.

We do not know when the first domestic cats were brought to the Subregion, but it is certainly likely that the first Europeans who settled in the Cape were accompanied by cats or at least that they were introduced shortly thereafter. What is known is that they accompanied him sooner or later to wherever he has settled.

The domestic cat, being an exceedingly versatile creature, has in countless parts of the Subregion settled and become feral very successfully.

They have a very wide habitat tolerance and have established themselves in as diverse situations as in parts of the Kalahari in Botswana, around solitary trading stores, and at the other extreme on Marion Island in the sub-Antarctic.

On Marion Island the introduction of domestic cats to the island is well documented. Van Aarde & Robinson (1980) recorded that five cats were brought to the island in 1949 to control house mice, *Mus musculus*, which were proving a problem in the meteorological station. A survey conducted in 1973/74 (Anderson & Condy, 1974) showed that the cats had become feral and were widespread on the island below the 450 m contour. A fullscale survey was initiated in 1974 (van Aarde, 1977) which confirmed that they were widespread. Further study showed that the intrinsic rate of natural increase was 23,3% per year (van Aarde, 1978), with a population numbering 2 100 (van Aarde, 1979). By 1977 the population was estimated to be 3 409 (van Aarde & Skinner, 1981). Furthermore, far from feeding predominantly on the house mice, *Mus musculus*, which are common on the island, they were preying on a series of seven species of marine birds including petrels, prions and sheathbills which constituted a high percentage of their prey (Table 254.1).

**Table 254.1**

Percentage occurrence of marine bird species in the prey remains of feral domestic cats on Marion Island (van Aarde, 1980a)

| Species | Percentage occurrence in prey remains |
|---|---|
| *Pachyptila salvini*, Salvin's prion | 60,05 |
| *Pterodroma mollis*, Soft-plumaged petrel | 9,40 |
| *Pterodroma macroptera*, Great-winged petrel | 10,05 |
| *Pterodroma brevirostris*, Kerguelen petrel | 12,04 |
| *Procellaria aequinoctialis*, White-chinned petrel | 0,74 |
| *Halobaena caerulea*, Blue petrel | 2,45 |
| *Chionis minor*, Lesser sheathbill | 0,82 |

The cats were seen to enter the burrows of the larger species and the birds became susceptible to predation when entering or leaving burrows or when courting. Distinct trails led from the cat lairs to burrow entrances. The common diving petrel, *Pelecanoides urinatrix*, which was at one time regarded as a common species on the island (Rand, 1954), by 1965/66 no longer nested on it (van Zinderen-Bakker, 1971).

This serious depletion of the avifauna led to an investigation of the population characteristics of the feral cats on the island with a view to the introduction of control measures (van Aarde, 1978; 1979; 1983; van Aarde & Skinner, 1981). A number of methods of control were tried, including trapping and hunting, but were proved to be ineffective. Trapping success was very low at 50 cats at 702,4 hours/cat and, under the conditions prevailing, hunting only succeeded in removing 190 cats over a period of three years.

In March 1977 feline panleucopaenia virus (cat flu) was introduced to the population. Ninety-six cats were trapped on the island, infected with the virus and released in various parts of the island. Monitoring in 1982 showed that numbers had decreased from 3 409 as estimated from the investigation in 1977 to an estimated 615, although this number probably was higher (van Rensburg, Skinner & van Aarde, 1987).

In a follow up operation in an endeavour to further reduce numbers, 16 hunters, divided into 8 teams of two each, shot 460 cats during the summer season of 1986/7 and this process will continue to the 1988/9 season (Bester, pers. comm.).

Van Aarde (1978) found that, on Marion Island, sexual maturity in feral domestic cats was attained at an age of about nine months old and litters were produced during the first season following their birth. The young were born during the summer months from August to March; no pregnant females were taken in the winter months from March to June.

Most of the cats on Marion Island were solitary, but van Aarde (1978) found that groups of two to five were observed throughout the year and the mean group size was 2,65 (n=79).

# XXXII. Family CANIDAE
## Foxes, wild dog and jackals

Members of this Family are found in a wild state over most of the world, with the exception of New Zealand, Australia, Antarctica and some oceanic islands. The dingo, *Canis dingo*, of Australia, apparently was introduced by visitors or settlers many centuries ago. Members occur in such diverse habits as the ice-bound Arctic to hot dry deserts such as the Sahara, the only association they tend to avoid being dense forest.

Members vary considerably in size but there is a general family resemblance between the species. The head is furnished with conspicuous erect ears. The muzzle is long and tapers to the naked black rhinarium, which encloses the nostrils. They have long slender legs, an adaptation to their hunting methods, and bushy tails.

The skull is long and narrow, the braincase rounded (Fig. 259.1). The dental formula in all but the bat-eared fox, *Otocyon megalotis*, is:

$$I\frac{3}{3}\ C\frac{1}{1}\ P\frac{4}{4}\ M\frac{3}{3} = 42$$

The number of teeth in the bat-eared fox varies from 46 to 50 (see Text No. 255 Skull).

The Family is represented in the Subregion by three Subfamilies: the Caninae which includes the two jackals, the side-striped, *Canis adustus*, and the black-backed,

*C. mesomelas*, and a fox, the Cape fox, *Vulpes chama*; the Otocyoninae, with a single species, the bat-eared fox, *O. megalotis*; and the Simocyoninae with a single species, the wild dog, *Lycaon pictus*.

Of the five species the wild dog is the only one that subsists almost entirely on flesh. Both the jackals include in their diet a high percentage of vegetable matter and insects, and the bat-eared fox is predominantly an insect-eating species.

The carnassial shear, comprised of the upper fourth premolar and the first lower molar tooth, is well developed in the wild dog and the jackals (Fig. XXXII.1), but is not differentiated in the bat-eared fox which, because of its insect diet, does not require a dentition that has the ability to slice flesh.

Jackals are the most abundant canids in the fossil record (Savage, 1978). The fossil remains of the extant black-backed jackal, *Canis mesomelas*, and the bat-eared fox, *Otocyon megalotis*, are recorded from the earliest Pleistocene deposits in the Subregion (Ewer, 1956). The side-striped jackal, *C. adustus*, is known only from the late Pleistocene; the Cape fox, *Vulpes chama*, and the wild dog, *Lycaon pictus*, from the middle Pleistocene (Savage, 1978).

The ancestors of the wild dog and the bat-eared fox are unknown and there are no clues to the links between the Miocene and Pleistocene canids.

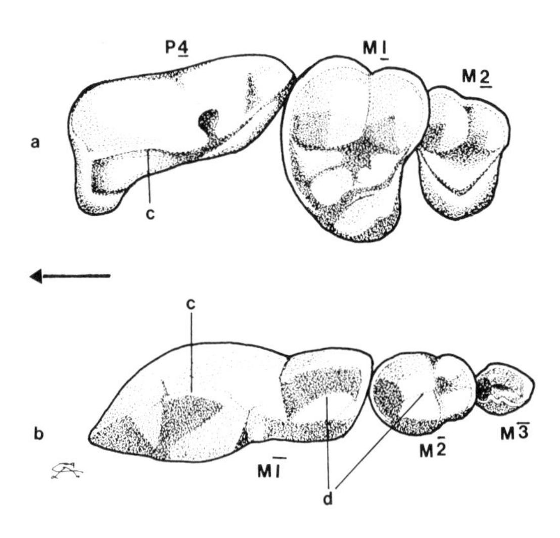


Fig. XXXII.1. Teeth: (a) upper and (b) lower carnassial and post carnassial teeth of a canid. The cutting blades (c) of $P^4$ and $M_1$, which together form the carnassial shear, occlude against each other serving as a slicing mechanism in cutting up tough food. The inner cusps of $M^1$ and $M^2$ fit into the basins in (d) $M_1$ and $M_2$ to form a crushing mechanism (after Ewer, 1973).

Key to the genera (Meester *et al.*, 1986)

1. Cheekteeth 7/8, less often 8/8; carnassial teeth scarcely differentiated; ears much enlarged, 20 percent or more of head and body length

   ... *Otocyon*

   Cheekteeth not more than 6/7, carnassials well differentiated; ears smaller, 15 percent or less of head and body length

   ... 2

2. Forefoot with 4 digits, no pollex; large, greatest skull length 180 mm and more, robust, with well-developed sagittal crest; $M^1$ with little or no sign of lingual cusps; $M^2$ about 1/3 or less of size of $M^1$; coat with vari-coloured blotches

   ... *Lycaon*

   Forefoot with 5 digits, small pollex present; smaller, greatest skull length about 175 mm and less; $M^1$ with two small lingual cusps and a talon; $M^2$ about half as large as $M^1$ or larger

   ... 3

3. Smaller, greatest skull length less than 120 mm; tail length more than half of head and body length; frontals flat, postorbital processes concave above

   ... *Vulpes*

   Larger, greatest skull length more than 130 mm; tail length less than half of head and body length; frontals elevated, postorbital processes convex above

   ... *Canis*

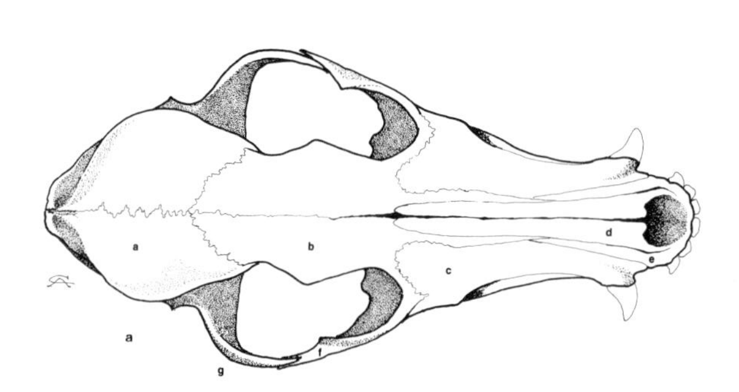

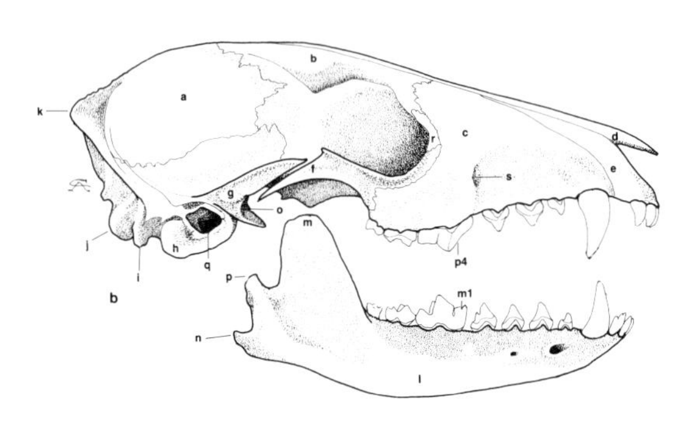

Fig. XXXII.2. Nomenclature of bones, teeth etc. of the skull of a carnivore: black-backed jackal, *Canis mesomelas*, dorsal and lateral view (a) parietal (b) frontal (c) maxilla (d) nasal (e) premaxilla (f) jugal (g) squamosal (h) ear bulla (i) paroccipital process (j) occipital condyle (k) supraoccipital crest (l) mandible (lower jaw) (m) coronoid (n) angular process (o) glenoid (p) condyle (q) auditory meatus (r) lachrymal (s) infraorbital foramen ($P^4$+$M_1$), $P^4$ upper fourth premolar, $M_1$ lower first molar tooth, both which together form the carnassial shear.

## Genus *Otocyon* Muller, 1836

No. 255

## *Otocyon megalotis* (Desmarest, 1822)

## Bat-eared fox
## Bakoorvos

Plate 21

### Colloquial Name

The colloquial name draws attention to the large ears, so characteristic of the species. The bat referred to is probably the Egyptian slit-faced bat, *Nycteris thebaica*, which is common and widespread in the Subregion and, for the size of its body, has very large ears. The Afrikaans name *bakoor-* is appropriate, but although the names *bakoorjakkals* or *draaijakkals* are often used, they are not jackals.

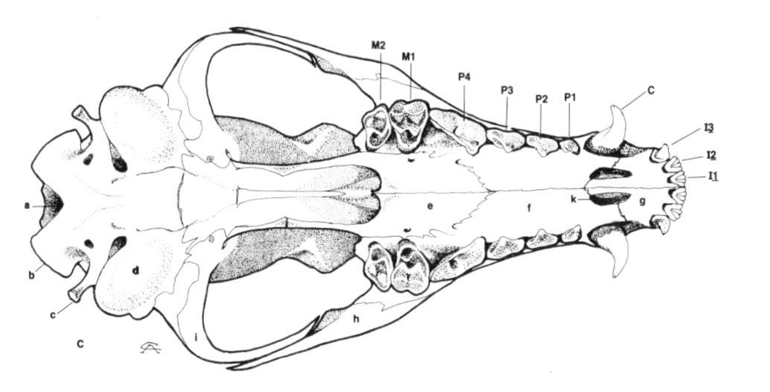


Fig. XXXII.3. Nomenclature of bones, teeth etc. of the skull of a carnivore: black-backed jackal, *Canis mesomelas*, ventral view (a) occipital foramen (b) occipital condyle (c) paroccipital process (d) ear bulla (e) palatine (f) maxilla (g) premaxilla (h) jugal (i) squamosal (j) pterygoid (k) anterior palatal foramen I1, 2, 3 upper incisor teeth; C upper canine; P1, 2, 3, 4 upper premolar teeth; M1, 2 upper molar teeth.

### Taxonomic Notes

Originally the species was described from a specimen from the "Cape of Good Hope" by Desmarest in 1822 under the name *Canis megalotis*, because of their close external resemblance to jackals. Their huge ears and different dental formula warrant inclusion in a genus of their own, distinct from both *Canis* and the true foxes of the genus *Vulpes*.

The East African population, which differs in certain features from the population in the Subregion, is distinguished under the subspecific name *O. m. virgatus* Miller, 1909.

### Description

Bat-eared foxes resemble small jackals in build and stand about 300 mm at the shoulder. They have a total length of about 800 mm and a mass of up to about 5,0 kg (Table 255.1). They are built more slightly than jackals, with slim legs and sharp, elongated muzzles. Characteristic features are the enormous ears, up to 130 mm long and 100 mm around the base, the broadly black-tipped, bushy tail, and the black limbs.

**Table 255.1**

Measurements (mm) and mass (kg) of adult bat-eared foxes, *O. megalotis*, from Botswana (Smithers, 1971)

| | Males | | | Females | | |
|---|---|---|---|---|---|---|
| | $\bar{x}$ | n | Range | $\bar{x}$ | n | Range |
| TL | 827 | 25 | 760–905 | 839 | 29 | 770–910 |
| T | 298 | 25 | 230–340 | 303 | 29 | 278–340 |
| Hf c/u | 149 | 25 | 140–161 | 150 | 29 | 139–165 |
| E | 124 | 25 | 119–137 | 124 | 29 | 114–134 |
| Mass | 4,03 | 22 | 3,40–4,91 | 4,11 | 29 | 3,18–5,36 |

On the upper parts of the body the hairs of the dense, fine underfur are about 30 mm in length. The base of the hairs is smoke-grey or buffy-grey for about 10 mm, the rest is off-white or buffy. The guard hairs are longer, about 55 mm, and form a dense coat overlying the underfur. The individual hairs are broadly black with white tips, giving the upper parts a grizzled appearance, which appears grey at a distance. When the white annulations towards the tip of the guard hairs are broad, individuals have a lighter appearance than those in which the annulations are narrower or not so clearly white. Interspersed among the guard hairs is a sprinkling of tactile hairs up to 65 mm long, which may be entirely black or with a white annulation near the tip. When broadly black-tipped guard hairs predominate down the centre of the upper parts, they produce a dark central band; when less so the dark band may not be so much in evidence or may be absent altogether.

The coat is soft and densely haired, and undergoes a distinct moult once a year. Details of the moult were reported by Smithers (1983). In Botswana the indigenous peoples hunt the bat-eared fox for its skin in the colder months from April to July, when the pelage is in prime condition.

In adults the hair on the forehead is white, extending as a band on either side to the base of the ears. The muzzle is dark brown, usually darker between the eyes. From below the eyes and from their hind corners there is a narrow black band which tapers out on the sides of the face. The chin and the area around the mouth are black. The insides of the ears are white, the edges fringed with a dense band of fine, pure white hair from the base to near the tips and around the outer edges of the pinnae on their outer margins. The backs of the ears are dark brown, darker or sometimes nearly black towards the tips. The lower part of the limbs is black in the front, lighter on the back; the feet are black above and below. The under parts vary in colour between individuals, being either whitish, buffy or buffy-grey, usually darker on the upper chest and lower belly where the darker bases of the hairs predominate. The hair of the tail is long, the individual hairs up to 80 mm; the top of the tail from near its base is black, with a broad black tip.

There are five digits on the front feet; the first which carries the dew claw is situated far back of the pads and does not come into contact with the ground (Fig. 255.1). It is functionless in this species, which is largely insectivorous, whereas in other carnivores, as for example in the felids, it plays an important part in holding the prey. The claws on the forefeet are long and slightly curved, up to about 20 mm across the curve, and are adapted ideally to digging. The claws on the four digits of the hind feet, on the other hand, are short, in some specimens a bare 7 to 10 mm long.

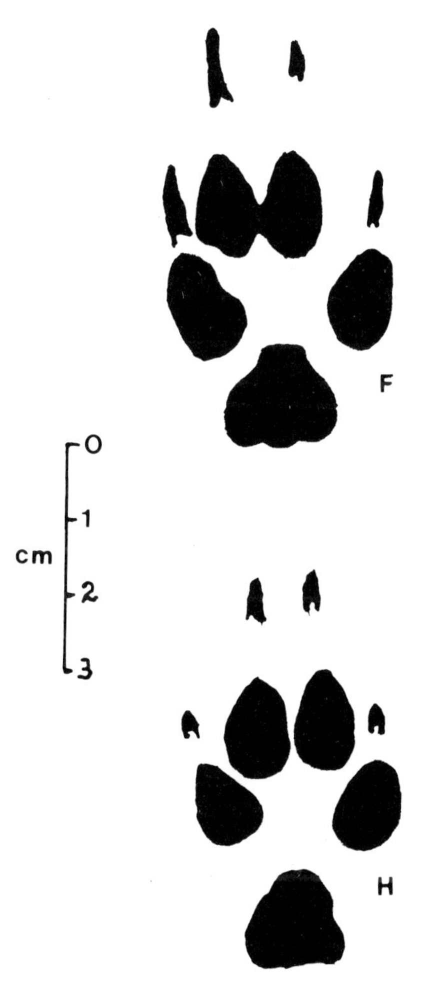


Fig. 255.1. Spoor: bat-eared fox, *O. megalotis*. F. Right forefoot H. Right hind foot.

The average size and mass of a series of males and females from Botswana (Table 255.1) reveal that, while the difference is slight, females tend to be larger and heavier than males.

**Skull** (Fig. 255.2)

The skull is elongated, narrowing evenly from the sides of the braincase to the front of the narrow muzzle. In younger individuals the teeth have high cusps; in older individuals the molars in the lower jaw wear to a flat surface, those in the upper wearing similarly, but retaining an unworn edge on their outer surfaces. The construction of the glenoid fossa allows little side to side action of the lower jaw, whose function, therefore, is more of a chopping than a grinding action, an ideal mechanism for dealing with insects and other softer-bodied invertebrates and ill-adapted for anything more substantial. The quick chopping action achieved in killing hard-bodied beetles prior to swallowing is achieved by a special adaptation of the lower jaw. The digastric muscle inserts on a flange situated vertically below or slightly in front of the glenoid, thus greatly increasing the muscle's efficiency in opening the mouth (Fig. 255.3). Timing indicates that the quick repetitive bite is not less than four or five bites per second.

Although the zygoma is stoutly built to accommodate the insertions of the masseter muscles, the temporalis muscles insert onto the sides of the braincase, and onto low crests, very obvious in older individuals, which lie on the upper sides of the braincase, leaving a wide smooth area on top of the skull devoid of muscle attachments. In juveniles the crests are poorly developed and barely discernible, becoming more obvious with age.

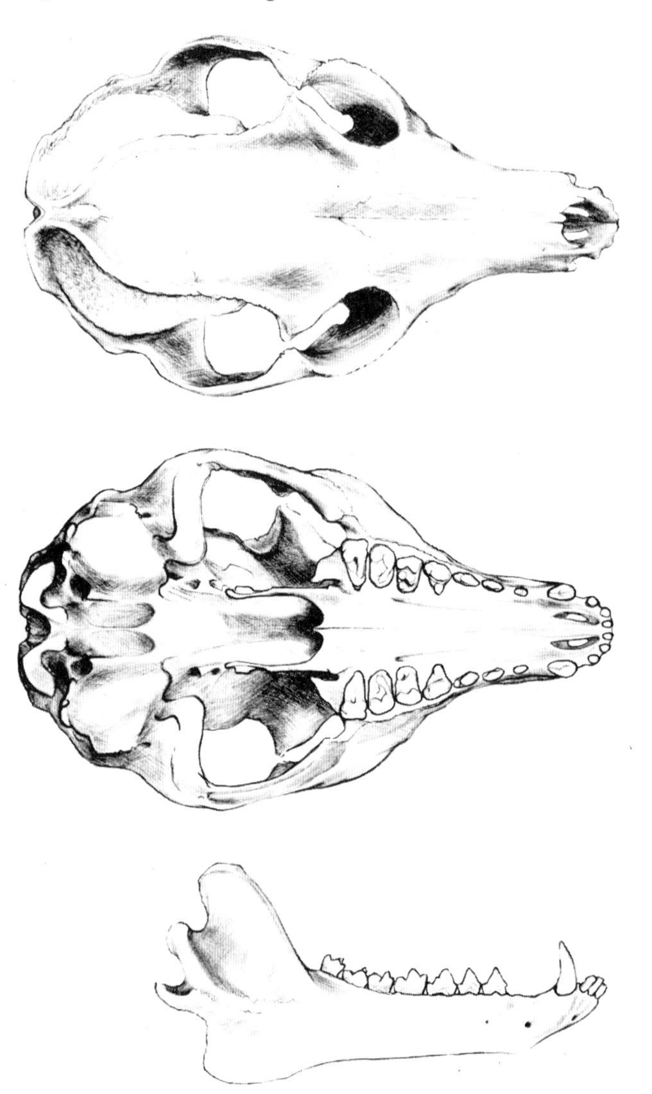

Fig. 255.2 Skull, bat-eared fox, *O. megalotis*. TL Skull 120 mm

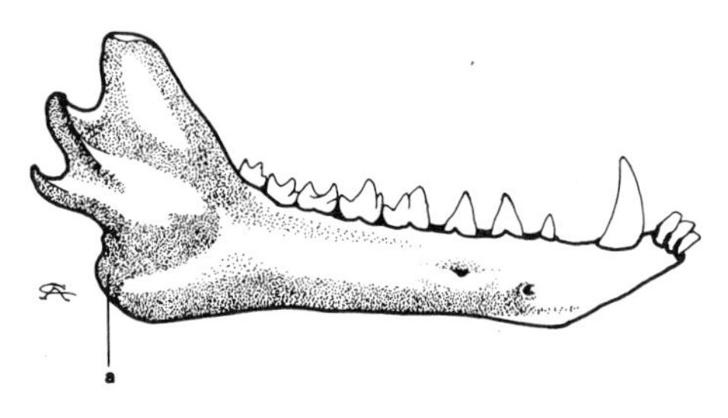

Fig. 255.3. Mandible: bat-eared fox, *O. megalotis*, to show (a) sub-angular lobe on which the digastric muscle inserts. In other canids it inserts further forward on the lower margin of the mandible.

Within the species there is considerable individual variation in the number of teeth, the commonest form being:

$I\frac{3}{3}\ C\frac{1}{1}\ P\frac{4}{4}\ M\frac{3-4}{4-5} = 46$ or 50

The bat-eared fox, therefore, can have more teeth than any other living heterodont placental mammal.

**Distribution**

The bat-eared fox, *O. megalotis*, occurs within two discrete distributional ranges on the continent. The northern range, in East Africa to as far south as the Mbeya area in southwestern Tanzania, is separated by some 1 200 km from the southern in the Southern African Subregion, which has a narrow extension into southern Angola in the northwest. It seems likely that, at some period during the Pleistocene, when conditions were drier than at present the two populations would have formed a continuum through the intervening country.

*South of the Sahara, excluding the Southern African Subregion*

They occur in southern **Somalia** north to about 5 °N, with an isolated record from the vicinity of the Nogal River in the northeast. In Somalia they are locally common, but of sporadic distribution. They are listed from the southern **Sudan; Ethiopia** and **Uganda**, where they are recorded from the flat central plains in the Karamoja district and in the Kidepo National Park in the extreme northeast. They occur in the central and southern parts of **Kenya** and in a number of National Parks and game reserves; and in the central and southwestern parts of **Tanzania**, the furthest south being the Mbeya area which appears to mark the southern limits of their distribution in East Africa. In **Angola** they have a marginal distribution in the southwestern parts of the country, between the escarpment and the coast.

*Southern African Subregion*

They occur widely in **Namibia** and are widespread in **Botswana**, excluding parts of the eastern and northern sectors. Their distribution extends narrowly into **Zimbabwe** in the northwest and throughout the southern parts of the country; and from there through to the Banhine Flats in southwestern **Mozambique**, south of the Zambezi River. They occur narrowly in the northern and western parts of the **Transvaal** as far southwestwards as Zeerust and throughout the northern, western, southwestern and central arid parts of the **Cape Province**.

The distribution range of this species appears to change in relation to short-term fluctuations in rainfall. Unknown in the Chobe National Park in northeastern Botswana prior to 1965, a pair were seen in that year near the eastern entrance to the park at Kasane, with numerous subsequent records in the park and on the Kalahari sand associations to the south. In March 1970 they were recorded for the first time in northwestern Zimbabwe. Unknown east of the Hwange National Park until 1968, in that year a specimen was collected on the Manyoli River, 180 km east of the park. In the southern part of Zimbabwe they were known from the Gwanda area, but not until 1967 on Nuanetsi Ranch further east; subsequently they have been recorded as far east as Buffalo Bend on the Nuanetsi River. MacDonald (1982) observed a single individual on Kenilworth Ranch in south-western Zimbabwe in 1970. A similar extension of their known range occurred in the Republic of South Africa. A specimen record and first sight record in 1967 from a farm in the Limpopo valley were cited by Rautenbach (1982). They were recorded for the first time in the Kruger National Park (Pienaar, 1970b) in June 1969. Stuart (1981) reported similar range extensions in the Cape Province. MacDonald (1982) was of the opinion that this range extension was in response to the low rainfall period of the 1960's and early 1970's. Furthermore, he provided evidence that *O. megalotis* increases in abundance in arid savannas with a mean summer rainfall of less than 300 mm per annum during periods when rainfall is above average, but shows a decrease in abundance during the same periods in medium rainfall savannas with a mean annual summer rainfall of more than 500 mm per annum.

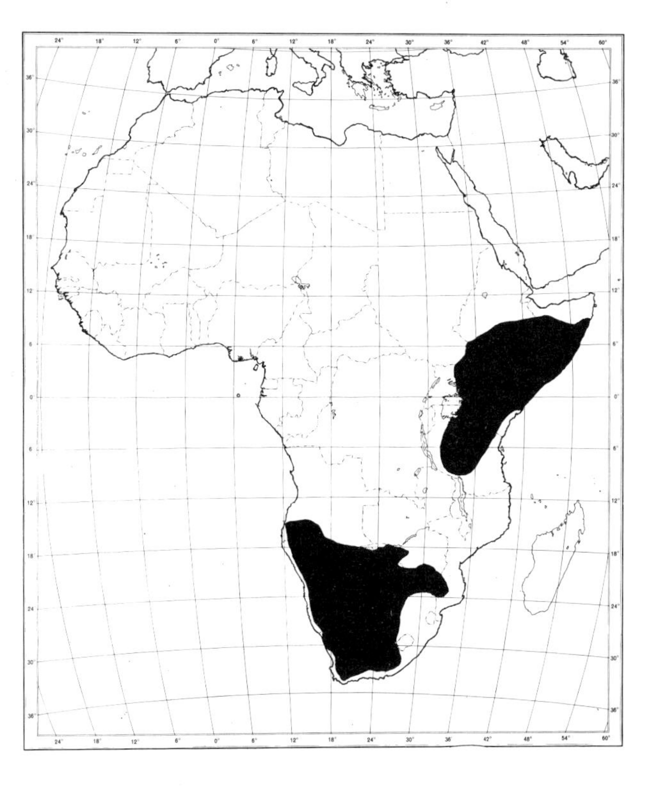

## Habitat

In the Southern African Subregion the species is associated with open country within the South West Arid, Southern Savanna and South West Cape Biotic Zones with a mean annual rainfall of about 100–600 mm. They occur on open grassland, with a preference for areas of short grass or grassland with much bare ground (Nel, 1978; Koop & Velimirov, 1982; Mackie & Nel, 1989), on degraded overgrazed areas, in open woodland with a scant undercover, and in Karoo scrub. Berry (1978) and Mackie & Nel (1989) suggested that short grass open veld with bare patches is the optimum habitat and this is found between the isohyets of 200 and 300 mm. Grass height and abundance of insects, particularly *Hodotermes mossambicus*, are strongly influenced by fluctuations in annual rainfall, lending support to this hypothesis. They do not occur in the central Namib Desert dune sea or in montane or evergreen forest.

As the harvester termites, *Hodotermes mossambicus* and *Microhodotermes viator* are such important food items, in some areas their habitat usage is governed to some extent by the occurrence of these termites. The distribution of the bat-eared fox coincides very closely with that of *H. mossambicus* and even *Microhodotermes viator* (Mackie & Nel, 1989).

## Habits

In most areas activity shifts gradually from diurnal in winter to nocturnal in summer (Mackie, 1988). This corresponds to the activity rhythm of a common prey item, *Hodotermes mossambicus* (Mackie, 1988; Nel, pers. comm.). However, in East Africa activity throughout the year tends to remain nocturnal (Lamprecht, 1979; Malcolm, 1986).

They dig well and adapt holes of aardvarks and springhaas, and also on occasion share burrows with Cape foxes, *Vulpes chama* (Nel, pers. comm.). The burrows are often on raised ground, possibly to avoid being submerged in heavy rain. These burrows reach a depth of about 1 m, and are up to 3 m in length. In captivity, at a time when the female was nearing the time of parturition, both male and female engaged in digging. A breeding burrow excavated on Nxai Pan, Botswana, in December 1964, had four entrances and three chambers, all interconnected. The main entrance entered the ground under a small spreading thornbush. The first chamber was 1,2 m from the entrance, the roof of the chamber 330 mm from the surface, and some 180 mm in diameter. From here another tunnel rose out 3 m to the surface. The third tunnel was 2,7 m long and had a chamber about 0,7 m from the surface and some 0,25 m high, about 0,46 m from the chamber in the main tunnel. The fourth tunnel was some 3 m long and had a chamber about 1,2 m from the entrance, some 0,3 m wide and 0,18 m high. This chamber was closer to the surface than the other two. The floors of the tunnels and chambers were perfectly clean with no sign of bedding material.

Bat-eared foxes feed in groups, and different groups intermingle freely at rich food patches; up to 15 individuals from four groups have been found to feed together in an area of less than 0,5 km$^2$ (Nel, 1978). Foraging ranges vary from 1,5–2 km$^2$ in the Kalahari to 0,47–1,28 km$^2$ in the south-eastern Orange Free State (Mackie & Nel, 1989) in the Subregion, and from 2,5–4,9 km$^2$ in East Africa (Malcolm, 1986). Family groups forage as a cohesive unit (although individuals may forage 100–200 m apart from others) from the time pups accompany their parents, until June-July when the family groups break up and the pups scatter. Mean group size, recorded in the Kalahari Gemsbok National Park from 1974–1980, was 2,72 (range 1–10), while the most common group size encountered was two (Nel, Mills & van Aarde, 1984). These authors also demonstrated a positive correlation between mean annual rainfall and group size.

Prey is located primarily through hearing; foxes often forage in a circular fashion and cast around. The posture of the head and ears is typical (Fig. 255.4). As prey is snapped up and chewed the prominent ears flip back. Sight appears to play a subsidiary role, and immobile prey is usually ignored. Depending on the main prey source during a foraging period the linear distance covered per time period varies: 0,87–1,28 km/h when foraging on clumped prey, such as termite colonies, and 0,56–0,83 km/h when foraging on dispersed prey items, for example beetles or beetle larvae. Individuals call other group members to food-rich patches (Nel & Bester, 1983). Bat-eared foxes exhibit a variety of visual displays (Nel & Bester, 1983), scent-mark, and also use tactile communication. They are extremely playful, often groom each other and are regarded as the most gregarious of the canids (Kleiman, 1967).

While dens are used when the pups are small, after weaning a family group dispenses with such shelter and they rest or sleep in the open, or more usually underneath shrubs or trees. When moving away from such resting places, most individuals defecate; this in time often leads to the formation of concentrations of faeces in a small area.

When disturbed groups members scatter in all directions, twisting and turning as they run. Quick turns are enhanced by sudden flicks of the tail, this habit earning them the name "draaijakkals" in certain parts of the country. However, this same colloquial epithet is also used for the Cape fox, *Vulpes chama*.

Fig. 255.4 Bat-eared fox listening for subterranean beetle larvae.

## Food

The principal food items in a sample of 72 stomach contents from Botswana are set out in Table 255.2.

**Table 255.2**

Percentage occurrence of the food items in a sample of 72 stomach contents of the bat-eared fox, *O. megalotis*, from Botswana (Smithers, 1971 and unpublished records)

| Food item | Percentage occurrence |
|---|---|
| Insecta | 88 |
| Scorpiones | 22 |
| Muridae | 17 |
| Reptilia | 14 |
| Wild fruit | 14 |
| Solifugae | 11 |
| Myriapoda | 7 |

Insects had by far the largest percentage occurrence in the sample at 88%. Within this, Isoptera at 56% had the highest occurrence, being represented by the harvester termite, *Hodotermes mossambicus*, at 56%. In three stomachs they constituted almost the sole content, with smaller amounts of *Macrotermes natalensis* and *M. bellicosus*. As the sample originated from Botswana, where scorpions are particularly common, especially at certain times of the year, they had a high percentage occurrence after insects of 22%. Among the remains *Parabuthus vaudus, Opisthophthalmus carinatus, O. wahlbergi* and *O. histrio* were recognisable.

Muridae had an occurrence of 17%, a range of six species being recorded, and Reptilia, at 14%, were represented by a range of seven species of lizards and two of snakes (Smithers, 1983). Wild fruits had a percentage occurrence of 14%; 11% were the berries of the raisin bush, *Grewia* spp, which frequently occur in the stomachs of other small carnivores.

Hunting spiders, Solifugae, had an occurrence of 11%, the remains recognised in 5% of cases as *Solpuga monteiroi*.

Myriapoda, at 7%, were represented in stomach contents by millipedes and the centipede, *Scolopendra morsitans*. Millipedes had a high occurrence in October at the commencement of the rainy season, but were not favoured at other times. This may be due to the noxious fluid which they secrete which is not in evidence when the millipedes first emerge.

Green grass, as opposed to dry cut stems normally ingested when eating harvester termites, had a percentage occurrence of 36% in the sample, a common item in the stomachs of other species, with probably only a mechanical action and little, if any, food value.

Unusual items were a large number of faecal pellets of duiker, *Sylvicapra grimmia*, and springbok, *Antidorcas marsupialis*, in one stomach, perhaps ingested with the termites; and a frog in another.

Bothma (1966c) found that in the Kalahari Gemsbok National Park harvester termites, *Hodotermes mossambicus*, had by far the highest percentage occurrence in eight stomachs. In the same area and in the Karoo, Viljoen & Davis (1973) found that invertebrates constituted the commonest food; plant food ranked high in the Karoo. Analyses of scats from the Kalahari Gemsbok National Park (Nel, 1978) showed *Hodotermes mossambicus* to predominate as a prey item, with invertebrates as a group contributing the major portion of the diet. In contrast to the findings of Bothma (1971) and Smithers (1971), however, few vertebrate remains occurred. Beetles (Coleoptera) were the next most frequent prey item on a year-round basis, although ants were important in the dry winter season. As in Botswana the occurrence of *Grewia flava* berries rose sharply in summer. Other important prey sources were Orthoptera (grasshoppers), Lepidoptera (moths) and beetle larvae. Analyses of scats from the Namib Desert likewise showed *H. mossambicus* to be the most important prey, with *Trinervitermes* sp. second, and some Coleoptera, Formicidae and Diptera pupae also being utilised (Bothma *et al.*, 1984). On the Cape West Coast, in the Postberg section of the West Coast National Park, termites again formed the major portion of their diet, in this case *Microhodotermes viator* (MacDonald & Nel, 1986). In the Orange Free State, Mackie (1988) similarly found termites (*H. mossambicus*) to predominate in the prey.

The dentition of the bat-eared fox is well-adapted for dealing with a diet consisting of small prey such as insects and their larvae, small rodents, scorpions, termites, *etc.* The jaw action in mastication is extremely fast. In dealing with large Coleoptera, observations in captivity show that these are picked up, crunched several times very quickly, then dropped, the process repeated until the prey is quiescent, when it is thoroughly masticated prior to swallowing. Hard-bodied insects in general are broken up into very small pieces, rendering their identification in stomach contents difficult. On the other hand, scorpions and sunspiders are not subject to such severe treatment and, although broken, are recovered from the stomach content in an identifiable condition. In the case of scorpions, the tail normally becomes severed from the body, but it is swallowed, together with the sting and poison sac.

Coleoptera larvae and termites when recovered are chewed, but are recognisable, in the case of termites as the head capsules. Small mice such as *Mus* spp or juveniles of larger species often remain nearly wholly intact, the skulls crushed. Larger mice are broken up into several sections and are subject to much more prolonged mastication. Reptiles are cut into small sections, but not masticated beyond identification.

### Seasonal variation in food

There is a seasonal variation in the foods utilised (Fig. 255.5). Consideration of the percentage occurrence of four of the major food items in 11 stomachs from February, during the warm wet season, 13 from May, a colder, drier month, and four from October just after the break of the rains, shows this variation. In February insects are plentiful and occur in every stomach examined, followed by wild fruits, scorpions and mice, in that order of occurrence. In May, in the drier, colder conditions, insects are not abundant and their percentage occurrence declines below that of mice, which then constitute the most important item in the diet. Wild fruits too are less freely available and scorpions are less in evidence than they were in February. With the onset of the rains in October and the return of warmer weather, insects again become the most freely available food item and their percentage occurrence in diet returns to the February level. Scorpions are in evidence after dark and are used more widely than they were in May. The wild fruits consist almost entirely of the raisin bush, *Grewia* spp, which ripen after December and are not utilised when they are still green.

Seasonal variation in food taken was also found in the Kalahari Gemsbok National Park by Nel (1978), where especially ants were more common in winter, and berries only appeared in the diet during summer, and by Mackie (1988) in the Orange Free State.

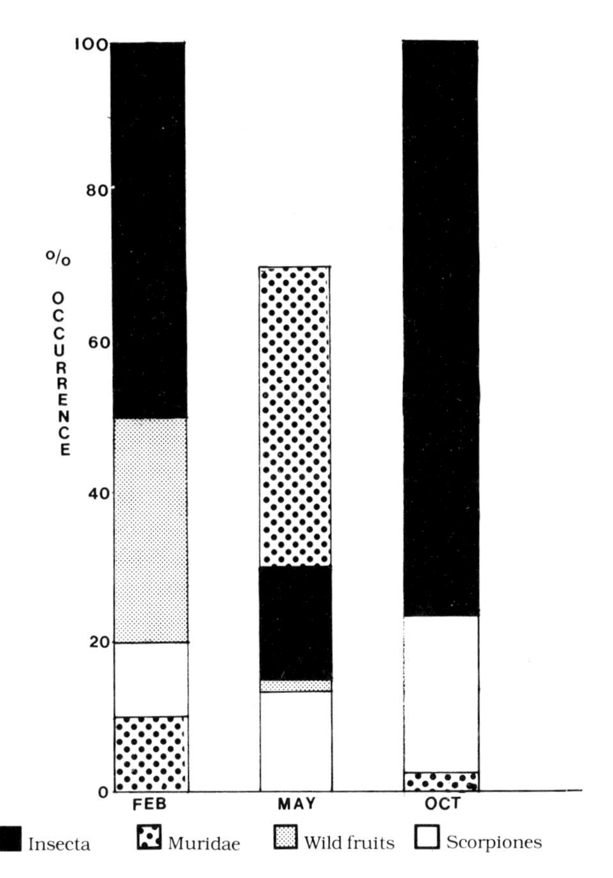


Fig. 255.5. Seasonal variation in food of the bat-eared fox, *O. megalotis*, in Botswana.

**Reproduction**

Of a series of 39 females from Botswana, taken over the months of the year, four, or about 10%, were found to be gravid in October and November, indicating strict seasonality in the time at which the young are born (Smithers, 1971). In the southwestern Kalahari births occur from October to early December (Nel *et al.*, 1984). This is at a time when insect numbers have increased markedly following the start of the rains. The young wean at about 10 weeks of age (Berry, 1978) when food is plentiful which ensures maximum survival of the litter. In captivity a female produced eight litters over a period of 12 years: one in September, the remainder in October and November (Smithers, 1983).

The average number of foetuses carried is five (range 4–6; n=4). In captivity average litter size was five (range 4–6; n=6). In Botswana, the largest family party seen was two adults and four young, the average number of young with two adults in 13 observations being 2,4. This suggests a heavy mortality in the early stages of life when predation plays a part. For example, Bothma & le Riche (1982) found they are a prime prey of leopards in the Kalahari Gemsbok National Park.

There is considerable variation in the mass at birth in individuals in litters. In a litter of five born in captivity the mass at birth varied from 99,4 g to 142,0 g and in near full-term foetuses in the field, the mass varied from 106,5 g to 140,5 g in the same potential litter. The hind foot lengths, however, show very little variation and in the former case the difference was 2 mm and in the latter 1 mm (Smithers, 1983).

The young are born in holes in the ground (see **Habits**).

Comprehensive observations on subsequent reproduction in captivity were reported by Smithers (1983).

The females have two pairs of inguinal mammae.

## Genus *Lycaon* Brookes, 1827

---

No. 256

### *Lycaon pictus* (Temminck, 1820)

### Wild dog
### Wildehond

Plate 21

---

**Colloquial Name**

Often referred to as the Cape hunting dog, there seems no good reason why Cape should be retained as the species has a wide distribution in Africa south of the Sahara and today only occurs marginally in the Cape Province. Hunting dog is acceptable, but wild dog is widely used and well entrenched, as is its Afrikaans name, *wildehond*.

**Taxonomic Notes**

Originally the species was described from a specimen from coastal Mozambique, under the name *Hyaena picta*, by Temminck in 1820. The specific name *picta* means painted in Latin and refers to the varicoloured coat which is blotched with patches of white, black and yellow. There is a tendency for individuals from the southern parts of the distributional range to have more white in their coats.

In the Republic of South Africa the wild dog is listed in the *South African Red Data Book* as an Endangered species (Smithers, 1986), and it is Endangered in Zimbabwe (Childes, 1988).

**Description**

The wild dog is unmistakable among the medium-sized carnivores. Characteristic features are the large rounded ears, the long legs, bushy, broadly white-tipped tails and blotched, black, yellow and white shaggy coats. Throughout their distributional range no two are exactly alike in pattern. The hair on the shoulders is about 40 mm long and, between the shoulders on the mid-back, slightly longer. The forehead and the area between the ears are usually whitish or yellowish, with a distinct dark stripe from between the eyes across the top of the head. The short broad muzzle is black or dark brown, with short hair. The hair on the limbs is much shorter than on the body. The rounded ears are dark, often with black fringes and have conspicuous tufts of white hair which arise from the lower, inner edges in front. The coarse, sparse hair on the body has little or no undercoat, the hair on the under parts is even sparser and shorter. The sheath of the penis is a prominent feature in males, caused by a profusion of sebaceous glands in the skin.

There are four digits on each foot equipped with short, powerful claws. The paws of the front feet are larger and broader than those of the hind feet and these mark clearly in the spoor (Fig. 256.1).

**Skull** (Fig. 256.2)

The skull is heavily built, with heavy ridges and a well developed sagittal crest which, joining the supraoccipital crest, continues across the top of the braincase to divide into two low, thick ridges which end at the postorbital bars. In relation to the rest of the skull the braincase, which is broadest at the posterior junction of the zygomatic arches with the skull, is small and pear-shaped, narrowest at the intertemporal constriction. The postorbital bars are incomplete, represented at most by blunt processes on the zygoma and frontals.

The zygomatic arches in particular are heavily built and swing widely out from the skull. These factors and the development of the sagittal crest allow for the attachment and accommodation of particularly well developed temporalis and masseter muscles which actuate the jaw action and give the wild dog its tremendously powerful bite.

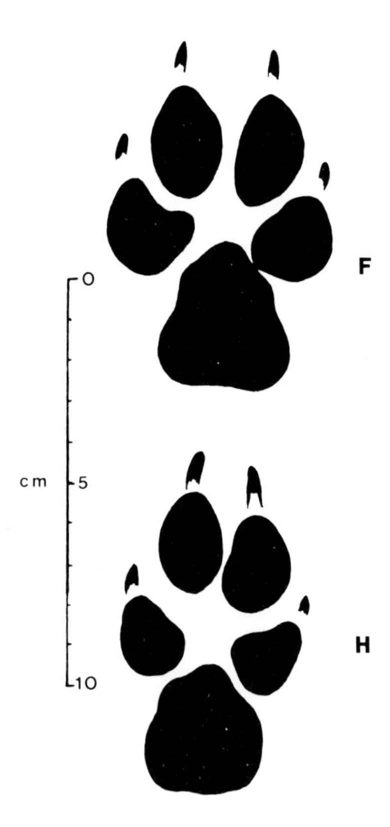


Fig. 256.1. Spoor: wild dog, *L. pictus*.
F. Right forefoot H. Right hind foot.

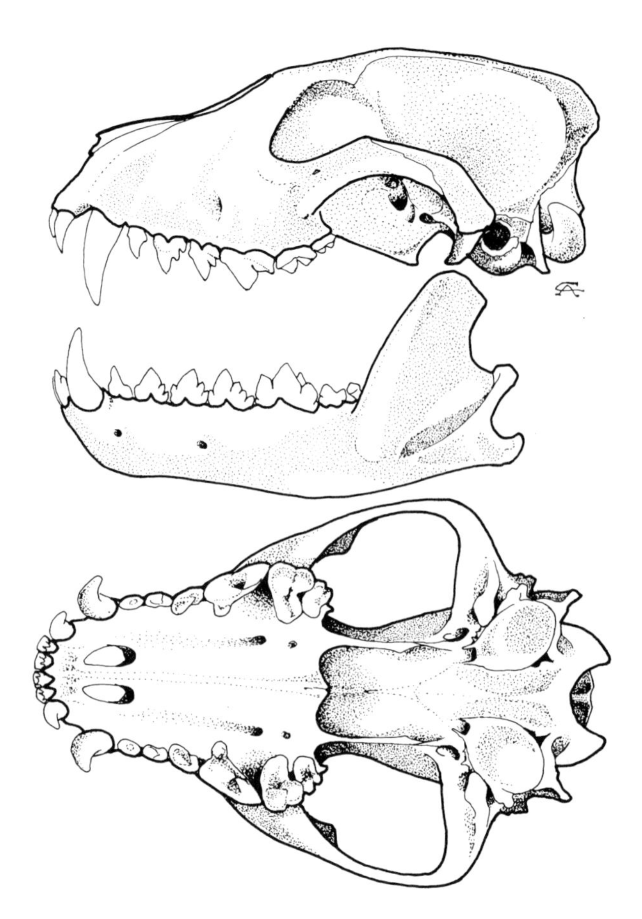

Fig. 256.2. Skull: wild dog, *L. pictus*.
TL Skull 210 mm.

In profile the skull is highest at the front of the braincase, the forehead sloping forward and levelling out at the nasals and, at the back, sloping gradually to the junction of the sagittal and supraoccipital crest, which project beyond the braincase. The forehead between the frontals is distinctly depressed centrally, the frontals on either side rising to heavy rounded ridges above the eyes; this depression continues forward to the nasals. The rostrum is short, but broad in relation to the skull, the palate broadest at the level of the carnassials, with little anterior narrowing. The bullae are ovoid and not particularly well developed, but have large openings, the paroccipital processes extending downwards beyond them.

In line with the rest of the skull the lower jaw is massive, the condyle heavily built and broad, the coronoid broad and heavy.

The dental formula is:

$I\frac{3}{3}\ C\frac{1}{1}\ P\frac{4}{4}\ M\frac{2}{3} = 42$

This is typically canid, the teeth showing an adaptation both to holding and slicing and a much lesser function of grinding than in some other canids. The outer upper incisors are larger than the remainder, heavily built and recurved, rather similar in shape to a canine. They wear to sharp edges to assist the short, sharp-pointed canines in holding the prey. The outer incisors in the lower jaw are less well developed and follow the normal incisor pattern. The back portion of the lower first molar is sectorial, adding to the slicing ability of the carnassial mechanism. The crushing that is necessary is performed by the second upper molar and the lower second and third molars which are less developed than the remainder of the teeth.

**Distribution**

There has been a spectacular reduction in the distribution of wild dogs in the Subregion since the days of early settlement (Skead, 1980). In 1684 Gravensbroek (Shapera & Farrington, 1933) recorded packs of 10 or 20 "wild dogs" disembowelling sheep and calves near the Cape, and Masson (1776) recorded them near Saldanha Bay a century later. From the early 19th century onward, records show that they were widespread from Namaqualand (Thompson, 1827), through the northern (Burchell, 1822) and northeastern Cape Province (Harris, 1838) and along the south coast at least to Mossel Bay (La Trobe, 1818). East of this Hewitt (1931) recorded them in the Addo district in 1906 and in the Albany and Bedford districts up to 1925. They no longer occur anywhere near these localities.

The species is now restricted to the larger National Parks and safari areas in the Subregion, with occasional sightings in the ranching country in Zimbabwe even as far as the Limpopo River in the southwest (Childes, 1988). Wild dogs wander very widely and turn up from time to time, without settling, in areas where they have not been known for many years. Their existence anywhere depends on the availability of an adequate supply of their bovid prey. Where indigenous populations of bovids have been replaced by domestic stock, to which they then turn, wild dogs become subject to control.

*South of the Sahara, excluding the Southern African Subregion*

In West Africa, the furthest west they are recorded is in the northern parts of the **Ivory Coast**. They are also listed from **Burkina Faso**, central and northern **Nigeria**, and western **Chad**, from where they penetrate northwards into the Sahel Zone, occurring also in the Sudan Zone. They are known from southern and southwestern **Algeria** in the Tanzerouft and Adrar des Foras and Aïr in northern **Niger**. They occur in the **Central African Republic** and in southwestern **Sudan**. They are recorded from **Ethiopia** and are discontinuously distributed in **Somalia**, only occurring in the Horn of Africa and in the central and southern parts of the country. They occur in **Kenya, Uganda** and **Tanzania**, but Kingdon (1977) showed that their distribution is shrinking in general. They occur in eastern and southeastern **Zaire**, in coastal **Gabon**, and throughout **Angola**, excluding the coastal desert. Although widespread in **Zambia**, their occurrence is today sporadic throughout the country. In **Mozambique**, north of the Zambezi River, they are widespread, although at the moment there are no records from the northwestern Tete

District. East of this they are widespread in **Malawi**, although rarely seen.

*Southern African Subregion*

They are widespread in **Mozambique**, south of the Zambezi River, but are not recorded within recent times in the extreme south and southeast. In **Zimbabwe**, where there has been a 40% decline in numbers in 10 years (Maddock, 1989), they are confined to the more remote, undisturbed areas, to the larger cattle ranches and to National Parks and game reserves, north and south of the plateau. In 1949 and 1952 packs penetrated into the suburbs of Bulawayo and they turn up from time to time on ranches in the midlands. They are widespread in **Botswana**, except in the more densely settled areas, although there are no records in the west, south of about 20°30′S.

Although recorded previously in the Kalahari Gemsbok National Park, they are not recorded within recent years (Eloff, pers. comm.). In **Namibia** they were contacted rarely in the past, and have not been reported or specimens taken within recent years. Sweatman (pers. comm.) recorded seeing four on the coastal road in Namibia about 150 km north of the Orange River mouth in 1964.

In the **Transvaal**, they are recorded in parts of the northwest and throughout the eastern areas, as far south as **Swaziland** which corresponds with their known distribution in southern Mozambique.

Pringle (1977) stated that in Natal the last pack was recorded in 1930, after which only vagrants have been seen, one in the Mkuzi Reserve in 1947/48 and two shot near Vryheid in 1960. They have been re-introduced subsequently into the Hluhluwe Umfolozi Game Reserve Complex in 1980.

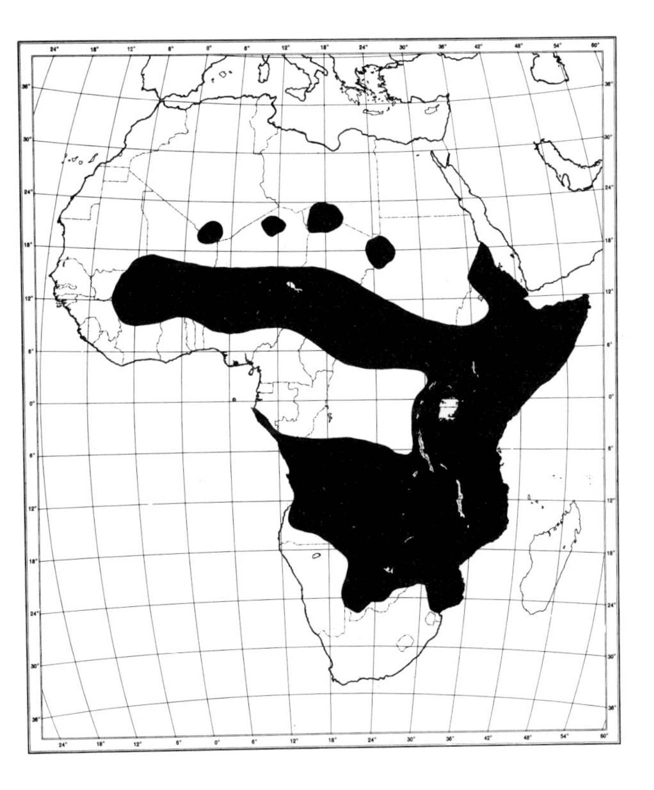

## Habitat

Wild dogs rely on sight rather than smell in hunting and it is, therefore, to their advantage to utilise relatively open country. They are associated with open plains and open savanna woodland. They avoid forest or woodland with a thick underbush or tall grass cover. They avoid montane forest, although they will use the adjacent montane grasslands. Nevertheless, their presence in an area is more strictly governed by the availability of their principal bovid prey. As they are independent of water, this is not a limiting factor, although they will drink where it is available. They are known to occur up to 1 800 m in Zimbabwe.

## Habits

The behaviour of wild dogs is highly specialised and they are specifically adapted to living in packs, one of the primary functions of which is to secure food. Estes & Goddard (1967) listed increased probability of success and more efficient utilisation of the food resources, with less disturbance of the prey, as some of the advantages of pack hunting. In addition the hunting section of the pack provides the food for the young and for those other members that remain behind for their protection.

Wild dogs are gregarious and, in the Kruger National Park, Maddock (1989) found that there are 28 packs comprising 359 individual animals or a density of some one/km$^2$. Mean pack size is 12,6 (range 3–28). In the Zambezi Valley mean pack size varied from 8,8 to 12 (range 3–25) from 1967–1974 and recent sightings show this has decreased only slightly (Childes, 1988)—the larger packs are among the largest in Africa. In Botswana pack size may have been larger, with several records of packs numbering 27–40. Today they never occur in such numbers.

The relationship between packs is not fully understood, but Kruuk (1972a) found that from time to time there is some interchange of members between them. Little inter-pack aggression has been recorded, this being avoided by ritual appeasement between individuals. The pack is a well coordinated, efficient hunting unit and the members are interdependent. The young occupy a particularly privileged position, to the extent that, after the first few weeks, the mother is not essential to their further upbringing, for members of the pack will either carry back or regurgitate food for them. This service is extended to members of the pack that remain in attendance on the young while the others are hunting or to sick or crippled members (Estes & Goddard, 1967).

Wild dogs hunt by sight, although stragglers will use their noses to follow the pack. Normally they hunt in the early to late morning and early to late evening, and Schaller (1972a) recorded hunting on moonlight nights. They are coursers, not stalkers, and a pack, moving on a broad front, will trot or walk up to potential prey in open country, not breaking into a run until the prey runs off. At the last minute the wild dogs turn towards the potential prey and course after it. Once on the run their prey is singled out among those fleeing, usually by the pack leader, and relentlessly pursued. Chases may continue for several kilometres and Kingdon (1977) recorded sustained speeds of up to 66 km/hour over a distance of some 2 km. Not all hunts are successful and it has been estimated that in 10–30% of cases the prey escapes. The prey itself appears to recognise the different intentions of a moving pack. Kruuk (1972a) recorded that gazelles will stand 50 m from a pack of walking wild dogs, but will take to flight 2 km from them if they are in motion and chasing. Prior to or during the course of the hunt, members of the pack may break away to grab fortuitous prey. Estes & Goddard (1967) recorded the taking of hares, springhaas and gazelle fawns in this manner, but in general, having once started the chase, nothing diverts them and they are oblivious to the presence of other prey, to non-food species, to vehicles or to man.

With smaller prey such as duiker, the wild dog that has secured it, which is often the leader, will be joined by other members and between them they tear it to pieces. Larger prey such as a wildebeest will be attacked on the run and pieces torn out of it, or it will be disembowelled while still running or standing until it collapses. This is the process usually employed by a pack when raiding cattle. They are not as prone to attack the larger adult bovids or zebra as the juveniles, and will avoid bunched cattle, tending to go for the solitary individuals.

Spotted hyaenas are serious competitors for food and at kills are actively resisted. Hyaenas, which lack the mobbing instinct, are no match for a pack of wild dogs and they often get a severe mauling. Their defence is to sit or lie down and snap at any dogs that attack from the front, sometimes protecting their hindquarters by sitting in holes or depressions in the ground until they can run off. Large aggregations of spotted hyaenas assembling at wild dog kills have been known to drive them off. Although competitors for food, there is some division of the resources between wild dogs and spotted hyaenas, the latter tending to take larger species.

Prior to the hunt and at the time of the kill, wild dogs become very excited, a manifestation of which is the loud twittering indulged in by pack members. It is an astonishing display of the close-knit nature of the pack to witness a wild dog kill and to see the adults, many of whom are obviously hungry, stand or lie around while the juveniles enjoy priority.

Kruuk (1972a) showed that the tail, just as in a domestic dog, is an indicator of the mood of the individual. Normally hanging down in a relaxed position, social attraction is demonstrated by curving it over the hindquarters, aggression by holding it stiffly upwards, submission, or the likelihood of taking to flight, by curving it between the back legs. The ritual greeting ceremony exhibited by adults on meeting evolves from the behaviour when young. Infantile begging for food on the return of the pack from hunting involves whining, face-licking, and nudging the corners of the mouth, which normally leads to regurgitation. In adults this may be extended to such actions as nudging of the mammae of females or nibbling at the mouth. Facial expression is rarely exhibited.

During the heat of the day they lie up in closely knit groups, usually in the shade. When there are females with young they tend to lie up in the vicinity of the breeding sites.

Vocalisation takes a number of forms, the best known being the musical *hooo-hooo* used by members of packs to relocate each other after they have become scattered. It is said that this can carry up to three or four kilometres (Estes & Goddard, 1967). Excitement prior to the hunt, when killing, feeding or when mobbing other predators, is expressed with a high-pitched, birdlike twittering, practically all pack members at times taking part. They yelp like hounds when chasing, or bark and growl when suddenly startled. Whining is part of the submissive behaviour, evolving from the squeaky whines of the young demanding food. Kingdon (1977) recorded a broken whine, used to entice the young from the den.

In East Africa, packs roam over areas as large as 1 500—4 000 km$^2$ (Reich, 1977). In the Kruger National Park, Reich (1977) found that the home ranges were smaller at about 450 km$^2$ and that there was a 10% to 20% overlap in the home ranges of adjacent packs. When a pack of wild dogs enters the home range of another pack it will be warned of its prior occupation as the home range will have been assiduously marked by the dominant male and female of the pack in occupation. Only these individuals in the pack scent-mark by anal-dragging, although body-rubbing was indulged in by all members. As they have no territories wild dogs do not mark boundaries. However, they do urine-mark fortuitously over their home range. When hunting, a dominant member will raise its legs from time to time and deposit a trickle of urine, other pack members following suit.

Predation on wild dogs is minimal, man being the only serious destroyer of them in numbers. They are killed from time to time by lions and leopards (Kingdon, 1977), but this is hardly a factor to be reckoned with. They are part of the unique African fauna and in spite of their reputation, wild dogs are not wantonly destructive and normally will kill only what they require to satisfy the needs of all members. It will be yet another debit entry in man's unenviable record if this interesting predator is allowed to go the way of other species in disappearing from the African scene. It is encouraging, therefore, that the Natal Parks Board has reintroduced wild dogs into the Hluhluwe Umfolozi Game Reserve complex.

### Food

The relative importance of prey varies throughout their distributional range. Childes (1988) listed data from Hwange and Gonarezhou National Parks, Matetsi, Chirisa and the Zambezi Valley, showing the major prey species to be impala, *Aepyceros melampus* (38,7%), followed by kudu, *Tragelaphus strepsiceros* (25,8%), waterbuck, *Kobus ellipsiprymnus* (6,1%), duiker, *Sylvicapra grimmia* (5,5%), sable, *Hippotragus niger* (5,5%) and steenbok, *Raphicerus campestris*, wildebeest, *Connochaetes taurinus*, bushbuck, *T. scriptus* and buffalo, *Syncerus caffer*, all 3,1%. Reich (1977) and Maddock (1989) in the Kruger National Park showed that impala, (93,9% and 75,4% respectively), was by far the commonest species taken, with 7,4% kudu and 2,5% each for duiker and steenbok. There are no comparable figures for Botswana, but from cursory observations, springbok, *Antidorcas marsupialis*, appear to be the principal food.

After feeding, the head, portions of skin, the heavier bones and hoofs are all that usually remain. They are fast eaters and between them will quickly demolish a duiker or gazelle. Van Lawick-Goodall & Van Lawick (1970) recorded the consumption of a Thomson's gazelle in 15 minutes. Wild dogs rarely scavenge and seldom come to the freshest of carcasses laid out to attract predators. Van Lawick-Goodall & Van Lawick (1970), however, recorded instances where wild dogs took over the kills of hyaenas. In these cases the prey was freshly killed and there do not appear to be any records of their taking carrion. They have been observed to cache food on several occasions on the Serengeti plains (Malcolm, 1980). All four dogs seen to cache later retrieved and ate the food.

### Reproduction

Van Heerden & Kuhn (1985) found that, in captivity, females became sexually mature at about 23 months old, and breed throughout the year. Compared with other canids, mating in wild dogs is accomplished in a relatively short time, the longest time recorded by Van Lawick-Goodall & Van Lawick (1970) for the wild dog being five minutes. During this process the pair are highly vulnerable, especially as in most cases the mating takes place in open country. Male wild dogs have a *bulbus glandis* like other canids, but the tie between the sexes at mating is of short duration.

The average gestation period is 72,4 $\pm$ 1,6 days (n=7). The average interval between litters, in females that bred regularly, was 11,7 months. The average litter size was 8,1 $\pm$ 1,88 (n=20), and the sex ratio at birth for 13 litters was 1 male : 0,6 females. The pups were born blind and left the den for the first time at 3–4 weeks old. When there was more than one female in the group, usually only the dominant female showed signs of oestrus and mated (van Heerden & Kuhn, 1985).

In the Kruger National Park, wild dogs breed seasonally (Reich, 1977; Maddock, 1989), producing pups between April and September, with a peak during the dry season in late May and early June. This mid-winter period comes at the end of the impala rut when out-of-condition rams are more readily available as prey and corresponds to high concentrations of bovids around water courses (Maddock, 1989). It is also the time when the country is open and visibility at its best.

The number in litters in the wild has been recorded as from two to 19 (Shortridge, 1934; Ansell, 1960a; Van Lawick-Goodall & Van Lawick, 1970; Rosevear, 1974), the average number being between seven and 10. The close-knit nature of the pack is no better demonstrated than by the fact that females will readily adopt (Schaller, 1972a) and even steal other females' pups (Kingdon, 1977).

The young are born in holes in the ground, disused antbear burrows or those which have been adapted by warthogs or spotted hyaenas. The breeding chamber is lined with grass or leaves. Sometimes more than one female occupies a breeding hole (Brand & Cullen, 1967). The young in the breeding holes are well guarded by members of the pack, who remain in attendance while hunting is carried out by other members.

Pup mortality is high, believed by Schaller (1972a) to be due to disease, caused, in some cases at least, by gastroenteritis caused by canine distemper virus. Although "rickettsial diseases" or more correctly canine ehrlichiosis has never been diagnosed in free-living wild dogs, it has been demonstrated that captive wild dogs are susceptible (van Heerden, pers. comm.). This disease may have led to the total loss of wild dog populations in the southern parts of the Kruger National Park in 1927–1933 reported on by Pienaar

(1963). Subsequently this disease was diagnosed in domestic dogs belonging to game rangers (van Heerden, pers. comm.). In many areas wild dog populations appear to remain static in spite of the high breeding potential of females, which is an indication of high losses in the young. Van Heerden (1985) found a high mortality amongst newborn captive bred pups, primarily as a result of diarrhoea, bone disease, heart failure, gastro-intestinal ulceration and various parasitic infections.

Although females will suckle their young for about three months, they start weaning at about 14 days, begging for food from members of the pack who regurgitate for them. Suckling is carried out in the hole or near the entrance, with the female standing up or lying down. Suckling lasts from two to three minutes at a time (Van Lawick-Goodall & Van Lawick, 1970). At about three weeks old the young clamber around and may be seen at the entrance of the den, which they leave when they reach the age of about two and a half months.

On the return of the hunters the young greet them with a characteristic ritual begging ceremony which consists of whining, nudging or biting at the corners of the mouth or the mammae of females and face-licking, all of which is designed to encourage them to regurgitate food. In this process the young may insert the whole muzzle into the mouth of the individual feeding them. Instances are known where adults will regurgitate for the young without the stimulation of begging (Van Lawick-Goodall & Van Lawick, 1970). On similar encouragement they will regurgitate for the adults that have remained in attendance on the young. A similar greeting ceremony, evolved from this juvenile behaviour, is used by the adults in meetings between pack members and members of other packs as a means of avoiding aggression.

In the event of disturbance at the breeding site the female may move the young to another hole, carrying them one by one in her mouth, by the head, leg, back or even tail, in what Schaller (1972a) called a haphazard manner.

As the pups grow up and join in hunts they may become stragglers. Van Lawick-Goodall & Van Lawick (1970) recorded that, although they are left behind, members of the pack will return and lead them to kills, where they enjoy priority of feeding.

In the early stages of life adult members of the pack take an active part in cleaning up the pups and may even assist the female in returning them to the hole when they stray. They will also feed the pups at the den, to the exclusion of the female, a further example of the cohesion of a wild dog pack.

Females have six or eight pairs of mammae (van Heerden & Kuhn, 1985).

---

No. 257

## *Vulpes chama* (A. Smith, 1833)

## Cape fox
## Silwervos

Plate 21

---

### Colloquial Name

It is desirable to retain the name Cape fox for this species to distinguish it from the other species, although it is not confined in its distribution to the Cape Province.

In prime condition the winter coat has a silvery appearance and is then prized for the manufacture of karosses. The Afrikaans *silwerjakkals* is widely used for the species, but they are not jackals and *silwervos* is more appropriate.

### Taxonomic Notes

No subspecies have been described.

### Description

Adult Cape foxes stand about 350 mm at the shoulder and have a total length of about 900 mm. The bushy tail is about two-thirds of the length of the head and body (Table 257.1). The pelage is soft and is comprised of a dense underfur of hairs which are crinkled and wavy and about 25 mm in length. These are grey at the base and buffy for about half their length. The underfur is overlaid by a thick guard coat, the individual hairs of which are up to 40 mm long and predominantly black, with light-coloured bases and silvery-white subapical annulations. At close quarters the upper parts of the body look silvery-grey, and grey at a distance. Sparsely scattered throughout the guard coat are slightly longer black tactile hairs. The tail is distinctly bushy, the individual hairs of the guard coat up to 55 mm long and slightly longer towards the tip. They have buffy-white bases and are broadly black or dark brown apically. This gives an overall impression of a dark, almost black, bushy tail. At close quarters the buffy underfur and lighter buffy colour of the bases of the guard hairs show through to give the tail a lighter appearance.

The upper parts of the forelimbs are reddish, the lower parts lighter in colour. The hind limbs have a dark brown, nearly black, patch on the back of the thighs. The hair on the feet is light reddish-brown.

The whole of the head and back of the ears are reddish, with some admixture of white hairs on the face; the cheeks have so much whitish hair intermixed with the red that they look almost white. In some individuals there is a narrow dark patch above the eyes and a dark patch between the eyes and the tip of the muzzle. The fronts of the ears are fringed with white hairs, the chin and an area around the mouth dark brown or greyish-white towards the front. The throat is pale buffy, the upper chest pale reddish; the remainder of the under parts is white, tinged reddish, the red tinge more pronounced on the middle of the belly.

They have five digits on the front feet and four on the hind. The claws on the front feet are thin, sharp and curved, about 15 mm in length across the curve. Those on the hind feet are the same shape and length.

The moult, which in some specimens is very distinct, takes place during the early part of the warm, wet season from about October to November.

**Table 257.1**

Measurements (mm) and mass (kg) of a series of Cape foxes, *V. chama*, from (a) Botswana (Smithers, 1971) and (b) the Orange Free State (Bester, 1980)

**(a)**

| | Males | | | Females | | |
|---|---|---|---|---|---|---|
| | $\bar{x}$ | n | Range | $\bar{x}$ | n | Range |
| TL | 906 | 14 | 880–948 | 892 | 10 | 860–977 |
| T | 360 | 14 | 293–393 | 360 | 10 | 345–380 |
| Hf c/u | 145 | 14 | 138–150 | 143 | 10 | 137–146 |
| E | 98 | 14 | 92–109 | 94 | 10 | 87–98 |
| Mass | 3,0 | 12 | 2,3–3,3 | 2,9 | 10 | 2,3–3,2 |

**(b)**

| | Males | | | Females | | |
|---|---|---|---|---|---|---|
| | $\bar{x}$ | n | Range | $\bar{x}$ | n | Range |
| TL | 937 | 41 | Not given | 934 | 33 | Not given |
| T | 351 | 44 | | 354 | 33 | |
| Hf c/u | 126 | 48 | | 122 | 32 | |
| E | 93 | 43 | | 90 | 33 | |
| Sh.ht | 361 | 12 | 320–430 | 353 | 9 | 330–370 |
| Mass | 2,8 | 24 | | 2,5 | 15 | |

### Skull (Fig. 257.1)

The skull is elongated and narrow, the rostrum narrow and slender with a distinct dip about the level of the second upper premolar. The upcurved zygomatic arch is weak, spreading widely posteriorly. The glenoid allows little or no sideways movement of the lower jaw, which is narrow and lightly built. In older specimens the sides of the rounded cranium are roughened for the attachment of the temporalis muscles which attach at their ends on low ridges near the top of the cranium on either side. These ridges arise from the postorbital processes and continue posteriorly to join at the front end of the short sagittal crest, which in turn joins the supraoccipital crest at right angles. The top of the cranium between these ridges is smooth and devoid of muscle attachments. The bullae are large for the size of the skull.

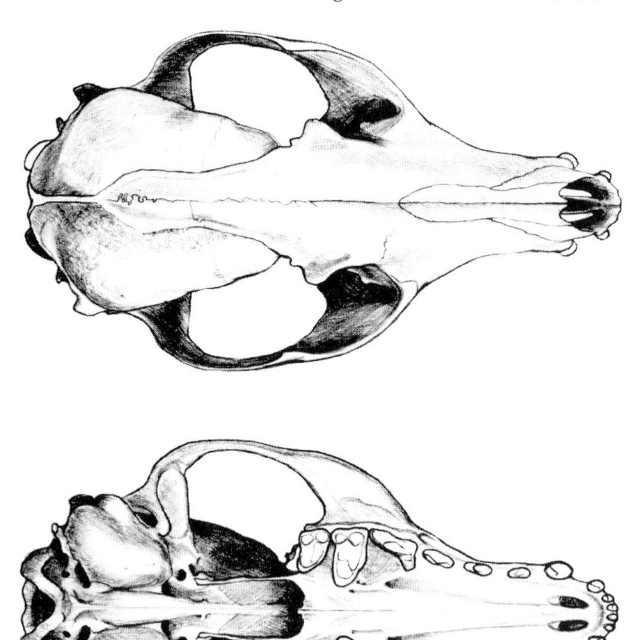

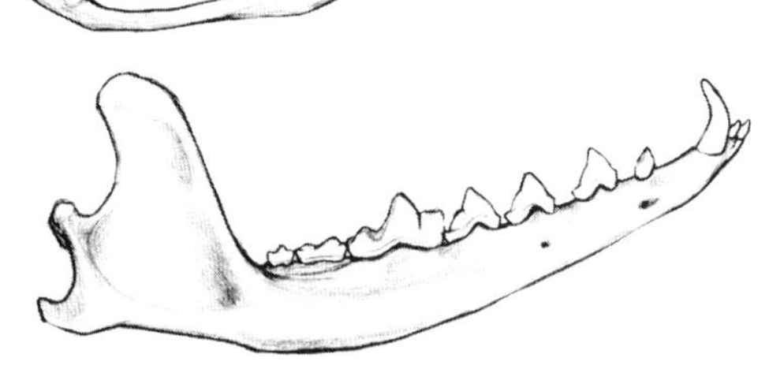

Fig. 257.1. Skull: Cape fox, *V. chama*.
TL Skull 115 mm

The dental formula is:

$I\frac{3}{3}\ C\frac{1}{1}\ P\frac{4}{4}\ M\frac{2}{3} = 42$

The third upper incisors are slightly enlarged, the canines long, curved and thin. When the jaw is closed the long upper canines project below the bone of the lower jaw. The carnassial shear is not well developed, although it retains some cutting ability. The upper fourth premolar has an enlarged protocone anteriorly on its inner edge.

In the upper jaw the two molars are broad and adapted to crushing. In the lower jaw the posterior section of the first molar, which constitutes over a third of the tooth, and the second molar, are similarly adapted; the third molar is very small.

While the cheekteeth have some cutting ability, sufficient to deal with food such as lizards and mice, they are adapted predominantly to dealing with insect food.

### Distribution

*South of the Sahara, excluding the Southern African Subregion*

They are recorded from the extreme southwestern parts of **Angola**.

*Southern African Subregion*

They are widespread in **Namibia**, except in the coastal Namib Desert and in parts of the northern and northeastern parts of the country. In **Botswana** they occur throughout the southern sector as far north as Lake Ngami and the Makgadikgadi Pan, but are absent from the eastern sector north of about Palapye. In the **Transvaal** they occur in the southwestern and southern parts of the province; in western and northwestern **Natal**; throughout the **Orange Free State** and widely in the **Cape Province**, except in the southeast and in mountainous and forested areas.

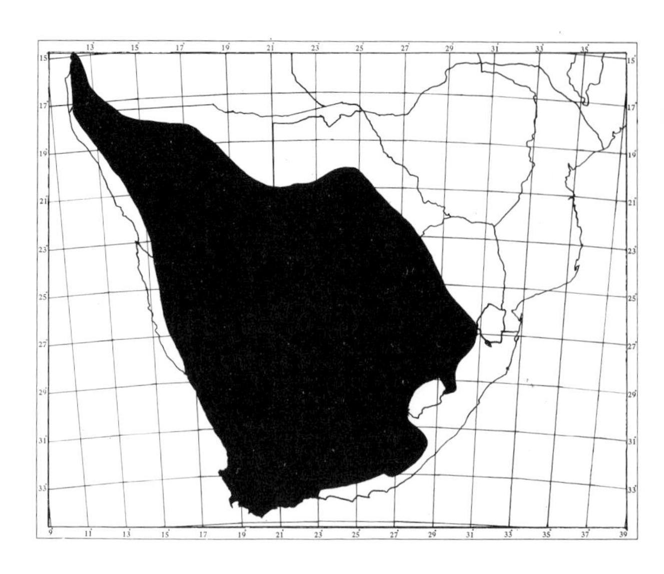

### Habitat

Throughout their range they are associated with open country, open grassland, grassland with scattered thickets, coastal scrub or semi-desert scrub, penetrating marginally into open dry woodland and into the *fynbos* in the southwestern parts of the Cape Province. Thirty specimens collected in Botswana were all taken in open habitat, 50%of the series from *Acacia* scrub, the balance from grassland, other types of scrub and cleared or overgrazed areas. In particular they are associated with the extensive areas of open grassland which surround the many pans which are a feature of the southern parts of the country. In the Republic of South Africa they are associated with the open scrub of the Karoo, the grasslands with thickets characteristic of parts of the northern Cape Province, the open grassland with few shrubs of Bushmanland, and the scrub of the West Coast Strandveld.

### Habits

Very little information is available on the habits of this species. They are predominantly nocturnal and difficult to observe, with peaks of activity just after sundown and before first light in the morning. They are generally solitary. During the day they lie up in holes in the ground or in the cover of stands of tall grass. They are accomplished diggers and either dig their own shelters or adapt those of other species, such as springhaas, to their own requirements, but more often are inclined to use ground surface cover.

They appear to have overlapping home ranges and tend to occur within optimum areas where food supplies are plentiful and cover available (Bester, 1982). Within this range, the territory which they will defend is probably only a limited area around the burrow in which a female has a litter. Hunting ranges vary from 1–4,6 km$^2$ in the Orange Free State (Bester, 1982).

Vocalisation is a high-pitched howl and a bark, sometimes one of a pair howling, the other dueting with a bark. The bark is also used as an alarm call, especially by the female in alerting her young to danger, when predators approach the breeding den. Calls are more common in the breeding season (August-October) (Bester, 1982). They growl and spit when showing aggression. When they are excited the tail is raised, its elevation indicating the level of excitement.

The Cape fox is asocial compared with other canids. The adults do not allogroom or have any contact with each other except at the time of mating and while the pups are small, although females maintain contact with their young until they are ready to disperse. Bester (1982) suggested that although foxes forage alone they might in fact have a social organization consisting of a pair.

They have a strong body odour and are assiduous urine-markers.

## Food

Comparison of the percentage occurrence of food items in stomach contents from a series of localities shows that mice and insects rank high in their diet (Table 257.2).

**Table 257.2**

Comparison of the percentage occurrence of various food items in stomach contents of the Cape fox, *V. chama*, from (a) Botswana (Smithers, 1971), (b) the Orange Free State (Lynch, 1975; Bester, 1982) and (c) the Republic of South Africa (Bothma, 1966b)

| | a | b | | c |
|---|---|---|---|---|
| | (n=23) | (n=58) (Lynch) | (n=193) (Bester) | (n=37) |
| Mammals | | | | |
| Sciuridae | — | — | 1 | — |
| Muridae | 52 | 55 | 36 | 35 |
| Insectivora | — | 14 | 2 | — |
| Lagomorpha | — | 10 | 4 | 8 |
| Bathyergidae | — | 5 | — | 14 |
| Bovidae | — | — | — | 3 |
| Domestic stock | — | 9 | 32 | — |
| Pedetidae | — | 3 | 2 | 3 |
| Carrion | — | 14 | 5 | 19 |
| Viverridae | — | — | 1 | — |
| Aves and eggs | 4 | 26 | 10 | 19 |
| Insecta | 61 | 51 | 30 | 35 |
| Coleoptera | 48 | — | — | — |
| Isoptera | 9 | 17 | — | — |
| Lepidoptera | — | — | — | — |
| Orthoptera | 30 | 16 | — | — |
| Hymenoptera | — | 2 | — | — |
| Arachnida | 26 | — | 2 | 14 |
| Scorpions | 13 | — | 1 | — |
| Solifugae | 26 | — | 2 | — |
| Myriapoda | 8 | 2 | — | — |
| Amphibia | — | 2 | — | — |
| Reptilia | 30 | 12 | 6 | 3 |
| Wild fruits | 4 | 5 | 6 | 16 |
| Green grass | — | 28 | 15 | 5 |

Compared with the two samples from the Orange Free State and the Republic of South Africa in which a wide range of small mammals was found in stomach contents, the Botswana sample contained murids only. On the other hand reptiles and Arachnida were far higher in the Botswana sample than in the other three.

Insects, which had the highest percentage occurrence in the Botswana sample, were represented by Coleoptera at 48%, in one case including larvae. A wide variety of Families occurred, the principal being Scarabaeidae, Carabidae and Dystiscidae. Orthoptera at 30% were represented by grasshoppers and crickets and termites at 9% by the harvester termite, *Hodotermes mossambicus*. Lynch (1975) recorded Scarabaeidae and Curculionidae in the Orange Free State sample, and Bester (1982) Coleoptera, Isoptera, Diptera, Orthoptera and Neuroptera.

**Table 257.3**

Breakdown by species of the Muridae represented in a sample of 23 stomachs of the Cape fox, *V. chama*, from Botswana (Smithers, 1971)

| Species | Percentage occurrence |
|---|---|
| Pouched mouse, *Saccostomus campestris* | 17 |
| Gerbil, *Tatera* spp | 9 |
| Multimammate mice, *Mastomys* spp | 9 |
| Namaqua gerbil, *Desmodillus auricularis* | 4 |
| Lesser gerbil, *Gerbillurus paeba* | 4 |
| Undetermined | 4 |

Murids (Table 257.3) in the Botswana sample consisted of a high percentage of slow moving pouched mice, *Saccostomus campestris*. The multimammate mice, *Mastomys* spp, only occur marginally to their range in Botswana. All the other species listed are particularly associated with the same type of habitat as the Cape fox. Lynch (1975) listed among the food: striped mice, *Rhabdomys pumilio*; gerbils, *Tatera* spp; pygmy mice, *Mus minutoides*, and large-eared mice, *Malacothrix typica*, while Bester (1982) found *Aethomys* sp as well, but not *R. pumilio*. Bothma (1966b) listed Namaqua rock mice, *Aethomys namaquensis*; climbing mice, *Dendromus* sp; multimammate mice, *P. natalensis*; pygmy mice, *M. minutoides*; Brants' gerbils, *T. brantsii*, and white-tailed mice, *Mystromys albicaudatus*, in the Orange Free State.

Birds were represented by the double-banded courser, *Rhinoptilus africanus*, and the crowned plover, *Stephanotis coronatus*, species associated with the open type of habitat in which the Cape fox is found.

Reptilia were represented in the Botswana sample by the whistling gecko, *Ptenopus garrulus*; the spiny agama, *Agama hispida*; the Mozambique rough-scaled sand-lizard, *Ichnotropis squamulosa*; Sundevall's writhing skink, *Lygosoma sundevallii*; the limbless skinks, *Acontias* sp and *Typhlosaurus* sp, and the amphisbaenian, *Monopeltis* sp. Snakes were represented by Peters' black worm-snake, *Leptotyphlops scutifrons*.

Hunting spider, *Solpuga*, remains were clearly recognisable but, in most cases, were unidentifiable; *Solpuga monteiroi*, however, was recognised in two stomachs. The same applied to scorpions, where *Uroplectes* sp was the only genus recognisable. Myriapods were represented by the centipede, *Scolopendra morsitans*, a species that is common in small carnivore stomachs.

Wild fruit in the form of the berries of the raisin bush, *Grewia* spp, occurred in one stomach. Grass was found at a percentage occurrence of 16%, a non-food that may be taken more for its mechanical action than for its food value.

In the Kalahari, Bester (1982) found that rodents occurred in 42% of scats (n=101), insects in 97%, solpugids in 5%, reptiles in 32% and birds in 16%, while in 32% of the scats plant material occurred. In contrast, in a small sample (25 scats) from the pro-Namib gravel plains in Namibia, murids occurred in 88% of the scats, Lagomorphs (*Lepus* sp) in 24%, birds in 8%, reptiles in 12%, insects in 24% and solpugids in 4% of the scats.

In parts of the Republic of South Africa the Cape fox is widely blamed for its depredations on small domestic stock up to the size of sheep and goats. Although there is no evidence for this, in the Orange Free State, for example, they are widely blamed for their predation on lambs, particularly in the age class of newly born to about a month old. On this basis during the years 1968 to 1976 over 2 000 Cape foxes were destroyed annually by Oranjejag, over 4 000 in 1974 (Bester, 1978).

Doubts as to whether these actions were justified were expressed by Roberts (1951), and Bothma (1966b) found no evidence of this predation. While Lynch (1975) recorded the remains of sheep in five out of 58 stomachs examined in the Orange Free State, he stressed the impossibility of determining whether these had been killed by the foxes or taken as carrion. In Botswana, where goats which were not kraaled at night were regularly killed by jackals, the Cape fox was not considered to be a problem animal (Smithers, 1983). Bothma (1966b) examined 40 stomachs from the Transvaal and came to the conclusion that the Cape fox is not a harmful predator and that control measures were not economically justifiable or ecologically desirable. Bester (1982) found that Cape foxes can only kill sheep lambs up to the age of three months, and that they account for 4,5% of the lamb crop. Larger sheep are only utilized as carrion.

## Reproduction

In the Orange Free State pups are born between August and October, with a peak in September; litters number two to five (Bester, 1980; Lynch, *in litt.*). Shortridge (1934) recorded a lactating female from Namibia in September, Smithers (1971) a gravid female in October in Botswana. Brand (1963) stated that in captivity in the National Zoological Gardens, Pretoria, the time of the birth of young extends from the middle of September to the middle of October, litters varying in number from one to four, with a gestation period of from 51 to 52 days.

Bester (1982) recorded that when burrows were excavated containing young, most were found to be too small for adults to enter. Parents on occasion carry pups to other burrows and "helpers" are found at dens occasionally. Ribbink (pers. comm.) mentioned that the male provisions the female soon after she has given birth to the pups. Mills (pers. comm.) once observed two litters being raised simultaneously in one burrow, while Bester (1982) found one litter consisting of eight pups in the Orange Free State, which may indicate a similar situation.

Females have one pair of inguinal and two pairs of abdominal mammae.

## Genus *Canis* Linnaeus, 1758

Key to the species (Meester *et al.*, 1986)

1. Carnassials relatively small, length less than 83 percent of $M^1 + M^2$ in upper jaw and less than 130 percent of $M_2 + M_3$ in lower jaw; tail-tip white; ears blackish-grey behind, normally less than 100 mm long; no dark saddle-patch on back, pale stripe normally present on sides
... *adustus*

   Carnassial/molar ratio (see above) more than 83 percent in upper jaw, more than 130 percent in lower jaw; tail-tip dark; ears reddish-brown behind, normally more than 100 mm long; dark saddlepatch on back
... *mesomelas*

No. 258

## *Canis adustus* (Sundevall, 1846)

## Side-striped jackal
## Witkwasjakkals

Plate 21

### Colloquial Name

The name jackal is derived from the Persian, Sagal, which presumably was applied to the golden jackal, *Canis aureus*. Side-striped refers to the longitudinal light-coloured bands on the flanks which, unfortunately, are not always obvious, but there are few other features that mark this drab-coloured species. The Afrikaans name is generally more appropriate, referring to the white tip of the tail.

### Taxonomic Notes

Coetzee (1977a) listed seven subspecies from the continent, only one of which, *C. a. adustus*, originally described from a specimen from "Caffraria Interiore", occurs in the Subregion. This indefinite type locality was later fixed by Roberts as the Magaliesberg, west of Pretoria.

### Description

Side-striped jackals stand about 0,38 m at the shoulder, and have a mass of between 8 and 10 kg (Table 258.1). They are a much less colourful species than their close relatives, black-backed jackals, *C. mesomelas*, lacking the distinct dark saddlemarking on the back and the rich reddish colour of the flanks and limbs of this species. At a distance they appear an overall grey or greyish-buff colour, with two characteristic features. The first of these is the light or off-white lateral bands, fringed with black, on their flanks. The white bands rise from just behind and slightly below the shoulder and run upwards towards the base of the tail. The second is the broad white tip to the tail, which is normally present, although occasionally it is missing.

**Table 258.1**

Measurements (mm) and mass (kg) of side-striped jackals, *C. adustus*, from Zimbabwe (Smithers, 1983)

| | Males | | | Females | | |
|---|---|---|---|---|---|---|
| | $\bar{x}$ | n | Range | $\bar{x}$ | n | Range |
| TL | 1082 | 50 | 960–1165 | 1075 | 50 | 1000–1170 |
| T | 361 | 50 | 305–390 | 354 | 50 | 310–410 |
| Hf c/u | 172 | 50 | 160–192 | 168 | 50 | 153–178 |
| E | 88 | 50 | 80–97 | 86 | 50 | 80–95 |
| Mass | 9,39 | 50 | 7,26–12,04 | 8,29 | 50 | 7,26–10,00 |

In the field the side-striped jackal gives the appearance of being similar in size to the black-backed jackal, but in series they are in fact slightly larger overall and distinctly heavier (Table 258.1). Their ears are shorter and more rounded than the black-backed jackal, but this is not usually apparent unless they are seen together. Like the black-backed jackal there are lighter coloured patches on the shoulders which contrast with the drab colour of the remainder of the flanks. The limbs are lighter coloured than the body, often tinged rufous, but never the rich reddish colour of the black-backed jackal. Their hind feet are plain buffy-white.

The hairs of the guard coat on the upper parts of the body are rather coarse; the individual hairs are broadly buffy at the base, with a narrow dark band, a white band and a broad jet black tip. On the shoulder the hair reaches a length of about 70 mm, increasing in length to 80 mm towards the base of the tail. On the base of the tail the hairs are very broadly buffy at the base with black tips, giving it the appearance of being lighter in colour than the remainder of the upper parts. The tail is predominantly black; the hairs have broad jet black tips; the tip is usually white. The white hair on the tip is longest of all, reaching a length of about 100 mm. The hair on the face and lower parts of the limbs is much shorter, a bare 10 mm. The underfur is dense and buffy in colour; it is wavy and shorter than the guard hairs and tends to be a richer buffy on the hindquarters than on the shoulders. The throat is light buffy-white. The remainder of the under parts is off-white; both the guard hairs and underfur hairs have grey bases. The base of the tail has long, buffy-white hair.

There are five digits on the front feet and four on the hind. The claws on the front are typically dog-like and up to about 20 mm over the curve; those on the hind feet are shorter at about 15 mm. The first digits on the front feet, carrying the dew claws, are situated far back of the plantar pads and do not mark in the spoor (Fig. 258.1). The impression of the plantar pad in the spoor is characteristic, the impression of the back showing little or no sign of a central evagination and appearing as a nearly straight line.

### Skull (Fig. 258.2)

The skull of the side-striped jackal is, in many respects, rather similar to that of the black-backed, but there are characters by which they may readily be distinguished. In profile the skull of the side-striped is flatter, there being less

**Plate 21**

255. Bat-eared fox, *Otocyon megalotis*
Bakoorvos
256. Wild dog, *Lycaon pictus*
Wildehond
257. Cape fox, *Vulpes chama*
Silwervos
258. Side-striped jackal, *Canis adustus*
Witkwasjakkals
259. Black-backed jackal, *Canis mesomelas*
Rooijakkals

PLATE 21
258
259
255
257
256
Dick Findlay

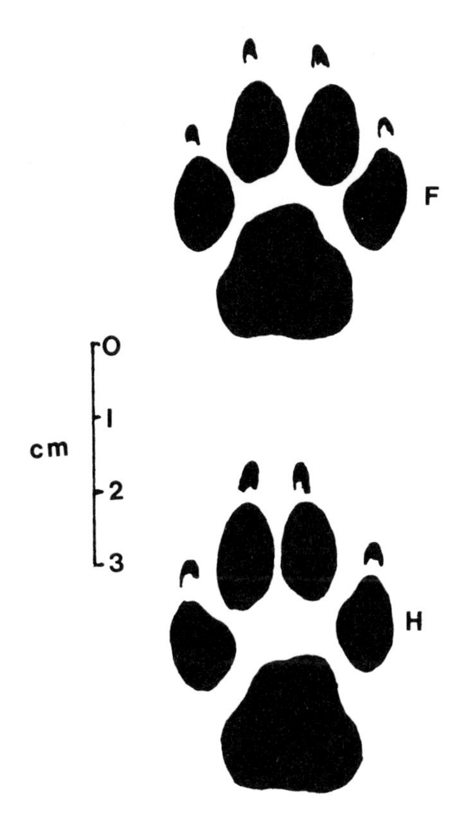


Fig. 258.1. Spoor: side-striped jackal, *C. adustus*.
F. Right forefoot H. Right hind foot.

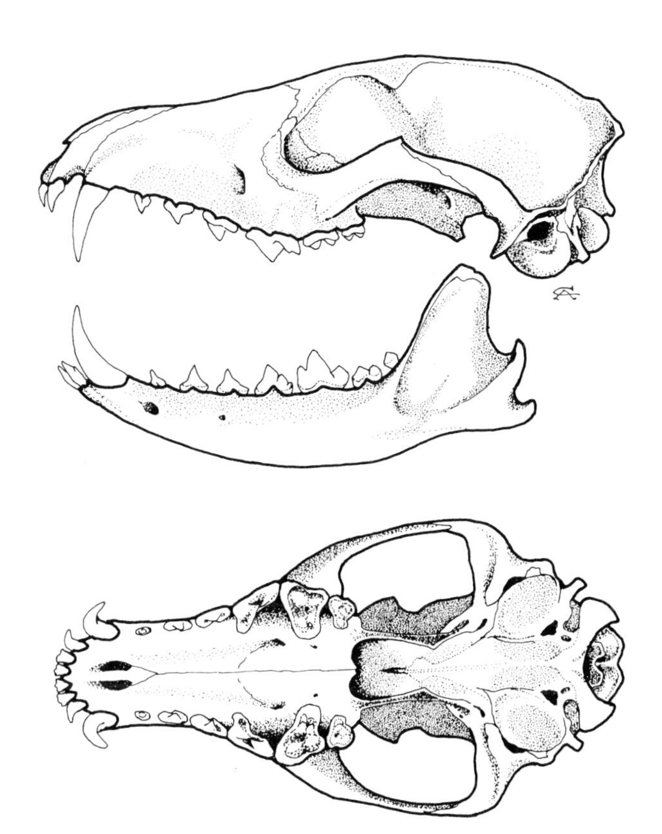

Fig. 258.2. Skull: side-striped jackal, *C. adustus*.
TL Skull 170 mm

of a marked difference between the height at the frontals and the front of the nasals. This is due to the narrow elongated rostrum which is longer and narrower in the side-striped than in the black-backed, a feature which is even more noticeable in life than in the skull itself. The elongation of the rostrum can be shown when the breadth at the third upper premolar is considered in relation to distance from the back of this tooth to the incisors and is compared in the two species. In the black-backed the ratio is about 31/42 or 74%, as opposed to about 28/55 or 51% in the side-striped.

In the side-striped there is a very distinct sagittal crest running from the supraoccipital crest right over the top of the braincase, reaching a height of two or three millimetres, and dividing forwards into two sharp ridges, to end in the postorbital bars. The zygomatic arches are lighter in build than in the black-backed, the postorbital bars represented by blunt processes on the frontals and zygoma.

The dental formula is similar to that of the black-backed:

$I\frac{3}{3}\ C\frac{1}{1}\ P\frac{4}{4}\ M\frac{2}{3} = 42$ and is typically canid.

The outer upper incisors are not quite as large as those of the black-backed. The canines, however, are generally longer and more curved. On the other hand the upper fourth premolar in the side-striped is smaller in proportion than in the black-backed, a feature which Ewer (1956) was able to demonstrate by comparing the length of this tooth against the ratio of its length to that of the first upper molar. This allows for a reliable separation of skulls picked up in the field (see key to the species). The teeth of the two species are otherwise very similar except that, because of the elongation of the rostrum in the side-striped, the third upper premolar now lies more in line with the remainder and not at an angle as in the black-backed jackal.

The dentition is adapted to holding and killing with the canines, cutting with the carnassials, and at the same time, a grinding function in the broad molar teeth.

**Distribution**

The side-striped jackal has a considerably wider distribution on the continent than the black-backed jackal, ranging widely south of the Sahara and into parts of West Africa. In the South West Arid Zone they are replaced almost entirely by the black-backed jackal, reflecting their habitat requirements which they find in better-watered, higher rainfall areas.

*South of the Sahara, excluding the Southern African Subregion*

There are records from northern **Nigeria**, a specimen from Gombe, and sightings from north of Benue, and the Borgu Game Reserve in the west. They occur in the **Central African Republic** and are recorded from localities in the southern **Sudan** and central **Ethiopia**. They are recorded from central and southern **Kenya** and from the extreme southwest and northeast of **Uganda** and along the northern shores of Lake Victoria. They are widespread in **Tanzania** and **Zambia**. Although there are few records from **Mozambique**, north of the Zambezi River, they probably occur throughout this sector, as they are common in **Malawi** and southern **Tanzania**. They are recorded from southern, western and eastern **Zaire**, and extend into southern **Gabon**. They occur widely in **Angola**, apart from the extreme southwest.

*Southern African Subregion*

With a fringing distribution in the extreme northern parts of **Namibia**, they occur in the vicinity of the Okavango Delta and in the extreme northern parts of **Botswana**, extending eastwards throughout **Zimbabwe**, except in the drier western and southeastern parts of the country. They are widespread in **Mozambique**, south of the Zambezi River, but corresponding with their absence in southwestern Zimbabwe, they are not recorded from the adjacent drier areas of the Banhine Flats in the northern parts of the Gaza District. There are many material records from the **Transvaal**, east of 31 °E where they are confined to the better-watered parts of this province. Southwards they range marginally into **Natal** in the extreme northeast, this marking their most southern occurrence on the continent.

**Habitat**

Unlike the black-backed jackal, the side-striped jackal avoids open savanna grassland, favouring more thickly wooded country, but not occurring in forest. In parts of their distributional range, as for example in the Hwange National Park, Zimbabwe, they are confined to the woodland in the

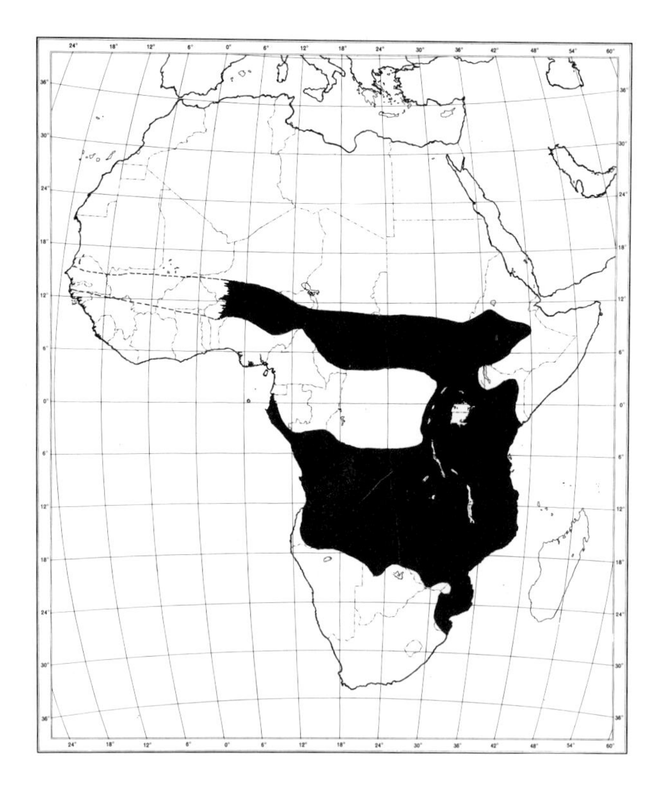

northern parts of the Park, but where this gives way southwards to more open country, they are replaced by the black-backed jackal. Throughout their distributional range they are associated with well-watered habitat.

## Habits

They are more strictly nocturnal than the black-backed jackal, but on occasion move after sunrise as late as 08h00, and just before sunset. Activity appears to continue throughout the night as there are records of their being seen at 02h30, although their main peaks of activity appear to be early in the night and just before sunrise in the morning. During the day they lie up in the cover of substantial shelter such as holes in the ground, disused antbear holes being commonly used, or in piles of boulders. Normally solitary individuals, pairs, and family parties comprising a female with young, have been recorded. They are terrestrial and move at a walk, or more typically at a slow trot, giving the appearance of being more sluggish in their actions than the black-backed, although under stress they show a good turn of speed when making for cover. If caught in live traps, they are less aggressive than the black-backed jackal and more easily handled, but they are just as wary of these and are difficult to trap. Under stress of trapping they smell very strongly and traps so contaminated are avoided by other species. They are not averse to moving into close proximity of dwellings or farm outbuildings and will enter peri-urban or urban areas freely, even being taken in the centre of cities (Harare, Zimbabwe), where there is cover in city parks or in vacant stands.

Vocalisation is a series of melancholy yaps, being distinguished from the call of the black-backed in that it lacks the long, drawn-out howl characteristic of that species. Under stress they chatter and the young whine, especially when hungry.

## Food

The 71 stomachs from Zimbabwe (Smithers & Wilson, 1979) on which the present assessment is based, were recovered from specimens taken predominantly in an agriculturally developed area where carrion was not as freely available as it is in a wild area where there are large predators. In the Okavango Delta in Botswana the side-striped jackal came in freely to carcasses laid out as baits and, where it is available, no doubt carrion figures at a higher occurrence than in the present sample.

**Table 258.2a**

Percentage occurrence of various food items in a sample of 71 stomachs of the side-striped jackal, *C. adustus* from Zimbabwe (Smithers, 1983)

| Food item | Percentage occurrence |
|---|---|
| Vegetable matter | 72 |
| Wild fruits | 48 |
| Peanuts | 10 |
| Maize | 7 |
| Beans | 3 |
| Sunflower seed | 2 |
| Pumpkin | 1 |
| Avocado | 1 |
| Mammalia | 35 |
| Insecta | 31 |
| Carrion | 11 |
| Aves | 11 |
| Reptilia | 1 |

In the 71 stomachs vegetable matter, in a number of forms, figures at by far the highest percentage occurrence (Table 258.2a). This included a range of wild fruits (Table 258.2b) and the seeds of agricultural crops. Full stomachs of the latter were recorded; in two these contained green maize, in another two, peanuts and in one, sunflower seeds.

**Table 258.2b**

Wild fruits identified

| Food item | Percentage occurrence |
|---|---|
| Wild fruits | 16 |
| Wild figs, *Ficus* spp | 10 |
| Mobola plums, *Parinari curatellifolia* | 6 |
| Mahobohobo, *Uapaca kirkiana* | 1 |
| *Solanum* spp | 1 |
| Jackal-berry, *Diospyros mespiliformis* | 1 |
| Wild raisin, *Grewia* spp | 1 |
| Undetermined | 17 |

Various mammals, predominantly rats and mice, had the next highest occurrence and included a wide range of species, the largest a scrub hare, *Lepus saxatilis* (Table 258.2c). As might be expected, multimammate mice, *Mastomys* spp, the commonest species in the area, had by far the highest occurrence.

**Table 258.2c**

Murid species, a mole-rat and lagomorph identified

| Species | Percentage occurrence |
|---|---|
| Multimammate mice, *Mastomys* spp | 17 |
| Angoni vlei rat, *Otomys angoniensis* | 3 |
| Pygmy mouse, *Mus* spp | 3 |
| Gerbil, *Tatera* spp | 1 |
| Pouched mouse, *Saccostomus campestris* | 1 |
| Water rat, *Dasymys incomtus* | 1 |
| Grooved-toothed mouse, *Pelomys fallax* | 1 |
| Mole rat, *Cryptomys hottentotus* | 1 |
| Scrub hare, *Lepus saxatilis* | 1 |

Insects were well represented at an occurrence of 31% by a preponderance of grasshoppers, crickets, beetles (larvae and adults), and termites, represented in two stomachs by the harvesters, *Macrotermes falciger*, and in one each by *M. natalensis* and *M. bellicosus*.

Carrion ranked noticeably low in occurrence at 11% and included the hair of a cow and a goat. Birds were represented by the remains of an adult guineafowl, *Numida mitrata*, its eggs and a chicken from the stomach of a specimen taken while raiding a poultry run. Reptiles occurred in one stomach, being the remains of two Schlegel's blind snakes, *Typhlops schlegelii*.

Forty percent of the stomachs contained broad-leaved green grass, a common non-food item in the stomachs of carnivores, in two cases forming the only item in the stomach. Hairballs, consisting predominantly of their own hair, occurred in two stomachs and pieces of electric flex and scraps of inner tubes from car tyres were also recovered.

Other food items not included in the present sample, from stomachs from Botswana, included carrion in the form of the skin and hair of wildebeest, eland, reedbuck and lechwe, the small quills of a porcupine and a young tortoise, *Testudo pardalis*. Although this sample is small, consisting of only 11 stomachs, the percentage occurrence of carrion at 45% is much higher than in the Zimbabwe sample, which is to be expected owing to its freer availability.

Shortridge (1934) considered the side-striped jackal as essentially a scavenger, but listed at the same time, among other foods, mammals, birds, lizards, insects and wild fruit. Stevenson-Hamilton (1929) stated that they are not entirely carnivorous, eating locusts and other insects and certain wild fruits.

From this evidence the side-striped jackal appears to be omnivorous, with a bias towards vegetable matter, warm-blooded prey and insects, and will take carrion freely when it is available.

**Reproduction**

Present evidence indicates that the females litter down just before or during the summer months from about August through to January (Maberly, 1963; Smithers, 1983). Litters consist of an average of 5,4 pups (range 4–6; n=5). Haagner (1920) has a record of seven in a litter from a female in the National Zoological Gardens, Pretoria. While Shortridge (1934) quoted Wolhuter who shot a female with 12 foetuses, this is unusual.

The young are born in holes in the ground, usually disused antbear holes, which the female adjusts to her own requirements, often opening a second escape hole from the breeding chamber. In Zimbabwe a breeding hole had its main entrance opening in a ditch, which allowed the female to emerge and move out of sight, except from adjacent high vantage points, 300 m in one direction and 200 m in the other. Breeding chambers examined in two holes were about three-quarters to one metre below ground level and two to three metres from the entrance. In one, the escape hole opened at the edge of a maize land and the female, which had a litter, was observed to scan the terrain carefully from this entrance as well as from the main entrance before finally emerging. While still suckling, the young may crawl to the entrance to lie just within its shelter in the sun, and at such times the females sometimes lie out in adjacent cover, keeping the litter under observation. Females with suckling young are sensitive to disturbance and they will carry the whole litter, one by one, to a new hole if unduly disturbed.

During the early growth stages of the young, the male operates independently. Later both the male and female will bring back food to the litter, either regurgitating this or carrying it back in their mouths. Small cubs are fed inside the lip of the hole; larger cubs are fed by depositing the food just outside the entrance.

Females have two pairs of inguinal mammae.

---

No. 259

## *Canis mesomelas* Schreber, 1778

## Black-backed jackal
## Rooijakkals

Plate 21

---

**Colloquial Name**

Black-backed refers to the broad, dark saddle which, on the upper parts of the body, extends from the neck to the base of the tail. This serves to distinguish them from the side-striped jackal, *Canis adustus*. The Afrikaans name, *rooijakkals*, is appropriate as the head, flanks and limbs in adult individuals are a rich reddish colour which is very apparent in the field.

**Taxonomic Notes**

Meester *et al.* (1986) relegated all Subregion material to *C. m. mesomelas*.

**Description**

The characteristic features of the black-backed jackal are the dark saddle on its back, which runs from the nape of the neck to the base of the tail, the black, bushy tail, and reddish flanks and limbs. In the field these features normally can be distinguished even at a distance.

Standing about 400 mm at the shoulder and a metre in total length, adult males have a mean mass of about 8 kg, females 7 kg. They are slightly lighter on average than the side-striped jackal (Table 259.1).

**Table 259.1**

Measurements (mm) and mass (kg) of black-backed jackals, *C. mesomelas*, from Zimbabwe (National Museums, Zimbabwe records)

| | Males | | | Females | | |
|---|---|---|---|---|---|---|
| | $\bar{x}$ | n | Range | $\bar{x}$ | n | Range |
| TL | 1050 | 39 | 960–1120 | 987 | 52 | 890–1095 |
| T | 329 | 39 | 280–365 | 314 | 52 | 250–370 |
| Hf c/u | 161 | 39 | 150–179 | 160 | 52 | 140–180 |
| E | 109 | 39 | 98–115 | 99 | 52 | 80–115 |
| Mass | 7,89 | 39 | 6,81–9,53 | 6,60 | 52 | 5,45–9,99 |

The head is dog-like, with a pointed muzzle and high upstanding pointed ears. The dark saddle is broadest at the level of the shoulders and tapers off to a narrow point at the base of the tail. At a distance it looks black but, at close quarters, is seen to be sprinkled liberally with silvery-white hairs. The individual hairs have broad silvery-white bands below their broad black tips, which show clearly against the black background. Sometimes these bands lie in juxtaposition, giving the appearance of white lines. Just behind the shoulders there are light-coloured patches within the black of the saddle.

In the winter coat, adults, in particular males, from the drier western areas develop the rich reddish colour to a high degree, making them very striking and handsome animals. The whole head, back and ears, flanks, limbs and basal third of the tail are then a deep russet red, usually darker on the thighs and on top of the muzzle. The lips and chest are white, the under parts white or tinged rusty. The lower parts of the limbs are usually lighter in colour. Females are generally less richly coloured than males and this is also true for individuals from the eastern areas where the face and muzzle tend to remain browner or greyer.

The guard hairs on the saddle, at the level of the shoulders, may reach a length of about 60 mm, tapering off to 40 mm at the base of the tail. They are longer on the tail at about 70 mm, reaching 90 mm at the tip. The individual hairs are coarse, buffy or buffy-grey at the base with a black band, a broad white band and broad jet black tips. The hair on the face is short, 10–15 mm, lengthening on the flanks to about 30 mm and to 40 mm on the rump. The underfur is whitish or buffy. The hairs are shorter than the guard hairs and wavy.

There are five digits on the front feet. The first, which carries the dew claw, is set well back from the remainder and does not mark in the spoor (Fig. 259.1). The hind foot has four digits. The claws are broad at the base and relatively short, measuring about 150 mm over the curve.

Males on average are slightly larger than females and heavier (Table 259.1).

**Skull** (Fig. 259.2)

The skull of the black-backed jackal is elongated. The braincase is pear-shaped, broadest at the level of the junction of the zygoma and tapering anteriorly.

In profile the skull is highest at the level of the frontals, sloping off gradually to the back of the braincase and more abruptly forward, to level out halfway along the nasals. The rostrum is narrow, the width at the canines about a third of the distance between the front of the eye orbits and the incisors. The depression between the frontals, which extends to the nasals, so noticeable in *Lycaon*, is barely perceptible, in some specimens only being present between the frontals and the posterior part of the nasals.

The supraoccipital crest is well developed and while the sagittal crest at its junction with the supraoccipital rises to

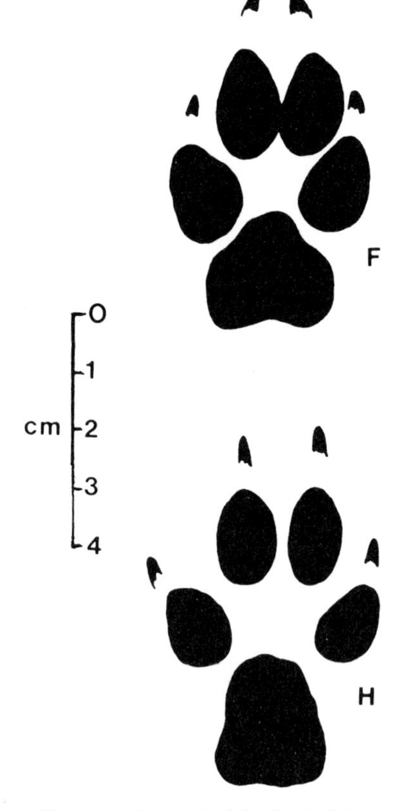


Fig. 259.1. Spoor: black-backed jackal, *C. mesomelas*.
F. Right forefoot H. Right hind foot.

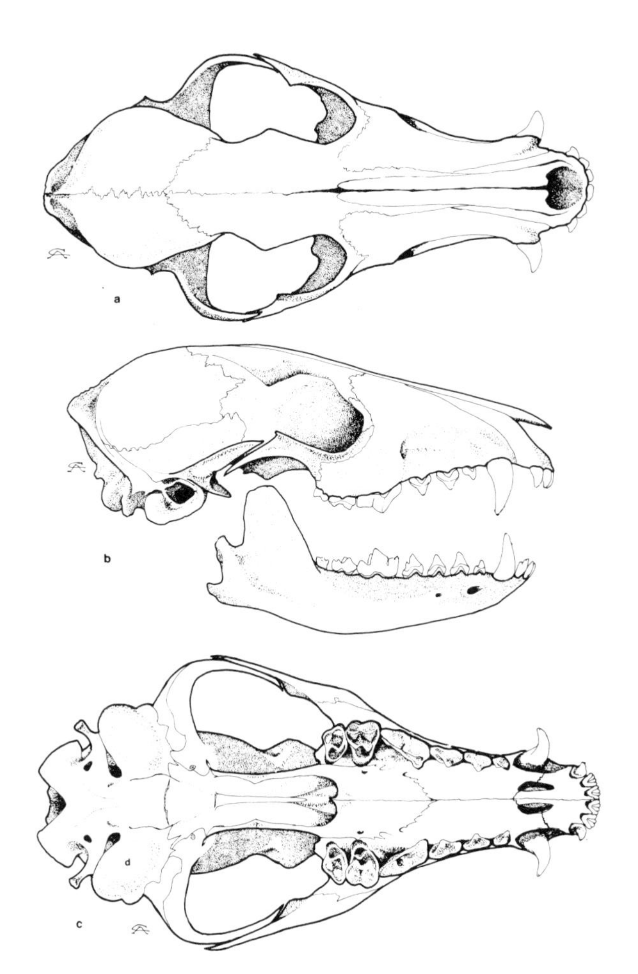


Fig. 259.2. Skull: black-backed jackal, *C. mesomelas*.
TL Skull 170 mm.
See also Fig. XXXII.2 and 3

its level, it is only apparent on the back of the skull, forward of which it divides into two low ridges which end on the postorbital bars. The area between the ridges on the top of the braincase is smooth and appears to be devoid of muscle attachment. The sides of the braincase on the other hand are rough to give attachment to the temporalis muscles. The zygomatic arches are broad and well developed in relation to the size of the skull; the postorbital bars are incomplete and represented by blunt processes on the zygoma and frontals. The bullae are rounded, the paroccipital processes fused to the back of the bullae.

The dental formula is:

$I\frac{3}{3}\ C\frac{1}{1}\ P\frac{4}{4}\ M\frac{2}{3} = 42$

which is typically canid. The upper outer incisors are larger, more pointed and more canine-like in build than the remainder; the lower are less so and more normal in shape. The upper canines are long, curved and sharp-pointed, with a sharp ridge on their posterior faces. The lower are similar, but slightly more recurved and shorter.

The palate broadens at the level of the third premolar, which is set at a slight angle to the toothrow. The fourth upper premolar, the upper component of the carnassial shear, is clearly adapted to slicing. The first and second upper molars are broad and well developed for crushing. In the lower jaw the first molar, the lower component of the carnassial, has the anterior two-thirds of the tooth adapted to cutting. The posterior third, which occludes on the broad first upper molar, is flattened and the second lower molar provides for crushing. The third lower molar is very small and, as it does not occlude on the face of the second upper molar, can take only a minor part in the crushing process.

The dentition allows for the catching and holding of prey with the canines, assisted by the upper outer incisor, for slicing with the well developed carnassial shear, and for the grinding of insect and other more fragile food by the broad molar teeth, all functions being necessary to an omnivorous species.

**Distribution**

The black-backed jackal occurs in two discrete areas on the continent separated by a distance of some 900 km—the northern area extending from the Gulf of Aden southwards to southern Tanzania and the southern area from southwestern Angola and Zimbabwe to the Cape Province. This corresponds in broad outline with the present distribution of species such as the bat-eared fox, *Otocyon megalotis*, and there is no doubt that at some drier period in the past there was continuity in their distribution.

In parts of East Africa the black-backed jackal co-exists with the golden jackal, *Canis aureus*, which replaces this species to the north and extends in its distributional range into parts of the Middle East, Europe and Asia.

*South of the Sahara, excluding the Southern African Subregion*

The species occurs in **Somalia** and is stated to be widespread and common, except in the central sector and in **Ethiopia**. There is a record from the southeastern **Sudan** and they occur throughout most of **Uganda**, central and northeastern **Tanzania** and as far south as Ilolo and Njombe, near the northern tip of Lake Malawi. They occur in southwestern **Angola**, but not north of about 13 °S coastally.

*Southern African Subregion*

They occur throughout **Namibia** including the Namib Desert. In **Botswana** they are common throughout, except in the extreme northeast, which coincides with their absence in adjacent parts of Zimbabwe. In **Zimbabwe** they occur throughout the southwest and eastwards on the plateau to the Rusape district, being absent north and northeast of the plateau. In **Mozambique** they occur as far north as the Save River. They are found throughout the **Transvaal**, the **Orange Free State, Lesotho, Swaziland, Natal** and the **Cape Province**, excluding the extreme southwestern and eastern parts.

**Habitat**

Black-backed jackals have a wide habitat tolerance, occurring in the South West Arid and Southern Savanna zones in

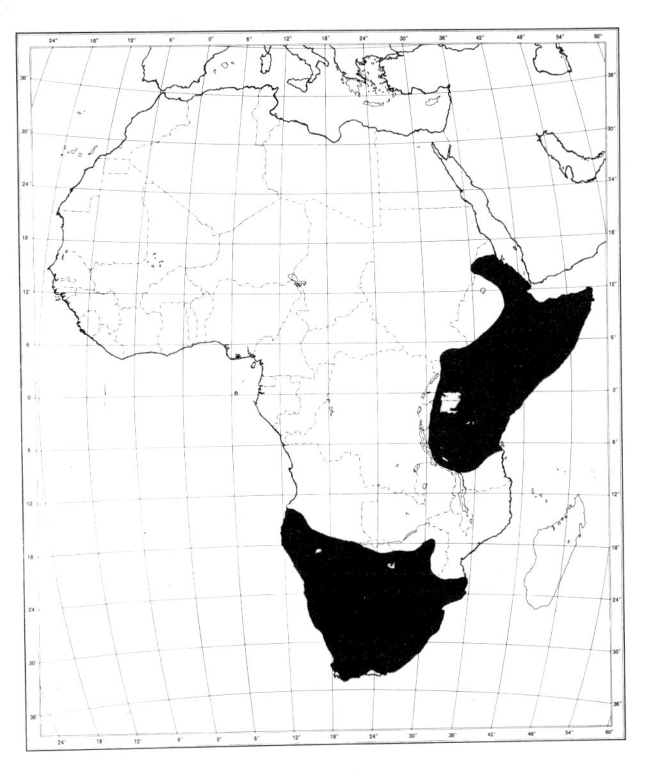

areas with a mean annual rainfall of up to about 1 000 mm. However, they are most common in the drier areas. Towards the northern and eastern limits of their distribution where the country is better-watered with a rainfall of 800–1000 mm, they are replaced by the side-striped jackal, *Canis adustus*.

In the Subregion they are absent from forest but, apart from this association, occur in a wide variety of habitats, with a tendency to be associated with open terrain. Near the limits of their eastern distribution in Zimbabwe and the Transvaal Lowveld/Mozambique, small numbers occur on the same ground as the side-striped jackal. Here black-backed jackals occupy the more open conditions of the plateau, with only side-striped jackals being found in the river valleys.

**Habits**

Black-backed jackals exhibit both diurnal and nocturnal activity, with their circadian activity pattern closely resembling that of their important prey animals, particularly rodents (Ferguson *et al.*, 1988). In National Parks and other areas, where human disturbance is negligible, they may be seen moving during daylight hours, whereas in intensively developed areas or where they are subject to control they are clearly nocturnal. Normally occurring in pairs or on their own, aggregations of up to eight or 10 may be found at carcasses and there are records of larger numbers of up to 30 being seen at seal carcasses on the Namibian coast (David, 1989) and at elephant carcasses in eastern Botswana (McKenzie, pers. comm.). Pairs and family parties, consisting of the parents with three or four half to three-quarter grown young, move and forage as a group.

Movement is normally at a trot, except when hunting for small vertebrates and invertebrates when they will walk around slowly, ears pricked, searching for prey. Their senses are acute, their sense of smell being developed particularly well. On the open plains in Botswana an individual was seen following up the down-wind scent of a dead springbok from a distance of well over a kilometre. It followed this scent without hesitation to join others already feeding. No doubt it had picked up the scent of the rather meagre remains at a distance considerably in excess of this. They are independent of water, which in the drier parts of their range is only available seasonally, but will drink when water is available.

They are wary and cunning and, where they are in contact with human developments, may be extremely difficult to trap. They will examine live traps set for them in detail, walking around them presumably attracted by the bait, but usually do not enter. Shortridge (1934) stated that in the more remote parts of Namibia, however, they ranked among the easiest of carnivorous animals to trap.

If encountered at night with dazzling lights they tend to keep well clear, glancing back from time to time as they move further away, or they may circle in a wide arc to catch the scent down wind. Where the disturbance factor is high, they become very wary of human beings and quickly slink off out of sight. Under cover of darkness they will penetrate freely into peri-urban or even urban areas and may be seen in the vicinity of farm buildings when hunting.

They may rest in holes in the ground (frequently using disused burrows of antbears, *Orycteropus afer*), in rock crevices or among piles of boulders, preferring this more substantial cover to that of the underbush or tall grass. However, in areas where human disturbance is absent, they prefer to rest in an open spot from where they have a good view of the surrounding terrain. Under these conditions they resort to resting under cover only to escape cold winds or the midday sun. On very cold still nights they have been found resting on flattened piles of dry elephant dung or on impala middens—presumably utilizing the insulating properties of the dung to conserve warmth (McKenzie, pers. comm.).

The territorial call is a long drawn out *nyaaaa*, followed by a stacatto *ya-ya-ya-ya*, and is one of the characteristic sounds of the African night. If cornered and under stress, they may "kecker" with a shrill chattering noise. The young whine like puppies, especially when hungry. A persistent *nya-nya-nya* call is given out when a large predator is sighted. This apparent mobbing behaviour has been seen to be directed at baboons (Ferguson, 1980) and baboons, caracals, cheetahs, leopards, lions and spotted hyaenas (McKenzie, pers. comm.). Skead (1973) found that they are more vocal during the winter months from June to August, when the majority of females come into oestrus, and believed that this peak in vocalisation is related to sexual activity.

Mated pairs are territorial and both males and females mark and defend the boundaries of their territories. Moehlman (1978) recorded that if the territorial pair encountered a female trespasser, the female of the pair would threaten it while the male of the pair stood aside and watched and, alternatively, if the trespasser was a male, the male of the pair would take action while the female stood aside.

The home ranges of the adult pairs are mutually exclusive. However, adult jackals may occasionally conduct extensive forays into neighbouring territories in search of food, and at large food resources, such as a carcass, jackals from neighbouring territories are well tolerated by the resident pair.

Adult home ranges in the Subregion have been found to vary from 3,4 to 21,5 $km^2$ (mean = 10,6 $km^2$) (Ferguson *et al.*, 1983). The home ranges of subadult jackals may approximate those of the parent jackals if the subadults remain as helpers; however, other subadults range over a wide area. Young jackals usually remain within the vicinity of their natal den for at least six months, but later disperse from 5 to 135 km from their natal home range. Subadult home ranges vary from 1,9 to 575 $km^2$ (mean = 85,2 $km^2$) (Ferguson *et al.*, 1983). The variation in home range sizes within the different components of the population is largely attributable to differences in topography, vegetation and food supply in different parts of the Subregion. Human presence and persecution may also influence this aspect of jackal biology.

**Food**

Table 259.2 (a-d) shows the incidence of various types of food items in the stomachs of a sample of 96 jackals collected in Botswana and Zimbabwe. Insects which had the highest percentage occurrence (52%) consisted mainly of grasshoppers and crickets, followed by beetles and termites. The beetles were predominantly Scarabaeidae, which are associated with carrion, but also included "rose beetles" which occur in very large numbers with the onset of the rains. Where identified the termites consisted of the harvester, *Hodotermes mossambicus*, in three cases, with single records of *Macrotermes* sp and *Pseudocanthotermes militaris*. Caterpillars, dragonflies and earwigs were recognised among the remainder of the insect food.

**Table 259.2a**

Percentage occurrence of various food items encountered in the stomachs of a sample of 96 black-backed jackals, *C. mesomelas*, from Botswana and Zimbabwe (Smithers, 1983).

| Food items | Percentage occurrence |
|---|---|
| Insecta | 52 |
| Orthoptera | 22 |
| Coleoptera | 19 |
| Isoptera | 17 |
| Lepidoptera | 1 |
| Odonata | 1 |
| Dermoptera | 1 |
| Undetermined | 4 |
| Carrion | 37 |
| Muridae | 29 |
| Vegetable matter | 25 |
| Solifugae | 10 |
| Reptilia | 7 |
| Scorpiones | 6 |
| Mammalia | 5 |
| Aves | 5 |
| Myriapoda | 2 |
| Amphibia | 1 |

**Table 259.2b**

Categories of carrion identified.

| Species | Number of occurrences |
|---|---|
| Springbok, *Antidorcas marsupialis* | 9 |
| Goat | 4 |
| Wildebeest, *Connochaetes taurinus* | 1 |
| Duiker, *Sylvicapra grimmia* | 1 |
| Impala, *Aepyceros melampus* | 1 |
| Giraffe, *Giraffa camelopardalis* | 2 |
| Undetermined | 15 |

Among the items identified as carrion (37% of stomachs), springbok and goat remains figured highly, followed by the skin and bones of springbok, wildebeest, giraffe, common duiker and a range of oddments such as paper, plastic bags (which probably were used originally as food containers), string, pieces of a leather harness and the remains of drag baits in the form of the intestines of antelopes. With reference to the latter it was noted on several occasions in Botswana that the jackal showed a preference for the stomach contents of antelope over the chopped up remains of intestines and flesh.

**Table 259.2c**

Murid species identified.

| Species | Number of occurrences |
|---|---|
| Angoni vlei rat, *Otomys angoniensis* | 4 |
| Multimammate mice, *Mastomys* spp | 3 |
| Gerbil, *Tatera* spp | 2 |
| Pouched mouse, *Saccostomus campestris* | 1 |
| Pygmy mice, *Mus* spp | 1 |
| Fat mouse, *Steatomys pratensis* | 1 |
| Unidentified | 18 |

While the murids (29%) remained largely unidentifiable, five species were recognised.

Vegetable matter ranked next, occurring in 25% of the stomachs. In Botswana raisin bush berries, *Grewia* sp, were of common occurrence and in addition the pips and pulp of tsamma melons, *Citrullus lanatus*, and *Ficus* spp fruits. Three stomachs from Zimbabwe were full of peanuts, which the animals dig up or pluck from the drying stocks.

Solifugae (sun spiders) occurred in 10% of stomachs, these apparently being palatable to a wide range of small carnivores. However, they are only available seasonally, being in evidence only during the summer months from about October to February.

**Table 259.2d**

Reptile species identified.

**Serpentes**
Peters' black worm-snake, *Leptotyphlops scutifrons*
Sundevall's shovel-snouted snake, *Prosymna sundevallii*
Quill-snouted snake, *Xenocalamus bicolor*,
Puff adder, *Bitis arietans*

**Sauria**
Spiny agama, *Agama hispida*

Reptiles were represented by a small range of snakes and lizards and ranked low as food.

Mammals had a percentage occurrence of 5% and included the springhaas, *Pedetes capensis*, in five stomachs; the scrub hare, *Lepus saxatilis*, in two; with single records of the yellow mongoose, *Cynictis penicillata*, and the large grey mongoose, *Herpestes ichneumon*.

Birds included the turtle dove, *Streptopelia capicola*, and Swainson's francolin, *Francolinus swainsoni*, together with the feathers of small birds. Black-backed jackals are known to frequent the roosting and breeding colonies of quelea, *Quelea quelea*, and to prey upon these as the opportunity permits.

Myriapods, in the form of the centipede, *Scolopendra morsitans*, were found in two stomachs and Amphibia in one.

Non-food items included blades of broad-leaved green grass which were found in 30% of the stomachs. These presumably are ingested for their mechanical action in the digestive process and are a common item in the stomachs of other canids. For this reason some authors classify grass as a food item (Bothma 1966b, 1971). Sand and fragments of dry grass stems are ingested fortuitously with the food. Hairballs were found in two stomachs, these consisting predominantly of jackal hair, with hair of springhaas and scrub hare intermixed.

There is a large measure of agreement in the findings of various authors on the food of this species (Avery *et al.*, 1987; Bothma, 1966c, 1971, 1984; Ferguson, 1980; Grafton, 1965; Lamprecht, 1978; Rowe-Rowe, 1976, 1978a; Stuart, 1976, 1977; Hall-Martin & Botha, 1980; Hiscocks & Perrin, 1987). From the various studies it emerges that the black-backed jackal is clearly omnivorous, with insects, carrion, warm-blooded prey and vegetable matter usually ranking high in its diet. The relative percentages of the various items in the diet vary widely with differences in habitat, rainfall and time of the year, and the overall conclusion is that the jackal is an opportunist, taking whatever prey is in greatest abundance or is most easily captured.

While it is generally accepted that most of the smaller vertebrate items in the diet are the remains of captured prey, Smithers (1983) emphasized the difficulties encountered in separating carrion from captured prey items in stomach samples. Although all remains of larger antelope were assigned the rank of carrion, it was noted that in doing so, doubt must always remain as to which category these sort of food items should be allocated.

Direct observations have served to confirm that the black-backed jackal is an efficient hunter of mammals up to the size of scrub hares and springhaas. The young of smaller antelope are also taken when available, and this component of the diet may be replaced by young sheep in farming areas. Sporadic reports have indicated that black-backed jackals may even kill adult antelope (Kruuk, 1972a; Lamprecht, 1978; Schaller, 1972a; Sleicher, 1973; van Lawick-Goodall & van Lawick, 1970). A recent study has shown that jackals can become regular hunters of adult antelope under certain conditions. McKenzie (1990) found that jackals in the Mashatu Game Reserve in Botswana co-operate in hunting adult impala, *Aepyceros melampus*, on a regular basis. Jackals foraging singly or in pairs were observed to suddenly rush towards a herd of resting impala, but would stop once the impala had taken fright and run off. This behaviour, also noted by Lamprecht (1978), was interpreted as a "testing" of the herds for any sign of weak or sick animals. Once a compromised individual was located, up to 12 jackals would congregate and corner the impala in thick bush. One of the jackals would then seize the animal by the throat. Other jackals quickly penetrate the thin flesh of the flank and sever the major arteries in the vicinity of the kidneys, thus dispatching the immobilized prey quickly and quietly. The prey was then rapidly consumed until all that remained was the skeleton and the contents of the rumen. Impala captured by jackals in this way were found to be old and in extremely poor condition, or to have been wounded previously. The co-operation between jackals from different territories in the hunting of large prey confirms the adaptability of this opportunistic species.

**Reproduction**

Black-backed jackals are one of the few mammalian species with a long-term pair bond (Moehlman, 1978). The females litter down in holes in the ground, very often in disused antbear burrows, which they adjust to their own requirements. They less frequently use caves or rock crevices. Carr (pers. comm.) reported that a breeding hole examined in the Transvaal had a wide chamber, one to two metres in diameter, excavated by the jackals, in which the young were accommodated. These holes often have two or more entrances as escape routes and it appears that these are opened by the jackals, as they are atypical of antbear burrows. The females may change the dens regularly, whimpering to the young as if to feed them and then leading them to a new den. If a pup gets left behind, the male of the pair remains with it until the female returns to lead it (Moehlman, 1978).

Both the male and female jackals take part in the rearing and feeding of the young. When they are small, food is regurgitated for them, and later it is carried back in the mouth and left for them to be eaten inside or often near the entrance to the hole. Moehlman (1978) found that in East Africa in 11 out of 15 litters the parents had what she termed "helpers". These were pups of the previous year's litter that remained with their parents and assisted them in raising the next litter. These helpers regurgitated food for the litter, as well as for the lactating mother and guarded the pups while their parents were absent, thus allowing them to spend a higher proportion of time foraging. The helpers also played with the young, groomed them and later helped to teach them to hunt.

She found that the presence of helpers is positively correlated with pup survival. If a pair was raising pups on their own, 0–2 pups would survive. In four pairs observed the ratio of pup survival was 0,5 pup per adult. With one helper the surviving pup ratio rose to 1,0 pup per adult. The largest family she observed had the two parents and three helpers, and had six surviving pups.

Moehlman (1978) found that the pups emerge from the den at about three weeks, are weaned by eight to nine weeks of age, and by 14 weeks no longer use the den and start to forage with their parents. The first 14 weeks are a critical period for the young, for they are subject to predation and to food shortages and this is the period when the major contribution to their survival is made by the assistance afforded to the parents by helpers.

In the Cape Province, Stuart (1981) deduced from the occurrence of pregnant and lactating females and back-dated births that the young are born from July to October. Antenatal litter sizes ranged from one to six; post-natal litters showed that three was the commoner number in litters which ranged from one to six. In Natal, Rowe-Rowe (1978a) found that most births took place from July to September, with a peak in July, and Fairall (1978) recorded births from August to October in the Kruger National Park.

Once the young start to follow the parents at the age of about three and a half months, they no longer sleep in dens, but use the cover of underbush. They may become separated during the day, but in the late afternoon the family group reassembles, contact being re-established by members vocalising in a distinctive yipping call. Family members only respond to family calls and ignore the calls of neighbouring individuals (Moehlman, 1978).

# XXXIII. Family MUSTELIDAE

## Otters, polecats, weasels, honey badger

Members of this Family are distributed widely throughout the world except in Australia, Madagascar and the polar regions. In the Subregion the Family is represented by five species, two of them aquatic and three terrestrial. In other parts of the world there are arboreal and even marine species, the latter represented by the sea otter, *Enhydra lutris*, of the northern Pacific Ocean. Mustelids are fierce hunters, preferring flesh, freshly killed by themselves, but will take carrion. The honey badger, *Mellivora capensis*, includes honey and bee larvae in its diet, and the otters, crabs and fish.

Five Subfamilies are recognised (Simpson, 1945), three of these represented in the Subregion: the Lutrinae, the Mellivorinae and the Mustelinae. The divisions between these are not clear cut.

The Lutrinae are distributed widely both in the Old and New Worlds and throughout much of Africa. The two species that occur in the Subregion are predominantly aquatic, the clawless otter, *Aonyx capensis*, occurring both in fresh and salt water, the spotted-necked otter, *Lutra maculicollis*, in fresh water only. Both species exhibit terrestrial activity, eating on dry land and moving across it in search of new feeding grounds, both at night and by day. They are short-legged, with broad heads, short muzzles and thick necks. They have long, stiff vibrissae and tails that are adapted to propulsion when swimming. These are muscular, thick at the base and taper to points, and, in the clawless otter, are flat underneath. The clawless otter, as the name implies, has no claws, but has small vestigial nails on some of its digits (Fig. XXXIII.1). Their digits are narrowly webbed, the propulsion in swimming, however, being carried out by the tail. In the spotted-necked otter the digits have claws and are broadly webbed. The pelages of both species have a sparkling sheen, making them valuable as commercial pelts. In the clawless otter the underfur is fine, dense and crinkled, the hairs of the guard coat longer and convexly oblong in cross-section. These glisten and give the coat its sheen.

The Subfamily Mellivorinae consists of the single species, the honey badger, *Mellivora capensis*, a powerful, thick-set species of fearless nature, which has been known to stand up to other species far larger in size.

The Subfamily Mustelinae is represented in the Subregion by two species, the striped polecat, *Ictonyx striatus*, and the African weasel, *Poecilogale albinucha*. The pelage of both species is black and white. The weasel has very short legs and a sinuous, snake-like body and short hair, the polecat has much longer hair and a less sinuous body, but is still short-legged. Both these are equipped with anal glands which secrete a strong smelling substance, used in deterring enemies.

Although the Mustelidae is the largest Family of the carnivores, only six genera are represented in Africa in the fossil record. The earliest known fossil remains of a mustelid

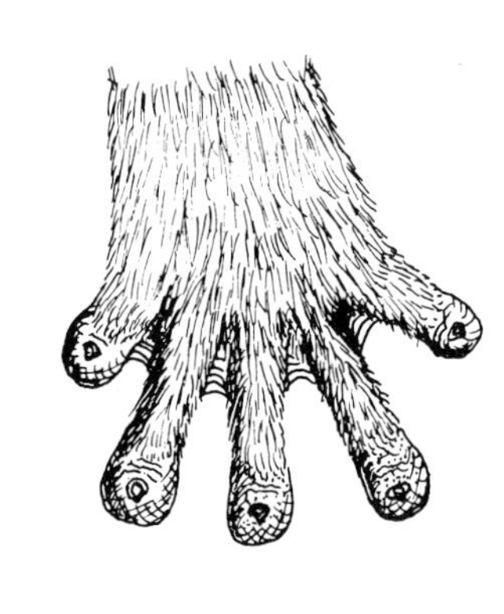


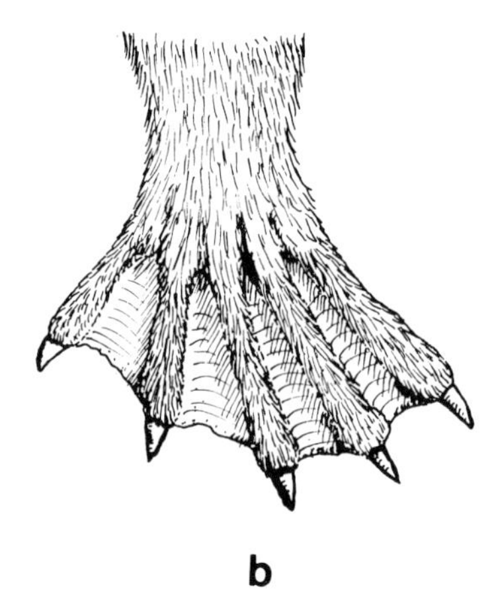


Fig. XXXIII.1. Feet: (a) clawless otter, *A. capensis*. (b) spotted-necked otter, *L. maculicollis*

in Africa were recovered from the late Miocene beds in Tunisia dated about 10 million to 5 million years old (Robinson & Black, 1969). Hendey (1974) recorded fossil remains of a polecat from Pleistocene beds at Hopefield, Cape Province, which he referred to the extant striped polecat, *Ictonyx striatus*, and similar remains of a honey badger, *Mellivora capensis*, from the late Pleistocene (Hendey, 1969). An extinct genus of lutrines, *Enhydriodon*, is recorded from Pliocene/Pleistocene sites in Namibia. This was a very large otter with affinities to the clawless otter, *Aonyx capensis*, and like this species was probably a crab eater (Savage, 1978).

Key to the Subfamilies (Meester *et al*., 1986)

1. Clearly modified for aquatic life; fur short and dense; tail long, thick and muscular, fleshy at base; 5 upper cheek-teeth, $M^1$ much enlarged, more or less square, as large as adjoining carnassial or larger

   ... LUTRINAE

   Not modified for aquatic life; fur longer, not dense; tail not thickened; no more than 4 upper cheekteeth, $M^1$ much smaller than carnassial, narrow

   ... 2

2. Heavily built, appearance badger-like; colour normally blackish below, separated from greyish dorsal colour by a whitish band; claws enlarged; ears small, at most one-third of hind foot length; tail short, roughly one-third of head and body length or less; greatest skull length 120 mm or more

   ... MELLIVORINAE

   Lightly built, appearance weasel-like; distinctive black and white or black and yellow stripes dorsally, blackish below; claws not enlarged; ears well over one-third of hind foot length; tail longer, roughly two-thirds of head and body length; greatest skull length less than 85 mm

   ... MUSTELINAE

## Subfamily LUTRINAE

Key to the genera (Meester *et al*., 1986)

1. Larger, greatest skull length normally 115 mm or more; feet with rudimentary webs, nails absent or small and blunt; postorbital process clearly developed; mastoid process projects prominently behind ear opening

   ... *Aonyx*

   Smaller, greatest skull length normally 110 mm or less; feet clearly webbed, with well developed claws; post-orbital process vestigial; mastoid process weak

   ... *Lutra*

## Genus *Aonyx* Lesson, 1827

No. 260

### *Aonyx capensis* (Schinz, 1821)

### Cape clawless otter
### Groototter

Plate 22

**Colloquial Name**

Clawless is certainly appropriate, immediately differentiating them from the spotted-necked otter, which has claws on all its fingers and toes. It is useful to retain the name Cape to distinguish them from their near relatives, the Zaire clawless otter. If, in Afrikaans, *kleinotter* is accepted for the spotted-necked, then *groototter* is appropriate for this species as they are much larger.

**Taxonomic Notes**

Two species occur on the continent, the Cape clawless otter, *A. capensis*, and the Zaire clawless otter, *A. congica*. While the two species are very similar, *A. congica* is slightly larger. Meester *et al*. (1986) listed only *A. c. capensis* from the Subregion, with a distribution as far north as Zambia and Angola.

**Description**

The clawless otter is the largest of the two species occurring in the Subregion and can attain an overall length of up to 1,5 m and a mass of up to over 16,0 kg (Table 260.1). The upper parts vary in colour from light brown to very dark, almost blackish-brown. The hindquarters are usually a shade darker than the fore. The under parts are lighter in colour than the upper, with patches of off-white on the chest and at the junction of the forelimbs; the belly is white. In some specimens the hair on the forehead, across the top of the head, and extending onto the shoulders has silvery tips, giving the effect of a mantle, reminiscent of that found in the Zaire clawless otter, *A. congica*. However, it is never as noticeable as in *A. congica* and, at its fullest development, simply imparts a silvery sheen to this part of the body. A characteristic feature which readily distinguishes the clawless from the spotted-necked otter, *Lutra maculicollis*, is the unspotted white area in the clawless otter which covers the chin, throat and upper chest and extends onto the sides of the neck, to just below the ears and onto the sides of the face below the eyes. The fringes of the ears are generally light in colour, but never white as in *A. congica*. The white area on the sides of the face continues forward to the base of the whiskers and around the upper lip to just below the nostrils. In some specimens there are distinct white or off-white patches on the inner sides of the eyes. The whiskers may be altogether white, or have dark bases and broad white tips.

**Table 260.1**

Measurements (mm) and mass (kg) of Cape clawless otters, *A. capensis*, from (a) Zimbabwe (Smithers, 1983) and (b) Tsitsikama National Park (van der Zee, 1979 & Arden-Clarke, 1983 respectively)

**(a)**

| | Males | | | Females | | |
|---|---|---|---|---|---|---|
| | $\bar{x}$ | n | Range | $\bar{x}$ | n | Range |
| TL | 1313 | 9 | 1110–1800 | 1570 | 2 | 1170, 1970 |
| T (mid anus) | 501 | 9 | 443–540 | 530 | 2 | 520 |
| Hf s/u | 142 | 9 | 130–156 | 140 | 2 | 140 |
| E | 26 | 9 | 24–28 | 25 | 2 | 25 |
| Mass | 12,25 | 9 | 10,00–15,44 | 14,30 | 2 | 12,26–16,34 |

**(b)**

| | Males | | | Females | | |
|---|---|---|---|---|---|---|
| | $\bar{x}$ | n | Range | $\bar{x}$ | n | Range |
| TL | 1 216 | 7 | 1130–1 280 | 1 215 | 2 | 1 145, 1 185 |
| T | 512 | 7 | 475–570 | 488 | 2 | 480, 495 |
| Mass | 13,1 | 7 | 10,0–16,4 | 12,4 | 2 | 11,7; 13,0 |

| | Males | | | Females | | |
|---|---|---|---|---|---|---|
| | $\bar{x}$ | n | Range | $\bar{x}$ | n | Range |
| TL | 1 323 | 6 | 1 290–1 380 | — | | |
| Mass | 14,6 | 6 | 13,5–17,8 | | 1 only 11,0 | |

The coat is comprised of a dense covering of guard hairs, up to about 25 mm long on the mid-back; these are longer towards the tail and shorter towards the head (10 mm). The guard hairs are thinner towards their light-coloured bases. Underlying the guard coat there is a dense underfur comprised of wrinkled white or off-white hair, much finer than the guard hairs. The guard hair coating is so dense, however, that the lighter bases of the guard hairs and the whitish underfur are obscured and can be seen only if the fur is ruffled against the lie of the hair. The skin is thick and the hair of the guard coat has a distinct sheen, which makes the skins very valuable for commercial purposes, for which they are in high demand.

They have five digits on the feet. Those on the hind feet are webbed for half their length. The webbing on the front feet is less in evidence and barely perceptible, unless the digits are pulled apart (Fig. 260.1). The front feet are devoid of claws, the digits adapted to feeling and grasping. The third and fourth, and in some cases the second digits on the back feet have rudimentary nails. These are semi-circular and just protrude from the skin. Each foot has a single large pad. The under sides of the digits are rough to assist in holding slippery objects. The head is broad and rounded towards the muzzle. The nasal apertures are set in slits in the rhinarium, which is small when compared with the size of the head. The edges of these slits can be brought together to close the nasal apertures when the individual is swimming under water. The tail is long and flattened underneath, adapted to act as an organ of propulsion when swimming.

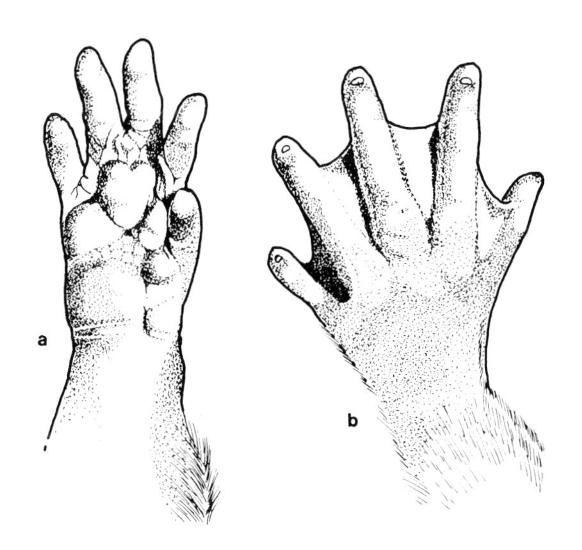


Fig. 260.1. Feet: clawless otter, *A. capensis*
(a) underside right front foot
(b) upperside right hind foot, to show webbing.

Rowe-Rowe (1975) gave masses of 16,4 kg for an adult male taken at Underberg and 13,6 and 18,2 kg for two males shot near Bulwer in Natal, while a captive Natal female had a mass of *c*. 11,8 kg. An adult female from the Transvaal had a mass of 12,0 kg (Scholtz in Rowe-Rowe, 1975) and a male trapped near Belfast had a mass of 12,8 kg (Skinner, unpubl.).

In moving on a muddy substrate the five digital pads on each of the feet, together with an indication of the front margin of the plantar pads, mark in the spoor (Fig. 260.2).

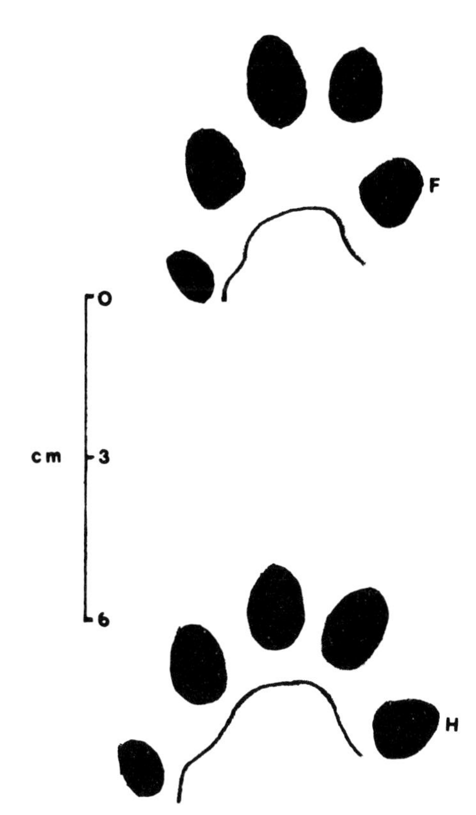


Fig. 260.2. Spoor: clawless otter, *A. capensis*
F. Right forefoot H. Right hind foot

**Skull** (Fig. 260.3)

The skull is heavily built. The cheekteeth, especially the fourth upper premolar and the molar, and the first lower molar, are massive. In adults the skull sutures close to the extent that they are not discernible on any part of the skull. The cranium is broad and flattened, broadest at the level of the ears and tapering sharply to the interparietal constriction, being 70 mm at the broadest point, narrowing to 25 mm. The cranium at the interparietal constriction continues forward, parallel-sided to the postorbital constriction, the postorbital bars being represented by distinct processes above and behind the eyes and on the zygomatic arch. In proportion to the size of the skull, the eye orbits are relatively small. The rostrum is very short and broad, its length from the front of the eye orbit to the incisors being a bare 1/5 of the total length of the skull. The zygomatic arch is thin and lightly built, relative to the massive construction of the skull, a factor common to the mustelids, which reflects the great development of the temporalis muscles at the expense of the masseters. In addition to the wide expanse of cranium to which the temporalis muscles are attached, there is a low crest to which part of this muscle is attached. This runs forward from about the level of the ear openings, dividing at the interparietal constriction and ending at the postorbital processes on either side. This crest does not join the supraoccipital crest, but broadens out before reaching it into a flat lozenge-shaped area, devoid of muscle attachment. The supraoccipital crest is thick and curved upwards.

In line with the general heavy build of the skull, the lower jaw is thick and massive, the coronoid process broad and high to accommodate the attachments of the temporalis muscle which activates its closing. The clawless otter, equipped with formidable canine teeth, has a powerful bite which can inflict most dangerous wounds on dogs and other adversaries and once it takes a grip is almost impossible to dislodge.

The glenoid cavity is deep and broad to accommodate the broad glenoid processes on the lower jaw. This allows for very little side to side movement as in other mustelids. It is sometimes difficult to disarticulate the lower jaw in the cleaned skull.

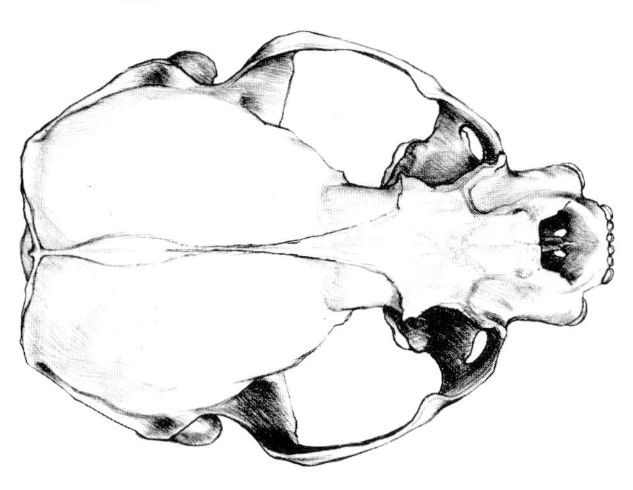

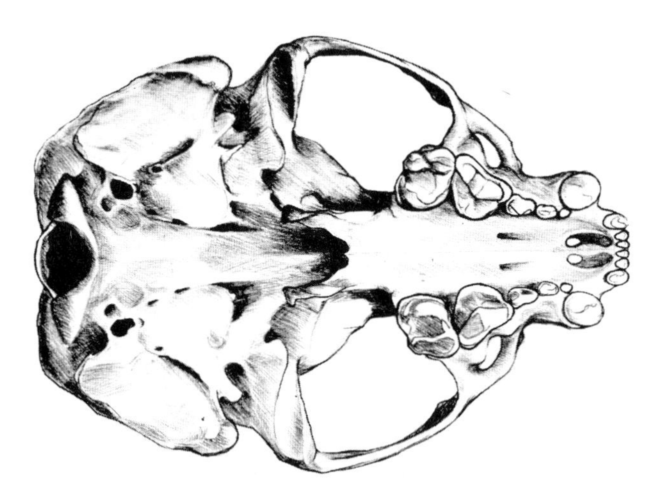

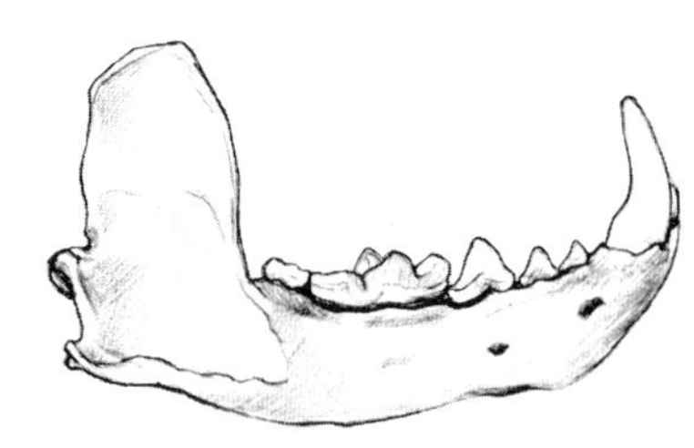

Fig. 260.3. Skull: clawless otter, *A. capensis*. TL Skull 130 mm

The dental formula is:

$I\frac{3}{3}\ C\frac{1}{1}\ P\frac{4}{3}\ M\frac{1}{2} = 36$

The outer, upper incisors are enlarged to assist the canines in holding. The upper canines are long, round and sharp, the lower distinctly recurved. The small first upper premolars lie in the toothrow, just inside the canines, which lie outside the toothrow. The first upper premolar is not always present or, in some specimens, is present only on one side. A feature of the teeth is the enormous development of the fourth upper premolars and first molar and the lower first molars. These are very heavy and broad and, while the outer edges of these teeth provide for cutting, this function is subservient to their crushing function. The second lower molars, for at least half their surface, occlude on the first upper molars, assisting in this function.

The ear bullae are small compared to the size of the skull and are closely adpressed to it and swollen only on their forward inner parts. The nasal passages are noticeably large.

**Distribution**

The Cape clawless otter, *Aonyx capensis*, is distributed widely on the continent south of the Sahara, where there is suitable aquatic habitat. They are as much at home in salt as in freshwater, and in parts of their range occur narrowly along the coast. It is impossible to draw up a distribution map showing only the aquatic habitat in which they have been recorded and the map therefore illustrates only the general area within which, in suitable aquatic conditions, they have been recorded.

The Zaire clawless otter, *A. congica*, occurs alongside *A. capensis* in the southeastern parts of the Congo basin, Gabon, Cameroun and in parts of Nigeria and Uganda, but is not specifically dealt with in the text or the map.

*South of the Sahara, excluding the Southern African Subregion*

They occur in **Senegal**, from where *Lutra leonori* Rochebrume, 1888 (= *A. capensis*) was described; **Guinea; Sierra Leone; Liberia**, where there are coastal as well as northeastern inland records; **Ivory Coast; Ghana**, where they are stated to occur in the larger rivers; **Nigeria; Benin** and eastwards into **Cameroun**. In **Niger** and **Chad**, they occur in Lake Chad and eastwards they are found in the southern **Sudan** and **Ethiopia** where they have been taken in Lake Tana. They occur in most of **Kenya's** National Parks and reserves and there are records from the central parts of the country. They occur widely in **Tanzania**. In **Zaire** there are records from the southern and southeastern parts of the country, the commonest and most widely distributed species, however, being the Zaire clawless otter, *A. congica*, which occurs throughout the Congo basin to near the coast and appears generally to replace *A. capensis*. There are a few records from **Angola**. They occur in **Zambia** and there are records from **Malawi**, where they occur near Zomba and in the Shire and other rivers. There are only two records from **Mozambique**, north of the Zambezi River.

*Southern African Subregion*

There are very large areas in the western parts of the Subregion where the clawless otter does not occur owing to the lack of suitable aquatic habitat. For example in **Namibia** they are found only in the Cunene and Okavango rivers in the north and in the Orange River in the south.

There is a tendency for the clawless otter to occur in the tributaries of major rivers and not in the main rivers themselves. This is apparent in **Zimbabwe** where they occur in the Mazoe River, which drains into the Zambezi River, from which they are absent. They were not recorded from the Zambezi River at the time of its flooding to form Lake Kariba or before this from any point between Victoria Falls and the Kariba Dam site or between this and the delta of the Zambezi River in Mozambique, where they are found. West of the Victoria Falls they are quite common, however, especially in the extensive areas of lagoons and swamps associated with the Zambezi and Chobe rivers, as well as in the eastern **Caprivi Strip** and in northern **Botswana**, where they occur in the Okavango Delta, and have been recorded from the Tuli area. They occur widely in northern and northeastern Zimbabwe and with the great increase in the number of farm dams and other water impoundments throughout the country, most of which have been stocked with fish, further suitable areas of habitat have been provided for them, and where these are large enough, they settle permanently.

In **Mozambique**, south of the Zambezi River, they occur in the delta of this river and there are sufficient records southwards to suggest a wide distribution wherever there is suitable habitat.

They are recorded from the **Transvaal** and the Limpopo River along the Botswana boundary. They occur in **Natal**, except in the central sector; in the eastern and southern parts of the **Orange Free State**; in the eastern, southcentral and southern parts of the **Cape Province** and along the Orange,

Vaal and other rivers. They are found in the coastal waters along the south coast.

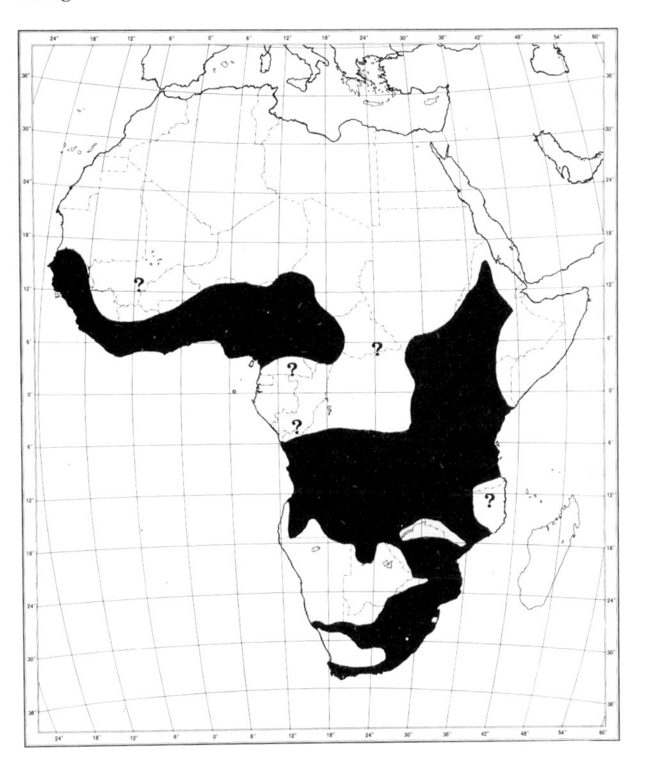

## Habitat

While predominantly aquatic, clawless otters wander widely from this habitat in their search of new feeding grounds. In this respect they are more terrestrial than spotted-necked otters which are confined more closely to aquatic habitat.

Throughout their range, clawless otters occur in rivers, lakes, swamps and dams and move freely up the tributaries of rivers into small streams, often right to their sources, providing that these habitats carry food supplies in the form of crabs, frogs, fish or other aquatic life. If they wander from water they invariably return to it, as it is an essential requirement. They take freely to estuarine and sea water, occurring commonly in limited parts of the coastal regions of the Cape Province, Natal and Transkei, feeding along the coast in rocky areas. Where they occur in coastal waters, a supply of fresh water is an essential habitat requirement.

The physiognomy of the associations in which the terrestrial aquatic habitat occurs can range from forest to woodland to open grassland and their occurrence bears no relation to surrounding terrain, providing the aquatic conditions are suitable and the surrounding terrain provides cover in which to rest. They occur in river systems penetrating deep into extremely dry terrain with a very low rainfall, for example along the Orange River in the Cape Province, where the mean annual rainfall in parts is 100 mm and less.

As fish are not an indispensable part of their diet, very small streams can supply their food requirements in the form of crabs and frogs. As these dry up they move down to more permanent water.

They occur in the Subregion from sea level to about 1 500 m.

## Habits

In the coastal waters of the Tsitsikama National Park, Cape Province, where the numbers are high at 1 otter/2 km of coastline (van der Zee, 1981), Arden-Clarke (1983) found that the main periods of activity were from 20h00 to 22h00, tailing off to about 07h00 and increasing from about 15h00. Rowe-Rowe (1975), in Natal, recorded that of 32 sightings, six were in the early morning (sunrise to 08h00), 24 were in the later afternoon (15h00 to sunset) and two just after dark.

During the heat of the day they rest in dry places, in holes in the ground, under rocks, in sheltered places in erosion gullies or in dense reed beds adjacent to their habitat. In the Tsitsikama National Park they use the shelter of bushes (van der Zee, 1979). These resting places, known as holts, are scattered throughout their home ranges. Arden-Clarke (1986) found that males in the Tsitsikama National Park had home ranges extending from 8,8 km to 12,8 km of coastline and traced 15 holts, used by the same individual, in a 12,8 km stretch.

At Betty's Bay, Cape Province, Verwoerd (1987) found that they lived in a clan type of social structure and had a degree of territoriality. In this sector, where human disturbance was a factor, there was an artificial clumping of their holts in the less disturbed areas, their activities being more restricted to the marine habitat where they foraged in the shallower water along the coast.

Clawless otters spend a large part of their active lives in water. After swimming and returning to dry land they first shake the head and then the whole body to get rid of surplus water. Thereafter, they will dry off all parts of their bodies by rubbing themselves in dry sand, dry debris or on short grass, this process continuing for a considerable period. When it is wet the coat lies closely adpressed to the body, giving it an additionally streamlined appearance, but nevertheless, the underfur becomes sodden, at least on the outside. When they have dried off, they will choose a sheltered place in which to sun themselves, lying about in all sorts of postures, flat on their backs with the legs outstretched, on their bellies or reclining on their sides (Smithers, 1983).

Clawless otters will walk at a leisurely gait, but generally progress by bounding along which carries them forward at a smart pace, or they will gallop with an undulating motion. They are generally solitary, but pairs and family parties of two adults and up to three young have been seen. Rowe-Rowe (1975, 1989) showed that, in Natal, the group size varies from one to five, with solitary individuals or two together being the more normal number. Arden-Clarke (1986) found that in the Tsitsikama National Park, of 56 observations, the mean group size was 1,71, with 35 observations of solitary individuals, five of two together, eight of three, three of four and one group of five.

Because clawless otters are inclined to move widely, extensive latrines are not formed and consist mainly of small accumulations of faeces that may be deposited over a period of days in the one place. These latrines are situated near the water and are characterised by the amount of crab shell remains and fish scales that they contain. They break down easily in light rain, leaving a scattered accumulation of undigested hard fragments and scales. Usually they can be distinguished from the scats of the water mongoose, *Atilax paludinosus*, as water mongoose scats contain rodent fur and other items normally not eaten by the otter, but where both are feeding extensively on crabs alone, identification is difficult. Although a latrine deposited on a cement weir was removed and the area well scrubbed down with detergent, the otter returned to use the same place some 10 days later. Rowe-Rowe (1975) observed that their latrines are situated near deep water, believing that this facilitates escape into it if they are disturbed. This was the case in a great number of latrines examined in Zimbabwe, although some were placed on raised ground in reed beds several metres from the water.

Clawless otters swim on the surface, with the head and sometimes part of the back showing. In deep water they will submerge the head, arch the back and dive, the tail held vertically as they disappear under water with very little disturbance. Rowe-Rowe (1975) recorded submergence for up to 49 seconds in a captive female, and an average of about 17 seconds (6–26 seconds) under field observations.

When hunting crabs in a farm dam, an otter dived eight times in the manner stated, after each dive coming up with a crab in its forepaws. On each occasion the crab was taken to a muddy promontory where, in a reed bed in shallow water, it could be heard, but not seen, crunching up the prey. The whole crab is eaten, only very few slivers of hard exoskeleton being discarded at the feeding site. This is in line with their behaviour in captivity where an individual would eat the largest crab available (90 mm across carapace), leaving no trace of it. This is different feeding behaviour from the water mongoose, *A. paludinosus*, which almost invariably leaves the shell of the carapace. In the field the finding of empty carapaces is a sign of the presence of the water mongoose and not the clawless otter.

Clawless otters are very playful, chasing each other around in the water, or treading water and mock fighting. They will play with small stones or sticks for lengthy periods, both in the water and out of it. The great dexterity and sensitivity of the forefeet can be appreciated better under these circumstances. In captivity a female otter would play for long periods with a tiny stone, dropping it into the water and then feeling around for it on the bottom, picking it up and repeating the process over and over again. Where the water was shallow her head would be raised out of it, the stone recovered purely by feeling around with the forefeet.

**Food**

In a terrestrial environment in Natal, Rowe-Rowe (1975) analysed over 800 spraints (scats) which revealed food items in the following order of occurrence: crabs and frogs, which ranked by far the highest, followed by far lesser amounts of fish, insects, birds, reptiles, mammals and molluscs. In trout streams and dams, crabs and frogs ranked by far the most important items of diet. Stuart (1977) reported on two stomachs, in one of which the remains of a duck and a hen were found and in the other frogs, crab fragments and a caterpillar. On the other hand, in a sample of 10 stomachs from Zimbabwe, fish had the highest occurrence at 78%, followed by crabs, *Potamonautes perlatus*, at 20% and frogs at 11%. In this sample the fish consisted of bream, *Tilapia* spp, and barbel, *Clarias* spp, the frogs the common platanna, *Xenopus laevis*, and the painted reed frog, *Hyperolius marginatus* (Smithers & Wilson, 1979).

In a marine environment, in the Tsitsikama National Park, van der Zee (1981) analysed over 1 100 scats and recorded over 35 species of crabs, fish and octopus. Calculated on a relative frequency basis the red rock crab, *Plagusia chabrus*, had the highest frequency at 27,9%, followed by suckerfish, *Chorisochismus dentex*, at 16,5% and the brown rock crab, *Cyclograpsus punctatus*, at 10,4%. Octopus, *Octopus granulatus*, had a frequency of 7,4% and small rock fish, *Clinus cottoides*, of a maximum length of 115 mm, 4,4%. The remaining items all had a relative percentage frequency of under 2,5%. At Betty's Bay, Verwoerd (1987) found that fish constituted 59% of the biomass of the food, followed by octopus 15%, red rock crabs 13%, and rock lobster 10%, brown rock crabs figuring poorly at 0,8%. A marine habitat is more stable than a terrestrial habitat and therefore there is no great seasonal change in the diet as is experienced inland (Rowe-Rowe, 1977). Preferred feeding areas in the marine environment were vertical rock faces just below the surface of the water, but they would also explore intertidal pools and crevices. During bad weather at sea they would move far inland in foraging. They fed in the early morning and late evening, activity continuing throughout the night (Arden-Clarke, pers. comm.).

Rowe-Rowe (1975) noted, from observations in captivity, that when otters hunt fish they swim under water, using sight to locate the prey, then spurt forward to capture it. With trout, Rowe-Rowe (1975) showed that the 100 to 200 mm size was the most favoured. In the Okavango River, Botswana, very much larger fish, estimated to have a mass of over 2 kg, were freely taken (Smithers, 1983). With barbel, Rowe-Rowe (1975) noted that, in captivity, an otter would pin a fish to the bottom of the pond with its front feet and immobilise it by biting the fish behind the head. After the otter had captured a fish, it would play with it, swimming to the surface and throwing the fish up in the air, then diving to recapture it. When the fish was benumbed by this process, the otter would swim after it, nose to its tail, before eventually recatching it and carrying it to the bank to be eaten. Rowe-Rowe (1975) stated that otters will eat small fish while treading water. When foraging for crabs they feel around with the sensitive digits on the front feet in holes and among rocks under water, bringing the prey onto dry land to be eaten.

Fish and frogs are normally eaten from the head first, which is at variance with the feeding behaviour of the spotted-necked otter, *L. maculicollis*, which eats a fish from the tail end. An exception to this was barbel, which, probably because of the bony structure of the head, was eaten from the tail, discarding the head. The water mongoose, *A. paludinosus*, behaves similarly with frogs, the head being eaten first. During feeding the otter immerses its head and chews the prey in the water or the food may be dunked in the water from time to time while being eaten. On completion of the meal they go through a lengthy and elaborate ritual of cleaning their faces and feet in the water.

Clawless otters can become problem animals where domestic ducks free-range on farm dams. They will also take water birds and wildfowl if the opportunity permits.

**Reproduction**

There are very few records to show when the young of the clawless otter are born. At Betty's Bay, Verwoerd (1987) recorded five litters which he estimated were born between April and June. Stuart (1977) recorded a foetus taken from a female in July and a juvenile with its eyes still closed taken in April, both from the Cape Province. In Zimbabwe juveniles were taken from March and April and, in Natal, Rowe-Rowe (1978b) recorded two taken at about a week old, in the last week in August, and a single juvenile estimated to have been born in November. This meagre information suggests that the young may be born at widely divergent times throughout the year, but further information is required.

Females have two pairs of abdominal mammae.

## Genus *Lutra* Brisson, 1762

---

No. 261

## *Lutra maculicollis* Lichtenstein, 1835

## Spotted-necked otter
## Kleinotter

Plate 22

---

**Colloquial Name**

The name spotted-necked appropriately describes one of the salient features of the species, as the front of the lower part of the neck and upper chest is either spotted or mottled. This feature clearly distinguishes them from the Cape clawless otter, *Aonyx capensis*. The Afrikaans name highlights its smaller size.

**Taxonomic Notes**

Coetzee (1977a) recognised five subspecies from the continent, two occurring in the Subregion: *L. m. maculicollis* in the southern and eastern areas and *L. m. chobiensis* Roberts, 1932 in the northern and western. *L. m. chobiensis* is slightly different in colour, being seal-brown against the chestnut-brown of *L. m. maculicollis*.

**Description**

The smaller spotted-necked otter found in the Subregion, has a longer, slimmer body than the clawless otter, *A. capensis*. It has a long tapering tail, which is dorsoventrally flattened to assist in swimming, and fully webbed feet, with short claws on each digit. The head is large and broad at the back, narrowing to the short, broad muzzle. The ears are a little more prominent than in the clawless otter, and more elongated, and are adpressed closely to the head. The whole animal is beautifully streamlined, an ideal adaptation to an aquatic life.

There is a scarcity of measurements and masses of specimens from the Subregion where the males appear to have an overall length of about 1,0 m, the females slightly smaller. Smithers (1971) took a young female in the Okavango delta in Botswana which had the following measurements (mm) and mass (kg): TL 965, T 390, Hf c/u 98, E 15, Mass 3,0; from the same area Rowe-Rowe (1975) recorded a male with a mass of 4,5 kg and reported that a female in the zoo at Colenso maintained a mass of about 3,3 kg. Mortimer (1963) recorded that a fully grown captive male had a mass of 4,5 kg, a female 3,5 kg.

Their colour varies from chocolate-brown to a deep, rich reddish-brown. The throat and upper chest are mottled or blotched with white or creamy-white. Very occasionally the mottling is lacking, as is seen in two specimens in the Port Elizabeth Museum. In some specimens there is some white mottling in the inguinal area and on the inside of the hind limbs. When they are wet, they look much darker, almost black or a very dark sepia. The upper lips and the area under the nostrils are white, which normally do not show in the field. In some specimens the flanks are slightly lighter in shade than the upper parts. The under parts are the same colour as the upper. In proportion to the size of the head, the rhinarium, which encloses the nostrils, is much smaller and narrower than in the clawless otter. The webs of the feet have a sparse covering of hair above and below; the covering on the first digits of the hind feet, however, is thick and generous, covering the digit to the base of the claws. The creamy-white claws on the front feet, which are up to about 10 mm long over the curve, are lightly built and very sharp. Those on the back feet are slightly shorter and not so well adapted for hooking (Fig. XXXIII.1).

The coat, which is soft to the touch, consists of a dense covering of guard hairs about 15 to 20 mm long, shorter towards the head, and an even denser covering of very fine, slightly shorter underfur. Although not apparent in the living animal, the colour of the bases of the guard hairs and the underfur is white or off-white. This is only apparent when the coat is ruffled against the lie of the hair. The soft hair with its beautiful sheen and the substantial nature of the skin renders spotted-necked otter skins of considerable commercial value for fabrication into articles of apparel and karosses.

**Skull** (Fig. 261.1)

The skull of the spotted-necked otter, while in general conforming to the typical mustelid shape, is lightly built. The bone structure is thin compared with the clawless otter. The braincase is ovoid, broad towards the back, narrowing sharply to the interparietal constriction and continuing nearly parallel-sided to the postorbital constriction. The rostrum is short and broad. The length from the incisors to the front of the eye orbits is only about one-fifth to one-sixth of the total length of the skull. The postorbital bar is represented by a small knob-like process behind and above the eye and a slightly better developed process on the zygomatic arch. In proportion the eye sockets are larger than in the clawless otter. The glenoid processes on the lower jaw, which form part of the hinge mechanism, are long and fit snugly into the groove in the upper part of the skull, allowing little or no sideways movement. Such a movement is only necessary in a species where the food has to be finely ground and is therefore unnecessary in the spotted-necked otter.

The condyle is broad and high, allowing for a firm attachment of the temporalis muscles which, at their posterior end, have a broad face for attachment to the sides of the braincase and to the low crest. This crest runs from the supraoccipital crest across the top of the braincase and divides at the level of the interparietal constriction, ending in the upper part of the incomplete postorbital bars. The zygomatic arches are weak, the bone broad, but thin, suggesting a reduction in function of the masseter muscles in favour of the temporalis.

The dental formula is:

$I\frac{3}{3}\ C\frac{1}{1}\ P\frac{4}{3}\ M\frac{1}{2} = 36$

The upper canines are set outside the toothrow. The first peg-like upper premolars lie immediately on their inner sides, in line with the remainder of the toothrow. The upper outer incisors are enlarged. The upper canines are sharp and relatively heavy, the lower are distinctly recurved. The carnassial shear allows for a measure of cutting, as the outer section of the upper fourth premolar occludes against the

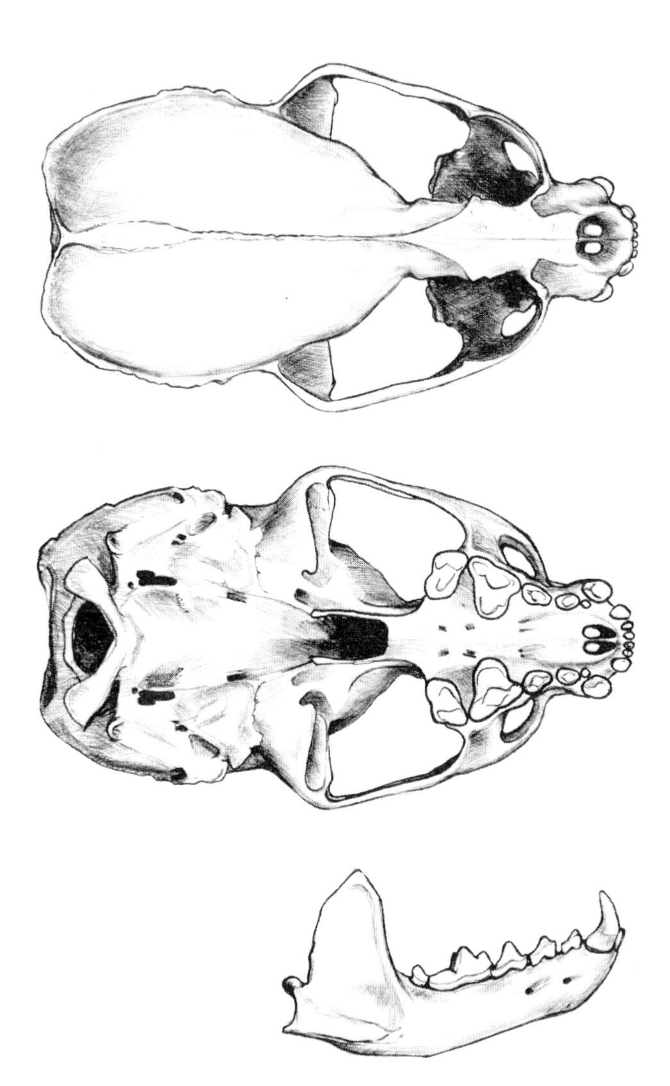

Fig. 261.1. Skull: spotted-necked otter, *L. maculicollis*.
TL Skull 112 mm

outer half of the first lower molar. The greater part of these teeth, however, is adapted to crushing, especially the inner part of the upper fourth premolar and the first molar which is very broad. The flat tables of these upper teeth occlude on the back half of the lower first molar and slightly on to the second, forming a broad crushing surface. The dentition, therefore, shows an adaptation to capturing and holding with the canines, a modest cutting function, but a primary adaptation to crushing the food.

**Distribution**

The spotted-necked otter has a wide distribution in Africa, south of the Sahara. In Morocco, Algeria and Western Sahara it is replaced by its near relative the common otter, *Lutra lutra*, which has a wide distribution in Europe, eastwards to Asia and Japan and southwards to India and Burma, Sumatra and Java.

While presenting the distribution map in the conventional manner, it must be borne in mind that the spotted-necked otter is an aquatic species and therefore will be confined to rivers, streams, dams and swamps within the areas demarcated.

*South of the Sahara, excluding the Southern African Subregion*

In West Africa they occur in **Sierra Leone, Liberia, the Ivory Coast, Nigeria, Gabon** and **Equatorial Guinea**. There are many records from the Congo River and its tributaries in **Zaire**. In the southern **Sudan** they occur in the north and northeast and in the White Nile; they are recorded from **Ethiopia**, the Rift lakes in western **Uganda** and in **Rwanda** and **Burundi**. They occur in **Malawi** at Mbamba Bay, Lake Malawi and widely in western **Zambia** above the Victoria Falls, in the upper parts of the Zambezi River and its tributaries; in the upper reaches of the Kafue River east of the Zambezi Escarpment and in Lake Bangweulu and the Chambeshi River which drains into Lake Tanzania. There are records from **Angola**.

*Southern African Subregion*

In **Namibia** they are confined to the Cunene River in the north. In the **Caprivi Strip** they are widespread and quite common in the Linyanti and Chobe swamps which extend into northern **Botswana** along the Chobe River and in the Okavango Swamps as far south as Maun. They do not occur in Zimbabwe. In **Mozambique**, south of the Zambezi River, they occur in the Zambezi River delta and in rivers in the southern parts of the country. In the **Transvaal** they occur in the southeast, but not in the dry western and northern parts of the province. While there are no material records from the **Orange Free State**, there are many sight records from widely scattered localities, excluding the drier northwest. In **Natal** they are confined to the upland regions, being less common in the intermediate areas and apparently absent from the plateau and low-lying and coastal regions except in the extreme south, where they occur near the coast at about 30°50'S. They are found in the eastern **Cape Province** and they are known from the Vaal River at Warrenton (Stuart, 1981).

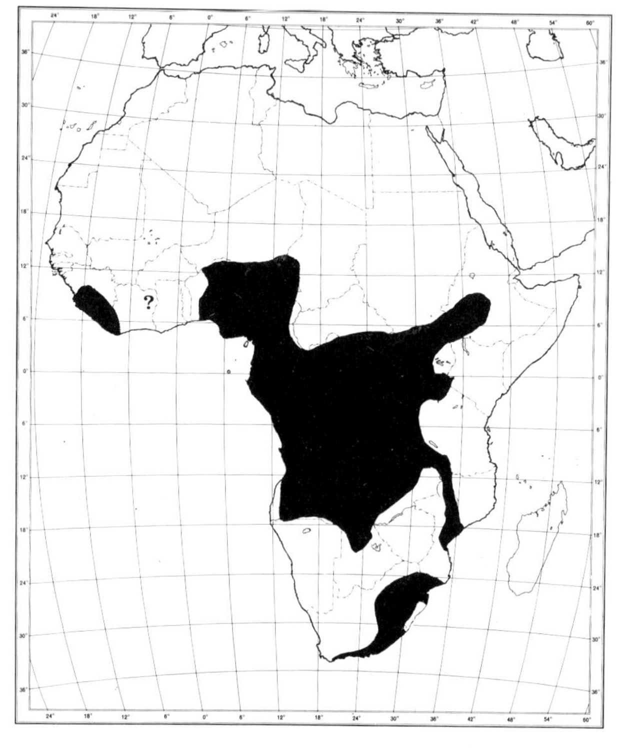

**Habitat**

The spotted-necked otter is an aquatic species confined to the larger rivers, lakes and swamps which have extensive areas of open water. They are confined more closely to this habitat than the clawless otter and they do not indulge in forays far from its margins. Their resting and swimming places, breeding sites and latrines are all near to the water's edge. On land they are clumsy and quickly become distressed (Mortimer, 1963). There do not appear to be any records of the spotted-necked otter entering estuarine or sea waters.

**Habits**

Spotted-necked otters are adapted ideally to an aquatic life, and only leave water marginally to breed, rest, defecate and urinate and at times to eat the fish which form one of their principal foods. On land they have a clumsy shuffling gait. With their streamlined bodies, flattened tails and broadly webbed feet, their movements in the water are lithe and graceful. When swimming on the surface seeking fish, they will arch the body suddenly, submerge the head and dive, creating very little disturbance, the tail following the curve of the body as they disappear. Proctor (1963) described how they will dive from 2 m into the water, leaving scarcely a ripple. On the other hand, when alarmed, they will fling themselves into the water by the shortest route in a crash dive, making a resounding splash. This could be a deliberate action to warn others of danger.

They will swim under the water for a few metres, then rise on to the surface for three or four metres before submerging again. They are perfectly at home in the roughest water, even where it is breaking over rocks, but under these conditions spend more time submerged. Proctor (1963), as an illustration of their litheness in the water, described how he observed an individual chasing a small fish near the surface which turned and leapt out of the water to land near the otter's tail; it was immediately seized, following a quick turn. Food taken in the water may be eaten there, the otter treading water in an upright position or lying on its back; or it may be taken to the banks and stored until there is sufficient for a full meal, which is eaten on the water's edge.

In the Subregion, Rowe-Rowe (1975) recorded schools of up to five, most of the records, however, being of solitary individuals or a family party of an adult and two young. Whereas clawless otters invariably shake themselves vigorously on emerging from the water, spotted-necked otters rarely do this, confining the action to a shake of the head. Rowe-Rowe (1975) stated that the spotted-necked otters defecated and urinated close to the water's edge, forming latrines in secluded spots where there was cover. Mortimer (1963) noted that the female would defecate with the tail held horizontally, the male with the tail held vertically.

Fitzsimons (1919), Shortridge (1934) and Roberts (1951) were of the opinion that spotted-necked otters are nocturnal. In the Linyanti Swamp in the eastern Caprivi Strip, where they are quite common, they appeared to be crepuscular, moving in the early morning up to about 08h00 and in the evening after about 16h30 (Smithers, 1983). In Lake Victoria, Proctor (1963) recorded crepuscular activity, fishing being in full swing at sunrise and continuing for about two and a half hours, after which they would retire to their holts or to brush and groom on the rocks. However, he recorded fishing and moving throughout the day, with increased activity between 16h00 and dusk. While activity rhythms can vary between areas, depending on the degree of disturbance, it seems that in general spotted-necked otters are crepuscular.

As the catching of fish under water is apparently carried out by sight, some light would seem to be a prerequisite and some diurnal activity necessary. Clear water, too, seems an obvious advantage to the species and may to some extent account for their large numbers in places like the Okavango and Caprivi swamps, where the crystal clear water is a feature. In the Caprivi where there were extensive areas of inundated semi-aquatic grasses around the open water, runs were formed in which they moved without being seen. If disturbed in these they would sit up in an erect posture and look around before lumbering off back into the water. Their vision does not seem to be acute and often it would take them a moment or two before they noticed the observer standing and watching them. In studying captive otters, Mortimer (1963) observed that their sight is good up to about 3 m, although objects could be detected at 9 m or more. He showed that in a room they were able to detect water in a flower vase or cup by smell and immediately would make for it. He was of the opinion that their hearing was good.

While the spotted-necked otter is generally a silent species, Proctor (1963) recognised four vocalisations: a shrill "chikkering" as a scold; or, when playing, a challenging mewing *yea-ea-ea-ea*; a squealing whistle when excited, and a challenging *ie-yang*, rarely heard. The commonest vocalisation appears to be a high-pitched squeak, changing to a trill.

Predation on spotted-necked otters may occur from two species: the crocodile, when they are in the water, and the python, when they are breeding on land, which they do in deep rocky crevices, inaccessible to other predatory species.

Under stress they emit a heavy musky smell which is persistent but not unduly unpleasant, as is that of the polecat.

They lie up in holes in river banks, in rock crevices, or in dense reed beds.

### Food

The main food of the spotted-necked otter is fish, but includes crabs, fresh water molluscs and frogs. Scat analysis by Rowe-Rowe (1975) in Natal gave the following percentage occurrence of food items:

| Item | Percentage occurrence in a trout stream | Percentage occurrence in a non-trout stream |
|---|---|---|
| Crabs | 57 | 50 |
| Fish | 56 | 42 |
| Frogs | 29 | 45 |
| Insects | 3 | 9 |
| Birds | trace | 17 |
| Unidentified | trace | 5 |

In the trout stream he showed that of the fish eaten, the great majority were up to 200 mm long. The order was slightly different in a non-trout stream where frogs had a slightly higher occurrence than fish. The diet included birds.

Fish are normally eaten from the tail first, sometimes the heads being discarded. The fish is grasped in the forepaws as the otter lies on its belly and chewed with the side of the mouth. Mortimer (1963) stated that live fish usually were played with in the water before being eaten, first being harried, teased and tossed around and then either landed or eaten in the water. In Lake Victoria, Proctor (1963) stated that fishing was carried out with tremendous vigour. The fish were caught and eaten with great rapidity, three or four bites being sufficient for a small fish. When satiated they would continue to catch fish, but then only played with them. Crabs are butted about with the nose before being eaten.

### Reproduction

There is a scarcity of information on the times at which the young are born. On Lake Victoria, Proctor (1963) estimated that this occurred about September; Ansell (1960a) in Zambia estimated November or December. Litters may number up to three, but two is the more normal number. Rowe-Rowe (1975) recorded females with one and two young. No birth dates are available. The young are born in holes in river banks, in rocky crevices or, where this type of cover is not available, in secluded areas in reed beds. Females have two pairs of abdominal mammae.

## Subfamily MELLIVORINAE

## Genus *Mellivora* Storr, 1780

---

No. 262

## *Mellivora capensis* (Schreber, 1776)

## Honey badger
## Ratel

Plate 22

---

### Colloquial Name

The generic name *Mellivora* is derived from the Latin *mel*, honey, and *voro*, to devour, a reference to one of its food items. Honey badger as a name is deeply entrenched, as is the Afrikaans name *ratel* which, in fact, is often used in English texts. Badger is normally applied to the European mustelid, *Meles meles*, the two species being very similar in form and, in broad terms, colour. The gait of the European badger and the honey badger is very similar, a slow lumbering trot. Both are accomplished diggers.

### Taxonomic Notes

Coetzee (1977a), in his review of the genus, recognised 10 subspecies for the continent, of which only one occurs in the Subregion: *M. c. capensis* which originally was described from a specimen from the "Cape of Good Hope" by Schreber in 1776.

### Description

The broad, light-coloured saddle, which runs from above the eyes to the base of the tail and which contrasts with the jet black lower parts of the body and limbs, renders the honey badger an unmistakable species in the field. The saddle, which extends from ear to ear across the top of the head, narrows slightly on the back of the neck, then widens out at the level of the belly, narrowing to a point at the base of the tail, or in some individuals extending slightly on to the top of the tail itself. The colour of this saddle varies from pure white to greyish-brown, always however, clearly differentiated from the jet black of the remainder of the body and limbs. In some individuals the centre part of the saddle is greyish, grizzled with white, and broadly fringed with pure white. Except where the saddle is pure white, no two appear exactly alike and there is considerable variation even within specimens from circumscribed areas.

The guard hair is harsh. On the upper parts of the body it is shorter towards the head, where it may measure about 10 mm, but reaches 35 mm about the level of the belly. The hair on the upper parts of the hind limbs, on the rump and the tail, is longest of all, up to 70 mm. When seen walking in the field this long hair tends to obscure the form of the limbs and tail. In some specimens there is very little sign of underfur, and in others it is present in the form of wavy hair slightly shorter and thinner than the main guard hair.

The ears are little more than thick ridges of skin and are hardly noticeable, except when close at hand. The eyes are small, the limbs short and stockily built. Adults stand about 250 to 280 mm at the shoulder and generally give the appearance of being slightly higher towards the rump. There are five digits to each foot. The claws on the front feet are elongated and powerfully built, reaching a length of 35 mm. Those on the back feet are much shorter at about 15 mm and more lightly built. The front claws are built like curved knives, broader on their top edges and sharp and knife-like below. Those on the back feet lack the knife edge and are broad and hollowed out underneath. The soles of the feet are thickly padded and naked to the wrists. All five digits and their claws mark clearly in the spoor (Fig. 262.1).

They have a pair of anal glands from which, when the individual is under stress, a foul-smelling excretion exudes which has a heavy, persistent, and to some handlers, extremely unpleasant smell. It appears that the honey badger is not so prone to use this defence mechanism as is the polecat, and is much more prone to attacking its aggressor than to driving it off by this means. These anal glands open just inside the anus and the honey badger is unusual in having an anal pouch very like that possessed by mongoose. Sikes (1964) recorded that the outpourings of the excretion are generous in quantity and suggested that marking is a symbol of territorial rights and a stimulus to courtship.

**Table 262.1**

Measurements (mm) and mass (kg) of honey badgers, *M. capensis*, from Zimbabwe (Smithers, 1983)

| | Males | | | Females | | |
|---|---|---|---|---|---|---|
| | $\bar{x}$ | n | Range | $\bar{x}$ | n | Range |
| TL | 954 | 8 | 902–1020 | 955 | 2 | 950–960 |
| T | 219 | 8 | 200–240 | 193 | 2 | 185–220 |
| Hf c/u | 133 | 8 | 123–145 | 118 | 2 | 115–120 |
| E | 43 | 8 | 40–48 | 41 | 2 | 35–47 |
| Mass | 11,7 | 8 | 7,9–14,5 | 11,6 | 2 | 9,5–13,6 |

The average size of a small series is given in Table 262.1 which unfortunately is unbalanced as there are data from only two females. The skin is very thick and loose and it has been said that, if a dog takes a grip on any part of it, the

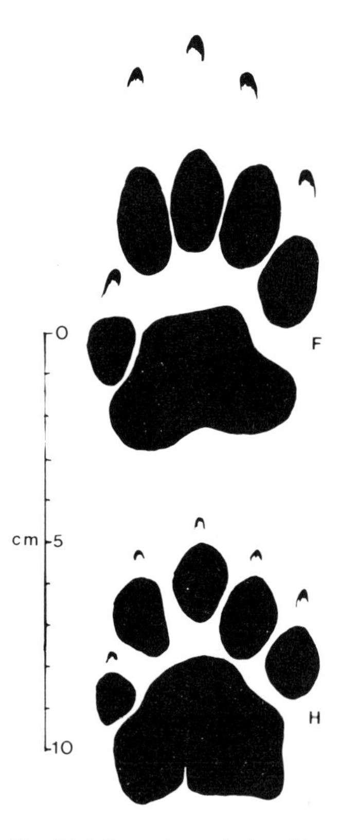


Fig. 262.1. Spoor: honey badger, *M. capensis*.
F. Right forefoot H. Right hind foot.

honey badger can turn around inside its skin and bite back. Within certain limits this is undoubtedly true.

**Skull** (Fig. 262.2)

The skull is massive, the bone thick and heavy, and of typical mustelid build. The braincase is much broader behind and tapers to its narrowest behind the eye sockets. Compared with the size of the skull, the eye sockets are small, the postorbital bar represented by small blunt processes, one above and behind the eye socket, the other on the zygomatic arch. In profile the skull is highest at the level of the ear bullae, sloping off evenly to the very broad, short rostrum. The skull sutures close before the individual is fully adult, and in adults are not apparent on any part of the skull. The zygomatic arch is relatively weak compared with the robust build of the skull. This reflects a reduction in the masseter muscles and an increase in size of the temporalis, which are afforded a wide base of attachment on the sides of the elongated braincase and on the low sagittal crest, which runs from the supraoccipital crest to the postorbital constriction. The supraoccipital crest, while not being greatly in evidence, is heavily built and consists of two irregular parallel ridges of thick bone.

The palate is broadest between the upper fourth premolar teeth, narrowing behind to the upper molars and continuing far behind them. The ear bullae are relatively flat, lying snugly against the skull; they are broad in front and narrower posteriorly, where they taper to a broad end.

In line with the rest of the skull, the lower jaw is massive, with a high coronoid to which the temporalis muscles are attached, giving them powerful leverage on the jaw. The transversely elongated glenoid articulation, which acts as a hinge for the lower jaw, allows it little side-to-side action, an unnecessary function in a species which does not have to grind its food. In some specimens the articulation is so tight that it is difficult to release the lower jaw from the rest of the cleaned skull.

The dental formula is:

$I\frac{3}{3}\ C\frac{1}{1}\ P\frac{3}{3}\ M\frac{1}{1} = 32$

The upper, outer incisors are distinctly enlarged, the remainder progressively smaller towards the centre. Those in the lower jaw are similar, but the enlargement of the outer is less distinct.

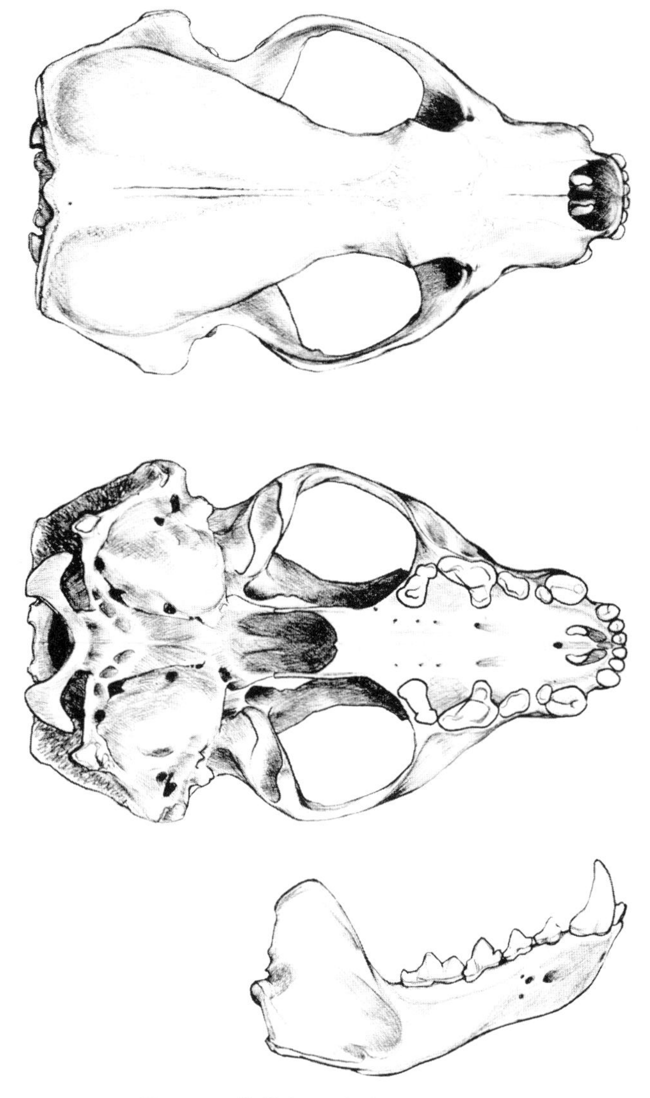

Fig. 262.2. Skull: honey badger, *M. capensis*.
TL Skull 145 mm

The upper canines are short, sharply pointed and stout. Those in the lower jaw are very distinctly recurved, with broad enlarged bases. To enhance crushing the posterior half of the lower first molar occludes on the first molar of the upper jaw, which lies at right angles to the tooth row and has a broad base on its inner side. Its outer edge, which lies free of the occlusion of the lower first molar, normally lies in the tooth row and thereby may assist to some extent in the sectorial action that is required. In line with the canines the cheekteeth are all heavily built.

The great development of the jaw musculature and the sturdy nature of the canine teeth, assisted by the outer incisors, allow a tremendous grip. When the individual is thoroughly roused, this grip is only released when the opponent is exhausted or dead or the honey badger itself has been despatched.

**Distribution**

The honey badger has a distribution which extends far beyond the confines of the African Continent to parts of Asia and India. Throughout this great range they are not common anywhere and in parts are considered rare. Present records suggest that they occur throughout the Subregion, although there remain areas from which no material is available.

*North Africa*

They occur in the mountainous parts of southern **Morocco**, extending to the borders of the Sahara; in **Western Sahara** (Rio de Oro) and central **Mauritania**. Judging from the low number of records from this part of the continent, they may be considered rare.

*South of the Sahara, excluding the Southern African Subregion*

From southern **Mauritania** they extend east to Timbouctou, **Mali**, in the Sahelian zone. They occur in **Sierra Leone** and in the northeastern parts of **Liberia**. In **Niger** there is a northern extension of their distribution into the Sahara. They occur in the **Sudan, Ethiopia** (*M. c. abyssinica* Hollister, 1910) and **Somalia**. South of this they are recorded from the **Congo Republic, Zaire** and the western parts of **Uganda, Kenya** and **Tanzania**. They are widespread in the southern parts of **Angola** and **Zambia**.

*Southern African Subregion*

They are widespread in the **Subregion**, apart from central Botswana, parts of the Cape Province and the Orange Free State. Nevertheless, they are one of the most widely spread species of small carnivores. They are widespread in **Namibia**, excluding the Namib Desert; **Botswana**; **Zimbabwe; Mozambique**, south of the Zambezi River and in the **Transvaal**. They are recorded from **Natal**, where they are rare south of 29 °S. In the **Cape Province** they are widespread, although not common anywhere.

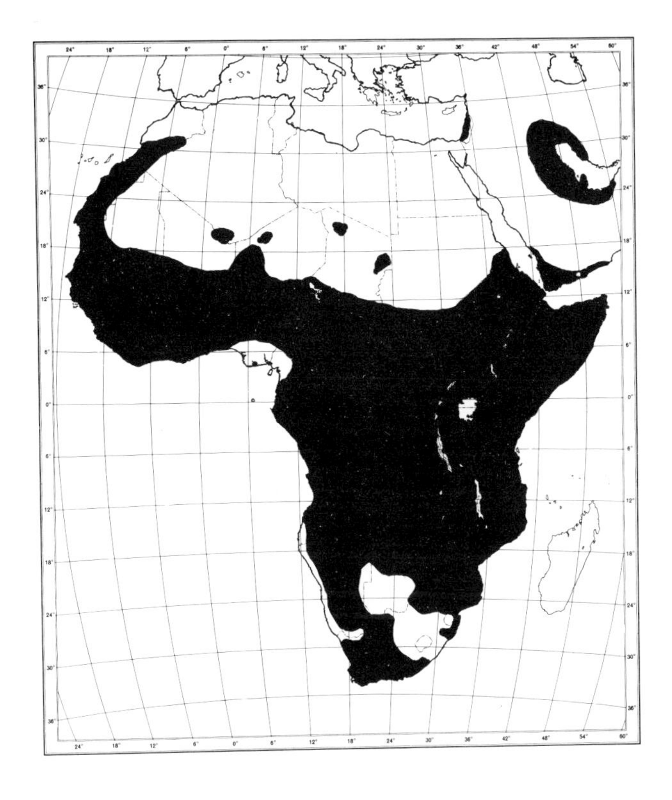

**Habitat**

Judging from their very wide occurrence, honey badgers are catholic in their habitat requirements and the only major association in which they do not appear to occur is dune desert. Although there are no records from the Namib Desert in Namibia, they can tolerate conditions of very low mean annual rainfall, in Namibia under 100 mm, and in parts of the Republic of South Africa at over 1 000 mm, and they occur from sea level (Rowe-Rowe, 1975) to over 1 500 m. Robinson (1976) listed them from forests in the Tsitsikama National Park and they occur at least on the fringes of montane forest in the eastern parts of Zimbabwe. Although they will use crevices in rocky areas in which to shelter, they are powerful diggers and will also dig refuges for themselves or adapt existing disused holes to their requirements. As they occur in arid country they do not appear to be dependent on water and, while common in and around the Okavango Swamps, they are also found in southwest Botswana, where surface water is only available seasonally.

**Habits**

While honey badgers are predominantly nocturnal, there are numerous observations of diurnal movement and it seems likely that they adjust their activities to suit their requirements. Most of the records of their raiding apiaries or fowl runs show that this takes place at night, and may have led to the supposition that they move only after dark. A number of carnivores show nocturnal activity in areas where they are subject to disturbance and considerable diurnal activity in reserved or wild areas and the honey badger appears to follow this pattern. In Mashonaland they are certainly nocturnal, while in Botswana, Smithers (1971) listed visual records from 09h00 to 17h00.

Generally solitary, there are many observations of two or more moving and hunting together. Smithers (1983) saw two together on four occasions in Botswana. These may well have been pairs, as Grimbeek (pers. comm.) trapped a pair in the Waterberg, Transvaal. They have a strong tendency to use tracks and roads along which they move at a lumbering trot, which carries them surprisingly quickly. They are courageous animals and, while normally shy and retiring, occasionally and without provocation they can become extremely aggressive.

In interspecific fighting, they have been known to put up a good fight against large animals. Stevenson-Hamilton (1912) quoted a ranger's report on an encounter between a lion and a honey badger which, from the condition of the bush around, had been killed only after putting up a spirited defence. In intraspecific fighting, Fitzsimons (1919), who witnessed such an encounter, recorded that each individual invited the other to bite first. Whichever did so was obviously at a disadvantage for the other would then lunge for the softer skin of the abdomen, a most vulnerable spot.

Sikes (1964) noted that, in captivity, normally docile individuals suddenly, and for no apparent reason, would develop "fury moods", when they became dangerous to handle. A return to docility was just as sudden. She concluded that these temperamental extremes were related to their natural habits, contributing to their reputation for ferocity and fearlessness. In captivity honey badgers show playfulness and are responsive, readily learning to recognise voices, tones of command and warnings. When disturbed or prowling, honey badgers vocalise with a soft repeated *haarr-haarr*. Under stress they growl loudly.

At times honey badgers can become problem animals, raiding poultry runs. Being very powerful and equipped with the long, knife-like front claws, they have no difficulty in tearing through wire netting. On gaining entry, they are inclined to kill far more than they can consume. To hold them requires a heavily built trap. Smithers (1983) described the catching of one in a steel live-trap. The honey badger tore off the end to escape, but not content with this, it attacked the trap, crushing in the side and the trigger mechanism. In encounters with dogs, honey badgers invariably come off best, as the dogs' teeth rarely penetrate the loose, thick skin. Stevenson-Hamilton (1912) recorded them walking off, little the worse for encounters with packs of dogs. This thick skin effectively protects them when raiding bee hives.

There is little doubt that Pocock (1922) was correct in stating that the coloration of the honey badger is one of the best known examples of warning coloration. Its diminutive external ears, too, are in keeping with the theory that it does not have to have sharp hearing, either to escape enemies, for it has few to fear, or capture its prey. When hunting, the honey badger moves with a slow rolling gait, nose close to the ground, sniffing here and there for prey, and they are not disturbed easily in this pursuit. Individuals observed feeding in the Kalahari sometimes had a chanting goshawk, *Melierax musiens*, in trophic association. The goshawks followed the honey badgers, catching insects and other small animals disturbed by the latter while hunting (Skinner, unpubl.; Marlow, 1983). Quite a high proportion of the prey, such as scorpions and burrowing reptiles, need to be dug up, a technique for which they are equipped ideally with their powerful front limbs and long, knife-like claws.

Although normally terrestrial, they have been known to climb trees in search of prey such as lizards, and to get at bee hives. They are accounted a problem in areas where indigenous people construct grass or bark hives, which are placed in trees, as they totally destroy these in getting at the contents. They will dig in the hardest ground to obtain access to hives of indigenous bee species, or large baboon spiders.

### Food

In addition to their carnivorous habits, Fitzsimons (1919) included wild berries and fruit in the diet of this species, and a liking for honey and the larvae of wild bees. Shortridge (1934) listed them as omnivorous and Stevenson-Hamilton (1912) included carrion and stated that insects feature prominently in their diet.

**Table 262.2**

Percentage occurrence of food items in the stomachs of seven honey badgers, *M. capensis*, from Botswana and Zimbabwe (Smithers, 1983)

| Food item | Percentage occurrence |
|---|---|
| Scorpiones | 71 |
| Muridae | 57 |
| Araneae | 57 |
| Sauria | 43 |
| Insecta | 29 |
| Myriapoda | 29 |
| Aves | 14 |
| Serpentes | 14 |
| Bee larvae and honey | 14 |

In a sample of seven stomach contents from Botswana and Zimbabwe, scorpions had the highest occurrence (Table 262.2), followed by mice, spiders, lizards, centipedes, grasshoppers, small birds, snakes, bee larvae and honey. If the opportunity permits, they will raid apiaries, and there are several records of their tearing the hives to pieces to get at the contents.

Scorpions figured highly in the diet, probably because six of the seven specimens originated in the dry country of western Zimbabwe and northeastern Botswana where scorpions are very common. Four of the six were taken during the warm, wet summer months when scorpions move widely at night. There is, therefore, some bias towards scorpions in the sample. In three cases the scorpion involved was *Opisthopthalmus betchuanicus*, a large species that excavates shallow resting places in sandy soils. In one specimen these scorpions comprised 90% of the stomach content. Spiders had a high occurrence, consisting entirely of large baboon spiders. A honey badger taken in Botswana was seen digging these out of the surface of Nxai Pan. Insects consisted predominantly of grasshoppers and Myriapoda, solely of the centipede, *Scolopendra morsitans*.

Murids were represented by multimammate mice, *Mastomys* spp, the lesser gerbil, *Gerbillurus paeba*, and gerbils, *Tatera* spp, all common in the area from which the honey badgers were collected. Lizards were represented by the whistling gecko, *Ptenopus garrulus*, the spotted scrub lizard, *Nucras intertexta*, and the common striped skink, *Mabuya striata*, and snakes by Schlegel's blind snake, *Typhlops schlegelii* and the herald snake, *Crotaphopeltis hotamboeia*. The square-tailed wedge-snouted amphisbaenian, *Tomuropeltis pistellum*, was identifiable in one stomach, small birds in another, with bee larvae and wax in a third.

Stevenson-Hamilton (1947) recorded the killing of a black mamba, *Dendroaspis polylepis*, by a honey badger and Ewer (1973) a 3 m long python, *Python sebae*. Indeed, there is a report from the Kruger National Park (*Afr. Wildl.* 18(1): 37) of a honey badger engaged in a fight with a 3 m python which continued, after it was first observed, for 15 minutes. The python was killed and it was reported that it was so mutilated that it looked as if it had been run over by a train. Having killed the python the honey badger immediately began to eat it and after being driven off, returned to it later. While no Amphibia were recorded from the seven stomachs from the Subregion, a specimen from Zinave, Mozambique had eaten eight rain frogs, *Breviceps mossambicus*. These are in evidence in the wet season during hatches of termites.

Marlow (1983) observed twice between 18h00 and 18h30 on different days, in the Kalahari Gemsbok National Park, a honey badger crossing the road with a large downy white-backed vulture chick, *Gyps africanus*, the first the size of a domestic fowl, the second weighing 4,25 kg, in its mouth. This was some half its own weight and it was assumed that it captured the vultures from their nests on top of nearby camelthorn, *Acacia erioloba*, trees. In Israel, Ilani (pers. comm.) observed an individual digging out molerats.

Normally honey badgers are not attracted by carrion, although they can be trapped on baits of the entrails of hares or birds.

### Reproduction

There is a paucity of information on the time of the year when the young are born. In the Kruger National Park, Transvaal, Fairall (1968) believed that they may breed throughout the year. A female from Botswana taken in November was heavily lactating (Smithers, 1971). Ansell (1960a) in Zambia recorded newly born young in December and half-grown juveniles under parental care in June. Two young constitute a litter. The females have two pairs of inguinal mammae.

## Subfamily MUSTELINAE

Key to the genera (Meester *et al.*, 1986)

1. Smaller, greatest skull length 56 mm and less; body sinuous; fur short and silky, black and yellowish-white; no white markings below eyes; white on forehead continuous with that on the neck; normally 1 lower molar, 28–30 teeth ... *Poecilogale*

   Larger, greatest skull length more than 56 mm; body not sinuous; fur long and thick, black and white; white markings present below the eyes; white on forehead separated from that on neck; 2 lower molars, 34 teeth ... *Ictonyx*

## Genus *Poecilogale* Thomas, 1883

No. 263

## *Poecilogale albinucha* (Gray, 1864)

## African weasel
## Slangmuishond

Plate 22

### Colloquial Name

This species has a superficial similarity to European weasels, *Mustela* spp. As their bodies are long, sinuous, and snake-like, the Afrikaans name is singularly appropriate. Alternative name: African striped weasel, the "striped" referring to the characteristic white longitudinal bands on their otherwise black bodies.

**Plate 22**

260. Cape clawless otter, *Aonyx capensis*
     Groototter
261. Spotted-necked otter, *Lutra maculicollis*
     Kleinotter
262. Honey badger, *Mellivora capensis*
     Ratel
263. African weasel, *Poecilogale albinucha*
     Slangmuishond
264. Striped polecat, *Ictonyx striatus*
     Stinkmuishond

PLATE 22
263
264
262
261
260
Dick Findlay.

### Taxonomic Notes

Meester et *al.* (1986) listed four subspecies: *P. a. albinucha* from the eastern Cape Province; *P. a. transvaalensis* Roberts, 1926 from the northeastern Transvaal; *P. a. bechuanae* from the northern Cape Province, and *P. a. lebombo* Roberts, 1931 from Natal. At the moment there is insufficient material to judge their validity.

### Description

African weasels have a total length of up to 500 mm and a tail about a third of this length. The males have a mean mass of about 260 g, the females about 170 g (Table 263.1). The legs are very short. The height at the shoulder in adults is about 50 mm to 60 mm.

**Table 263.1**

Measurements (mm) and mass (g) of African weasels, *P. albinucha*, from Zimbabwe (Smithers, 1983)

| | Males | | | Females | | |
|---|---|---|---|---|---|---|
| | x̄ | n | Range | x̄ | n | Range |
| TL | 445 | 6 | 414–508 | 425 | 11 | 400–465 |
| T | 155 | 6 | 128–163 | 157 | 11 | 136–166 |
| Hf c/u | 36 | 6 | 33–39 | 32 | 11 | 30–36 |
| E | 18 | 6 | 15–19 | 16 | 11 | 14–18 |
| Mass | 263,0 | 6 | 218,0–355,0 | 173,0 | 11 | 116–257,0 |

In both Roberts' (1951) and Rowe-Rowe's (1972a) sample the average total length and length of the tail are greater in males than in females. Rowe-Rowe (1972a) showed that the mass of males is about 50% greater than females, which is reflected in the present sample.

The body and limbs are jet black, the forehead and top of the head pure white, the white colour extending to the ears on either side and continuing in the form of two broad bands on to the back of the neck. These in turn break up into two dorsal and two lateral bands, which rejoin near the base of the tail. The longitudinal bands on the body may be pure white, white tinged yellow, yellow or ochre-yellow, no two individuals being exactly similar. The two lateral bands are usually broader than those on the dorsal side of the body and, arising from behind the shoulders, curve downwards along the flanks. The tail is covered with white hair about 30 mm in length. The individual hairs are black basally with broad white tips.

There is considerable individual variation in the breadth of the white bands on the body. In a Botswana specimen the lateral bands reach a breadth of about 15 mm compared with those in other specimens in which they barely reach 7 mm. In some the dorsal bands run so close to each other that the black central band between them appears as a narrow line; in others they are further apart. Sometimes the central black band between the dorsal white bands narrows towards the head, breaking up into irregular black spots on the top of the head. The hair of the under parts is jet black with a narrow fringe of white hairs on the chin.

The pelage consists of a sparse covering of underfur which is overlaid by the guard coat, the hairs of which are about 10 mm long on the body, shorter on the limbs.

There are five digits on each foot. The claws on the front feet are strongly curved and longer than those on the back and all five digits on the feet and their claws mark in the spoor (Fig. 263.1).

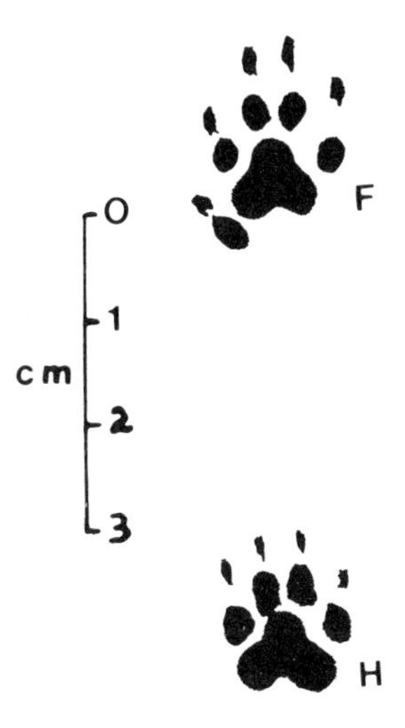


Fig. 263.1. Spoor: African weasel, *P. albinucha*. F. Right forefoot H. Right hind foot.

### Skull (Fig. 263.2)

The skull is typically mustelid with an ovoid braincase, which is broader behind, and tapers forward to just behind the eye orbits; these are small in relation to its size. The eyes are situated far forward in the skull, the distance from the front of the eye orbits to the front of the skull being about one fifth of its total length. The rostrum is short and broad, giving the individual a snub-nosed appearance. The socket of the lower jaw (the glenoid) lies just behind the middle point of the skull. The postorbital bars are incomplete, being reduced to two small processes, one above and just behind the eye orbit, the other on the zygomatic arch. The sides of the braincase provide a broad attachment for the temporalis muscles which activate the closure of the lower jaw. The zygomatic arch is relatively weak suggesting that the main jaw activation is more dependent on the temporalis muscles and less on the masseters. For the size of the skull the lower jaw is stoutly built and the coronoid process is high in relation to the length. The condyle of the lower jaw, which hinges on the upper part of the skull, is very broad and fits tightly into the socket in the upper, allowing little or no side to side action of the jaw. In some specimens it is difficult to release the lower jaw from the upper. This is an indication of a carnivorous diet which requires cutting rather than a side to side grinding action of the jaw. The ear bullae are elongated and flattish and taper to narrow points in front.

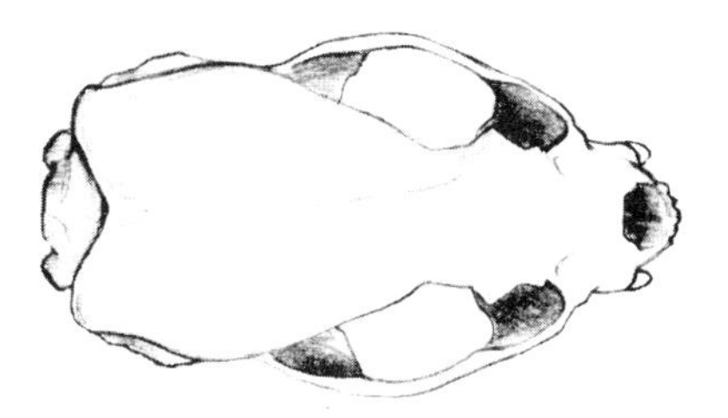

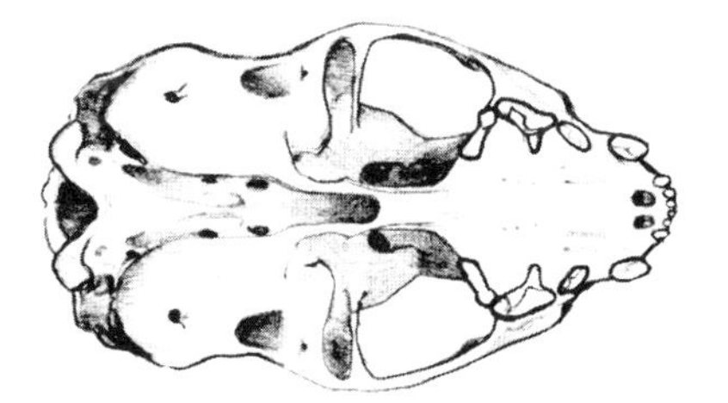

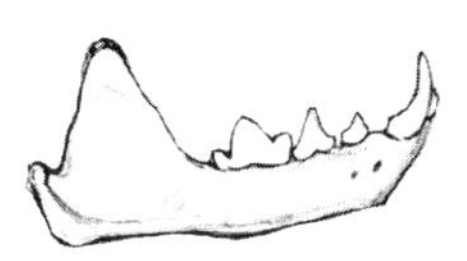

Fig. 263.2. Skull: African weasel, *P. albinucha*. TL Skull 48 mm.

The dental formula is:

$I\frac{3}{3}\ C\frac{1}{1}\ P\frac{2}{2}\ M\frac{1}{1} = 28$

The carnassials are adapted to slicing; the single molar in the upper jaw is long and lies nearly at right angles to the line of the cheekteeth, occluding in part on the back portion of the molar in the lower jaw. The tooth row is short, not occupying more than one-third of the total length of the skull.

### Distribution

This species is apparently rare in most parts of its range and overlooked so easily that there are relatively few specimens in collections. It appears to be quite common in Natal (Rowe-Rowe, 1975) and in the Ambaca area, inland of Luanda, Angola (Hill & Carter, 1941).

*South of the Sahara, excluding the Southern African Subregion*

They are recorded from west of the Rift Valley in **Kenya**; southwestern **Uganda; Tanzania; Rwanda; Burundi; Zaire**, excluding the forests of the Congo Basin; **Angola; Zambia** and **Malawi**.

*Southern African Subregion*

There are single records from **Namibia** from Leonardville in the central part of the country, and from near Deebeti in the eastern sector of **Botswana**. They occur in the eastern and northeastern parts of **Zimbabwe**, with a single record from Lupane in the west. Their occurrence in the eastern parts of Zimbabwe on the border with **Mozambique**, south of the Zambezi River, suggests that they probably occur in adjacent parts of that country, but at the moment there is only a single record from the Maputo District in the south. They occur in the **Transvaal**, in the eastern parts of the **Orange Free State** and widely in **Natal**. Their distribution extends into the eastern parts of the **Cape Province** as far west coastally as the Knysna district and they also occur in the northern and northeastern parts of the province.

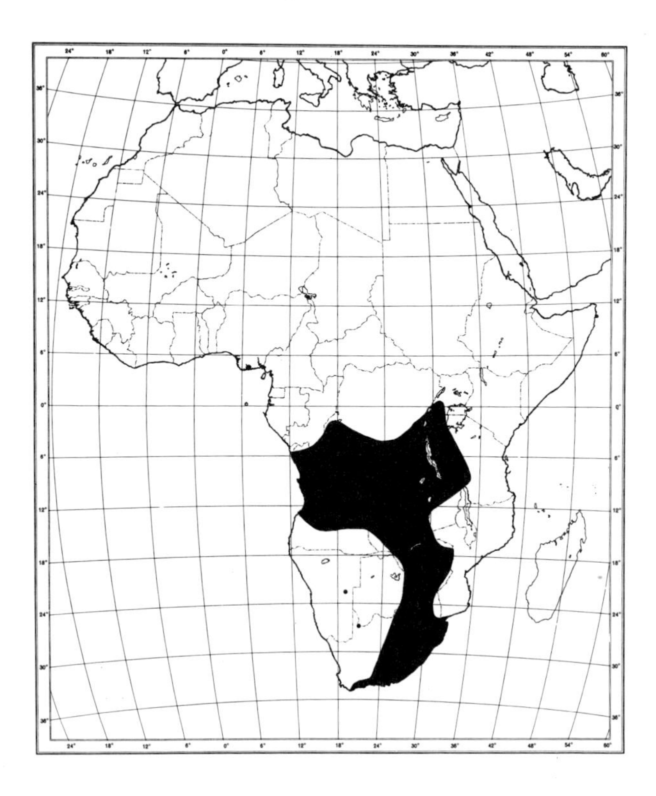

### Habitat

The African weasel is a savanna species particularly associated with moist grassland areas having an annual rainfall in excess of 600 mm (Rowe-Rowe, 1990).

### Habits

African weasels are usually solitary, terrestrial and predominantly nocturnal, occasionally being seen in daylight. Owing to their small size, their short legs and low slung body, observations on African weasels in the field are meagre. Most records in the field are of solitary individuals, but they may occur in groups of two to four, usually a female and her young. Rowe-Rowe (1972a) stated that they are not good climbers, although they will do so in captivity, when they would clamber up the sides of the cage, but when they attempted to climb along the top, invariably lost grip with the back feet and eventually dropped to the ground. They were obviously not adept at negotiating the tree trunks available in the cage and frequently the back feet would slip off.

In walking the head is held low, the tail extended horizontally, and the back slightly arched. In running the same posture is adopted, but the back is more arched. The run may develop into the loping gallop in which the individual moves in a series of bounds.

While individuals will raise their heads and forequarters and look around, they were never seen to sit up on the haunches as do other mustelids. The length and sinuous nature of the body probably makes this difficult. They are good burrowers, often excavating their own holes (Rowe-Rowe, 1990). Rowe-Rowe (1975) described how they made a burrow 50 mm in diameter, almost vertical for about 100 mm, then horizontal for up to about 200 mm, terminating in a chamber 100–150 mm in diameter. When excavating, the loosened soil is pulled away with the front feet, the individual reversing to move it out of the way. Rowe-Rowe (1972a) described how two together in turn, would help to excavate a burrow. As they have been ploughed up in agricultural lands, they do use burrows, possibly adapting those of rodents to their own requirements.

A characteristic feature was the yawning and stretching which preceded emergence from the sleeping box. The individual would poke its nose out of the hole, sniffing the air, often with the eyes closed, and yawn several times before emerging.

Defecation and urination usually took place in the same corner of the cage, up against the vertical wall, but also inside the sleeping box. African weasels are equipped with perineal glands from which they can eject a yellowish fluid with a very heavy, sweet, pungent smell. Preceding ejection, the hair on the tail and on the lower part of the back is raised and the tail held vertically. Alexander & Ewer (1959) stated that, in a badly frightened individual, the fluid can be ejected to a distance of a metre in a thin stream, but normally it is not ejected forcefully. The smell is not nauseating as in the case of the polecat.

Adult calls can be divided into those for threat, defence and greeting. The warning calls of African weasels and striped polecats are similar, as are the aggression calls which are high amplitude sounds uttered suddenly (Channing & Rowe-Rowe, 1977).

### Food

The diet consists almost exclusively of small rodents, but on occasion small insectivores and young birds on the ground are taken (Rowe-Rowe, 1978a). As a specialist killer of small mammals, it is capable of killing rodents up to its own size using a well directed bite at the back of the neck accompanied by a lateral rolling to bowl the prey over and break the spine by treading vigorously against it with the hindfeet (Rowe-Rowe, 1990).

### Reproduction

In South Africa they breed during spring and summer. Copulation lasts 60–80 minutes and the gestation period of 32 days is the shortest of any carnivore without delayed implantation (Rowe-Rowe, 1978b). One to three, altricial, naked young weighing 4 g are born in a litter. Canine teeth erupt on about Day 35 when young first eat solid food and the eyes open at about 52 days. They first kill prey at 13 weeks and are full grown at 20 weeks. They usually rear only one litter per season unless this dies at an early stage, when the female will mate again.

The females have a pair of abdominal and a pair of inguinal mammae, but may occasionally have an extra pair of inguinal mammae (Rowe-Rowe, 1972a).

# Genus *Ictonyx* Kaup, 1835

No. 264

## *Ictonyx striatus* Perry, 1810

## Striped polecat
## Stinkmuishond

Plate 22

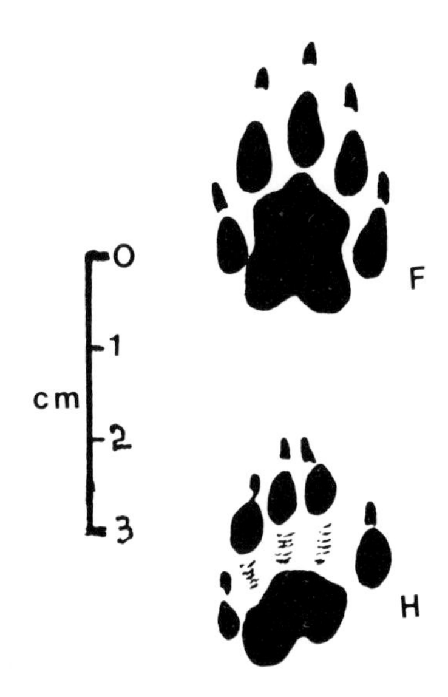


Fig. 264.1. Spoor: striped polecat, *I. striatus*.
F. Right forefoot H. Right hind foot.

### Colloquial Name

As the coat is distinctly striped black and white, "striped" very aptly describes this polecat. The Afrikaans *stinkmuishond* is descriptive, but *muishond* applies also to the weasel and the mongoose.

### Taxonomic Notes

Meester *et al.* (1986) listed 10 subspecies from the Subregion, noting that too many subspecies have been described. It is probable that far fewer will be recognised eventually.

### Description

The striped polecat is one of the most easily recognised species of small carnivores on account of its black and white colour pattern and long hair. It is unlikely to be confused with the African weasel, *Poecilogale albinucha*, which is also black and white with a similar pattern, but which is much smaller and has a sinuous body. Their conspicuous coloration is no doubt a warning to enemies who, if they are imprudent enough to interfere with them, are likely to be tainted by the nauseating fluid which the striped polecat can release at will from its anal glands. The long-lasting, clinging smell is likely to remind them for a long time after that this small black and white mustelid is best avoided.

The overall colour is jet black, with a series of four bands of pure white which, arising from a white patch on the head, run the length of the upper parts to the base of the tail. These white bands vary in width in individuals; the inner two are usually narrower. Running roughly parallel from the head to just in front of the hind limbs, they then swing outwards to rejoin at the base of the tail. The outer bands lie similarly and are always broader and more conspicuous. On the forehead, just between and extending above the eyes, there is a white patch varying in shape and size in individuals. Above the eyes and between them and the base of the ears is a still larger white patch, which varies in size and shape in individuals. The tips of the ears are fringed with short white hair. The base of the tail is black in some specimens, in others flanked with white, being a continuation of the white bands on the back. The remainder shows white, although the black bases of the hairs show through conspicuously. In some specimens the tip of the tail is broadly pure white.

The under parts and limbs are jet black. The hair on the upper parts is long and silky. The hair on the white bands is pure white throughout its length, and on the black parts of the body, jet black.

There is some variation in the length of the individual hairs of the guard coat on the upper parts, but in all specimens it is shorter on the head, barely reaching 6 to 7 mm long and much longer on the hindquarters, about 50 to 60 mm. The hair on the tail is longer, reaching 70 to 80 mm in some specimens. The individual hairs are either pure white or have broad black bases and broad white tips. The underfur is fine and silky, pure white on the white parts of the body, jet black on the black parts.

There are five digits on each foot. The claws on all five digits of the front feet are long, strong and curved, up to 18 mm long over the curve; those on the hind feet are much shorter, less curved and up to about 10 mm long over the curve. All five digits on the feet mark in the spoor (Fig. 264.1).

In some lights the coat has a distinct sheen. The rhinarium is small, the muzzle bluntly pointed and the ears rounded. The soles of the feet are naked.

In the series available males appear to be slightly larger and heavier than females, although the number of females available is small (Table 264.1).

**Table 264.1**

Measurements (mm) and mass (g) of a series of striped polecats, *I. striatus*, from Zimbabwe and Botswana (Smithers, 1983)

| | Males | | | Females | | |
|---|---|---|---|---|---|---|
| | $\bar{x}$ | n | Range | $\bar{x}$ | n | Range |
| TL | 627 | 27 | 566–670 | 604 | 8 | 565–633 |
| T | 261 | 27 | 236–295 | 257 | 8 | 248–263 |
| Hf c/u | 63 | 27 | 56–70 | 59 | 8 | 50–64 |
| E | 30 | 27 | 26–36 | 29 | 8 | 26–31 |
| Mass | 974 | 27 | 681–1460 | 713 | 8 | 596–880 |

### Skull (Fig. 264.2)

As in the case of other mustelids the skull is solidly and heavily built, the braincase broad at the back and tapering sharply towards the anterior. The rostrum is short and blunt, the distance between the front of the eye sockets to the front of the maxillary bone, which projects slightly anterior to the incisor teeth, only about a quarter of the total length of the skull. While there is no sagittal crest, two low ridges run from the centre of the supraoccipital crest, widening anteriorly to join the postorbital processes, giving an extra attachment on either side of the braincase for the temporalis muscles. These and the broad area of attachment provided by the broadening of the braincase, provide an extensive area of attachment for this powerful muscle that activates the closing of the jaw. The palate is broad posteriorly between the upper fourth premolars, narrowing sharply behind the molar teeth.

The dental formula is:

$I\frac{3}{3}\ C\frac{1}{1}\ P\frac{3}{3}\ M\frac{1}{2} = 34$

The canines are short and strong, the front part of the carnassial shear adapted to slicing. The broad molar tooth in the upper jaw occludes on the rear portion of the first and on the front portion of the small second molar tooth in the lower jaw, providing for crushing and grinding, especially of insect food. The outside incisor in the upper jaw is distinctly larger than the remainder and no doubt assists the canine in the holding of larger prey. The lower jaw is heavy, the canine teeth distinctly backwardly projecting towards their tips; the small second molar is set towards the inside of the tooth row.

The ear bullae are very broad and flat, tapering to a narrow point anteriorly. The zygomatic arches, while broad and strong towards their bases, are centrally thin and weak, the postorbital processes reduced to small knobs.

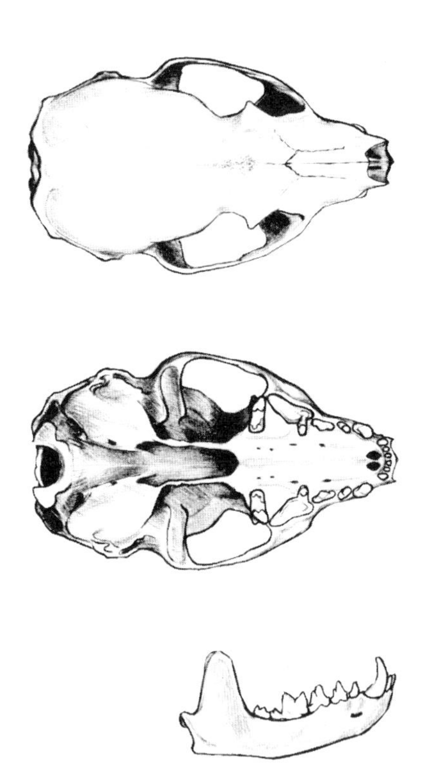

Fig. 264.2. Skull: striped polecat, *I. striatus*.
TL Skull 68 mm

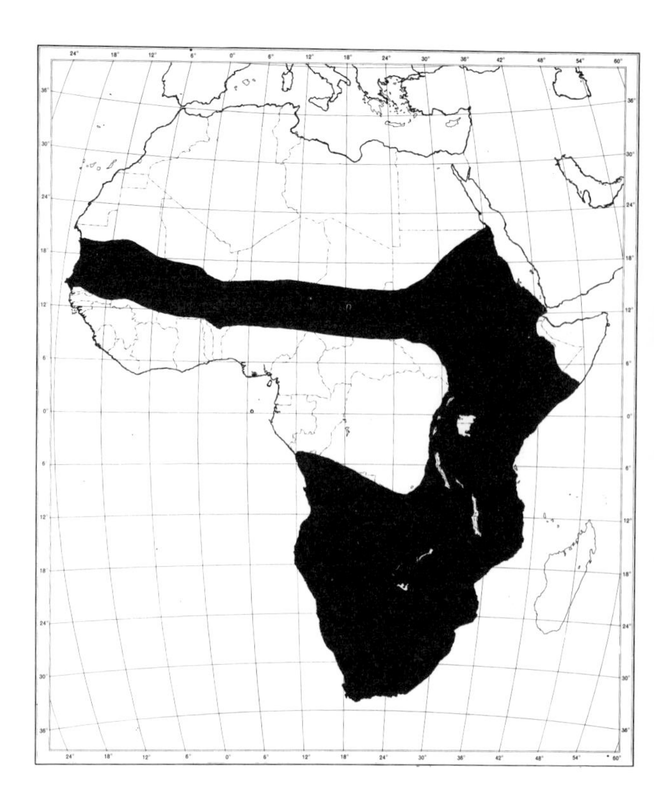

## Distribution

The striped polecat, *I. striatus*, is confined to Africa south of the Sahara where it has a wide distribution, being absent only from the forests of the Congo basin, the Guinea Zone and the forests of West Africa, the arid regions of northeastern Somalia and adjacent parts of Ethiopia. However, they can utilise desert areas as is shown by their occurrence in the Namib Desert in the Subregion (Coetzee, 1969).

*South of the Sahara, excluding the Southern African Subregion*

They occur in the Adrar Mountains in the southeastern parts of **Mauritania**; in **Senegal** (*I. s. senegalensis* J.B. Fischer, 1829) eastwards in the Sahel and Sudan zones to the coast of the Red Sea in the northeastern **Sudan**. South of this they are recorded from **Ethiopia**, excluding parts of the southeast; **Somalia**, excluding the northeast; **Kenya; Uganda; Rwanda; Burundi; Tanzania** and southeastern **Zaire**. They occur there as they are recorded from **Malawi** and from adjacent parts of **Zambia**, where they are widespread and from **Angola**.

*Southern African Subregion*

They occur widely in **Mozambique**, south of the Zambezi River; they are recorded from **Zimbabwe**, with no records at the moment from the northeastern parts of the country; they occur in **Botswana, Namibia** and throughout the remainder of the Subregion.

## Habitat

The striped polecat has a wide habitat tolerance in the Subregion, occurring in drainage lines in desert, where there is some scrub cover, in open grassland, savanna woodland and forest. They are found at altitudes from sea level to over 1 500 m. Coetzee (1969) recorded the species from the sand dunes and hummocks of the Namib Desert and Smithers & Wilson (1979) from rainfall areas of up to 1 400 m in the eastern parts of Zimbabwe. Rowe-Rowe (1975) stated that they occur in Natal in a variety of habitats including open grassland, savanna, thornbush, rocky areas, natural forest and exotic plantations. Shortridge (1934) described it as one of the most ubiquitous mammals in southern Africa. Within its distributional range it is absent locally. Wherever they occur, they are nowhere common and in some parts are considered rare.

## Habits

Striped polecats are nocturnal, terrestrial and solitary (Rowe-Rowe, 1975). In Botswana they are late movers, not normally being seen before about 22h00 (Smithers, 1971). While adapted to a terrestrial life, they will climb trees under stress (Fitzsimons, 1919). Occasionally they are seen in pairs or a female with young.

Movement is usually at a fast trot, with the back arched. When hunting, this trot may be arrested suddenly as the individual casts around with the nose close to the ground in search of prey. If suddenly disturbed, they break into a fast galloping run as they seek the safety of a hole or other refuge. In the relaxed trot the tail is carried horizontally or nearly so, the nose close to the ground. Rowe-Rowe (1975) recorded that the polecat will sit on its haunches, raising the forequarters off the ground.

In soft sandy substrate they dig their own burrows, but more commonly use the disused holes of other species or the shelter of piles of rocks, crevices in loose stone walls, under tree roots or fallen logs. Shortridge (1934) recorded an individual that lived under the floor of an outhouse and Rowe-Rowe (1975) recorded their use of stacks of maize stalks in agricultural lands. Within their home range they appear to have a knowledge of the refuges available, for when disturbed, they make for these directly and quickly disappear into their shelter. They are prone, however, to take up aggressive attitudes if suddenly disturbed. The hair of the body and tail is erected, appearing to double their size; the tail is raised or curved forward over the back, and the individual stands high on the legs. If cornered they growl or will scream loudly and turn the hindquarters to the aggressor, looking over their shoulders, and may eject the pungent excretion from the anal glands, which is highly offensive and persistent. The use of anal glands appears to be the ultimate defence in confrontation with larger enemies and while the black and white pelage is to some extent a disruptive camouflage, it is more a warning coloration to would-be enemies.

## Food

The two principal food items of the striped polecat are insects and mice, but they will also take reptiles, birds, amphibia, spiders, scorpions, hunting spiders, millipedes and centipedes.

Examination of the stomach contents of 36 from Zimbabwe and Botswana (Smithers, 1983) and 21 from Natal (Rowe-Rowe, 1975) show close similarities. In both, insects had by far the highest percentage occurrence at 61% and 62% respectively, followed by mice at 17% and 33% (Table 264.2).

**Table 264.2a**

Percentage occurrence of various food items in a sample of 36 stomachs of the striped polecat, *I. striatus*, from Zimbabwe and Botswana (Smithers, 1983) compared with 21 from Natal (Rowe-Rowe, 1978a)

| | Percentage occurrence | |
|---|---|---|
| **Food item** | **Zimbabwe and Botswana** | **Natal** |
| Insecta | 61 | 62 |
| Muridae | 17 | 33 |
| Reptilia | 17 | — |
| Araneae | — | 10 |
| Scorpiones | 11 | — |
| Solifugae | 8 | — |
| Myriapoda | 5 | 5 |
| Aves and eggs | 3 | 10 |
| Amphibia | 3 | 5 |
| Vegetable matter (seeds) | — | 5 |
| Chrysochloridae | — | 5 |

While in Natal spiders (Araneae) had an occurrence of 10%, they appear to be replaced in the northern region by scorpions at 11% and hunting spiders (Solifugae) at 8%, the last two-named being readily available in the more arid parts from which the sample originates. Birds figure more prominently at 10% in the Natal sample than in the other at 3%. Grass figures in both samples, but probably as a non-food, ingested fortuitously or for its mechanical action on the digestive system.

**Table 264.2b**

Insecta identified

| | Percentage occurrence | |
|---|---|---|
| **Food item** | **Zimbabwe and Botswana** | **Natal** |
| Coleoptera | 25 | 14 |
| Coleoptera grubs | 19 | 38 |
| Orthoptera | 14 | 10 |
| Gryllidae | 8 | 19 |
| Isoptera | 3 | – |
| Blattidae | 3 | – |
| Lepidoptera | 3 | 14 |
| Dermaptera | – | 5 |

Insects in both samples consist predominantly of beetles and beetle larvae, in the Natal sample larvae figuring very prominently (Table 264.2b). The striped polecat with its long front claws is adapted ideally to digging up subterranean food of this sort. Grasshoppers and crickets figure in both samples and Lepidoptera higher in the Natal samples.

In the northern sample rats, mice and reptiles had the next highest occurrence at 17%. Mice were represented by gerbils, *Tatera* spp, juvenile fat mice, *Steatomys* spp, and multimammate mice, *Mastomys* spp. In one the sole content of the stomach was nine juvenile multimammate mice, probably taken from a nest.

Reptiles were represented by the amphisbaenians, the Kalahari round-snouted, *Zygaspis quadrifrons*, and the long-tailed wedge-snouted, *Tomuropeltis longicauda*; snakes by the herald snake, *Crotaphopeltis hotamboeia*; lizards by the sand lizard, *Eremias namaquensis*. Amphibia were represented by Mozambique rain frogs, *Breviceps mossambicus*. Rowe-Rowe (1975) listed a burrowing frog, *Tomopterna* sp, from a stomach of this species. Scorpions occurred at 11% and hunting spiders at 8%, with smaller occurrences of baboon and wolf spiders and centipedes, *Scolopendra morsitans*, birds and amphibians.

In the Natal sample, Rowe-Rowe (1975) listed among the mammals taken multimammate mice, *Mastomys* spp; vlei rats, *Otomys* sp; white-tailed rats, *Mystromys albicaudatus*, and Hottentot golden moles, *Amblysomus hottentotus*. The rats and mice had a percentage occurrence of 33%.

Spiders and birds, including a francolin chick, and birds' eggs occurred at 10%, with lesser occurrences of centipedes, frogs and seeds.

When hunting, the striped polecat moves purposefully, poking its muzzle into loose litter and other places where insects are to be found. Subterranean larvae are located in this manner and then dug out with the aid of the long claws of the front feet. Insects and other smaller prey, located on the surface, are simply picked up with the mouth. Larger prey such as frogs and lizards are stalked and either bitten on the head or arrested with the front paws and then bitten. Rowe-Rowe (1975) described how they will approach a snake cautiously, slinking towards it, body held close to the ground and then bite it on the back and sometimes shake it vigorously. Then they may drop it and retreat rapidly, repeating this process until the reptile is quiescent, when it is held down with the forefeet and bitten near the head. However, shaking is not as characteristic of the polecat as it is of some viverrids such as the civet, *Civettictis civetta*. If the snake attempted to strike, the polecat quickly would avoid the thrust, catch it near the tail and render it quiescent by vigorous shaking, often then continuing to bite it over the length of its body.

In dealing with rats and mice, the polecat bites on any part of the body available, biting and releasing until the prey is immobilised, when the killing bite usually is directed to the neck.

### Reproduction

There is a paucity of information on the times at which the young are born. In the northern parts of the Subregion, a female carrying two minute foetuses was taken in August and juveniles in March, May and as late as July. A series of 10 females taken between March and August showed no signs of breeding. It seems likely on this basis that the young are born during the summer. Females have their first litter from an age of 10 months. Rowe-Rowe (1975) stated that if a female in captivity successfully rears a litter, she will not produce a second litter until the following season. If, on the other hand, the young die at an early age, she will mate again.

Rowe-Rowe (1978b) recorded that copulation lasts 25–106 minutes. During copulation the female is very vociferous, emitting loud yaps in decreasing frequency and amplitude (Rowe-Rowe, 1975). The gestation period is 36 days (n=3); litter size is one to three, although in zoological gardens, Rowe-Rowe (1975) listed litters of three, four and five, the maximum number reared being three. Mass at birth is 10 to 15 g. The young are altricial, being born hairless, with the eyes and ears closed. At birth the dark stripes are apparent in the pink skin. The eyes open during the sixth week and the lower canines erupt at about 32 days. The young in the nest both squeak and yap, and later, at about three weeks old, mew when separated from the female. The young polecats are weaned by about eight weeks, when live prey in the form of insects is captured and eaten, and a week later they are killing rats (Rowe-Rowe, 1975).

Females have two pairs of mammae, one pair abdominal, one pair inguinal.

# XXXIV. Family VIVERRIDAE

## Mongoose, civets, genets and suricate

The Viverridae is a large and diverse Family represented in the Subregion by three Subfamilies, the Viverrinae, Herpestinae and Paradoxurinae, comprising 13 genera and 16 species. Although heterogeneous, there has been an almost universal agreement over the years for the close association of the species listed as members of this Family.

In the Subregion the Subfamily Viverrinae is represented by the civet, *Civettictis civetta*, and the genets, *Genetta* spp. In the former the skull is similar but more heavily built and the carnassials less blade-like and better adapted to crushing. The Subfamily Herpestinae is represented by 11 species of mongoose and the suricate. The teeth are adapted in various ways to the diet, ranging from those of the suricate, on an insect diet, to those of the slender mongoose, *Galerella* spp, in which they are all-purpose, giving them a slicing as well as a crushing ability.

The third Subfamily, the Paradoxurinae, is represented by one species, the tree civet, *Nandinia binotata*, which has a well developed carnassial shear, but only one upper molar tooth. It is unique among living Carnivora in that the posterior portions of the ear bullae are unossified.

Members occur in Africa and Asia and two of the species that occur in the Subregion, the small spotted genet, *Genetta genetta*, and the large grey mongoose, *Herpestes ichneumon*, have distributions that extend beyond continental limits into the Middle East and southern Europe.

Except for the civet, *Civettictis civetta*, which is of heavy build with a relatively stocky body, the members have long tails, short legs, and long sharp muzzles. All members of the Family are equipped with scent glands, the anal glands being particularly well developed.

They have five digits on each foot armed with claws, some specifically adapted to digging, others, such as those possessed by the genets and the tree civet, partly curved, sharp and partly protractile and adapted to holding the prey.

Corresponding with their rather elongated, sharp muzzles, their skulls are longer than broad. The rostrum is usually long, except in the Herpestinae. The dental formula is diverse, the number of teeth present varying from 36 to 40. There are always three incisors in each jaw half and a canine tooth, the diversity being due to the varying number of premolar and molar teeth. In the skull the ear bullae are large and show a constriction anteriorly that marks the internal septum that divides the bullae into two sections.

Most of the species are either nocturnal or crepuscular, but some of them such as the slender mongoose, *Galerella sanguinea*, the Cape grey mongoose, *G. pulverulenta*, the suricate, *Suricata suricatta*, the banded mongoose, *Mungos mungo*, the dwarf mongoose, *Helogale parvula*, and the yellow mongoose, *Cynictis penicillata*, are predominantly diurnal. Some are purely terrestrial, others such as the tree civet, *N. binotata*, in particular, are arboreal.

The Family is a very ancient one, originating in Eurasia in late Eocene times, some 45 million to 40 million years ago. Savage (1978) stated that members of the Miacidae, known from their fossil remains of some 40 million years ago, are impossible to distinguish from early viverrids on their dental characters. The earliest known from Africa is *Kichechia zamonae*, from early Miocene deposits in East Africa (Savage, 1978). In the Subregion, Hendey (1974) recorded three viverrids from Pliocene deposits in Namibia and they are well represented from the Pleistocene Epoch in the Subregion.

Key to the Subfamilies and genera (Meester *et al.*, 1986)

1. Feet compressed, claws short; coat spotted; no bony tube to auditory orifice; lower jugal section of postorbital process poorly developed

   ... 2

   Feet with digits more separated and fossorial claws; coat not spotted; with bony tube to auditory orifice; postorbital process well developed (Subfamily HERPESTINAE)

   ... 4

2. Bullae imperfect, wall of posterior (ectotympanic) portion permanently cartilaginous; paroccipital process directed backwards, away from bullae; feet more subplantigrade, hind feet with metatarsal pads broad and nearly reaching heel, but with hair at bases of toes (Subfamily PARADOXURINAE)

   ... *Nandinia*

   Bullae normal; paroccipital process lying against posterior part of bulla; feet more digitigrade and terrestrial, hind feet with no, or only a narrow, bare area on tarsus (Subfamily VIVERRINAE)

   ... 3

3. Large, greatest skull length exceeding 140 mm, hind feet exceeding 129 mm

   ... *Civettictis*

   Smaller, greatest skull length less than 110 mm, hind feet less than 100 mm

   ... *Genetta*

4. Four toes on fore and hind feet

   ... 5

   Five toes on forefeet, 4 or 5 on hind feet

   ... 7

5. Only 3 premolars in each toothrow, 36 teeth; interorbital width less than 2/3 of postorbital constriction; orbits closed by a bony ring; foreclaws much enlarged; back indistinctly banded; tail slender, not bushy

   ... *Suricata*

   Four upper, 3–4 lower premolars, 38–40 teeth; interorbital width about equal to or wider than postorbital constriction; orbits not closed posteriorly; foreclaws not markedly enlarged; back not banded; tail bushy

   ... 6

6. Skull height including bullae about 34–35 mm; upper carnassial sectorial, without hypocone on posterobuccal surface; anterior portion of bulla inflated, nearly as deep as posterior portion

   ... *Paracynictis*

   Skull height including bullae about 28 mm; upper carnassial more molariform, broad lingually, hypocone present; anterior part of bulla not inflated

   ... *Bdeogale*

7. Hind foot with four digits; skull relatively high, greatest height, measured at external auditory meatus, and including anterior part of bulla, just less than half of condylo-incisive length; anterior part of bulla much enlarged, posterior portion only slightly inflated; six cheekteeth; ears relatively large, seldom less than 9 percent of head and body length

   ... *Cynictis*

   Hind foot with five digits, although hallux is often reduced and may even be absent; skull relatively lower; anterior part of bulla usually uninflated, but if inflated then not dominant over posterior part; five or six cheekteeth

   ... 8

8. $P_4$ with posterior lobe (metacone) elongated, distance between protocones of $P_4$ and $M_1$ (Fig.1a) greater than distance between lingualmost point of contact of these two teeth and a line drawn between their lingual surfaces (b)

   ... 9

   $P_4$ with posterior lobe not so elongated, distance between protocones of $P_4$ and $M_1$ (Fig.1a) less than distance between lingualmost point of contact of the two teeth and a line drawn between their lingual surfaces (b)

   ... 10

9. Larger, condylobasal length of adult skull more than 100 mm; anterior chamber of bulla flattish and much smaller than inflated posterior portion

   ... *Herpestes*

   Smaller, condylobasal length of adult skull less than 70 mm; anterior chamber of bulla inflated, more comparable in size to posterior portion

   ... *Galerella*

10. Six upper cheekteeth; tail length more than ¾ of head and body length

    ... 11

    Five upper cheekteeth; tail length less than ¾ of head and body length

    ... 12

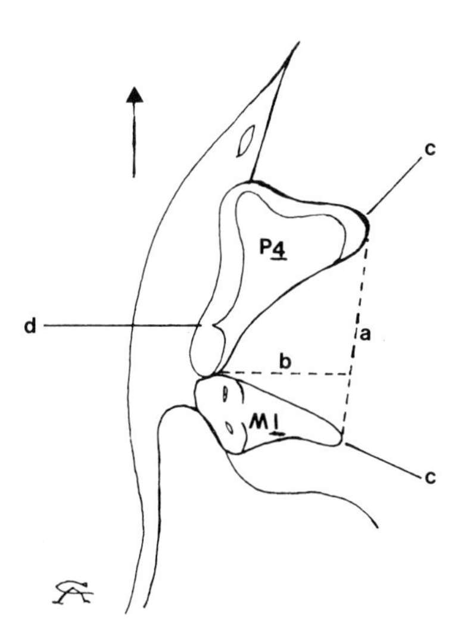


Fig. XXXIV.1 $P_4$ and $M_1$ of a herpestine showing (a) the distance between the protocones of these two teeth, and (b) the distance between the lingualmost point of contact of $P_4$ and $M_1$ and a line drawn between their lingual surfaces.

11. Hallux vestigial or untraceable; colour brownish, tail usually not white; carnassial poorly developed, both upper molars flat-crowned; palate does not extend far back beyond toothrow, width of post-dental palate greater than its length

... *Rhynchogale*

Hallux less reduced; colour greyish, tail-tip usually white; upper molars cuspidate; palate extends further back behind toothrow, length of post-dental palate greater than its width

... *Ichneumia*

12. Large, head and body length more than 470 mm, condylo-incisive length more than 100 mm in adults; claws short

... *Atilax*

Smaller, head and body length less than 460 mm, condylo-incisive length less than 90 mm; claws longer

... 13

13. Posterior (ectotympanic) part of bulla much larger than anterior (entotympanic) part; larger, head and body length usually more than 300 mm, condylo-incisive length of adults more than 57 mm; lower part of back transversely banded

... *Mungos*

Posterior part of bulla projects only slightly more than inflated anterior part; smaller, head and body length less than 250 mm, condylo-incisive length less than 53 mm; back not banded

... *Helogale*

## Subfamily PARADOXURINAE

## Genus *Nandinia* Gray, 1843

No. 265

## *Nandinia binotata* (Gray, 1830)

### Tree civet
### Boomsiwet

Plate 23

### Colloquial Name

The colloquial name so commonly used for this species, palm civet, is unfortunate as they are by no means particularly associated with palms in the southern part of their distributional range.

### Taxonomic Notes

Allen (1939) listed four subspecies: *N. b. binotata* originally described from Bioko Island (Fernando Póo), and ranging through West Africa and western central Africa; *N. b. intensa* Cabrera & Ruxton, 1926 from the Congo Basin and Angola; *N. b. arborea* Heller, 1913 from East Africa and *N. b. gerrardi* Thomas, 1893 from Malawi, Mozambique and eastern Zimbabwe.

### Description

The tree civet is a medium-sized viverrid, about 930 mm overall, with a tail about half this length, or almost equal in length to the length of the head and body (Table 265.1). In build it is very similar to a genet, but slightly larger and heavier.

**Table 265.1**

Measurements (mm) and mass (kg) of tree civets, *N. binotata*, from eastern Zimbabwe (Smithers & Wilson, 1979)

| | Males | | | Females | | |
|---|---|---|---|---|---|---|
| | $\bar{x}$ | n | Range | $\bar{x}$ | n | Range |
| TL | 937 | 6 | 927–956 | 932 | 4 | 875–976 |
| T | 469 | 6 | 460–484 | 492 | 4 | 477–513 |
| Hf s/u | 84 | 7 | 82–86 | 88 | 4 | 86–89 |
| E | 37 | 7 | 31–40 | 39 | 4 | 37–41 |
| Mass | 1,99 | 7 | 1,36–2,44 | 1,90 | 4 | 1,39–3,12 |

Among the branches of forest trees they look dark brown, the tail bushy. Closer at hand it can be seen that the upper parts are covered with small, irregularly shaped, very dark brown, almost black, spots on a lighter brown background colour. A characteristic feature is the two white or yellowish spots, one above each shoulder blade; these are very distinct in some and less distinct in others, but always present in specimens from the Subregion. From the top of the head to near the shoulders the black spots tend to coalesce to form an irregular and, in some specimens, a distinct black line. The flanks and the lower part of the limbs are unspotted. The bushy tail shows a little dark spotting or banding towards the base, but is generally an uneven buffy-brown colour, darker to almost black towards the tip in some individuals. The upper parts of the body in some lights have a blackish sheen. The under parts are lighter in colour than the upper, and in some specimens are distinctly yellowish on the under parts of the front limbs and from the upper chest to the base of the tail. The feet are naked to the wrist and ankle respectively. The hair is soft and woolly and exceptionally dense. The individual hairs of the guard coat, which are about 15 mm long on the forehead, increase in length towards the rump where they measure about 30–35 mm. These have broad, dark-coloured bases and a broad whitish or buffy annulation, which shades to brown towards the black tip of the hair. Interspersed throughout the guard coat, on the upper parts and on the flanks, are long tactile hairs which are predominantly black and about 50 mm long. The underfur, like the guard coat, is particularly dense but is slightly greyer towards the bases of the hairs; on the rump the base of the hairs is tinged yellowish. The hairs of the guard coat on the tail are about 40 mm long, the whole liberally interspersed with black tactile hairs 50 mm long. The underfur is greyish, the bases of the individual hairs tinged yellow.

There are five digits on each foot armed with sharp, curved, protractile claws about 6 mm long, the first digits not marking in the spoor (Fig. 265.1). In the male there are two scent glands situated just in front of the penis. In the female these are sited in front of the vulva.

In size or mass there does not appear to be any noticeable difference between males and females, except that in the small series available, while the tails of the males are on average equal to the length of the head and body, those of the females are longer (Table 265.1).

### Skull (Fig 265.2)

The skull is very similar in shape to that of the two species of *Genetta*, elongated, with a short but broader rostrum. The

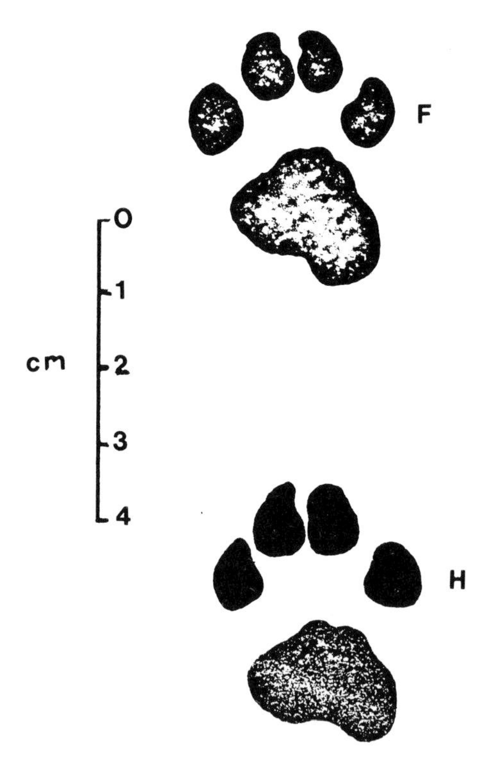


Fig. 265.1. Spoor: tree civet, *N. binotata*.
F. Right forefoot H. Right hind foot.

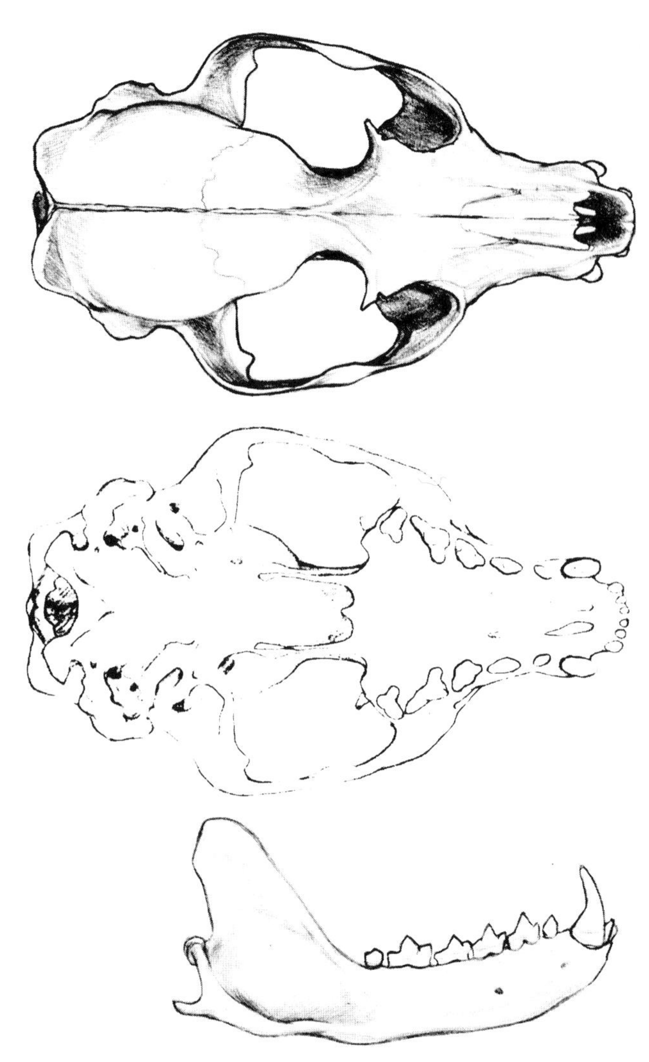

Fig.265.2. Skull: tree civet, *N. binotata*.
TL Skull 90 mm

whole bone structure, however, is heavier, the skull more robustly built. The postorbital constriction is markedly narrower than the interorbital; the postorbital bars are incomplete and represented by well developed supraorbital processes and smaller processes on the zygomatic arches.

The strongly developed supraoccipital crest slopes backward and is joined at right angles by the high sagittal crest, which may protrude from the braincase up to 5 mm in old individuals. It continues forward to the postorbital constriction, decreasing in height towards the front of the skull.

The posterior part of the ear bullae is unossified and is normally lost in the preparation of the skull. This feature is unique in extant mammals, although known in fossil forms. In other closely allied species in which the bullae are fully ossified, the paroccipital processes cover part of the posterior part of the bullae, but in *Nandinia*, as this section of the bullae is not ossified, they have no bone to attach to and consequently they are isolated and conspicuous and are a feature of the skull of this species.

The dental formula is:

$I\frac{3}{3}\ C\frac{1}{1}\ P\frac{4}{4}\ M\frac{1}{2} = 38$

In dealing with West African material, Rosevear (1974) gave the number of teeth as 40, there being two molars in the upper jaw, but in 14 specimens from eastern Zimbabwe the upper second molar is missing, no root sockets being present, and no other signs of it are visible on the bony plate which holds it. The outer upper incisors are more heavily built than the remainder, the lower less so. The lower incisors are bifid, the canines strongly developed and ridged longitudinally on both the inside and outside faces. The carnassials have well developed blades and are adapted to slicing, the upper with a well developed protocone. The posterior second molar in the lower jaw is tiny. The lower jaw is massive for the size of the species; the glenoid articulation is broad and deep, and the canines are more strongly curved than those in the upper jaw.

**Distribution**

Tree civets are confined in their distribution to Africa south of the Sahara, in various types of forest, and occur from Sierra Leone in West Africa to Kenya in East Africa and from there narrowly southward, occurring only marginally in the Subregion in the extreme northeast.

While it is possible to record the limits of distribution within which the species occurs, their occurrence within these limits depends on the availability of suitable habitat in the form of various types of forest. In parts, therefore, their distribution is discontinuous and patchy. This applies particularly to the eastern and southern parts of their range, for in the northern parts, apart from the Benin gap, the forest in which they occur forms a continuum over a very large part of their northern range.

*South of the Sahara, excluding the Southern African Subregion*

They occur from **Sierra Leone** to **Zaire** in suitable habitat; and in **Ghana; Nigeria** and **Cameroun**. They occur in the extreme western parts of **Kenya** at the northeastern corner of Lake Victoria and in **Uganda**. They occur in the extreme southwestern parts of the **Sudan** and in northeastern, eastern and southern **Tanzania** and from the Northern and Southern Provinces of **Malawi**. Sweeney (1959) drew attention to the deforestation of recent years and the extensive planting of conifers, which most likely has led to a shrinkage in their range. Deforestation in Mozambique and eastern Zimbabwe certainly has had the same effect. They occur in central and northern **Angola**, and from the extreme northwestern corner of **Zambia** in dry evergreen forest.

*Southern African Subregion*

In the eastern districts of **Zimbabwe** they occur narrowly along the border with Mozambique, from 18°45'S to 20°30'S, and in adjacent parts of **Mozambique**, with a record from near Vila Fontes (1734C), which suggests the possibil-

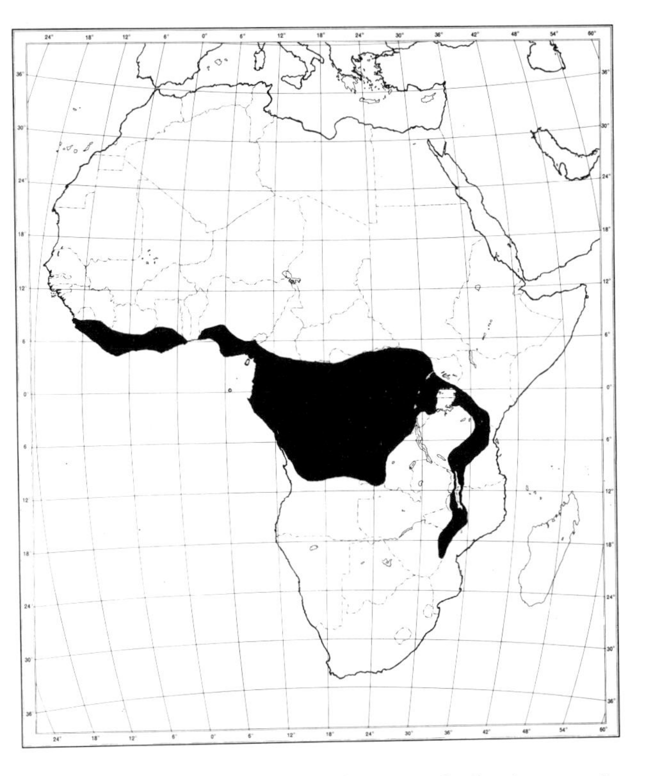

ity of a northeastern connection between the border records and their occurrence in Malawi.

## Habitat

Throughout their range tree civets are associated with forest. In Zimbabwe, they occur in montane and subtropical rain forest in areas of mean annual rainfall of 1 000 to 1 400 mm, associations which today are discontinuous and patchy.

## Habits

The tree civet in the southern parts of its range is solitary and nocturnal, seldom being seen until an hour or so after sundown and retiring to its daytime resting place before first light in the morning. Although predominantly arboreal and most often observed high in the canopy of forest trees 30 to 50 m and upwards from the ground, they have been trapped at ground level and therefore certainly exhibit some terrestrial activity. They have been observed to leap with agility from branch to branch of the canopy, running along these to escape the disturbance of a dazzling light. Thornycroft (1958) reported how one leapt to the ground at a steep angle, legs and tail fully outstretched, giving the impression of floating through the air, and making a perfect landing some distance from the tree. This process was repeated. Taylor (1970) ranked the tree civet as the most efficient at jumping of the African viverrids. Like genets, tree civets climb down trees head first, appearing as much at home whether going up or down. Taylor (1970) recorded how a tree civet, while walking along a branch, hugs the branch close to its body, the body held low, the base of the tail slightly elevated. The tail, which is long and heavy, is held higher than the horizontal or often vertically, the end curved downwards, acting as a balancing organ. When climbing up and down vertical branches it grips with both front feet and then moves both back feet in unison up to the front feet, and then repeats the process. During the day they sleep curled up. Ansell (1960a) recorded the finding of two juveniles asleep during the day in the top of a large tree in Zambia.

## Food

From meagre evidence the tree civet emerges as an omnivore, its principal food, however, being vegetable matter in the form of fruit and berries. However, little has been put on record concerning the food of the species.

In a series of 10 stomachs from Zimbabwe, vegetable matter had by far the highest percentage occurrence (Table 265.2). This included wild figs, *Ficus* spp, in five stomachs, rough-leaved corkwood, *Commiphora edulis*, and raisin bush berries, *Grewia* spp, in one stomach each. Guavas, which grow wild in the area in which the specimen was taken, occurred in one and unidentifiable pulp in another.

**Table 265.2**

Percentage occurrence of various food items in a series of 10 stomachs from tree civets, *N. binotata*, from Zimbabwe (Smithers, 1983)

| Food item | Percentage occurrence |
|---|---|
| Vegetable matter | 60 |
| Aves | 30 |
| Muridae | 10 |
| Isoptera | 10 |

Where individuals were taken in the act of raiding, there were remains of chicken feathers in two stomachs and the remains of a small turkey in one. In the one stomach containing Isoptera, the termite *Odontotermes* sp constituted the sole content of the stomach which was over half full. Coaton & Sheasby (1972) stated that these fungus-growing termites occur in leaf litter, on and in dead branches and fallen logs, and under soil canopies over the trunks of living trees.

The remains of a single specimen of the red veld rat, *Aethomys chrysophilus*, was found in one stomach and the toes and skin of a juvenile baboon, *Papio ursinus*, in another; the latter unusual item was presumably taken as carrion. One stomach contained the remains of a juvenile fruit bat, *Epomophorus* sp.

## Reproduction

The only published information appears to be the recording of a gravid female in July in eastern Zimbabwe which carried two small foetuses (Smithers & Wilson, 1979). In Zambia, Ansell (1960a) took a juvenile at about a month old in October. In captivity, Crandall (1964) reported a litter of two born in spring at the New York Zoological Gardens, and Zuckerman (1953) a similar event in Regent's Park, London.

# Subfamily VIVERRINAE

## Genus *Civettictis* Pocock, 1915

No. 266

## *Civettictis civetta* (Schreber, 1776)

## African civet
## Afrikaanse siwet

Plate 23

## Colloquial Name

The use of the name civet cat or *siwetkat* in literature and everyday use is incorrect. The African civet is a viverrid belonging to the mongoose Family and is only distantly related to cats, which belong to another Family, the felids. In fact, it is singularly unlike a cat in either its form or its habits. The name African civet is used to distinguish *C. civetta* from other species of civets.

## Taxonomic Notes

Petter (1969) concluded that the African civet had diverged so far from the main evolutionary line of other civet species on dentition alone that it justified separate generic status. Meester *et al.*, (1986) have adopted this view.

## Description

While individuals vary extremely in colour pattern throughout their range, no two being exactly alike, certain features such as the combination of black, grey and white pattern on the neck, head and ears and the black lower parts of the limbs, are common to all. Even these vary in the degree of whiteness, as opposed to grey, and the breadth of the black bands, which separate the white or grey areas on the head and neck.

In general, the head, ears and neck are clearly marked. A black band runs across the front of the face above the eyes. The black nostrils are outlined on either side by pure white patches which continue on to the upper lip. The chin and mid-throat are black. The forehead is whitish or grey. The front of the rounded ears are white, the back of the ears basally black, with distinct white tips. The forequarters from the top of the head onto the shoulders, and the upper parts of the forelimbs, are differentiated from the remainder of the body, being greyish or whitish with some rather indistinct spotting, contrasting with the more distinct pattern of the remainder of the body. Alternatively, the forequarters may show distinct transverse banding, running from the upper parts of the forelimbs across the top of the body to the upper parts of the forelimbs on the other side. In some specimens the lighter background colour is tinged rusty, especially on the shoulders and down the mid-back. A distinct white or grey neck stripe is a feature. This runs from behind the ear to the front of the shoulder, broadening posteriorly and bordered by black, above and below. Below this the whitish or greyish colour of the forehead continues broadly on to the side of the upper part of the neck.

The sides of the body from the chest to the base of the tail have a distinct pattern of black markings on a greyish or whitish background. The black markings take the form of irregular spots, rosettes or bands and no two specimens are exactly the same. The lower parts of the limbs are black, one of the few features of colour that seem to be common to all specimens examined.

The hair is long and coarse, especially so on the middle of the upper parts of the body where it forms, when erected in the threat display, a distinct crest extending from the forehead to the tip of the tail. The hair of this crest increases in length from the forehead posteriorly and reaches its maximum length of about 100 to 120 mm on the posterior parts of the back. The base of the hair is white or light grey, the remainder black. The under parts of the tail are broadly banded white or grey, the tip broadly black.

On average females have a greater mass than males, although in size they are very similar (Table 266.1). They have five toes on the fore and hind feet, the first toes set far back from the other four and not marking in the spoor, which characteristically shows the marks of the curved claws (Fig. 266.1).

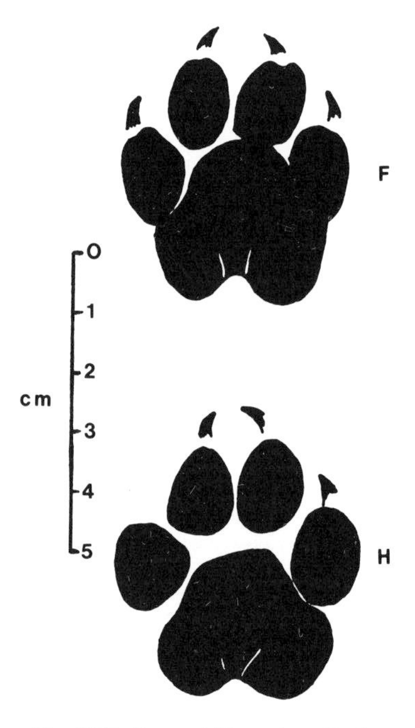


Fig. 266.1. Spoor: African civet, *C. civetta*. F. Right forefoot H. Right hind foot.

**Table 266.1**

Measurements (mm) and mass (kg) of African civets, *C. civetta*, from Zimbabwe (Smithers & Wilson, 1979)

| | Males | | | Females | | |
|---|---|---|---|---|---|---|
| | $\bar{x}$ | n | Range | $\bar{x}$ | n | Range |
| TL | 1296 | 8 | 1225–1374 | 1296 | 11 | 1250–1370 |
| T | 462 | 8 | 416–500 | 469 | 11 | 423–492 |
| Hf c/u | 140 | 8 | 135–148 | 139 | 11 | 130–148 |
| E | 58 | 8 | 55–60 | 58 | 11 | 54–63 |
| Mass | 10,92 | 8 | 9,53–13,17 | 11,58 | 11 | 9,65–12,71 |

**Skull** (Fig. 266.2)

The skull of the civet is elongated and heavily built; the braincase long and oval in shape, slightly narrower in front; the rostrum narrow. In profile the skull is curved evenly across the top and rather flat, there being little difference in height between its highest point, at the front of the braincase, the front end of the rostrum or the occipital part of the skull. The supraoccipital crest is markedly developed and heavy. The sagittal crest in adults is well developed and tapering in height, continuing forward across the top of the skull to near the front part of the braincase, where it divides into two low ridges which end at the supraorbital processes. These are broad and blunt, there being no postorbital bars, their lower ends represented by low blunt processes on the zygomatic arches. The zygomatic arch is heavy, giving a strong base for attachment of the masseter muscles which together with the temporalis muscles activate the lower jaw. The latter have a broad area of attachment on the lateral surfaces of the braincase and on the sagittal crest. Attached to the broad, high coronoid process of the lower jaw, the well developed temporalis muscle provides for a more than normally powerful bite. The lower jaw, in line with the rest of the skull, is heavily built.

The ear bullae are large and roughly oval, the front chambers much smaller and less in evidence than the hind which are rounded and swollen. The paroccipital processes, which lie at the back of the bullae, are well developed and closely enclose them; their points extend well beyond the bullae ventrally. The interorbital and intertemporal constrictions are not well marked.

The dental formula is:

$$I\frac{3}{3}\ C\frac{1}{1}\ P\frac{4}{4}\ M\frac{2}{2} = 40$$

The outer upper incisors are enlarged to assist the canines in holding prey and are set apart from the rest of the incisors. The canines are short but heavily built and rounded, their outer faces smooth. All the cheekteeth are heavy, the first and second upper molars, particularly the first, much larger and broader than in other members of the Family. The second molar in the lower jaw is well developed, broad and flat-faced. The fourth upper premolar and first lower molar, which together form the carnassial shear, show no adaptation to slicing as in other carnivores. The teeth are blunt and broad for crushing, an adaptation to the omnivorous diet of the species.

**Distribution**

*South of the Sahara, excluding the Southern African Subregion*

The African civet is confined to Africa, south of the Sahara, and has a distribution from **Senegal** through all the other West African countries eastwards to **Ethiopia**. Southwards it occurs in the extreme southern part of **Somalia**; in **Kenya; Uganda; Zaire; Angola; Tanzania; Zambia** and **Mozambique**, north of the Zambezi River.

*Southern African Subregion*

In **Botswana** they are confined to parts of the eastern border areas with the Transvaal and Zimbabwe, occurring throughout the Okavango Delta, south to about 20 °S and westwards to the Namibian border. In **Namibia** they are confined to the northeastern and eastern parts of the country, south to about 21 °S. Coetzee (*in litt.*) reported that the State Museum, Windhoek, Namibia has a specimen from Florine Farm 499 (2419D4) taken in 1974 which is far outside the present known limits of distribution. It appeared from spoor that two individuals were involved, and their occurrence caused

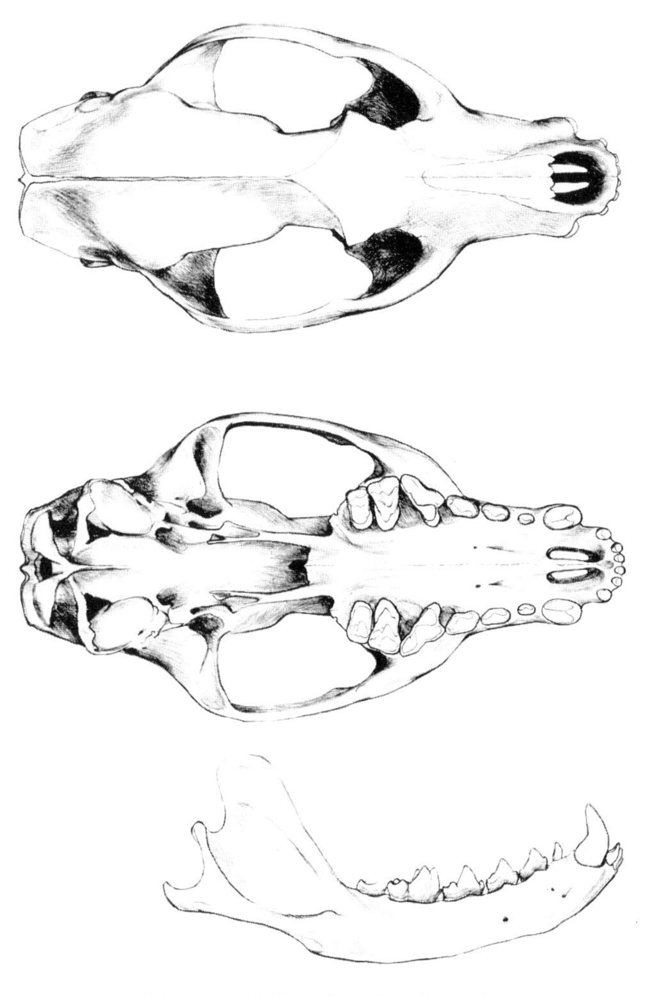

Fig. 266.2. Skull: African civet, *C. civetta*.
TL Skull 155 mm

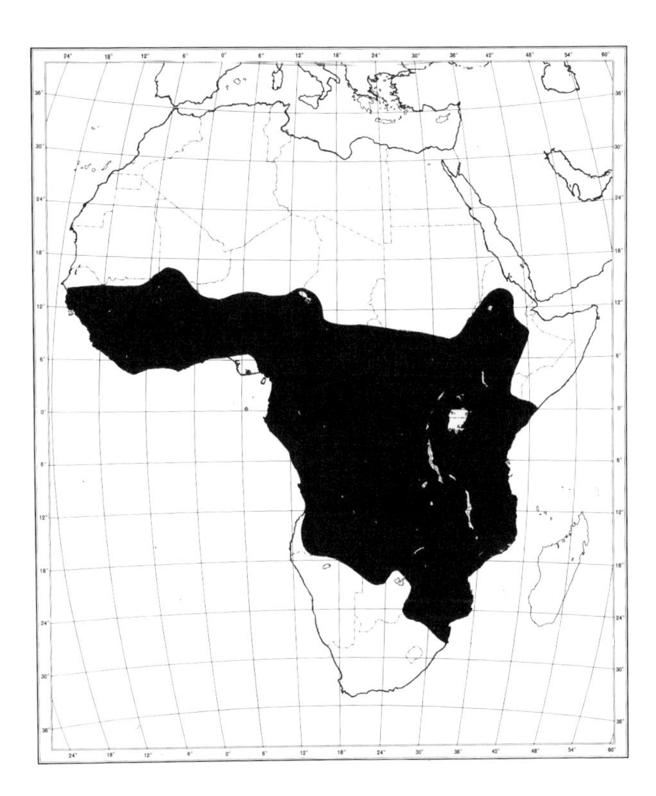

interest as they were previously unknown there. Coetzee stated that it remains to be proved whether an endemic population exists and that their normal range extends southwards, or whether the years of high rainfall have provided conditions for range extension. There are records from southern **Mozambique**. The species occurs throughout **Zimbabwe**. In the remainder of the Subregion it has a restricted distribution. It is confined to the central, northern and eastern parts of the **Transvaal** and there are reports of their occurrence in the extreme northeastern parts of **Natal**.

## Habitat

They occur in forest throughout their range in the Subregion, where they are confined to well-watered savanna, not occurring in the dry western and southern areas. In the Subregion they are found up to 1 650 m. They will drink when water is available, but they do not appear to be dependent on it. Well-watered areas provide good cover in the form of underbush and, in particular, more trees and shrubs that provide succulent fruit and high populations of insects, resources which are essential habitat requirements for civets. While they occur in the *Brachystegia/Julbernardia* woodland of Zimbabwe, they are commoner where there is permanent water.

## Habits

Civets are terrestrial, solitary and predominantly nocturnal, and are active just before sunrise and for a short time thereafter. Randall (1977) showed that the peak of activity takes place from one to two hours after sunset, gradually tailing off towards midnight, after which activity generally ceases. They are poor climbers, but are known to clamber along low stout branches of fig trees to get at the ripening fruit. Otherwise they rely on the natural fall of ripe fruit or on other mammals and birds pulling it off or knocking it to the ground for them. It is unusual to see more than one, although family parties consisting of an adult and two young have been observed. Great use is made of paths and roads along which they move slowly and purposefully, characteristically with the head held low. When disturbed suddenly, civets will either flatten and lie still or stand motionless. On such occasions Randall (1977) found that two defence strategies may be adopted, either the individual will slink off, or it will remain lying and hiding, and allow the observer to approach to within a few metres before exploding out of hiding and bounding away. It appeared that under these circumstances the individual was relying on its camouflage to avoid early detection. Ewer & Wemmer (1974) stated that piloerection occurs mainly as a defensive threat. In free-ranging individuals it is accompanied by a sideways turn of the body so that the whole spectacular erection of the 100 mm hair is fully visible to the opponent.

Some individuals in traps give a low threatening growl and, if sudden movements are made, a loud coughing spit. Ewer & Wemmer (1974) listed, among other vocalisations, a scream given during the course of fighting, teeth-clicking when an individual snaps at another, the mewing by the young, or other types of miaowing during copulation or by the female during oestrus. They also recorded a contact call which can be imitated by saying *ha-ha-ha* with the lips closed. In the wild, however, civets are quiet and when observed moving or feeding at night they do so silently, and on sensing danger, move off quietly without vocalisation or at most with a low "wuff". Ewer & Wemmer (1974) found that their senses of smell and hearing are acute.

Civets deposit their faeces at latrines or civetries. Randall (1974) found that these normally are located adjacent to paths and roads, some used frequently and then abandoned for periods up to several months. Even when the accumulation of scats is removed, they tend to use the original site. In his study area in the eastern Transvaal, these were located in hollows in clearings or at the edge of clearings, although in Zimbabwe they were found in *Asparagus* thickets, in grassland and in the cover of dense reed beds. Civetries are communal and may be used by a number of individuals.

Civets mark smooth-surfaced objects along the routes they normally use, backing up to their objects and applying a secretion from the everted perineal glands. This secretion retains its smell and can be detected over periods of up to three months. This secretion, known to the trade as "civet", was collected at one time from captive individuals for use in the perfume trade, but has been replaced largely by synthetics now (Rosevear, 1974).

## Food

From the examination of stomach contents recorded by various authors (Bothma, 1965, 1971; Smithers, 1971; Rosevear, 1974; Wilson, 1975) and more general remarks by others (Shortridge, 1934; Stevenson-Hamilton, 1957; Maberly, 1955; Pienaar, 1964; Neal, 1971, and Pienaar, Rautenbach & de Graaff, 1980) the civet emerges as an omnivorous feeder.

Analysis of a sample of 27 stomach contents from Zimbabwe reveals that insects, wild fruit, murids, reptiles, birds, Amphibia, Myriapoda, Araneae, in that order of percentage occurrence, constituted the food of this sample (Table 266.2). Most of these specimens were taken in the Harare District on a series of farms, where the availability of carrion is minimal. Where carrion is more freely available it is made wider use of as a food resource (Randall, 1977).

**Table 266.2a**

Percentage occurrence of various food items in a sample of 27 stomach contents from civets, *C. civetta*, in Zimbabwe (Smithers & Wilson, 1979)

| Item | Percentage occurrence |
|---|---|
| Insects | 59 |
| Wild fruit | 52 |
| Murids | 41 |
| Reptiles | 22 |
| Birds | 15 |
| Amphibia | 11 |
| Myriapoda | 11 |
| Araneae | 4 |
| Pisces | 4 |
| Green grass | 22 |

Insects, which had the highest percentage occurrence, consisted predominantly of grasshoppers and adult beetles. Beetle grubs occurred as a trace only. These have to be dug up and the feet and claws of the civet are ill-adapted to this function, compared with other mongoose such as the white-tailed, *Ichneumia albicauda*, or the suricate, *Suricata suricatta*, with their long front claws. Tenebrionidae, Scarabeidae and Cerambycidae were all represented, most of the specimens of medium to large size. Isoptera were represented by *Hodotermes* sp and *Macrotermes* sp, both of which forage on the ground surface and do not need to be dug up. The Lepidoptera were not identified, but consisted of the remains of moths and butterflies together with "bagworms" (Table 266.2b).

**Table 266.2b**

Insects identified

| Item | Percentage occurrence |
|---|---|
| Orthoptera | 26 |
| Coleoptera | 26 |
| Isoptera | 15 |
| Lepidoptera | 11 |
| Formicidae | 4 |
| Undet. | 26 |

**Table 266.2c**

Wild fruits identified

| Item | Percentage occurrence |
|---|---|
| *Ficus* spp | 8 |
| *Uapaca kirkiana* | 8 |
| *Pseudolachnostylis maprouneifolia* | 4 |
| *Diospyros mespiliformis* | 4 |
| *Parinari curatellifolia* | 4 |
| *Ziziphus mucronata* | 4 |
| Undet. | 26 |
| Cape gooseberry, *Physalis peruviana* | 4 |

Wild fruits, the second highest on a percentage occurrence basis, are an important food resource. In addition to those listed here (Table 266.2c), Randall (1977) provided a much more extended list from the eastern Transvaal, including:

Marula, *Sclerocarya birrea*
Raisin bush, *Grewia* spp
Guarri, *Euclea* spp
Bird plum, *Berchemia discolor*
Milkberry, *Manilkara mochisia*
False marula, *Lannea stuhlmannii*
Wild vine, *Cissus cornifolia*
Wild date palm, *Phoenix reclinata*
Monkey pod, *Cassia petersiana*

Maberly (1955) included the bridelia, *Bridelia* sp, and Smithers & Wilson (1979) the Cape gooseberry, *Physalis peruviana*. The high occurrence of mahobohobo, *Uapaca kirkiana*, in the sample (Table 266.2c) reflects the ready availability of this species on frost-free hillsides in the Harare District, Zimbabwe, from where the bulk of the sample was taken. Cape gooseberries have become well established in the wild in this area, along stream banks and in grain lands in valleys (Smithers, 1983).

Murids were represented by multimammate mice, *Mastomys* spp, at an occurrence of 18%. Common and ubiquitous, they are the most freely available murid species. The Angoni vlei rat, *Otomys angoniensis*, ranked next at 11%, a species which has restricted habitat requirements, being confined generally to damp areas along streams, wet vleis and swamp, areas frequented by civets in their search for food. The pouched mouse, *Saccostomus campestris*, and the pygmy mouse, *Mus minutoides*, occurred, but at much lower percentages (Table 266.2d). Reptiles included snakes and lizards which, at an occurrence of 22%, ranked high among the food utilised (Table 266.2e). Birds, at an occurrence of 15%, were represented by francolin, *Francolinus* sp, the turtle dove, *Streptopelia capicola*, and laughing dove, *S. senegalensis*. Amphibia at an occurrence of 11%, consisted predominantly of the common African toad, *Bufo regularis*, the red toad, *B. carens*, and the clawed toad, *Xenopus laevis*. Araneae were represented by portions of legs and chitinous remains of large unidentifiable spiders.

**Table 266.2d**

Murids identified

| Species | Percentage occurrence |
|---|---|
| Multimammate mice, *Mastomys* spp | 18 |
| Angoni vlei rat, *Otomys angoniensis* | 11 |
| Pouched mouse, *Saccostomus campestris* | 4 |
| Pygmy mouse, *Mus minutoides* | 4 |
| Undet. | 4 |

**Table 266.2e**

Reptiles identified

| Species | Percentage occurrence |
|---|---|
| **Sauria** | |
| Agama, *Agama* spp | 8 |
| Common striped skink, *Mabuya striata* | 4 |
| Limbless skink, *Typhlosaurus cregoi* | 4 |
| **Serpentes** | |
| Cape centipede eater, *Aparallactus capensis* | 4 |

**Note**: In specimens from Mozambique the spiny agama, *Agama hispida*, and the variable skink, *Mabuya varia*, were identifiable. Bothma (1971) included the rock leguaan, *Varanus exanthematicus*, and the blind snake, *Typhlops schlegelii*.

Randall (1977) showed that millipedes occur very commonly in civet diet, yet in the Zimbabwe sample the percentage occurrence was only 7%, a further 3% being the remains of centipedes, *Scolopendra morsitans*.

Fish remains occurred at 4%, but whether this was in the form of carrion could not be ascertained. Ewer & Wemmer (1974) showed that captive civets do not hesitate to put their faces in water to catch small fish, picking them out with a scooping bite.

The folded-up remains of broad-leafed grass are a feature of civet scats in latrines, in some cases constituting practically the whole mass of the individual scat. At an occurrence of 22% it is apparently an important item, probably ingested more for its mechanical action than as an item of food. Randall (1977) showed that there is a tendency for grass in scats to be related to the eating of snakes, and to a lesser degree, frogs. In stomach contents it is possible, in many cases, to see that this broad-leafed grass has been eaten whilst still green.

A breakdown of the food on a seasonal basis, October to April, the warm, wet summer months, as opposed to May to September, the colder, drier months, reveals changes in the principal food resources utilised (Table 266.3). Generally available throughout the year, the occurrence of murids remains fairly static, noticeable changes being in the utilisation of Reptilia, Amphibia and Insecta, which are less in evidence during May to September, the dry, colder months of the year. Myriapoda are not available at all during this period except to species equipped to dig for them. While some wild fruits are available during all the summer months, there is a peak of availability during the latter part of the cold, dry season from May to September, reflected in the slightly higher percentage occurrence during this period. Randall (1975) found that green grass was taken as frequently in winter as in summer, a fact with which these figures agree. Randall (1977) recorded a highly significant seasonal occurrence of herbivore stomach contents and faeces in scats, concluding that these are purposefully taken.

**Table 266.3**

Comparison of the percentage occurrence of the principal food items on a seasonal basis in a sample of 27 stomach contents from civets, *C. civetta*, in Zimbabwe (Smithers, 1983)

| Item | Percentage occurrence | |
|---|---|---|
| | October to April | May to September |
| Insecta | 70 | 43 |
| Wild fruit | 40 | 57 |
| Muridae | 30 | 43 |
| Reptilia | 30 | 14 |
| Aves | 10 | 21 |
| Amphibia | 20 | 7 |
| Myriapoda | 20 | — |
| Green grass | 20 | 21 |

Although not represented in the Zimbabwe sample, both Maberly (1955) and Randall (1977) recorded scrub hares, *Lepus saxatilis*, as being taken by civets, the former showing that the civet had considerable difficulty in accomplishing the kill. Randall (1977) included banded mongoose, *Mungos mungo*, and slender mongoose, *Galerella sanguinea*, Stevenson-Hamilton (1957) a domestic cat, and Bothma (1965) guinea fowl. It is unlikely that civets could deal with larger live prey, in spite of the statements that have appeared in print expressing the view that they will take the newly-born young of antelopes (Stevenson-Hamilton, 1957; Shortridge, 1934; Bothma, 1971). As carrion, however, the remains of impala, *Aepyceros melampus*, kudu, *Tragelaphus strepsiceros*, bushbuck, *T. scriptus*, and wildebeest, *C. taurinus*, are recorded by Randall (1977). The dentition of the civet is not adapted specifically for dealing with tough food and they have difficulty in dealing even with large rats (Ewer & Wemmer, 1974). The side to side chewing has to be continued for lengthy periods before they are reduced to a suitable state for swallowing and the alternate method of holding down the food with the front paws while tearing off parts with the teeth has to be employed.

The civet does not pluck birds and, in dealing with large species, holds them down and pulls the flesh from the body. The techniques used in prey capture, while clearly not as efficient as those of the felids, are nevertheless sufficient to deal with the type of prey normally utilised.

Prey capture takes a number of forms (Ewer & Wemmer, 1974), a runaway bite delivered on any part of the prey's body, followed by release and retreat, or a bite and throw, where the prey is held long enough to be thrown aside with a quick action of the head, this often accomplished by a quick leap in the air. In the bite and shake, the grip is retained and the prey shaken with violence so as to break the vertebrae. This technique is frequently used with snakes; the prey is thrown down and the civet leaps aside to avoid the chance of being bitten. In the killing bite the grip is retained, the jaws biting home firmly and repeatedly without total withdrawal of the teeth. Occasionally this is more deliberate; the bite is aimed at the head and is accompanied by shaking.

While fish, frogs and aquatic insects are caught under water, the civet does not dunk its food as is commonly observed in clawless otters, *Aonyx capensis*, or water mongoose, *Atilax paludinosus*.

Insects are freely available during the warm, wet summer months, and have the highest percentage occurrence, being replaced by other food resources during the cold, dry months.

**Reproduction**

Records of time of births are sparse, but this may occur during the warm, wet summer months. In the Republic of South Africa there are records from November and December (Pienaar, 1964); August and October (Stevenson-Hamilton, 1950); October (Maberly, 1955); August, November and December (Fairall, 1968), based predominantly on the sightings of juveniles. In Botswana and Zimbabwe gravid females were recorded in the months of October, December and January, with sightings of juveniles under 1,8 kg in December and January and at 1 kg in May (Smithers & Wilson, 1979), suggesting that the birth season may well extend later into the summer months.

Litters consist of two to four young, born in disused antbear, *Orycteropus afer*, holes, or in the shelter of piles of rocks or other similar situations, affording substantial cover.

At any early stage of development (150–200 g) the foetus clearly shows the pelage pattern which will be perpetuated in the adult. While there is a close similarity in these markings within members of a litter, they vary tremendously between litters. There is wide variation in the pelage pattern. In members of a litter of four from Botswana the forequarters show the black transverse bands, the posterior part of the body being distinctly black spotted with some narrow transverse bars.

## Genus *Genetta* G. Cuvier, 1816

Roberts (1951) recognised four species as occurring in the Subregion: *G. genetta; G. tigrina; G. rubiginosa* and *G. mossambica*. Coetzee (1977) in reviewing the African species recognised the occurrence of *G. genetta* (Linnaeus, 1758) in the Subregion, but regarded the status of the other three species (Roberts, 1951) as uncertain. He dealt with these three species under *G. tigrina sensu latu* (in its broadest sense) under three sections: a. the *tigrina* section which includes *G. tigrina* (Schreber, 1778); b. the *rubiginosa* section which includes *G. t. rubiginosa* Pucheran, 1855; and c. the *mossambica* section, which includes *G. (tigrina?) mossambica* Matschie, 1902.

With material from the northern parts of Botswana and Zimbabwe, it is possible, on the basis of Cabral's (1970) findings from material from Angola, that what we have considered as *G. tigrina* might in these areas include both *G. pardina* I. Geoffroy, 1832 and *G. angolensis* Bocage, 1882. For purposes of this work *G. genetta* (Linnaeus, 1758) and *G. tigrina* (Schreber, 1778) as a group are recognised. Nevertheless, there is a need for a detailed study of members of this genus, especially in the southern parts of its distributional range.

The acknowledgement of the generic name *Genetta* to G. Cuvier, 1816 arises from Opinion No. 417, 1956 of the International Commission for Zoological Nomenclature which ruled that Okens, 1816 name was not available.

Key to the species *G. genetta* and the *G. tigrina* group of species in the Subregion (after Meester *et al.*, 1986)

1. Small-spotted; tail-tip white; hind feet black; distinct crest of long black hair forming an erectile crest from shoulders to base of tail, hair of crest 44–70 mm long ... *genetta*

   Larger-spotted; tail-tip black; hind feet not black; dorsal crest lacking or at best poorly developed, hair of crest less than 43 mm long ... *tigrina*

No. 267

## *Genetta genetta* Linnaeus, 1758

## Small-spotted genet
## Kleinkolmuskejaatkat

Plate 23

### Colloquial Name

While the spots on the body of this species are in general smaller than those on the body of genets of the *G. tigrina* group, there are exceptions to this. The same can be said of the colour of the spots which are usually black, but are sometimes black-tinged or fringed with rusty, and even in some totally rusty in colour.

The name small-spotted genet has been in use for a very long time and is well entrenched, although not entirely appropriate. It would have been better if the colloquial name had been applied to the dorsal crest possessed by the small-spotted genet, which is lacking in genets of the *G. tigrina* group in the Subregion.

### Taxonomic Notes

Cabral (1969) in his review of the genus in Angola showed that *G. genetta* occurs in three discrete distributional blocks: in North Africa; West to East Africa, and in the southern parts of the continent, a view with which Ansell (1968) agreed, and one which is accepted for purposes of this review. Rüppell (1936) expressed the view that a single species ranges from Europe to the Cape. Whatever the situation in other parts of the continent may be or what more extensive study may reveal, the fact remains that specimens from Spain, the type locality of *G. g. genetta* Linnaeus, 1758, and individuals from parts of the Subregion are so similar that it is not difficult to believe that *G. genetta* has indeed the range stated by Rüppell. Coetzee (1977a) listed five subspecies, two of which occur in the Subregion: *G. g. felina* (Thunberg, 1911) in the mountainous areas of the Cape Province, south of the Orange River, and *G. g. pulchra* Matschie, 1902, throughout the remainder of the distributional range in the Subregion, with an extension of range into Angola, Zambia and Mozambique, south of the Zambezi River.

### Description

The small-spotted genet is a short-legged species with an elongated body and a white-ringed tail which is about the same length as the head and body. The body is spotted, with a dark central dorsal band from just behind the shoulders to the base of the tail. The muzzle is pointed and the ears are upstanding and rounded.

The background colour of the body varies from almost pure white in specimens from the western drier parts of the range, to white tinged with buff or off-white from the eastern parts. The spots and bars on the upper parts are dark in colour, never completely black. These are usually tinged rusty or sometimes entirely rusty in the lighter coloured specimens. No two specimens are exactly alike. Two distinct black bands arise from near the inner edges of the ears and swing downwards over the front of the shoulders. A further two indistinct bands extend from the back of the neck towards the flanks, usually breaking up into spots or short bars and may continue downwards behind the shoulders. Sometimes a third pair of bands, usually indistinct and broken, arises on top of the shoulders, soon giving way to a line of spots. The spots on the flanks tend to run in irregular lines along the body to the hindquarters.

A characteristic feature of the species is the distinct, usually jet black band which arises just behind the shoulders on the mid-back and continues onto the base of the tail. The hair of this band is much longer and coarser than the hair on the rest of the upper parts. When the individual is under stress, this can be erected at will to form a high, upstanding crest.

Characteristic features of the face are the distinct white patches under the eyes and the black patches at the base of the vibrissae. In addition there are usually two indistinct white bands on the inner side of the eyes, running on to the forehead. The black patches at the base of the vibrissae continue along the upper lip around the mouth to the black chin, which often has an indistinct white median patch.

The front limbs are usually darker than the background colour of the upper parts and sometimes have small spots, especially near the body. The hind limbs are spotted on the upper half but distinctly suffused with black on the lower parts, especially from the ankle to the feet. The upper parts of the feet are lighter. In some specimens this black suffusion broadly encircles the ankle. The long tail has about eight encircling white bands and a white tip; these white bands are sometimes rusty-tinged on top. The under parts of the body, in the lighter coloured specimens, are white, with some spotting on the lower chest and upper belly, or greyer in the darker specimens.

The hair of the guard coat is rather coarse and wiry; the hair on the face is short, about 8 mm, and increases in length towards the hindquarters, where it reaches about 30–35 mm. The individual hairs are either dark or rusty-tipped on the bars and spots, or white or off-white on the remainder of the upper parts. The hair on the dorsal crest is about 45 mm long just behind the shoulders, increasing to 75 mm on the hindquarters. The dense underfur is greyish, darker on the spots and bars. The hair on the base of the tail is about 65 mm long, tapering off to about 35 mm at the tip.

The sharp, curved, protractile claws on the front feet are light coloured and similar to those on the hind. There are five digits to each foot, the first digit on each set back from the remainder. The first digits do not mark in the spoor (Fig. 267.1).

There is a pair of large scent glands, in males situated just behind the penis, in females behind the vulva. These open in a longitudinally orientated, Y-shaped slit. Under stress or in marking the secretion has a heavy musky smell which is very persistent.

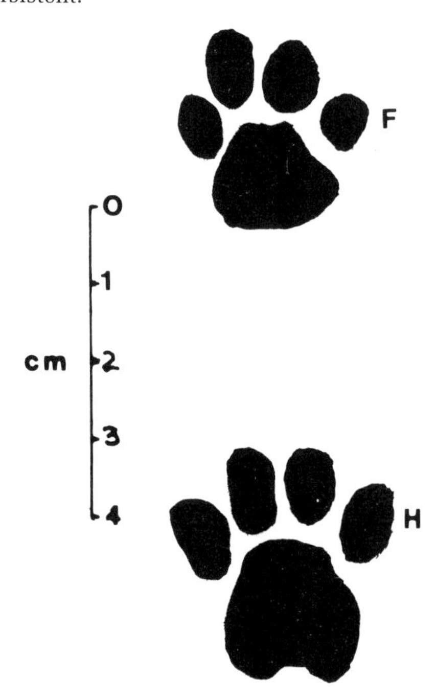


Fig. 267.1. Spoor: small-spotted genet, *G. genetta*. F. Right forefoot H. Right hind foot.

There does not appear to be any noticeable difference in size between males and females, but specimens from Botswana appear larger than those from Zimbabwe (Table 267.1).

**Table 267.1**

Measurements (mm) and mass (kg) of small spotted genets, *G. genetta*, from (a) Zimbabwe (Smithers & Wilson, 1979) and (b) Botswana (Smithers, 1971)

**(a)**

| | Males | | | Females | | |
|---|---|---|---|---|---|---|
| | $\bar{x}$ | n | Range | $\bar{x}$ | n | Range |
| TL | 943 | 22 | 890–1 030 | 917 | 14 | 890–952 |
| T | 461 | 22 | 435–510 | 443 | 14 | 408–469 |
| Hf s/u | 88 | 23 | 80–97 | 87 | 14 | 82–91 |
| E | 51 | 20 | 40–57 | 54 | 13 | 50–60 |
| Mass | 1,8 | 16 | 1,6–2,61 | 1,9 | 13 | 1,5–2,3 |

**(b)**

| | Males | | | Females | | |
|---|---|---|---|---|---|---|
| | $\bar{x}$ | n | Range | $\bar{x}$ | n | Range |
| TL | 953 | 42 | 860–1 050 | 936 | 12 | 890–1 024 |
| T | 464 | 42 | 430–516 | 459 | 12 | 417–516 |
| Hf s/u | 90 | 37 | 82–97 | 88 | 11 | 83–92 |
| E | 54 | 35 | 50–60 | 55 | 12 | 51–65 |
| Mass | 2,0 | 20 | 1,8–2,3 | 1,8 | 10 | 1,5–2,2 |

**Skull** (Fig. 267.2)

In fully adult specimens with well worn teeth, the skull of the small-spotted genet, *G. genetta*, in profile rises to its maximum height at the level of the ear openings, sloping abruptly backwards to the supraoccipital crest and gently forwards to the nasals. The nasals are concave at the level of the first upper premolar, and at the postorbital constriction there is a slight dip.

The cranium is ovoid, broadest at the level of the back of the zygomatic arches and narrowing to the postorbital constriction, which is slightly broader than the interorbital. The rostrum is narrow and elongated; the breadth, at its broadest point, is about half the distance between the front of the eye orbits and the incisors.

The zygomatic arches are lightly built, with no sign of the lower processes of the postorbital bars which, on the temporal region, are reduced to blunt extensions of the bone. In a sample of 46 male and 33 female skulls, the supraoccipital crest is well developed, sloping slightly backwards and rising to a maximum height of about 4 mm from the cranium. The sagittal crest, at its greatest development is about 3 mm high, and extends from the supraoccipital crest on to the back of the braincase, tailing out completely at this point. In some specimens the sagittal crest, while tailing out at the back of the braincase, is discernible, although barely so, as two low ridges which run forward to the temporal region and which broaden out on top of the braincase, leaving an oval smooth area devoid of muscle attachments. The ear bullae are elongated; the greatest width of the bullae is about 40% of the length. The anterior chamber is only slightly less developed than the posterior.

The dental formula is:

$I\frac{3}{3}\ C\frac{1}{1}\ P\frac{4}{4}\ M\frac{2}{2} = 40$

The outer upper incisors are slightly longer than the remainder, the upper canines curved and sharp, with two longitudinal grooves on the inner and outer faces near the tip of the teeth. The outer cusps on the upper fourth premolar are sectorial, the outer anterior cusp bifid. The second upper molar is small in comparison with the first. The space between the interpterygoid processes is narrow, and, while bulging outward at about its mid-point, is more nearly parallel-sided than in the *G. tigrina* group.

The inner cusp of the third upper premolar was present in 42 out of 45 male skulls, being absent altogether in one and barely perceptible in two, and was present in all 33 female skulls. Its development varies from a tiny to a very well developed and obvious cusp.

**Distribution**

Outside the continent of Africa the small-spotted genet occurs in Spain, France and in parts of Germany, Switzerland and Belgium, as well as in the Balearic Islands (Eller-

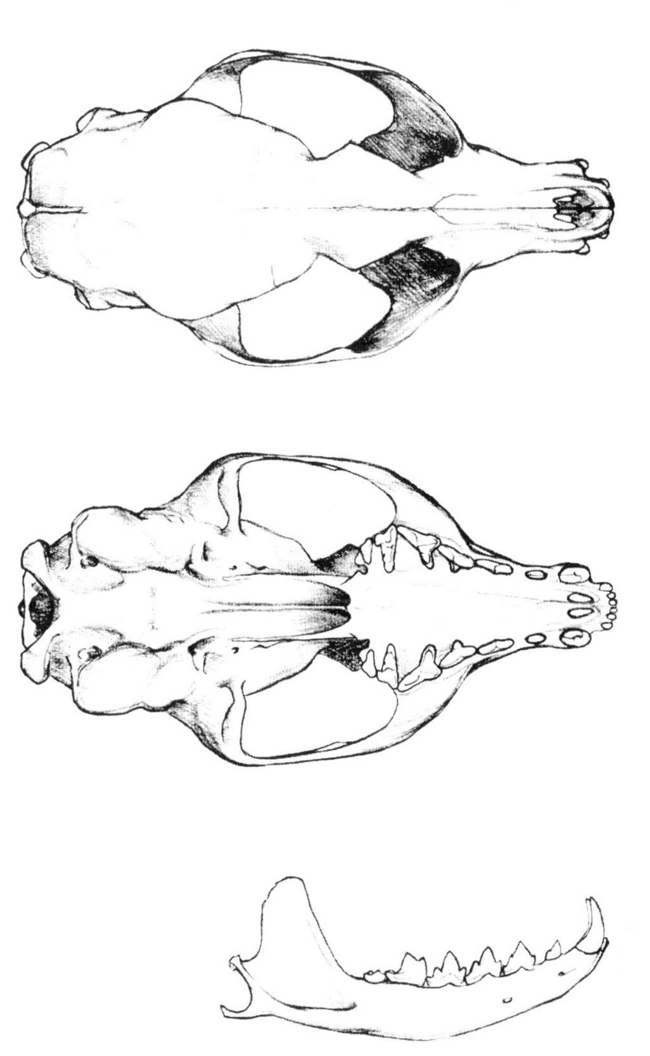

Fig. 267.2. Skull: small-spotted genet, *G. genetta*. TL Skull 90 mm

man & Morrison-Scott, 1951). Harrison (1968) listed specimens from Israel, South Arabia and the Yemen.

*North Africa*

They occur in **Morocco, Algeria** and **Tunisia**; in northwestern coastal **Libya** and narrowly inland in the Gharian area.

*South of the Sahara, excluding the Southern African Subregion*

They occur in **Senegal; Nigeria**, north of about 10°N; the northeastern **Sudan** and from the coast of the Red Sea. They are widespread in **Ethiopia**; they are found throughout the southern parts of **Somalia** and along the coast. They are recorded from **Uganda**, where they are stated to be less common than in **Kenya**, where they are widespread. There are a number of records from **Tanzania**, all these, however, being from north of 9°S. Southwest of Tanzania there is a break in distribution, the nearest records in a southwest direction being from the Zambezi Valley in **Zambia**. They occur in the eastern parts of **Angola** from just north of Luanda, narrowly southwards, coastally, and in the southwestern and southern central parts of the country.

*Southern African Subregion*

They are widespread in **Namibia**, excluding the Namib Desert, and in **Botswana**. In **Zimbabwe** they occur throughout the western and southern sectors and on the central plateau east to the Harare District, being replaced eastwards by the *G. tigrina* group. In **Mozambique** they only occur south of the Save River in the more arid western areas, adjacent to the Zimbabwe and Transvaal borders. In the **Republic of South Africa** they are widespread, excluding most of Natal, Swaziland, the eastern parts of Lesotho and the extreme eastern parts of the Cape Province, east of about

28 °E and the forested coastal area of the southern parts of the country.

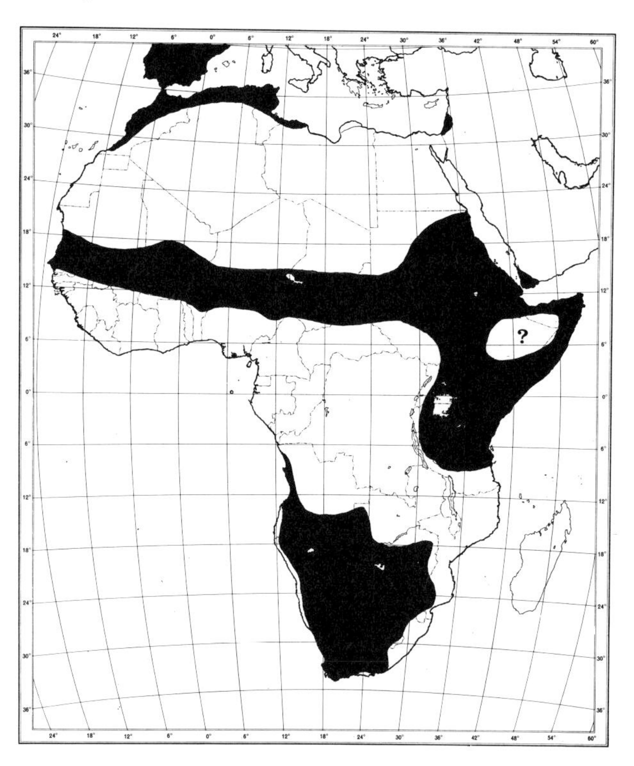


## Habitat

In the greater part of their distributional range, small-spotted genets occur in open, arid associations, conditions in which group genets do not occur. In the Subregion they occur widely, both in parts of the Southern Savanna Zone and in the South West Arid Zone. Where they occur in woodland savanna, they tend to utilise the more open areas of woodland and dry grassland or the dry vlei areas that form a mosaic with the woodland. Their distribution shows that they occur in rainfall areas lower than 100 mm, and up to about 800 mm. Essential habitat requirements include cover, in the form of scrub or underbush, or holes in the ground or in trees in which to shelter during daylight hours. They are independent of a water supply. In the eastern parts of the Subregion, where the mean annual rainfall is higher than in the west, they are replaced by the group genets. Taking a broad transect across the Subregion from Namibia to Mozambique this is illustrated clearly.

## Habits

The small-spotted genet is a strictly nocturnal species. In Botswana where they are very common, the earliest sightings were just after dark, at 19h00, with records through until 02h00. Most records are of solitary individuals or two together. While they are proficient climbers and will take to trees voluntarily when hunting or under stress, most of their activities are on the ground and they therefore are accounted as a terrestrial species. In parts of their range, as for example in Namibia and Botswana, there are no trees for them in which to take refuge and they use holes in the ground in which to rest during daylight hours, or to hide in under stress. Resting places include hollow logs and holes in trees, and they have been disturbed from underbush cover, an individual in Botswana being found among the branches of a thick, low *Acacia* bush, where debris had been trapped. In western Zimbabwe and Botswana they are known to use the shelter of piles of boulders and disused antbear and springhaas holes. In Botswana they use holes in calcareous cliffs that are a feature of the fringes of Kalahari pans. They make no attempt to adjust holes in the ground to their requirements, the claws being ill-adapted to digging, nor do they carry in bedding material. The type of shelter used is very similar to the observations made by Delibes (1974) on the species in Spain. Movement on the ground can be rapid. The body is held low, the tail trailing out horizontally behind. Normal movement is at a fast trot, the body and tail held in a similar position. When stalking prey, movement can be very slow until a favourable position is reached for the final rush in to the kill.

## Food

In an analysis of the contents of a sample of 107 stomachs from Zimbabwe and Botswana, the largest mammal recorded was the house rat, *Rattus rattus*, which averages just over 100 g; the largest bird, a turtle dove, *Streptopelia capicola*, with a mass of about 50 g. The species is perfectly capable of dealing with small hares and probably young guineafowl as well, but there is no clear evidence of their tackling the adults. When raiding poultry, they tend to take the younger birds, leaving the adults alone.

When dealing with all prey, the action is a stalk and pounce, or rush in to kill. The prey is grabbed with the sharp claws of the forelimbs and bitten repeatedly at any convenient part of the body without releasing it. There is no sign of the well-oriented neck bite characteristic of the felids. If the prey is not killed quickly, however, they will throw themselves on their side in cat-like fashion, and rake the prey into submission with the back claws, and when it is nearly dead, will crush the head with a few bites. With birds, everything is eaten including the beak and legs, except some feathers that may be loosened in the process. With all types of vertebrates the prey is chopped into sections convenient for swallowing without any great degree of mastication, which makes its identification easier.

Analysis of 107 stomachs from Zimbabwe and 78 from Botswana taken through the year, shows a close measure of agreement between the relative percentages of the food items: the five major food items, Insecta, Muridae, Arachnida, Aves and Reptilia occurring in that order of priority (Table 267.2).

### Table 267.2a

Percentage occurrence of various food items in the stomach contents of 29 specimens of the small-spotted genet, *G. genetta*, from Zimbabwe (Smithers & Wilson, 1979) and 78 from Botswana (Smithers, 1971) taken through the months of the year

| Food Item | Percentage occurrence Zimbabwe | Botswana |
|---|---|---|
| Insecta | 66 | 72 |
| Muridae | 59 | 54 |
| Arachnida | 31 | 36 |
| Aves | 10 | 6 |
| Reptilia | 10 | 18 |
| Soricidae | 3 | 1 |
| Amphibia | 3 | — |
| Myriapoda | 3 | 5 |
| Wild fruits | — | 5 |
| Muscardinidae | — | 1 |
| Lepidoptera | — | 1 |
| Chiroptera | — | 1 |

In the Zimbabwe sample, Insecta consisted of Coleoptera, adult beetles of various Families; Orthoptera, mainly grasshoppers; and Isoptera, in that order of occurrence. In Botswana Orthoptera, grasshoppers, predominated, followed by Isoptera, Coleoptera, and Lepidoptera. In both about 10% of the total sample consisted of unidentifiable chitinous chips. The Isoptera consisted of *Hodotermes mossambicus*, *Odontotermes* sp and *Macrotermes falciger*. Muridae had

**Plate 23**

265. Tree civet, *Nandinia binotata*
Boomsiwet
266. African civet, *Civettictis civetta*
Afrikaanse siwet
267. Small-spotted genet, *Genetta genetta*
Kleinkolmuskejaatkat
268. Large-spotted genet, *Genetta tigrina*
Rooikolmuskejaatkat
269. Suricate, *Suricata suricatta*
Stokstertmeerkat
270. Selous' mongoose, *Paracynictis selousi*
Kleinwitstertmuishond

PLATE 23

the second highest occurrence in the two samples. The high percentage of multimammate mice, *Mastomys* spp, in the Zimbabwe sample, as opposed to the much lower percentage in Botswana, is a reflection of this murid's common and widespread occurrence in the former country and their restricted distribution in the latter, where they do not occur in the drier central and southern half of the country, where the genet occurs. The house rat, *Rattus rattus*, common in built-up areas and in farm outbuildings in Zimbabwe, has not been recorded so far in Botswana; the lesser gerbil, *Gerbillurus paeba*, is distributed marginally in Zimbabwe in the west and southeast and common throughout Botswana (Table 267.2b).

**Table 267.2b**
Muridae identified.

| Species | Percentage occurrence Zimbabwe | Botswana |
|---|---|---|
| *Mastomys* spp | 21 | 9 |
| *Mus* spp | 10 | 9 |
| *Tatera* spp | 7 | 6 |
| *Saccostomus campestris* | 3 | 7 |
| *Gerbillurus paeba* | — | 7 |
| *Steatomys pratensis* | 3 | 7 |
| *Thallomys paedulcus* | — | 3 |
| *Otomys angoniensis* | — | 1 |
| *Aethomys* spp | — | 1 |
| *Rattus rattus* | 7 | — |

In the Zimbabwe sample, Arachnida were represented by a high occurrence of spiders, Araneae, with lesser amounts of Scorpiones and hunting spiders, Solifugae. The situation in Botswana is reversed, scorpions having the highest occurrence, followed closely by Solifugae, with only a small percentage of spiders (Table 267.2c).

**Table 267.2c**
Arachnida identified.

| Item | Percentage occurrence Zimbabwe | Botswana |
|---|---|---|
| Araneae | 17 | 2 |
| Scorpiones | 7 | 27 |
| Solifugae | 7 | 24 |

In the Zimbabwe sample, Reptilia were represented by the striped skink, *Mabuya striata*, at a percentage occurrence of 10%; in the Botswana sample by a comprehensive list of seven species of snakes and nine species of lizards (Table 267.3). Among these, Sundevall's skink, *Lygosoma sundevallii*, was the commonest species occurring.

**Table 267.3**
Percentage occurrence of various species of Reptilia in the stomach contents of 78 small-spotted genets, *G. genetta*, from Botswana (Smithers, 1971) taken through the year

| Species | Percentage occurrence |
|---|---|
| **Serpentes** | |
| Spotted purple-glossed snake, *Amblyodipsas ventrimaculatus* | 1,5 |
| Peters' black worm-snake, *Leptotyphlops scutifrons* | 3 |
| Spotted quill-snouted snake, *Xenocalamus bicolor* | 3 |
| Quill-snouted snake, *Xenocalamus* sp | 1,5 |
| Shield snake, *Aspidelaps scutatus* | 1,5 |
| Centipede-eating snake, *Aparallactus capensis* | 1,5 |
| Puffadder, *Bitis arietans* | 1,5 |
| **Sauria** | |
| Sundevall's skink, *Lygosoma sundevallii* | 9 |
| Bibron's gecko, *Pachydactylus bibroni* | 1,5 |
| Spotted gecko, *P. punctatus* | 1,5 |
| Cape gecko, *P. capensis* | 3 |
| Dwarf gecko, *Lygodactylus capensis* | 1,5 |
| Skink, *Mabuya* sp | 1,5 |
| Whistling gecko, *Ptenopus garrulus* | 1,5 |
| Kalahari lined blind skink, *Typhlosaurus lineatus* | 1,5 |
| Striped skink, *Mabuya striata* | 1,5 |

All the remaining items occurred at relatively low percentages. Wild fruits were represented in both samples, a food item not normally included by writers dealing with this aspect of the species. In both samples raisin bush berries, *Grewia* sp, were identified.

Soricidae, musk shrews, normally are not palatable to small carnivores, so that the occurrence, at small percentages, of *Crocidura* spp is unusual. This also applies to the dormouse, *Graphiurus murinus*. In one stomach there were the remains of a bullfrog, *Pyxicephalus adspersus*.

In the Botswana sample there is one record of the Cape serotine bat, *Eptesicus capensis*, being eaten. Carpenter (1970) described the taking of bats by the large-spotted genet, *G. tigrina*, and included this species in their diet.

From this evidence the small-spotted genet in the Subregion has a diet consisting predominantly of insects, mice, arachnids, birds and reptiles, with other food items such as frogs, centipedes and fruits playing very much a secondary role. Some of these secondary foods can be very important to the species under certain circumstances. On occasion they will take carrion and they can become problem animals where poultry is concerned.

### Reproduction

From present evidence the young are born during the summer months of the year from about August to April. Two to four constitute a litter, the average number being 2,6 (n=11). Two out of the eleven gravid females carried four foetuses implanted 2R 2L (Smithers, 1983). The gestation period is 10–11 weeks and it takes nine weeks from birth to weaning and becoming fully active. Females litter down in holes in the ground, disused antbear and springhaas holes and holes in termite mounds, in hollow trees, piles of boulders and other situations where excavation is not required. No bedding material is brought into the nests.

Females have two pairs of abdominal mammae.

---

No. 268

## *Genetta tigrina* (Schreber, 1776)

## Large-spotted genet
## Rooikolmuskejaatkat

Plate 23

---

### Colloquial Name

None of the colloquial names applied to any of the species in the past are appropriate, for *G. tigrina* is not necessarily large-spotted, nor *G. rubiginosa* rusty-spotted; in fact, some specimens of *G. genetta* are clearly rusty-spotted. If eventually three or even four species are accepted as occurring in the subregion, other names will have to be sought.

### Taxonomic Notes

The treatment used here follows Meester *et al.* (1986), three subspecies being recognised: *G. t. tigrina* from the southwestern Cape Province along the coast to southern Natal; *G. t. rubiginosa* Pucheran, 1855 from Natal, Lesotho, northeastern Orange Free State, Transvaal, Zimbabwe, southeastern and northern Botswana, northeastern Namibia and Mozambique, south of the Zambezi River, and *G. t. zambesiana* Matschie, 1902 from the Tete district of Mozambique, which may well range south of the Zambezi River.

## Description

The complex comprising the group *G. tigrina*, the large-spotted genets, are all short-legged species with elongated bodies and white-ringed tails, about the same length as the head and body. The spots and other dark markings on the body, which are generally larger than in *G. genetta*, can vary from almost black, with a sprinkling of rusty-coloured hairs in varying proportion, to individuals in which they are overall rusty in colour. There is great variation in the colour of the bands and spots even in the individual specimens; sometimes the bands are entirely black, the spots ringed rusty. The darker bands on the tail normally follow the colour of the spotting with varying degrees of a sprinkling of rusty hairs on the otherwise dark bands, or the bands may be almost totally black. There are eight or nine lighter bands on the tail usually approximate in colour to the ground colour of the upper parts. One feature of the tail which helps to distinguish the species from *G. genetta* is that it is almost without exception broadly black-tipped in the *G. tigrina* group, in *G. genetta* white-tipped.

The ground colour of the upper parts varies from off-white to greyish-white or white tinged buffy. The colour of the face is sometimes slightly lighter in colour. Two dark bands arise from the back of the head and swing downwards over the shoulders, where they usually break up into spots or bars. Two further bars arise from the back of the neck between the outer bars. These are usually not so distinct and extend over the shoulders, giving way to bars and spots. From the top of the shoulders to the base of the tail there is a very distinct mid-dorsal band, as in *G. genetta*. The hair forming this band is never as coarse or long, however, as in *G. genetta*, and even when the hair of the body and tail is erected under stress, it does not show as a distinct crest.

The hair of the guard coat is softer and less wiry than in *G. genetta*. The hair on the face is about 8–10 mm long, increasing in length towards the hindquarters, where it reaches about 20–25 mm and is therefore shorter than in *G. genetta*. The individual hairs are either dark in colour, or on the spots or bars are rusty-tipped; those on the ground colour are white or off-white with narrow dark tips. The hair on the mid-dorsal band at the level of the hindquarters is normally about 30–35 mm long, but in some specimens reaches about 40 mm. The dense underfur on the ground colour is pale greyish at the base with light buffy tips, darker on the spots and bars. The individual hairs are soft, fine and wavy.

The facial markings are very similar to those of *G. genetta*, but are not so contrasting. There are two white or off-white patches under the eyes and a brown or dark brown patch at the base of the vibrissae. There are two indistinct white bands on the inner side of the eyes running on to the forehead, which except in the dark spotted and barred individuals, are never so distinct as in *G. genetta*. In some specimens the brown or dark brown patches at the base of the vibrissae are continued narrowly around the mouth and on to the chin where they tend to become grey. The greater part of the chin, however, remains white or off-white as opposed to the black chin in *G. genetta*. The lower parts of the front limbs are unmarked and about the same colour as the background colour of the upper parts. The lower parts of the hind limbs are similar. The under parts of the feet are slightly darker in the specimens with dark markings, and only in these is the ankle suffused with black or blackish-brown, which never reaches the intensity found in *G. genetta*.

The under parts are lighter in colour than the ground colour of the upper parts and may be suffused with buffy or grey, the spotting generally confined to the lower chest and upper belly. The claws and feet are similar to those of *G. genetta*, and the situation of the anal glands identical.

As with *G. genetta* there do not appear to be any noticeable differences in measurements or mass between males and females. The series from Botswana is larger and slightly heavier than that from Zimbabwe (Table 268.1).

The spoor is indistinguishable from that of *G. genetta* (Fig. 268.1).

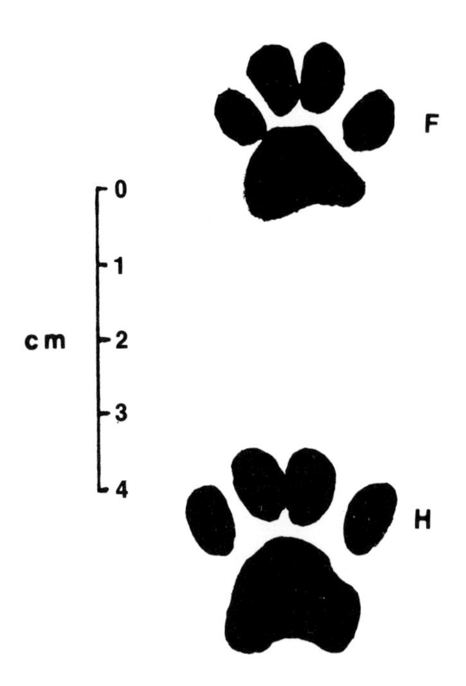


Fig. 268.1. Spoor: large-spotted genet, *G. tigrina* group. F. Right forefoot H. Right hind foot.

**Table 268.1**

Measurements (mm) and mass (kg) of large-spotted genets, *G. tigrina* group, from (a) Zimbabwe (Smithers & Wilson, 1979) and (b) Botswana (Smithers, 1971)

**(a)**

| | Males | | | Females | | |
|---|---|---|---|---|---|---|
| | $\bar{x}$ | n | Range | $\bar{x}$ | n | Range |
| TL | 939 | 32 | 845–1 020 | 916 | 28 | 865–1 010 |
| T | 451 | 32 | 415–530 | 454 | 28 | 395–495 |
| Hf s/u | 86 | 32 | 81–90 | 84 | 28 | 80–89 |
| E | 45 | 32 | 41–50 | 44 | 27 | 41–48 |
| Mass | 1,8 | 28 | 1,4–2,3 | 1,7 | 28 | 1,5–2,0 |

**(b)**

| | Males | | | Females | | |
|---|---|---|---|---|---|---|
| | $\bar{x}$ | n | Range | $\bar{x}$ | n | Range |
| TL | 1043 | 7 | 970–1 080 | 1035 | 7 | 1 005–1 060 |
| T | 512 | 7 | 475–535 | 513 | 7 | 475–540 |
| Hf s/u | 92 | 7 | 87–98 | 91 | 7 | 85–93 |
| E | 50 | 7 | 47–51 | 55 | 7 | 51–65 |
| Mass | 2,1 | 7 | 1,7–3,2 | 2,0 | 7 | 1,5–2,5 |

**Skull** (Fig. 268.2)

The skulls of the *G. tigrina* group are built more massively than those of *G. genetta*, the average mass of a series of 25 of each being: *G. tigrina* group 16,5 g; *G. genetta* 10,5 g. In line with this the canine teeth are longer and heavier in most specimens but, like so many skull characters that authorities have used to separate these species, there are exceptions to this, where it is impossible to separate the two. The continuation of the sagittal crest right across the top of the braincase in the *G. tigrina* group, as opposed to its confinement to the back of the braincase in *G. genetta* is useful, but can be used only to separate old adult specimens. While it is present in all the *G. tigrina* group skulls examined, it also occurs in three out of 61 *G. genetta* males and one out of 40 females. Cabral (1969) published photographs of the under parts of the skulls of *G. genetta* and *G. pardina*, which show that the interpterygoid space in the former is much broader, the pterygoid processes bulging outwards. In the latter the space is much narrower, the pterygoid processes lying nearly parallel to each other. In the present sample from the northern parts of the Subregion, this is very variable.

Rosevear (1974) illustrated the relative proportions of the anterior, as opposed to the posterior, chambers of the bullae in *G. genetta* and *G. genettoides*. Unfortunately he was unable to compare *G. genetta* with *G. pardina* owing to the lack of material. In the present sample the anterior chambers of the ear bullae do appear to be larger in proportion in *G. genetta* than in the *G. tigrina* group and might be a character worth detailed investigation.

In the G. *tigrina* group the upper ends of the postorbital bars are better developed than in G. *genetta* and appear as sharp, pointed processes directed slightly backwards. In addition, in fully adult specimens the postorbital constriction in the G. *tigrina* group narrows to a much greater extent than in G. *genetta*. Taking a series of 25 of each, in the G. *tigrina* group this averages 11,7 mm (10,2–13,8) as opposed to 14,7 mm (11,1–16,9) in G. *genetta*.

The dental formula is the same as in G. *genetta*:

$I\frac{3}{3}\ C\frac{1}{1}\ P\frac{4}{4}\ M\frac{2}{2} = 40$

The inner cusp on the upper third premolar, in a sample of 23 adult males, is present in one, tiny and barely perceptible in 12, and absent in 10. In 45 G. *genetta* skulls it is generally present and obvious, but in one it was absent and in two barely perceptible.

The situation at the moment, therefore, is that there are no clear constant characters showing the differences between the two skulls, a state of affairs which Rosevear (1974) found to rule in West Africa as well. In any revision of the G. *tigrina* group, a detailed morphometric treatment of skull characters will have to be applied to see if this will resolve the present impasse.

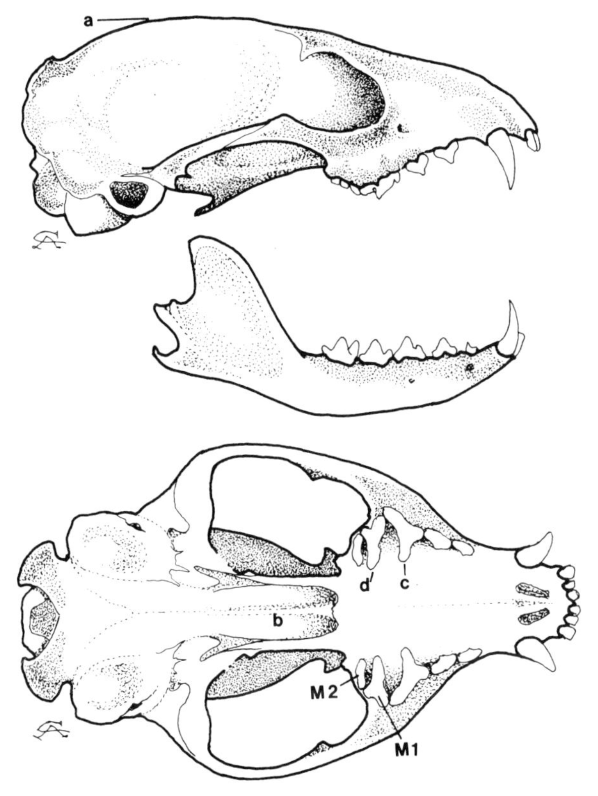


Fig. 268.2. Skull, *Genetta tigrina* group:
(a) sagittal crest (b) interpterygoid (mesopterygoid) space
(c) and (d) protocones
M1 first molar, M2 second molar.
TL Skull 94 mm.

### Distribution

Even if we accept the findings of Cabral (1969, 1970) and Ansell (1978) which show that species, other than those included by Coetzee (1977a) in the G. *tigrina* group, occur on the borders of the Subregion and indeed in parts within it, we are not in the position to show what their limits are in the Subregion. All that can be done at the moment, therefore, is to map the distribution of the G. *tigrina* group as a unit and leave the sorting out of the limits of distribution of any species, which may be shown later to be included in it, to a later revision.

*Southern African Subregion*

They occur in the extreme northeastern parts of **Namibia** in the vicinity of the Okavango River. In **Botswana** they are common throughout the Okavango delta and its associated swamp areas in the northeast, along the Chobe River as far as the Zimbabwe border and in the eastern better-watered parts of the country, from the Tate Concession south to Gaborone and east to the Transvaal and Zimbabwe borders. In **Zimbabwe** they occur widely throughout, except in the more arid parts of the extreme west, where they are absent from the central and southern sectors of the Hwange National Park south to the plateau at Plumtree. They occur widely throughout **Mozambique**, except in a limited area of the Banhine Flats in the southwest which is dry and arid. In the **Tranvaal** they are distributed widely except in the drier northwestern, southern and southeastern parts of the province, and there are records from **Swaziland**. They occur throughout **Natal** and have a relatively narrow distribution in the **Cape Province** coastally from the eastern part of the province to the southwestern sector.

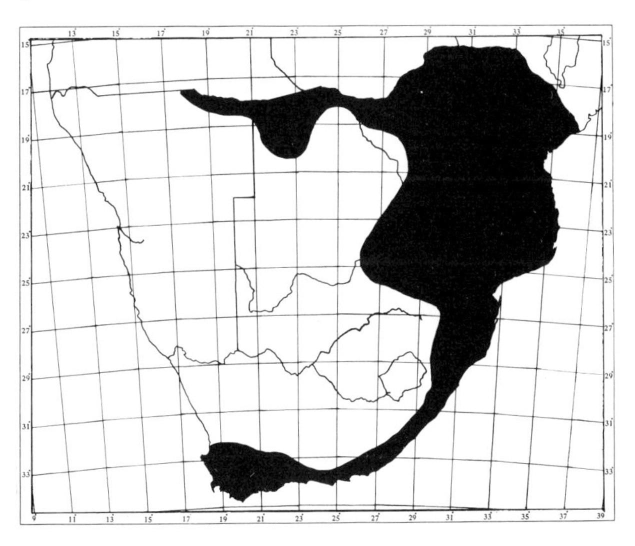

### Habitat

In the Subregion genets of the G. *tigrina* group occur both in the Cape Macchia Zone in the southern parts of the Cape Province and in savanna woodland in the higher rainfall areas of the eastern sector. They are associated particularly with riverine associations, especially in the drier parts of their distributional range and do not occur in the South West Arid Zone. Throughout their distributional range they appear to be associated particularly with well-watered country. In the eastern sector of the Subregion they occur in areas with a mean annual rainfall of about 450 mm and over, and are absent from areas where the rainfall is less than this. Cover appears to be an essential habitat requirement and while they may be found in open grassland or vlei areas within woodland associations when foraging, they are found much more frequently within the woodland itself. They appear to favour agriculturally developed areas where murids are numerous, these being one of their principal foods.

### Habits

The G. *tigrina* group is almost exclusively nocturnal and if active during daylight hours, this is certainly atypical behaviour. They normally move from the daylight resting places an hour or two after sunset and continue to be active until about 02h00. These resting places are holes in trees, hollow logs, under tree roots or in disused antbear or springhaas holes, under piles of boulders or in fact in any readymade substantial shelter of this sort. In Zimbabwe they have been known to use the shelter of the roofs of houses, farm outbuildings, stacked hay bales and other shelters, often in close association with man's activities. Accomplished climbers, they take to trees readily when hunting or under stress, climbing to the highest clumps of foliage to hide or taking shelter in the forks of branches. They have considerable power of leaping and are able to leap from tree to tree over distances of three or four metres. In spite of their relatively short legs they can move rapidly on the ground, the head held low and the tail trailing out horizontally behind. More characteristically they slink, moving fairly slowly, on the alert for danger or in search for food and when thoroughly alarmed make off in a series of bounds towards cover. They will sit up on their back legs, balancing with the tail, to gain a wider view of the surrounding terrain. Under stress they emit a heavy musky odour from the secretion of the anal glands and this smell often indicates points where they have urinated.

Normally solitary, pairs occasionally are found moving together, but it appears from the lack of observations of females moving with juveniles that the litter remains in the vicinity of the breeding site until the juveniles are ready to move on their own.

### Food

A sample of 136 stomachs of specimens of the *G. tigrina* group from Zimbabwe and 30 from Botswana shows that insects and murids rank high among the various food items recorded (Table 268.2). In the case of the Botswana sample, where insects predominated, there might well have been a bias against murids, as a high proportion of the sample was taken at the end of a four year drought, when murid numbers were at a low ebb and, as will be seen from Table 268.2, they had turned more to a diet of insects, Arachnida, Myriapods and wild fruit, all of which ranked higher than in the Zimbabwe sample.

**Table 268.2a**

Percentage occurrence of various food items in the stomachs of 136 specimens of the *G. tigrina* group from Zimbabwe (Smithers & Wilson, 1979) and 30 from Botswana (Smithers, 1971) taken through the year.

| | Percentage occurrence | |
|---|---|---|
| **Food item** | **Zimbabwe** | **Botswana** |
| Insecta | 40 | 90 |
| Muridae | 68 | 47 |
| Arachnida | 9 | 27 |
| Aves | 15 | 7 |
| Reptilia | 8 | 3 |
| Soricidae | 3 | — |
| Amphibia | 2 | 3 |
| Myriapoda | 3 | 10 |
| Wild fruits | 8 | 17 |
| Arthropoda | — | 3 |
| Pisces | 1 | — |
| Leporidae | 1 | — |

Among the insects Coleoptera ranked high in the Botswana sample, followed by Orthoptera, in the form of grasshoppers and crickets, and Isoptera, represented by harvester termites. Lepidoptera and Formicidae, true ants, occurred as minor items in the Zimbabwe sample (Table 268.2b).

**Table 268.2b**

Insecta identified.

| | Percentage occurrence | |
|---|---|---|
| **Item** | **Zimbabwe** | **Botswana** |
| Coleoptera | 7 | 37 |
| Orthoptera | 10 | 27 |
| Isoptera | 6 | 23 |
| Lepidoptera | 3 | — |
| Formicidae | 4 | — |

Muridae, which had a higher occurrence in the Zimbabwe sample than in Botswana, are represented by a high proportion of multimammate mice, *Mastomys* spp, the common and most widespread species in the country (Table 268.2c). In Botswana this genet occurs in areas where there are multimammate mice and there is no ready explanation as to why they were not represented, except that the pouched mouse and the gerbils may have been more freely available.

**Table 268.2c**

Muridae identified.

| | Percentage occurrence | |
|---|---|---|
| **Species** | **Zimbabwe** | **Botswana** |
| Multimammate mice, *Mastomys* spp | 40 | — |
| Angoni vlei rat, *Otomys angoniensis* | 4 | 1 |
| Pygmy mice, *Mus* spp | 3 | — |
| Pouched mouse, *Saccostomus campestris* | 3 | 17 |
| Gerbil, *Tatera* spp | 3 | 10 |
| Veld rat, *Aethomys* spp | 1 | 7 |
| House rat, *Rattus rattus* | 1 | — |
| Four-striped mouse, *Rhabdomys pumilio* | 1 | — |
| Climbing mouse, *Dendromus melanotis* | — | 7 |

The pouched mouse, *Saccostomus campestris* occurs in both samples, at quite a high level in Botswana when compared with Zimbabwe. It is a slow moving mouse which ranges widely on open ground, when it becomes vulnerable to predation. The gerbils, *Tatera leucogaster* and *T. brantsii*, occur commonly and widely in Botswana. The house rat, *Rattus rattus*, has not been recorded in Botswana and the four-striped mouse, *Rhabdomys pumilio*, quite apart from being a diurnal species and therefore not so freely available to a nocturnal predator, has a limited and patchy distribution in Botswana.

Birds, in the Zimbabwe sample, were represented in five out of 11 cases by chickens, pigeons, young peafowl and an ornamental pheasant, the genets concerned being shot while raiding. They have a bad reputation among farmers who have free-ranging poultry. As a whole, however, they should not be condemned for this type of depredation, for it is usually the individual which, finding a ready source of food, will return for another meal, and if this animal is removed, it will take time for another to find this food source. Properly penned birds are in no danger from genets who are incapable of breaking through wire netting, although they are past masters at finding weaknesses which they will enlarge to enter. The remaining six records were of small birds up to the size of a turtle dove, *Streptopelia capicola*.

Arachnida were represented predominantly by scorpions and hunting spiders; in both samples hunting spiders were well represented, particularly so in the Botswana sample. Although seasonal in occurrence, they appear to be very palatable to a wide range of small predators (Table 268.2d). Reptilia were represented poorly in the Botswana sample by the remains of a gecko and a chameleon, *Chamaeleo dilepis*, better so in Zimbabwe by four species of snakes and three of lizards (Table 268.3). These are a regular item in their diet, and both in Mozambique and Natal reptiles are represented in stomachs (Table 268.4).

**Table 268.2d**

Arachnida identified.

| | Percentage occurrence | |
|---|---|---|
| **Item** | **Zimbabwe** | **Botswana** |
| Araneae | — | 3 |
| Scorpiones | 3 | 7 |
| Solifugae | 2 | 16 |

**Table 268.3**

Reptilia recorded in a sample of 136 stomach contents of *G. tigrina* group genets from Zimbabwe (Smithers & Wilson, 1979).

**Serpentes**
Schlegel's blind snake, *Typhlops schlegelii*
Peters' black worm snake, *Leptotyphlops scutifrons*
Olive grass snake, *Psammophis phillipsii*
Puff adder, *Bitis arietans*

**Sauria**
Common striped skink, *Mabuya striata*
Transvaal flat gecko, *Afroedura transvaalica*
Kirk's rock agama, *Agama kirkii*

**Table 268.4**

Additional reptile species recorded in stomachs of genets of the *G. tigrina* group in Mozambique and Natal (Broadley, pers. comm.).

**Mozambique**
**Serpentes**
Long-tailed worm snake, *Leptotyphlops longicauda*
Sundevall's shovel-snouted snake, *Prosymna sundevallii*

**Sauria**
Tropical house gecko, *Hemidactylus mabouia*
Baobab gecko, *H. platycephalus*
Gecko, *Pachydactylus* sp

**Natal**
**Serpentes**
Boomslang, *Dispholidus typus*

**Sauria**
Gecko, *Pachydactylus* sp

Amphibia occurred in both samples. They were unidentifiable in Botswana, but in Zimbabwe were represented by the bull frog, *Pyxicephalus adspersus*, in one stomach, and by five golden-backed grass frogs, *Hylarana darlingi*, in another. This latter frog inhabits grassland and therefore is available more freely to the genet than species more associated with aquatic conditions. Broadley (pers. comm.) stated that tree frogs, *Leptopelis* sp, have also been recorded in Natal. Myriapods were represented by the centipede, *Scolopendra morsitans*, in both samples, an invertebrate commonly recorded in the stomachs of small carnivores. Wild fruits ranked high in the Botswana sample and included raisin bush berries, *Grewia* sp, and the fruits of the jackal-berry, *Diospyros mespiliformis*, and in the Zimbabwe sample, wild figs, *Ficus* sp, occurred in five stomachs and dusty berries, *Rubus* sp, in one.

On this evidence, the principal foods of genets of the *G. tigrina* group appear to be mice and insects, augmented by reptiles, invertebrates and wild fruits. In the present sample there was no evidence to show that they are attracted by carrion, and at the many carcasses laid out in Botswana to attract larger predators, genets were never recorded as visitors.

The normal method of hunting is by stalking the prey and then pouncing. The action is similar to that of *G. genetta*. The prey is bitten wherever it can be caught and then repeatedly bitten until quiescent; the teeth are not fully retracted from the prey in the process, the claws of the front feet being used to hold it. If not killed by this method, it may be bitten on the head, an action observed with larger mice and birds such as turtle doves, *Streptopelia capicola*. In dealing with house rats, *Rattus rattus*, which are tough and less readily killed, the genet will hold them with the front feet while biting them, then roll over on its side and rake the prey with the claws of the back feet.

In two captive individuals, there was no sign of the shaking of the prey mentioned by Ewer (1973), but this has been observed elsewhere. Rowe-Rowe (1971) recorded that an individual in captivity made its first killing and eating of live vertebrate prey at the age of 28 weeks. Post-killing play consisted of nosing the prey and poking at it with the paw, and never lasted more than half a minute. Smithers (1983) reported that two captive individuals, taken as adults, acted similarly, but sometimes would sit for a considerable period watching the prey for movement before commencing to eat.

Both with this species and the small-spotted genet, *G. genetta*, there is a marked seasonal variation in the food eaten. During the warm, wet, summer months insects and other invertebrates rank high in their diet and during the cold, dry months of the year when insect life is at a low ebb, their place is taken by murids and birds. Ewer (1973) answered the question as to what small carnivores eat, by replying "what is available". This is confirmed by examination of the seasonal variation in the food items utilised. As one resource becomes more readily available it is more heavily utilised and as it decreases in availability so its place is taken by another resource which for seasonal reasons becomes available more readily than the other.

#### Reproduction

In spite of the fact that genets of the *G. tigrina* group are quite common in parts of the Subregion, there are few records of the times at which the young are born. Shortridge (1934) listed a litter of three found in a hollow tree in northern Namibia in October; Maberly (1963) recorded a suckling female in the eastern Transvaal in September, and Pienaar (1964) three newly-born in February in the Kruger National Park. Rautenbach (1978) recorded two gravid females in November in the Transvaal.

In a sample of 128 females from the northern parts of the Subregion, gravid and lactating females were taken over the period August to February, indicating that the young are born during the warm, wet months of the year, about August to March. Gravid females carried two to five foetuses, and the average number was 2,9 (n=10). Juveniles that were still suckling, at a mass of between 194 g and 500 g, were taken in October and November and one at 800 g in January.

In Zimbabwe litters have been recorded in hollow trees, in a pile of loose boulders and in a house roof and they will use the same type of shelter that the adults use for resting in during daylight hours, in which to litter down. The absence of records of females moving with young and the taking of free-ranging young with a mass of 800 g suggests that they remain dependent on the shelter of the breeding site until ready to move on their own. Rowe-Rowe (1971) showed that a captive free-ranging genet aged 23 weeks was moving only within an area of about 600 $m^2$.

Females have two pairs of abdominal mammae.

## Subfamily HERPESTINAE

## Genus *Suricata* Desmarest, 1804

---

No. 269

## *Suricata suricatta* (Schreber, 1776)

## Suricate
## Stokstertmeerkat

Plate 23

---

#### Colloquial Name

In English, meerkat is often used, but as the name is applied to other mongoose species as well, suricate is more appropriate. The name apparently is of French derivation borrowed from the Dutch, who in turn may have picked up the name from some native South African language.

In Afrikaans *graatjiemeerkat* is used by Kritzinger *et al.* (1968), but *stokstertmeerkat* is entrenched, referring to the thin tapering tail.

#### Taxonomic Notes

Meester *et al.* (1986) recognised two subspecies: *S. s. suricatta* which occupies the whole species range, except the Namib Desert and pro-Namib of Namibia and Angola, and *S. s. marjoriae* Bradfield, 1936 of the Namib Desert and pro-Namib, north of Swakopmund, replaced in Angola by *S. s. iona* Cabral, 1971.

#### Description

About 500 mm overall, suricates have a thin tapering tail that is about three-quarters of the length of the head and body. Their hindquarters are stockier than the fore, and they have a rounded, rather broad head and a short, sharp-pointed muzzle.

The colour varies considerably through the distributional range. Overall the colour is silvery-brown, individuals from the northwestern areas are much paler than those from the southern parts of their range. The species is characterised by the distinct darker mottling on the upper parts which extends from the shoulders to the base of the tail, sometimes forming into distinct transverse bars towards the rump. The slender tapering tail has a characteristic darker tip. They all have dark circles around the eyes which, in life, tend to accentuate their size. The eyes are relatively small with a fine dark line extending from above them towards the top of the ears. The small ears are dark, in the southern form surrounded by black hair, in the northern this is largely obscured by lighter, in some, white hair. The nose is brown, the short hair above it either white or mixed brown and white. The limbs are lighter in colour towards the feet than on the remainder of the body; the tail is the same colour as the upper parts for over half its length, ending in a dark tip.

The under parts, from the upper chest to the base of the tail, are very sparsely haired, the dark-coloured skin showing through, giving them a dark appearance. The throat and chin are covered with a denser covering of short hair; the chin is greyish. In the paler specimens this hair may be white, extending upwards around the ear. The hair is closely adpressed to the body. The hair of the guard coat is about 15 mm long on the shoulders, increasing in length towards the base of the tail where it is over 20 mm. The hair on the flanks of the hindquarters may reach a length of over 30 mm, with a sparse admixture of longer hairs up to 40 mm, which may have a tactile function. The hair at the base of the tail is long, tapering off evenly in length towards the tip, the hair of the dark tuft about 12 mm long.

The individual hairs of the guard coat on the upper parts are light-coloured at the base with two dark annulations separated by a light-coloured one, and a silvery-white tip. In some individuals the hairs have dark tips. The mottled and banded pattern of the upper parts is governed by the overlapping, between individual hairs, of the outermost dark band which in southern material is dark brown, in northern a lighter brown. The silvery overall colour is created by the free admixture of guard hairs with broad silvery-white annulations, the tips narrowly brown.

There are four digits on each foot. The front feet are bare underneath to the wrist; the hind are bare to the ankle. Each digit has a distinctly swollen digital pad. The claws on the front feet are strong, curved and some 15 mm long across the curve, ideally adapted to digging. Those on the back feet are much shorter, not more than about 8 mm across the curve. When burrowing, a forward and downwards movement of the posterior and superior ridges of the ear effectively closes the ear and prevents the entry of dust and debris into the external auditory meatus (Fig. 269.1).

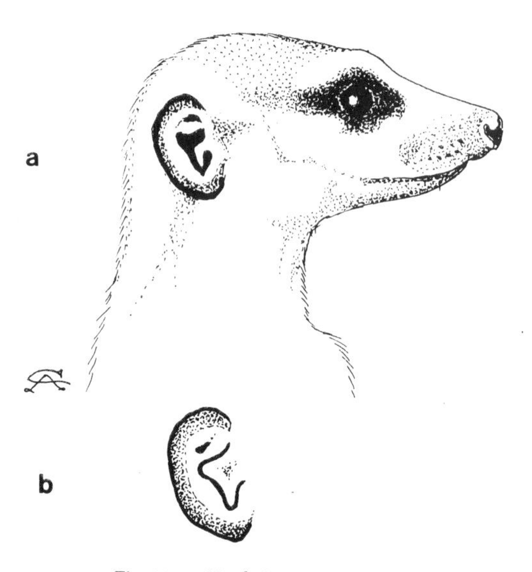


Fig. 269.1. Head: *Suricata suricatta*
(a) ear open (b) ear closed as when burrowing
(after Ewer, 1973).

The anus and the openings of the paired anal glands lie in a deep pouch with naked lips, which when closed, totally encircle them, showing externally as a transverse slit. The lining of this pouch is ridged to form transverse creases which Ewer (1973) suggested is for storing the secretion of the anal glands.

The measurements and mass of a series of males and females show that there is no difference in size between the sexes (Table 269.1); Lynch (1979) combined data from males and females.

**Table 269.1**

Measurements (mm) and mass (g) of suricates, *S. suricatta*, from (a) Botswana (Smithers, 1971) and (b) the Orange Free State (Lynch, 1979).

**(a)**

| | Males | | | Females | | |
|---|---|---|---|---|---|---|
| | $\bar{x}$ | n | Range | $\bar{x}$ | n | Range |
| TL | 502 | 18 | 450–530 | 491 | 8 | 450–515 |
| T | 220 | 17 | 205–240 | 227 | 8 | 190–230 |
| Hf c/u | 71 | 17 | 63–74 | 70 | 8 | 65–74 |
| E | 21 | 14 | 18–26 | 18 | 8 | 17–20 |
| Mass | 731,0 | 6 | 626,0–797,0 | 720,0 | 8 | 620,0–960,0 |

**(b)**

| | Irrespective of sex | | |
|---|---|---|---|
| | $\bar{x}$ | n | Range |
| TL | 510 | 20 | 499–545 |
| T | 214 | 20 | 199–235 |
| Hf s/u | 65 | 20 | 62–68 |
| E | 19 | 20 | 17–20 |
| Mass | 734,0 | 20 | 616,0–900,0 |

(Adjustment Hfs/u to Hfc/u + 8 mm)

**Skull** (Fig. 269.2)

In profile the skull, which is lightly built, is high and rounded, the highest point at about the level of the glenoid articulation, falling off evenly forward to the nasals and more rapidly towards the back. From the dorsal view the braincase is broadest at the level of the bullae, but only narrows very slightly forward to the postorbital constriction. This lies tucked up behind the postorbital bars which, in adult specimens, connect around the back of the eye sockets.

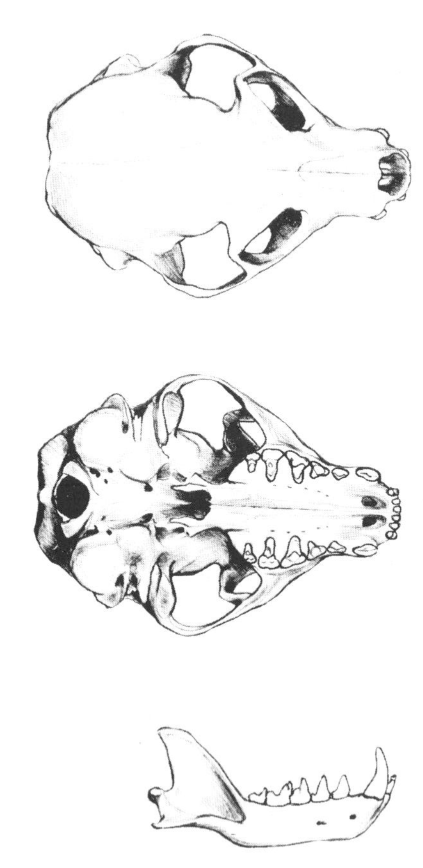

Fig. 269.2. Skull: suricate, *S. suricatta*.
TL Skull 65 mm

The eye sockets are large, over 20% of the total length of the skull, the rostrum narrow and projecting forward of the eye sockets. The supraoccipital crest is represented by a low ridge, which in some specimens is barely perceptible, there being no sign of a sagittal crest. The hind chambers of the ear bullae are ovoid, large and inflated and lie roughly at right angles to the long axis of the skull; the anterior chambers are smaller, about half the size of the posterior. The zygomatic arches are thin, the coronoid processes of the lower jaw only of medium height, suggesting that the temporalis and masseter muscles are called upon to deal with relatively soft food only.

The dental formula is:

$I\frac{3}{3}\ C\frac{1}{1}\ P\frac{3}{3}\ M\frac{2}{2} = 36$

The incisor rows are slightly curved, the outer upper incisors slightly larger than the remainder, the lower bifid and distinctly sloping outward. The upper canines are straight and slightly flattened on their inside faces, the lower distinctly recurved. The third upper premolar has a distinct protocone, the fourth premolar and first molar with distinct cusps on their inner extensions; the second premolar is small. All the cheekteeth have high cusps, with no sign of adaptation of the fourth upper premolar and lower first molar to slicing. The hind part of the first lower molar is relatively flat and this, with the occlusion of the first and second upper molars on this flat surface and on the second lower molar, provides for the necessary grinding up of the hard chitin of insects. This indicates an adaptation to an insectivorous diet.

## Distribution

Except for a narrow extension of distribution into the Iona National Park in the extreme southwestern part of **Angola**, suricates are restricted in their distribution to within the limits of the Southern African Subregion.

*Southern African Subregion*

In **Namibia** they are absent from the greater part of the northern and northeastern parts of the country, but are otherwise widespread, occurring into the Namib and pro-Namib deserts in the west, at least north of Swakopmund. They occur throughout the southwestern parts of **Botswana** north to about 21 °S and east to the Makgadikgadi Pan, but are absent from the eastern parts of the country. In the **Transvaal** they are confined to the southern parts of the province, not extending eastward as far as the Swaziland border. They are widespread throughout the **Orange Free State**, but occur only marginally in the northwestern parts of **Natal**. They occur widely in the **Cape Province**, but are absent from the extreme northwest and southeast and from just north of Cape Town to near Port Elizabeth, along the coast and for some distance inland.

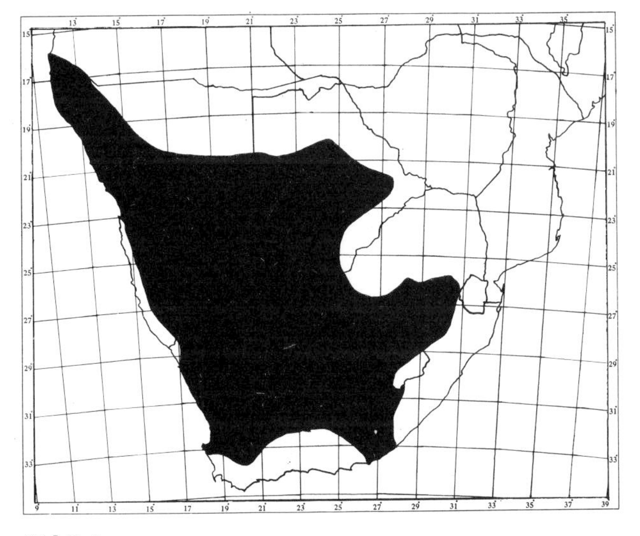

## Habitat

Suricates are clearly an open, arid country species, with a tendency to use areas where the substrate is hard or stony. They occur widely through the South West Arid Zone but are not confined to this entirely, occurring also in the *fynbos* in the south and southwestern parts of the Cape Province, and eastwards into the Orange Free State, Transvaal, marginally into northeastern Natal and into the southern savannas, in areas of mean annual rainfall of up to about 600 mm. In the northwestern part of their distributional range they closely follow the extension of the South West Arid Zone narrowly into southeastern Angola in the area which has a 100 mm to 400 mm mean annual rainfall. Within this distributional range, however, they are absent from desert and forest and generally avoid mountainous terrain. Although widely distributed through the arid sandy areas of the Kalahari, they tend to be localised, being associated particularly with the fringes of the many dry pans and fossil river beds that are a feature of this area. They tend to associate more with hard, often stony or calcareous substrate. Warrens may be constructed in this type of ground from which they forage into open scrub or woodland or on to completely open ground. They are common in parts of the Karoo where there is the barest cover of low xerophytic scrub.

## Habits

Suricates are diurnal, appearing shortly after sunrise. They initially sit at the entrances of the burrows on their haunches, sometimes clustering together, depending upon the temperature, to warm themselves in the early sunlight. At such times mutual and self-grooming is very much in evidence, as is continual murmurings between individuals. The length of the morning rest depends upon the hunger state of the individuals, as in times of drought little time is spent on grooming at the burrow entrance as feeding begins immediately (Knight, pers. comm.). They are continually on the alert, turning their heads from side to side on the look-out for predators, their main predators being the larger raptors, and martial eagles, *Polemaetus bellicosus*, in particular. Jackals, *Canis mesomelas*, are also a major threat. A shrill, sharp bark from the posted sentry causes the whole colony to dive for the burrows, disappearing from sight, often while uttering an hysterical scream. Individuals will then stick their heads out, still barking in a terrier-like fashion, cautiously surveying the scene for danger, in the absence of which they again emerge and take up their sitting positions. From the sitting position one may drop its front legs and move around, which is a sign for the others to follow suit. There is a division of labour, for example, sentinels and baby-sitters (the former males, the latter females) are posted and they are relieved from time to time. In times of food shortages, such as droughts, the sentinel behaviour is abandoned occasionally in order to feed.

Troop size varies from 2–30 and the troop moves around within their territory. They may travel up to 6 km during a day's foraging and normally return to the same burrow to sleep at night. There may be two or three such burrows in which they sleep, apart from many burrow systems which they use as bolt holes and temporary burrows (Goss, 1986). Suricates are adept at digging and excavate their own burrows, which have many entrances, but they also expel ground squirrels, *Xerus inauris*, and yellow mongoose, *Cynictis penicillata*, from sites excavated by the ground squirrels. They often share burrows with these two species. In digging, once the soil has been loosened with the front claws it is dragged out by holding the front feet together to act like a scoop, and thrown backwards between the back legs. Through continual turning up of soil in the construction of the burrows, which are 80–150 mm in diameter, the warren sites eventually may become raised above the level of the surrounding ground, looking like broad, raised mounds. Deserted warrens are sometimes found which have been vacated temporarily, perhaps because they have become vermin-infested or because food supplies in the vicinity are exhausted. Deserted burrows are marked by the lack of freshly excavated soil.

Suricates are particularly active in the early morning and late afternoon and, particularly in summer, may take a siesta in the shade of trees or within a burrow during the heat of the day. When walking and foraging, the head is held low, the tail trailing, the back sloping forward, due to the wideness and heavier build of the hips compared with the forequarters. As they move they continually pause to sniff the ground or dig with the long front claws, turning over stones or scratching in debris for the insects which form their principal food. They vocalise continually when out of the burrow to maintain a cohesive group. The young keep up an incessant, loud churring squeal for the first few months when out foraging. This appears to enable adults to locate and feed them quickly and efficiently. Sentries also maintain a peeping call, presumably to broadcast that all is clear.

Suricates make use of communal latrines situated near their burrows, and do not bury the faeces. Latrines consist of areas approximately 1 $m^2$ in size which are recognised by numerous shallow diggings and dark insectivorous faeces. Visits to latrines may precipitate simultaneous defecation by a large number of the group. Scent-marking is undertaken largely (or possibly exclusively) by the dominant male and female in the group. Burrow entrances are particularly frequently marked using the anal gland and individuals also wipe saliva onto each other, a behaviour which may have a social bonding significance (Goss, 1986).

Play occurs among members of a troop around the burrows or siesta sites during the morning, midday and evening rest periods. Play consists of chasing, hugging and rolling and is largely confined to the younger animals when they are in the immediate vicinity of a burrow. During times of drought little play occurs and individuals enter the burrows immediately after foraging (Knight, pers. comm.).

Strangers are usually vigorously repelled by the group by aggressive chasing. Partial acceptance is only secured as a result of great determination and dogged persistence on the part of the new member or members (Goss, pers. comm.). Recruitment of strangers into a troop appears to take place in early summer and is a time of great unrest in the troops. Males as well as females appear to change troops occasionally. Individuals initially approach troops carefully from a distance, and progressively venture closer if the resident troop attitude is not too aggressive. However, individuals sometimes have to persist for days to gain acceptance (Knight, pers. comm.).

Encounters between troops are spectacular affairs, with members of both troops adopting a peculiar cohesive bobbing wave action, with tails held erect, as the intruders and residents advance on each other as a closed group. During the skirmishes some individuals may be severely wounded.

Honey badgers are regarded with suspicion, whilst bat-eared foxes and Cape foxes (the latter capable of killing an individual suricate) may be severely intimidated by the group. Snakes are often mobbed and molested until they seek refuge down a hole or in a tree and may sometimes be killed by the suricates.

## Food

Reptiles occur in the diet, geckos forming a very large part at certain times of the year, and Goss (pers. comm.) observed a baby hare being caught and devoured. Fitzsimons (1919) recorded a captive suricate killing venomous snakes by crushing the skull and then eating them; in the wild they appear to rather ward off snakes by nipping at the tail. Viljoen & Davis (1973) examined two stomachs from the Kalahari Gemsbok National Park, finding that invertebrates ranked highest by volume, these including Coleoptera, Lepidoptera, both adults and larvae, Hymenoptera and spiders. Stuart (1977) recorded that in three stomachs examined from the Cape Province, all contained Coleoptera, adults or larvae, as well as termites, various other types of insects, Myriapoda, Arachnida and in one, a lizard.

In a sample of 23 stomachs from Botswana, insects had by far the highest percentage occurrence, followed by scorpions at a much lower figure, reptiles and myriapods (Table 269.2).

**Table 269.2**

Breakdown of the food items in a sample of 23 stomachs of suricates, *S. suricatta*, from Botswana (Smithers, 1983)

| Food item | Percentage occurrences |
|---|---|
| Coleoptera larvae | 91 |
| Scorpiones | 35 |
| Orthoptera | 17 |
| Coleoptera adults | 17 |
| Isoptera | 9 |
| Reptilia | 13 |
| Myriapoda | 13 |

A breakdown of the insect material showed that beetle larvae had the highest occurrence, at 91%; in eight stomachs they constituted the whole content, in a further four over 80% of the content. The search for subterranean larvae is, no doubt, the reason for the persistent digging engaged in by individuals. Scorpions, being almost entirely nocturnal, are only available to a diurnal predator if dug out of the ground or secured by turning over the stones under which they take shelter. Suricates are immune to the sting of scorpions (Knight, pers. comm.).

Reptiles were represented by lizards including:
Spiny agama, *Agama hispida*
Namaqua sand lizard, *Eremias namaquensis*
Legless skink, *Typhlosaurus lineatus*
Spotted scrub lizard, *Nucras intertexta*.

Myriapods were represented by the centipede, *Scolopendra morsitans*, and by millipedes.

Lynch (1979) provided very full data on his examination of 98 stomach contents from the Orange Free State on a qualitative (Table 269.3a) and on a seasonal basis (Table 269.3b). He compared the winter and summer diets of the suricate and the yellow mongoose on a percentage occurrence basis:

| | Winter | | Summer | |
|---|---|---|---|---|
| Suricate, *S. suricatta* | Lepidoptera | 42 | Lepidoptera | 32 |
| | Coleoptera | 29 | Orthoptera | 26 |
| | | | Diptera | 26 |
| Yellow mongoose, *C. penicillata* | Isoptera | 76 | Isoptera | 74 |
| | Lepidoptera | 13 | Orthoptera | 20 |

He concluded that suricates have a more catholic insectivorous diet than the yellow mongoose, *C. penicillata*.

**Table 269.3a**

Percentage occurrence of food items in a sample of 98 stomachs of the suricates, *S. suricatta*, from the Orange Free State (Lynch, 1979)

| Food item | Percentage occurrences |
|---|---|
| Coleoptera | 58 |
| Lepidoptera (pupae, larvae) | 43 |
| Isoptera | 40 |
| Orthoptera | 34 |
| Diptera (pupae, larvae) | 23 |
| Arachnida | 21 |
| Hymenoptera | 15 |
| Dermaptera | 12 |
| Chilopoda | 10 |
| Dictyoptera | 10 |
| Diplopoda | 9 |
| Reptilia | 5 |
| Amphibia | 5 |
| Aves | 2 |
| Hemiptera | 1 |

**Table 269.3b**

Seasonal analysis of five food categories which were present most frequently in a sample of 98 suricate stomachs from the Orange Free State (Lynch, 1979)

| Percentage occurrence | Winter | n | Summer | n |
|---|---|---|---|---|
| Coleoptera | 44 | 62 | 92 | 36 |
| Lepidoptera | 37 | 62 | 53 | 36 |
| Isoptera | 27 | 62 | 61 | 36 |
| Orthoptera | 19 | 62 | 47 | 36 |
| Diptera | 15 | 62 | 25 | 36 |

## Reproduction

Young are born in burrows in summer after a gestation period of 11 weeks (Lynch, 1979; Degre & Robert, 1987). Lynch (1979) gave the mean number of foetuses per female as 2,9 (n=34).

Although it is known that under captive conditions females can have more than one litter within a year, there is no evidence at the moment that they have more than one in the season in the wild. In the Orange Free State, Nel (pers. comm.) reported that a captive, but free-ranging, female had two litters in the season, one in September, the second in March. The male took an active part in guarding the young, the female sitting to suckle them.

Females have three pairs of abdominal mammae.

## Genus *Paracynictis* Pocock, 1916

No. 270

## *Paracynictis selousi* (De Winton, 1896)

## Selous' mongoose
## Kleinwitstertmuishond

Plate 23

### Colloquial Name

During the time that the famous hunter F.C. Selous lived at Essexvale, just south of Bulawayo, Zimbabwe, he made an extensive collection of small mammals. These included this mongoose which De Winton named after him.

### Taxonomic Notes

Coetzee (1977a) recognised four subspecies: *P. s. selousi* (De Winton, 1896) from Zimbabwe and the northern and eastern Transvaal; *P. s. sengaani* Roberts, 1931 from northeastern Natal and southern Mozambique; *P. s. ngamiensis* Roberts, 1932 from northern Botswana, northern Namibia and Angola, and *P. s. bechuanae* Roberts, 1932 from eastern Botswana.

Meester *et al.* (1986) listed *P. s. selousi*, which occurs throughout the Subregion, except in northeastern Natal and the Maputo district of Mozambique, south of the Zambezi river, *P. s. ngamiensis* Roberts, 1932 and *P. s. bechuanae* Roberts, 1932 as synonyms; and *P. s. sengaani* Roberts, 1931 from Zululand and southern Mozambique.

### Description

Selous' mongoose is smaller, at a total length of up to 0,75 m, than the white-tailed mongoose at 1,0 m, with which it is sometimes confused. Both have white tails but, whereas in the white-tailed, the tail is pure white for over three-quarters of its length, in Selous' only a short section towards the tip is pure white. This, coupled with the disparity in size and the fact that Selous' is generally greyer or tawny in colour, as opposed to the darker colour of the white-tailed, helps to distinguish them in the field. Proportionately, the length of the tail in the two species is the same, being about 40% of the total length or about 70% of the length of the head and body. At a distance the colour of the upper parts in Selous' looks greyish or tawny-grey; at close quarters, however, the coat is grizzled, the white annulations on the guard hairs showing distinctly against the background colour.

The soft hair is short on the face and head, barely reaching a length of about 15 mm, increasing in length towards the rump where it reaches about 40 mm. The hair on the tail is longest of all, about 50 mm towards the base and up to 100 mm on the white tassel at the end of the tail. The colour of the under parts is lighter than the upper, being either grey or tawny-grey depending on the general colour of the individual. The guard coat is thick, the individual hairs dark at the base, each with a narrow white band, a broad dark grey or dark brown band, a narrow white band and a narrow dark tip. The undercoat is thick, the woolly crinkled hairs are dark at their bases with buffy or buffy-grey tips, which, showing through the guard coat, affect the general colour of individual specimens. The upper parts of the limbs are black or nearly so in the greyer specimens, dark brown in the tawny-grey specimens. The four digits on each foot are armed with heavy claws. Those on the front feet are slightly curved and about 8–10 mm long, but usually show considerable wear; those on the back feet are straight and about the same length. All four digits mark in the spoor (Fig. 270.1). The muzzle is pointed. The rhinarium which encloses the nostrils is small for the size of the head, with a fine depression (the philtrum) between the nostrils in front which, continuing downwards, divides the hairy portions of the upper lip.

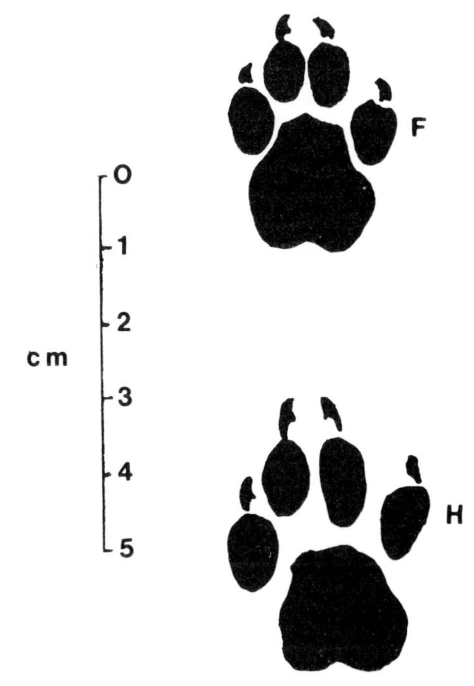


Fig. 270.1. Spoor: Selous' mongoose, *P. selousi*. F. Right forefoot H. Right hind foot.

The feet are covered with short hair right up to the base of the plantar pads, each digit with a distinct swollen digital pad at the base of the claws. The ears are typically viverrid but large for the size of the head. They lie closely adpressed to the sides of the head and are covered partially by the long hair lying in front of them.

There does not appear to be any noticeable difference in measurements and mass between males and females (Table 270.1).

**Table 270.1**

Measurements (mm) and mass (g) of Selous' mongoose, *P. selousi*, from Botswana (Smithers, 1971)

| | Males | | | Females | | |
|---|---|---|---|---|---|---|
| | $\bar{x}$ | n | Range | $\bar{x}$ | n | Range |
| TL | 774 | 22 | 733–890 | 744 | 25 | 635–810 |
| T | 377 | 21 | 288–435 | 325 | 23 | 307–367 |
| Hf c/u | 116 | 20 | 106–124 | 112 | 25 | 103–120 |
| E | 43 | 20 | 39–48 | 45 | 20 | 41–50 |
| Mass | 1746 | 18 | 1390–2156 | 1746 | 21 | 1263–1873 |

### Skull (Fig. 270.2)

The skull of Selous' mongoose is elongated; in profile it is highest at the level of the ear openings, sloping gently forward to the top of the eye sockets and then more sharply to the nasal openings. The braincase is ovoid, narrowing slightly to the interorbital constriction, which lies tucked in behind the postorbital bars which enclose the eye sockets in adult specimens. The rostrum is short and broad, the distances from the front of the eye sockets to the incisors about 33% of the total length of the skull. The supraoccipital crest is well developed, sloping backwards from the braincase and up to 5–6 mm high. The sagittal crest is obvious but much less developed, running forward over the top of the braincase and tailing off where it divides to end, on each side, at the postorbital bars. The zygomatic arches are of medium build; their width is half the total length of the skull. For the size of the skull the ear bullae are large, the two chambers of about equal size. The coronoid of the lower jaw is not particularly high, suggesting that strong jaw action in feeding is not essential.

The dental formula is:

$I\frac{3}{3}\ C\frac{1}{1}\ P\frac{4}{4}\ M\frac{2}{2} = 40$

The upper canines are short, rounded and slightly recurved, the lower distinctly recurved. Both the upper and lower outer incisors are slightly larger than the remainder. The first upper and lower premolars are not always present. They were absent on one side of the lower jaw in a sample of 43 adult skulls. The fourth upper premolar teeth have two well

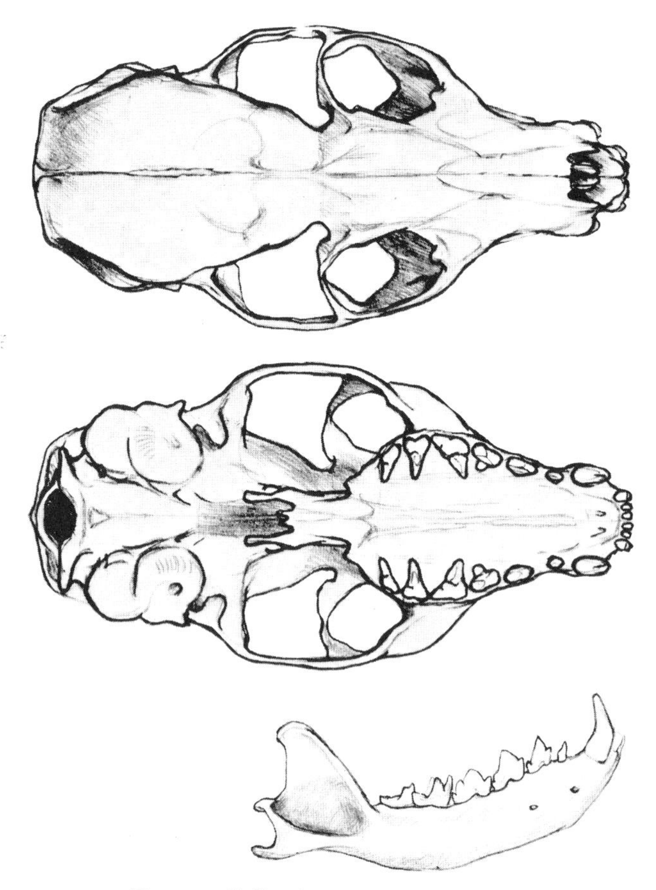

Fig. 270.2. Skull: Selous' mongoose, *P. selousi*.
TL Skull 90 mm

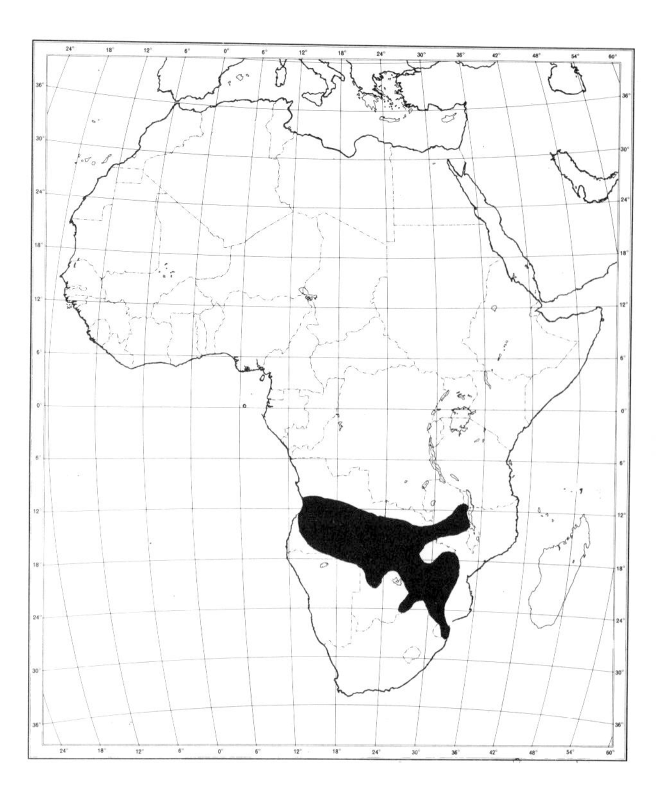

developed cusps on their outer edges and a low cusp on their inner sides. The first molar in the lower jaw has three high cusps towards the front of the teeth, the hind end of the teeth low and flat. The carnassial shear which is composed of these teeth, therefore has little slicing ability and is not specifically adapted to this function; it appears better adapted to a diet of insects and other soft food.

**Distribution**

Selous' mongoose are confined in their distribution to the southern part of the continent, from Angola in the west to the western shores of Lake Malawi, extending southeastwards to the northeastern parts of Natal. They are not common in any part of their distributional range and, while the map represents our knowledge up to this date, it is possible that they will be shown in time to occur still further northeastwards in Zimbabwe and into parts of Mozambique than present information indicates. At the moment there are no records from Zambia between about 29 °E and 32 °E, but there seems no good reason why they should not occur and it is probable that the lack of knowledge in this sector is due to a lack of collecting. Again, the northeastern parts of Zimbabwe are little known and the same situation pertains there.

*South of the Sahara, excluding the Southern African Subregion*

They occur in central and southern **Angola** from the coast at Lobito Bay east to about 18 °E. They are known from western and south-central **Zambia**, although not north of about 11 °S, and again in the eastern parts of the country, and also in **Malawi** from the western shores of Lake Malawi at Selima.

*Southern African Subregion*

In **Namibia** their occurrence is strictly marginal and they are found only in the extreme northeastern parts of the country close to the Quito/Okavango river confluence. Corresponding to this, in **Botswana** they occur along the Okavango River, in the extreme northwest and throughout the delta as far south as Lake Ngami and northeastward in the Savuti to the Chobe River and eastwards in the Chobe Valley to the Zimbabwe border. From the Chobe River they occur southwards narrowly along the Zimbabwe border and rather more widely westwards in the eastern parts of Botswana along the Transvaal border to about 24 °S. In **Zimbabwe** they occur throughout except in the northeast, and in **Mozambique** they are found narrowly along the Zimbabwe border from about 18 °S to the eastern borders of the Transvaal, south to inland from Maputo at about 26 °S.

They are recorded from the northern and eastern parts of the **Transvaal** and they extend southeastwards to northeastern **Natal**, which marks their most southern limits as at present known.

**Habitat**

Selous' mongoose is a savanna species, absent from desert, semi-desert and forest. They are not dependent on the availability of water as none is available in parts of their distributional range. They are known from areas with a mean annual rainfall from about 400 mm to 1 000 mm, yet they do not appear to occur in other areas of similar rainfall which otherwise appear suitable, although they may have been overlooked. From the data that are available, the habitat types in which they are found include *Acacia* scrub and woodland, if these have a sandy substrate. Here they can excavate their own burrows more easily, but on the other hand, they are known to use holes excavated by other species in harder ground. In this type of habitat they tend to be found in association with the more open areas, where there is cultivation or where bush clearing has taken place; on floodplain, or grassland where the grass is short and provides only a scanty cover. Both Shortridge (1934) and Ansell (1960a) associated the species with sandy open country.

**Habits**

Selous' mongoose is a terrestrial and nocturnal species. The great majority of a series of 25 specimens in the National Museum of Zimbabwe collection were taken between 21h30 and 22h00. They are normally solitary, although pairs have been recorded. During the day they lie up in burrows, which they excavate for themselves in sandy ground, the entrances often under the shelter of a low bush, but at other times out in the open. The burrows may have two or more entrances. A burrow excavated in Botswana had an entrance at the base of a termite mound and was connected with the galleries within it. In the construction of their own burrows they dig deeply. Roberts, quoted by Maberly (1963), excavated a burrow in Zululand which led to passages and chambers to a depth of 1,5 metres.

Under stress they will go to ground in any convenient hole. Under these circumstances in Botswana, when followed with a dazzling light, they used springhaas and aardvark holes.

The normal movement is a quick walk, the head and body held low to the ground and the tail held horizontally, pausing frequently to investigate possible food sources. They are avid diggers and scratchers, and will excavate among litter or at the bases of tufts of grass for subterranean beetle larvae, the long front claws ideally adapted to this purpose. Every now and then they will rise on the legs and hold the head high, looking and listening for signs of danger. Judging from the size of the ear bullae in relation to the skull, their hearing is acute, which may assist them in locating subterranean food or movements in the surrounding grass. Their action when moving, with the head held low and the nostrils close to the ground, suggests that their location of food is mainly carried out by smell.

### Food

Shortridge (1934) stated that the diet of Selous' mongoose includes rats, mice, small birds, eggs of birds and reptiles, tortoises, lizards, snakes and insects and quoted a number of authorities, some of whom listed small vertebrate prey or reptiles first on their lists.

In a sample of 51 stomachs from Botswana and Zimbabwe, insects had by far the highest percentage occurrences of any of the food items (Table 270.2). In only seven of the 51 stomachs were insects absent. Four of these were from specimens collected in June when insect life is at its lowest ebb. In all four of these murids were the sole content of the stomachs.

**Table 270.2a**

Percentage occurrence of food items in a sample of 51 stomachs of Selous' mongoose, *P. selousi*, from Zimbabwe (Smithers & Wilson, 1979) and Botswana (Smithers, 1971)

| Food item | Percentage occurrence |
|---|---|
| Insecta | 82 |
| Solifugae | 22 |
| Scorpiones | 18 |
| Muridae | 16 |
| Reptilia | 14 |
| Amphibia | 10 |
| Araneae | 8 |
| Myriapoda | 8 |
| Aves | 4 |

A breakdown of this insect food shows that there was a fairly even occurrence of adult beetles, termites and grasshoppers (Table 270.2b). Coleoptera were represented by the Families Scarabaeidae, dung beetles; Carabidae, ground beetles; Curculionidae, weevils; Dytiscidae, water beetles; and Elateridae, click beetles. Out of 22 occurrences of Isoptera, 11 were identifiable as *Hodotermes mossambicus*, four as *Macrotermes falciger*, with eight unidentifiable. In one, *H. mossambicus* comprised the sole content of a full stomach. Orthoptera consisted predominantly of grasshoppers and crickets, with lesser occurrences of grasshoppers of the Families Tettigoniidae and Pamphagidae, and cockroaches. Coleoptera larvae ranked next, consisting, where identifiable, of ground beetles, Tenebrionidae, dung beetles, Scarabaeidae, and click beetles, Elateridae. Two stomachs were packed with ground and dung beetle larvae.

**Table 270.2b**

Insecta identified.

| Food item | Percentage occurrence |
|---|---|
| Orthoptera | 43 |
| Isoptera | 43 |
| Coleoptera adults | 37 |
| Coleoptera larvae | 27 |
| Lepidoptera | 10 |
| Neuroptera | 2 |
| Hymenoptera | 2 |
| Undet. | 16 |

Lepidoptera were represented by butterflies of the Family Pieridae and Noctuidae and in two by caterpillars of hawk moths, Sphingidae. Among other food items of lesser occurrence lacewings, Neuroptera, and Formicidae, *Pheidole* sp, ants were identified. Eight stomachs contained insect remains so thoroughly masticated that they were unidentifiable (Table 270.2b). Hunting spiders, Solifugae, where identifiable, were represented in two by *Solpuga monteiroi*; scorpions by *Opisthophthalmus wahlbergi* and *Parabuthus granulatus*.

Among the remains of Muridae, which are chopped up into small pieces, the fat mouse, *Steatomys pratensis*, and the climbing mouse, *Dendromus* sp, were the only species identified with certainty.

Reptiles consisted of four species of lizards and four snakes (Table 270.2c). Amphibia were identified in three stomachs as toads, *Bufo* spp, Delalande's burrowing frog, *Tomopterna delalandii*, and Bocage's burrowing frog, *Leptopelis bocagii*.

**Table 270.2c**

Reptiles identified.

**Sauria**
Spotted ground gecko, *Pachydactylus capensis*
Spiny agama, *Agama hispida*
Wahlberg's snake-eyed lizard, *Panaspis wahlbergi*
Striped scrub lizard, *Nucras taeniolata*
Striped skink lizard, *Mabuya striata*

**Serpentes**
Shield snake, *Aspidelaps scutatus*
Peters' black worm snake, *Leptotyphlops scutifrons*
Cape wolf snake, *Lycophidium capense*
Bibron's burrowing adder, *Atractaspis bibronii*

Araneae, while generally unidentifiable, were in one case recognised as the remains of a large baboon spider; Myriapoda occurred in two, as the centipede, *Scolopendra morsitans*, and Aves by the remains of a small bird still in the egg, together with the egg shells of a small ground bird, thought to be a lark.

On the basis of this evidence, Selous' mongoose appears to subsist mainly on an insectivorous diet, augmented with other soft-bodied invertebrates and lesser amounts of murids and reptiles.

### Reproduction

Information on when the young of Selous' mongoose are born is scanty. Smithers (1971) took two gravid females in Botswana, one with four, the other with three foetuses, in February and September respectively. Smithers & Wilson (1979) recorded a gravid female with three foetuses from the Hwange National Park in August and two juveniles at 450 g taken in December and January, and another at 900 g in February.

## Genus *Bdeogale* Peters, 1850

No. 271

## *Bdeogale crassicauda* Peters, 1852

## Bushy-tailed mongoose
## Borselstertmuishond

Plate 24

### Colloquial Name

Alternative name: Four-toed mongoose, but *P. selousi* also has four toes.

*Dikstertmuishond* is used in Afrikaans, but Kritzinger *et al.* (1968) applied this name to the polecat, *Ictonyx striatus*.

### Taxonomic Notes

Five subspecies have been described: *B. c. tenuis* Thomas & Wroughton, 1908 from Zanzibar; *B. c. nigrescens* Sale & Taylor, 1970 from Kenya; *B. c. omnivora* Heller, 1913 from Tanzania; *B. c. crassicauda* and *B. c. puisa* Peters, 1852 from Mozambique. The specimens from the Subregion most closely fit Peters' description of *B. c. crassicauda*, originally described from Tete on the Zambezi River.

Two other species of *Bdeogale* are known from the continent: *B. nigriceps* Pucheran, 1855 from northern Angola, parts of Zaire and northwest to Nigeria, and *B. jacksoni* (Thomas, 1894) in central Kenya and southeastern Uganda.

### Description

In the field the bushy-tailed mongoose looks black, with a tail about 60% of the length of the head and body, and stands about 150 mm at the shoulder. Close at hand, however, it can be seen that, whereas the limbs and tail are jet black, the head and body are grizzled, the white annulations on the guard hairs contrasting with the general black background of the coat. There is a tendency in some Zimbabwe specimens for the white annulations on the guard hairs to be missing or so fine that they do not produce the grizzled appearance on parts of the upper parts.

The hairs of the guard coat are about 5 mm long on the forehead, increasing in length towards the rump where they reach a length of 45 mm. The individual hairs are black at the base with two or three white annulations or with one white annulation near the base, the remainder black. The guard hairs are distinctly flattened. The hair on the tail is particularly long, up to 60 mm, and does not taper off in length very much towards the tip. The under parts are sparsely haired, the hair generally black without annulations except on the throat and, to a lesser extent, on the belly. The limbs are covered with shorter, entirely black hair.

The dense underfur in Zimbabwe specimens is greyish-buff, dark towards the base of the hairs which are crinkled and shorter than the guard hairs. In some specimens the underfur tends to show through the guard coat, especially on the flanks, and this imparts a slightly lighter grey colour to these parts.

There are four digits on the fore and hind feet. The front have stout, curved claws, which usually show considerable wear, and are up to 8 or 9 mm long over the curve. Those on the hind are obviously not subjected to the same wear and measure up to 10 or 11 mm over the curve.

The hind foot is haired up to the back of the plantar pads; the forefoot has a short naked section immediately behind the pads. The digits have distinct digital pads under the base of the claws.

The ears are typically viverrid. The rhinarium which encloses the nostrils has a fine depression in front which, continuing downwards, divides the hairy portions of the upper lip.

While the sample of material from the Subregion is small, there does not appear to be any noticeable difference in size between males and females; however, the former appears heavier on average (Table 271.1).

**Table 271.1**

Measurements (mm) and mass (g) of bushy-tailed mongoose, *B. crassicauda*, from Zimbabwe (Smithers, 1983)

| | Males | | | Females | | |
|---|---|---|---|---|---|---|
| | $\bar{x}$ | n | Range | $\bar{x}$ | n | Range |
| TL | 693 | 3 | 655–740 | 695 | 4 | 672–720 |
| T | 259 | 3 | 229–285 | 249 | 4 | 230–265 |
| Hf c/u | 89 | 3 | 87–94 | 89 | 4 | 87–90 |
| E | 37 | 3 | 34–39 | 37 | 4 | 33–40 |
| Mass | 1 929 | 3 | 1 816–2 100 | 1 569 | 4 | 1 339–1765 |

**Skull** (Fig. 271.1)

The skull of the bushy-tailed mongoose is elongated, the zygomatic width almost exactly 50% of the total length. The braincase is ovoid, broadest at the level of the glenoid articulation and narrowing to the postorbital constriction which averages about 85% of the interorbital width. Even in older specimens with heavily worn teeth the postorbital bars, which enclose the back of the eye socket, are never complete.

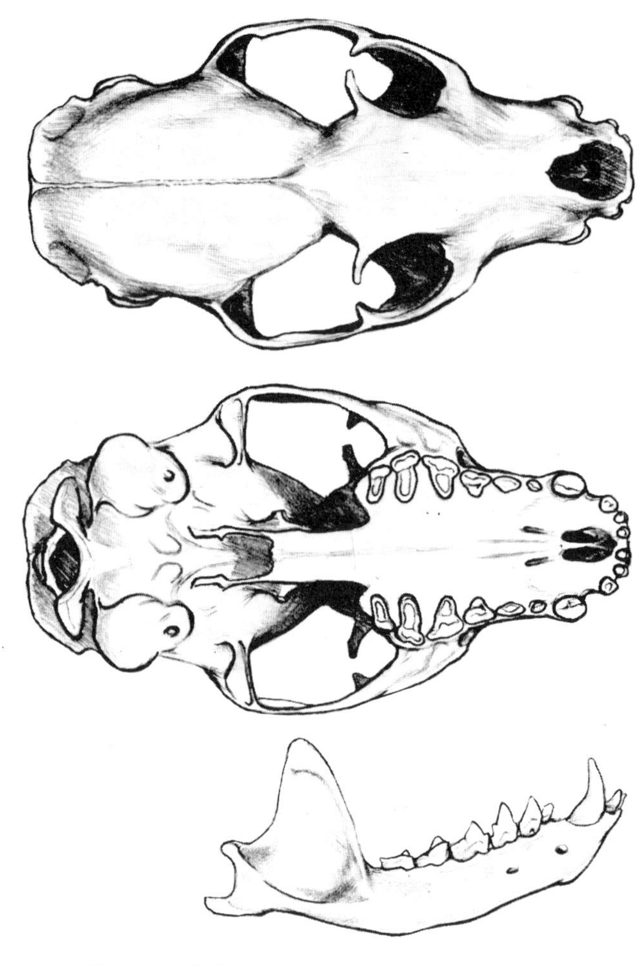

Fig. 271.1. Skull: bushy-tailed mongoose, *B. crassicauda*.
TL Skull 93 mm

The rostrum is longer than in some other viverrids, the distance between the front of the eye sockets to the incisors some 31% of the total length of the skull. The nasals, however, end well back of the incisors about the level of the diastema between the outer incisors and the canines. The front part of the skull, anterior to the glenoid articulation, is twice the length of that part lying posterior to it. The supraoccipital crest is well developed, reaching a height of about 4 mm in adults; the sagittal crest is high at the back of the braincase, tapering off anteriorly and generally disappearing altogether at the level of the postorbital constriction. The zygomatic arches are heavily built, suggesting well developed masseter muscles and this, coupled with the high coronoid process of the lower jaw to which the temporalis muscles attach, indicates a powerful jaw action.

The dental formula is:

$I\frac{3}{3}\ C\frac{1}{1}\ P\frac{4}{4}\ M\frac{2}{2} = 40$

The upper incisors are long, well separated from each other and form a curved row. The lower lie tightly together. In both jaws the outer are slightly larger than the remainder. The upper canines are nearly straight, with sharp cutting edges in front and behind and flattened inner surfaces; the lower are distinctly recurved. While the outer parts of the fourth upper premolars extend over the outer edges of their counterparts in the lower jaw and therefore provide some cutting ability, this is poorly developed, the edges being blunt. The first premolars in both jaws are small and peg-like, the lower lying tightly up against the second. The second upper premolar is of normal shape, but the third and fourth are broader than in viverrids of comparable size, the two molars wearing to broad rectangular surfaces.

The two pairs of upper molars are much lighter in build than in *B. jacksoni* and *B. nigriceps*, in which they are heavy and square-faced, a feature which clearly separates *B. crassicauda* from them. Correspondingly, in the lower jaw the fourth premolar and the two molars are broad and rectangular, the dentition as a whole indicating an adaptation to crushing rather than slicing.

## Distribution

Bushy-tailed mongoose are confined in their distribution to the eastern parts of the continent, from southeastern Kenya southwards to central Mozambique, southeastern Zaire and eastern Zimbabwe. They also occur on Zanzibar Island from where *B. c. tenuis* was described by Thomas & Wroughton (1908). They are not common anywhere throughout their range and there are very few specimens in collections. Therefore, it is difficult to draw up a map which will show their distributional limits accurately.

*South of the Sahara, excluding the Southern African Subregion*

They are recorded from **Kenya** and **Tanzania** and are widespread but nowhere common in **Malawi**. They are recorded from the eastern parts of **Zambia**. They occur in south eastern **Zaire** and in **Mozambique**, north of the Zambezi River, from where *B. c. puisa* was described by Peters in 1852 from Mocimboa in the northeast, and there is a visual record from near Morrumbala (SE 1735A) in Zambezia Province.

*Southern African Subregion*

In **Zimbabwe** they occur near the Kariba Dam, on the Mashonaland Plateau and in the Eastern Districts as far south as the Melsetter District (SE 1932D1) about 20°S. In **Mozambique**, south of the Zambezi River, they occur in the central parts of the country south to about 20°S, which marks their southernmost limits of occurrence.

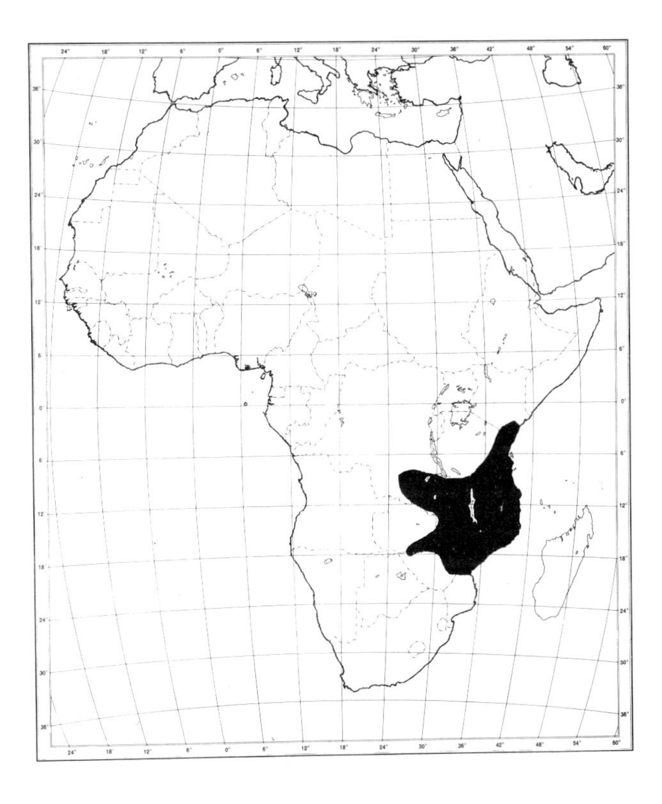

## Habitat

Owing to the rarity of the bushy-tailed mongoose and the consequent paucity of specimens in collections, or observations of the habitat in which they occur, it is difficult to assess their habitat requirements.

In Mozambique they occur on the floodplains of the lower Shire and Pungwe rivers where, on the drier, raised areas, there is an open association of *Acacia* woodland. On the other hand, in northeastern Zimbabwe they occur on granite koppies in association with yellow-spotted dassies, *Heterohyrax brucei*, and red rock rabbits, *Pronolagus rupestris*, at altitudes of up to 1 500 m, and in the Eastern Districts at the Haroni/Lusitu River confluence on the fringes of lowland forest at altitudes of 230 m. Sale & Taylor (1969) in Kenya recorded the trapping of specimens around the base of hills with rocky outcrops and boulders which provided habitat for other small carnivores.

In parts of Zimbabwe they occur in *Brachystegia* woodland where at low altitudes they are found in riverine associations in the Zambezi Valley and in the adjoining mopane woodland. In most of the localities in which they have been taken there is sufficient broken country, at least in the vicinity, to provide habitat for rock dassies. Coe (pers. comm.) recorded that in parts of Kenya they are associated with rocky areas in which dassies occur and it may be that they require this sort of habitat in which to lie up and have their young, but further information is required.

## Habits

Little or nothing is known of their habits. Sale & Taylor (1969) in Kenya, who trapped a number near rocky habitat, stated that they are shy, solitary and apparently nocturnal.

## Food

There is a scarcity of published information on their diet. In a sample of seven stomach contents from Zimbabwe, insects were present in six stomachs, reptiles in four, with smaller occurrences of other food items (Table 271.2).

**Table 271.2**

Number of occurrences of various food items in a sample of seven stomachs of the bushy-tailed mongoose, *B. crassicauda*, from Zimbabwe (Smithers & Wilson, 1979)

| Food item | Number of occurrences |
|---|---|
| Insecta | 6 |
| Reptilia | 4 |
| Amphibia | 2 |
| Muridae | 2 |
| Myriapoda | 2 |
| Araneae | 1 |
| Scorpiones | 1 |
| Gastropoda | 1 |
| Grass | 1 |

Isoptera, termites, were found in three stomachs, in two *Macrotermes falciger* and *Odontotermes badius*, in one, *Trinervitermes rhodesiensis*; Orthoptera and grasshoppers in one; adult Coleoptera in two, and Coleoptera larvae in one.

Reptiles were represented in four stomachs by the following lizards and snakes:

| | Number of occurrences |
|---|---|
| **Sauria** | |
| Variable skink, *Mabuya varia* | 3 |
| Kirk's rock agama, *Agama kirkii* | 1 |
| **Serpentes** | |
| Common house snake, *Boaedon fuliginosus* | 1 |

Amphibia occurred in two stomachs and included the red toad, *Bufo carens*; the toad, *B. pusillus*; Bocage's burrowing frog, *Leptopelis bocagii*; the savanna ridged frog, *Ptychadena superciliaris*, and the Mozambique ridged frog, *P. mossambica*. Muridae in one case was identified as a juvenile multimammate mouse, *Mastomys* sp; Myriapoda as millipedes; Araneae as a baboon spider, *Harpactira* sp, and the gasteropods as the slug, *Laevicaulis natalensis*. The scorpion could not be identified and it was presumed that the dry grass was ingested with the termites and had no food value. It therefore appears that the bushy-tailed mongoose is predominantly insectivorous, but will eat other invertebrates, small mammals and reptiles.

### Reproduction

No information is available for the Subregion.

## Genus *Cynictis* Ogilby, 1833

No. 272

## *Cynictis penicillata* (G. Cuvier, 1829)

## Yellow mongoose
## Witkwasmuishond

Plate 24

### Colloquial Name

All the names so far applied to the species are not fully appropriate, as in the northern parts of the Subregion they are grey, whereas in the greater part of their southern range they are yellow. Occasionally red meerkat (*rooimeerkat*) has been used. However, yellow mongoose is most frequently used; *geelmeerkat* may be used in Afrikaans. Lynch (1980) reported that in earlier literature both *Suricata* and *Cynictis* are referred to as "mierkat"; "mier" = the Afrikaans for termite and "kat" = mongoose; both species are associated with termite *Trinervitermes* mounds in the Orange Free State. He was not sure whether they were named after this association or because of the termites they consume, but thought the name appropriate, especially for *Cynictis*.

### Taxonomic Notes

Roberts (1951) and Ellerman *et al.* (1953) recognised 12 subspecies of yellow mongoose, distinguished predominantly on the basis of their colour, size and the length of the hair and tail. Lundholm (1955b), working with a series of 450 specimens from widely separated areas in the Subregion, showed that these characters grade from one end of their distributional range to the other, although not all in the same direction. To take examples, in the case of colour, specimens from the south are yellow, those from the north grey, with a gradual transition in favour of grey northwards. In the case of the size of the head and body, specimens from the central part of the Subregion, e.g. in southern Botswana, are smaller than those from the west, while those from the east are larger. The tails are longer in specimens from the west compared with those from the east. Therefore Lundholm concluded that subspecies could not be recognised. He applied the name "cline complex" to explain the situation, naming it after the most distant geographically situated subspecies *Cynictis penicillata*, cline complex *penicillata* (from the Uitenhage area)—*cinderella* (from northwestern Namibia). This rather cumbersome nomenclature is of little concern, as long as it is realised that throughout their distributional range clinal variations exist.

### Description

Because of the variations seen in the yellow mongoose in so many characters, it is impossible to give a general description that fits them throughout their range. The colour varies from the richly coloured tawny-yellowish, larger specimens of the southern part of the range to the grizzled, greyish, smaller specimens of northern Botswana. The former have long, white-tipped tails and long-haired coats, the latter have shorter tails with no white tip, the body covered with short hair.

Yellow mongoose have five digits on the front feet and four on the hind feet. The first digits on the front feet are set far back of the other four and do not mark in the spoor. The second to fifth digits on the front feet are armed with long claws, those on the second to fourth measuring up to 10 mm over the curve, those on the hind feet shorter at about 7 mm. The upper lip is entire, lacking a philtrum.

**Table 272.1**

Comparison of the measurements (mm) and mass (g) of yellow mongoose, *C. penicillata*, from (a) Botswana (Smithers, 1971) and (b) the Orange Free State (Lynch, 1979)

**(a)**

| | Males | | | Females | | |
|---|---|---|---|---|---|---|
| | $\bar{x}$ | n | Range | $\bar{x}$ | n | Range |
| TL | 496 | 36 | 412–582 | 506 | 30 | 447–580 |
| T | 210 | 36 | 181–250 | 211 | 30 | 180–245 |
| Hf c/u | 67 | 38 | 61–78 | 67 | 29 | 61–76 |
| E | 30 | 33 | 24–36 | 30 | 27 | 25–38 |
| Mass | 589 | 20 | 478–797 | 553 | 18 | 440–797 |

**(b)**

| | Irrespective of sex | | |
|---|---|---|---|
| | $\bar{x}$ | n | Range |
| TL | 580 | 20 | 526–615 |
| T | 240 | 20 | 218–266 |
| Hf s/u | 71 | 20 | 66–76 |
| E | 35 | 20 | 32–39 |
| Mass | 829,7 | 20 | 715,0–900,0 |

(Adjustment Hfs/u to Hfc/u + 8 mm).

Lynch (1979) showed that there was no significant difference in size between adult males and females.

### Skull (Fig. 272.1)

In profile the skull is highest at the level of the ear openings, sloping gently to the level of the top of the eye sockets and then more sharply forward to the nasal openings.

The braincase is pear-shaped, narrowing towards the postorbital constriction which is tucked in, well in front of the postorbital bars, which are closed in adult specimens, completely encircling the back of the eye sockets. These bars are broad towards their tops and hollowed out inside to accommodate the eyes, narrowing towards the zygomatic arches.

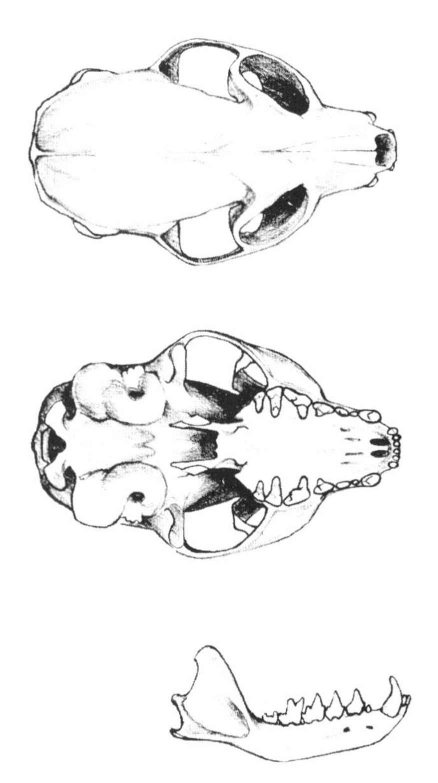

Fig. 272.1. Skull: yellow mongoose, *C. penicillata*.
TL Skull 60 mm

The rostrum is short and broad, the distance between the front of the eye socket to the incisors being about 30% of the total length of the skull. The zygomatic arch is weak, the supraoccipital crest represented by a low, poorly developed ridge. The sagittal crest is absent, the top of the braincase having a smooth lozenge-shaped area, devoid of muscle attachments. The poor development of the zygomatic arches and the lack of a sagittal crest suggest relatively weak masseter and temporalis muscles adapted to a diet of soft food. The front chambers of the ear bullae are developed well and are about the same size as the rear chambers.

The dental formula is:

$I\frac{3}{3}\ C\frac{1}{1}\ P\frac{4}{4}\ M\frac{2}{2} = 40$

The upper canines are long, sharp and slightly flattened on their inside faces, the lower strongly recurved. The first upper and lower premolars are tiny and peg-like, the lower lying tightly up against the second. In a sample of 41 skulls, the first uppers were absent in one, the lower were absent on both sides in three, and in another five were absent on one side or the other.

The upper fourth premolar is large in proportion to the other teeth and has some slicing ability in its outer edge; its counterpart in the lower jaw, the first molar, has three high cusps. In general the dentition is best adapted to a diet that does not require a well developed slicing mechanism. The two upper molars are elongated, lying at right angles to the tooth row and are relatively flat-faced. The hind portion of the first in the lower jaw is flattened; the second molar has three cusps in front, a flat central section and a low cusp at the back. This provides for the crushing that is required for insect and other soft food.

## Distribution

*South of the Sahara, excluding the Southern African Subregion*

Except for a few records near the southern border of **Angola**, between the Cunene and Okavango rivers, the limits of distribution of the yellow mongoose lie within the borders of the Subregion.

*Southern African Subregion*

They are widespread in **Namibia**, except in the Namib Desert. In **Botswana** they occur widely, but are absent immediately north of the Okavango Delta and in the extreme northeast and eastern parts of the country. They are found, however, in the Tamafupa area on the Zimbabwe border in the northeast and extend narrowly in this sector into **Zimbabwe**, in the southern parts of the Hwange National Park. In the south they occur narrowly in the Beit Bridge area.

They occur in the western **Transvaal**, with an incursion just to the north of the Soutpansberg and west of the Sand River (Taylor & Meester, 1989), but are absent from the central, northwestern and eastern parts of the province. They are widespread in the **Orange Free State**, but only occur in the northwestern parts of **Natal**. They occur throughout the **Cape Province**, excluding the mountainous and forested areas in the south and the eastern regions of the northeastern Cape Province and Transkei.

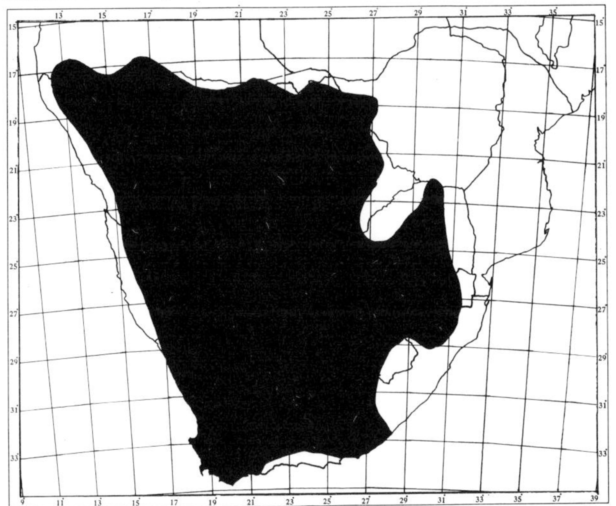

## Habitat

The yellow mongoose is an inhabitant of the open country on a sandy substrate of the South West Arid Zone as far as the pro-Namib in the west, extending narrowly into the southern savannas in the northern and northeastern parts of its range and quite widely in the east where it occurs in the Transvaal and right through to the northwestern parts of Natal and southern parts of Zimbabwe. However, they do not occur in desert or in forest or, within their distributional range, in areas of thick bush. Where they occur in more closed associations, such as the *Combretum/ Terminalia* scrub of Botswana, they are associated within this with the more open areas such as vleis and open grassland around water holes. Within their range they occur in areas of mean annual rainfall of between about 100 mm and 800 mm, but everywhere are independent of water supplies.

## Habits

Yellow mongoose are predominantly diurnal, although some nocturnal activity has been recorded. Herzig-Straschil (1977) recorded that, in the S.A. Lombard Nature Reserve, they were observed to leave the burrows between 08h00 in summer time and around 10h00 in winter, the latest that they were seen outside the burrows being 19h00. Although most other authors are in agreement (Fitzsimons, 1919; Shortridge, 1934; Roberts, 1951), in Botswana specimens were taken after dark (20h45 and 22h00) and they were seen moving at night at several localities (Smithers, 1971). Fitzsimons (1919) suggested that night prowling may result from living in the vicinity of man.

Yellow mongoose are a common feature of the open country of the Karoo in the Cape Province, and the Orange Free State. Although Lynch (1980) regarded *Cynictis* as a solitary species which is usually found singly or in pairs, he stated that *Cynictis* exhibits signs of being in the evolutionary process of becoming a social species. Larger groups encountered usually consist of a family group, *i.e.* an adult pair plus two or three juveniles, accompanied possibly by two subadults of the previous parturition season. In the central Orange Free State, Lynch (1980) found the mean clan size to be 4,1 ± 1,9. On the other hand, Wenhold (1990) found a group of 13, comprising seven adults and six juveniles, in the northern Orange Free State. Fitzsimons' (1919) single allegation of a colony of 50 has been quoted by several authors in the past, including Smithers (1983), so that the literature abounds with this report, wrongly ascribing it to several authors (Lynch, 1980). Without any doubt, Fitzsimons (1919) must have been confusing *Cynictis* with *Suricata*; possibly the colloquial name mierkat was responsible for this confusion.

They frequently share warrens with Cape ground squirrels, *Xerus inauris*, and suricates, *Suricata suricatta*. However, sometimes solitary burrows are found, occupied by a pair or a family party of four or five. While the yellow mongoose certainly excavates its own burrows, the question remains, when warrens are shared with the other species, as to which pioneered the original excavation. Of the three species, the ground squirrel and the suricate are probably the most avid diggers and may be the pioneers of the warren, the yellow mongoose taking advantage of this; on the other hand, the yellow mongoose also digs, and most certainly adjusts the burrows to its own particular requirements. In areas where the other two species do not occur, *Cynictis* excavates extensive burrow systems on its own (Wenhold, 1990). Because of the soil which is thrown up in excavation, the more extensive warrens are sometimes eventually situated on a low mound above normal ground level.

Using tunnels, *Cynictis* (also the two other species) is able to avoid the above ground temperature extremes that exist. In the Orange Free State, Lynch (1980) found that mean burrow temperature during summer fluctuated by only 0,7 °C over a 24 hour period and by only 0,8 °C during winter. Furthermore, burrow temperatures were only 13,3 °C colder during winter than during summer. This is phenomenal if compared to mean air temperatures which ranged from -4 °C during winter to 39 °C during summer—a variation of 43 °C outside the burrow.

Observations show that the yellow mongoose wanders far more widely from the environs of the warrens than the other two species and if disturbed at a distance from its home warren, will take to any hole for shelter. It may well be that, like the dwarf mongoose, *Helogale parvula*, temporary refuges are known throughout the home range, to the nearest of which an individual will retreat on threat of danger. However, when disturbed, they frequently run the longer distance back to the shelter of the home warren. No arboreal tendencies have been observed in the yellow mongoose.

Meredith (1982) has implicated *Cynictis* in 75% of all incidences of rabies epizootics in South Africa. Zumpt (1982) studied *Cynictis* in this context and particularly its association with the suricate, *Suricata suricatta*, and the ground squirrel, *Xerus inauris*, with which it frequently shares warrens. He noted that animals infected with rabies show no fear of man, but no other information has been published on the habits of rabid *Cynictis*. During rabies epizootics Zumpt (1982) found that 25% of animals in an area survive and he suspected that some of these animals act as reservoirs for the further spread of the disease.

## Food

Herzig-Straschil (1977) analysed a sample of 76 stomachs from the Transvaal, showing that invertebrates had the highest percentage occurrence at 87%, with vertebrates at 28%. Among invertebrates harvester termites, *Hodotermes* sp., had the highest occurrence at 67%. In Botswana (Smithers, 1971) termites also had the highest occurrence among the invertebrate food, predominantly *H. mossambicus*. Indeed, the distribution of the yellow mongoose in the Subregion follows closely the distribution of *H. mossambicus* as given by Coaton & Sheasby (1975).

Stuart (1977) examined the contents of six stomachs from the Cape Province which revealed that Coleoptera larvae and adults, in that order, constituted the two food items of highest occurrence in the sample. Other items were crickets, caterpillars, ants, termites, grasshoppers and birds, all these being of low occurrence compared with the adult and larval beetles.

Although Zumpt (1968a p.90) found mice to be important, this was undoubtedly mice and rats dying as a result of a plague outbreak, as he states that "a large number of dead mice and rats were found in the field during April and September". Moreover, Pirie (1927) and Fourie (1938) reported that *Cynictis* readily ate rodent carcasses during plague epizootics and that such epizootics could be detected in the change in contents of scats from insect chitin to rodent hair.

### Table 272.2a

Percentage occurrence of food items of the yellow mongoose, *C. penicillata*, in a sample of 54 stomachs from Botswana (Smithers, 1971).

| Food item | Percentage occurrences |
|---|---|
| Insecta | 91 |
| Muridae | 15 |
| Scorpiones | 13 |
| Reptilia | 11 |
| Myriapoda | 4 |
| Aves | 2 |
| Amphibia | 2 |
| Solifugae | 2 |
| Araneae | 2 |

In a sample of 54 stomachs from Botswana (Table 272.2a), insects had by far the largest percentage occurrence, being found in 91% of the stomachs. This was followed by murids—15%; scorpions—13%; reptiles—11%, with lesser percentages of centipedes, birds, frogs, hunting spiders and true spiders. In this sample, as opposed to Stuart's (1977), while Insecta still had the highest occurrence, within this category termites ranked highest, followed by adult beetles, grasshoppers, crickets and beetle larvae, with much smaller percentages of ants and cockroaches (Table 272.2b). Isoptera (termites occurring in 20 stomachs) were identified in 13 stomachs as the harvester, *H. mossambicus*. In seven cases they represented over 80% of the stomach content, in four the sole content. Adult Coleoptera were represented by Scarabaeidae, dung beetles, and were nearly equalled in occurrence by Orthoptera, consisting principally of grasshoppers and crickets. Coleoptera larvae consisted of ground beetle larvae, Tenebrionidae, at a high percentage occurrence, followed by ants and cockroaches at minor percentages.

### Table 272.2b

Insects identified.

| Food item | Percentage occurrences |
|---|---|
| Isoptera | 37 |
| Coleoptera adults | 33 |
| Orthoptera | 32 |
| Coleoptera larvae | 28 |
| Formicidae | 2 |
| Blattidae | 2 |
| Undet. | 20 |

After insects, murids ranked next, with the much lower percentage occurrence of 15%. Among identifiable species, multimammate mice, *Mastomys* spp, the fat mouse, *Steatomys pratensis*, and the pygmy mouse, *Mus* spp, were recognised. In the four stomachs which contained reptiles no snakes were present, all the remains being of lizards (Table 272.2c).

### Table 272.2c

Reptiles identified.

| Species | No. of occurrences |
|---|---|
| **Sauria** | |
| Black and yellow sand lizard, *Eremias lugubris* | 3 |
| Spotted sand lizard, *Meroles suborbitalis* | 1 |
| Spiny agama, *Agama hispida* | 1 |
| Striped Kalahari blindworm, *Typhlosaurus lineatus* | 1 |
| Worm lizard, *Zygaspis quadrifrons* | 1 |
| Wahlberg's ground gecko, *Colopus wahlbergi* | 1 |

Although no Amphibia were recorded in the samples examined, Herzig-Straschil (1977) listed Delalande's burrowing frog, *Tomopterna delalandii*, and Garman's square-marked toad, *Bufo garmani*, in stomachs of specimens from Bloemhof, and Lynch (1979) recorded Amphibia in stomachs in the Orange Free State (Table 272.3).

Myriapoda were represented in two stomachs by the centipede, *Scolopendra morsitans*. Small birds were present, possibly larks. Similar small percentage occurrences of hunting spiders and true spiders were noted. Herzig-Straschil (1977) recorded that in the Bloemhof district they occasionally would feed on sunflower seeds, one stomach which she examined being more than half full of these seeds. Most of the stomachs she examined contained plant material, but most of this is probably ingested fortuitously with termites and other insects and cannot be considered as important in their diet. Zumpt (1968a), however, recorded their eating the leaves of a succulent plant, *Chortolirium angolense*, which he suggested was taken for its water content, while Wenhold (1990) reported *Cynictis* feeding on the fruit of *Opuntia* sp, as well as other vegetable matter.

Lynch (1979) analysed 156 stomach contents from the Orange Free State, on a qualitative (Table 272.3) and on a seasonal basis (Table 272.4), confirming that the yellow mongoose is predominantly insectivorous, but will take mice, small birds, reptiles and amphibians as well.

### Table 272.3

Percentage occurrence of insect and other foods taken by the yellow mongoose, *C. penicillata*, in (a) a sample of 156 stomachs from the Orange Free State (Lynch, 1979) and (b) 24 scats from north-west Orange Free State (Shepherd *et al.*, 1983)

| Food item | Percentage occurrence | |
|---|---|---|
| | (a) | (b) |
| Isoptera | 74 | 92 |
| Orthoptera | 48 | 96 |
| Coleoptera | 42 | 100 |
| Lepidoptera | 22 | 8 |
| Aves | 11 | 38 |
| Arachnida | 11 | 25 |
| Amphibia | 10 | — |
| Mammalia | 9 | 75 |
| Hymenoptera | 9 | 46 |
| Reptilia | 6 | 4 |
| Dermaptera | 6 | 58 |
| Diptera | 5 | — |

| Food item | Percentage occurrence (a) | (b) |
|---|---|---|
| Dictyoptera | 3 | — |
| Diplopoda | 1 | — |
| Chilopoda | 1 | 4 |
| Hemiptera | — | 37 |
| Crustacea | — | 4 |

**Table 272.4**

Seasonal analysis (%) of four food categories which were present most frequently in a sample of 156 yellow mongoose stomachs from the Orange Free State (Lynch, 1979)

| Percentage occurrence | n | Isoptera | Orthoptera | Coleoptera | Lepidoptera |
|---|---|---|---|---|---|
| Winter | 79 | 72 | 42 | 37 | 19 |
| Summer | 77 | 75 | 48 | 44 | 25 |

Yellow mongoose are good diggers and commonly scratch in piles of debris and in dung in their search for termites and other insect food. They are generally regarded as problem animals as they will take hens' eggs and free-ranging chickens, but normally are deterred by the wire netting around the runs. However, as Earlé (1977) and Wenhold (1990) found that their study animals were apparently incapable of opening chicken eggs, it seems likely that not all yellow mongoose utilise this food source.

*Cynictis* also utilises carrion extensively as a source of food. The occurrence of *Pedetes capensis* and *Lepus* sp in their diet found by Lynch (1980) is probably the result of eating carrion, as yellow mongoose have been observed feeding avidly on the remains of *Pedetes capensis* (Wenhold, 1990).

## Reproduction

Zumpt (1969) examined a series of 676 yellow mongoose from the Orange Free State, western Transvaal and northeastern Cape Province and recorded gravid females from mid-July to the end of December, with a peak in October. Lynch (1980) recorded births from August to November in the Orange Free State, with no apparent peak. More recently, in the northern Orange Free State, Wenhold (1990) found that births occurred in October and December. At the National Zoological Gardens, Pretoria, Brand (1963) reported on the birth of six litters, four of two, and two of one each, between September and November. In the northern parts of the Subregion gravid females have been taken from October to March, with a single record in July. Lynch (1980) found the mean number of embryos/foetuses = 2,3 (n=12) and the mean number of young per litter = 1,8 (n=10). The foetuses are irregularly implanted in the uterine horns. The young are born in chambers in the burrows which are clean with no bedding material.Females have three pairs of abdominal mammae.

# Genus *Herpestes* Illiger, 1811

No. 273

# *Herpestes ichneumon* (Linnaeus, 1758)

# Large grey mongoose
# Grootgrysmuishond

Plate 24

## Colloquial Name

This is the larger of the two species of grey mongoose, the smaller being the small grey mongoose, *Galerella pulverulenta*. Large grey mongoose seems accurately descriptive and appropriate. It is also known as the ichneumon, which is derived from the Greek meaning "tracker", a name given to it in ancient times as they were reputed to dig out and eat crocodile eggs. It was also known in Egypt, in ancient times, as Pharaoh's rat.

Although it happens that the species was described originally from a specimen from Egypt, and the name Egyptian mongoose is also used, they have a very wide distribution on the continent and beyond, and there no longer seems to be any valid reason for associating them with that country.

## Taxonomic Notes

G.M. Allen (1939) listed 10 subspecies from the continent, Monard (1940) added another and Rosevear (1974) a further two.

Meester *et al.* (1986) recognised two subspecies from the Subregion: *H. i. cafer* (Gmelin, 1788) which occurs in the southwestern Cape Province from Hermanus coastally to Natal, in the eastern Transvaal, eastern Swaziland, Mozambique and in eastern, northeastern and northern Zimbabwe, and *H. i. mababiensis* Roberts, 1932 which occurs in northern Botswana.

## Description

The large grey mongoose is a relatively short-legged species with an elongated body. The tail, which includes the hairs of its long black tassel, is longer than the length of the head and body (Table 273.1). The head is long and the muzzle pointed. The ears, which are of the typical mongoose type, are adpressed closely to the sides of the head, and are covered partially by the long hair. The rostrum is short, the eyes set far forward in the head. In the field the body looks grey, the head slightly darker and the lower part of the limbs black. The characteristic feature, however, is the long tail with its distinct broad black tip. At close quarters the body is seen to be grizzled grey owing to the dense cover of long, coarse guard hairs. These are up to 80 mm long towards the hindquarters, and each hair is annulated with five to six black and white alternating bands and has a white tip. This hair on the flanks and hindquarters is long enough to hide most of the hind legs when the individual is walking.

**Table 273.1**

Measurements (mm) and mass (kg) of large grey mongoose, *H. ichneumon*, from Zimbabwe (Smithers & Wilson, 1979)

| | Males | | | Females | | |
|---|---|---|---|---|---|---|
| | $\bar{x}$ | n | Range | $\bar{x}$ | n | Range |
| TL | 1 084 | 10 | 1 005–1 168 | 1 092 | 8 | 1 050–1 125 |
| T | 517 | 10 | 452–576 | 528 | 8 | 485–563 |
| Hf c/u | 111 | 10 | 105–115 | 111 | 8 | 108–114 |
| E | 36 | 10 | 30–38 | 38 | 8 | 30–42 |
| Mass | 3,41 | 10 | 2,61–4,09 | 3,12 | 8 | 2,38–4,06 |

The underfur is soft, fine and greyish, reddish-buffy or yellowish and varies in colour depending on its position on the body. In most specimens it is greyer on the forequarters and flanks than on the posterior parts of the upper parts of the body and the base of the tail, where the other colours are in evidence. The hair on the under parts is shorter and scantier than on the upper parts, especially from the chin to the chest and on the lower belly. The hair towards the base of the tail is long, up to 80 mm, and tapers off in length towards the tip to about 40 mm. The hair of the black tassel on the end, however, is much longer, up to 130 mm.

The large grey mongoose, like other mongoose, has a pair of scent glands, their openings situated adjacent to the anus, each of which is surrounded by a thick semi-circular wall, forming a basin enclosing the anus and the glandular openings. Unlike other species of mongoose, even under the type of stress actuated by handling in live traps, and the proximity of human beings, these glands are not used to any extent and at most only a faint odour is detectable. When handled in live traps, they are much less excitable than other species, such as genets and water mongoose, and are inclined to lie flat and quietly.

The feet have five digits; the first digit is short, situated behind the plantar pad and normally does not mark in the spoor (Fig. 273.1); the remainder are long with swollen digital pads. The claws are long and curved, up to 15 mm across the curve on the front feet and about the same length on the hind.

## Skull (Fig. 273.2)

The skull of the large grey mongoose is long and narrow, the greatest width of the zygomatic arches just less than half the total length of the skull. The braincase is elongated and

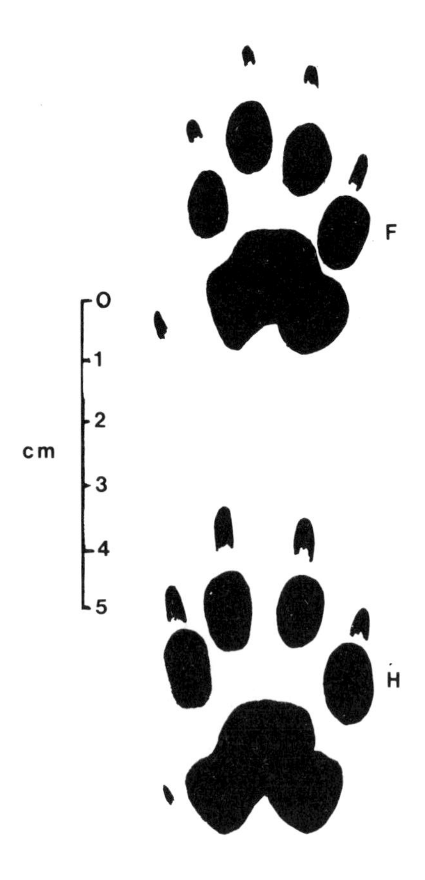


Fig. 273.1. Spoor: large grey mongoose, *H. ichneumon*.
F. Right forefoot H. Right hind foot.

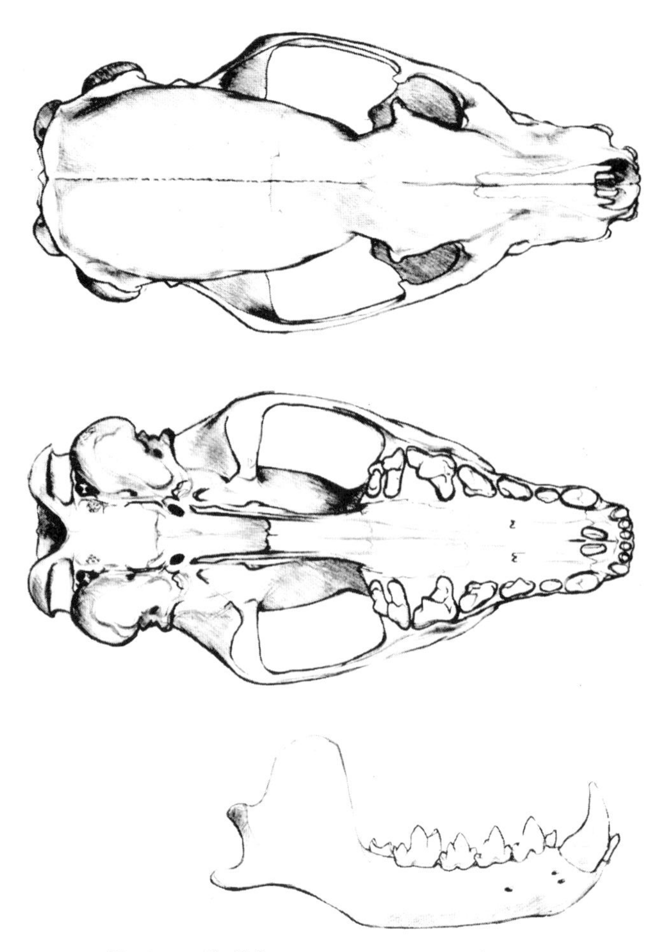

Fig. 273.2. Skull: large grey mongoose, *H. ichneumon*.
TL Skull 100 mm

ovoid, the postorbital constriction about 50% of the greatest width of the braincase, at the level of the junction of the maxillary process with the skull. In profile, from the inflated frontals to the back, the skull is almost level, but in front falls off in an even convex curve to the short, rather narrow rostrum.

The supraoccipital crest is well developed, rising to 7 mm from the skull. The sagittal crest is apparent but not well developed and continues across the top of the braincase to the postorbital constriction. In older specimens with well worn teeth, the postorbital bars are complete. The zygomatic arches are broad and strongly built.

The dental formula is:

$I\frac{3}{3}\ C\frac{1}{1}\ P\frac{4}{4}\ M\frac{2}{2} = 40$

The outer, upper incisors are considerably larger than the remainder and, in unworn sets of teeth, are round and elongated. Their counterparts in the lower jaw are less so, but are broad towards their tips. The upper canines are of moderate size, those in the lower jaw more recurved. The first upper premolar, the smallest of the teeth, lies midway between the canine and the second, but in the lower jaw is tucked up against the second premolar. While the upper second molar is relatively small and narrow, it occludes tightly against its counterpart in the lower jaw, providing a broad platform for crushing. The carnassials have high cusps, suggesting an adaptation to crushing, rather than slicing. The anterior chambers of the ear bullae are small compared with the posterior, which rise to a high rounded apex from the skull.

At the age of 2,5 months all their deciduous teeth have erupted. Three months later the permanent molars erupt. The first premolars are replaced at nine months of age (Ben-Yaacov & Yom-Tov, 1983).

## Distribution

Outside the African continent the large grey mongoose, *Herpestes ichneumon*, occurs in Europe, in Spain and Portugal and in the Middle East, and countries bordering on the eastern Mediterranean. On the continent itself they have a wide distribution from North Africa to the Cape Province.

*North Africa*

They are found in parts of southern **Morocco**; eastwards they occur in **Algeria**, and in central, northern **Tunisia**. The only record from **Libya** is from the Gialo Oasis in the northeast and they occur in parts of **Egypt**.

*South of the Sahara, excluding the Southern African Subregion*

In West Africa they occur in southern **Mauritania; Senegal; Gambia; Guinea; Guinea Bissau; Sierra Leone; northern Liberia; Ghana** and **Nigeria; Zaire**; central and northern **Cameroun**; northern **Gabon** and in a large part of the western **Congo Republic**. They are found in the southeastern parts of the **Sudan; Ethiopia** and **Somalia**, in the vicinity of the Juba and Uebi Schebeli rivers and their associated swamps in the south. They occur in the better watered parts of **Uganda** and **Kenya** and are distributed widely in **Tanzania**; the Central and Southern Provinces of **Malawi**, and throughout **Zambia** and **Angola**.

*Southern African Subregion*

In **Namibia** they occur only in the extreme northeast in the Okavango River drainage; in northern **Botswana**, in the Okavango Delta and along the Chobe River; in **Zimbabwe** in the Zambezi Valley and northeastern and eastern parts of the country; and throughout **Mozambique**, south of the Zambezi River, except in the Banhine, which is dry with a mean annual rainfall of less than 400 mm. In the Republic of South Africa they are confined to the extreme eastern parts of the **Transvaal**; to southern and coastal **Natal** and narrowly along the southern coastal areas of the **Cape Province** as far as Bredasdorp.

## Habitat

Throughout their distributional range large grey mongoose are associated with riparian conditions irrespective of the

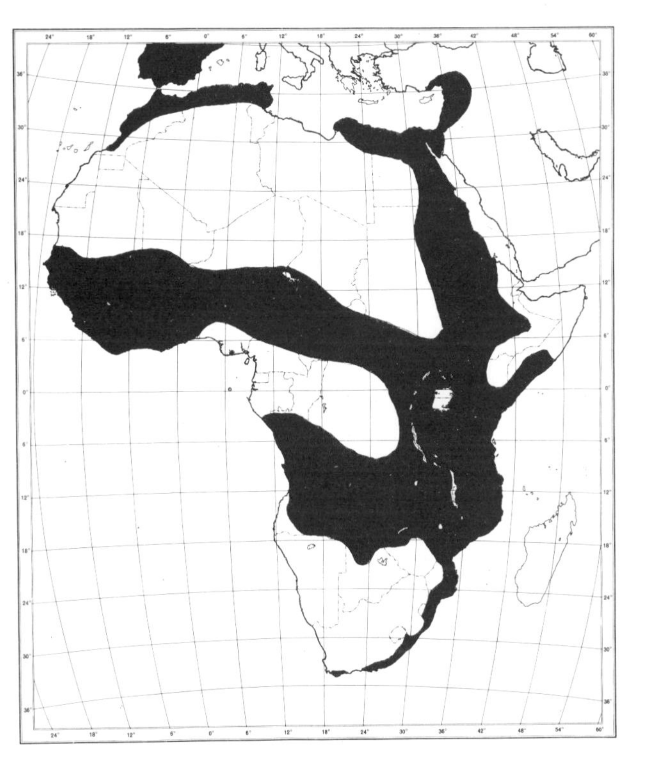

type of vegetational associations in which these occur. They frequent reed beds along rivers, the fringes of lakes, dams and swamps. In spite of their close association with these wet conditions they wander widely in adjacent dry terrain when foraging or when moving from one well-watered site to another, using roads and paths. In the northern part of the Subregion they do not occur in montane habitat or forest.

## Habits

Although authors disagree as to whether they are nocturnal with some diurnal activity (Maberly, 1963), or largely diurnal (Pienaar, 1964), in the northern parts of the Subregion they are clearly diurnal, as shown by observations between 09h00 and 18h00, particularly in riverine underbush, and by spoor on roads after dawn rain. In Zimbabwe they have been trapped between 06h00 and 09h00 on several occasions. Upon realising they are observed they will freeze, lying flat with head and tail pressed to the ground, being difficult to distinguish as the long hair, pressed out from the sides, obscures the outline of the body (Smithers, 1983). They are entirely terrestrial, and are not averse to hunting and moving in shallow water and in muddy areas and are reputed to swim well (Shortridge, 1934; Rosevear, 1974).

Pairs move together and family parties of up to five have been seen. Hewitt (1931) recorded 14 together in the Komgha district in the Republic, a larger number than would be expected in non-gregarious species. Maberly (1963) recorded sightings of four to six together in the Knysna district. Pups are always accompanied by at least one adult, not necessarily the mother, and there is some sharing of duties such as baby-sitting (Ben-Yaacov & Tom-Tov, 1983). The adults always hunt without pups and bring food to them, continuing to do so until they are a year old. Solitary individuals are seen frequently, but one of the pair may be overlooked. When pairs are moving together, one animal tends to closely follow the other with its snout close to the anus of the leader, the pattern followed by the young when accompanying their mother, the scent glands acting as a sort of "adhesive" device in a manner somewhat similar to that in the caravanning in young shrews and in young striped weasels, *Poecilogale albinucha* (Kingdon, 1977; Smithers, 1983).

Large grey mongoose mark their home ranges using items such as big stones situated near their trails. They mark by squatting and extruding anal gland secretion onto the marked place or by dragging the pelvis along the ground. When stressed they mark more frequently. Permanent latrines are used by all family members to mark home ranges (Ben-Yaacov & Tom-Tov, 1983). Under extreme stress, individuals will erect the body and tail hair, appearing to double their size and vocalise with a high-pitched *kie-kie-kie* which, rising in intensity, is very unpleasant at close quarters to the human ear. In traps they will growl softly, although normally they remain silent.

Large grey mongoose can be playful. Rensch & Dücker (1959) described play as involving stalking, circling, rising on the hind legs, head-waving and seizing objects symbolising prey. They would play-fight, face off with arched backs and lashing tails and when quarrelling over food make explosive spitting sounds and fall on their backs, biting and clawing. Adults catch large prey by neck-biting and small items by head-biting and these are eaten from the head.

## Food

The large grey mongoose is a powerful digger and will excavate at the base of dead trees and in debris in search of beetles and other prey. They will kill and eat both murids and snakes, a favoured prey in the southwestern Cape Province being puffadders, *Bitis arietans* (Stuart, 1983). They also take fish, crabs and frogs, as well as mammals, birds, insects and reptiles (Stuart, 1983).

Stuart (1983) in his analysis of 105 scats from the southwestern Cape Province found that murids, particularly *Otomys irroratus* and *Rhabdomys pumilio*, were the principal prey. They also took birds from prinias to cormorants and terrestrial gasteropods amongst other items (Table 273.2). Neither fish nor crabs were represented in a sample of 19 stomach contents from Zimbabwe where murids had the highest percentage occurrence, followed by birds, frogs, reptiles and insects (Table 273.3).

**Table 273.2**

Percentage occurrence of prey items in 105 large grey mongoose, *H. ichneumon*, scats (Stuart, 1983)

| Prey item | Percentage occurrences |
|---|---|
| Mammal | |
| Rodent (uniden.) | 17,0 |
| *Rhabdomys pumilio* | 5,5 |
| *Otomys irroratus* | 5,5 |
| *Bathyergus suillus* | 1,0 |
| *Praomys verreauxi* | 0,8 |
| *Cryptomys hottentotus*(?) | 0,3 |
| Shrews (uniden.) | 1,0 |
| *Myosorex varius* | 0,3 |
| *Chrysochloris asiatica* | 0,3 |
| Felid (kitten) | 0,5 |
| *Procavia capensis* | 0,3 |
| Bird | |
| Unidentified | 4,2 |
| Egg | 1,3 |
| Reptile | |
| Serpentes (uniden.) | 3,7 |
| *Bitis arietans* | 2,1 |
| Sauria (uniden.) | 0,5 |
| *Mabuya*sp. | 0,5 |
| Fish | |
| Unidentified | 1,0 |
| Crustacean | |
| Unidentified crab | 0,3 |
| Arachnid | |
| Scorpion | 0,5 |
| Solifugid | 0,5 |
| Spider | 0,3 |
| Myriopod | |
| Millipede | 0,3 |
| Insect | |
| Coleoptera | 12,0 |
| Orthoptera | 10,5 |
| Mollusc | |
| Freshwater gasteropod | 0,3 |
| Terrestrial gasteropod | 2,4 |
| Plant material | |
| Green grass | 12,0 |
| Dry grass | 4,5 |
| Seed | 4,5 |

**Table 273.3**

Percentage occurrence of various food items in a sample of 19 stomachs of the large grey mongoose, *H. ichneumon*, from Zimbabwe (Smithers & Wilson, 1979)

| Food item | Percentage occurrences |
|---|---|
| Muridae | 63 |
| Aves | 37 |
| Amphibia | 16 |
| Reptilia | 16 |
| Insecta | 16 |

The murids consisted of the Angoni vlei rat, *Otomys angoniensis*, at 37%, followed by multimammate mice, *Mastomys* spp, at 21%, with a single occurrence of the grooved-toothed mouse, *Pelomys fallax*.

Amphibia were represented by: the Angola river frog, *Rana angolensis*; Gray's grass frog, *R. grayi*, and the mottled shovel-snouted frog, *Hemisus marmoratus*. Reptilia were represented by skink lizards, *Mabuya striata*, and the olive grass snake, *Psammophis phillipsii*. The insect remains consisted of beetles and grasshoppers.

The large grey mongoose, probably because of its diurnal habits, when it is likely to be disturbed in such predation, is generally not considered a problem where poultry is kept.

The occurrence of vlei rats, grooved-toothed mice and Amphibia reflect the type of habitat with which they are associated.

Although the sample is small, a breakdown of nine stomachs from the wet, warm months of the year, October to April, compared to 10 from the cold, dry months, reveals that there appears to be no substantial change in the feeding habits seasonally (Table 273.4).

**Table 273.4**

Breakdown of the percentage occurrence of various food items in the stomachs of nine large grey mongoose, *H. ichneumon*, from the warm, wet months from October to April, compared with 10 from the dry, cold months from May to September.

| Food item | Percentage occurrence | |
|---|---|---|
| | 9 stomachs October to April | 10 stomachs May to September |
| Muridae | 67 | 60 |
| Aves | 33 | 40 |
| Amphibia | 11 | 20 |
| Reptilia | 11 | 10 |
| Insecta | 11 | 20 |

In the case of the slight rise in the utilisation of Amphibia and Insecta during the period May to September, all records are from the months of August and September.

Ewer (1973) recorded that the large grey mongoose deals with eggs in the same manner as the banded mongoose and slender mongoose, throwing them with the front feet between their back legs on to a stone or other hard object.

**Reproduction**

There is a paucity of information on the times at which the young are born and where females litter down. Extrapolating from data in Israel, pups are born from October to November in nesting places in thickets. In Zimbabwe two juveniles with a mass of 372 g and 398 g were taken together in December, and one of 900 g in January. In the Cape Province, Stuart (1977) reported that in February an adult with two subadults was seen.

Large grey mongoose live in polygynous families of one male with up to three females with their cubs. Mating takes place over two months in early spring (September) and they usually give birth to only one litter per year, except if the litter is lost when they mate again. They will also mate again if food is abundant, such as during a rodent population explosion, when a second litter is produced. During pro-oestrus both female and accompanying male emit "pip" tones. During oestrus several non-ejaculatory copulations occur. When intromission occurs both emit "pip" tones. During one period of 35 minutes, 10 such matings took place; ejaculatory matings usually last 6–7 minutes. In between matings the male chases the female vigorously, even biting her aggressively (Ben-Yaacov & Yom-Tov, 1983). Gestation lasts about 60 days and mean litter size is 3,3 (range 1–4; n=10; S.D.=0,67). Pups first appear outside the nesting place at about six weeks. When newly born, their eyes are closed, and they only react to movement on Day 21 and sound on Day 25. At four weeks they are fully mobile and at 10 weeks show hunting behaviour. They remain with the family until one year of age or older.

## Genus *Galerella* Gray, 1865

The history of this genus is a classical example of the controversy between "splitters and lumpers". Ellerman *et al.* (1953), for example, listed five subspecies of *G. pulverulenta* and 24 subspecies of *Herpestes sanguineus*, all of which are now included in two species of the genus *Galerella*. More recently Cabral (1989) suggested that they be regarded as superspecies. For further details see Watson & Dippenaar (1987).

Meester *et al.* (1986) noted the confused state of the taxonomy of this genus and recognised two groupings: the *sanguinea* group in which the body is drab brown to yellowish-grey in colour, the tail tip normally black; 13 subspecies are recorded from the Subregion: and the *ratlamuchi* group in which the body is reddish in colour, the tail tip dark but not black, with four subspecies recorded from the Subregion. This treatment is followed in this work.

The present situation warrants further examination in the hope that other characters will be found which will throw further light on this complex issue.

Key to the species (Meester *et al.*, 1986)

1. Colour dark brown, drab-brown, or grizzled reddish or yellowish, with a clearly contrasting dark tail-tip; smaller, skull length normally less than 64 mm in males, 63 mm in females
   ... *sanguinea*

   Colour grizzled grey, tail-tip indistinctly or not at all contrasting; larger, skull length normally more than 67 mm in males, 63 mm in females
   ... *pulverulenta*

---

No. 274

## *Galerella sanguinea* (Rüppell, 1836)

### Slender mongoose
### Swartkwasmuishond

Plate 24

---

**Colloquial Name**

Slender is an appropriate name as they have long, sinuous bodies and long slender tails. The Afrikaans name *rooimuishond*, often used, is misleading, as they are not invariably reddish in colour. *Swartkwasmuishond* is more appropriate.

**Plate 24**

271. Bushy-tailed mongoose, *Bdeogale crassicauda*
    Borselstertmuishond
272. Yellow mongoose, *Cynictis penicillata*
    Witkwasmuishond
273. Large grey mongoose, *Herpestes ichneumon*
    Grootgrysmuishond
274. Slender mongoose, *Galerella sanguinea*
    Swartkwasmuishond
275. Small grey mongoose, *Galerella pulverulenta*
    Kleingrysmuishond
276. Meller's mongoose, *Rhynchogale melleri*
    Meller se muishond

PLATE 24
271
272 b
272 a
274 b
273
275 b
274 a
275
276
Dick Findlay

### Taxonomic Notes

*Sanguinea* section (drab brown to yellowish-grey in colour, tail tip normally black)

Meester *et al.* (1986) listed under the *sanguinea* section 13 subspecies from the Subregion, the limits of occurrence of these being imperfectly known:

*G. s. cauni* (A. Smith, 1836) from the western Transvaal; *G. s. punctulata* (Gray, 1849) from Durban, Natal; *G. s. ornata* (Peters, 1852) from the Tete district of Mozambique; *G. s. swinnyi* (Roberts, 1913) from Transkei, which Watson & Dippenaar (1987) now recommend be given specific status; *G. s. swalius* (Thomas, 1926) from the Berseba district, Namibia; *G. s. caldata* (Thomas, 1927) from Gobabis, Namibia; *G. s. kalaharica* (Roberts, 1932) from central Botswana; *G. s. kaokoensis* (Roberts, 1932) from the Kaokoveld, Namibia; *G. s. bradfieldi* (Roberts, 1932) from Damaraland, Namibia; *G. s. okavangensis* (Roberts, 1932) from northeastern Namibia; *G. s. khanensis* (Roberts, 1932) from near Swakopmund, Namibia; *G. s. ngamiensis* (Roberts, 1932) from northern Botswana and *G. s. erongensis* (Roberts, 1946) from the Eronga Mountain, Namibia.

*Ratlamuchi* section (reddish colour, tail tip dark, not black)

They listed four subspecies from the Subregion under this section:

*G. s. ratlamuchi* (A. Smith, 1836) from the northern Cape Province; *G. s. aurata* (Thomas & Wroughton, 1908) from Tete, Mozambique; *G. s. ignitoides* (Roberts, 1932) from Macequece, Mozambique and *G. s. upingtoni* (Shortridge, 1934) from near Upington, northern Cape Province.

### Description

Slender mongoose, as the name suggests, are small, short-legged and slenderly built, with a sinuous body and a long tail which characteristically has a broad black or dark tip in the Subregion. Barely 0,6 m in total length, the tail is about 88% of the length of the head and body. The average mass of adult males is 637 g, females 459 g (Table 274.1).

**Table 274.1**

Measurements (mm) and mass (g) of slender mongoose, *G. sanguinea*, from Zimbabwe (Smithers & Wilson, 1979)

| | Males | | | Females | | |
|---|---|---|---|---|---|---|
| | $\bar{x}$ | n | Range | $\bar{x}$ | n | Range |
| TL | 595 | 25 | 560–652 | 555 | 19 | 506–600 |
| T | 278 | 25 | 240–299 | 261 | 19 | 233–272 |
| Hf c/u | 65 | 25 | 60–69 | 58 | 18 | 52–60 |
| E | 25 | 25 | 21–28 | 24 | 18 | 22–25 |
| Mass | 637 | 24 | 523–789 | 459 | 15 | 373–565 |

The great variation in the general colour has been dealt with already and correspondingly the length and texture of the guard coat also varies. In the *ratlamuchi* group, the hairs of the guard coat on the upper parts are long and soft with little or no annulations, much softer and less harsh to the touch than in the *sanguinea* group. In the *sanguinea* group, in the greyer, redder or yellower specimens, the hairs of the guard coat are between 30–38 mm long on the hindquarters, graduating in length to the head where the hair is much shorter, on the forehead about 5 mm long. The hair towards the base of the tail is particularly long, up to 40 mm in some specimens. The hairs of the guard coat on the upper parts are annulated with light and dark bands. The general colour is governed largely by the colour of the penultimate annulation, or by the hairs being broadly coloured towards the tip. A typical guard hair from the hindquarters of a greyer specimen has a light base (3 mm), a dark band (4 mm), a light band (3 mm), a dark band (5 mm), a light band (3 mm), a dark band (5 mm), a light band (3 mm), a dark band (4 mm) and a light tip (5 mm). Some have a broad dark base, only two dark bands and a dark tip. Although the hairs on the shoulders are shorter, they still have four dark bands. The hairs of the guard coat on the hindquarters of reddish specimens have only one or two dark bands, the hair being broadly tipped reddish. The hair on the under parts, which is sparse, lacks annulations, being greyer in grey specimens, redder or yellow in the more brightly coloured. In the grey specimens the transition from annulated to plain hair on the flanks is abrupt; in the more lightly coloured redder or yellow specimens it is less so. A feature of the hair of the upper parts is that from about the upper chest the hair is directed forward, with a parting at the level of the lower throat where the hair swings sideways and then backward to join the flow backwards on the side of the lower throat. The profile of the face, from the forehead to the rhinarium, is slightly convex. The rhinarium, which encloses the nostrils, is small and is either pinkish-brown or light brown and has a shallow slit in front which, continuing downwards, divides the hair on the upper lip.

The ears are typically viverrid, closely adpressed to the sides of the head, the opening partially covered by the longish cheek hairs. There are five digits on each foot. The first digits, however, are situated back of the plantar pads and generally do not mark in the spoor, except in a soft substrate (Fig. 274.1). All the claws are sharp and curved, those on the front feet up to 7 mm in length across the curve, those on the back about the same length. There is a narrow web connecting the four digits of each foot. The anus and anal gland openings are enclosed in a nearly circular sac surrounding the anus.

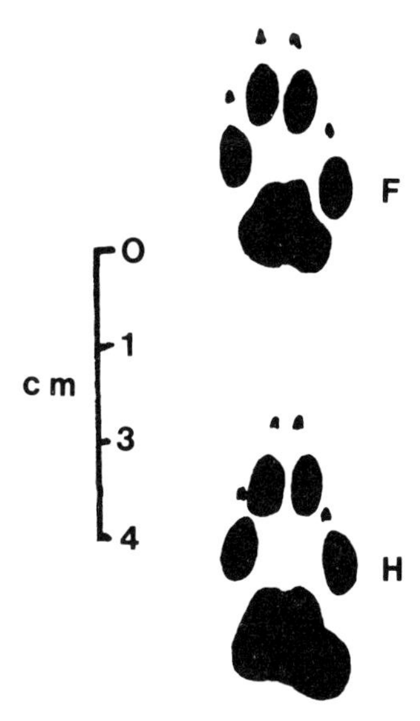


Fig. 274.1. Spoor: slender mongoose, *G. sanguinea*.
F. Right forefoot H. Right hind foot.

**Skull** (Fig. 274.2)

The braincase of the slender mongoose, *Galerella sanguinea*, is roughly oval, broadest at about the level of the ear openings and narrowing in front to the postorbital constriction, which in this species lies tucked in, close up to the postorbital bars. In adult specimens the postorbital bars are complete, enclosing the back of the eye sockets. The rostrum is short and broad, the distance from the front of the eye sockets to the incisors being only about a quarter of the total length of the skull. The flange-like supraoccipital crest is well developed in adult skulls, the sagittal crest, however, except at its junction with the supraoccipital, is represented across the top of the braincase by a barely perceptible ridge. In relation to the size of the skull the zygoma are fairly heavily built, the zygomatic width about half the total length of the skull.

The coronoid process of the lower jaw is high, giving powerful leverage for the temporalis muscles. The front portions of the ear bullae are inflated only slightly less than the hind.

The dental formula is:

$I\frac{3}{3}\ C\frac{1}{1}\ P\frac{4}{3}\ M\frac{2}{2} = 38$

The incisors are set in a straight line, the outer upper distinctly enlarged. The canines are sharp and slightly flattened on their inner sides; the upper nearly straight, the lower distinctly recurved. The first upper premolars are small and peg-like and are not present in all skulls. In a sample of 131 skulls, they were absent in 8% and present on one side only in 9%. All the upper premolars have high sharp cusps. The upper fourth premolar, the carnassial, is

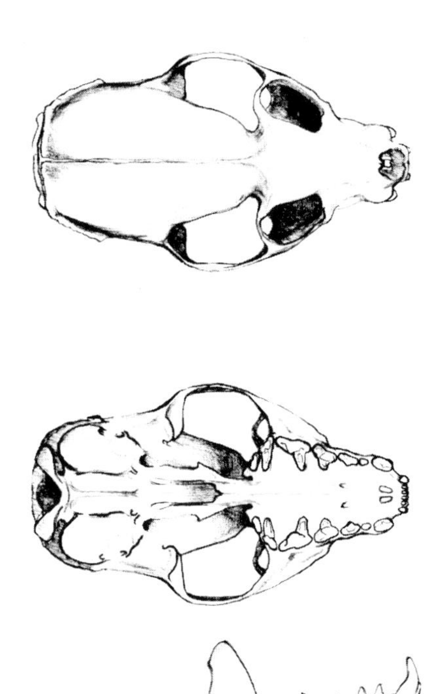

Fig. 274.2. Skull: slender mongoose, *G. sanguinea*
TL Skull 67 mm

well developed, its length over 30% of the total length of the toothrow. The three premolars in the lower jaw are also sharp and high-cusped; the first molar, the lower component of the carnassial shear, is large, its length over 20% of the total length of the cheekteeth row. The upper first molar is elongated, its long axis at right angles to the toothrow; the second is also elongated but tiny; the lower second molar has a roughly square top. The carnassial shear is well developed; the outer hind cusp of the lower first molar enlarged with a sharp cutting edge.

Primarily adapted to an insectivorous diet, the development of the carnassials allows the slender mongoose to deal with tough food such as reptiles and murids.

## Distribution

The slender mongoose has a wide distribution in Africa, south of the Sahara, occurring from Senegal to the coast of the Red Sea in the Sudan and south to the Cape Province.

### *South of the Sahara, excluding the Southern African Subregion*

They are listed from **Senegal, Sierra Leone**, and from a wide range of localities in **Liberia**. They occur in forest and coastal scrub in **Ghana** and in the Guinea savanna in **Nigeria**. In **Niger** they are recorded from two localities in the Asben, much further into the desert than in other areas. They occur in the **Central African Republic**, western **Sudan** and in the northeast on the coast of the Red Sea, near Suakin. They also occur in southwest **Ethiopia**; the northern and southern parts of **Somalia**; the central, western and southern parts of **Kenya**; from a wide range of localities in **Tanzania** and **Uganda**, and the Rift Lakes in **Zaire**, from Lake Albert south to Lake Tanzania, and in the Katanga. They are believed to be widespread in **Angola**, are found widely throughout **Zambia** and occur in **Malawi**. At the moment there are only two records from **Mozambique**, north of the Zambezi River.

### *Southern African Subregion*

They have a wide distribution in **Namibia**, excluding the Namib Desert, and along the Orange River in the south. They are widespread in **Botswana** and are recorded from the Kalahari Gemsbok National Park in the extreme southwest. They are widespread in **Zimbabwe**; in **Mozambique**, south of the Zambezi River, and in the **Transvaal**. In **Natal** they occur coastally and for some distance into the midlands, but not to the Drakensberg in the west and there are no records from near the Orange Free State and Transvaal borders in the northwest. They occur in parts of **Lesotho** and in the central and southern parts of **Orange Free State**, but not in the northeast. In the **Cape Province** they occur north of the Orange River and in the Eastern Province they are found east of about 25 °E.

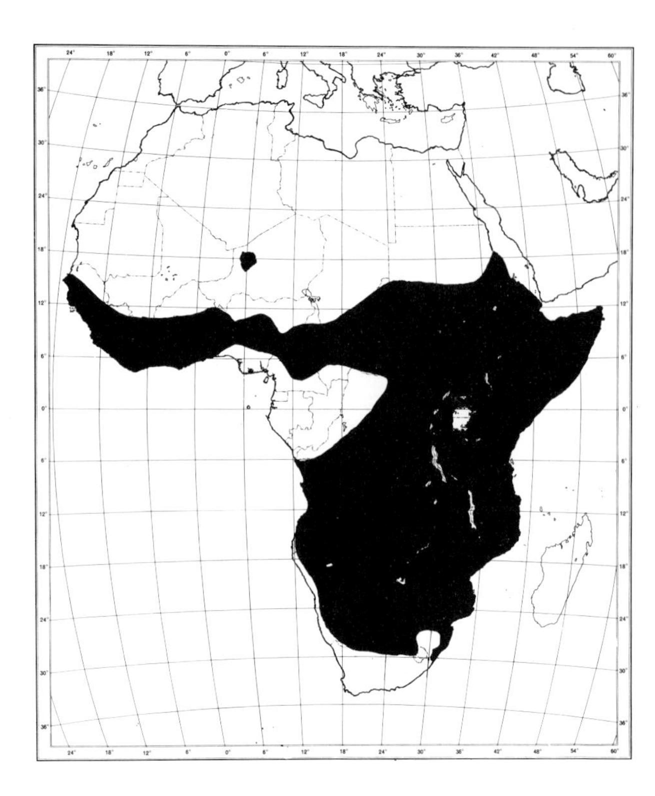

## Habitat

In the Subregion the slender mongoose is catholic in its habitat requirements, occurring from arid regions where the mean annual rainfall is less than 200 mm, to the better watered areas, where the mean annual rainfall exceeds 1 400 mm. They are not found in desert, being absent from the Namib Desert. While they are absent from the greater part of the karroid regions of the Cape Province, the reason is probably not climatic but may be due to competitive exclusion in favour of the small grey mongoose, *G. pulverulenta*. At the perimeter of their range, however, the two species overlap to a limited extent.

Providing there is some cover in the form of holes in the ground, hollow logs, fallen trees or the shelter of rocks, they will colonise open areas. While they will use disused aardvark holes, they have the advantage over other species in being small enough to use holes in termitaria, for which there is less competition. They occur in woodland and even on the fringes of montane or lowland forest, but are not found within the forest itself. They occur from sea level to altitudes of 1 500 m, in the northern parts of their range, occurring up to 3 600 m in Ethiopia. In view of their wide altitudinal range of distribution it is curious that, in Natal, they do not reach the Drakensberg (Pringle, 1977), although they are common in the coastal area.

## Habits

Slender mongoose are predominantly diurnal, not being in evidence in the morning until well after sunrise, after the day has warmed up and they do not move at all in cold, overcast weather. They are less in evidence in the afternoon, retreating to shelter about an hour before sunset. Smithers (1983) surprised an individual at about 08h30 one morning, lying stretched out full length on the side of an anthill, sunning, near the entrance of its resting hole. They are terrestrial and solitary. They are good climbers and will take to trees under stress or when hunting normally. They are found on the ground but if disturbed, will take to the nearest thick cover readily or disappear down holes.

They are alert and quick in their movements and normally move at a quick walk with a smooth action. The tail trails behind in a low curve with the black tip turned up, the nose to the ground, the back slightly arched. When running the body is held flat, with the tail straight out behind. Characteristically, when caught in the open or crossing a road and diving for cover, the tail flips up into a vertical position, just before the cover is reached. When excited they erect the hair on the body and tail, which seems to increase their size greatly. When disturbed they often freeze, standing motionless until the sound is located, or rise up on their back legs balancing, with or without the aid of the tail, to obtain a better view. In certain circumstances they can stand right up on the back feet, balancing with the tail, the front legs held tight in to the body.

They habitually use roads or tracks, moving in and out of the tall grass fringes to hunt. This feature of their behaviour makes them easier to see and no doubt accounts for the many records in literature of their being taken by birds of prey. In captivity they are very sensitive to large birds flying overhead. They will watch these carefully and they appear to recognise the difference between crows, louries and other non-raptors and birds of prey. In the former case, once satisfied that there is no danger, they take little notice; in the latter they at first freeze and then dive for cover.

Baker (1982) identified five different vocalisations in captive slender mongoose: a loud, sharp "spit", a growl, a snarl and a "buzz", which are used in agonistic encounters. Growling and spitting are produced when threatening a conspecific or warding off attackers, snarling when two animals approach each other in attack. The fifth vocalisation, a "huh-nwe" call, is a distress call.

**Food**

In a sample of 60 stomachs of slender mongoose from Zimbabwe and Botswana, the percentage occurrence of the various food items is set out in Table 274.2a.

**Table 274.2a**

Percentage occurrence of food items in a sample of 60 stomachs of slender mongoose, *G. sanguinea*, from Zimbabwe (Smithers & Wilson, 1979) and Botswana (Smithers, 1971)

| Food item | Percentage occurrence |
|---|---|
| Insecta | 73 |
| Sauria | 27 |
| Muridae | 25 |
| Aves | 8 |
| Wild fruit | 7 |
| Serpentes | 4 |
| Amphibia | 2 |
| Myriapoda | 2 |
| Slugs | 2 |
| Araneae | 2 |

Insects had by far the highest percentage occurrence in the sample, the greater proportion of the stomach contents, however, being unidentifiable as they were ground up very finely and consisted of a mass of chitinous chips. Within this ground-up mass, grasshoppers predominated, followed by termites, beetles and ants. Grasshoppers constituted over 60% of the content of two stomachs, termites, *Macrotermes bellicosus*, the sole content of one.

Lizards, Sauria, ranked next after insects, represented by a wide range of species listed in Table 274.2b.

**Table 274.2b**

Lizards identified.

Spotted scrub lizard, *Nucras intertexta*
Variable skink, *Mabuya varia*
Common striped skink, *Mabuya striata*
Striped skink, *Mabuya punctatissimus*
Black and yellow sand lizard, *Eremias lugubris*
Cape rough-scaled sand lizard, *Ichnotropis capensis*
Wahlberg's snake-eyed skink, *Panaspis wahlbergi*
Tree agama, *Agama cyanogaster*
Arnold's skink, *Proscelotes arnoldi*
Common flap-necked chameleon, *Chamaeleo dilepis*
Smooth-headed skink, *Mabuya homalocephala*

Serpentes, where identifiable, included:
Bibron's burrowing adder, *Atractaspis bibronii*
Peters' black worm snake, *Leptotyphlops scutifrons*
Schlegel's blind snake, *Typhlops schlegelii*.

Murids ranked next after lizards, multimammate mice, *Mastomys* spp, the striped mouse, *Rhabdomys pumilio*, and the grooved-toothed mouse, *Pelomys fallax*, being identified. Unidentifiable remains consisted of teeth, scraps of bone and traces of fur. Birds were represented by the feathers of small birds. Wild fruit included raisin bush berries, *Grewia* sp, and wild figs, *Ficus* sp, and in one stomach dusty berries, *Rubus* sp. Herzig-Straschil (1977) listed the Cape dwarf gecko, *Lygodactylus capensis*, in a stomach from Bloemhof. Stevenson-Hamilton (1947) stated that they will kill the "deadly black mamba", *Dendroaspis polylepis*, and Skinner (unpubl.) witnessed the killing of a 1,5 m cobra near Louis Trichardt, northern Transvaal. In captivity, while they will kill and eat small snakes, the larger ones are left strictly alone. The Amphibia and Araneae were unidentifiable. The Myriapoda consisted of the centipede, *Scolopendra morsitans*, a species palatable to a wide range of small carnivores. While insects appear to constitute the principal food of the slender mongoose, lizards and mice rank high as secondary foods.

A breakdown of the food utilised in the cold dry months from May to September, as opposed to the warm wet months from October to April, reveals a change in the percentage occurrence of various items (Table 274.3). This is understandable as, from the onset of the rains, about October, insects become freely available, being less in evidence in the cold dry months, when the utilisation of murids increases as an offset to the scarcity of insects. The same applies to birds, where the occurrence in the period October to April falls off thereafter to a low percentage.

**Table 274.4**

The percentage occurrence of various food items in samples of 10 stomachs of the slender mongoose, *G. sanguinea*, taken in the dry, cold months from May to September, compared with 12 from the warm, wet months from October to April. The samples originated from Zimbabwe and Botswana (Smithers, 1983)

| Food item | Percentage occurrence | |
|---|---|---|
| | 10 stomachs May to September | 12 stomachs October to April |
| Insecta | 30 | 68 |
| Muridae | 40 | 17 |
| Reptilia | 30 | 25 |
| Aves | 20 | 8 |
| Wild fruit | — | 17 |

Reptiles, consisting predominantly of lizards, remain fairly static throughout the year, with wild fruits more available during the warm wet season.

A captive slender mongoose dealt with eggs in the same way as has been observed in the case of the banded mongoose, *M. mungo*, and the dwarf mongoose, *H. parvula* (Smithers, 1983). Being unable to enclose the egg in its teeth on account of its size, it would position it with the front feet and then hurl the egg between its back legs against the wall or other hard object until it was broken, then lap up the contents.

**Reproduction**

Little information on the times when the young are born is available. Indications are that they are born during the warm, wet summer months from about October to March. This is reinforced by the collection of free-ranging juveniles at 90 g in November, 110 g in March and 300 and 400 g in May and June. Such a time would favour predominantly insectivorous species. Implantation in four of five gravid females was 1R 1L, in one 1R, the mean number of foetuses recorded in five females being 1,8 (1–2). The young are born in holes in the ground, in termitaria, crevices in rocks, under tree roots, in hollow logs or in any substantial shelter available.

The hair in juveniles lacks the annulations on the guard hairs, the hairs being unicoloured and woolly. In a 90 g juvenile from the Lowveld of Zimbabwe, where the adults generally are tinged reddish-yellow, the whole of the head and shoulders was reddish, the hindquarters darker and the tail, even at this stage, had a distinct dark tip. The under parts were very sparsely haired and were slightly lighter in colour than the upper parts.

Roberts (1951) recorded that females of the *sanguinea* section had two pairs of abdominal mammae, and those of the *ratlamuchi* section three pairs.

---

No. 275

## *Galerella pulverulenta* (Wagner, 1839)

## Small grey mongoose
## Klein grysmuishond

Plate 24

---

### Colloquial Name

They are often referred to as the Cape grey mongoose as the type specimen came from the Cape of Good Hope. As *Herpestes ichneumon* is by far the larger, this lends weight to the use of "small grey" for this species.

Alternative name: Cape grey mongoose

### Taxonomic Notes

Meester *et al.* (1986) listed six subspecies as occurring in the Subregion: *G. p. pulverulenta* (Wagner, 1839) from the Cape Province; *G. p. ruddi* (Thomas, 1903) from Little Namaqualand, Cape Province; *G. p. nigrita* (Thomas, 1928) from central and northern Namibia, which may include the following two subspecies: *G. p. shortridgei* (Roberts, 1932) from the Ruacana Falls, northern Namibia and *G. p. annulata* (Lundholm, 1955) from northwestern Kaokoveld, Namibia; and *G. p. basutica* (Roberts, 1936) from the Maluti Mountains, Lesotho.

### Description

The species originally was described from the Cape of Good Hope by Wagner in 1839 and, throughout their range in the Republic of South Africa, at a distance they give the impression of being overall dark grey. At close quarters, however, the coat is seen to be grizzled white or buffy and black; specimens from parts of Namibia are generally lighter than those from further south. The individual hairs of the guard coat are annulated with bands of these colours which, lying in juxtaposition, give the whole a grizzled appearance. The guard hairs have four to six black annulations interspersed with white, the width of the bands varying considerably. The hair is short on the head and closely adpressed to it, the individual hairs up to about 5 mm long, reaching a length of up to 50 mm on the hindquarters. The hair on the base of the tail is up to 55 mm and tapering off evenly in length towards the tip. The underfur on the upper parts is slightly darker on the base than at the tip, the individual hairs fine, wavy and much shorter than the guard hairs.

The colour of the under parts is similar to the upper. However, there is a loss of the grizzling, especially on the upper chest and belly. The ears, which are typically viverrid in shape, are closely adpressed to the sides of the head and are partly covered in front by a band of longer hair which arises from the side of the head.

The muzzle is pointed. The rhinarium which encloses the nostrils is small, with a central depression which continues downwards and divides the haired section of the upper lip.

Lynch (1981) provided details of the sizes and mass of adult *G. p. pulverulenta* (Table 275.1). This shows that they have a total length of about 0,64 m, the males with tails about 85% of the length of the head and body, in the females 90%. The average total length of their skulls is 69,8 mm in males, 67,4 mm in females.

Specimens of *G. p. nigrata* from central and northern Namibia, which formerly were considered to represent a separate species, lack the grizzling on the guard hairs and, in the field, look overall black. In the hand they are dark brown in colour with a wide band of black or very dark brown from the muzzle to the tip of the tail, the whole of the distal third of which is black. The guard hairs which form the dorsal black band are narrowly brown on the base and broadly black towards the tips. On the flanks and limbs these are dark brown, but are slightly lighter in colour on the limbs than on the flanks. In this subspecies there is no sign of grizzling on the hairs of the guard coat.

In *G. p. shortridgei* from the northern Kaokoveld, Namibia and southern Angola the upper parts are chestnut-red or yellowish-orange, the flanks yellow-ochre. The yellowish-orange tail has a broad black tip some 90 mm in length. The under parts of the body are buffy to yellowish-buff.

**Table 275.1**

Measurements (mm) and mass (g) of adult small grey mongoose, *G. pulverulenta* (Lynch, 1981)

| | Males | | | Females | | |
|---|---|---|---|---|---|---|
| | $\bar{x}$ | n | Range | $\bar{x}$ | n | Range |
| TL | 647 | 101 | 545–760 | 631 | 81 | 550–687 |
| T | 297 | 101 | 205–340 | 298 | 81 | 220–332 |
| Hf s/u | 69 | 101 | 59–75 | 64 | 81 | 52–75 |
| E | 27 | 101 | 59–75 | 25 | 81 | 16–33 |
| Mass | 911 | 39 | 680–1250 | 683 | 28 | 491–900 |
| TL skull | 69,8 | 101 | 63,0–74,2 | 67,4 | 81 | 62,8–71,8 |

### Skull (Fig. 275.1)

The braincase of *G. p. pulverulenta* is ovoid, broadest at the level of the ear openings, narrowest in front at the postorbital constriction, which lies tucked in behind the postorbital bars and is narrow, not above 45% of the greatest width of the braincase or 17% of the total length of the skull. The rostrum is short, the distance from the front of the eye orbits to the base of the incisors about 70% of the diameter of the orbit. In older specimens there is a slight, barely noticeable, sagittal crest, slightly higher where it joins the supraoccipital crest, which is well developed and may reach a height of about 3 mm.

The zygoma are stout for the size of the skull, the zygomatic width about 50% of the total length of the skull.

The dental formula is:

$I\frac{3}{3}\ C\frac{1}{1}\ P\frac{4}{3}\ M\frac{2}{2} = 38.$

The outer incisor teeth are slightly larger than the remainder in both the upper and lower jaw. The upper canines are slightly curved, sharp and slightly flattened; the lower canines are distinctly recurved. The first upper premolar is small, the fourth adapted to cutting by occlusion of its outer edge on the first lower molar and in part on the fourth lower premolar. At the same time there is provision for crushing in the development of the large protocone on the front inner edge of the upper fourth premolar and the back of the first lower molar together with the other molar teeth. The second molar in the upper jaw is very small, but nevertheless, in occluding on the first molar in the lower jaw, plays a part in this function.

The two chambers of the ear bullae are about equal in size.

### Distribution

*South of the Sahara, excluding the Southern African Subregion*

They occur in the southwestern parts of **Angola**.

*Southern African Subregion*

They occur widely in the northwestern, western, southwestern, southern and eastern parts of the **Cape Province**, with a marginal extension into the southern parts of **Namibia**. There is a break in distribution in Namibia between about 25°30'S and 22°00'S. The species is represented in northern Namibia by *G. p. shortridgei*, *G. p. nigrata* and *G. p. annulata*. They occur in the **Orange Free State**, excluding the northern sector, extending eastwards into northwestern **Natal** in the Royal National and Giant's Castle National

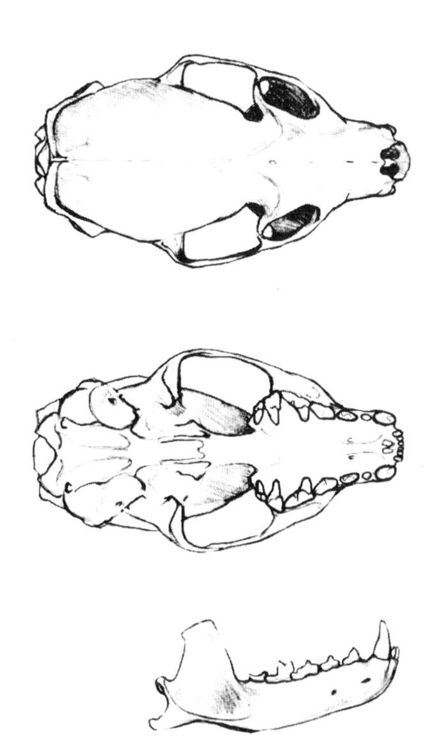

Fig. 275.1. Skull: small grey mongoose, *G. pulverulenta*.
TL Skull 70 mm

Parks and into parts of **Lesotho**. They occur sympatrically with the slender mongoose, *G. sanguinea*, in the Orange Free State and in the northeastern and northern parts of their distributional range in the Cape Province.

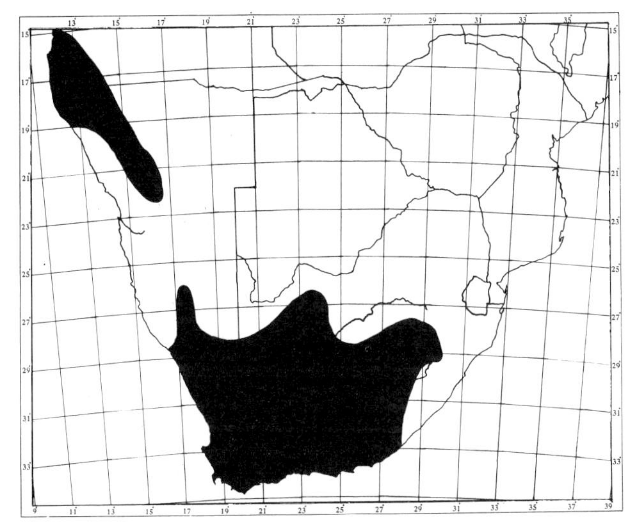

## Habitat

Small grey mongoose have a wide habitat tolerance. The southern subspecies, *G. p. pulverulenta*, is found in areas of forest as well as in open country (Stuart, 1977) and from sea level along the southwestern coast of the Cape Province to 1 900 m in Natal (Nash, 1972) where this subspecies gives way to *G. p. basutica*.

In the northwestern Cape Province and Namibia *G. p. ruddi* occurs in areas with a mean annual rainfall of less than 100 mm, and *G. p. basutica* where rainfall reaches over 1 000 mm.

In the southwestern Cape Province they occur in the *fynbos* characteristic of this sector, and eastwards along the coast. Robinson (1976) recorded that they are widespread in the forested areas of the Tsitsikama National Park.

## Habits

The small grey mongoose is a diurnal species, active from shortly after sunrise until about sunset. Their activities usually slacken off during the heat of the day and recommence late in the afternoon.

Normally solitary, occasionally they occur in pairs and the lack of observations of females moving with young may be due to the fact that the young are weaned in the breeding holes and eventually leave these only at a stage when they are capable of looking after themselves. Although predominantly terrestrial, they will climb trees, either of their own volition when hunting, or under stress, but they are in no sense arboreal. They move at a quick pace on their short legs, pausing to sniff here and there or to scratch in debris in search of insects, which form their principal food. They are quite common in parts of the Karoo where the scrub cover is sparse.

Where there is insufficient vegetational cover to provide shelter at night, they make use of holes in the ground, the shelter of piles of rock, holes in termitaria or holes and crannies in outcrops. Like the slender mongoose, *G. sanguinea*, they will live in close association with man, using the shelter of holes under the floors of outbuildings, stone walls, or any other substantial cover available. They will even penetrate into the periurban areas of cities and settle there.

The claws of the front feet are not particularly well developed, so that they are poor diggers and, while they may adjust existing holes to their own requirements, they do not dig their own burrows, relying either on holes dug by other species or on natural shelters.

Like other small carnivores they tend to move along existing tracks and paths and frequently are observed crossing roads. Unlike their near relatives the slender mongoose, *G. sanguinea*, they do not cock their tails in the air when diving for cover as they cross roads, but hold these close to the ground as they move.

## Food

Fitzsimons (1919) rated insects high in the diet of the small grey mongoose, including grasshoppers and locusts, and among vertebrate prey, rats and mice, reptiles and ground birds, their eggs and young. He described how, in captivity, they would kill and eat puffadders, *Bitis arietans*, always eating the head first, and after eating their fill, would return later to eat the remainder. Shortridge (1934) quoted two correspondents whose list of food items agreed with that of Fitzsimons (1919), but also included the eggs of tortoises, and grubs. There is no evidence to support the suggestion that they may be resistant to snake venom.

In a sample of 11 stomachs Stuart (1977) from the Cape Province showed that insects had by far the highest occurrence, followed by murids and birds, with a lesser occurrence of Arachnida, reptiles and fruit. In addition he had records of their taking carrion in the form of birds and hares killed on roads (Table 275.2). C.H. Langley (*in litt.*) has three records of this species attacking Cape grysbok lambs in the Rondevlei Bird Sanctuary.

**Table 275.2**

Percentage occurrence of various food items in a sample of 44 stomachs of the small grey mongoose, *G. pulverulenta*, from the Cape Province (Stuart, 1981)

| Food item | Percentage occurrence |
|---|---|
| Insecta | 66 |
| Muridae | 52 |
| Carrion | 14 |
| Aves | 9 |
| Reptilia | 9 |
| Solifugae | 9 |
| Araneae | 4,5 |
| Myriapoda | 2 |
| Amphibia | 2 |
| Seed and grape skins | 7 |

From this evidence it seems that the small grey mongoose is predominantly insectivorous, with murids, carrion and birds also ranking high in their diet.

Insects caught on the ground are held down with the front feet, then taken directly in the mouth. Larger prey such as mice are stalked, the mongoose crouching down and watching for a favourable moment before dashing out to secure them, biting at any available part of the prey's body and worrying it before delivering the killing bite on the head. Small mice are chewed in the side of the mouth allowing for the maximum cutting ability of the carnassial teeth. Larger and tougher prey is held with the front feet firmly on the ground and then torn apart; the pieces are then cut up with the teeth before swallowing. Insects are thoroughly masticated, making anything but broad identification of the remains difficult.

**Reproduction**

Stuart (1977) recorded two gravid and two lactating females of *G. p. pulverulenta* taken in August, one gravid female in September and a lactating female in January, from the Cape Province. He listed four juvenile specimens in the collection of the Albany Museum, taken in August, September, December and January, and a report of two juveniles estimated to be a few weeks old found near Port Elizabeth in October. This suggests that the females litter down from about August through to December. Fitzsimons (1919) recorded finding juveniles in a hollow tree, but apart from this nothing seems to have been put on record as to where they normally have their litters.

## Genus *Rhynchogale* Thomas, 1894

No. 276

## *Rhynchogale melleri* (Gray, 1865)

## Meller's mongoose
## Meller se muishond

Plate 24

**Colloquial Name**

While there is a tendency to favour descriptive colloquial names, it is historically interesting to retain the name of the individual after which a species is named, as has been done in this case.

**Taxonomic Notes**

Meester *et al.* (1986) listed two subspecies from the Subregion: *R. m. melleri* from central Mozambique, Zimbabwe and extralimitally to Malawi, Zambia, southeastern Zaire and Tanzania, and *R. m. langi* Roberts, 1938 from the eastern Transvaal, Swaziland and southern Mozambique.

**Description**

At a distance Meller's mongoose appears as a medium to large-sized species with a light brown body, about 0,8 m overall. The tail is slightly less than half the overall length, or about three-quarters the length of the head and body (Table 276.1). Throughout their range, in the northern parts of the Subregion, the tail may be black, brown or white and when it is white the species may be confused, when seen at a distance, with the white-tailed mongoose, *Ichneumia albicauda*. The white-tailed mongoose, however, is considerably larger and generally appears black, at least from the mid-back to the base of the tail.

**Table 276.1**

Measurements (mm) and mass (kg) of Meller's mongoose, *R. melleri*, from Zimbabwe (Smithers, 1983)

| | Males | | | Females | | |
|---|---|---|---|---|---|---|
| | $\bar{x}$ | n | Range | $\bar{x}$ | n | Range |
| TL | 827 | 15 | 572–892 | 824 | 8 | 825–875 |
| T | 360 | 15 | 312–385 | 358 | 8 | 320–377 |
| Hf c/u | 102 | 15 | 97–106 | 98 | 8 | 95–103 |
| E | 38 | 15 | 31–43 | 37 | 8 | 35–40 |
| Mass | 2,31 | 15 | 1,75–2,67 | 3,07 | 8 | 2,41–2,84 |

At close quarters the upper parts of Meller's mongoose are coarsely grizzled, caused by the broad buffy, brown or dark brown annulations on the hairs of the guard coat, which is hard and wiry to the touch. The individual hairs of the guard coat may be basally white or off-white with broad brown or light brown tips or with two darker, almost black annulations. A lighter, very pale brown annulation separates these from the still paler brown tip.

The underfur is dense, the individual hairs fine, shorter than those of the guard coat, wavy and greyer at the base, and grey-brown or ashy-grey tinged brown towards their tips.

The hair on the forehead is about 8–10 mm long, increasing in length towards the rump where it may reach a length of 40 to 45 mm. The hair on the tail of the black-tailed specimens reaches a length of about 80 mm midway and up to 125 mm at the tip, in the white-tailed phase 80 mm midway along the tail, but is never so long at the tip, barely reaching 90 mm.

In the black-tailed individuals the hair of the tail is broadly white or brownish-white at the base; the remainder of the hair is black, the hair on the end of the tail wholly black. In the white-tailed individuals the hairs have white bases with a broad black annulation and broad white tips. The hair on the tip of the tail is wholly white. Ansell (1960a) recorded that in Zambian specimens there is some variability in the colour of the tail, some being basally yellowish-brown, becoming darker midway with a black tip, others showing some banding of brown and lighter colour. The lower parts of the limbs are darker than the upper parts of the body, the forelimbs lacking the grizzling towards the feet. The hind limbs are covered with plain brown hair with little or no grizzling, and are darker on their insides. In some specimens the mid-back towards the rump is darker than the remainder of the upper parts owing to a preponderance of broadly dark brown-tipped guard hairs. The under parts are generally lighter in colour than the upper and may be browner or whiter in line with the general colour of the upper parts.

There are five digits on each foot. The claws on the second to fifth are short, curved and sharp, about 8 mm long across the curve. Those on the hind are slightly heavier and less curved and about the same length. Each digit has a swollen pad at the base of the claw, those on the hind feet generally longer and larger than those on the fore. The larger size of the hind feet shows in the spoor (Fig. 276.1).

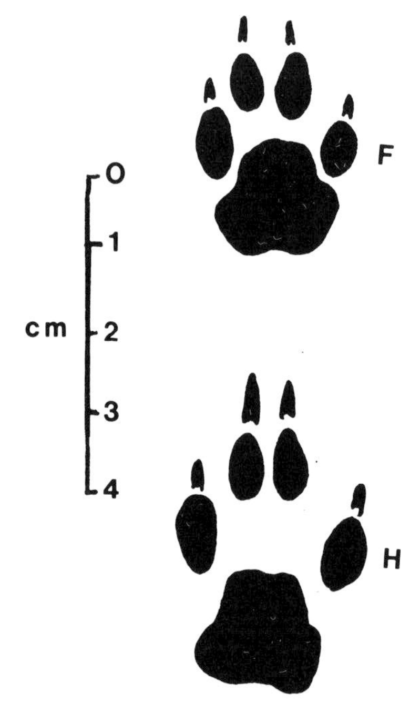


Fig. 276.1. Spoor: Meller's mongoose, *R. melleri*.
F. Right forefoot H. Right hind foot.

One of the characteristic features of Meller's mongoose, as opposed to the white-tailed or Selous', is that there is no central vertical slit on the front of the rhinarium, and the upper lip is entire and covered with short, fine hair.

The anus and anal glands open into a circular pouch which closes to a transverse slit.

**Skull** (Fig. 276.2)

The skull of Meller's mongoose is lightly built and elongated, the width across the zygomatic arches about half the total length of the skull. In profile the top of the skull is highest about the level of the mid-point of the zygomatic arches, sloping gradually back to the supraoccipital crest and rather more sharply forward to the nasals. The braincase is ovoid, widest just behind the glenoid articulations, narrowing forward to the postorbital constriction which is broad, about 70% of the width of the widest part of the braincase. From the point where the sagittal crest divides into two to join the postorbital processes, the top of the skull is enlarged, rising about 4 mm from the general level of the braincase and continuing forward at this level. The eye sockets are set so that the eyes point rather more forward than in other viverrids, the distance between the fronts of the eye sockets is only half the width across the backs. The zygomatic arches are thin and weak. The coronoid of the lower jaw is of medium height, suggesting that the masseter and temporalis muscles are not developed particularly well and consequently the jaw action is not very powerful. The food eaten by the species is soft and does not require powerful jaw action. The supraoccipital crest slopes backwards rising to a height of about 5 mm; the sagittal crest is low and becomes insignificant where it divides into two at the broadened section on the top of the skull. The rostrum is short and broad, the distance from the front of the eye sockets to the incisors is 34% of the total length of the skull. The front chamber of the ear bullae is much smaller than the hind which is roughly rounded and rises to a high rounded apex. The palate is broad, the cheekteeth in the upper jaw set in a curved line so that the palate is broadest at the level of the fourth premolar.

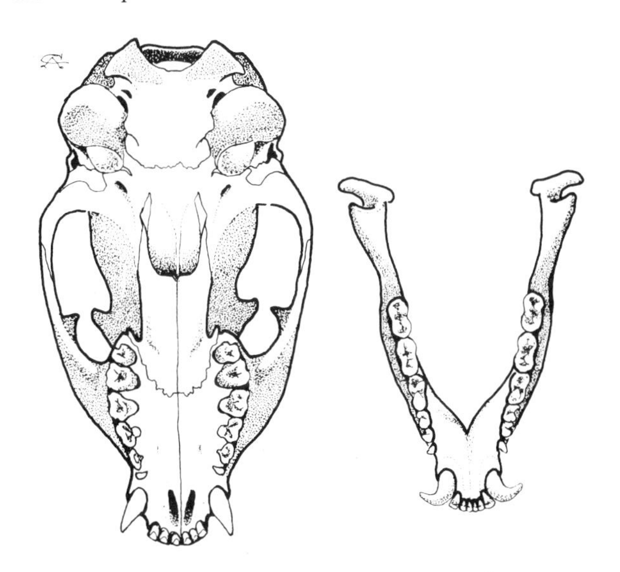

Fig. 276.2. Skull: Meller's mongoose, *R. melleri*.
TL Skull 90 mm

The dental formula is:

$I\frac{3}{3}\ C\frac{1}{1}\ P\frac{4}{4}\ M\frac{2}{2} = 40$

The outer upper incisors are slightly larger than the remainder; the incisor row is curved. The upper canines are thin, sharp and slightly curved, the lower distinctly curved and heavier than the upper. The first upper premolars are tiny, situated behind the mid-point between the canines and the second premolars. The fourth upper premolars are broad and molariform, the first and second molars are also broad-faced and wear rather flat. The first lower premolars are set behind the mid-point between the canines and second premolars. The fourth are broad with high cusps. The first molars have three high cusps on the front, the back half of the teeth flattened. The second molars are similar but the cusps are lower. There is no sign of a slicing ability in the configuration of the carnassials, which are adapted to a grinding function rather than cutting.

**Distribution**

They appear to be confined to the more eastern parts of the continent from about 6 °S to 27 °S, not occurring west of about 24 °E in Zambia. Ansell (1978) noted that their precise limits of distribution in Zambia remain uncertain but they probably do not occur west of the Zambezi River. Throughout their range Meller's mongoose are nowhere common but their apparent discontinuous distribution may be due to a lack of knowledge of the species' presence rather than their absence.

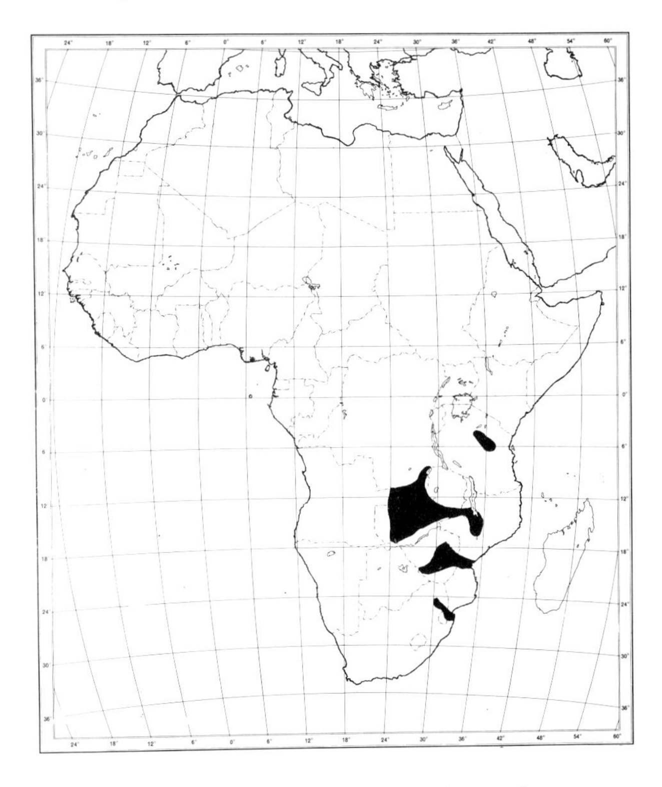

*South of the Sahara, excluding the Southern African Subregion*

There are two records from central **Tanzania**, but there are no records southward between this and eastern **Zambia** and the Southern Province of **Malawi** or westwards between this and the records from **Zaire** in the Mweru Wantipa area. In the extreme southeastern parts of Zaire there are three records and in western **Zambia** there are a number of records east of the Zambezi River and south to the borders of the eastern Caprivi Strip at Sesheke. East of this, while there is a record from the southern Luangwa Valley, they appear to be absent from the Zambezi Valley throughout its length in Zambia.

*Southern African Subregion*

In **Zimbabwe** their distribution appears to be confined to south of the central plateau from Bulawayo east to Mutare, but only as far south as about 21 °S in the west and 20 °S in the Eastern Districts. In central **Mozambique** their distribution follows the Zimbabwe distribution very closely and continues eastwards to the coast. South of this there is an island of distribution which extends from the southeastern parts of the **Transvaal** from 24 °S, north of Swaziland eastwards to the extreme southern parts of Mozambique which marks their southern limits in the Subregion.

**Habitat**

Meller's mongoose is a savanna species particularly associated with open woodland or grassland with termitaria. Both in Zimbabwe and Malawi they are found in open *Brachystegia* woodland, being associated with the more open grassland or vlei areas where particular species of termites, *Macrotermes* spp and *Hodotermes* spp, are found; these termites are their principal food.

## Habits

Meller's mongoose is nocturnal, not appearing until well after sunset and continuing to be active until about midnight. Twelve out of the 18 specimens in the collection of the National Museums of Zimbabwe were killed at night. Except in one case where a female was moving with two juveniles, all records are of solitary individuals, and all observations indicate that they are terrestrial.

## Food

Ansell (1965) reported on the stomach contents of a specimen from Chipengali, eastern Zambia, which contained only termites and two centipedes. Apart from this observation little seems to have been published on the food of Meller's mongoose. Thomas (1894) quoted a collector as saying that wild fruits are always found in the stomachs and Ansell (1965) trapped one on a bait of pumpkin seeds.

Termites occurred in 23 samples of stomachs from Zimbabwe, in 18 being identified as *Macrotermes falciger* and in one each as *M. natalensis* and *Hodotermes mossambicus*. In 10, termites constituted the whole content, in one 80%, the balance consisting of grasshoppers and a centipede, *Scolopendra morsitans* (Table 276.2). Other food items occurring were a Peters' black worm snake, *Leptotyphlops scutifrons*, a frog and the remains of black beetles in one stomach each and grasshoppers in three stomachs. Most of the stomachs contained small pieces of dry grass presumably ingested with the termites.

**Table 276.2**

The percentage occurrence of food items in a sample of 23 stomachs of Meller's mongoose, *R. melleri*, from Zimbabwe (Smithers, 1983)

| Food item | Percentage occurrence |
|---|---|
| Isoptera | 100 |
| Orthoptera | 13 |
| Reptilia | 4 |
| Myriapoda | 4 |
| Coleoptera | 4 |
| Amphibia | 4 |

Although the sample is relatively small, it is a remarkable example of a small carnivore subsisting predominantly on a single food item. Coaton & Sheasby (1972) showed that *Macrotermes* spp occur on and in the dung of cattle and other herbivores, on dead grass and surface leaf litter, on dead trees, fence posts and under canopies constructed over the trunks of living trees. They are distributed widely in the Subregion, their termitaria being very large, up to 6 m high in the case of *M. falciger*, 2,7 m in the case of *M. natalensis*, these being a conspicuous feature of the landscape.

The feeding habits of Meller's mongoose are not known, but from the build of the claws they are scratchers rather than diggers, the short curved claws on the front feet being ill-adapted to the latter pursuit.

## Reproduction

The only information available at the moment from the Subregion is of a female with three foetuses taken in November and a female taken from an antbear hole with two young in January in the Harare District, Zimbabwe. A litter of two newly-born young were taken in a cave in rocky hills near Fort Jameson, Zambia, in December (Ansell, 1960a). Females have two pairs of abdominal mammae.

# Genus *Ichneumia* I. Geoffroy, 1837

No. 277

## *Ichneumia albicauda* (G. Cuvier, 1829)

## White-tailed mongoose
## Witstertmuishond

Plate 25

## Colloquial Name

Within the Subregion the colloquial name is descriptive of the most obvious and useful field character distinguishing the species.

A phase of Meller's mongoose, *Rhynchogale melleri*, also has a white tail, and confusion can occur, although in this case the body is brown, never appearing black as in the white-tailed mongoose.

Selous' mongoose also has some white on the tail, but this never covers the whole tail; furthermore, it is a good deal smaller overall. In the Subregion to date, only two black-tailed specimens have been recorded, one a melanistic specimen from Zimbabwe and the other from the Transvaal.

## Taxonomic Notes

Meester *et al.* (1986) listed a single subspecies from the Subregion: *I. a. grandis* (Thomas, 1890) which occurs throughout the species' range in the Subregion and extends into Zambia; the nominate form has a wide distribution on the remainder of the continent.

## Description

The white-tailed mongoose is among the larger and heavier of the viverrids occurring in the Subregion, individuals reaching a total overall length of over 1,5 m and a mass of over 5 kg (Table 277.1). The tail is long, about 40% of the total length and is pure white for about four-fifths of its length. It stands out in marked contrast with the generally black or darker appearance of the remainder of the body and limbs. The large size and greater development of the white on the tail are useful characters in distinguishing the species in the field. Both features help to distinguish them from Selous' mongoose, *Paracynictis selousi*, which is smaller, and in which only a short section of the tail near the tip is white.

**Table 277.1**

Measurements (mm) and mass (kg) of white-tailed mongoose, *I. a. grandis* from Zimbabwe (Smithers & Wilson, 1979)

| | Males | | | Females | | |
|---|---|---|---|---|---|---|
| | $\bar{x}$ | n | Range | $\bar{x}$ | n | Range |
| TL | 1101 | 18 | 920–1510 | 1016 | 25 | 911–1076 |
| T | 421 | 19 | 346–470 | 442 | 25 | 392–485 |
| Hf c/u | 139 | 19 | 130–147 | 138 | 25 | 130–148 |
| E | 46 | 19 | 42–50 | 45 | 25 | 37–50 |
| Mass | 4,49 | 14 | 3,63–5,22 | 4,14k | 25 | 3,62–4,99 |

In the field, the white-tailed mongoose gives the appearance of being higher and heavier in the hindquarters than in the fore, which is accentuated by the fact that the hair on the hindquarters is much longer than on the fore. The body and limbs are blackish, the head slightly greyer, although this is not always appreciated at a distance. At close quarters it can be seen that the head is grizzled white and black, giving a grey appearance. The body is not an even black but only generally so, there being many whitish hairs showing, and the underfur, which is buffy, shows through the black-tipped hair of the guard coat. The only parts of the individual that are an even jet black are the limbs which are this colour for the greater part of their length.

The hairs of the guard coat on the head are short, barely reaching a length of 10 mm and lie closely adpressed to it. They increase in length towards the hindquarters, on which they reach lengths of about 90 mm. Most of the individual hairs have two silvery-white bands, separated by a black band, and a broad black tip; a few, however, are entirely black. The dense underfur consists of a thick mat of buffy or off-white wavy hairs, much shorter than those of the guard coat.

The hair on the basal fifth of the tail is about the same length as that on the hindquarters, increasing slightly in length where the tail shows white and tapering off in length towards the tip. The guard hairs on the white section have a broad black annulation about midway up the hair and are broadly white-tipped; towards the tip of the tail the individual hairs are pure white. The under parts have a covering of underfur sparsely intermixed with guard hairs.

The central slit on the front of the rhinarium continues downward to divide the haired section of the upper lip.

There are five digits on the fore and hind feet, the first digits small and set well back from the plantar pads (Fig. 277.1). The soles of the front feet are naked; this naked section is short, not reaching the wrist. Similarly, on the hind feet the naked section only reaches the level of the first digit and is not continued back to the ankle. This reflects a more digitigrade form of locomotion in which only the foot and a small portion of the limb behind it is applied to the ground.

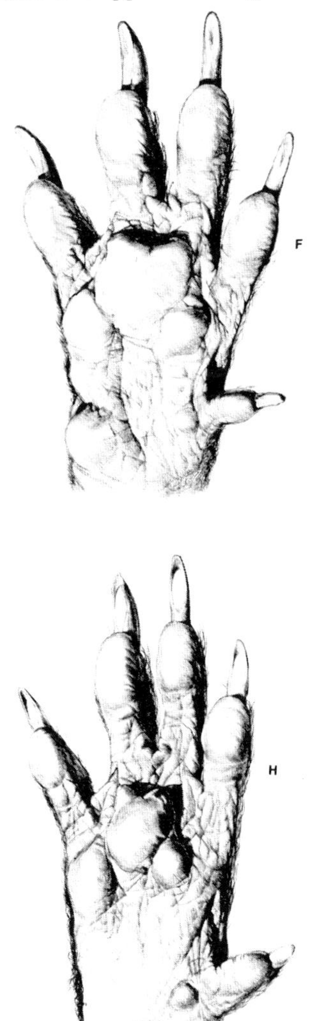


Fig. 277.1. Soles of feet: white-tailed mongoose, *I. albicauda*. F. Right forefoot H. Right hind foot.

The claws on the four toes of the front feet are broad, strong and curved and attain a length of about 13 mm over the curve. Those on the back feet are straighter but still broad at the base and about the same length. The digital pads on digits two to five on the back feet are broader and more swollen than those on the front. The hind feet as a whole are heavier and broader than the front. This shows in the spoor and reflects the extra support necessary to carry the heavier hindquarters (Fig. 277.2).

There does not appear to be any noticeable difference in size or mass of males and females, although males tend to be slightly heavier (Table 277.1).

**Skull** (Fig. 277.3)

In profile the skull of the white-tailed mongoose is highest at the level of the postorbital bars, which are complete in adults, the skull sloping only slightly to the back but more sharply forward to the nasals. The braincase is ovoid but the postorbital constriction is broader in this species ($\bar{x}$=230 mm) than in Meller's mongoose ($\bar{x}$=219 mm), Selous' mongoose ($\bar{x}$=180 mm) or the large grey mongoose ($\bar{x}$=187 mm) (Table 277.5). The braincase is broadest at the level of its connection with the zygomatic arches.

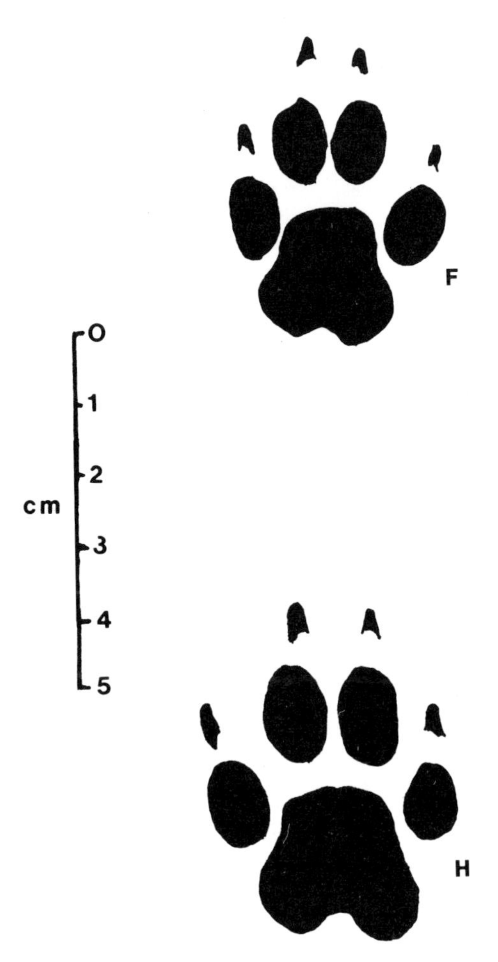


Fig. 277.2. Spoor: white-tailed mongoose, *I. albicauda*. F. Right forefoot H. Right hind foot.

The supraoccipital crest is well developed in adults, sloping backwards and rising up to about 4–5 mm from the surface of the braincase. The sagittal crest is distinct but not particularly well developed and divides just behind the postorbital constriction to fade out before it reaches the postorbital bars on each side.

For its size the skull is rather heavily built; the zygomatic arches stout, the rostrum broad.

**Table 277.5**

Comparison of some skull measurements (mm) in four species of mongoose, the range in brackets.

| | n | Width postorbital $\bar{x}$ | $M^1$-$M^1$ $\bar{x}$ | Condylo-basal length $\bar{x}$ |
|---|---|---|---|---|
| *I. albicauda* | 24 | 230 | 350 | 1116 |
| | | (215–254) | (327–381) | (1089–1187) |
| *R. melleri* | 28 | 219 | 272 | 877 |
| | | (199–247) | (243–300) | (805–940) |
| *H. ichneumon* | 13 | 187 | 323 | 1053 |
| | | (169–214) | (307–339) | (1033–1099) |
| *P. selousi* | 18 | 180 | 258 | 823 |
| | | (159–206) | (245–272) | (760–862) |

The dental formula is:

$I\frac{3}{3}\ C\frac{1}{1}\ P\frac{4}{4}\ M\frac{2}{2} = 40$

The upper incisors, which lie in a curved row, have a distinct shelf on their inner sides caused by wear which is especially noticeable on the outer pair which are larger than the remainder. The upper canines are slightly flattened on their inner sides and are slightly curved, heavily built and taper sharply to the points. The upper first premolar is present in most cases, only absent in one of the 32 adult skulls examined. While the upper fourth premolar has some cutting ability this is not well developed and in general this tooth, together with the two molars and their counterparts in the lower jaw, are adapted more obviously to crushing than cutting. All these are heavily built teeth. The lower molars have high cusps, especially at the front of the teeth. The outer incisors in the lower jaw are longer than the remainder.

The front chambers of the ear bullae are small in comparison with the hind which are swollen and rise high from the braincase when viewed from below.

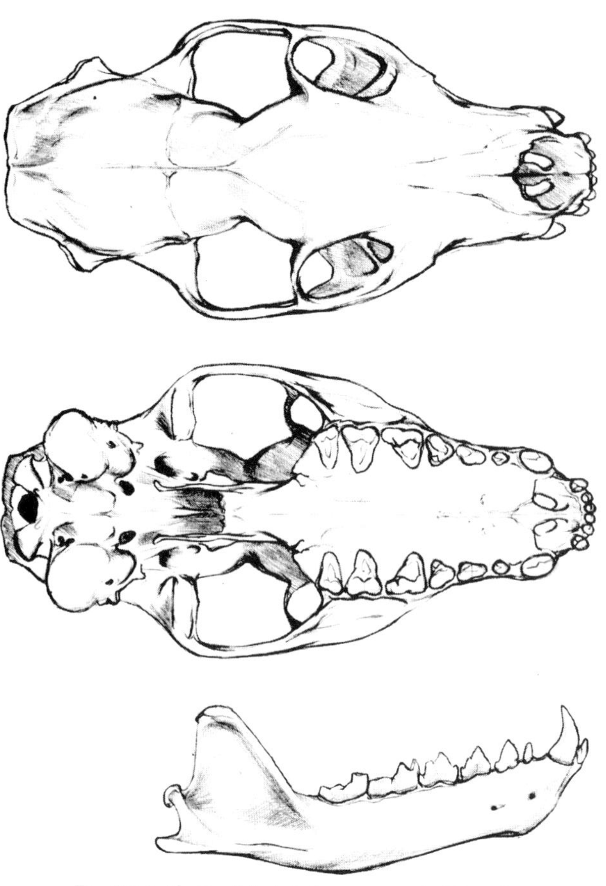

Fig. 277.3. Skull: white-tailed mongoose, *I. albicauda*. TL Skull 110 mm

**Distribution**

Outside the continent the white-tailed mongoose occurs in the Oman, at the southeastern corner of the Arabian peninsula. On the continent they have a wide distribution from Senegal to the southeastern parts of Egypt and south of this to the eastern parts of the Cape Province. Within this distributional range they are absent from forest, desert, semi-desert and the more arid parts of the southwestern part of the continent. In spite of this they do occur marginally in the Sahel Zone in West Africa where local conditions are suitable.

*South of the Sahara, excluding the Southern African Subregion*

They are recorded from **Senegal**, **Guinea Bissau**, and they occur throughout central and northern **Nigeria**. There are sight records from the vicinity of Lake Chad, along Chad's southern boundary with Zaire in Guinea savanna, along the cultivated banks of the Nile in the **Sudan** and marginally into the southeastern parts of **Egypt**, north to about 24 °N on the Red Sea. They occur in **Ethiopia** east to about 40 °E, in parts of **Somalia**, and widely in **Uganda** and **Kenya**, excluding the northeast. They have a wide distribution in **Tanzania**, and in adjacent parts of **Zaire** they occur throughout the Rift Valley and in the southern parts of the country. There are records from central and northern **Angola**, and they occur widely throughout **Zambia**, although there are no records west for the Barotse Province, and in **Malawi**. In **Mozambique**, north of the Zambezi River, information is sparse, only two visual records being available.

*Southern African Subregion*

They occur marginally in the extreme northeastern parts of **Namibia**; in the Okavango Delta in northern **Botswana** and along the Chobe River to its junction with the Zambezi River. In **Zimbabwe** they are widespread except in the more arid western and southwestern areas and occur commonly throughout **Mozambique**, south of the Zambezi River, except locally in arid areas such as the Banhine. In the **Transvaal** they occur in the central and eastern parts of the province; in the **Orange Free State** and throughout **Natal**. They are confined to the eastern parts of the **Cape Province** to the coast at about 33°27′S which marks their southernmost limits on the continent.

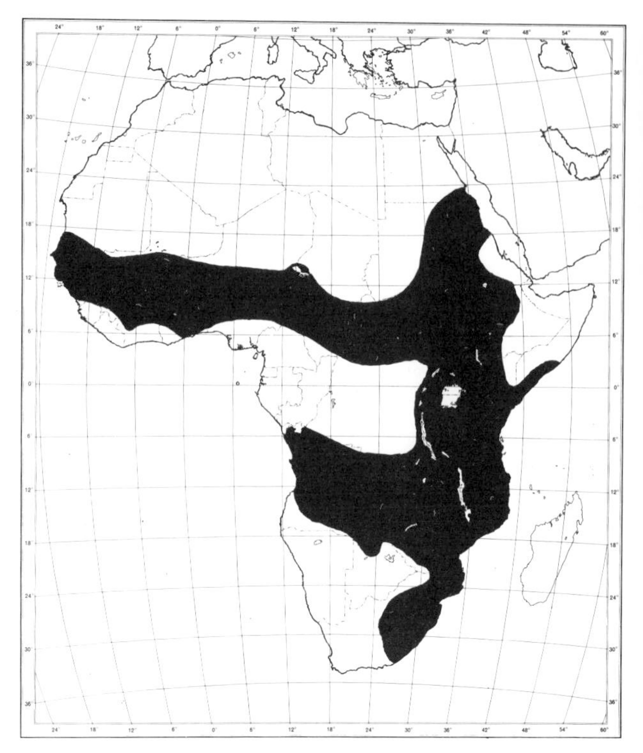

**Habitat**

The white-tailed mongoose is a species associated with savanna woodland in well-watered areas and does not occur in desert, semi-desert or forest. It is almost entirely absent from the open areas of the South West Arid Zone except marginally in the central eastern parts of the Cape Province.

In Botswana they are confined to the Okavango Delta and its associated river systems, although they will wander narrowly into the surrounding dry country. In Zimbabwe, where they are common and widespread, they are associated everywhere with savanna woodland in well-watered terrain, but are not found within forest.

In the Cape Province, Stuart (1977a) showed that while they occur in the better-watered Eastern Province, they are absent from the central and western parts of the province. In the drier eastern parts of the province they occur in parts along the Orange River.

**Habits**

White-tailed mongoose are nocturnal, being in evidence from about 20h30 and moving late into the night, up to 01h30—later than most small carnivores, whose activities appear to tail off by midnight. There does not seem to be any pre-dawn movement. Normally solitary, it is nevertheless quite common to find pairs or family parties moving together at night, even when the young are well grown. It is sometimes difficult to distinguish juveniles from adults until they are caught. In parts of their range in the Subregion they are one of the commonest small carnivores and frequently are seen crossing roads at night, their white tails which stand out clearly in the dazzling light contrasting with the dark body, and often the white tail is seen before the eyes blink. When followed with a head lamp they are prone to hide in grass clumps or thick undercover, crouching low with their heads well down, the tail flat on the ground. They lie so tight that they can be taken with a hand net if approached carefully. As they are difficult to catch in live traps this has proved an effective way of catching individuals for marking. They are terrestrial, with little or no ability to climbing trees.

Even on low thick branches they are ill at ease and under stress take to thick cover or holes in preference to climbing. However, they can climb up the sides of wired enclosures with agility.

Although the long coat gives the impression that they are short legged, the legs are in fact surprisingly long and they are capable of a good speed over short distances. Under certain circumstances they will freeze if disturbed, and if cornered they erect the long hair on the body and white tail, giving the individual a formidable appearance. They walk with a fast, restless gait, with the head held low, the heavy hindquarters giving the back a forward slope, the tail trailing with the tip turned up. If they sense danger while walking they will pause, raise the head with the ears pricked forward, rising high on the legs to try and locate the source. They have not been observed to sit up on the back legs, so characteristic of Selous' mongoose, the slender mongoose and the banded mongoose, but rather support themselves on the front feet on a convenient high object to look around.

They are accomplished diggers, the strong front claws ideally adapted to this purpose. A pair used the refuge of two large fallen trees which, in falling together, had provided a tunnel which the mongoose had enlarged to provide a shelter. However, they do not appear to dig their own burrows, using disused antbear or springhaas holes to rest in during the day. They will also use holes in rocky koppies, adjusting such holes to their convenience. They also use holes in termitaria which previously have been opened up by aardvarks or other species. It is not known whether in the wild they use bedding material.

## Food

The evidence available shows that the white-tailed mongoose is predominantly insectivorous, including in its diet a high percentage of termites, beetles, grasshoppers, crickets and beetle larvae. They are frequent visitors to kraals and manure heaps where they grub for beetle larvae and termites.

Although there are also reports that the white-tailed mongoose feeds on game birds and mammals the size of dassies (Stevenson-Hamilton, 1912; Fitzsimons, 1919; Shortridge, 1934; Maberly, 1963) these have not been confirmed. A captive female would take house rats, *Rattus rattus*, with masses up to about 180 g, but had some difficulty in tackling them (Smithers, 1983).

In a sample of 65 stomachs from Zimbabwe, insects had by far the largest percentage occurrence at 86%, followed by Amphibia, Muridae and Reptilia and much smaller percentages of a range of other foods. Among the Orders of insects found, Isoptera, termites, had the highest occurrence, followed by Coleoptera adults, Orthoptera and Coleoptera larvae (Table 277.2).

**Table 277.2**

Percentage occurrence of various food items, including various Orders of Insecta, and number of occurrences of Reptilia identified in a sample of 65 stomachs of white-tailed mongoose from Zimbabwe (Smithers & Wilson, 1979)

| Food item | Percentage occurrence |
|---|---|
| Insecta | 86 |
| Amphibia | 31 |
| Muridae | 18 |
| Reptilia | 15 |
| Wild fruit | 6 |
| Earthworms | 6 |
| Aves | 5 |
| Soricidae | 1,5 |
| Myriapoda | 1,5 |
| Solifugae | 1,5 |
| Scorpiones | 1,5 |

**Insecta**

| Order | Percentage occurrence |
|---|---|
| Isoptera | 43 |
| Coleoptera adults | 35 |
| Orthoptera | 26 |
| Undet. | 20 |
| Coleoptera larvae | 15 |

**Reptilia**

| Species | Number of occurrences |
|---|---|
| **Sauria** | |
| Variable skink, *Mabuya varia* | 3 |
| Flap-necked chameleon, *Chamaeleo dilepis* | 2 |
| Cape rough-scaled sand lizard, *Ichnotropis capensis* | 1 |
| Sundevall's writhing skink, *Lygosoma sundevallii* | 1 |
| **Serpentes** | |
| Fitzsimons garter snake, *Elapsoidea fitzsimonsi* | 1 |
| Savanna vine snake, *Thelotornis capensis* | 1 |
| Common house snake, *Boaedon fuliginosus* | 1 |
| Mole snake, *Pseudaspis cana* | 1 |
| Shield snake, *Aspidelaps scutatus* | 1 |

Among the Isoptera, *Macrotermes falciger* predominated, occurring in 13 stomachs, in three constituting the whole content, in four others over 40% of the content; this was followed by *Hodotermes mossambicus* in six and *M. bellicosus* in three; the remainder were not identified. Where they could be identified, adult Scarabaeidae were the commonest Coleoptera occurring, with smaller amounts of Carabidae, Tenebrionidae and the larvae of dung beetles, Scarabaeidae. In five stomachs, adult Coleoptera constituted over 90% of the content. Orthoptera consisted mainly of grasshoppers, locusts and crickets.

Amphibia had the next highest occurrence after insects, in four being identifiable as the common African toad, *Bufo regularis*, in nine as *Bufo* sp, with single occurrences of the Mozambique rain frog, *Breviceps mossambicus*, Delalande's burrowing frog, *Tomopterna delalandii*, and the mottled shovel-nosed frog, *Hemisus marmoratus*.

Muridae were identified in five stomachs as multimammate mice, *Mastomys* spp, and in one each as the grooved-toothed mouse, *Pelomys fallax*, bushveld gerbil, *Tatera leucogaster*, and the pygmy mouse, *Mus minutoides*.

Reptilia consisted of four species of lizards and five of snakes (Table 277.2).

Vegetable matter was found in only four stomachs, therefore not forming an important food. It consisted of unidentifiable pulp, maize pips and the fruit of the mobola tree, *Parinari curatellifolia*. Earthworms were found in four stomachs and the unidentifiable remains of small birds in three.

The remains of a shrew, *Crocidura* sp, Myriapoda, millipedes, sun spiders and scorpions were recognised in one stomach each.

## Reproduction

There is meagre information on the time of the year at which young are born and where the females have their litters. Two neonates with the umbilical cord still attached were ploughed up near Harare, Zimbabwe, in January, possibly from a springhaas hole. From the evidence of juvenile scats and spoor at the entrance to another hole under a pile of rocks in the same area, excavated in December, the females use holes in which to litter down.

Four gravid females had three foetuses each, one female one foetus only. In each of the four cases implantation was 2R1L and in the one 1R, one to three young constituting a litter. Females have three pairs of abdominal mammae.

# Genus *Atilax* F. Cuvier, 1826

No. 278

## *Atilax paludinosus* (G. Cuvier, 1829)

## Water mongoose
## Kommetjiegatmuishond

Plate 25

### Colloquial Name

Throughout their range they occur in the vicinity of rivers, streams and dams. The Afrikaans *kommetjiegatmuishond* refers to the sac which, like a cup, surrounds the anal opening and its associated glands, which is possessed by other viverrids.

### Taxonomic Notes

Twelve subspecies have been described from the continent (Allen, 1939). Meester *et al.* (1986) considered that only the nominate *A. p. paludinosus* occurs in the Subregion.

### Description

In a series of 12 adults and five juveniles of the water mongoose from the Harare District, Zimbabwe, there is a wide variation in the general colour of the upper parts. This varies between individuals, both adult and juvenile, which are almost black to others which are reddish-brown or russet. The heavy guard coat, glossy and harsh to the touch, with hairs about 50 mm long contributes to this as, in some cases, it is dense enough to obscure the colour of the underfur, in others open enough to allow the colour of the underfur to show through it. Moreover, in four of the 12 adult specimens, the hairs of the guard coat are annulated, giving the upper parts a grizzled appearance. In two adult specimens from the Okavango, Botswana, the annulations on the individual guard hairs are white, or off-white, the underfur buffy, giving the specimen a generally much greyer colour.

Corresponding with the colour of the upper parts, the under parts may be dark, the short greyish-brown underfur, the individual hairs of which are about 10 mm long, showing through the sparse guard coat. In the individuals with generally russet upper parts, the under parts are correspondingly russet.

The underfur is soft and woolly, the individual hairs kinked and twisted, and about 20 to 25 mm in length. The colour of the underfur varies from dark greyish-brown, brown to reddish-brown, no two being exactly alike. In one, the base of the hair is dark greyish-brown, the tips buffy, the remainder even in colour throughout. The hair in front of the ears grows very long and thick and completely covers the external ear when swimming, protecting it from water as it remains dry (Trendler, pers. comm.).

In life the head appears heavy and broad. The muzzle is short with a broad black rhinarium with a slit down its front which continues downwards to divide the hair on the upper lip. The ears are broad and rounded, closely adpressed to the sides of the head, and are obscured partially by the long hair. The tail, which is about two-thirds of the length of the head and body, is covered with long hair.

The five digits on the fore and hind feet are long, without an interdigital web, which is present in all other viverrids (Fig. 278.1). The digital pads are smooth and, even throughout the length of the digits, are without the distinct apical bulbs seen in the large grey or white-tailed mongoose. This is a useful character in distinguishing the spoor of the water mongoose (Fig. 278.2). In walking the digits tend to splay, which facilitates walking on wet, muddy substrates. The claws on the front feet are stout and curved, the longest 11 mm; those on the back slightly longer and less curved.

The measurements and mass of a series of 12 adult males and 12 adult females, all with a full set of permanent teeth, are given in Table 278.1.

**Table 278.1**

Measurements (mm) and mass (kg) of water mongoose, *A. paludinosus*, from (a) Zimbabwe (Smithers & Wilson, 1979) and (b) mass from some Cape Province specimens (Stuart, 1981)

**(a)**

| | Males | | | Females | | |
|---|---|---|---|---|---|---|
| | x̄ | n | Range | x̄ | n | Range |
| TL | 878 | 12 | 818–970 | 848 | 12 | 792–895 |
| T | 357 | 12 | 310–410 | 348 | 12 | 330–400 |
| Hf c/u | 113 | 12 | 110–115 | 112 | 12 | 107–118 |
| E | 37 | 12 | 30–45 | 35 | 12 | 32–37 |
| Mass | 3,4 | 12 | 2,9–4,0 | 3,4 | 12 | 2,4–4,1 |

**(b)**

| | Males | | | Females | | |
|---|---|---|---|---|---|---|
| Mass | 2,9 | 18 | | 2,6 | 9 | |

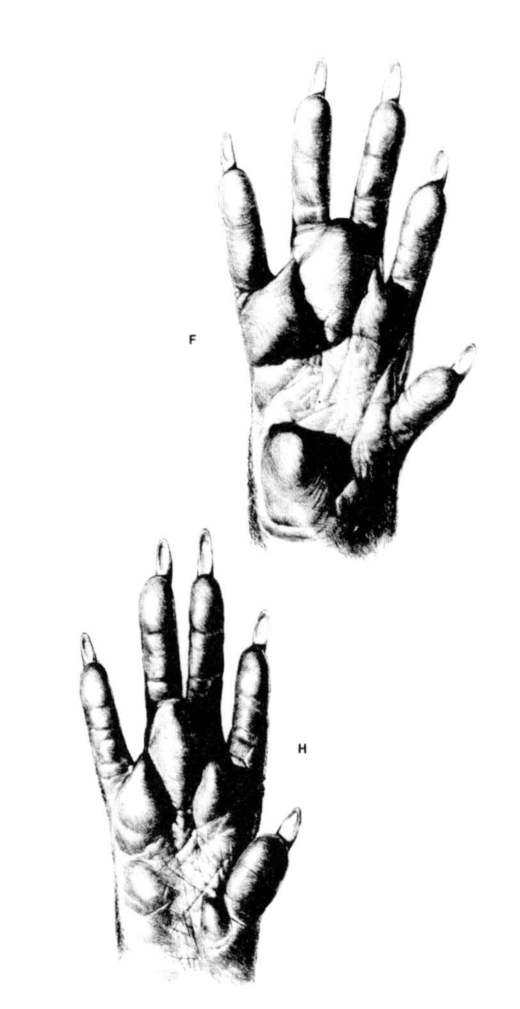


Fig. 278.1. Soles of feet: water mongoose, *A. paludinosus*. F. Right forefoot H. Right hind foot

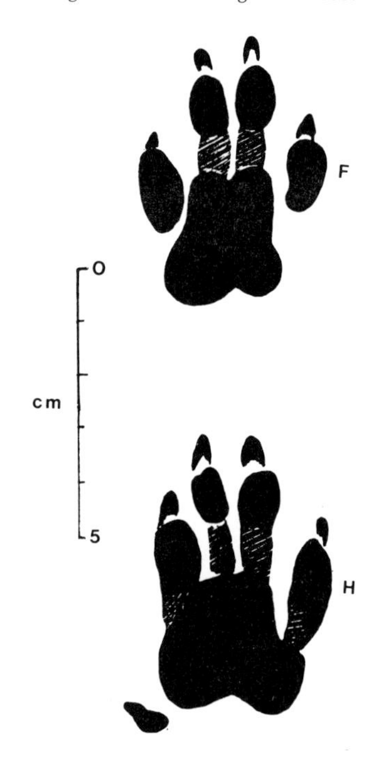


Fig. 278.2. Spoor: water mongoose, *A. paludinosus*. F. Right forefoot H. Right hind foot.

**Skull** (Fig. 278.3)

The skull of the water mongoose is elongated, the elongation extenuated, when viewed from above, by the flange-like development of the supraoccipital crest, which in old adult specimens with heavily worn teeth may measure up to 15 mm at its broadest point. The braincase is pear-shaped, broadest about the middle, the postorbital constriction marked. The postorbital processes in old adult specimens meet the jugal processes to form a ring behind the eye socket. In proportion to the length of the skull the eye sockets are relatively small, their diameter at the widest point only 20% of the condylobasal length, and less than the distance from the front of the eye socket to the incisor teeth. The rostrum is short and broad; the zygoma spreads widely at the back, the width over 50% of the total length of the skull. The thickness of the zygomatic arch varies and is seemingly not correlated with age or sex, for in skulls with well developed sagittal crests and worn teeth, it may only measure 6 mm, while in skulls of young specimens it may reach 8 mm.

In old adult individuals the sagittal crest is well developed and rises to a height of about 4 mm across the top of the braincase to join the supraoccipital crest at right angles at the back of the braincase. It continues forwards to divide into two ridges, ending in the supraoccipital processes. This and the roughened surfaces of the sides of the braincase indicate a powerful set of temporalis muscles which are required to actuate the crushing action of the jaws. The lower jaw is broad and heavily built, the coronoid process wide and high.

The dental formula is:

$I\frac{3}{3}\ C\frac{1}{1}\ P\frac{3}{3}\ M\frac{2}{2} = 36$

In material from West Africa, Rosevear (1974) found that there is variation in the number of premolars in the upper and lower jaw. In a sample of 24 specimens from the northern parts of the Subregion the upper first premolar was present in only two, and then only on one side, in one case the right hand side, in the other the left hand side.

The outer, upper and lower incisors are larger than the others, the upper larger than the lower. The inner two in the lower jaw, in particular, show the bifid points sometimes seen in unworn teeth of the permanent set. The incisors are set in a straight transverse row.

The canines are heavily built, those in the lower jaw more curved than in the upper, which taper sharply to the points. The upper canines have narrow blade-like processes on the front and back, running nearly the whole length of the teeth. In the lower canines these are less in evidence and tend to be present on the inner side of the teeth only. In some skulls the canines remain pointed, even when the premolars and molars show signs of heavy wear, but more generally the canines wear to blunted points.

The posterior section of the ear bullae are rounded and prominent, the anterior section small and flat. The paroccipital processes which are so much in evidence in other viverrids, such as *Nandinia binotata*, enclose the lower part of the ear bullae only and do not protrude beyond them.

The carnassial teeth show little sign of ability to slice. In heavily worn teeth the fourth upper premolar tends to wear flat, the lower first molar retaining three cusps which are blunt and rounded. The carnassials show a distinct adaptation to crushing rather than slicing.

At birth pups are equipped with i1 and 2, after which i3, c1, p3, p2 and p1 erupt; the deciduous set is complete on about Day 4. Replacement by the permanent set then follows: I1, I2, M1, after which there is some variation with regard to the remaining incisor, molar and premolars. Permanent canines are only complete by about Day 243 (Baker & Meester, 1986).

## Distribution

The water mongoose is confined in its distribution to the African Continent, south of the Sahara.

*South of the Sahara, excluding the Southern African Subregion*

In West Africa they are recorded from **Guinea Bissau**, which appears to be as far west as they have been recorded to date; from **Sierra Leone; Nigeria; Benin; Ghana; Liberia; Cameroun; Equatorial Guinea** and **Gabon**. They occur in **Ethiopia** and throughout **Zaire**, extending into the **Congo Republic**, with many records from the Rift lakes. They are found in

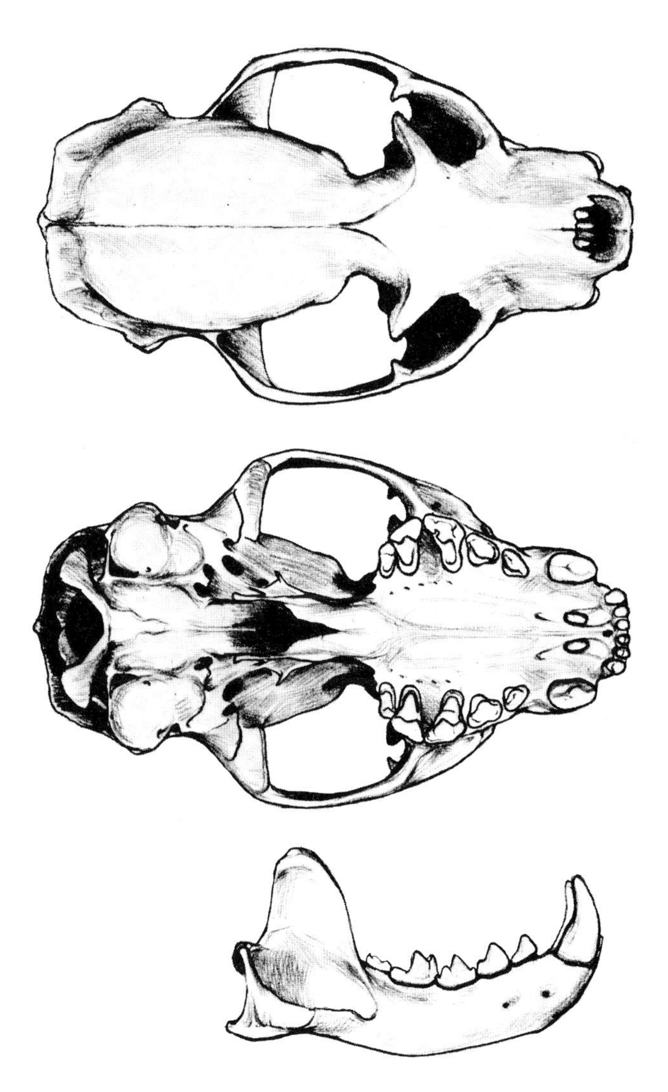

Fig. 278.3. Skull: water mongoose, *A. paludinosus*. TL Skull 110 mm

**Uganda**, the southwestern and southern parts of **Kenya**, in suitable habitat in **Tanzania** and north of the Zambezi River in **Mozambique**. They occur throughout **Zambia** and **Malawi** and are found in **Angola**.

*Southern African Subregion*

In **Namibia** they are confined to the extreme north and northeast along the Cunene and Okavango rivers and in the south along the Orange River about as far as 19°E. In **Botswana** they are confined to the Okavango River, the Okavango Delta and the Chobe River and their associated swamps. In **Zimbabwe** they are recorded from west of the Victoria Falls on the Zambezi River, but not east of this in the valley within Zimbabwe limits. There are no records from the Zambezi River throughout its length in Mozambique, except from the delta.

In spite of this they occur both in Zimbabwe and **Mozambique** in the upper reaches of tributaries of the Zambezi and Limpopo rivers. In Zimbabwe they occur on the plateau from Bulawayo eastwards to the Eastern Districts, but are absent from most of the country north and south of this. This corresponds with their absence in adjacent parts of Botswana and the Transvaal. They are distributed widely in Mozambique, south of the Zambezi River; in the **Transvaal**, excluding the dry western, and parts of the northern areas, and in **Natal**. They occur in the **Orange Free State**, excepting the drier central and western sectors. In the **Cape Province** they are found wherever there are streams and permanent water, in the form of vleis or large dams, but are absent from the arid northwest, north of about 31 °S, the northern parts of the province, north of the Orange River and much of the central Karoo. There is a record from the Orange River at 21 °E which suggests that in time they may occur all along the river westwards as they occur in the same river at *c.* 19 °E.

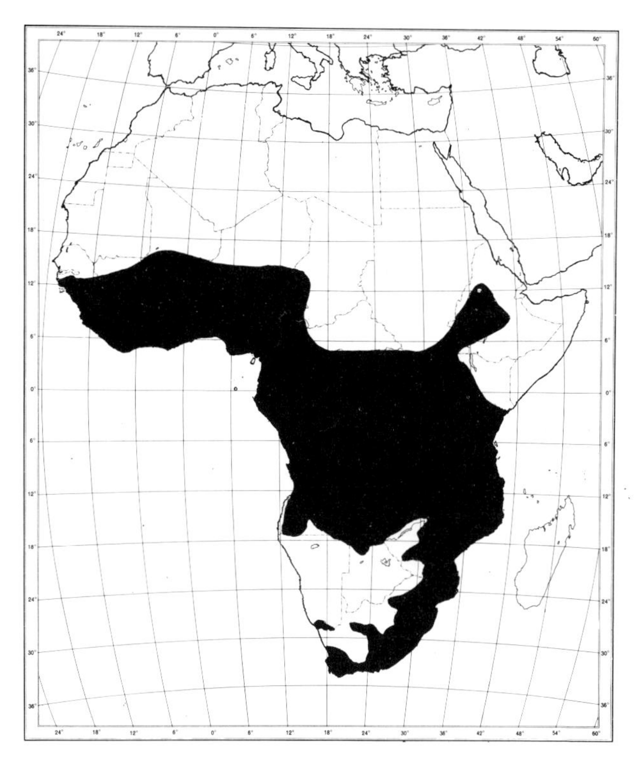

## Habitat

Throughout their wide distributional range water mongoose are associated with well-watered terrain, living in close association with rivers, streams, marshes, swamps, wet vleis, dams and tidal estuaries, where there is adjacent cover of reed beds, or dense stands of semi-aquatic grasses. Their close association with a wet habitat is emphasised in Botswana where they only occur in and around the Okavango Swamp and its associated river systems (Smithers, 1971). In these conditions in the Subregion they occur from sea level to 1 800 m (Hewitt, 1931).

While closely associated with this type of habitat, they will wander some distance from it, either in search of new feeding grounds or in foraging, and have been seen and trapped 0,5 km from water in dry *Brachystegia* woodland. While commonly found along small tributary systems or rivers, when these temporarily dry up they do not vacate the area, like the clawless otter, but remain. Examination of scats and stomach contents at this time shows that they turn to terrestrial food resources (see **Food**).

## Habits

In the northern parts of their range in the Subregion, water mongoose are crepuscular. Observations in the field indicate activity from first light in the morning until about 08h30, or 09h00 in overcast or cool weather and commonly from about 17h30 in the afternoon until the fading of the last light at about 19h00. In captivity, activity continued up to about 12h30, after which they retired, being active again from first light at about 05h30 until about 08h30.

During regular weekly observations with dazzling lights, operating from about 20h30 to midnight no water mongoose were seen in an area in Zimbabwe in which 14 individuals had been trapped and marked (Smithers, 1983). However, they are very sensitive to dazzling lights and will make for cover or run in a distracted manner to escape the beam, thereby being overlooked.

They are terrestrial and solitary, although adult females may be accompanied by juveniles. They will wander some distance from the fringes of aquatic habitat and have been trapped alongside roads in dry terrain. Spoor indicates that, under these conditions, like so many other small carnivores, they make use of paths when moving from one area to another.

They use resting places for some time. The nocturnal resting places are piles of grass and other debris in thick reed beds, usually situated on raised ground out of reach of flood water, in one instance, deep within the shelter of a *Phragmites* reed bed adjacent to a stream, under a dense matted mass of fallen leaves and stems on the dry ground. Another resting place was discovered in the shelter of a curve in a dam wall close to the outlet pipe, where an individual was in the habit of lying out in the sun, sheltered from the wind, on cold mornings (Smithers, 1983).

Authors agree that water mongoose will swim (Fitzsimons, 1919; Sclater, 1900; Stevenson-Hamilton, 1912). They do this voluntarily (Trendler, pers. comm.) and they are excellent swimmers. They fully immerse themselves when searching for prey with eyes open, and even after extended swimming periods the undercoat remains dry. On numerous occasions spoor show that they enter the water near the top reaches of dams and cross to the other side. They move up and down water courses, the spoor indicating that in some parts they wade, in others they walk along the muddy banks (Smithers, 1983). Fitzsimons (1919) gave an account of an individual under stress taking to the water and remaining in the shelter of a reed bed with only its nose showing above water, where it remained motionless until found by a dog.

Upon capture on being approached, they exhibit a "frenzy of fear" and are inclined to damage themselves in their efforts to escape.

They are vocal animals, and Baker (1988a) analysed vocalisations of water mongoose sonagraphically; she placed sounds in three main categories, "bray" being produced during mating and in agonistic encounters, "grizzle" being vocalisations during distress or warning, and "humph" being attention or appeasement calls. The variety of calls is poor, but their variability is extensive. They utter a high-pitched spitting sound like a bark when cornered or a snort when nervous or curious which they do while keeping the head near the ground and raising their hindquarters (Trendler, pers. comm.). They utter two guttural "miaows" when calling for attention or food. Being solitary, the calls probably only represent those essential for maintaining compatibility during brief encounters.

They have a well developed sense of smell and Baker (1988b) described four methods of scent-marking: defecation, urination, anal-marking and cheek-rubbing. Anal-marking is frequently used, more so by females than males, particularly by females in the breeding season. Scats are always deposited in middens (Baker, 1988b), and in the wild they usually defecate on shrubs 50–200 mm high (Louw & Nel, 1986). Urination is performed in the squatting position by females; females occasionally and males invariably lift a hind leg. Anal-marking is achieved by depressing the open anal sac onto an object, occasionally using the hand-stand position. Initially black, with the passage of time the substance becomes creamy. In stressful situations they may forcibly eject anal fluid which is strong-smelling and volatile. Cheek-marking occurs frequently and, only when the female is ready to copulate does she cease to do so (Baker, 1988b).

## Food

In the absence of quantitative data on prey availability in studies undertaken thus far, the diet of water mongoose is a product of its environment and reflects the degree of opportunism resorted to by the water mongoose when feeding.

This is well illustrated in Table 278.2 where it can be seen that the composition of scats from water mongoose on the coast at Betty's Bay was different from scats collected from mongoose foraging inland at the Mountain Zebra National Park, the Cape Province, and Natal.

**Table 278.2**

The percentage of all the items in the scats in which an item is recognisable as remains of prey from particular Orders from (a) Betty's Bay (Louw & Nel, 1986), (b) Mountain Zebra National Park (du Toit, 1980) in the Cape Province and (c) Natal (Rowe-Rowe, 1977), and from stomachs in Zimbabwe (Smithers & Wilson, 1979).

| Prey item | Area | | | |
|---|---|---|---|---|
| | a | b | c | d |
| | n=247 | n=100 | n=210 | n=29 |
| Mammalia | 1,8 | 8,0 | 14,0 | 23,6 |
| Aves | 1,6 | 22,0 | 14,0 | — |
| Pisces | 2,6 | — | 2,0 | 4,5 |
| Amphibia | 2,1 | — | 14,0 | 29,0 |
| Mollusca | 11,0 | — | 43,0 | — |
| Crustacea | 25,6 | 32,0 | — | 23,6 |
| Isopoda | 30,3 | — | — | — |
| Insecta | 12,3 | 17,0 | 2,0 | 19,0 |
| Fruit | 12,0 | 21,0 | 2,0 | — |
| Uniden. | — | — | 3,0 | — |

Frogs' eggs constituted 30% of the content of one stomach. Prey items are carried onto the drier fringes of streams and pools to be eaten. Heads of platannas are eaten first, followed by the remainder of the body. *Bufo* sp toads are killed by a head bite and then palpated on the ground which Baker (1989) presumes is to remove noxious substances. Crabs are undoubtedly a favoured food item in all areas (Table 278.2) and in studies at the Palmiet River and Kobee Valley (Louw & Nel, 1986) and Lake St Lucia (Whitfield & Blaber, 1980) these are forked out from under overhanging roots and other crannies in river banks with the long digits of the agile forefeet. Small specimens are crunched up whole; larger ones are pinned to the ground with a forepaw and the nippers removed with the teeth and discarded (Baker, 1989). The crab is then turned upside down and the meat from inside the carapace eaten, the carapace being discarded, after which the legs and nippers are eaten. Upturned dry carapaces found on river banks are an indication of the presence of this species. Clawless otters, which also eat crabs, normally crunch up the carapace (Smithers, 1983). When it has finished eating, the mongoose wipes its mouth with the forefeet.

**Table 278.3**

Percentage occurrence of species of Muridae in a sample of 19 stomachs of water mongoose, *Atilax paludinosus*, from Zimbabwe (Smithers & Wilson, 1979)

| Species | Percentage occurrence |
|---|---|
| Angoni vlei rat, *Otomys angoniensis* | 10 |
| Multimammate mice, *Mastomys* spp | 5 |
| Pygmy mouse, *Mus minutoides* | 5 |

Lombard (1958) included freshwater mussels in the diet of captive animals even though they were not available to them in the area from which the sample was taken. These were thrown forcibly onto a hard surface with the front feet in order to break open the shell.

In rodent prey, the killing bite commonly spans the antero-dorsal part of the cranium and the prey is then often shaken to death and consumed from the anterior end, parts of the cranium being found in scats. Unlike other mongoose species, large eggs are broken by rearing up on the hind legs and throwing the egg vertically downwards (Baker, 1989).

In an estuarine situation at Lake St Lucia, Whitfield & Blaber (1980) found that crabs were the dominant food, followed by penaeid prawns, insects, frogs and fish, together with lesser amounts of vegetable matter and mammals.

**Reproduction**

Only meagre information exists on which time of the year the young are born in the wild. Fitzsimons (1919) recorded the birth of two to a captive female in Port Elizabeth in August, and another two juveniles, at an estimated age of 4 and 6 weeks, were taken in the eastern Cape in January and September. In the Transvaal, two four-week old pups were taken in mid-October and a six-week old pup in mid-March (Trendler, pers. comm.). In Zimbabwe two gravid females were taken in November and December, one with one foetus, the other with two foetuses, and juveniles of 1,9 kg in October and 1,9 kg in February. These data suggest that the young are born during the early part of the warm, wet summer months.

Fitzsimons (1919) noted that a female in captivity had her young in a nest of grass in the dark corner of her cage. Baker & Meester (1986) gave no dates for when their captive litters were born. Six litters were born, mean size 2,5 (S.D.=0,54) and birth mass about 125 g. Pups are born fully furred, the eyes open on about Day 11 and the auditory meatus opens on about Day 21, although ear pinnae are extended at birth. They are weaned at about Day 36. Males grow slightly faster than females. Females have three pairs of abdominal mammae.

## Genus *Mungos* E. Geoffroy & C. Cuvier, 1795

No. 279

## *Mungos mungo* (Gmelin, 1788)

## Banded mongoose
## Gebande muishond

Plate 25

**Colloquial Name**

The present names in both languages describe the characteristic conspicuous transverse banding on the lower part of the back.

**Taxonomic Notes**

Coetzee (1977a) recognised 13 subspecies from the continent of which two, *M. m. grisonax* Thomas, 1926 and *M. m. taenionotus* (A. Smith, 1834), occur in the Subregion.

*M. m. grisonax* of northwestern Transvaal, Botswana, Namibia and parts of Angola is lighter in colour than *M. m. taenionotus* of the northeastern Cape Province, Natal, eastern Transvaal, Zimbabwe and Mozambique, south of the Zambezi River. In southern Natal, in *M. m. taenionotus*, the upper parts are dark reddish-brown, this colour particularly noticeable between the black bands on the lower back. In *M. m. grisonax* of Botswana and Namibia on the other hand, the upper parts are light grey, with only a faint tinge of reddish-brown between the black bands. In the area intermediate between these two extremes of colour there is a gradation in colour.

**Description**

Banded mongoose come into the category of small mongoose, adults being about 550 mm in total length, with tails about half this length or about 60% of the length of the head and body (Table 279.1). The feature which distinguishes them from other species is the series of about a dozen black transverse bands on the upper parts between the mid-back and the base of the tail. The coat is distinctly grizzled, especially on the head and shoulders, caused by the lie of the black and white or reddish-brown annulations on the hairs of the guard coat. This grizzling continues on to the tail which is tipped black in the darker specimens, dark brown in the lighter. The individual hairs of the guard coat are light in colour at the base, with two broad black bands and a narrow dark tip interspersed with two light-coloured bands. It is the colour of the lighter bands which governs the overall colour of the upper parts, being whitish in the light-coloured specimens, reddish-brown in the darker. The guard coat is thick and harsh. The individual hairs on the head are short, not above about 6 mm long, lengthening towards the rump, where in the eastern specimens they reach a length of

45 mm, and in the western are shorter at about 35 mm. In both the hair is slightly shorter on the tail.

### Table 279.1

Measurements (mm) and mass (kg) of banded mongoose, *M. mungo*, from (a) Zimbabwe and Botswana (Smithers, 1983) and (b) from the Transvaal (Rautenbach, 1978)

**(a)**

| | Males | | | Females | | |
|---|---|---|---|---|---|---|
| | x̄ | n | Range | x̄ | n | Range |
| TL | 539 | 10 | 500–586 | 535 | 8 | 504–610 |
| T | 205 | 10 | 178–240 | 217 | 8 | 200–245 |
| Hf c/u | 74 | 10 | 67–82 | 72 | 8 | 66–81 |
| E | 23 | 10 | 21–27 | 22 | 8 | 20–27 |

**(b)**

| | Males | | | Females | | |
|---|---|---|---|---|---|---|
| | x̄ | n | Range | x̄ | n | Range |
| TL | 585 | 12 | 562–615 | 590 | 5 | 545–670 |
| T | 226 | 12 | 202–252 | 247 | 5 | 190–238 |
| Hf c/u | 79 | 12 | 63–90 | 78 | 5 | 72–84 |
| E | 27 | 12 | 23–36 | 25 | 5 | 22–26 |
| Mass | 1,3 | 5 | 1,0–1,6 | 1,4 | 2 | 1,3–1,5 |

The underfur is much less in evidence than in other viverrids, being present on the upper parts of the darker specimens (*M. m. taenionotus*), the individual hairs fine and short with dark bases and lighter tips. While there is a fine sprinkling on the shoulders and mid-back of the lighter specimens (*M. m. grisonax*), the individual hairs with buffy bases and lighter tips, the undercoat is to all intents and purposes absent on the hindquarters.

The colour of the limbs follows the overall colour of the body. The muzzle is pointed. The rhinarium is small and lacks the central slit on the front found in some viverrids. The upper lip is intact. There are five digits on the front feet, four on the back. The first digit on the front is small and situated at the side of the planter pad, but armed with an unusually large curved claw about 8 mm across the curve, which usually marks in the spoor (Fig. 279.1). The other four digits on the front feet have long, sharply curved claws up to about 20 mm long. Those on the back feet are heavier, less curved and shorter at about 14 mm. The anus is enclosed in a subcircular pouch into which the anal glands open. There is no difference in size between the sexes (Table 279.1).

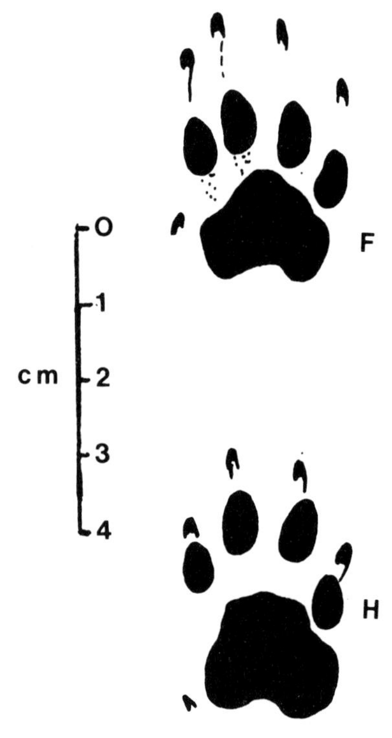


Fig. 279.1. Spoor: banded mongoose, *M. mungo*.
F. Right forefoot H. Right hind foot.

**Skull** (Fig. 279.2)

In profile the skull of the banded mongoose is highest at the level of the ear openings, sloping sharply back to the supraoccipital crest and evenly forward to the nasals. The braincase is pear-shaped, broadest at the level of the ear openings and narrowing forwards to the postorbital constriction, which is about 68% of the total length of the skull and lies well back of the upper portion of the postorbital bars. The postorbital bars are incomplete, being represented by small processes on the zygomatic arch and the frontals. The zygoma are thin and weak, the rostrum short and broad. Two-thirds of the skull lie in front of the glenoid articulation. The supraoccipital crest is poorly developed, not more than about 1,5 mm high in old adult specimens and there is no sign of a sagittal crest.

The dental formula is:

$I\frac{3}{3}\ C\frac{1}{1}\ P\frac{3}{3}\ M\frac{2}{2} = 36$

The outer upper incisors are considerably larger than the remainder; the upper canines slightly curved, short, rounded and sharp, the lower distinctly recurved. The upper and lower first premolars are absent and all the cheekteeth have low, rounded cusps. The carnassials are better adapted to crushing than slicing. This factor together with the weak zygoma and lack of a sagittal crest all suggest an adaptation to a diet of relatively soft or insectivorous food.

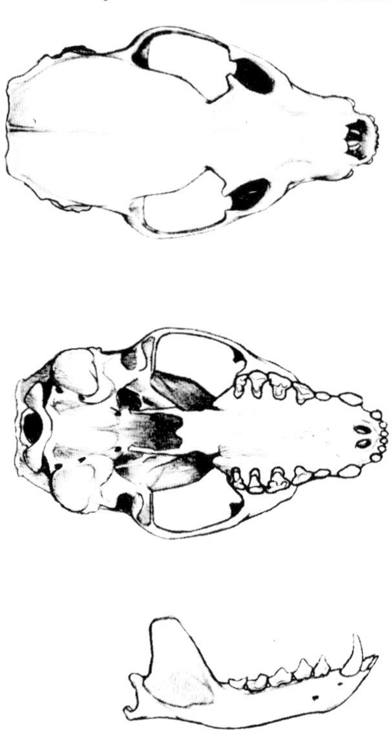

Fig. 279.2. Skull: banded mongoose, *M. mungo*.
TL Skull 70 mm

### Distribution

The banded mongoose is confined in its distribution to the continent, south of the Sahara. Within this range it is generally absent from forest, desert and semi-desert areas.

**Plate 25**

277. White-tailed mongoose, *Ichneumia albicauda*
Witstertmuishond
278. Water mongoose, *Atilax paludinosus*
Kommetjiegatmuishond
279. Banded mongoose, *Mungos mungo*
Gebande muishond
280. Dwarf mongoose, *Helogale parvula*
Dwergmuishond

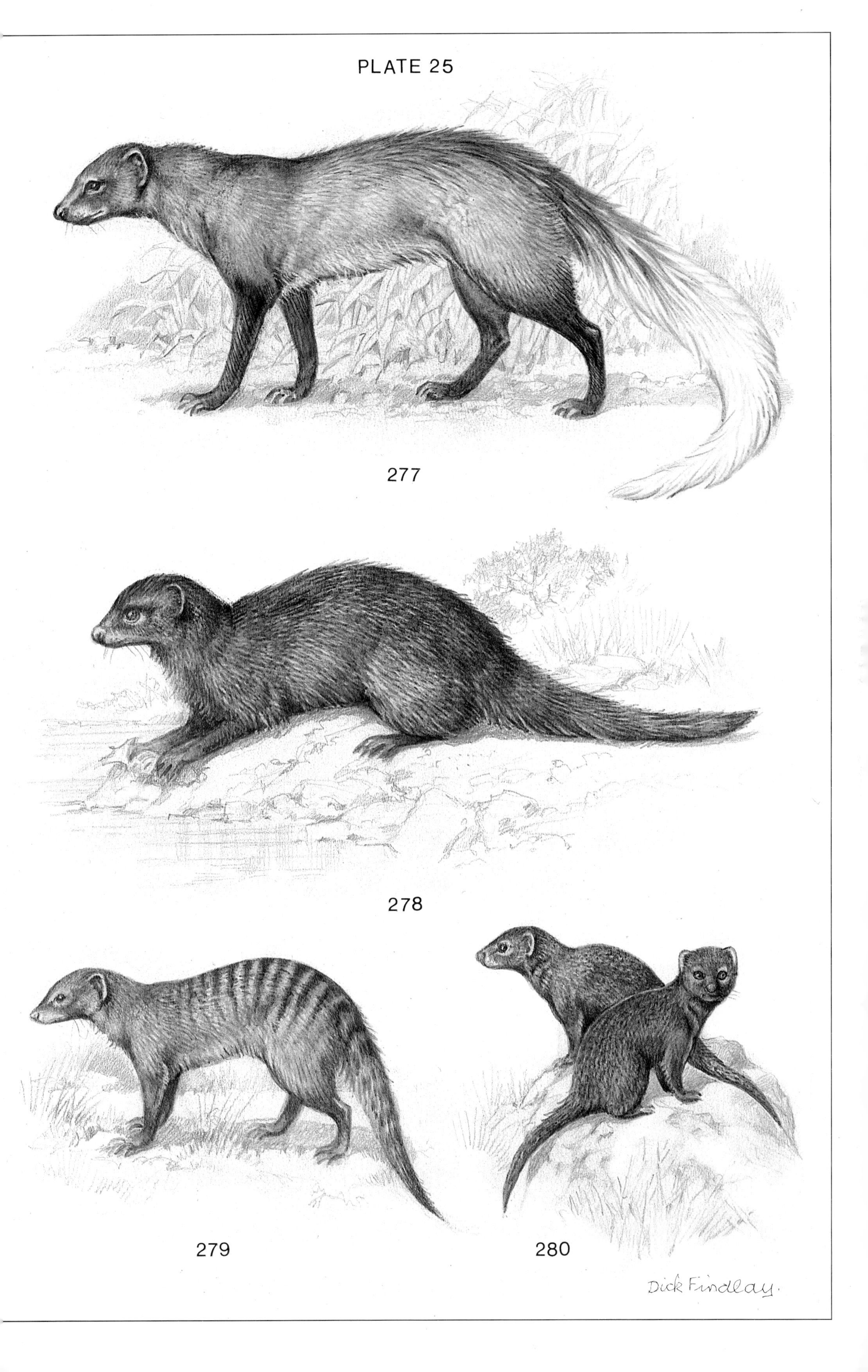
PLATE 25
277
278
279
280
Dick Findlay.

*South of the Sahara, excluding the Southern African Subregion*

Recorded from **Senegal; Gambia**, which was fixed as the type locality of *M. m. mungo* (Gmelin, 1788), by Ogilby (1835); **Guinea Bissau; Guinea** and **Benin**. Few records exist from the part of West Africa between Gambia and northeastern **Nigeria**, where they are stated to be rare. There are records from **Cameroun** and the **Central African Republic**, and they occur in the southern **Sudan** and in **Kenya**. There are records from southern **Somalia** and a single record from the northeast, and they are known from near Massawa, **Eritrea**. They occur in the central, northern and southwestern parts of **Tanzania** and coastally at Dar-es-Salaam. They are known to be distributed widely in northeastern **Mozambique**, as far north as the Rovuma River and in **Zambia**, although absent from the Zambezi Valley. They are found in the eastern parts of Zaire as far south as Lake Kivu, and in the northeastern, southern and southwestern parts of the country. There are records from central **Angola**.

*Southern African Subregion*

They have a wide distribution in northeastern **Namibia** south to about 23 °S, which corresponds with the situation in northern **Botswana** where their distribution extends over the border narrowly into northwestern **Zimbabwe** and along the eastern border with the Transvaal. Corresponding to the situation in Zambia, in Zimbabwe they are absent from a greater part of the Zambezi Valley between 27 °E and 29 °E, occurring narrowly in the northeast, east and southern areas. Widely distributed in **Mozambique**, south of the Zambezi River, and in the northern parts of the **Transvaal**, south to about 26 °S, their distribution extends southward to **Natal** in a narrow coastal strip (*c.* 80 km) to about 31 °S, which marks their southern limit on the continent.

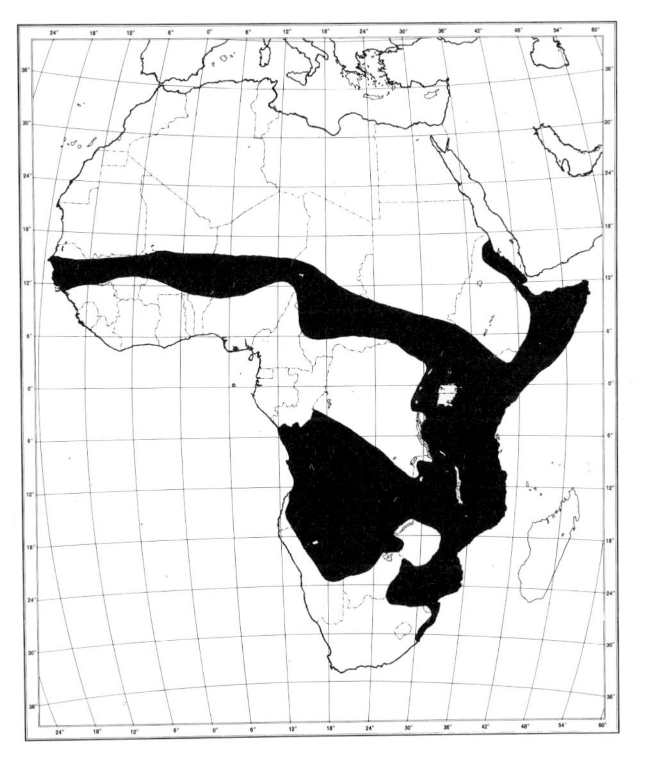

### Habitat

Banded mongoose have a wide habitat tolerance, but do not occur in desert or, in the southern parts of their range, in semi-desert, and therefore are absent from large parts of the South West Arid Zone. In the Subregion they occur in parts of the riverine forests of the Zambezi, Limpopo and other major rivers in the east, and in *Acacia* woodland in dry areas. In northern Botswana they are associated with dense belts of *Acacia* woodland in which the highest concentrations of the tsetse fly, *Glossina* spp, are found. Although they do occur commonly in riverine conditions, it is believed that it is the physiognomy of the vegetation rather than the presence of water that controls their occurrence; woodland, underbush and accompanying fallen logs and other substrate detritus and, in addition, the presence of termitaria are apparently essential habitat requirements.

### Habits

Banded mongoose are diurnal and gregarious; the pack emerges from refuges in the warmth of the morning sun and takes to them towards the late afternoon, retiring before the sun sets. No nocturnal activity has been recorded for the species. In the Subregion packs may vary in number from a few to over 30 (Table 279.2). When foraging the pack may scatter, the individuals maintaining contact by a continuous twittering. The more widely the pack scatters, the more highly pitched becomes the twitter. In this pursuit they are noisy and may be heard some distance away, either by twittering or the scratching and digging as they search for food. When danger threatens, individuals vocalise with a trident chittering upon which the pack will freeze, members rising on the back legs to the full standing position, balancing with the tail on the ground and looking around. The pack will then slip away with little noise, moving considerable distances before resuming their interrupted activities or disappear into the nearest thick cover or down holes. If put under severe stress they will make for any sort of cover that may be available, such as springhaas or aardvark holes, hollow logs or under fallen trees. There appear to be certain temporary refuges within their home range which are known to them and to which they will retreat. Simpson (1964a) recorded the finding of three such refuges located within an area of more than 2,5 km$^2$. The central refuge usually consists of holes in a termite mound.

Although terrestrial, under stress they will take to trees and climb with agility on broad sloping branches, also to the tops of high termitaria which they use as vantage points to survey the surrounding terrain. Simpson (1964a) recorded that a pack, chased by wild dogs, *Lycaon pictus*, took to the high branches of a tree that had been pushed over by elephants.

**Table 279.2**

Numbers of individuals in packs of banded mongoose

| Authority and locus | Average number in packs | Maximum number observed in packs |
|---|---|---|
| **Namibia**<br>Shortridge, 1934 | 6–12 | 30 |
| **Zimbabwe**<br>Simpson, 1964a | — | 35 |
| **Botswana**<br>Smithers, 1971 | 8–12 | 30,<br>several over 20 |
| **Transvaal**<br>Kruger National Park<br>Pienaar, 1964 | — | 75 |

Their senses are acute, smell being used to locate subterranean grubs, and they will react quickly when they see movements of grasshoppers or other insects. Simpson (1964a) stated that they more easily detect higher pitched sounds and are intensely curious, quick to investigate new sounds or strange objects. If the alarm is given they take to their refuges, and after a few moments peer out of the entrance, smelling the air and looking around, trying to locate the source of danger. While foraging there appears to be little time for intraspecific aggression, each individual giving the impression that the search for food is the primary occupation. As they move, the nose is held close to the ground, and they pause every few seconds to scratch or dig. When there are disputes over food, there is always submission to the dominant individuals in the pack.

The social organisation has not been studied in detail in the Subregion but there is a suggestion in Simpson's (1964a) observations that they may well be a matriarchal society. He noted that the females appeared to dominate the males. This dominance was established by placing the foreleg over the shoulder and gripping the other softly at the back of the head.

Scent-marking with the anal glands takes place frequently within the range, on stones, logs or other prominent or new objects, or on other members of the pack.

Rood (1975) found that in Uganda the mean home range size of five packs was 80,4 ha, two of the largest packs having ranges exceeding 1 km$^2$. Packs were active from an hour after sunrise to sunset, with a rest period during the hottest part of the day. The dens were in disused antbear holes, in erosion gullies and termite mounds, most of them used for only a few days and then abandoned, but a few preferred dens were occupied for up to 54 days and re-used repeatedly. Interactions between packs were aggressive, the larger packs dominating the smaller. Pack life is of adaptive significance directed to the protection of the young from predation and to their care. Packs bunch around young when disturbed and bunch to attack certain predators and competitors. When packs are disturbed on open ground they aggregate, any young present being in the centre of the pack which then moves to the nearest cover.

Banded mongoose care for invalids in the pack, warning and grooming them as well as affording them preferred access to food (Pilsworth, 1977).

### Food

Banded mongoose eat insects, grubs, myriapods, snails, small reptiles, the eggs and young of ground nesting birds and wild fruits (Shortridge, 1934; Maberly, 1963). Analyses of a sample of 14 stomachs from Zimbabwe and Botswana are in agreement with these findings (Table 279.3). In this sample insects in some form occurred in every stomach, represented principally by Coleoptera and their larvae, followed by grasshoppers, mole crickets, formicid ants, their eggs and larvae, and caterpillars.

**Table 279.3**

Number of occurrences of various food items in a sample of 14 stomachs of the banded mongoose, *M. mungo*, from Zimbabwe (Smithers & Wilson, 1979) and Botswana (Smithers, 1971)

| Food item | Percentage occurrence |
|---|---|
| Insecta | 10 |
| Reptilia | 6 |
| Wild fruits | 5 |
| Amphibia | 1 |
| Scorpiones | 1 |
| Solifugae | 1 |
| Myriapoda | 1 |
| Araneae | 1 |

Reptiles were represented in six stomachs by the round-snouted amphisbaenian, *Zygaspis quadrifrons*; Peters' black worm snake, *Leptotyphlops scutifrons*, both of which are burrowers; the striped skink, *Mabuya striata*; the variegated sand skink, *Mabuya varia*; the black-lined plated lizard, *Gerrhosaurus nigrolineatus*, and the olive grass snake, *Psammophis phillipsii*. Vegetable matter had the next highest occurrence, represented by unidentifiable pulp and small wild fruits including raisin bush berries, *Grewia* spp.

From the evidence available, banded mongoose diet is predominantly insectivorous, augmented by soft-bodied invertebrates that they may find while scratching in debris. Vegetable matter in the form of wild fruit also ranks high, together with reptiles, represented by lizards and snakes.

When foraging, individuals operate independently, scratching in fallen leaves and other debris, under stones, in the bark of and under fallen logs, forking around in any crevices they find that might hold food items. In digging for subterranean larvae they scratch several times with each front foot in succession. Small items are simply picked up in the mouth, larger ones held down with the front feet and then pulled apart. In dealing with toads and hairy caterpillars individuals roll them around and repeatedly paw them, thus removing the noxious secretion and bristles before eating them. In captivity, live mice and small live snakes are pounced on and bitten on any convenient part of the body, then shaken to death and, held down by the front feet, pulled to pieces to be eaten. Toads are similarly held down, and the skin stripped off. Simpson (1964a, 1966c) described the method used by the banded mongoose in dealing with larger eggs which is similar to that used by the slender mongoose, *G. sanguinea*, and the dwarf mongoose, *H. parvula*. The egg is positioned by the front feet and hurled between the back legs on to a rock or other hard object. The process is repeated until the egg is broken, when it is licked out of the shell.

### Reproduction

Simpson (1966c) recorded that females become sexually mature at nine to 10 months, the males slightly later. He recorded that the female takes an active and deliberate role in the courtship, lying on her back and wrestling with the male or flattening herself against his back and anal-marking him which he reciprocates. The partners are very playful, jumping around and pouncing on each other. The male circles the female with his tail in the air. His anal glands enlarge and the female becomes covered with the whitish secretion from these glands. Neal (1970) reported that mounting is repeated several times, with a short chase between each mounting, on one occasion a second male taking part and mounting the female after the first had separated from her. The gestation period is about two months (Rosevear, 1974).

Shortridge (1934) recorded a female with six foetuses taken in November in Namibia and juveniles not more than 14 days old in December. Skinner (unpubl.) found a female moving four young of about this age in the Soutpansberg, northern Transvaal in December; she was carrying one pup, with the other three following behind. Dixon (1966) saw juveniles in the Ndumu Game Reserve, Natal in November and December, and Rowe-Rowe (1978a) recorded litters of two to eight in October, December and February. This meagre evidence points to the young being born during the warm, wet summer months from October through to about February.

The litters are born in grass-lined chambers in the warrens (Simpson, 1966c), in holes in the ground or in termite mounds (Rowe-Rowe, 1978a). At birth the young have a mass of about 20,0 g and are blind; their skin is dark in colour with a sparse covering of hair, which shows faintly the dark banding on the back, characteristic of the adults. The eyes open about the 10th day. At two weeks of age the pelage is well developed but does not attain the full mature coloration and pattern until they are about three months old. Neal (1970) recorded that when a pack left to forage a female would remain to suckle and look after eight young and, on the return of the pack, all the females would nurse any of the young without distinction. The growth of the young is rapid, although there is a wide variation between individuals (Simpson, 1964a). He recorded that a young male reached a mass of 1,75 kg at an age of five months.

Rood (1974) noted that in Uganda reproduction within the pack, is synchronised. Typically several females come into oestrus about the same time and consequently produced their litters within a few days of each other. The young suckle from any lactating female and are groomed, played with and transported by all pack members. The young leave the den when three to four weeks old for short foraging expeditions and accompany the adults regularly at five weeks old on their morning foraging. Up to this age one or more adult male pack members stay at the den with the young while the pack is away, thus enhancing their chances of survival against the depredations of snakes and other ground predators. Rood (1975) found that mortality in individuals over six months old is 10% annually and that less than 50% of the juveniles survive to the age of three months. Mating between members of separate packs was observed during aggressive encounters between them.

The females have three pairs of abdominal mammae.

## Genus *Helogale* Gray, 1862

Two species are recognised as occurring on the continent by Coetzee (1977a): *Helogale hirtula* in Ethiopia, Somalia and

Kenya, with long shaggy fur and cheekteeth which are heavily built and not typically adapted to slicing, and *H. parvula* with short fur and lightly built cheekteeth adapted to slicing. *H. parvula* occurs in the remainder of the genus' range southwards, with some overlap in range with *H. hirtula* in East Africa.

---

No. 280

## *Helogale parvula* (Sundevall, 1846)

## Dwarf mongoose
## Dwergmuishond

Plate 24

---

### Colloquial Name

They are the smallest species of mongoose occurring in the Subregion.

### Taxonomic Notes

Meester *et al.* (1986) listed three subspecies from the Subregion: *H. p. parvula* from northeastern Natal and KwaZulu, the Transvaal, southern Mozambique, Zimbabwe and eastern and northeastern Botswana; *H. p. mimetra* Thomas, 1926 from northwestern Botswana and northern Namibia, and *H. p. nero* Thomas, 1928 from Usakos, Eronga Mountains to Kamanjab, southeastern Kaokoveld, Namibia. They noted that the species is in need of revision.

### Description

The dwarf mongoose in overall length is not more than about 400 mm, with a tail about half that length and a mass of about 300 g (Table 280.1). At a distance they look black or very dark brown, but at close quarters it can be seen that the upper parts are grizzled with little flecks of pale colour against a dark brown background. There is some variation in this general colour. The hair on the head is short, about 2 or 3 mm long, closely adpressed to the skin and gradually increasing in length towards the tail where, on the hindquarters, it reaches a length of about 15 mm. The individual hairs of the guard coat are dark with white or off-white annulations, one near the dark tip and a second lower down, giving the coat a "pepper and salt" appearance. There is a liberal admixture of longer hairs in the guard coat especially near the hindquarters which have broad dark tips, and which may have a tactile function. The underfur is dense; the individual hairs are fine and woolly, dark at the base, buffy towards their tips in the lighter coloured specimens, wholly dark buffy in the darker. The hair on the tail is similar to that on the upper parts, only slightly longer at about 18 mm. The hair on the under parts is sparser than on the upper parts but similar in colour.

**Table 280.1**

Measurements (mm) and mass (g) of dwarf mongoose, *H. parvula*, from Botswana (Smithers, 1983)

| | Males | | | Females | | |
|---|---|---|---|---|---|---|
| | x̄ | n | Range | x̄ | n | Range |
| TL | 375 | 34 | 340–410 | 387 | 19 | 340–410 |
| T | 166 | 24 | 152–183 | 165 | 19 | 142–188 |
| Hf c/u | 46 | 23 | 41–51 | 46 | 19 | 41–49 |
| E | 17 | 21 | 15–21 | 18 | 18 | 14–21 |
| Mass | 269 | 13 | 223–341 | 265 | 11 | 213–341 |

The rhinarium, which encloses the nostrils, is tiny with a slight shallow depression on the front between the nostrils. Continuing downwards, it divides the hair on the upper lip. The ears are of typical mongoose shape, closely adpressed to the sides of the head, but more obviously so than in some other species, as the hair surrounding them is short.

They have five digits on the front feet, the first, the thumb, lying behind the plantar pad, and five digits on the hind feet, the first set far back of the others, but still marking in the spoor (Fig. 280.1). The claws on the front feet are long, curved and sharp, measuring up to 10 mm across the curve and are adapted to digging. Those on the hind feet are slightly shorter, up to about 8 mm. The anus and openings of the anal glands are enclosed in a subcircular pouch, the lips of which close to a transverse line. The hind foot is naked nearly to the ankle, the forefoot naked to the wrist.

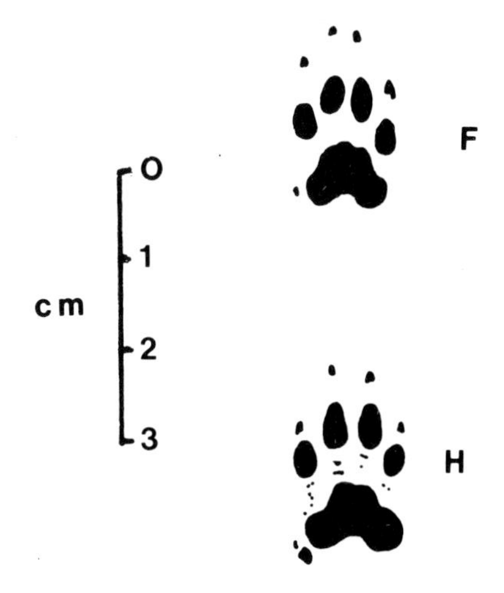


Fig. 280.1. Spoor: dwarf mongoose, *H. parvula*.
F. Right forefoot H. Right hind foot.

**Skull** (Fig. 280.2)

The braincase of the dwarf mongoose is pear-shaped, narrowing in the front to the postorbital constriction, which lies close up to the postorbital bars which are incomplete even in fully adult specimens. The supraoccipital crest is well developed in adult specimens, the sagittal crest never more than a low ridge which continues over the top of the braincase to divide and end on the processes of the postorbital bar. For the size of the skull the zygomatic arches are relatively heavy, suggesting well developed masseter muscles. The coronoid of the lower jaw is high and wide to accommodate the insertion of the temporalis muscles, which activate the lower jaw.

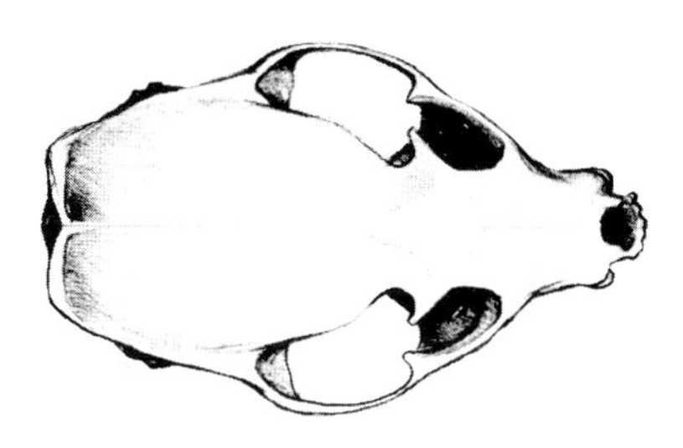

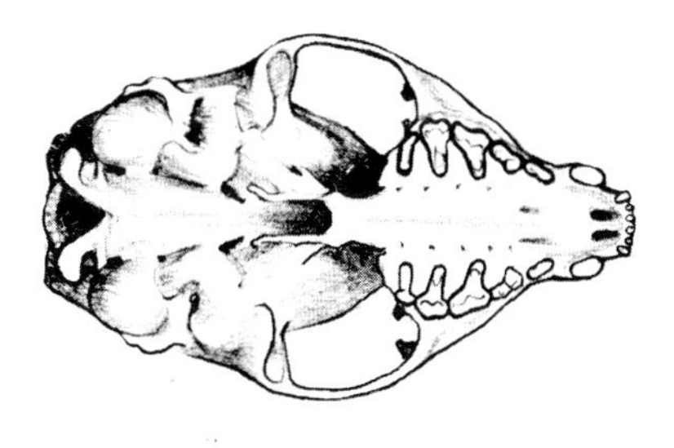

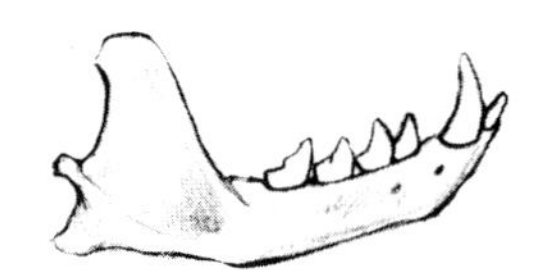

Fig. 280.2. Skull: dwarf mongoose, *H. parvula*.
TL Skull 50 mm

The front chambers of the ear bullae are slightly larger than the hind. The rostrum is short, the distance between the front of the eye sockets to the incisor teeth is about a quarter of the total length of the skull. The eye sockets are small in diameter, about a fifth of the total length of the skull.

The dental formula is:

$I\frac{3}{3}\ C\frac{1}{1}\ P\frac{3}{3}\ M\frac{2}{2} = 36$

The outer upper incisors are larger than the remainder. The upper canines are long, reaching below the level of the base of the lower, and taper to very sharp points. The carnassials are not adapted particularly to slicing. The lower first molar has three high cusps on the front and a broad grinding surface on the back half of the tooth. The remaining molars as well have high cusps, the adaptation being towards the handling of a generally insectivorous diet.

## Distribution

The dwarf mongoose, *Helogale parvula*, has a distributional range extending from southern Somalia to the northeastern parts of Natal and the Transvaal, and westwards narrowly through the northern parts of the Subregion to southwestern and central Angola and the extreme southeastern parts of Zaire.

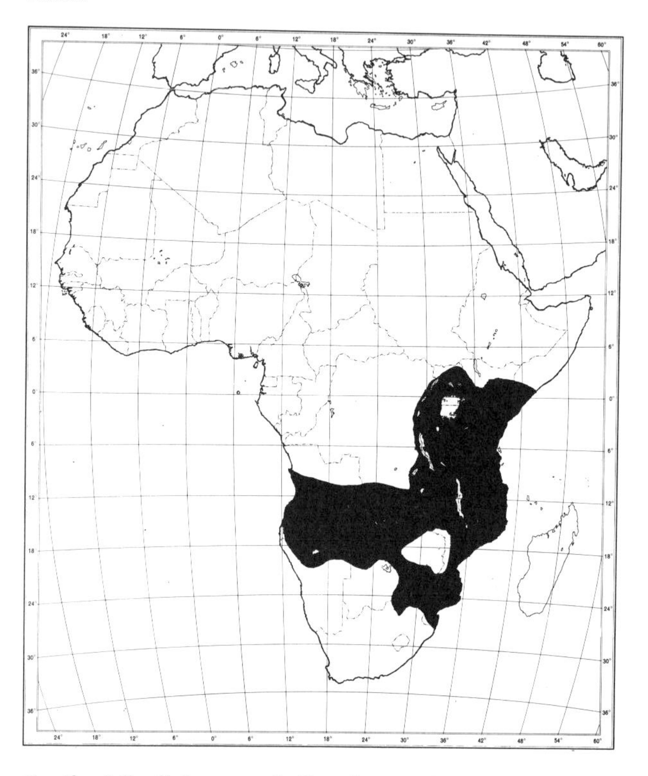

*South of the Sahara, excluding the Southern African Subregion*

They occur in eastern **Uganda**, in central and southern **Kenya** and in southern **Somalia**. There are two records from the extreme southern parts of **Zaire** near the borders of Angola and Zambia, but none from the Rift Valley. They are recorded, however, from the southern end of Lake Tanzania. They have a wide distribution in **Tanzania** and **Zambia**, excluding the Barotse Province. They occur in **Angola** as far north as the Quanza River (*c.* 10 °S). In **Mozambique**, north of the Zambezi River, there are coastal records from Mocimboa, in the Cabo Dalgado District and Mossuril in the Mozambique Province, and they occur in **Malawi**.

*Southern African Subregion*

They occur in northern **Namibia** and are widespread in **Botswana** throughout the northern parts of the country, being common in the Okavango Delta, and narrowly along the Zimbabwe and Transvaal borders south to about 24 °S. In **Zimbabwe** they occur along the western border with Botswana and north and south of the central plateau, being absent on the plateau itself, east of Bulawayo, and not occurring in the Eastern Districts. In the **Transvaal** they have a wide distribution in the north, northwestern and eastern parts of the province and may well be present in the eastern parts of **Swaziland** as there is a record from Golela in the south. They are widespread in **Mozambique**, south of the Zambezi River, but do not occur at the higher levels along the Zimbabwe border. They occur in the extreme northeastern parts of **Natal** which marks their southernmost limits in the Subregion.

## Habitat

The dwarf mongoose is a savanna species associated with semi-desert and dry open woodland and grassland wherever sufficient hiding places abound such as termite mounds with adjacent accumulations of debris in the form of leaf litter, fallen trees or branches. In the northern parts of the Subregion the great majority of observations were made in *Terminalia/Combretum* scrub, which is normally found on sandy ground, but within this they tend to use areas of hard ground with active or quiescent termitaria, using the holes as shelters. In Zimbabwe they generally are confined to altitudes below 1 100 m, not occurring on the plateau or in the Eastern Districts. They do not occur in forest and are not dependent on the availability of water.

## Habits

Dwarf mongoose are diurnal, seldom moving out of their holes until the sun is well up in the morning and usually retiring before sunset. They are not in evidence in cold, rainy or overcast weather. In the field they clamber up high termitaria and on the branches of fallen trees. Terrestrial dwarf mongoose live amicably as a group, which is a matriarchy led by an alpha pair with a life-long bond, dividing group duties between them (Rasa, 1977, 1985; Rood, 1990). Rasa (1985) believes that this division of labour is the highest observed in a mammal; while some guard, others baby-sit, attack predators or conspecific intruders. Troop size varies from 2–32 (Rasa, 1985, 1987). The "territory" averages 0,98 $km^2$ or more and within this the troop will occupy a different termite mound each day (Rasa, 1985). Being small they use the ventilation holes made by the termites without adjustment. The mounds used are those of *Macrotermes falciger* which have a characteristic tall cone structure up to 2 m above ground. They forage for 2,5 hours in the early morning and again for 2,5 hours in the afternoon. In the middle of the day they take a siesta, again within termite mounds, those of *Odontotermes* sp with no structure above ground being preferred (Rasa, 1985). *Macrotermes* cultivate fungus gardens within these mounds, their galleries surrounding them. Most of the mound is underground. The fungus requires a particular temperature to flourish and the mounds are pierced with ventilation shafts to keep them cool (Ledger & Bannister, 1979). It is these shafts that are used by the mongooses (and other animals) to provide a secure home.

In the morning the troops move out from the stop-over mounds to forage, the individuals scattering to do so, but nevertheless maintaining contact by vocalising in abrupt "perrips" or musical "chucks" and by posting guards. On the alarm call, a sharp *chu-chwee* being given by one of the troop, usually the sentinel, the remainder will freeze, then after a time rise on to their back legs, and balancing with the tail, search around for the cause of the disturbance, the head moving quickly from side to side, the body motionless. This alarm call is given on the appearance of birds of prey or jackals (Rasa, 1985). Rasa (1976a) showed that there is a division of responsibility among members of the troop towards sentinel duty, certain male members contributing more than others. If the troop is far from the vicinity of a residence-mound, they appear to know temporary refuges in hollow trees, under fallen trees or in hollow logs, or in shallow burrows within their home range, to which they retreat quickly. Some of these obviously are used frequently as there are scats near the entrances or the burrows have been adjusted by excavation to meet their requirements. In these cases the burrows are relatively shallow, not more than about 150 mm below the surface of the ground and up to 1,8 m in length.

They mark objects in their territory near the termite mounds in which they sleep with both cheek and anal glands. Marked objects are invariably (82%) in the northern quarter of the mound. All members mark the same objects or marking "posts" and the smell of these anal secretions is detectable for up to three weeks which is the time taken for a group to make a circuit of its territory. There is little overlap between territories and no correlation between territory size and group size (Rasa, 1987).

Alloparenting takes place and up to three members—a female and two males—remain with the young while the group forages (Rasa, 1977). When the group returns at midday another set of babysitters takes over. When the group moves to another mound, the dam and other females carry the pups until they can walk themselves, from about 3,5 weeks of age. Food provisioning and invalid care has been reported for incapacitated animals (Rasa, 1976). An individual is warmed, groomed and afforded access to food.

The residence-mounds are marked by substantial accumulations of scats in the vicinity of the entrances as compared to temporary refuges. In digging, once the soil has been loosened with the front claws, it is dragged out by holding the front feet to act like a scoop, and thrown backwards between the back legs.

Dwarf mongoose are sun-lovers and they will lie sunning themselves in the early morning on the ground or on logs near the entrances of the residence-mounds. At such times mutual and self-grooming is very much in evidence. In the former, one walks under the head of the other that it is about to groom, turns its head and nibbles at the neck and shoulder region with the incisor teeth. The other then reciprocates, continuing the grooming down the body to the base of the tail. This nibbling is apparently a reflex action, as Rasa (1976a) recorded that even a naked blind juvenile of 10 days old, when scratched on the side of the neck or back with the finger, attempts to reciprocate by nibbling on any object in the vicinity or if no object is available continues the movement in the air. Willingness to be groomed on the under parts is shown by an individual rolling on to its side or back, the groomer forcibly lifting up the legs of the one to be groomed with the nose and nibbling on the inguinal or belly region.

In self-grooming, nibbling, licking and scratching with the hind feet are all employed; the cleaning of the front paws by licking is a very common type of self-grooming.

Smithers (1983) observed play both in the field and in captivity, in the form of mock fighting. Two individuals roll around on the ground interlocked, or stand up on their back legs facing each other, the front legs touching, and the opponents making mock slashes with the teeth at the side of each other's necks. When such play becomes too rough for either opponent the one lies down on its side, moving the uppermost free front legs backwards and forwards as if pushing the opponent away. Play then ceases. This submissive action is used by the juveniles when suddenly confronted by an adult or on occasions where disputes arise among members of the troop over food, *etc.* It is also apparent when a strange individual is introduced to an established troop in captivity. Strangers of either sex or age are accepted by the troop after some initial sorting out of status.

Rasa (1985) described in vivid detail a take-over attempt by one troop of a mound of an occupying group. With tail hairs extended at right angles, the residents charge the intruders, attacking as a closed group. The bone of contention is always a particular mound which both troops claim for the night. Such key mounds are invariably inhabited by horny-plated lizards. Rasa (1985) concluded that dwarf mongooses do not defend a territory, but have regular routes they traverse through the bush. At certain "key"-mounds these cross the routes of other troops and when troops meet here, there is a "battle" in which some individuals are severely injured. The larger troops invariably win such fights, occupying the mound in question for the night.

Apart from predation where raptors such as chanting goshawks, *Melierax canorus*, play a major role, Rasa (1985) mentioned two other interesting inter-specific relationships. One was with hornbills, *Tockus* spp, where these follow dwarf mongoose troops, catching the grasshoppers which fly up from the disturbing animals, in return providing an early warning system for approaching raptors. The second was with horny-plated lizards, *Gerrhosaurus major*, inhabiting the termite mounds and which feed on fecal pellets of the mongooses.

The main predators of dwarf mongoose are the large grey mongoose, *Herpestes ichneumon*, the slender mongoose, *Galerella sanguinea*, as well as black-backed jackals, *Canis mesomelas*, honey badgers, *Mellivora capensis*, chanting goshawks, *M. canorus*, tawny eagles, *Aquila rapax*, martial eagles, *Polemaetus bellicosus*, pythons, *Python sebae*, spitting cobras, *Naja nigricollis* and puffadders, *Bitis arietans* (Rasa, 1983; Rood, 1990).

**Food**

Stevenson-Hamilton (1912) stated that the food of the dwarf mongoose consists of termites, snails, locusts, scorpions, centipedes, earthworms, reptiles and the eggs of ground birds and of snakes. Shortridge (1934) stated that they are largely insectivorous. Stevenson-Hamilton's contention is largely borne out by the examination of 27 stomachs from the northern parts of the Subregion where all the items he mentioned occur, with the exception of the eggs of birds and snakes. The percentage occurrence of insect material in the sample was by far the highest, the remaining items all appearing at relatively small percentages (Table 280.2).

**Table 280.2**

Percentage occurrence of various food items in a sample of 27 stomachs of the dwarf mongoose, *Helogale parvula*, from the northern parts of the Subregion (Smithers, 1983)

| Food item | Percentage occurrence |
|---|---|
| Coleoptera adults | 37 |
| Coleoptera grubs | 33 |
| Orthoptera | 33 |
| Isoptera | 33 |
| Insecta undet. | 44 |
| Araneae | 11 |
| Myriapoda | 4 |
| Scorpiones | 4 |
| Solifugae | 4 |
| Reptilia | 4 |
| Muridae | 4 |

Dwarf mongoose masticate their food very thoroughly, breaking up insect material into very small pieces, making it difficult to provide accurate identifications. Among the identifiable remains, chips of chitin of adult Coleoptera ranked high at 37% and included the remains of scarabaeid beetles. Coleoptera grubs were identified in 33% of the stomachs. Isoptera were represented by *Hodotermes mossambicus*, *Macrotermes bellicosus* and *Odontotermes latericius*; Orthoptera by crickets and grasshoppers. Among other identifiable material Myriapoda were represented by the centipede, *Scolopendra morsitans*; reptiles by the sand lizard, *Eremias* sp, the striped skink, *Mabuya varia*, and the herald snake, *Crotaphopeltis hotamboeia*, and Muridae by the pouched mouse, *Saccostomus campestris*. Traces of caterpillars, dipterous pupae and saturnid larvae were also identified.

Rasa (1985) observed them eating eggs which are very restricted in their availability for dwarf mongoose. The eggs from small birds are bitten open at the end and the contents licked out, while larger eggs such as those from crested francolins, *Francolinus sephena*, are clasped in front of them on the ground and thrown backwards under the body and upwards so that the egg is propelled against a hard object to break it open. They then either lick up the contents or use their paws to scroop and then lick these.

Water is not an essential requirement, for in a very large part of their range it is not available to them, except seasonally. They make clumsy attempts to lap, often immersing their heads; the more normal method is to dip their paws and lick the water off them (Rasa, 1985).

With flying insects the mongoose jump and catch them in their forepaws or, if settled, they pounce with both forefeet and pin the insects to the substrate before taking them in the mouth. Large insects such as locusts almost always were eaten from the head first. Rasa (1973a) noted that with insects that are capable of stinging, the lips are pulled back from the teeth as they are being chewed.

Small snakes and blind worms are tackled by a single member of the group. These are bitten a short distance behind the head then dropped, bitten again, perhaps several times, then shaken violently until they are quiescent when they are pinned down with the forepaws and eaten head first. The response to larger snakes may involve the whole group, the dominant female taking the lead and advancing on the snake with her hair erected. If unsuccessful in catching the snake by the neck she would jump back and try again. In the meantime other members of the group would encircle it and catch it by the tail, shaking it vigorously until it was disorientated, allowing one of the group, usually the larger male or dominant female, to catch it by the neck, bite it and spring back out of harm's way. This process is repeated until the snake is eventually killed by one of the adults with a bite behind the head (Rasa, 1985). Then he or she eats it from the head first, allowing the remainder of the group to partake of what is left. Usually the dominant female takes the first turn at eating, driving off the male if he happens to have killed it (Smithers, 1983).

Rasa (1973a) showed that when the dominant male and female were presented with a number of live mice, they would continue killing them until all were dead, then take one each to eat, and leave the remainder for the rest of the group.

They never share their smaller prey with other members of the group (Rasa, 1985). Larger insects are pinned down by one forefoot, bitten on the head, chewed and swallowed. Centipedes and lizards are shaken to immobilise them. After capture, multimammate mice, *Mastromys* spp, are pinned down with the forefeet and then killed with a bite through the head. The head is held upright between the forepaws, the head eaten and then the trunk, hooking the neck skin with the foreclaws and pulling it down, simultaneously pulling on the neck with the mouth, thus effectively skinning it like taking off a glove. The entrails are extracted with the teeth, pulled to one side, and the carcass consumed, the process complete in 3–4 minutes.

**Reproduction**

Shortridge (1934) captured a juvenile not more than a month old in Namibia in April and half-grown individuals in April and July. Smithers (1971) took two females with minute foetuses in February in Botswana and recorded juveniles at 140 g in March and April. In captivity a female gave birth in January, indicating a summer breeding season in the Subregion, as in East Africa they breed in the rainy season when insects are plentiful (Rood, 1990).

Each pack contains a dominant pair which sires most members of the group (Rood, 1980). The alpha female is in oestrus for five days during which time the alpha male guards her from subordinate males (Rood, 1990) and copulates often with her, as many as 2 386 times and ejaculating in 10% of these (Rasa, 1985). Rood (1990) noted that copulation takes 21 seconds (n=67) and ejaculation occurs in 16%. Late in oestrus, the alpha male may mate with subordinate females, which come into oestrus synchronously with the alpha female, who then mates with the beta male. In 13 years Rood (1990) observed that subordinate females only became pregnant 12 times and when this happened, the resultant number of young counted at first emergence from the den was no larger than a single litter size (Rood, 1980). This probably resulted from infanticide as Rasa (pers. comm.) has observed this in a captive colony. Subordinate females may lactate and nurse the alpha female's young (Rood, 1980). The death of a breeder usually results in replacement from within the pack by the oldest adult of the same sex.

Litters of two to four are usual in the field, but in captivity up to seven are born, with a high degree of mortality, reducing the survival rate to between one and two. In the field Rasa (1986) observed a mean litter size of 3,04 per group for groups of all sizes, with a survival of 2,42 after four months. However, groups of six or more individuals did not lose any young during this particularly vulnerable period, whereas groups of five or less suffered a 70% loss. Rood (1990) found a similar mean for litter size, but found that large groups had significantly larger litter sizes than small groups. Rasa (1977) showed that in captivity, if the young of each litter are removed shortly after birth, a female is capable of producing up to five litters in a single breeding season, and that if a litter is reared successfully she can have a second litter later in the year.

Females litter down in termitaria. The young vocalise with a rapid *tseep-tseep-tseep*. When the female or another of the colony visits them, this type of vocalisation ceases (Rasa, 1977). Females carry the young by holding them across the back or by the scruff of the neck. The young keep up a continual high-pitched *peep-peep-peep* during the time they are not suckling until they are about a week to two weeks old.

# XXXV. Family OTARIIDAE
## Fur seals

In the first edition of *The Mammals of the Southern African Subregion* the Otariidae (fur seals) and the Phocidae (true seals) were considered, following Nel (1971), as families of the Order Pinnipedia. While this may appear a logical arrangement as they are all marine mammals and have adaptations to this way of life, including among other features their generally streamlined shape, the reduction of the ear pinnae and the possession of flippers as opposed to the conventional limbs of terrestrial mammals, they have close relationships with the Carnivora which, by separating them at ordinal rank, obscures this relationship.

Mitchell & Tedford (1973) described an ancestral family, the Enaliarctidae, from fossil remains from California dated from the beginning of the Miocene epoch some 22,5 million years ago. These fossil remains were derived with reasonable certainty from primitive ursids (bears) which were evolving into an otariid form. They had carnassial teeth, a carnivore characteristic, and other features showing resemblances to the ursids on the one hand, and others showing resemblances to the otariids. Probably about 15 to 13 million years ago the ancestral enaliarctids gave rise to the otariid seals, *Arctocephalus*, being probably the genus most like the ancestral otariid. The earliest known otariid is *Pithanotaria* which was about 1,5 m in length and was described from the late middle Miocene, about 11 million years ago.

Less is known about the fossil history of the phocid seals, the earliest known fossil material being from the early middle Miocene about 14 million years ago. While there is a paucity of material, it appears that these earliest phocids included *Leptophoca lenis*, representing the phocine branch of the Family, and *Monotherium wymani*, the monachine branch, both being equally old. Therefore there must have been an earlier common form, but this as yet remains undiscovered. There is no doubt, however, that they originated from carnivore stock as did the otariids, but what particular group remains obscure (King, 1983). Judging from the formation of the ear region, phocid seals have affinities with the Mustelidae and Procyonidae rather than the Ursidae, and they have other features as well suggesting affinities with the first two named. King (1983) suggested that the phocid seals probably came from a stock of primitive mustelids closely allied to *Potamotherium*, a possible early Miocene mustelid.

The Family Otariidae is represented in Subregion seas by three species: the Cape fur seal, *Arctocephalus pusillus pusillus*, the Antarctic fur seal, *A. gazella*, and the Subantarctic fur seal, *A. tropicalis*.

Extralimitally it includes seven fur seal species: the Australian, *Arctocephalus pusillus doriferus* (Wood Jones, 1925); the South American, *A. australis* (Zimmerman, 1783); the Juan Fernandez, *A. philippii* (Peters, 1866); the Galapagos, *A. galapagoensis* (Heller, 1904); the Guadalupe, *A. townsendi* (Merriam, 1897); New Zealand, *A. forsteri* (Lesson, 1828), and the Alaska or Pribilof, *Callorhinus ursinus* (Linnaeus, 1758). It also includes five species of sea lions: Steller's, *Eumetopias jubatus* (Schreber, 1776); Californian, *Zalophus californianus* (Lesson, 1828); Southern, *Otaria byronia* (Blainville, 1820); Australian, *Neophoca cinerea* (Peron, 1816), and Hooker's, *Phocarctos hookeri* (Gray, 1844). The walrus, *Odobenus rosmarus* (Linnaeus, 1758), is closely related to the Otariidae, but in a Family of its own, the Odobenidae.

Commonly known as eared seals to distinguish them from the true seals of the Family Phocidae, which have no external ears, the pelage of fur seals of the genus *Arctocephalus* consists of a dense coat of underfur overlaid by a guard coat of longer hair. Stripped of this guard coat, their skins with their durable coat of underfur, are of considerable commercial value. The first digit of the foreflipper is approximately the same length or slightly shorter than the second digit, while all the digits on the hind flipper are of similar length.

Members of this Family and the Phocidae move in different ways when on land. In the Otariidae the hind flippers can be turned forward under the body and used in a four-footed motion, whereas in the Phocidae they cannot be turned forward and are not used in locomotion on land. The under surfaces of the fore and hind flippers in the Otariidae are naked, in the Phocidae they are well furred.

In the skull the arrangement of the nasal bones distinguishes members of the two Families (Figs. XXXV.1 and XXXVI.1).

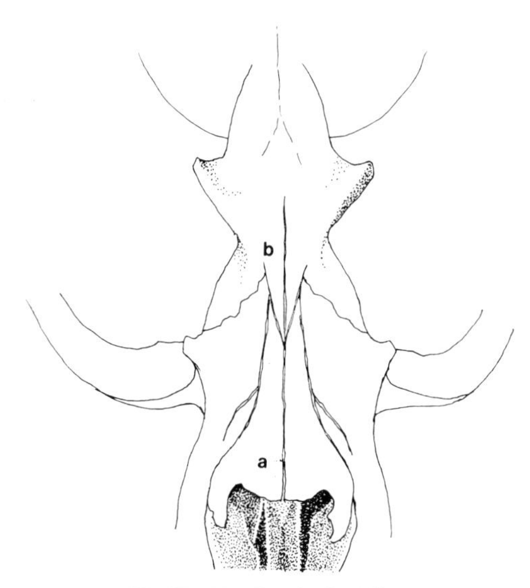

Fig. XXXV.1. Family Otariidae.
Front view of the skull, *Arctocephalus tropicalis*.
Nasals (a) not forming a wedge between the frontals (b).

## Genus *Arctocephalus* F. Cuvier, 1826

The generic name is derived from the Greek *arktos*, a bear, and *kephale*, a head, referring to the bear-like appearance of the head.

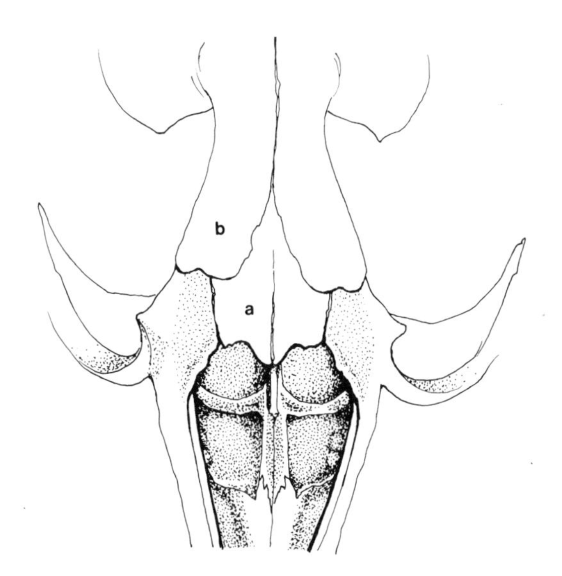

Fig. XXXVI.1. Family Phocidae.
Front view of the skull, *Lobodon carcinophagus*
Nasals (a) forming a wedge between the frontals (b).

Key to the species after Nel (1971)

1. Post-canine teeth with small accessory cusps; ventral edge of jugal arch lying dorsal to dentary part of maxilla ... *pusillus*

   Post-canine teeth without, or with weak, accessory cusps; ventral side of jugal arch on the same level as the dentary part of the maxilla ... 2

2. Size larger, bulls up to 200 kg, cows up to 50 kg; the bulls with chest and neck silvery-grey, the cows with creamy coloured throat, chest and neck, the bulls lacking the crest on top of the head and with long, visible ears often covered with short white hair; flippers long in relation to size of body ... *gazella*

   Size smaller, bulls up to 150 kg, cows up to 50 kg, the bulls with chest and neck cream to burnt orange, the cows similar, the bulls with a prominent crest, especially when under stress, and with short, black, fleshy, sparsely haired ears; eyelids hairless; flippers short and broad ... *tropicalis*

---

No. 281

## *Arctocephalus pusillus* (Schreber, 1776)

## Cape fur seal
## Kaapse pelsrob

Plate 26

---

### Colloquial Name

Nine species of fur seal are known, and it is useful therefore to retain the name Cape to distinguish *A. pusillus* from these other species. The specific name *pusillus* is derived from the Latin meaning small, as the original description was based on a pup.

### Taxonomic Notes

Two subspecies are recognised: the Cape fur seal, *A. p. pusillus*, the subspecies occurring in the Subregion, and the Australian fur seal, *A. p. doriferus* (Wood Jones, 1925), which occurs around the coasts of Australia and Tasmania. The two subspecies differ in the length of the crest that unites the mastoid process with the jugular process which is proportionally longer in the Australian fur seal.

### Description

Adult male Cape fur seals have a mean total length of 2,15 m and a mean mass of 247 kg; the females are smaller at 1,56 m and 57 kg respectively. The coarse coat of the bull is dark blackish-grey and females are an intermediate brownish-grey colour, lighter below. Pups have a velvety black coat at birth which is moulted during March and April. The new coat is silver-grey in colour but fades during summer to a darker colour.

The ears are narrow, pointed and about 40 mm long. The forelimbs with scalloped edges are not incised into lobes and have five rudimentary nails. The hind limbs are directed forwards and are incised into flipper-like digits, the three middle digits with large claws, the fifth with a rudimentary claw and the first without a claw.

The dental formula is:

$I\frac{3}{2}\ C\frac{1}{1}\ P\frac{6}{6} = 36$ (Rand, 1956b).

### Table 281.1

Measurements (m) and mass (kg) of Cape fur seals, *Arctocephalus pusillus* (David, 1987)

**Adult males**

| | |
|---|---|
| TL | 1,95–2,30 m |
| Mass | $\bar{x}$ = 247,0 kg (200–350 kg) |

**Adult females**

| | |
|---|---|
| TL | 1,20–1,60 m |
| Mass | $\bar{x}$ = 57,4 kg (40–80 kg) |

Rand (1959) noted that, in summer just before the rut, bulls may attain estimated weights of up to 360 kg.

### Distribution

The species occurs in two discrete regions in the southern oceans.

*Australia and Tasmania*

The Australian fur seal, *A. p. doriferus*, is confined to the coasts and islands of Australia and Tasmania.

*Southern African Subregion and Angola*

The Cape fur seal, *A. p. pusillus*, is confined to the islands and coasts of southern Africa from southern Angola along the coast of Namibia and the Cape Province to Algoa Bay, with occasional wanderers as far east as East London. Adults range some 160 km out to sea (Rand, 1959). This species is widely dispersed in 24 established breeding colonies and 10 known non-breeding colonies on the southern African coast (Oosthuizen & David, 1988), and has been recorded on Marion Island in January 1982 (Kerley, 1983a).

### Terrestrial haulout

They haul out on most of the small offshore islets and islands, the better known including the Seal Islands in Algoa, Mossel and False bays. They occur on many small rocky islets, parts of which remain dry at high tide, and on rocky promontories such as Cape Cross and False Cape Fria on the Namibian coast.

In movement on land the front and hind flippers bend at right angles to the body and lift it clear of the ground, the ridges on the soles of the front flippers helping to maintain a grip, especially on slippery rock. They may amble along with consecutive movement of the flippers; slightly faster by the consecutive action of the front flippers and dragging the tail; or gallop along using the two front flippers in unison and then the two back flippers in unison, with a hunching movement of the body. They climb well and will drop from heights, the chest bearing the shock of landing. In hauling out in heavy seas their timing to take advantage of an incoming wave and judgement to avoid being washed back is superb.

### Food

Rand (1959) reported that small schooling fish constituted 80% by volume of the fish food eaten, 60% of all the main edible food items. Ranking high among the fish are maasbankers, *Trachurus trachurus*, pilchards, *Sardinops ocellata*, and Cape mackerel, *Scomber japonicus*. In addition to these he listed 21 other species of fish eaten. Octopuses, squid and cuttlefish rank high in their diet; rock lobsters and crustaceans are eaten, but compared with fish and cephalopods, form an insignificant part of their diet. In foraging, the Cape fur seal scatters and tends to become a solitary feeder. However, small groups of two or three may feed together and it is likely that a number of groups may join to form larger congregations at favourable feeding locations.

Young seals pick up and swallow water-worn stones and gravel. These are found in 25% of the stomachs of yearlings; their function remains obscure.

### Reproduction

Eighteen of the 24 known localities where Cape fur seals breed along the South African and Namibian coast are on islands and six are situated on the mainland, including the four largest (David, 1987; Oosthuizen & David, 1988). The breeding sites are situated predominantly on rocky ground but also on flat sandy beaches, some parts of which may only be tenable at low tide. These sites are used during the breeding period by males that manage to establish territories and adult females hauling out to pup, other classes being forbidden access until all the females have mated (Rand, 1959).

Large adult males haul out about mid-October and establish territories, the females following a few weeks later to give birth to a single pup. Most pups are born in late November and early December, 90% of them within a 34-day period. The newly born pups are 0,6 to 0,7 m in total length, with a mass of 4,5 kg to 7,0 kg. They are black in colour, the first moult taking place in March/April to the silvery-brown adult coat. The pups suckle within an hour of birth and the adult females remaining with them on shore for the first week. Females come into oestrus five or six days after the birth of the pup (Rand, 1955). The gestation period is approximately a year. About one week after the birth of her pup the female leaves it for periods of up to several days while she returns to the sea to forage. On returning to land she bellows for her pup which may answer by bleating, eventually tracing it by scent among those in the vicinity of her usual resting place (Shaughnessy, 1979).

For some weeks before the onset of the breeding season there is a notable decrease in the number of seals on land. Adult males arrive at the breeding sites with a large food reserve in the form of blubber and those that establish a territory usually do not move off it for a period of up to six weeks. Much of the reserved energy is used in establishing and maintaining their territories, in herding females and in the other activities associated with breeding. The establishment of territories starts even before the arrival of the females, breeding territories being established shortly after their arrival. While the males that arrive early in the season establish territories without much effort, those arriving later may have to fight their way from the sea to find unoccupied ground. Once established, territories are vigorously defended. Chest to chest combats are frequent, efforts being made by the contestants to make each other lose balance. Serious wounds on the tail and pelvic region are common and if one of the contestants is pushed into another territory, its territorial male may also take part in the contest, biting indiscriminately at one or other of the opponents.

The pupping site coincides with the territory of a territorial male and, as soon as the female comes into oestrus after the birth of her pup, she is served. The grouping of the females around a territorial male gives the impression of harems. Rand (1967) did not think that the males fight over the females, but they do exercise a subtle control over their movements. Rand (1967) recorded harems of seven to 66 cows. The mating season is brief, covering a few weeks only, and by early December the cows start to disperse and by mid-December most harems have disappeared. With the Cape fur seal it is rare for males to establish territories and then not to receive any cows, but this does happen when territories are situated on the fringe of the main breeding area.

The females, as they come ashore, lay claim to space within a male's territory. In the process of its establishment the females fight viciously, this fighting sometimes settled by intervention from the territorial male. Generally this spatial sorting disappears once the females have produced their pups.

Non-breeding mature adult males, or adult males suffering from injuries, may be found in specific parts of the breeding site, adjoining the main breeding colony. Young males herd together away from these breeding sites.

During the first few days of the pup's life the maternal bond is very strong, and the female will fight vigorously over ownership of what she considers to be her own pup. This bond is maintained even more strongly by the pup, some females appearing indifferent to the whereabouts of their offspring. While their mothers are away very young pups congregate on "playgrounds". As they grow up they start to explore the rock pools and reefs around the breeding site, but avoid rough water. At first they are clumsy swimmers but soon develop proficiency. By the time they are three to four months old their mothers may be absent for long periods and hunger activates them to seek edible matter. They then also start to explore deeper water. When seven months old they may stay away from land for three or four consecutive days.

During the winter months the young seals mix freely with the other age classes but may form discrete groups on the beaches above the high water mark. When the young females reach sexual maturity in their third year (Shaughnessy, 1979), they leave these groups and follow the pattern of the older females, hauling out to join the males and females at the breeding sites.

The pups continue to suckle from their mothers for nine to 11 months, although some young continue to suckle into the second year. The weaning process appears to be gradual and pups supplement their milk diet by limited foraging three to four months before weaning (David & Rand, 1981). Females have two pairs of inguinal teats but the mammary glands coalesce in a sheet-like layer under the blubber (King, 1983).

**General**

Shaughnessy & Payne (1979) estimated that the annual mortality of Cape fur seals caused by trawl netting for fish in South African waters amounts to over 4 000 annually. Fur seals tend to congregate in the vicinity of trawlers and, if they enter the nets while the trawl is being hauled in, may drown before it is pulled aboard or alternatively enter it near the surface and may escape as it is being hauled aboard. In the area in which the investigation took place Shaughnessy & Payne (1979) estimated that the total population was about 320 000 seals, the proportion of the population killed annually amounting to 0,013%.

Cape fur seals are known to have died through being caught and strangled in discarded portions of fish net and cordage thrown overboard from fishing vessels. This comes about by their predilection for playing with flotsam.

Best & Shaughnessy (1979) recorded that the Cape fur seal has been exploited for about 370 years, a Dutch expedition taking 45 000 near the Cape of Good Hope between March and October 1610. They recorded an account of Morrell's sealing voyage to the southwest coast of Africa in 1828/1829 which showed that only some of the colonies now known to exist, were present in those days, and that they were less abundant than today.

The first contact on record by Europeans with the Cape fur seal was that by the crew of Diago Cao's ship who reported that, at Cabo de Santa Maria (then Cabo do Lobo) 144 km south of Benguella, Angola, in 1483, the rocks were alive with seals.

The first recorded report of seals from the coastline of the Subregion is that of Vasco da Gama who in 1497 anchored at St Helena Bay, 130 km north of Table Bay, and sampled the roasted meat of the "sea wolf" cooked by Khoikhoi, pronouncing their manners and methods of cooking "revolting". Calling at Mossel Bay in 1497 he reported in detail on the seals on Seal Island in the bay (Skead, 1980). From this time onward visits to capes and islands off the coast of the Subregion by voyagers became more frequent in their search for fresh food supplies. This included Cape fur seals; rock dassies, *Procavia capensis*; jackass penguins, *Spheniscus demersus*, and their eggs and the eggs of other sea birds.

Sir James Lancaster who called at Robben Island in 1601 recorded that they killed seals and "made oyle of them and some of the youngest we did eate which to us seemed good meate". In 1608 the seals on this island, then in "unspeakable numbers", were put to a rather different use as Cornelius Matelief reported that "our men amused themselves by clubbing fully a hundred to death", no mention being made of the utilisation of the carcasses. The consistent killing of seals on Robben Island, which continued thereafter, reduced the numbers to such an extent that, by the time of Van Riebeeck in the 1650's, they had to be sought on the islands further north, such as Dassen and the islands in Saldanha Bay (Skead, 1980).

Commercial exploitation apparently started on an extensive scale about the 1650's, for Van Riebeeck's journal reports that "the yacht *Goede Hoope* returned from an island in Saldanha Bay with 2 700 seal skins apparently left there by a French ship which could not take them as they already had a full load (Skead, 1980).

Uncontrolled exploitation of the Cape fur seal which continued late into the 19th century led to the diminution of numbers, in parts rendering further hunting uneconomic. In 1893, with an appreciation of the serious position, they were protected by an Act of the Cape Government. This and other legislation has led to an increase in their numbers over the years. Under the Sea Birds and Seals Protection Act of 1973 the management of Cape fur seal populations became the responsibility of the Sea Fisheries Institute, Cape Town. The scientific and technical staff of this organisation has contributed substantially to the knowledge necessary for the proper management of the species and is responsible for setting the quotas so that culling may proceed on a sustained yield basis. Four islands in Saldanha Bay were incorporated into the Langebaan National Park in 1986, and most of the other continental islands and some offshore rocks were ceded to the Cape Department of Nature and Environmental Conservation on two occasions, in 1979 and 1987, and have been promulgated as nature reserves.

In 1980 the population of Cape fur seals was estimated at 1 035 000, of which about one third occur in the territorial waters of the Republic of South Africa, the remainder in Namibian waters, including South Africa's islands off its coast. Of the 24 breeding colonies only nine, in that year, were subject to culling. The total pup quota awarded for all nine colonies was 84 460, of which 32 100 were to be taken from Republic of South Africa colonies, the balance from Namibia. This amounts to 32% of the total pup crop in the nine colonies, the actual harvest eventually falling considerably short of the quota awarded (David, *in litt.*).

Despite the fact that, under control and with a knowledge of overall population numbers and recruitment rate, the exploitation of a renewable natural resource on a sustained yield basis is a legitimate and proper undertaking, the harvesting of seals arouses deep emotions and many people would like to see it cease. To some extent these emotions are roused because it is the under-yearling seals, between the ages of seven to 10 months, that are culled and because the traditional "stun and stick" method of killing is still in use. The method of killing has been investigated by Veterinary and Medical Authorities in various parts of the world who remain satisfied as to its criteria of humaneness. Many other methods have been investigated but in no case has an improvement been found (Shaughnessy, 1976). Although the method may appear primitive it is similar to the method used to kill livestock in abattoirs.

Seals can be a problem in line and net fishing, in the former eating the catches and in the latter damaging nets and becoming entangled in these and the lines by which they are operated. Fishermen claim that seals seriously reduce fish populations. Best (1973b) stated that a primary aim of the South African Government in the management of the Cape fur seal is to ease the effects of their predation on the fish stocks. However, as yet there is no adequate scientific basis upon which to predict whether a reduction in the Cape fur seal population would have a positive or negative impact on sustainable yields of commercial fish species ((Butterworth, Duffy, Best & Bergh, 1988). Conversely modern fishing techniques for locating and capturing fish have improved to the point that seal populations can be affected seriously by reduction of fish populations, their principal food.

There is little evidence to show that oil spills affect seals, although peak mass for oiled pups is lower than for unoiled pups (Bonner, 1978). Organochlorine contamination of seals has been described from many industrialised coastlines but there is little evidence to connect high concentrations of pollutants with abnormalities in the seals. Bonner (1978) reported, however, that in the Californian sea lion, *Zalophus californianus*, there is some evidence that high pollutant levels in females can result in premature births.

Human disturbance can affect seals on their breeding grounds at the time of pupping and Van Haaften (1974) suggested that the increase in tourism had been partly responsible for the decrease in seal numbers around the Netherlands.

No. 282

# *Arctocephalus gazella* (Peters, 1875)

## Antarctic fur seal
## Antarktiese pelsrob

### Colloquial Name

This species was named after SMS Gazelle, the ship that brought the original specimen back from Iles Kerguelen in 1874.

Throughout the greater part of their distributional range the Antarctic fur seal occurs south of the Antarctic Convergence as opposed to the Subantarctic fur seal, *A. tropicalis*, which is generally confined to the seas north of it. The Antarctic fur seal, nevertheless, occurs north of the Convergence on the Prince Edward, Crozet and Macquarie islands.

Sometimes called the Kerguelen fur seal, as the original specimen was taken on the island, it seems preferable to distinguish them on the basis of the association of *A. gazella* with the colder Antarctic and *A. tropicalis* with the relatively warmer Subantarctic waters.

### Taxonomic Notes

Formerly the two species *A. gazella* and *A. tropicalis* were considered subspecies of *A. tropicalis* (King, 1959a). Repenning, Peterson & Hubbs (1971) accorded them full specific rank. Brown *et al.* (1974) noted that the acceptance of this change awaits the test of time but, in view of the many differences in their morphology and life history, they are considered here as two species.

While the key highlights some of the characters used to distinguish the two species, the fuller field key provided by Kerley (1981) is a convenient and useful guide to their identification (See Field characters: *A. tropicalis* and *A. gazella* No. 283). Hybridisation occurs occasionally where the two species live sympatrically (Kerley, 1983b).

### Description

Adult female Antarctic fur seals vary in colour on the upper parts from grey to slightly brownish, some individuals almost russet. The chin is the same colour as the upper parts, the throat and breast cream or cream-tinged yellow and they have a lateral stripe of the same colour from the insertion of the flippers extending back along the body. This cream colour may become brownish but never orange as in *A. tropicalis*. The under parts from the insertion of the flippers over the belly are dark ginger in colour, and around the insertion of the flippers rich chestnut, the flippers black towards their extremities. The short hair around the eyes and bordering the lips is brownish. The ears are naked at their black tips, the middle portion of the ear lighter coloured than the upper parts of the body. The underfur on the upper parts is dark fawn in colour and darker on the belly.

The adult males are silvery-grey and lack the creamy coloured throat and chest of the females. They have a grizzled "mane" of relatively long hair which covers the neck, shoulders and breast down to the insertion of the flippers, so that the entire front of the male, when sitting alert, is protected by it. They have a dark yoke from the insertion of the flippers over the shoulders behind the mane. The under parts between the flippers are rich chestnut, shading to a lighter hue on the belly. The underfur is darker than that of the cow and is reddish (Bonner, 1968).

The hair on the mane of bulls of *A. gazella* reaches a length of about 60 mm, on *A. tropicalis* 32 to 35 mm and correspondingly the hair on the upper parts of the former is longer at 42 to 43 mm than that of the latter at 20 to 21 mm. Male *A. gazella* have a mass of up to 230 kg, females 50 kg, with total lengths of 1,95 m and 1,4 m respectively (Bonner, 1968; McCann & Doidge, 1987). The males have a less well developed crest of long hair on top of the head than in *A. tropicalis*.

### Skull

As far as skull characters are concerned, Repenning *et al.* (1971) noted that the most prominent features are that *A. tropicalis* has a narrower palate than *A. gazella*; the post-canine teeth are smaller in *A. gazella*, the last two on each side being distinctly smaller and button-like in shape; the lateral appearance of the upper post-canine tooth row is straighter and less arched in *A. tropicalis* than in *A. gazella; A. gazella* has shorter and broader nasal bones, and male *A. gazella* have larger and longer skulls than *A. tropicalis*, although in the females the skulls are similar in size (Fig. 282.1). Kerley & Robinson (1987) found that these two species can be distinguished on size and shape characteristics of the skull.

The dental formula is:

$I\frac{3}{2}\ C\frac{1}{1}\ PC\frac{5-6}{5} = 34$ to 36 (Bester, pers. comm.).

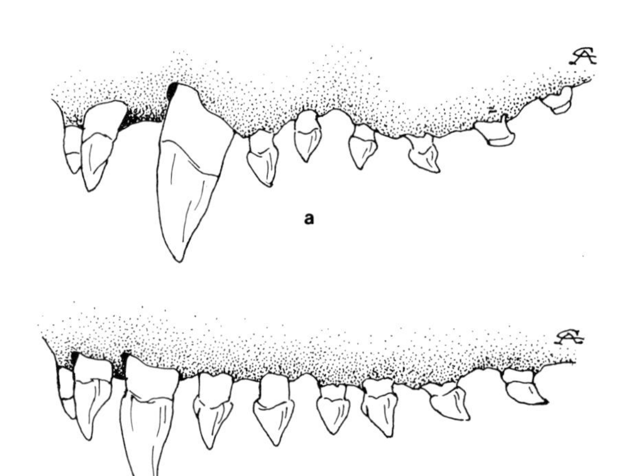


Fig. 282.1. Upper toothrow
(a) *Arctocephalus gazella* (b) *A. tropicalis.*

### Distribution

They are generally confined to the seas and the islands lying to the south of the Antarctic Convergence, with a northerly extension to the Prince Edward, Macquarie and Crozet islands which lie to the north of the Convergence and Iles Kerguelen which lie on it, and extending westwards to Heard Island and eastwards to the vicinity of the Antarctic Peninsula.

Their southernmost limits are not well known but they have been recorded in winter on the pack ice southwest of Bouvet Island (Bester, 1979), found breeding at the South Shetland Islands (McCann & Doidge, 1987) and ashore at Mawson Station (67°36'S, 62°52'E), Antarctica (Shaughnessy & Burton, 1986). Payne (1979a) noted instances of *A. gazella* penetrating north of the Convergence and *A. tropicalis* south of it. An *A. gazella* pup tagged on South Georgia was recovered on the coast of South America and there are five records of *A. tropicalis* at South Georgia which is several hundred kilometres south of the Convergence. Kerley (1983b) recorded that on the Prince Edward Islands, which lie north of the Convergence, *A. gazella* hauls out to breed in numbers estimated to be 300–400, against those of *A. tropicalis* at about 35 000. In a similar situation it has been found that they co-exist at Iles Crozet (Jouventin, Stahl & Weimerskirch, 1982) and at Macquarie Island which they share with non-breeding New Zealand fur seals, *A. forsteri* (Shaughnessy & Fletcher, 1987). The Convergence is therefore not an absolute boundary between the two species.

**Terrestrial haulout**

Antarctic fur seals spend about 30% of their lives on land to rest or reproduce. In hauling out on Marion Island they show a preference for open vegetated areas behind landing beaches (Kerley, 1983b) on the southwest side of the island. The territorial bulls are very aggressive to arrivals from the sea side and it is safer for human observers to approach the breeding colonies from the shoreward direction. After a rapid increase in late November, numbers peak in December, the height of the breeding season, followed by a second peak to moult in autumn (March). After the pups are weaned in April, both females and pups are absent from the island until the next summer. Males also depart in April and start returning in October.

**Food**

The principal food of the Antarctic fur seal is krill, *Euphausia* spp, but they will also take fish and cephalopods, and remains of penguins have been found in stomachs (Doidge & Croxall, 1985). On Marion Island, Kerley (pers. comm.) recorded unidentified squid beaks and the remains of either rockhopper or gentoo penguins in stomachs. Stones and gravel are found often in stomachs. The purpose of these has not been explained fully and several reasons have been advanced, the most plausible being that they swallow them to allay pangs of hunger.

**Reproduction**

On South Georgia, Bonner (1968) recorded the sequence of events leading up to pupping and mating and the history of the colonies thereafter. Some adult bulls start to haul out in the early days of September, but these may not remain until the onset of the breeding season. Practically all the harem bulls have hauled out and established territories by early December, although by then only about one-third of the cows has arrived. The first cows start to haul out about the middle of November. Bulls try to establish and maintain as large a territory as possible. When the population is sparse, these territories may have a radius of about 15 m, but on more densely populated sites are usually not over 5 m in radius. The territorial boundaries are usually marked by physical barriers such as rocks or boulders.

The first bulls that arrive are usually spaced so far apart that little fighting takes place, but fighting becomes commoner as more bulls arrive until the whole area available is taken up. Late-comers patrol up and down in the shallow water looking for a favourable opportunity to dash ashore and may be successful in traversing the first rank of territories by charging through them before having to come to grips with an established territorial bull. In the fighting that ensues opponents slash at each other's necks and chests, the heavy mane affording substantial protection and bites on these parts rarely cause more than superficial wounds. Serious injuries may be incurred, however, on other parts of their bodies which are not protected so well. The loser in these contests may have to fight his way back to the sea, unless he can find a route free of occupied territories. Bulls are less aggressive towards neighbouring territorial bulls and, on their territorial boundaries, skirmishing may result more in demonstrations than contests, the bulls challenging each other and making lunges which seldom connect.

The most successful bulls have territories near the sea, the least successful further inland among the tussock grass, where their harems may consist of a single cow only. Adult younger bulls may not be able to secure a territory on land and remain in the water close to the shore where they may slip ashore sometimes and copulate with cows in oestrus that have been served inland already and are on their way to the sea.

Most cows arrive in early December to seek pupping sites. They show a preference for dry, sheltered shingle beaches. The bulls make no attempt to gather cows, but will try and prevent cows from leaving their territories once they are there, by placing themselves between them and their territorial boundaries. The cows have their pups within a few days of arrival. The pup is active from birth, calling to its mother in its search for food, to which she replies. This duet is one of the most characteristic sounds of the breeding sites. If the bond between the mother and pup is broken during the early critical stage, by disturbance, through territorial fighting or other causes, the cow may not be able to recontact her pup and it may become a starveling.

Kerley (1985) showed that the mean birth mass of pups was 4,2 kg and they were weaned in about 112 days. The pups of the Subantarctic fur seal, *A. tropicalis*, although with the same mean birth mass, weaned in about 300 days. Cows come into oestrus within a few days after parturition, and abandon their pups temporarily and take to the sea on feeding expeditions. During the first three months after the birth of their pups, the females may be absent on these expeditions for about 40 days in total.

The pups start to moult when 50 to 60 days old, the moult being complete by the time they are 90 days old. As they grow older the pups tend to congregate on the inland side of the breeding sites.

The territorial aggressiveness of bulls declines steadily as the breeding season passes, and by mid-January there is a noticeable fall-off in the number of the territorial bulls on the site, although the number of cows remains about the same as at the height of the season. When bulls relinquish their territories these may be taken over by younger bulls. If the territorial bulls return they may lie about on the beach or may take steps to oust some of these younger bulls from their former territories. By mid-May all the cows have departed.

Young seals, most of them males, are conspicuous throughout the breeding season in the tussock grass areas inland from the breeding sites and on neighbouring beaches. The territorial bulls are intolerant of these young males and they have to gain access to the tussock grass resting sites along well marked corridors through the breeding colonies. They also congregate on the half-tide marks fringing the breeding sites and in the shallows offshore.

Because of their greater tendency to wander, most of the seals seen away from the breeding sites are juveniles. Because of crowding on the breeding sites, at the height of the season when the territorial boundaries are obscured, it is difficult to estimate the number of cows in the harems of territorial bulls. Bonner (1968) gave the figure as six to 11 from direct observation and from pup and bull counts about 12 to 16, with an average of 15.

Pup mortality is highest on crowded beaches, the principal cause being starvation, which mainly results from the failure of mother-pup bonding. Skull injury caused by bites inflicted by cows and liver rupture resulting from trampling by bulls are the other main causes of death. Killer whales, *Orcinus orca*, are potential predators but are rare in the seas around South Georgia (McCann & Doidge, 1987).

Females have two pairs of inguinal mammae.

No. 283

## *Arctocephalus tropicalis* (Gray, 1872)

## Subantarctic fur seal
## Subantarktiese pelsrob

Plate 26

### Colloquial Name

This species was described originally from a specimen from an unknown locality, but has also been called the Amsterdam Island fur seal.

### Taxonomic Notes

Previously this species and the Kerguelen or Antarctic fur seal, *A. gazella*, were thought to be subspecies of *A. tropicalis* (King, 1959b), those breeding north of the Antarctic Convergence *A. t. tropicalis* and those breeding south of it, *A. t. gazella*. Repenning, Peterson & Hubbs (1971) in reviewing the taxonomic status of the species, came to the conclusion, however, that they were worthy of full specific status, a view followed here.

### Description

Adult male *A. tropicalis* are much larger than adult females, the bulls with a mass of up to 165 kg (Amsterdam Island; Prevost & Mougin, 1970), 158 kg (Gough Island; Bester, 1987) and 117,5 kg (Marion Island; Kerley, 1987). The cows have a mass of up to 54 kg (Amsterdam Island; Tollu, 1974) and 50 kg (Marion Island; Condy, 1978). A conspicuous feature of the bulls is the distinct tuft of long hair which forms a crest on top of the head. The upper parts of the bodies in the bulls vary in colour from a grizzled black to a dark buff with a ginger tinge. This colour extends over the top of the head, coming to a point between the eyes. This contrasts with the conspicuous cream to burnt orange colour of the throat and chest which extends upwards to the level of the ears and continues around the eyes and across the bridge of the nose. It varies in extent, but in some individuals may reach to the anterior insertion of the foreflippers.

Around the lower side of the insertion of the foreflippers there is a brown or dark chocolate-coloured area which may extend, as a broad band, across the under parts of the body between the foreflippers. The belly may be dark chocolate or light brown. The fur which covers the flippers from their insertions to the level of the nails is fawn to dark chocolate in colour (Bester, 1977).

Older bulls tend to have an overall ginger-brown tinge, the chest fur russet, probably due to staining, and the top of the crest may be lighter in colour. Very old bulls have yellowish-white to grey-white crests, throats, faces and upper parts, the only darker areas being around the flippers and on the head (Bester, 1977). Very dark individuals are known, which are almost black overall with lighter chests.

Condy & Green (1980) showed that the guard coat is made up of two types of hairs which are longer in cows than in bulls. The outer layer is comprised of the longest and thickest hairs, which are relatively straight and elliptical in section. Towards their tips, however, they curve upwards and away from the body, become flattened and taper to a fine point. An inner layer of guard hairs is shorter and more spherical in section, and is characterised by being bent almost at a right angle and curving towards the body. The hairs of the dense underfur are wavy and generally reddish-brown in colour. The white whiskers are very long, in some individuals reaching half way down the chest, but in older individuals wear down and may reach only the corners of the mouth.

The colour of the adult cows is softer in tone than in the bulls, varying from dark grey to grey, the throat and chest conspicuously burnt orange which extends upwards on the sides of the head in a crescent across the forehead. The belly is brown or fawn and between this and the greyish upper parts there is a lighter coloured band from the foreflippers extending towards the tail. The cows lack the crest on top of the head, although rarely it may be present (Bester, 1977).

The essential differences in the skulls and teeth of this species and *A. gazella* are given under *A. gazella* (**Description** and Figs 282.1 and 283.1).

The dental formula is:

$I\frac{3}{2}\ C\frac{1}{1}\ PC\frac{5-7}{4-6} = 28$ to 40 (Bester, pers. comm.)

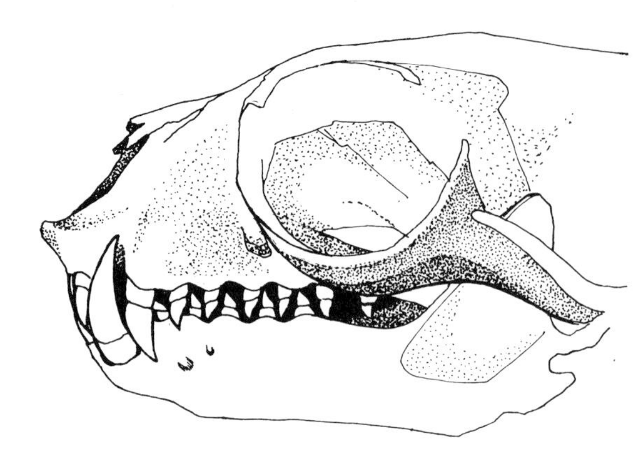

Fig. 283.1. Anterior portion of skull and toothrows, *Arctocephalus tropicalis*

### Field characters, *A. tropicalis* and *A. gazella*

Condy (1978) noted that field identification is dependent on colour, external morphological differences and vocalisation. Kerley (1981) provided the following notes to assist identification in the field of the two species of fur seals, *A. tropicalis* and *A. gazella*.

| FEATURE | SPECIES DESCRIPTION | |
|---|---|---|
| **Body size** | | |
| **Bulls** | *A. tropicalis* | *A. gazella* |
| | Up to 158 kg (Gough Island, Bester, pers. comm.), with a stout and compact appearance. The shoulders are massive and the neck is short. | Up to 200 kg on South Georgia (Payne, 1979b), with less massive shoulders and a more sinuous appearance, and long necks. |
| **Cows** | Up to 50 kg (Condy, 1978) with a compact body. | Up to 50 kg (Payne, 1979b) with a slender sinuous body. |
| **Immatures** | Difficult to distinguish. *A. gazella* has a more slender appearance than *A. tropicalis*. | |
| **Colour** | | |
| **Bulls** | *A. tropicalis* | *A. gazella* |
| | Chest and face to behind the eyes is cream to burnt orange. The belly is light fawn to dark orange, frequently with a dark brown band between the fore flippers, as well as at the insertion of the flippers. | Chest and neck are silvery-grey with long guard hairs giving the appearance of a silvery mane. There is a darker band below the mane at the level of the foreflippers, the insertion and ventral region between the foreflippers. |
| **Cows** | Chest and face are cream to fawn with the belly fawn to light brown. The back is grey to brown, occasionally darker. | Generally silvery in appearance with creamy throat and chest, slightly darker belly and brown flipper insertions. |
| **Immatures** | Similar in coloration, although *A. gazella* is always lighter and more silver in appearance. | |
| **Pups** | The pups are black before first moult and at this stage are very similar. *A. gazella* pups have a grizzled face giving them the appearance of having a white face. | |

**Crest**
**Bulls**

| *A. tropicalis* | *A. gazella* |
|---|---|
| The crest is prominent in the adult bulls. | No crest present, but there is a slight top knot of guard hairs. |

**Cows**

| | |
|---|---|
| Crest is rarely present. | Crest is never present. |

**Immatures**

Young *A. tropicalis* males may have a slight crest, but otherwise it is not present.

**Vibrissae**
**Bulls**

| *A. tropicalis* | *A. gazella* |
|---|---|
| The bulls have very long white whiskers commonly extending to below the ears and in extreme cases to halfway down the chest. They are shortened by wear and may be bitten off during fights. | Whiskers are not so long and appear to be thinner and less luxuriant. |

**Eyes**

| *A. tropicalis* | *A. gazella* |
|---|---|
| The eyes are oval and less prominent. | Eyes are smaller and almond-shaped, but prominent. |

**Ears**

| *A. tropicalis* | *A. gazella* |
|---|---|
| The ears are naked at the tips with dark hair on the proximal two-thirds. They are not prominent above the fur. | Naked at the tips with light hair on the proximal two-thirds. Ears protrude prominently above the fur. |

**Flippers**

| *A. tropicalis* | *A. gazella* |
|---|---|
| The flippers especially the hind flippers are relatively short and broad. | The flippers are relatively long and slender. The distance from the insertion of the nails to the extremity of the hind flipper is nearly twice that for *A. tropicalis*. |

In addition, Bester & Wilkinson (1989) showed that linear measurement of the hind flipper length could be used to distinguish between pups of the species when 40–50 days old.

## Vocalisations

The two species have distinctly different vocalisations. *A. tropicalis* has a more extensive repertoire of vocalisation. The most comparable vocalisation for field identification is the gutteral challenge of the adult bulls (Bester, 1977). In *A. tropicalis* this can be described as a deep growl, whereas in *A. gazella* it is like a series of rapid wheezy coughs or exhalations ("Uughff-Uughff").

## Hybridisation

Adult bulls have been observed with features that are typical of both *A. gazella* and *A. tropicalis*. These specimens are very dark, big, with short broad flippers and frequently a crest. Their vocalisations are indecisive, having qualities of both *A. tropicalis* and *A. gazella*.

Research on the skull morphometrics of male Antarctic and Subantarctic fur seals and their putative hybrids supports the contention of Condy (1978) that these two species hybridise at the Prince Edward Islands (Kerley & Robinson, 1987).

## Distribution

They occur in Subantarctic waters, north of the Antarctic Convergence, reaching the coast of the Subregion as vagrants. Bester (1984) listed them as breeding at Amsterdam and St Paul islands, Iles Crozet, Gough Island and the Tristan da Cunha group of islands, and on Marion and Prince Edward islands. Stragglers are recorded from South Georgia (Payne, 1979a), the Argentine coast (Castello & Pinedo, 1977) and Juan Fernandez Archipelago (Torres & Aguayo, 1984). From 1981/82 it has been recognised that both *A. tropicalis* and *A. gazella* occur at Macquarie Island which they share with non-breeding New Zealand fur seals, *A. forsteri*, and that breeding territories contain cows and pups of both *A. gazella* and *A. tropicalis*, as well as *A. tropicalis* bulls (Shaughnessy & Fletcher, 1987). Recently *A. tropicalis* was recorded at Heard Island during the summer haulout of *A. gazella* there, and one pup was born (Goldsworthy & Shaughnessy, in press).

Shaughnessy & Ross (1980) recorded 22 strandings on the coast at points between Cape Town and Richards Bay, the first near Port Elizabeth in June 1966. This two-year-old female lived in the Port Elizabeth Oceanarium for 2 years and 10 months until its death. The occurrence of the species on the South African coast appears to be seasonal, 19 of the 22 individuals, mainly subadult and adult males and immature females, stranding between May to September, the winter and early spring months (Shaughnessy & Ross, 1980). At this time they are scarce on Marion and Gough islands (Condy, 1978; Bester, 1981a). The source of these stranding vagrants is unknown. Shaughnessy & Ross (1980) suggested that, as the largest population occurs at Gough Island and as this is expanding rapidly (Bester, 1980a), they might well have come from there. On the other hand the Prince Edward Islands are nearer, but the population there is smaller, and at least one immature seal, tagged on Marion Island, found its way to Saldanha Bay in 1984 (Bester, 1989).

## Terrestrial haulout

Fur seals, like other seals, spend a portion of their lives on land, either for the purposes of resting or reproduction. In hauling out on the coast of Marion Island they show a distinct preference for rugged, uneven terrain on the windward and exposed coast of the island. The many flat, smooth-surfaced beaches on the leeward side are not used to the same extent (Condy, 1978). On islands such as Gough Island, with slightly more temperate climates, the cooling effect of wind and spray is important to them in thermoregulation, but probably does not apply on Marion Island to the same extent as it lies near the Antarctic Convergence where air and sea temperatures are lower (Bester, 1982a). Condy (1978) suggested that their use of this terrain on Marion Island may be influenced by a number of factors such as their habit of pupping in caves and crevasses, the fact that elephant seals, *Mirounga leonina*, use the smoother beaches, and the possibility that the present population is a descendant that survived the onslaughts of the sealers only because it made use of the more inaccessible and inhospitable beaches. Bester (1982b) stated that on Gough Island their distribution and the choice of the sites which they use for the haulout is influenced primarily by thermoregulation and that former exploitation made itself felt only initially. The presence of *M. leonina* on this island does not influence their choice of sites for the haulout (Bester, 1980b).

The haulout takes place on established breeding colony sites and on non-breeding sites. Colonies on the established breeding colony sites consist almost exclusively of territorial males and females with newly born calves. On the less successful breeding sites fewer females haul out, but immatures are abundant. On the non-breeding sites the colonies consist of adult males, a few adult females and a preponderance of subadult males. In addition "idle" sites are established, the colonies occupying these sites composed almost entirely of adult and subadult males (Bester, 1982b).

Adult males in the idle colonies are not very active. Bester (1977) found that 94% of their time is spent in total inactivity, with less than 2% of interactions between adult males and 4% in non-social activities, such as moving around and grooming. The subadults in these colonies are more active than the adults, there being some interaction between them.

In contrast to this the breeding sites are hives of activity, the territorial males in particular being active in territorial defence, in herding adult females and other activities associated with breeding, and the females in attendance of their offspring.

Seals are affected by high ambient temperatures and high levels of solar radiation and at the non-breeding and idle sites in particular they take to the water under these conditions to cool off. The territorial males in breeding colonies only resort to the sea under high environmental temperatures and when there are no females in their territory. When they do they return to their territories after a cooling off period in the sea.

On both Gough and Marion islands the total numbers of seals on the islands have two peaks during the summer months. After a rapid increase in numbers during late October, the first peak falls during the middle of December which is the height of the breeding season. There is an increase in numbers during February/March, the second peak following in March/April, the height of the moult haulout (Bester, 1981; Kerley, 1983c).

**Food**

Shaughnessy & Ross (1980) examined stomach contents of eight individuals which had stranded on the South African coast and found squid, Histioteuthidae, in seven and fragments of crustaceans in one. No remains of fish were found in any of the eight examined. Rand (1956a) recorded that, at Marion Island, fish were more important than squid and, for the same area, Condy (1981) estimated that their diet is comprised of 50% squid, 45% fish and 5% krill.

On Gough Island in 220 stomachs examined, squid constituted almost the exclusive food item recorded, fish only occasionally being found. The diurnal haul out pattern of this species at Gough Island suggests that they feed from dusk to dawn in order to take advantage of the vertical migration of pelagic squid which move towards the surface at night (Bester & Laycock, 1985). Neither at Gough Island, where the crayfish, *Jasus tristanii*, was extremely abundant nor at Amsterdam Island, where *J. paulensis* was equally common, were these eaten. At Amsterdam Island the adult fur seals feed on rockhopper penguins, *Eudyptes chrysocome*, from August to April; squid and mackerel, *Scomber japonicus*, are the most important foods for the rest of the year (Tollu, 1974). In contrast the species at Gough and Marion islands do not supplement their diet with penguins (Condy, 1981; Bester & Laycock, 1985).

**Reproduction**

On Gough Island with the rapid increase in the haulout of the males during November, those landing on the breeding sites engage in intra-sexual fighting leading to the establishment of individual territories. These territories tend to be delineated by natural topographical features such as large rocks or ledges which influence their size, which may vary from 5,0 m² to 63 m². Territory size is also governed by position, and those bordering on the sea are smaller than those inland. In addition those established early in the season may decrease in size through competition and, late in the season, may increase in size due to incorporation of neighbouring abandoned territories. The physical nature of the beach contributes to the number of territories that can be formed.

Although serious fighting may take place in the establishment of a territory, once established, neighbouring territorial males tolerate each other, but indulge in boundary displays, which never culminate in prolonged fighting. These displays take the form of rushes to the boundary with open-mouthed guttural threats. Slashes may be directed at the opponents' face and chest. Group aggression, where several territorial males may converge on a trespasser infringing mutual boundaries, are common, each of the territorial males, however, remaining within their territorial boundaries.

In fierce fighting in the establishment of territories, the opponents position themselves chest to chest, lunging and slashing at each other. If a bite results in a firm grip the opponent may be shaken or pushed backwards. In the process they tear the opponent's skin at the point of contact. Fighting may leave the contestants exhausted and badly injured. Very little fighting is seen at the non-breeding sites on which the injured, and the males which have failed to establish territories, take refuge.

The bulk of the females arrives at the breeding sites in an advanced state of pregnancy about a week after the large-sized males of territorial status. Pupping peaks in mid-December, a single young being produced at a birth. Kerley (1985) showed that, like the Antarctic fur seal, *A. gazella*, the mean birth mass was 4,2 kg, but that the period to weaning was longer at about 300 days, compared with *A. gazella* at about 112 days. Twinning seldom occurs, and one case is known where twins were raised to weaning in the wild (Bester & Kerley, 1983).

Adult females can be aggressive towards other females when numbers are high or when they are herded together by the territorial male. Aggregations of females tend to space themselves out but disputes are settled by threats and at the most biting.

The newly born pups are inept in finding the females' nipples and, when searching for them, bleat. The female may either turn on her side to expose the nipples or assume a sitting position during suckling and, during the process, may caress the pup with a front flipper, sometimes with a hind one. Females will only suckle their own pups and are extremely aggressive towards strange pups.

A female hauling onto a beach where her pup is located, gives a pup attraction call to which a number of pups will respond. Recognition of her own pup among others is by nuzzling or sniffing and when this contact is established, if the female moves up the beach, the pup follows, and if it encounters obstacles, the female will pick it up in her jaws and assist it to surmount them (Bester, 1977).

The females remain with their pups for about a week before returning temporarily to the water for a brief period. As soon as they come into oestrus, which they do soon after their pup is born, they are herded actively by the territorial males and copulation ensues. The length of the period of oestrus is not known for *A. tropicalis*, but in the New Zealand fur seal, *A. forsteri*, it lasts up to 14 hours (Miller, 1975).

The territorial males take no notice of the pups, some of which are killed by being trampled on by them in the melée of herding and other breeding activities. Starvation may be the main cause of pup deaths (Bester, pers. comm.).

At the age of about two weeks the pups start to associate with one another. By the time they are four to five weeks old most of them have congregated at the back of the beach. By six weeks old they have taken to the surf zone or swim in rock pools. They keep close to the rocks, avoiding the rough water (Bester, 1977).

By about February/March the pups moult out of their black woolly natal coats, the majority being fully moulted by 15 weeks old. The new under-yearling coat is not fully attained by some until about August or September (Bester, 1981a). The under-yearlings are characterised by their small size, the flippers disproportionately small compared to their plump bodies, due mainly to the fluffy nature of their coats.

Females have two pairs of inguinal mammae.

# XXXVI. Family PHOCIDAE

## True seals

This Family, members of which occur in the Northern and Southern Hemispheres, consists of 10 genera and 19 species, only four of which occur in the Subregion: the leopard seal, *Hydrurga leptonyx*; the crabeater seal, *Lobodon carcinophagus*; the southern elephant seal, *Mirounga leonina*, and the Weddell seal, *Leptonychotes weddellii*, which was recorded on Marion Island in October 1979 (Gleeson, pers. comm.).

Most commonly known as the earless seals, all the members occurring in the Subregion have two pairs of upper incisor teeth and reduced claws on the hind flippers.

King (1983) noted that the otariid subfamily names are not generally used now, and referred to the Phocinae as the "northern phocids", the Monachinae as the "southern phocids".

Key to the genera adapted from Nel (1971)

1. Size very large, up to about 6,5 m; body thickset; two upper and one lower incisor teeth; canine at least five times the size of the adjacent incisors; proboscis present in adult males (Fig. 284.1).
   ... *Mirounga*

   Size smaller, up to about 4,0 m; body less thickset; two upper and two lower incisor teeth; no proboscis in adult males
   ... 2

2. Total length less than 2,7 m, cheekteeth with four to six cusps (Fig. XXXVI.2.a)
   ... *Lobodon*

   Total length in excess of 2,7 m, cheekteeth with one to three cusps
   ... 3

3. Cheekteeth with three cusps, the central cusp long and recurved; upper incisor teeth not antero-laterally orientated (Fig. XXXVI.2.b)
   ... *Hydrurga*

   Cheekteeth with one cusp; upper incisor teeth strongly antero-laterally orientated (Fig. XXXVI.2.c)
   ... *Leptonychotes*

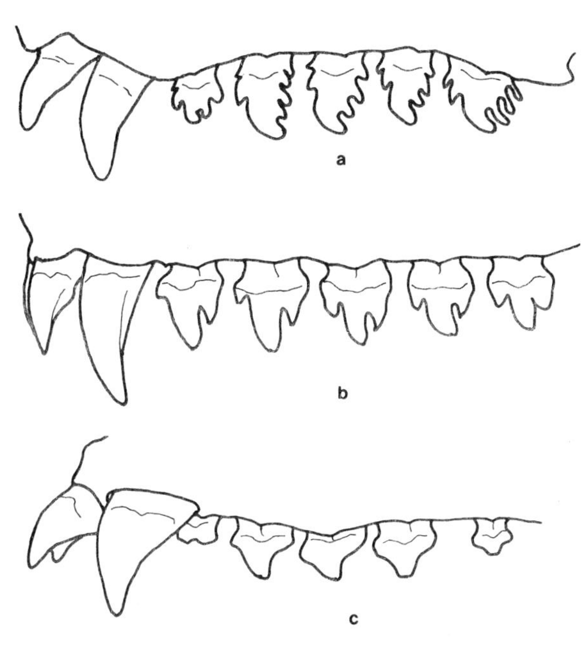


Fig. XXXVI.2. Upper toothrow:
(a) *Lobodon carcinophagus* (b) *Hydrurga leptonyx*
(c) *Leptonychotes weddellii* (after King, 1964)

## Genus *Mirounga* Gray, 1827

No. 284

## *Mirounga leonina* (Linnaeus, 1758)

## Southern elephant seal
## Suidelike olifantrob

Plate 26

### Colloquial Name

So called from their enormous size and the swollen, proboscis-like nose possessed by the adult males (Fig. 284.1). Often referred to as the sea elephant or *see-olifant*. *Miouroung* is the Australian native name for the elephant seal; *leonina*, lion-like, refers partly to size and partly to their roaring (King, 1983).

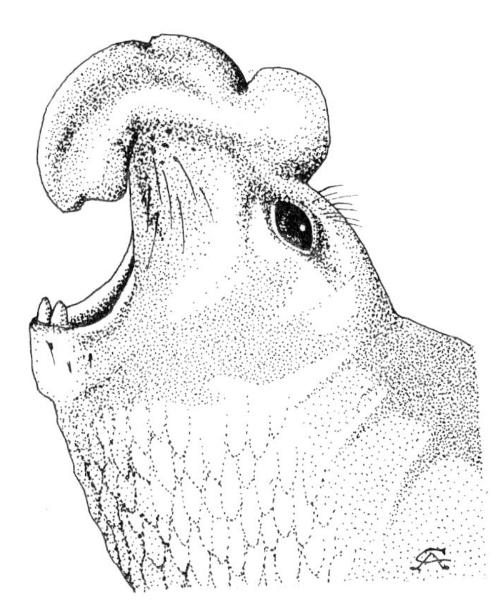

Fig. 284.1 Proboscis of male *Mirounga leonina*.
After Briggs & Morejohn (1976).

### Taxonomic Notes

Two species of *Mirounga* are known, this species and the northern elephant seal, *M. angustirostris* (Gill, 1866), which occurs on the eastern side of the North Pacific Ocean and is found on islands off Alaska, California and Mexico.

The body colour of the two species is very similar. The northern species is slightly smaller and when they are relaxed, the proboscis-like nose of the males is very long and hangs down over the mouth for about 300 mm. Unlike the southern elephant seal, which can bend its body backward far over the vertical line into a U-shape, the northern is far less flexible and can barely bend back over the vertical line.

### Description

Southern elephant seals are so large that there are practical difficulties of obtaining their mass in the field. Laws (1953) pointed out the difficulties in obtaining measurements of the total length when it is measured over the curve of the body, which cannot be obtained with an accuracy of less than 150 mm. In addition the variation in the size of the proboscis and the thickness of the blubber layer may affect measurements to the extent of 300 mm to 400 mm. Adult bulls have a mass of about 3 500 kg, cows 900 kg (King, 1983). Laws (1960) recorded total lengths of about 4,6 m for males and 2,9 m for females and drew attention to literature references to bulls of up to 7,6 m and even up to 9 m. He stated that at South Georgia the last of the very large bulls was killed about 1940 and suggested that formerly they reached larger sizes.

During the breeding season the adult bulls are dark greyish-brown in colour with a bluish sheen, becoming lighter through the summer until just before the moult in mid-January when they are chestnut or golden-brown in colour. After the moult the colour is dark grey, tinged brown. Except on the top of the proboscis and on the extremities of the flippers they are covered with short stiff hair. The adult females are drab-brown, lighter in colour ventrally. There is some variation in colour, individuals being grey-brown or reddish-brown, but they never attain the golden colour of the adult males (Laws, 1953).

The foreflippers are armed with stout grey-brown-coloured claws which have a series of three or four transverse lighter coloured bands across them, 3–4 mm in width. In the males these claws wear down much more than in the females. X-ray photographs of elephant seal foetuses show that their milk dentition is feebly developed, the teeth being resorbed before they are born. At birth only about 20% of the pups show any erupted teeth, the lower canines being the first to appear at the age of about eight days. The pups have a full set of functional teeth about 11 days after they wean.

The dental formula is:

$I\frac{2}{1}\ C\frac{1}{1}\ P\frac{4}{4}\ M\frac{1}{1} = 30$ (Laws, 1953).

### Distribution

The southern elephant seal is circumpolar in distribution, occurring in Subantarctic seas, but with records as far north as St Helena, from where it was recorded as early as 1656, and as far south as 77°40'S (Carrick, Csordas & Ingham, 1962).

Visits by the southern elephant seals to the southern coastline of the Subregion are fairly frequent. Best (1971a) recorded that, up to that date, 23 records were known, a further five being added as an addendum to this paper. Half of the 24 records of known date occurred during the summer months of December to February. In addition Ross (1969a) listed records from islands off Luderitz, Namibia. A further 95 hitherto unpublished sightings for the period 1913–1987 appear in Oosthuizen, David & Ross (1988).

The southern elephant seal ranges very widely. An individual tagged as a pup on South Georgia on the 6th November 1965 was found at Quoin Point, near Bredasdorp, Cape Province, on the 25th December, 1966, having travelled 4 825 km (Vaughan, 1967). At least two branded seals from Heard Island, one from Iles Kerguelen, and seven from Ile de la Possession found their way to Marion Island, covering 2 740, 2 640 and 1 100 km respectively (Bester, 1988). Marion Island is the most likely origin of elephant seals visiting the Subregion, but they may have come from any of the breeding colonies (Oosthuizen *et al.*, 1988).

### Terrestrial haulout

(Information for Marion Island from Condy, 1977a)

In hauling out the southern elephant seal prefers to do so on beaches which have a flat, smooth topography with a substrate of sand, smooth rounded stones or pebbles. They avoid the rough, rocky, uneven beaches favoured by the Subantarctic fur seal, *Arctocephalus tropicalis*. On Marion Island they prefer haulout beaches on the leeward side of the island; the rougher beaches, favoured by the fur seals, are mainly on the windward side. As a result there is very little overlap of the two species during the haulout periods.

The southern elephant seal hauls out for several purposes, the adult cows in order to pup, the adult cows and bulls for purposes of mating (see **Reproduction**), and all age classes in order to undergo the moult, or occasionally, in the case of subadults, to rest.

Seals in all age classes older than under-yearlings haul out once a year to moult. The subadult males and females haul out from early November before the adults, the subadult males hauling out so that their numbers reach a peak in early December, about five weeks before the females. The subadult male haulout is synchronised to fall between the two haulout periods of the bulls. The cows haul out from the second week in December, their numbers reaching a peak in late January and all have departed by early March. During the moult the bulls and cows tend to aggregate separately and, where there is access to areas of tussock grass inland, lie up in these while moulting. The wallows so caused consist of a complex of waterlogged hollows and mounds and give the area a distinctive appearance, and the manuring of the area has a profound influence on the vegetation and invertebrate fauna of the site and the areas below it (Panagis, 1984).

Although a few bulls remain on the island after the end of the pupping and mating season, the main haulout for moulting starts in mid-January, the peak being reached in mid-February. By early May they have all departed. While the cows complete their moult within 25 days, the bulls take 28 to 42 days.

Individuals in their second year of life start to haul out in early November, the peak being reached by mid-December, and most of them have departed by early February. In late March there is another less spectacular haulout.

The cows are absent from the island from early March to early September, the bulls from early May to early August. Some subadults haul out right through the winter, but leave before the bulls start to return for the mating. Some of the yearlings also remain on the island over the winter, leaving by mid-September, their departure precipitated by the arrival of the cows. Although bulls have arrived by mid-September, they do not molest the yearlings, but their arrival precipitates a decline in their numbers.

During the moult the old hair is shed in patches or sheets which are composed of the shed epidermis of the skin holding the shed hair together. In young individuals the new epidermis and hair then appear, but in males over five years old, the new hair may take up to 10 days to appear.

The process of moulting necessitates an increased blood supply on the outside of the layer of blubber which makes it difficult if not impossible for the elephant seal to maintain its body temperature in waters near freezing point and hence the necessity for the process to be carried out on land. During moulting the individuals tend to lie closely together, packing more closely on cold days than on warm days (Laws, 1960).

### Food

Southern elephant seals feed predominantly on squid and fish; crustaceans and other invertebrates constitute only a small part of their diet. In inshore waters they feed mainly on fish, on squid elsewhere, and it is assumed that the year-round diet probably includes about 75% cephalopods and 25% fish (Laws, 1984).

As the adult bulls spend up to nine weeks on land during the summer months and expend large energy resources during the breeding season, provision has to be made for this by a build-up in the form of blubber during the winter while they are at sea. The adult cows spend up to about 30 days during the parturition and mating period, during which they may lose up to 300 kg in suckling and attendance on their pups and a further 30 days ashore during the moult. Therefore they have to build up food resources against these periods ashore (Laws, 1960).

Most stomachs contain sand and stones which Laws (1960) suggested are related to the periods of fasting while ashore, serving to relieve pangs of hunger through keeping the stomachs distended.

### Reproduction

On Marion Island the sequence of events in the haulout for pupping and mating follows a regular annual pattern (Condy, 1977b). The adult bulls spend the winter months at sea and start to haul out in early August. Bulls that in previous years had attained territorial status may return to the same beach on which they had held this status previously. As soon as they arrive, fighting may take place to establish a hierarchy, which eventually leads to one of them becoming dominant (the beachmaster) over the others. By the time the cows arrive the territorial status and male hierarchy have been established. Changes can take place, however, in the hierarchy among the bulls at any stage during the haulout period.

**Plate 26**

281. Cape fur seal, *Arctocephalus pusillus*
Kaapse pelsrob
283. Subantarctic fur seal, *Arctocephalus tropicalis*
Subantarktiese pelsrob
284. Southern elephant seal, *Mirounga leonina*
Suidelike olifantrob
286. Leopard seal, *Hydrurga leptonyx*
Luiperdrob

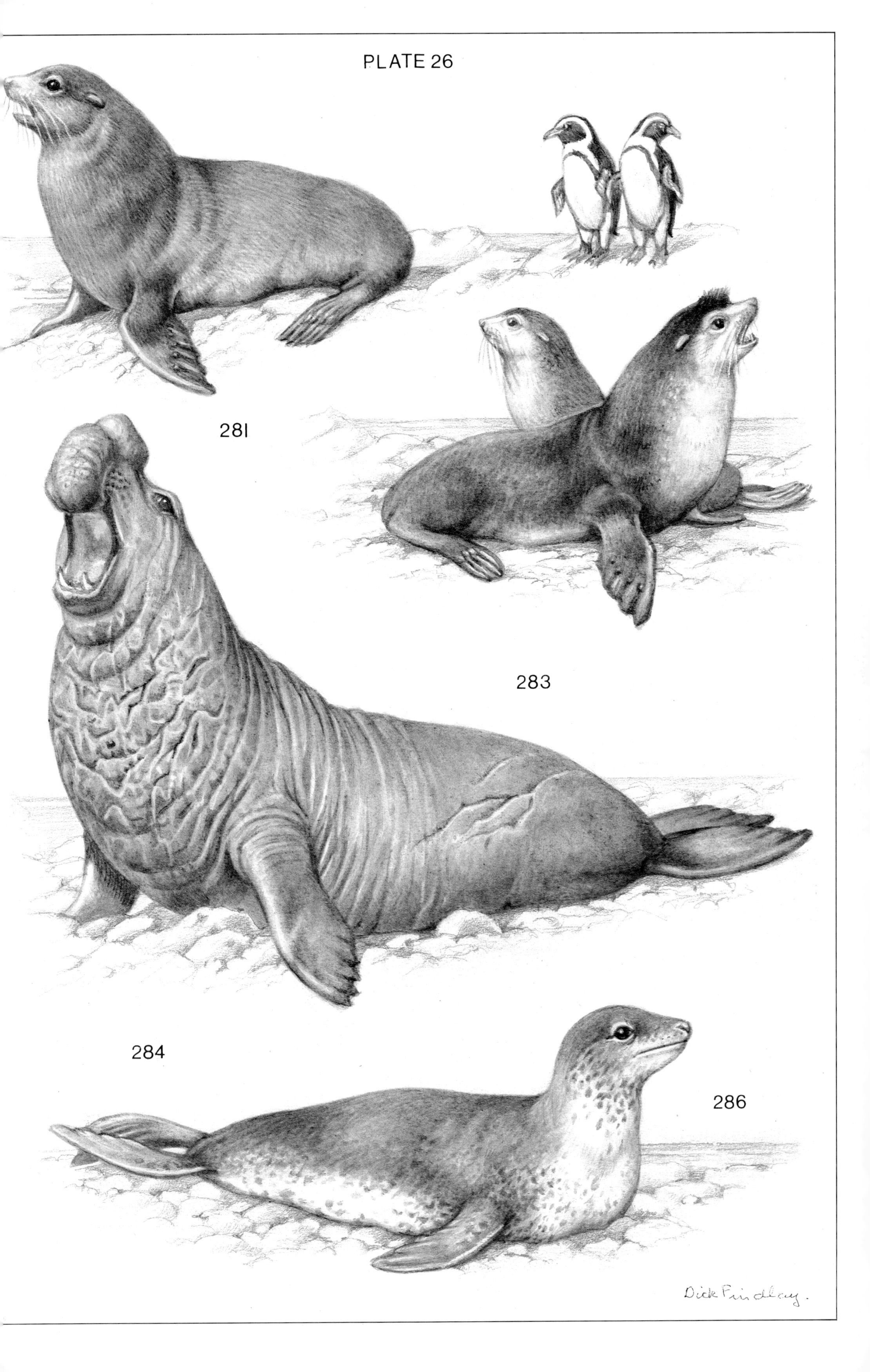
PLATE 26
281
283
284
286
Dick Findlay.

On Macquarie and Heard islands, Carrick *et al.* (1962) gave details of the hierarchy among the bulls. The beachmaster, the dominant bull, is an adult bull with a large harem. Older beachmasters are the largest, usually badly scarred, bulls up to 4,25 m long, 14 or more years old, with a fully developed proboscis. Younger beachmasters are experienced, with a small harem. The beachmaster is able to maintain sole possession of a harem of up to 60 cows, but when the breeding beach has 60 to 130 cows, he accepts an assistant beachmaster on the periphery of the colony and especially on the seaward side who serves the excess cows and, when over 130 are present, a second assistant beachmaster. Challengers are bulls without harems who, by fighting, are striving to attain one. Bachelor bulls are subordinates 3 to 4 m in length, 6 to 13 years old, whose proboscis lacks the central groove of the larger bulls and who may be slightly scarred. Bachelors avoid conflicts with the more dominant bulls.

Carrick *et al.* (1962) recorded that on Macquarie and Heard islands when the bulls first arrive ashore, which they do ahead of the cows, they lie around peacefully. The arrival of the cows heralds the start of the formation of the harem. The beachmaster will defend his harem from challengers. He usually takes up a position near the seaward fringe of his harem so that he can intercept cows before they reach the water and can warn off intruding bulls arriving from that direction. Once a cow reaches the water he is unable to herd her back to the harem. A bull challenging the beachmaster roars his challenge, with inflated proboscis, and approaches. If the challenger is the weaker of the two, he usually will not press home his challenge. If they are equal in size they will approach closely and rear up, turning their heads from side to side, and eventually lunge at each other, with more than two-thirds of their bodies off the ground. Contestants may also try to push each other off balance and if one falls, the other tries to pin him down, biting and slashing at the head and other parts of his body. These fights between evenly matched contestants may last up to 50 minutes (Wilkinson, pers. comm.) (Fig. 284.2).

Fig. 284.2. Males *Mirounga leonina* in fighting attitude.

If one contestant gives up he deflates his proboscis and backs away, uttering short, high-pitched cries and usually is chased back into the water. A single roar from a beachmaster is usually sufficient to chase off challengers.

On Marion Island the cows, most of which are pregnant and give birth to a single pup within two to seven days of their haulout, start to arrive in late August, their numbers reaching a peak in mid-October. They come into oestrus 17 to 22 days after the birth of their pup (Van Aarde, 1980a).

The breeding beaches on Marion Island, the location of which is established for ease of haulout of the cows, compared with most breeding beaches elsewhere, are circumscribed in size and each usually accommodates a single harem. On Macquarie and Heard islands where suitable beaches are much more extensive and the populations larger, Carrick *et al.* (1962) recorded several harems with up to 600 cows in each. On the other hand on Marion Island the total number of cows does not exceed 1 300, and owing to the smaller size of suitable haulout beaches, the harem sizes are much smaller. On Iles Kerguelen, van Aarde (1980b) recorded harems of five to 1 350 individuals. He found that the surface structure of the beaches had an important influence on the size of the harem, the highest densities being found on the sandy beaches, followed by vegetated humps, pebble beaches and cobble beaches.

Cows on Marion Island remain ashore for a period of about 28 days from the time of their arrival in late August. Their numbers decline rapidly from mid-October and by mid-November all have departed. The male pups at birth have a mass of about 40 kg, the female pups 34 kg (Wilkinson, pers. comm.). They have furry black natal coats, with curly hair about 25 mm long, brownish-black at the base, black towards the tips. The hair begins to shed at 13 days of age, the moult proceeding from the fore and hind flippers, then the head, neck and remainder of the body. This moult, to a silvery-grey colour, the soft velvety hair about 10 mm long, is complete by the time the pups are about five weeks old and ready to take to the sea. They are weaned when 22 days old. The mothers' milk contains about 50% fat and 10% protein (Le Boeuf & Ortiz, 1977) and at Marion Island males weigh 112 kg at weaning, while females are significantly lighter at 97 kg, this representing a threefold mass increase from birth to weaning (Wilkinson & Bester, in press). Laws (1960) showed that in the South Orkney Islands, where growth potential is greater than in the southern Indian Ocean (Bryden, 1968), pups increase their girth from 0,9 m at birth to 1,6 m at weaning and their weights quadruple in 21 days. This results from the accumulation of blubber which enables pups to survive the weaning period until they learn to feed.

Weaned pups congregate in large pods on the inland side of the breeding sites. Pups fast until they have lost around 30% of their weaned mass, with late-weaned pups fasting for a shorter period than early weaners (Wilkinson & Bester, in press). The last pups leave Marion Island early in January (Panagis, 1981; Wilkinson & Bester, in press). On Gough (Bester, 1980b), Marion (Panagis, 1981) and Kerguelen islands (Lenglart & Bester, 1982), they undergo a post-weaning dispersion phase beginning early in November.

Mortality in the pups arises from a number of causes. Pup deaths in large harems are caused most frequently by starvation when the pup gets separated from its mother. Bester & Lenglart (1982) showed that pup mortality is higher in large than in small harems on Iles Kerguelen and that a density-dependent mechanism acts primarily through pup mortality as a function of the density of bulls active in and around harems. Pups get killed by trampling during the melée of mating and other activities during the breeding period, or are drowned when they get washed away in heavy seas in the early stages of their lives, while they are still weak. Pups may try and suckle from cows other than their mothers and either get killed by them or suffer wounding from which they may die. Stillbirths are rare but miscellaneous causes such as rockfalls cause deaths. Predation by killer whales, *Orcinus orca*, appears to be a significant cause of pup deaths. Although adult bull elephant seals normally escape from killer whales, the pups, when first taking to the sea, and the cows, when arriving to haul out, are vulnerable. Killer whales visit Marion Island in numbers seasonally. They first start to arrive in August, with a peak in numbers in late November, which coincides with the time the pups are starting to learn to swim (Condy, van Aarde & Bester, 1978). Condy (1977b) suggested that the decrease in the elephant seal population on Marion Island is due to the lowered recruitment of the third year age class of cows through predation by killer whales.

Ross (1969a) and Oosthuizen *et al.* (1988) listed five unusual records of the birth of a pup on the coast of the Subregion.

**General**

The numbers of southern elephant seals breeding on Marion Island are declining (Skinner & van Aarde, 1983), while fur seal numbers are increasing rapidly (Kerley, 1983b). The forces responsible for this have not been identified as yet, but man-induced changes in food availability (as a result of exploitation) and climatic changes may be responsible for these trends.

## Genus *Lobodon* Gray, 1844

No. 285

### *Lobodon carcinophagus* (Hombron & Jacquinot, 1842)

### Crabeater seal
### Krapvreterrob

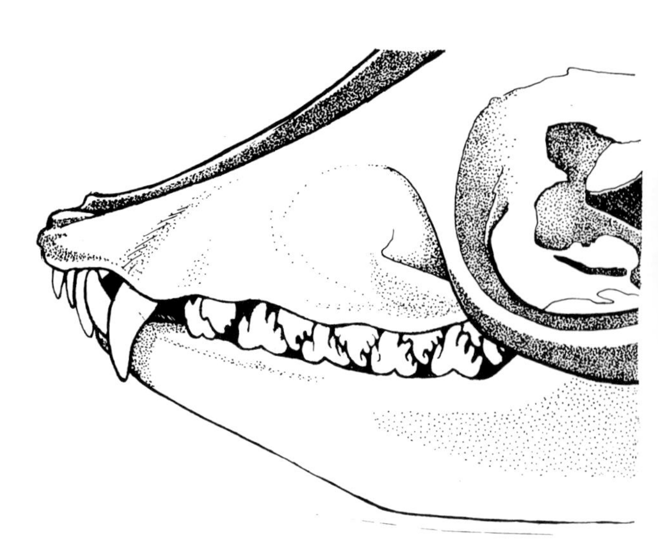

Fig. 285.2. Toothrows, *Lobodon carcinophagus*.

**Colloquial Name**

The well entrenched name crabeater is misleading, for the principal food of the species is krill. The specific name is derived from the Greek *lobos*, a lobe and *odous*, a tooth, referring to the lobed character of the teeth (Fig. 285.2).

**Taxonomic Notes**

No subspecies are recognised.

**Description**

Crabeaters, the most abundant seals in the world, are slim, lithe seals that can move very fast over the ice. Adult males reach a total length of about 2,32 m, females 2,74 m (Nel, 1965). The largest male in a small series examined by Bryden & Erickson (1976) had a mass of 220 kg, a female 242 kg.

Fig. 285.1 Crabeater seal, *Lobodon carcinophagus*

Young adults are silvery-brownish-grey on the upper parts with chocolate-brown markings on the shoulders and flanks, the under parts pale greyish. The flippers and tail are dark in colour. The colour of the body fades throughout the year, very quickly during the summer months to a creamy-white. In January the creamy-white coat is moulted to be replaced by a darker coat, which in older individuals becomes progressively paler with age (King, 1983).

The cheekteeth have up to six cusps, the upper set interlocking with the lower to provide a sieving mechanism for separating the krill from the water (Fig. 285.2).

The dental formula is:

$I\frac{2-3}{1-2}\ C\frac{1}{1}\ P\frac{4}{4}\ M\frac{0-2}{0-2} = 26–38.$

**Distribution**

Crabeater seals have a distribution that is circumpolar and pelagic, inhabiting the seas in the vicinity of the Antarctic Continent, vagrants reaching the coasts of eastern South America, as far north as 23 °S, New Zealand, Australia, and South Africa. They prefer the areas of pack ice where the ice covers 30% to 70% of the water surface (Erickson, Siniff, Cline & Hofman, 1971).

The first record from the coast of the Subregion was that of Courtnay-Latimer (1961) on a female which hauled out on the beach at Hamburg near East London in July 1957. Since then Ross, Shaughnessy & Best (1978) recorded a further nine individuals from localities on the coast from False Bay in the west to East London in the east. The origin of these is unknown, but it is likely that they came from the western Atlantic sector where they are particularly abundant (Ross *et al.*, 1978). Eight of the South African records occurred between late December and early March, six from January.

**Pack ice and fast ice haulout**

Siniff, Stirling, Bengtson & Reichle (1979) studied them on the pack ice over a period of three years during September and October on the western side of the Antarctic Peninsula. They found family groups, male-female pairs and lone seals at low densities. The family groups generally seek the larger ice floes, the pairs and single seals the smaller. Larger concentrations of non-breeding seals are found in the fast ice areas.

Family groups consist of an adult male, an adult female and her pup, the adult male not necessarily the father of the pup. In these groups the pup lies close to its mother, usually in contact with her. Pups separated from their mothers bawl loudly and remain distressed until contact with her is re-established.

Large concentrations of crabeater seals are found on fast ice, smaller groups on pack ice in November. Almost no aggressive behaviour is seen amongst these, at most it is confined to low intensity encounters of brief duration between males and females. Both sexes are present in these concentrations whose members are apparently sexually inactive and most of them are immature. In taking to the water they swim in closely-knit groups along the edge of the ice, behaviour which may have evolved in response to predators, especially leopard seals.

Crabeater seals cannot open and maintain breathing holes in the ice as can Weddell seals, *Leptonychotes weddellii*, but they use the Weddell seals' holes without strife, except when the female Weddells have pups and become aggressive towards intruders. When the two species are seen together on the ice, they ignore each other.

Stirling & Siniff (1979) who studied the vocalisation of this species found that when they were in the water under the ice near a breathing hole, they emitted a deep, very loud monosyllabic call, almost like a groan. Nel (1966) reported that when disturbed, while lying on the ice, they hiss and bark.

**Food**

Crabeater seals feed almost exclusively on krill, *Euphausia* spp, a small shrimp-like crustacean. They swim into the middle of a school of krill with their mouths open, then close their mouths and force the water out between their sieve-like teeth, retaining the krill in their mouths, which they then swallow (King, 1961).

The cheekteeth are adapted to this way of feeding, the many processes on their sides effectively blocking up the space between adjacent teeth, yet allowing the water to escape through the interstices between them (Fig. XXXVI.1).

At the back of the tooth rows in the upper and lower jaw there are bony protuberances, covered with soft tissue which, when the jaw is closed, effectively close what would otherwise be an opening at the back of the tooth rows and making the sieve-like action of the teeth more effective.

King (1961) noted that two muscles are concerned in the action of the tongue, the geniohyoid drawing it forward and the genioglossus depressing it. The tongue lies in the bowed out mandibles and it is tempting to guess at its action in the sieving process. Moved forward and downward the tip would close the open space between the canines and the teeth posterior to them and between the upper and lower incisors as the jaw closes, the elevation of the tongue then forcing out the water whose only escape then would be through the sieve-like teeth. To effect this closure the tongue need not contact the incisor and canine teeth as the palate and the anterior parts of the mandible are close together and an effective closure is possible at this point.

**Reproduction**

Little is known about the mating and pupping behaviour of the crabeater seal since these activities take place during the Antarctic spring when access to the pack ice is difficult.

The male lies two to four metres from the female and her pup, waiting for her to become receptive. If he approaches her before she is ready to receive him, she chases him away aggressively, biting at his head and neck. His "ownership" of the female is subject to challenge by another male and he may be driven off by a challenger. Several males in turn may attempt to displace the resident male, eventually one being successful in doing so. Several challenges per day can be experienced by a resident male in attempts to take over his female. From tracks on the fast ice Siniff *et al.* (1979) found that males attempt to defend an area up to about 50 m from their female.

In the male-female pairs the two lie in close physical contact, the male at right angles to the female with his head resting on the female's side, or with his chest over her back. If the female tries to move off the male herds her by positioning himself between her and the edge of the ice floe. Siniff *et al.* (1979) observed intense mutual aggression between the male and female which they suspect is precopulatory behaviour. The male bites the upper back and neck of the female and attempts to mount her, the female in turn swivelling around and biting at the male's neck or shoulder. Through this aggression the pair get covered in blood. Copulation has not been observed. By the end of October solitary adult females are seen, which most likely are females that have completed the full cycle of pupping, mating and separation from the males.

From these observations Siniff *et al.* (1979) outlined a probable sequence of events in the reproductive cycle. A pregnant female hauls out on a suitable ice floe on which to give birth. Then she is joined before or after parturition by an adult male. The female comes into oestrus after the pup is weaned, mating taking place on the ice. The growth of the pup is probably faster than in most other seals, as the ice is less stable, natural selection having favoured a short period of lactation of 14 to 21 days and a weaning weight of 80 to 110 kg (Shaughnessy & Kerry, 1989).

The gestation period is thought to be about 12 months. The pups are born between mid-September and early November and at birth have a total length of 1,3 to 1,4 m. Females have their first pup between two and three years of age (Ross, 1977b). The natal coat of the pups is soft and woolly and greyish-brown in colour.

**General**

Mass die-offs of crabeater seals are known. Laws & Taylor (1957) recorded that, in 1955, of 3 000 crabeaters, most of them young, which wintered on the sea ice off the east coast of Graham Land, 85% died from what was thought to be a virus infection. As the continental population has been estimated to be to the order of 30 million (Erickson *et al.*, 1971), die-offs of this magnitude have little impact on the population as a whole.

Body scars on crabeaters suggest attacks from leopard seals, *Hydrurga leptonyx*, or killer whales, *Orcinus orca*. At times crabeater seals may represent a more important food source for leopard seals than krill or penguins (Siniff & Bengtson, 1977). Siniff *et al.* (1979) found a leopard seal with a partially eaten crabeater carcass and recorded that they chased leopard seals back into the water where they had the obvious intention of aggressive attack on crabeater pups on the ice. Killer whales appear to be the only predator of importance.

## Genus *Hydrurga* Gistel, 1848

The scientific name probably originates from the Latin *Hydra*, a mythical water creature, and the Greek *ourgos*, a worker, in referring to its aquatic habits, and the Greek *leptos*, small and *onux*, a claw.

---

No. 286

## *Hydrurga leptonyx* (Blainville, 1820)

## Leopard seal
## Luiperdrob

Plate 26

---

**Colloquial Name**

So named from the spotting on the body and their predatory habits.

**Taxonomic Notes**

No subspecies are recognised.

**Description**

Adult male leopard seals have a length of some 3,0 m and a mass of about 300 kg (King, 1983); the females are considerably larger at 4,0 m and 450 kg (Nishiwaki, 1972). The upper parts of the body are charcoal-grey or bluish-grey in colour with a silvery sheen and are usually darker on top of the head and body than on the flanks. The whole body has black or grey dots and blotches scattered over its surface. The under parts are light grey from the throat to the genital opening.

Leopard seals undergo an annual moult about January, a process which does not interfere with their normal activities. The old coat is by that time dingy yellowish in colour, the moult starting around the base of the hind flippers and progressing forward to reveal the silvery-grey-coloured new coat (Gwynn, 1953).

A feature of the leopard seal is its very large elongated head and the very large gape to its mouth. The skull is indeed the second longest among the Phocidae, only being surpassed by that of the male southern elephant seal, *M. leonina*, which is, in body size, much larger.

The post-canine teeth are like a saw, each tooth with three high cusps, the central one cone-shaped and longer than the other two, with a sharp point and slightly bent back at the tip (Fig. XXXVI.2).

The dental formula is:

$I\frac{2}{2}\ C\frac{1}{1}\ PC\frac{5}{5} = 32$

**Distribution**

The leopard seal is a species of the Antarctic pack ice which usually hauls out in the winter on to the islands that lie near or to the south of the Antarctic Convergence, such as Iles Kerguelen and Heard and Macquarie islands. They occur year-round at Iles Kerguelen (Bester & Roux, 1986) and Heard Island (Gwynn, 1953). Beyond this they occur as far westwards as the seas in the vicinity of the Falkland Islands and Tierra del Fuego and eastwards to Australia and New

Zealand. Six sightings have been recorded on Marion Island (Panagis, pers. comm.; Wilkinson, pers. comm.).

They have been recorded from the southern coast of the Subregion, the first record being of an individual which stranded about 60 km north of East London in September, 1946, now in the collection of the East London Museum (Roberts, 1951). The second, which came ashore in October 1969 at Hout Bay, Cape, and which died in captivity, is now in the collection of the South African Museum, Cape Town (Best, 1971b).

**Terrestrial haulout**

From November to May leopard seals live on the pack ice around the Antarctic Continent and migrate northwards to the vicinity of the Subantarctic islands in the winter and spring months from May to October. They are solitary animals both on the ice and when they haul out on the islands, tending to lie separately from one another. On Iles Kerguelen, Bester (1981b) reported that they lie up on the beds of kelp in the vicinity of colonies of macaroni penguins, *Eudyptes chrysolophus.*

During the haulout leopard seals make a curious crooning noise which is sometimes made when they are sleeping and which can be heard at a considerable distance. They may also trumpet loudly and make a resonant booming noise (Gwynn, 1953).

Apart from resting or sleeping, leopard seals, once having hauled out, do not engage in any activity. Gwynn (1953) recorded one instance of their engaging in what he thought was play, the two seals circling around each other, occasionally breaking away to repeat the process over a period of half an hour.

**Food**

Penguins are one of their principal foods, but they also take seals, particularly pups, krill, squids, occasionally fish and carrion. They have been recorded as taking the remains of crested penguins, *Eudyptes robustus* (Horning & Fenwick, 1978) and Adelie penguins, *Pygoscelis adeliae* (Ingham, 1960). Gwynn (1953) reported on a two-year-old leopard seal taking an elephant seal pup, *Mirounga leonina*, and they are known to take Weddell seals, *Leptonychotes weddellii* and crabeater seals, *Lobodon carcinophagus.* Siniff & Bengtson (1977) noted that at times crabeater seals may be a more important food source than either krill or penguins.

The individual taken at Hout Bay, Cape, and kept in captivity, caught and ate a black-backed gull, *Larus dominicanus*, that settled on its pool, leaving behind most of the feathers and the neatly fleshed skeleton. Fish below 300 mm were swallowed whole, larger specimens fleshed by repeated shaking until only the head and vertebral column were left (Best, 1971b).

Leopard seals in turn fall prey to killer whales, *Orcinus orca* (Siniff & Bengtson, 1977).

**Reproduction**

Leopard seals give birth to their young on the pack ice during the summer months from late October to mid-November (Siniff & Stone, 1985). In the vicinity of Heard Island, Gwynn (1953) reported that in August many of the females were pregnant but by September they had become increasingly rare. It was assumed that they were then departing for their breeding grounds on the pack ice.

Courtship is unknown in the wild, but Marlow (1967) recorded observations from a pair in captivity in the Taronga Park Zoological Gardens, Sydney. Vocalisations were made under water by the male and were answered by the female. These consisted of a "gargling" sound which could be heard in the air over 45 m. These vocalisations continued on and off from October to November and were accompanied by grunting at the level of the water. Copulation was observed in 0,6 m of water, the female floating prone, the male grasping her around the thorax with his forelimbs. Copulation continued for 10 minutes.

A pregnant female held in restraint gave birth to a stillborn pup which had a length of 1,6 m and a mass of 29,0 kg. At birth its eyes were open, the canine teeth and one incisor erupted above the gums (Brown, 1952).

In addition to this record Gwynn (1953) quoted the recovery of a pup on South Georgia and another born in natural but exceptional circumstances on the Falkland Islands. The natal coat is soft and thick, dark grey dorsally, with a darker central strip down the back. The flanks and under parts are white, irregularly spotted with black (King, 1983).

## Genus *Leptonychotes* Gill, 1872

The generic name is derived from the Greek *leptos*, small, *onux*, claw, and *otes*, possessing, referring to the small claws on the hind limbs.

---

No. 287

## *Leptonychotes weddellii* (Lesson, 1826)

## Weddell seal
## Weddell se rob

---

**Colloquial Name**

Named after Sir James Weddell who commanded a British sealing expedition in 1822–1824 into that part of the Antarctic seas now called after him.

**Taxonomic Notes**

The genus is monotypic.

**Description**

Weddell seals are spindle-shaped and very fat, not streamlined like the crabeater seal, *Lobodon carcinophagus*, and their heads are small for the size of their bodies. The females are on the average larger than the males, with a total length of 3,0 m and a mass of about 400 kg, the males 2,8 m in total body length with a mass of about 360 kg (Nishiwaki, 1972). King (1964) noted that the maximum size recorded for females is 3,29 m, for males 2,97 m. The flippers are located far forward on the body, and the hind limbs are broad.

The adult fur is dark brownish-grey on the upper parts of the body, darker towards the hind limbs, with irregularly shaped, lighter coloured spots. The flippers and hind limbs are darker in colour than the body. The under parts are predominantly white.

Fig. 287.1 Weddell seal, *Leptonychotes weddellii*

The dental formula is:

$I\frac{2}{2}\ C\frac{1}{1}\ P\frac{3}{3}\ M\frac{2}{2} = 32$

The outer upper incisors are four times the size of the inner (Fig. XXXVI.2). The post-canine teeth are strong and functional; the cranium has a low sagittal crest.

**Distribution**

Weddell seals have a circumpolar Antarctic distribution and live further south than any other mammal, their southern limit being about 80 °S. They usually inhabit the fringe of the Antarctic Continent and the fast ice shelf, but adults have been recorded from the pack ice (Stirling, 1969a).

Outside their normal range of distribution vagrants have been recorded from the Islas de Lobos, Uruguay; the Islas Juan Fernandez, Chile; Wellington, New Zealand; South Australia; Iles Kerguelen and Marion Island. The record from the latter, a sub-adult male which had a small wound, with a total length of about 2,0 m, was observed in a breeding rookery of southern elephant seals, *Mirounga leonina*, in October 1979, remaining ashore for 10 days (Gleeson, pers. comm.).

**Food**

Weddell seals feed predominantly on fish, squid and crustaceans (Dearborn, 1965).

**Reproduction**

Weddell seals' pups are born in traditional pupping colonies on the fast ice where cracks make exit holes easy to maintain (King, 1983), or less commonly on beaches, in areas where the break up of the ice precedes parturition (Smith & Burton, 1970). Females remain on the ice with their pups for the first few days of their lives. Several females may share an ice hole. During the latter part of the first week and during the second week the females enter the water, leaving their pups for periods up to six hours. However, the females do not feed until their pups are weaned (Mansfield, 1958; Reijnders, Plötz, Zegers & Gräfe, 1990). Siniff *et al.* (1977), however, concluded that when food resources are available, nursing Weddell seals will use them. Most pups enter the water with their mothers before they are two weeks old, moving in and out of the water with them.

The cow-pup pairs space themselves out on the ice. The space between them is greater during the early part of the pupping season than later when the pairs tend to move nearer the ice-holes or cracks in the ice. Pups grow quickly from birth till they are five weeks old. The peak in growth rate coincides with the pups' first entry into the water. It then decreases in proportion to the time spent in swimming.

Females can have their first pups at an age of four years (Laws, 1984), but the males do not mate until they are at least six to eight years of age (Stirling, 1971). Males are territorial and aggressive towards strange males. During the mating season males remain in the water, spending most of the time defending a three-dimensional territory (Stirling, 1977). However, they will court females on the ice, approaching them head-on and emitting a repertoire of vocalisations, but copulation has not been witnessed on ice, perhaps because females have a lactational anoestrus (Reijnders *et al.*, 1990). Cline, Siniff & Erickson (1971) witnessed copulation under the ice. The male clasped the female with his flippers and when she attempted to escape he bit her on the base of the neck. When the female's pup appeared on the scene, she broke away to attend to it.

The gestation period is nine to 10 months (Stirling, 1971) and a single new-born pup has a mass of about 29 kg (Reijnders *et al.*, 1990). The time of birth of the young varies with latitude. At latitude 60 °S births commence from the first week in September (Mansfield, 1958). At 78 °S these are delayed until the fourth week of October (Lindsey, 1937).

Neonates have a soft, grey natal coat which moults after three or four weeks to a dark coat similar to that of the adults. They wean at six to seven weeks of age and cows lose 38% of their body weight during lactation (Reijnders *et al.*, 1990).

**General**

Seals that spend the winter months on the fast ice of the Antarctic Continent must have adaptations to allow them to cut and maintain breathing holes in the ice. In the Weddell seal the outer upper incisor teeth and canines are heavily built and are antero-laterally orientated for the purpose of cutting through the ice and maintaining these holes open. This adaptation of the teeth is unique to the species. Continual abrasion of the teeth in this operation causes heavy wear, first of the upper canines, followed later by the outer incisors and much less commonly of the inner upper and lower incisor teeth. Severe abrasion can cause exposure of the pulp cavity and abscesses can develop (Stirling, 1969c). They are competent divers and have been known to reach depths of 600 m and to remain under water for at least 73 minutes (Kooyman, 1969; 1981), being second only to elephant seals whose depth record is estimated at 894 m (Le Boeuf, Costa, Huntley & Feldkamp, 1988).

Weddell seals are relatively free of predation except from man, leopard seals, *Hydrurga leptonyx*, and possibly from killer whales.

The Weddell seal is highly vocal in both repertoire and volume and their calls are readily audible to an observer on the surface of the ice (Wilson, 1907). Kaufman *et al.* (1975) recorded that the males vocalise with deep chugs and soft tapping noises, the chugs preceding surfacing or diving, the tapping following the chugs after diving. The chugs may be preceded by short whistles or wheezes. They also moan, trill and chirrup. When on the surface of the ice they will threaten each other with mouths wide open and clack their teeth, or in close contact rise up on their flippers and lunge at each other, although this rarely leads to physical damage.

# Order TUBULIDENTATA

## XXXVII. Family ORYCTEROPODIDAE
### Aardvark

The aardvark, *Orycteropus afer*, is the only surviving representative of the Order Tubulidentata. Fossil evidence suggests that the members of the Order, the earliest known from the early Miocene beds of East Africa, spread from Africa to Europe and Asia during the Miocene and early Pliocene and to Madagascar where the fossil remains of an aberrant form, *Plesiorycteropus madagascariensis*, have been found.

Four genera are known, three of them as fossils. *Leptorycteropus* apparently was not specialised for eating termites or ants, having a complete set of cheekteeth, large canine teeth and a heavier mandible than the extant aardvark. From the form of the bones of the front legs it was equipped poorly for digging, and was probably omnivorous (Patterson, 1978). *Plesiorycteropus* of Madagascar is only known from about 50 isolated bones and *Myorycteropus* from an equally poor representative collection of fossil material. The genus *Orycteropus*, which includes our extant aardvark, *O. afer*, had a number of near relatives whose fossil remains have been found in Europe, the Middle East and Africa. Among these, *O. gaudryi*, which had no teeth, from the late Miocene beds of Iran is the best known, some 20 reasonably complete skeletons having been recovered (Patterson, 1978).

In the Subregion the Order is comprised of one Family and a single species, the aardvark, *Orycteropus afer*.

## Genus *Orycteropus* G. Cuvier, 1798

No. 288

## *Orycteropus afer* (Pallas, 1766)

## Aardvark
## Erdvark

Plate 27

**Colloquial Name**

Although the English name of antbear is commonly used, it is unfortunate as they are in no way related to or resemble bears. The name aardvark is more appropriate as they do in some ways resemble pigs and are closely associated with the soil, both in their diggings for food and shelter.

**Taxonomic Notes**

Many subspecies have been described; Meester (1972b) listed 18 from the continent, south of the Sahara, but at the same time pointed out that, owing to the scarcity of material, many of these may not be valid. Only *O. a. afer* occurs in the Subregion (Meester *et al.*, 1986).

**Description**

Superficially aardvarks show some resemblance to pigs in their possession of long muzzles and ears and pale yellowish-grey, sparsely haired bodies. However, here the resemblance ends, for in shape they are unique among African mammals. They are much heavier in the hind quarters than in the fore. They have very thick, tapering tails and unusually heavy, powerful limbs, narrow elongated muzzles and long tubular ears. In profile the body is arched, the highest point about the lower part of the back, sloping off gently to the muzzle and more abruptly to the tail.

The pale colour of the body tends to become stained with the soil in which they burrow and, where they live on heavy red soils, the body stains reddish. The hair on the limbs and base of the tail is darker than on the body, often black. Most of the tail and head, however, is lighter in colour than the body, usually off-white or buffy-white.

The tubular ears are very sparsely haired, outstandingly long, and can be folded flat to exclude detritus in burrowing. The nose is a muscular swelling, capable of considerable movement, enclosing the two vertical slits of the nostrils. The septum between these nasal slits is equipped with a series of thick, fleshy processes. The nostrils are surrounded by a dense mat of hair which effectively seals the nostrils off when they are closed and acts as a dust filter. Below and above the eyes there are lines of long sensory bristles and further tufts of these low down on the sides of the face between the eyes and the ears. These serve to alert the individual to obstructions and so prevent damage to the eyes during burrowing and foraging.

There are four digits on the front feet and five on the back feet. They have distinct webs between the second and third, and third and fourth digits on both feet (Fig. 288.1). The claws on the forefeet are long and spatulate, with sharp edges, the claws on the third digits longer than the remainder. Those on the hind feet are shorter and more curved. While each digit has a well developed digital pad near the base of the claw, there are no plantar pads on the front feet. The claws, backed by the powerful limbs, give the aardvark its prodigious digging abilities.

Aardvark spoor on tracks show clearly the marks of three of the four broad front claws, with three, sometimes four, of the hind lying close behind or slightly overlaying them. The tail is held clear of the ground. They walk on their toes but when they pause, they sink on to their haunches, and the whole of the hind feet then mark, with the impression of the tail between them (Fig. 288.2).

Both sexes are equipped with scent glands, the orifices of which lie at the base of the penis and sides of the vulva respectively, from which exudes a thick yellow secretion used in marking.

Judging from the sizes and masses of a series of 15 males and 16 females from the northern parts of the Subregion, there does not appear to be any noticeable difference between the sexes (Table 288.1). There is a tendency for females to be lighter in colour on the face and tail than males.

Side.

Underside.

Fig. 288.1 Forefoot of an aardvark, *Orycteropus afer*.

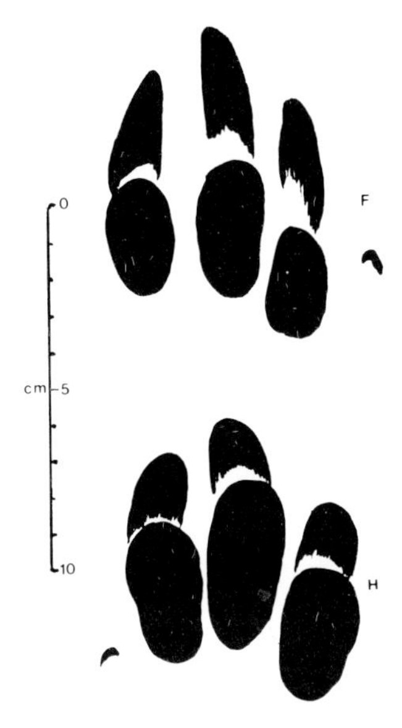


Fig. 288.2. Spoor: aardvark, *O. afer*.

**Table 288.1**

Measurements (mm) and mass (kg) of aardvarks, *O. afer*, from Zimbabwe (Smithers, 1983).

| | Males | | | Females | | |
|---|---|---|---|---|---|---|
| | $\bar{x}$ | n | Range | $\bar{x}$ | n | Range |
| TL | 1600 | 15 | 1490–1750 | 1580 | 16 | 1400–1730 |
| T (mid anus) | 544 | 15 | 443–620 | 539 | 16 | 464–630 |
| Hf c/u | 256 | 15 | 240–268 | 247 | 16 | 225–280 |
| E | 180 | 15 | 167–210 | 177 | 16 | 165–185 |
| Mass | 53,3 | 15 | 41,3–64,5 | 51,4 | 16 | 40,4–57,7 |

Why the aardvark, *O. afer*, has teeth at all is something of a mystery for the nature of its food, as we know it, does not require mastication. This function is provided for in the aardvark by their having a muscular pyloric area in their stomachs which functions rather like a gizzard, grinding up the food, mixed as it is with sand or soil. They have enlarged salivary glands and long ribbon-like tongues and are organised for a rapid transfer of the prey from the tongue to the stomach. This appears to preclude the necessity for teeth.

## Skull

The skull of the aardvark is elongated and narrow, the bone structure lightly built (Fig. 288.3). In profile it is flat, except for a slight upward bulge in front of the eyes, the outstanding feature being the greatly elongated rostrum which tapers off to the nasal openings. The postorbital bars are represented by a process above and behind the eye sockets, with little or no sign of a similar process on the zygoma, which are thin and weakly developed. Viewed from above the skull is broadest just in front of the eyes, the flattened braincase bulging out at the level of the hind insertion of zygomatic arches. The thick supraoccipital crest lies in a plane with the top of the braincase, extending backwards for 3 to 5 mm from its rear edge. Below this crest there is a broad flat surface between it and the occipital foramen which provides ample surface for attachment of the muscles which actuate and carry the greatly elongated head. The ear bullae are unossified and are lost in the cleaned skull.

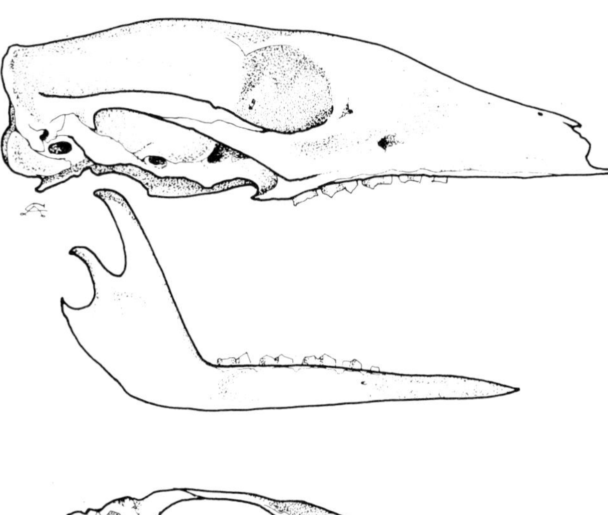

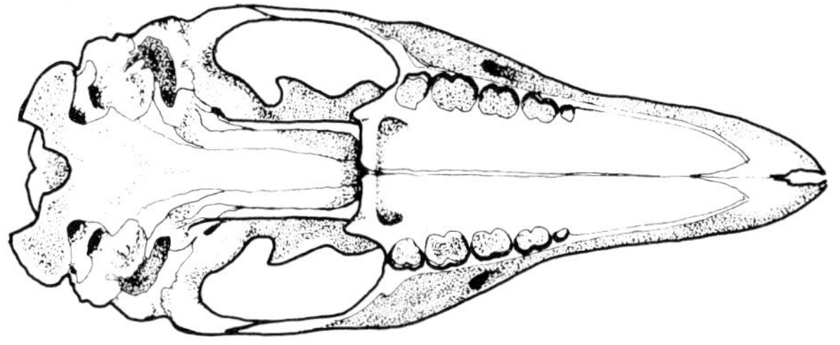

Fig. 288.3. Skull: aardvark, *O. afer*.
TL Skull 200 mm.

The mandible is unique, being thin, elongated and tapering, and the sides are swollen outwards to accommodate the cheekteeth. The condyle is a flat, rounded convex plate which hinges on a flattened, concave surface on the skull, allowing a back to front movement of the lower jaw in masticating the food.

The extant aardvark, *O. afer*, has no incisor or canine teeth. The cheekteeth consist of two upper and two lower premolar teeth and three upper and three lower molar teeth in each jaw half. Sometimes the premolar teeth are preceded by other tiny, vestigial, peg-like premolars. The premolar and molar teeth have no roots and they lack enamel. The skull is elongated, the zygomatic arches broad anteriorly, tapering posteriorly, where they are thin and lightly built. The palate is flat and roughly parallel-sided and they have a tympanic ring but no bony ear bullae (Fig. 288.3).

Although adult aardvarks have a greatly reduced set of teeth, they have a very extended set of minute milk teeth which Broom (1909a) showed, in a young individual, 0,85 m overall, to consist of:

$$DI\tfrac{3}{3}\ DC\tfrac{1}{1}\ DP\tfrac{6}{6}\ DM\tfrac{0}{0} = 40$$

These teeth do not show above the gum and are absorbed. The presence of six premolars removes the aardvark from a relationship with any other extant mammal to a relationship with some ancestral Mesozoic ancestor.

The dental formula in adults is:

$$I\tfrac{0}{0}\ C\tfrac{0}{0}\ P\tfrac{2}{2}\ M\tfrac{3}{3} = 20$$

Irregularly there may be an extra premolar on either side in the upper and lower jaw or a reduction of the premolars in both the upper and lower jaws. The third upper molars are round, the three teeth in front of them pinched in centrally. All the teeth have relatively flat surfaces, the outer edges of the larger teeth higher than the general surface indicating that the action of grinding the food is directed more backwards and forwards than from side to side.

## Distribution

Aardvarks have a wide distribution on the continent, south of the Sahara, but are nowhere common, and, owing to their nocturnal and secretive habits, there are relatively few specimens in collections, and they are rarely seen. Their distribution is governed to some extent by the availability of food. Generally they are absent from forest and desert and they avoid rocky or stony terrain. Within their wide distributional range there are many areas where they are locally absent, either because the terrain is unsuitable or a food supply lacking, as, for example, in the Transvaal where Rautenbach (1978a) had no records from parts of the central, eastern parts of the province.

*South of the Sahara, excluding the Southern African Subregion*

They occur from **Senegal** westwards to northern **Cameroun**, *O. a. senegalensis* Lesson, 1840 being described from the western extremity of their range in West Africa. They occur in northern **Sierra Leone**; northern **Ghana** and **Nigeria**, excluding the southern High Forest Zone. Throughout West Africa they occur in the Guinea, Sudan and in parts of the Sahel zones. They occur in the **Sudan** and **Ethiopia**. There is little information from **Somalia,** but they are included on the faunal list of this country.

In **Zaire** the subspecies *O. a. erikssoni* Lönnberg, 1906 occurs in the northeastern parts of the forests of the Congo Basin, the only area from which they are recorded in this type of association, as well as north and southeast of this and eastwards in the Rift Valley. They are recorded from **Uganda; Kenya; Tanzania; Zambia; Angola; Mozambique,** north of the Zambezi River and **Malawi.**

*Southern African Subregion*

They are widespread in **Namibia**, excluding the coastal Namib Desert; in **Botswana; Zimbabwe,** and **Mozambique,** south of the Zambezi River. They are widespread in the **Transvaal; Orange Free State; Natal** and the **Cape Province.**

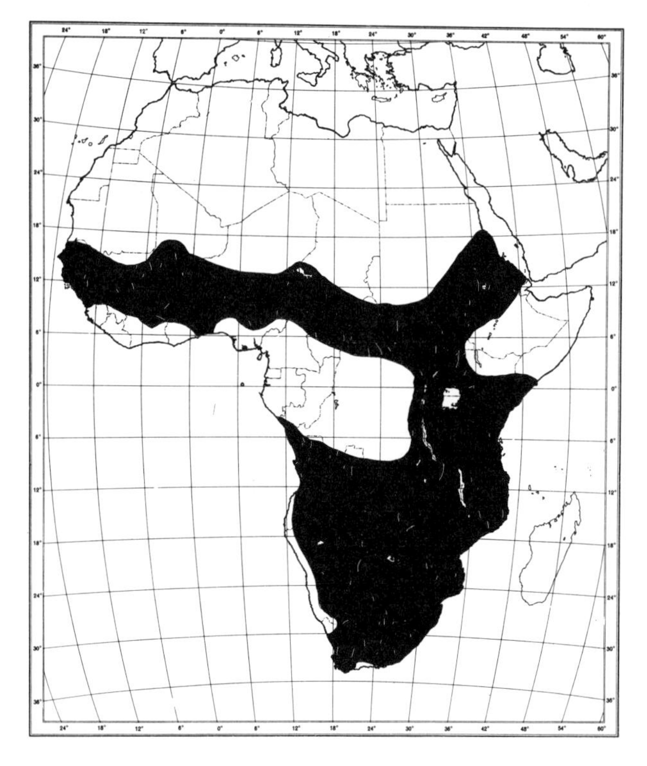

## Habitat

Aardvarks have a wide habitat tolerance, occurring in the Subregion both in the Southern Savanna and the South West Arid zones. Within these they are found in open woodland, scrub and grassland, especially where these are associated with sandy ground. Nevertheless, they are capable of utilising heavy soils and are found in areas of mopane woodland and other types of hard ground, and on the heavy red soils of parts of the Subregion. They will utilise the raised sandy islands in floodplain, both for digging their permanent burrows and for feeding in the termitaria which are a common feature of these islands. Unprecedented high floods do occasionally flood them out of these situations; many burrows during the high floods of 1956 were inundated in the Okavango in Botswana. Water is not an essential requirement and they occur in terrain where it may only be available seasonally. They are associated particularly with heavily utilised grassland where there are termite populations. Melton & Daniels (1986) found that in Natal they showed a preference for open areas and avoided rocky areas which tended to reduce prey abundance and make digging difficult. Similar observations have been recorded by Willis (1988) in the southern Orange Free State.

## Habits

Aardvarks are solitary and almost exclusively nocturnal, but under exceptional circumstances may be seen during daylight hours. If they are flooded out of their burrows, San people of Botswana spear them as they lie sleeping in the sun on nearby raised ground. Kingdon (1971) recorded that a captive aardvark regularly sunned itself for an hour each day at about 10h00. Generally they are found singly and are late movers, seldom being seen before 21h00, and forage both on dark as well as on bright moonlight nights (van Aarde, Willis, Skinner & Haupt, 1990). Recorded estimates of distances travelled per night vary from two to 14,7 km (Melton, 1975; van Aarde, 1984). In the southern Orange Free State, van Aarde *et al.* (1990) recorded the mean home range size as 3,5 $km^2$, where the estimated sizes of the home ranges occupied by adult males varied from 2,0 $km^2$ to 4,7 $km^2$, whilst the home ranges of females varied from 4,4 $km^2$ to 4,6 $km^2$. An analysis of the distances moved per hour suggested that the mean hourly foraging speeds for males varied from 183 m/h to 828,6 m/h, with those of females from 464,4 m/h to 943,2 m/h. Radio-tracking on the Tussen-die-Riviere Game Farm, Orange Free State showed that minimum distances covered during a night of foraging varied from 0,035 km to 8,43 km (van Aarde *et al.*, 1990).

When foraging, aardvarks move slowly with their noses close to the ground. They move around irregularly searching for prey. Their sense of smell is well developed, as can be seen by the extensive area of finely convoluted olfactory epithelium surrounding the olfactory bulbs, which underlie the swollen part of the skull in front of the eyes. Their hearing is acute and, if suddenly disturbed at close quarters, they may freeze momentarily and then take off at a fast run. Their eyesight does not appear to be keen, because as they run off, they often crash their way through bushes, as if unable to perceive the easier routes open to them.

Apart from small exploratory scratchings, which show clearly the impression of the broad front claws, aardvarks appear to make three types of excavations. The first are shallow diggings, often in flat ground or penetrating termitaria, which are only sufficiently deep to give access to the food. Aardvarks have a habit of excavating these in the compacted soils of farm roads, causing damage to vehicles. Some of these burrows may penetrate a termitarium to a depth sufficient to cover the head and shoulders of the animal, or allow it to disappear altogether. These excavations are not used as refuges and normally are not revisited. The second type of burrow, dug overnight, is a temporary refuge and may penetrate several metres shallowly underground. These may be re-used over a period of a day or two or may be returned to sporadically. They usually have a chamber at the end to allow the individual to turn around. If excavated in the walls of earth dams they can cause serious loss of water, if not the destruction of the impoundment itself, which makes aardvarks unpopular in farming lands. The third type of burrow is the most permanent and is used as a shelter in which the young are born. Dorst & Dandelot (1972) stated that the females use these, the males being more nomadic. These permanent shelters may extend deeply into the ground, have an extensive burrow system with numerous chambers, and several entrances. Melton (1976) listed one with five entrances and another, which was a 13 m burrow, with three entrances and chambers 1 m wide and 0,8 m high. This type of burrow may be used fairly regularly. Aardvarks are captured successfully by setting fall-traps at the burrow entrance after they have entered.

Judging from the spoor, the occupant of a burrow enters and emerges head first. Often occupied burrows are characterised by swarms of small flies which congregrate in the shade inside the entrance. After withdrawing into the burrow for the daytime rest, the occupant closes the burrow immediately behind it with soil. In the Karoo, burrow temperatures at a depth of one metre are buffered and remain around 10 °C, protecting aardvarks from the extremes of temperature (Skinner, unpubl.). Kingdon (1971) described how they sleep curled up with the tail and hind feet covering the snout, an attitude also adopted by a captive juvenile at the National Museum, Bulawayo.

Burrows, when unoccupied, provide both shelter and safe refuge for a wide range of mammals, birds, reptiles and insects. Smithers (1971) in Botswana recorded their use by 17 species of mammals, a bird and two reptiles, and no doubt this list could be extended considerably. Some of these will use occupied burrows, as does the ant-eating chat, *Myrmecocichla formicivora*, which excavates a nesting site in the roof of the burrow near the entrance. The very survival of some of these species may depend on the shelter which these burrows provide.

Aardvarks can burrow at a prodigious rate and, if observed as they enter, can rarely be dug out, as they dig much faster than their pursuers can. Bryden (1900) recorded his efforts with assistants to dig out one which was seen to enter a hole, and the undertaking was abandoned after the burrow had been dug out to a distance of 32 m. Skinner (unpubl.) noted that on release an aardvark burrowed so quickly in deep red loam soil that he was out of sight in 30 minutes.

Little is known about specific inter-relationships. On one occasion on the S.A. Lombard Nature Reserve in the western Transvaal, a dead female was found which had been involved in a fight with another aardvark the previous night. She had succumbed after a frantic fight judging from the flattened vegetation covering 10 m$^2$ and the cause of death seemed to be internal damage as the result of heavy scratches inflicted by the claws of the adversary (Fig. 288.4) (Skinner, unpubl.). It has been reported that heavy scratches may also be inflicted during mating.

Fig. 288.4 Female aardvark killed in intra-specific fight

Aardvarks fall prey to the larger predatory species as well as to indigenous people who find their flesh very palatable. To the Shona people of Zimbabwe the aardvark also has ritual significance and the snout and digits are eagerly sought after by witch doctors. An unattended road kill is almost invariably stripped of these parts.

The only noise recorded for aardvarks is a vigorous sniffing made with the nose pressed close to the ground (Kingdon, 1971) and even when captured alive in snares they do not vocalise. Aardvarks bury their faeces, scraping a shallow hole, defecating in it, and then covering it up with soil. They do not use latrines, although Melton (1976) recorded fresh droppings buried alongside old. The droppings are ovoid and consist predominantly of sand and other indigestible matter, and look like ovoid cakes of sandy soil.

**Food**

Formicid ants constitute a substantial part of aardvarks' diet, which also includes termites. In the sample of 20 stomachs from Zimbabwe, and in scat analyses from Natal and the Orange Free State, ants predominated over termites (Smithers, 1983; Melton & Daniels, 1986; Willis, 1988) (Table 288.2). Their diggings in termitaria are usually more obvious than those in flat ground where ants' nests are to be found. This may have led to the assumption that termites are a preferred food. Termites were taken mainly during the wet season and ants during the dry (Melton, 1976; Willis, 1988). Certain mound-building termites are quiescent during the dry, colder months of the year and remain deeper in the termitaria, which may be the reason for seasonal differences. Large numbers of ants' eggs and larvae as well as adults were present in the Zimbabwe stomach sample; the only other food recognised was the pulp and pips of melons. Meeuse (1955, 1958, 1962) first drew attention to the importance of aardvarks for the germination of the cucurbit, *Cucumis humofructus*. The fruit is dug up and eaten and due to its high moisture content, may well be a source of water, particularly in arid regions. The aardvark disperses the seeds in its droppings. Mitchell (1965a) confirmed this, noting the seeds germinating in aardvark droppings. The relationship contains the basic elements of a symbiosis. The fruits of this plant develop underground from the flower stems, which force their way into the soil to a depth of 200 to 300 mm. The pulp is soft but the seeds are hard, and pass undamaged in the digestive process to be buried with the faeces in a situation favourable for germination. Kingdon (1971) recorded an individual stomach containing over 40 scarabaeid pupae. These pupae develop in pellets of dung, cached 200 to 300 mm underground—an indication of the powers of detection possessed by the species. The teeth of aardvarks are unsuitable for dealing with anything except the softest food.

Aardvarks apparently locate food by smell. They walk leisurely around with the nose close to the ground and they pause from time to time to dig. Many of these digs are exploratory, being bare surface scratchings. On locating an ants' nest in flat ground, they dig until the nose and mouth can be inserted. While the next step cannot be observed, it is presumed that the long, rounded, sticky tongue is inserted into the tunnels, then withdrawn into the mouth covered with ants, which either adhere to the saliva or are held on the tongue by biting on its tough covering. During the process the aardvark squats down on its hind limbs, with the forelimbs extended forward, until further excavation is required or the site is abandoned. Digging may continue in termitaria until the whole body enters the excavations, as more and more sections of tunnels are opened up. When digging the individual may sit on its haunches or stand as the soil is excavated with the strong spatulate claws on the front feet. The soil is then pushed back under the body, to be thrown clear with the hind feet. Usually these diggings may be recognised by the marks of the broad front claws and the trail of the tail and the spoor of the hind feet on the loose, excavated soil.

**Table 288.2**

a. Analysis of the stomach contents of a sample of 20 aardvarks, *O. afer*, from Zimbabwe (Smithers, 1983); b. Analysis of the contents of 20 aardvark faecal samples from the Tussen-die-Riviere Game Farm, southern Orange Free State (Willis, 1988).

a.

| Food item | Number of occurences | |
|---|---|---|
| **Formicidae** | | 15 |
| *Camponotus* sp | 2 | |
| *Dorylus* sp | 2 | |
| *Alaopone* sp | 1 | |
| *Anoplolepis custodiens* | 1 | |
| *Crematogaster* sp | 1 | |
| *Typhlophone* sp | 1 | |
| **Isoptera** | | 13 |
| *Macrotermes falciger* | 3 | |
| *Odontotermes badius* | 2 | |
| *Odontotermes* sp | 1 | |
| *Trinervitermes rhodesiensis* | 2 | |
| *T. rapulum* | 1 | |
| *Allodontermes tenax* | 1 | |
| *Hodotermes mossambicus* | 1 | |
| *Pseudacanthotermes militaris* | 1 | |
| **Melon pulp and pips** | | 1 |

b.

| Food item | Proportion (percentage by number) | |
|---|---|---|
| **Formicidae** | | 71,14 |
| *Anoplolepis custodiens* | 43,95 | |
| *Aenictus eugenii* | 11,45 | |
| *Dorylus ?helvolus* | 9,47 | |
| *Messor capensis* | 2,60 | |
| *Monomorium albopilosum* | 1,86 | |
| *Crematogaster* sp | 1,15 | |
| *Monomorium havilandi* | 0,30 | |
| *Pheidole* spp | 0,24 | |
| *Solenopsis* sp | 0,04 | |
| *Camponotus* sp | 0,02 | |
| *Camponotus ?fulvopilosus* | 0,02 | |
| *Monomorium* sp | 0,02 | |
| *Tetramorium* sp | 0,02 | |
| **Isoptera** | | 21,52 |
| *Trinervitermes trinervoides* | 13,79 | |
| *Hodotermes mossambicus* | 7,73 | |
| **Muscoid fly puparia** | | 0,24 |
| **Seeds** | | 7,11 |
| *Chenopodium album* | 4,95 | |
| *Amaranthus deflexus* | 0,56 | |
| *Erodium* sp | 0,40 | |
| *Portulaca oleracea* | 0,36 | |
| Aizoaceae | 0,34 | |
| *Stachys* sp | 0,12 | |
| *Celosia* sp | 0,10 | |
| *Bulbostylis zeyheri* | 0,06 | |
| *Amaranthus* sp | 0,04 | |
| *Plectranthus* sp | 0,04 | |
| *Anagillis arvensis* | 0,02 | |
| *Argemone subfusiformis* | 0,02 | |
| *Digitaria* sp | 0,02 | |
| *Lippia* sp | 0,02 | |
| *Mesembryanthemum* sp | 0,02 | |
| *Polygonum aviculare* | 0,02 | |
| *Sherardia arvensis* | 0,02 | |

In the Umgeni Valley in Natal, Melton & Daniels (1986) from faecal analysis found that *Dorylus* sp formicids predominated in the diet, having a mean percentage occurrence of 78,2%; *Odontotermes* sp termites 12,2%; followed by 9,5% unidentified ant species, and 0,1% *Hodotermes mossambicus* and *Trinervitermes* sp.

## Reproduction

Young have been born in captivity in the northern hemisphere in spring, autumn and winter (Hodges, pers. comm.) and in the Subregion in July in the Karoo (Skinner, unpubl.), while 11 instances of neonates or near-term foetuses have been recorded in July, September and November in Zimbabwe (Smithers, 1983). Gravid females with small foetuses have been recorded in February, April, May and June. All these records are of single young, although Melton (1976) stated that on rare occasions there may be two. Sampsell (1969) gave a protracted gestation period of seven months. Implantation may occur in either uterine horn. At birth both males and females weigh 1,7 kg (n = 4 females, 3 males; range 1,3–1,9 kg; Hodges, pers. comm.). The altricial young are born in a maternity den in the wild and remain alone in the den, the mother returning from time to time to nurse (Skinner, unpubl.). After a few weeks (Verheyen, 1951 gave two weeks, but this seems unlikely), the young may accompany the mother, and they dig for themselves at about six months of age. It is not known how long the juveniles remain in company with the mother. Melton (1976) recorded a female accompanied by two young of different sizes.

# Order PROBOSCIDEA

## XXXVIII. Family ELEPHANTIDAE
## Elephants

The earliest known ancestor of the Proboscidea was a small pig-like creature named *Moeritherium*, whose fossil remains were found at Fayum in Egypt. It lived in swamp on the fringes of the Tethys Sea that covered parts of North Africa during the Eocene Epoch about 50 million years ago. What is now the Sahara Desert was then a mosaic of swamp and plains. It stood about 0,6 m at the shoulder, had no trunk, but its teeth and skull marked it as an early representative of a wide range of proboscids which in later geological ages included the ancestors of our present-day elephants. Many forms arose from the early proboscids, each adapting to the diverse niches open to them. On the basis of their fossil remains, these various forms have been classified into five Families: the Moeritheridae, the Gomphotheridae, the Mastodontidae, the Dinotheridae and the Elephantidae. Only the Family Elephantidae still occurs today, all the others are extinct.

The true elephants, the Elephantidae, include modern elephants and two species of mammoths, the imperial mammoth, *Mammuthus imperator*, and the woolly mammoth, *Mammuthus primigenius*, both now extinct. As the colloquial name implies, the latter had a coat of fine, soft, yellow-brown hair, about 25 mm long, overlaid with a coat of long, coarse, dark rust-coloured hair about 500 mm in length. They had very thick skin, with a thick layer of fat underlying it, very small ears about 400 mm in length, and long, inwardly curving tusks. Their foreheads were distinctly swollen and, like *M. imperator*, their backs sloped towards their hindquarters, more so than in modern elephants. Both the long hair and fat layer under the skin were adaptations to the rigors of the extremely cold climate in which they lived at the high latitudes of the Northern Hemisphere. The woolly mammoth survived up to the time that man was well established on the earth, as is confirmed by the rock paintings of Europe which depict groups of men catching them in pits and despatching them with rocks and stone tools. Woolly mammoths trapped in boggy places in Siberia became frozen into the permafrost. In the early 1900's local inhabitants dug up frozen mammoth meat to feed their dogs. A scientific party investigating a well preserved specimen reported eating such meat, as did one of the Tsars and his party at a banquet in Leningrad.

Typical mammoths also differed from modern elephants in their simple molar teeth that were not replaced as they are in modern elephants. Modern elephants have complex molar teeth, with a series of flattened transverse plates of enamelled dentine. *Stegodon*, which lived in Asia and whose fossil remains have been recovered from Pliocene beds, had 14 ridges on the molars and looked very like the Indian elephant, *Elephas maximus*. It was the ancestor of both the Indian and African elephant, *Loxodonta africana*, the two living species which represent the Family Elephantidae.

Both the Asiatic and the African species are intelligent and respond well to domestication. Both have been employed by man for working, for ceremonial purposes and, in early historical times, for war. The Asiatic elephant was domesticated earlier, over 3 000 years ago. The Romans trained African elephants, and the forest elephant, *L. a. cyclotis*, was used in Zaire as recently as 1982 (Won Wa-Musiti, pers. comm.) for levelling an aircraft landing strip. The African elephant is reputed to be more temperamental and to require more rigid discipline and exercise, thus proving less successful as a working animal for logging operations. Even under optimum vegetational conditions the African elephant takes too long to obtain its food requirements, leaving too little time for working. Under the conditions in which the Asiatic elephant works in the Burma forests, food is superabundant and they can obtain their requirements in a far shorter time.

In spite of a diminution in numbers, in parts of Africa where elephants have been afforded protection, as they have in the Subregion, their numbers have increased to the extent that in some places population control is exercised.

### Genus *Loxodonta* Anonymous, 1827

No. 289

### *Loxodonta africana* (Blumenbach, 1797)

### African elephant
### Afrika-olifant

Frontispiece

#### Colloquial Name

The name is derived from the Greek for an elephant, *elephas*, in Latin *elephantus*. The name "pachyderms", often applied to elephants, refers to their thick skins.

#### Taxonomic Notes

Despite the view of some authors (Frade, 1955; Azzaroli, 1966) that the forest elephant, *L. cyclotis* (Matschie, 1900), was specifically distinct from the savanna or bush elephant, *L. africana*, Backhaus (1958) who found considerable intergrading where their distributions overlap in the northeastern parts of Zaire, concluded that they were conspecific, as did Ansell (1974b), who divided them into two divisions, *africana* and *cyclotis*.

Because of the huge size of the species, comparative data are difficult to obtain. Morrison-Scott (1947) provided data on the height of the forest elephant, *L. a. cyclotis*, obtained from the Belgian Congo (Zaire) Elephant Training Centre. This showed that they are small elephants. Captured at about 10 to 12 years of age, they were measured yearly until they ceased growing at about 20 to 25 years of age. At the latter age the average height (n = 200) was 2,35 m for males and 2,10 m for females; exceptional individuals reached 3,00 m in males and 2,50 m in females.

In *L. a. africana* the ears have a well developed triangular lobe, its apex directed downwards. *L. a. cyclotis*, on the other hand, has no well developed lobe and the outline of the whole ear is therefore much more rounded (Fig. 289.1).

Frade (1931) considered that the number of toe nails was a good distinguishing character, *L. a. africana* having four on the forefeet and three on the hind, *L. a. cyclotis* five on the forefeet and four on the hind. However, both subspecies have five well formed digits both on the fore and hind feet, but the nails are inclined to be lost in *L. a. africana*, perhaps through the nature of the terrain in which they live as opposed to that of *L. a. cyclotis*. Morrison-Scott (1947) found that the best characters distinguishing the two subspecies were the shape of the mandibles and condyles. In *L. a. cyclotis* the mandibles formed a long, narrow spout, in *L. a. africana* the spout was short and wide. The condyles in *L. a. cyclotis* are ovoid in shape, in *L. a. africana* they are spherical.

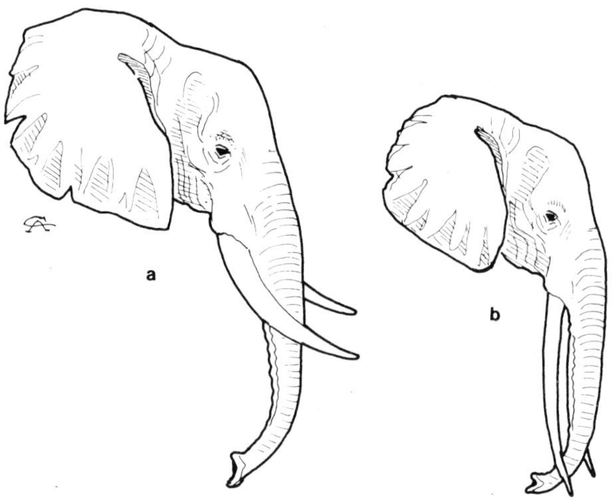

Fig. 289.1.
Ears: (a) African elephant, *L. a. africana*
(b) Forest elephant, *L. a. cyclotis*

Noack (1906) described what he called the pygmy elephant from the Gabon, *Elephas africanus pumilio* (=*L. a. pumilio*), which was 1,20 m high at the shoulders. The type specimen lived in the New York Zoological Gardens up to its death in 1915, by which time it had a shoulder height of 2,03 m which is within the range of size of *L. a. cyclotis*. Stories of pygmy elephants persisted for many years, but generally have been discounted.

Within the *africana* division Ansell (1974b) recognised four subspecies: *L. a. africana*, *L. a. knockenhaueri* (Matschie, 1900), *L. a. oxyotis* (Matschie, 1900) and *L. a. orleansi* Lydekker, 1907.

**Description**

Through their universal portrayal in books and films and their wide use in circuses and exhibitions in zoological gardens, elephants hardly require description for they are well known even to many people who have never seen one in the wild. Creased, folded and covered with papillae which give it a gnarled appearance, the skin is thickest on the legs, forehead, trunk and back, where it may reach a thickness of 30–40 mm. The skin is thinnest on the back of the ears. The body is sparsely covered with bristly hairs, the juveniles with more hair than the adults. Adults have well developed eyelashes and thick hair at the ear orifices.

The cylindrical tail, which may reach a length of 1,5 m in an adult bull, is flattened towards the tip and is usually fringed on either side with long, black, bristly hairs about 400 mm long, although these may be worn off. These hairs are much in demand for making into ornaments. Kolb (1731) reported that Europeans in the Cape used these hairs as pipe cleaners. The skin colour is grey or brownish-grey, but often the colour is obscured in the wild by their habit of dusting and mud-wallowing and they tend to assume the colour of the soil in which they carry out this practice. The skin has no sweat glands.

Elephants have five nails on the front feet and four on the hind. Sometimes the outer nails on the front feet and the outer and inner on the hind are missing, having been torn out or worn away. The feet have a thick layer of cartilage which acts as a shockabsorber. When placed on the ground in walking, the soles splay out and, when the foot is raised, they shrink. This layer allows them to move without making a sound. The soles of the feet are horny and superficially cracked, the mosaic of cracks visible in the spoor (Fig. 289.2).

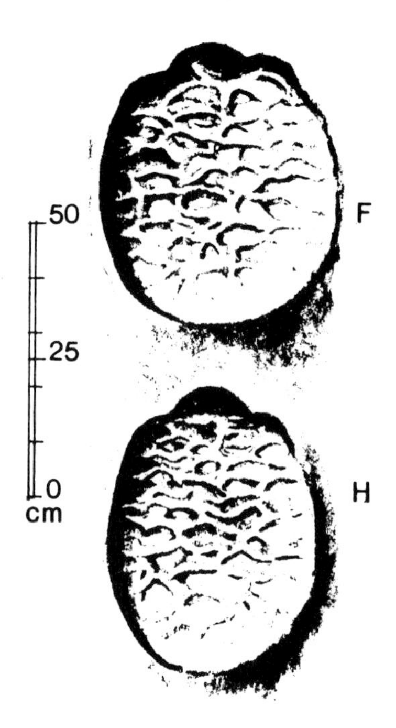

Fig. 289.2 Spoor of the elephant, *Loxodonta africana*

The trunk is an organ of extreme dexterity, with a prehensile tip on both upper and lower sides, unlike the Indian elephant which has only a tip on the upper side. This remarkable organ serves many uses.

The flaps of the ears are very large and in adult bulls may reach a vertical height of nearly 2 m and a breadth of 1,2 m. Elephants, with their huge body size, increase their surface area to dispense heat generated within the body by evaporation through the skin and thermoregulate using their ears as the main window for heat loss (Wright & Luck, 1984). Although the ears weigh only some 20 kg each, they constitute 20% of the elephant's surface area. They have an extensive vascular system with a blood-flow rate of between five and 12 litres per minute. The ears give out about three-quarters of the heat loss required to maintain body temperature. Wright & Luck (1984) measured water loss from the skin of various parts of a 1 200 kg elephant and concluded that it was capable of losing 0,23 l of water/m$^2$/h on average. The estimated surface area was 11 m$^2$, so that some 2,5 l of water would be lost per hour of a 12 hour day, i.e. approximately 30 l of water was used for evaporative cooling. They normally drink about 160 l of water per day. Even in the Namib Desert they dig *goras* or water holes in the dry river beds; in addition they are assisted in reducing excess body heat by the cool air and advective fog coming off the cold Benguela Current on the west coast. In more tropical regions their habits of swimming and wallowing are ways of reducing heat gain and promoting heat loss by keeping the skin wet. Ear-flapping, so characteristic of elephants standing in the shade on hot days, causes air convection over the body and ear surfaces, cooling the blood in the vessels and so assisting in regulating the body temperature.

The relatively small eyes are green or hazel in colour. They have nictitating membranes but no tear ducts, so that when the eyes "water", the tears run down the cheeks. The mouth is small and spout-shaped.

Elephants belong to the Testiconda, *i.e.* species in which the testes remain within the body cavity. The single pair of mammae in females is situated between the forelegs and is the only reliable way of distinguishing the sex of post pubertal animals in the field (Cumming, pers. comm.), although the angle of the forehead in females tends to be more rounded and convex in males and is commonly used. The profile of the back in males tends to be straighter than in females. In elephants in poor condition the top of the pelvic girdle and backbone stick out prominently above the body contours.

Elephants have temporal glands on both sides of the head, with their external orifices midway between the outer canthus of the eye and the external auditory meatus. Their secretion may be seen often as a dark mark on the dry skin and may be a copious secretion when stressed. Musth is a condition closely associated with increased sexual activity in the bull and is dealt with under **Reproduction**.

The tusks are elongated upper incisor teeth. The heaviest pair of tusks on record, now in the possession of the British Museum (Nat. Hist.), are from Kenya with a mass of 102,3 kg and 97,0 kg respectively. Such massive tusks have not been recorded yet from the Subregion where, according to Best & Best (1977), the heaviest came from the Limpopo Valley at 64,3 kg, and a pair from Fishan, Zimbabwe weighed 57,7 kg and 48,5 kg. Recently, Hall-Martin (1984) recorded a pair from the Kruger National Park weighing 55,5 kg and 56,6 kg. Tuskless individuals of both sexes are known. In females this is usually due to a recessive genetic characteristic and in males the result of injury. Tuskless elephants have a reputation for aggressiveness.

The whole mass of the huge head, the trunk and tusks is carried by the forelimbs and as a consequence the front feet are larger and more rounded than the hind which are more oval, features which show clearly in the spoor (Fig. 289.2).

No living mammal exceeds the elephant in the height at the shoulder. The Fenykoevi elephant bull from Angola, now mounted in the foyer of the United States National Museum in Washington, measured just over 4 m. The practical difficulties in obtaining the mass of elephants precludes the production of averages. Moss (1976) recorded that the heaviest bull elephant on record had a mass of 6 569 kg. A bull taken during control operations in eastern Zambia, which had an estimated age of 60 years, had a mass of 6 004 kg (Robertson-Bullock, 1962). Old adult bulls in the Subregion may be considered, at an estimate, to have masses of between 5 500 kg and 6 000 kg. The females usually have masses of about two-thirds that of the males from the same area.

Considerable thought has been given to visual methods of obtaining quick age assessments in the field. A useful guide is given by Hanks (1979) based on body size within a family unit (Fig. 289.4) and the relative size of footprints and fecal boli may also be useful (Western, Moss & Georgiadis, 1983; Jachmann & Bell, 1984). Accurate ageing of elephants, however, can only be carried out on tooth replacement and wear (Laws, 1966; Sikes, 1971; Jachmann, 1988). Tusk size is no criterion, for it can vary with the nutritional status of the habitat. Elephants have a life expectancy of about 60 years, although occasionally they may exceed this age.

## Skull

The skull of the elephant is rounded and very large, the maxillary and premaxillary bones extending far below the level of the upper tooth row and forming bony supports on either side for the bases of the tusks. In older adults there is no sign of the sutures between the bones and the whole skull is fused into a solid structure. In the female skull there is a distinct nuchal eminence not present in the male. The bony structure of the skull is "honey-combed" and, in a full grown adult bull, may be as much as 300 to 400 mm thick at the frontal region. The brain cavity is small and situated low down at the back of the skull. The eye sockets are situated towards the front of the skull and, in life, house eyeballs that are almost identical in size to that of man. Their situation gives a very limited line of sight to the sides and rear.

The tusks, which grow throughout life, are enlarged upper incisors which replace the tiny milk tusks which may only reach a size of about 40 mm and are shed at about a year old. At an early stage of development the permanent tusks have a cap of smooth enamel which, however, is quickly lost, the tusks being composed entirely of "dentine" or ivory. Ivory is the only dentine that shows a characteristic cross-grained matrix—a means by which elephant ivory can be distinguished from imitations. Their bases, lying within the bony projections of the skull, remain covered with a cement layer throughout life, and they continue to grow both in length and girth. Normally one or other tusk is subject to greater wear and as a consequence there is always a discrepancy in mass between the individual tusks in pairs. The bases are hollow and the tapering cavity is filled with a highly vascular pulp. While a break towards the tip of a tusk is not a serious factor, a break through to the pulp can cause malformation in growth or, more serious, infection involving the whole root structure. There is a superstition among the Ndebele people of Zimbabwe that to view the pulp leads to impotency. As a consequence they always shake this clear of a tusk out of sight of others, where it will not be seen, averting their own eyes while they do so.

During their lifetime elephants grow six molar teeth. However, two molars normally occur on each side of the upper and lower jaws and are in use at the same time. As each successive molar tooth comes into use, it moves forward in the jaw, becoming worn and breaking down towards its forward edge, the roots being resorbed. The next one then moves forward from the back of the jaw to replace it. Each tooth that erupts is longer and wider than the previous one. Laws (1966) showed that the six molars develop fully and erupt at the following approximate ages:

| | Age in years |
|---|---|
| M1 | 1 |
| M2 | 2 |
| M3 | 6 |
| M4 | 15 |
| M5 | 28 |
| M6 | 47 |

Eventually only the last molar M6 remains and by the age of about 60, through breaking down the front of the tooth, it may be represented by a fragment only. At this stage elephants usually decline physically, owing to their inability to masticate their food properly.

The heavy lower jaw hangs like a swing on the temporalis muscles. The action in grinding the food consists of a backward and forward movement of the jaw, the grinding taking place on the forward movement.

## Distribution

By 1903 elephants had practically ceased to exist in the Subregion; their disappearance was effected in the space of 60–70 years (Bryden, 1903). This was not surprising as, at that time, 1 200 000 lbs of ivory were being imported into England alone each year, for which 50 000 elephants were reputedly slain, and Bryden (1889) predicted on this basis that they would soon be extinct in the Subregion.

Skead (1980) gave a detailed account of the history of elephants in the Cape Province, which highlights the shrinkage in their range from the time of their first being reported at Mossel Bay by Vasco da Gama in 1497 to their present day survival in only the Addo Elephant National Park and the Knysna Forest. Apparently elephants were never recorded on the Cape Peninsula itself, the nearest record being from Tiervlei (Leibbrandt, 1896). Verburgh's expedition to the hinterland in 1652 recorded them between Cape Town and Saldanha Bay (Thom, 1952) and other parties recorded them at Clanwilliam, Verlorenvlei, Piketberg and Lambert's Bay. Further north, two were killed between the Groen and Buffels rivers in Namaqualand in 1680 (Mossop, 1935) and elephants were reported from the south bank of the Orange River as far inland as about 100 km east of Goodhouse. In Bushmanland and the Karoo they were recorded just west of the Augrabies Falls in 1779 (Barnard, 1950) and in the Kenhardt district. Robert Jacob Gordon encountered elephants when he explored the Eastern Cape in 1777 and 1778, but not in large numbers. He also recorded seeing small herds near the present town of Kakamas and commented on their aggressive behaviour towards the local San communities (Raper & Boucher, 1988). Burchell (1824) in 1812 recorded that the Khoikhoi had killed 39 elephants on the Makkwarin River, 25 km northeast of Kuruman, and elephants were still to be found in that area until about 1816 (La Trobe, 1818).

In the 17th century ivory was a valuable commodity in great demand in Europe, a factor not overlooked by early settlers in the Cape, who urged the Khoikhoi to bring them tusks. At this time, however, the Khoikhoi found that elephants were too formidable to attack. Soon they were taught how to deal with them, at first using pitfalls where they were slowly put to death by the wounds of assegaais and arrows (Valentyn, 1726). From the early part of the 18th century hunters, traders and settlers in the hinterland took their toll of elephants. For the year 1736 Theal (1909) reported that elephant hunters were away from Cape Town for eight or nine months at a time before "returning with their wagons laden with ivory" but would not reveal their routes or hunting grounds. By 1755 no elephants could be found west of Port Elizabeth (Bryden, 1889). Thunberg (1793 or 1795) recorded his discussion in 1773 with Jacobus Bata, a farmer who lived between Montagu and Swellendam. Then 81 years of age, Bata stated that, in earlier days, elephants were plentiful as far west as the Cape and that he often had shot four or five, even 12 or 13 in a day, and had once shot 22. In 1775 Sparrman (1786) recorded that elephants were being "shot at continually" and by that time had been largely expelled from the George to Plettenberg Bay sector, and "had taken refuge in the almost entirely unexplored country of Sitsikamma". Thomas Charles Bain, a road engineer who cut the first road through the Tsitsikamma Forest, starting in 1879, reported that "the number of elephants cannot be less than 200".

In the Subregion, elephants are not a forest species and their occurrence in the Knysna Forest is due to their being forced into this unnatural environment by man. They once roamed over a much larger area (Mackay, 1983). While forest may appear to provide a rich and varied diet, it does not provide the abundance of palatable grasses which are so important to the healthy survival and reproduction in elephant populations. From the time that the original stock was forced into this environment this factor militated against them (Koen, 1988). However, it was by no means the only factor leading to their decline. In 1858 the Cape Colony published strict protection measures for elephants when Government Notice 263, "Preservation of Elephants and Buffaloes", was issued. It seems that the Knysna forest conservancies which were established at this time were as much concerned with the conservation of the depleted elephant herds of the forests as they were with the trees (Grove, 1987). Preservation measures continued in 1860 and 1876 when elephants in the Addo Bush and Knysna Forest were afforded protection. Capt. Harrison, the Forestry Officer in charge of the area, estimated that some 400 to 600 elephants still remained in the George/ Tsitsikamma areas. He also reported that they continued to be destroyed (Phillips, 1925) and this destruction was still going on in 1889 (Superintendent of Woods and Forests, 1889). As late as 1920, in spite of their low number, Maj. P.J. Pretorius shot two bulls, one with a shoulder height of some 3,8 m, which was mounted later for the South African Museum, Cape Town (Pretorius, 1947). The Knysna Elephant Survey of 1969/70 recorded that there were probably not more than 10 left, which by 1990 had been reduced to four. Nearby, in the Addo Elephant National Park, numbers have increased steadily at 7% per annum since the 1920's and now number some 160.

In Natal, the bush around the present-day suburb of Berea in Durban was noted for its large elephant population. Traces of elephant paths, numerous in the 1860's, were still discernible in the 1880's (Little, 1884). Between 1850–1875 immense numbers of elephants were destroyed in Zululand (Bryden, 1889). In 1873, £17 199 worth of ivory was exported through Natal and in 1885 this had declined to £4 100. The last elephants were shot at the Umgeni River in 1854 (Tait, in Skead, 1987), but there seems little doubt that there continued to be movements into northern Zululand from southern Mozambique which have continued up to the present day, resulting in a fluctuating population of 50 to 150 individuals being found in Tongaland (Klingelhoefer, 1987).

From the time that white settlement at the Cape began in 1652 the demand for ivory had been an encouragement to expansion into the interior. The first trekboers in the early 17th century were attracted by easy access to ivory (van der Merwe, 1938). In 1875 the value of ivory exported from the Cape Colony was £60 402 and this had declined to £2 150 in 1886 (Bryden, 1889). When the first European travellers visited the Transvaal in the late 1820's and 1830's, Harris recorded that in the Magaliesberg "the whole face of the landscape was actually covered with wild elephants. There could not have been fewer than three hundred within the scope of our vision" (Harris, 1840). The economic viability of early Voortrekker settlement in the Transvaal was based almost exclusively on the ivory trade—principally for manufacture into trinkets and ornaments, piano keys and billiard balls—and Schoemansdal (just west of the town of Louis Trichardt) was set up as a flourishing mercantile headquarters in 1848 (Carruthers, 1988). In these early days large tuskers appear to have been abundant, many tusks requiring two or three men to carry them, and in 1855 some 90 000 kg of ivory were exported from the northern Transvaal (Huet, 1869). However, so great was the slaughter that by 1856 no elephants could be found in the Warmbaths district (Churchill, 1856; Gassiott, 1852). By 1875 they had all but disappeared from the Transvaal and could only be located in what is now Zimbabwe, the eastern Transvaal Lowveld and Mozambique (Erskine, 1875; Da Costa Leal, 1870). In 1902, just a few years after the Sabi Game Reserve had been proclaimed, the warden reported that there were no elephants in the reserve and that they were locally extinct in the Transvaal (Stevenson-Hamilton, 1903). Two years later the first elephants entered the game reserve from Mozambique (Stevenson-Hamilton, 1905) and the nucleus of the present large population (maintained at about 7 000) of the Kruger National Park emanated from this source—a process that took 50 years.

From the turn of the century in 1700 the ivory trade formed the basis of the economy in Mozambique until about 1800 (Alpers, 1975). Even before then, in three years from 1512–1515 the Portuguese exported 69 000 kg of ivory from Beira and it is reported that in 1544 great quantities could be obtained at Delagoa Bay, not necessarily originating from Mozambican territory. For example, 1 720 kg were exported from the town of Lourenzo Marques (now Maputo) from 1759–1761 (Alpers, 1975). During 1879–1883, the peak of ivory entering Europe was reached, 848 000 kg per year being imported, only 29 000 kg of which originated from South Africa where destruction of elephant herds had taken place over a long period of time, compared to 142 000 kg of this annual total from Mozambique (Spinage, 1973).

Similar levels of decimation took place in Zimbabwe. As recently as 1871–1875 Bryden (1889) reported that vast numbers of elephants occurred in Matabeleland and Mashonaland, but 10 years later it was difficult to come across a single elephant. Cumming (pers. comm.) has estimated that the Zimbabwe population was certainly below 4 000 elephants in 1900. The first game laws came into effect in 1902 and the first National Park (Hwange) was declared in 1930. The recovery of the elephant population at 5% per year from 1905–1965 has been remarkable and ivory exports from elephants killed in Zimbabwe show an exponential increase of 15% per year from 1950–1980, and probably reflected both the increase in elephant populations and increasing conflict between elephants and expanding human populations (Cumming, 1981). Reflecting this trend, Davison (1950) estimated the population of elephants in Hwange at 1 000 in 1930 and 2 000 in 1944, while the estimate in 1979 was 15 564 ± 15% (Williamson, 1979). Likewise, Cumming (1981) reported on a healthy expanding population in the Sebungwe Region where the populations were low 100 years ago (Selous, 1893) and by 1919 were seldom seen (Paxton & Jack in Cumming, 1981). An estimate of 724 was made in 1924, while the population was estimated at 8 000 to 12 000 in 1979. A further 4 649 were killed in tsetse control operations in the 1960's. Cumming (1981) mentioned that the elephant population in Gonarezhou National Park closely parallels that in the Sebungwe, expanding from 1 000 animals in 1925 to some 7 000 in 1970.

A similar tale of decimation in the 19th century and

recovery in the 20th century is reported for Botswana. Livingstone (1857) reported that a year after the discovery of Lake Ngami, 900 elephants were killed in 1850 on the Lake shore alone. In 1855 elephants were scarce in Bamangwato, being hunted in Ngamiland and towards the Zambezi in 1857 and by 1860 the best days for elephant hunting had passed (Spinage, 1973). For five years from 1846 to 1850 great execution was wrought by ivory hunters. Today populations have recovered dramatically, even in the privately owned Northern Tuli Game Reserve in southeastern Botswana, increasing from a few animals in the 1950's to about 685 or one elephant/km$^2$ in 1990 (Le Roux, 1988).

In Namibia elephants occurred on the Fish River in the Keetmanshoop district in 1761/1762 (Mentzel, 1787). By 1900 they were regarded as very scarce south of the Kunene River in Owambo (Moeller, 1899; Bryden, 1903) and Fischer reported that the last herd of elephants in the area of the Etosha National Park was exterminated in 1881. They previously probably occurred throughout Namibia (Skead, 1980; De Villiers & Kok, 1984). Shortridge (1934) only encountered elephants in the Kaokoveld, isolated parts of the Kavango, Outjo district and Owambo. Small herds recolonized the Etosha National Park beginning in the 1950's and, following the provision of borehole water in the 1960's, elephants recolonized the park in large numbers, reaching a peak of 2800 in the dry season of 1983 (Lindeque, 1988). Viljoen (1988) discussed early reports of sightings of elephants in the Kaokoland as far back as 1793 and indicated that elephants have always found a refuge there. He found little evidence to support seasonal migration between elephant populations in the western Kaokoland and those in the Etosha National Park up until 1983. More recently, however, Lindeque (pers. comm.), using satellite tracking, found that there is indeed occasional movement between the different subpopulations.

Some credit for the recovery of African elephant populations has tended to be given to procedures in colonial Africa emanating from the Convention for the Preservation of Wild Animals, Birds & Fish in Africa held in London in 1900, where European powers first attempted to act in concert with one another for the protection of game, the initiative for which came from the Governor of German East Africa in 1895 (Carruthers, 1988). Clause 11 of the Convention prohibited the killing or hunting of young elephants, the establishment of severe penalties for this including the confiscation of all elephant tusks weighing less than five kilograms. Unfortunately the regulations introduced were too complicated and therefore impractical to execute, although it did reflect a genuine desire to protect numerous species of game by the European powers. The problem lay with the attempt to control the international trade in animal products, particularly ivory. Moreover, the Portuguese and German colonies were reluctant to accept the terms of the Convention which dragged on until the outbreak of war in 1914 when the project was finally abandoned. Indeed, the value of wild animals as an economic resource (for white settlers) overrode the sentimental attitudes espoused by the imperial powers (Carruthers, 1988).

Everywhere in the Subregion, elephants have shown a remarkable capacity for recovery, to such an extent that populations have to be managed carefully and controlled to prevent permanent damage to their habitat. This must be one of the truly great conservation achievements and reflects immense credit on early administrators, conservationists and the conservation authorities in the countries involved; a species nearing extinction has been brought to a situation where it is essential that it is managed as a renewable resource to ensure its survival — it is something of which we can all be truly proud.

*South of the Sahara, excluding the Southern African Subregion*

In West Africa, present records indicate a discontinuous distribution of the subspecies *L. a. oxyotis*, from the western **Mali** to **Nigeria**; from Lake Chad and the southern sector of **Chad**; the northeastern **Central African Republic**; the southern and southeastern **Sudan** and narrowly into western **Ethiopia**. Except in the southern Sudan their present status

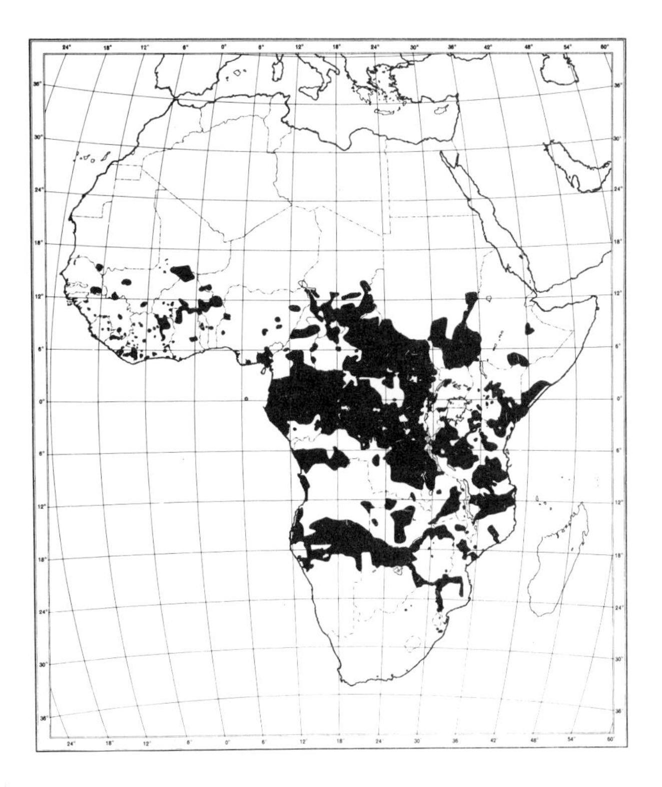

Map by courtesy of EEC/WWF African Elephant Programme in collaboration with GEMS/GRID and ELSA

is poorly known and in many parts they may be extinct locally. *L. a. oxyotis* is replaced in northeastern Ethiopia by a relict population of *L. a. orleansi*, whose distribution at one time extended into northern Somalia. *L. a knockenhaueri* occurs in southwestern **Somalia; Kenya; Uganda** and **Tanzania** and is replaced southwards in **Mozambique**, north of the Zambezi River; **Malawi; Zambia;** southern **Zaire** and in **Angola** by *L. a. africana*. The forest elephant, *L. a. cyclotis*, occurs from **Liberia** to the Congo basin in **Zaire**, in the High Forest Zone intergrading with *L. a. africana* in northeastern Zaire and Uganda.

*Southern African Subregion*

*L. a. africana* occurs in northern and northeastern **Namibia** and widely throughout northern and in parts of eastern **Botswana**. In **Zimbabwe**, while they are absent except as vagrants from the whole of the central plateau and adjacent developed areas, they are present north and south of this in the low country of the Zambezi and Limpopo valleys. They occur throughout **Mozambique**, south of the Zambezi River, except along the Zimbabwe border from about 19 °S to 21 °S and in the southeast. In the **Transvaal** they occur in the Kruger National Park and in two private game reserves on its western boundary, with vagrant excursions into the northern and northeastern parts of the province from Botswana and Zimbabwe. South of this there are three areas where they are still found, one in the Addo National Park and a precarious remnant in the Knysna Forest. The third group occurs in Tongaland in northeastern KwaZulu which originated from vagrants from southern Mozambique which settled in the area. Today there is a viable population in the area. Elephants have been reintroduced to several game reserves including the Hluhluwe Game Reserve and Pilanesberg National Park.

**Habitat**

African elephants are catholic in their habitat requirements. They occur in country as diverse as the riverine valleys of the coastal Namib Desert to the high rainfall areas of the eastern parts of the continent with their lush woodland, thick underbrush and heavy grass cover. They range almost anywhere except where man has either exterminated them or subjected them to too much disturbance. A supply of water, preferably fresh, is an essential habitat requirement, as well as some shade in which to shelter during the hottest hours of the day and food in the form of grasses and browse plants.

The occurrence of some 84 elephants in the riverine valleys of the western desert region of Kaokoland, in an area with a mean annual rainfall of 150 mm, is only possible because the rivers provide narrow (100 m wide) ribbons of savanna winding through the desert. These elephants owe their ability to survive in these adverse conditions to their mobility, travelling long distances for food and water and to taking advantage of the occurrence of rain (Viljoen, 1988).

**Habits**

Elephants are gregarious, are both diurnal and nocturnal, particularly in hot environments, and live in family groups consisting of an adult female with her offspring and a number of closely related females with their offspring. On reaching puberty the young males within these groups leave of their own accord. These family groups may coalesce to form herds. The bulls usually join up with the family herds only when a female is in oestrus and thereafter leave to rejoin male herds or to remain on their own. Bulls in musth actively seek out herds containing females in oestrus. The male herds are temporary associations, for members leave and rejoin them at will. Very old bulls often live solitary lives. Much larger associations may be found numbering hundreds of individuals of all age classes and sexes. These associations are formed naturally or when the lead cows in family herds are shot or the population as a whole is subjected to heavy hunting or control pressures.

While elephants show no territorial behaviour, they do have home ranges which vary greatly in size between various habitats. In Kaokoland, Viljoen (1988) found the mean home range for 52 of the desert-dwelling elephants to be 2 172,3 ± 426,5 km$^2$, with that of bulls being slightly larger than that of family groups. This is considerably larger than home range sizes in the Zambezi Valley of 94 to 263 km$^2$ reported by Dunham (1988) and probably reflects lower availability of food and water as the annual rainfall is ten times as great. Similar variations were found in East Africa, with home ranges varying from 350 km$^2$ in Tsavo east to 1 580 km$^2$ in Tsavo west and 15 to 52 km$^2$ in Manyara (Douglas-Hamilton, 1973; Leuthold & Sale, 1973).

Elephants are normally peaceful, but individuals, especially if sick or injured, can be aggressive and extremely dangerous. Females in groups with young are particularly unpredictable. Aggressive tendencies take the form of raising the head and trunk and extending the ears perpendicular to the body, often kicking up dust with the front feet, and screaming. Swaying or shaking the head, they may then initiate a mock charge which usually breaks off before reaching their objective. However, the mock charge may develop into an attack, when, with the trunk tucked in below the jaw, they charge forward, trumpeting and screaming, with tusks directed at the enemy.

Fights between males are extremely rare (Poole, 1989a). When they become enraged, however, they do great damage to each other with their tusks and aggression can persist until one or the other is seriously wounded or killed. An encounter witnessed in the Hwange National Park, Zimbabwe left a trail of broken trees, trampled bushes and a copious blood spoor (Smithers, 1983). Normally tolerant of other species, they are less tolerant of lions, rhinoceros and hippopotamus, which they have been known to kill, and there are instances where they killed sable antelope at dwindling water supplies (Child, 1968b) and chased off zebras, warthogs and buffaloes. Their ears express their mood, an enraged elephant bearing down on one with ears held outward is a sight that is never forgotten. Unfortunate victims may be caught by the trunk and thrown around or more generally are crushed to the ground with the base of the trunk, or impaled on the tusks. Cases are on record where victims were buried or covered with branches and debris, more cases than can be explained purely by chance.

With their trunks elephants can break down substantial tree branches to get at the fresh outer twigs and leaves. They pluck bundles of grass by curling the end of the trunk around the stems and pulling the plant up by the roots. They then beat it against their leg to get rid of the soil, thereafter conveying the food to the mouth with the trunk. They drink large quantities of water (up to 200 l in one drinking session) by filling the trunk with water and squirting it into their mouths, or cool themselves by spraying the water over their bodies. During droughts they will dig for water, using first the tusks and then the trunk. In sandy soil they will excavate a deep round hole, barely larger than the diameter of the trunk, to reach water, waiting patiently until the water seeps in. In Botswana these holes reached a depth of over 0,8 m, the water in them only available to elephants and man.

In extreme situations, where fresh water is not available, elephants will drink brackish water. This has been known to kill them if the concentration of salts is too high, as happened in a drought year in northeastern Botswana (Smithers, 1983) and one year in Hwange National Park when elephants drank some saline water at a pumped pan (Cumming, pers. comm.). Weir (1972) found that the largest congregations of elephants in Hwange National Park gathered at man-made waterholes where the water is sodium-rich and numbers decreased as sodium decreased. Sodium content was usually correlated with carbonate and bicarbonate alkalinity. At water supplies with insufficient sodium elephants utilised local concentrations of water-soluble sodium in the soil. This is called geophagia, eating saline or calcareous soils, loosening it with the nails of the front feet and scooping it up with the tip of the trunk. However, there is no evidence of any physiological benefit to elephants of a sodium-rich diet.

Whenever they reach water, which may be daily, or in drier areas only every third or fourth day, they will bathe, spraying themselves or lying down in the water. Sometimes they submerge completely, with only the tip of the trunk showing. They are perfectly at home in water and are known to cross regularly to islands in the Zambezi in search of food, either by walking on the bottom with their trunks acting as "snorkels" or by swimming. They are partial to wallowing in mud or dusting themselves to protect the skin from the hot sun or to rid themselves of parasites. Tree and stone-rubbing are indulged in regularly and stout overhanging branches and tree stumps at convenient heights, especially near water holes, become polished by this activity. They move at a steady walk, often at night, and tend to string out into single file, thus creating well worn paths which are used over many years and are a feature of "elephant country".

Elephants, in the course of their meanderings, can cover very long distances. Lindeque (pers. comm.) and Calef (pers. comm.) using radio-telemetry, have documented seasonal migrations up to 200 km in Namibia and northern Botswana respectively. They tend to move to seasonally preferred feeding areas and water supplies. When the fruits of the fan palm, *Hyphaena* spp, the manketti tree, *Ricinodendron rautanenii*, or the marula, *Sclerocarya birrea*, are ripe, one can be fairly certain of finding elephants in the vicinity in these groves feeding on the fruits. During certain times of the year they will move to graze on stands of palatable grasses such as *Panicum maximum* and *Urochloa trichopus*, or reed and papyrus beds along swamps or rivers. The grasses are particularly attractive when in seed and elephants will feed effectively by drawing in trunk-fulls of seed-laden grass heads (Cumming, pers. comm.) They are partial to sweet, clean water and will travel long distances to obtain it. Vagrant movements take them far from their normal habitat and in Zimbabwe they have been known to turn up in the peri-urban areas of cities where they had not been seen for many years.

While their eyesight is not very acute, their hearing is good and their sense of smell is very keen and the act of raising the trunk and testing the air is a common feature of their behaviour. Vocalisation consists of trumpeting and screaming when upset and they maintain contact with a deep rumbling. Formerly this was thought to emanate from their stomachs, but is now known to be produced by the vocal cords. A feeding herd can be very noisy as branches are broken down or plucked off. On sensing danger, however, the whole herd will stand still as they test the air, the contrast between the noise of their feeding and the dead silence when they are alert is very pronounced. Recently infrasonic components of calls have been shown to play a major role in communication between individuals even several kilometres apart (Poole, Payne, Langbauer & Moss, 1988). Vocalisations largely inaudible to man also occur in the Asiatic elephant (Payne, Langbauer & Thomas, 1986) and may explain aspects of group cohesion and synchronized behaviour.

**Food**

Elephants both browse and graze, utilising a very wide range of species. Williamson (1975) has shown that, in the Hwange National Park, Zimbabwe, 87 browse species, 42 grass species and 36 herb species are eaten. The ratio between the types of food varies both with their availability and the season, there being a tendency to eat more grass after a season of good rainfall. Browsing stimulates coppicing which can lead to an increase in primary production. Among the very many species of browse plants eaten, mopane, *Colophospermum mopane*, ranks high under Subregion conditions and elephants prefer to browse on regrowth from previously damaged trees (Anderson & Walker, 1974; Viljoen, 1988). Other species replace mopane in different parts of their range. The bases of perennial grass stems are normally richer in carbohydrates than the remainder of the plant, and in plucking and eating grasses they carefully shake off or knock the clumps against trees or parts of their bodies to get rid of adhering soil, which would not be palatable and would cause tooth impaction.

Elephants can be very destructive in their feeding habits, pushing over trees, pulling them up by the roots, or breaking off branches to get at the young fresh foliage. In doing so, however, they may improve the habitat for some species by opening it up to grassland or providing a new micro-habitat under the fallen trees conducive to the germination of the seed of other plant species or providing cover for small mammals and ground-living birds. Where elephant populations exceed their food supply, especially where their movements are restricted, they can devastate the habitat (Martin, Craig & Booth, 1989). They are indeed only second to man in their capacity for altering their environment.

Thompson (1975) showed that, in the Chizarira Game Reserve in Zimbabwe, there was a real danger that the reserve would lose its mufuti, *Brachystegia boehmii*, woodland as a result of bark-stripping by elephants. In one area, of 500 trees marked, 66,8% were damaged so badly that they died, 20,4% were damaged and only 12,8% were undamaged. Damaged trees were susceptible to further attack by insect borers and fungi, even if only a part of the bark was stripped off. Hanks' (1979) contention that this was a classic example of compression is only partially correct, because a major contributing factor was elephant population growth (Cumming, 1981). Not only were elephants displaced from the Zambezi Valley when Lake Kariba flooded and people were resettled, but a population growth rate of 5% per annum resulted in a doubling of the Reserve elephant population in the period between 1960 and 1975.

In the Sengwa Wildlife Research Area, severe reduction of trees was already apparent in 1968 (Jacobson & Cumming in Cumming, 1981). From 1972, there was a marked decline in basal area covered by *Acacia tortilis*, a species favoured by elephants for bark-stripping. The biomass of trees in miombo woodland in particular decreased by 45% over a five-year period (1972–1976) primarily as a result of removal by elephants of large trees which were not replaced due to the effects of fire and further ravages by elephants. The opening of the canopy and coppicing of damaged trees resulted in more browse for smaller browsers (Guy, 1981). In 1980–82 elephants were culled, reducing the density from 2,9 to 0,7 elephants per km$^2$, following which the number of trees and canopy cover regenerated rapidly (Coulson, in Martin *et al.*, 1989). Regrettably there are few areas in Africa where elephants have large areas in which to range freely. Therefore control of numbers becomes of paramount importance to avoid devastation.

Elephants eat the bark of certain trees, the umbrella thorn, *Acacia tortilis*, and knob-thorn, *A. nigrescens*, being especially favoured. They loosen the bark with their tusks and then strip it off. They also like the roots of certain woody species such as *Combretum* spp, zebrawood, *Dalbergia melanoxylon*, and *Terminalia* spp which may have some medicinal properties. In the Sengwa Wildlife Research Area, Sharp (1982) analysed samples of the diet from stomachs and faeces for plant parts and crude protein and fibre. The proportion of browse (mainly wood) peaked in the hot dry season and reached a minimum during the early wet season. The proportional stomach fill of males was significantly less than for females, whether the latter were lactating or not. Crude protein reached a minimum during the hot dry season and fibre content a maximum. Diet quality was significantly correlated with proportions of leaf and wood in the stomach. The minimum dietary crude protein content was below estimated maintenance requirements for some five months of the year. Excepting for bark, the proportions of major plant components in the stomach were significantly correlated with those in the faeces. Elephants digest only about 40% of what they eat (Moss, 1976). Consequently they need about 170 kg of green food (Guy, 1975) and *ca.* 160 litres of water daily. Elephants spend a high proportion of their time feeding; Wyatt & Eltringham (1974) put this as high as 74% in Uganda.

Where elephants concentrate the droppings can benefit the environment. Coe (1972a) found that a 10 year old female elephant produced on an average 100 kg of dung in a 24 hour period. Droppings also provide an optimum micro-habitat for the germination of certain tree seeds including camelthorn, *Acacia erioloba*, and ana tree, *A. albida* (Viljoen, 1988), through fertilization and contributing to the litter mass.

**Reproduction**

Within the Subregion, where summer rains fall from November to April, conceptions peak at this time. This has been found in Mana Pools National Park (Kerr, 1978), Chizarira National Park (Craig, 1984), Hwange National Park (Williamson, 1975), Gonarezhou (Sherry, 1975), Kruger National Park (Smuts, 1975) and Etosha National Park (Lindeque, 1988). However, the production of sperm in mature bulls is independent of season (de Villiers, 1988) and some conceptions occur in every month.

Craig (1984) made a most interesting discovery following observations on foetal size from culling operations. He found that foetuses fell into two distinct categories and, with a gestation period of nearly two years, he deduced that conceptions were distinctly seasonal and the foetuses resulted from conceptions in two summers. This has proved without doubt that they have a breeding season restricted to the wet months of the year within the Subregion.

Oestrus may last up to six days. Large musth (see later) males over 35 years old guard oestrous females and do all the mating in mid-oestrus. An oestrous female may mate with males 25–35 years of age during early and late oestrus, but rarely in mid-oestrus (Poole, 1989b). Only oestrous females solicit guarding from musth males and give loud, low frequency calls that may attract males and incite competition between them. This results in their mating with males which are old, vigorous and healthy (Poole, 1989b). Bulls will fight over cows, although this behaviour is rare, but similarly ranked musth males will fight if they meet one another.

Craig's (1984) discovery emanated from his deductions that, in estimating conception date from birth weight and gestation length, in large foetuses, growth rate of the embryo in early stages is slow, deviating from a linear relationship. This resulted in an error of up to two months in estimating time since conception date for elephant foetuses. He used a gestation period of 660 days in making his calculations. The gestation period for a captive cow at the Johannesburg Zoological Gardens for four births was 668,75 ± 12,2 days, with a mean calving interval of 1078 days (range 830–1462 days); a single stillborn calf weighed 165 kg, and of the four calves, two were born in August, one in January and one in November (Wilkinson, pers. comm.). A single young is produced at birth, although twins have been recorded (Roth & Austen, 1966; Sikes, 1971), with an incidence of about 10% in the Etosha National Park (Lindeque, 1988). At the time of birth females will seek a shady secluded retreat, often near water, and may clear the ground prior to squatting and giving birth. At this time the female may be accompanied by other females, often with their calves, who act as guards. The calf, in dropping free from the female, severs the umbilical cord, and the adhering membranes are removed carefully by the female with her trunk or by caressing with her forefoot (Sikes, 1971). The calf's first reaction on attaining a steady footing is to search for the mammae which are situated between the front legs of the female, and to suckle with the mouth. Only occasionally has the female been observed to eat the afterbirth.

At birth calves stand about 900 mm at the shoulder. They are pinkish in colour and have more hair on their bodies than the adults. At this stage their eyesight is poor and they maintain contact with the females by feeling with their trunks. They may continue to suckle for two or three years, although normally they wean at about two years, depending on conditions. This would have the effect of increasing the birth interval, thus reducing the rate of increase of the population. If a nursing mother dies, her calf may be adopted by other nursing mothers.

Young elephants are subject to predation by lions and remain close to their mothers, rarely moving more than a few metres from her side during their first few months of life. Where they are not within the social protection of the herd they remain vulnerable up to a shoulder height of 1,4 m (Fairall, pers. comm.). Very young elephant calves walk under their mothers' bellies, between their legs. The mothers and other females in the herd will defend them vigorously at this stage.

Maternal care of the young is intensive for the first two years of life. The mother will ensure it is safely positioned under her belly when moving, assist it over obstacles and up and down steep slopes, squirt water over it and dust it regularly. Calves are very playful and may irritate the females with their gambolling, when they will smack them smartly with their trunks, which quickly brings them to heel. Playing calves are very vocal, squeaking and squealing with much ear-flapping and barging into each other. They will bellow loudly if hurt. By the age of one to two years, calves have learnt some degree of threat display and take part in the strong bond of mutual cohesion within the herd (Sikes, 1971). An injured member may be assisted to its feet and supported by other herd members, and if mortally wounded, may be defended vigorously by other members of the herd, actions in which even the young calves may take part.

Under optimum habitat conditions females may conceive from about nine years of age (Sherry, 1975; Smuts, 1975; Kerr, 1978; Dunham, 1988; Lindeque, 1988), while males reach puberty about a year later. However, Laws, Parker & Johnstone (1975), using data from populations in East Africa, have hypothesised that as habitat resources decrease and population density increases, so fecundity declines. Age at first conception would be one of the first characteristics to be delayed, followed by a lengthening in calving interval.

Males are not "socially mature", that is do not compete successfully with older males for oestrous females, until they are over 35 years of age (Poole, 1989b). Females may remain sexually mature to an age of 55 years, sometimes over 60 years (Sikes, 1971). Lindeque (1988) gave the mean calving interval as 3,8 years in the Etosha National Park, with a lactation anoestrus lasting 1,8 years — in both instances a year longer than that for elephants in the Kruger National Park (Smuts, 1975). On the other hand, using only the indirect methods available to him, Viljoen (1988) found the age at first mating for Kaokoveld elephants to be not less than 15 years and the mean calving interval to be 9,5 years. This lower reproductive rate may reflect the harsh environment in which they live. Under savanna conditions, Calef (1988) has shown that the maximum rate of increase for the species is about 7% per year, a rate of increase observed under natural conditions in the Addo Elephant National Park (Hall-Martin, pers. comm.).

Musth is the term referring to a period of increased sexual activity and aggressiveness in elephant bulls, particularly noticeable in Indian elephants, where the temporal glands of only bulls secrete fluid. In both species temporal glands discharge a copious, strong-smelling, watery secretion which runs down the sides of the face during musth and this is accompanied by increased plasma testosterone concentrations (Jainudeen, Katongole & Short, 1972; Hall-Martin & van der Walt, 1984; de Villiers, 1988). There is considerable evidence that musth is a reliable indicator of good condition, as African elephant bulls in poor condition do not come into musth and wounded bulls drop out of musth (Poole, 1989a).

Temporal glands are functional in all age groups and both sexes of African elephants (de Villiers, 1988), except in very young calves (Laws, 1970). Only bulls over 24 years old experience musth (Poole, 1987; de Villiers, 1988). Musth in African elephants was first reported by Poole & Moss (1981) and is characterized by copious secretions from the temporal gland, constant dribbling of urine, a greenish coloration of the penis, increased aggression and frequent association with female groups (Poole, 1982). Among individuals 25–35 years old the duration of musth is short and sporadic (several days to weeks), while older bulls experience longer (2–5 months), more predictable periods of musth (Poole, 1987). Bulls in musth undergo profound behavioural changes, and spend most of their musth period in searching for cows in oestrus, often far from their normal ranges (Barnes, 1982; Poole, 1982; Hall-Martin, 1987). Temporal gland fluid, plasma and urinary concentrations of testosterone show a marked increase during musth (Poole, Kasman, Ramsay & Lasley, 1984; de Villiers, 1988), similar to male Asiatic elephants. De Villiers (1988) has suggested that temporal glands in African elephant bulls are used primarily for olfactory signals of dominance in the hierarchy. The factor determining dominance rank in non-musth bulls is body size, but musth bulls rank above larger non-musth bulls in agonistic interactions (Poole, 1989a).

Fig. 289.3
The relative sizes of elephants in a family group compared to an average lead cow (after Hanks, 1979)
(a) adult female (b) subadult (15 years old)
(c) intermediate (6 years old) (d) juvenile (2 years old)
(e) infant (1 year old)

# Order HYRACOIDEA

Dassies

## XXXIX. Family PROCAVIIDAE

The dassies are in many characters primitive or generalised subungulates that have changed, in the course of evolution, from the forms known as fossils from the Oligocene Epoch. By that time they had evolved into a large and diverse assemblage, represented by six genera and including species of much larger size than those known today. One of the Plio-Pleistocene forms, *Gigantohyrax maguirei*, from Makapansgat in the Transvaal, like so many other fossil species known from this period, was about three times larger than the extant rock dassie, *Procavia capensis*. *G. maguirei*, known from the anterior two-thirds of a skull with full upper dentition, had already lost the second and third upper incisor teeth and the canine possessed by earlier forms, and resembled the extant rock dassie in this aspect of its dental formula very closely. Other smaller dassies are known from this geological age, some such as *Procavia antiqua* and the larger *P. transvaalensis* occurring in fossil deposits at Taungs and in the Transvaal (Maglio & Cooke, 1978).

There is ample evidence to show that extant dassies are related most closely to the dugongs and the elephants, and in the past, authors have placed them together in a Superorder Paenungulata which included, in addition, the manatees which do not occur in the Subregion.

The Family Procaviidae is represented in the Subregion by three genera: *Procavia*, *Heterohyrax* and *Dendrohyrax*, each by a single species, *P. capensis*, *H. brucei* and *D. arboreus*.

*Heterohyrax* was regarded as a subgenus of *Dendrohyrax* by Ellerman *et al.* (1953), but, in a subsequent review, Bothma (1967) advanced valid reasons for their separation. These are based on cranial and ecological differences and is the view followed here.

Bothma (1971a) recorded the differences in the position of the penis in relation to the anus in *P. capensis* and *H. brucei*, drawn to his attention by Coetzee (*in litt.*). In the former the distance between them is 20–25 mm, in the latter 65–70 mm. In addition, Hoeck (1978) recorded the differences in penis structure between *H. brucei*, *P. johnstoni* of East Africa and *D. arboreus* and in their territorial vocalisations as illustrated by sonograms. He recorded the call of *H. brucei* as shrill and long, lasting up to 1,5 seconds and given repeatedly for up to 5 minutes. *D. arboreus* starts with several cracking sounds followed by loud and repeated screams. In *P. johnstoni* it is a repeated barking, becoming louder towards the end of the sequence, the last barks tailing off to guttural noises. The screaming of *D. arboreus* is one of the characteristic noises of the African night and at times sounds almost human. In *H. brucei* and *D. arboreus* it appears that only the males produce these calls, in *P. johnstoni* and in *P. capensis* both sexes vocalise. These differences support the existence of three genera.

Dassies, in particular the rock dassie, *P. capensis*, and the yellow-spotted dassie, *H. brucei*, are, in parts of the Subregion (Zimbabwe, parts of Botswana and Mozambique), of considerable economic importance to African people who make use of the meat and skins, the latter traded as dried skins or processed and made up into karosses. The nature of the skin and pelage is such that the processed article is both durable and long-lasting.

Dassie intestinal tracts have certain features that are unusual among mammals (Rahm & Frewein, 1980). Posterior to the stomach and connected to it by the small intestine they have a large sac in which there are bacteria which break down by fermentation the cellulose in the food. Posterior to this and connected to the sac by a short length of intestine they have a caecum, which has two horn-shaped processes at its anterior end, a structure encountered frequently in birds. The caecum is a fermentation chamber that produces large amounts of volatile fatty acids which serve as an energy source (Leon, 1980; Eloff & van Hoven, 1985).

Dassies have one pair of enlarged upper incisor teeth and two pairs of lower, the other front teeth being absent. There is a considerable space between these teeth and the cheekteeth which in pattern are not unlike those of a rhinoceros. Their ears are very short and they have four functional digits on the front feet and three on the hind (Fig. 290.1). The digits are all armed with nails except the inner digit on the hind foot which is armed with a long nail which is almost claw-like.

Key to the genera (Bothma, 1971a)

1. Molars hypsodont, $P_1$ sometimes absent, length of $P^{1-4}$ much less than that of $M^{1-3}$; mammary formula: 1 pair pectoral and 2 pairs inguinal; temporal ridges in close contact or form a sagittal crest; rock dassies, living in colonies; diurnal, and sometimes nocturnal on moonlight nights
   ... *Procavia*

   Molars brachyodont, $P_1$ always present, length of $P^{1-4}$ just less than, equal to or exceeding length of $M^{1-3}$
   ... 2

2. Length of $P^{1-4}$ just less than or equal to length of $M^{1-3}$; rock dassies living in colonies; mainly diurnal but sometimes nocturnal on moonlight nights; mammae 1 pair pectoral and 2 pairs inguinal, varying to 2 pairs inguinal only; skull flat dorsally, temporal ridges in close contact or form a sagittal crest
   ... *Heterohyrax*

   Length of $P^{1-4}$ exceeding length of $M^{1-3}$; tree dassies living solitarily or in pairs; nocturnal or partly diurnal; usually 1 pair of inguinal mammae, but in two subspecies the number varies and may be 1 pair pectoral and 1 pair inguinal or 1 pair pectoral and 2 pairs inguinal; skull concave dorsally, temporal ridges beaded and far apart
   ... *Dendrohyrax*

### Genus *Procavia* Storr, 1780

No. 290

### *Procavia capensis* (Pallas, 1766)

### Rock dassie
### Klipdas

Plate 27

#### Colloquial Name

The "dassie" colloquially used in English in South Africa is Afrikaans and is derived from the Dutch *das* or badger, the name applied by the Dutch settlers in the Cape to this species. Elsewhere in Africa "hyrax" is used more frequently, which is a usage more of the scientific community.

The name *steen-dasch* (stone badger) was applied to this species by the Dutch. Captain Joris van Spilbergen in 1601 reported finding, on Isla d'Elizabeth (Dassen Island) "beasts in shape like a stone badger" which were "very tasty like lamb or mutton" (Skead, 1972). Later visitors to the island referred to them as dassies or rock rabbits. Van Spilbergen must have been the pioneer of animal translocation in southern Africa for, in the same year, he sent his yacht back to Dassen Island to collect live dassies for the colonisation of Isla de Cornelia (Robben Island), the experiment, however, proving unsuccessful. In 1654 Van Riebeeck imposed an embargo on catching them on Dassen Island until they had time to multiply (Skead, 1972).

### Taxonomic Notes

The species, although then known for many years, was described first in 1766 by Pallas, who saw one for the first time in a tavern in Cape Town, where it was kept as a pet.

Many subspecies have been described, but Meester *et al.* (1986) recognised only *P. c. capensis* from the entire Subregion, except where replaced in northern Namibia by *P. c. welwitschii* (Gray, 1868).

### Description

Rock dassies are small, tail-less, compact animals, about 500 mm in total length, the males having a mass up to about 4,5 kg, the females lighter and smaller (Table 290.1).

The colour of the upper parts of the body varies throughout their wide distributional range from a yellowish-buff to a reddish or greyish-brown. The pelage has a grizzled appearance due to the banding on the individual hairs. Individuals from one area may exhibit extensive colour variation (Bothma, 1966a). This variation in colour led early workers to ascribe many subspecific names to the variously coloured populations, none of which is recognised today. In general the palest specimens originate from the northwestern parts of Namibia, where the mean annual rainfall is 125–250 mm, the darkest from the eastern, where the mean annual rainfall is 1 000–1 500 mm (Bothma, 1966a).

In the centre of the back there is an elongated patch of long hair, which is black in *P. c. capensis*, white or pale yellow in *P. c. welwitschii*, the individual hairs up to 40 mm in length. This hair overlays the dorsal gland, the function of which is commented on under **Habits**. Behind and at the bases of the ears there are conspicuous patches of off-white or buffy-coloured hair.

The body is thickly haired; the hair of the guard coat is harsh; the individual hairs are up to 25 mm long, dark at the base with a subapical lighter band of varying width and a black tip. The underfur is soft and woolly; the hairs have dark grey or grey-brown bases and broad light-coloured tips. The hair on the lower part of the limbs and feet and on the head is shorter than on the remainder of the body. The area above the eyes, around the mouth and on the feet is lighter in colour than the body. The forehead, however, tends to be darker. The under parts lack the banding on the hair, are lighter in colour than the upper, and the hair is generally longer.

A feature of the pelage of the rock dassie is the long black tactile hairs which, scattered among the coat, extend far beyond the level of the guard coat and may reach a length of up to 60 or 70 mm. There are also a few of these under the chin and above each eye. The whiskers on the upper lips reach a length of 100 mm. These tactile hairs assist the individual in orientating itself in the dark rocky crevices.

The limbs are short and sturdy. The forefoot has four digits, the outer digit the shortest, each digit with a flat nail. The curved claw is used in self-grooming. The soles of the feet are naked, the skin thick and padded with glandular tissue, an exudation from which serves to keep the surface permanently moist. The padded feet ensure increased traction and allow the rock dassie to negotiate steep and often smooth rock faces or to climb trees with agility (Fig. 290.1).

The head is carried on a short neck and has a short, rather pointed snout. The hind portion of the lower jaw is very broad so that when viewed from the side the neck appears to be very thick. The pupil of the eye is kidney-shaped and lies horizontally, the concave edge on top. Johnson (1901) noted the existence of a peculiar shield in the dassie eye which he named an 'umbraculum'. Millar (1973) has suggested this has evolved in response to predation by black eagles, *Aquila verreauxi*, which frequently appear to attack from out of the sun. Dassies are the predominant prey of black eagles (Davies, pers. comm.). Being somewhat thermolabile, dassies have to bask in the sun, thereby exposing themselves to attack (Millar, 1973).

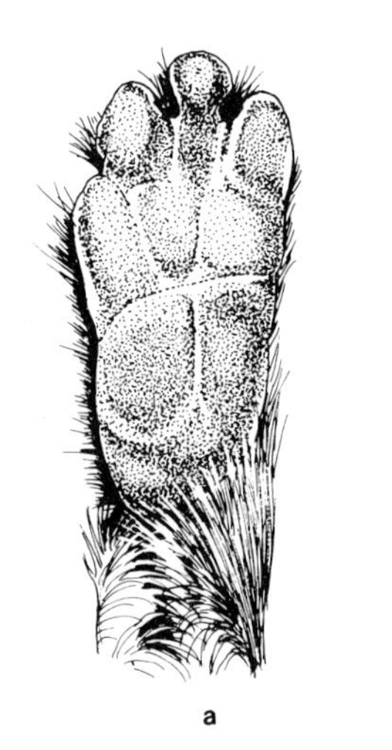


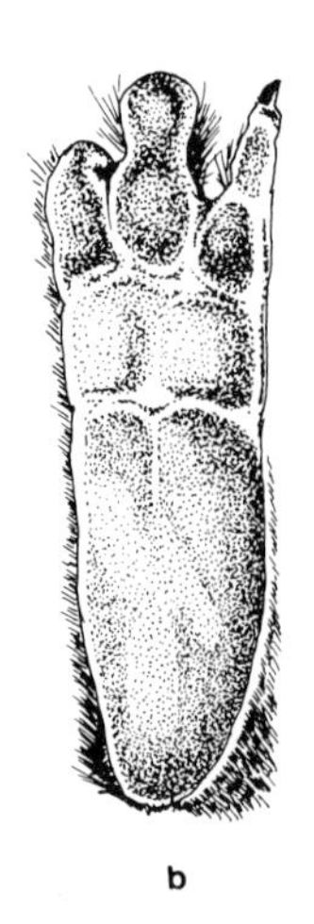


Fig. 290.1. Feet, ventral view: Rock dassie, *Procavia capensis*
(a) Forefoot
(b) Hind foot, showing claw on inner digit.

**Table 290.1**

Measurements (mm) and mass (kg) of adult rock dassies, *P. c. capensis*, from Zimbabwe (Smithers & Wilson, 1979) and the Orange Free State (van der Merwe, *in litt.*), and *P. c. welwitschii*, from Namibia (Bothma, 1967).

**Zimbabwe**

| | Males | | | Females | | |
|---|---|---|---|---|---|---|
| | $\bar{x}$ | n | Range | $\bar{x}$ | n | Range |
| TL | 531 | 10 | 495–600 | 511 | 10 | 455–550 |
| Hf s/u | 74 | 10 | 70–80 | 69 | 10 | 64–76 |
| E | 34 | 10 | 30–40 | 31 | 10 | 29–35 |
| Mass | 3,52 | 10 | 3,21–4,65 | 3,09 | 10 | 2,47–3,46 |

**Orange Free State**

| | Males | | | Females | | |
|---|---|---|---|---|---|---|
| | $\bar{x}$ | n | Range | $\bar{x}$ | n | Range |
| TL | 560 | 15 | 532–577 | 553 | 13 | 525–585 |
| Hf c/u | 75 | 14 | 71–79 | 69 | 13 | 65–77 |
| E | 35 | 15 | 32–41 | 35 | 13 | 34–40 |
| Mass | 3,76 | 15 | 3,16–4,34 | 3,56 | 13 | 3,01–4,15 |

**Namibia**

| | Irrespective of sex | | |
|---|---|---|---|
| | $\bar{x}$ | n | Range |
| HB | 464 | 24 | 365–500 |
| Hf s/u | 66 | 24 | 60–76 |
| E | 24 | 26 | 23–34 |

### Skull

Features of the rock dassie skull are the widely spaced eye sockets which are elongate-oval, the short rostrum and the two upper, ever-growing incisor teeth, one on each side, separated by about the width of one tooth. The lower mandible is exceptionally broad, especially at the back. The skull is flattened on top, the occipital region vertical and broad for the size of the skull. The zygomatic arches are broad and heavily built and this, coupled with the widening of the bone structure at the back of the mandible, which is ridged at its edges, indicates a powerful set of masseter muscles. In the rock dassie these are the major muscles operating the lower jaw, the temporalis being secondary. As a measure of the comparative size of these two muscles, the masseters comprise 53% of the total bulk of the muscles actuating the lower jaw, as opposed to the temporalis at 23% (Knight, *in litt.*).

Even in the oldest specimens examined, the postorbital bar, while appearing complete, has a junction of cartilage which is often lost in preparation. The ear bullae, viewed from below, are flattish, the swelling confined to their inner surfaces, the paroccipital processes extending far below them.

The dental formula is:

$I\frac{1}{2}\ C\frac{0}{0}\ P\frac{4}{3}\ M\frac{3}{3} = 32$

A characteristic feature is the distinctly larger size of the molar teeth compared with the premolars. This is a useful feature in distinguishing the skull of the rock dassie, *P. capensis*, from the yellow-spotted dassie, *Heterohyrax brucei*, in which the cheekteeth are of much more even size (Fig. 290.2).

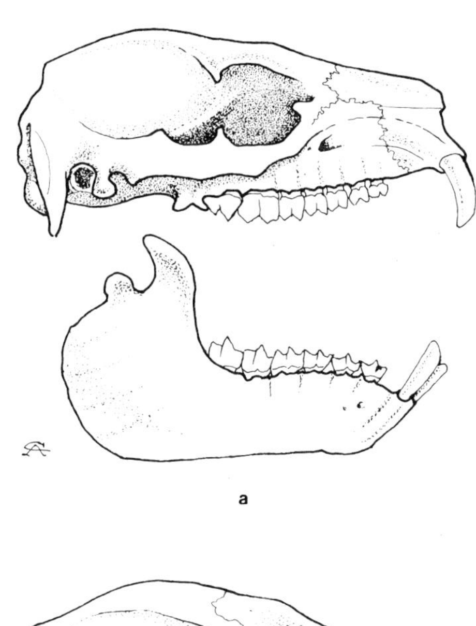
a

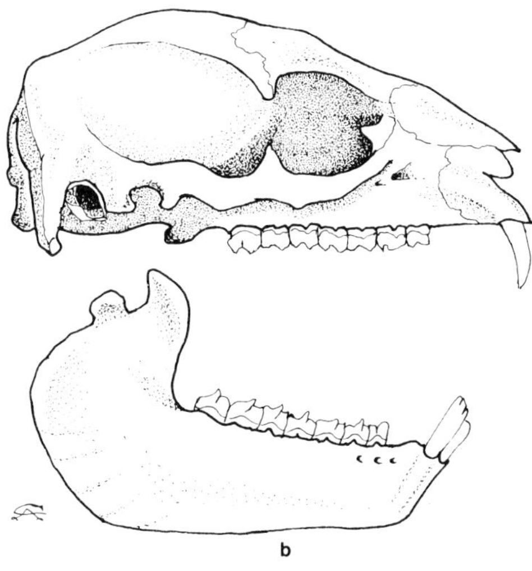
b

Fig. 290.2. Skulls, lateral view
(a) Rock dassie, *Procavia capensis*
(b) Yellow-spotted rock dassie, *Heterohyrax brucei*

The first premolar in the lower jaw is usually absent or, if present, is thin and splint-like, and in juveniles up to about 10 months old, the deciduous canine may persist. In the male rock dassie the upper incisor teeth are triangular in section and, through occlusion on the points of the outer incisors in the lower jaw, which slope forward, are honed constantly to needle-like points. In the female the upper incisors are rounded in front and each occludes on the two incisors in the lower jaw, wearing to more chisel-like points. In the male the outer incisors in the lower jaw occlude on the backs of the upper and themselves wear to flat points, with sharp outer edges. The inner pair is thin and round and much smaller than the outer. In the female the pairs of incisors on either side become concavely worn on their points through the action of the upper incisors and the inner pair is proportionately larger than in the male. The cheekteeth rows are distinctly outwardly curved, particularly on the outer sides of the teeth, which, as they become worn, remain as upstanding, sharp-cutting edges. In juveniles the lower incisor teeth are tricuspid, in adults unicuspid through the loss of the tricuspid crowns through wear. In old *P. c. welwitschii* the tricuspid nature of the teeth shows in the two grooves on the front of these teeth.

The length of the upper premolar toothrow $P^{1-4}$ (mean = 16,18 mm) is much shorter than that of the molar toothrow $M^{1-3}$ (mean = 20,95 mm). The first premolar in the lower jaw is absent.

### Distribution

Extralimitally numbers of species have been described (Honacki, Kinman & Koeppl, 1982; Meester *et al.*, 1986), all of which are considered as synonyms of *Procavia capensis*. On this basis the species has a very wide distribution on the continent and extends into countries in the Middle East, including the Sinai Peninsula of eastern Egypt, Israel, Lebanon, Syria and parts of Arabia. Within this wide distributional range, however, they only occur where there is suitable habitat and their distribution therefore is patchy and discontinuous.

*North Africa*

In **Algeria** they are recorded from the isolated massifs of Ahaggar and Adnar des Ifonas in the south; in similar terrain in the Aïr of northern **Niger**, in the Akakus Mountains and the Tibetsi in southern **Libya** and in the coastal mountains bordering the Red Sea and in the Sinai Peninsula in **Egypt**.

*South of the Sahara, excluding the Southern African Subregion*

They are recorded from **Senegal** eastwards to the mountainous country of the eastern **Sudan, Ethiopia** and **Somalia** and from there southwards in northeastern **Zaire**, and all countries east of the Rift Valley to the borders of the Subregion, with the exception of Zambia, from where there are no records, although there are suggestions the species could exist in southeastern Zambia (Spassov & Roche, 1988). In **Angola** they occur on the inland escarpment as far north as about Benguela.

*Southern African Subregion*

They occur in parts of northwestern and narrowly in the west of **Mozambique**, south of the Zambezi River; in southeastern **Zimbabwe**; in eastern **Botswana**; the **Transvaal**; parts of **Swaziland** (but not in the Lubombo Mountains); **Natal**, excluding the northeast; widely in the **Orange Free State** and **Cape Province**; in the inland escarpment and adjacent rocky areas in **Namibia**, north to the Angola border.

### Habitat

As the name implies the rock dassie only occurs where there are outcrops of rock in the form of krantzes, rocky koppies or rocky hillsides, or piles of loose boulders accompanied by an association of bushes and trees of species which provide browse, which forms a major part of their diet. It is necessary that these rocky areas provide crannies and crevices in which they can shelter. The slot height through which dassies move is just over twice the skull height, 66,1 mm (± SE 1,3; n=45) *cf.* 151 mm (± 4,6 SE; n=69) (George & Crowther, 1981). Granite formations with piles of huge boulders, from which the overlying soil has been washed away, and dolomite intrusions in the Karoo are specially favoured, as are sandstone krantzes with loose, rocky, overhanging slabs. They also occur in erosion gulleys in areas such as the Karoo, one habitat they have colonised recently.

The rock dassie appears to be more versatile than its near relative the yellow-spotted dassie, *Heterohyrax brucei*, with which it lives in close association in many parts of its range. They will use quite small piles of rocks, not favoured by the yellow-spotted dassie. As a consequence they frequently are found colonizing outlying koppies far from the main ranges shared by the two species.

### Habits

Rock dassies are predominantly diurnal, only emerging from their resting places in cool weather after the sun is well up

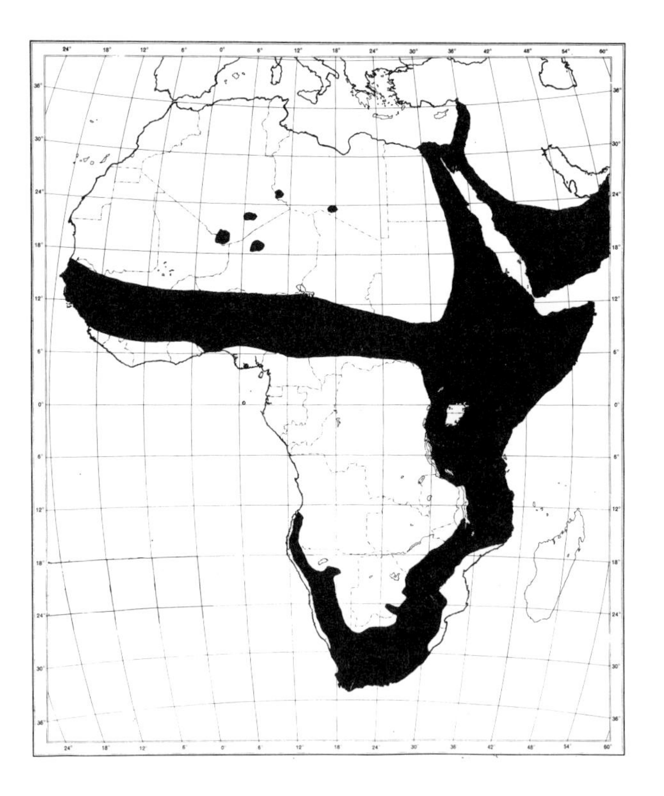

in the morning and retiring before it sets in the evening. Dassies have a labile body temperature which can drop a few degrees at night (Sale, 1970b). Their first reaction after their cautious emergence in cool weather is to seek a warm spot in the sun, well sheltered if it is windy, and to sun themselves. Often whole family parties indulge in this pursuit. In warmer weather with a half to full moon they will feed before dawn or after sunset and are only exclusively diurnal when it is cold and they require to augment their body heat by sunning (Fairall & McNairn, 1981; McNairn & Fairall, 1984). The shape of their bodies is such that it is difficult to distinguish them among the smaller rocks lying around, although they do not always choose to conceal themselves and will sit on the top of rounded boulders in a totally exposed position. When sunning they remain keenly alert and one of the older females assumes the role of sentinel, and when danger threatens gives the warning call, when they all dive for the shelter of their rocky retreats. If this crier is removed, usually another female will take her place (McNairn *in litt.*).

They have also been known to use the shelter of culverts under roads and holes in stone walls. Thomas (1964) recorded their use of antbear and other holes in the ground where overpopulation forces them from rocky habitat and which they probably reach by dispersing at night. Due to the formation of the feet, rock dassies are incapable of burrowing and have to rely on existing shelters.

Rock dassies are gregarious, living in colonies which vary in size according to the area of rocky habitat and amount of food available. Sometimes a family party of four to six will occupy a small pile of isolated rocks, while on extensive, continuous ranges of krantzes, where estimates of numbers are difficult, hundreds may be present, divided into harems.

Dassies are territorial, one male associating with up to 17 adult females and juveniles and one to two peripheral males. Males are forced to disperse when mature, whereas females disperse voluntarily at a later age. As a result one to two year old and old males feature strongly in black eagle diet (Davies, 1989).

Their padded feet allow for movement even on smooth surfaces and they are very agile in leaping from rock to rock, in negotiating steep rock faces or clambering about on the branches of trees. The sweating, which takes place on the pads, increases their traction.

Providing it is warm and sunny they may be found feeding at any time during the day, except when very hot, with peaks in feeding activity in the early morning and late afternoon. In winter the peak periods are later, or one peak only in the morning and earlier in the afternoon. If food is not available in the immediate vicinity of their habitat they will travel 500 m down to a river to feed (Fourie, 1983). They are adept at tree climbing and will move out on the finer branches to reach the succulent fresh leaves. If disturbed when feeding in trees, they will drop or jump to the ground from considerable heights, racing back to the rocky shelters, or take refuge in dense stands of vegetation.

Rock dassies spend the greater part of their time outside the shelters doing very little. Sale (1970b) showed that in East Africa only about 5% of the time is spent in active pursuits, consisting of foraging or moving. In very hot weather they seek the shade of rocks or overhanging foliage.

Observation of rock dassies in captivity shows that, in the shelter, heaping and huddling are commonly indulged in, as a means of conserving energy (Fairall & McNairn, 1981). When heaping in the shelter a number of individuals pack themselves tightly together, heads facing outwards, in two layers, often but not always with the young on top. Sometimes both these attitudes can be seen when they are resting outside the shelters. In captivity *P. capensis* may heap up to four deep, often as many as 20 to 25 in the heap (McNairn, pers. comm.).

When resting in the open many attitudes are adopted. Straight sitting with the head held in to the body is the commonest, but they will also lie on their sides or on their bellies with the legs stretched out to cool off by losing heat to the rock (Davies, pers. comm.).

Heaping and huddling in the dark shelters are related to the dorsal spot and gland which underlies it, for in both postures the nose of one animal is brought into relatively close contact with the spot of the neighbour. Sale (1970b) suggested that its function is one of close range identification under these conditions. In a closely related species, *P. johnstoni*, Sale (1970b) showed that the piloerection of the hair of the dorsal spot has a function in submission and aggression. Fourie (1974) found the same applied in the case of *P. capensis*.

Aggression is demonstrated by piloerection of the hair of the dorsal spot, baring of the teeth, angry growling and teeth grinding. Serious fights are seldom witnessed as usually the threat is sufficient to send the submissive individual in search of another sunning site or to the shelter of the hole. Head-on encounters generally are avoided for they may lead to aggression. Sale (1970b) suggested that the fan pattern adopted in huddling is a mechanism to avoid head to head encounters. Submission is demonstrated by the individual presenting his rump or side to the aggressor, without piloerection of the hair on the dorsal spot.

Fourie (1977) traced no less than 21 (plus four non-vocal) acoustic communications in the repertoire of the rock dassie, including grunts, growls, wails, squeals, twitters and snorts. The best known is the sharp bark made by the dominant male or female in a colony on the recognition of danger, which is followed usually by their taking cover. Squeals alert them without eliciting flight. The repetitive bark often heard in the field is a territorial advertisement and spacing mechanism of the breeding males (Davies, pers. comm.). Whistles, chirrups and twitters are associated with contact and teeth gnashing with threat or when they are barred from reaching food.

Self-grooming with the lower incisor teeth or scratching with the claw-like nails of the hind feet is regularly engaged in. Dust-rolling during the cooler parts of the day probably assists in keeping them free of ecto-parasites. It seems to be most prevalent after a long session of basking, and between sessions of basking, and does not seem to be correlated with ambient temperature. Dusting appears to dissuade the attention of flies which do bother them (McNairn, pers. comm.).

Under stress of overpopulation or at times of local food shortage the rock dassie is capable of traversing considerable distances between areas of suitable rocky habitat. In Botswana they were observed occupying isolated koppies up to 20 km from the nearest range of krantzes.

Rock dassies fluctuate greatly in numbers. During the

early 1980's, simultaneous declines were reported from many areas in southern Africa, viz. Matobo Hills, Magaliesberg, Drakensberg, Karoo. While drought plays an important role (Hoeck, 1982, 1989), disease cannot be ruled out as a factor influencing animals in such crowded conditions. Predator eradication may have led to simplification of these fluctuations and destabilised the relationship between dassies and the vegetation resource (Kolbe, 1983; Davies, pers. comm.).

The long upper incisor teeth of the males, which are triangular in section, overlay the lower lip and are visible when they are at rest. These teeth are exceedingly sharp and are effective organs of defence and aggression.

Rock dassies in parts of their range are independent of water, obtaining their moisture requirements from their food, but when water is available, they will drink regularly. In the Karoo they scamper about the rocks drinking from puddles after showers and fighting over possession of a puddle (Davies, pers. comm.).

Louw, Louw & Retief (1972) found that the renal efficiency of the species is high and that, although they require free water when on a dry diet, or access to some succulent food or dew, their efficient kidney function allows them to exist on minimal moisture intake. Rock dassies are efficient thermoregulators allowing body temperature to decline as an energy conserving mechanism (Sale, 1970b). They have a labile body temperature which they regulate, but cannot withstand high ambient temperatures indefinitely. They utilise behavioural means, such as extending the body to alleviate heat stress, finally retreating into the cooler crevices should the need arise.

Rock dassies urinate and defecate in latrines, which, occasionally, through continued use, may assume very large proportions. In the Cedarberg Mountains in the western Cape Province a deposit measured some 3 m and was nearly 1 m deep. Because of the slope of the floor of the sandstone cavern the faecal pellets tended to run off the top surface, leaving a crystallised mass of urine, which was clear amber in colour. It was claimed that crystallised dassie urine has medicinal properties and was marketed at one time under the name "hyracium".

The diet of black eagles, *Aquila verreauxi*, in the Karoo consists of 74,3% rock dassies, the remainder being mainly red rock rabbits, *Pronolagus* (Davies, 1989).

## Food

Rock dassies are mixed feeders, selecting phenological stages of all their food plants to obtain the required diet and utilising plant parts most advantageous to them during a particular season. They will eat a variety of grasses, forbs and shrubs, including some that are highly aromatic and others known to be poisonous to other species (Sale, 1965b). In Botswana, Smithers (1971) included species of bushwillows, *Combretum* spp; wild figs, *Ficus* spp; jacket plums, *Pappea* sp; and shepherd's tree, *Boscia* spp, all associated with their rocky habitat. The *Boscia* and *Ficus* are most favoured. Where grass is available they will graze freely. In some areas, especially where their predators have been reduced in numbers and they occur in very large numbers, they become subject to control as they compete with domestic stock for grazing, exceeding the recommended stocking rate by a factor of 15 (Fairall, pers. comm.). In adverse seasons or where populations are abnormally high they may take to eating the bark of trees. In parts of Natal Drakensberg they noticeably reduce the regeneration of trees (Feely, pers. comm.).

Rock dassies are very fast feeders. Sale (1966b) found that with *P. johnstoni* in East Africa the total time occupied by feeding was less than an hour a day. The food is chopped off with the long row of cheekteeth; the incisor teeth are used, predominantly in the spring, to strip the bark off trees. In captivity solid foods such as carrots may be held with the forefeet so that the side of the mouth may be brought into play. Occasionally both the incisor teeth and the fore-feet may be used to bring a twig or bunch of grass stems into proximity of the mouth. Through wear the cheekteeth are left with a sharp outer edge, which assists in cropping the food.

Large shrubs are favoured over Karoo bushes and grass in the Karoo (Fourie, 1983; Davies, pers. comm.). Dassies use their forelimbs to reach out and pull down sprigs/branches. Heavy grazing around colonies has a profound effect upon the local vegetation community, sculpting favoured *Grewia* bushes into strange shapes, clearing grasses and leading to a preponderance of unpalatable plants eg. *Hermannia burkei*.

## Reproduction

Millar (1972) found that mating is triggered by photoperiod and not by annual changes in rainfall or temperature. He showed that in the southwestern Cape Province rock dassies of both sexes have a short period of sexual activity. In males, testes mass, spermatogenic activity and testosterone content of the testes increased in February, peaking in March, declining thereafter, testes being quiescent by May. This period varies in different areas and is progressively later at lower latitudes (Table 290.2). Following a long gestation period of 230 days (Millar, 1971), the time of parturition in the Cape Province occurs in September/October, in the Karoo in November, but is progressively later at lower latitudes (Table 290.2). For example, in the Orange Free State the peak period of parturition is a month later and in Zimbabwe about March/April (Smithers, 1983). Millar (1972) could find no clear-cut environmental factors, which consistently occur with decreasing latitude, which appeared to constitute favourable conditions for the birth and early development of the young. In parts of Namibia the rock dassie thrives even where the rainfall is negligible and temperatures can exceed 40 °C. Nevertheless in the southwestern Cape Province the peak of births takes place at a time when the *fynbos* association is in prime condition at the end of the winter rains, in the Karoo at the start of the rainy season, and in the Orange Free State, a summer rainfall area, births peak after the summer rains have commenced (van der Merwe & Skinner, 1982).

Litter size in all mammals is genetically determined and environmentally influenced, and in dassies it can vary from one to six, and may be modified by local conditions, age and nutritional state of the dam. Adverse nutritional conditions influence the size of litters by decreasing the rate of ovulation (Millar, 1972). Age specific fecundity has been reported by Fairall, Vermeulen & van der Merwe (1986)—Table 290.3. In the Orange Free State of 49 adult females culled, 51% had twins, 33% triplets, 8% singles , 6% quadruplets and 2% quintuplets (van der Merwe & Skinner, 1982). There is apparently no reproductive senility in female dassies (Fairall, pers. comm.). They will conceive for the first time at 16 to 17 months of age (Fairall, pers. comm.), at which age a small proportion of the males may have active testes provided their body mass exceeds 2,3 kg (van der Merwe & Skinner, 1982).

The young are born in the rock shelters and are precocial, being born fully haired, with their eyes open. The males at birth have a mean mass of 231,2 g, the females significantly less at 165,0 g. The mass at birth depends to a large extent on the number in the litter. Millar (1972) found that in a litter of two their mass was 310,0 g and 260,0 g, in a litter of four 160,0 g, 150,0 g, 160,0 g and 185,0 g.

Within a day of birth rock dassies are capable of agile movement on the rocks and of eating solid food. The young, however, suckle from birth on any female, weaning at about one to five months of age. In the majority of females, however, lactation ceases after about three months.

Newborn young climb on to any adult's back within hours of birth. Sale (1965a) stated that this physical association with the adults and the scenting of the young has the advantage of their then being recognised as members of the colony. Female dassies show little interest in their young except to suckle them and parental care is very poor. The young soon become very playful and mix freely with the young of the yellow-spotted dassie, *Heterohyrax brucei*, which in some areas share the same rocky habitat, but they do not interbreed.

**Table 290.2**

Times of mating of rock dassies, *P. capensis*, in the Subregion (Millar, 1972; Smithers & Wilson, 1979; van der Merwe & Skinner, 1982)

| Area | Time of mating | Time of parturition |
|---|---|---|
| Southwestern Cape Province | February | September/October |
| Karoo | February/March | November |
| Eastern Cape Province | March/April | October/November |
| Orange Free State | March/April | November/ December |
| Transvaal | May/July | December/February |
| Zimbabwe | August/September | March/April |

**Table 290.3**

Mean age-specific fecundity of the Tsitsikama rock dassies, *P. capensis*, with standard deviations (S.D.) (Fairall, Vermeulen & van der Merwe, 1986)

| Age | Sample size n | Mean number of young per female ±S.D. |
|---|---|---|
| 1 year | 10 | 0,0±0,0 |
| 2 years | 8 | 2,0±0,0 |
| 3 years | 12 | 2,4±0,5 |
| 4 years | 6 | 3,2±0,7 |
| 4+ years | 2 | 4,0±0,0 |

**WITHDRAWN**

No. 291

*Procavia welwitschii* (Gray, 1868), given full specific rank in the first edition, is now considered to be a subspecies of *P. capensis* (Meester *et al.*, 1986).

## Genus *Heterohyrax* Gray, 1868

No. 292

## *Heterohyrax brucei* (Gray, 1868)

## Yellow-spotted rock dassie
## Geelkoldas

Plate 27

### Colloquial Name

This refers to the colour of the hair on the dorsal gland which in the rock dassie in the Subregion, *P. capensis*, is black, white or very pale yellow and in this species varies in colour from yellowish to ochre.

### Taxonomic Notes

Meester *et al.* (1986) listed two subspecies from the Subregion: *H. b. ruddi* (Wroughton, 1910) from western Mozambique, Zimbabwe and eastern Botswana and *H. b. granti* (Wroughton, 1910) from the Transvaal. *H. b. brucei* was described from a specimen from Ethiopia.

### Description

Yellow-spotted dassies have a total length of about 500 mm, and a mass of some 3,0 kg. In series they are slightly smaller than the rock dassie, *P. capensis*, and the muzzle is slightly narrower (Table 292.1).

Bothma (1966a) recorded the high degree of individual variation in the colour. There are two basic colour patterns more or less representative of two allopatric subspecies, recognisable mainly on the basis of the length of the upper toothrow, and a third colour group, members of which do not conform to either of these (Bothma, 1966a). The first group, representative of *H. b. granti* (Wroughton, 1910), occurs in areas of relatively higher mean annual rainfall, above 1 250 mm. The members of this group are dark brown with a reddish tinge and are flecked on the upper parts with off-white. The dorsal spot is creamy-buff or reddish-ochre, the belly pale yellow, dirty white or off-white. They are representative of the populations in parts of the eastern and northeastern Transvaal. Specimens from the Soutpansberg in the northern Transvaal show affinities with the second group typical of *H. b. ruddi* (Wroughton, 1910) which occur in lower rainfall areas of less than 1 250 mm and are paler on the upper parts. In the third group the colour of the upper parts is intermediate between that of the first and second group and, within the borders of the Republic, it is impossible to provide a description that fits the group as a whole. Further north, in parts of Zimbabwe, the colour of the upper parts is grey, drab grey or light grey, in parts with a brown tinge, the dorsal spot is yellowish, the under parts white or off-white. In the northern parts of their range populations tend to be even in colour, those from the Matobo Hills, Zimbabwe, being light grey and from localities further east showing varying degrees of a brown tinge.

Two of the best features in distinguishing the yellow-spotted dassie from the rock dassie in the field are the distinct white or off-white patches above the eyes and the lighter colour of the sides of the face in this species. Although the rock dassie has pale patches above the eyes, these are never white and generally are inconspicuous.

The upper parts of the body are grizzled, due to the light subapical bands of the hairs lying irregularly together, which give the appearance of light spots and bands. The hair of the guard coat is softer than in the rock dassie; the individual hairs are black-tipped and up to 30 mm long. The underfur is dense, the hairs narrowly dark grey at their bases and buffy towards the tips.

Just as in the rock dassie, there are long black tactile hairs scattered over the upper parts, up to 70 mm long, patches of these above the eyes and under the chin and whiskers up to 90 mm in length. These have a tactile function and assist the individual in orientating itself in the rock crevices.

**Table 292.1**

Measurements (mm) and mass (kg) of adult yellow-spotted dassies, *H. brucei*, from Zimbabwe (Smithers & Wilson, 1979)

| | Males | | | Females | | |
|---|---|---|---|---|---|---|
| | $\bar{x}$ | n | Range | $\bar{x}$ | n | Range |
| TL | 497 | 5 | 465–530 | 516 | 12 | 485–560 |
| Hf s/u | 68 | 5 | 65–70 | 69 | 12 | 65–73 |
| E | 32 | 5 | 30–33 | 32 | 12 | 29–34 |
| Mass | 3,01 | 5 | 2,72–3,18 | 3,01 | 12 | 2,32–3,63 |

### Skull

In both the rock dassie, *Procavia capensis*, and this species the upper incisor teeth in the males are triangular in section, the apex of the triangle lying on the forward face of the teeth. In the females the front faces of the teeth are rounded, not showing the clearly triangular shape as in the males. In this species the two upper incisor teeth are set wider apart than in the rock dassie, where they are separated by about the breadth of a single tooth. In younger specimens the lower incisors are seen to be trilobed on their cutting edges, these teeth lying sloping forwards, the two outer occluding on the rear faces of the upper incisors and so continually honing them to sharply pointed tips and lateral edges.

**Plate 27**

288. Aardvark, *Orycteropus afer*
Erdvark
290. Rock dassie, *Procavia capensis*
Klipdas
292. Yellow-spotted rock dassie, *Heterohyrax brucei*
Geelkoldas
293. Tree dassie, *Dendrohyrax arboreus*
Boomdas

PLATE 27

In this species the upper cheekteeth are of a more even size, there being less discrepancy between the sizes of the premolar and molar teeth than in the rock dassie, *P. capensis*, where the three molar teeth are far larger than the premolars, the second upper molar being the largest tooth in the row (Fig. 290.2). The dental formula is:

$I\frac{1}{2}\ C\frac{0}{0}\ P\frac{4}{4}\ M\frac{3}{3} = 34$

In this species the first lower premolar tooth is present, in the rock dassie it is absent.

The upper incisor teeth are relatively narrower than in the rock dassie, *P. capensis*, and about equal to those of the *P. c. welwitschii*, but wider than those of the tree dassie, *D. arboreus*. The length of the upper premolar toothrow, $P^{1-4}$ (mean = 15,95 mm) is less than that of the upper $M^{1-3}$ (mean = 16,42 mm) (Bothma, 1967).

**Distribution**

The yellow-spotted dassie has a wide distribution on the continent, and extends from the Transvaal northwards to Ethiopia and west to parts of Angola. Within the limits shown they are found only where there is suitable rocky habitat.

*South of the Sahara, excluding the Southern African Subregion*

They are recorded from the southern and southeastern **Sudan; Ethiopia; Somalia; Uganda; Kenya; Tanzania; Malawi; Mozambique,** north of the Zambezi River; in the extreme southeastern parts of **Zaire**, in central and eastern **Zambia** and in central **Angola**.

*Southern African Subregion*

They occur throughout **Zimbabwe**, except in the western and southeastern sectors; in **Mozambique**, south of the Zambezi River, in the western parts of the Vila Pery District and as far east as Gorongosa Mountain in the Beira District; in the eastern sector of **Botswana** and in the northern parts of the **Transvaal**, this marking their southernmost limits on the continent.

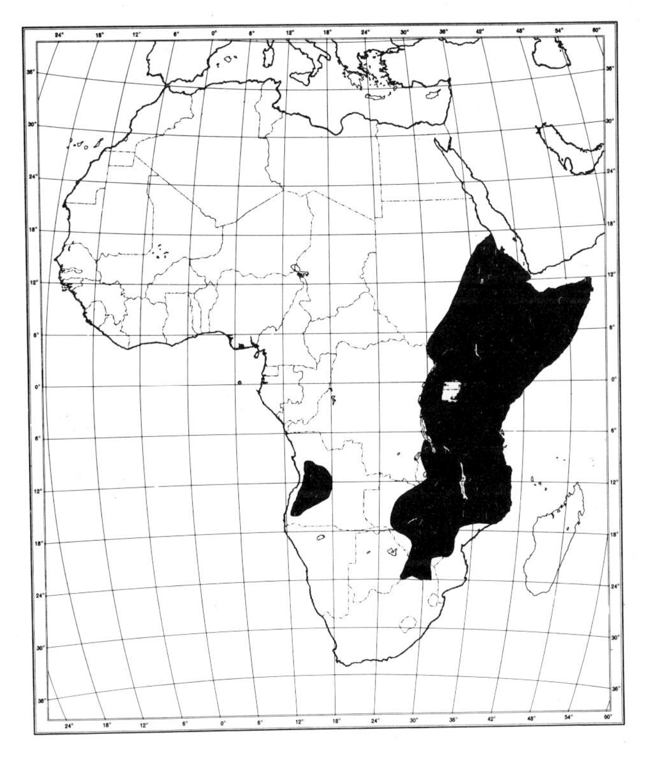

**Habitat**

The yellow-spotted rock dassie occupies similar habitat to the rock dassie and in many parts of their distributional range the two species live on the same rocks, use identical crevices and often are seen basking in the sun alongside each other. The yellow-spotted dassie is found less often occupying isolated rocky koppies, further from areas where the two species occur together, than the rock dassie, *P. capensis*. As they sit on the rocks together this species usually can be distinguished by its lighter coloured spots above the eyes and the lighter colour of the sides of its face.

**Habits**

There do not appear to be any obvious differences in the habits of the yellow-spotted as opposed to the rock dassie and observations given under the latter apply equally to the former.

It has been stated that dassies "chew the cud" and certainly, while at rest, the jaw movements suggest this. Authorities, however, refute this as they are not ruminants and therefore incapable of this action and the chewing action of the jaw is probably displacement behaviour.

**Food**

The yellow-spotted dassie is predominantly a browser but, more particularly during the warm, wet summer months, their diet includes grass as well. In East Africa, Hoeck (1975) showed that, where the rock dassie, *Procavia johnstoni*, and the yellow-spotted dassie occupy the same habitat, the rock dassie is predominantly a grazer, the yellow-spotted predominantly a browser, both species increasing their intake of grass during the wet season.

Hoeck (1975) noted that, although in East Africa yellow-spotted dassies will feed on up to 64 species of plants, their staple diet is provided by about two to 11 species depending on the situation of their habitat.

In Botswana where this species and the rock dassie, *P. capensis*, occur together, both will feed at the same time on the leaves, shoots and fruits of the wild fig, *Ficus pretoriae*, the bushwillow, *Combretum* spp, and the fever-berry tree, *Croton* spp (Smithers, 1971). In the area where these observations were made grass was not available.

In western Zimbabwe, Wilson (1975) recorded their feeding on the fallen fruits of the jackal berry, *Diospyros mespiliformis*; the raisin bush, *Grewia flavescens*; the leaves and fruits of the buffalo thorn, *Ziziphus mucronata*; the leaves of the bushwillow, *Combretum* spp; fever-berry, *Croton* spp; the Transvaal gardenia, *Gardenia volkensii*, and the fresh leaves and twigs of the apple-leaf, *Lonchocarpus capassa*. Only one grass species has been recorded as being eaten, *Brachiaria deflexa*. In times of drought they have been observed to eat the bark of trees. Like the rock dassie they are independent of water, obtaining their moisture requirements from their food.

**Reproduction**

In the northern parts of the Subregion gravid females have been taken widely throughout the year and it may be that, when more detailed information becomes available, they will be shown to have their young at any time throughout the year.

The average number in litters is two and, from the evidence of near full-term foetuses, mass at birth ranges from about 220 to 230 g. The young are born fully furred and just as precocious as the newly born of the rock dassie. Females have a pair of pectoral and two pairs of inguinal mammae (Bothma, 1967).

---

No. 293

## *Dendrohyrax arboreus* (A. Smith, 1827)

## Tree dassie

## Boomdas

Plate 27

---

**Colloquial Name**

In the Subregion the close association of this species with trees gives them their name. In other parts of Africa (Kenya; Rudnai, pers. comm.) they live in a rocky habitat like our rock dassie, *Procavia capensis*, and the yellow-spotted rock dassie, *Heterohyrax brucei*.

### Taxonomic Notes

Three species of *Dendrohyrax* have been described from the continent: the West African, *D. dorsalis* (Fraser, 1855); the East African, *D. validus* True, 1890, and the southern, *D. arboreus*, which is the only species occurring in the Subregion. Of the eight subspecies of *D. arboreus*, only one, *D. a. arboreus*, occurs in the Subregion.

### Description

Tree dassies are about the same size as rock dassies (Table 293.1), but differ from all the other species in having longer fur which gives them a woolly appearance. The fur may reach a length of 45 mm on the shoulders, as opposed to a bare 25 mm in the rock dassie.

Just as with the other dassies there is considerable variation in the colour of the upper parts of the body, which is a grizzled greyish-white with a brownish tinge. Those from the areas of mean annual rainfall of 1 000–1 500 mm are the darkest, those from areas of 750–1 000 mm, paler (Bothma, 1967). The head is usually slightly darker in colour than the remainder of the body. The under parts are creamy-white to pure white.

The individual hairs of the guard coat have a broad buffy band below the black tip, giving the coat the grizzled appearance. Underlying the guard coat there is a dense underfur, the hairs fine and wavy and dark brown or grey-brown in colour.

The hairs on the dorsal gland are white or off-white and 45 to 50 mm long; the ears are fringed with short hair of the same colour. The light patches above the eyes are indistinct and barely distinguishable in life. The long tactile hairs scattered over the body, which are a feature of the rock dassie, are not in evidence in the tree dassie, but they have black whiskers up to 80 mm in length, a patch of long hair on the eyebrows up to 60 mm long, and a patch under the chin up to 40 mm long.

The limbs are short and sturdy. The forefeet have four digits, each with a flat nail; the hind feet have only three, the inner digit armed with a curved claw used in self-grooming. The soles of the feet are padded as in the rock dassie.

### Table 293.1

Measurements (mm) of tree dassies, *D. arboreus*, from the Subregion (Bothma, 1967)

| | Irrespective of sex | | |
|---|---|---|---|
| | $\bar{x}$ | n | Range |
| HB | 475 | 9 | 428–520 |
| Hf s/u | 63 | 10 | 59–67 |
| E | 32 | 8 | 29–36 |

### Skull

The braincase of the tree dassie is distinctly raised above the plane of the front part of the skull, and the frontals are hollowed out. Characteristic features which distinguish the skulls from those of the other dassies are the broad beadings above the orbits and between these and the interparietals. In adults the postorbital bars are complete; the muzzle is narrower and longer in the rock dassie.

The dental formula is:

$I\frac{1}{2}\ C\frac{0}{0}\ P\frac{4}{4}\ M\frac{3}{3} = 34$

The diastema between the incisors and the first premolars is much wider than in the rock dassie and more comparable to that in the yellow-spotted dassie; the rows of cheekteeth are wider apart in front than in either of the other two species. The upper incisors are separated widely and are never as heavily built as in the rock dassie, the teeth tending to diverge towards the tips. The cheekteeth increase evenly in size from front to back and in this respect they more closely resemble those of the yellow-spotted dassie, *H. brucei*. In the males the upper incisors are triangular in section with distinct ridges on the front; in the females the teeth are more rounded in front and lighter in build. The outer incisors in the lower jaw occlude on the backs of the upper incisors, continually honing them to sharp points and edges. The lower incisors are deeply tricuspid.

The length of the upper premolar toothrow $P^{1-4}$ (mean = 16,20 mm) is longer than that of the molar toothrow $M^{1-3}$ (mean = 16,10 mm) (Bothma, 1967).

### Distribution

The tree dassie, *D. arboreus*, is replaced in eastern Tanzania and its offshore islands by *D. validus* and in the forests of the Congo Basin and the coastal forests of West Africa by *D. dorsalis*, both very closely allied species.

Being associated with well developed woodland or forest, their continued existence locally is dependent on this type of habitat. In parts of their distributional range (e.g. parts of Mozambique) they may well have had a wider distribution in the past, but the clearing of vast areas of forest for agricultural purposes has rendered the habitat unsuitable and they no longer occur there. They have never been recorded in Angola, Zimbabwe or the Transvaal and their present distribution east of Lake Malawi is uncertain as the area has not been adequately explored zoologically.

*South of the Sahara, excluding the Southern African Subregion*

They occur in **Uganda;** in central and southwestern **Kenya;** western **Tanzania;** eastern and southeastern **Zaire**, and throughout **Zambia**, excluding the western areas. They occur widely in **Malawi** and they may well occur at least in parts of northwestern **Mozambique**, although at the moment there are no records.

*Southern African Subregion*

In **Mozambique**, south of the Zambezi River, they are confined to the central parts of the country from about 19°45'S to the Save River, not reaching the Zimbabwe border in the west. Southwards they are recorded from the southern parts of **Natal** and from the eastern parts of the **Cape Province** as far west coastally as about 27°E.

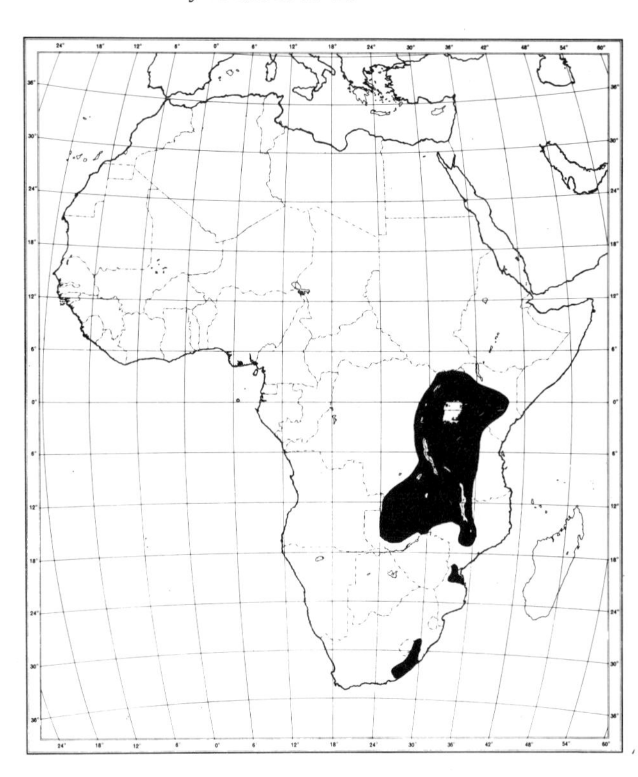

### Habitat

In the southern part of their distributional range tree dassies occur in the better developed forests of the eastern Cape Province and Natal. Further north in central Mozambique they occur in lowland evergreen forests, such as the Amatonga and Dondo, as well as in the evergreen riverine forests of the Save River. They use holes in trees, dense matted masses of creepers or the thick foliage of trees in which to rest during daylight hours, and the association in which they occur must provide these requirements and not be too open.

### Habits

Unlike the rock and yellow-spotted dassies, the tree dassie in the Subregion is predominantly a solitary species, only one adult or an adult female and her young occupying a single shelter, arboreal and almost entirely nocturnal. An East African subspecies, the Ruwenzori tree dassie, *D. a. ruwenzorii*, is diurnal and generally solitary, but in the alpine zone at higher altitudes lives among rocks like the other species (Kingdon, 1971; Rudnai, 1984b). Being nocturnal, and as their eyes are poor reflectors of spotlights at night, tree dassies are difficult to observe. However, they are very noisy and in the early part of the night and again in the hours before sunrise one can get a fair estimate of how many are around, for as soon as one vocalises, the others follow suit. This vocalisation is indulged in by both sexes and is an unearthly noise, starting off with a series of cackling barks followed by piercing tremulous screams which rise to a high crescendo. When a few are vocalising at the same time the forest resounds with what sounds like an orgy of mass murder. Other vocalisations include growling, barking and grinding their teeth.

Tree dassies have latrines, just like other dassies. These are situated normally in the low fork of a tree or on the ground beside a tree trunk. They are rather more sluggish in their actions than rock dassies, although agile in the trees, sometimes leaping from one branch to another or climbing out on to the thinner branches. During the day they lie up in hollow trees or among thick masses of creepers or other foliage. Shortridge (1934) stated that tree dassies tame easily and are far better-tempered than rock dassies.

### Food

The food requirements of the southern tree dassie have not been studied and we can only assume that, like some of the other subspecies of *D. arboreus*, the food will consist of browse in the form of leaves, fruit and young shoots of trees and perhaps grass, for they will descend from the trees to the ground to feed. In East Africa the species is recorded as eating insects (Rudnai, pers. comm.).

### Reproduction

Shortridge (1934) suggested that there is no particular breeding season. One to three constitute a litter. Apart from these brief remarks there is no information on record concerning reproduction in this species. Kingdon (1971) reported that *D. a. ruwenzorii* breeds all the year round, with a gestation period of some 7–8 months. Rudnai (1984a) gave a mean litter size of two for *D. a. stuhlmanni* in Kenya.

Rudnai (1984a) found that the young prefer inguinal teats, probably due to their higher milk yield, and suckling was first observed when the young were four hours old. There is no forceful displacement between siblings. Suckling is initiated more often by the young than by the mother. Average suckling time is 168 sec (n=394) and most suckling occurred shortly after sunrise and before sunset.

Females have a varying number of mammae, usually one pair inguinal but sometimes with the addition of a pair of pectoral mammae or one pair pectoral and two pairs inguinal (Rudnai, 1984a).

# Order SIRENIA

## The Dugong

Sirenia are remarkably adapted to a coastal, estuarine or riverine life. The Order includes three Families, two with living representatives. The Dugongidae are represented by one species, the dugong, *Dugong dugon*; the Trichechidae by three species, the Amazon manatee, *Trichechus inungius*, the American manatee, *T. manatus*, and the African manatee, *T. senegalensis*; and the Hydromalidae by a single species, Steller's sea cow, *Hydromalis stelleri*, the largest member of the Order, reaching a length of 10 m, which is believed to be extinct as there were at most only about 2 000 in the Bering Sea in 1741, when first discovered by Dr Wilhelm Steller, a ship's doctor. Fearless of man, they soon fell prey to sealers and whalers. In 1963 the crew of a Russian whaling ship reported a group of marine creatures which were not whales or seals and which in size and other features matched the description of the Steller's sea cow (Nishiwaki, 1972). Therefore there remains the faint possibility that they are not extinct.

The dugong is the only member of the Order found in the Subregion where it has a relatively marginal occurrence on the east coast.

Two manatees occur in the New World, the American manatee in the region of the Caribbean and the Amazon manatee in the Amazon and Orinoco rivers in South America and one in Africa, the African manatee, which occurs from Senegal to Angola. The Amazon manatee lives entirely in fresh water, the other two are at home in either fresh or salt water.

In the case of the Amazon manatee, Coffey (1977) reported that between 1938 and 1942 thousands of carcasses were exported from Brazil. Throughout their wide distributional range, dugong numbers have been reduced drastically and, in parts, they have become locally extinct. Although vigorously protected by legislation in many parts of their range, the enforcement of this under marine conditions is difficult; furthermore they fortuitously fall prey to net fishing, drowning if held under water. The creation of coastal National Parks, as have been gazetted in parts of their range including Mozambique, can do much to ensure their future existence, but outside these their continued existence seems uncertain. Absolute population sizes are not known for dugongs, but it appears that they are most abundant in Australian waters where they are protected.

The Order has an extensive fossil record, showing that they once had a wider distribution than they have today. Dugong fossils have been found widely in Europe, the West Indies and in lands bordering the Pacific Ocean. Simpson (1945) placed them in a superorder of herbivorous subungulates, the Paenungulata, which includes the elephants and the dassies.

The name of the Order, Sirenia, is derived from the mythical sirens of Greek folklore who by their sweet singing enticed ships to the close proximity of the rocks on which they lived, the crews perishing in the ensuing shipwrecks. Odysseus on his homeward voyage plugged his crew's ears with wax and lashed himself to the mast to protect his ship from a similar fate. The many tales of mermaids undoubtedly stem from sightings of manatees and dugongs whose pectoral mammae so closely resemble these of the human species.

# XL. Family DUGONGIDAE

## Dugong

### Genus *Dugong* Lacépède, 1799

No. 294

### *Dugong dugon* (P.L.S. Müller, 1776)

Dugong
Dugong

**Colloquial Name**

This is derived from the Malay name for the species, *duyong*.

**Taxonomic Notes**

No subspecies are recognised.

**Description**

Adult dugongs have a total length of about 3 m, with masses of up to 400 kg and, although larger specimens have been reported, Marsh, Spain & Heinsohn (1978) believed that the maximum lengths for males is about 3,15 m, for females

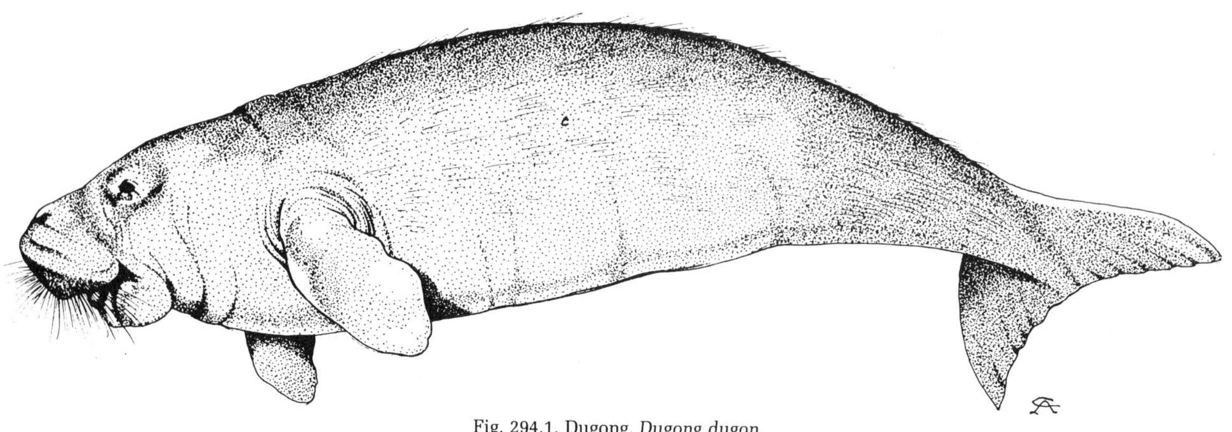

Fig. 294.1. Dugong, *Dugong dugon*.
Males recorded up to 3,2 m, females 3,1 m.

3,05 m. An adult female from Santa Carolina, southern Mozambique, had a mass of 405 kg.

The adults are slate-grey in colour, slightly darker on the head, neck, outer surface of the flippers and upper parts of the tail flukes. The under parts are slightly lighter in colour.

The body is streamlined from its widest point about the shoulders to the tail, the thick rough skin with scattered hair follicles showing, but nearly naked except for a few scattered hairs. However, the lips and around the mouth are profusely covered with stout, bristly hairs. The upper lip is so very thick and heavy that Hill (1945) remarked that it appeared to him as a truncated proboscis rather than just a modified upper lip. The eyes are tiny and have no eyelids and, because of the thickness of the skin on the skull, they lie external to the eye sockets. They are protected by nictitating membranes lubricated by oil glands.

The crescent-shaped nostrils are situated on top of the massive snout in such a position that they are not seen when the individual is viewed from the front. Dugongs cannot close their nostrils completely, like whales, but they have nasal ducts which extend for about 100 mm just below the skin behind the nostrils; these ducts are surrounded by muscles which, when contracted, serve to close the ducts. The ears are simple small openings in the skin at the sides of the head.

They have a pair of flippers, each with a bony structure of five digits enclosed within the muscle and skin. The boneless tail flukes are broad, the hind margin between the two points slightly crescent-shaped, without any sign of a notch centrally. They have no hind flippers, the pelvic girdle represented by two small rods of bone free of the vertebral column. They have a clearly defined navel near the centre of the abdomen and the females have a pair of mammae situated one on either side, just behind the foreflippers.

The skull is heavily built; the premaxillary bones, which are particularly thick and solid, project downwards in front to about the level of the lower part of the front of the lower jaw. The first pair of upper incisor teeth are shed early in life, the second pair, situated on the ends of the premaxillary bones, developing into tusks in both sexes. In the females they barely project beyond the bone, in old males they reach their maximum development as a pair of tusks up to 300 mm long, which have sharp outer margins.

It is difficult to distinguish between premolar and molar teeth since there is no replacement of milk teeth. During life there is a total of six pairs of cheekteeth in both jaws. The anterior teeth, like those of the elephant, progressively fall out, their roots being resorbed and their sockets closing. Further teeth are added posteriorly during growth, the process continuing until only two pairs of teeth remain in each jaw in old individuals. These appear to have persistent pulps and may continue to grow throughout life (Marsh *et al.*, 1978).

**Distribution**

Although dugongs have a very wide distribution in the warmer seas of the world, their distribution is patchy and discontinuous owing to their habitat requirements. In many parts of their range their numbers have become reduced drastically through over-exploitation and in others they have become locally extinct.

*Extralimital to the continent*

They occur around islands in the Indian Ocean such as the **Comoros** and **Madagascar**; along the southwest coast of **Asia**, the Gulf of Mannar, between **India** and **Sri Lanka**; to the Arafura Sea and Coral Sea north and northeast of **Australia**; to tropical islands in the Pacific Ocean such as the **Philippines**, and northwards to **Taiwan** and islands south of **Japan** such as Okinawa and Amami-Oshima. They are now believed to be extinct in the water around Borneo, the Phillipines, Marshall Islands and most of the islands in the Indian Ocean (Yalden *et al.*, 1986).

*North Africa*

They at one time occurred commonly in the Red Sea, being in parts plentiful (Glover Allen, 1942). By 1932 they were accounted as rare and as seldom occurring north of 25°, but as still being present in small numbers southwards; however, they are heading for extinction (Yalden *et al.*, 1986).

*The east coast of Africa, outside the Southern African Subregion*

They appear sporadically in the Gulf of Aden on the northern coast of **Somalia** and some survive in the waters adjacent to Brava and Kisimayo in the south. They occur along the coast of **Kenya** and **Tanzania** and in the waters around the offshore islands of Pemba, Zanzibar and Mafia. They are still quite common along the northern coast of **Mozambique**, south to about Moma on the coast of Zambezia Province, but are only sporadic in occurrence between this and Quelimane and absent from Quelimane south to the Save River.

*Southern African Subregion*

They occur in the coastal waters of **Mozambique**, south of the Zambezi River, from just south of the mouth of the Save River to Maputo Bay and have been recorded as vagrants as far south as Umhlali, some 50 km north of Durban, on the coast of **Natal**.

**Habitat**

Dugongs are a coastal marine species that tend to avoid fresh water at the mouths of large rivers as this inhibits the growth of the sea grasses on which they feed. They seldom stray into areas of deep sea water. Grzimek (1972) gave the range as water from 1 m to 12 m deep, with a temperature range of 20° to 30°C. Their preferred habitat is in coastal lagoons, where coral outcrops, lying off-shore, provide sheltered conditions from the disturbed water of the open sea and the sandy bottom allows for the growth of the food plants on which they live. Kingdon (1971) reported that during the months of November to March when the winds are gentle and the surface waters warm and not rough, they move outside the reefs into deeper water to feed. Later during April to October when the seas are rough, they seek the more sheltered bays nearer the coast. In shallow water they tend to move in with the tide and into deeper water on the ebb. Hughes & Oxley-Oxland (1971) reported similar movements at Antonio Enes on the coast of the Zambezia Province, in northern Mozambique, where, from March to April, they frequent the shallower seas around the offshore islands, moving into the estuary in November to January.

**Habits**

Dugongs are gregarious, on the Mozambique coast congregations of up to 30 are known, although the more usual number is about six. In other parts of their range, in former times, much larger congregations were known. It is reported that in Moreton Bay, Brisbane, Australia, many hundreds were seen together extending over an area three miles long and some 270 m wide. In the Larnu area of coastal Kenya, Kingdon (1971) recorded congregations of over a hundred and Marsh *et al.* (1972) over 500 on the southern Somali coast. Most sightings today off the coast of the Subregion are of solitary individuals, pairs, or a pair with a juvenile. The family bond appears to be strong, for Kingdon (1971) quoted eyewitness accounts of large males attempting to interfere when females or juveniles were caught in nets.

They swim slowly just under the surface of the water at a speed given by Grzimek (1972) as 8–10 km/h (4,3–5,4 knots) and Nishiwaki (1972) as 2,0 knots, with an escaping speed of 5,0 knots. In the clear waters off the Mozambique coast they can be seen from the air against the light coloured sands as they move from feeding ground to feeding ground. Swimming is carried out by up and down movements of the tail with its flukes. The front flippers are used as stabilisers and to assist in maintaining their position while feeding, and take no part in the forward motion.

They rest lying on the bottom, rising periodically to breathe every few minutes. Marsh *et al.* (1978) showed that in shallow water, when followed in a dinghy, they could swim submerged between breaths for about three minutes, then had to surface frequently. Anderson & Birtles (1978) recorded the times of 370 dives in Australian water, the mean dive being 73,3 seconds, the maximum time under water 400 seconds. Dugongs are normally quiet and, even when rising to breathe, do so silently and with little disturbance. Jones (1967) who observed them in captivity over a long period stated that they make no sounds, but Kingdon (1971) recorded squeaky calls which probably have a function in underwater communication. Marsh *et al.* (1978) noted that the Australian aborigines reported "whistlers" in the herds that they regard as the dominant individuals. They also recorded observations by others of chirping sounds and the vocalisations of a young captive female which produced at least three different sounds. Out of the water their eyes "water" copiously which is probably the secretion from the glands which lubricate the eyes and nictitating membrane. In the Far East these "tears" are supposed to have powerful aphrodisiac qualities. Dugongs have sensitive hearing and make off if approached by boats with engines. However, they will move close to boats anchored when fishing, but make off if the occupants walk around or knock on the sides.

**Food**

Dugongs are vegetarians, living predominantly on sea grasses of the Families Potamogetonaceae and Hydrocharitaceae, which grow in meadows on the sandy bottom of relatively shallow waters of lagoons, sheltered from the open seas by coral reefs or on the fringes of these on the sides facing the open sea or around islands.

Off the coast of Mozambique, Hughes & Oxley-Oxland (1971) recorded that the dense beds of the sea grasses *Holidule uninervis* and *Cymodocea ciliata* are their preferred feeding grounds. In the Red Sea similar types of sea grasses are their principal food, Gohar (1957) recording that they feed almost entirely on *Diplanthera* (=*Holidule*) *uninervis*. Jones (1967) recorded their dependence on sea grasses, for in Polk Bay, between India and Sri Lanka, torrential rains with heavy flooding into the bay killed the sea grasses and many dugongs died as a result. Apparently this food is sensitive to a drop in the salinity of the water and the absence of dugongs on the Mozambique coast, except in transit, near the mouth of major rivers such as the Zambezi or Save is probably due to the fact that the sea grasses are absent. On the East African coast, Kingdon (1971) listed the sea grasses *Syringodium* sp, *Cymodocea ciliata*, *Halophila* sp, *Zostera* sp and *Holidule uninervis* as being utilised by dugongs. He noted that these grasses are sensitive to seasonal conditions, mostly disappearing at certain times of the year, causing local food movements in search of fresh pastures.

Where they are subject to disturbance, dugongs feed predominantly at night. Off the Mozambique coast they may be seen feeding during daylight hours on the sea grass meadows. As they feed the bottom gets stirred up, leaving a murky trail in the water which, when seen at low tide, looks like a pathway through the meadow. The grasses are raked up with the aid of the heavy coarse bristles around the mouth. Grzimek (1972) recorded that the flippers are used to stuff the food into their mouths and that they have been observed to stack the grasses in heaps, allowing it to stand for a time before eating so as to get rid of sand and other marine creatures. The food is shaken under water to get rid of sand before being masticated by the teeth and horny gums. When feeding they rise to the surface every few minutes for air.

Best (1981) recorded that when feeding they cut a swathe 3–8 m long and 200–260 mm wide through the sea grasses, these representing feeding bouts between respirations. In other parts of their range, outside the Subregion, he listed 19 species of sea grasses that are eaten, their daily intake of food being 10%-15% of their body mass.

**Reproduction**

Knowledge of the breeding behaviour of dugongs is meagre. In courtship behaviour in captivity, Jones (1967) recorded that the male nudged and nuzzled the female's neck, then turned belly upwards for a few minutes, the female doing likewise, and both rolled together side to side. However, the conditions of observation were by no means ideal as the water was shallow, not allowing them to orientate themselves vertically. Grzimek (1972) stated that, when copulating, the pair rises out of the water vertically, belly to belly. Most adult dugongs are scarred rather heavily, especially on the neck and shoulders, which may have been inflicted during mating. In the wild, courtship, mating and the birth of the young are presumed to take place in sheltered lagoons, Hughes & Oxley-Oxland (1971) recording that they move to this shelter on the Mozambique coast during the rainy season of November to Jauary where the young are born. A single young is produced at a birth, rarely twins.

A lactating female was collected off Paradise Island, Santa Carolina, southern Mozambique, in July. She was not accompanied by a calf, so there is no indication of when she may have given birth (Smithers, unpubl.).

Newly born dugongs are sparsely haired, losing this as they grow up. Juveniles have dark brown upper parts and are pale brown on the belly. Behaviour at birth is not fully confirmed, but it is said that the young at birth may be assisted to the surface by the mother and transported on her back for a time, as in the case of the manatee, *Trichechus* sp. She is reported to suckle the young while lying on the surface of the water on her back, holding it with one of her flippers. In the early stages of life the young is said to make use of its flippers for propulsion, the tail remaining curved underneath as in the foetal position (Kingdon, 1971).

# Order PERISSODACTYLA

## XLI. Family RHINOCEROTIDAE

## Rhinoceros

Four genera of fossil rhinoceros are known from the early Miocene Epoch of some 23 million to 19 million years ago, whose ancestors, at present unknown, must have lived during the Oligocene Epoch which preceded it. These four genera are *Brachypotherium*, *Aceratherium*, *Dicerorhinus* and *Chilotherium*.

The two rhinoceros, the white rhinoceros, *Ceratotherium simum*, and the black rhinoceros, *Diceros bicornis*, arose from a common ancestor and fossil remains recorded from Plio-Pleistocene beds of some four million to three million years old show that they occurred throughout Africa during this period. A fossil species, *Ceratotherium praecox* Hooijer & Patterson, 1972, whose remains have been recovered from fossil beds at Langebaanweg, was among the commoner of the large mammals in the assemblage, dating back some seven million years ago.

Both species of rhinoceros formerly occurred widely in the southern parts of Africa. The white rhinoceros, however, never occurred very far south of the Orange River and generally was absent from the Orange Free State and parts of the southern Transvaal, although in the east it occurred throughout most of Natal, except in the extreme south. The black rhinoceros, on the other hand, had a wider distribution and occurred throughout most of southern Africa, except in parts of the Orange Free State and southern parts of the Transvaal (du Plessis, 1969).

With the increase in European settlement of southern Africa from the 17th century both species were exterminated gradually throughout their range. By the end of the 19th century the southern white rhinoceros was reduced to only one population of about 50 to 100 in the southern part of the area which now forms the Hluhluwe-Unfolozi Game Reserve in Natal. It appears the population estimate of 20 for this time was a deliberate under-estimate to convince the politicians of the urgency of the situation (Emslie, pers. comm.). As a result the Hluhluwe and Umfolozi Game Reserves were proclaimed in 1897, which along with St Lucia makes them the oldest game reserves in Africa. The black rhinoceros did not fare much better, being reduced by 1930 to only about 85 to 135 black rhinoceros in northern Hluhluwe-Umfolozi Game Reserve, with a further 15 in the Mkuzi Game Reserve in Natal. The species was extinct in the Cape by 1880 and the last black rhinoceros in the Transvaal was seen in the Kruger National Park in 1936. Happily, the proclamation and protection of these Natal reserves, coupled with the development of rhino capture techniques, led to both species being saved from extinction in South Africa. To date a staggering 3 440 white and 185 black rhinoceros have been translocated from Natal reserves to form new populations both in the Subregion and abroad (Meiklejohn & Strauss, pers. comm.). Similar action with the black rhinoceros has been taken by other National Parks organisations in the Subregion.

Key to the genera after Ansell (1974a)

1. Lips square and broad to pluck grass; pronounced nuchal hump visible when the head is raised; skull longer and narrower, with occipital part produced backwards beyond the condyles; high crowned molars and premolars adapted for grazing
   ... genus *Ceratotherium*

   Upper lip pointed and prehensile—a finger-like projection which aids browsing; no nuchal hump; the back has much more of a hollow/saddle appearance when viewed from the side; ears are more rounded and "trumpet-like"; skull shorter and broader, with occipital part not produced backwards beyond the condyles; molar teeth are lower crowned with high cusps to support browsing
   ... genus *Diceros*

## Genus *Ceratotherium* Gray, 1868

No. 295

### *Ceratotherium simum* (Burchell, 1817)

### White rhinoceros
### Witrenoster

Plate 28

#### Colloquial Name

The colloquial name white rhinoceros is entrenched and originates from the name given to them by the early Dutch hunters, *witte renoster*, or in Afrikaans *witrenoster*, which was used to distinguish them from the black rhinoceros, *Diceros bicornis*. Barrow (1801/4), Harris (1852) and Selous (1908) used the name *wit* or white, so it has been in use for nearly 200 years. In spite of this, both *C. simum* and *D. bicornis* are grey, and they are inclined to assume the colour of the soil on which they live through mud-wallowing and dusting. One of the most obvious characters that differentiates them is the square lips of *C. simum* (Fig. 295.1) and the hooked, prehensile upper lip of *D. bicornis* (Fig. 296.1), which are adaptations to and in their feeding habits, and they may also be referred to in this way.

#### Taxonomic Notes

Burchell (1817) originally described this species from a specimen from "the interior of South Africa", the type locality later being fixed by Shortridge (1934) as near Kuruman, Cape Province. Two subspecies are recognised, *C. s. simum* from the southern part of their distributional range and *C. s. cottoni* (Lydekker, 1908) from central Africa which are somewhat higher in the legs and less long in the body (Cave, 1962).

#### Description

With a shoulder height of up to 1,8 m for males and 1,77 m for females (Kirby, 1920), with a mass of some 2 000–2 300 kg for males and females 1 600 kg, the white rhinoceros ranks as Africa's third largest land mammal. They have a barrel-shaped body and short, thick-set limbs. Characteristic features include the long head with long, continually growing horns, one in front and a shorter one behind; pointed ears fringed with hair; wide squared-off lips; a distinct hump on the neck and a hump on the back, just in front of the thighs (Fig. 296.2). The thick skin is

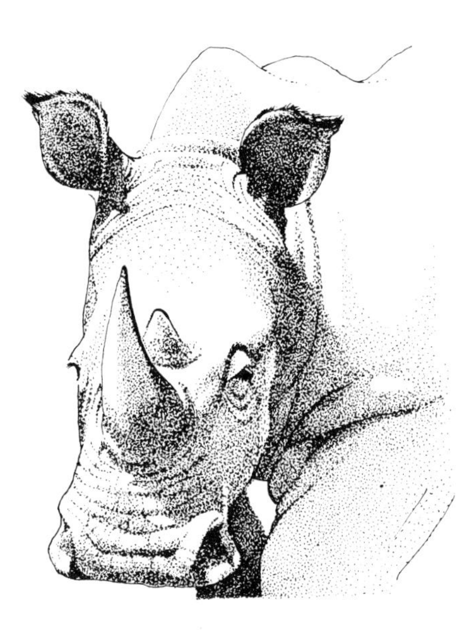

Fig. 295.1. Head: white rhinoceros, *C. simum*, to show the square-shaped lips of the species and the hump on the neck which shows clearly when the head is raised.

prominently folded on the front of the shoulders, on the upper part of the hind limbs and at the junction of the forelimbs and the body.

The colour of the skin is grey, but like that of the elephant, is often obscured by a coating of soil or mud. The skin on the body appears naked, but at close quarters is seen to have a sparse coating of bristly hairs. The skin may reach a thickness of about 20 mm on the shoulders, the thick dermis covered with a thin layer of epidermis barely 1 mm thick. Scattered over the surface of the skin are sweat glands which, when the individual is under stress, exude droplets of sweat. Underlying the skin there is a thick layer of fat which, on the abdomen, may reach a thickness of 50 mm.

The horns, which are composed of a mass of tubular filaments similar in substance to hair, are outgrowths of the skin and are not attached to the bone of the skull. The front is almost invariably longer than the hind, 1,58 m being the record length of a front horn from the Subregion (Best & Best, 1977), its accompanying rear horn 0,566 m. In the white rhinoceros, *C. s. simum*, the front horn has a straighter transverse edge in front. The lower lip has a hard surface; the upper is sensitive and soft which allows the individual to detect and then crop grass to within 10 mm of the ground. The tail is relatively short, in adults up to about 1,0 m, and has a sparse fringe of bristly hair.

The limbs have three digits, each armed with broad, stout nails, which mark clearly in the spoor. The front feet are slightly larger than the hind. However, there is a less marked difference between them than in the black rhinoceros. The cushioned pads on the soles of the feet have a hard surface with a mosaic of irregular cracks and, characteristically, have a distinct indentation on their rear edges, which marks in the spoor, and distinguishes the spoor from that of the black rhinoceros in which the indentation is absent (Plate I).

**Skull** (Fig. 295.2)

The skull is more elongated in this species than in the black rhinoceros, the occipital crest rising high at the back of the skull. The crest has a broad rugose area on top to provide a firm attachment for the huge muscles that actuate the raising and lowering of the heavy head. The high crest also provides for a broad area at the back of the skull for the attachment of the other neck muscles. The zygomatic arches are heavily built to give a firm attachment for the masseter muscles that actuate the lower jaw, which, at their posterior edges, broaden out to give these an extra wide area of attachment for the lower end of these muscles. The lower jaw is massive, particularly so at the level of the posterior angle, the condyles very broad and fitting into deep sockets.

The earliest known fossil form of the species, *Ceratotherium praecox* Hooijer & Patterson, 1972, has been recorded from Langebaanweg, Cape Province. In other parts of Africa

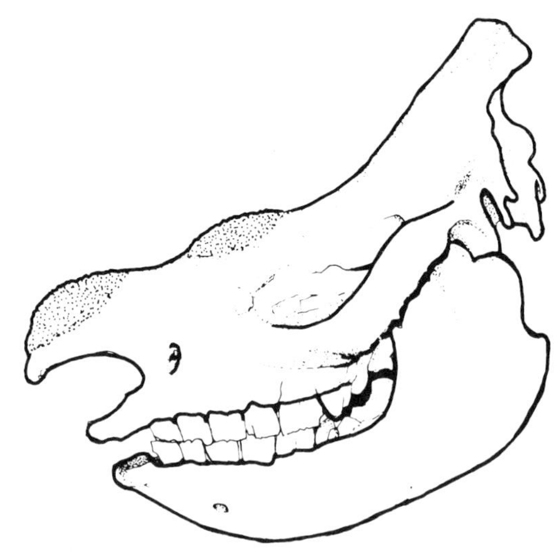

Fig. 295.2. Skull: white rhinoceros, *C. simum*. TL Skull 0,76 m.

this species is known from fossil beds laid down some seven million years ago. It has four incisor teeth which are lacking in the extant white rhinoceros. The dental formula of the white rhinoceros, *C. simum*, is:

$I\frac{0}{0}\ C\frac{0}{0}\ P\frac{3}{3}\ M\frac{3}{3} = 24$

The upper and lower second molars are the largest of the cheekteeth. All cheekteeth are broad-faced and have convoluted enamel layers on their biting surfaces and are adapted to grinding up the food.

In the deciduous dentition they have four premolars on either side in the upper and lower jaws, the anterior premolar being the last to erupt and which, in adolescence, is lost and not replaced. Some, however, may persist into early adulthood. There is no sign of the incisors or canines in the deciduous dentition, which are sometimes present in the black rhinoceros, *D. bicornis*.

**Distribution**

The white rhinoceros, from the evidence of skeletal remains and their depiction in rock art, at one time occurred from the coastal areas of Morocco, Algeria and Tunisia, through the Sahara and East Africa to the Republic of South Africa.

In the wild the northern white rhinoceros is now only found in the Garamba National Park in Zaire, while the southern white rhinoceros is now spread throughout much of the Southern African Subregion. There is no doubt that at one time, during the Pleistocene Epoch, their distribution was continuous from Morocco through the Sahara to parts of the Cape Province, the break caused by climatic changes which rendered the intervening terrain unsuitable for them.

Renshaw (1904) recorded that at the turn of century there were only about 10 alive in Zululand and in 1916 Vaughan-Kirby, the first Game Conservator in Zululand, estimated that only 20 individuals survived in the reserves. However, the first official estimate in 1930 revealed that there were 120 in the Umfolozi Reserve and 30 on adjacent ground and by 1960 an aerial count gave a total of just over 700. Since then numbers in the Zululand reserves have more than doubled and up to October 1989 a total of 1 240 have been relocated out of South Africa and 2 199 within South Africa (total 3 439) (Strauss, pers. comm.). White rhinoceros have been moved to the following countries (figures correct to 31/12/1983—Meiklejohn, pers. comm., 1990): **Subregion**—Cape 80, Natal 487, Orange Free State 23, Transvaal 931, Bophuthatswana 330, Ciskei 6, Transkei 15, Venda 6, Botswana 97, Namibia 88, Swaziland 96, Zimbabwe 152; **Africa, excluding Subregion**—Angola 10, Kenya 23, Mozambique 85 (although Emslie (pers. comm.) believes Mozambique now holds the dubious distinction of the species going extinct twice), Zambia 4; **Elsewhere**—Argentina 6, Belgium 19, Burma 4, Canada 6, Cuba 2, Czechoslovakia 7, Denmark 2, East Germany 5, Great Britain 64, Holland 62, India 5, Israel 8, Italy 6, Japan 37, Java 2, Portugal 2, Saudi Arabia 1, Spain 33, Sweden 2, Switzerland

4, Taiwan 7, USA 257, West Germany 96. The majority were relocated inside South Africa. They have not done so well in the sourveld areas of Natal (eg. Chelmsford) or in the drier parts of the northern Transvaal (Emslie, pers. comm.). Once again this represents a remarkable effort by conservationists in the Subregion in removing a subspecies from the endangered category.

The northern subspecies, *C. s. cottoni*, is endangered, with a drastic reduction in numbers and shrinkage in their distribution (Kingdon, 1979).

*South of the Sahara, excluding the Southern African Subregion*

The northern white rhinoceros now only survives (a group of 25–30) in Garamba National Park, northeastern **Zaire**. A further 13 are in zoological gardens, of which only one female is breeding (Hodges, pers. comm.). Following introductions from Natal, there are about 40 southern white rhinoceros in **Kenya**.

*Southern African Subregion*

At the end of the 19th century they were restricted to what is now the Umfolozi Game Reserve, but spread during the 1930's and 1940's to the Hluhluwe Game Reserve. At first confined to the Umfolozi-Corridor-Hluhluwe Game Reserve Complex, subsequently they have been reintroduced to the Mkuzi, Itala and Ndumu Game Reserves in **Natal** and many other reserves including the Kruger National Park and Pilanesberg National Park.

The last record of individuals in the three neighbouring countries was of one which was shot in Zimbabwe at Mpanda's Kraal in the northeast of the country in 1895. In Botswana, Selous (1908) stated that he shot one at Thamma Setsi (Tamuseche Pan) on the Zimbabwe border in 1874, but they persisted beyond this date in this area as he recorded their spoor in 1877. In Mozambique one was shot at Marcorsa (SE 1733 D4) by the late Sir Hugh Beadle in 1935.

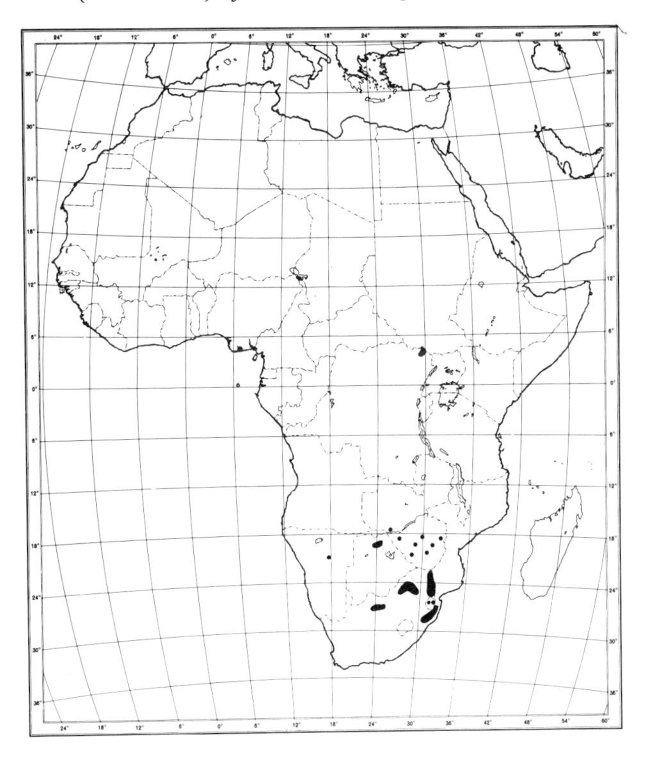

### Habitat

Player & Feely (1960) listed four basic habitat requirements: areas of short grass, for which they have a marked preference; stands of medium tall *Panicum maximum* which they find under trees (Emslie, pers. comm.); the availability of water for drinking and in which to wallow; adequate bush cover, and relatively flat terrain.

These requirements are met in the wooded grasslands, common in many parts of the Subregion, where they formerly occurred. This woodland carries the palatable grasses which form their principal food. Reintroduced to areas where these conditions prevail, the species is flourishing. The type of woodland is a secondary consideration, for its function is to provide shade from the sun during the hotter parts of the day. Steep slopes within the habitat are avoided, although they will traverse them freely to feeding grounds or to water.

Melton (1987) found that white rhinoceros showed a reduction in broad scale habitat selectivity during winter, changing from favouring the *Acacia nigrescens* open woodland in west Umfolozi in summer to using habitats at random during winter.

### Habits

White rhinoceros occur in small groups consisting of a single dominant or territorial bull, subordinate bulls, cows and their offspring. Territorial bulls occupy clearly defined territories, which they defend against the trespass of other bulls from neighbouring territories. In the Umfolozi Game Reserve in Natal, these territories vary in size from 0,75 km$^2$ to 2,60 km$^2$ (Owen-Smith, 1973); somewhat smaller than those of the black rhinoceros, *D. bicornis*. The boundaries of these territories often coincide with topographic features such as watercourses, crests of watershed ridges, or roads. The boundaries have narrow, common zones 50–100 m wide, visited by neighbouring territorial bulls. Territorial bulls mark their territories by spray urination or defecating on latrines along the boundaries. Owen-Smith (1973) recorded that, only on five occasions during his study in Umfolozi, territorial bulls moved more than 100 m beyond their own territorial boundary where this had an available water supply. Where water is not available seasonally within their territories, the territorial bull will leave it every three or four days to drink.

Territorial bulls trespassing into the territory of an adjacent bull normally take avoidance action and serious fights are usually averted. Encounters may take the form of short charges with much dust raising or, at closer quarters, horn clashing. Where a territorial bull is accompanied by a female in oestrus, however, serious fighting may ensue. Wounding may be caused by the horn or by heavy shoulder battering and may lead to internal injury. A deposed territorial bull may be allowed to remain in the territory providing he clearly demonstrates his submissiveness. Subordinate bulls respond to territorial bulls with snorting, snarling or shrieking, but seldom actually engage in fighting, although they have been killed in such encounters.

Where a territory does not include a water supply, a narrower corridor is used leading to it. Within the territory the dominant bull usually has a number of favourite resting places in which he lies up in the shade during the heat of the day, either standing or reclining on his belly or side. The territorial bull alone sprays urine which is directed backwards between the hind legs. Having defecated, he scatters his dung by kicking with the back feet. Sometimes the urine emerges as a stream and the dung is deposited without scattering. These actions are common near territorial boundaries, but may take place anywhere within the territory. However, when the territorial bull has to leave his territory to drink, he urinates in a stream in the manner of subordinates (Owen-Smith, 1973).

Subordinate bulls are tolerated by a territorial bull, providing they remain submissive, and they spend most of their lives within his territory, although they make occasional explorations outside it. Several subordinate bulls may live in a territory of a single territorial bull.

Cows on the other hand have home ranges that overlap with those of other cows and may overlap the territories of as many as seven territorial bulls (Owen-Smith, 1973). In areas with good grazing and water the home range of individual cows may be as small as 6–8 km$^2$. With deteriorating food supplies this may increase to 10–15 km$^2$ and, if there is no water available, be increased to 20 km$^2$.

Communication within the species depends heavily on olfactory signals (urine and dung constituents), which individual rhinoceros detect through their sensitive sense of smell as they cross the paths of other members of their community and encounter their dung middens. Vocalisations and subtle displays are used for direct communication; Owen-Smith (1973) recognised 10 of the former and 15 of the latter. Territorial bulls are normally silent, even in encounters, but occasionally may snort when another moves nearby. During courtship of a female, they may squeal when trying to block a female in oestrus from leaving their territory. Other members of the group may snort or snarl, which is a sign for others to keep their distance; they pant, when maintaining contact or as a sign to join up; shriek, as an attack inhibiting signal; squeal for eliciting protection or as a distress signal in calves; or puff when suddenly alarmed.

Subtle displays may involve pulling the ears back as a sign to the others to keep off; advancing steps often accompanied by a snarl are used as a threat; charges; prodding with the horn or staring at each other, horn against horn, as intimidatory gestures. Horn against horn clashing is a more intense ritual attack, which may develop into horn-wrestling and finally jabbing with the horn. Side-rubbing may be a means of more closely cementing the bonds within a group and head-flinging in the young is an invitation to play. Although white rhinoceros have preputial glands in the region of the penis or vulva, olfactory communication appears to be limited to the odours of the urine and dung. Frequently territorial bulls will ascertain whether cows within their territories are in oestrus, but cows take little notice of each other. Calves are inquisitive and will investigate other members of the group, sometimes even cars and road signs!

White rhinoceros walk slowly, their heads held close to the ground, their nostrils in close contact with it to the extent that, in sandy soil, the broad mouth may mark clearly in the spoor. When in a hurry they move with a graceful trot, timed from a vehicle as up to 28 km/h, and under stress canter and gallop at up to 40 km/h. They tend to use established routes to water or to preferred grazing areas. In cool cloudy weather with high winds they tend to shelter in thickets. Cows and subadults do not seem so prone to use established sheltering places as do territorial bulls.

White rhinoceros pay little attention to other mammalian species, even at close range. Pienaar (1970a) recorded an unusual incident of an elephant killing one at a water hole. Predation on them, except by man, is minimal, although rarely they may be killed by lions.

Fork-tailed drongos, *Dicrurus adsimilis*, often hawk insects by flying along the sides of resting rhinoceros and frequently they are accompanied by red-billed oxpeckers, *Buphagus erythrorhynchus*, which remove ticks from their hides. Terrapins may also remove ticks while rhinoceros are wallowing in a pan. The birds serve the useful purpose of warning them of approaching danger.

White rhinoceros have poor sight but acute senses of smell and hearing. They respond more readily to moving objects, which are only discerned at ranges of 10–25 m, than to those at rest. Owen-Smith (1973) recorded that, when downwind, they respond with alertness to human scent at about 0,8 km, and continually investigate odours when moving. The ears which can be rotated independently, orientate quickly to face any strange sound and move continually, even when the individual is apparently asleep. They are generally temperamentally quieter and less prone to provocation than black rhinoceros.

During the summer months, white rhinoceros indulge in mud-wallowing or lying in muddy pools as a means of thermoregulation, but more especially for the purpose of coating the body with a layer of mud as a means of ridding themselves of ecto-parasites. Following mud-wallowing they will rub themselves on the trunks of trees or boulders which eventually, through continued use as rubbing posts, become debarked and polished. Mud-wallowing is infrequent during the winter months (Owen-Smith, 1973).

**Food**

White rhinoceros are grazers with a preference for feeding on short grass, which they are capable of cropping to within 25–60 mm of the ground (Owen-Smith, 1988). Lacking incisor teeth, the movable and extremely sensitive upper lip is extended over a grass clump, pressing the grass against the hard lower lip to be cropped with an upward movement of both lips. Sometimes the process is assisted by a slight movement of the head. As the individual feeds the head is held low, the wide nostrils maintaining contact with the grass. They are selective feeders. Owen-Smith (1973) gave the bite width of an adult female as about 200 mm and estimated that about 48% of daylight hours are taken up in feeding. Feeding rate on short grass averaged 78 bites per minute. In doing so they stand in one place, moving the head in an arc, then take a step forward to repeat the process. In wetter years when the grass is taller they do not crop the grass as short, and their bite rate is greatly reduced (Emslie, pers. comm.) They may chew the food for a moment or two, but do not ruminate.

Owen-Smith (1973) showed that, in Natal, four species of grasses constituted 74% of the food intake, these being: red grass, *Themeda triandra* (an important dry season food resource); buffalo grass, *Panicum maximum*; small buffalo grass, *P. coloratum*, and common signal grass, *Urochloa mosambicensis*, the first-named being by far the most heavily utilised, sprouting green grass being preferred. In a study of wet season feeding behaviour of grazers in west Umfolozi in 1984, Emslie (pers. comm.) found that 42% of the grass biomass in white rhinoceros feeding patches was made up of *Urochloa mosambicensis* and *Panicum maximum*. Both these species favour lower-lying, more alluvial soils. *P. maximum* is also a species often found in shady sites under trees. These two species contributed 51% to the diet. *Themeda triandra*, *Sporobolus smutsii* and *Panicum coloratum* contributed a further 33% to the diet. White rhinoceros were found to preferentially graze the shorter, more erect central tillers of *P. coloratum* than the longer, more prostrate side stoloniferous tillers (Emslie, 1985; Diamond, 1986). Some 30 other species are eaten to a lesser extent. Other species such as the resinous turpentine grass, *Cymbopogon plurinodis*, are rigorously avoided. Owen-Smith (1973) recorded geophagia, especially around termitaria.

White rhinoceros drink water regularly and are dependent on its availability. Owen-Smith (1973) found that most drinking is done between 17h00 and 21h00 and continues after sundown, less drinking taking place during the day. A drinking frequency of every 2–3 days was most usual during the dry season.

**Reproduction**

White rhinoceros breed at any time of the year, but in Natal there are peaks of calving in March & July.

Bulls start holding territories at an age of 12,5 years (Condy, 1973) and can detect when cows are in pro-oestrus for they form a close attachment with a cow for a considerable time before mating. During this period bulls will take active steps to prevent cows from leaving their territory, chasing cows, squealing and sometimes horn-clashing with a pro-oestrous cow until she remains. While in pro-oestrus she will drive him off with snarling and snorting. Interested subordinate males are driven off actively by the territorial bull during this period (Owen-Smith, 1973).

Females breed from an age of four years (Owen-Smith, 1988). The oestrous cycle length is approximately 28 days (n=5) based on the inter-oestrus intervals and hormonal profiles of captive *C. s. cottoni* (Hodges, pers. comm.). One calf was born after a gestation period of about 16 months and had a birth weight of about 40 kg.

The female usually moves away from the group to give birth. At birth the wrinkled skin is pale grey with a pink tinge. For the first three days following parturition the calf is unsteady on its feet, thereafter it keeps close to its protective mother. Bigalke, Steyn, de Vos & de Waard (1950) recorded that the outer horny layer of the skin is moulted at about one and a half to four months, revealing a new paler skin. A further moult takes place at about 10 months.

The calf is weaned at about a year old and separates from its mother at about two or three years of age. If the female loses her next calf, the bond between them may be re-established. During the association of the cow and her calf, the calf usually precedes its mother when moving, being guided by gentle prods of her horn. This is in contrast to the

black rhinoceros, *D. bicornis*, where the calf usually runs by her side or behind her.
Females have a pair of inguinal mammae.

## Genus *Diceros* Gray, 1821

No. 296

## *Diceros bicornis* (Linnaeus, 1758)

## Black rhinoceros
## Swartrenoster

Plate 28

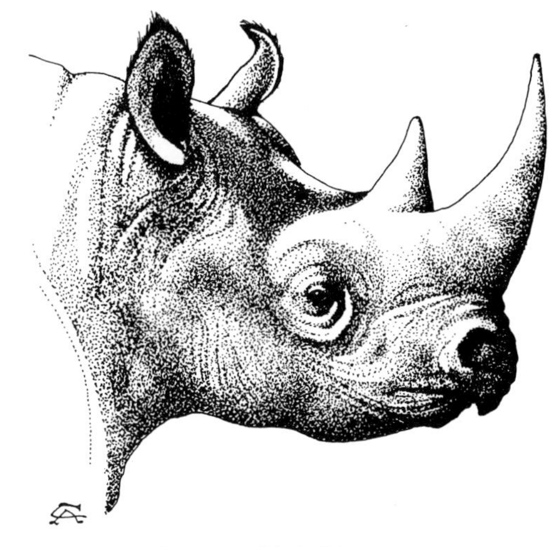

Fig. 296.1. Black rhinoceros, *D. bicornis*, to show the hooked lip of the species.

**Colloquial Name**
Alternative name: Hook-lipped rhinoceros.

**Taxonomic Notes**
While seven subspecies have been described (Groves, 1967), more recent research (du Toit, 1987) has not supported this degree of taxonomic splitting, and the African Elephant and Rhino Specialist Group (of the International Union for the Conservation of Nature) now recognizes four conservation units within the continent (du Toit, Foose & Cumming, 1987). These are a northwestern group in Cameroun and the Central African Republic (it is no longer certain if any of these survive), an eastern group in Kenya and northern Tanzania (designated as *D. b. michaeli*), a desert group in Namibia (*D. b. bicornis*), and the relatively large bushveld group extending from Natal through Zimbabwe and Zambia into southern Tanzania (*D. b. minor*). In addition to *D. b. minor* and *D. b. bicornis* (which has recently been reintroduced to the Cape Province), the Subregion also has a small population of *D. b. michaeli*, originating from Kenya, in the Addo Elephant National Park.

Fig. 296.2. Outline of the body:
(a) black rhinoceros, *D. bicornis*.
(b) white rhinoceros , *C. simum*.

**Description**
Adult black rhinoceros stand about 1,6 m at the shoulder and have a mass of up to about 1 000 kg. The mean mass of live individuals from the Hluhluwe Game Reserve, Natal is males 852 kg (n=8), females 884 kg (n=6) (Hitchins, 1968b).

Some characteristic features which serve to distinguish them from their near relative, the white rhinoceros, *Ceratotherium simum*, include their possession of a prehensile upper lip (Fig. 296.1), which is used in grasping the twigs of the woody plants on which they feed, the shorter head, longer neck and smaller, rounded ears. The outline of the back is also different in the two species, the black rhinoceros lacking the nuchal hump, which is a well developed and obvious feature of the white rhinoceros (Fig. 296.2). The black rhinoceros carries its shorter head higher than the white rhinoceros.

In overall colour they are dark grey. Like the elephant and the white rhinoceros, they tend to take on the colour of the ground on which they live, through their habit of wallowing in mud and dusting themselves after bathing. The skin is thick, with a sparse scattering of hairs. They have eyelashes and hairy fringes to the ears and the end of the tail. The folding of the skin is confined to an area above the knees, on the front limbs, across the nape behind the ears and on the flanks. Scattered throughout the skin are sweat glands which exude droplets of sweat when the individual is under stress.

The horns are composed of a mass of tubular filaments, similar in substance to hair. They grow from the skin and are not attached to the underlying bone, but the bony surface of the skull is rugose under the bases of the horns to allow a firm attachment of the skin to the skull in these areas. In Zululand the front horn in black rhinoceros is invariably longer than the back. In Hluhluwe-Umfolozi in 1973 only 2,5% of males had anterior horns = posterior, and none shorter (n=120). For females the figures are 14,2% and 5,7% (n=106). For 1985 the figures are for males 0% and 0% (n=58) and females 29,0% and 4,3% (n=69) (Hitchins, 1989). The shape of the horns also depends upon the habitat. Horns in Kaokoveld for example are much straighter than those in Zululand, presumably as a result of different wear patterns. The maximum front horn length recorded by Best & Best (1977) for a specimen from northern Natal is 1,05 m, with a rear horn of 0,52 m, which is surpassed by several from East Africa where the maximum is 1,20 m and 0,445 m respectively.

The limbs have three digits each, with broad, stout nails which mark clearly in the spoor (Plate I). The front feet are larger than the hind as they have to carry the great mass of the huge shoulders, neck and head. The cushioned pads on the soles of the feet have a hard surface with a mosaic of irregular cracks. In Kenya, Rob Brett has been able to identify individuals based on photographs of the wrinkle patterns left behind in the spoor. The pads are rounded at the back and lack the indentation characteristic of the white rhinoceros. This aids in distinguishing the spoor of the two species, as does the size of the nails which are larger in the white rhinoceros.

Black rhinoceros suffer from skin lesions caused by a filaria parasite. At their fullest development these lesions take the form of black, blood-encrusted areas which ulcerate and haemorrhage. Usually these are situated on the skin behind the shoulders, but also occur on the chest, neck and forelegs. All adult Natal black rhinoceros have these lesions, but they are absent in rhinos from central Africa (Leader-Williams, pers. comm.) and are not found on desert rhinoceros in Namibia, no doubt due to the absence of flies that serve as specific vectors for the parasite (du Toit, pers. comm.). The calves are free of these until they are about six months old, when the lesions begin to appear as bare pink patches on their chests. By the age of three years they are found on the chest and sides, but only appear behind the shoulders of the individual at the age of four and a half to five years. These lesions are not related to their state of health and appear on perfectly healthy individuals (Feely, pers. comm.). Oxpeckers, *Buphagus* spp, which frequent the backs of rhinoceros in search of ticks, flies and the blood issuing from these lesions, tend to keep the lesions open by their activities. The association of the rhinoceros with these birds has mutual benefits, for, by their loud chattering and calling, they alert the rhinoceros to danger, even when the animal is resting or sleeping.

**Skull** (Fig. 296.3)

The skull of this species is less elongated, the supraoccipital crest not extending upwards and backwards to the extent seen in the white rhinoceros. The occipital crest lacks the broad rugose area on top seen in the white rhinoceros and is narrower. The zygomatic arches are heavily built to give a firm attachment for the masseter muscles that activate the massive lower jaw. While ancestral forms of rhinoceros possessed cutting incisor teeth and, in some, canines, these are absent in the black rhinoceros whose dental formula is:

$I\frac{0}{0}\ C\frac{0}{0}\ P\frac{3}{3}\ M\frac{3}{3} = 24$

The premolar teeth are molariform, all the cheekteeth being broad-faced and adapted to grinding up the food.

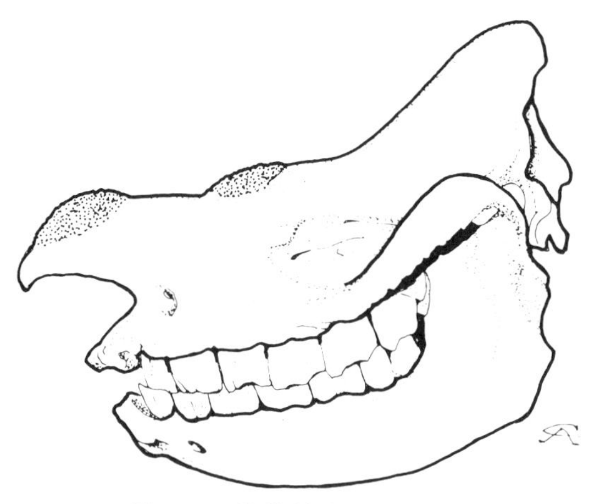

Fig. 296.3. Skull: black rhinoceros, *D. bicornis*. TL Skull 0,55 m.

## Distribution

It is a sad reflection that a species which formerly had such a wide range in the Subregion, should have suffered such a drastic reduction in its distributional range within historical times. World population estimates were: 1960–100 000; 1970–63 000; 1980–14 800; 1990–3 000 (Emslie & Adcock, 1990a).

Van Riebeeck's Diary of 1652 recorded rhinoceros as occurring on the slopes of Table Mountain and as being common on the Cape Flats. At that time no European was aware that two species occurred in Africa and this species did not have a distinguishing name. Names differentiating the two species must have come into use towards the end of the 18th century, when the hunters and pioneers entered the area north of the Orange River and first saw the white rhinoceros. From this date onwards the distribution of both species of rhinoceros shrunk in the face of human pressures. The last black rhinoceros was shot in the Cape Province at Graaff Reinet in 1880. The horns of this individual are now in the collection of the Reinet House Museum, Graaff Reinet. It was shot in the parsonage garden by James Murray on the instructions of his brother, the Rev. Charles Murray, as it was eating his vegetables. The last record from the Orange Free State is dated 1842. In the Transvaal, the last record of a naturally occurring black rhinoceros was of a solitary female seen in the Kruger National Park in 1936 (Penzhorn, 1971). In Natal, the proclamation of the Hluhluwe and Umfolozi Game Reserves in 1897 and the Mkuzi Game Reserve in 1912 came just in time to save them from extinction in this province. In Zimbabwe populations survived mainly in Lowveld areas where low rainfall and trypanosomiasis constrained farming activities (du Toit, pers. comm.)

Since these days, with a growing appreciation of wildlife as a natural resource with economic, recreational and aesthetic values, as a further measure to ensure the future of the species, surplus black rhinoceros have been translocated to a number of areas in the Subregion where they formerly occurred. Since 1962 a total of 131 Hluhluwe-Umfolozi and Mkuzi *D. b. minor* animals have been moved to re-establish seven new populations: Ndumu Game Reserve (which now has also become a donor reserve, with 19 animals translocated from Ndumu to date); Kruger National Park (12 also brought in from Zimbabwe), Itala Game Reserve, Pilanesberg National Park, Weenen Nature Reserve, Eastern Shores and Andries Vosloo Kudu Reserve in the Cape (Emslie & Adcock, 1990a). Their limits of distribution are still rapidly altering, for example within recent years in Zimbabwe, the remnants of two isolated populations in the Chipinga and Mtoko districts, threatened by land development, were translocated to the Gonarezhou National Park.

The distribution, as depicted, shows a scattered and discontinuous occurrence and, except where they are afforded protection in National Parks and reserves, the continued existence of some of the smaller island populations is doubtful. In Kaokoland and Damaraland in northern Namibia, 43 were removed in 1970–72 as a conservation measure to the Etosha National Park (Hofmeyr *et al.*, 1975). The remaining rhinoceros were almost wiped out by poachers, only a relict population of some 60 rhinos remaining by the early 1980's. Following extensive protection measures records for 1987–88 show there are about 100 rhinoceros now occurring in the area (Britz & Loutit, 1989).

Outside South Africa, Namibia and Zimbabwe, the species is close to extinction owing to continued poaching, which is fuelled by the high demand for rhinoceros horn as a component of traditional medicines in Asia and, to a lesser extent, as a raw material for the manufacture of Yemeni dagger handles. Markets for horn remain despite major efforts by international conservation agencies to stop the trade (du Toit, pers. comm.).

There are currently at least 600 black rhinoceros in South Africa, 400 in Namibia and 1 500 in Zimbabwe. Two small populations of *D. b. bicornis* have been reintroduced recently from Namibia to the Vaalbos and Augrabies National Parks in the Cape. An unknown but very small number still survive in northern Botswana. Six *D. b. minor* have been reintroduced recently into Swaziland. In Mozambique, a few scattered survivors are still present in remote areas of dense bush (du Toit, pers. comm.). Only in Mozambique can it be regarded as endangered. Elsewhere in the Subregion populations have been increasing under sound scientific management. Contrast this with the decline, due to poaching, in the rest of Africa, from an estimated 63 000 in 1970 to 4 000 (including those in the Subregion) in 1986 (du Toit *et al.*, 1987) and one can appreciate the great effort put into conservation by authorities within the Subregion.

An interesting translocation was that of seven black rhinoceros in 1961/62 from the Kenya Game Department to the Addo Elephant National Park (Penzhorn, 1971; Hall-Martin & Penzhorn, 1977). These represent the subspecies *D. b. michaeli* and, with the species now endangered in Kenya, effective steps have been taken to ensure the short-term genetic conservation of the Addo rhinoceros which in 1989 numbered 20. The National Parks Board is presently negotiating with zoological gardens to import animals for a breeding programme for the subspecies' conservation in the Park (Hall-Martin, pers. comm.). Details of their biology can be found in the cited publications.

*South of the Sahara, excluding the Southern African Subregion*

While a small number (under 50) of black rhinoceros have been reported in **Cameroun** and the **Central African Repub-**

**lic**, the survival of these animals has not been confirmed. There is also no recent confirmation of a remnant population in the Akagera National Park, Rwanda. The only other remaining wild populations are in **Kenya** (300–400), **Tanzania** (probably under 200), **Zambia** (under 50) and a very small number in **Malawi** (du Toit, pers. comm.).

*Southern African Subregion*

They still exist in Kaokoland and Damaraland in northwestern **Namibia**, and in the eastern parts of the Etosha National Park. The largest concentration (some 100 animals) is in the Otjovasandu area in the southwest of the park (Cilliers, 1989). There are other widely scattered records south to 21°30'S and east to about 17°E. A small number have been reintroduced from Namibia into the Augrabies Falls and Vaalbos National Parks in the Cape Province (Raath & Hall-Martin, 1989).

In **Zimbabwe**, previously confined to the Zambezi Valley and adjacent parts of the escarpment from the western end of Lake Kariba to the Mozambique border, they have been translocated to the Hwange National Park and Matobo National Park. During the period 1986–1989, 160 were established on private ranches, as part of an ongoing programme to develop four major breeding groups under free-range conditions (du Toit, pers. comm.). In **Mozambique**, south of the Zambezi River, they may still occur in the Gorongoza National Park. In **Natal** they occur in the Hluhluwe-Corridor-Umfolozi Game Reserve Complex. A few survive in the area north of the Mkuzi Game Reserve and east of the Pongola River, and a small number have been reintroduced to Ndumu (16), Itala (34), Eastern Shores (15) and Weenen (5) Game Reserves. In the Transvaal there have been reintroductions from Natal to the Kruger National Park (81) and Pilanesberg National Park (30). In addition, seven *D. b. minor* have been sent to the USA to take part in a captive breeding programme (Emslie & Adcock, 1990a).

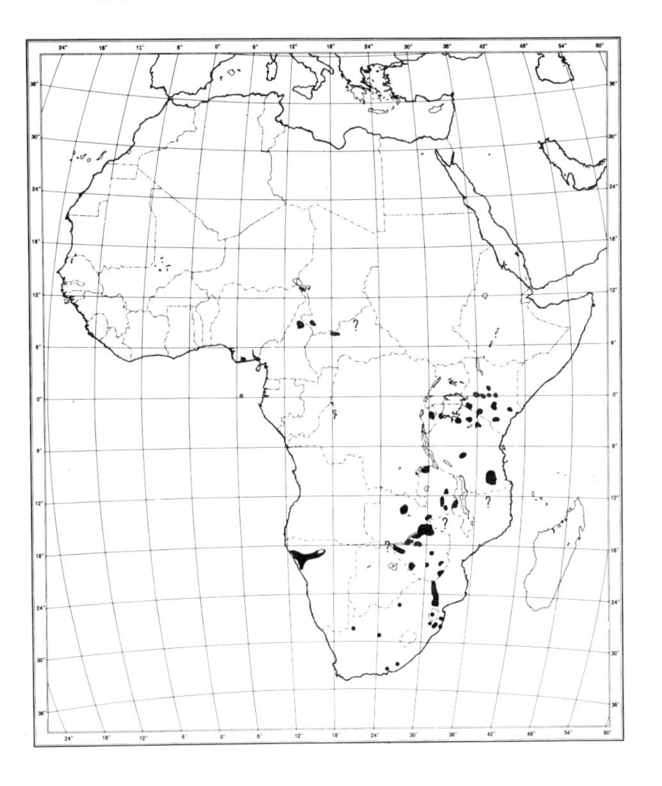

## Habitat

The black rhinoceros requires a habitat providing adequate shrubs and young trees up to about 4 m high, including well developed woodland or thickets in which to shelter during the heat of the day or in inclement weather. A water supply, not only for drinking but also in which to bathe and mud-wallow, is also important.

While not usually associated with open plains country, the black rhinoceros occurs in a wide range of habitats ranging from forest to savanna woodland and scrub, from sea level to at least 1 500 m in the Subregion and up to 2 700 m in East Africa (Kingdon, 1979).

They are dependent on water and, in the Subregion, are seldom found more than 10 or 15 km from it. Kingdon (1979) stated that in East Africa the maximum dry season distance from water was found to be about 25 km. Where it is not available, they will dig for it in the sand in river beds, excavating with their forelegs.

The early stages of bush encroachment favour this species, especially if this is coupled with heavy grazing (Emslie, pers. comm.). However, later successional trends from closed *Acacia nilotica* woodland to lowland forest dominated by *Euclea schimperi*, *Berchemia zeyheri* and *Rhus pentheri* have reduced habitat quality in the Hluhluwe Game Reserve, and is likely to have contributed to the decline in the Hluhluwe population which has taken place over the last 20 years. Interestingly many of the most rejected species (e.g. *Euclea crispa*, *Lippia javanica*) in Hluhluwe have grown up on bush-cleared sites in wetter, low-lying sites. By way of contrast favourable food plants have grown up in cleared sites in drier areas of the complex. In addition, Emslie has found grass interference to be very important. Black rhinoceros prefer the smaller sizes of *Acacias* but when these are hidden they are forced to eat the larger and less preferred plants. They avoid feeding in the tall grass areas of northern Hluhluwe, except along paths. In both Hluhluwe and Umfolozi young tamboti, *Spirostachys africana*, thickets were key habitats, with *S. africana* being the dominant item in the black rhinoceros summer diet, accounting for between 20–25% of woody browse eaten. Emslie & Adcock (1990b) also found that size structure changes in the vegetation were important to the rhinoceros even if the species composition remained very similar (e.g. mature *S. africana* and *Acacia grandicornuta* woodland was rejected). Riverine bush, tamboti thickets, ridges and lowland forest margin habitat were amongst the most preferred habitats in Hluhluwe. In Umfolozi one of the most preferred habitats was heavily grazed short grass country with a few small *Acacias*.

## Habits

Black rhinoceros tend to be solitary, the only stable bond being between the female and her calf, but even this is only of a temporary nature, persisting into the female's next pregnancy and ceasing altogether with the birth of her next calf. Other associations, such as that of an adult male with a female, or with a number of individuals of all age classes, are transitory.

Black rhinoceros are not strictly territorial in the sense of defending delimited areas against others of their species, but each adult does tend to remain within a specific home range which may overlap with the home ranges of other members of the population. The size of a bull rhinoceros' home range and its location (relative to waterpoints, female home ranges and other features of importance to the species), is determined by the dominance status of the individual, the establishment of which may involve some fighting when the animals are living at medium to high densities in typical bushveld situations (du Toit, pers. comm.).

The size of their home ranges differs according to sex, age and the type of habitat, immature animals usually occupying larger areas than adults. In the Hluhluwe Game Reserve, Hitchins (1969) found that the size of the home range varied according to the nature of the habitat. Where there is a high proportion of thicket and dense stands of woody plants, a young female had a home range of some 3 000 ha in Umfolozi (Emslie & Adcock, 1990a). In Hluhluwe, Hitchins found home ranges to be smaller at 500 to 750 ha. Hitchins (1969) found that they do not occupy territories in the sense of areas exclusively held and defended against other black rhinoceros. Joubert (1969) believed that in Namibia the size of the home range varies with the density of the population as well as the availability of food and cover. Where their feeding areas are far from water, they are nomadic in habit and will share tracks, feeding and resting sites and water supplies with others. Loutit (1984) estimated the home range size as about 500 km$^2$ in Kaokoland.

Although adult bulls are inclined to be aggressive towards other bulls, they deliberately tend to avoid contact. Serious fighting, however, does take place, especially between bulls over a female in oestrus, between bulls and cows, but rarely between cows. There is a higher mortality in males (11 cases) than females (five cases) (Hitchins & Anderson, 1983). In meetings between bulls there may be some testing behaviour, which takes the form of one rushing forward with lowered head and screaming, to simply lifting the head and staring. A bull will approach a cow with a stiff-legged gait, head swinging from side to side, or may jerk the horn in the air. If the cow shows signs of aggression, the bull usually retires. In fighting, the front horn is used to buffet the other, the action taking place with tail raised, ears flattened and with much screaming and squealing.

During the heat of day they retire to the shade of thickets or woodland to sleep, either standing motionless or lying with their legs curled under them. They tend to rest on the tops of ridges but they will also lie in dusty hollows, sometimes in the full sun, or by water holes or mud wallows. Sometimes they sleep lying flat on their sides, a position never adopted by the white rhinoceros (Feely, *in litt.*). As they are unable to roll right over, they wallow in mud or dust on one side, then rise, and wallow on the other side. While asleep the ears move restlessly, rotating in all directions, or flick quickly from back to front.

Black rhinoceros deposit their dung in latrines but will also defecate on paths or fortuitously anywhere in their home range. The latrines may be used by a number of individuals. Usually a small bush marks the centre of the latrine. After deposition the dung is vigorously scraped by the bulls with alternate kicks of the hind feet which leave scrape marks on the ground which, in soft ground, may reach a depth of 0,3 m (Feely, *in litt.*). Possibly the adherence of portions of the dung to the hind feet may mark the presence of the individual on tracks. In northern Natal, many latrines are used by both species of rhinoceros (Feely, *in litt.*). Smell is very important to rhinoceros and they have been observed to change direction by 90 degrees to investigate the presence of strange rhinoceros (Emslie, pers. comm.).

Urination may take place in a fine stream or the urine may be ejected by the bulls in a spray in short bursts, backwards on to a bush or other object. Cows likewise, when moving, may squirt small quantities of urine. Spraying of urine may have the effect of advertising the individual's presence in an area.

Both lions and spotted hyaenas have been reported as attacking adults, with the outcome usually in favour of the rhinoceros. Adults exhibit no fear of the larger predators and generally disregard even the near presence of other mammals. They normally give way to elephants, but aggressive encounters during drought conditions at waterholes with these and with buffaloes have been recorded. In parts of their distributional range predation on calves is a rare occurrence, but has been reported in the Hluhluwe Game Reserve in Natal (Deane, 1962), where Hitchins (1969) believed spotted hyaenas, *Crocuta crocuta*, take a toll of the young, and Hitchins & Anderson (1983) provided circumstantial evidence to support this. Goddard (in Moss, 1976) witnessed five incidents in which spotted hyaenas tried unsuccessfully to pull down calves.

In Hluhluwe females and males were active most of the night, but only for a third to half of the day respectively (Owen-Smith, 1988).

Black rhinoceros vocalise in a number of ways, the most commonly heard being the repeated loud snort given when the individual gets a fright or is angry. They grunt and growl when fighting and may squeal or scream loudly.

They appear heavy-footed when walking, but are extraordinarily agile when provoked. At a gallop they can cover the ground at speed and can spin around within their own length. Their sight is poor, but their senses of hearing and smell are acute.

While they have a reputation for being irascible and bad-tempered, this depends on circumstances and the individual. Normally human scent will make them move off, but their reactions depend on whether they have been hunted or harried, or left in peace, and they do sometimes charge from 50 to 70 m away. A charging black rhinoceros may swing away from a rifle shot or, at closer quarters, to a loud shout, and they seldom return to press home an attack. They are unlikely to charge uphill and like to retreat into cover. When seriously annoyed or when wounded they may work out their anger on inanimate objects such as bushes or termite mounds, attacking them with lowered horns, and demolishing them.

**Food**

They have a simple stomach, and digestion of herbage takes place mainly in the voluminous sacculated caecum where most fermentation takes place (Clemens & Maloiy, 1982). They browse, manoeuvering food into their mouths with the aid of the prehensile upper lip, biting shoots off with the premolar teeth and grinding the food in the massive molar teeth. They will push over higher growth to obtain edible parts. Sticks and thorns are included in the diet, different parts of different plants being utilised. In some cases only the outer tips of the shoots are taken, in others the twigs as well. Small forbs which grow low on the ground are also eaten and small quantities of grass are taken at certain times of the year, usually during the wet season (Moss, 1976). They are selective feeders and generally reject dry plant material (Goddard, 1968).

In both Hluhluwe and Umfolozi *Acacia* spp or their close relatives comprised at least half of the 10 most preferred species, and as they grew in size they became less and less preferred (Emslie & Adcock, 1990b). The most preferred species were *A. gerrardii*, *A. senegal* and *A. borleae*. The more common *A. karroo* and *Dichrostachys cinerea* were less preferred, but more important in the diet, accounting for about a fifth of woody browse eaten in summer.

Despite the different species composition of the Umfolozi and Hluhluwe study areas, the striking feature of the black rhinoceros feeding was the very similar contribution to the diet by a number of important species that occurred in both areas (*) (Table 296.1).

**Table 296.1**

Percentage contribution of the top 10 woody species in the woody diet of black rhinoceros, *D. bicornis*, in the Hluhluwe and Umfolozi Game Reserves (Emslie & Adcock, 1990b)

| | Hluhluwe | Umfolozi |
|---|---|---|
| **Spirostachys africana* | 22,5 | 24,1 |
| *Acalypha glabrata* | 13,9 | |
| **Dichrostachys cinerea* | 10,8 | 10,5 |
| **Acacia karroo* | 8,2 | 10,3 |
| *Berchemia zeyheri* | 6,1 | |
| *Acacia caffra* | 5,2 | |
| **Acacia nilotica* | 3,8 | 4,7 |
| **Acacia gerrardii* | 3,6 | 5,1 |
| *Hibiscus* spp | 3,4 | |
| **Maytenus nemorosa* | 3,2 | 3,1 |
| *Acacia borleae* | 5,4 | |
| *Ehretia rigida* | 4,3 | |
| *Acacia tortilis* | 4,3 | |
| *Schotia capitata* | 2,9 | |

Through browsing, rhinoceros prune the bushes on which they feed, so that they become rounded on the sides and top. The bushes show little sign of the breaking or tearing which characterises elephant feeding.

In Kaokoland, Namibia, of the 103 plant species encountered, rhinoceros utilise 74 (Loutit, Louw & Seely, 1987). Apart from expected species such as *Acacia albida*, *Euphorbia virosa* was also fed upon and this plant and *Merremia* spp had the highest water content. The high tannin content and other defence mechanisms such as formidable spines on *E. virosa* did not deter the rhinoceros from eating them, nor did the very high crude fibre content of *Commiphora virgata*, *Sterculia africana* and *Euphorbia damarana*. However, in deserts, food selection may be influenced by other factors than nutritional value. For example, in parts of East Africa, *Euphorbia tirucalli* forms 70% of their diet during the dry season (Goddard, 1968), the rhinoceros obtaining their moisture requirements in this way. This was also the case with *D. b. michaeli* in the Addo National Park where they selected succulent plants with a high moisture content in the dry season (Hall-Martin, Erasmus & Botha, 1982).

From studies undertaken in the Subregion, one can conclude that black rhinoceros feed on an unusually wide variety of species, and they are flexible, shifting their preferences according to availability of species. They can also utilise plants unavailable to other herbivores because of their formidable chemical and morphological defences.

In the Zambezi Valley, Zimbabwe in the 1982/83 and 1983/84 wet seasons, rainfall was only about half the mean over 17 years. This resulted in reduced vegetative growth and at least 38 rhinoceros died of malnutrition in the subsequent dry seasons. Most (22) of these animals were under 10 years of age, with the next biggest category (18) being those 31–40 years of age (Dunham, 1985). This indicates how important it is not to exceed carrying capacity with species such as rhinoceros which cannot be translocated rapidly from one area to another.

In the well-watered Hluhluwe Game Reserve, they drink nightly, as they do in the hot, dry months in the Etosha National Park, but in the cooler months they drink every second night (Owen-Smith, 1988).

**Reproduction**

Black rhinoceros may breed at any time of the year in the Subregion. In the Hluhluwe/Umfolozi Game Reserve there are minor peaks in births in January and again from June to August. Hitchins & Anderson (1983) found that females may produce calves when only 6,5 years of age, but this is exceptional and they usually only conceive after seven years of age.

In Natal, Anderson (1983) found that pro-oestrus lasts six to seven days and is characterised by frequent tail-erecting by the female. During this time the male was in attendance and oestrus lasted only one day. During pro-oestrus complex encounters between a bull and a cow occur, the cow squirting small amounts of urine on to the ground, the bull then sniffing this and performing "flehmen" (Moss, 1976). Initially events are largely governed by the cow. The bull approaches her circumspectly in a stiff-legged gait, his hind legs dragging on the ground, and, face to face, they spar with their front horns or nudge one another with the sides of their heads. The bull horns the cow between the hind legs and under the stomach. She may attack him from time to time, but during courtship no serious or vicious fighting takes place (Goddard, 1966; Schenkel & Schenkel-Hullinger, 1969). The length of the oestrous cycle was 35 days (S.D. = 7,7; n=10), although captive animals cycled approximately every 25 days (n=7), based on inter-oestrous intervals and urinary hormone profiles (Hodges, pers. comm.). Observations confined to daytime showed that copulation occurred two to seven times (n=47); duration of copulation varied from 12 to 43 minutes and the number of ejaculations ranged from twice in 12 minutes to nine times in 43 minutes. Following a gestation period of 15 months, a single calf of about 40 kg is born. Calving intervals in Hluhluwe were 44 months and in Umfolozi 30 months.

Calves walk and suckle within three hours of birth. At this stage the females are extremely intolerant of disturbance. At birth calves are lighter in colour than adults and are sparsely haired. They are alert and playful and appear to have keener eyesight than their mothers. Suckling at first takes place standing up, but as they grow older, the calves have to lie down on their bellies to reach the teats, a pair being situated in the cow's inguinal region. During the early life of the calf the cow tends to keep to thick bush, the calf always in close proximity, walking at her side or behind her. At a few weeks of age the calf starts to browse, but continues to suckle for about a year. The cow calls the calf by emitting a high-pitched mew, while the calf, if it has strayed, calls the cow with a bellowing squeal. The cow will defend her young vigorously. Goddard (1966) witnessed a cow killing a lion in these circumstances.

The calf is rejected by the cow at two to four years of age, either during the cow's next pregnancy or at birth of the new calf. If rejection of the calf takes place after the new calf is born, the rejection by the female may be active and vicious (Moss, 1976). The calf continues to grow until seven to eight years old. It may join another calf, a bull or another female, the females being usually more tolerant of their presence. Spermatogenesis commences in males after eight years of age, but no male was observed holding a territory or mating which was under nine years of age (Hitchins & Anderson, 1983).

In the first two years of their lives mortality is high. Goddard (1966) estimated that there was about a 16% loss, caused by predation by lions and spotted hyaenas or lowered resistance to disease caused by lack of food or water.

# XLII. Family EQUIDAE
## Zebra

Churcher & Richardson (1978) regarded the African fossil equids as being descendants of immigrants that crossed into northeastern Africa during the late to middle Miocene Epoch some 15 to five million years ago. The earliest known of these immigrants was a small equid, *Hipparion primigenium*, which is known from the late middle to early late Miocene beds of East Africa. It was a forest dwelling species that became extinct by the end of the Pleistocene Epoch, perhaps being unable to compete with the antelopes. A much larger species, *Equus burchelli mauritianus*, from North Africa was the ancestor of the later, modern *E. burchelli* subspecies. The origins of the mountain zebra, *E. zebra*, and the extinct quagga, *E. quagga*, are obscure. The latter is poorly represented in the fossil record, some of the material being of doubtful validity. Churcher (1970) described a distorted palate with seven teeth from the early Pleistocene which he ascribed to *E. quagga*. Churcher & Richardson (1978) thought that *E. quagga* might well represent the ancestral condition seen in *E. b. mauritianus* as represented by fossil remains from the middle Pleistocene.

Today the Family is represented by three living species of zebras: *Equus grevyi* Oustalet, 1882 of East Africa; *E. zebra* Linnaeus, 1758 of the Subregion and southwest Angola, and *E. burchelli* which has a wide distribution from the north-eastern parts of the Subregion west to Angola and north to East Africa. Ansell (1974a) gave the chromosome numbers of the three species: *E. grevyi* 2n=46; *E. zebra* 2n=32; and *E. burchelli* 2n=44. The quagga, *E. quagga*, which occurred in the southwestern parts of the Subregion, became extinct towards the end of the 19th century.

In the equids the mid-toe on the foot is fully developed and ends in a hoof, only the vestiges of digits two and four (the splint bones) being present.

The dental formula of the zebra is similar to all extant equids; the deciduous dentition is:

$$i\frac{3}{3}\ c\frac{1}{1}\ p\frac{4}{4} = 32$$

and the dental formula of the permanent dentition in adults is:

$$I\frac{3}{3}\ C\frac{0-1}{0-1}\ P\frac{3}{3}\ M\frac{3}{3} = 36 \text{ or } 40$$

In the females the canine teeth are rudimentary or absent, but they are present in the males. In the juveniles the deciduous canines are present but never pierce the gums.

The deciduous first premolars are rudimentary and are soon shed, not to be replaced. The deciduous incisors have narrow necks and the permanent incisors are columnar with broad cutting faces. The incisor teeth have an enamel-lined hollow (the infundibulum) running down the centre for a variable length. As the incisor teeth wear down to flat surfaces, the shape of the infundibulum can be used as a criterion for age class determination. This has been defined for the Cape mountain zebra, *E. z. zebra* (Penzhorn, 1987), Hartmann's zebra, *E. z. hartmannae* (Joubert, 1971b) and Burchell's zebra, *E. burchelli* (Smuts, 1972). The cheekteeth have high crowns, with folds of enamel on their occlusal surfaces.

Key to the species after Meester, Davis & Coetzee (1964)

1. The dark stripe running down the middle of the upper parts of the body forming a distinct "gridiron" pattern on the croup; a dewlap present; ears large, their mean length over 200 mm

   ... *E. zebra*

   The dark stripe not forming a "gridiron" pattern on the croup; no dewlap; ears smaller, their mean length under 200 mm

   ... *E. burchelli*

## Genus *Equus* Linnaeus, 1758

No. 297

## *Equus zebra* (Linnaeus, 1758)

*E. z. zebra* Linnaeus, 1758

## Cape mountain zebra
## Kaapse bergsebra

Plate 28

### Colloquial Name

While it is not usual to apply colloquial names to subspecies, in this case it is convenient to retain the name Cape mountain zebra in order to distinguish them from Hartmann's mountain zebra, *E. z. hartmannae*, of Namibia and Angola. In Afrikaans the alternative name *Kaapse bergkwagga* is often used.

### Taxonomic Notes

Only two subspecies have been described, the Cape mountain zebra, *E. z. zebra*, from the Cape Province, and Hartmann's mountain zebra, *E. z. hartmannae*, of Namibia and Angola.

Mountain zebra differ from Burchell's (plains) zebra in that the black stripes on their heads and bodies are narrower and consequently more numerous. There is a marked contrast between their width and the width of the black stripes on the rump which are clearly much broader and show no sign of "shadow" stripes between them. Mountain zebra have white under parts, with a central narrow black stripe running from the chest to the belly. The black body stripes fade out on the lower parts of the flanks. In Burchell's zebra the black body stripes continue around the under parts. Mountain zebra have a distinct dewlap and are smaller in body size than Burchell's zebra. There is some variation in the colour of the dark stripes which may be black or deep chocolate-brown, which may be a factor of the moult. Heinichen (1969) showed that both subspecies have the same number of chromosomes, namely 2n=32, and thus belong to the same species, *E. zebra*.

### Description

No two zebras are alike in the striped pattern of the coat, and the two sides of the body do not match each other exactly. The ground colour is white with black stripes, the black stripes on the body narrower than on the rump, those on the neck slightly broader than those on the body, and those on the head narrowest of all. The legs are distinctly black-striped to the hooves. The stripes on the hind legs are broader than on the forelegs and there are black patches just above the hooves. The black body stripes do not continue on to the under parts, discontinuing abruptly on the lower parts of the flanks. The under parts are white, with a central longitudinal black stripe. The upper two or three black stripes on the rump are exceptionally broad, with no "shadow" stripes between them as in Burchell's zebra. On the rump, from the front of the pelvis to the base of the tail, the black markings form a "gridiron" pattern, a characteristic feature of the mountain zebras.

The tip of the muzzle is black and immediately behind this there is a characteristic orange-coloured suffusion on the top and sides. The ears are rounded and, when viewed from the front, have white tips and black margins. On the back they are white at the bases, then black with white tips. Along the top of the tail there is a narrow black stripe which extends to the whisk of long black or blackish-brown hair towards the tip, the hair dangling below the level of the hock.

Their hooves are compact, with hard ventral surfaces, presumably an adaptation to the type of terrain in which they live (Grobler, *in litt.*) (Plate I).

Cape mountain zebra stallions stand about 1,27 m at the shoulder and are estimated by Hall-Martin (*in litt.*) to have a mass of about 234 kg; the mares stand 1,24 m at the shoulder, with a mass of 240–250 kg (Table 297.1). They are therefore smaller is size and mass than Burchell's zebra, *E. burchelli*, or Hartmann's mountain zebra, *E. z. hartmannae*.

The ears of the Cape mountain zebra are noticeably larger than those of Burchell's zebra, having a mean length of 220 mm (Hall-Martin, *in litt.*), compared with 167 mm (16 stallions) and 174 mm (16 mares) for Burchell's zebra (Smuts, 1974).

**Table 297.1**

Measurements (mm) and mass (kg) of adult specimens of the Cape mountain zebra, *Equus z. zebra* (Hall-Martin, *in litt.*)

| | Males | | | Females | | |
|---|---|---|---|---|---|---|
| | $\bar{x}$ | n | Range | $\bar{x}$ | n | Range |
| TL | 2690 | 1 | — | 2610 | 5 | 2550–2690 |
| T | 420 | 1 | — | 430 | 5 | 400–470 |
| Hf c/u | 510 | 1 | — | 480 | 5 | 470–490 |
| E | 220 | 1 | — | 220 | 5 | 210–230 |
| Sh.ht | 1270 | 1 | — | 1240 | 5 | 1160–1285 |
| Mass | — | —* | — | 234,3 | 5 | 204–257 |

*Estimated as 250–260 kg (Hall-Martin *in litt.*).

These figures include the masses of two old specimens which were in poor condition and had died natural deaths. The mean is therefore likely to be slightly greater when dealing with healthy individuals (Hall-Martin, *in litt.*).

### Skull

The skull of *E. z. zebra* has been subjected to detailed study by Smuts & Penzhorn (1988). The over-all features are similar to those of *E. burchelli* although 11 small structural differences are described. For further details of the equid skull see *E. burchelli* **Skull** and Fig. 298.3.

**Plate 28**

295. White rhinoceros, *Ceratotherium simum*
     Witrenoster
296. Black rhinoceros, *Diceros bicornis*
     Swartrenoster
297. Mountain zebra, *Equus zebra*
     Bergsebra
298. Burchell's zebra, *Equus burchelli*
     Bontsebra

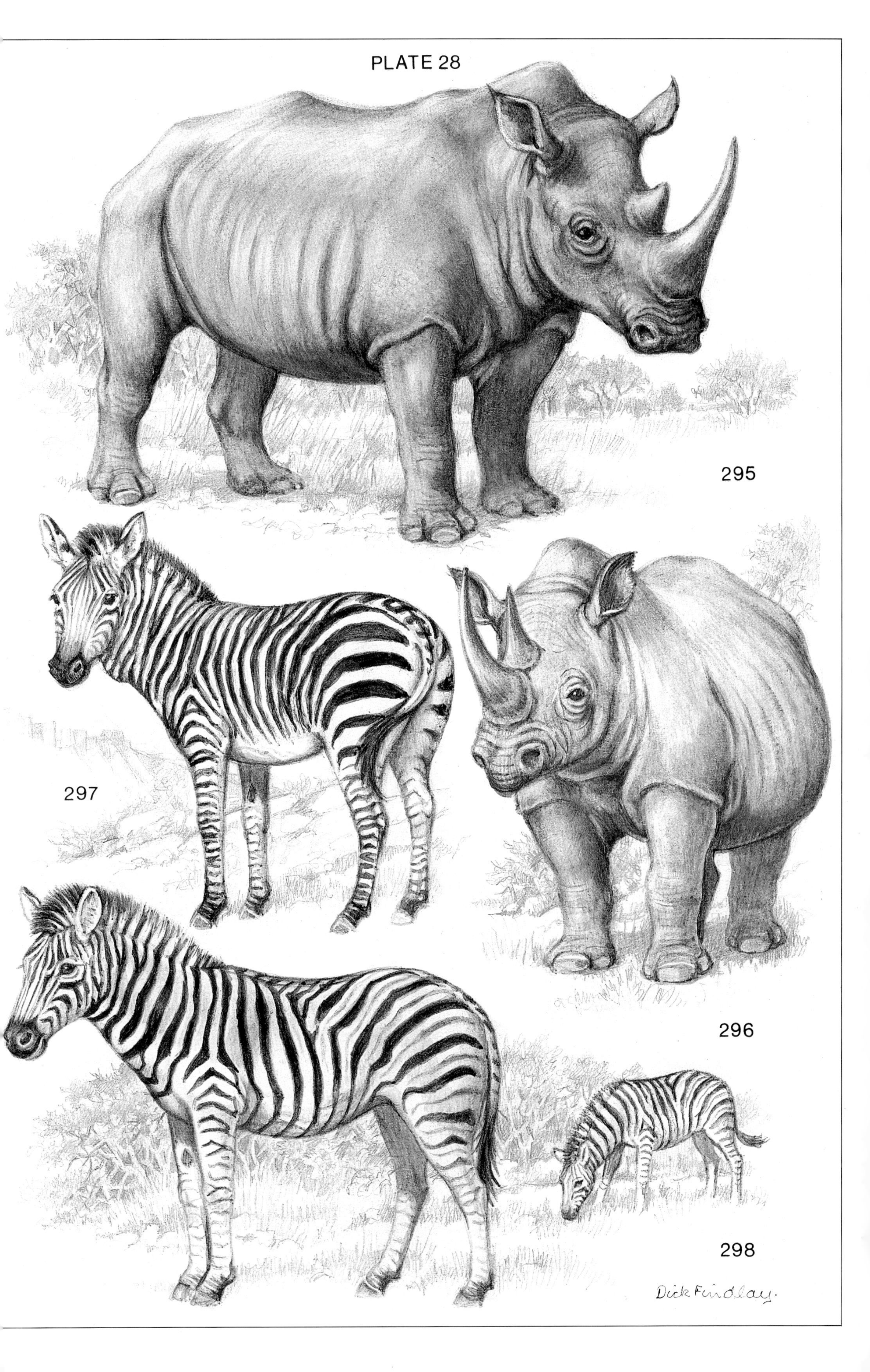
PLATE 28
295
296
297
298
Dick Findlay.

## Distribution

Historically Cape mountain zebras occurred throughout the mountainous areas of the Cape Province from Paarl Rock eastwards to the Amatola Mountains in the Cathcart area and northwards to the Nuweveld, Suurberg and Stormberg mountains (Millar, 1970a). Reports of mountain zebras in the Kamiesberg, Namaqualand, most probably were of Hartmann's mountain zebras (Sidney, 1965). Whatever subspecies they were, they no longer occur in this area.

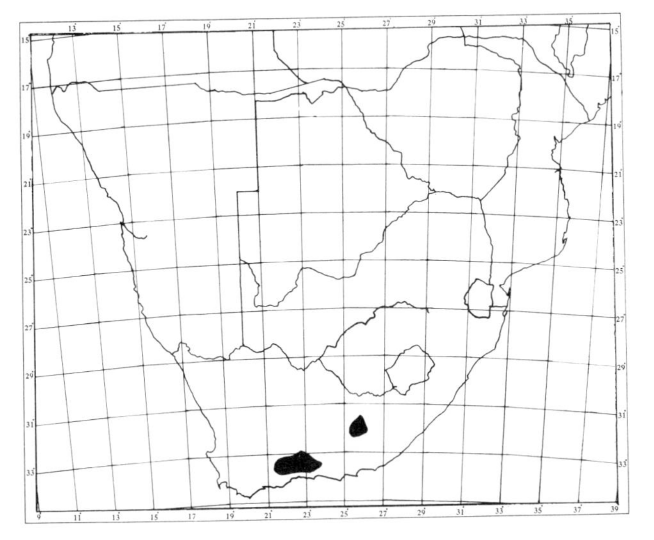

In the early 1930's it was apparent that, unless they were afforded special protection, Cape mountain zebras would become extinct. In 1937 the State proclaimed the farm Babylons Toren in the Cradock District a National Park, which then contained five stallions and a mare. By 1945 only two stallions and a young mare remained, to which were added five stallions and six mares from a neighbouring farm Waterval, donated by Mr. H.J. Lombard (Penzhorn, 1975). This retrieved the situation and from this nucleus, with the purchase and addition to the park of several adjoining farms, the population increased to 220 (by 1980) and is maintained at its present level of *ca.* 220 zebras. As many as 40 zebras are removed annually to re-establish breeding herds elsewhere within their original range (Penzhorn, 1988). Some 280 zebras have now been redistributed in this way and the total population of *E. z. zebra* was *ca.* 474 in 1985 (Smithers, 1986).

*Southern African Subregion*

Today they are confined to the Mountain Zebra National Park, Cradock, with small isolated populations in the Gamka, Kamanassie, Kouga and Baviaanskloof mountains (Millar, 1970a).

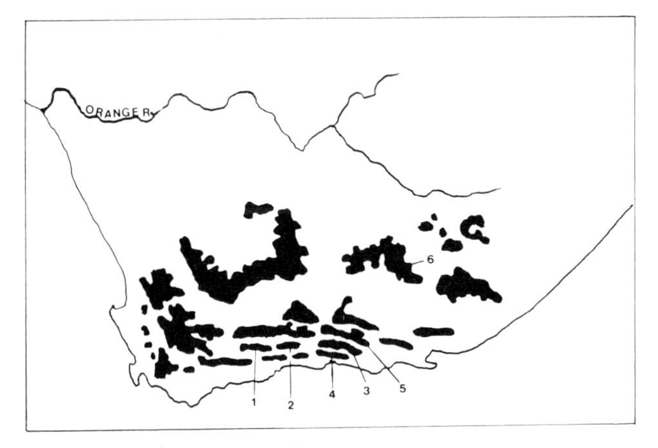


Fig. 297.1. Mountains of the Cape Province where the Cape mountain zebra, *Equus z. zebra*, formerly occurred, with numbered areas where small numbers are still found:
1. Gamka Mountains 2. Kamanassie Mountains 3. Kouga Mountains 4. Outeniqua Mountains* 5. Baviaanskloof Mountains 6. Mountain Zebra National Park (after Millar (1970a) and Penzhorn (1975)).
*May now no longer occur.

## Habitat

As the colloquial name suggests, Cape mountain zebras are closely confined to mountainous areas that offer the required types of grazing and a plentiful water supply and shelter in the form of kloofs and ridges. While they occur up to altitudes of about 2 000 m, Millar (1970a) stated that during winter with harsh weather conditions they tend to move to lower altitudes than those occupied during the summer months. They occur on plateaux and the slopes of mountains, particularly in areas where there are stands of red grass, *Themeda triandra* (Grobler, *in litt.*).

## Habits

Penzhorn (1975, 1979) studied the species in the Mountain Zebra National Park, and the following information is available largely as a result of his work. Cape mountain zebras are gregarious and predominantly diurnal. They are most active for an hour or two after dawn and in the late morning and late aternoon and this activity continues until sunset in the summer months and after dark in the winter. Between periods of activity they rest as a herd, either standing or lying down, not necessarily seeking shade when doing so. They drink water daily, during the late morning and then again in the afternoon and have a distinct preference for clear water, avoiding muddy water.

Dusting is regularly practised. The individual rolls in the sand, first on the one side, then stands up and rolls on the other side. They rarely roll right over from one side to another. Self-scratching and nibbling are common and mutual grooming between two partners, lasting up to 20 minutes at a time, is of regular occurrence. This consists of nibbling at the neck, mane, shoulders and other parts of the body.

The social organisation is based on the breeding herd, consisting of a stallion and his mares together with their foals. Penzhorn (1975) stated that the largest herd he encountered consisted of 13 individuals, comprising a stallion, five mares and seven foals. The mean number in 21 herds was 4,7 individuals, with a range of two to 13, which is nearly identical with the figures given by Joubert (1971b) for Hartmann's mountain zebra in Namibia. These herds remain stable over many years. At De Hoop Nature Reserve the mean period of herd tenure was found to be 7,42 ± 4,98 and 8,78 ± 2,98 for six stallions and nine mares respectively whose life histories were known (Lloyd & Rasa, 1989). Should the stallion die his place is taken by another, although sometimes the herd may split up (Penzhorn, 1984b). Mares usually remain in breeding herds for life.

Herd stallions have been known to maintain their status within the herd for up to 15 years, but if they do not remain in good physical condition, they may be displaced by younger stallions. This can lead to serious fighting involving biting and kicking, severe wounds being inflicted on the antagonists. Breeding herds are formed initially when a stallion, at about five years old, acquires a mare from an established group. At a younger age he is unlikely to have the necessary stamina to withstand the opposition to this from the herd stallion. He may also acquire a mare or mares from a split herd that has lost its stallion. While in the long established herd the role of the stallion is relatively passive, with the establishment of a new herd, with looser ties, the stallion has to actively herd the mares and foals to prevent them from leaving, especially those mares he may have acquired recently.

The herd moves either by the initiation of movement from the stallion or a mare. When danger threatens, a mare with a foal usually takes the lead in moving away. The stallion maintains a defensive position at the rear. At water the stallion leads to check for possible danger.

In the smaller herds Penzhorn (1975) detected a social hierarchy among the mares, established by threat gestures. In the larger herds each individual appears to have learnt its relative position and threat gestures are rare. In all breeding herds the herd stallion is dominant. Mares with new-born foals become extremely aggressive towards other members, which may lead to a temporary rise in their status.

Threat behaviour takes the form of pulling back the ears against the head, lowering the head, with neck outstretched and teeth bared, tail-lashing and finally a rush towards the antagonist. Moving away is an adequate response to threat, but may be accompanied by a kick in defence.

Vocalisation includes a high-pitched alarm call from the stallion when danger threatens and a drawn-out squeal uttered by a bachelor when confronted by the herd stallion. The herd stallion may utter an alarm snort as well. This is actuated, on sensing danger, by an audible intake of air through the nose, a sharp expelling of air, followed by an audible intake. Penzhorn (1975) listed a soft sound of contentment when feeding, audible over short distances only.

Cape mountain zebras are not territorial. The home ranges of the breeding herds overlap and show some change seasonally. They are sensitive to adverse weather conditions and during heavy rainstorms cease to feed and stand with their backs to the rain. On cold mornings they tend to use east-facing slopes and stand with their bodies at right angles to the sun's rays. They use kloofs and shallow caves for shelter (Penzhorn, 1975).

The major factors in dispersion are the movement of foals of both sexes from their natal groups to bachelor groups and from there to breeding herds (Lloyd & Rasa, 1989). Fillies left maternal herds at 18,8 ± 6,0 months and colts six months later at 24,4 ± 6,0 months. "Bachelor" groups were almost always of mixed sex and fillies remained associated with these groups for 8,7 months, compared to 29,9 months for colts. There is a distinct social hierarchy in these bachelor herds (Grobler, *in litt.*) and they are less rigid in their structure than breeding herds.

Cape mountain zebras react to the flight or alarm signals of black wildebeest, *Connochaetes gnou*, but they seldom react to the smaller species of antelope such as springbok or blesbok. Unlike Burchell's zebra, the Cape mountain zebra does not appear to associate with antelope.

After the first bout of activity in the early morning they rest, either standing or lying down, and thereafter during the day rest at irregular intervals. In the Mountain Zebra National Park, unlike Hartmann's mountain zebras in Namibia, they made no attempt to seek shade, resting in the open, the foals spending longer periods resting than the adults.

**Food**

Cape mountain zebras are predominantly grazers but will take limited amounts of browse as well. They spend more than half of the daylight hours feeding, which they tend to do in the vicinity of their drinking places. More time is spent grazing during the daylight hours in summer than in winter. As they require a greater food intake in winter, feeding may extend into the night (Penzhorn, 1975). The grass is gathered with the lips, then held between the incisors and plucked by an upward, downward or sideways jerk of the head.

Penzhorn (1975) observed them feeding on the following grasses in the Mountain Zebra National Park: *Aristida congesta; Cymbopogon plurinodes; Cynodon incompletus; Digitaria eriantha; Eragrostis chloromelas; E. curvula; E. lehmanniana; Merxmuellera disticha; Setaria neglecta; Themeda triandra* and *Tragus berteronianus*. Browse plants included *Acacia karroo, Eriocephalus ericoides, Lycium* sp and *Pentzia incana*.

Grobler (*in litt.*) in a quantitative study in the same park found that although they feed on a variety of grasses, the principal species utilised were red grass, *T. triandra*, turpentine grass, *C. plurinodes*, and spear grass, *Heteropogon contortus*, in that order. Seasonally they would feed on the seed heads of *S. neglecta* and *E. curvula*. He considered browsing as atypical of the species and of rare occurrence. Certain grasses are uprooted totally in feeding and the entire plant is eaten. They drink daily and are partial to mineralised soil licks.

Penzhorn (1975) found that there were three main grazing periods during daylight hours: from dawn to about 08h30 in winter, later in summer; from 10h00 to 12h30 in winter, irregular in summer, and from 14h00 to dusk in winter, 16h00 to dusk in summer.

Penzhorn (1975) recorded that foals nibbled grass when only a few days old, which corresponds with observations by Joubert (1971b) on Hartmann's mountain zebra in Namibia. Up to the age of about 14 weeks the foals of both species and of Burchell's zebra, *E. burchelli*, (Smuts, 1972) eat the faeces of adults, particularly that of their own mothers. They would paw the faeces and eat only parts of two or three pellets, perhaps as a means of obtaining a supply of intestinal micro-organisms that are required to break down the cellulose in their food.

**Reproduction**

Foals are born year-round, births peaking in summer (Penzhorn, 1985a; Penzhorn & Lloyd, 1987). Mares may produce their first foals at four to five years of age, the mean length of time between the birth of foals being 18 months (Grobler, *in litt.*). The gestation period is given by Penzhorn (1975) as about one year. A single foal is produced at a birth.

Penzhorn (1985a) found that when the rains are late the conception date can be delayed. First conception occurred at 26 months and mean age at first foaling was 66,5 months (range 38–105, n=29; Penzhorn, 1985a). Mares may continue to produce foals up to an age of 21 years and possibly longer, and stallions may remain fertile for up to 19 years in the wild (Penzhorn, 1985a).

Testis mass of adult stallions (70 g) was appreciably less than that of other zebra species. Up to the age of 29 months, histologically the testes were prepubertal, but at 48 months spermatogenic activity was at a very low level, showing a marked increase from 54 months. From 6,5–19 years stallions showed marked spermatogenesis, no matter what the season (Penzhorn & Van der Merwe, 1988). During the first weeks of its life the foal remains in close association with its mother, seldom venturing more than a few paces from her (Penzhorn, 1984b). She actively discourages contact between her foal and other members of her group, irrespective of their social status. When suckling, the foal stands parallel to its mother with its tail towards her head. It conveys its desire to suckle to the mother by pressing its body against her chest as it moves to suckle across her front. This behaviour is apparently important, for foals seeking to drink by direct approach to the teats are often unsuccessful.

Penzhorn (1975) found that many young males left their breeding herd voluntarily at an age of just over 22 months, when their mother's new foal was about four months old. The young females leave the herd during their first oestrus to wander alone or be successfully herded by a bachelor. On occasion they may join bachelor herds until herded by a male. Unlike Hartmann's zebra, the mothers apparently do not forcibly expel the foal from the herd.

When a foal is very young it is tolerated by mares within its group and if a foal loses its mother, another mare with a foal may adopt it (Penzhorn, 1975). Lloyd & Harper (1980) recorded a mare rejecting her own foal and adopting the foal of another mare. The herd stallion is normally indifferent towards foals, but may actively discourage contact between foals in his group and "strangers" from other groups.

The mortality rate for foals at De Hoop was high, 26% of 42 foals dying. Nine of the 11 foals which died were the offspring of subordinate mares. Mortality appears to be related to behavioural factors, as subordinate mares defend their foals vigorously which suffer broken legs probably inflicted by dominant mares (Lloyd & Rasa, 1989).

---

No. 297A

## *E. z. hartmannae* Matschie, 1898

## Hartmann's mountain zebra
## Hartmann se bergsebra

---

**Colloquial Name**

The reason for the retention of the name Hartmann's mountain zebra for this, a subspecies, is for the purpose of distinguishing them from the Cape mountain zebra, *E. z. zebra*.

### Taxonomic Notes

See notes under the Cape mountain zebra.

### Description

Hartmann's mountain zebras differ from Cape mountain zebras in that they are slightly larger. The stripes are about equal in width especially on the rump, but in some individuals the light stripes may be slightly wider. Hairs on the rump are 10,0±1,8 mm long, oval or oblong in cross-section, with an irregular waved mosaic pattern along the entire length (Fig. XLII.1) (Buys & Keogh, 1984). The dark stripes are composed of black hairs but around the muzzle the black hairs are interspersed with red hairs medially (Findlay, 1988). The black hairs are 4,55±0,65 mm long, the red hairs being 20% shorter. Findlay (1988) suggested the red colour is produced by a different growth intensity rather than different pigmentation. Dust-rolling tends to obscure the light colour of the coat, tinging it various shades of red, a feature commonly seen in colour slides and published colour photographs.

Adult males stand about 1,5 m at the shoulder, with tails 0,5 m long and ears 280 mm long. There is no difference between the sexes except that males are heavier, averaging 298 kg (n=22), females 276 kg (n=23), and males over seven years old average 336 kg (Joubert, 1971b).

The hooves of Hartmann's mountain zebras grow extremely fast to compensate for the heavy wear to which they are subjected on the rocky substrate on which they live. This is manifest under captive conditions where, unless a special hard substrate is provided, the hooves grow and distort, requiring continued maintenance.

### Skull

In shape the skull of Hartmann's mountain zebra is identical to that of the Cape mountain zebra, but in overall measurements of old adult males, it is slightly larger. As in the Cape mountain zebra, the canine teeth are prominent in adult males, while those of the females are rudimentary and normally do not cut through the gums (Joubert, 1971b). The tooth formula is the same as in other members of the family. For further details of the equid skull see *E. burchelli* **Skull** and Fig. 298.3.

### Distribution

They are confined to Namibia, with a marginal extension in the extreme southwest of Angola. It has been stated (Shortridge, 1934) that mountain zebras were still found in the Kamiesberg in 1912 and Sidney (1965) quoted Lang who stated that they occurred as far south of the Orange River as Kamieskroon (Lat. 31 °S) in the Cape Province. No mountain zebras occur naturally in these areas today and it is impossible to say whether, if they did, they were either of the two subspecies or an intermediate between them. They have been introduced to the Hester Malan Reserve, Springbok, Namaqualand and to the Cape Point Nature Reserve (Fairall, pers. comm.).

*South of the Sahara, excluding the Southern African Subregion*

They occur in the Iona National Park in southwest **Angola**.

*Southern African Subregion*

In **Namibia** they occur in the mountainous transition zone between the Namib Desert in the west and the plateau in the east. Their distribution today is discontinuous, in the north occurring from the Angola border in Kaokoland southwards to about the Ugab River and eastwards to farms in the Outjo District. South of this there is a small island of occurrence in the Erongo Mountains in southeastern Damaraland on the borders of the Omaruru and Karibib districts and a much more extensive area of occurrence southwards on the escarpment from the Swakop River south to the Naukluft Mountains and eastwards along the Kuiseb and Gaub drainage into the Khomas Hochland. Southwards there is a break in their distribution and they reoccur in the Fish River Canyon and Huns Mountains near the Orange River.

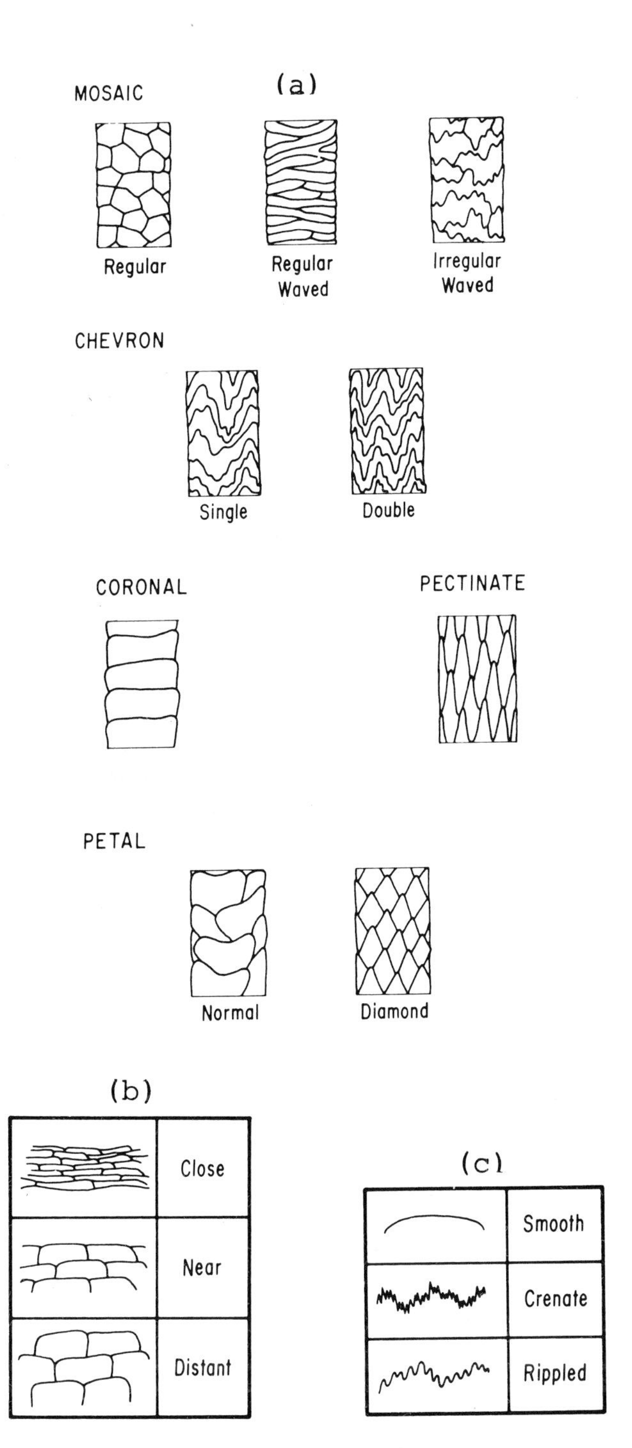


Fig. XLII.1 (a) Hair cuticular scale patterns
(b) Distance between scale margins
(c) Form of scale margins (Keogh, 1983)

### Habitat

The preferred habitat of Hartmann's mountain zebras is the ecotone of mountainous areas and flats. Seasonally they make wide use of sand flats. Viljoen (pers. comm.) found that their use of these areas depends on the food supply offered. As the food supply on the mountains reaches low levels at the end of the dry season about September, they move to the flats, later returning to the mountains as the food supply there improves. They also exhibit considerable local movement to areas where local rain has improved the grazing, sometimes covering distances up to 100 km. They use kloofs and krantzes as shelter from cold winds.

Joubert (1971b) stated that they must drink at least daily during the hot, summer months and often do so twice a day, and that water is an important limiting factor in their distribution. In spite of this apparent water dependence, in the

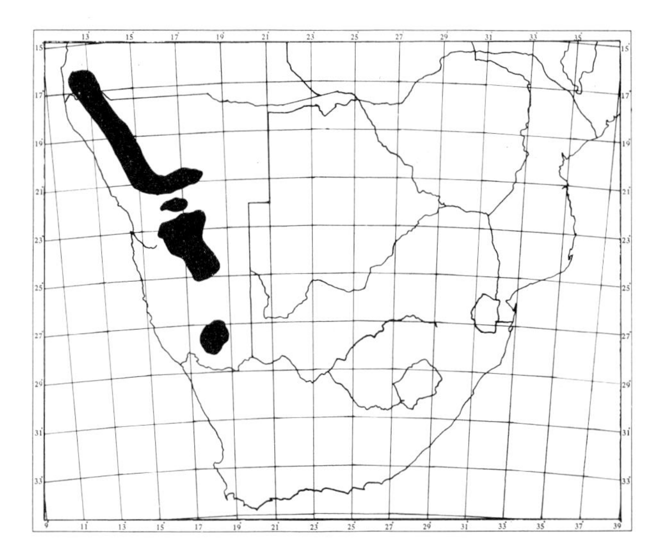

Iona National Park in southwestern Angola they occur on the open sandy plains where in order to make use of the nutritious desert grasses, they must endure extended periods away from a water supply (Huntley, 1972a). In this area water is available in the adjacent mountains where Burchell's zebra, *E. burchelli*, occurs, a species that is apparently more water dependent than Hartmann's mountain zebra.

## Habits

Hartmann's mountain zebras are gregarious and diurnal. The periods of major activity are shortly after first light in the morning and in the afternoon from 15h00 until sunset, but even during the intervening period they may be active for short periods. Most of the periods of activity are taken up in grazing, but not all members of a group are engaged in this activity at the same time, a factor which probably results in increasing vigilance for the group (Joubert, 1971b). In grazing they move slowly in a zig-zag pattern, with the group members narrowly scattered. Where they are undisturbed, they may drink at any time of the day, but where regularly hunted, they water during the night.

Their social organisation is similar to that of the Cape mountain zebra and is based on the family group of a stallion with his mares and their foals, stallion groups, and, occasionally, a solitary stallion. Under certain circumstances family groups come together to form herds of up to 30 individuals (Viljoen, pers. comm.). Family groups are formed when a dominant stallion, against strong competition from other stallions, obtains possession of a number of females and manages to retain them. When a group has been established in this way, the dominant stallion alone serves the females in his group. A male without a group has little or no chance of mating (Joubert, 1971b). A young female who is not yet sexually mature, after being driven from a family group, usually joins up with a bachelor group. Joubert (1971b) quoted an instance where such a female came into oestrus but, in spite of the fact that fully grown males were present who exhibited flehmen, they did not mate with her. She mated instead with the dominant male in a nearby family group.

When family groups approach each other this may lead to aggressive behaviour between their dominant males. Opposing males try to gain psychological advantage by a confident approach to each other with feigned kicking, nasogenital or head-rump contacts, tail-lashing and lateral displays (Joubert, 1971b). These displays serve to reduce the psychological pressures built up between the antagonists and prevent the issue developing into fighting. Withdrawal without loss of face takes the form of the individuals adopting grazing attitudes and moving off.

Bachelor groups may attach themselves temporarily to family groups, the dominant male of the family group fraternising with members of the bachelor group. Bachelor males exhibit submissiveness to the dominant male, circling around him and uttering high-pitched submissive calls and lowering their heads.

Family groups may lose their dominant male through death or loss of status. In the latter instance they usually join bachelor groups, but otherwise family groups are stable units. Joubert (1971b) found a distinct hierarchy among the mares in the groups, the association between the individual mares being much stronger than that between the mares and the stallion. Joubert (1971b) found that no other activity takes up so much time, even in old established groups, than the affirmation of social status between the individual mares.

The home ranges of the groups overlap considerably and are affected by factors such as the availability of food and water, topography and population pressures. Seasonally the size of the home range varies, normally being much larger during the dry months of the year. In the case of the bachelor groups the home ranges are better defined, but they tend to move with the moving populations.

Vocalisation is similar to that of the Cape mountain zebra. Joubert (1971b) listed the sound of contentment, uttered when grazing or resting, as being achieved by forcing air through the closed lips, causing them to slap together. The alarm is a sudden, short, explosive snort which alerts the whole group. They also use the characteristic Burchell's zebra, *E. burchelli*, call of *kwah-ha*, repeated as an alarm, but they use it less frequently than do Burchell's zebras. The submissive call is a high-pitched squeal, often heard in the bachelor groups and also used by the foal at the time of being expelled from the group by the mare.

Hartmann's zebras are subject to predation by spotted hyaenas, lions, leopards and cheetahs. Viljoen (pers comm.) observed from spoor and other signs that a stallion had not only kicked to death an adult spotted hyaena, *C. crocuta*, but had pressed home its attack over a distance of a hundred metres, repeatedly kicking the hyaena, even after death, until the bushes and grass around were spotted with its blood.

During the hot summer months, from about October to February, they rest in the shade of trees and they will shelter from cold wind in krantzes and kloofs.

Among the young bachelor males play-fighting is common. Individuals bite each other's knees and manes and try to push each other down to the ground, and knock each other's shoulders. These attacks are never pushed home but serve the function of determining which of the antagonists is the strongest and fittest (Joubert, 1971b). There is a clear hierarchy in bachelor herds related to age and size. Hartmann's mountain zebras regularly dust bathe throughout the day, with peaks after the morning grazing and before the afternoon grazing reaches its peak (Joubert, 1971b). Dust bowls are located in sandy or loamy soil and may be up to 2,5 m in diameter and 300 mm deep. Except when dust bathing, the adults seldom lie down, although this is common behaviour in the foals, which will lie out in the full sun. Grooming of foals by their mothers is common practice, but no grooming has been observed between adults (Joubert, 1971b). Foals are playful, racing or chasing each other, play-fighting or indulging in a greeting ceremony of nose to nose contact or rubbing the head on the other foal's rump. This is a replica of the ceremony used by adults.

The survival rate for foals is high, probably due to the protection offered to the young by the other members of the group, especially the mares. Adverse weather conditions, especially drought, take the heaviest toll, although they also fall prey to leopards and cheetahs.

## Food

Hartmann's mountain zebras are grazers, but the types of grasses utilised have not been studied. Joubert (1971b) listed more than 30 species of grasses identified in the mountainous zone in which they occur, which, therefore, may include most of the preferred species. They are dependent on water and, where surface water is not available, they will dig for it, at times excavating to depths of a metre or more in likely places. The digging is carried out with a scraping movement of the front hooves. This also makes water available to a wide range of small mammals and birds whose survival depends on it.

### Reproduction

Most matings (81%) in the Etosha National Park occurred between November and April, peaking in December (Westlin-van Aarde *et al.*, 1988). Mares are capable of having their first foal at three years of age. Only a single record of the period of gestation is available which comes from a pair kept in captivity in Windhoek, where it was recorded as 364 days (Joubert, 1974b). No births have been seen in the wild, but as parturition approaches, mares become hostile to their last foals and actively drive them away. They may remain as members of her group or leave it to be absorbed into others. This may take place when the foal is weaned and about a year to 14 months old.

Young Hartmann's foals have shorter muzzles than the adults, their stripes are less distinct, and they have long woolly hair covering their bodies. The foal is protected actively by its mother who, in the first few hours of life, will continually smell and lick it, thus contributing to her recognition of it in the early stages. Later recognition appears to be by visual means, repeatedly confirmed by direct contact (Joubert, 1971b). Foals may start to nibble grass from the age of three days, but are not weaned until they are about 10 months old, when the mares drive them off.

As in the Cape mountain zebra, females have a pair of inguinal mammae.

---

No. 298

## *Equus burchelli* (Gray, 1824)

## Burchell's zebra
## Bontsebra

Plate 28

---

### Colloquial Name

This species was named after the well-known traveller and naturalist, W.J. Burchell, who brought the original specimen from South Africa and presented it to the British Museum. The name zebra is derived from the Italian or Portuguese form of the name given to the species in Zaire.

### Taxonomic Notes

Ansell (1974a) listed seven subspecies from the continent; three are from the Subregion, of which one, *E. b. burchelli*, is now extinct. Of the remaining two, he considered that *E. b. antiquorum* occupies a distributional range from southern Angola across northern Namibia, northern Botswana, the Transvaal to Natal; and *E. b. chapmani* from northeastern Botswana, Zimbabwe to southern Mozambique. In *E. b. antiquorum* there is some loss of the striping on the lower parts of the legs; in *E. b. chapmani* the legs are striped to the hooves, the pattern often black. There appear to be wide areas of intergradation, as for example in western Zimbabwe, and individuals with these different intensities of marking are found in the same area.

### Description

Body hair is 9,4±4,0 mm long, oval or oblong in cross-section, with an irregular waved mosaic pattern along the entire length (Fig. XLII.1) (Buys & Keogh, 1983). The characteristic striped pelages of zebras make them easily recognisable. In all the species that occur in the Subregion no two individuals are exactly alike and, in any population, there are some that do not conform to the general pattern. Smuts (1974) illustrated examples of Burchell's zebra in which the whole of the top of the back is broadly black and others in which the black stripes on the hind quarters are narrow, broken, or in parts missing altogether. Similarly the shadow stripes are of every gradation from distinct to missing altogether.

As a general rule, however, Burchell's zebra may be distinguished from the two mountain zebras, *E. zebra* by the possession of yellowish or greyish shadow stripes between the black on the hind quarters, the lack of the "gridiron" pattern on top of the hind quarters, from in front of the pelvis on to the tail, and the absence of a dewlap, which are features of the mountain zebras. Here too there are exceptions and Burchell's zebras rarely have three or four transverse "gridiron" markings at the base of the tail. The black striping is usually broader on the body and hind quarters than on the neck and head, where it forms a pattern of narrow neat stripes, which continue through on to the mane. The ears are white behind, sometimes with transverse black bars, and are upstanding with rounded tips, the front portion of the mane forming a black tuft of hair between them. The tail has a tuft of long black hair at the end, the dorsal longitudinal black band continuing on to the top of the tail where it is flanked by black bars. The front of the muzzle and around the chin is black.

Zebras invariably appear to be in prime condition with well rounded bodies and shining coats. Usually the stallions can be recognised as their necks are thicker than those of the mares.

Adult zebras stand about 1,36 m at the shoulder, with a mass of about 320 kg and there is no difference between stallions and mares in the southern part of their distributional range. This is at variance with the situation in East Africa where the mares of *E. grevyi* are smaller and lighter. In the Kruger National Park, stallions of Burchell's zebra are 22% heavier than *E. grevyi*, the mares 32% (Smuts, 1974).

Smuts (1974) listed the mean, maximum and minimum measurements and mass of 26 age classes of Burchell's zebra, *E. burchelli*, from the Kruger National Park. Table 298.1 provides the data from the 12 years old age class.

Spoor—Plate I.

**Table 298.1**

Measurements (mm) and mass (kg) of adult Burchell's zebras, *E. burchelli*, (12 years old) from the Kruger National Park (Smuts, 1974)

| | Males | | | Females | | |
|---|---|---|---|---|---|---|
| | $\bar{x}$ | n | Range | $\bar{x}$ | n | Range |
| TL* | 2784 | 3 | 2770–2841 | 2832 | 4 | 2753–3005 |
| T | 469 | 3 | 446–488 | 452 | 4 | 419–497 |
| Hf c/u | 514 | 3 | 482–531 | 516 | 4 | 509–525 |
| E | 163 | 3 | 155–169 | 172 | 4 | 165–176 |
| Sh.ht | 1338 | 2 | 1318–1358 | 1337 | 4 | 1303–1367 |
| Mass | 313,0 | 5 | 291,4–339,4 | 302,2 | 6 | 289,9–323,6 |

*Measured over the curve from the grinding surface of the first upper incisors to the fleshy tip of the tail.

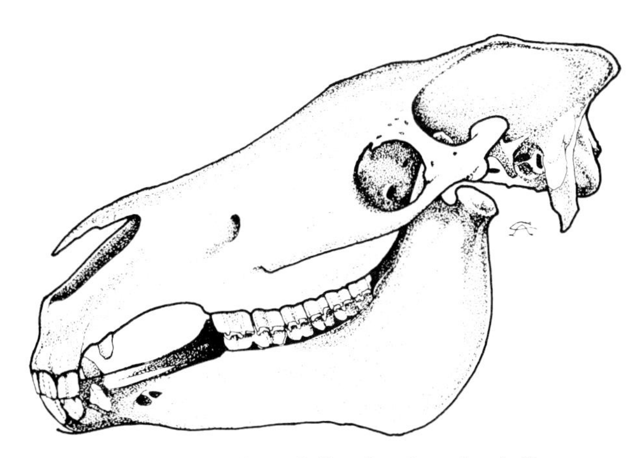

Fig. 298.1. Skull: Burchell's zebra, *Equus burchelli*
TL Skull 520 mm

**Skull** (Fig. 298.1)

The skull is elongated, three-quarters of the total length lying in front of the eye orbits which are situated at its broadest part. Smuts & Penzhorn (1988) have compared skulls and mandibles from *E. burchelli* with those of *E. zebra*. They have described eleven structural differences in detail. These are not great and for further particulars, refer to the scientific publication. There is a wide diastema between the incisors and the first premolar in which the canine teeth are situated.

In most cases, while these remain in the bone, they do not cut through the gum surface. In relation to the size of the skull the ear bullae are small and the paroccipital process is thick and well developed, descending far below the level of the bullae. The eye orbits are ringed with bone and the zygomatic arches are thick and heavily built to accommodate the attachment of the well developed masseter muscles which actuate the lower jaw.

The lower jaw is massive, broad at the back and roughened on its faces to provide firm attachment of the muscles. The coronoid rises high above the condyle to give leverage for the temporalis muscles, the condyle hinging on an open socket in the upper jaw to allow sideways and back to front movement in grinding the food.

The dental formula of the deciduous teeth is:

$i\frac{3}{3}\ c\frac{1}{1}\ p\frac{4}{4} = 32$

Late term foetuses and foals at birth show the first incisor and the second, third and fourth upper premolar erupted. The milk incisors have narrow roots, broadening out abruptly to broad curved faces. The permanent incisors are more columnar and have much broader grinding faces. As they wear, the enamel layer in front remains raised as the dentine behind wears away, giving a sharp cutting edge to the teeth. Soon after birth the alveolus of the deciduous first premolar opens and the development of the tooth is complete before the third premolar. This tooth is not replaced in the permanent set and sometimes only occurs in the upper jaw where it may reach the same length as the other cheekteeth, but more usually is either peg-like or molariform in shape. Often it is pushed out by the second permanent premolar which tends to occupy its position. However, it may be retained throughout the life of the individual and its presence is therefore indicated in the dental formula of the permanent set of teeth (Erz, 1964). In the permanent set of teeth the first molar is the first permanent tooth to develop, the permanent set being completed with the eruption of the third incisor. The dental formula of the permanent set of teeth is:

$I\frac{3}{3}\ C\frac{1}{1}\ PD\frac{1}{1}\ M\frac{3}{3} = 44$

As in the domestic horse, *E. z. zebra* and *E. z. hartmannae*, male and female Burchell's zebra show dimorphism in the permanent canine teeth. Both the deciduous and permanent canines of the females are similar in shape, being small and thin, and both may be seen together in the same jaws at the same time, the permanent canine lying behind the deciduous canine. They usually do not cut through the gums. In the males the permanent canine is much larger, broader and spade-shaped and forms a prominent part of the permanent set of teeth.

Smuts (1972) defined 27 age classes for Burchell's zebra in the Kruger National Park, from birth to 20 years of age, based on tooth eruption and wear, the shape of the table surface of the incisors, and the corresponding shape of the infundibulum. With wear of these teeth beyond the depth of the infundibulum the hollow disappears on the first incisors at the age of 15 years and on all these teeth by 17 years.

## Distribution

Although there was some confusion in the historical record between Burchell's zebra and the now extinct quagga, *E. quagga*, the consensus of opinion suggests that Burchell's zebra never occurred south of the Orange River. Their present day distribution shows a marked shrinkage and, in the Republic of South Africa, naturally occurring populations are found only in reserved areas in the northern and eastern Transvaal, in particular the Kruger National Park, and in northeastern Natal and Swaziland. However, within recent years, they have been reintroduced widely to private properties and parks on a countrywide basis.

*South of the Sahara, excluding the Southern African Subregion*

The furthest north record is from the Bor District of the **Sudan** and there was reported to be a herd of 96 in the Lake Chamo area of **Ethiopia**. They do not occur in northeastern **Kenya**, but otherwise have a wide distribution throughout the country, and a marginal distribution in southwestern **Somalia**. They occur widely in **Tanzania;** throughout **Zambia** and in the Katanga Province of **Zaire**; throughout **Mozambique**, north of the Zambezi River and in southern **Angola**, north to about 14 °N.

*Southern African Subregion*

In **Namibia** they are confined to the northern and northeastern areas from the Kaokoveld to the Botswana border; throughout **Botswana**, north of Lake Ngami and the Makgadikgadi Pan and in the area of the Tuli Circle. In **Zimbabwe** they are absent from the central plateau and the Eastern Districts, but occur north and south of the plateau. In the **Transvaal** they are confined to conservation areas in the north and the Kruger National Park and adjoining private nature reserves in the east. In **Mozambique**, south of the Zambezi River, they are still found widely south to about 25 °30′S, but are absent from the extreme south and from the greater part of the eastern, more heavily settled areas. In **Natal** they appear never to have occurred south of the Umhlatuzi River or above 700 m above sea level. They are still found in the Umfolozi-Corridor-Hluhluwe Game Reserve complex and the Mkuzi Game Reserve and have been re-introduced into the Ndumu Game Reserve. They also occur naturally in the Hlane Wildlife Sanctuary and on adjoining ground in Swaziland (Feely, pers. comm.).

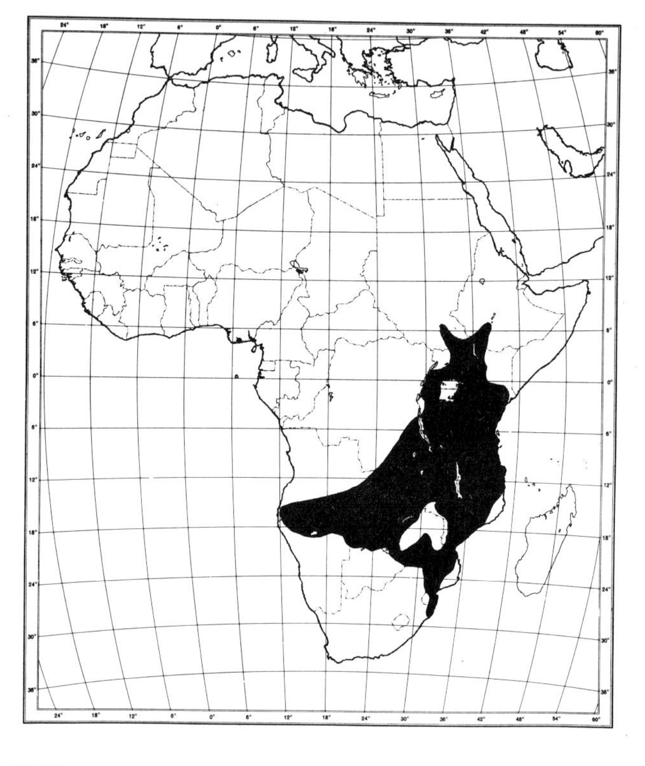

## Habitat

Burchell's zebras are a savanna plains species, partial to open areas of woodland, open scrub and grassland, where water is available. They do not occur in forest or dune desert and avoid areas of dense woodland except in transit. As they are dependent on water, they are seldom found more than 10 or 12 km from it. In parts of their distributional range, as for example in northern Botswana, they are associated with floodplain grassland. Smuts (1972) in the Kruger National Park found that Burchell's zebras, although a species of great adaptive flexibility, nevertheless had a definite choice of habitat. This actuates them to undertake daily and seasonal movements to areas where better grazing conditions and water supplies are available. They are dependent on the availability of the latter and cannot use even optimum grazing areas unless it is present.

## Habits

Burchell's zebras are gregarious, living in small family groups consisting of a stallion and one or more mares and their foals. Surplus stallions, rejected from the family group, form bachelor groups or they may remain solitary. Smuts (1974) found that the youngest stallion leading a family group was four years old and that most of these groups were led by stallions between four and a half and 12 years old. Where there are high concentrations of zebras, stallions may not secure the lead of a group until they are between five and six years old.

The average size of these family groups varies within restricted areas and appears to be correlated with the conditions of the habitat and the level of predation. In prime open grassland habitat such as the Ngorongoro Crater in East Africa, where the density of zebras is 192 per 1 000 ha (Turner & Watson, 1965b), the average family group size is 7,7, whereas in the Kruger National Park where it is 9 per 1 000 ha, the average family group size is from 4 to 4,5 (Smuts, 1974). Smuts concluded that the densely overgrown condition of the Kruger National Park does not favour zebras. Factors such as ease of predation and loss of contact with the group by the stallion inhibit larger group sizes.

Burchell's zebras are non-territorial but sub-populations occupy home ranges of varying size. In the Kruger National Park, Smuts (1972) recorded home ranges by marking individuals in groups and found that these varied in size from 111 $km^2$ to 262 $km^2$ in different parts of the park. There was no correlation between the size of the group and the size of its home range. The home ranges of the groups overlapped and where they were studied over a two-year period, it was found that they varied in size from year to year and that a group might utilise two separate home ranges in succeeding years.

In the smaller of the home ranges studied (111 $km^2$) there was a good water supply and well grassed parkland. In a larger area (207 $km^2$), while water supplies were more than adequate, the terrain was covered by fairly dense woodland with tall, unpalatable grasses, so that the group had to move over a larger area to obtain food. Within the home range Smuts (1972) found that there were foci of activity around water supplies, while other areas were used less frequently.

In zebra herds, which may be made up of many family groups, the stallion groups tend to take up positions on the periphery of the herd, away from the concentrations of family groups. When the herd is on the move the stallion groups tend to take up position at the rear or on the flanks and only under extreme conditions integrate with it. When the herds do move individual stallions become prone to attack by the stallions of family groups and by the adult mares. This is similar to the rear position taken up by a family group stallion when his group is attacked by predators. Lions and spotted hyaenas both prey on zebras, the latter particularly on the foals. They are timid and shy, especially when approaching water, which they do circumspectly. They are found frequently in association with wildebeest and other species, and the zebras' acute sense of sight, smell and hearing is of benefit to the group as a whole.

Smuts (1974) recorded that young foals are occasionally killed by kicks from adults and a dispute at a waterhole led to the killing of a mare by a bull elephant. When under attack by predators the family group stallion will defend members of his group vigorously, as will the mares defend their foals. Defence is by biting or kicking. Cullen (1969) recorded a mare killing a spotted hyaena with a kick of the front feet and a stallion biting and casting aside another. During and immediately after these attacks zebras vocalise with excited barks.

The function of the striped coat of zebras has led to much speculation. It may have a value in camouflage under certain light conditions. It has also been suggested that it tends to confuse a predator as to their direction of movement or to confuse it at close range, when confronted by a group, but none of these explanations is entirely acceptable. Each individual is, however, uniquely marked and no two are exactly alike, a feature which has been used widely in field recognition.

Burchell's zebras are reluctant to take to water, as was shown during the flooding of the Zambezi Valley in the creation of Lake Kariba. They would remain on small islands, adjacent to larger areas of dry land, when other species had swum to safety, even when harried by beaters. Child (1968a) recorded that those individuals that did swim were exhausted after 180 m.

Their characteristic vocalisation of *kwa-ha-ha* no doubt gave them the name quagga, which is used so often but is now generally reserved for the extinct, *E. quagga*.

They are very partial to rolling in dust and often the white stripes become stained, obscuring their natural whiteness.

In the Kruger National Park, Smuts (1972) showed that parts of the Burchell's zebra population had significant local and full-scale movements, some of which even took them outside the boundaries of the park. Other sections of the population remained relatively sedentary or had more restricted movements which were not strongly directional. These movements never attained the scope of those seen in northern Namibia where they covered distances of between 100 and 160 km (Ebedes, 1972) or in the Serengeti in East Africa where they exceeded 200 km (Grzimek & Grzimek, 1960). In the Kruger National Park these movements take place between winter and summer grazing areas. In the summer grazing area their water requirements are provided for in seasonal pans and pools in rivers and if these become depleted, they are compelled to return to their winter ranges. These movements take place along well defined paths, the animals moving in single file and the family and stallion groups maintaining their individuality. They are led by an adult mare, the stallion groups remaining towards the rear. During such movements grazing is confined to the occasional taking of a mouthful of grass. Smuts (1972) found that the zebras always leave their summer grazing area before the water supplies are depleted.

### Food

Burchell's zebras are predominantly grazers, but occasionally will browse and feed on herbs. In the Kruger National Park, Smuts (1972) from direct observations on feeding, listed 50 species of grasses utilised, detailing the parts of the grasses eaten, whether inflorescence, leaves, sheaths or stems. In addition he included a sedge and, among the browse, eight species of herbs, the leaves, twigs or pods of nine shrubs or trees, and wild fruits. In Zambia, Ansell (1960a) and Darling (1960) recorded browsing and Tinley (1966) in Botswana recorded their digging for the succulent rhizomes of grasses.

Burchell's zebras have strong, sensitive, mobile upper lips which they use to push the herbage between their incisor teeth which then cut it free. They are partial to feeding on areas of short grasses but will feed on almost any grass species provided it is short and in the young growing stage. In East Africa, Stewart & Stewart (1970) found that red grass, *Themeda triandra*, and couch grass, *Cynodon dactylon*, were selected by them consistently, irrespective of whether they were abundant in the pasture. Growth flush after a burn or stimulated by percipitation is very attractive to them and they will move to these areas. However, Smuts (1972) found that in the Kruger National Park they would feed in areas of long grass, taking a few mouthfuls here and there and not grazing lower than about 100 mm to 150 mm from ground level. He found that they were partial to recently burnt or scorched secondary mopane, *Colophospermum mopane*, and round-leaved teak, *Pterocarpus rotundifolius*, eating both the leaves and scorched twigs, and also observed them grazing in smouldering grasses. They also eat the herb *Tribulus terrestris* in overgrazed or trampled areas, a species which has toxic effects on sheep.

### Reproduction

Dominant stallions in family groups test the reproductive status of females by urine-smelling and exhibiting flehmen. In this act the stallions raise their heads high and may canter around with their nostrils in the air and their lips curled back. The females in oestrus and in a receptive condition stand with widely straddled legs and tails raised, when copulation may follow.

Foals may be born at any time throughout the year. Smuts (1974) showed, however, that in the Kruger Park there was a peak in foaling in December and January, over 85% of all births taking place from October to March. With good rains

Fig. 298.2. Two zebdonks: hybrids between a donkey jack and a Burchell's zebra mare, and their mother, a Burchell's zebra, *E. burchelli*. Van Niekerk's ranch, Halfway House, western Zimbabwe.

in the early part of the summer season, about October and November, breeding activity increases markedly with an increase in conception rates, and it appears that green growth, stimulated by rainfall, is an important factor in this process. The gestation period is from 360 to 390 days. A single foal is born at a birth and there are no records to date of twins in the wild. About the time of parturition the mare becomes restless, but never wanders far from her group. She lies down to give birth, the group remaining in the vicinity. Birth mass is from 30 to 35 kg. The mare rarely eats the afterbirth. Within the first year of life mortality is high. Smuts (1974) concluded that the primary cause was predation by lions and spotted hyaenas, disease and accidents being secondary factors.

The mother-foal bond is very close-knit and the mare will actually drive off any other zebra that comes too close. The foal stays very close to its mother and if the group is disturbed the mare and her foal take a lead position, protected by those behind and by the stallion at the rear. She will actively defend the foal against predators. The foal weans at about 11 months old, but may continue to suckle for a time thereafter. The females have one pair of inguinal mammae.

Burchell's zebras mate freely with donkeys (Fig. 298.2). In semi-domestication such hybrids remain tactile and were used in pioneer days in Zimbabwe by Zeederberg in tandem with mules in his coaches which plied between Bulawayo, Zimbabwe and the Republic of South Africa. In the early 1950's an ox wagon drawn by two mules, two zebdonks and two mules was a familiar sight in Bulawayo where they were used to deliver bulk milk supplies. In the cattle ranching areas in southwestern Zimbabwe, where there were free-ranging donkeys, these hybrids, from donkey stallions and Burchell's zebra mares, were not uncommon. They would range with the cattle and donkeys, but when the cattle were driven in to the dip tank, they had the habit of taking fright and galloping off, with the cattle following, and therefore were strongly disliked by the ranchers.

Zebdonks retain the zebra striping on the front and outside of the legs, which sometimes extends on to the rump. They have upstanding manes, a dark line down the mid-back, and may show, under the brownish-grey coat, indistinct striping on the mid-back.

# Order ARTIODACTYLA

## Even-toed ungulates

Members of this Order are characterised by the fact that the main mass of their bodies is borne by the third and fourth toes on the feet, which are equipped with keratinous hooves. This differentiates them from the Perissodactyla, the odd-toed ungulates, in which the mass is borne by the third, central, toe alone. The even-toed ungulates are a very successful assemblage, members occurring throughout the world, except in the Polar and Australasian regions, although they have been introduced to the latter.

The Order is represented in Africa by six Families: the Suidae, the pigs; the Hippopotamidae, the hippopotamus; the Tragulidae, the water chevrotin, *Hyemoschus aquaticus* (Ogilby, 1841), which does not occur in the Subregion and is confined to parts of West Africa and Zaire; the Giraffidae, the giraffe; the Cervidae, represented in the Subregion by the introduced fallow deer, *Cervus dama*, and the Bovidae, which includes in the Subregion the buffalo, 33 species of antelope and the introduced Himalayan tahr, *Hemitragus jemlahicus*.

The Suidae and Hippopotamidae are non-ruminant members of the Order, the former are omnivores and both groups have single chambered stomachs. They have one or more pairs of incisor teeth in the upper jaw, and the lower and upper canine teeth are enlarged and tusk-like.

Except for the water chevrotin, *H. aquaticus*, the remaining members of the Order usually have no upper canine teeth, although on rare occasions they are found in bovid skulls. The upper incisor teeth are missing, their place being taken by a tough pad against which the lower incisor teeth occlude.

All members of the Order are herbivores and are important in the food chain. Green plants convert the sun's energy, through the chlorophyll in their cells, into food for herbivores which convert it into protein, making this available to other forms of life. Mammals cannot digest the cellulose and lignin in plant material as their digestive systems do not produce the enzymes necessary to carry out this process. They achieve this by means of symbionts in the digestive tract which may be considered a major evolutionary adaptation for the utilisation of herbage by mammals in terrestrial environments. Microbial fermentation or symbiont-aided digestion is characteristic of the large intestine of mammals even in omnivores such as the pig, but, in many herbivores, the caecum and colon have greatly enlarged, thereby increasing the size of fermentation chambers, for example the dassie, dugong and the equids which all exhibit postgastric microbial digestion. In the Lagomorpha both the large intestine and the stomach are of equal importance. On the other hand, the ruminants and other mammals such as the hippopotamus exhibit pregastric symbiont-aided digestion, with enlarged compartmentalised stomachs.

Some herbivores also exhibit coprophagy; for example, the Lagomorpha which produce two types of faecal pellets. One type is the usual hard pellet produced from the central stream from food passing through the hindgut and the other is soft and formed in the caecum and excreted much more infrequently (Bjoernhag, 1985). The latter are picked up direct from the anus by the animal and reingested. The pellet, containing bacteria, is enclosed by a gelatinous layer. When reingested such pellets are retained in the fundus or body of the stomach in which significant fermentation takes place.

Symbiont-aided digestion is most highly developed in the ruminants. Symbiont digestion of cellulose and other insoluble polysaccharides requires space and time for it to be effective. Herbage, after being cropped, passes down the oesophagus into the greatly expanded reticulorumen which serves as a major storage and fermentation vat and in buffalo for example, its capacity amounts to about 15% of body mass.

Ruminants owe their name to their ability to return the coarse plant matter of the reticulorumen content to the mouth for rechewing. A bolus is passed back up the oesophagus and the chewing reduces particle size of the plants thus facilitating fermentative action of the digestive enzymes produced by the microbes in the rumen. This is called chewing the cud and the food is mixed at the same time with large quantities of saliva — cattle secrete 200 litres of saliva daily.

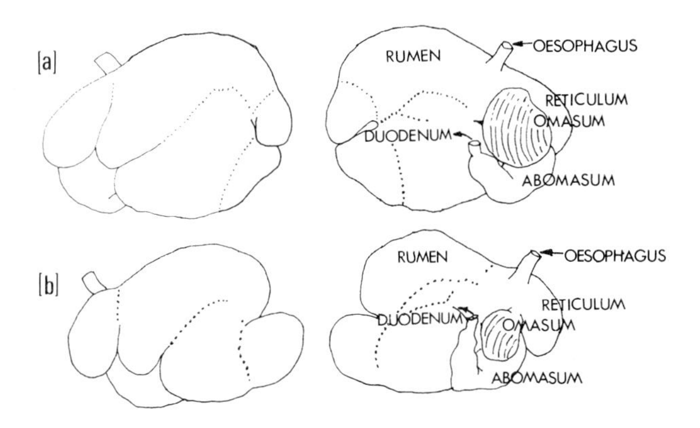


Diagrammatic plan of the four chambered stomachs of two ruminants left and right aspects.
(a) the buffalo, a grass and roughage eater
(b) the dik-dik, a concentrate selector (from Hofmann 1973).
Note the difference in blind sacs and omasal size
The rumen plus the reticulum = reticulorumen.

The fauna and flora in the rumen of different species differ and they may also differ with the animal's diet. The host does not utilise directly the sugars set free by the action of microbial enzymes but these are utilised by the microorganisms themselves. Because of the anaerobic environment sugar catabolism by the microorganisms is a fermentation resulting in the production of volatile fatty acids. As they are absorbed through the rumen wall, the latter constitute the host's share in the carbohydrates of the food. In addition, the microorganisms themselves pass from the rumen via the reticulum and the omasum to the abomasum or true stomach. Here their digestion commences and they represent an important source of protein to the host.

Microorganisms in the rumen utilise ammonia and urea for the synthesis of proteins. Urea, following protein digestion, is returned from the liver via the saliva to the rumen where it is reutilised. The microorganisms also synthesise many vitamins especially of the B group. There are thus several advantages for the ruminant in symbiont-aided digestion (Skinner, *in litt.*).

Recently much has been published about the palatability of woody plants to browsing ruminants (Owen-Smith & Cooper, 1987) and particularly the role of tannins about which there is much controversy. Du Toit, Bryant & Frisby (1990) found that foliage of heavily browsed *A. nigrescens* was higher in nutrients and lower in condensed tannins than foliage from lightly browsed trees, resulting in increased palatability. In addition to differences in functional anatomy of the digestive tract, which are in turn related to feeding habits such as browsing or grazing, it has been postulated recently by Murray (pers. comm.) that grazers may be site or bite selectors. He suggested that wildebeest and hartebeest select patches of grass for their nutritional quality. Their mouth parts are such that they cannot select plant parts and select instead the sward, remaining on that site until it has been grazed down. Other grazers have mouth parts which enable them to select plant parts; they move from place to place, and Murray called these bite selectors, for example, tsessebe. All members of the Order have skin glands which play an important role in intraspecific relations, such as the marking of territories. They either have long limbs, specialised for walking or running, or, in the very large species, heavily built limbs for supporting the great mass of the head and body. Members have unique characters in their skeletal structures in addition to the form of the hooves. The talus, one of the ankle bones, has rounded articulations on the upper as well as on the lower end with no constricted neck between them. Other hoofed mammals (equines) have only one articulation above the constricted neck. The talus also has an articulation on the back to accommodate the calcaneum, the heel bone. This feature is present in members that are long extinct. All artiodactyls, except the pigs, have bony bars, the postorbital bars, behind the eyes.

Artiodactyls usually have two or four mammae, and have a single young at a birth, less commonly twins. The Suidae, the pigs, however, may have from four to 12 mammae and correspondingly larger litters which in the wild number up to eight.

Among the members there are some that are predominantly solitary, the male and female only associating at the time of the rut. Others live in small family groups and others in herds, some of the grazers at times forming huge aggregations numbering thousands of individuals. Association in herds or larger units gives protection from predators. Instigative behaviour is evinced in the herds. When an individual senses danger and takes to flight, the whole herd will do likewise. Among the various types of groups the maternal group is the most cohesive.

Members of the Order, in particular those of the Family Bovidae, are of great importance from an economic, aesthetic and recreational viewpoint, more so than most other families of mammals. Game farming is today an established venture and has demonstrated that wildlife, if utilised on a sustained yield basis, is, as a source of protein, a renewable natural resource of considerable economic value.

In the earlier days of settlement of the southern part of the continent, wildlife was overexploited to the point of the local extinction of species. This can be seen by the shrinkage in the distributional ranges of so many species within historical times. Some, such as the black wildebeest, *Connochaetes gnou*, and the bontebok, *Damaliscus dorcas dorcas*, through man's encroachment on the development of their natural habitat and through over-exploitation, came dangerously close to joining the blue antelope, *Hippotragus leucophaeus*, and the quagga, *Equus quagga*, as extinct species. Happily through the timely and dedicated efforts of individuals and organisations interested in their survival, together with an enlightened appreciation of our wildlife, the future of the black wildebeest and bontebok are assured. Today, quite apart from its economic value in utilisation, landowners appreciate the presence of wildlife on their properties, and species such as springbok, *Antidorcas marsupialis*, blesbok, *Damaliscus dorcas phillipsi*, and many others have been reintroduced to areas where they had become extinct. In some cases these reintroductions, carried out in the first place for their aesthetic values alone, have led to an increase in the numbers of the species concerned to a point where culling has become necessary, and the venture has then become of economic value in the meat produced. The growth of the private game reserve, to which not only bovids but representatives of other families as well, have been introduced, including carnivores and some of the larger species such as square-lipped rhinoceros, *Ceratotherium simum*, bring to their owners financial gain. They also provide the general public with an aesthetic resource as an outlet for their desire for open space and a chance to view wildlife. The National Parks Board and Provincial Administrations provide similar amenities.

Hunting under controlled conditions is today internationally recognised as an accepted form of wildlife utilisation. With the growth of human populations and the development of land for agricultural and pastoral purposes, the Republic of South Africa cannot provide the same facilities for hunting as the less developed countries, which still possess extensive undeveloped areas with naturally occurring bovid populations. Other countries lying within the limits of the Southern African Subregion provide for big game hunting at a sophisticated level, which brings in substantial revenues to the governments concerned and to the private companies who administer the hunting. In South Africa the provision of these facilities devolve mainly upon the private sector, with landowners offering hunting on their properties.

These various types of wildlife utilisation, especially of bovids, are sound conservation measures, for, with the demand for land in the face of escalating human populations, unless wildlife can be shown to have an economic value, its future is bleak. Aesthetic values in themselves are insufficient to withstand developmental pressures.

Bovids have elaborate courtship behaviours, many of which warrant further study. In the territorial species, the males defend their territories from trespass by other male challengers or strange males. They accomplish this more by advertising themselves or by engaging in ritual displays than by actual aggression, involving fighting. This behaviour saves valuable energy.

The hairs of the different Artiodactyl species have been described in detail by Keogh (1983) and Buys & Keogh (1984) and are only referred to briefly in this text. Their descriptions are particularly useful for prey identification. The hair cuticular scale patterns, distance between scale margins and form of scale margins are illustrated in Fig. XLII.1a,b,c (see page 581).

Among the Artiodactyla the Family Bovidae has proved difficult to classify and no two authors are in complete agreement as to the treatment that should be afforded to members. The classification used in this work follows Ansell (1972) with amendments and includes only those species which occur naturally or have been introduced to the Subregion.

Key to the Families after Ansell (1972)

1. At least one pair of upper incisors; non-ruminant ... 2

   No upper incisors; ruminant ... 3

2. Muzzle long, ending in a flat disc containing the nostrils; feet narrower; with lateral hooves not touching the ground; tail thin; hair on body noticeable, at least dorsally ... SUIDAE

   Muzzle broad, not ending in a disc; feet broader, with lateral hooves reaching the ground; tail thick (and shorter in proportion); body hairs sparse and inconspicuous, giving generally a naked appearance ... HIPPOPOTAMIDAE

3. Lower (incisiform) canine lobed; horns simple, skin covered with bony projections ... GIRAFFIDAE

   Lower (incisiform) canine simple, not lobed; horns either covered with a horny sheath or bony and deciduous ... 4

**Plate I Spoor**

295. White rhinoceros, *Ceratotherium simum*
296. Black rhinoceros, *Diceros bicornis*
297. Mountain zebra, *Equus zebra*
298. Burchell's zebra, *Equus burchelli*
299. Bushpig, *Potamochoerus porcus*
300. Warthog, *Phacochoerus aethiopicus*
302. Hippopotamus, *Hippopotamus amphibius*

PLATE I

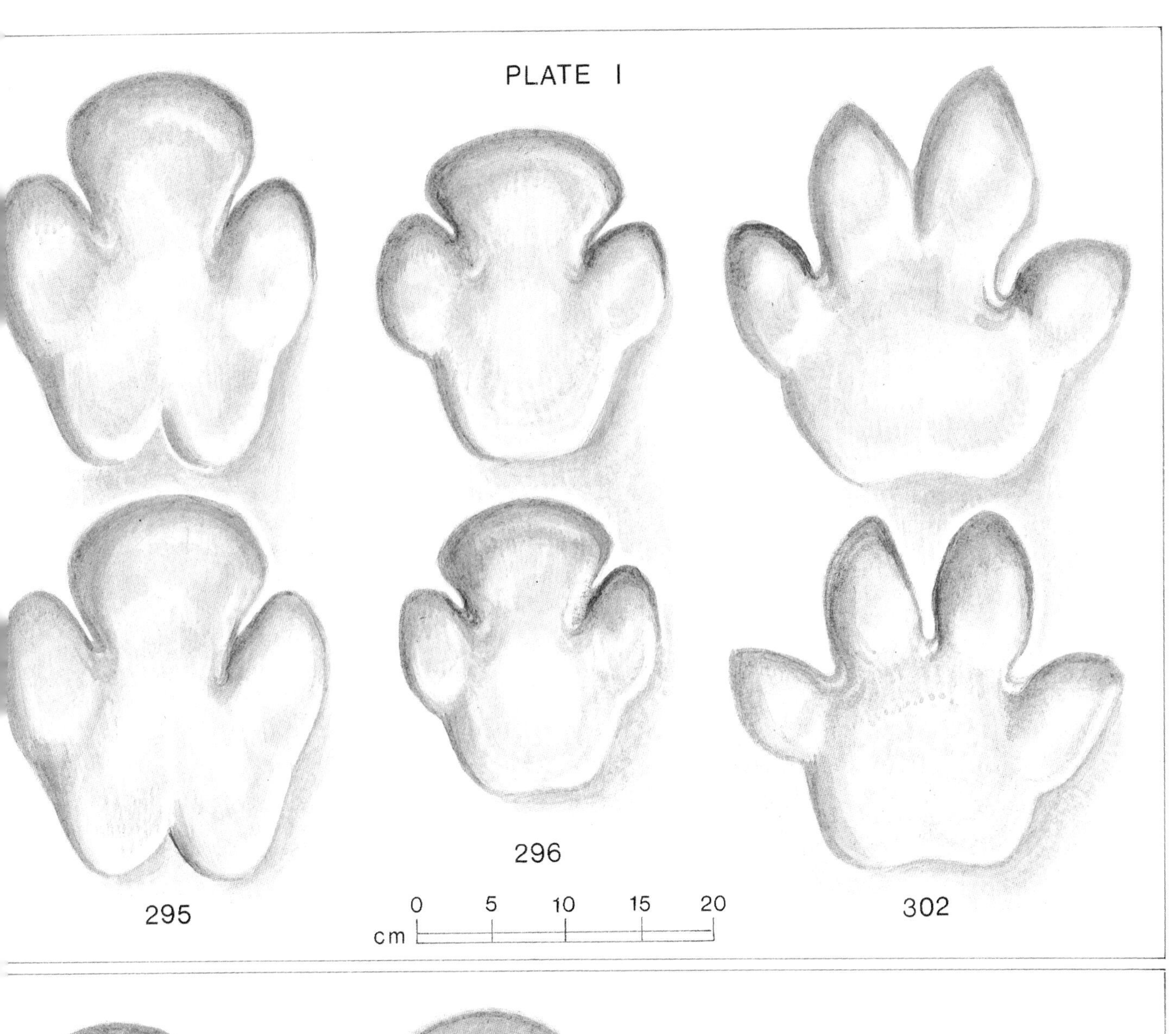


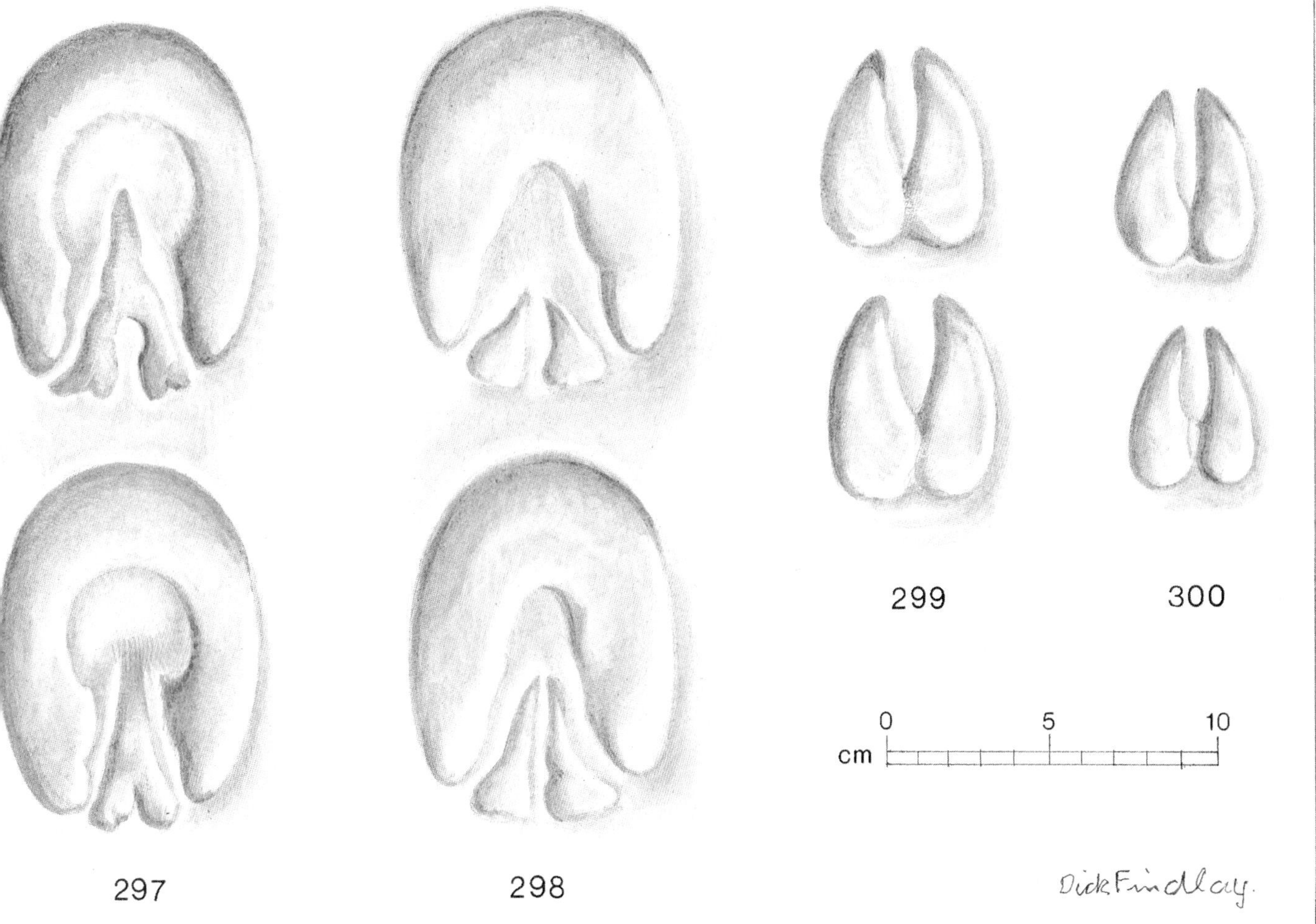

4. Horns in the form of bony, deciduous, branched antlers; upper canine teeth present
   ... CERVIDAE (introduced)

   Horns in the form of non-deciduous, unbranched, horny sheaths or bony cores (a); no upper canine teeth (b)
   ... BOVIDAE

(a) In many species of Bovidae in which the females are normally hornless they may very occasionally possess horns which, however, are small and little developed.

(b) Deciduous upper canines are rarely present, as an abnormality, in the Bovidae.

# XLIII. Family SUIDAE
## Pigs

Members of this family are characterised by having a stout body with thick, tough skin, either sparsely or generously covered with bristly hair. They have short, thin tails with a tuft of bristles at the tip and relatively short limbs. The central pair of digits is longer than the two lateral digits, which do not reach the ground except where it is very soft. The lateral digits are armed with claw-like hooves, the central pair, which bears the weight of the individual, is armed with well developed flattened hooves. The head is elongated, tapering forwards towards the snout on the end of which is an oval, tough cartilaginous disc, supported internally by the prenasal bone, which encloses the nostrils. The edge of this disc is used in digging for food. The upper canine teeth curve upwards and outwards and their faces, occluding against the lower canine teeth, keep their tips and edges very sharp.

The fossil remains of suids are known from Oligocene deposits of some 30 million years old in other parts of the world. In Africa they are first known from the lower-middle Miocene beds in Namibia dated at about 20 to 15 million years old, from which *Xenochoerus africanus* (Stromer, 1926) was described (Cooke & Wilkinson, 1978). Suids are sparsely known from the Pliocene Epoch but are common in Pleistocene deposits dating from about 1,8 to 0,1 million years ago from which numerous species have been described. Some species from this Epoch such as *Notochoerus capensis* Broom, 1925, from the Vaal River gravels, were very large, nearly twice the size of the extant warthog, *Phacochoerus aethiopicus*. Fossil remains of bushpig are rare in Africa, even in the late Pleistocene Epoch.

On the basis that in the extinct Cape warthog, *P. aethiopicus* (Pallas, 1767), the root formation in the third molar teeth is delayed until well after the last columns of these teeth come into use, whereas in the warthog, *P. africanus* (Gmelin, 1788), the roots form on these teeth well before the hindmost columns come into use, some authorities such as Cooke & Wilkinson (1978) use the name *P. africanus* for the extant warthog and *P. aethiopicus* for the extinct Cape warthog. Generally this treatment has not been accepted.

Key to the genera (Meester *et al.*, 1986)

1. Lower canines completely abrading with upper, thus without widely spreading upper tusks; three upper incisors; full dentition 42 to 44
   ... *Potamochoerus*

   Lower canine wearing against only the lower part of the upper, leaving summits free as wide-spreading tusks; only one upper incisor; full dentition 34
   ... *Phacochoerus*

## Genus *Potamochoerus* Gray, 1854

No.299

### *Potamochoerus porcus* (Linnaeus, 1758)

### Bushpig
### Bosvark

Plate 29

#### Colloquial name

As the species is associated throughout its distributional range with thick cover, the colloquial names in both languages are appropriate.

#### Taxonomic notes

Ansell (1972) recognised 11 subspecies as occurring on the continent, but admitted that some have been described on inadequate material. Two of these are recorded as occurring in the Subregion: *P. p. nyasae* Forsyth Major, 1897, from Zimbabwe, northeastern Botswana and parts of Mozambique, and *P. p. koiropotamus* (Desmoulins, 1831) from the remainder of the Subregion.

#### Description

The overall colour of adult bushpigs varies greatly throughout their distributional range and also with age. Those from West Africa are more rufous, from Gabon a richer yellow than those from the Subregion, where they are generally reddish-brown, or reddish from the northeastern parts of Zimbabwe. The body is covered with hairy bristles, $66,3 \pm 28,6$ mm long, large and circular in cross-section, covered with an irregular waved mosaic cuticular scale pattern; the scale margins are deeply rippled crenate (Fig. XLII.1) (Buys & Keogh, 1984). They have a mane of long, paler, erectile hair, either yellower or more buffy than the body, extending from the head to the base of the tail. The forehead, top of the face and cheeks are pale, the lower parts of the face black or dark brown, the under parts similarly coloured, the limbs black. On the sides of the face, at the level of the angle of the lower jaw, they have a thick patch of very long whitish or yellowish hair, which is very conspicuous in some individuals, and may extend forwards along the lower edges of the jaw. The ears are much more pointed than those of the warthog and the adults have tufts of long hair arising from the tips with short whitish or yellowish hair along the outer edge. In some individuals there are distinct patches of paler hair just under the eyes. The hooves are broader than in the warthog, a feature which shows in the spoor (Plate I).

The whole head is elongated more evenly and is longer than that of the warthog and lacks the warts on the face which are such a conspicuous feature of their near relative.

Males appear to be slightly larger than females (Table 299.1) and approximately half adult mass is obtained by one year (Seydack, 1983).

**Table 299.1**

Measurements (mm) and mass (kg) of bushpigs, *P. porcus*, from (a) Zimbabwe (Smithers & Wilson, 1979) and (b) eastern Cape Province (Seydack, 1983)

**(a)**

| | Males | | | Females | | |
|---|---|---|---|---|---|---|
| | $\bar{x}$ | n | Range | $\bar{x}$ | n | Range |
| TL | 1553 | 6 | 1322–1728 | 1459 | 4 | 1346–1540 |
| T | 402 | 6 | 355–432 | 361 | 4 | 305–432 |
| Hf c/u | 275 | 6 | 253–305 | 270 | 4 | 254–290 |
| E | 175 | 6 | 151–203 | 178 | 4 | 161–190 |
| Mass | 61,7 | 6 | 46,0–82,0 | 59,2 | 4 | 48,0–66,0 |

**(b)**

| | Males | | Females | |
|---|---|---|---|---|
| | $\bar{x}$ | Range | $\bar{x}$ | Range |
| Mass | 73,1 | 55–93 | 68,9 | 54–85 |
| | 72,2 | | 68,4 | |
| | 69,2 | | 66,5 | |
| | 58,4 | | 57,5 | |
| | 34,2 | | 32,9 | |

**Skull** (Fig. 299.1)

There is sexual dimorphism in skull structure. Male skulls differ in having a dorsal extension of the maxilla from the base of the canine and a parallel rugose thickening of the nasals (Breytenbach, 1977). In profile the highest point of the skull lies near the back and from this point it slopes gently forward to the nostrils, much less abruptly so than in the warthog. The rostrum is narrow and elongated and in old individuals the bony structure supporting the rhinarium fuses firmly to the skull, accentuating still further the elongation of the rostrum. In old male individuals the tips of the maxillary flanges are expanded into thick, rounded rugosities which in life are overlayed by thickened skin which may play a part in the head to head pushing which is a feature of aggressive action. The rostrum is hollowed out on either side to accommodate the powerful muscles that actuate the rhinarium in rooting and digging. The eye orbits are not set so high in the head as in the warthog and lack the supraorbital ridges, their setting being lower down on the sides of the skull.

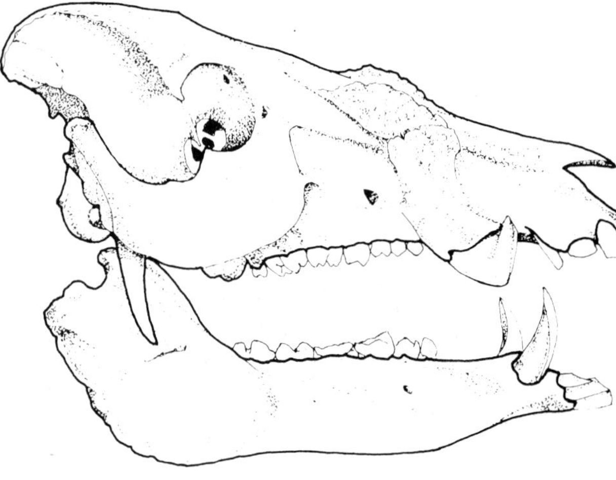

Fig. 299.1 Skull: bushpig, *P. porcus*
TL Skull 380 mm.

As the mandible is long and massive the muscles actuating it must be powerful. Because of the build of the skull there is little space on the sides of the head behind the eye orbits for the attachment of the temporalis muscles, which play a part in this actuation, and they are poorly developed. The major part of this actuation falls, therefore, on the masseters which are particularly powerful and provided with firm attachments on the thick zygomatic arches and on the broad mandible.

The supraoccipital ridges are thick and rugose. The back of the skull arches high from the occipital condyles and provides a firm base for the attachment of the neck muscles which actuate the movement of the heavy head. The paroccipital processes are long, but not as long as in the warthog, and provide attachment for the digastric muscle which pulls the jaw backwards in opening the mouth.

The dental formula is:

$I\frac{3}{3}\,C\frac{1}{1}\,P\frac{4\text{-}3}{3\text{-}4}\,M\frac{3}{3} = 40, 42 \text{ or } 44.$

The deciduous dentition is

$i\frac{3}{3}\,c\frac{1}{1}\,p\frac{3}{3} = 28.$

The bushpig has a heterodont $M^3$ omnivore dentition. All permanent teeth have erupted by 796 days, $M^3$ being the last to erupt (Seydack, 1983). The incisors are heavily built and persist throughout the life of the individual. Gaps separate the maxillary 2nd and 3rd incisors, the canine and first premolars. The inner, upper pair curves around from the sockets so that the points meet in front; the outer pair is much smaller and rounder than the other two. The lower incisors point forward and are elongated, rising 28 to 30 mm from the jawbone. The upper incisors occlude on the back of the lower, not point to point, and the third upper incisors often wear round holes in the back of the outer lower teeth. The tips of the lower incisors wear to flat surfaces caused by abrasion in rooting.

The upper canines are enclosed towards their bases by thick outgrowths of bone and wear to a flat surface in front by occlusion on the lower canines and on the outside by rooting. They project outside the mouth cavity but never reach the length seen in warthogs, although they are massive teeth. The lower canines are formidable weapons and are maintained sharp-pointed and sharp-edged by occlusion against the upper. They lie at an angle sloping outwards from the mandible, making them readily available as defensive or offensive weapons. Mean measurement of lower canines taken along the lower frontal edge from the alveolar edge to the tip for males was 55,6 mm (n=47) and for females 45,3 mm (n=59) (Seydack, 1983).

The upper first and second premolars and the first lower premolar may or may not be present or may occur irregularly. In the usual case the upper P1 erupts, but may be lost subsequently. The lower P1 only erupts in exceptional cases and is lost much sooner than the upper P1 (Seydack, 1983). They have high cusps and do not wear as flat as the other cheekteeth. The third upper and lower premolars are similarly higher cusped than the remainder. The molars, which have no deciduous precursors are brachyodont (low-crowned) and bunodont (blunt rounded crowns) which in old individuals still retain some ridging indicating a chopping action rather than grinding during mastication. Seydack (1983) found that cementum growth layers in bushpig teeth are consistently related to chronological age but the technique has a number of drawbacks which detract from its routine use.

The ear bullae are sub-conical and extend downward from the braincase. In some old individuals the bullae are connected to a process of the pterygoid bone by an extension of bone from their extremities. In the warthog there is no such connection.

The build of the skull with its long snout, forwardly sloping lower incisors, short canines and bony support for the rhinarium are all adaptations to its search for food by rooting and digging. They are deep rooters and can easily excavate to depths of up to 200 mm in soft soil.

**Distribution**

Although the bushpig has a wide distributional range on the continent, south of the Sahara, within this they only occur where there is suitable habitat. In East Africa, for example, they occur along the major river systems and associated swampy areas in Somalia and not in the surrounding arid terrain, and in Kenya have the same type of discontinuous distribution which it is impossible to reflect properly on a small-scale map. The same applies in the Subregion where, although shown on the map to occur widely in the eastern Transvaal, Pienaar (1963) showed that in the Kruger National Park they are of limited occurrence. The area demarcated on the map therefore must be interpreted with this proviso in mind.

*South of the Sahara, excluding the Southern African Subregion*

In West Africa they occur in and on the fringes of the High Forest regions in **Senegal; Guinea; Sierra Leone; Liberia; Ghana; Nigeria** southeastwards to **Cameroun; Gabon** and **Congo Republic**. They are widespread in **Zaire** and they occur widely in **Uganda, Kenya** and **Tanzania**, with records from southern **Ethiopia** and southern **Somalia**. They are distributed widely in **Angola**, excluding the southwestern parts and in **Zambia, Malawi** and **Mozambique**, north of the Zambezi River.

*Southern African Subregion*

They are not recorded in Namibia. In **Botswana** they are confined to the Okavango Swamps and adjacent river systems, such as the Chobe River, and occur narrowly in the northeastern and parts of the eastern sectors. In **Zimbabwe** they are widespread and still occur even in the intensively agriculturally developed parts of the country, but do not occur in the more arid west. In **Mozambique**, south of the Zambezi River, they are widespread, as well as narrowly in the west, north and eastern parts of the **Transvaal**. They are widespread in parts of central and eastern **Natal**, and in the eastern **Cape Province** occur narrowly along the coast to the George District at about 22°E. Judging from the historical record their distribution in the Subregion has not altered to any great extent, although they may have been exterminated locally in parts or driven back in the face of human developments.

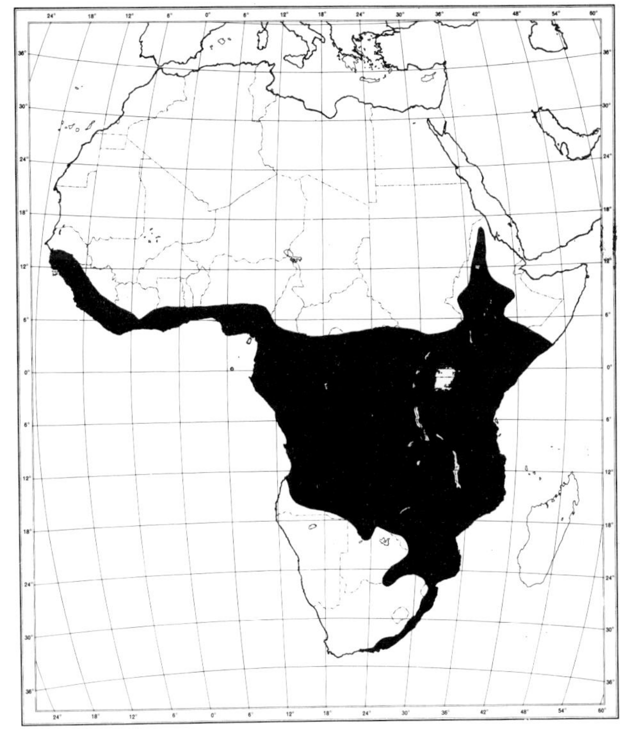

**Habitat**

Bushpigs are associated particularly with forest, thickets, riparian undercover, reed beds or heavy cover of tall grass, where there is water. Dense cover and water are among their essential requirements and as a consequence, although they have a wide distribution on the continent, they only occur where these conditions pertain. Such conditions sometimes penetrate into otherwise drier country, as in northern and eastern Botswana, where bushpigs remain in close proximity to their preferred type of habitat.

Agricultural developments have favoured bushpigs, when these lie adjacent to adequate cover, at least 2 ha for diurnal resting (Cooper & Melton, 1988). Where the cultivation of valleys leaves the adjacent rocky hillsides with their cover undisturbed, bushpig habitat is improved by the provision of ample food supplies in the form of sugar cane, maize, peanuts, beans and other crops. In spite of intensive control measures they have increased in number to the extent of becoming a serious problem, particularly during the winter months in sugar cane growing areas (Cooper & Melton, 1988).

**Habits**

Bushpigs are predominantly nocturnal, with some crepuscular and even diurnal activity where they are protected (Maberly, 1950; Breytenbach & Skinner, 1982). In areas where they are subject to control, on the other hand, they are strictly nocturnal. In agricultural areas in Zimbabwe, for example, they only become active late in the evening after 21h00 and continue their activity up to at least 02h00.

They are gregarious, moving in groups or sounders of four to six (Skinner *et al.*, 1976) occasionally up to 12. In Natal, Scotcher (1973) gives a mean of 2,3 (n=3) and in Uganda Ghiglieri *et al.* (1982) 3,2 (range 2,1–5,0; n=7) pigs in a sounder. Sounders consist of a dominant boar and sow, other sows and juveniles or piglets. Where there are aggregations of sounders those with piglets are inclined to be more aggressive than those without. Wilson (1969a) quoted an incident when a sow with young treed a game guard for several hours.

The dominant boar in a sounder will guard and lead the piglets to feeding areas and will challenge and aggressively drive off dominant boars of other sounders from their feeding grounds. Such encounters seldom lead to actual contact, the confrontation taking the form of threat display. Dominant boars will advance on one another, shoulder bristles raised, tails wagging furiously, jaws snapping, pawing the ground and throwing up dust or clods of earth. They will lie down and roll over, again advancing to the fray, circling and making little charges or, head to head, they may push each other around, until one or other loses confidence and concedes the ground, moving away with his sounder following (Skinner, Breytenbach & Maberly, 1976). Dominant sows also exhibit aggression and will demonstrate at strange boars or sows. The close association of the dominant boar with the young continues until they are about six months old, after which both parents become intolerant of them and drive them off.

Information on the size of their home range is conflicting, but it appears that in some areas these are very large. In Zimbabwe, bushpigs moved to feeding grounds at night over distances estimated to be up to 4 km from their resting places. Continued use of the same routes to feeding areas leads to the formation of narrow, clearly marked paths.

Tree-marking by tusking is described by Skinner *et al.* (1976) who found that tree girth influences their choice of trees on which to tusk and rub. Jones (1978) described scent glands situated on the sides of the boar's face which open around the base of the upper canines, and suggested that the tusking of trees is subsidiary to the application of the secretions of these glands in scent-marking. The males also have digital glands which no doubt function for the same purpose.

Like warthogs, bushpigs wallow in mud, probably as a means of temperature regulation and as a protection against biting insects. When sleeping or resting they lie up in any dense cover and remain alert. When flushed the sounder tends to disperse in all directions, only later rejoining. Bushpigs are difficult to drive for they have a tendency to break back through a line of beaters. Under these circumstances they can become aggressive and a passing slash with the lower canines can cause serious wounds. When wounded they can become dangerous. In such encounters the sharp lower canines do the damage; the upper canines do not appear to be used either for this purpose or for digging, although they become heavily worn down in rooting.

Bushpigs are cunning and wary and are almost impossible to eradicate even in the face of intensive control. They swim well, as was shown during game rescue during the flooding of Lake Kariba, where Child (1968a) reported that individuals were picked up still swimming strongly after 1200 m, and they will freely cross rivers. Under stress and in the absence of other cover, Child (1968a) reported that they will hide in the water, one individual being observed to rest his head on a floating branch in deep water to remain afloat.

When foraging, individuals in sounders grunt softly, probably as a means of maintaining contact. The dominant boar in a sounder may give the alarm by uttering a long, drawn, resonant grunt which actuates the sounder to run for cover.

Only two ages for longevity have been recorded—14,6 and 13,1 years (Flower, 1931; Jarvis & Morris, 1960), and four estimates from cementum lines have been made—14 years for a male and female and 15 years for a male and female from cementum line counts for skulls found in the Knysna Forest (Seydack, 1983).

**Food**

Bushpigs root with the hard upper edge of the snout in much the same way as warthogs, but tend to feed in damper places or in litter, generally making less use of hard ground than warthogs. They are omnivorous and will root and browse. Rooting is directed at the underground rhizomes of grasses and at bulbs and tubers. It also gives them access to earthworms and the pupae of defoliating insects which they eagerly devour, their keen sense of smell enabling them to locate these. Phillips (1926) and Thomas & Kolbe (1942) both recorded that bushpigs root for the rhizomes of ferns, and Milstein (1971) included the corms of nutgrass. Wild and cultivated fruits are also eaten, including wild figs, mangoes, guavas, avocado pears, pineapples and pawpaws. When raiding pawpaws they tusk the trees down to get at the fruit (Skinner *et al.*, 1976). They are a problem in maize lands, especially when the cobs are green, doing more damage by flattening the crop in the process than by the amount they eat which, however, can be considerable. They also take sugar cane, beans, peas, peanuts, sweet potatoes, marrows, pumpkins, potatoes and oats, and in fact most agricultural crops are attractive to them.

Milstein (1971) reported that they killed and ate chickens, newborn kids and lambs, and Willemse (1962) recorded an individual that entered a pigsty, attacked the sow, and ate several piglets. Carrion, even in its most putrid form, is eaten and several authors quoted in Skinner *et al.* (1976) recorded that they can scent this from many kilometres away. They also recorded their eating the flowers of arum lilies and fallen *Acacia* pods, as well as succulent plants of various types.

Maberly (1950) recorded their association with vervet monkeys and baboons which dislodge fruit from trees and make it available to them, and which follow them around for vegetable and arthropod food which they have missed. Phillips (1926) recorded that, in the Knysna Forest, bushpigs follow elephants for the food which they dislodge from trees and for food items in their faeces. They also root in certain soils for their mineral content.

Breytenbach & Skinner (1982) noted that bushpigs, while omnivorous, were highly selective in their feeding habits. They recorded that in the Lake St Lucia area of Natal they ate the roots and corms of a fern; the leaves, corms, roots, fruit and bulbs of 18 species of monocotyledonous plants, and the seeds, fruit and roots of 40 species of dicotyledons. They recorded seasonal variation in the foods utilised, fruit being replaced in the winter by non-temporal food sources such as bulbs. Because of their habit of using latrines in the ecotone of forest and grassland and their habit of eating seeds and fruits, Breytenbach & Skinner (1982) accounted them as efficient dispensers of the diaspores of forest precursor species. They noted that bushpigs were generally in poor physical condition for nearly all the year except in late January at the height of the fruiting season. During winter they were active longer during the 24 hour period, which they attributed to the poor quality and scarcity of food.

**Reproduction**

In the northern parts of the Subregion the young are born during the summer months from October to February (Sowls & Phelps, 1968; Seydack, 1983). The sow constructs a nest of grass in woodland or on broken, rocky hillsides or other places where the chance of disturbance is minimal. Although the process of nest-building does not seem to have been observed, it appears that the sow plucks bunches of high-standing grass and carries these to a chosen site, piling it up until it resembles a small haystack and then boring into it to litter down. The young are thus provided with a bed of grass, insulating them from the ground, and a thick cover as protection from weather conditions. Two nests examined near Bindura, Zimbabwe, resembled low hay ricks and measured approximately 3 m across and were about 1 m deep. Both were in clearings in scrub bush on hillsides. These blend in with the surroundings and are not as obvious as might be supposed. Skinner *et al.* (1976) recorded nests as being constructed in *Acacia* thickets and Phillips (1926) stated that, in the Knysna Forest, sows litter down in the stumps of hollow trees.

The size of litters is usually three to four, but up to eight have been recorded (Phillips, 1926; Milstein, 1971) and while their reproductive rate is considered to be lower than in the warthog, juvenile mortality is also apparently lower (Thomas & Kolbe, 1942). Young bushpigs are hardier than young warthogs and do not require the shelter of burrows to survive as they are better able to control their body temperature.

At birth the young have a mass of betwen 700 and 800 g, and are rufous-brown with conspicuous yellowish or buffy stripes. These become indistinct at about three months, fading out altogether thereafter, when the body is then covered with bright orange-rufous bristly hair. At five to six months the dorsal stripe becomes white and the forehead becomes paler in hue. The markings of the very young act as a very effective camouflage in the dappled shade of the habitat.

The sows have three pairs of abdominal mammae and, except during suckling, take very little notice of the young, their care being entrusted to the dominant boar of the sounder who is assiduous in his attention to them.

Bushpigs have been known to crossbreed with domestic pigs (see *S. scrofa*).

## Genus *Phacochoerus* F. Cuvier, 1817

No.300

## *Phacochoerus aethiopicus* (Pallas, 1766)

## Warthog
## Vlakvark

Plate 29

**Colloquial name**

Both names are descriptive. The English name refers to the characteristic and conspicuous facial "warts"; the boars have two pairs, the sows only one. *Vlakvark* refers to their tendency to be associated with vleis, floodplain and open grassland areas, as distinct from the *bosvark* which prefers denser vegetation.

**Taxonomic notes**

Seven subspecies are recognised from the continent, of which three occur in the Subregion: *P. a. aethiopicus* which now survives only in the northern Cape Province; *P. a.*

*sundevalli* Lönnberg, 1908 from Natal northwards to the Transvaal, Mozambique and Zimbabwe, and *P. a. shortridgei* St Leger, 1932 from Namibia and Botswana.

### Description

Warthogs have been described unflatteringly by authors as "incarnations of hideous dreams" (Lydekker, 1908) or as "the most astonishing objects that have disgraced nature" (Pitman, 1942) and while they may not have the grace of an impala or the dignity of a lion, they are an integral and very interesting part of the spectrum of African wildlife.

Adult boars stand about 0,7 m at the shoulder and have a mass of up to 100 kg; females are 0,6 m and have a mass of up to 70 kg (Table 300.1). They are grey in colour. Both sexes have a crest of long black, brown or yellowish bristly hair from between the ears to the base of the tail which, when they are relaxed, hangs down over the sides of the shoulders and body, but can be erected under stress.

The body is covered very sparsely with coarse bristles 28,8±6,4 mm long, distinctive and exceptionally large in cross-section, with an irregular waved cuticular mosaic scale pattern and with scale margins deeply rippled crenate ( Fig. XLII.1) (Buys & Keogh, 1984). The tail has a terminal tuft of blackish hair. On the sides of the face, at the level of the angle of the lower jaw, there are well developed "side whiskers" of long white hair which are conspicuous, especially in juveniles, and which may continue as bands of short white hair to just behind the ears. Inside the ears there are patches of long white hair.

For the build of the body the legs are slender and relatively short. Characteristic features are the elongated head, which slopes sharply forward to the snout, in which the protuberant eyes are set high up near the back, and, in particular, the distinctive facial warts. The males have two pairs of these, a very large pair, rising some 120 mm from the skin just below the eyes on the side of the face and a second and much smaller pair on the cheeks. Females have a pair just below the eyes, but these are much smaller, barely rising to 30 mm, and the cheek warts are absent. These "warts" from which the colloquial name is devised, are outgrowths of the skin and not abnormal growths as are true warts.

The canine teeth grow out sideways from the jaws as protuberant tusks. In old adult females the upper tusks tend to curl over the top of the snout more than in the males. The lower tusks, whose edges and tips are kept sharp by occlusion against the upper, are smaller and less in evidence. They are, nevertheless, more important in defence than the upper pair with their sharp points and edges. The bases of the tusks are enclosed in a thick outgrowth of bone which causes the snout to broaden out at the level of their bases. The nostrils are enclosed in a hard, cartilaginous, rounded disc with a hard upper edge used in digging. The ears are prominent, rising to high rounded points. Females have four mammae, one pair inguinal and one pair abdominal.

The hooves are narrower than those of the bushpig, a feature which shows in the spoor (Plate I).

**Table 300.1**

Measurements (mm) and mass (kg) of adult warthogs, *P. aethiopicus*, from Natal (Mason, 1985a)

| | Males | | | Females | | |
|---|---|---|---|---|---|---|
| | x̄ | n | Range | x̄ | n | Range |
| TL | 1323 | 56 | 1165–1440 | 1182 | 74 | 1090–1268 |
| Hf c/u | 264 | 56 | 242–280 | 247 | 74 | 225–262 |
| Sh ht | 682 | 56 | 612–720 | 598 | 74 | 543–657 |
| Mass | 79,6 | 56 | 59,2–103,9 | 56,5 | 74 | 44,6–69,1 |

### Skull (Fig. 300.1)

The skull slopes sharply forward from the brain case to the nostrils, the broadest part being at the level of the lower part of the zygomatic arches just below the eyes. From this point the skull narrows evenly forward to about the level of the upper premolar teeth, then broadens out to the bony sockets of the upper canines, narrowing forwards again to the nasal openings. The rostrum is considerably elongated. For the size of the skull, the eye sockets, which are set back and elevated, are small, and there are distinct supraorbital ridges on the inner sides. The supraoccipital crest is well developed, lying at an angle backwards of the braincase, leaving a wide face at the back for the attachment of the massive neck muscles which support the weight of the head. The paroccipital processes are long, extending nearly to the level of the bottom of the angle of the mandible.

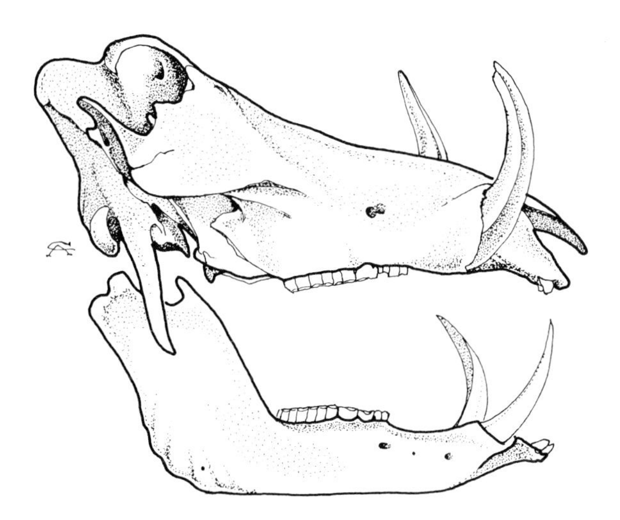

Fig. 300.1. Skull: warthog, *P. aethiopicus*
TL Skull 400 mm.

The mandible is massively built, flattens out in front, and widens laterally to accommodate the bony sockets of the canines and lower incisors. The incisor teeth slope forwards. The dentition is

$I\frac{1}{2\text{-}3}\ C\frac{1}{1}\ P\frac{3}{2}\ M\frac{3}{3} = 32–34$

but there is more variation in the tooth formula of this species than in any other ungulate. The loss of teeth, which proceeds with age, affects all the teeth except the canines and the third molars, which have semi-persistent pulps and continue to grow for up to three to four years, lengthening in the process. The growth of the third molars eventually forces out the teeth in front of them but, lengthening as they grow, they continue to provide 40–50 mm of flat molar surfaces for the chewing of the food. In old adults the tooth formula may reduce, in the extreme to

$I\frac{0}{0}\ C\frac{1}{1}\ P\frac{0}{0}\ M\frac{1}{1} = 8$

The upper and lower incisors are rounded. The cheekteeth have flat grinding surfaces. The third molars, which persist throughout life and continue to grow, do so by eruption from the back parts of the teeth below bone level. As growth proceeds and the teeth elongate, those in front of the third molars are slowly displaced until in older individuals, apart from the canines, they remain the only teeth persisting. In very old individuals the roots of the forward portion of the teeth atrophy, leaving only the surface grinding portion which may break away. The process is very similar to that found in elephants.

There is very little space on the back of the braincase for the attachment of the temporalis muscles which are poorly developed. The masseters and digastric muscles on the other hand are well developed, with broad attachments on the wide zygomatic arches and mandible, giving a powerful action to the lower jaw. The open glenoid allows for a considerable side to side movement of the mandible necessary for the grinding of the food.

### Distribution

Originally described from a specimen from Guinea, the warthog has a distribution from Senegal and Guinea in West Africa, in the Sudan and, in part, in the Sahelian zones and Guinea savannas, to Ethiopia and south to the northern parts of the Republic of South Africa. Within this they may be absent locally, through having been extirpated in the face of human development, and nowhere do they occur in forest or desert.

*South of the Sahara, excluding the Southern African Subregion*

They occur in **Senegal** and in the southern parts of **Mauritania**; in **Guinea** and in the northern parts of **Sierra Leone** and northern **Ghana**. They are recorded from central and northern **Nigeria**; from the southern and southwestern **Sudan** and south central **Ethiopia**. Hemprich & Ehrenberg (1832) described *P. haroia* from **Eritrea** and Dorst & Dandelot (1970) extended their distribution in this sector to the coast of the Red Sea. They are widespread in **Somalia, Kenya, Uganda** and **Tanzania**. There are records from the northern sector of **Zaire** along the border with the **Central African Republic**, from the east in the Rift Valley and throughout the southern parts of the country west to about 18 °E, excluding the forests of the Congo Basin. They have a wide distribution in **Angola**, excluding the desert in the southwest, and they occur throughout **Zambia**. They are widespread in **Malawi** and they occur throughout **Mozambique**, north of the Zambezi River.

*Southern African Subregion*

In **Namibia** they occur in the central, northern and eastern parts of the country, south to about 24 °S, excluding the more arid coastal strip, with only scattered records south of this. They are widespread in **Botswana**, but are rare in the southern parts and do not occur in the settled southeastern sector.

They occur widely in **Zimbabwe**, excluding the intensively farmed areas on the Mashonaland Plateau, and in **Mozambique**, south of the Zambezi River, excluding the extreme southern sector.

In the **Transvaal** they occur narrowly in the west, north and east, and in the **Cape Province** marginally along parts of its northern border with **Botswana** and in the central and northern parts of the Kalahari Gemsbok National Park. In **Natal** they are confined to the northeast where they are abundant in the game reserves.

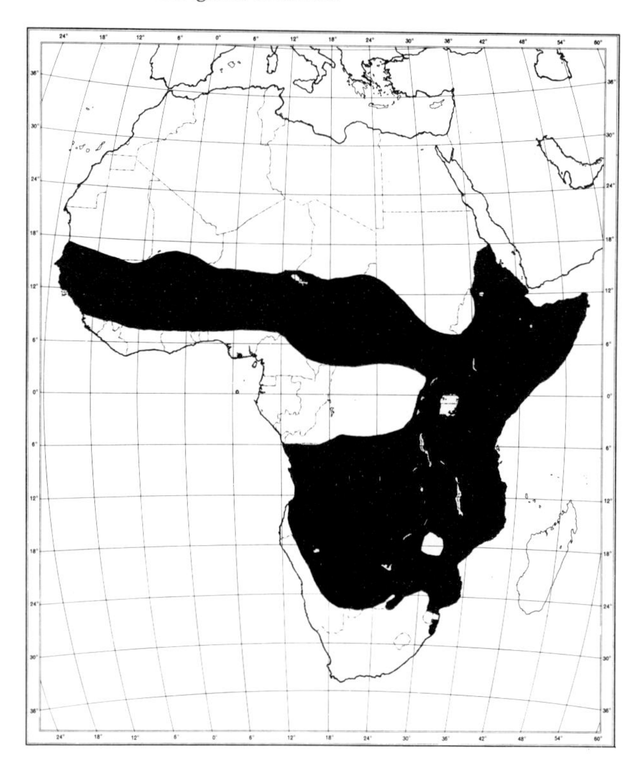

## Habitat

Warthogs are associated particularly with open ground, grassland, floodplain, vleis and in open areas around waterholes and pans, but they will also utilise open woodland and open scrub. They are partial to areas of burnt ground, where the grass is freshly sprouting. While found where water is available this is not an essential habitat requirement and they occur in areas where it may only be available seasonally (Bigourdan, 1948; Smithers, 1971). They avoid thick bush, riverine and montane forest, forest and desert.

## Habits

Warthogs are diurnal, lying up during the night in holes in the ground, usually disused antbear, *O. afer*, holes which they adjust to their own requirements. They use their forefeet for digging, moving the loosened soil by shovelling it out of the holes with their snouts. In Uganda, Clough (1969) reported that they dig their own holes, but this is atypical of their behaviour in the Subregion where aardvark holes are most commonly used. Less commonly they have been observed to use sink-holes in erosion gulleys or caves (Cumming, 1975).

Aardvarks excavate both shallow feeding holes and more permanent and much more extensive burrow systems. Warthogs use both types, the former sometimes only just deep enough to enclose them. The latter are adjusted and chambers opened up in the burrow system.

These holes are very important in the lives of warthogs, affording them protection against adverse climatic conditions and predators. In inclement weather they remain in these holes, only emerging if it clears up. They are also reported to use them as protection from the sun (Stevenson-Hamilton, 1947), although during the hottest time of the day they may rest in the shade of underbush, or in thickets or stands of tall grass. They exercise caution in leaving the holes, often spending several minutes testing the air from the shelter of the entrance before finally emerging. While the piglets enter these holes head first, the adults enter them backwards. When chased they accomplish this by a last minute turn around just outside the entrance; this performance is often accompanied by clouds of dust.

Some tenure of holes exists, warthogs moving to what appears to be predetermined holes. If these happen to be already in use, they will move on in search of another, occupation being determined on a sort of "first come, first served" basis (Cumming, 1975). They change holes frequently and individual holes may be used intermittently by different individuals or sounders.

Warthogs are not dependent on the availability of water, but where it is available they drink regularly. They are great mud wallowers, the mud covering serving as a protection against biting flies and in thermoregulation.

The social unit is the family group or sounder, consisting of an adult male, adult female and her offspring. There remains some difference of opinion as to the durability of the male attachment to the sounder. In Zimbabwe, Cumming (1975) found that while up to 10 individuals may form a sounder, the more usual number is five or less. The number of individuals in a sounder varies seasonally and is usually larger during the rainy season, (from October to February) than during the dry season. Larger sounders fragment when farrowing commences at the onset of the rains. Cumming (1975) recognised no less than 19 types of sounders from solitary individuals to groups consisting of adults and mixed age classes. Solitary individuals accounted for 27% of all sounders observed, 75% of these being solitary males.

Maternity groups consist of one or more adult females with their offspring, either juveniles or juveniles and yearlings or the latter grouping with subadults as well. Bonds between females in these groups might last for a number of years. Adult males join them when the females come into oestrus.

Bachelor groups consist of adult males and younger males, but these associations are temporary, lasting up to about three months. The younger males may associate together for longer periods, until they become fully mature, but at the time of the rut they tend to disperse.

Cumming (1975) found that the most durable bonds are between females and between females and their offspring, the latter remaining together for a period of up to 27 months and in an exceptional case up to three years. When the females become pregnant they tend to desert the group or to drive out the young of the previous year, which then form heterosexual groups which are not considered to be stable social units. Cumming (1975) found that there was some evidence that the groups associated into a clan system, comprising groups in which all the members were related, but observed that further study was required before this was established clearly. He found no evidence to suggest that warthogs are territorial but they may defend a small area around the entrance of nesting holes against others. Groups had widely overlapping home ranges, the groups tending to avoid each other in the overlapping areas. They shared a number of nesting holes. The female home range varied between 64 ha and 341 ha and averaged 171 ha for 15 of his radio-tagged individuals. The male home range was only slightly larger, at an average of 179 ha for 10 tagged individuals and varied between 65 ha and 374 ha. He found that the home ranges tended to be larger during a drought period, coupled with a low population density, and that once established they would adhere to them for long periods, if not for life. Some movement outside the limits of these home ranges did take place to take advantage of the flush of green grass following dry season burns, but these movements were temporary. Encounters were observed, particularly at waterholes, where adult males drove off younger males or even at times adult females. There were indications of dominance, adults showing intolerance to others in feeding areas.

Warthogs scent-mark by wiping the sides of their mouths on objects (Cumming, 1975). They also mark by urine spraying and wiping with the exudation from the eyeglands, which may sometimes be noticed in the field as dark patches just in front of the eyes.

Serious encounters between warthogs are rare, but during the mating season there may be a considerable degree of aggressive display between adult males, especially when a strange male approaches a group which has a male in attendance. This may take a number of forms including a rush towards each other, often without contact, pawing of the ground, running sideways with the legs held stiffly and mane raised, lunging, or at close quarters dropping onto the knees, their heads touching, as they attempt to push each other backwards. During the farrowing season females can become aggressive towards each other, indulging in much head-pushing.

Warthogs are quick to respond to the warning calls of other mammals or birds, particularly oxpeckers, *Buphagus* spp, in attendance searching for ticks, and is of importance, as they have a limited range of vision, being relatively short-sighted and short-legged. They will chase off other species aggressively, excepting predators, that move too near when they are feeding or drinking, but, on the other hand, are often chased off themselves.

They have been known to defend themselves successfully against the attack of a solitary cheetah and Cowie (1961) recorded an incident in which two adult males successfully defended themselves against a pack of 16 wild dogs. They are no match, however, for lions which have been known to dig them out of their holes. Their strictly diurnal habits are some measure of protection against spotted hyaenas and leopards, but there are records of their falling prey to both species.

Warthogs defecate fortuitously. They are prone to rubbing themselves on any convenient object and to scratching themselves with their hind legs. Social grooming is common behaviour among members of a group, taking the form of nibbling and grooming of each other's inguinal and axillary regions. Greeting, which may occur when a new individual joins a group or when two strangers meet, consists of slow movement towards each other, with outstretched necks, ears held flat against the neck, until the tips of their noses touch. This may develop into a head to head encounter or, having touched noses, they may return to their feeding. Their movements are generally leisurely, but under stress they will trot off at a fair speed, with their tails held vertically, which may assist the group in maintaining contact.

Although noticeably quiet, warthogs grunt, snarl and snort. Grunting is used by the adults to maintain group contact. The piglets, under these circumstances, use a whistling squeak. Snarling and snorting occurs with aggressive display or when defending themselves. During the preliminaries to mating the males chomp their jaws as they approach the females and the resulting teeth-gnashing can be heard up to distances of 50 m (Feely, pers. comm.).

**Food**

Warthogs spend the greater part of the daylight hours in search of food. In general they are vegetarians, living on annual and perennial grasses which grow in lawn-like swards, and are partial to freshly sprouting grasses after a burn and also to rooting on the underground rhizomes of grasses. They prefer to graze on short grass, but will also eat sedges, herbs, shrubs and wild fruits. They show a preference for grasses growing in damp areas, where these remain fresh and the rhizomes succulent and full of moisture. In areas where warthogs root for underground rhizomes, the soil becomes churned up to a depth of 100 or 150 mm. Characteristically, in rooting, the individual kneels on the front legs so as to bring the upper edge of the hard snout to bear as an efficient digging tool. The kneeling position provides a firm base for the leverage of the head and neck in the process. As a result they develop callouses on the joints of the forelegs which can be seen clearly in the field. Warthogs can root in this way even in very hard soils, an ability not possessed by bushpigs. They exhibit geophagia, osteophagia and coprophagia (Mason, 1982).

When feeding they walk with their noses close to the ground, smelling out underground sources of food, which they will then root up. The greater part of their food, however, consists of fresh green grasses, the shoots of which they nibble off when the grass is short or which they crop when it is longer. Juveniles have a full set of incisors but these appear ill-adapted to feeding except for a very restricted nibbling action, as the occlusion of the teeth is minimal. It may be that, like a hippopotamus, close cropping is carried out mainly by lip action (Mason, 1982).

Warthogs are selective feeders and can be seen pushing aside unwanted grass to get at the more preferred new shoots close to the ground. They will strip off the flowering and seeding heads of grasses, pulling the standing stems through their mouths to comb off the flowering and seeding parts. Juveniles are particularly partial to this food as it is available seasonally.

In KwaZulu, Mason (1982) recorded grazing on: gonya grass, *Urochloa mosambicensis*; buffalo grass, *Panicum maximum*; small buffalo grass, *P. coloratum*; old-lands grass, *Chloris virgata*; finger grass, *Digitaria argyrograpta*; *Sporobolus nitens*; *S. smutsii*; couch grass, *Cynodon dactylon*, and Durban grass, *Dactyloctenium australe*. He recorded that there was a seasonal variation in proportions of the different grasses selected.

Cumming (1975) gave a list of 39 species of grasses eaten by warthogs in his study area in Zimbabwe and showed that there is a greater percentage of time spent in rooting during winter from June to September than during summer, when they turn to grazing. Wild fruits also form part of their diet and groups may be seen eating the fallen fruits of trees such as wild figs, *Ficus* spp; marula, *Sclerocarya birrea*, and wild oranges, *Strychnos* spp. They also eat berries and will strip bark from trees and shrubs. There are a number of well authenticated records of their eating carrion (Wilson, 1975) and they are also reported to have killed and eaten snakes and a litter of rats (Cumming, 1975). This is, however, atypical feeding behaviour. Unlike bushpigs they are not considered a problem in agricultural areas.

**Reproduction**

Mason (1986) found that the males reach sexual maturity at 17 to 18 months old, but although they display sexual interest in females, few participate in breeding because of competition with older, larger males. The males court the females in oestrus by approaching them with a springy, hip-rolling gait and with their tails wrapped around their flanks or carried half upright in a bent position (Simpson, 1964b; Cumming, 1975). The males follow closely behind the females as they move around, now and then placing their chins on top of the hindquarters of the females. If a female is receptive she will back on to the male, and copulation may follow (Simpson, 1964). Cumming (1975) recorded that boars would visit holes during the mating season to join oestrous females which might emerge and sometimes they sleep in the same holes.

Sub-adult males which approach oestrous females are chased away by the adult male. Cumming (1975) found that from the observation of radio-tagged groups warthogs are polygamous or possibly promiscuous.

In Zimbabwe, piglets are born shortly before or just after the start of the summer rains (September to December) (Roth, 1965; Child, Roth & Kerr, 1968), peaking in November/December (Cumming, 1975). This time varies locally within narrow limits. For example, the season further north in Zambia is from June to August, peaking in July/August (Ansell, 1960a). In KwaZulu, Mason (1982) recorded a peak in mating in May. Piglets are born late in October with births in exceptional years as early as August. Farrowing occurs early in the rainy season which is the most favourable period for the lactating female as fresh green grass is freely available.

In Zimbabwe, Child *et al.* (1968) recorded that in 97 pregnancies the average number of foetuses was 3,0, with a range of one to eight. In KwaZulu, Mason (1982) recorded that in 61 pregnancies the mean was 3,26, with a range of one to five births taking place following a gestation period of 167 to 175 days. The mass at birth appears to vary inversely with the size of the litter and there is considerable discrepancy in size and development among foetuses of the same potential litter (Child *et al.*, 1968; Mason, 1982). Bigourdan (1948) recorded birth masses of 480,0 g to 620,0 g in litters of three to four and 800,0 g to 850,0 g in twins. Females attain sexual maturity at 18 to 19 months of age.

The litters are born in burrows. The piglets lie huddled together on a shelf-like tapering recess at the far end of the burrow which is raised above the level of the main chamber floor, thus minimising the possibility of their being drowned during heavy rain (Mason, 1982). These burrows provide a sheltered micro-climate for the piglets which have been shown (Sowls & Phelps, 1966; Cumming, 1975) to be sensitive to low temperatures at night and may die unless provided with warm shelter. Warthogs have almost bare skin and virtually no subcutaneous fat to provide insulation against cold. The floor of the resting chamber is sometimes floored with grass brought in by the female. Mason (1982) found that during the very early part of the piglets' life, the mother, if unduly disturbed, might carry them in her mouth to a new burrow.

The large number of foetuses recorded does not mean corresponding numbers in litters and it has been shown that there is a prenatal loss of some 9,13% in KwaZulu (Mason, 1982) *cf.* 16,92% for Zimbabwe (Child *et al.*, 1968). In addition, many may be stillborn or die shortly after birth. The higher numbers of piglets occasionally seen with females may be due to recruitment from litters of other females, which is a common occurrence. Furthermore, up to 50% of young suckling piglets may die during their first six months of life (Bradley, 1968). They have little resistance to sudden changes in temperature and, if for climatic reasons there are large temperature fluctuations, high losses occur. Losses by predation are also high during their early life when they become prey even to medium-sized carnivores such as jackals.

Piglets, which at birth are coloured like adults, with no sign of patterning, will graze at about a week old, may be weaned at about nine weeks old, but frequently continue to suckle until about five months old. They remain with their mother for about a year and mature at about 17–18 months.

Just before she gives birth to a litter, members of the previous litter are driven off. If she does not become pregnant or if she loses a number of her litter, a total or partial reunification of the group may take place, always however, with a bias towards allowing for the return of female offspring. Such reunifications are a common occurrence. Pregnant sows leave the group with the advent of parturition.

Fig. 301.1. Feral pig, *S. scrofa*.

Females have two pairs of inguinal mammae.

**INTRODUCED**

No. 301

## *Sus scrofa* Linnaeus, 1758

## Feral pig
## Wilde huisvark

Apart from the two indigenous species of pig, the bushpig, *Potamochoerus porcus*, and the warthog, *Phacochoerus aethiopicus*, domestic strains of pigs have taken to the wild and bred successfully, thereby qualifying for inclusion. These may have adopted this free living state voluntarily, from stock which has been allowed free range or may have been deliberately released. Thomas & Kolbe (1942) recorded that the Forestry Department released domestic pigs into its plantations in the southwestern parts of the Cape Province (Kluitjieskraal) and in the George area, in an endeavour to control the pine tree emperor moth, *Nudaurelia cytherea*, whose caterpillars defoliate pine trees, and that the pigs flourished in both areas. Once the caterpillars are fully grown and ready to pupate they do so some 50 mm deep in loose soil where they are rooted out easily by the pigs. Botha (*in litt.*, 1986) reported that feral populations were present in plantations at Franschhoek in 1944; Lebanon (near Grabouw) in 1946; Swellendam in 1947; Garcia in 1951 and in Jonkershoek, Nuweberg and Highlands in 1953. At least up to the late 1940's there were feral domestic pigs living in the vlei at Kleinmond which were shot occasionally. By 1986 only those on Kluitjieskraal, Franschhoek and Garcia still existed, albeit in diminished numbers.

Mr Martin Melck of Kersefontein in the Piketberg District of the Cape Province reported in 1973 that he had about 200 feral domestic pigs on his farm which he hunted with dogs, rationing the meat to his staff. Skead (1980) reported that there was a herd of feral domestic pigs living in the mountains near Broekhuizen's Poort, 14 km west of Grahamstown, and Botha (*in litt.*, 1986) reported that there was a feral population on Ganskraal farm on the southern slopes of the Riviersonderend Mountains, 10 km west of the town. A boar was taken from this population in 1985 and translocated to Garcia to strengthen the genetic pool there. In the Wemmershoek area of the Cape Province they are the preferred food of leopards (Norton, pers. comm.)

Crosses between bushpig, *P. porcus*, and feral domestic pigs are known. Milstein (1971) reported that a hybrid was acquired by the Conservation Officer in the Hans Merensky Nature Reserve in the northeastern Transvaal. This was one of a litter of eight, four boars and four sows, produced by a domestic sow which escaped while on heat and was served by a bushpig boar in the mountainous area near Tzaneen. The hybrid showed many bushpig characteristics.

# XLIV. Family HIPPOPOTAMIDAE

## Hippopotamus

This Family is comprised of two living genera, *Choeropsis* and *Hippopotamus*, both with one species each. The former is represented by the pygmy hippopotamus, *C. liberiensis*, of the forests and coastal plains of West Africa and the latter by the hippopotamus, *H. amphibius*, which occurs widely in sub-Saharan Africa, and is the only species occurring in the Subregion.

Fossil hippopotamids are known from the Pleistocene deposits of the Old World but they never reached the New World. Early forms had a dental formula of

$I\frac{3}{3}\ C\frac{1}{1}\ P\frac{4}{4}\ M\frac{3}{3} = 44$

The exant hippopotamus, *H. amphibius*, has a dental formula of

$I\frac{2}{2}\ C\frac{1}{1}\ P\frac{3\text{-}4}{3\text{-}4}\ M\frac{3}{3} = 36\text{-}40$

Remains of the earliest hippopotamids are represented by teeth with few skull remains or postcranial skeletal material, but in *Hippopotamus* the dentition is remarkably conservative throughout their known evolutionary history, the molar teeth being quite distinct in formation from those of the Suidae (Coryndon, 1978).

The earliest known member so far recognised was found in Miocene beds, some 20 million years old, in Kenya (Coryndon, 1978). In the Subregion the earliest fossil remains come from middle Pleistocene deposits of about one million years old, these remains closely resembling the extant hippopotamus, *H. amphibius*. This form, named *H. kaisensis*, by the end of the Pleistocene Epoch occurred widely in Africa and spread by way of Israel to Europe, reaching northeastern England. With the coming of the last glacial period their distribution shrunk, their descendants surviving now only in the warmer climate of Africa (Coryndon, 1978).

## Genus *Hippopotamus* Linnaeus, 1758

No.302

## *Hippopotamus amphibius* Linnaeus, 1758

### Hippopotamus
### Seekoei

Plate 29

### Colloquial Name

The English colloquial name is derived from the Greek which means "water or river horse". Their association with the mouths of rivers most probably led to their being called "sea cows or seekoeie" which has been adopted in Afrikaans.

### Taxonomic notes

Three subspecies are listed by Meester *et al.* (1986) from the continent, of which two occur in the Subregion: *H. a. capensis*, which was described originally in 1825 by Desmoulins from the lower reaches of the Berg River, Cape Province, and *H. a. constrictus* Miller, 1910 from northern Namibia, which may be a synonym of *H. a. capensis*.

### Description

Hippopotamus are characterised by their great size, short, barrel-shaped body, smooth naked skin and short, stout legs. Their heads are broad and heavy, with the eyes and the nostrils mounted on top. Their mouths are wide and very large, the jaws armed with tusk-like canines and incisor teeth. In proportion to the head the ears are small and upstanding. The tail is short and flattened, with a sparse brush of bristles towards the tip. The lips, sides of the head and neck and tips of the ears have a sparse covering of bristly hair.

The colour of the body is greyish-black with a pink tinge, pinkish-yellow in the folds of the skin and around the eyes and ears. The gape of the mouth is flesh-coloured. The eyes are raised on bony protuberances on the top of the head. The slit-like nostrils, which can be closed at will, are situated on top of the rhinarium. When the head is partially submerged in the resting position the eyes and ears are, as a consequence, above the surface of the water. The only other parts of the body showing above the water are the back of the head with the upstanding ears and portion of the back. The short legs have four toes, each with heavy broad nails, which mark clearly in the spoor (Plate I). Males are larger than females (Table 302.1).

**Table** 302.1

Measurements and mass (kg) of hippopotamus, *H. amphibius*, from the Kruger National Park (Pienaar *et al.*, 1966a)

| | Males | | | Females | | |
|---|---|---|---|---|---|---|
| | $\bar{x}$ | n | Range | $\bar{x}$ | n | Range |
| Sh.ht(m) | 1,5 | 32 | 1,29–1,72 | 1,44 | 36 | 1,1–1,58 |
| Length lower canine (mm) | 223 | 32 | 125–308 | 142 | 36 | 76–203 |
| Mass | 1490 | 32 | 971–1999 | 1321 | 36 | 995–1674 |

### Skull (Fig. 302.1)

Features of the skull of the hippopotamus include the high supraorbital ridges, the anterior heavy broadening of the jaws to carry the heavy teeth and the high supraoccipital and sagittal crests.

For the massive size of the skull the braincase is surprisingly small. The zygomatic arches are very thick and swing widely outwards at the back to allow space for the temporalis muscles. In old specimens the postorbital bar is complete, usually with a distinct bony knob at the junction of the two bones.

The massive zygoma give firm anchorage for the masseter muscles; the high sagittal and supraoccipital crests extend the restricted surface of the sides of the small braincase for the attachment of the temporalis muscles. Both these muscles require to be extra powerful to move the massive lower jaw with its accompanying huge, heavy teeth. In a cleaned skull the lower jaw may have a mass of up to 16 kg.

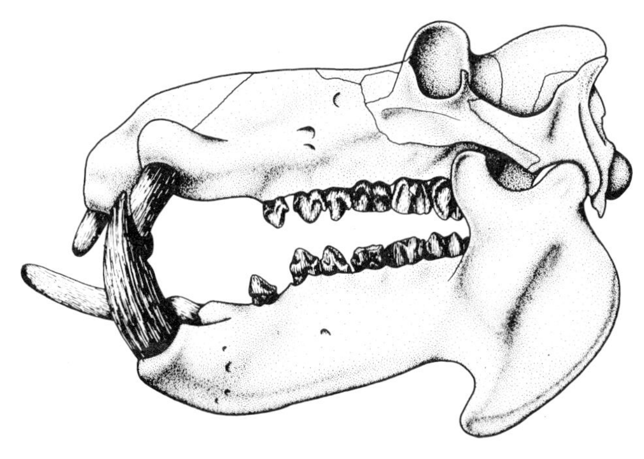

Fig. 302.1. Skull: male hippopotamus, *H. amphibius*. TL Skull 650 mm

In the permanent set of teeth the canines and incisors are continually growing. The canines in the lower jaw are the largest and heaviest of the teeth. They are triangular in section, with the flat face on the inner side, and are distinctly ridged along their length, which may reach 700 mm overall or 300 mm above the gum level. The inner face of the canines, through occlusion with its short counterpart in the upper jaw, is continually honed to a flat surface, keeping the point and sides of the tooth sharp.

The inner incisors in the lower jaw are round and may reach a length of about 170 mm above the gum. Although, like the canines, they wear by occlusion on their inner faces, they remain round and blunt-pointed. The outer incisors are small and round-pointed.

The canines in the upper jaw, through wear, remain short but very sharp-edged. The incisors are short and rounded.

At birth hippopotamus appear to have only the central incisors and canines protruding through the gums. These are shed within the first few months of their life. Four deciduous premolars may be present below bone level. The second, third and fourth are replaced by permanent teeth; the first is present only in the milk set and not subsequently replaced, although it may persist quite late in the life of the individual.

The dental formula in an adult with full dentition is:

$I\frac{2}{2}\,C\frac{1}{1}\,P\frac{3\text{-}4}{3\text{-}4}\,M\frac{3}{3} = 36\text{–}40$

While the cheekteeth are adapted to grinding, the positioning of the canines and incisors renders them useless in feeding. The cropping of grass is taken over by the hard edges of the lips and these teeth function as weapons of defence only.

**Distribution**

Hippopotamus occur widely on the continent south of the Sahara and were once found in the lower Nile, from where the first specimen was described by Linnaeus in 1758, disappearing from this area about 1815 (Ellerman & Morrison-Scott, 1951). Van Riebeeck's Diary recorded the presence of hippopotamus in 1652 in the swamp that is now Church Square, Cape Town, and they were then quite common in the vicinity of the Cape. The distribution map reflects the subsequent great reduction in their range in southern Africa. As they are amphibious, they are necessarily confined within this wide range to adequate aquatic habitats, resulting in a discontinuous and patchy distribution. As they are great wanderers, they may be expected to turn up from time to time outside these demarcated limits. They can cause serious damage to crops and become a problem and be subject to control measures, leading to their local extirpation. Their meat and fat are highly prized for cooking purposes and their hide is sought after for the manufacture of sjamboks and their teeth for curios.

*South of the Sahara, excluding the Southern African Subregion*

They are recorded from parts of **Gambia; Guinea Bissau; Sierra Leone; Liberia;** the **Ivory Coast; Ghana** and **Nigeria**, northeast to Lake Chad. They are still common in the Parc National de Saint-Fores in western **Chad** and they occur in **Gabon, Congo Republic** and in parts of **Equatorial Guinea**. In the **Sudan** they are now extinct in the Nile downstream of about 50 km south of Khartoum, but are common in the south in the "Sudd". They are listed from **Ethiopia**; southern **Somalia**; from the northern (Lake Turkana), central and southern parts of **Kenya** and parts of **Uganda; Tanzania** and **Zaire**. They are recorded from rivers in **Angola**; throughout **Zambia**; in **Malawi** and **Mozambique**, north of the Zambezi.

*Southern African Subregion*

They occur marginally in **Namibia** in the extreme northeast and there may still be a few in the lower Cunene River as they occurred there in former times. They are common in the Okavango Swamps and on the Chobe River in northern **Botswana**; throughout most of **Zimbabwe**, except in the western area; they occur in the northeastern and eastern **Transvaal** and occasionally in parts of **Swaziland** Lowveld; in **Mozambique**, south of the Zambezi River and marginally in **Natal** in the northeast, and south, coastally, to about 20 °S, which now marks their southern limits on the continent.

**Habitat**

An essential habitat requirement is sufficient open water in which they can submerge totally. They prefer shallow standing water near sandy banks on which they can bask in the sun. If undisturbed, they will use these pools over a period of many years providing food supplies remain available to them within their range of normal movement. Seasonal flooding may cause them to move temporarily from their established resting pools but, providing this has not altered their condition seriously, they will return as the flood subsides. They find temporary resting places during flooding in oxbows or up the side tributaries of major rivers.

**Habits**

Amongst the ungulates only hippos are truly amphibious, feeding mostly nocturnally on dry land and spending much of the day in water, where mating and calving take place. During daylight they live in social groups varying in size and composition; solitary animals are generally territorial bulls or females about to give birth. Apart from a proportion of adult bulls living solitarily, the groups consist of females with calves, or bachelors in association (Klingel, 1979). Social groups break up in the evenings and the animals come ashore to graze when they amble singly or in female-young units; a cow may be accompanied by as many as four young in ascending age, the youngest keeping nearest to the dam.

Klingel (in press) found that some 10% of bulls are territorial, occupying territories in which they are dominant over all conspecifics and where they have exclusive mating rights. The size of territories varies depending on the breadth and depth of rivers, but he found this varied from 50 to 100 m in the Ishasha River, Uganda, included 250 to 500 m of shoreline in Lake Edward, while in swamps territories were arranged in a mosaic pattern.

Bulls maintain territories for long periods of time and Klingel (in press) believed this could span the whole adult life of a bull of some 20 to 30 years. Territorial bulls may be challenged and this is dependent on density and also climatic changes affecting territory size. Territories are advertised through dominant behaviour and ritualised defecation combined with urination. Defecation in the same places and flapping their tails from one side to another, result in the accumulation of impressive dung piles measuring several square metres. Dung piles do not function as markers and are not produced only by the territorial bull, but by all males passing the site. Such piles are also found where the hippopotamus graze, outside the territories, as well as along footpaths.

Fights between neighbouring territorial bulls are ritualized frontal combats with splashing of water demarcating the boundary. Partners hardly make contact, advancing and retreating in response to the opponent's actions. However, where serious fights occur for territorial possession, the bulls fight in reverse parallel position, slashing at each other's flanks with the lower canines. These attacks can result in serious injury leading to death and invariably result from challenges by non-territorial bulls.

Klingel (1983, 1988) found that relationships between territorial bulls and other bulls were extremely friendly provided the latter were subordinate. This they demonstrate in an elaborate display with head down and, while on land, creeping along sniffing the territorial bull's genital region without him seeming to take notice. Apart from the territorial bull, recognisable by the larger size of his head and his thick neck, few dominance relationships seem to exist in hippopotamus groups. The only stable associations are those of a cow and her young until these are fully grown at six to eight years. In the evenings when hippopotamus depart to

**Plate 29**

299. Bushpig, *Potamochoerus porcus*
Bosvark

300. Warthog, *Phacochoerus aethiopicus*
Vlakvark

302. Hippopotamus, *Hippopotamus amphibius*
Seekoei

PLATE 29

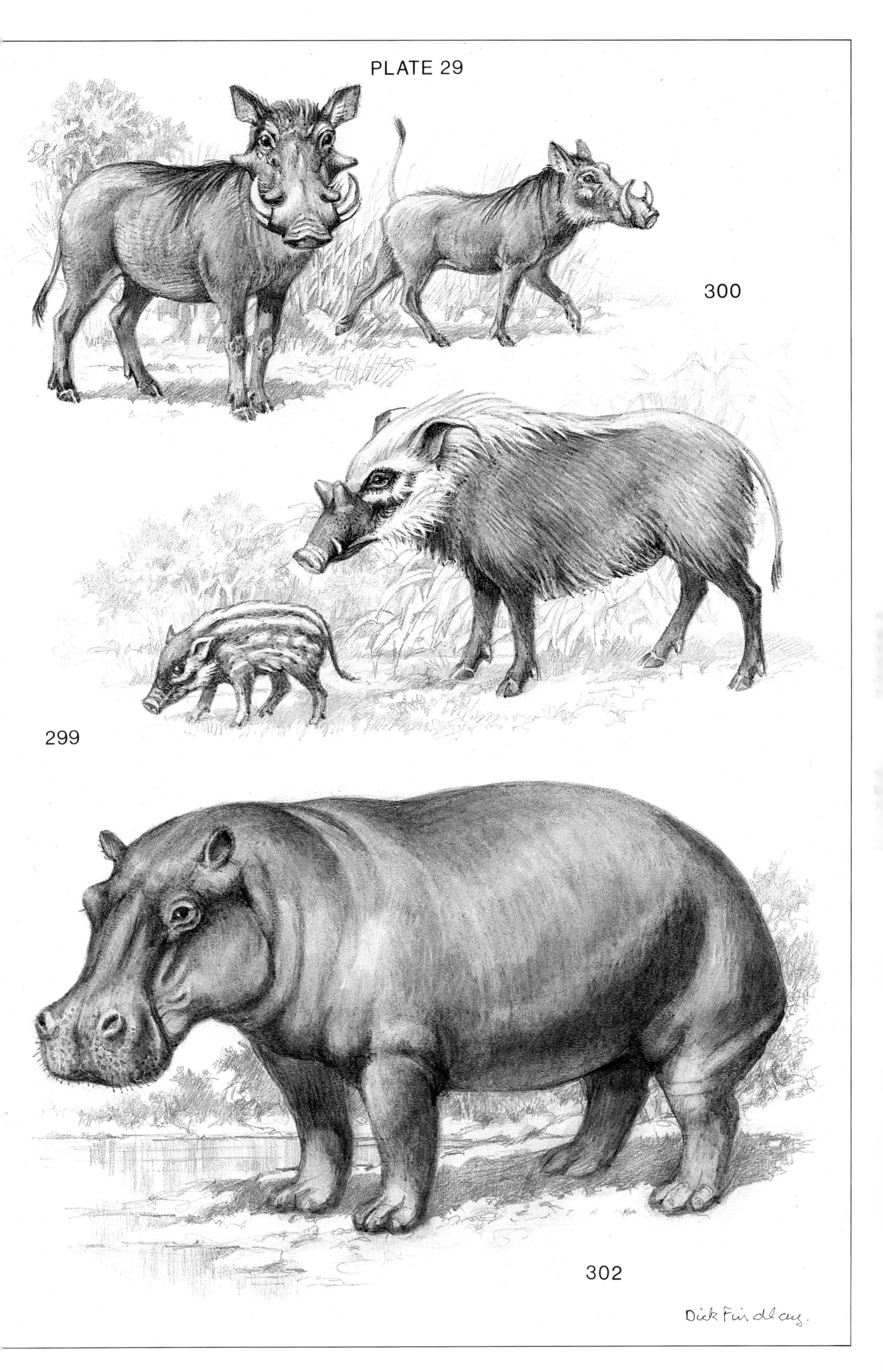

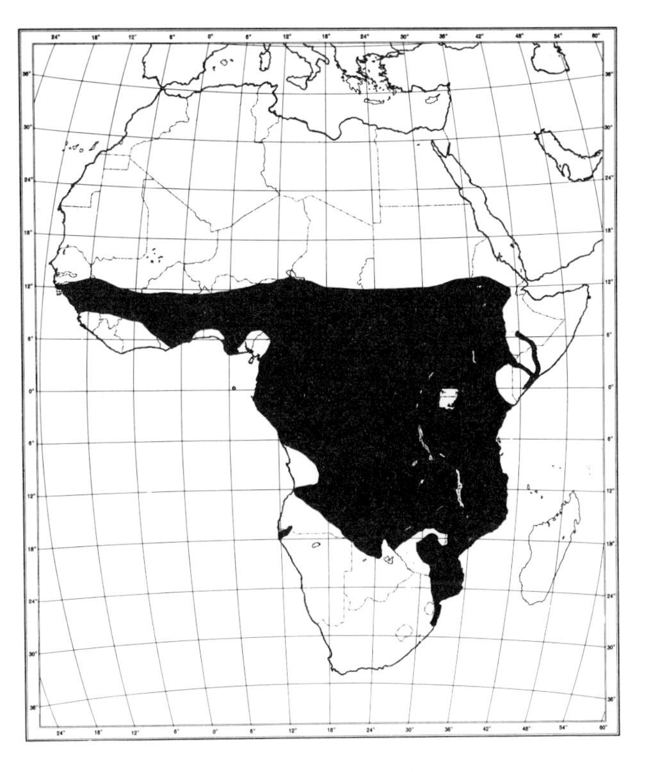

graze, the social groups break up. Hippopotamus do not spend the whole night feeding and may rest, lying down under bushes or even return to the water. Grazing areas are not subdivided into territories and change with season and availability of forage. On dry land they tend to use established routes, the ground eventually becoming bare. Hippopotamus paths characteristically have a central ridge where the grass is still intact. On river banks the exits are worn deeply into the ground. These gorge-like passages are short, only a few metres long and a metre or so deep. In extensive areas of swamp, such as the Okavango in Botswana, the movements of hippopotamus create deep, clear channels through the reed beds and permit freer movement of the water. While on dry land they appear ungainly, but they are more agile than one would suppose and can run surprisingly fast for their great bulk.

Hippopotamus will walk on the bottom in deep water and can be seen doing this where the water is clear, such as in the Okavango, Botswana, or in the Mzima Springs in the Tsavo National Park in Kenya. Even under these conditions they tend to use the same paths which, on a sandy bottom, become clearly marked.

Where food is plentiful they tend to remain in the vicinity of the resting pool but will move freely up to eight or 10 km and are known to move much further when food is scarce locally. Individuals of both sexes are prone to vagrant movements and may be found in farm dams and other water impoundments far from their normal haunts. The wanderings of "Hubert" (or "Huberta" as she was later called after her death when it was established that she was a female), a hippopotamus from Lake St Lucia, Natal, to the Cape Province, over a period of three years and for a distance of close on 1 800 km, is well documented (Chilvers, 1931).

The hairless skin is kept soft and pliable by the secretions of subdermal glands scattered over its surface. The hippopotamus normally avoids thermal stress on land by taking to the water for most of the day, but it can keep its body temperature to normal levels under adverse conditions on land (Wright, 1987). The glands in the skin secrete a reddish viscous fluid.

Adult hippopotamus can remain under water for five to six minutes at a time, the young for much shorter periods. Just before submerging they fill their lungs with air and, as the water closes over them, sphincter muscles close the nostrils and hearing ducts to prevent the entry of water. On returning to the surface they empty the lungs with a loud blast, which can be heard over considerable distances. They may also exhale under water. They are not able to float, but in deep water push themselves to the surface with their hind feet. When swimming on the surface of the water they propel themselves forward with a "jumping" action. The four toes are not webbed to aid swimming. They are well adapted to life in water, the nostrils, ears and eyes raised high on the top of the head so that only the top of the head need remain above the surface to keep these three keen senses ready to alert them to danger. While generally associated with fresh water, they have been observed in the sea. In the 19th century a whaleboat from a Yankee whaler harpooned and killed one of a group of at least three hippopotamus about 3 km (1,5 n.m.) offshore in about 2 m (1 fathom) of water between Bazaruto Island and the mainland, Mozambique (Nordhoff, 1856). More recently, at the time of the floods in Natal (1957, 1984), hippopotamus were seen in the sea a few kilometres off the mouth of the Umfolozi river by Player (pers. comm.) who has also seen both hippopotamus and elephants a few hundred metres offshore on other occasions.

Hippopotamus, especially the females with young, can become aggressive quickly and there are many reports of small boats being overturned or badly damaged and the occupants bitten to death in these attacks. Aggression is demonstrated by opening the mouth, displaying the imposing teeth, and by making short charges through the water, sometimes directed at intruders who venture too close to the edge of the waters in which they are resting. They have been known to demonstrate against anything unusual that they may encounter on their way to graze at night.

Vocalisation, which takes the form of a deep roaring grunt followed by four or five shorter ones in quick succession, can be heard over great distances and is particularly in evidence at sunset.

### Food

Hippopotamus are selective nocturnal grazers, consuming about 40 kg of grass per night (Klingel, 1983), the types of grasses utilised depending on their availability. Scotcher, Stewart & Breen (1978) in two study areas in the Ndumu Game Reserve, northern Natal, showed that in the one, buffalo grass, *Panicum maximum*, *Urochloa mosambicensis*, and couch grass, *Cynodon dactylon*, occurred predominantly in their diet, in the other, *Hemarthria altissima* and *Echinochloa pyramidalis*. Around Lake St Lucia, *Ischaemum arcuatum* is a preferred species (Feely, pers. comm.).

Hippopotamus are very close croppers and will graze on stands of grass such as couch grass, *C. dactylon*, until they are of lawn-like appearance. This is accomplished with the horny edges of the lips. The grass is plucked with an upward movement of the head. Like ruminants, hippopotamus have a compound stomach with three compartments but no rumen, nor do they ruminate (Arman & Field, 1973). Grass is digested and fermented in the stomach with the aid of microorganisms before passing into the small intestine (van Hoven, 1974). In general they prefer to feed on open areas of short green grass. Where there are large numbers of hippopotamus their trampling and over-utilisation of grazing areas can cause soil erosion and control measures to reduce their numbers have had to be carried out in many parts of Africa. Without these controls Nature herself would carry out the same task through death by starvation, so reducing numbers to within the carrying capacity of the habitat. In such cases management is both desirable and economically rewarding, making meat available to the local people and enabling hides, which have a high commercial value, to be processed properly.

Hippopotamus are notorious crop raiders and can become a problem where crops are grown near rivers in which hippopotamus live. People have invented many devices to ward them off.

### Reproduction

Mating in hippopotamus takes place in the water, the female remaining submerged, except for brief intervals to breath; the male's head is not submerged. The gestation period is from 225–257 days (Asdell, 1964). In the Subregion they calve throughout the year but seasonal calving peaks have been reported in the Kruger National Park (Pienaar, van Wyk & Fairall, 1966a; Smuts & Whyte, 1981). Females have their first calves at about four years old. Males reach puberty when they are about seven years old (Skinner, Scorer &

Millar, 1975). When about to calve, the female leaves the group and finds a secluded site in shallow water to give birth to the single young, hindlegs emerging first, which has a mass of about 50 kg (Klingel, 1988) and which is capable of going into deep water within a few minutes of being born. Like adults, young hippopotamus are unable to float. The female and young remain apart from any groups for the first few days. This is associated with the critical period of imprinting, a process which ends after 10 to 14 days when mother and young rejoin the other hippopotamus (Klingel, 1983). On rejoining the group the calf initially stays near the shore while the mother feeds in the vicinity. Later it accompanies her to the feeding grounds, and when older still it may stay behind when the mother goes grazing. In the water, calves are often seen resting their heads on the backs of adults as their legs are too short to enable them to stand on the submerged sandbanks. When in deeper water, a young hippopotamus often sits on its mother's back. Suckling of the calves is carried out in the water. Calves do not appear to be able to remain under water for as long as the adults and normally submerge for only two or three minutes at a time.

Calves are prone to predation by crocodiles, which are, however, no match for an adult. On land, calves fall prey to lions and hyaenas, against which the female will put up a spirited and often successful defence. In the Luangwa Valley, Zambia, adult hippopotamus were killed regularly by lions, although not in large numbers (Feely, pers. comm.).

The females have a pair of inguinal mammae.

# XLV. Family GIRAFFIDAE

## Giraffe

This Family is represented by two living genera and two species: the okapi, *Okapia johnstoni*, of the lowland forests of East Africa and Zaire, and one of the last living African ungulates to be described, and the giraffe, *Giraffa camelopardalis*, which has a wide distribution in sub-Saharan Africa, although it has been exterminated in many parts of its range through over-exploitation.

Giraffe are large, ruminating artiodactyls standing up to 3 m at the shoulder, with characteristically long necks. The skulls have subconical paired ossicones which are covered by skin and resemble short, blunt horns. These are possessed by both sexes, and are usually larger in the males than in the females. They may also have paired "horns" in the nuchal region and single frontal "horns" in the males. Their dental formula is:

$I\frac{0}{3}\ C\frac{0}{1}\ P\frac{3}{3}\ M\frac{3}{3} = 32$

The earliest known fossil giraffids were found in early Miocene deposits about 22 million years ago in Libya from which two species were described, *Zarafa zelteri* Hamilton, 1973 and *Prolibytherium magnieri* Arambourg, 1961. In the former the spike-like paired ossicones extended sideways from the head, in the latter they were shaped like butterfly wings, the lower edges overlapping the eye sockets, the upper parts extending like flattened horns above the level of the head. Churcher (1978) suggested that the display of these flattened "horns" may have been more important than their use as bludgeons in intimidating opponents.

Heintz (1975) concluded that Africa was the original centre for the evolution of the early giraffids which gave rise to the extant species. *Samotherium africanum* Churcher, 1970, first known from the middle Miocene beds in North and northeastern Africa dated about 15 million years ago, was much larger, judging from the teeth, than our modern giraffe whose fossil record dates from the late Miocene beds of Africa, some 10 to 5 million years ago. Fossil material from these beds at Langebaanweg of this age are close to *G. jumae* Leakey, 1965 originally described from East Africa.

### Genus *Giraffa* Brisson, 1762

---

No. 303

### *Giraffa camelopardalis* (Linnaeus, 1758)

### Giraffe
### Kameelperd

Plate 30

---

#### Colloquial Name

The name giraffe appears to have its origin in the Arabic word *xirapha*, one who walks swiftly. The specific name *camelopardalis* refers to their size and marking, as being "big as a camel" and "spotted like a leopard".

#### Taxonomic notes

While at one time several species of giraffe were recognised, it is generally accepted today that they are all subspecies of *G. camelopardalis*.

Meester *et al.* (1986) listed two subspecies from the Subregion: *G. c. capensis* (Lesson, 1842) from the eastern Transvaal, southwestern Mozambique and southern and southeastern Zimbabwe, and *G. c. angolensis* Lydekker, 1903 from northwestern Zimbabwe, northern Botswana and northern Namibia.

#### Description

Unmistakable among African wildlife, the giraffe with its long neck is the tallest animal in the world. Shortridge (1934) recorded a specimen from Kenya that stood 5,88 m, but this is exceptional and the average height is about 4,9 m to 5,2 m for males and 4,3 m to 4,6 m for females. In the eastern Transvaal the average mass is 1191 kg for males *cf.* 828 kg for females (Hall-Martin, 1975). Child (pers. comm.) recorded some measurements from northern Botswana (Table 303.1).

Body hairs are $9{,}5 \pm 2{,}5$ mm long, circular or oval in cross-section, pigment in half the cortex only in some hairs, and the irregular waved mosaic scale pattern is at a sharp angle to the hair shaft. Scale margins are deeply rippled crenate (Fig. XLII.1) ( Buys & Keogh, 1984). The tops of the "horns" are covered with black hair, giving them a knob-like appearance and, from the back of the head to the top of the shoulders, they have a mane of stiff, brush-like hair.

The body, from the chin to the upper parts of the limbs, is covered in large, irregularly shaped patches of colour divided from one another by a network of light-coloured, off-white, white or yellowish-white bands. The colour of the patches is due to variation in hair colour and is very variable and tends to darken with age. It may be chestnut-brown, dark brown or nearly black, colours which may vary on the individual. The lower part of the flanks is occasionally black or dark chocolate, the upper parts lighter in colour. The forehead and top of the muzzle are evenly coloured, usually the same colour as the patches on the neck or slightly lighter. The shape of the patches, the width of the intervening lighter bands and the colour of the lower parts of the limbs have been used to distinguish the various subspecies. In our southern giraffe, these patches have well defined, even outlines and the lower part of the limbs is very faintly marked with small blotches of colour which are usually slightly lighter than the colour of the body patches. Towards the hooves the limbs are generally white. The front of the ears is whitish and there is usually a distinct lighter area just behind the ears which runs under the throat. Underneath the hair, the skin is uniformly pigmented dark grey (Ackerman, 1976).

All the megaherbivores have special mechanisms by which they thermoregulate and it seems the patches are of significance in the giraffe, acting as windows through which giraffes dissipate heat.

It has been stated that females reach a height of 4,3 m in five years (Foster, 1966), which is an incredibly fast growth rate. Males average about 5,0 m in height.

Spoor—Plate II.

**Table 303.1**

Measurements (mm) of giraffe, *G. camelopardalis*, from (a) northern Botswana (Child, pers. comm.) and measurements (mm) and mass (kg) of a series of over eight year old individuals from (b) the eastern Transvaal (Hall-Martin, *in litt.*)

**(a)**

| | Males | | | Females | | |
|---|---|---|---|---|---|---|
| | $\bar{x}$ | n | Range | $\bar{x}$ | n | Range |
| TL | 4848 | 4 | 3919–5224 | 4138 | 4 | 3759–4456 |
| T | 1231 | 4 | 965–1500 | 860 | 4 | 750–902 |
| Hf c/u | 1181 | 4 | 1099–1352 | 1103 | 5 | 1041–1178 |
| E | 228 | 4 | 216–242 | 210 | 5 | 203–216 |
| Sh.ht | 3036 | 4 | 2559–3490 | 2737 | 5 | 2032–3010 |
| Ht hq. | 2498 | 4 | 2243–2770 | 2396 | 4 | 2336–2458 |

**(b)**

| | Males | | | Females | | |
|---|---|---|---|---|---|---|
| | $\bar{x}$ | n | Range | $\bar{x}$ | n | Range |
| TL | 5050 | 15 | 4860–5270 | 4440 | 16 | 4160–4750 |
| Sh.ht | 3310 | 15 | 3130–3470 | 2800 | 16 | 2720–2920 |
| Mass | 1191,8 | 18 | 973,0–1395 | 828,4 | 18 | 703,0–950,0 |

**Skull** (Fig. 303.1)

A feature of the skulls of adult giraffes is the two prominent backward sloping horns which arise from the top of the braincase. In life these are covered with hairy skin, except at the blunt tips which are calloused. Unlike the horns of antelope, where the bony horn core grows out from the skull, in newly born giraffe the horns are soft and cartilaginous. As the young giraffe grows, ossification of these soft horns proceeds from a number of independent nuclei within them, the solid bone core formed eventually fusing with that of the skull. These horns are not so well developed in females as in males which may have yet a further median horn arising from the forehead between the eyes. This may originate in the same manner as the other horns or simply be an enlarged knob on the skull. In addition, in male skulls the whole of the upper part of the skull tends to be rugose, these rugosities sometimes growing to a size where they resemble supernumerary horns which may be found on any part of the skull. Female skulls are much smoother than males and lighter in build. The median horn is absent or represented by a low bulge. The skull is longer in front of the eye sockets which, situated laterally, give the individual a wider range of vision than is possessed by most mammals.

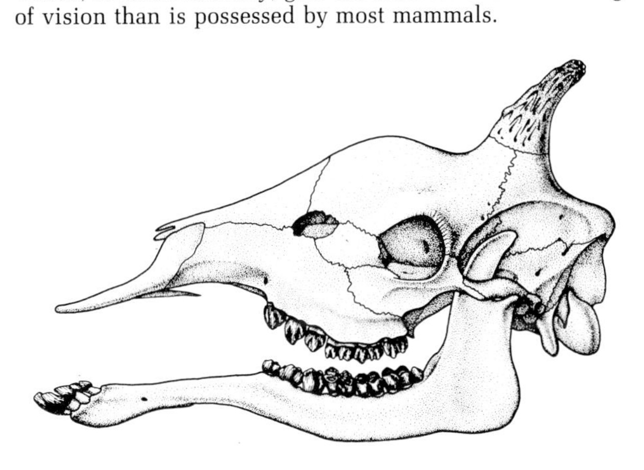

Fig. 303.1. Skull: male giraffe, *G. camelopardalis* TL Skull 560 mm

The portion of the skull in front of the cheekteeth is elongated and, relative to the rest of the skull, lightly built. The long lower jaw carries on its forward edge the three forward sloping incisor teeth on either side with their broad tips, and in addition, in individuals over six years old, the lower canine teeth which, at their points, broaden out widely into two or three lobes. The row of teeth is arranged in an open half circle, the broad points of the teeth adapted to stripping off the leaves and smaller shoots of the twigs in browsing.

The dental formula of the deciduous teeth is:

$i\frac{0}{3}\ c\frac{0}{1}\ p\frac{3}{3} = 20$

and of the permanent set:

$I\frac{0}{3}\ C\frac{0}{1}\ P\frac{3}{3}\ M\frac{3}{3} = 32$

The molar teeth are nearly square in section and both these and the premolars are adapted to grinding up the food. The permanent teeth in a giraffe do not erupt until it is about three years old, the canine teeth erupting last of all when the individual is about six years old or more (Hall-Martin, 1976).

**Distribution**

Within historical times the limits of distribution of the giraffe have shrunk dramatically and the present picture shows that, throughout their range from the eastern Transvaal to West Africa, their occurrence is patchy and discontinuous. Both Le Vaillant (1796) and Lichtenstein (1812) recorded them from the vicinity of the Orange River in the Cape Province and they at one time occurred in Morocco and in parts of the Sahara (Dekeyser, 1955). Although by the end of the last century shrinkage in their range had already taken place, rinderpest, poaching and settlement have further contributed to their local disappearance. With the establishment of reserves they nevertheless are not an endangered species and, with the enlightened appreciation of wildlife, they have been re-introduced widely onto farms and private game reserves with success in parts of the Republic of South Africa and Zimbabwe.

*South of the Sahara, excluding the Southern African Subregion*

In West Africa they occur in a number of National Parks and Reserves from eastern **Senegal; Mali**; southwestern **Niger**, on the northern banks of the Niger River; **Nigeria**; northern **Cameroun**, south of Lake Chad; southern **Chad**; the northeastern **Central African Republic** and southern and southeastern **Sudan**. They are recorded from southern **Somalia**; central and eastern **Kenya**, excluding the coastal strip; northern **Uganda** and from the northern and central parts of **Tanzania**.

Southwards there is a break in distribution, their next occurrence being in the form of an isolated population in the Luangwa Valley in **Zambia**. They also occur in the extreme southwest of the country, extending westwards narrowly into southern **Angola** along its southern border with the Caprivi and Namibia.

*Southern African Subregion*

In **Namibia** they occur in the extreme northeastern parts of the country south to about 20°S on the Botswana border, with two isolated populations in the western Kaokoveld. They are confined to the northern parts of **Botswana** and extend into the Hwange National Park in northwestern **Zimbabwe**, and also occur in the southwest and southeast. In **Mozambique** they occur in the southwest as far north as the Save River and narrowly in the eastern parts of the **Transvaal**.

**Habitat**

Giraffes occur in a wide variety of dry savanna associations ranging from scrub to woodland, providing that these include the particular range of food plants necessary to cover their seasonal requirements. They do not occur in forest and generally are not associated with open plains. In the Namib Desert they occur along river courses where *Acacia* trees abound. While they will drink regularly where water is

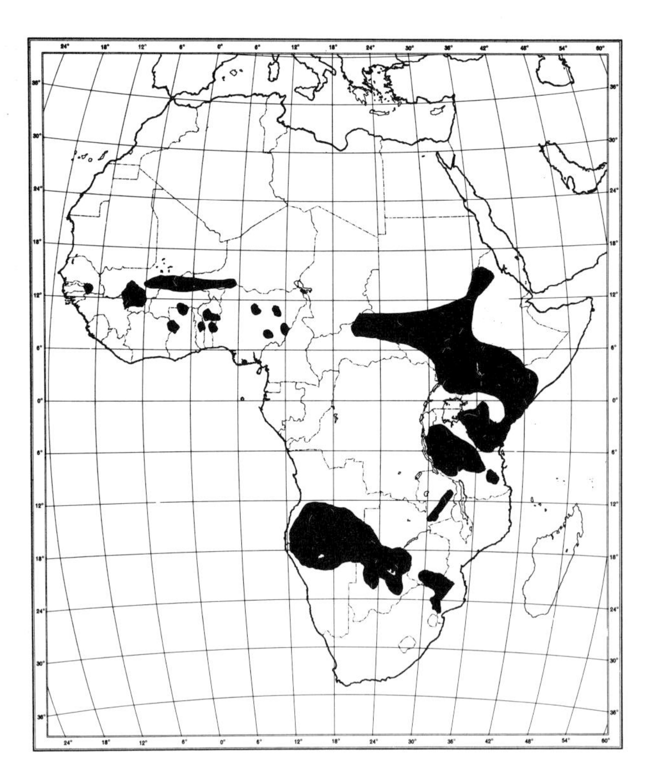

available they are not dependent on it and can obtain their moisture from their food plants.

### Habits

Giraffes are predominantly diurnal but they will also feed and move during the hours of darkness. During the hottest hours of the day they rest, either standing or lying down in the open or in shade, with their necks erect. Taller and heavier males make use of different orientations towards the sun to reduce radiation, while females and calves select shadow (Kuntzsch & Nel, 1990). Individuals in a resting herd may be approached quite closely. In deep sleep, which has been observed in captivity and which lasts only for a few minutes at a time, the individual bends its head back against the body, a position sometimes seen in juveniles in the wild.

When a giraffe lies down the forelegs are folded underneath the body and then the hind legs are bent. To get up it rises slightly on the forelegs, then rises on the hind legs, and finally straightens the fore.

They walk in an unusual way, the two legs on one side swing more nearly in unison than in other species, and they gallop in an ungainly manner, with tail twisted over the rump. Arbuthnot (1954) estimated that the maximum speed attained at the gallop was only some 56 km/h, which is far less than some other species attain and which is perhaps surprising in view of the tremendous length of their legs. As they gallop the neck swings backwards and forwards in rhythm with the leg movements. They can also jump fences up to about 1,5 m high (Dagg & Foster, 1976).

Although generally considered voiceless, giraffe grunt or snort when alarmed and Hart (1966) recorded the bleating of an individual when darted. During capture operations using vehicles and lasoos, snorting and grunting were heard regularly as they were guided to the holding pens. Dagg & Foster (1976) reported that captive giraffes bellow when they are hungry and moo gently when lonely and that females call their young with a whistling sound.

Rubbing against trees or other objects is common practice. Because of the length of the neck they are unable to scratch the sides of the head and neck with the hind feet as other species do and have to rely on rubbing to alleviate the irritation of ticks.

Their senses of hearing and sight are keen but there is some disagreement on their sense of smell. At the London Zoo, giraffes refused food that had been prepared by keepers who had previously handled mice or chewed tobacco (Dagg & Foster, 1976). A herd in Botswana certainly scented lions moving in thick bush nearby, shifting their focus of attention from the observer towards the lions.

Giraffes are generally docile and will approach stationary vehicles, but especially the females with young will mount a spirited defence against lions which, apart from man, are their only serious predators. Davison (pers. comm.) and Dagg & Foster (1976) each recalled incidents where a giraffe killed a lion with a single blow of the front foot. In spite of this, giraffes appear high on the list of prey species of the lion. Defence against attack takes the form of chop-kicking with the front feet, like a horse, striking with a stiff foreleg or a swinging kick with the hind foot. Henschel (1986) observed spotted hyaenas take a newborn calf which was knocked over by its mother who was chop-kicking in this fashion, accidentally prostrating it and killing it while protecting it from the hyaenas.

"Sparring" occurs when two males stand close together, head to head or head to tail, and swing at each other with the horns. This rarely leads to serious damage to either, although there are reports of one male occasionally being knocked down but getting up again. A report (Clarke, pers. comm.) indicated that once down, death can occur. The function of sparring has been stated by Coe (1967b) to be related, in bachelor herds, to the hierarchy within them and to lead to cohesion within the community.

Social bonds are not developed strongly and giraffes appear to have a loose herd structure made up mainly of females and young, but bachelor herds and mixed herds are also found. There is apparently no consistency in the ratio of males to females in a herd, or in the size of these. Herds rarely consist of the same individuals for more than a few days. The bulls are mainly solitary, wandering from herd to herd. Immature males sometimes form herds within which a hierarchy is established. Leadership of the herd tends to be arbitrary and it is impossible to tell which adult fills this role (Dagg & Foster, 1976). They do not defend a territory. In East Africa, their home ranges have been estimated by Dagg & Foster (1976) as 62 km$^2$ for males and 85 km$^2$ for females. In the eastern Transvaal Lowveld, with its dense population, Langman (1973) gave these as 22,8 km$^2$ and 24,6 km$^2$ respectively.

In several parts of their range they occur on one side of a river and not on the other (Lundi River in Zimbabwe, and Save River in Mozambique). This is understandable where major rivers with permanent water form barriers, for it is known that in captivity a water barrier effectively contains them. But, in the two examples, these rivers are in parts dry and sandy in the dry season, yet the giraffes do not cross.

### Food

Giraffes are predominantly browsers, utilising a wide range of food plants, but will graze occasionally on fresh sprouting palatable grasses. Hall-Martin (1974) showed that, in the eastern Transvaal, their food varies with the time of the year. During the hot wet months from November to March, when there is a plentiful supply of browse, they feed mainly on various species of *Acacia*, *Combretum*, *Terminalia* and *Ziziphus*. Various species of *Acacia* are the most important and preferred food plants for giraffe. Sauer, Skinner & Neitz (1982) showed that the leaves had a higher protein content than that of other species eaten and was a better food source than species of *Combretum* which nevertheless ranked high in their diet. Sauer *et al.* (1982) listed the common hook-thorn, *A. caffra*; sweet thorn, *A. karroo*; three horned acacia, *A. senegal*, as preferred species, and the red bushwillow, *Combretum apiculatum*; russet bushwillow, *C. hereroense*; leadwood, *C. imberbe*; large-fruited bushwillow, *C. zeyheri*; mopane, *Colophospermum mopane*; sickle bush, *Dichrostachys cinerea*, and jackal-berry, *Diospyros mespiliformis*, as important foods. During the hot dry months from August to November, when the leaf mass is drastically reduced, they will turn to evergreens or semi-deciduous species such as *Euclea*, *Maytenus*, *Schotia* and *Diospyros*. The fruits of *Acacia* and *Combretum* are included in their diet, as well as the flowers of trees such as the knob thorn, *Acacia nigrescens*. At this time they tend to take more woody material than they do when fresh leaves are available and will utilise species not taken at other times of the year, such as mopane, *Colophospermum mopane*. The nutritional value of the food during this hot dry period is low and, during poor seasons, can lead to malnutrition or even starvation ending in death.

The finer shoots of trees and shrubs are pulled into the mouth by curling the long tongue around them and are held between the teeth in the lower jaw and the hard pad in the upper. The leaves and other edible portions are stripped off the twigs with a backward pull of the head. If small branches are broken off in the process, these are discarded. Giraffes can browse up to a height of about 5 m which is higher than can be reached by other browsing species. Where trees are higher than this, a browse line may be created below the canopy but where they are lower, browsing may tend to level its top. When drinking or browsing on low-growing shrubs the front legs are bent or alternatively splayed out to the sides, to provide a firm footing.

Giraffes are partial to salt licks but appear to have to rely on other species to pulverise the ground and loosen up the deposit as they have not been observed to do this themselves.

They search for suitably mineralised soil by walking over an area with the head lowered towards the ground. On locating a suitable site, they assume the drinking position, either licking the soil up with the tongue or taking a mouthful, then raising the head to the standing position so as to move the soil back to the molars for chewing (geophagia) (Langman, 1978). Osteophagia involves picking up bones and chewing them. Both these actions are commoner during the dry season from April to July and may be an attempt to gain a balanced ratio of calcium and phosphorus in the diet (Langman, 1978).

**Reproduction**

The giraffe, which is the only ungulate species with a gestation period longer than a year, will breed throughout the year, although there is a positive correlation between rainfall one month before conception and conception (Hall-Martin, Skinner & van Dyk, 1975). Daylength exerts a stimulus on conception indirectly via the nutritional status of the vegetation, *Acacia* and *Combretum* trees being seasonally deciduous.

A male has been known to breed at two years and eight months of age and others between three to four years in captivity, but it is unlikely that giraffes in the wild would normally breed as early as this, although they are physiologically capable of doing so (Hall-Martin, Skinner & Hopkins, 1978).

Females in the wild become sexually mature at 4,5 years (Hall-Martin & Skinner, 1978). The gestation period is 457 days. The mass at birth is 102,0 kg and the height at the shoulder about 1,5 m (Skinner & Hall-Martin, 1975). While a single young is produced at a birth, there is one case on record where, in the eastern Transvaal, stillborn twins were observed and, in captivity, live twins were born in Quebec in 1975, which were thriving in 1976 (Dagg & Foster, 1976). The females leave the herd to give birth.

The young are born with the female standing, her back legs bent to lessen the drop to the ground. In the process the umbilical cord snaps during the fall. Within an hour of birth the young stands up, its first reaction usually being to seek the teats for its first feed (van Aarde, 1976). The calf lies out isolated for the first one to three weeks of its life. In the relaxed position its head lies resting on its rump. While it appears that the female may choose the general area for the lying up, it is uncertain whether she or the calf chooses the exact lying up place. The female may forage up to 3 km from the area where the calf is lying. Calves wean at between six to eight months of age and the calf/female bond breaks down near the time of the female's next parturition when the calf is about 14 months old. Two or more infants and juveniles together with females form nursery herds, and from these herds calving pools may form consisting of numbers of calves and juveniles, which are left in the charge of one or two females (Langman, 1977).

Young calves are playful, running together and kicking up their legs. When two meet they may perform a nosing ceremony, touching noses and then jumping apart, which has been interpreted by Mejia (1972) as being a means of cementing the bonds among them.

The mortality rate among calves is high. In East Africa figures up to 73% during the first year of life have been given (Foster, 1966) and 48% in the eastern Transvaal (Hall-Martin, 1975).

Females have two pairs of inguinal mammae.

**INTRODUCED**

# XLVI. Family CERVIDAE

## Deer

Members of this Family are widespread in Europe, Asia and the New World. Both the red deer, *Cervus elaphus*, and the fallow deer, *C. dama*, have been introduced to the Subregion, but only the fallow deer has become feral and therefore qualifies for inclusion. Unlike members of the Bovidae, most members of this Family possess upper canine teeth, although in some members of the Family which occur in other parts of the world, they are absent (Ansell, 1972). In most species only the males carry the antlers, which are shed seasonally. The exceptions are the musk deer, *Moschus moschiferous*, and the Chinese water deer, *Hydropotes inermis*, which have no antlers, and the reindeer, *Rangifer tarandus*, in which both sexes have them. There is some archaeological evidence to suggest that fallow deer may have occurred in Egypt and Ethiopia (Brentjes, 1969), and Heck (1968) showed a former African range from northern Morocco to northern Tunisia and in Egypt, attributing their disappearance to increasing desiccation and heavy hunting pressure.

**INTRODUCED**

## Genus *Cervus* Linnaeus, 1758

No. 304

## *Cervus dama* Linnaeus, 1758

## European fallow deer
## Europese takbok

**Taxonomic notes**

Two subspecies have been described: the European fallow deer, *C. dama dama*, and the Persian fallow deer, *C. dama mesopotamica*.

## Description

Male fallow deer stand about 0,9 m to 0,95 m at the shoulder, and have a mass, in large males, of up to 110 kg; the females are slightly smaller. Many colour varieties are known, many of them produced by selection. The summer pelage is deep fawn with prominent white spots on the flanks. They have a broad white stripe on the lower part of the flanks between the fore and hind limbs and a second nearly vertical white line on the posterior part of the thighs. The winter pelage is greyish-fawn and is rough and thick. The throat and chin are white, this colour extending upwards to the sides of the face below the eyes and along the lower jaw. They have a conspicuous white patch above the eyes. In the males the forehead and top of the muzzle are dark, lighter in colour just behind the rhinarium. They have a broad black line down the mid-back which extends on to the top of the tail, the under surface of which is white. The lower parts of the limbs are whitish with patches of deep fawn on the forelegs above the knees. Among the many varieties of colour known, there are those with black bodies, others with porcelain-coloured or white bodies (Fig. 304.1). In the Subregion the males shed their antlers annually, about November, regrowing them into the velvet stage by early February.

Fig. 304.1 European fallow deer, *C. dama* (male).

## Distribution

The European fallow deer, *C. d. dama*, occurs from Turkey westwards through Europe. At one time they occurred in Great Britain, but apparently became extinct during the last period of glaciation. They were reintroduced to England probably by the Normans in the 11th Century (Chapman & Chapman, 1975) and it is from this stock that they were introduced to southern Africa.

It is not known with certainty who was responsible for the first introductions into southern Africa. Fallow deer were kept in the grounds of Newlands House, Cape Town, in 1869, and when this was sold by the Government, the stock which numbered 100 was sold for two hundred pounds to a farmer in Somerset West. Cecil John Rhodes has been attributed falsely with the first introduction, but this did not take place until 1897 when a number were released on his Groote Schuur estate on the Cape Peninsula (Chapman & Chapman, 1980).

Chapman & Chapman (1980) reviewed the situation up till this date and showed that they have been introduced to 32 of the 113 districts of the Cape Province. Three from Groote Schuur Estate were transferred to Robben island, Table Bay,

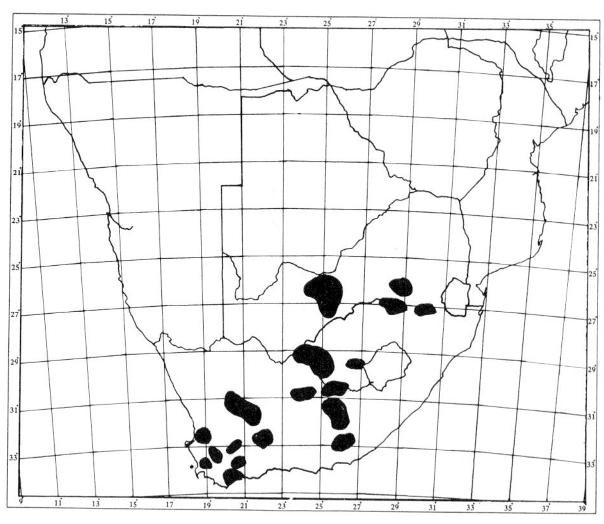

in 1963 and by 1977 the population had grown to about 40. Sir Percy FitzPatrick introduced them to his farm in the Orange Free State in 1900. In 1972 von Richter, Lynch & Wessels (1972) reported that 183 were present in this province. They were introduced into the Transvaal in about 1900 when Mr Fick of Palmietfontein farm, near Volksrust, exchanged tame springbok for fallow deer with the Zoological Gardens, London; by 1967 over 350 were present.

## Habitat

European fallow deer are catholic in their habitat requirements and have adapted well to a wide variety of vegetational areas in the Subregion. Chapman & Chapman (1980) recorded that on the slopes of Table Mountain they flourish in a habitat of oak and pine woodland with areas of open grassland at altitudes from about 65 m to 500 m above sea level. In the eastern parts of the Cape Province they thrive in an area of scrub on brackish soils, vleis and low-lying ground inundated during the wet season, which appears to be the preferred habitat in this area. They also frequent dense riverine bush. In the Orange Free State they occur on Highveld grassland at altitudes of over 1400 m.

## Habits

In Europe fallow deer are predominantly nocturnal, the old males markedly so. They vocalise when alarmed with a loud bark and seek safety in cover.

## Food

Predominantly browsers, they will eat leaves, herbs, nuts and berries and the bark of trees and, to a lesser extent, will graze. While they will drink water, they are not dependent on its availability.

## Reproduction

The older males are territorial during the rutting season, marking their areas by urinating in scrapes under trees and flaying trees with their antlers. They have postorbital glands, the secretion from which is rubbed on trees and becomes transferred from them to the antlers in tree-flaying. During the rut the males are noisy, vocalising loudly in a series of "burps", and the fawns bleat. The rut lasts for about four weeks during the autumn when the males will herd the females. The young are born after a gestation period of about eight months. A single fawn is usually born, but twins and even triplets occur. The females leave their fawns in dense cover during the early part of their lives while they forage.

The males spend the summer apart from the does and their fawns, reassembling with them at the time of the rut. The females conceive at two years of age.

# XLVII. Family BOVIDAE

## The antelopes and buffalo

This Family is represented in the Subregion by an assemblage of 34 species arranged in nine subfamilies.

The fossil record shows that, in Africa, the earliest known bovids were recovered from the early Miocene beds of Libya dating from about 20 million years ago (Hamilton, 1973). *Walangania africanus* Witworth, 1958, from similarly dated beds in Kenya, is possibly an early bovid.

## 1. Subfamily ALCELAPHINAE

Formerly two tribes of this Subfamily were recognised, the Connochaetini and the Alcelaphini (Ansell, 1972). Vrba (1979), however, proposed to reinstate the genus *Sigmoceros* for Lichtenstein's hartebeest, as it appears to have characters more closely allied to those of the wildebeests, *Connochaetes* spp, than to the hartebeests, *Alcelaphus* spp. In view of this, Meester (1986) pointed out that the two commonly recognised tribes, the Connochaetini and Alcelaphini, do not represent natural groupings and therefore cannot be maintained.

Alcelaphines of the hartebeest-wildebeest-bontebok/blesbok group appeared first in the fossil record about five million years ago and appear to have been almost but not quite wholly African in their evolution (Vrba, 1979). Gentry (1978) believed that both living species of *Alcelaphus* and *Sigmoceros* were descended from *Rabaticeros*, a species of which *R. porrocornutus* is known from early Pleistocene deposits at Swartkrans, Transvaal (Vrba, 1979). Primitive alcelaphines have also been found in Pleistocene deposits at Langebaanweg, Cape Province.

Wildebeest are known from their fossil remains in North and East Africa and from lower, middle and upper Pleistocene beds in South Africa from whence *C. gnou antiquus* Broom, 1913 was described. Wildebeest survived in North Africa into the late Pleistocene Epoch and perhaps into the Neolithic (Ficheur & Brives, 1900).

Horn cores of *Damaliscus dorcas* or a probable ancestor of that species are known from Florisbad and Vlakkraal in the Cape Province (Gentry, 1978).)

**Characters of members of the Subfamily**

Size medium to large; horns present in both sexes, either ridged basally and twisted, without downward curve (*Alcelaphus, Sigmoceros* and *Damaliscus*) or smooth and initially curving downwards (*Connochaetes*); well developed face glands present in preorbital fossae, though in some individuals the fossa may be very reduced; pedal glands well developed on forefeet only, absent or at most rudimentary on the hind feet; no inguinal glands; one pair of mammae; tail long and either crested (*Alcelaphus, Sigmoceros* and *Damaliscus*) or hairy and rather equine looking (*Connochaetes*); no ethmoid fissure.

**Species occurring in the Subregion**

Black wildebeest, *Connochaetes gnou*
Blue wildebeest, *C. taurinus*
Lichtenstein's hartebeest, *Sigmoceros lichtensteinii*
Red hartebeest, *Alcelaphus buselaphus*
Bontebok, Blesbok, *Damaliscus dorcas*
Tsessebe, *D. lunatus*

## 2. Subfamily CEPHALOPHINAE

The Subfamily Cephalophinae is represented in the Subregion today by three species of duiker, one each of the genus *Philantomba, Cephalophus* and *Sylvicapra*. They are extremely uncommon as fossils, but Broom (1934) described *C. parvus* from teeth from Pliocene or early Pleistocene beds at Taung, Cape Province, which Wells (1967) believed to be conspecific with the extant blue duiker, *P. monticola*.

**Characters of members of the Subfamily**

Size very small to medium; horns short and simple, present (*Cephalophus* and *Philantomba*) or absent (*Sylvicapra*) in females; face glands and pedal glands present; inguinal glands present or absent; mammae two pairs; tail short; a coronal tuft on the head; face blaze present or absent, and either plain-coloured, or with body pattern according to species; preorbital fossa present; ethmoid fissure absent; females tend to be larger than males.

**Species occurring in the Subregion**

Blue duiker, *Philantomba monticola*
Red duiker, *Cephalophus natalensis*
Common duiker, *Sylvicapra grimmia*

## 3. Subfamily ANTILOPINAE

The Subfamily Antilopinae is represented in the Subregion by two Tribes, the Antilopini and the Neotragini, with one living species of the former and seven of the latter.

### Tribe Antilopini

The Tribe Antilopini is represented in the Subregion by the springbok, *Antidorcas marsupialis*.

Three fossil species are known from the Subregion: *A. recki* Schwarz, 1932; *A. bondi* Cooke & Wells, 1951, and *A. australis* Hendey & Hendey, 1968 of which Hendey (1974) believed that *A. recki* is ancestral to the living springbok. *A. recki* is known from Kromdraai, Transvaal (Vrba, 1973). *A. bondi* was described originally from Chelmer, Zimbabwe from late Pleistocene beds and is known from early Pleistocene deposits at Swartkrans and at Kromdraai, Florisbad and Kalkbank in the Transvaal (Vrba, 1973). *A. australis* is known from a number of middle and late Pleistocene deposits at Swartklip, Elandsfontein and other coastal deposits in the Cape Province. Gentry (1978) suggested that it may have been a form peculiar to the southern Cape Province.

**Characters of the Antilopini**

Size small to medium; horns medium to long, ridged, and varied in shape, but not simple spikes (*c.f.* Neotragini); females horned; face and pedal glands present; inguinal glands present or absent; mammae one or two pairs; tail short to very short; face pattern usually well marked; preorbital fossa present (may be shallow); ethmoid fissure present or absent.

**Species occurring in the Subregion**

Springbok, *Antidorcas marsupialis*

### Tribe Neotragini

The Tribe Neotragini is represented in the Subregion by seven species. Fossils related to most of the genera are known, but are not common (Gentry, 1978). A *Raphicerus* has been found in the upper Pleistocene beds in South Africa that is indistinguishable from living grysbok or steenbok, but fossil remains from the middle and upper Pleistocene at Elandsfontein, Cape Province are of a larger species which had more inclined horn cores, with a tendency towards posterolateral keels. Fossil remains of a klipspringer, *Oreotragus major* Wells, 1951, are known from the Pliocene and lower Pleistocene beds at Makapansgat, Transvaal. They differ from living klipspringer in having slightly longer rows of premolar teeth in relation to the molar rows.

**Characters of the Neotragini**

Size small; horns short and spike-like, usually ridged basally; females hornless; face glands present; inguinal glands absent (except in *Ourebia*); *tail short to rudimentary; mammae two; false hooves present or absent; preorbital fossa present; ethmoid fissure present or absent.

**Species occurring in the Subregion**

Klipspringer, *Oreotragus oreotragus*
Damara dik-dik, *Madoqua kirkii*
Oribi, *Ourebia ourebi*
Steenbok, *Raphicerus campestris*
Grysbok, *R. melanotis*
Sharpe's grysbok, *R. sharpei*
Suni, *Neotragus moschatus*

## 4. Subfamily AEPYCEROTINAE

This Subfamily is represented in the Subregion by the impala, *Aepyceros melampus*. Fossil remains are known from diverse East African strata, more than three million years old.

**Characters of members of the Subfamily**

Size medium; horns lyrate, strongly ridged; females hornless; no face, pedal or inguinal glands; metatarsal glands with prominent tuft of black hair on hind leg; mammae two pairs; no false hooves; tail medium length; a black stripe on each thigh; no preorbital fossa or ethmoid fissure; a premaxillo-maxillary vacuity present (otherwise found in *Neotragus moschatus*); general build slender and gazelle-like.

**Species occurring in the Subregion**

Impala, *Aepyceros melampus*

## 5. Subfamily CAPRINAE

The Subfamily Caprinae is represented in the Subregion by a single introduced species, the Himalayan tahr, *Hemitragus jemlahicus*, and therefore has no fossil history in this part of the world. However, a Tribe of this Subfamily, the Ovibovini is represented in the fossil record from the Pliocene or lower Pleistocene beds at Makapansgat, Transvaal from whence *Makapania broomi* Wells & Cooke, 1956 was described. The Ovibovini are represented in the northern hemisphere by the muskox, *Ovibos moschatus*, which occurs in the Arctic Zone of North America and the takin, *Budorcas taxicolor*, of Tibet.

**Characters of the Subfamily**

Size medium; horns long in males, either scimitar-shaped, or curving downwards and backwards; females horned, but horns less developed than in males, as well as smaller; no face, pedal or inguinal glands; mammae one pair; no preorbital fossa or ethmoid fissure.

**Species occurring in the Subregion**

Himalayan tahr, *Hemitragus jemlahicus* (introduced).

## 6. Subfamily PELEINAE

The Subfamily Peleinae, which today is represented in the Subregion by a single species, the grey rhebok, *Pelea capreolus*, has been variously placed with the Reduncinae and the Antilopinae. Fossil *Pelea* are known from caves in the Transvaal (Vrba, 1975) dating from as far back as the early Pleistocene.

**Characters of members of the Subfamily**

Size medium; horns short, straight and ridged, found only in males; no face or inguinal glands; pedal glands present; males with preputial gland; rhinarium swollen and glandular; mammae two pairs; false hooves united across midline; coat woolly; no preorbital fossa; ethmoid fissure present.

**Species occurring in the Subregion**

Grey rhebok, *Pelea capreolus*

## 7. Subfamily HIPPOTRAGINAE

Members of this Subfamily include in the Subregion the now extinct blue antelope, *H. leucophaeus*, two extant species of *Hippotragus* and a single species of *Oryx*. In the later Pleistocene of South Africa the fossil remains of three species of *Hippotragus* are known. A small species, probably referable to the blue antelope, *H. leucophaeus*, occurred in the middle and upper Pleistocene, and roan, *H. equinus*, were found at Sterkfontein, Transvaal, in the upper Pleistocene or early Holocene beds. *H. gigas* L.S.B. Leakey, 1965, described from Olduvai, Tanzania, which occurs abundantly in the middle and upper Pleistocene beds at Elandsfontein, Cape Province, became extinct about 0,4 to 0,3 million years ago. It differed from the roan, *H. equinus*, and the sable, *H. niger*, in the formation of the horn cores and shorter premolar toothrow and was larger. Fossil remains of the sable, *H. niger*, are recorded from mid Pleistocene beds at Swartkrans, Transvaal. Klein (1974) showed that fossil remains of both the roan, *H. equinus*, and the blue antelope, *H. leucophaeus*, occurred together in similarly dated deposits in the Cape Province.

**Characters of members of the Subfamily**

Size large; horns present in both sexes, long, ridged, and either straight, scimitar-like or twisted; face glands absent or at most slightly developed; pedal glands present on all four feet; no inguinal glands; mammae two pairs; tail long and tufted; face pattern usually distinct, except in the extinct *H. leucophaeus*; ethmoid fissure small or absent.

**Species occurring in the Subregion**

Blue buck, *Hippotragus leucophaeus* (extinct)
Roan, *H. equinus*
Sable, *H. niger*
Gemsbok, *Oryx gazella*

## 8. Subfamily BOVINAE

The Subfamily Bovinae includes three Tribes: the Boselaphini, the Bovini and the Tragelaphini.

The Boselaphini, which is mainly a fossil group, is represented by two living species which occur in India, the nilgai, *Boselaphus tragocamelus*, and the four-horned antelope, *Tetracerus quadricornis*. Fossil remains of members of this Tribe are known from North and East Africa, but the most interesting is a large species with divergent horn cores, *Mesembriportax acrae* Gentry, 1974 from Langebaanweg, Cape Province.

The Bovini includes three living genera, *Bos*, the cattle and bison of Eurasia and North America; *Bulbalis*, the Asiatic water buffalo, and *Syncerus*, the African buffalo. The genus *Syncerus* is represented by fossil remains dated as previous to two million years old from deposits at Sterkfontein, Swartkrans and Kromdraai in the Transvaal (Vrba, 1976) and from later deposits at Melkbos, Cape Province (Hendey, 1968). It was larger than the extant buffalo, *S. caffer*, and differed from it in that the hollowed horn cores show that the horns extended outwards at their bases and did not immediately turn downwards. In the middle Pleistocene beds of eastern and southern Africa dating from

* Situation in *N. moschatus* unknown.

about three-quarters of a million years ago, a very large, long-horned buffalo, *Pelorovis antiquus*, has been recovered and forms ancestral to this are known from Makapansgat, Transvaal and from Langebaanweg, Cape Province. The fossil remains show that the horns were less dorso-ventrally compressed and they lacked the heavy bosses of the horns characteristic of the extant buffalo. Other species of *Pelorovis* have been recovered from lower Pleistocene beds of about 1,8 to 1,5 million years old in East Africa. *Bos primigenius*, known from the late Pleistocene beds of North Africa, is interesting as it survived into Neolithic times and perhaps into Roman times (Gentry, 1978).

The third Tribe of the Subfamily Bovinae, the Tragelaphini, is today represented in the Subregion by a group of medium to large-sized antelopes. The fossil remains of eland, *Taurotragus arkelli* L.S.B. Leakey, 1965 are known from Olduvai, Tanzania dating from the early Pleistocene Epoch, about one to a half million years ago, predating those from Elandsfontein, Cape Province, recovered from mid-Pleistocene deposits, which Gentry (1978) stated could safely be referred to the extant species, *T. oryx*.

Teeth very similar to those of the living kudu, *Tragelaphus strepsiceros*, are known from Olduvai, Tanzania and Swartkrans, Transvaal, dating from the early Pleistocene, about two million years ago.

The only definite evidence for the ancestry of the bushbuck, *T. scriptus*, comes from horn cores recovered from Pliocene or early Pleistocene beds in East Africa and tooth remains from Makapansgat, Transvaal. The horn cores agree with those of the living bushbuck in their strong keeling. Horn cores from Pliocene beds at Langebaanweg show that the horns of this species were set more upright in the skull than in the living nyala or bushbuck.

## Tribe Bovini

**Characters of members of the Tribe Bovini**

Size very large and form heavy; horns present in both sexes, not ridged; no face, pedal or inguinal glands; mammae two pairs; tail long and tufted; plainly coloured; no preorbital fossa or ethmoid fissure.

**Species occurring in the Subregion**

African buffalo, *Syncerus caffer*

## Tribe Tragelaphini

**Characters of members of the Tribe Tragelaphini**

Size medium to large; horns twisted, present or absent in females; no face or pedal glands; inguinal glands present or absent; mammae two pairs; tail varied, long and tufted to medium and bushy; frontal tuft, mane, throat and ventral fringes variously developed; face and body pattern of white spots and stripes variously developed; no preorbital fossa; ethmoid fissure present; males distinctly larger than females.

**Species occurring in the Subregion**

Sitatunga, *Tragelaphus spekei*
Nyala, *T. angasii*
Bushbuck, *T. scriptus*
Kudu, *T. strepsiceros*
Eland, *Taurotragus oryx*

## 9. Subfamily REDUNCINAE

This Subfamily is represented in the Subregion by two genera, *Redunca* and *Kobus*, the former with two species, the latter with three.

Members of this Subfamily are moderate to large-sized antelopes commonly associated with water and today are confined to Africa. Only the males carry horns which are ridged and are without keels or spiralling. In the Subregion the reedbuck, *R. arundinum*, is common as a fossil in the middle and upper Pleistocene beds at Elandsfontein, Cape Province, and other sites showing that they have not changed over a period of about half a million years (Hendey, 1968; Hendey & Hendey, 1968), although possibly they had shorter horns than the living reedbuck. An earlier form, *R. darti* Wells & Cooke, 1956 is known from the late Pliocene or lower Pleistocene at Makapansgat. It was larger than the mountain reedbuck, *R. fulvorufula*, and has less upright horn cores. Broom (1913) described *Kobus venterae* from the upper Pleistocene in South Africa, which Gentry (1978) stated was indistinguishable from the lechwe, *K. leche*. A short-horned *Kobus*, perhaps related to *K. sigmoidalis* of the Pliocene and lower Pleistocene of East Africa, is known from Langebaanweg, Cape Province (Gentry, 1978). *Kobus sigmoidalis* is thought to be an ancestor of the waterbuck, *K. ellipsiprymnus*.

**Characters of members of the Subfamily**

Size medium to large; horns medium to long, bowed, lyrate or hooked, and ridged; females hornless; face glands a little developed in *Kobus vardonii*, otherwise absent; foot glands absent, or at most rudimentary; inguinal glands present or absent; mammae two pairs; tail of medium length, bushy in some species; no preorbital fossa; ethmoid fissure present.

**Species occurring in the Subregion**

Reedbuck, *Redunca arundinum*
Mountain reedbuck, *R. fulvorufula*
Waterbuck, *Kobus ellipsiprymnus*
Lechwe, *K. leche*
Puku, *K. vardonii*

## Family BOVIDAE

Key to the Subfamilies (Ansell, 1972)

1. Face gland well developed and lying in a preorbital fossa (a) ... 2

   Face gland absent or rudimentary, no preorbital fossa ... 4

2. Pedal glands either completely absent (*Oreotragus*) or well developed on all four feet; tail short or rudimentary; mammae two pairs; body size small to medium ... 3

   Pedal glands well developed on forefeet only, rudimentary or absent on hind feet; tail medium to long; mammae one pair; body size medium to large ... Alcelaphinae

3. Head tuft present; no ethmoid fissure, no reduction of nasals, and no development of proboscis ... Cephalophinae

   No head tuft (except in *Madoqua*, which has an ethmoid fissure, reduced nasals and a proboscis) ... Antilopinae

4. Hind leg with metatarsal glands, marked by a prominent black tuft of hair; false hooves absent (b); premaxillo-maxillary vacuity present (c) ... Aepycerotinae

   No such metatarsal gland ... 5

5. Horns present or absent in females, but where present developed in similar form to those of males, though smaller; no "goatee" beard on chin or heavily developed mantle reaching on to the forelimbs ... 6

   Horns present in both sexes, but in less developed form, as well as smaller, in females; either a "goatee" beard on chin in males, or a mantle of long hair on throat and forelimbs in both sexes ... Caprinae

6. Pedal glands on all four feet ... 7

   Pedal glands absent, or at most rudimentary ... 8

7. Size medium; horns, present only in males, spike-like; coat woolly

   ... Peleinae

   Size large; horns in both sexes, long and not spike-like; coat not woolly

   ... Hippotraginae

8. Horns either more or less smooth throughout and present in both sexes, or spiral, usually keeled, and present or absent in females

   ... Bovinae

   Horns distinctly ridged, not spiral or keeled, and absent in females

   ... Reduncinae

*Notes to the above key:*

(a) The fossa may be shallow, or even almost untraceable, particularly in some Alcelaphinae, but the gland itself is always well developed.

(b) False hooves are also absent or rudimentary in *Raphicerus* and *Neotragus*, both easily distinguished from the Aepycerotinae in several other features.

(c) A similar vacuity is found in *Neotragus moschatus*; both otherwise easily distinguishable.

## Subfamily ALCELAPHINAE

Key to the genera (Meester *et al.*, 1986)

1. Horns smooth throughout and directed downwards initially; prominent tuft of facial hairs, neck mane, and fringe of hairs either on throat or on chest between forelimbs; colour either bluish-grey or blackish

   ... *Connochaetes*

   Horns directed upwards from the base; no facial tuft, mane fringe on chest or throat; colour variously rufous, yellowish or brownish, not bluish-grey or blackish

   ... 2

2. Face not markedly elongated; horns not on a pedicle, and with only slightly more than a single curvature

   ... *Damaliscus*

   Face much elongated; horns set on a pedicle, and with a distinct double curvature

   ... 3

3. Horn pedicle short and broad; occiput about level with base of horns; horns flat and curved inwards towards each other before bending back; forehead convex

   ... *Sigmoceros*

   Horn pedicle long; occiput in front of base of horns; horns not curving inwards as above; forehead flat

   ... *Alcelaphus*

## Genus *Connochaetes* Lichtenstein, 1814

Key to the species after Meester *et al.* (1986)

1. Horns directed forward and downwards before curving up; nasals and muzzle not noticeably elongate; tail white; no pedal glands on hind feet

   ... *gnou*

   Horns directed outwards and slightly downwards before curving up; nasals and muzzle noticeably elongate; tail black; pedal glands on hind feet

   ... *taurinus*

The blue wildebeest, *C. taurinus*, has rudimentary pedal glands on the hind feet (Ansell, 1969) which are absent in the black wildebeest, *C. gnou*. Although these two species occupy different habitats in nature, when placed together artificially they have been found to interbreed and recently evidence has been produced to show that the hybrids are fertile (Fabricius & Oates, 1985; Fabricius, Lowry & van der Berg, 1988).

No. 305

## *Connochaetes gnou* (Zimmerman, 1780)

## Black wildebeest
## Swartwildebees

Plate 30

### Colloquial Name

The colloquial name black wildebeest is well entrenched although not accurately descriptive of the colour, which is buffy-brown. At a distance, however, they appear darker than their close relatives, blue wildebeest, *C. taurinus*, which are in fact silvery-grey in colour. The characteristic and most obvious feature of black wildebeest is their white tails and often they are referred to as white-tailed wildebeest or white-tailed gnu. *Gnu* is a Khoikhoi name referring to the bellowing snort which they use when alarmed.

### Taxonomic notes

No subspecies are recognised.

Although they rarely occur sympatrically with *C. taurinus*, occupying a different habitat, they will interbreed when kept together artificially and the hybrids are fertile (Fabricius, Lowry & van den Berg, 1988). The appearance of the hybrids is intermediate between the two parent species. Chromosome number is 2n=58 (Wurster & Benirschke, 1968).

### Description

Male black wildebeest stand about 1,2 m at the shoulders and have a mass of about 180 kg; females are smaller and lighter.

Hairs are 60,2±10,1 mm long, with an irregular waved mosaic pattern along the length (Fig. XLII.1) (Keogh, 1983). The general colour is buffy-brown, old males being darker, almost black. Their faces are usually darker than the colour of the body. The juveniles have shaggy, fawn-coloured coats and horns that rise straight up from the head and only start to curve at about a year old. The characteristic feature in the field is the tail, which is dark at the base, the remainder with long, off-white hair reaching nearly to the ground. Black wildebeest are rather ungainly looking. The back slopes from the massive humped shoulders to the slender, lightly built hindquarters. Their heads are elongated, albeit not to the extent seen in blue wildebeest. Their manes are high and upstanding, the hairs at the base light-coloured, but black towards the tips. They have a distinct beard of long hair. An elongated patch of long hair on the chest extends from between the forelegs nearly to the belly. The conspicuous brush of long hair between the eyes and the nostrils divides into two outswinging moustaches on either side of the face.

The hooves on the front feet are slightly larger than those on the hind feet as they carry the extra weight of the heavy shoulders and head; the tips of the hooves are sharp-pointed (Plate II).

**Table 305.1**

Shoulder height (mm) and mass (kg) of adult black wildebeest, *C. gnou*, from (a) Tussen-die-Riviere Game Farm, Orange Free State (Vrahemis, pers. comm.) and (b) S.A. Lombard Nature Reserve, western Transvaal (Skinner, van Zyl & van Heerden, 1973)

**(a)**

| | Males | | Females | |
|---|---|---|---|---|
| | $\bar{x}$ | n | $\bar{x}$ | n |
| Sh.ht | 120,6 | 164 | 115,7 | 72 |
| Mass | 161,1 | 164 | 130,0 | 72 |

**(b)**

| | Males | | |
|---|---|---|---|
| | $\bar{x}$ | n | Range |
| Mass | 134,0 | 24 | 123,6–138,1 |

Both sexes carry horns which arise from expanded bases, sweep downwards and forwards and then curve upwards. The tips tend to curve inwards. The maximum horn length recorded by Best & Best (1977) is 699 mm for a pair from the Orange Free State. The horns of the females are lighter in mass and thinner than those of the males.

**Distribution**

*Southern African Subregion*

Black wildebeest are endemic to the Subregion. They formerly ranged in hundreds of thousands, over the central, northern and northeastern parts of the Cape Province, throughout the Orange Free State, extending into Natal and the southern parts of the Transvaal. Their decline in numbers, which brought them to the point of extinction, was due to over-exploitation and agricultural development, and their survival was ensured only by protection on farms and reserved areas within part of their former range as shown on the map. Brand (1965) estimated that not more than 1 800 survived in the entire Subregion in that year, but since then, through the efforts of the National Parks Board, Provincial Nature Conservation Departments and private individuals, the species is no longer endangered and a surplus stock has been made available for introduction and reintroduction. In 1985 numbers in the Orange Free State exceeded 7 000 (Vrahemis, pers. comm.)

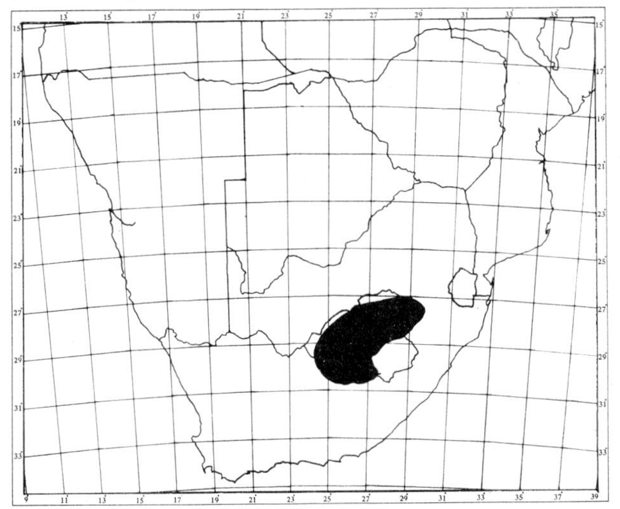

**Habitat**

Black wildebeest are a species of the central plateau open plains, formerly associated with the Karoo in the Cape Province and the grasslands of the Orange Free State and Transvaal.

**Habits**

Black wildebeest are gregarious with a social organisation involving territorial males, female herds and bachelor groups. The territorial males are closely attached to their territories on a year-round basis, although there is some loosening of this bond after the rut. An adult male may acquire a territory either by displacing a territorial male, which is no longer able to defend it, or by finding and establishing one of its own in a vacant area. Males may become territorial by the age of four years. Before this they are less able to maintain their status or to displace existing territorial males. When a territorial male is displaced he usually joins a bachelor group (von Richter, 1971b).

Territorial males are the nucleus of the population and they alone partake in the rut, taking vigorous steps to prevent non-territorial males from mating. They advertise their possession of a territory by scent-marking with the faeces and urine and the various glands on the body, including the preorbital and the interdigital glands, by threat, by vocalising and by adopting certain advertising stances (von Richter, 1972). Territorial males paw vigorously in their territories prior to defecating. Kneeling and horning of the ground is a threat gesture and rolling, coupled with pawing and ground-horning, has been interpreted as a threat (Estes, 1969). They advertise their presence with a very loud, two syllabled call which has been described as *ge-nu* and led to the colloquial name sometimes used for the species. Certain characteristic stances are adopted by the territorial males who may hold their heads high, cantering in a stiff-legged manner. They gallop at high speed, moving their heads up and down and lashing their tails, or cavort around each other, lashing and swishing their tails and tossing their heads, sometimes kicking out with their back legs (von Richter, 1972).

A territorial male is circumspect when approaching another territory and does so in the submissive attitude, with the head held below shoulder level, and in most cases will adopt a grazing attitude. Only in high intensity encounters do the contestants resort to horn interlocking and head pushing, and serious fighting, while it does occur, is rare. Four cases have been reported of males dying with horns interlocked (Vrahemis, pers. comm.).

The female herds, which consist of females and their offspring and occasionally a subadult male, wander freely over their territories and, outside the rut, are disregarded by the territorial males. During the rut, however, territorial males herd females into tight groups, serving those that are in oestrus. Should they relax their herding, the female herd may move on to another territory, and this leads to threat displays and fighting amongst the males. They are also subject to harassment from adult males from the bachelor groups which have no territories and are trying to acquire one (von Richter, 1971b). The female herds are closely knit and when broken up by disturbance, reunite thereafter. Herd size varies with the density of the population and individuals in a herd may number up to 60 (von Richter, 1971b). Average herd size for female herds in various areas in the Orange Free State was 28,4 (n=144) (Vrahemis, pers. comm.)

With the appearance of the next calf crop the females no longer tolerate their yearlings and drive them away. The female yearlings simply keep their distance from their mothers and remain with the female herd, but the males leave it to join the bachelor groups. The females, now with small calves, tend to group together within the herd, those without calves associating with the yearling males (von Richter, 1971b). Von Richter believed that there may be a hierarchy within the female herds, yearlings and females without calves being subordinate to females with calves. In flight a female with calf usually leads the herd.

Bachelor groups are loose associations of adult, subadult and yearling males. Displaced territorial males may also join bachelor groups. Outside the rut territorial males may join bachelor herds temporarily and if they maintain their status, will reoccupy their former territories later. Bachelor groups are important units within the social organisation, serving as reservoirs of potential territorial bulls and providing protection for them as they grow up. An outstanding feature of the bachelor groups is the lack of aggression between members (von Richter, 1971b). Average size of bachelor herds in the Orange Free State was 20,6 (n=52) (Vrahemis, pers. comm.).

During the summer the female herds and bachelor groups are active in the early morning and late afternoon and lie up during the heat of the day. They are also active before dawn and after sunset. During the colder winter months the midday resting period is reduced and they may be active throughout most of the hours of daylight. Territorial males do not conform to this pattern as they may be called upon to defend their territories at any time.

When resting they do not always seek shade, but when lying in the sun, they tend to orientate themselves with the head or hind quarters towards it. Young calves lie close to their mothers. In heavy rainstorms they present their hind quarters to the onslaught, but will continue to feed. Very strong winds cause the herds to become restless and they readily take to flight (von Richter, 1971b). On the approach of danger the herd will stand in an alert position with heads up, snorting, twitching their tails and stamping the ground. If suddenly disturbed the herd may dissolve into tumult, the individuals bucking, tossing their heads, snorting and throwing their back legs high in the air before galloping off. If the danger is distant the whole herd will whirl around in a sudden turn, their conspicuous white tails waving, to look for the cause of the stampede. Stevenson-Hamilton (1947) remarked that the extraordinary antics and capers of the black wildebeest formed a constant theme for anecdote among the early pioneers and hunters. The snort is made by a quick exhilation of air through the nose, and has a curious metallic ring to it.

It is likely that, in historical times, black wildebeest were subject to extensive local movements, if not migrations, which, with human development of their range, are now impossible. Their occurrence in Natal may have been due to a local movement from the Orange Free State during the winter months in search of better feeding grounds (Grout, 1862). At present, as they are restricted, they are prone to over-utilise their habitat.

They have the reputation of being irascible, and in captivity untrustworthy, quickly becoming aggressive and dangerous.

Vrahemis (pers. comm.) reported that between 1985–1987 only 20 cases of malignant catahrral fever, reportedly a problem with this species, were diagnosed on farms of 205 landowners in the Orange Free State. Both species of wildebeest are carriers and outbreaks occur in cattle herds which are in proximity to wildebeest populations. As a result movement of wildebeest is now strictly controlled (D. Meltzer, pers. comm.).

### Food

Black wildebeest are predominantly grazers, but during the cold winter months they will browse on karroid bushes. Van Zyl (1965) stated that in the S.A. Lombard Nature Reserve, in the western Transvaal, their main diet, based on plants eaten during three months or more in the year, consisted of 63% grass and 37% karroid shrubs. The latter is probably an over-estimate on a year-round basis. He listed 41 plant species utilised by them. They turn to the karroid browse after the first winter frosts when the nutritional value of grass starts to decline. Among the grasses *Sporobolus* spp; red grass, *Themeda triandra*, and couch grass, *Cynodon dactylon*, are important as food. The karroid shrubs include *Nenax microphylla; Salsola rabieana; Osteospermum leptolobum; Nolletia ciliaris* and *Pentzia* spp which are eaten when not browsed down by other herbivores. Black wildebeest show a distinct preference for grazing where the grass is short. Vrahemis (pers. comm.) found, following 9 000 observations over a 2 year period on a tame animal, that it took over 90% grass and 3% shrubs. They are dependent on water and will drink regularly, usually in the late afternoon, and very seldom during the heat of the day.

### Reproduction

Black wildebeest are seasonal breeders, shortening day length being the proximate factor influencing the onset of breeding. Skinner, van Zyl & Oates (1974) showed that in the western Transvaal mating peaked during autumn in March/April, with 54,5% of matings in March and 40% in April. Mating continued to July. The gestation period is 8,5 months (Skinner, van Zyl & van Heerden, 1973). The bulk of the young is born in December and January. The absence of large predators in the areas where black wildebeest occur today greatly enhances their survival rate. Calving percentage in the Orange Free State was 75% (Vrahemis, pers. comm.).

The female remains with the herd at the time of the birth of the single calf, not selecting a specific site for the purpose. Just before the birth she becomes restless and repeatedly lies down and gets up, eventually giving birth in a recumbent position.

Birthweights of 14,0 kg (range 12,5–15,5 kg; n=4) have been reported by Vrahemis (pers. comm.) Females calve in the late morning (09h00–11h00) (Vrahemis, pers. comm.) and may chew on the afterbirth, but have not been seen to eat it as do blue wildebeest. Shortly after birth the calf, after being licked clean by its mother, totters to its feet and is very soon capable of following her. The bond between the mother and calf is very strong, the calf remaining close to her during the early part of its life. Females have a pair of inguinal mammae.

No. 306

## *Connochaetes taurinus* (Burchell, 1823)

## Blue wildebeest
## Blouwildebees

Plate 30

### Colloquial Name

The blue wildebeest is also referred to as the brindled gnu, a name which has now largely fallen out of use. The colour is actually a silvery-grey, sometimes with a brown tinge, but in some lights might be interpreted as being a bluish-grey.

### Taxonomic notes

Ansell (1972) listed five subspecies from the continent, of which only one, *C. t. taurinus* (Burchell, 1823) occurs in the Subregion.

Chromosome number is 2n=58 (Gerneke, 1967).

### Description

Adult male blue wildebeest stand about 1,5 m at the shoulder and have a mass of about 250 kg; the females are smaller at 1,35 m and 180 kg (Attwell, 1977).

The humped shoulders and deep necks contrast with the more lightly built hindquarters and their legs look slender compared with the size of the body. The slope from shoulder to hindquarters is more pronounced than in black wildebeest. Their heads are massive and elongated, broadening out at the nostrils and lips. Their chins have a distinct beard of long black hair.

The hairs on the body are 60±31 mm long and concavo-convex in cross-section. Scale margins are rippled crenate, with three scales across the width of the hair (Fig. XLII.1) (Keogh, 1983). The adults are dark grey in colour, tinged brown, with a silvery sheen and look almost black at a distance. On the neck and shoulders and extending back to about the middle of the body there is a series of dark-coloured bars which gives them a brindled appearance. They have manes of long black hair which droop over their shoulders, long whisks of black hair on the ends of their tails, which nearly touch the ground, and a fringe of long black hair down the throat. In adult males the face from the top of the head to the nostrils is black, often, however, with a russet tinge on the forehead. The sides of their faces are greyish, lighter in colour than their bodies, and are often tinged russet. In juveniles and females the bodies are browner than in adult males and they have more of a russet colour on their foreheads, which may extend broadly from the forehead to between the eyes. Very young individuals are fawn-coloured over-all, with a darker face and a dark stripe along the back, and therefore are distinguished easily in wildebeest herds. Occasionally very young individuals with black faces may be observed.

*C. t. johnstoni* Sclater, 1896 had a white band across the muzzle anterior to the eyes and originally was described from the Southern Province of Malawi, where it is now extinct. South of this in the Gorongoza National Park, Mozambique, populations show no sign of the white band, but further south in the Zinave National Park on the Save River 2% of the population have white muzzle bands (Smithers & Tello, 1976).

**Plate 30**

303. Giraffe, *Giraffa camelopardalis*
Kameelperd
305. Black wildebeest, *Connochaetes gnou*
Swartwildebees
306. Blue wildebeest, *Connochaetes taurinus*
Blouwildebees

PLATE 30
303
306
305
Dick. Findlay.

The hooves on the front feet tend to wear to rounded tips and to be larger than those on the hind feet, reflecting the extra weight of the shoulders, neck and head carried by the front legs (Plate II).

Both sexes carry the unridged horns which, arising from swollen bosses, sweep outward and slightly downward and then rise upwards to the inwardly pointed tips, which often are directed slightly backward. The horns of females are lighter in build than those of males. In juveniles the horns rise straight up from the head and only show the start of the outward curve at the age of about eight months. The horn bosses do not develop until the wildebeest are about two years old, up to which time the bosses of the horns are covered with tufts of long russet-coloured hair. The world's record pair of horns, which at their greatest width measured 860 mm, came from the northern Transvaal (Rowland Ward, 1986).

### Distribution

Today blue wildebeest occur in two main, widely separated areas. The northern area extends from southwestern Kenya to northwestern Mozambique, the southern area from Zambia marginally into South Africa, with an isolated population in the Luangwa Valley in Zambia.

Although Gordon Cumming (1909) recorded taking a specimen, in extraordinary circumstances, in the Britstown district in 1843, south of the Orange River, this species was generally confined to the country north of the river. This particular individual had by some means managed to get its foreleg over its horn and could not run and was killed by his Khoikhoi servants (Skead, 1980). Du Plessis (1969) listed historical records which show that at one time they were widespread in the Transvaal and that they occurred as far south as the Orange and Vaal rivers.

*South of the Sahara, excluding the Southern African Subregion*

Southwestern **Kenya** marks their most northerly limits on the continent. They occur southwards in parts of central and eastern **Tanzania**, extending into northeastern **Mozambique**, north of the Zambezi River. There is a break in their distribution in Mozambique southwards from about the central parts of the Zambezia District to the northern parts of the Beira District. Apart from the isolated population in the Luangwa Valley in **Zambia** (*C. t. cooksoni* Blaine, 1914) this break extends westwards to where they occur in the western parts of Zambia and in central and southeastern parts of **Angola**. They are now extinct in Malawi.

*Southern African Subregion*

They have a restricted distribution in **Namibia**, only occurring in parts of the northern and northeastern sectors and marginally along the Botswana border south to the Kalahari Gemsbok National Park. They are widespread in **Botswana**, but less common in the south and are absent from the more densely settled areas in the east. In **Zimbabwe** they occur only in the northwest and in the southern parts of the country. In **Mozambique**, south of the Zambezi River, they occur from about the Gorongoza National Park southwards, excluding the southeastern part of the country. In the **Transvaal** they occur in parts of the north and east of the province. The Transvaal Museum has a series taken in 1914 from near Golela in the eastern extension of the Transvaal, south of Swaziland, but although they have been reintroduced to the area, they became extinct at some period since that date. They are abundant in northeastern **Swaziland**, on the Hlane Game Reserve and adjoining areas. Southwards they occur in the Umfolozi-Corridor-Hluhluwe Game Reserve in **Natal**. Today they have only a marginal occurrence in the northwestern parts of the **Cape Province**.

### Habitat

Blue wildebeest are associated particularly with savanna woodland, with the availability of shade and drinking water as essential habitat requirements. Open woodland dominated by the knob thorn, *Acacia nigrescens*, was the preferred habitat in northern Natal; other associations utilised included *Acacia* spp and the tamboti, *Spirostachys africana*

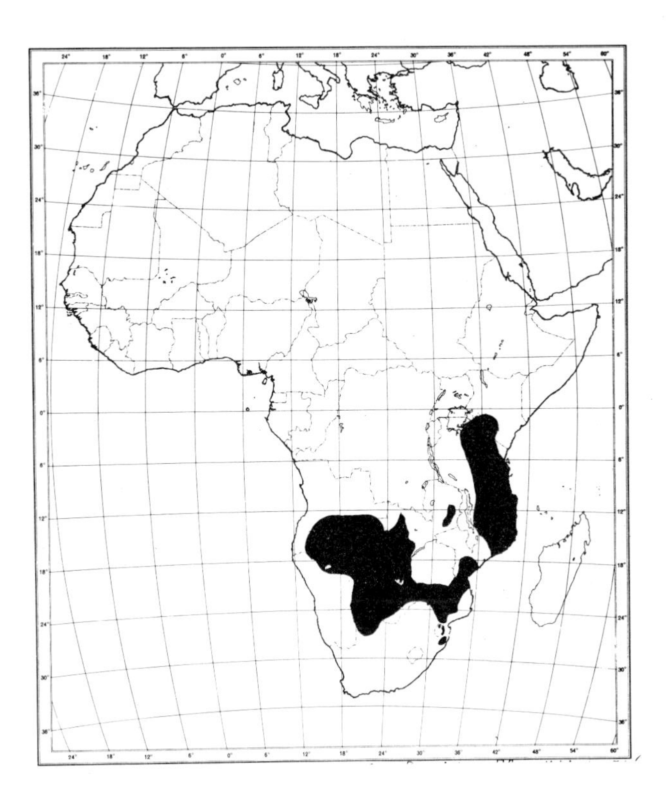

(Attwell, 1977). In the eastern Transvaal, Hirst (1975) stated that the situation is similar. Seasonal movements during the dry season to short grass areas on sandy river banks, when the other short grass communities are heavily overgrazed, take place, as well as long distance migrations to seek better grazing.

### Habits

Blue wildebeest are gregarious, occurring in herds of up to 20 or 30 or in much larger aggregations numbering up to thousands. Their social organisation consists of territorial males, female herds and bachelor groups. In the Kruger National Park, territories are set up and maintained all year round. Bulls in the migratory sub-population maintain these territories in the breeding area while the female herds are in other parts of their range (Whyte, 1985). In the Kalahari Gemsbok National Park bulls also maintain territories for as long as environmental conditions are favourable. In times of drought bulls tend to lose condition and, as water points dry up, abandon territories and join bachelor herds (Skinner & Knight, unpubl.). When a bull from a neighbouring herd approaches a territorial bull, he will chase him off or they will drop on to their knees and horn spar, butting with their heads thumping together. The impact is taken on the horn bosses and injuries rarely result from these encounters which are threats rather than actual fighting.

Territorial sexually active bulls employ a number of ritual displays directed to individual situations (Estes, 1969). When other bulls approach his territory, the territorial bull adopts a threat display with his neck held erect, his head directed horizontally, as he advances towards them in a "rocking horse" canter. This is usually sufficient to dissuade them from trespassing, but it may develop into horn-sparring or head-butting. While herding, a territorial bull will advance on the females with lowered head and swishing tail, circling around them, or he will chase them, with his body low to the ground, tail streaming out behind, bawling and grunting. Bulls may also display in front of females, rising high on their back legs and holding this position momentarily before dropping on to the front feet.

The female herds consist of females with their offspring of the year. They are the most numerous and most cohesive groups in the social system. In East Africa, Estes (1966) stated that the average number in a herd is 10. These herds move around over the territories established by the bulls and strangers endeavouring to join them are usually rejected. Their home ranges may be up to about 2,5 km².

The bachelor groups are loose associations of adult males and young males evicted from the nursery herds which do not have a territory. They occupy areas on the fringes of the home range of the population, usually the least desirable parts of the habitat, and thus do not compete with the nursery herds for food.

Whereas in some parts of their distributional range blue wildebeest move over relatively small distances when not fenced in, in others they are subject to wide movements. In the Kruger National Park, two of the sub-populations between the Sabie and Olifants rivers used summer ranges in the north and winter ranges in the south near the Sabie River (Braack, 1973). One of these had its migration routes disrupted by the erection of a veterinary game-proof fence on the western boundary, resulting in a sub-population crash from some 6 000 wildebeest to 750 (87%), and the termination of its migratory habits (Whyte, 1985; Whyte & Joubert, 1988). Other sub-populations are either sedentary or vagrant, moving to areas of optimal habitat created by fire and/or rainfall. Within the Kalahari Gemsbok National Park, the resident wildebeest populations confine their movements predominantly to the dry riverbeds, moving in response to local rainstorms, grazing conditions and the availability of palatable drinking water supplies. They confine their activities within a radius of 10 km of fresh water (Child, Parris & le Riche, 1971; Mills & Retief, 1984a,b; Dreyer, 1987; Knight, pers. comm.). Blue wildebeest drank water daily each morning (19,4 ± 3,7 l/individual) in contrast to gemsbok which drank similar quantities every five days (Dreyer, 1987).

In East Africa the aggregation of hundreds of thousands of, in particular, blue wildebeest and their mass movements, have been documented well. Similar aggregations and movements take place in Botswana involving up to, and sometimes in excess of, 100 000 individuals. Liversedge (pers. comm.) recorded seeing a mass of wildebeest which he estimated was 16 km long and about 10 deep, moving northeastwards towards the Makgadikgadi Pan in 1980. Some of the mass movements in Botswana are directed to and from the vast, open, short grass plains which fringe the Makgadikgadi Pan, others develop in a southwesterly direction. From the central Kalahari mass movements are occasionally made to Lake Xau and also to the southwest into the Gemsbok and Kalahari Gemsbok National Parks (Knight, pers. comm.).

These northeasterly movements during exceptionally dry seasons have been characterised by large die-offs in 1930/31 and again in 1964 (Child, 1972), when an estimated 1 500 *C. taurinus* died. However, the encroachment of cattle farming into the Kalahari and the erection of veterinary fences (as on the western boundary of the Kruger National Park) have influenced the direction of movements drastically and resulted in considerably increased die-offs, particularly amongst the wildebeest (Williamson & Williamson, 1985), some 50 000 dying of starvation around Lake Xau in 1983 (Williamson & Mbano, 1983; Parry, 1984). As the initial movement develops, herds met with *en route* join up, the numbers increasing as the movement progresses. These movements do not follow fixed routes, only a general direction, and local rain or fire may, by producing a flush of green grass, delay the movement or cause a deviation from the route intended. In each of the three years in which wildebeest congregated at Lake Xau, the previous season's rainfall was 25–50% below the long-term average (Williamson & Williamson, 1988). At the onset of the first summer rains the wildebeest departed, returning to the southwestern Kalahari. The prime motivation for this northeast-south west migration is for water and does not occur during periods of high rainfall (Williamson & Williamson, 1988). As the access to water diminishes, wildebeest populations will decrease.

Blue wildebeest are sensitive to localised rain storms and will move in their direction in search of fresh grazing. Talbot & Talbot (1963) in East Africa found that even when they are crosswind or downwind from local rain, they will move in its direction. Scent therefore cannot be playing the only role in its detection. Distant thunder causes movement in the direction of storms over distances of 25 km, which suggests

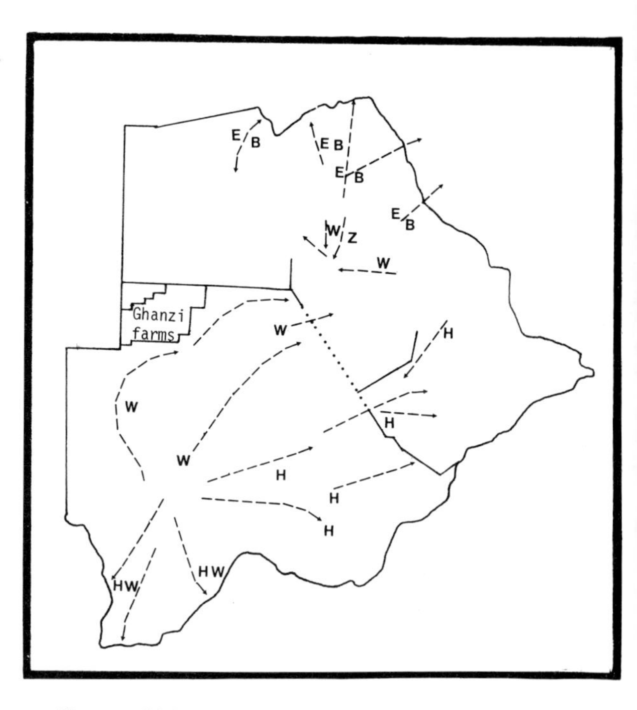


Fig. 306.1 Major migratory routes and main obstructing fences during dry season ungulate (and elephant) migrations (--→) in Botswana. Wildebeest (W); Hartebeest (H); Zebra (Z); Buffalo (B) and Elephant (E). Main cordon fences (————) and programmed fencing (. . . . .) (Williamson, pers. comm.)

that hearing is important, but sight appears to be the primary sense involved. Nevertheless, behaviour of the wildebeest is not infallible and Talbot & Talbot (1963) described how when wildebeest arrived at the site of heavy thunderstorms they found that the rain had fallen on hills and not on adjacent dry grassland.

After two days the wildebeest returned to the riverside from which they had come, a distance of some 90 km.

Talbot & Talbot (1963) recognised five distinct types of vocalisation. Adult males snort, either in alarm or as a challenge, grunt and low. Females snort and low and have a sharp warning snort in communicating with calves. The young bleat when separated from their mothers. The alarm snort is often heard at night.

Blue wildebeest have pedal glands on the front feet and large preorbital glands. The exudation from these smells like tar and can be detected when the observer is in the proximity of large herds. Territorial males mark their territory by dropping on to their knees and rubbing the preorbital glands on the ground or on bushes or tree trunks. The pedal glands scent-mark on the ground as they move, facilitating following by other individuals. During the rut pawing of the ground and use of the preorbital glands by rubbing the sides of the face in soil is very much in evidence and can signal aggression.

During the rut the great majority of bulls is inactive and they remain either in bachelor herds or alone. However, there is a continuing interchange of bulls in these herds, as previously sexually inactive bulls become active and active bulls retire from attendance on their harem herds. Active bulls defend an area up to 30 m in diameter around themselves or their harem herd and not necessarily an area of ground. The size of this zone depends on the density of the population and is spacial and moveable (Talbot & Talbot, 1963).

Where there are relatively few wildebeest at the time of the rut, or just prior to it, bulls may establish territories which are defended against the trespass of other bulls and within which they will herd females from the nursery herds to form harem herds. Some of these territories may be maintained on a long-term basis, others may be broken down, at least temporarily, by seasonal movements.

Berry, Siegfried & Crowe (1982) found that in the Etosha National Park, Namibia, blue wildebeest spend 53% of their time standing, lying or resting in the shade, 33% grazing,

12% moving, 0,5% drinking and 1–15% in social encounters. Mixed herds graze less and rest and move more than bachelor herds, increase in temperature being largely responsible for inactivity during daylight hours when they seek shade under trees. They are able to satisfy their nutritional requirements during short feeding bouts in between resting in summer. In cool, overcast weather they may continue to be active throughout the day and may remain active on moonlight nights, but are less active when it is dark. They drink at any time during the day except during the last hour before sunset, with a preference for five to seven hours after sunrise (Berry *et al.*, 1982). Orientation of the body of wildebeest in Etosha is related to sun and wind direction, but this is not so where adequate shade is available (Ben-Shahar & Fairall, 1987).

**Food**

Blue wildebeest are grazers, with a preference for feeding on areas of short, green lawn-like grassland. They are particularly partial to fresh sprouting grass on burnt areas or fresh green grass sprouting after rain. They rarely eat grass that is more than 100 or 150 mm high. In northern Natal, Attwell (1977) found, from rumen content analysis, that 96% of the content was grass. Their preference for and ability to make use of short grass is reflected in the adaptation of the snout, which is wide, making them capable of cropping from lawn-like grassland and less successful in dealing with taller types from which the leaves have to be selected and stripped. Murray (pers. comm.) classified them as site selectors in contrast to grazers which select for plant parts or bite selectors.

In the open knob thorn, *Acacia nigrescens*, association in northern Natal, Attwell (1977) found that, in the valleys away from the woodland, *Panicum* spp and *Digitaria argyrograpta* are utilised. In the woodland and especially on the hillslopes red grass, *Themeda triandra*, was an important food. Towards the end of the dry season, when the other communities are heavily grazed, they will move on to stands of couch grass, *Cynodon dactylon*. Within the Kalahari Gemsbok National Park wildebeest select for *Stipagrostis obtusa* and *Eragrostis porosa* within their preferred riverbed habitats. Movements into the adjacent red dune grass communities take place in late winter where they select for *Stipagrostis ciliata* (Knight, pers. comm.).

**Reproduction**

Braack (1973) gave the rut in the Kruger National Park as falling between April and the first week in June. Blue wildebeest in Zululand have a bimodal breeding season. Attwell (1977) showed that the rut peaks in April, with some mating again in August. The calving season peaks from mid-November to the end of December, with some births about May. In the Kalahari Gemsbok National Park, births were synchronised within a three-week period, but occurred in December 1985, January 1986 and February 1987 and 1988 (Knight, pers. comm.). Fairall (1968), while agreeing that there is an inherent rhythm in their breeding activities, stated that they may be influenced by prevailing climatic conditions.

Sinclair (1977) provided evidence to show that synchronisation of oestrus was enhanced in blue wildebeest by correspondence of the lunar and oestrous cycles. He furthermore suggested that sensitivity to the lunar cycle is enhanced when the abundance of green grass declines in May resulting in nutritional levels declining below a certain threshold. Females in oestrus are restless, moving around from one territorial bull to another and mating with several. Estes (1969) recorded the mating of a female in oestrus with three different bulls in the space of three minutes. Sexual activity during this period is very marked and must affect the territorial bull's physical well-being, allowing little time for grazing and resting (Estes, 1969). The bulls court the females in oestrus by stretching their necks forward and laying their heads as far back as possible. They will then approach a female, rising on their hind legs. Copulation is observed infrequently and may take place more commonly at night.

The period of gestation is about 250 days (Mentis, 1972). The female may separate herself from the herd at the time of the birth of her single calf, and normally lies down to give birth. At birth the calves have a mass of about 22 kg and, after being licked clean by their mothers, can stand within a few minutes and run with her within five minutes. Within a day they can fully maintain their place within the herd. Estes (1966) suggested that births were synchronised so that a glut of precocious, fast-developing calves would mean that a smaller percentage would be taken at their most vulnerable age. He found that there was a lower mortality amongst calves born at the peak of the calving season than amongst those born at other times.

The young stay close to their mothers, lying down as the opportunity permits. Lost calves bleat loudly for their mothers, who will only suckle their own calf. They are very frolicsome, chasing each other with tails flying, and butting each other with their heads. Within 14 days after birth, they start to nibble grass, but the mother continues to suckle them until about eight months. From six months they are perfectly adapted to digesting grass although their smaller body size is still a limiting factor to utilising cellulose (Hofmann, pers. comm.). There is evidence from the Kruger National Park which suggests that the population there may be limited by lion predation in years when preferred short grass areas become rank due to above average rainfall (Whyte, 1985). Young females may spend their life with the herd. Young males, however, are evicted at about two years of age, joining bachelor herds which tend to live on the periphery of the breeding area or of the harem herds. Females produce their first calf at just over two years of age. The females have a pair of inguinal mammae.

## Genus *Sigmoceros* Heller, 1912

No. 307

## *Sigmoceros lichtensteinii* (Peters, 1849)

## Lichtenstein's hartebeest
## Lichtenstein se hartbees

Plate 31

**Colloquial Name**

This species is named after the famous naturalist and traveller, W.H.C. Lichtenstein, who travelled in southern Africa during the years 1803–1806.

**Taxonomic notes**

No subspecies are recognised.

**Description**

Adult Lichtenstein's hartebeest stand about 1,25 m at the shoulder. The males have an average mass of about 177,0 kg, the females 166,3 kg (Table 307.1). They have humped shoulders which give their backs a sloping appearance similar to red hartebeest, *A. b. caama*.

The hairs are 9,8±2,1 mm long, reniform in cross-section, with an irregular waved mosaic scale pattern along their entire length (Fig. XLII.1) (Keogh, 1983). The colour of the body is yellowish-tawny with an indistinct saddle of a more rufous colour on the upper parts of the body which extends from the shoulders to the base of the tail. The chin, the fronts of the lower parts of the legs and the tuft of hair on the end of the tail are black. In some individuals there is a dark patch on the forehead and an indistinct dark band on top of the muzzle. The rump and base of the tail are white, the tip black. The upper parts of the hind legs to the hock are white.

Lichtenstein's hartebeest have a habit of rubbing the sides of their faces on their flanks, especially after ground-horning. This leaves a dark patch on their flanks just behind the shoulders. Dowsett (1966) believed that this is caused by the application to the flanks of the sticky secretion from the preorbital glands. This sticky patch is accentuated by the adherence of dust and ash from burnt grass, when it stands out most conspicuously. It generally washes out in rainy weather.

Spoor—Plate II.

**Table 307.1**

Measurements (mm) and mass (kg) of adult Lichtenstein's hartebeest, *S. lichtensteinii*, from Zambia (Wilson, 1966c)

| | Males | | | Females | | |
|---|---|---|---|---|---|---|
| | $\bar{x}$ | n | Range | $\bar{x}$ | n | Range |
| TL | 2380 | 6 | 2090–2540 | 2360 | 5 | 2010–2420 |
| T | 48 | 0 | 400–510 | 450 | 5 | 410–470 |
| Hf c/u | 550 | 6 | 540–570 | 530 | 5 | 510–550 |
| E | 210 | 6 | 200–230 | 210 | 5 | 190–230 |
| Sh.ht | 1230 | 6 | 1220–1360 | 1250 | 5 | 1190–1300 |
| Mass | 177,1 | 10 | 156,7–203,9 | 166,3 | 10 | 160,4–181,2 |

In Zimbabwe, Booth (1986) recorded the mass of females as being from 125 kg to 177 kg.

Both sexes carry the curved S-shaped horns. These arise from the top of the head, from a much less well developed bony pedicle than is found in red hartebeest. The bases of the horns are rounded and spread broadly like flanges on top of the head. The horns rise from these to bend forward and outwards, then inwards and backwards to the diverging tips. The base of the horns is ridged, this ridging tails out just above the flanges and is never as pronounced as in the red hartebeest.

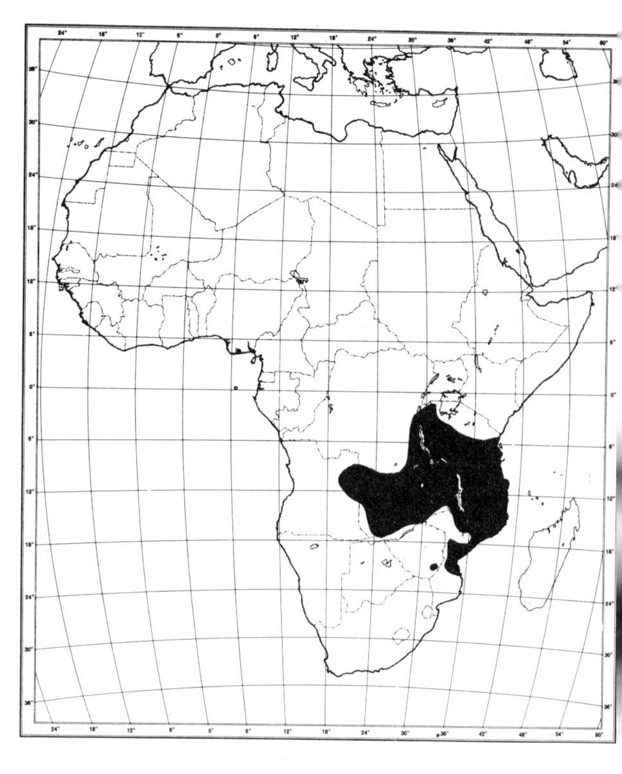

## Distribution

Lichtenstein's hartebeest occurs from northeastern Tanzania southwards to the northern parts of the Inhambane District in Mozambique, where, at least until about 1976, a small relict population still survived. If these no longer survive, the furthest south they occur is in southeastern Zimbabwe. In the first report of the game warden Van Oordt of the Pongola Reserve, which was situated just south of Swaziland, he reported in 1895 the presence, among other species, of hartebeest and tsessebe (Pringle, 1982). As he recognised the difference between these two species and as this area is ecologically unsuitable for the red hartebeest, *A. buselaphus*, it appears that Lichtenstein's hartebeest, *S. lichtensteinii*, may have been present in this area at one time. The Transvaal Museum has in its collection a skull of this species collected by their taxidermist, Mr P. Krantz, which came from near Acornhoek in the eastern Transvaal about the turn of the century. Furthermore, letters in its archives suggest that as late as 1916 they may still have occurred in the vicinity of the Njelelle and Nuanetsi rivers in the northern Transvaal. Similar historical evidence indicates that this species may have occurred recently and more widely in the Transvaal Lowveld and possibly further south (Milstein, 1988). They have been re-introduced to the Kruger National Park, Transvaal.

### *South of the Sahara, excluding the Southern African Subregion*

They occur in northwestern, central and southern **Tanzania**; in southeastern **Zaire**; northeastern **Angola**; widely throughout **Zambia**, except in the southwest and in the Zambezi valley in the south; in **Malawi** and in **Mozambique**, north of the Zambezi River.

### *Southern African Subregion*

They occur widely in the central parts of the Vila Pery and Beira districts in **Mozambique**, south of the Zambezi River, and may still occur in the extreme southern part of the Beira District and possibly in the northeastern part of the Inhambane District. They occur in southeastern **Zimbabwe** in the Ghona-re-Zhou National Park and on a number of privately owned ranches.

## Habitat

Lichtenstein's hartebeest is a savanna species particularly associated with the ecotone of open woodland and vleis or floodplain grassland (Tinley, 1977; Booth, 1980). As grazers their habitat must provide a supply of perennial grasses to sustain them and surface water, on which they are dependent.

Tinley (1977) in Gorongoza, Mozambique, found that there was a seasonal movement from one sector of the habitat to another. In the wet season they moved out of the miombo, *Brachystegia* sp, woodland of the higher zones on to the Rift Valley floor and back again during the dry season. This was probably a movement in response to the availability of food.

## Habits

Lichtenstein's hartebeest are gregarious, rarely occurring in herds larger than 10 individuals (Booth, 1986). The herd size may vary from place to place. In Zambia, Wilson (1966c) showed that the average number was three (1–5), with a single record of a herd of 15. In Mozambique, Tinley (1977) recorded herds of six to 12, and in Zimbabwe, Booth (1980, 1986) recorded a mean of 5,3 and the largest herd counted numbered 16. In Gorongoza, Tinley (1977) observed aggregations of up to 72 in October.

Lichtenstein's hartebeest are territorial. In Zambia, Dowsett (1966a) found that males, accompanied by eight or nine females and their offspring, established territories which were just over 2,5 km$^2$ in the most favourable habitat. Other males, with one to five females and their offspring, were forced into establishing their territories in inferior habitat. Territories were maintained on a year round basis and might be occupied for as long as the herd males were strong enough to defend them during the rutting season.

The territorial bull is the leader. He maintains a position some distance from his females and their young, more often than not downwind of them, and remains keenly on the alert for their welfare. Relying mainly on sight, he may take up his position on elevated ground such as a termite mound to keep them and the surrounding terrain in view. When the herd takes to flight he brings up the rear, often stopping to look around. Wilson (1966c) observed that in control operations in Zambia this habit was often his undoing as more males were shot than females.

At the time of the rut, territorial males herd females into harems within their territories. Fighting is commonplace during the rut as wandering males attempt to take over females from other territorial males or the possession of territories is challenged. Dowsett (1966a) reported on a fight which lasted over an hour, the loser lying exhausted by his efforts for over an hour thereafter. He also witnessed a territorial male chasing an intruder for over 1,5 km. Territorial males will not allow young males of between 10 months and a year old to remain with his harem females. The composition of the harem is relatively stable. However, females may leave the harem herd and return of their own accord after a day or two or may join other harem herds. Dowsett (1966a) suggested that dominance among the females is governed by age, for in most sparring bouts the younger females give way.

Males mark their territory by horning the ground randomly within the territory. The male will drop to his knees, turn his head from side to side and dig up the soil with his horns, then rub the preorobital glands on it. He will rub his face on his flanks which characteristically marks the sides of the body just behind the shoulders. The horned areas are very conspicuous, when not obscured by tall grass, and may extend over an area of some 1,3 $m^2$ (Dowsett, 1966a). They apparently do not deliberately use the preorbital glands in marking vegetation on the ground, but Booth (1986) suggested that the secretions are deposited on thick tall grass as the animals are feeding and thus mark the territory against intruders. Dung piles are a feature of these territories and no doubt play a part in territorial marking as well.

When alarmed an inquisitive Lichtenstein's hartebeest may vocalise with a "sneeze-snort" through the nostrils and may bellow when fighting. This may be accompanied by stamping the ground with a foreleg before trotting off, tail swinging from side to side. They have good eyesight and can spot observers at several hundred metres, but their sense of smell is not so well developed and Dowsett (1966a) stated that they can be approached, if the observer keeps out of sight, equally well up or down wind. When the herd takes to flight an adult female takes the lead, the herd racing off for a distance before reverting to a "rocking horse" canter which takes them to a safe distance.

Bachelor herds can only establish home ranges in less favourable habitat. They are less stable than the harem herds, periodically moving their home ranges. On the one hand, males attaining maturity leave the herd in an endeavour to establish territories, while on the other, the herd may be joined at the time of the rut by juvenile males evicted from harem herds by territorial males.

Lichtenstein's hartebeest are most active in the morning and afternoon. Booth (1980) recorded that, during the summer, they would retire to shade about 09h00 and recommence grazing after 17h00. During winter the activity period was lengthened, but they invariably rested up during the midday heat. Wilson (1966c) suggested that they may graze at night. In the Kafue National Park, Zambia, Mitchell, Shenton & Uys (1965) showed that Lichtenstein's hartebeest ranked high in the diet of large predators, and calves figured among the kills of wild dogs and leopards.

**Food**

Lichtenstein's hartebeest are almost exclusively grazers, although Wilson (1966c) recorded a small percentage of browse in the stomachs of 52 specimens examined in eastern Zambia. This included the leaves of the velvet bushwillow, *Combretum molle*; the horn pod tree, *Diplorhynchus condylocarpon*; the fruits of the kudu berry, *Pseudolachnostylis maprouneifolia*; and the sourplum, *Ximenia caffra*. Booth (1980), in southeastern Zimbabwe, recorded their browsing on the bean tree, *Markamia acuminata*; the apple leaf, *Lonchocarpus capassa*; camwood, *Baphia* sp; raisin bush, *Grewia* spp; sickle bush, *Dichrostachys cinerea*; and caper bush, *Capparis* sp. The leaves of mopane, *Colophospermum mopane*, zebrawood, *Dalbergia melanoxylon*, and knob thorn, *Acacia nigrescens*, which were recorded in stomachs, may have been fortuitously picked up while grazing.

Tinley (1977) listed a wide range of grass species included in the diet of the species in Mozambique. During the summer months they fed on *Urochloa mosambicensis*; *Cymbopogon excavatus*; spear grass, *Heteropogon contortus*; and red grass, *Themeda triandra*, eating the burnt stems, leaves and basal parts of *H. contortus* and the burnt parts and post-fire green flush of *T. triandra*. Indeed they show a preference for burnt areas, not only for the flush of fresh green grass following the fire, but are also partial to the ash and burnt parts of grasses. During the dry season they fed on these and a wider range of grass species including Rhodes grass, *Chloris gayana*; finger grass, *Digitaria milanjiana*; *Echinocloa* spp; *Enteropogon macrostachyus*; spear grass, *H. contortus*; *Hyparrhenia* spp; buffalo grass, *Panicum maximum*; small buffalo grass, *P. coloratum*; *Paspalum acrobiculatum*; *Setaria aylesii*; *Sporobolus* spp; and the sedge, *Maerua brunnescens*. In southeastern Zimbabwe, Booth (1980) recorded *Ischaemum afrum* and *Setaria sphacelata* in stomach contents and observed their feeding on *U. mosambicensis* and blue buffalo grass, *Cenchrus ciliaris*, the two last-named being abundant grasses in the area.

**Reproduction**

Lichtenstein's hartebeest are seasonal breeders. In Mozambique and Zimbabwe calves are born in September. Many females captured in August aborted full-term calves in the first week in September (Tinley, 1977; Booth, 1980). Rutting by bulls occurs from November to January in Zimbabwe (Booth, 1986). When courting females in oestrus, territorial males approach with their noses extended forward, their tails stiffly horizontal. The oestrous females stand with their legs apart, their hindquarters towards the male and their tails curled. Wilson (1966c) recorded that after anal sniffing and rubbing his preorobital glands on the female's hindquarters, a male eventually mounted her four times in as many minutes. Dowsett (1966a) noted that not more than two females came into oestrus at the same time in the harem herd. The gestation period is 240 days (Kenneth & Ritchie, 1953); females have their first calves at about two years old. The birth mass is about 15 kg (Wilson, 1966c). In Zimbabwe calves are born in September (Booth, 1986), and many cows captured in Mozambique in August 1972 and translocated to Zimbabwe gave birth or aborted near full-term foetuses in the first week in September.

Although the calves are capable of following their mothers from the time of their birth, she usually beds them down while she goes off to graze or to drink. Unlike some other bovids she makes no attempt to conceal them, bedding them down even on open burnt ground (Mitchell, 1965a). A single young at a birth appears to be the rule. Females occasionally may be accompanied by as many as three calves because of the tendency for calves to be bedded down together (Booth, 1980).

## Genus *Alcelaphus* Blainville, 1816

No. 308

### *Alcelaphus buselaphus* (Pallas, 1766)

### Red hartebeest
### Rooihartbees

Plate 31

**Colloquial Name**

The name hartebeest is derived from the Dutch name *hartbeest* given to the species by the early settlers. The first record of the name in South African literature appears in Van Riebeeck's *Daghregister* (1660) where he recorded that "Meester Pieter ein hartbeest geschooten hadde" at a locality just north of Paarl, Cape Province. Often referred to as Cape hartebeest, this name is not appropriate as they are by no means confined to the Cape Province. The extinct North African hartebeest, *A. b. buselaphus*, was known many years before the red hartebeest, *A. b. caama*, and was called the "bubal".

**Taxonomic notes**

Ansell (1972) recognised 12 subspecies of which only one, *A. b. caama* (G. Cuvier, 1804) occurs in the Subregion.

Chromosome number is 2n=39/40 (Wurster & Benirschke, 1968).

## Description

Adult male red hartebeest stand about 1,25 m at the shoulder and have a mass of about 150 kg; the females are slightly smaller with a mean mass of about 120 kg (Table 308.1).

The shape of the body and head is characteristic of members of the genus which have high humped shoulders, sloping backs and elongated heads, held high on their upright necks.

The hairs are 27,2±14,8 mm long, reniform in cross-section, with a regular waved mosaic scale pattern—three scales across the width (Fig. XLII.1) (Keogh, 1983). Together with a small amount of underfur, the hairs are densely packed forming a most effective reflective surface. At a distance the general colour of the body of adults is reddish-brown, but this varies and in some individuals it is yellow-fawn or tawny. While not always obvious in the field, they have a saddle of a darker colour than the remainder of the body, which extends on the mid-back from the shoulders to the base of the tail, broader towards the tail than on the shoulders. This saddle is less obvious in the females than in the males and in some females is barely perceptible. A characteristic feature of the colour pattern is the well defined pale yellow or off-white colour of the rump, which looks white in the field. Covering the upper and hind parts of the haunches, it contrasts markedly with the colour of the remainder of the body and is a useful feature in identifying the species. There are dark patches on the front of the shoulders which extend down the front of the forelegs, either to stop short at the knees or to continue downwards to the hooves and up the back of the leg to the fetlock joints. The hind legs are black from halfway down the thighs to the knees, in some cases right to the hooves.

Spoor—Plate II.

The forehead is black, with a broad patch of reddish-brown across the face between and in front of the eyes and a black band on top of the muzzle. These and the other black markings on the body have an iridescence which in some lights gives them a plum-coloured sheen. In strong light the iridescence is so pronounced that, when the individual is standing facing the observer, the black on the forehead and muzzle shines white and thus has given rise to the widely current belief in parts of Botswana that some individuals have white face blazes. Behind the horn pedicles there is a black patch which extends on to the sides of the face behind the eyes. The sides of the face and neck tend to be lighter in colour than the top of the face. Arising from the base of the ears are two narrow black bands which join to form a single band down the ridge of the neck. In some cases the origin of this band is obscured as it arises from the black patch behind the horn pedicles which extend to the base of the ears. The hair inside the long pointed ears is white. The under parts are lighter in colour than the upper parts.

Red hartebeest have preorbital glands which open to the surface in small pores just in front of the eyes. These glands exude a waxy substance much sought after by Bushmen as medicine.

**Table 308.1**

Measurements (mm) and mass (kg) of adult red hartebeest, *A. buselaphus*, from (a) Botswana (Smithers, 1971) and (b) from S.A. Lombard Nature Reserve, western Transvaal (bi) Skinner *et al.* (1973) (bii) Kilian (pers. comm.)

**(a)**

| | Males | | | Females | | |
|---|---|---|---|---|---|---|
| | x̄ | n | Range | x̄ | n | Range |
| TL | 2144 | 8 | 2073–2200 | 2096 | 3 | 2070–2110 |
| T | 470 | 8 | 404–504 | 472 | 3 | 430–500 |
| Hf c/u | 557 | 8 | 534–572 | 524 | 3 | 175–192 |
| E | 195 | 8 | 192–201 | 185 | 3 | 175–192 |
| Mass | 152,0 | 8 | 137,0–156,0 | 120,0 | 3 | 105,0–136,0 |

**(bi)**

| | Males | | |
|---|---|---|---|
| | x̄ | n | Range |
| Mass | 119,8 | 24 | 103,0–132,0 |

**(bii)**

| | | | |
|---|---|---|---|
| Mass | 148,79 | 12 | 131,0–165,2 S.D. 11,75 |

Both sexes carry horns, those of the males heavier in build than those of the females. Set closely together at their bases, they rise straight up from a high pedicle at the top of the skull, curving forward and then backward, almost at right angles. They are heavily ridged for about three-quarters of their length, leaving only the tips smooth. The outside of the forward curve of the horns in older individuals tends to lose the ridging through wear. The longest horns on record came from Namibia and measured 750 mm (Rowland Ward, 1986).

## Distribution

Accepting that the North African hartebeest, *A. b. buselaphus*, is now extinct, hartebeest of the genus *Alcelaphus* have a wide but discontinuous distribution on the continent south of the Sahara. They still occur from Senegal eastwards to Ethiopia and Somalia and south to the northern Cape Province. Some of the subspecies such as the western hartebeest, *A. b. major*, of West Africa and Swayne's hartebeest, *A. b. swaynei*, of parts of Ethiopia and Somalia have been exploited to the point of extinction.

In the southern parts of the Subregion the distribution of red hartebeest, *A. b. caama*, has shrunk markedly within historical times. Van Riebeeck's *Daghregister* for 1659 to 1662 (Thom, 1958) stated that at that time they occurred near the Fort (Cape Town). Writers in the 18th century make frequent mention of the species which showed that they occurred throughout what is today the Cape Province (Sparrman, 1786; Thunberg, 1793 or 1795; Le Vaillant, 1796). They occurred in parts of the Orange Free State and in the western and northwestern parts of the Transvaal (du Plessis, 1969), as well as in Natal (Buckley, 1876; Hardley, 1950; Pringle, 1963), but they are now extinct in Natal, although they were reintroduced in recent times to the Giant's Castle Game Reserve (Vincent, 1962). Today they wander southwards across the Botswana border on to farms in the Northern Cape Province, on some of which they have been afforded protection.

There seems good evidence that the population on De Beers farm, Rooipoort in the Kimberley District, grew from a naturally occurring population (Secretary, De Beers Consolidated Mines, *in litt.*), although there was, in addition, a translocation from the Transvaal (Smithers, 1971). They certainly occurred naturally on neighbouring farms (Drooglaagte, Talbot, pers. comm.) prior to 1900. Within recent years red hartebeest have been reintroduced to many farms and reserves in South Africa.

Their status today in Angola, where they are recorded in a narrow sector from between the Cunene and Cubango rivers in the south of the country, is uncertain.

*Southern African Subregion*

In **Namibia** they occur in a belt of country from the Angola border southeastwards to the Botswana border, not occurring in the northeast or in the western and southern parts of the country. In **Botswana** they occur widely south of the Okavango Delta and the Makgadikgadi Pan, and are absent from most of the eastern sector of the country except where the Kalahari associations extend eastwards to the Transvaal border between Mahalapye and Artesia. In the **Cape Province** they occur narrowly in the north along the Botswana border. In the **Transvaal**, Rautenbach (1978a) stated that there are no naturally occurring populations surviving, but they have been reintroduced to farms where they are protected.

**Plate I Spoor**

303. Giraffe, *Giraffa camelopardalis*
305. Black wildebeest, *Connochaetes gnou*
306. Blue wildebeest, *Connochaetes taurinus*
307. Lichtenstein's hartebeest, *Alcelaphus lichtensteinii*
308. Red hartebeest, *Alcelaphus buselaphus*
309. Bontebok/Blesbok, *Damaliscus dorcas*
310. Tsessebe, *Damaliscus lunatus*

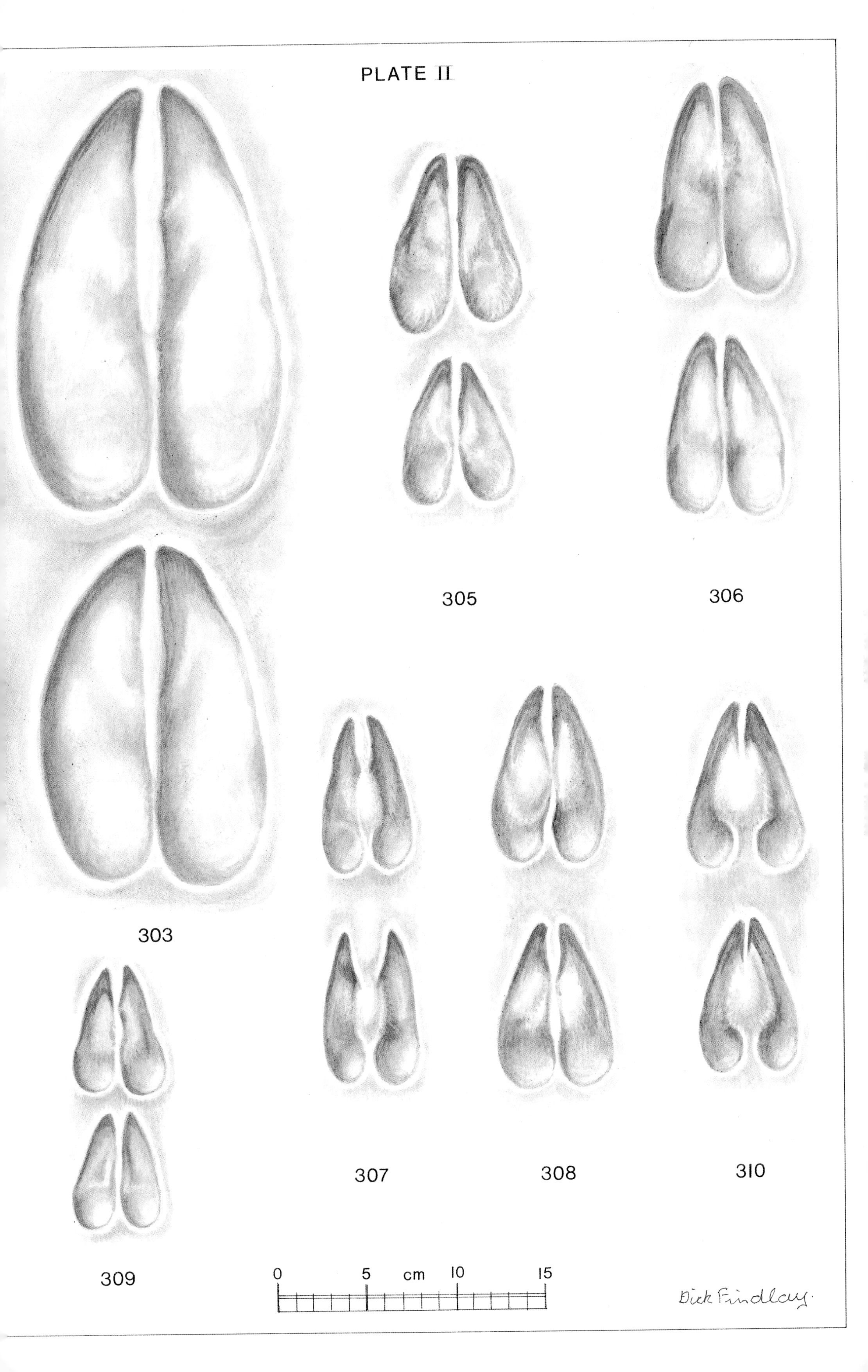
PLATE II
303
305
306
307
308
309
310
0
5
cm
10
15
Dick Findlay

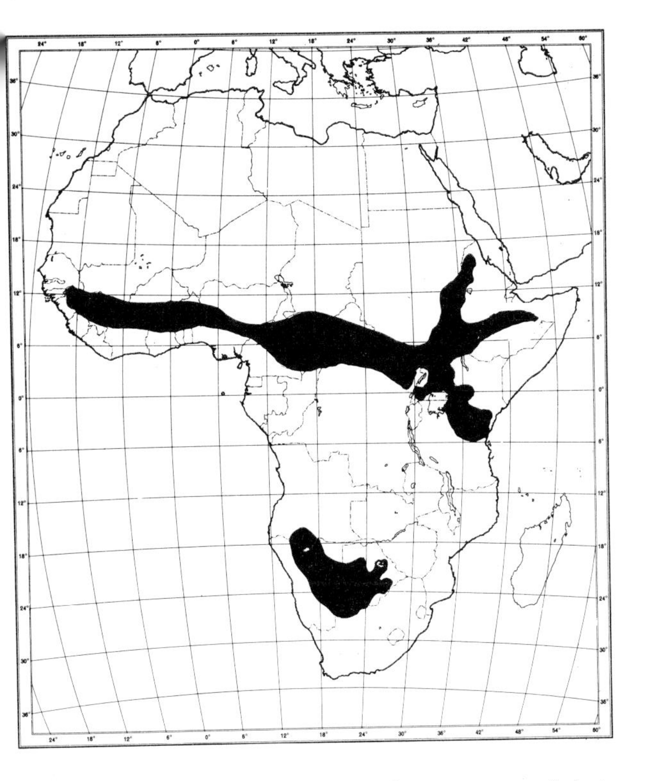

Red hartebeest wander far from the perimeter of their distributional range and have been recorded as vagrants in the vicinity of the Hwange National Park, **Zimbabwe** and on ranches near the Botswana border south of the plateau. They remain for periods of up to several years, but eventually disappear. Four were moved from south of the Hwange Park into the Park itself, but disappeared shortly thereafter.

### Habitat

Red hartebeest are associated predominantly with open country, occurring on grassland of various types including floodplain grassland and extensive areas of vleis, in semi-desert bush savanna and to a lesser extent in open woodland. They avoid the more closed types of woodland, except in transit, which in some areas such as northeastern Botswana act as barriers through which they are reluctant to move. In the Subregion they remain common and widespread in the semi-desert associations of Botswana and in parts of Namibia. Here there are vast stretches of dry grassland with scattered low bush. In Botswana they tend to utilise the open grassland surrounding pans. Throughout their distributional range they are dependent on surface water which affects their movements westwards.

### Habits

Red hartebeest are gregarious, occurring in small herds of up to about 20, as well as in much larger herds of up to 300 and at certain times of the year in Botswana, in aggregations of over 10 000 (Smithers, 1971). These aggregations, composed of a number of normally separate herds, are found between August to May, but more commonly in November/December. The reason for aggregating has not been studied, but in summer may be due to movement to preferred feeding grounds following rain as, like some other species such as springbok and wildebeest, they are subject to irregular dispersal related to local rainfall, a feature of the southern parts of Botswana.

The social organisation of naturally occurring populations has not been studied in detail, but in the Orange Free State, Kok (1975), working with an introduced population, found that the males herded females and were territorial, actively defending their territories against other trespassing males. Harem herds were stable for up to three years and consisted of females with their offspring, a dominant bull and young bulls. Members of a herd tend to lie scattered and not in a compact group.

Vicious fighting between bulls may take place, especially at the time of the rut. A territorial bull may be displaced by another bull, but has been known to regain his position later. During the temporary absence of the territorial bull leadership of the harem herd may be taken over by an adult female.

Bachelor herds consist of males of all ages. Harem herds occupy the better grazing areas and bachelor herds have to make do with the less favourable areas (Kok, 1975). Although solitary males were not uncommon in Botswana (Smithers, 1971), they were rare in the Orange Free State (Kok, 1975).

Red hartebeest are most active in the early morning and late afternoons, but during cool weather may continue to be active, grazing throughout the day. In very hot weather they may seek shade, but do not show any regular pattern, and in winter they lie out in the full sun, often in open places (Ben Shahar & Fairall, 1987). Evaporative water loss is reduced by two physiological adaptations, a rise in body temperature during the day and panting (Taylor, Robertshaw & Hofmann, 1969). This and the dense reflective red pelage enable hartebeest to survive on open grass plains.

Their senses of smell and hearing are acute, but their sight appears to be poor. When disturbed curiosity actuates the herd to pause in flight, milling around as if to sum up the situation. They run at a bounding gallop and can attain considerable speed. When doing so they tend to take a swerving course, a few metres to the left, then a few to the right, showing alternate flanks to the pursuer (de Graaff, 1975a).

### Food

Red hartebeest are predominantly grazers. In the naturally occurring populations in Botswana stomach contents contained grass, with a negligible proportion of browse. However, in re-introduced herds in the S.A. Lombard Nature Reserve, western Transvaal, van Zyl (1965) recorded that the food consisted of 56% grass and 44% browse. In another study in this Reserve, Kilian (pers. comm.) found browse contributed significantly to the diet of red hartebeest only during the most limiting period (September/October) before the onset of the first rains; in other seasons they were overwhelmingly grazers. However, in the Orange Free State, Kok & Opperman (1975) found that browse constituted 40% of the diet.

Among grass species utilised by red hartebeest in the Transvaal, Kok & Opperman (1965) listed lovegrasses, *Eragrostis* spp; *Panicum stapfianum*; red grass, *Themeda triandra*; couch grass, *Cynodon dactylon; C. hirsutus*, and *Sporobolus* spp. *T. triandra* is a highly palatable grass and is eaten throughout the year.

### Reproduction

Red hartebeest are short-day seasonal breeders. In the western Transvaal the rut commences at the beginning of March and lasts until the end of April. In the Orange Free State, Kok (1975) found that the rut peaked in February. The great bulk of the calf crop (82,5%) is born in late Septemer to November just before the onset of the rains; no calves are born from March to August (Skinner *et al.*, 1973; Kilian, pers. comm.). The gestation period is eight months (Skinner *et al.*, 1973).

The territorial bull keeps a check on the reproductive status of his females by vulval sniffing. He courts females in oestrus by advancing on them with head outstretched and ears partially lowered and nudges them with his snout. Copulation may be attempted numerous times before it is successful. Skinner *et al.* (1973) found indications that oestrus lasts only for a day.

Females have their first calves at about three years of age. Before parturition females become restless and eventually leave the harem herd to have their calves in secluded places, such as in stands of tall grass or in thick scrub. The female eats the afterbirth and after cleaning up the calf, leaves it hidden while she grazes nearby, or she may rejoin the harem herd temporarily. From time to time she will revisit the calf to suckle and clean it, licking up its urine and eating its faeces to lessen scenting of the hide (Kok, 1975). During the first few days of their life calves, if approached, lie motionless with their heads lowered to the ground, the ears laid flat.

When the calf is strong enough to follow its mother she leads it back to the harem herd where she protects it from interference by other herd members. Kok (1975) recorded that mothers recognise their calves at distances up to 300 m and if the herd takes to flight the calves rejoin their mothers in flight. He recorded that calves that are unable to keep up with the herd will fall flat on the ground and lie still, as an avoidance reaction to following predators. As the calves grow up they tend to form calf groups within the harem herds, and the bond between mother and calf slowly weakens.

Calves will nibble at grass from the age of two weeks old and, although they will suckle up to eight months old (Skinner, *et al.*, 1973), they usually are weaned by about seven months (Kok, 1975). Females have one pair of inguinal mammae.

## Genus *Damaliscus* Sclater & Thomas, 1894

Key to the species after Ansell (1972)

1. Face with a white blaze; lower part of limbs white or partly white; smaller, shoulder height not exceeding 1,02 m

   . . . *dorcas*

   Face without a white blaze; limbs wholly coloured; larger, shoulder height about 1,17 m or more

   . . . *lunatus*

---

No. 309

## *Damaliscus dorcas* (Pallas, 1766)

## Bontebok/Blesbok
## Bontebok/Blesbok

### *D. d. dorcas* (Pallas, 1766)

### Bontebok
### Bontebok

Plate 31

---

#### Colloquial Name

The name applies to their "many coloured" coats which include white and several shades of brown, in parts glossed purple. While it is not normal practice to apply colloquial names to subspecies, the colloquial names bontebok, *D. d. dorcas*, and blesbok, *D. d. phillipsi*, are both well entrenched and warrant retention.

#### Taxonomic notes

Previously the bontebok and blesbok were considered to be separate species, but the consensus of opinion today is that this cannot be upheld and they are both considered as subspecies of *D. dorcas*.

Chromosome number is 2n=38 (Wurster & Benirschke, 1989). Recently (Fabricius, van Hensbergen & Zucchini, 1989) it has been shown using a discriminant function analysis, that the two subspecies and their hybrids can be separated on the basis of colour pattern.

#### Description

Bontebok are medium-sized antelope standing about 0,9 m at the shoulders. Adult males have a mean mass of 61,0 kg (Table 309.1), females are lighter and slightly smaller. It is difficult to recognise the sexes in the field, except that the horns of the females are more slender than those of the males and hardly thicken up at the base. The adult males are generally darker in colour and their white scrotums are conspicuous.

**Table 309.1**

Mass (kg) of adult bachelor bontebok rams, *D. d. dorcas*, from the Bontebok National Park, Swellendam (Skinner, Dott, de Vos & Millar, 1980).

| | Males | | |
|---|---|---|---|
| | $\bar{x}$ | n | Range |
| Mass | 61,0 | 24 | 59,6–63,6 |

At close quarters the back is seen to be rust-brown in colour. The crown of the head, the sides of the face and neck, the flanks, thighs and front portion of the rump and upper parts of the limbs are dark brown to nearly black. The sides of the face and neck, the flanks and the upper parts of the limbs are glossed with a purple sheen. The front of the face is white from the base of the horns to the nose, this blaze narrowing just above the eyes. However, there is considerable variation in this character; David (1970) showed that in 19% of bontebok the face blaze is divided by a brown band as it is in the blesbok.

The under parts, the lower parts of the limbs and the rump patch are white, with a dark brown suffusion just below the knees, on the front surface of the forelegs. The ears are brown, slightly lighter in colour than the body. The tail is white for about half its basal length and the remainder is dark brown or black with long black hair towards the tip.

Spoor—Plate II.

Detailed examination of the microstructure of bontebok and blesbok hair shows no specific variation apart from colour (Fig. XLII.1) (Keogh, 1983). The principal differences between the bontebok and the blesbok are summed up by Bigalke (1955) as follows:

| **Bontebok**, *D. d. dorcas* | **Blesbok**, *D. d. phillipsi* |
|---|---|
| The general body colour is a rich dark brown, darker on the sides of the head, the flanks and upper parts of the limbs. These darker parts have a purple gloss. | The general body colour is a reddish-brown, without a purple gloss. |
| As a rule the white face blaze is not divided by a transverse brown band but is constricted between the eyes. | As a rule the white face blaze is divided by a narrow brown band between the eyes. |
| The patch on the buttocks is pure white and the white extends around the base of the tail. The upper surface of the basal part of the tail is also white. | The patch on the buttocks is generally not white but merely paler than the body colour. The basal end of the tail is white or pale brown. |
| With the exception of the brown stripe on the front of the forelimbs, and sometimes also a brown patch on the front of the hind limbs, just above the hooves, the limbs are white from the knee downwards. | On the outer surface the fore and hind limbs are dark brown in colour. |
| The horns are usually black on the upper surface of the rings. | The horns are usually straw-coloured on the upper parts of the rings. |

The pure white patch on the rump of the bontebok is probably the best character in the wild in distinguishing them from blesbok.

Both the bontebok and blesbok have preorbital glands (see **Habits**). They have pedal glands on the forefeet only and no inguinal glands. The preorbital glands are larger in the male than in the female and exude a yellowish-black sticky secretion, which mats the hair and forms tear marks on either side of the face. Territorial males after applying this secretion to grass stems transfer it from them to their horns, a procedure which appears to be unique to the bontebok (Lynch, 1974).

Their long face, high withers and sloping hindquarters give them a characteristic outline compared with other medium-sized southern African antelope, which is reminiscent of that of their close relatives, the wildebeest and hartebeest.

Both sexes carry the ridged horns which, rising from the top of the head, curve backwards and outwards and then slightly forwards towards the unridged tips.

## Distribution

*Southern African Subregion*

Bontebok are confined in their distribution to a restricted area in the southwestern **Cape Province**, lying between Bredasdorp and Cape Agulhas. Historically their area of occurrence was somewhat larger, extending from Bot River to Mossel Bay and inland to the Sondereind and Langeberg mountains (Bigalke, 1955). Many of the early travellers first saw them near Caledon, where Isaac Schrijerer's Journal of 1689 recorded that more than 1 000 were seen. Sparrman (1786) also recorded their presence in this area. In these early times there was a measure of confusion in identification between the bontebok and the blesbok. Cornwallis Harris (1840) wrote of "bontebok" as far north as the Magaliesberg in the Transvaal, which were certainly blesbok. Since the time of the early settlement in the Cape there was a distance of some 320 km between the limits of distribution of the two. Bryden (1936) noted that blesbok were never found in the Cape Province, west of Colesberg, and did not occur in the Great Karoo. At one time the species *D. dorcas* must have had a wide and continuous distribution in southern Africa. Through climatic changes at some geological period of time it became split into two populations which, over the intervening ages, have diverged in characters, leading to the recognition of the two subspecies we see today, the bontebok, *D. d. dorcas*, and the blesbok, *D. d. phillipsi*.

It is appropriate that tribute be paid to Mr. P.V. van der Byl, his son, Mr. A. van der Byl, and the van Breda and Albertyn families, for without their recognition of the perilous situation of the species they might well have become extinct. The van der Byls took steps in 1837 to set aside a portion of their farm "Nacht Wacht" near Bredasdorp as a reserve for a nucleus of some 27 individuals. This example was followed by adjoining landowners on the farms De Groote Eiland, Bushy Park and Zoetendals Vallei (Bigalke, 1955). In 1931 the first Bontebok National Park was proclaimed on an area near Swellendam and 84 bontebok were moved to it by truck. By 1969 it was estimated that the numbers had grown to around 800. Since then the National Parks Board of Trustees have made available their surplus stock to farmers and reserves in the Cape Province and by these measures have ensured the survival of the species for the future. Bontebok, nevertheless, remain the least common antelope in the Southern African Subregion.

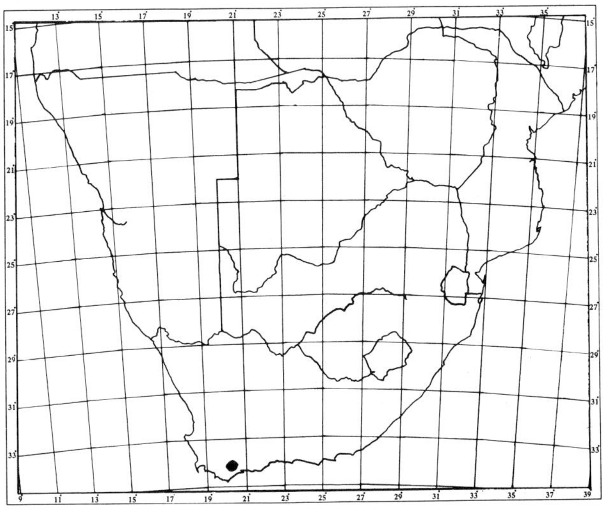

## Habitat

Bontebok live in a narrow sector of coastal plains at an altitude of from 60 to 200 m above sea level within the Cape *fynbos* zone, a sandy, alluvial plain with stony ridges and gravel terraces. The plain provides the grasses (see **Food**) on which they feed, and an association of shrubs 300 to 700 mm high, including *renosterbos*, *Elytropappus rhinocerotis; Aspalathus spinosa; Montinia caryophyllacea; Oedera imbricata; Berkheya armata*; and *Corymbium scabrum*, which provide shelter (David, 1973). Water is an essential habitat requirement and is found in the many small streams and rivers which occur and whose banks provide, in their riparian *Acacia* associations, more substantial cover in the form of small trees. The habitat lies in a winter rainfall area, rain falling in all months of the year, with a peak during spring from September to November, which is the lambing season. The average mean annual rainfall is about 550 mm. Areas of short grass, cover and drinking water are among their essential habitat requirements.

## Habits

Bontebok are a diurnal, gregarious, grazing species. Their social organisation consists of territorial males, female herds and bachelor groups. The territorial males establish and maintain a mozaic of territories varying in size from four to 28 ha on an all year round basis. Some males may hold their territories for much longer periods, even for the duration of their adult lives. They rarely manage to establish a territory before they are three years of age, generally five years (David, 1970). They acquire these by deposing a territorial male from his territory or by establishing a new one. They defend these from trespass by other males by a complicated system of ritual displays, seldom if ever resorting to fighting.

Female herds consist of a small number of adult females with their young, in total numbering up to about eight, which are non-territorial and wander at will over the home ranges of the territorial males. During the rut the territorial male courts females when they enter his territory and takes steps, by herding and ritual displays, to entice them to remain within it (see **Reproduction**). There is a hierarchy among the members of the female herds, established by threat postures, horn-clashing or battling with the horns. Adult females demonstrate against strange attentive males, driving them off with a bucking bounce, kicking out with the hind legs.

Bachelor groups are much larger, consisting of males of all ages, including old decrepit males and young males. They may also include a small number of females. They are an important unit in the social structure as they provide security for young developing males, who may later become territorial males, a haven for decrepit old males, deposed territorial males, which are accepted amicably as members, and a temporary refuge for immature females. There is no hierarchy within bachelor groups and no aggression between members. Play-fighting between yearlings may occur, consisting of horn-twisting and head-pushing (David, 1970).

Young males leave their mothers at about 12 months old, when she produces her next offspring. They may remain solitary for a time but eventually join bachelor groups until sexually mature. They are not forced out of the female herds by their mothers or by the territorial males, as happens in the case of wildebeest and impala, but leave of their own accord. Bachelor groups are loose associations and when, in their wide movements, they enter the territory of a territorial male, they may so overwhelm him by numbers that he is not able to drive them out. While he may chase individual males, he eventually gives up and confines his actions to various threat postures. Normally males in bachelor groups give way to territorial males without encounter. Yearling females which join bachelor groups remain with them until they are about two years old before joining the nursery herds.

David (1973) described in detail some 30 challenge reactions used by territorial males in driving off trespassing males which include lateral presentation of the body to intruders, head-dipping and nodding, alarm-snorting, bucking, bouncing with kicking with the hind legs, defecating and urinating postures, soil-horning and head to tail sniffing, the individuals standing side to side. All these usually end up with the trespasser moving off and actual encounters are rare.

While the many complicated challenge threats are all used by the territorial male in retaining his dominance in his territory, the most important seems to be the manner in which he advertises his possession of it. He will assume the "proud" posture with head held high, ears extended sideways, often standing on raised ground so that he is clearly visible. Marking of the territory by defecation and urination used by other species is not important to the bontebok. Their latrines are scattered about the territory and generally are disregarded by other males.

Territorial males endeavour to retain adult females if they show signs of leaving their territories. They may do this by courting them with a display consisting of an approach with the muzzle pointed forward, horns laid low along the back and tail curled upwards. They display in this way and prance up to her or run straight at her with head held high and ears forward. If the female is determined to leave, however, the male may allow her to do so. If the herd is disturbed, the territorial male takes up a defensive position in the rear, standing broadside on in a wide stance or in the urinating posture, which has been interpreted as a symbolic threat. The scent-marking which they carry out by applying the black secretion of the preorbital glands to grass stems, is apparently not recognised by others.

Horning of bushes or of the latrine patches by territorial males, often used on trespass by bachelor intruders, was suggested by David (1973) to be a threat display. Serious fighting is rare and even when fighting occurs no injuries result. Contestants may drop on their knees with their foreheads close to the ground and feint at each other without actual contact. These encounters only last a few seconds before one gives up and retires.

While the territorial males invariably use latrines, a central one in the territory is often used to lie on during the day. The bachelor males defecate randomly, as do the females and juveniles.

The periods of greatest activity are in the early morning and late afternoon. They rest during the hotter hours of the day in thickets, where they tend to cluster together. During periods of heavy rain they seek the shelter of trees or stand facing away from the wind with their heads held low.

In common with the blesbok, bontebok have a characteristic habit on hot days of standing in orientated groups facing the sun with their heads held low. They remain alert during this time, occasionally shaking their heads and snorting or stamping their feet, then running in a circle to resume their place in the group.

### Food

Bontebok are almost exclusively a grazing species, with a preference for feeding on short grass. Nolte (1973) examined the fresh rumen contents of bontebok from the De Hoop Provincial Nature Reserve, Cape Province against the epidermal characters of a series of grasses collected in the Reserve and ascertained that they contained the following percentage of various grasses:

| **Species** | Percentage |
|---|---|
| *Bromus* sp. | 25 |
| *Pseudopentameris macrantha* | 22 |
| *Plagiochloa uniolae* | 16 |
| *Eragrostis capensis* | 14 |
| *Bromus diandrus* | 5 |
| *Merxmuellera stricta* | 3 |
| Undet. | 15 |

### Reproduction

Bontebok are short-day seasonal breeders, mating in early autumn in the Bontebok National Park, where the rut takes place between the months of January to mid-March, with some activity continuing until April (David, 1973). The territorial males court the females with a display involving curling the tail over the back and holding the head low with the muzzle outstretched and the tail horizontal. Flehmen does not occur in bontebok. A male may sniff the vulva of a female and if she is not receptive she will run around him closely to avoid his attentions. During this "mating circling" the female holds her head low in the submissive attitude. During the rut the frequency of the courtship display may be as high as once an hour, but is not confined to the period of the rut and may be performed in all seasons of the year. When the male performs to females about to leave a territory, it may actuate them to remain (David, 1970). The annual cycle in the male matches that in the female (Skinner *et al.*, 1980).

Conception rate is influenced by rainfall (which in turn affects grass cover) prior to the breeding season (Novellie, 1986), as well as food availability, as influenced by competition for food by grazers. The gestation period is between 238 and 254 days. Lambs are born in the spring, between September and November, with late arrivals up to the end of February, the peak months being September/October. Females become sexually mature at just over two years old, having their first lambs at about three years old. The young females remain with their mothers after their new lambs are born, as a member of the herd (David, 1975).

Females have one pair of inguinal mammae.

---

No. 309

## *D. d. phillipsi* Harper, 1939

## Blesbok
## Blesbok

Plate 31

---

### Colloquial Name

*Bles* is the Afrikaans for a blaze and refers to the white face marking which extends from the horns to the nose and is broken by the brown band just above the eyes.

### Taxonomic Notes

See notes under bontebok, *D. d. dorcas*.

### Description

The blesbok is very similar to the bontebok (for differences see notes on bontebok). The outline of the front hooves is slightly larger than the hind hooves in the spoor (Plate II). The horns are illustrated in Fig. 309.1. The world's record pair originated from Molteno, Cape Province, and measured 0,508 m (Best & Best, 1977).

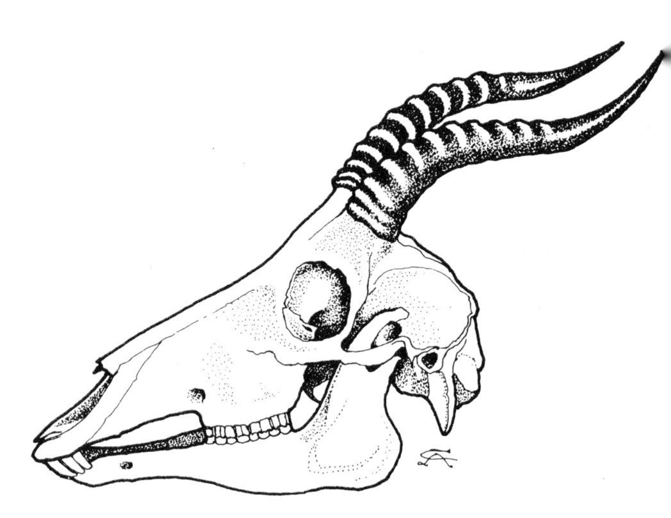

Fig. 309.1. Skull: blesbok, *D. d. phillipsi*
TL skull 310 mm

### Distribution

*Southern African Subregion*

Blesbok are endemic to the Subregion. Their present distribution is to a large extent artificial as there have been wide introductions and reintroductions and they now occur in protected herds on fenced farms and reserves. Because of these wide translocations they have a wider distribution today than they had in the past. The limits shown on the map represent the area within the Subregion where naturally occurring populations were found in the past and where they still may be seen today albeit under enclosed conditions. The Magaliesberg probably represented their northern limits in this sector, yet through introduction, they may be seen today in many areas right through to the northern parts of the province on scattered farms and reserves (Kettlitz, 1962a).

From the time of the first settlers in the Cape and the commencement of exploration of the hinterland there was a gap of some 300 km between the limits of distribution of the bontebok and the blesbok. Blesbok were hunted relentlessly for their meat and hides and, as far back as 1893, Bryden (1893) noted that although they formerly occurred in countless thousands, they seldom were seen even then. They were first seen in the treks northeast from the Cape on the open grassland of the Middelberg/Richmond areas. They were common in parts of the eastern **Cape Province**, in the **Orange Free State** and northwestwards to near the Molopo River, the present boundary with **Botswana**. They occurred on the grasslands of the southern parts of the **Transvaal** and marginally into **Natal**, where Anderson (1888) recorded hunting them along the upper reaches of the Tugela River. In Lesotho, Arbousset & Daumas (1846) stated that they occurred to the west of the Maluti Mountains.

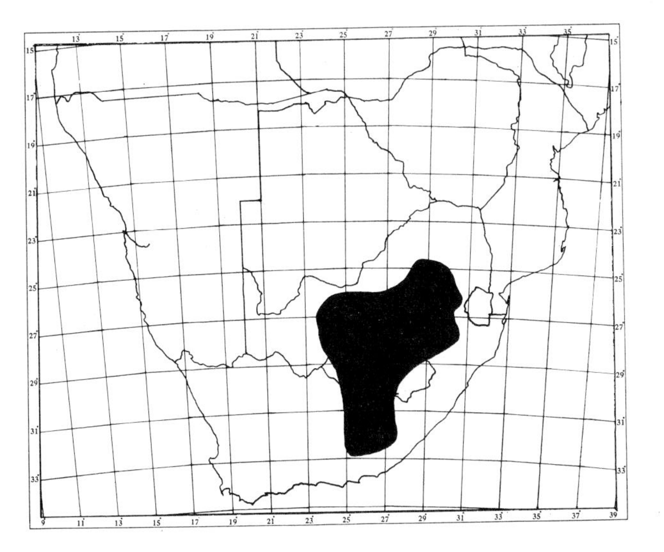

## Habitat

When first encountered by Europeans at the end of the 17th century all reports indicated that they were restricted to grasslands and were not seen until the karroid areas of the central parts of the Cape Province had been traversed. Their former distribution indicates that they were confined to the Highveld plateau grasslands where water was available.

## Habits

Blesbok are gregarious, diurnal grazers. Their habits are very similar to those of bontebok. They are active in the early morning and late evening and lie up during the hotter hours of the day in the shade of bushes or trees. They appear to be susceptible to heat for, during the summer months, they will seek the shade of thickets, moving deep into them. At this time the territorial males become soporific and can be approached very closely. Like bontebok, they tend to rest together in small groups.

When moving to their feeding or drinking places, or retiring to their night resting sites, blesbok string out in long single files. This continuing activity forms distinct paths. They are much more active during cool, overcast weather, but during heavy rainstorms they take shelter under trees or bushes or stand with their backs to the direction of the rain, with their heads held low.

The characteristic habit of standing in orientated groups with their heads towards the sun and their faces close to the ground is common to both bontebok and blesbok. Authorities differ as to whether they are indeed sleeping in this posture or not. They occasionally indulge in violent head shaking, snorting or stamping their feet and then running in a small circle to resume their places in the group.

As in bontebok, bachelor groups are the largest and reach peak numbers during the rut. They consist predominantly of young males and occupy home ranges in areas not occupied by territorial males (Novellie, 1975). During the autumn rut in March/April, the harem herds consist of from two to 25 females, usually about 10, attended by a territorial male which will actively drive other males away from his females. While much of this antagonism is of a ritual nature, du Plessis (1968) recorded serious fighting, the males dropping on to their knees and attempting to thrust their opponents in the flanks. These fights do not last long but are indulged in at speed and with vigour, and males have been found which apparently had been killed in these encounters. The territorial male of the harem herd courts females in oestrus, with his head held forward and his tail curled over his back in the same way as in the bontebok.

Males occupy a network of territories at least during the rut between March and May, which Novellie (1979) found in the Transvaal to have an average area of 0,023 km$^2$ (range 0,009–0,041 km$^2$).

After the rut territorial activities such as herding of the females and boundary encounters drop in intensity and during winter and spring territories were virtually undefended (Novellie, 1975). In November there was a rise in intensity of territorial behaviour and territorial males tended to remain in their areas for longer periods, but herding of females and aggression towards intruders were erratic. During the rut territorial males are strongly attached to their territories and will return to them if driven off. They maintain their territories by means of complicated challenge displays and actions. These include lateral presentation, head to shoulder sweeps with the head, mutual anus-smelling, horn-angling towards the opponent, digging into the ground with the horns, and in intense excitement, leaping high in the air, horn-clashing and fighting. They mark their territories by inserting grass stems in their preorbital glands so as to smear them with secretion or by wiping the glands across vegetation. They perform a process unique to the species of transferring the glandular secretion from the grass stems to the base of the horns by stroking their horns across the grass with a sideways movement of the head. Lynch (1971) found that some territorial males had a deposit of this black waxy substance up to 3 mm thick between the horn annuli. Females, bachelor males and calves also perform this process. The territorial males create dung patches in their territories and tend to lie up on them during resting periods. These middens are a focal point in the life of the territorial male, especially during the rut. It is a rendevous for social contact and a point at which many of the challenge displays are carried out in warning off other blesbok males (Lynch, 1971). Blesbok dung middens were associated often with the remains of termite mounds and provide a focus of mammal activity by virtue of their association with peripheral vegetation of high quality and the visibility afforded by patches of bare ground for behavioural and anti-predator purposes (Coe & Carr, 1978).

Snorting, with feet-stamping in the alert position, head held high, hind legs apart, and front legs straight, is also used as a ritual challenge. All these displays, which usually are sufficient to cause withdrawal of the trespasser, serve to minimise actual fighting. Aggression between adult females in harem herds has been recorded by Lynch (1971). However, this is confined to threatening with the horns, but never reaches the extent of horn-clashing.

Blesbok have interdigital glands and pawing, especially of the dung heaps, by territorial males may be an additional factor in marking. It also occurs in conjunction with other challenge displays such as face-wiping, horning or defecating. Challenge rituals are terminated usually by mock grazing, the individuals then moving apart. Should one, however, raise its head at this juncture, it may be taken as a threat and horn-clashing follows.

During the cold, dry season from about June to August very large aggregations, consisting of all sexes and age groups, are found. Lynch (1971) recorded up to 650 individuals in one such aggregation. Female herds, however, still maintain their identity, tending to frequent particular areas. Both the female herds and aggregations have well defined home ranges at this time. By September these large aggregations begin to split up into female and bachelor herds and territoriality among adult males becomes noticeable from November, reaching its highest intensity about April. Veld burning can cause disruption of the social organisation, for fresh sprouting grass is much sought after by blesbok and the entire population may move to an area after a burn.

Unlike the bontebok, where the general herd structure remains unchanged throughout the year, the social organisation of the blesbok undergoes marked structural changes during the months of the year. Blesbok females are not associated intimately with the territorial males throughout the year, only during the rut, and do not occupy the same home ranges on a year round basis (Lynch, 1971).

### Food

Blesbok are predominantly grazers, although van Zyl (1965) recorded that they will browse occasionally. They are partial to sprouting grasses which appear after a burn, and will move on to burnt areas even before the green flush is apparent. Where these areas are some distance from a water supply, they will move off it only for the purposes of drinking in the early morning and late afternoon, then return to it. During winter du Plessis (1968) recorded that blesbok enter a period of minimal activity which lasts until the grass sprouts with the onset of the rains. During this time they graze lightly and selectively in small groups. Du Plessis (1968) stated that blesbok avoid grasses with more than one season's growth and showed that there is a marked difference in the species of grasses utilised on burned as opposed to unburned areas. Among the species of grasses eaten some, such as *Setaria flabellata*, are important in winter but remain untouched in summer, indicating a seasonal change in the species utilised. Some species such as *Ctenium concinnum*; bristle grass, *Aristida junciformis*; and sour grass, *Elyonurus argenteus*, are consistently avoided. Du Plessis (1968) gave a list showing the relative importance in the diet of six species of grasses from a burned and seven from unburned areas at Rietvlei, Transvaal. The four principal species from the former are red grass, *Themeda triandra*; weeping lovegrass, *Eragrostis curvula*; *Chloromelas* sp and *Setaria nigrirostris*, and from the latter *Eragrostis pseudosclerantha*; *T. triandra*; *E. curvula* and *Chloromelas* sp.

### Reproduction

Blesbok are short-day seasonal breeders, mating in autumn, and further oestrous synchronisation is induced by the presence of the male (Marais, 1988). The oestrous cycle was determined by measuring plasma progesterone peaks and is about 30 days (Marais, 1988). The bulk of the lamb crop is born between November and January, with a peak in December (Skinner *et al.*, 1974). Where parturition occurred as late as February/March this was confounded by dystocia, females dying while giving birth, so that although breeding is theoretically possible outside autumn, other factors limit this occurrence (Marais, 1988). Prior to the rut, which occurs from March to May, territorial males start to herd females in an endeavour to retain them within their territories. Exhibiting the courting display with their heads held forward, the horns lying back and their tails curved over their backs, they advance on the females with stiff legs and, moving in a semi-circle in front of them, cause the females to cluster. Once they have grouped the females in their territory they will keep them there by circling them from time to time. Lynch (1971) recorded a territorial male that successfully herded 34 females. In spite of this, females do slip away from harem herds to join others and whole harem herds may move from territory to territory. Well-fed blesbok ewes kept in proximity with the ram cycled throughout the year. The length of the cycle, as indicated by cyclic production of progesterone, was 28–32 days. During the breeding season when a ram was introduced to ewes which previously had been isolated from the ram, this caused the previous non-cyclic ewes to cycle in synchrony. This synchronisation caused the bulk of the lamb crop to arrive within a short period. The short autumn mating season is timed when nutrition has been adequate for several months, improving body condition and the chances of ovulation and conception. Following gestation, lambing occurs after the first summer rains when nutrition is again adequate for lactation and growth (Marais, 1988).

Female blesbok become sexually mature at about two and a half years old, in some cases possibly earlier (du Plessis, 1968). Skinner *et al.* (1974) gave the gestation period as about 240 days and a single young is born at a birth weighing six to seven kg. Females remain with the herd to give birth, which usually takes place in the forenoon. Females do not eat the afterbirth as do some hartebeest. The cream-coloured calves can stand up a few minutes after being born, but are unsteady. Some 20 minutes later, however, they can run with their mothers. They start suckling when about an hour old.

Yearlings are very interested in new-born calves and have to be chased off by the female. Females will suckle their own calves only, driving others away, and when calves get separated from their mothers they bleat loudly, the mothers responding with deep grunts, until contact is re-established. Calves are weaned at about four months old but remain attached to their mothers for another six months, then tend to leave them, and will form calf groups either within the female herds or join mixed aggregations or bachelor herds. Male calves may remain in the same herd as their mothers until calving time, but females sometimes remain with their mothers for up to two years.

Females have a pair of inguinal mammae.

---

No. 310

## *Damaliscus lunatus* (Burchell, 1823)

Tsessebe

Tsessebe

Plate 31

---

### Colloquial Name

The name comes from the Tswana name for the species, *tshêsêbe*.

### Taxonomic Notes

Ansell (1972) listed seven subspecies of *D. lunatus* which include not only the tsessebe, *D. l. lunatus*, which occurs in the southern part of the continent, but also two subspecies of the topi of East Africa and Zaire, *D. l. jimela* (Matschie, 1892) and *D. l. topi* Blaine, 1914; the tiang, *D. l. tiang* (Heughlin, 1863) of East Africa; the korrigum; *D. l. korrigum* (Ogilby, 1837) of the Sudan and westwards to Senegal; and two other subspecies without colloquial names, *D. l. lyra* Schwarz, 1914 of the Central African Republic and Chad and *D. l. purpurescens* Blaine, 1914 of Cameroun and Nigeria.

In *D. l. lunatus* the number of chromosomes is 2n=36 (van der Veen & Penzhorn, 1987).

### Plate 31

307. Lichtenstein's hartebeest, *Alcelaphus lichtensteinii*
Lichtenstein se hartbees
308. Red hartebeest, *Alcelaphus buselaphus*
Rooihartbees
309a. Blesbok, *Damaliscus dorcas phillipsi*
Blesbok
309b. Bontebok, *Damaliscus dorcas dorcas*
Bontebok
310. Tsessebe, *Damaliscus lunatus*
Tsessebe
322. Impala, *Aepyceros melampus*
Rooibok

PLATE 31
310
322
309a
309b
308
307
Dick Findlay.

**Description**

The tsessebe is a large antelope, standing about 1,2 m at the shoulder. Adult males have a mean mass of about 140 kg (n=16), the females 126 kg (n=32) (Child, Robbel & Hepburn, 1972) (Table 310.1). The body hairs are 8,7±1,4 mm long, concavo-convex in cross-section, with gutters and an irregular waved mosaic cuticular scale pattern along their length (Fig. XLII.1) (Keogh, 1983). The general colour of the body is dark reddish-brown with a distinct iridescent purplish sheen and a dark, almost black suffusion on the top of the head and muzzle. The lower parts of the shoulders and the upper parts of the forelegs, both inside and outside, are darker than the general colour of the body, often nearly black. The upper parts of the hind legs and thighs are also conspicuously darker than the colour of the body. The tail is basally yellowish-white with a black or dark brown tassel of long hair towards the tip. The back of the ears, hind parts of the rump, inside of the hind legs and abdomen are yellowish-white. They have a patch of yellowish-white above the darker part of the inside of the front legs. The lower parts of the legs are brownish-yellow, the front legs with a narrow band of dark brown on the front. Juveniles lack the darker markings on the body and are generally yellowish-red in colour.

Spoor—see Plate II.

The horns possessed by both sexes bend outwards in a uniform curve, without any abrupt change, then inwards and slightly forwards. They are ringed for nearly their full length, only the tips being smooth. The record length of 469 mm is shared by pairs from northern Botswana and Angola (Best & Best, 1977).

**Table 310.1**

Measurements (mm) of tsessebe, *D. lunatus*, with moderate and heavy tooth wear, from northeastern Botswana (Child *et al.*, 1972)

| | Males | | | Females | | |
|---|---|---|---|---|---|---|
| | $\bar{x}$ | n | Range | $\bar{x}$ | n | Range |
| TL | 2160 | 21 | 2070–2290 | 2130 | 45 | 1900–2260 |
| T | 450 | 20 | 40–52 | 420 | 44 | 360–510 |
| Hf c/u | 550 | 21 | 518–570 | 533 | 46 | 482–560 |
| E | 196 | 21 | 184–206 | 192 | 46 | 177–209 |
| Sh.ht | 1260 | 21 | 116–134 | 1250 | 44 | 1080–1320 |

**Distribution**

Following Ansell (1972), who considered that the seven known forms were all subspecies of *D. lunatus*, this species has a wide but scattered and discontinuous distribution from Senegal to eastern Ethiopia and southwards to the eastern Transvaal. The distribution of the tsessebe has shrunk considerably in historical times. The original specimen on which the description of the species is based was collected by Burchell in 1812 just northeast of Kuruman. They were common in the western Transvaal in earlier times, but do not appear ever to have extended much further south than the Vaal River.

Carr (1986) stated that as a result of a survey in the Transvaal it was estimated that there were 1 000 individuals outside the Kruger National Park, 1 163 in the Park according to a 1985 survey, and 71 in the Pilanesberg National Park, Bophuthatswana. Translocations have taken place to the northern Cape Province the Etosha National Park, Namibia and Natal and generally there has been an increase in numbers over recent years. Naturally occurring populations outside the Kruger National Park occur only in the northwestern Transvaal (250 individuals) and the Klaserie Game Farm (49 individuals).

*South of the Sahara, excluding the Southern African Subregion*

The species occurs from **Senegal** eastwards, in the Sudan and Sahel savannas, through northern **Nigeria**; the **Central African Republic** to the southern **Sudan** and parts of eastern **Ethiopia**. It occurs in southeastern and southwestern **Uganda**, extending marginally in **Zaire**; in western **Tanzania** and in a narrow coastal sector from southern **Somalia** and **Kenya** to northeastern Tanzania. In **Zambia** they occur on the Chambeshi flats in the northeast, extending marginally into Zaire, and in the southwest of the country west of the Zambezi River extending into eastern **Angola**.

*Southern African Subregion*

The species occurs in the extreme northeastern parts of **Namibia**; throughout the northern and in scattered localities in the eastern sector of **Botswana**; in the **Caprivi Strip**, extending marginally into northwestern **Zimbabwe**. They also occur in Zimbabwe in scattered localities in the central parts of the country and south of the central plateau. In **Mozambique**, Sidney (1965) recorded eight areas in which at that date they still occurred. Smithers & Tello (1976) noted that up to 1970 a few still survived in the extreme southeastern parts of the Beira District, but disappeared thereafter. Before the fencing of the border between the Kruger National Park and Mozambique, vagrants used to cross from the Park into Mozambique which is no longer possible and it is believed that they are now extinct in Mozambique. In the **Transvaal** they occur in the Kruger National Park where the bulk of the population is found north of the Letaba River. Outside the Park they occur in private game reserves on its western boundary and isolated localities in the Waterberg. They have been reintroduced to Nature Reserves in the Transvaal, to the Itala Game Reserve in northern Natal and to the Etosha National Park, Namibia.

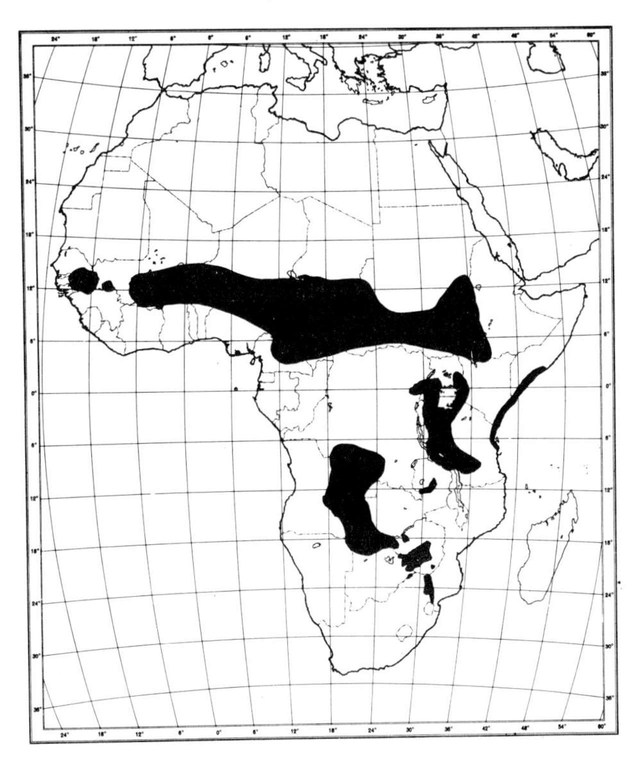

**Habitat**

The habitat requirements of tsessebe include the availability of palatable grasses, water and shelter. In Botswana they favour the fringes of grassland where this forms an abrupt ecotone with woodland, whose importance appears to derive more from the shade it provides rather than from concealment. Tsessebe prefer to keep potential danger in sight and will take to the open frequently when disturbed (Child *et al.*, 1972). They are dependent on water and while they will utilise areas in which water is available in seasonal pans, they will leave the area as these dry up. During the rains they will move away from floodplains, on which the greater part of their time is spent during the dry season, into neighbouring woody vegetation to make use of palatable grasses and seasonally available water supplies. Garstang (1982) summed up their habitat requirements and came to the conclusion that they were highly dependent on open surface water within an open woodland habitat and that bush encroachment accounts for reductions in range and numbers. Artificial waterpoints should be camouflaged to resemble natural pools or tsessebe may be averse to using them.

## Habits

Tsessebe are gregarious, occurring in small herds. Their social organisation includes the presence of territorial males, breeding herds, which in northeastern Botswana averaged 3,6 individuals with a range of one to 21 (n=589), and bachelor groups which averaged eight individuals with a range of two to 31 (n=76) (Child *et al.*, 1972). Aggregations do occur on preferred feeding grounds. Child *et al.* (1972) recorded an aggregation of 58 individuals together in the Moremi Game Reserve, 120 on the Chobe River floodplain and 194 on burnt ground in the Mababe Depression, Botswana.

Territorial males establish and maintain territories which they patrol regularly and which, in the Kruger National Park, were estimated to be 2–4 km$^2$ (Joubert, 1972). In patrolling they maintain a steady gait, with their ears extended forward in an alert attitude, and defecate at regular intervals. While both sexes mark with the preorbital glands, the territorial males are particularly active in doing so. They usually mark on an upright grass stem which is inserted into the gland to become covered with the transparent sticky secretion. They also rub the sides of their faces on the ground, usually on a termite mound or on a sandy patch, falling on their knees to do so. Both sexes horn the soil, especially after rain, which in the case of the territorial males probably has a scent marking and visual function in inhibiting trespass to the territory. Pocock (1910) showed that tsessebe have well developed interdigital glands on the front feet, less well developed on the hind feet, which no doubt in the case of territorial males when they paw or scrape in the ground, form yet another means of territorial marking. Advertising their presence by standing on raised ground is regularly used by the territorial males as a deterrent to trespassers on their territory. They will approach trespassers, throwing their heads up and down, or may rear up. This either elicits a similar response in the trespasser and the two may then wheel around each other, or the intruder may break off the challenge. Serious fighting is unusual but the two may drop on their knees and horn-clash or, if the fight reaches a high intensity, they may interlock their horns and engage in vigorous pushing which may raise clouds of dust. The victor may then chase off his opponent.

Unlike the blesbok, tsessebe harems remain permanently associated with their territorial male (Garstang, 1982). This can be to their disadvantage when a territorial male becomes infertile for some or other reason (Skinner, pers. comm.). Herding his females is achieved by a ritualised dominance display by the territorial male. In this display the male raises his head with his nose pointing forward, the ears held rigidly to the sides of the neck pointing towards the ground. His movements are slow and deliberate, the front legs lifted high at the knee with each stride forward (Joubert, 1972).

Yearling males are evicted from the harem herds by the territorial males soon after the commencement of the calving season (October) and this gains momentum in January as the rut approaches. These yearling males aggregate to form or join established bachelor groups. The bachelor groups do not have a fixed area of activity, but establish themselves on the periphery of the established territories (Joubert, 1972).

Although rather an ungainly species with their high shoulders and sloping backs, tsessebe are reputed to be the fastest of any of the antelope occurring in the Subregion and they can sustain a lumbering gallop for great distances. They are inquisitive and curious to the verge of stupidity and will stand in the open even after a number of members of the herd have been shot. This factor among others certainly contributed to their disappearance from many parts of their former distributional range.

## Food

Tsessebe are almost exclusively grazers and in the drier grasslands show a preference for grass up to 0,6 m tall, although at certain times of the year they frequent patches of 3 m tall *Sorghum verticilaster* in the Mababe Depression in Botswana (Child *et al.*, 1972). They make heavier use of burnt than unburnt areas, a factor well known to the Bushmen in Botswana who burn the vleis annually for the specific purpose of attracting this species onto them to facilitate hunting. They are bite selectors (selecting plant parts) in contrast to wildebeest, for example, which are site selectors (selecting grass patches) (Murray, pers. comm.).

## Reproduction

Tsessebe are seasonal breeders. In the Transvaal the rutting behaviour commences in early January, it peaks in March, and the bulk of the calf crop is born in October, with occasional births in November and early December (Garstang, 1982). In northern Botswana the rut peaks in March/April and calves are born from October to December (Child *et al.*, 1972), the bulk of the calf crop being born within a 40 day period.

The females make no attempt to hide their young, even in the very early stages of their lives, and shortly after birth they join their mothers. While their mothers forage, groups of young tend to join up into nursery herds of two to five, which bed themselves down in slight depressions. One or more of the mothers usually remains close to the calves and the remainder of the breeding herd joins them at the first sign of danger.

Males become sexually mature in time for the rut in their fourth year of life, at about 40 to 42 months of age, whereas females calve for the first time when about 36 months old. One young is born at a birth with a mass of between 10–12 kg.

Females have one pair of inguinal mammae.

# Subfamily CEPHALOPHINAE

The Subfamily is represented in the Subregion by three genera: *Cephalophus*, *Philantomba* and *Sylvicapra*, and three species, one from each genus. They are small to medium-sized antelope, with plain-coloured bodies, with no pattern. They have short tails and tufts of hair on top of the head between the ears. Both sexes of *Cephalophus* and *Philantomba* and the males of *Sylvicapra* have short, simple horns. Preorbital glands are present in all species, pedal glands are present in *Philantomba* and *Sylvicapra*, which also has inguinal glands. Females have two pairs of mammae. The blue duiker, *Philantomba monticola*, and red duiker, *Cephalophus natalensis*, occur in forested areas, the common duiker, *Sylvicapra grimmia*, in savanna woodland and grassland.

Key to the genera (Meester *et al.*, 1986)

1. Horns normally present in both sexes, although possibly reduced in females, directed backwards in plane of face; ear proportionately shorter and rounded at tips
   ... 2

   Horns normally absent in females, in males directed upwards, forming an obtuse angle with plane of face; ears longer and pointed
   ... *Sylvicapra*

2. Smaller, greatest skull length below 150 mm, often considerably less; mass below 9 kg
   ... *Philantomba*

   Larger, greatest skull length over 150 mm; mass over 9 kg
   ... *Cephalophus*

## Genus *Philantomba* Blyth, 1840

No. 311

## *Philantomba monticola* (Thunberg, 1789)

## Blue duiker
## Blouduiker

Plate 32

## Colloquial Name

The southern representatives of the species have, in certain lights, a faint bluish sheen on the coat which gave them their name.

**Taxonomic Notes**

Ansell (1972) listed 16 subspecies from the continent, of which three occur in the Subregion: *P. m. monticola* from the Cape Province; *P. m. bicolor* (Gray, 1863) from eastern Natal, Swaziland and the Eastern Districts of Zimbabwe, and *P. m. hecki* Matschie, 1897 from Mozambique, south of the Zambezi River, extending northwards to Malawi.

**Description**

Blue duikers are the smallest antelopes found in the Subregion. Adult males stand about 300 mm at the shoulder, with a mass of about 4 kg; the females are slightly larger, with a mass of about 4,6 kg (Table 311.1).

Blue duikers give the impression of being slightly higher at the hindquarters than at the fore, the musculature of the thighs being better developed than that of the shoulders. The legs are slim, the head broad between the small, rounded ears, the muzzle short and pointed. The large eyes are situated more forwardly in the head than in most small antelope.

The body hairs are 20,0±2,6 mm long, oval or concavo-convex in cross-section, with a regular waved cuticular scale pattern along their entire length (Fig. XLII.1) (Keogh, 1983). The colour varies considerably in the three subspecies. In the Eastern Districts of Zimbabwe, the colour of the upper parts in *P. m. fuscicolor* is a dark smoky-brown, darker on the head and rump, with a distinct dark bluish sheen in some lights. The chin, throat and inner parts of the thighs are white, and the remainder of the under parts is slightly lighter in colour than the upper. The fronts of the legs are browner than the body, with a distinct reddish tinge and white flecks. The sides of the face are lighter in colour than the upper parts. The ears are white in front and dark smoky-grey behind. The top of the tail is the same colour as the upper parts and white underneath.

*P. m. hecki*, of the coastal areas of Mozambique, is much more richly coloured, rusty-brown on the upper parts, more smoky-brown on the nape of the neck and down the mid-back, darkening towards the base of the tail. The chin and the whole of the under parts are pure white, the limbs light chestnut with some white flecking. The top of the tail is nearly black, white underneath.

In specimens of *P. m. monticola* from the southern coastal forests, the body is dark blue-grey, the limbs light rusty-brown. The tail is the same colour as the upper parts and white below.

The preorbital glands, which lie on the sides of the face in front of the eyes, are slightly protuberant. The glands have a row of minute pores, each gland with a few hairs near its opening, and on pressure the glands exude an opaque liquid. Blue duikers also have pedal glands between the hooves of the feet which secrete a whitish liquid with an acrid smell. The preorbital glands are rubbed on stems of trees, logs and twigs, low branches and other rigid vegetation to mark their territory, and the pedal glands mark their movements in their forest habitat.

The hair on the body is sleek, about 15 mm long on the shoulders and 20 to 25 mm long near the base of the tail. It is shorter on the sides of the face below the eyes but longer, up to 15 mm, on the top of the muzzle and head, with a well developed tuft between and around the horns.

Spoor—see Plate III.

**Table 311.1**

Measurements (mm) and mass (kg) of blue duikers, *P. monticola*, from Natal (Bowland *in litt.*)

| | Males | | | Females | | |
|---|---|---|---|---|---|---|
| | $\bar{x}$ | n | Range | $\bar{x}$ | n | Range |
| TL | 619 | 31 | 540–685 | 638 | 22 | 575–690 |
| T | 72 | 31 | 50–90 | 73 | 21 | 55–90 |
| Hf c/u | 165 | 32 | 154–175 | 163 | 21 | 154–170 |
| E | 52 | 32 | 48–55 | 51 | 22 | 38–56 |
| Sh.ht | 298 | 32 | 265–335 | 300 | 21 | 250–360 |
| Mass | 4,1 | 32 | 3,2–4,9 | 4,6 | 22 | 3,4–5,9 |
| Horns | 45 | 32 | 33–56 | 31 | 21 | 24–39 |

Both sexes carry tiny horns which slope backwards in the line of the face. They are coarsely ringed at the base and smooth towards the slightly diverging tips. Often the horns are almost obscured by the hair tuft between them on the top of the head. The horns are about 45 mm long in males and about 31 mm long in females; the longest so far recorded from the Subregion is a pair in the Kaffrarian Museum, King William's Town, which measures 57,2 mm (Best & Best, 1977).

**Distribution**

Blue duikers have a wide distribution which extends from the coastal areas of the Cape Province to parts of West Africa. Because of their specialised habitat requirements their distribution is discontinuous and patchy.

*South of the Sahara, excluding the Southern African Subregion*

They occur in southeastern **Nigeria**, east of the Cross River, eastwards to the southern **Sudan**; narrowly in western and throughout the southern parts of **Uganda** and in southwestern and the extreme southeastern parts of **Kenya**. In **Tanzania** they occur in the northwest, around Lake Victoria, in the west and southwest and in the forests of the Usumbara and Uluguru mountains, with a break in distribution southwards to appear again in similar habitat in the extreme southeast. There is some doubt as to whether they still occur on Zanzibar Island and its two adjacent islets from whence *C. m. sundevalli* Fitzinger, 1869 was described, but they occur on **Pemba Island** north of this. They occur throughout **Zaire**; they extend northeastwards into the **Congo Republic**; **Gabon**; **Rio Muni** and the island of **Bioko**. In **Angola** they occur in the west, as far south as Benguela and in suitable habitat in the north and east of the country. In **Zambia** they occur in parts of the North Western Province, with an isolated population in the southern Kasempa District and in the Northern and North Eastern Provinces as far south as Feira on the Zambezi River. In **Malawi** they occur in the Nyika and Lengwe National Parks. In **Mozambique**, north of the Zambezi River, there are no recent records, although Peters (1852) recorded them from the Quelimane area and they may still occur in forest in this part of the country.

*Southern African Subregion*

They occur in forests in the Eastern Districts of **Zimbabwe** and east of this in similar habitat in the Vila Pery and Beira Districts of Mozambique, south of the Zambezi River. There are no recent records from the Inhambane District, from where they were recorded by Peters (1852), due to the extensive removal of forests in this sector. In **Natal** they occur from the Umfolozi River system southwards mainly in the coastal areas but also in suitable habitat in the central parts of the province, and in the **Cape Province** they occur narrowly along the coastal areas westwards to the vicinity of George.

**Habitat**

Blue duikers are specialised in their habitat requirements and throughout their wide distributional range are confined to forests, thickets or dense coastal bush. Within these associations they frequent forest glades and the slightly more open parts of the underbush cover, but require the denser underbush to lie up in or in which to take cover when disturbed.

**Habits**

Because of the nature of their habitat blue duikers are seldom seen. They commonly live in pairs, sometimes with sub-adult offspring. The pair occupies the same home range of about 0,75 ha, with both the male and female scent-marking, and they usually forage and sleep or rest close to each other. Three pairs, captured and radio-collared in two different study areas, were monitored for over a year. During this period the pair-bond remained intact and their territorial boundaries, maintained by both, did not change. Established pairs groom each other frequently and often go through an extensive greeting ceremony where they rub noses and orbital glands and nibble each other's head tufts, neck and shoulders. This greeting ceremony is not only confined to territorial pairs; on one occasion a lone female approached an established or territorial pair and went

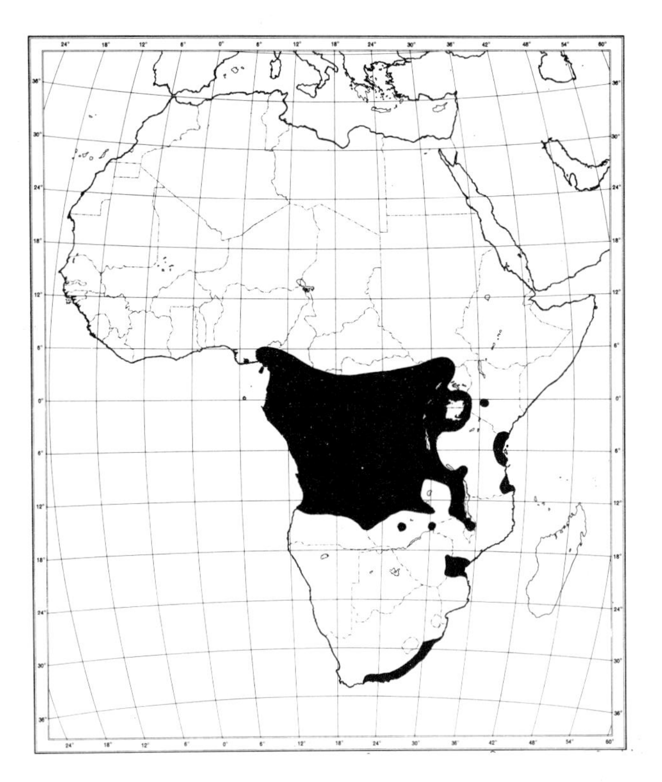

through an intensive greeting ceremony with the paired female, while she, the lone female, and the male ignored each other (Bowland, 1989). After weaning, in particular, males are seen often with the young, rather than the female (Bowland, 1989). Females with their single young have been seen, but it is not known how long they remain together.

Crawford (1984) found that, in the Tsitsikama National Park, they were active throughout the day. They are very active in the early morning and late afternoon and if a position is taken up in the forest, with a view over open glades, the observer may be lucky enough to see them emerge from the dense undergrowth to feed on fallen leaves, flowers and fruit on the forest floor and occasionally browse on young shoots. Blue duikers spend about eight hours a day foraging or moving about their home range. Intensive radio-tracking showed that they do not move about at night and spend a large portion of the day resting or ruminating.

Within their dense habitat blue duikers create well marked paths between bed-sites and feeding grounds. People aware of this habit catch many in snares set across these paths. Though normally silent, they do have an adequate vocal repertoire, for example when caught they utter loud cat-like "miaows"; alarm "whistles" are usually heard as the animal flees from an intruder, and rapid low-key snorts are issued when the animal is curious (Bowland, 1989).

**Food**

Direct observations of blue duikers have revealed that they eat mainly fallen leaves, fruit and flowers, and that they browse infrequently. The foraging activities of monkeys, seen by many as wasteful, frequently provide duikers with fruit and leaves and it is not unusual to see duikers feeding below a troop of monkeys in the forest. Frugivorous birds, often gathering in large numbers in fruiting trees, dislodge ripe fruit which are relished by the duikers. The wind too frequently blows off leaves, fruit and flowers. Trees provide food by their natural turnover of leaves and shedding of ripe fruit (Bowland, 1989). Blamey & Jackson (1956) stated that in dune scrub in Natal blue duikers have been seen to feed on buckweed, *Isoglossa woodii*; the leaves of the wild silver oak, *Brachylaena discolor*; stinging nettles, *Urera tenax*, and the fruit of the thorny rope, *Dalbergia armata*.

In the Eastern Districts of Zimbabwe, many of the forest trees and the underbush bear fruit which is eaten by blue duikers. Stomachs containing up to 90% of wild fig fruits, *Ficus* spp, have been recorded, which include *F. capensis*, *F. craterostoma*, *F. exasperata*, and *F. natalensis*. The fruits of the wild olive, *Olea africana*, the water berry, *Syzygium cordatum*, and red milkwood, *Mimusops* spp, are eaten. They also eat the fallen sepals of wild strelitzia, *Strelitzia nicolai*. Although Blamey & Jackson (1956) recorded that they will graze on fresh green grass sprouting after fire, in Natal no grass was found in stomach contents. In Zimbabwe they appeared to be feeding on wild fruits and tiny forbs sprouting in the grassland, but not on the grass itself. Bowland (1989) found that, as browsers, their principal food is freshly fallen leaves of eight species, fruit from 10 species, flowers from four species, and they browsed on shoots only of *Dalbergia armata*, *Bequaertiodendron natalensis* and the lily, *Chlorophytum modestrum*. These food items they seek on the fringes of forest glades or in glades within the forest. Indeed, he found it difficult to positively identify fallen leaves eaten and this component should be much greater.

**Reproduction**

Myers (1972) stated that the male courts the female by nibbling at her neck and shoulders, rubbing his preorbital glands against her cheeks, prancing in front of her and presenting his horns. There are understandably very few lambing records for blue duikers in the wild, but all indications are that breeding occurs throughout the year. In Natal, Bowland (1989) saw three-month-old lambs in all months except January, June and September and in captivity lambs were born in February, July, September and November. Brand (1963), von Ketelhodt (1973, 1977) and Böhner *et al.* (1984) all reported births in captive blue duikers throughout the year. One lamb is born at a time and the mass at birth is 490 g (n=2), the mass doubling by 30 days (Bowland, 1989). The gestation period is 207 days (range 196–216) and the ram may cover the female again within 14 days of parturition, but the lambing interval is usually about 265 days (Böhner *et al.*, 1984).

Females have two pairs of inguinal mammae. Böhner *et al.* (1984) reported that sexual maturity is attained at nine months in males in captivity and from 6 to 17 months in the female.

## Genus *Cephalophus* A. Smith, 1827

No. 312

## *Cephalophus natalensis* A. Smith, 1834

## Red duiker
## Rooiduiker

Plate 32

**Colloquial Name**

So called from the rich red colour of their pelage.

**Taxonomic Notes**

Ansell (1972) listed 11 subspecies from the continent, of which two are recognised by Meester *et al.* (1986) as occurring in the Subregion: *C. n. natalensis* which occurs in southern and northeastern Natal, the eastern Transvaal and southern Mozambique, and *C. n. robertsi* Rothchild, 1906 which occurs in Mozambique, north of the Limpopo River. The existence of the species in the Transvaal is currently precarious (Pienaar, 1963; du Plessis, 1969; Carr, 1984).

**Description**

Red duikers are smaller than the common duiker, *Sylvicapra grimmia*, standing about 420 mm at the shoulder and having a mass of about 12,0 kg.

**Table 312.1**

Measurements (mm) and mass (kg) of red duikers, *C. natalensis* from Natal (Bowland *in litt.*)

| | Males | | | Females | | |
|---|---|---|---|---|---|---|
| | x̄ | n | Range | x̄ | n | Range |
| TL | 864 | 9 | 809–900 | 890 | 8 | 855–950 |
| T | 96 | 8 | 70–115 | 103 | 8 | 85–125 |
| Hf c/u | 231 | 9 | 220–245 | 227 | 8 | 220–240 |
| E | 77 | 9 | 74–81 | 77 | 8 | 72–80 |
| Sh.ht | 412 | 9 | 380–480 | 418 | 8 | 385–450 |
| Mass | 11,7 | 9 | 9,8–12,6 | 11,9 | 9 | 10,3–13,2 |
| Horns | 70 | 8 | 45–80 | 35 | 7 | 20–44 |

The upper parts of the body of Natal specimens are a deep chestnut-red colour, the lower part of the flanks and the under parts a pale chestnut. The nape and throat turn ash-grey as the animal ages. Specimens from Mozambique tend to be more orange in colour on the upper parts of the body. They have a crest of long bushy hair on the top of the head which is partly chestnut, partly black in colour and often conceals the horns. The sides of the head, the sides and under parts of the neck and inner upper surfaces of the limbs are tawny or pale fawn, the throat white. The ears are short and rounded with a fringe of black hair on the outside margins, the insides whitish. The upper parts of the neck, the pasterns and hind part of the hocks are dark in colour, with a tinge of dull violet or grey. In front and below the eyes there is a bare glandular patch about 20 mm long on which opens a series of elongated pores from which small bristles arise. On pressure these pores exude a clear sticky fluid with a faint aromatic odour. Exudate from these glands is dabbed onto stems and branches by the animal as it moves about its home range. The upper parts of the tail are the same colour as the back, darkening towards the whitish tip.

Spoor—see Plate III.

Both sexes carry a pair of short, straight horns which have coarse basal rings and longitudinal striations but are smooth towards the tips and rise from the top of the head, lying in the line of the face. The longest pair recorded from the Subregion came from Natal (KwaZulu) and had a length of 101 mm (Best & Best, 1977).

### Distribution

While the distribution of the red duiker as shown on the map appears extensive, occurring as they do from parts of the Sudan southward, in the eastern parts of the continent to Natal, their distribution within this range is patchy and discontinuous. While this is to some extent a natural phenomenon in a species with specialised habitat requirements, in parts of their range the clearing of forests and thickets to make way for agricultural development has destroyed their habitat. In Natal, Vincent (1962) recorded that they have disappeared from most of the coastal areas and survive only in the thick scrub and evergreen forests of the northeast, in gullies in the Lebombo Mountains and in a protected forest in the Inanda district in the south. They have been reintroduced successfully to coastal regions in southern Natal, namely Vernon Crooks' Nature Reserve and the Umzumbe Conservancy (Bowland, pers. comm.). Red duiker have disappeared from a large portion of their former range in the Transvaal. The inland tropical forest types have been degraded severely by commercial afforestation in the higher rainfall areas and by agriculture in the drier areas. With this continuing trend of habitat destruction the population of red duiker can be expected to decrease still further (Carr, 1984).

*South of the Sahara, excluding the Southern African Subregion*

They occur in northeastern **Zaire**; southern **Sudan**; western **Uganda** and southern **Kenya**. In **Somalia** they are confined to the riverine forest of the Juba River, which is being destroyed rapidly. In **Tanzania** they occur in the north, east and throughout the southern parts of the country, and in **Mozambique**, north of the Zambezi River, are confined to the eastern sector. At one time they occurred in the southern parts of **Malawi** but are now extinct, only being found today in the Nyika National Park in the north, where they occur in montane rain forest up to altitudes of 2300 m (Dyer, pers. comm.) and in the Vipya Mountains (Liggett, pers. comm.).

*Southern African Subregion*

They are confined to the eastern parts of **Mozambique**, south of the Zambezi River; in **Swaziland** they are found in the Lubombo Mountains and in thickets in the adjoining lowveld (Hlane Game Reserve), and in **Natal** they occur as far south as the Umzumbe area. In the Transvaal they are restricted to suitable habitat in three main areas: the western fringe of the Ingwavuma/Ubombo population of Natal/Kwazulu; the eastern Transvaal escarpment population around Nelspruit, and the Soutpansberg population (Carr, 1984). In the **Transvaal** there is an isolated population on the southern slopes of the Soutpansberg, in the vicinity of Louis Trichardt and up to 50 km east of this (Skinner, unpubl.) and they occur in the southeastern parts of the province.

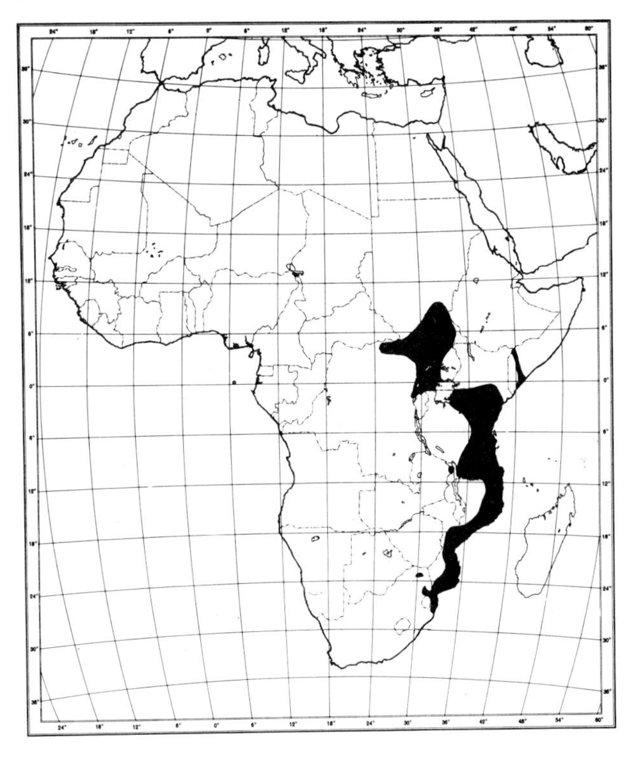

### Habitat

Throughout their range, red duikers are associated with forests, forest clumps and dense thickets. They occur in riverine forest, on forest-clad mountain slopes, in thickly wooded ravines and in dense coastal bush. In East Africa they occur in montane forest.

### Habits

Red duikers are usually found either solitarily or a female with her offspring, or in pairs or small groups (3–5) in a loose association. They are shy and secretive and, because of the type of habitat in which they occur, they are difficult to observe. If they become aware of an observer they seldom stand for more than a few seconds before bounding away into thick bush, often emitting a hoarse alarm "whistle". They are diurnal, with peaks in activity at dawn and dusk, and are reluctant to move around at night.

Heinichen (1972) recorded that they vocalise with a loud *tchie-tchie* sound which is louder and more penetrating than that of a suni, *Neotragus moschatus*. They use communal dung heaps and the home range usually covers an area of 6–8 ha. These may overlap to an extent of 80–100% and a defended territory is not present as in blue duikers (Bowland, 1989).

### Food

The red duiker is an extreme concentrate selector and even less able to digest fibre than the common duiker (Hofmann, pers. comm.). Red duikers browse primarily on fallen leaves, wild fruits and flowers and fine stems of low-growing shrubs. Heinichen (1972) recorded their feeding on the sickle bush, *Dichrostachys cinerea*; the black monkey orange, *Strychnos madagascariensis*; Natal gardenia, *Gardenia cornuta*; the needle bush, *Azima tetracantha*; *Asparagus falcatus* and *Justicia protracta*. She also noted the following from the examination of a stomach content: the spiny monkey orange, *Strychnos spinosa*; the duiker berry, *Sapium integerrimum*; *Justicia* sp; *Commelina africana* and raisin bush, *Grewia* spp. Bowland has observed red duiker eating the freshly fallen leaves of *Cussonia sphaerocephala*, *Strychnos spinosa*, *Celtis africana*, *Ficus stuhlmanii*, *Sapium integerrimum*, *Harpephyllum caffrum*, *Barringtonia racemosa*, *Apodytes dimidiata*, *Acacia robusta* and *Ziziphus mucronata*.

### Reproduction

The female produces one young at a time. Breeding occurs throughout the year, three-month-old lambs having been observed in the wild in February, July and August, and captive ewes have lambed in February, July, October and November. The average mass at birth is 979 g (n=2) and the lambing interval is about 235 days (Bowland, pers. comm.), which is similar to observations made on blue and common duikers, suggesting a gestation period of 210 days, but this needs to be confirmed.

The females have two pairs of inguinal mammae.

## Genus *Sylvicapra* Ogilby, 1837

No. 313

## *Sylvicapra grimmia* (Linnaeus, 1758)

## Common duiker
## Gewone duiker

Plate 32

### Colloquial Name

They are named after their characteristic habit, when disturbed, of making off at high speed in a series of plunging jumps and diving (Afrikaans *duik* = dive) for cover. They may be referred to as the grey duiker but in some parts of their distributional range they vary from rufous to yellow in colour.

### Taxonomic Notes

Ansell (1972) listed 19 subspecies from the continent, stating that their validity and limits of distribution are doubtful. Of these Meester *et al.* (1986) listed six as occurring in the Subregion: *S. g. grimmia* (Linnaeus, 1758) from the southern and western Cape Province; *S. g. burchelli* (H. Smith, 1827) from the eastern Cape Province and perhaps Natal; *S. g. caffra* Fitzinger, 1869 from northeastern Natal, the Transvaal, eastern and southwestern Zimbabwe, eastern Botswana and southern Mozambique; *S. g. splendidula* (Gray, 1871) from northwestern Zimbabwe, northern Botswana, and the Caprivi Strip; *S. g. steinhardti* Zukowsky, 1924 from the northwestern Cape Province and parts of Namibia and Botswana, and *S. g. orbicularis* (Peters, 1852) from central and northern Mozambique. It is likely that when more material and data become available this list will be reduced.

### Description

Common duikers are small antelope, the adult males standing about 500 mm at the shoulders, the females about 20 mm higher. Adult males have a mass of between about 15 to 18 kg, females 16 to 21 kg. In parts of Botswana the males have a mass of up to 21,2 kg, the females up to 25,4 kg (Table 313.1).

The hairs are oval in cross-section, with three scales across the width having a mosaic pattern (Fig. XLII.1) (Keogh, 1983). Throughout their wide distributional range, and even in the Subregion, they exhibit considerable variation in colour and size. The colour of the upper parts varies from a greyish-buff in *S. g. caffra* to a reddish-yellow in *S. g. splendidula*. In some areas there is a considerable colour variation within populations. The under parts are usually white, which may or may not extend on to the inner sides of the limbs. In some the under parts are tinged red, grey or off-white. The hair of the coat is short and sleek, the individual hairs on the upper parts being about 15 mm long. In the Lephepe sector in Botswana, within the population of those with normal coats, there are some in which the hair reaches a length of 30 mm and is wavy and curly, especially on the back (Smithers, 1971).

The black band on the top of the muzzle may extend from the forehead to the nostrils, but in some it is restricted to the lower part of the face near the nostrils. The forehead often contrasts with the colour of the body in varying darker shades of dull rufous. They have a tuft of long black or dark brown hair between the base of the horns. The front of the long slender forelegs is dark brown or black, the tufted tail short and narrow, the ears long and relatively narrow.

They have preorbital, pedal and inguinal glands. The preorbital glands are conspicuous, appearing as short black lines just below the front corners of the eyes. They open to the surface in a series of minute pores, lying within the naked black line, and exude a tarry-like substance. The pedal glands on the front feet open between the hooves. The inguinal glands open at the crease between the belly and the inner surface of the thigh.

Spoor—see Plate III.

**Table 313.1**

Measurements (mm) and mass (kg) of common duikers, *S. grimmia*, from (a) Botswana (Smithers, 1971) and (b) Natal (Schmidt, 1984)

**(a)**

| | Males | | | Females | | |
|---|---|---|---|---|---|---|
| | $\bar{x}$ | n | Range | $\bar{x}$ | n | Range |
| TL | 1097 | 23 | 1030–1160 | 1135 | 37 | 1050–1250 |
| T | 129 | 23 | 105–160 | 150 | 36 | 122–195 |
| Hf c/u | 326 | 25 | 290–349 | 327 | 38 | 245–355 |
| E | 129 | 24 | 115–148 | 129 | 37 | 118–145 |
| Mass | 18,7 | 24 | 15,3–21,2 | 20,7 | 37 | 17,1–25,4 |

**(b)**

| | Males | | Females | | |
|---|---|---|---|---|---|
| | $\bar{x}$ | n | $\bar{x}$ | n | Range |
| TL | 1036 | 2 | 1064 | 4 | 1037–1122 |
| T | 112 | 2 | 112 | 4 | 105–123 |
| Hf c/u | 304 | 2 | 296 | 4 | 291–304 |
| E | 118 | 2 | 110 | 4 | 102–114 |
| Sh.ht | 613 | 2 | 570 | 4 | 540–610 |
| Mass | 16,2 | 2 | 16,7 | 4 | 15,3–18,5 |

**Skull** (Fig. 313.1)

The milk dentition in the common duiker is:

$i\frac{0}{3}\ c\frac{0}{1}\ d\frac{3}{3} = 20$

At birth the deciduous incisors and lower canines are either partially or fully erupted and the upper and lower premolars are just starting to erupt. The first permanent tooth to erupt is the first lower molar which appears within two to three months of birth. The second lower molar erupts

**Plate 32**

311. Blue duiker, *Philantomba monticola*
Blouduiker
312. Red duiker, *Cephalophus natalensis*
Rooiduiker
313. Common duiker, *Sylvicapra grimmia*
Gewone duiker
325. Roan, *Hippotragus equinus*
Bastergemsbok
326. Sable, *Hippotragus niger*
Swartwitpens

PLATE 32
312
311
325
326
313
Dick · Findlay . '86.

at 8,5–10,5 months, the third at about 17 to 23 months. The permanent premolars appear at 26–48 months and the incisors and canine teeth at 60 months and older (Wilson, Schmidt & Hanks, 1984).

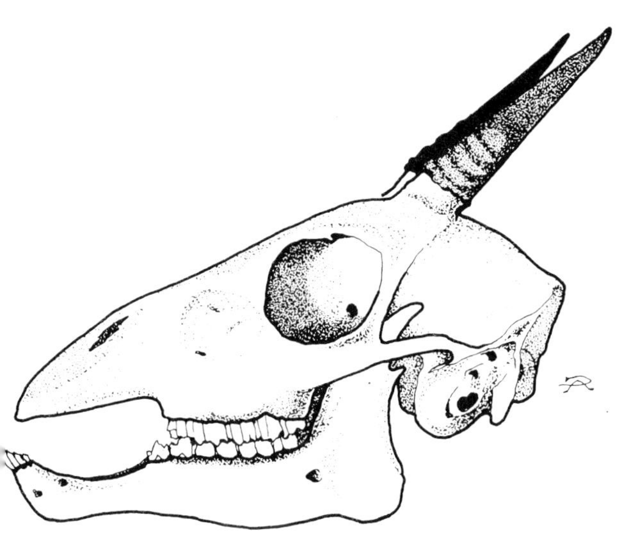

Fig. 313.1 Skull: common duiker, S. *grimmia*
TL skull 180 mm

The full adult dentition is attained by the age of six months (Wilson, Schmidt & Hanks, 1984) and consists of:

$I\frac{0}{3}\,C\frac{0}{1}\,P\frac{3}{3}\,M\frac{3}{3} = 32$

Only the males carry the short straight horns which, heavily ridged at their bases, arise close together from the top of the head, diverging slightly outwards, slope backwards and rise to smooth, sharp points (Fig. 313.2). Very occasionally females grow short, stunted horns. The world record horns of S. g. *grimmia* came from the Transvaal and measured 181 mm (Best & Best, 1977).

**Distribution**

Common duikers have a very wide distribution in Africa south of the Sahara. They are catholic in their habitat requirements, but they do not occur in forest. However, when disturbed they will hide in forests. Within the distributional range shown they are absent from desert regions, but will penetrate this type of terrain along watercourses where there is some vegetation to provide shelter, as for example in the Namib Desert in the Subregion and in the Somali Arid Zone. They avoid open grassland where there is no cover, except on the open grasslands of Nyika (Malawi) where the grass is long.

They are resilient to heavy hunting and persist in the face of intense agricultural development providing this leaves some peripheral bush cover, and they occur even in the peri-urban and urban areas of cities.

*South of the Sahara, excluding the Southern African Subregion*

They occur throughout the Guinea and Sudan savannas of **West Africa**, north of the forest zone, in which they do not occur. In the **Central African Republic** they are confined to the central and northern parts of the country, and also in the southeastern corner near Obo. They are recorded from the southern **Sudan** and **Ethiopia** and extend in this sector to the shores of the Red Sea. In **Somalia** they are confined to the vicinity of the Juba and Uebi Shebeli rivers which carry them far into arid terrain. They are widespread in **Kenya**, except in the north and northeast, and in **Uganda** and **Zaire**, except in the forests of the Congo basin, extending into the southeastern parts of **Gabon** and the southern **Congo Republic**. They are also widespread in **Angola, Zambia, Mozambique**, north of the Zambezi River and **Malawi**.

*The Southern African Subregion*

They occur throughout **Namibia**, penetrating the coastal Namib Desert along dry watercourses; **Botswana; Zimbabwe** and **Mozambique**, south of the Zambezi River. In the **Republic of South Africa** they are recorded as widespread throughout the country.

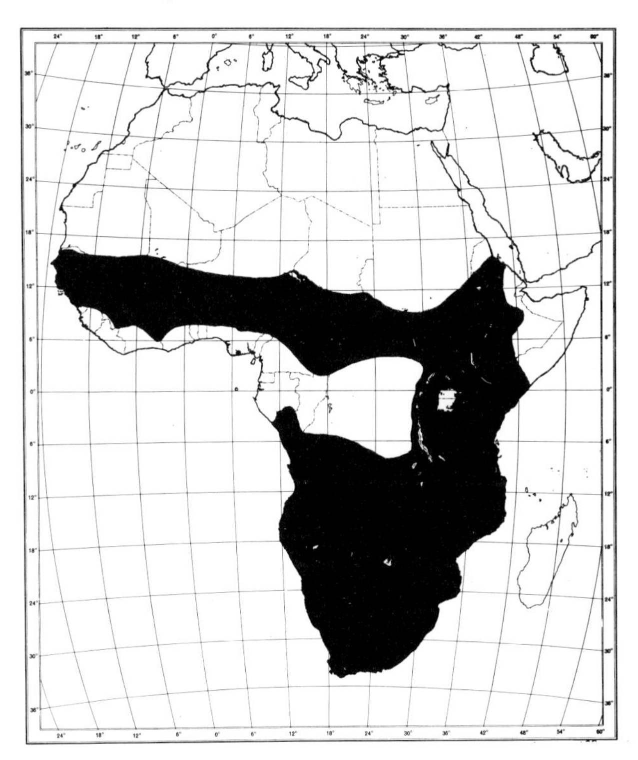

**Habitat**

The presence of bush is an essential habitat requirement of the common duiker in the Subregion. This provides shelter and shade, as well as the leaves, twigs, flowers and fruit which constitute their main food. They use woodland with ample underbush, but tend to avoid associations such as *Baikiaea* which are too open under the canopy, and they do not occur in open short grassland. They are found on the fringes of forested areas but avoid the forests themselves. When seen on grassland of medium to tall grass, they are seeking the low-growing forbs and other browse plants found there and may rest up in the stands of tall grass. In the northern parts of the Subregion they occur widely in *Acacia* woodland and scrub. In the southwest they occur in the Cape Macchia. Throughout their range they are found on the fringing scrub of agricultural lands or in the lands themselves, after the crops reach sufficient height to provide cover. They occur from sea level up to altitudes of over 1 800 m in the Drakensberg (Vincent, 1962) and in other parts of Africa on high mountains right up to the snowline.

**Habits**

Common duikers are solitary, but pairs can be seen during periods when females are in oestrus, and females with their single young move together. Their main periods of activity are in the late afternoon, extending well into the hours of darkness, and in the early morning. On cool or overcast days they may be active throughout the day. In areas where they are subject to continued disturbance or control, they tend to become more nocturnal. Activity after dark is sporadic, some individuals lying up by 20h00, others continuing their activities up to about 01h00, but activity generally ceases thereafter until about 04h00.

The mean size of the home range of the common duiker is about 21 ha and can vary between 12,1 and 27,4 ha throughout the year (Allen-Rowlandson, 1986). They rest and ruminate in the shelter of bushes or stands of tall grass and when approached, will lie tightly, springing up almost under one's feet to bound off with characteristic plunging jumps in a zig-zag course and disappear into the nearest cover. They are fast movers and outstrip most dogs. When caught in the beam of lights at night they react either by momentarily lowering their heads or by moving off a few paces and then lying down, after which they can be approached quite closely, but with their acute sense of hearing, a slight rustle or breaking of a twig sends them plunging off. Usually a quiet species, the common duiker's alarm call is a nasal snort which is not heard often. When caught in snares, they are difficult to handle, scream very loudly and kick violently with their hind legs; the sharp hooves and horns can cause injury.

### Food

Common duikers are concentrate feeders (Hofmann, 1973), and Boomker (1981) found that the caecum plays an important role in fibre digestion and energy yield in this species, especially in winter when food quality is low. Common duikers are almost exclusively browsers, only very rarely eating grass. Their diet consists of the leaves, twigs, flowers, fruits and seeds of a wide variety of trees and shrubs and they are great raiders of cultivated crops and ornamental shrubs, although the damage they do to these is minimal. They will also dig for tubers and roots and nibble at the bark of trees. Hofmann (1973) found 400 g of mushrooms in one stomach. In Zambia, Wilson (1966a) listed 45 species of plants, the leaves of which are eaten by duikers. In addition he recorded the eating of fruits and seeds of 33 species and the flowers of 15. His sample included a further list of unusual items such as the resin of the velvet bush willow, *Combretum molle*; the horn pod tree, *Diplorhynchus condylocarpon*, and the Prince of Wales feathers tree, *Brachystegia boehmi*. In two stomachs he found guineafowl chicks, *Numida mitrata*. There are records in literature of duikers taking young birds. Wilson & Clarke (1962) recorded ducklings, Maberly (1964) turkey chicks and Stoneham (1955), in East Africa, chickens. One individual had a lizard in its stomach. In Botswana, Smithers (1971) examined stomachs containing high percentages of mopane caterpillars, *Gonimbrasia belina*. Hofmann (1973) saw one swallow a striped mouse in Kenya and found globular bezoars made up of small mammal hairs in their abomasum.

Among cultivated crops, beans are very much sought after, as are the leaves and tubers of sweet potatoes, tomatoes, maize and groundnuts. Both the dry leaves and soft green cobs of maize are eaten, but they have also been observed eating the dry seeds in piles of detritus from shellers.

Among the many foods listed by Smithers (1971) from Botswana, the fruits of the snake berry, *Solanum* spp, were commonly found in their stomachs, as well as the pulp and pips of tsamma melons, *Citrullus lanatus*, which no doubt are important in this arid area, not only as a food but as a source of moisture. Common duikers are independent of water and even when it is freely available they rarely drink. They can become a nuisance in urban gardens as they are partial to roses and other ornamental shrubs, as well as annual plants. Duikers are delicate feeders, nipping off the outermost fine twigs of their browse with its fresh new leaves and buds. The fruits of large trees such as the wild figs, *Ficus* spp, become available to them through the feeding habits of monkeys, baboons and birds who drop or knock fruit to the ground. They will stand on their hind legs, steadying themselves on the branches with the forelegs, to reach the fruit and twigs of shrubs.

Sommerlatte (1979) recorded that in forestry plantations in the eastern Transvaal young pine trees in their first year of growth were seriously damaged, especially during the dry season, by the browsing of duikers. By the time the trees were two years old, however, they were immune to this damage. Allen-Rowlandson (1986) listed food items of duikers occurring in commercial plantations and on adjacent farmland and recorded their utilisation of exotic timber species.

### Reproduction

Lambs are born at any time of the year, gravid or lactating females having been taken in every month. For example, in Botswana, of 39 adult females taken over the year, only one was not gravid or lactating (Smithers, 1971). There is insufficient evidence to support the suggestion of peaks in births during the rainy season in Botswana and Zimbabwe (Smithers, 1971; Smithers & Wilson, 1979).

Usually duikers produce a single young at a birth, the foetus almost invariably developing in the right-hand uterine horn. The gestation period is about 191 days (seven months) (Wilson, pers. comm.). Females mature early and can conceive at about eight to nine months old, but usually lamb for the first time at 18 to 20 months (Wilson & Clarke, 1962).

The female retires to give birth in the cover of dense vegetation and after cleaning and suckling the newly-born lamb, leaves it hidden. At birth the young have a mass of about 1350 to 1900 g (Wilson, 1968). The young are precocious and stand up and attempt to suckle shortly after birth and run actively within 24 hours (Wilson & Clarke, 1962). The female returns to the hiding place of the lamb from time to time to suckle it. In captivity, Wilson & Clarke (1962) noted that if handled the lambs move to another site. In the early stages the young "freeze" if disturbed, remaining motionless with their heads flat on the ground, their ears folded back. Common duikers mature very rapidly, individuals of six or seven months of age closely approximating the size of the adults.

Females have two pairs of inguinal mammae.

## Subfamily ANTILOPINAE

Simpson (1945) regarded this Subfamily as being comprised of two tribes, the Antilopini and Neotragini. He included the impala, *Aepyceros melampus*, but for the reasons given in the text on this species, they are regarded as being worthy of a Subfamily of their own.

## Tribe Antilopini

These are medium-sized antelopes, both sexes with ridged, lyrate horns, those of the females noticeably lighter in build than those of the males. They have preorbital and pedal glands and a dorsal gland on the mid-back surrounded by long, white, erectile hairs, but no inguinal glands. The tail is short. The body has a distinct pattern including a longitudinal dark flank band.

The Tribe is represented in the Subregion by the springbok, *Antidorcas marsupialis*.

## Genus *Antidorcas* Sundevall, 1847

No. 314

## *Antidorcas marsupialis* (Zimmerman, 1780)

## Springbok
## Springbok

Plate 33

### Colloquial Name

The stotting of the springbok, which is so characteristic of the species, gave them their colloquial name. The specific name *marsupialis* derives from *marsupium*, a pouch, referring to the dorsal fan of long white hairs which, when not erected, lies flat, as in a pouch, hidden by the light brown hair of the back.

### Taxonomic Notes

Ansell (1971) listed three subspecies: *A. m. marsupialis* from the southern part of the species' distributional range; *A. m. hofmeyri* from the southern parts of Namibia and Botswana, and *A. m. angolensis* from northern Namibia and Angola. These are also suggested by Groves (1981). Robinson (1975) came to the conclusion, however, after a comparison of the size of skulls and by karyological and electrophoretic examination, that little support exists for the continued recognition of subspecies. Those recognising subspecies probably have not accounted for the interaction between heredity and the environment on certain traits.

## Description

Springbok stand about 750 mm at the shoulder. The hindquarters appear higher than the forequarters, giving the back a sloping appearance. In series the males are slightly heavier than the females at about 41 kg; the females 37 kg (Table 314.1).

In the springbok Findlay (1989) found that visual differences in the coat are attributable to melanin (differing in quantity and translucency but not in colour), to horny cells (pale yellow in white hairs), and to the medulla. Brightness is altered directly by the melanin content of hair—contrasts in brightness have the same disruptive effect as those in colour for a colour-blind predator, enhancing the power of camouflage. The hairs are concavo-convex in cross-section with gutters and an irregular waved mosaic scale pattern, two or three scales across the width (Fig. XLII.1) (Keogh, 1983).

Always appearing sleek and trim, they are a colourful species, the back a bright cinnamon-brown with a distinct broad, dark reddish-brown horizontal band which extends from the upper parts of the foreleg to the hip, separating the upper parts from the pure white under parts. The banding could also act as an intraspecific communicating mechanism at close quarters. The white of the under parts continues on to the flanks, the back and the sides of the forelimbs and shows on the front of the thighs, further enhancing the colourful appearance of the body. It also continues upwards, on the central part of the rump, narrowing forwards to tail into the dorsal crest of long, 100 to 120 mm, white hair which normally is not seen unless the crest in the "pouch" is erected, the reason for which remains obscure. The white hair in the "pouch" differs in that it is implanted into the skin at right angles to the surface (Findlay, 1989). At all other sites, the hair lies at a slope. In the pouch the *arrector pili* muscles run in bundles in a craniocaudal direction lying between the hair follicles. On stiffening the longitudinal arrector muscle mass the white hair becomes bunched together and stands out—the porcupine fans its quills in a similar way. Between the white of the rump and the cinnamon-brown of the sides of the thighs there is a broad vertical band of dark reddish-brown. The tail is white, with a terminal tuft of long black hair.

The face is white, with a reddish-brown line from in front of the eye to the angle of the mouth and a similarly coloured patch on the forehead. The ears are outstandingly long, narrow and pointed. The outside of the hind and front of the forelimbs is the same colour as the back. The neck is noticeably long for the size of the body, the legs long and slender, the sharp points of the hooves showing clearly in the spoor (Plate III).

Springbok that are predominantly either "black" or white are known, both occurring in herds with normally coloured individuals. The former are predominantly chocolate-brown, the latter mainly white. The "black" individuals are glossy black at birth, the colour changing soon thereafter to the dull chocolate-brown. At four months old white hairs appear on the upper lip and spread until the white face blaze is fully developed (Kruger, Skinner & Robinson, 1979).

**Table 314.1**

Measurements (mm) and mass (kg) of a series of adult springbok, *A. marsupialis* (Smithers, 1971)

**Botswana**

| | Males | | | Females | | |
|---|---|---|---|---|---|---|
| | $\bar{x}$ | n | Range | $\bar{x}$ | n | Range |
| TL | 1501 | 30 | 1390–1623 | 1484 | 13 | 1375–1580 |
| T | 244 | 30 | 146–286 | 256 | 13 | 200–305 |
| Hf c/u | 427 | 30 | 400–455 | 416 | 13 | 395–462 |
| E | 177 | 30 | 153–195 | 173 | 13 | 150–187 |
| Mass | 41,0 | 30 | 33,0–47,6 | 37,1 | 13 | 30,4–43,5 |

**Table 314.2**

Mean measurements (mm) and mass (kg) of adult springbok, *A. marsupialis* from (a) the eastern Transvaal (representative of *A. m. marsupialis*); (b) the Kalahari Gemsbok National Park (representative of *A. m. hofmeyri*) and (c) Kaokoland, Namibia and the Namib Desert in the Iona National Park, Angola (representative of *A. m. angolensis*) (Kruger, Skinner & Robinson, 1979)

**Eastern Transvaal**

| | Males | | | Females | | |
|---|---|---|---|---|---|---|
| | (a) | (b) | (c) | (a) | (b) | (c) |
| | n=21 | n=9 | n=10 | n-21 | n=9 | n=10 |
| TL | 1 141 | 1 278 | 1 247 | 1 122 | 1 243 | 1 217 |
| T | 234 | 254 | 241 | 230 | 259 | 238 |
| Hf c/u | 371 | 428 | 421 | 361 | 416 | 406 |
| E | 152 | 178 | 179 | 151 | 167 | 169 |
| Sh ht | 749 | 857 | 843 | 724 | 714 | 816 |
| Mass | 31,2 | 41,6 | 31,1 | 26,5 | 35,4 | 31,9 |

**Skull** (Fig. 314.1)

The skull in springbok is typically bovid and there is sexual dimorphism, with those of males more heavily built.

The milk dentition is:

$i\frac{0}{3}\ c\frac{0}{1}\ p\frac{3}{3} = 28$

In springbok the milk incisors and canine are much smaller than their permanent successors and $p_1$ is phylogenetically lost and $p_2$ appears as a small, non-functional, peg-like tooth; $p_4$ is the main functional tooth before eruption of $M_1$ and $M_2$. The replacement pattern follows that of mammals from front to rear and $i_1$ is lost at 12 months and eruption of $I_2$, $I_3$ and C occurs between 13 and 17 months of age (Rautenbach, 1971b). The full adult dentition is attained at 22 months of age and consists of:

$I\frac{0}{3}\ C\frac{0}{1}\ P\frac{2}{2}\ M\frac{3}{3} = 28$

Fig. 314.1. Skull: male springbok, *A. marsupialis*
TL skull 250 mm

The horn primordium in the foetus differs from the surrounding epidermis in being thicker, with many more melanocytes (Findlay, 1989). The horns start to grow soon after birth, increasing rapidly after eight weeks, when they can be used to age males in the field. In females variation in horn length at different ages is large (Skinner *et al.*, 1971).

Springbok males have heavily ridged horns sloping slightly backwards, to diverge outwards and curve sharply inwards in a hook at their tips. The longest male horns on record measured 492 mm (Best & Best, 1977). In the females the horns are distinctly smaller, wider apart at the base, lightly ridged and much thinner than in the males (Fig. 314.1).

**Distribution**

Except for a narrow extension into southwestern Angola, springbok are confined in their distribution to within the limits of the Subregion. Within historical times they were almost exterminated in the Orange Free State and the Transvaal and, to a large extent, in the Cape Province, except in the north. However, they have been reintroduced widely to reserves and private game farms within their former range and introduced to others extralimital to this. In the Cape Province this process has taken place to the extent that it is almost impossible to draw a map showing the areas in which the populations occur naturally. With the possible exception of farms on the Botswana border, all springbok in the Cape Province are held within fenced areas. In the western parts of the Cape Province they probably never occurred south of about Van Rhynsdorp, although in the east they were found through to the coast in the Port Alfred sector. Within their present distributional range they are absent from mountainous areas and rocky hills.

*South of the Sahara, excluding the Southern African Subregion*

They are restricted in their occurrence to the coastal Namib Desert west of the escarpment in **Angola**, from the Cunene River north to about Benguela.

*Southern African Subregion*

They are widespread in **Namibia**, except in the north and northeast. They occur in the southern parts of **Botswana** and in the west, north to about 20 °S on the Namibian border, but nowhere today in the whole of the eastern sector. Their northern limits in Botswana coincide with the open semi-desert scrub from Lake Ngami eastward to the Makgadikgadi Pan. In the northern parts of their range they are today comparatively rare as compared with 10 years ago, especially in the eastern part of the Makgadikgadi Pan. The widespread reintroduction of springbok to all provinces of the Republic of South Africa makes it impossible to be certain of the limits of occurrence of naturally occurring populations.

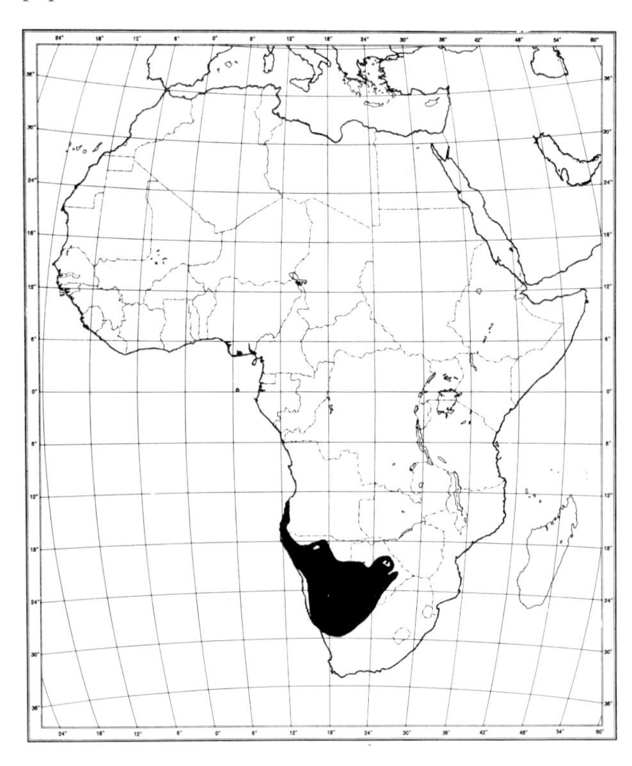

**Habitat**

Springbok are typically a species of arid regions and open grassland. In the southern parts of Botswana, in the semi-desert scrub association, they are partial to the wide, short grass fringes of pans, or to the pans themselves on fossil river beds and valley terrace where they have a short grass or karroid bush cover (Williamson, 1987). In the Kalahari Gemsbok National Park, Child, Parris & Le Riche (1971) showed that they have a preference for dry river beds and valley terrace rather than the adjacent dune scrub. Bigalke (1972) showed that where water is available they will drink. Child *et al.* (1971) found that temperature had a marked influence on drinking and that they could utilise highly mineralised water, unpalatable to most other species. They can exist without drinking water provided they can obtain sufficient moisture from succulent plants which they eat.

Springbok occur in areas where surface water is unavailable or only available seasonally and under these conditions satisfy their moisture requirements by browsing on succulent karroid vegetation, by digging for succulent roots or by eating fruits such as *Solanum* spp which have a high moisture content (Smithers, 1971). Greenwald (1967) compared the water economy of captive springbok with that of other species and found that they were able to survive indefinitely without drinking water while eating food containing 10% moisture. Factors which influence their choice of habitat include the availability of their preferred food plants, their mineral content and the height and the density of the vegetation, which control movement and affect visibility (Bigalke, 1972). Throughout their distributional range they avoid mountainous areas, rocky hills, thick woodland and areas of tall grass, favouring more open habitats.

**Habits**

Springbok are gregarious, moving in small herds during the dry months of the year from about April to October. In arid regions, where rainfall is sporadic and localised, the herds move to areas where rain has fallen in order to feed on the fresh, green vegetation, and then form aggregations which may number up to thousands of individuals of all ages and sexes.

The sporadic appearance of even larger aggregations, numbering hundreds of thousands, is documented by Skinner (in prep.). Until the end of the last century these "treks" continued on such a scale that Cronwright-Schreiner (1925) estimated that a swathe of country "over a hundred miles long by fifteen miles wide, was covered by the trekbokken moving in an unbroken mass, giving the veld a whitish tint, as if covered with a light fall of snow". Smaller mass movements have been recorded in recent times in unfenced areas in the South West Arid zone (Skinner, in prep.). The opening up of the northern Cape Province to farming, with the introduction of domestic stock and the fencing of huge tracts of country, put an end to "treks" in that province, and hunting pressures, together with rinderpest at the end of the last century, all contributed to reduction in numbers of springbok and cessation of treks.

The smaller winter herds, which can be studied more easily than the larger summer concentrations, consist of mixed herds of adults and juveniles of both sexes and bachelor herds (Bigalke, 1970). Territorial males are noticeable because of their solitary station and distance from one another (Skinner, unpubl.). Mixed herds consist of up to about 100 individuals, each herd with numbers of adult males usually associating on the periphery. With the onset of lambing, which may take place at any time throughout the year, these herds disrupt (Skinner, van Zyl & Oates, 1974). The females congregate with their lambs and the year-old males are driven out by territorial males. The bachelor herds consist largely of mature adult males but may include much younger males. Bigalke (1972) recorded that bachelor groups could be seen at any time of the year and numbered between two and 50 individuals, up to 300 being on record in the Kimberley area.

Males are territorial but may not remain permanently on their territories throughout the year, although they seldom leave them during the autumn in the Highveld (Novellie, 1975) or in the Kalahari Gemsbok National Park from December to September (Williamson, 1987). The peak in breeding activity varies, depending on the vagaries of the seasons. Territorial males defend a territory and will endeavour to retain the female herds in it by herding, but if the female herd as a whole moves off, they may allow it to do so. Herding is more intense during the rut. When herding, the male's head is stretched forward, the horns laid back and the tail held stiffly horizontal, lifted vertically or even curved forward. While being herded the females may "stot" with heads held high, other members of the herd following suit. Defence of the territory is by advertising and fighting. The territorial males take up conspicuous positions to show their presence to other rams and as an anti-predator mechanism. Territories are generally in open areas and are marked by conspicuous latrines. When crossing a territory to drink, other territorial rams will adopt a submissive posture towards the resident male or avoid his territory altogether (Jackson, pers. comm.). Solitary males have a unique urination-defecation ritual not used by the immatures, but also sometimes by bachelors. Spreading the legs far back and widely spaced, with the belly close to the ground, they urinate, then bring the legs forward and squat to defecate on the same spot (Novellie, 1975). This is considered to be a display of territorial behaviour (Estes, 1967) and may be preceded by pawing of the ground and concluded by tail wagging.

Although springbok have preorbital glands, there is no evidence to show that these are used in marking. Horn sweeping tends to make the territorial males more conspicuous, but though predominant, is not confined to territorial males and is also observed in bachelor males and females (Jackson, pers. comm.). This is directed at low bushes, the horns often being stained green with the herbage. Springbok groom themselves frequently, rubbing parts of their bodies with the sides of the muzzle, nibbling with the incisor teeth and rubbing with the horns. They will scratch themselves with their hind hooves, horns onto the back of the neck, and all of these actions contribute to their neat, clean appearance. Bigalke (1972) could find no evidence of mutual grooming.

The tail moves almost incessantly, flicking from side to side, especially when the individual is tense. When the springbok runs off, the tail is pressed close to the rump. Playful sparring is indulged in by young males. Adult females show aggression to other females, to juveniles or to males by lowering their horns and making stabbing movements. Fighting among adult males consists of horn interlocking and side to side wrestling. Horn stabs occasionally cause deaths but generally one or other of the opponents desists before either is seriously hurt; there is also sparring in bachelor herds which can become quite aggressive (Jackson, pers. comm.).

Springbok have two periods in which they are particularly active, one in the early morning, the other in the late afternoon (Davies & Skinner, 1986a), but this may vary with some activity at midday depending on climatic conditions. They also exhibit some activity after dark, during which time territorial males may move off their territories to higher ground, possibly to avoid excessive cooling as they are cold and not heat stressed animals. They also browse during this time (Jackson, pers. comm.). Solitary males will rest lying in the open, the herds often seeking the shade of low bushes, but they do not appear to require shade to the same extent as other species (Hofmeyr, 1981; Williamson, 1987). Hofmeyr (1981) has shown that by orientating their bodies with the long axis towards the sun, springbok, theoretically, may reduce radiation and hence heat load, by up to 62%. In addition the unusually thin pelage has a high conductance, thought to be an adaptation to facilitate heat loss during and after sprinting (Hofmeyr & Louw, 1987).

Normally they move slowly but can quickly break into a fast trot. Proud trotting is a springy, high stepping trot which is usually accompanied by head-tossing. Speeds of up to 88 km/h at the gallop, with the ears folded back, have been recorded by Bigalke (1972). When suddenly alarmed they perform gigantic leaps which may carry them 2 m off the ground and forward for a considerable distance. A herd alarmed by a shot may react in this way, the individuals leaping in all directions until they settle down to move away, first at a gallop, then settling down to a trot.

While stotting is a spectacular action it is not unique to springbok, being recorded in other species as well, including oribi, *Ourebia ourebi*. It comes into play when individuals are under stress or being chased. The back is arched, the legs held stiffly downwards, the dorsal fan of white hair fully erected as the individual leaps off the ground. It descends to the ground with all four legs landing simultaneously, and then shoots up into the air again, repeating the behaviour several times. The head is usually held low during stotting but may be held in the normal standing position or with the chin slightly raised. During stotting full exposure is given to the white dorsal fan which may act as a signal to other members of the herd.

Springbok are very vocal at certain times of the year. Several authors have commented on the sounds they make (Bigalke, 1972; Novellie, 1975; David, 1978). They emit a variety of sounds, the most common of which are loud grunting bellows. Small lambs will bleat and dams respond with a low pitched bellow. When alarmed they may emit a high-pitched whistling snort. On green veld following rain, rams become very vocal on their territories, emitting low-pitched, grunt-like bellows while rounding up ewes or chasing off intruders. This is also evident in the Kalahari Gemsbok National Park in winter (Skinner, unpubl.) In general, however, communication is by sight, and up-and-down movement of the head, or even by the simple means of taking up a conspicuous position. Scent is of little importance except during flehmen (Jackson, pers. comm.).

**Food**

Springbok have been characterised on morphophysiological grounds to belong to the intermediate group of feeders (Hofmann & Stewart, 1972), with a tendency to become concentrate selectors when forage is optimal (Hofmann, unpubl.). In the Kimberley district their food during the winter months from about June to August consists of the shoots and leaves of karroid shrubs and the leaves of several shrubs and trees. Grasses appear to be of little importance as they are low in crude protein and energy value at this time of the year. During the summer months from about October to March sprouting green grasses and herbs are utilised predominantly (Bigalke, 1972). Liversidge (1970) listed 33 plant species eaten, noting that they ate a variety of grasses in the early summer months of August to December. Near Campbell the species of grasses eaten included bristle grass, *Aristida congesta; Enneapogon brachystachyus* and six species of *Eragrostis*. Liversidge (1970) also found that grasses predominated in rumen samples from October to March, dicotyledons from June to August. Bigalke (1972) analysed the rumen contents of individuals from three farms in the Kimberley district and found that the karroid shrubs *Pentzia incana* and *P. tenuifolia*, *P. globosa*, *P. lanata*, the shrub *Rhus ciliata*, and *Acacia tortilis* were important food plants. In the western Transvaal, van Zyl (1965) listed 68 species of plants that were eaten, of which he accounted 20 to be the main food plants, nine of them grasses and 11 shrubs. Among important species of grasses he listed red grass, *Themeda triandra*; couch grass, *Cynodon* spp; buffalo grass, *Panicum* spp; love grass, *Eragrostis* spp, and *Sporobolus* spp. In the Kalahari Gemsbok National Park, Leistner (1967) listed 57 species eaten, including grasses, shrubs and ephemerals. He found that the grasses *Stipagrostis obtusa* and Kalahari sand-quick, *Schmidtia kalahariensis*, the shrubs *Monechma australe* and *Rhigozum trichotomum*, and the legume, *Cullen (=Psoralea) obtusifolia*, appeared to be preferred foods and another 14 species of shrubs and ephemerals were eaten frequently. Springbok also dig up roots and and tubers in the Kalahari Gemsbok National Park, all of which have a moisture content exceeding 62% in the dry season: *Acanthosicyos naudinianus*, *Brachystelma* sp., *Cucumella cinerea* and *Talinum tenuissimum* (Williamson, 1987).

In Botswana, Smithers (1971) recorded stomachs containing the leaves of camel thorn, *Acacia erioloba*; shepherd's tree, *Boscia albitrunca*; rhigozum, *Rhigozum trichotomum*; ganna, *Salsola* spp; *Zygophyllum* sp; raisin bush, *Grewia* spp; the leaves and pods of *Acacia detinens*; the fruit and leaves of buffalo thorn, *Ziziphus mucronata*; green and dry leaves of mopane, *Colophospermum mopane*, and the fruits of the snake berry, *Solanum* sp.

Davies, Botha & Skinner (1986), in a comparison, found that Karoo shrubs were preferred by springbok and lignified grasses by merino sheep. The diet of adult rams and ewes differed. Rams selected more palatable shrubs, especially *Salsola* spp and more *Eriocephalus ericoides*. Ewes selected more *Delosperma* sp, *Plinthus karooicus* and significantly more *Eberlanzia spinosa*. These dietary differences between the sexes are considered a consequence of springbok social organisation. Ewes are free to wander anywhere and favoured the rand vegetation. Rams were either territorial and selected plants abundant in the less-favoured pan vegetation or were bachelors and forced into sub-optimal habitat.

Davies & Skinner (1986b) showed that, in the Karoo where they were sympatric with merino sheep, springbok showed a better spatial utilisation of the vegetation, being at all times more dispersed than the sheep which were largely dependent on the proximity of food to watering sites which led to clustering and over-exploitation of the vegetation. Moreover springbok rams and ewes utilised different habitats and different plants. The larger body size of rams and the larger fermentation vats in their digestive systems permit them to utilise poorer (more fibrous) food than females and young.

Springbok will use mineral licks but to a much lesser extent than other species, possibly because of the higher mineral content of their diet (Leistner, 1967). Where fresh water is available in the Kalahari Gemsbok National Park, springbok drink 2,63 ± 0,45 l/individual every second day (Dreyer, 1987).

**Reproduction**

Springbok do not have a restricted breeding season (Skinner & van Jaarsveld, 1987). Territorial males are more tolerant of intruders than is the case for some other species and, even during the peak of the breeding season, were observed in company with bachelor herds (Novellie, 1975). Mating appears to be confined almost exclusively to the territorial males. When courting, the males usually approach the females at a walk, but they may also trot towards them with their heads held high and ears vertical. The trot has a bouncy appearance and may be accompanied by head tossing, and is referred to by Bigalke (1972) as the "proud" trot. Leg-tapping ("Laufschlage"), a courting action which precedes copulation, proceeds without the male's leg touching the female, and is reduced to a lateral side to side movement of the front leg. Territorial males vocalise loudly with grunting bellows. They may also take up conspicuous positions on open ground. The oestrous cycle is 16 days and under conditions of good nutrition there is a postpartum oestrus at 9–15 days (Liversidge & de Jager, 1984). Males test the reproductive status of females which are in their territory by vulva or urine-sniffing, followed by flehmen in which a male lifts his head into a horizontal position and, having turned it to one side, draws the upper lip upwards and breathes in through the open mouth. Flehmen is sometimes performed by females after sniffing another female's urine (Novellie, 1975).

Skinner & van Zyl (1970) showed that springbok rams are fertile throughout the year, the great bulk of the lamb crop being born during the summer in the summer rainfall areas (van Zyl & Skinner, 1970) and in July in the winter rainfall areas (Scully, 1898; Skinner, Nel & Millar, 1977) when ample green food is available. The gestation period is 25 weeks and the mean mass at birth 4,01 kg (n=13) (Skinner, unpubl.; van Zyl & Skinner, 1970; Liversidge & de Jager, 1984). The females eat the afterbirth (Skinner, unpubl.) and hide their lambs in tall grass or underbush where they remain for a day or two. During this period they lie tightly and can be captured by hand. Thereafter they quickly gain mobility and if disturbed will race off. At two weeks old the young lambs begin to nibble on plants and by six weeks graze for lengthy periods. At about three to four weeks old they are running strongly with the herd. Females with young lambs tend to form nursery herds, the young remaining together resting while the females graze in the vicinity. Lambs are weaned at about 120 days under good conditions (Liversidge & de Jager, 1984). While the young females remain with the herds, the young males may be evicted from about six months of age and join the bachelor herds.

Ewes are physiologically capable and, if conditions are favourable, may conceive at the age of about six months (Skinner & van Zyl, 1970; Liversidge & de Jager, 1984). On the other hand, rams only produce sperm from the age of one year (Skinner & van Zyl, 1970) and probably would be capable of mating only after 18 months of age when they are more fully developed. Indeed, Crowe & Liversidge (1977) provided indirect evidence for this with their hypothesis that differential mortality among rams results from the demands of gaining and maintaining a territory from the age of 19 months. In addition, Liversidge & de Jager (1984) observed a hand-reared ram to mate for the first time at 24 months.

The females usually have one pair of inguinal mammae, but individuals with two pairs are known (Bigalke, 1958).

## Tribe Neotragini

These are small antelope. The males only have short, spike-like horns, usually ridged basally (except in the klipspringer, *Oreotragus oreotragus*, in which both sexes are horned). Preorbital glands are present, but they have no inguinal glands (except in the oribi, *Ourebia ourebi*). The females have two pairs of mammae. Most members have pedal glands (except the klipspringer, *O. oreotragus*).

Key to the genera (Ansell, 1972)

1. No pedal glands; coat of peculiar bristly texture; hooves truncated, the animal walking on the extreme tips ... *Oreotragus*

   Pedal glands present; coat and hooves normal, not as described above ... 2

2. Nasals shortened and premaxilla elongated; muffle small and hairy above ... *Madoqua*

   Nasals not so shortened and premaxilla not so elongated; muffle large, with bare area above, extending back nearly to the hind angle of the nostrils ... 3

3. Inguinal glands present; a bare patch below the ear; a knee tuft present on each front leg ... *Ourebia*

   No inguinal glands; no bare patch below the ear; no knee tufts ... 4

4. Pedal glands opening into interdigital space by a long cleft; surface of preorbital glands invaginated; horns at an angle to the facial plane ... *Raphicerus*

   Pedal glands opening into interdigital space by a small circular orifice; surface or preorbital gland not invaginated; horns more or less in line with facial plane ... *Neotragus*

## Genus *Oreotragus* A. Smith, 1834

No. 315

### *Oreotragus oreotragus* (Zimmermann, 1783))

### Klipspringer
### Klipspringer

Plate 33

**Colloquial Name**

The English name is borrowed from the Afrikaans and is fully descriptive of the rocky habitat with which they are associated and the agility with which they are able to jump from rock to rock and bound up the sides of steep rock faces.

## Taxonomic Notes

Ansell (1972) listed 11 subspecies from the continent of which four occur in the Subregion. First described from a specimen from the Cape peninsula, *O. o. oreotragus* occurs in the Cape Province and as far east as about the Orange Free State; *O. o. transvaalensis* is found in the Transvaal and Natal and possibly in southern Mozambique; *O. o. tyleri* in Angola and Namibia; and *O. o. stevensoni* in Zimbabwe and Botswana. The limits within which these subspecies occur, remain uncertain.

## Description

Klipspringer are small antelope standing about 0,6 m at the shoulder; adult males have a mass of about 10 kg; the females are larger with a mass of 13 kg (Table 315.1). Distinctive pithy stiff hairs have an unusual appearance in cross-section, with a narrow soft cortex and a regular mosaic scale pattern along the width (Fig. XLII.1) (Keogh, 1983).

Their colour varies, depending on the area from which they originate. In the southwestern Cape Province, in *O. o. oreotragus*, the colour of the coat is yellow, speckled with brown; in those from the Transvaal, *O. o. transvaalensis*, it is a bright golden-yellow, and in those from western Zimbabwe, *O. o. stevensoni*, it is greyer and duller.

In the individuals from the Transvaal, *O. o. transvaalensis*, the bright golden-yellow on the upper parts is grizzled with black, caused by the dark bands on the individual hairs. The flanks lack this grizzling and are a bright rusty colour, especially on and just behind the shoulders. The under parts are white. Their short, stumpy tails are the same colour as the upper parts, tending to be lighter underneath. The forehead and top of the head is darker than the back, the sides of the face lighter in colour.

The general colour of the coat is imparted to it by the colour of the tips of the spiny guard hairs, or the penultimate band of colour on these hairs. The individual hairs on the back are light-coloured at the base, darkening towards the brown, yellow or golden-yellow tips; some of the hairs have narrow black tips. The hairs are hollow, flattened and spiny, a unique feature among southern African antelope. The adax also has flattened hairs, shaped rather like a cricket bat. This enables a greater amount of radiant heat to be reflected. They are springy in texture and adhere very loosely to the skin.

In days gone by this hair was prized as a stuffing for saddles. It ranges in length from 15–28 mm and forms a thick coat which insulates their bodies from extremes of heat and cold, in the former case aiding the conservation of body moisture, protecting them from heat loss, and reflecting much of the heat from their surroundings during the heat of the day.

Klipspringer walk on the tips of their hooves which are cylindrical-oval in shape, with a long, narrow sole and blunt tips, an adaptation to their life among rocks (Fig. 315.1). On soft ground the spoor shows as paired rounded depressions (Plate III).

Fig. 315.1. Hoof: klipspringer, *O. oreotragus*.

They have preorbital glands which open to the surface in a naked, black, forwardly sloping slit in front of the eyes. Pocock (1910) could not detect any sign of pedal glands. It may be that the way klipspringer walk, on the tips of the hooves, would render pedal glands ineffective.

The ears are covered sparsely with black hair at the back, with a white patch about midway up their inner edges. The insides are profusely covered with long white hair. The lower parts of the limbs are whitish, with a black band just above the hooves, which extends a short distance up the front of the forelimbs and to the ankle joint on the hind limbs. The false hooves on the forelimbs are much better developed than those on the hind.

**Table 315.1**

Measurements (mm) and mass (kg) of adult klipspringer, *O. oreotragus*, from Zimbabwe and Botswana (Smithers, unpubl.)

| | Males | | | Females | | |
|---|---|---|---|---|---|---|
| | $\bar{x}$ | n | Range | $\bar{x}$ | n | Range |
| TL | 862 | 13 | 820–920 | 905 | 10 | 883–1000 |
| T | 76 | 13 | 65–90 | 84 | 10 | 65–103 |
| Hf c/u | 223 | 13 | 215–230 | 224 | 10 | 215–240 |
| E | 93 | 13 | 87–100 | 92 | 10 | 85–99 |
| Mass | 10,6 | 13 | 9,1–11,6 | 13,2 | 10 | 10,5–15,9 |

In the Subregion only the males carry horns. In *O. o. schillingsi* of Tanzania both sexes have horns. These are widely spaced on top of the head and rise vertically upwards with a slight forward curve and are ringed for about a third of their length from the base; the tips are smooth. The world record pair of horns came from the eastern Transvaal and measured 159 mm (Best & Best, 1977).

## Distribution

Within their wide distributional range from the Cape Province to East Africa, klipspringer distribution is patchy and discontinuous on account of their specialised habitat requirements. There is a lack of information from Nigeria to the Sudan where they probably occur in suitable habitat in the Guinea and Sudan savanna zones. Norton (1980) stated that, in the sheep farming areas of the central Karoo, klipspringer at one time occurred in reasonable numbers, but have been largely wiped out by hunters.

*South of the Sahara, excluding the Southern African Subregion*

They were considered so rare in **Nigeria** in 1965 that they may not occur there now, and they are not recorded eastwards over a distance of some 3 000 km (Happold, *in litt.*), only reoccurring in the southern **Sudan**. They occur in the highlands of **Ethiopia** and in the mountain chain in northern **Somalia**. They occur in northern and northeastern **Uganda** and in the extreme southwestern parts of the country. They are confined to western **Kenya** and are widespread in **Tanzania**, except in the southeast. In **Zaire** they are confined to the western parts of the Rift Valley, in the east of the country, and in the extreme southeast. They are widespread in **Zambia**, except in the southwest and parts of the northwest, and in **Malawi**. They occur throughout **Mozambique**, north of the Zambezi River, except coastally. In **Angola** they are confined to the southwest, excluding the coastal desert.

*Southern African Subregion*

They are confined to the mountainous escarpment and broken plateau regions of central **Namibia**. In **Botswana** they occur only in the eastern sector. They are widespread in **Zimbabwe** and in **Mozambique**, south of the Zambezi River, they are confined to the western areas. In the **Transvaal** they occur in the west, north and east of the province, southwards into **Swaziland** where they occur in the Malolotja Nature Reserve in the west, as well as south of Manzini, and in the Lubombo Mountains. In **Natal** they occur in the Umfolozi Game Reserve and in parts of the Lebombo range of hills and in the Drakensberg over about 2 400 m, from the Giant's Castle Game Reserve to the Royal Natal National Park. In the **Orange Free State** they are confined to a restricted area in the central and eastern parts of the province. In the **Cape**

**Province** they occur in the west and northwest, along the valley of the Orange River to about 23 °E and coastally in the south.

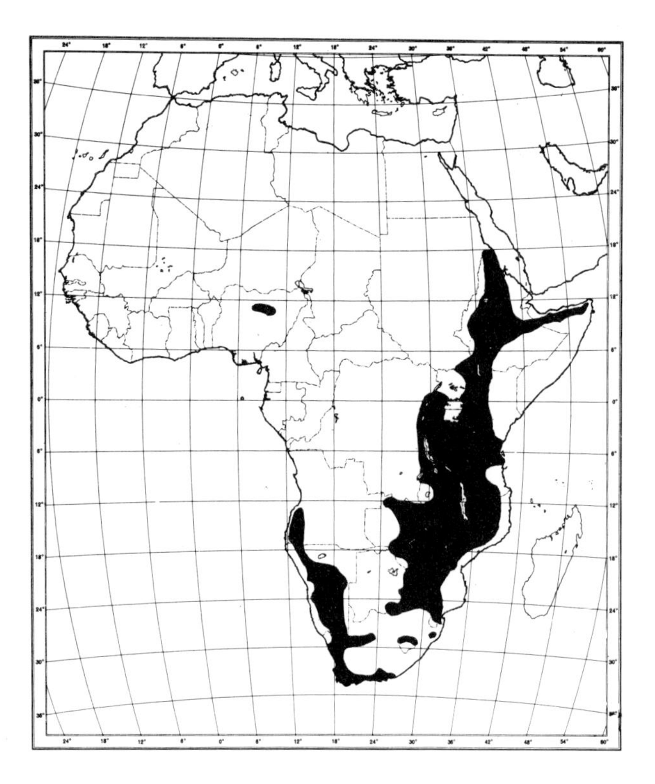

### Habitat

Klipspringer are closely confined to a rocky habitat. Mountainous areas with krantzes, rocky hills or outcrops, extensive areas of rocky koppies, or gorges with rocky sides provide suitable habitat. As this type of terrain is patchy and discontinuous, so is their occurrence.

They are capable of moving over long distances between rocky areas and often are found on isolated koppies in flat country 10 km apart (Vaughan-Kirby, 1899; Shortridge, 1934; Niethammer, 1942; Wilson & Child, 1965).

### Habits

Klipspringer are found most commonly in pairs, as solitary individuals or in small family groups of a male, female and her offspring. Although up to six may be found congregated at a preferred feeding site, these are loose, temporary associations and if they are disturbed, they split up. Wilson & Child (1965) noted that in eastern Zambia of 168 sightings of klipspringer, 74 were of two, 66 of one, 16 of three, 10 of four, with single sightings of groups of five and six, and in southern Namibia, Tilson & Norton (1981) recorded a mean group size of 2,6 (n=265).

Klipspringer are adept at bouncing up steep rock faces or leaping from rock to rock with agility. Quite often they may be seen standing motionless on a rock pinnacle scanning the scene, with their four hooves together in a characteristic klipspringer pose. They will leave their rocky habitat to browse or graze on the surrounding flatter ground, occasionally even at night, but if disturbed, their first reaction is to make for rocky shelter. They are active in the early morning, but more so in the late afternoon from about 16h00 until dusk, resting up in the shade during the hotter hours of the day. In cool weather they are active throughout the day. The individuals of a pair may lie up close to each other. They have a curious habit of hiding themselves from observers behind a rock, looking around it, with only their heads showing, as they watch their approach.

Klipspringer are territorial, an adult male establishing and defending an area which Norton (1980) noted varied in size according to the mean annual rainfall. In Ethiopia, Dunbar & Dunbar (1974) found that in an area with a mean annual rainfall of 1 300 mm, the area was 8 ha. In the Karoo where the mean annual rainfall is 400 mm, the area was 15 ha, and in the northwestern Cape Province where it is 160 mm, the area was 49 ha (Norton, 1980). Food availability is probably the predetermining factor.

Aggressive defence of the territory, by both male and female, is uncommon. Usually the male chases trespassers out of his territory and no fighting takes place. Norton (1980) recorded an instance of two males actively fighting while a female looked on. The loser was gored so badly that he retired to the bush exhausted and seriously wounded.

Dung heaps are scattered throughout the territory on flat ground, with a tendency to establish them on the border. Apparently they are used over long periods, for in eastern Botswana they measured up to 900 mm in diameter, the droppings 100 mm deep in the centre (Smithers, 1971).

The territories are defended by visual displays by the dominant male, by scent-marking and by the creation of dung heaps (Norton, 1980). In visual displays the dominant male advertises his presence by standing in conspicuous places and by horning of bushes or low branches, warning trespassers off. Scent-marking may be carried out by either partner, but if the female scent-marks, the male usually follows her and overmarks. This is carried out by selecting a bare twig of a small bush which is inserted into the open preorbital gland situated in front of the eye. This leaves a 4 mm to 6 mm smear of black, tarry, glandular exudation on the twig. Norton (1980) found that the frequency of this type of scent-marking was twice that of dung-marking and believed that it has an important role in the maintenance of the pair bond. Scent-marking is carried out usually after a resting period, before commencement of activity, and is associated with defecating which takes place at this time.

Rechav *et al.* (1978), working in the Matobo Hills, Zimbabwe, found that the tick, *Ixodes neitzi*, locates its mammalian host by its attraction to the preorbital exudate. By using a gustatory sense the ticks respond to the preorbital exudate washed down the twigs on to the ground, climb up them and remain on the top of the twigs, awaiting the return of the klipspringer to remark the twig, when they gain access to them. The ticks complete their life cycle on the red rock rabbit, *Pronolagus randensis*.

Klipspringers are subject to predation by leopards (Grobler & Wilson, 1972), spotted hyaenas, caracals, baboons, black eagles, *Aquila verreauxi*, and martial eagles, *Polemaetus bellicosus*, and lambs by black-backed jackals (Tilson, 1977). When predators are spotted at a distance, klipspringers "freeze" and watch. If the predator closes in, either sex including subadults will give a loud alarm call, which Tilson (1977) described as a high-pitched and very loud forceful exhalation of air which can be heard up to 0,7 km. The male and female may duet, the female calling immediately after the male (Tilson, 1977). The duet alarm call is loud, repetitive and highly directional and has the function of communicating their alertness to the predator, more than warning conspecifics. Together with other responses it acts as a pursuit deterrent, the klipspringer at the same time keeping the source of danger in view, while remaining conspicuous. Klipspringers can outrun and outmanoeuvre predators in their rocky habitat and have been observed to turn away once the duetting call is given (Tilson & Norton, 1981).

### Food

All recent evidence shows that klipspringers are predominantly browsers (Wilson & Child, 1965; Smithers, 1971; Qvorttrup & Blankenship, 1974), grass forming only a small proportion of the food. Under certain circumstances they will eat grass (Dunbar & Dunbar, 1974); in other circumstances even when fresh green grass is freely available, they will not touch it (Wilson & Child, 1965). They have very little capacity to digest cellulose in their rumen and like all concentrate selectors have a relatively large caecum or distal fermentation chamber (Hofmann, pers. comm.).

In a sample of 74 stomach contents, collected in a tsetse fly control programme in Zambia, Wilson & Child (1965) showed that 90% of contents of all stomachs was browse, consisting of leaves, berries, fruit, seed pods and flowers.They found a seasonal preference for various types of food, some food plants such as *Euphorbia tirucalli* and *Vellozia equisetifolia* showing signs of marked over-utilisation. Among the browse plants eaten they listed the leaves of *Brachystegia* sp; the horn-pod, *Diplorhynchus mossambicensis*; kudu berry, *Pseudolachnostylis maprouneifolia*; false marula, *Lannea edulis*; large sour plum, *Ximenia caffra*; *Dolichos malosanus*; velvet bushwillow, *Combretum molle*; *Aloe chabaudii*; the rubber hedge euphorbia, *E. tirucalli*, and *V. equisetifolia*. The berries of the kudu berry, *P. maprouneifolia*, the fruits of the large sour plum, *X. caffra*, and the pods and flowers of the sickle bush, *Dichrostachys cinerea*, were recognised in the sample.

In Zimbabwe, Smithers & Wilson (1979) included a number of items listed by Wilson & Child (1965) for Zambia and, in addition, the fruit and leaves of the buffalo thorn, *Ziziphus mucronata*; the berries of the raisin bush, *Grewia* sp; the leaves and fine twigs of the knob thorn, *Acacia nigrescens*; *Acacia* spp flowers; *Aloe chabaudii* flowers, and the fruits of the jackal berry, *Diospyros mespiliformis*. Klipspringers are independent of water and are found in areas where it is available only seasonally. However, they will drink when it is available and do so from temporary pools held in depressions in the rocks or from water holes on streams in the immediate vicinity of their rocky habitat.

Norton (1980) found that there was a marked increase in the time taken in feeding during the cold, dry months of the year as opposed to warm, wet summer months. He found that they fed unselectively on a wide range of plant species. In one of his study areas they were observed to feed on 41 species of shrubs and herbs, in the other, 62 species. As with the other feeding records quoted, the flowers, fruits, young shoots and leaves were all eaten. They tended to move when feeding, taking a bite here and there, but would settle where a plant was flowering or carrying palatable fruits, spending a long time pulling these off, but leaving the other vegetative parts. They would stand on their hind legs to enable them to reach items of food to a height of 1,2 m.

Norton (1980) recorded osteophagia and geophagia from termitaria.

### Reproduction

Lambs may be born at any time throughout the year. In the northeastern parts of the Subregion pregnant females were taken from June to February, in Zambia, from all months, excepting December and January (Wilson & Child, 1965). Norton (1980) concluded that klipspringer breeding seasons are variable, depending on local conditions.

The foetus is invariably implanted in the right hand horn of the uterus. The gestation period is given by Kenneth & Ritchie (1953) as 214 days, by Cuneo (1965) as seven to seven and a half months. Norton (1980) questioned the length of these periods and from observations on a captive individual believed that it might be 150 days.

A single young with a mass of just over a kilogram is produced at a birth (Wilson & Child, 1965). They are born in the shelter of rocks or in thick vegetation in the rocky habitat. The young remain hidden for the first two to three months of their lives. At least during the very early part of their lives, the young, if approached, lay their heads flat on the ground, with their ears flat and make no attempt to move off. Their cryptic coloration makes them very difficult to see when lying up in shelter. The young are weaned at about four to five months of age, (Norton, 1980).

Norton noted that horn growth started at about four months. The horns protruded above the hair at five and a half to six months, after which they grew rapidly up to 12 months and reached adult size at about 17 to 18 months. His study showed that horn length was useful in identifying young males of 12 to 18 months old, that had already reached adult body size, but was unreliable thereafter.

Females have two pairs of inguinal mammae.

# Genus *Madoqua* Ogilby, 1837

No. 316

## *Madoqua kirkii* (Günther, 1880)

## Damara dik-dik

## Damara dik-dik

Plate 33

### Colloquial Name

Drake-Brockman (1910) suggested that the origin of the name dik-dik stems from the rapidly uttered, sharp, whistling call, *ghuss-ghuss*, as they bound away when disturbed.

### Taxonomic Notes

Four other species of dik-dik occur on the continent: Swayne's, *M. swaynei* Thomas, 1894; Phillips', *M. phillipsi* Thomas, 1894; and Günther's, *M. guentheri* Thomas, 1894, all from the Somali Arid Zone, and Salt's, *M. saltiana* (Desmarest, 1819) from the Sudanese Arid Zone.

*M. kirkii* occurs in East Africa, where it is represented by six subspecies, and in the Subregion and southwestern Angola it is represented by one subspecies, *M. k. damarensis* (Günther, 1880).

### Description

Damara dik-dik are a small species, standing about 400 mm at the shoulder, with a mass of about 5 kg (Table 316.1).

Individual hairs have a colour variation which is distinctive amongst bovids: dumb-bell-shape or concavo-convex in cross-section, grooved, with two or three scales across the width, giving an irregular wavy appearance (Fig. XLII.1) (Keogh, 1983).

The upper parts of the body are yellowish-grey in colour, the hairs with subterminal whitish or pale yellow annulations and dark tips, which impart to the whole of the upper parts a grizzled appearance. The hair on the upper parts, at the level of the shoulders, is about 25 mm in length; on the rump it is about 30 mm. The hair on the face, the crown of the head and around the ears is a pale rusty colour, paler on the sides of the neck but richer on the shoulders and flanks. The hind parts of the thighs are lighter in colour than the flanks; the chest and belly and inside of the thighs are pure white. The ears are rusty-yellow behind with dark fringes, the insides pale yellowish-white. The hair on the forehead is up to 45 mm long, ginger or orange-brown and lies adpressed to the head, except when the individual is alarmed or during courtship, when it is erected to form a distinct crest. The eyes are ringed with white hair. The large prominent preorbital glands lie in front of the eyes and are used in scent-marking (see **Habits**). Among the characteristic features of the Damara dik-dik is the elongated, proboscis-like, mobile snout, which can be extended in any direction in seeking food. There is no external rhinarium as in other antelope, the nostrils being plain openings which cannot be closed, as they can in species such as the springbok, *Antidorcas marsupialis*.

The hooves have well developed black rubbery pads at the back which lie in contact with the ground. These act as shock absorbers as the feet strike the hard ground which is a feature of the terrain in which they live.

While it is known that two of the East African dik-diks, *M. phillipsi* and *M. saltiana*, have pedal glands, which open through narrow cylindrical tubes between the hooves, the Damara dik-dik lacks these. They have in their place small invaginated folds of skin on the fore and hind feet, with tufts of hair about 15 mm in length, but no underlying glands.

Spoor—Plate III.

**Table 316.1**

Measurements (mm) and mass (kg) of a series of Damara dik-dik, *M. kirkii*, from Namibia (Shortridge, 1934; Tinley, 1969a)

| | Irrespective of sex | | |
|---|---|---|---|
| | $\bar{x}$ | n | Range |
| TL | 635 | 14 | 580–690 |
| T | 46 | 14 | 32–56 |
| Hf c/u | 202 | 14 | 188–216 |
| E | 82 | 14 | 78–86 |
| Mass | 5,1 | 4 | 4,6–5,5 |

Only the males carry the spike-like horns which are stout at the base and are ridged and longitudinally grooved. They arise from just behind and above the eye orbits and lie backwards, only slightly elevated above the line of the face. They diverge and curve slightly forward towards the tips. The longest pair on record measures 101,6 mm (Best & Best, 1977), whose provenance is unknown. The great majority of the larger trophies come from the Namib Desert, southwestern Angola.

## Distribution

The species *M. kirkii* occurs in two discrete areas on the continent separated by some 2 000 km. This division of what at one time must have been a continuous distribution has been brought about by climatic changes which took place during the Pleistocene Epoch, resulting in the intervening terrain experiencing a slightly wetter climate with consequent vegetational changes rendering it unsuitable for the species.

Within these two areas of occurrence they are discontinuously distributed on account of their specialised habitat requirements. Within the limits shown on the map, therefore, they only occur where there is suitable habitat, which in parts occurs only in scattered patches.

*South of the Sahara, excluding the Southern African Subregion*

In **Namibia** they occur from Kaokoland southwards to Brukkaros Mountain (25°50′S) in the central hilly parts of the country; in the north they occur as far east as the Grootfontein district. In the northwest they penetrate into the coastal Namib Desert down watercourses with associated thickets.

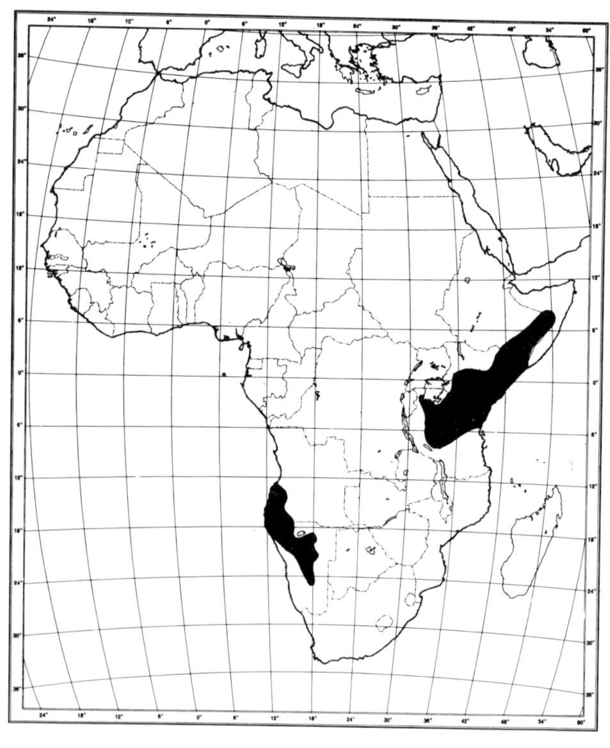

## Habitat

The typical habitat of the Damara dik-dik is dense woodland and thicket on stony or hard clay ground with a well developed shrub understorey, but with little or no grass (Tinley, 1969a). They avoid rocky outcrops, but occur in close association with these around their fringes. They are also found on hillsides and in riverine thickets which act as avenues of suitable habitat, carrying them deep into otherwise desert or semi-desert country. Where the substrate is stony and calcareous and there is suitable vegetation they occur in flat country.

In northern Namibia they occur in woodland with a canopy of 8 m to 14 m and an undershrub layer of up to 2 m. This woodland and thicket association is dominated by tambotie, *Spirostachys africana*; purple pod terminalia, *Terminalia prunioides*; red umbrella thorn, *Acacia reficiens*; weeping wattle, *Peltophorum africanum* and in parts mopane, *Colophospermum mopane*. The undershrub layer differs in various localities, but includes shrubs such as lavender croton, *Croton subgratissimus*; various species of raisin bush, *Grewia* spp; sickle bush, *Dichrostachys cinerea* and white berry bush, *Securinega virosa*.

The riverine woodland is dominated by various species of thorn trees, *Acacia* spp; leadwood, *Combretum imberbe*; buffalo thorn, *Ziziphus mucronata* and in parts mopane, *C. mopane*, with an understorey of mustard tree, *Salvadora persica*; tamarisk, *Tamarix usneoides*; ebony tree, *Euclea pseudebenus*; torchwood, *Balanites welwitschii* and tangles of *S. persica* which are much sought after by Damara dik-dik (Tinley, 1969a). Along the Cunene River the riverine association includes extensive areas of fan palms, *Hyphaene* sp.

Throughout the range of the species in the Subregion they are confined to areas with a mean annual rainfall of between 75 and 500 mm, in the lower rainfall areas normally confined to riverine associations. Suitable habitat in northeastern Namibia occurs in a higher rainfall zone unsuited to dik-dik.

During the middle of the rainy season, which extends from about December to April, Tinley (1969a) recorded that they exhibit local movements, in evasive response from areas with a heavy growth of grass, to areas where the substrate is more open.

## Habits

Damara dik-dik occur singly, in pairs or in family parties of three. During the dry season between the months of April to August small groups of up to six may be seen together. So far their social structure has not been studied in depth, but it is possible that the males may establish territories during the mating season.

They are a shy species and, when suddenly disturbed, give vent to a single explosive whistle as they run for cover to the deepest part of the thicket. Shortridge (1934) said that "even when running (for cover) the shadows cast are more conspicuous than the animals themselves as they vanish like wisps of smoke". In reaction to sudden fright they may also bound away stiff-legged, stotting, with their legs tucked up under their bodies and at each contact with the ground giving a short explosive whistle. They vocalise in communication with a high-pitched, quavering whistle made with the nostrils extended downwards (Tinley, 1969a).

They may spend as much as 51% of their time inactive during the day (Kamau, 1988), standing or lying down in thick shady cover ruminating, often in situations overlooking open glades. They are active at sunrise, in the late afternoon and at dusk, with some activity after dark. This behaviour, together with their ability to allow body temperature to rise to 44°C during the day, losing it at night, and their thin, elongated legs, allow dik-dik to gain and lose heat rapidly in changing environmental temperatures (Kamau, 1988).

**Plate 33**

314. Springbok, *Antidorcas marsupialis*
 Springbok
315. Klipspringer, *Oreotragus oreotragus*
 Klipspringer
316. Damara dik-dik, *Madoqua kirkii*
 Damara dik-dik
317. Oribi, *Ourebia ourebi*
 Oorbietjie

PLATE 33
314
315
316
317
Dick Findlay.

Communal dung heaps are a feature of the home ranges of Damara dik-dik, their use of these following a distinct pattern. A male approaches the heap, smells the dung and then walks on the heap and proceeds to paw the dung into a heap with the forefeet. He then urinates on this and may dig again before defecating. Females do not dig in the dung. Neither sex covers its dung as do some other species such as steenbok, *Raphicerus campestris*. After the use of the heap both sexes walk to the nearest grass clump or to shrubs and deftly insert tips of grass or twigs into their preorbital glands, often choosing those that have been previously marked in this way. This leaves a black tarry secretion, which may build up into blobs by constant marking by a series of individuals (Tinley, 1969a). The act of digging in the heap applies scent to the feet which scent marks their trail.

Damara dik-dik are preyed upon by leopards, *Panthera pardus*, and caracals, *Felis caracal* (Tinley, 1969a).

### Food

Dik-dik are extreme concentrate selectors. Due to their small body size they must feed on plant parts with a high nutrient content (Hofmann, 1973; Hoppe, 1984). Grasses are only eaten when sprouting and highly nutritious, but even then form a very small proportion of their diet. They pick up a lot of nutritious litter, like seed pods, from the ground. Hoppe *et al.* (1983) found that Damara dik-dik fed selectively on dicotyledon leaves and fruits which were rich sources of cell contents, this food source being fermented rapidly in the reticulorumen, but that cellulytic activity was low. As they eat and ruminate frequently throughout the day the reticulorumen is supplied continuously with food, fermentation being a continuous process, and the unfermented cell wall components are passed out quickly. Tinley (1969a) provided a list of 28 species of browse plants and four grasses eaten during the rainy season in the Etosha National Park, Namibia, and a further list of 22 species of browse eaten during the dry winter season from May to October. The browse includes the stems, twigs, shoots, leaves, flowers and fruits of plants and includes items of fresh litter, including fruits, of wild fig, *Ficus petersii*; bird plum, *Berchemia discolor*; and mustard tree, *Salvadora persica*, which they eat during the wet season. The stems and leaves, flowers and fruits of 11 species of herbs are eaten during this season, none during the dry season. The leaves, shoots and twigs of various thorn trees, *Acacia* spp, are eaten throughout the year, as well as those of the sickle bush, *Dichrostachys cinerea*, and tambotie, *Spirostachys africana*, which, with spike thorn, *Maytenus* sp, the leaves of the purple pod terminalia, *Terminalia prunioides*, and the tambotie, *S. africana*, rank as the chief dry season foods. Browse eaten during the wet season includes the worm cure albizia, *Albizia anthelmintica*; white berry bush, *Securinega virosa*; bitter karee, *Rhus marlothii*; and buffalo thorn, *Ziziphus mucronata*; and during the dry season the shepherd's tree, *Boscia albitrunca* and *B. foetida*; lavender croton, *Croton subgratissimus*; raisin bush, *Grewia* spp; mustard tree, *S. persica*, and purple pod terminalia, *T. prunioides*.

When feeding dik-dik tend to have an active period, followed by rest. These periods alternate during the day and, although the main periods of activity are during the morning and late afternoon, individuals may be seen feeding even during the heat of the day. The long proboscis-like snout is extended to test and search for the preferred foods. Where browse is out of reach they will stand on their hind legs to reach it, balancing themselves with their forelegs against the shrub stems or bending the thinner twigs down (Tinley, 1969a). Most of the feeding is done on the ecotones of thicket and glade where food is plentiful. When feeding in more open areas they tend to keep to the thicket fringes where they are difficult to see. Food is made available to them by elephant, rhinoceros, kudu and giraffe breaking down the browse plants, thus providing ground litter which they utilise. Wind and rain also make palatable litter available to them.

While they are independent of drinking water, they will drink from puddles when it is available.

### Reproduction

There is little information available on this facet of the life history of the Damara dik-dik. In the Etosha National Park, Tinley (1969a) recorded a juvenile about a month old seen in February and a female with a foetus in the same month. Courtship was also observed at this time. The males court the females by approaching them in a stiff-legged walk, the head held low with the nose pointed forward and the crest on the forehead fully erected. The females, if receptive, react to this in a crouching, supplicatory pose (Tinley, 1969a). Tinley's (1969a) observations suggest that, in the Subregion, the young are born during the rainy season from about December to April. It certainly would be to the advantage of the species if the young were born at about this time of the year as food would then be most plentiful for the nursing mothers.

Kellas (1955) gave the gestation period as six months, one young being produced at a birth. The young remain with their mothers until her next offspring is born. The females have two pairs of inguinal mammae.

## Genus *Ourebia* Laurillard, 1841

No. 317

## *Ourebia ourebi* (Zimmermann, 1783)

## Oribi
## Oorbietjie

Plate 33

### Colloquial Name

Almost certainly derived from the Khoikhoi name *orabi*.

### Taxonomic Notes

Thirteen subspecies were listed by Ansell (1972) as occurring on the continent, of which three are found in the Subregion. Originally *O. o. ourebi* was described from a specimen purported to have been taken at the "Cape of Good Hope". As they never occurred so far west, Roberts (1951) fixed the type locality as the Uitenhage district which was the nearest to the Cape where they are known to occur. The subspecies *O. o. ourebi* occurs throughout the southern part of the species' distributional range; *O. o. hastata* (Peters, 1852) in eastern and southeastern Zimbabwe and northern Mozambique, and *O. o. rutila* Blaine, 1922, in northeastern Botswana, northwestern Zimbabwe and northeastern Namibia.

### Description

Oribi are small antelope, adult males standing about 0,6 m at the shoulder, with a mass of about 14,0 kg. The females are slightly larger and heavier than the males (Table 317.1). The body hairs are 25,2±2,6 mm long, deeply concavo-convex, with a large medulla in cross-section; the hair is guttered with an overall pattern of regular waved mosaic scales becoming irregular towards the tip; the scale margins are smooth (Fig. XLII.1) (Keogh, 1983). The colour of the upper parts of the body is a yellowish-rufous, contrasting with the pure white of the under parts which extends upwards over the rump to the base of the tail and high on to the front of the chest. The coat is fine and silky and inclined to curliness on the back. There is a marked difference between the summer coat, which is shorter and smoother, and the winter coat, which tends to be thicker and more shaggy.

The face is distinctly and characteristically marked with two white blazes, one on either side of the nostrils, and they have distinct white crescent-shaped bands above the eyes which extend slightly forward on to the face. Another characteristic feature of the species and one which, together with the white markings on the face, distinguishes them from steenbok, *Raphicerus campestris*, is the tail which is black and bushy on the upper surface, white on the under and stands out clearly against the white rump. On the other hand, the tail of the steenbok is the same colour as the upper parts and their white face markings are never as distinct as those of the oribi. Only male oribi have horns, which rise straight up from the top of the head, curve slightly forwards and often diverge slightly towards the tips. Unlike the steenbok these are strongly ridged towards the bases, those of the steenbok being smooth. The longest horns on record are from Zomba, Malawi and measured 190,5 mm (Best & Best, 1977).

In most individuals there is a patch of black or brown hair between the base of the horns extending narrowly on to the forehead. The ears are noticeably large, narrow and pointed and there is a small circular patch of hairless skin just below them on the sides of the head. Pocock (1910) stated that the thin skin in this region is devoid of glands. Oribi do have preorbital glands situated close to the inner corners of the eyes, pedal glands between the hooves of all four feet, and inguinal glands covered with a mat of fine white hair in the groins. The inguinal glands secrete a powdery material that smells like "cold cream" (Pocock, 1918b). Oribi have tufts of hair on their forelegs just below the knees which overlie an area of thickened skin, which is not glandular.

Spoor—Plate III.

**Table 317.1**

Measurements (mm) and mass (kg) of oribi, *O. ourebi*, from the southeastern Transvaal (Viljoen, 1982)

| | Males | | | Females | | |
|---|---|---|---|---|---|---|
| | $\bar{x}$ | n | Range | $\bar{x}$ | n | Range |
| TL | 1023 | 13 | 970–1150 | 1028 | 12 | 890–1095 |
| Hf c/u | 294 | 13 | 260–316 | 290 | 12 | 265–31 |
| E | 225 | 13 | 178–255 | 225 | 12 | 185–250 |
| Sh.ht | 578 | 13 | 510–635 | 591 | 12 | 510–635 |
| Ht hq. | 578 | 13 | 510–635 | 591 | 12 | 510–635 |
| Mass | 14,0 | 12 | 10,5–17,4 | 14,2 | 12 | 7,5–17,0 |

## Distribution

Oribi have a wide distribution on the continent from Senegal to Ethiopia and south to the Cape Province. South of the equator their distribution is patchy and discontinuous, due in part to their specialised habitat requirements, although there are areas where they are not found which appear suitable for them. Found to be on the decline in some areas, they remain locally common in others.

*South of the Sahara, excluding the Southern African Subregion*

They occur in the Guinea savanna and Sudan Zone from **Senegal** to western **Ethiopia**; in the northern and southwestern parts of **Uganda**; in southwestern and southeastern **Kenya** and in southern **Somalia** in the vicinity of the Juba and Uebi Scebeli river systems. In **Tanzania** they occur throughout the western and northwestern parts of the country, with an isolated population in the extreme southeast. In **Zambia** they occur widely except in parts of the northeastern sector. There are records from the extreme southern parts of **Zaire** and they occur in central, southern and southeastern **Angola**. In **Malawi** they are restricted to National Parks and Game Reserves in the Central and Southern Provinces.

*Southern African Subregion*

They occur in the extreme northeastern parts of **Namibia** and in northern **Botswana**. They occur in **Zimbabwe** and in the Gazuma Pan National Park in the northwest and from northern Mashonaland in a narrow sector southeastwards to the Mozambique border. In **Mozambique**, south of the Zambezi River, they are found in the central sector south to the vicinity of the Save River and in the northern parts of the Gaza District. In **Swaziland** they occur in the Ndzindza Nature Reserve. In the **Transvaal** they occur in the northeast and in the grasslands in the southern part of the province. In the **Orange Free State** there are visual records from the south and northeast of the country. In **Natal** they occur in the northwest, in parts of the central and in the southern parts of the province, with an extension into the extreme eastern parts of the **Cape Province**. The most southern limits of distribution are in the Division of Dias, Bathurst District, where they occur between the Kariega and Fish rivers, where in 1984 the total population numbered 238 individuals (Bezuidenhout, pers. comm.).

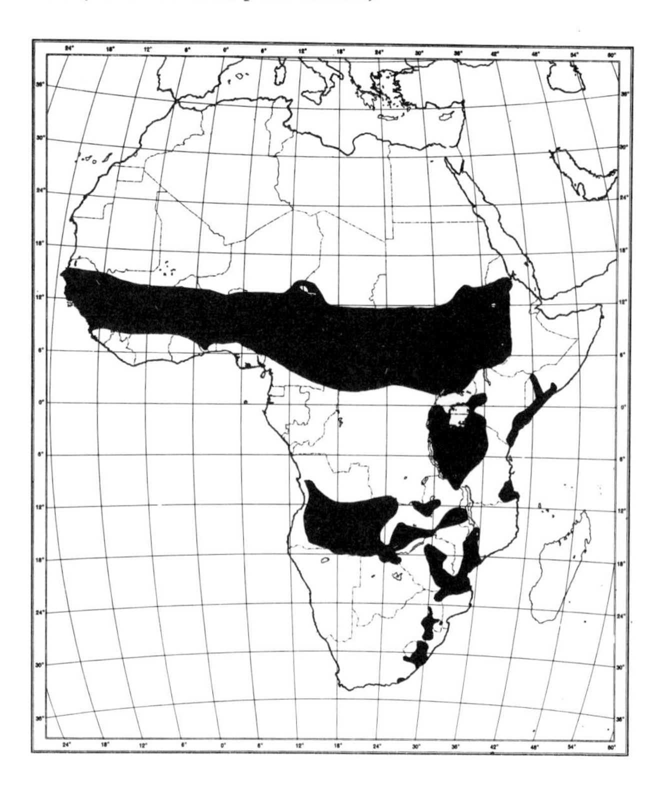

## Habitat

Oribi prefer an open habitat. They occur on open grassland or flood-plain, with or without a sparse scattering of trees and bushes, or in the more extensive grassed vleis that are a feature of parts of their distributional range. Within these habitat types they do not occur where there is a dense cover of tall grass, preferring the areas where the grass is short and at the same time affords some cover in parts in the form of isolated stands of grass up to about 300 to 400 mm in height, in which they take cover during resting periods (Viljoen, 1982). When resting, they tend to choose slightly raised ground, perhaps to improve their field of vision as they lie up with heads erect. From these vantage points they can detect the approach of predators or other dangers quickly. Cropping and trampling of tall grass by cattle opens up the habitat and renders it suitable for oribi; with the removal of cattle and the subsequent heavier growth of grass, oribi numbers may decline (Horsfield, pers. comm.). Oribi also prefer burnt areas and Shackleton & Walker (1985) suggested that any management policy to increase numbers should take cognizance of this as it will increase the forage preferred by oribi. Oribi are not found in forest or in arid areas. In the eastern Transvaal escarpment the preferred grassland is areas where *Themeda triandra* and *Rendlia altera* are dominant (Shackleton & Walker, 1985). In parts of their range, as for example in southwestern Zimbabwe and the Magaliesberg foothills in the Transvaal, they are associated with stony ground. Afforestation of their prime habitat and hunting with dogs by local inhabitants has caused their distribution to shrink and numbers to decline (Viljoen, 1982).

## Habits

Most often oribi are encountered solitarily, in pairs or a male and one or two females and their offspring. These parties on occasion join up temporarily to form small groups of up to a dozen (Ansell, 1960a). Viljoen (1982) recorded group sizes of 1,84 (1–6) and 1,72 (1–5) in two areas in the southeastern Transvaal. Reilly (1987) noted that in the Golden Gate Highlands National Park, to which they were introduced, the group size never exceeded four, with a mean of 2,5. Tait (1969) stated that, in the Transvaal, the family parties have seasonally demarcated home ranges in which they remain until the food supply becomes exhausted, when they move to a better area. The adult males are territorial, marking territories by glandular secretions and advertising their presence. Oribi mark grass stems with their preorbital glands, leaving a small amount of black secretion on them (Gosling, 1972). Males show a distinct attachment to their territories, at least during the rut. Viljoen (1982) recorded that in over 86% of cases when a female urinated and defecated, the male smelled the spot, marked a grass stem with the preorbital glands, over-marked the spot and scratched on it. Oribi create communal dung heaps in open areas such as on pathways. These have no territorial function and the males only make use of them if they happen to be in the vicinity (Viljoen, 1982).

If suddenly disturbed they will give the snorting whistle alarm call as they bound off, stotting with a rocking-horse motion. If this happens in tall grass they will bound up now and then as they run, holding their heads erect, enabling them to scan the surrounding ground. They are, however, very inquisitive and often, after running for a couple of hundred metres, will stop and gaze back at the source of disturbance.

In Natal, Oliver, Short & Hanks (1978) found that the size of the home range of the adult males averaged about 0,05 $km^2$. In the southeastern Transvaal, Viljoen (1982) found that the mean size of a territory was 0,034 $km^2$. In more suitable habitat densities of 4,56 and 2,68 oribi/$km^2$ have been found, but these decline to 1,5/$km^2$ under less favourable conditions (Oliver *et al.*, 1978; Shackleton & Walker, 1985).

**Food**

Based on morphological features of their digestive system, Hofmann (1973) suggested they were the first African antelope to become entirely a grazer, forbs forming a minor part of their diet. In the eastern Transvaal, Viljoen (1980) listed eight species of grasses identified as being eaten by oribi, among which four were utilised and appeared to be preferred species throughout the year. These were *Eulalia villosa;* red grass, *Themeda triandra;* oat grass, *Monocymbium ceresiiforme*, and thatch grass, *Hyparrhenia hirta*. The other four species were generally less used during the winter months: grey beard grass, *Trachypogon spicatus; Tristachya hispida;* red-top brachiaria, *Brachiaria serrata*, and broad-leaved blue grass, *Diheteropogon amplectens*. Shackleton & Walker (1985) considered that, a little further north in the Mount Sheba Nature Reserve, on the escarpment, *T. triandra* and *Panicum natalense* were the preferred species of grass. Reilly (1987) found that in the Golden Gate Highlands National Park they showed a preference for the grasses *Sporobolus centrifigus* and *T. triandra* and would dig for the corms of *Watsonia* sp.. Oliver *et al.* (1978) found, in Natal, that oribi show a high preference for sprouting grass in burnt areas. Mortality among oribi is more pronounced during the months of July to October in Natal (Oliver *et al.*, 1978), for the decline in the crude protein content of the food during the winter months leads to a lowering of their condition, rendering them prone to the effects of climatic stress and disease.

Even when drinking water is available they do not drink (Viljoen, 1982), obtaining moisture from succulent herbage such as *Eulalia villosa*.

**Reproduction**

Oribi are seasonal breeders; Skinner (unpubl.) reported mating in May in the Eastern Transvaal, the main lambing season falling during the warm wet summer months from October to December, with occasional records later in the year (Oliver *et al.*, 1978; Viljoen, 1982; Thompson, 1973). The gestation period is 210 days (Kenneth & Ritchie, 1953; Viljoen, 1982). A single young at a birth is the invariable rule. The females hide their offspring in clumps of grass when they move off to feed, returning to suckle them from time to time. If approached in the early stages the young lower their heads flat on the ground and remain motionless. Viljoen (1982) noted that the young remain hidden for periods of up to three to four months, after which they join the family group. Females have two pairs of inguinal mammae.

## Genus *Raphicerus* H. Smith, 1827

No. 318

### *Raphicerus campestris* (Thunberg, 1811)

### Steenbok
### Steenbok

Plate 34

**Colloquial Name**

The English name is borrowed from the Afrikaans *steen*, a brick, referring to the overall colour of the species. Steinbok has been used, which is unfortunate as it is the German name for the ibex, *Capra ibex*.

**Taxonomic Notes**

Ansell (1972) listed eight subspecies, of which Meester *et al.* (1986) listed five for the Subregion. Ansell (1972) added that a study of adequate series would probably lead to a reduction in the number of these. Whatever may be the resolution of the issue, there are obviously wide areas of intergradation of the presently named subspecies and a revision is overdue.

**Description**

Steenbok are small, graceful antelopes with long slender legs and slim bodies. They stand about 0,52 m at the shoulder. The males have a mass of about 11 kg, the females slightly heavier at 11,3 kg (Table 318.1).

Body hairs are 29,97±5,9 mm long, oblong, concavo-convex or dumb-bell-shape in cross-section, with large regular mosaic scales at the base petal becoming longer and broad at the tip; scale margins are smooth (Fig. XLII.1) (Keogh, 1983). The colour varies throughout their distributional range and is an even rufous-brown, rufous-fawn or reddish on the upper parts, sometimes with a distinct silvery sheen. The under parts are pure white or off-white. The top of the tail is the same colour as the upper parts and is white underneath. The muzzle is pointed, the forehead darker and more richly rufous-coloured than the upper parts, with a dark "Y" shaped marking on the forehead between the horns. However, the muzzle markings are not present on all individuals.

The ears are outstandingly large and coloured on the back like the upper parts or with a slightly darker tinge. They have black fringes on the centre parts of the ears.

Steenbok can be confused very easily with oribi, *Ourebia ourebi*, in the field, as they are very similarly coloured. Oribi, however, have longer necks, are taller at the shoulder and characteristically the tops of their tails are black. This shows distinctly in the field and is the best character in distinguishing them from steenbok.

Steenbok, like Sharpe's grysbok, *Raphicerus sharpei*, lack the false hooves found in the grysbok, *R. melanotis*. The hooves are narrow and sharp-pointed, features which show in the spoor (Plate III).

**Table 318.1**

Measurements (mm) and mass (kg) of steenbok, *Raphicerus campestris*, from Botswana (Smithers, 1971)

| | Males | | | Females | | |
|---|---|---|---|---|---|---|
| | $\bar{x}$ | n | Range | $\bar{x}$ | n | Range |
| TL | 843 | 38 | 773–910 | 856 | 39 | 790–920 |
| Hf c/u | 273 | 39 | 253–290 | 271 | 38 | 250–287 |
| E | 114 | 37 | 101–125 | 113 | 38 | 100–126 |
| Mass | 10,9 | 37 | 8,94–13,17 | 11,29 | 39 | 9,65–13,17 |

Only the males have the widely spaced horns which grow vertically and nearly parallel with a slight forward curve towards the tips. There are, however, exceptions to this and horned females turn up from time to time. The horns are indistinctly ringed towards their bases but are otherwise smooth and rise to sharp points. The world's record horns originate from the Cape Province and have a length of 190,5 mm (Best & Best, 1977).

### Distribution

Steenbok occur on the continent in two discrete areas, one in East Africa, the other in the Subregion, with extensions of distribution into Angola and Zambia. These are separated today by about 1 000 km. It is likely that, at some period during the Pleistocene Epoch, when climatic conditions were drier than they are today, their distribution would have been continuous from East to South Africa. Within the distributional ranges shown on the map they occur only where there is suitable habitat.

*South of the Sahara, excluding the Southern African Subregion*

Formerly more widespread in **Kenya**, they are now absent from the densely settled areas in the west, being confined to the southern and eastern sectors, nearly as far as the Somalia border. However, they are not recorded in Somalia. Southwards they occur widely in **Tanzania**, excluding the west and south. Between Tanzania and western **Zambia**, where they occur only in the southwest, there is a break in their distributional range. Westwards they occur in **Angola** south of about 12 °S, excluding the coastal desert.

*Southern African Subregion*

They are distributed widely in **Namibia**, where they narrowly penetrate the coastal Namib Desert down avenues of dry watercourses. They are widespread in **Botswana**. In **Zimbabwe** they are absent from the Zambezi Valley east of Binga, the northeast and parts of the southeast, occurring only on the plateau eastwards to the Mozambique border and extending into **Mozambique** in the northern Vila Pery District to Mocassa. Apart from this record, in Mozambique they are confined to the southern parts of the country from the Save River southwards. In the Republic of South Africa they are widespread in the **Cape Province**, except in parts of the Eastern Province, and they occur throughout the **Orange Free State, Transvaal** and in the central and northern parts of **Natal**.

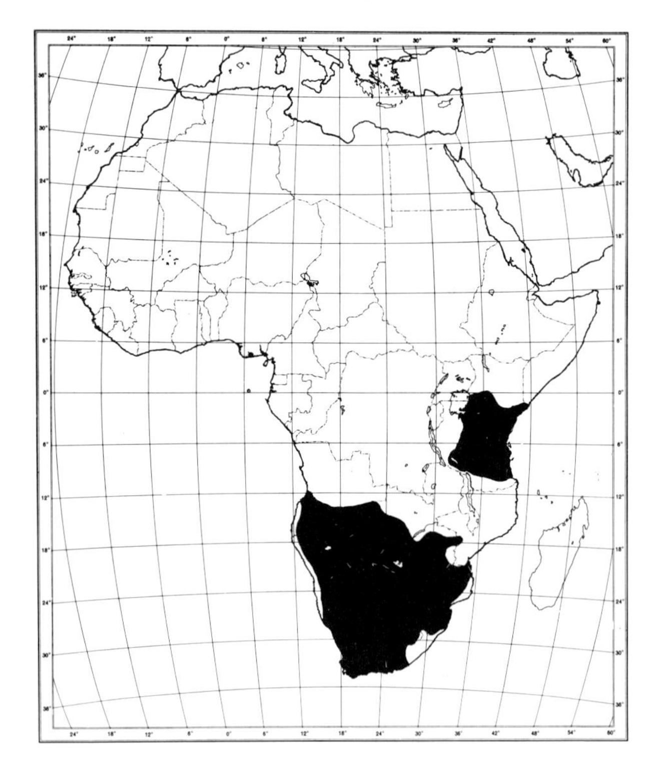

### Habitat

The steenbok is a species which inhabits open country and they do not occur in forest or thick woodland, or on rocky hills or mountains. They are absent from desert, although in Namibia they penetrate into the coastal Namib Desert down dry watercourses to which, under these circumstances, they are confined.

Although specifically associated with open grassland, this must provide some cover in the form of stands of tall grass, scattered bushes or scrub and the forbs which are an important part of their diet. They generally avoid the wide open, short grassed plains which do not provide them with cover, although they will utilise these marginally where there is adjacent cover of scrub or woodland. They are also found in open woodland and on clearings in woodland including airstrips, fire breaks and cultivated lands and are partial to the fringes of newly constructed roads where there is fresh sprouting vegetation. They select areas with a low-standing crop of grass, as a heavier grass crop obscures forbs, their favoured food plants and is a barrier to visability, rendering them vulnerable to predation. The upper canopy of woodland is not an important influence on their habitat requirements (Cohen, 1987).

### Habits

Steenbok lead solitary lives except when a female has a lamb or when she is in oestrus with an attendant male. They are generally diurnal, with peaks of activity during hot weather in the early morning and late evening, but during cool, overcast weather they may be active at any time during the day. They have some nocturnal activity, especially in areas where they are subject to disturbance.

They establish well defined but overlapping territories which both sexes will defend against trespassers. Each territory encompasses resting places, latrines and preferred feeding places. In the Kruger National Park territories are about 0,03 km$^2$ (Cohen, 1987) which provide for their requirements of cover and food, whereas in the Kuise valley in the Namib they were larger at 0,58 km$^2$ (Cloete, 1983). Defence of these territories, as in many other species, takes the form of demonstrations rather than actual combat. Juvenile trespassers usually move off on sighting adults. When fighting ensues between adults it does not result in physical damage.

Steenbok have preorbital glands which show as dark marks just in front of the eyes, pedal glands between the hooves on the front and back feet, and a throat gland, all of which no doubt are used in marking the territory. The latrines tend to be situated near the perimeter of the territories, acting as markers. When defecating or urinating steenbok clear a patch with their front hooves, defecate or urinate and then carefully cover it up by scraping soil over the spot with their front hooves.

Through thermoregulatory behaviour, association with shady trees like *Acacia albida* and *Savadora persica*, and selection of succulent plant parts they are largely independent of drinking water in the Namib Desert (Cloete & Kok, 1986). In Botswana they were recorded as avid diggers for succulent bulbs, roots and rhizomes as food and to provide for their moisture requirements.

During the hottest part of the day they lie up in the cover of tall grass or scrub, tending to use specific small areas within the territory for this purpose. In these they lie tightly, only flushing when closely approached. When alarmed, they will lie down often in the grass with their ears flattened

**Plate III Spoor**

311. Blue duiker, *Philantomba monticola*
312. Red duiker, *Cephalophus natalensis*
313. Common duiker, *Sylvicapra grimmia*
314. Springbok, *Antidorcas marsupialis*
315. Klipspringer, *Oreotragus oreotragus*
316. Damara dik-dik, *Madoqua kirkii*
317. Oribi, *Ourebia ourebi*
318. Steenbok, *Raphicerus campestris*
319. Grysbok, *Raphicerus melanotis*
320. Sharpe's grysbok, *Raphicerus sharpei*
321. Suni, *Neotragus moschatus*
322. Impala, *Aepyceros melampus*
324. Grey rhebok, *Pelea capreolus*

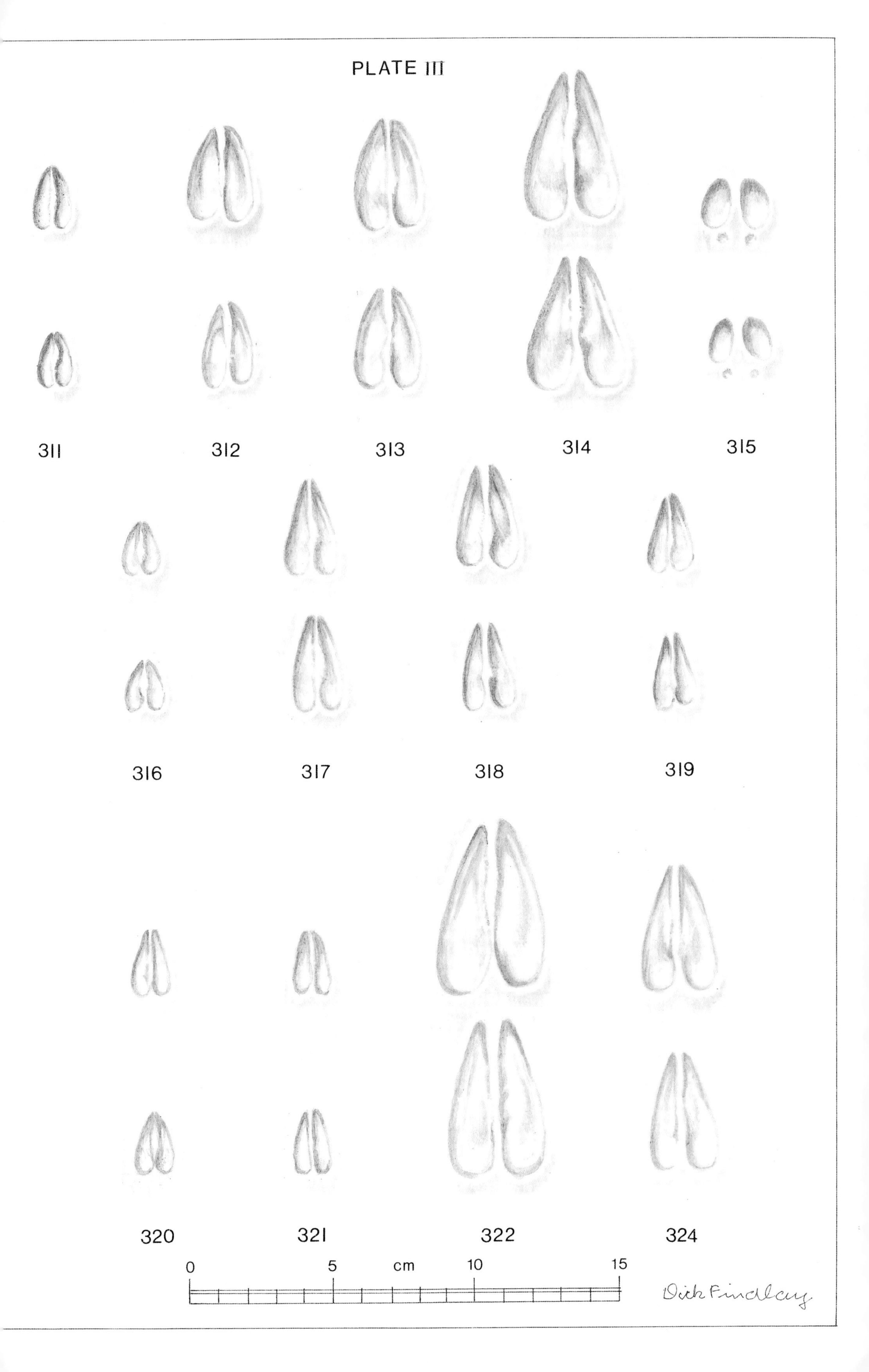
PLATE III
311
312
313
314
315
316
317
318
319
320
321
322
324
0
5
cm
10
15
Dick Findlay

against their heads and hide themselves, but when flushed they spring up and rush off, head thrust forward, to pause momentarily and glance back at the disturbance. They generally rely on their fleetness of foot to carry them out of danger.

Wilson & Kerr (1969) found in a sample of 102 gravid females that 67 foetuses were males and 35 females. However, in a sample of over 300 foetuses from KwaZulu, Mentis (1970) found a normal 1:1 ratio of males to females, indicating that an adequate sample size is essential, but local factors operative at specific times may influence the foetal sex ratio. In a sample of 4 600 adult steenbok in the Kruger National Park, Cohen (1987) found a sex ratio of 1,04 females per male.

Steenbok are resilient in the face of high hunting pressure and environmental changes brought about by development, as is shown by their wide distribution which has shown little change since historical times. They still occur right up to the fringes of rapidly developing towns and in intensively farmed areas.

They are preyed upon by most of the large and medium-sized mammalian predators, as well as the martial eagle, *Polemaetus bellicosus*. Young steenbok are particularly susceptible. Under severe stress and in the absence of other cover, they will hide in holes in the ground.

### Food

Steenbok are mixed feeders, preferring a richer diet of easily digestible forbs and grasses to which their stomachs are adapted, having a small rumenoreticulum and presumably a high fermentation rate (Hofmann, 1972). In a sample of 91 stomachs from Zimbabwe the proportions were 70% forbs and browse and 30% graze (Smithers, 1971). In the Kruger National Park, Cohen (1987) listed 227 species of plants utilised by steenbok, representing forbs (67%), trees and shrubs (19%), creepers and lianas (6%) and grasses (8%). He noted that they would take leaves, the tips of shoots, flowers, fruits and seed pods. He adjudged them selective and highly mobile feeders, choosing the most delicate components in the herb layer. They will dig for bulbs and make use of the remaining portions of bulbs and tubers left in the excavations made by porcupines. Huntley (1972), observing a male steenbok in captivity, found it to be a selective feeder which showed an extremely high preference for forbs.

### Reproduction

Steenbok lamb at any time of the year. Of 188 female specimens examined in southeast Zimbabwe, pregnant individuals were found in every month of the year, with indications of a peak in births about November/December, shortly after the onset of the rains. A similar trend was found in a sample of 188 specimens from Botswana, of which 70% were pregnant (Smithers, 1971). Bigalke (1963) had a captive female which mated at six or seven months of age and lambed at a year old. The gestation period is around 168 to 173 days or less (Hofmeyr & Skinner, 1969). Mass at birth is about 0,9 kg. A single young is born and twins are rare.

Usually lambs are dropped in the shelter of stands of tall grass, shrubs or among rocks, and concealed there while the mother feeds nearby (Robinson, 1977). Cohen (1987) found that in the Kruger National Park the lambs remain in concealment for up to three to four months. On the slightest disturbance the young lie flat in this shelter with their ears folded back and their heads on the ground and at this stage can be approached closely and in some cases handled. On the approach of the female for suckling and cleaning, the lamb will move out of concealment, the female finding it by visual means; sometimes the female gives a snort to which the lamb responds (Robinson, 1977). Prior to suckling nasal contact is made. Suckling proceeds over a mean period of seven minutes, 15 seconds. Suckling takes place with the female standing or lying down; in the latter position the lamb kneels. Females have two pairs of inguinal mammae.

No. 319

## *Raphicerus melanotis* (Thunberg, 1811)

## Grysbok
## Grysbok

Plate 34

### Colloquial Name

Although the general colour of the body is reddish-brown, there are numerous white hairs scattered through the pelage on the upper parts of the body along the back which give it a greyish tinge, hence the use of *grys* = grey in Afrikaans.

### Taxonomic Notes

No subspecies are recognised.

### Description

Grysbok are small antelope standing about 0,54 m at the shoulder and having a mass of about 10,0 kg (Table 319.1). They give the appearance of being higher at the hindquarters than at the forequarters.

The body hairs are 35,8±3,7 mm long, dumb-bell-shape or large oval or concavo-convex in cross-section; the cuticular scale pattern is regular waved mosaic towards the tip, with two to three scales across the width of the hair (Fig. XLII.1) (Keogh, 1983). The colour of the upper parts of the body is rufous-brown, liberally sprinkled with white hairs, giving a grizzled appearance to the pelage. Most of the face, neck, legs and flanks lack the white hairs and are yellow-brown which merges into a uniform buffy on the under side of the neck, under parts of the body and insides of the legs. The chin is brownish-yellow. They have large ears, buffy-white on the inside, greyish on the back. The tail is short and the same colour as the upper parts of the body.

This species has a pair of supplementary hooves above the fetlocks which are usually absent in its near relative, Sharpe's grysbok, *R. sharpei*.

Spoor—Plate III.

**Table 319.1**

Measurements (mm) and mass (kg) of grysbok, *R. melanotis* from the Cape Province (Stuart, *in litt.*)

| | Males | | | Females | | |
|---|---|---|---|---|---|---|
| | $\bar{x}$ | n | Range | $\bar{x}$ | n | Range |
| TL | 771 | 4 | 750–810 | 793 | 5 | 720–815 |
| T | 58 | 4 | 40–72 | 54 | 5 | 44–60 |
| Hf c/u | 245 | 4 | 240–250 | 248 | 5 | 235–265 |
| E | 113 | 4 | 105–115 | 115 | 5 | 110–120 |
| Mass | 10,0 | 4 | 10,0 | 10,5 | 5 | 8,8–11,4 |

Only the males have horns which rise nearly vertically from the head with a slight forward curve, and are inconspicuously ridged. The longest horns known measure 123,8 mm (Best & Best, 1977).

### Distribution

The grysbok is endemic to the southwestern and southern parts of the Cape Province.

*Southern African Subregion*

They occur from the Cedarberg Mountains in the southwestern **Cape Province** to the Vredenburg area and southwards and eastwards coastally as far as the Albany and Bathurst districts, with records from the Komga district on the border of Transkei. Although there is a visual record from the Lady Grey/Aliwal North district, this is a grassland area, a veld type not usually utilised by grysbok, and until material evidence is forthcoming, the record is not shown on the map.

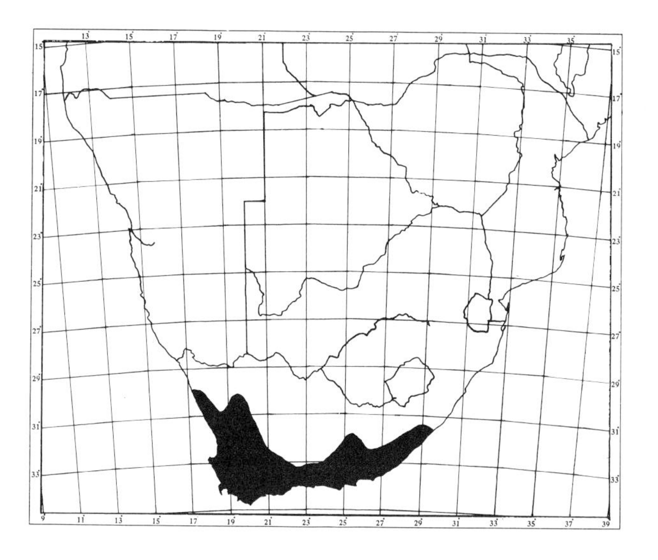

## Habitat

They are associated predominantly with thick scrub bush, particularly along the lower levels of hills. They also occur in the same type of habitat in broken country or in kloofs, in coastal forest or in dry succulent veld where there is cover of scrub bush. Providing there is adjacent dense cover their habitat is improved by agricultural developments such as the establishment of orchards and vineyards.

## Habits

They are relatively more active at night than during the day, and occur in groups of a female with her young or adult males and females together during the breeding season. Manson (1974) recorded that the males were territorial and had territories the size of which depended on the season and the type of habitat, and ranged from 0,013 to 0,094 $km^2$. Novellie, Manson & Bigalke (1984) found that the average home range of three males at Jonkershoek, Cape Province, was 0,025 $km^2$ and that of a female 0,011 $km^2$. The male's home range overlapped that of the female for only a brief period during the investigation. The home range of an adjacent juvenile overlapped that of the female but not that of the male. In captivity they noted that males were intolerant of other males, but the females tolerated other females. There was a clear dominance hierarchy among the females. In encounters, threat displays were poorly developed and direct attack of opponents the rule. Within the territory a dung heap, up to a metre in diameter and up to 100 mm deep, was used by all the members of the group and played an important role in the social organisation. Members used this dung heap in a ritual manner by sometimes first smelling, then performing a stereotype urination-defecation sequence on the heap. The males marked their territories by first smelling, then by applying their preorbital glands to tufts of grass or branches and also by nibbling twigs. Young males become territorial on reaching sexual maturity. When disturbed they run off with the head held low and make for the nearest thick cover.

## Food

They are predominantly browsers; grass is not important in their diet. Manson (1974) provided a lengthy list of plant species utilised in various areas in the southwestern Cape Province. In the Darling district in July *Euclea racemosa* and *Zygophyllum flexuosum* figured prominently, and in the Stellenbosch district, in addition to a list of 16 plant species, grapes figured prominently in November. He showed from a questionnaire to fruitgrowers that Cape grysbok were widely blamed for doing damage in orchards of apples, pears, plums and peaches and in vineyards. On the Cape Peninsula they damage vines by nibbling off the young shoots at night. Stuart (*in litt.*) noted the presence of the leaves of the Port Jackson wattle, *Acacia saligna*, in stomach contents. They are independent of a water supply.

## Reproduction

Females have their first lambs at an age of 17 to 26 months of age, the males becoming sexually mature at an age of 17 to 18 months. Females in oestrus raise their tails to the horizontal position. Most mounts by a male are unsuccessful, while he frequently utters bleating sounds, often just before mounting. After an ejaculatory thrust the male pays no further attention to the female. There is an autumn increase in the intensity of male courtship responses and an increase in preorbital marking by males in spring. The gestation period is not known but is not more than 192 days (Manson, 1974). Novellie *et al.* (1984) recorded that in captivity females gave birth to single lambs in most months of the year, with a peak in spring and early summer, from September to December. Under favourable conditions a female may have up to two lambs in the year. After a period of time the females become aggressive towards their offspring, evicting them. The females have two pairs of inguinal mammae.

---

No. 320

# *Raphicerus sharpei* (Thomas, 1897)

## Sharpe's grysbok
## Sharpe se grysbok

Plate 34

---

## Colloquial Name

This species was named after Sir Arthur Sharpe who first collected the specimen in southern Angoniland, Malawi from which the species was described. It is sometimes known in Afrikaans as the *tropiese grysbok* to distinguish it from the Cape grysbok, *R. melanotis.*

## Taxonomic Notes

Ansell (1972) recognised two subspecies, *R. r. sharpei* from the northern parts of the species' range, and *R. r. colonicus* Thomas & Schwann, 1906 from the southern parts. The limits of these subspecies and their validity are not clear. Haltenorth (1963) considered the Zambezi River below the Victoria Falls as the boundary. Meester, Davis & Coetzee (1964) regarded *colonicus* as a synonym of *sharpei.*

## Description

Sharpe's grysbok is slightly smaller than the Cape grysbok, *R. melanotis*, standing about 450–500 mm at the shoulder and having a mass of about 7,5 kg. The females are slightly larger than the males (Table 320.1).

The body hairs are 29,6±8,3 mm long, concavo-convex in cross-section, guttered, with a regular mosaic cuticular scale pattern. Scale margins are smooth but rippled at the tips, with two or three scales across the width (Fig. XLII.1) (Keogh, 1983). The colour of the body is a rich reddish-brown. The upper parts, shoulders and flanks are sprinkled liberally with white hairs. The general colour of the upper parts of the body is distinctly redder than in the Cape grysbok, *R. melanotis.* The sides of the face and outer parts of the limbs, the forehead and upper parts of the muzzle are yellowish-brown, lacking the whitish grizzling seen on the upper parts of the body, although in some individuals there may be a few scattered white hairs on the forehead. They have a short, dark band on top of the muzzle which extends from the rhinarium, tapers posteriorly, and disappears about the level of the front of the eyes. The sides of the muzzle between the eyes and the rhinarium are whitish and there is a whitish ring around the eyes. The under parts of the body, the under side of the neck and insides of the legs are buffy-white. The ears are shorter than those of the steenbok, *R. campestris*, with buffy-white hair inside and dark on the outside, where they are covered very sparsely with yellowish-red hair.

The hair on the upper parts of the body is fairly long and does not lie as smoothly on the body as does the shorter hair of the steenbok, *R. campestris*. Sharpe's grysbok lacks the false hooves present on the hind legs of its near relative, the Cape grysbok, *R. melanotis*.

They have preorbital glands which show as small areas of black naked skin, about 2 mm in diameter, pitted to about 3 mm deep (Ansell, 1964c), not "a large area of naked skin" as is seen in the steenbok, *R. campestris*, or the Cape grysbok, *R. melanotis* (Pocock, 1910, 1918). They have as well a preputial gland, the orifice of which lies anterior to the opening of the urethral canal. The pedal glands, which they have on both front and hind feet, open into the interdigital cleft which is well covered with hair. In the Cape grysbok, *R. melanotis*, the interdigital cleft is very sparsely haired (Ansell, 1964c).

Spoor—Plate III.

**Table 320.1**

Measurements (mm) and mass (kg) of Sharpe's grysbok, *R. sharpei*, from southeastern Zimbabwe (Smithers & Wilson, 1979)

| | Males | | | Females | | |
|---|---|---|---|---|---|---|
| | $\bar{x}$ | n | Range | $\bar{x}$ | n | Range |
| TL | 751 | 12 | 710–800 | 757 | 11 | 725–800 |
| T | 58 | 12 | 50–70 | 59 | 11 | 45–70 |
| Hf c/u | 201 | 12 | 195–220 | 204 | 11 | 193–210 |
| E | 90 | 12 | 83–98 | 91 | 11 | 85–98 |
| Mass | 7,3 | 12 | 6,8–8,9 | 7,7 | 11 | 6,4–8,9 |

Only the males carry the short horns which rise from the top of the head above the eyes, slope slightly backward and from their broad round bases taper abruptly to sharp points. The world record length is 104,8 mm. The longest horns recorded from the Subregion are 63,5 mm for a pair from southern Zimbabwe (Best & Best, 1977).

## Distribution

*South of the Sahara, excluding the Southern African Subregion*

The farthest north they have been recorded on the continent is the Kahama district of **Tanzania**, which lies about 160 km south of Lake Victoria. They also occur south of this in the central parts of the country, in the west to the southern end of Lake Tanzania and in the east to the Rovuma River, the border with Mozambique. They are recorded from southeastern **Zaire**; widely throughout **Zambia**, except west of the Zambezi River; in **Malawi** and in **Mozambique**, north of the Zambezi River, where there are several records from the Tete District. No specimens are presently available from the northeastern parts of Mozambique but, as they occur in southern Tanzania and in Malawi, they are likely in time to be shown to occur.

*Southern African Subregion*

They occur widely in **Zimbabwe**, except in the dry western parts of the country; in the extreme northeastern parts of **Botswana** and widely in **Mozambique**, south of the Zambezi River, as far south as the extreme southern parts of the Maputo District, and in the eastern part of **Swaziland**. They occur in the northern and northeastern parts of the **Transvaal** where they are not common. In the northern Transvaal they have been collected on the northern, more arid aspects of the Soutpansberg.

## Habitat

Sharpe's grysbok occurs in areas of low-growing scrub and grass of medium height, up to about 400–500 mm, avoiding areas where there are solid stands of high grass such as *Hyparrhenia* spp. In northern Botswana suitable habitat is found on dry sandy areas where, through logging practices, *Baikiaea* woodland has been removed, leaving a thick secondary growth of low bushes and regenerating trees with a grass cover. In other areas such as in parts of Zimbabwe, they live in rocky terrain with low bush and grass cover, often around the bases of koppies and stony ridges. In Zimbabwe and Zambia they also occur in *Brachystegia* woodland where there is good undercover. In the Hwange National Park, Zimbabwe, they are common in riverine vegetation,

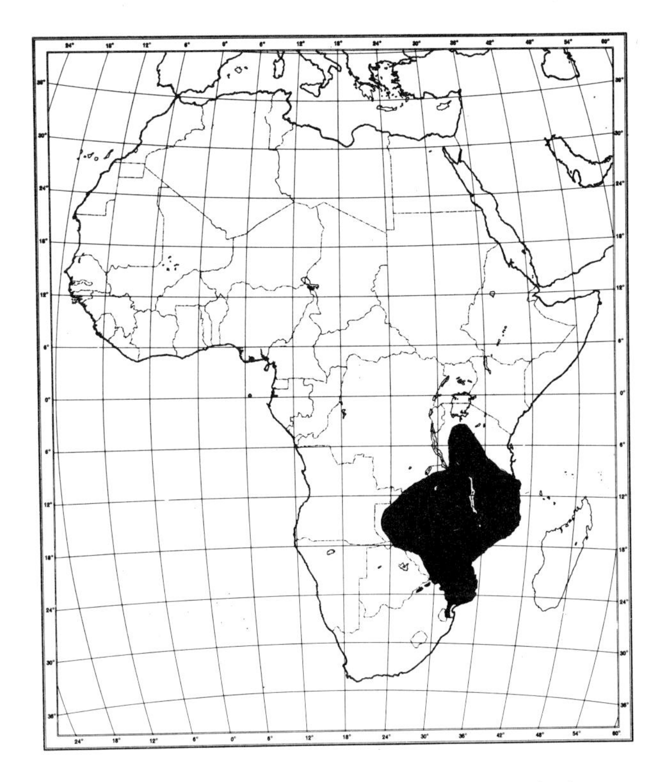

and also occur in broken country where there are thickets at the base of koppies (Wilson, 1975).

Although all these observations point to the association of the species with good ground cover and this seems to be a feature of their habitat in most parts of their distributional range, Wilson (1975) recorded that in the Hwange National Park they were also found in pure stands of mopane, *Colophospermum mopane*, with very little good cover, which seems atypical.

## Habits

Very little is known about the habits of this species. Being predominantly nocturnal and living in a concealing habitat, they are difficult to observe and they are inclined to lie up very tightly and unless disturbed by close approach remain hidden in the undergrowth. When they do run off they do so crouching low to the ground as they run through the thick underbush, making them difficult to see. Quite often the disturbance of the undergrowth and a glimpse of a reddish body is all that can be seen of them. In this behaviour they are very different from the duiker, *S. grimmia*, or the steenbok, *R. campestris*; the former bounds through the undergrowth and the latter, although not usually seen in such thick underbush, does not crouch like Sharpe's grysbok when flushed.

They usually occur solitarily, in pairs or a female with her single offspring. They may be seen foraging in the early morning or late afternoon. They lie up in the heat of the day in dense cover. When a clear view can be obtained of this species they are seen to hold their heads low, the outline of the back giving the impression that the hindquarters are higher than the shoulders and are hunched up, almost as if they had been kicked under the tail or as if they were ever ready to run off. They are shy and secretive and can be overlooked in areas where in reality they are reasonably common.

## Food

Predominantly a browser, in a sample of 91 stomachs collected from southeastern Zimbabwe the contents consisted of 70% browse and 30% grass. Among the browse plants leaves of the following were identified: velvet bridelia, *Bridelia mollis*; thornbush, *Acacia* spp; sand olive, *Dodonaea viscosa*; buffalo thorn, *Ziziphus mucronata*; false marula, *Lannea edulis*; horn pod, *Diplorhynchus condylocarpon*; beechwood, *Faurea saligna*; and bitter albizia, *Albizia amara* (Smithers & Wilson, 1979). Wild fruits did not feature highly but included kudu berry, *Pseudolachnostylis* maprouneifolia, and raisin berry, *Grewia flavescens* (Wilson, 1975).

### Reproduction

Kerr & Wilson (1967) recorded gravid females in most months of the year, suggesting an all-year-round breeding season, and the information given by Smithers & Wilson (1979) appears to substantiate this. Strijbis (1977) gave the gestation period as seven months. Females have two pairs of inguinal mammae.

## Genus *Neotragus* Von Dueben, 1846

No. 321

## *Neotragus moschatus* (von Dueben, 1846)

## Suni
## Soenie

Plate 34

### Colloquial Name

This is derived either from the Kikuyu name for the species, *kasuni*, or from the *suni* of the Wachagga people of Kenya.

### Taxonomic Notes

Meester *et al.* (1986) listed two subspecies as occurring in the Subregion: *N.m. livingstonianus* (Kirk, 1865) from northeastern Zimbabwe and *N.m. zuluensis* (Thomas, 1898) from northeastern Natal and KwaZulu, southern Mozambique and southeastern Zimbabwe. Originally the species was described from a specimen from Chapani Islet, Zanzibar Harbour.

### Description

The suni is a tiny antelope, adult males from the Subregion standing about 360 mm at the shoulder, with a mean mass of about 5,0 kg. The females are slightly larger and heavier, with a mean mass of 5,4 kg (Table 321.1). In East Africa they are a kilogram lighter. The subspecies *N. m. zuluensis*, which occurs in the Subregion, is a rich rufous-brown colour, the lighter coloured tips of the hairs on the upper parts giving them a faintly speckled appearance. The body hairs are 18,6±2,9 mm long, oval or oblong in cross-section, with a regular waved mosaic cuticular scale pattern along the entire length; two or three scales across the width (Fig. XLII.1) (Keogh, 1983). The mid-back from the neck to the base of the tail is a darker rufous colour than the flanks and legs. The under parts, including the inside of the legs, the chin and upper throat, are white. The hair on the forehead and top of the head is a dark rufous-brown, darker and richer in colour than the upper parts of the body. The sides of the face are lighter in colour than the upper parts of the body. Just above the eyes they have indistinct white patches, the top of the snout with a broad black band from the rhinarium to between the eyes. The legs are slender and lighter in colour than the upper parts, with a conspicuous encircling narrow band of black just above the hooves, and no false hooves. The tiny hooves are long and slender and tend to be upturned towards their sharp tips. The ears are broad, rounded at the tips and almost totally devoid of hair on the insides, which are pinkish in colour. The backs of their ears are sparsely covered with dark ashy-coloured hair. The upper surface of the tail is darker brown than the body and is white below. The under parts of the body are whitish.

Suni have preorbital glands on the sides of the face in front of the eyes, covered with short hair. These secrete a sticky substance which to the human nose does not appear to have a smell, but which probably has a function in marking. Heinichen (1972), however, never observed them making use of these glands for this purpose, although in East Africa adult males use them for marking their territories (Hoppe, pers. comm.).

Spoor—Plate III.

**Table 321.1**

Measurements (mm) and mass (kg) of adult suni, *N. moschatus*, from Mozambique and northeastern KwaZulu

**Mozambique**

| | Males | | | Females | | |
|---|---|---|---|---|---|---|
| | $\bar{x}$ | n | Range | $\bar{x}$ | n | Range |
| TL | 699 | 6 | 659–727 | 692 | 3 | 663–716 |
| T | 97 | 6 | 91–110 | 96 | 3 | 93–98 |
| Hf c/u | 197 | 6 | 193–204 | 195 | 3 | 193–198 |
| E | 80 | 6 | 77–84 | 75 | 3 | 72–78 |
| Mass | 5,0 | 6 | 4,5–5,2 | 5,4 | 3 | 5,1–5,9 |

**KwaZulu** (Lawson 1986)

| | Males | | | Females | | |
|---|---|---|---|---|---|---|
| | $\bar{x}$ | n | Range | $\bar{x}$ | n | Range |
| TL | 734 | 5 | 714–765 | 742 | 6 | 665–789 |
| T | 82 | 5 | 66–97 | 89 | 6 | 80–95 |
| Hf c/u | 197 | 5 | 193–201 | 194 | 6 | 187–204 |
| E | 78 | 4 | 77–79 | 76 | 6 | 73–79 |
| Sh.ht | 365 | 5 | 314–385 | 359 | 6 | 322–383 |
| Mass | 5,1 | 4 | 4,9–5,3 | 5,5 | 6 | 5,0–6,0 |

Only the males carry horns, which are widely spaced on the top of the head and lie back from it in the plane of the forehead. They are straight and strongly ridged for most of their length, but smooth near the tips. The greatest length recorded is 134 mm in a trophy from Mozambique (Rowland Ward, 1986).

### Distribution

Suni are confined to the eastern parts of the continent from the False Bay Park in KwaZulu north to the Marsabit area in Kenya. Within the limits shown their occurrence depends on the availability of suitable habitat.

*South of the Sahara, excluding the Southern African Subregion*

In **Kenya** they occur in the central and southern parts of the country and in **Tanzania** in the eastern sector, including the offshore islands of Zanzibar and its associated islets and Mafia Island. In **Mozambique**, north of the Zambezi River, they occur in the eastern parts of the Niassa District and widely in the districts of Cabo del Gado, Mozambique, Zambezia and in parts of the Tete District, but not as far north as the Zambian border. In the Southern Province of **Malawi** they are confined to the Lengwe and Liwonde National Parks.

*Southern African Subregion*

In **Mozambique**, south of the Zambezi River, they occur westwards to near the Zimbabwe border and throughout most of the remainder of the country, except in the high country in the west of the Vila Pery District along the Zimbabwe border. In **Zimbabwe** they occur narrowly in the eastern parts of the Mtoko District in the northeast and in the southeast of the country. There are unconfirmed reports of their occurrence in the Zambezi Valley as far east as the Mana Pools National Park. In the **Transvaal** they are confined to the northern parts of the Kruger National Park in the east, and in the northeastern parts of **Natal**, south to the

**Plate 34**

318. Steenbok, *Raphicerus campestris*
Steenbok
319. Grysbok, *Raphicerus melanotis*
Grysbok
320. Sharpe's grysbok, *Raphicerus sharpei*
Sharpe se grysbok
321. Suni, *Neotragus moschatus*
Soenie
324. Grey rhebok, *Pelea capreolus*
Vaalribbok

PLATE 34
318
319
320
321
324
Dick Findlay.

False Bay Park in the Lake St Lucia area, which marks their most southerly limits of distribution.

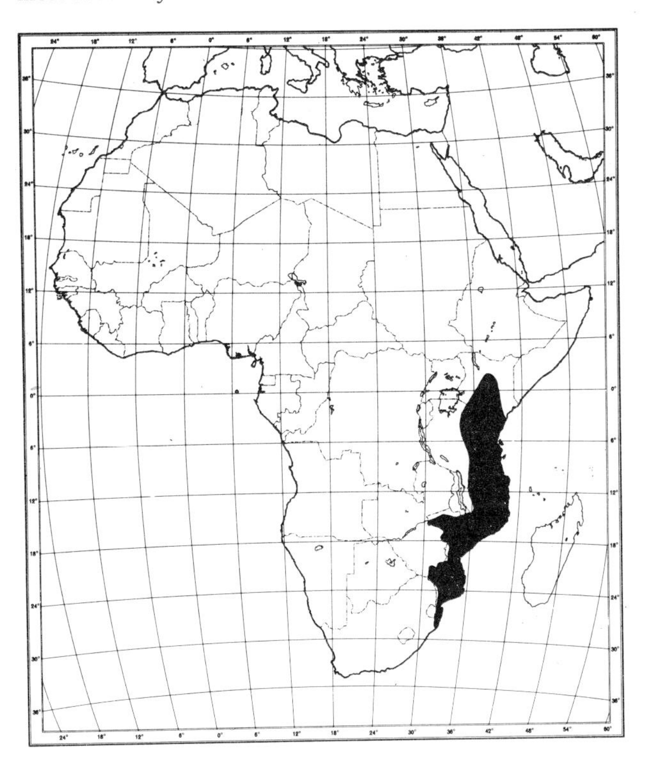

## Habitat

Suni are associated particularly with an evergreen association, consisting of a closed canopy woodland, with an understorey of shrubs with a high stem density and a low ground cover. In northern KwaZulu they occur in thickets, sand forest, pallid sand bushveld and dune forest (Lawson, 1986) and in southeastern Zimbabwe in dry *Commiphora, Combretum* woodland with dense underbush.

## Habits

Suni occur solitarily or in pairs or family groups consisting of a male and female and her offspring. Owing to the nature of the habitat observation is difficult and there may be a closer association of individuals in a pair than is suggested by the many sightings of apparently solitary individuals. If it happens that they are facing away from the observer the constant tail-flicking is often the only clue to their presence. The white of the underside of the tail extends outwards to the edges, making it more obvious as it flicks from side to side. In the males the white scrotum is also an obvious feature when viewed from behind (Hoppe, pers. comm.).

Suni are shy and wary and, if suddenly disturbed, they will freeze, standing motionless for considerable periods, before jumping away, vocalising with a high pitched *chee-chee*, to race for the cover of the nearest thicket. Heinichen (1972) recorded that a male, which she often found in the same place, soon became used to her presence and would lie down under a bush and watch her. She stated that the females appear to be much more alert than the males.

Their main periods of activity seem to be in the early morning and late afternoon. During cool weather they are more active from earlier in the afternoon. During the hot midday hours they lie up in dense thickets. Lawson (1986) found that the main period of activity of individuals in captivity was in the early morning, with lesser periods of activity in the late afternoon and middle of the night. The males were at all times more active than the females.

Lawson (1986) and Heinichen (1972) suggested that suni are territorial, which has since been confirmed by Lawson (1986). While the part played by females in the defence of their territory is not established, males actively defend the whole of their home range (territory). In northeastern KwaZulu, Lawson (1986) recorded that, using the "fieldworkers estimate" of Macdonald, Ball & Hough (1980), the size of male territories varied from 0,005–0,011 $km^2$ and for females from 0,009–0,046 $km^2$. While male territories had well defined borders with very little overlap, territories of females often were situated almost entirely within the territory of a male. Both sexes and in particular males undertook exploratory excursions which took them temporarily outside their territories.

Suni deposit their faeces in middens which are a feature of their territories. In their use the individual scratches a depression in the midden, urinates in it and then squats to defecate in the same place. When pairs are together, if a female uses the midden the male frequently follows her, repeating the process in the site she has used. Lawson (1986) used counts of middens to give a crude estimate of the relative density of suni in different areas.

Mutual grooming was a common feature of their behaviour and took the form of one individual grooming the head, neck and shoulders of a second individual, which then reciprocated. Allogrooming was also practised.

Because of their habit of using pathways through dense underbush, suni are snared easily. Taylor (1978) recorded that, in Natal, poaching is the cause of more deaths than natural predation. Insofar as northeastern KwaZulu was concerned Lawson (1986) stated that, outside conservation areas, suni had disappeared due to destruction of their habitat and excessive hunting. In parts the increase in populations of nyala, with a corresponding decrease in the density of the shrub layer which was critical to the survival of suni, had led to the decrease in numbers of suni or their disappearance in some areas. Suni fall prey to crowned eagles, *Stephanoaetus coronatus*, and pythons, *Python sebae*.

## Food

Hoppe (pers. comm.) showed that individuals in captivity were highly selective in their feeding habits, only eating leaves. They would pluck these from the plants, leaving even the finest twigs. Suni, like dik-dik, are not equipped to digest cellulose properly which in any case passes through their digestive system too quickly to be utilised. Their food, however, provides soluble plant sugars and other substances which provide for their nourishment (Hoppe, pers. comm.). From experiments with suni in captivity which were given access to a wide variety of food items, Lawson (1986) found that they had a preference for fresh fallen leaves and that although they would take wild fruits, flowers and the growing tips of shoots, they were not dependent on these food items. Given access to leaf litter and fresh browse, they showed a distinct preference for the former. This corresponds with the findings of Hoppe *et al.* (1983) who examined the rumen contents of suni in East Africa and found that their contents consisted of 84% dicotyledonous leaves, 4% stems, 6% fruit and 6% monocotyledonous material. Heinichen (1972) recorded that in northeastern KwaZulu they ate mushrooms and Taylor (1978) noted that they ate the fallen fruits of the wild fig, *Ficus* sp. in the Mkuzi Reserve, Natal.

Lawson (1986) showed that suni had a high metabolic rate and would feed for a relatively short period, up to 20 minutes, with intermittent ruminating periods like most concentrate selectors (Hofmann, 1973). This is unlike grazing ruminants which will feed for prolonged periods before resting and ruminating. The intake of food for the period 06h00 to 18h00 for the suni was on average 134 g for males, 104 g for females. While the most active period for feeding was at dawn, they had a lower period at dusk and another lower peak in the middle of the night. They are independent of drinking water, obtaining their moisture requirements from their food.

## Reproduction

In captive suni, pubertal ovarian activity commences at 350±23,1 days (range 307–386 days; n=3) and length of the oestrous cycle is 21,3±0,4 days (range 20–25 days; n=15) (Loskutoff *et al.*, 1990). Suni breed well in captivity and, in enclosures in northeastern Natal, Lawson (1986) recorded lambing in most months of the year, a single lamb at a birth, and the intercalving interval is seven months. Three male lambs weighed 750g, 640g and 720g and one female lamb 830g at birth. In the wild, Taylor (1978), in Natal, recorded young in June and February; Smithers & Wilson (1979) recorded a female with a near full-term foetus in September in southeastern Zimbabwe, and Smithers & Tello (1976) two gravid females in Mozambique in December. A captive ewe at De Wildt Estates gave birth to a stillborn lamb with a mass of 0,75 kg. Lawson (1986) recorded, from his observations of suni in captivity, that males mature at the age of eight months, females at about 12 months. The males court the females by approaching them from the side or rear and stroking their belly or ribcage with a foreleg. Copulation was not observed and it was presumed to take place at night. After several unsuccessful attempts at mating, males were observed to stot, jumping in the air with all four feet clear of the ground.

Lambs up to about a week old hide, their mothers visiting them two or three times during the day to suckle and clean them. The lambs start to take solid food at about four days old and by 32 days old will ruminate.

In captivity, Lawson (1986) stated that rams at the age of eight months had to be separated from adult rams as they started to fight. Young males removed to separate enclosures showed no signs of overt fighting, although a definite dominance hierarchy was noted. The introduction of a young female to the enclosure with the young males, however, caused fighting.

Females have their first lamb at the age of about 17 months, the mean inter-calving period being 221 days (Lawson, 1986).

At birth calves had three deciduous premolar teeth, and the first permanent molar teeth were starting to erupt. By the age of 550 days they have their full complement of permanent teeth.

## Subfamily AEPYCEROTINAE

Impala, the only representative of this Subfamily, are medium-sized antelopes. The males have strongly ridged, lyrate horns; the females are hornless. They have no preorbital, pedal or inguinal glands. The metatarsal glands on the hind legs are covered with a prominent tuft of black hair. They have two pairs of mammae. They do not have false hooves. They have tails of medium length, and a black stripe on the back of each thigh. They are of slender, gazelle-like build.

There still remain disagreements as to the affinity of the impala, *Aepyceros melampus*, the sole representative of this Subfamily. Simpson (1945) placed them with his Antilopinae; Pocock (1910) and Lydekker & Blaine (1914) thought that they warranted a rank on their own; Ellerman *et al.* (1953) thought that they might be allied to *Kobus* and *Redunca*. Oboussier (1965) considered them close to the Reduncinae, though distinct enough to be kept separate. Ansell (1972) in view of the general, although not unanimous, agreement as to their distinctiveness, retained them as the sole representative of the Subfamily Aepycerotinae.

## Genus *Aepyceros* Sundevall, 1847

No. 322

### *Aepyceros melampus*

### *A. m. melampus* (Lichtenstein, 1812)

### Impala
### Rooibok

Plate 31

#### Colloquial Name

Originally described from a specimen from "Southern Bechuanaland" (the former British Bechuanaland and what is today part of the northern Cape Province), the name was anglicised most probably from the Tswana name *phala*, although it has been claimed that it is derived from the Zulu name for the species, *impala*.

#### Taxonomic Notes

Ansell (1972) listed six subspecies from the continent, only two of which occur in the Subregion: the impala, *A. m. melampus* (Lichtenstein, 1812), which has an eastern distribution, and the isolated population of the black-faced impala, *A. m. petersi* Bocage, 1879, which is found in northern Namibia and southwestern Angola and is dealt with separately in the text.

#### Description

Impala are one of the most graceful and beautiful of the antelopes, with their shiny reddish coats and long slender legs. Adult males of *A. m. melampus* stand about 0,9 m at the shoulder and have a mean mass of about 50 kg; the females are slightly smaller, with a mean mass of about 40 kg (Table 322.1).

The length of body hairs is 50±7,5 mm; in cross-section they are triangular with blunted corners ("cricket bat" shape). The cuticular scale pattern is irregular waved mosaic from base to tip. Scale margins are smooth or with distinct large crenations; three to four scales cover the width of the hair (Fig. XLII.1) (Keogh, 1983). The upper parts of the body are a rich reddish-brown. The flanks, from behind the shoulders, are pale fawn, tinged reddish, and the under parts are pure white. They have white patches above their eyes which extend in front of these as narrow white bands, white throats and a dark brown or nearly black patch high up on the forehead. On the lower part of the back of the hind legs they have conspicuous oval tufts of black hair, just above the ankle joints, which overlie glandular areas in the skin. On their rumps from the level of the base of the tail, on either side, there are distinct black bands, broader at their tops than lower down, which extend down the back of the thighs. On either side of these there are pale fawn areas against which the black bands stand out very conspicuously. The top of the tail is broadly black, this band of colour tapering towards the base of the tail and continuing on to the top of the hindquarters as a fine black line. The under parts of the tail are white. The insides of the ears are white and they have contrasting black tips. The upper parts of the limbs are pale fawn like the flanks, tending to be lighter in colour towards the hooves. The limbs are paler on their insides.

The hair is closely adpressed to the body and barely reaches a length of 10 to 12 mm on the top of the shoulders. The individual hairs on the upper parts are off-white at their bases with broad reddish-brown tips. On the upper parts of the body in particular the coat has a distinct sheen. The hair is longer on the white under parts, where it may reach a length of 15 mm.

Spoor—Plate III.

**Table 322.1**

Measurements (mm) and mass (kg) of a series of adult impala, *A. m. melampus*, from (a) Zimbabwe (Smithers & Wilson, 1979) and (b) mass (kg) from the S.A. Lombard Nature Reserve, Western Transvaal (Skinner, 1971).

**(a)**

| | Males | | | Females | | |
|---|---|---|---|---|---|---|
| | x̄ | n | Range | x̄ | n | Range |
| TL | 1625 | 25 | 1386–1805 | 1548 | 25 | 1438–1670 |
| T | 298 | 25 | 239–327 | 274 | 25 | 225–304 |
| Hf c/u | 437 | 25 | 407–453 | 420 | 25 | 398–435 |
| E | 148 | 25 | 132–165 | 144 | 25 | 132–158 |
| Mass | 54,5 | 25 | 46,8–65,9 | 40,9 | 25 | 31,8–51,8 |

**(b)**

| | | | |
|---|---|---|---|
| Mass | 63±2,2 | 12 | 52,3–78,6 (mass peak March, nadir September) |

Only the males carry the lyrate horns which swing back from their heads, then bow outwards, then inwards and slightly forward to their sharp, inwardly directed points. They are strongly ridged for about two thirds of their length, but smooth towards the points (Fig. 322.1). The world's record horns came from the Limpopo River and have a length of 809,7 mm over the front curve (Best & Best, 1977).

Fig. 322.1 Skull: impala, *A. melampus*
TL skull 275 mm

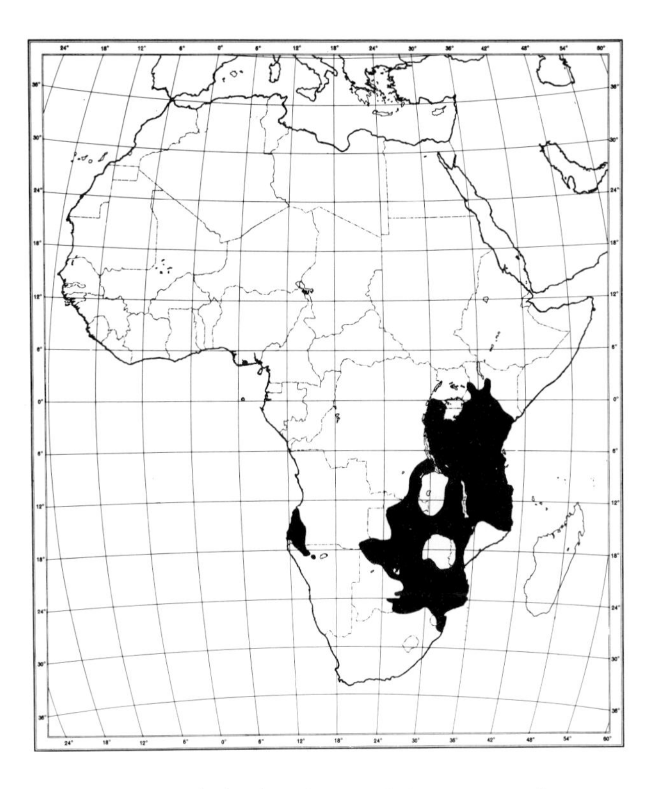

## Distribution

Impala are distributed widely in the eastern woodland parts of Africa, from northern Kenya south to northern Natal, extending westwards in the more southerly parts of their range to the extreme southern parts of Angola.

In the Subregion they have been introduced widely, and reintroduced to privately owned lands and game reserves in Zimbabwe, the Transvaal and Natal where they are now distributed widely throughout.

*South of the Sahara, excluding the Southern African Subregion*

In **Kenya** they occur widely in the central and southern parts of the country, but do not occur in the drier northeastern and eastern sectors. They occur in southwestern **Uganda** and widely throughout **Tanzania**. They are restricted to the extreme southeastern parts of **Zaire**, excluding southeastern Katanga. In **Zambia** they occur widely, except in the northeast and in parts of the western border areas abutting on to **Angola**, where they only occur in the southeast and where *A. m. petersi* occurs in the southwest.

*Southern African Subregion*

They are confined to the northern, northeastern and eastern sectors of **Botswana**, with deep incursions into the arid eastern parts of the Kalahari in fossil riverbeds fringed with *Acacia* woodland or scrub. In **Zimbabwe** they are distributed widely, although absent from the *Brachystegia* woodland in the northeast. They are distributed widely in **Mozambique**, south of the Zambezi River, except in the western parts of the Vila Pery District and today do not occur in the southern Inhambane and Gaza Districts. In the **Transvaal** they are widespread, except in the southern grasslands. They occur in eastern **Swaziland** and south to the northeastern parts of northern **Natal** as far as the Mhlatuze River. In **Namibia** *A. m. petersi* occurs in the extreme northwest, west of the Etosha Pan. Recently *A. m. melampus* have been introduced onto Namibian game ranches for hunting, a practice which could affect the conservation of *A. m. petersi*.

## Habitat

Throughout their distributional range impala are associated with woodland, preferring light open associations. In the northern parts of the Subregion they are associated particularly with *Acacia* and mopane, *Colophospermum mopane*, but also occur in other types of woodland association such as *Baikiaea*, *Combretum* and in parts *Terminalia*. While they generally avoid open grassland and floodplain, they occur on the ecotone of this and the woodland and will graze on open grassland with a flush of fresh, green grass. They are absent from montane areas.

Cover and the availability of surface water are essential habitat requirements. In parts of Botswana, where they penetrate narrowly in *Acacia* associations into arid terrain, they make use of spillage at wells and boreholes.

## Habits

Impala are gregarious, occurring in small herds of from six to 15 or 20 and in larger congregations of 50 to 100 during the wet season and early (cold) dry season. Mean group size in northwest Zimbabwe varied between 9,8 in November when food was most scarce to 23,4 in January following the start of the wet season (Murray, 1980).

In the Subregion their social organisation consists of males, which are territorial only during the rut, and bachelor and breeding herds. The bachelor herds are comprised of adult and juvenile males, the adults being potential territorial males. The breeding herds are comprised of adult and juvenile females, juvenile males and at times, other than during the rut, include a number of adult males. In addition nursery herds have been observed, consisting solely of juveniles, but these are of a temporary nature, the members later rejoining the breeding herds (Vincent, 1979).

The bachelor herds tend to occupy areas away from those of the breeding herds, where they are less subject to disturbance. This is most apparent during the rut when members of the herd are subject to aggression from the territorial males. They are less cohesive than the breeding herds and adults leave them during the rut to establish their territories, returning to the herd when the rut is over. Just prior to the rut adult members destined to become territorial become aggressive, and this leads to spacing within the herd, and therefore a loss of cohesion.

In Natal, Vincent (1979) found that from January onwards, members of the bachelor herds become increasingly restless, alert and aggressive towards the other adult males; this aggressiveness is accompanied by "roaring" and other intimidatory displays. The "roaring" in impala is more like a long drawn-out bark which is not as staccato or sharp as that made by bushbuck or kudu during the rut.

Adult males eventually break away from the bachelor herds and establish territories for themselves, which vary in size from 50–80 $km^2$, the average size being some 66 $km^2$ (Vincent, 1979). In other areas the size may vary as there is a relationship between the density of a population and the size of the territory. In the southern parts of the species' distributional range these territories are established by males between the ages of 4,5–8,5 years (Murray, 1982) only during the rut and are relinquished thereafter.

In northern Zimbabwe breeding groups of from 30–120 impala occupy discrete home ranges. The breeding group or clan only assembled together into a single large group when green grass was plentiful. Although casual observation suggests that impala move freely from group to group, observations of marked animals reveal that members of neighbouring clans seldom associate with one another (Murray, 1981).

This phase in their life history, which affects boths sexes and which leads eventually to reproduction, is due to the release of high levels of hormones triggered by the switch to shortening daylength, with sexual activity in males increasing from about March onwards to the peak of the rut in May (Kruger National Park; Fairall, 1972). The territorial males clear their territories of non-juvenile males some four to six weeks before the mating period (Murray, 1982).

At the height of the rut the breeding herds, which consist of adult females and juveniles of both sexes, are disrupted by the activity of the territorial males herding females in oestrus and chasing out males. Yearling males may be found in two's or three's on the fringes of the breeding herd or forming discrete groups on their own. While these yearlings are capable of breeding, they generally are debarred from doing so by the territorial males.

Territorial males defend their territories aggressively from other males which try to evict them. In addition to direct aggression the territories are defended by a series of vocalisations and other displays designed to demonstrate the dominance of the territorial male. The alarm snort is used when intruders approach and may be followed by chasing. Snorting and chasing also occur outside the rutting period, but never to the extent witnessed during the rut.

From the time that males show territorial behaviour, which in the southern parts of their distributional range is from January onwards, "roaring" may be heard. When roaring, the tail is extended, the head and nose directed forward. This is a manifestation of potential aggression and dominance and increases in intensity as the peak of the rut is reached in May. Roaring may also be heard at night, as defence of the territory continues during the hours of darkness. Although not so obvious in the case of impala as in some other species such as blesbok, the mere presence of the male in his territory is a deterrent to intruders and he may further advertise his presence by strutting around. He may scare off intruders by lowering of his horns accompanied by bobbing of his head, but if they are not intimidated, he may attack them. Low intensity fighting, with horn-clashing and head-pushing with horns interlocked, may result. More serious fighting may follow, the combatants silent during its progress, but breaking off to roar thereafter. Fighting in impala is not prolonged and is usually over in a few seconds but it can be prolonged, in some instances, leading to serious injury or even death. The lowering of the horns, with head-bobbing, is used also as a threat by the territorial male when herding females and may be accompanied by low intensity "roaring". It is also used in evicting yearling males from breeding herds and males encroaching on to their territories.

Territorial males scent-mark their territories by rubbing their foreheads and the fronts of their faces on twigs and grasses. This is seen most commonly during the rut and is not practised by the females (Jarman & Jarman, 1974). The behaviour of the territorial males at the time leading up to the peak of the rut is the psychological trigger that starts off the series of events leading to the onset of oestrus in the females (Fairall, 1972).

Impala are predominantly diurnal, with some nocturnal activity. They stand or lie down to rest during the hotter hours of the day in shady places. When active they keep moving slowly with tails wagging, ears twitching and feet stamping, caused by the irritation of biting flies. In response to such irritation, or spontaneously during periods of rest, impala may be seen to groom their bodies in an apparent licking motion with an upward movement of the head. In fact, the second and third incisors, and the incisiform canine, are used for this purpose. These teeth are thin and needle-like, and are arranged in the form of a comb on both sides of the lower jaw. The upward movement of this comb-like array against the skin provides an effective means of removing parasites from the pelage (McKenzie, 1990). One limitation of this adaptation is that the neck and head region obviously cannot be groomed by an animal's own teeth. This is compensated for by reciprocal allo-grooming wherein two impala will stand face to face and groom the neck and head region of their partner with their teeth on a one-for-one basis (McKenzie, 1990).

When alerted beyond the distance at which they will flee from intruders, they will merely watch carefully. A nearer approach may cause them to move off slowly but, if suddenly alerted within the flight distance, they may break wildly in all directions, leaping over bushes and imaginary objects with astonishing grace and agility. They then reform to stream off to safety. They are fleet of foot and run with a bounding motion, crossing tracks in graceful leaps which may carry them over distances of up to 12 m in a manner described by Stevenson-Hamilton (1947) as "floating through the air . . . their bodies in the form of a perfect arc". In headlong flight under stress they will race without hesitation at great speed through narrow openings in dense bush or between trees in woodland until they are out of range of danger. When startled, impala kick back and up with the hind feet and Kingdon (1982) believed this action releases puffs of scent from the black-tufted ankle glands. Presumably this helps impala to regroup, particularly in thick bush.

During the rut the territorial males create dung heaps which are scattered randomly within their territories. At other times both sexes urinate and defecate anywhere they happen to be.

**Food**

Impala both browse and graze (intermediate mixed feeders —Hofmann, 1973), the intensity of either depending on the locality in which they occur and the season of the year. In northern Zimbabwe, the proportion of grass to leaf in the diet reached a peak of 75% in January following the onset of the wet season and then declined to a minimum of 9% in June/July at the start of the dry season. The proportion of grass in the diet reflected the availability of green grass in the habitat (Dunham, 1980). During the dry season they tend to move to riverine areas where green grass is still available. Browse, however, also forms an important part of their diet, particularly in the dry season, even when there is an abundant supply of green grass of a preferred species such as *Panicum repens* (Attwell & Bhika, 1985). The browse consists of the leaves and fine twigs of shrubs and trees, either eaten while green or picked up dry from the ground. Various forbs are taken, the fine twigs with thin, fresh leaf buds nipped off near the tips. They are also partial to wild fruits. A very wide range of browse plants is eaten, the list of species depending on their availability within the area in which the impala occur. Common to most areas in which impala are found, the fine twigs and fresh leaves of *Acacia* spp are a common item in their diet. The seedpods of some species such as the umbrella thorn, *A. tortilis*, are particularly sought after. Where available the fine twigs and leaves of *Combretum* spp; *Boscia* spp; *Grewia* spp; *Ziziphus* spp; *Maytenus* spp; *Dichrostachys* spp; *Commiphora* spp; *Terminalia* spp and many other genera of browse plants are eaten. Dry fallen leaves of tambotie, *Spirostachys africana*, mopane, *Colophospermum mopane*, and bush willow, *Combretum apiculatum*, also form an important dietary component in some areas during the dry season. Wilson (1975) listed some 28 species of browse plants eaten by impala in the Hwange National Park, Zimbabwe; Monro (1979) 46 from the Nylsvley area in the northern Transvaal.

Similar long lists of grass species eaten by impala are available. Common throughout large parts of their distributional range, some species appear regularly on lists and are important in their diet. These include finger grass, *Digitaria eriantha*; red grass, *Themeda triandra*; couch grass, *Cynodon dactylon*; buffalo grass, *Panicum maximum*; *Eragrostis* spp and *Urochloa* spp, their occurrence in stomach contents varying with their local availability and their seasonal condition. Wilson (1975) listed 13 species from the Hwange National Park and Monro (1979) 23 from the northern Transvaal.

Recently Van Rooyen & Skinner (1989) found that the monocotyledon: dicotyledon ratios in the diet differed between the sexes. The percentage dicotyledons was 31% for

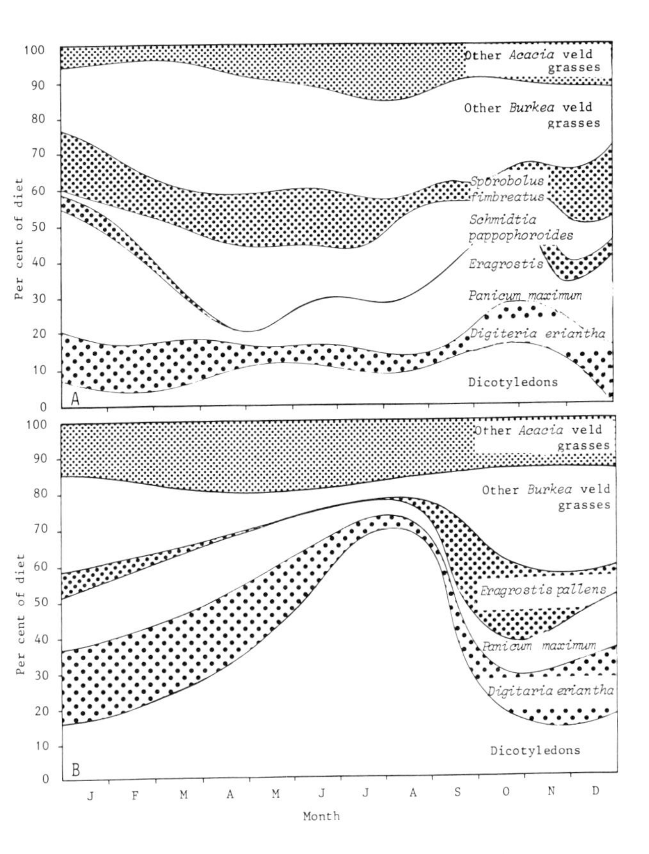


Fig. 322.2 Schematic presentation of probable diet composition of impala at Nylsvley as it varies with season (from Skinner, Monro & Zimmerman, 1984).

territorial males, 48% for females and 49% for bachelors. These differences are attributed to social organization as, during autumn, adult males hold a demarcated territory, excluding bachelor herds which are forced to feed elsewhere. In this study mature bachelors were found only in the koppies surrounding territories. Territorial males may thus select prime habitat to attract females. Very little grass grew on the koppies so this may be reflected in the diet. Territorial males and females occupy the same home range, but on the one hand males constantly defend territories with little time to devote to selective feeding, while on the other hand, females select for dicotyledons which have a superior nutritional value, enabling them to meet the higher energy demands of pregnancy and lactation.

As their range dries out, impala increase the time spent feeding per day, and move further in search of food and water. In northern Zimbabwe the home range size of breeding groups increased from 40 km$^2$ in April to 150 km$^2$ in November and movements of individuals of up to 8 km have been recorded (Murray, 1982).

Impala are dependent on the availability of drinking water. Young (1972a) reported that, in the Kruger National Park, they remained within 8 km of water and half his records show that herds were within 1,6 km of it. Where it is freely available they drink daily and are more dependent on water during the dry season than during the wet. However, under certain circumstances, they can obtain their moisture requirements from succulent food.

**Reproduction**

Impala are short-day breeders, with a restricted mating season in autumn (Skinner *et al.*, 1974; Skinner & van Jaarsveld, 1987). Murray (1982) found that, in Zimbabwe, the peak of the rut varied across a 20 day interval in five years, the timing being influenced by the lunar cycle, most mating taking place between full moons in each year. The lambs are born during the months of November to January after a gestation period of 194–200 days (Fairall, 1971).

Early on in the establishment of their territories males are preoccupied with demonstrating their possession. Later their attention becomes focused on the females. The breeding herds are mobile, their home ranges overlapping several male territories. Having herded females from these, the territorial male investigates their reproductive status by genital-smelling and licking, courting those in oestrus by approaching them with head lowered and nose held forward. If the female is receptive copulation may follow. The male may mount the female repeatedly in brief contacts lasting up to 10 seconds, and after successful copulation the male usually snorts and "roars". Ewes cycle for the first time at the beginning of May and only cycle twice (Fairall, 1983). After conception the single blastocyst implants in the right hand uterine horn. In northern Zimbabwe the most successful rutting male was observed to copulate with more than 15 females per season (Murray, 1982). Theoretically, this figure can be manipulated and Fairall (1985) has shown that manipulating the sex ratio can lead to increased productivity under game ranching conditions. Through the process of herding females and chasing off yearling males, the breeding herds tend to scatter, but aggregate later. While the territorial male endeavours to keep the herded females within his territory, they will move off it if he does not persist in these activities. Non-pregnant ewes display complete anoestrus during the winter months (Marais, 1988).

The male sexual cycle peaks in autumn (Skinner, 1971; Hanks, Cumming, Orpen, Parry & Warren, 1976) and reaches a nadir (low point) in spring. This parallels a decline in body condition (Monro & Skinner 1980), fat reserves of male impala declining rapidly during the rut (Dunham & Murray, 1982). Fat reserves of female impala decline to a minimum in January/February, when milk production, and thus the females' energy requirements, are at a maximum. So far twins have not been recorded from the Subregion, and only once in East Africa (Kayanja, 1969). The females break away from the herds to give birth in isolation, parturition taking place in thick underbush or in tall grass. At birth the lamb has a mass of about 5 kg and is fully haired except on the lower parts of the limbs. Jarman (1976) recorded that the female eats the afterbirth.

The whole of the calf crop is born within a restricted period of a few weeks, the timing varying with the locality. In the Zambezi Valley, Zimbabwe, lambing peaks in November *cf.* December in the southwest (Child, 1964). In the extreme northern Transvaal near Messina lambing peaks in January, lower levels of nutrition delaying conception, but in most of the Transvaal there is a peak in December (Skinner *et al.*, 1977).

Females conceive at just over two years of age and allowing for this period, Skinner (1969) found that a female which lived to the age of 15 years in the wild had 13 lambs, a 100% lambing record. The young are left hidden for a period of a day or two, but are capable of following their mothers 24 hours after birth when they rejoin the herds. Lambs at first are uncoordinated in their movements and their mothers are forced to stay close to them (Vincent, 1972). When the breeding herds include females with young, the young are seldom in close association with their mothers, except when suckling.

Predation by spotted hyaenas and other large predators including cheetahs is high during the early stages of their life, when jackals and pythons also take their toll.

Juvenile females grow up in the breeding herds, remaining with them throughout their lives. Juvenile males at the yearling stage are driven out of these breeding herds by the territorial males at the time of the rut when they may remain together in small groups for a time. Kerr (1965) showed that although the males may produce spermatozoa at 13 months old, they are not able to establish and hold territories and do not take part in the rut until they are over three years old. Eventually they join the bachelor herds and grow up in the shelter of these to become potential territorial males at the age of about three years. Between the ages of 1–4 years, 73% of males in northern Zimbabwe dispersed, most moving between 0,4–3,2 km and taking up residence in the area used by a neighbouring breeding herd (Murray, 1982). Longer distance movements by young male and female impala occurred in the Hluhluwe Game Reserve during a period of colonization of a neighbouring reserve (Hitchins & Vincent, 1972).

Females have two pairs of inguinal mammae.

No. 322

## *A. m. petersi* Bocage, 1879

## Black-faced impala
## Swartneusrooibok

### Colloquial Name

They are so called on account of the characteristic dark coloured face blaze on top of their muzzles which extends from the nostrils to the top of the head.

### Taxonomic Notes

The black-faced impala originally was considered to be worthy of full specific status, *A. petersi*, distinct from the impala, *A. melampus*, but Ellerman *et al.* (1953) and Ansell (1972) both considered it as a subspecies of *A. melampus*. This has been confirmed in a pilot cytogenetical study by Grimbeek (1984). The original specimen from which the subspecies was described came from the Mossamedes District in southwestern Angola.

### Description

Joubert (1971a) showed that adult males have a mean mass of 63,0 kg, females 50,4 kg (Table 322.3). They are darker in colour than the impala. The upper parts of the body lack the rich reddish-brown colour of the impala and are duller brown, with a distinct purplish-black sheen. Some individuals are darker brown down the middle of the back from the shoulders to the base of the tail. In adults the sides of the face and backs of the ears are reddish-brown. Between the darker upper parts and the white under parts the flanks are light fawn, lacking the faint red tinge seen in the impala. They have a distinct purplish-black band about 40 mm broad extending from near the nostrils to just in front of the eyes which continues on to the top of the head as a thinner dark band. From the base of the ears through the line of the eyes they have dark bands which taper out on their cheeks, and white patches in front of the eyes. The ear tips are more extensively black than in the impala and their tails are longer and much bushier, being considered by Shortridge (1934) to be as full and bushy as those of reedbuck. In the original type, a male, of *A. m. petersi*, the tail was given by Bocage (1878) as 380 mm. The mean lengths of those of the impala, *A. m. melampus*, are, males 298 mm, females 274 mm (Smithers & Wilson, 1979). Black-faced impala have the same black bands on the rump as the impala, the black line on top of the tail extending on to the body, the under parts of the tail pure white. The hair is closely adpressed to the body and is 10–12 mm long. The individual hairs have silvery-white bases, a band of light brick-red and broad dull brown tips. The white hair on the tail reaches a length of 100 to 110 mm. The world record horns from Angola measured 673,5 mm (Rowland Ward, 1986).

**Table 322.3**

Average mass (kg) of a series of adult black-faced impala, *A. m. petersi*, from northern Namibia (Joubert, 1971a)

| | Males | | | Females | | |
|---|---|---|---|---|---|---|
| | $\bar{x}$ | n | Range | $\bar{x}$ | n | Range |
| Mass | 63,0 | 10 | Not available | 50,4 | 9 | Not available |

### Distribution

*Angola*

They occur in southwestern **Angola** as far north as the Benguela District.

*Southern African Subregion*

They are confined to northern **Namibia** between the Otjiomborongbonga area (*c.* 12°45′E) and Swartbooisdrift on the Cunene River, southward to the Kaoko Otavi area, Otjivosandu, in the southwestern part of the Etosha National Park, and the Kamanjab district just south of the Park, which marks their most southern limits of distribution.

### Habitat

Joubert (1971a) gave the habitat requirements of the black-faced impala as dense riverine vegetation bordering on vegetation zones of moderate density and suggested that the availability of water supplies is a necessary requirement. They reach their greatest density at Omuhonga, in the vicinity of a waterhole in the river, where the river winds through a flat valley floor with rocky hills on either side, the floodplain extending in width up to about 2,5 km. The floodplain has a riverine woodland of ana trees, *Acacia albida*, camel thorn, *A. erioloba*, and leadwood, *Combretum imberbe*, together with fan palms, *Hyphaene benguellensis*, wild figs, *Ficus petersii*, some semi-deciduous trees and an underbush of shrubs. Interspersed within this riverine woodland are open glades.

### Habits

Black-faced impala are gregarious, occurring in small herds of from three to 15 individuals, occasionally up to about 20 (Joubert, 1971a). Aggregations of larger herds are formed during or after the lambing season, these splitting up into the smaller herds after all the lambs have been born. Solitary males, but no solitary females, were seen by Joubert (1971a), but occasionally two females occurred together. At night the herds lie up on open terrain, joining up for this purpose into numbers of up to 150 individuals. The black-faced impala tend to keep to the dense riverine vegetation during the day, lying up in the thickets.

Their social structure involves solitary males and harem herds consisting of females with their offspring, accompanied by a dominant male. While Joubert (1971a) made no mention of bachelor herds, they may occur, as in the case of the impala, and consist of young males and non-dominant adult males.

### Food

Black-faced impala are intermediate mixed feeders. Joubert (1971a) stated that during the rainy season they both browse and graze with apparently the same intensity. At this time they tend to move away from the floodplains onto the ecotone with the open woodland. During the dry season they make more use of the floodplain and riverine vegetation, with an emphasis on browsing.

Joubert (1971a) provided a list of 21 browse plants and 12 grasses utilised by black-faced impala in northern Namibia. They make wide use of *Acacia* spp pods, which have a high protein content, as well as their flowers, leaves and shoots, and the fruit, bark and leaves of shrubs such as the small sour plum, *Ximenia americana*. The grasses include *Aristida* spp; couch grass, *Cynodon dactylon; Eragrostis* spp, and small buffalo grass, *Panicum coloratum*.

Within most of the areas where they occur they have to compete with goats for food, these being accounted by Joubert (1971a) as a menace to their existence. In parts goats outnumber the black-faced impala by about 100 to 1, resulting in a high level of competition for such foods as *Acacia* spp pods.

### Reproduction

Black-faced impala are seasonal breeders, having a short and marked lambing season; the young are born from the end of December, with a peak in January. Newly born lambs are of rare occurrence in February (Joubert, 1971a). A single lamb is produced at a birth, with a mass of about 5,0 kg. During the first nine months their mass increases by approximately 2,69 kg per month in males, 2,58 kg per month in females. Their mass increases less in the next period and from the 22nd month they gain only 0,79 kg per month in males and 0,67 kg per month in females. The most rapid growth takes place in the first 20 to 22 months after birth (Joubert, 1971a). Joubert (1971a) recorded that one female produced twins, one of which was totally ignored and eventually died. Females have two pairs of inguinal mammae.

## Subfamily CAPRINAE

Although principally Palearctic, Oriental and Nearctic, this Subfamily is included as the Himalayan tahr, *Hemitragus jemlahicus*, is feral in the Subregion, occurring on Table Mountain, Cape Province.

The Himalayan tahr is a medium-sized antelope. Both sexes have long, curved horns, but the horns of the females are developed less than those of the males. No face, pedal or inguinal glands are present. The females have one pair of mammae.

**INTRODUCED**

## Genus *Hemitragus* Hodgson, 1841

Three species of this genus are known, these being considered more generally as subspecies of the oldest named, *H. jemlahicus*, the Himalayan tahr (Ellerman & Morrison-Scott, 1951). *H. j. jemlahicus* occurs, as the colloquial name indicates, in the Himalayas from Kashmir in the west to Sikkim; *H. j. hylocrius*, the Nilgiri tahr, occurs in the southern parts of India in the Nilgiri Hills, and *H. j. jayakari*, the Arabian tahr, in the Oman in the southeastern tip of Arabia. The generic name *Hemitragus* means semi-goat which aptly describes the look of these mammals. Often they are referred to in Afrikaans as the *bergbok*. The Himalayan tahr, *H. jemlahicus*, is included in this work for, following an accidental release, they established themselves on Table Mountain, Cape Province.

No. 323

## *Hemitragus jemlahicus* (H. Smith, 1826)

## Himalayan tahr
## Himalaja tahr

In the early 1930's Groote Schuur Zoological Gardens,which is situated on Groote Schuur Estate on the slopes of Devil's Peak, Table Mountain, near Cape Town, obtained a pair of Himalayan tahr from the National Zoological Gardens, Pretoria. They escaped from their enclosure which had a 1,5 m high fence and established themselves either on Devil's Peak or on Table Mountain. By the 1960's at the latest, the progeny of this single pair occurred widely on the north face of the mountain. In 1971 with the help of many volunteers the Mountain Club organised a survey which revealed a total count of 264. In 1972 Lloyd (1975a) reported a total number of 330, by which time their distribution extended over the north/northwest and south/southeast faces of both Devil's Peak and Table Mountain and the Saddle which links them and the northwest faces of the Twelve Apostles range. There were unconfirmed reports at this time that they had crossed Constantia Nek on to the Constantiaberg.

Fig. 323.1 Himalayan tahr, *H. jemlahicus*.

This uncontrolled increase in the numbers of Himalayan tahr, within a Nature Reserve and especially a reserve with a unique flora, posed a serious threat. Tahr occur in fairly large groups which tend to remain in restricted areas and have the ability, like goats, to eat any sort of plant material. Over-utilisation of the habitat became apparent with almost total destruction of vegetation in certain areas and resulted in soil erosion problems. The *fynbos* association which covers the mountain is particularly vulnerable to misuse of this type. Recently burnt areas are favoured by the tahr and frequently become excessively eroded. Recognising the dangers attendant on the growing population, the Cape Department of Nature Conservation initiated a research study to investigate the problems involved. As a result of this survey it was recommended that, as total eradication was probably impossible, there should be a drastic reduction in the population, particularly in areas which had been utilised heavily (Lloyd, 1975a). During the years 1975 to 1981 over 600 tahr were removed by Parks and Forestry officials and members of the Cape Department of Nature Conservation. A survey conducted by the Mountain Club and officials of the Parks and Forestry showed that at the end of April 1981, 88 tahr were still living on Table Mountain. This figure seems extraordinarily low in the light of previous surveys and from the fact that it is known that they have a reproductive capacity of 20%. The matter is being investigated further.

During the first four months of the year the males are found either in bachelor herds or alone. With the onset of the rut in May the males join the females, then accompanied by immatures and juveniles in nanny-kid herds. While the males are separated from the females they tend to occupy open slopes of the mountain which have a dense, tall *fynbos* association and are not precipitous. The nanny-kid herds on the other hand occur in precipitous areas, such as narrow ledges or terraces or close to cliffs which provide this type of habitat (Lloyd, 1975a). Lloyd (1975a) found that the average number in the nanny-kid herds was 5,6 (n=101); these herds, however, continually fluctuate in numbers due to intermingling or splitting up. The average herd size of males was 2,1 (n=82).

The males have a heavy mane of long fleecy hair on their necks, shoulders and chests and may have a mass of up to 105 kg. The females are smaller than the males. Both sexes are reddish-brown to dark brown in colour and have large eyes, small pointed ears, naked noses and short, goat-like tails. They lack preorbital glands and the males lack the beard present in other subspecies. Both sexes carry the goat-like horns which curve back from the top of the head in an even curve. The females have a single pair of inguinal mammae. They have one young during the summer months. They nurse their young for six months and by the time the young are 18 months old they are fully grown (Grzimek, 1972).

## Subfamily PELEINAE

These are medium-sized bovids. The males have ridged short, straight horns; the females are hornless. No preorbital, inguinal or pedal glands are present. The rhinarium is swollen and glandular. The females have two pairs of mammae. They have false hooves united across the midline, and a woolly pelage (Ansell, 1972).

The Subfamily is only known to occur in the Subregion where it is represented by the Grey rhebok, *Pelea capreolus*, which inhabits hilly country.

## Genus *Pelea* Gray, 1851

No. 324

## *Pelea capreolus* (Forster, 1790)

## Grey rhebok
## Vaalribbok

Plate 34

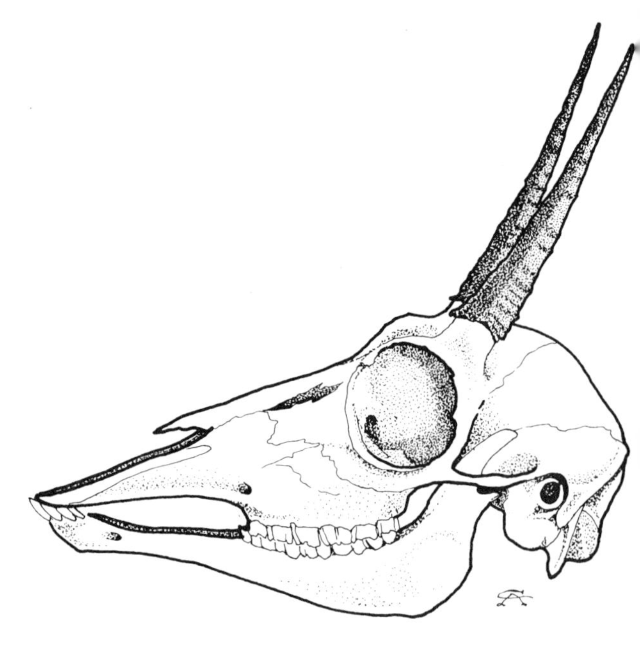

Fig. 324.1. Skull: grey rhebok, *P. capreolus*
TL skull 285 mm

### Colloquial Name

The name roebuck appears frequently in the earliest records of settlers in the Cape, probably because the grey rhebok reminded them of the roebuck (roe deer), *Capreolus capreolus*, of Europe. By degrees the pronunciation and spelling changed over the years through roebuck, rabuck, reebok, raybuck and so on to rhebok in English and *ribbok* in Afrikaans (Skead, 1980). The name *ribbok* in Afrikaans is also applied to the mountain reedbuck, *Redunca fulvorufula*, which is differentiated under the name *rooiribbok*. The generic name *Pelea* is derived from the Tswana name for the species, *phele*.

### Taxonomic Notes

The species is monotypic.

### Description

Grey rhebok are slender, graceful antelope which stand about 0,75 m at the shoulder and have a mass of about 20,0 kg. They have a long, slender neck and very long, narrow, pointed ears and, unlike the reedbuck, *Redunca arundinum*, and the mountain reedbuck, *R. fulvorufula*, they have no preorbital glands. They have no inguinal glands, but pedal glands are present on all four feet; the glandular sacs contain a semifluid, pale-coloured, evil smelling secretion. They have no subauricular patches as are seen in the mountain reedbuck and in some reedbuck. The rhinarium is characteristic, being very large, swollen and extending backwards from the nostrils. In the living individual it remains studded with drops of moisture and slight pressure after death yields droplets of moisture from its glandular structure.

The hair is soft, short, thick and woolly. Body hairs are 30,9±14,9 mm long, oval or circular in cross-section, having a regular waved mosaic scale pattern at the base, irregular along the shaft and tip; scale margins are smooth but rippled at the tip (Fig. XLII.1) (Keogh, 1983). The individual hairs have subterminal brown and terminal pale tips. The upper parts of the body and flanks are greyish-brown, with a fulvous tinge on the face and legs. The under parts, including the under parts of the tail, are pure white. The legs tend to be darker in front and have false hooves; the true hooves are short, triangular and compact. The long, narrow, pointed ears are covered with white hair inside. They have white patches around the eyes and some white on the sides of the muzzle and chin.

Spoor—Plate III.

Only the males carry horns which, like those of the steenbok, rise straight up from the top of the head at about a right angle to the plane of the face, with a slight forward curve. They are ringed for about half their length (Fig. 324.1). The world's record pair, which originated in the Subregion, measures 292,1 mm and a pair of similar length originated in the Cape Province (Rowland Ward, 1986).

### Distribution

Grey rhebok are confined in their distribution to within the borders of the Subregion. While there must remain some doubt as to whether they ever occurred on Table Mountain, they certainly occurred on the mountains near Stellenbosch. In general their distribution has not shrunk to the extent seen in other species, although they no longer occur in the northern Cape Province, in parts of the western Transvaal and southeastern Botswana. This may be due in some part to the fact that the flesh is unpalatable to most people and that the nature of their habitat renders them less obvious. Within the limits shown on the map they only occur where there is suitable habitat, consequently their distribution is discontinuous and patchy.

*Southern African Subregion*

They occur widely in the **Cape Province**, except coastally in the southwest and in the north; in the eastern parts of the **Orange Free State**; in **Lesotho** and in the Drakensberg in **Natal**, where they occur over 1 400 m above sea level. They occur in the central and southern parts of the **Transvaal** and in **Swaziland**.

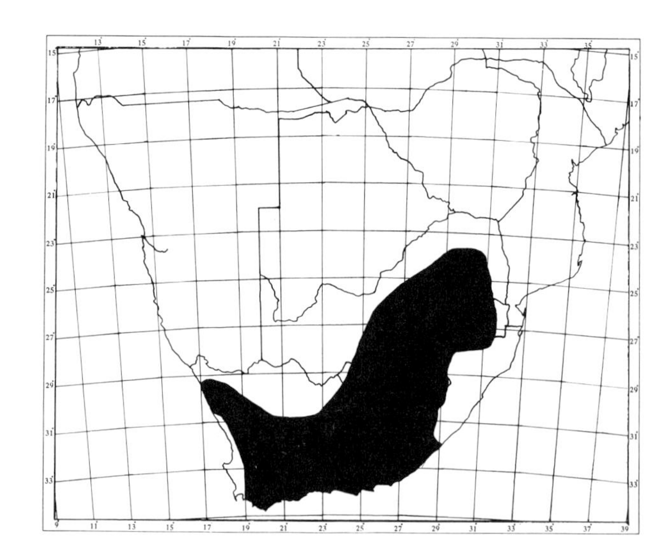

### Habitat

Throughout the greater part of their distributional range grey rhebok are associated with rocky hills, rocky mountain slopes and mountain plateaux with a good grass cover. They appear to be able to utilise a more exposed habitat than that preferred by the mountain reedbuck, *R. fulvorufula*. Vincent (1962) noted that on the slopes of the Drakensberg, Natal, they occupied the grassy slopes between 1 400 m and 2 500 m above sea level, seldom being found at lower altitudes. They are independent of a water supply.

## Habits

Esser (1973) found that grey rhebok live in small family parties numbering up to about 12 individuals, consisting of an adult male and several females and their young. He recognised only the two groupings, solitary males and family parties, and while during his study he did not observe larger aggregations, he noted that other authors mentioned parties of up to 30 which were probably the result of family parties temporarily joining up. He did not observe the formation of bachelor herds which are a feature of the social organisation of other bovids. The family parties remain within a defined home range throughout the year. The males are territorial and defend a part of this home range, designated as their territory, against the trespass of strange males.

Changes in numbers of individuals in family parties take place between the months of July and the beginning of October; the numbers in parties remain static in June and in December/January.

Esser (1973) believed that male grey rhebok become physically mature at about 1,5 to 1,75 years old, at which stage they start to try and establish a territory of their own. If a male leaves the family party before this, he will remain solitary until old enough and in a physical condition to establish his own territory. The young males usually leave the family parties shortly before the lambing season. Esser (1973) witnessed an adult male which in his endeavours to establish a territory, attacked two territorial males. Eventually after a number of fights he managed to displace one of the territorial males from part of his territory which he took over as his own. Adult males do not form family parties until they have established and are maintaining a territory. Males that fail to establish territories are forced to the peripheries of the territories of established males.

In order to advertise that a territory is occupied and will be defended, the territorial male advances on a trespassing male with exaggeratedly slow movements, displaying laterally and frontally towards the trespasser, at the same time snorting and stamping, which usually has the effect of chasing away the trespasser.

Acoustic signals form an important role in communication. Esser (1973) recognised three vocalisations; snorting, moaning and hissing. Snorting is uttered both by the males and females and may continue to be uttered over a period up to three-quarters of an hour, when the source of disturbance is not recognised.

Grey rhebok are active throughout the day in the summer time, about half the day spent in short periods of resting, while in winter this is reduced to about one-third to one quarter of the day. During both seasons they rest during the warmer part of the day from about midday to 15h00. During winter they cover greater distances in foraging than during the summer (Esser, 1973).

Grey rhebok are accomplished, graceful leapers and jump over barriers with apparent ease to land gracefully on the other side. When alarmed and in flight they move off with the characteristic "rocking horse" movement seen in the reedbuck, displaying the white underside of their tails as markers to those that follow. When pursued they run very swiftly in direct and swerving flight.

## Food

Grey rhebok rumens have a small percentage fill, large ostia and evenly dense papillation. They are predominantly browsers (Ferreira, 1983; Beukes, 1988), with a tendency to being mixed feeders (Hofmann, 1973). In the southern Orange Free State dicotyledons comprised 88% of their diet (Ferreira, 1983; Ferreira & Bigalke, 1987), exceeding 90% in winter and declining by 10% in summer as determined by faecal analysis. Observations when feeding on *Leucosidea sericea*, *Cliffortia nitidula* and a *Euryops* sp. suggest they select plant parts as well as plants. In the Bontebok National Park, Swellendam, Beukes (1988) found dicotyledonous shrubs and forbs made up 96,9% of their diet; the genera *Disparago*, *Metalasia* and *Aspalathus* were the most important food plants, and roots, seeds and flowers made up 5,8 to 14,6% of rumen contents from June to October, probably due to the greater abundance of flowering annuals at this time.

## Reproduction

During the rut, which falls about April, the territorial males are very active, defending their territories and testing their females for signs of oestrus by smelling of the vulva. Males court females in oestrus by tapping the insides of the females' back legs with their forelegs, and copulation may follow. The gestation period is 261 days (Brand, 1963). A single calf is born at a birth. The calves are born early in the warm, wet season of the year about November/December, and in captivity from about September to December (Brand, 1963). The females have two pairs of inguinal mammae.

# Subfamily HIPPOTRAGINAE

All members of this Subfamily are large. Horns are present in both sexes, either long and swinging backwards from the head in a curve, or straight. Preorbital glands are absent or, at most, poorly developed; they have pedal glands on all four feet but no inguinal glands. The females have two pairs of mammae. The tail is long and tufted. All members have distinctive facial patterns.

Two genera occur in the Subregion, *Hippotragus* and *Oryx*, the former with two species, the latter with one.

Key to the genera after Meester *et al.*, (1986)

1. Horns rising nearly vertically above the eye orbits, then evenly curve backwards
   ... *Hippotragus*

   Horns rising behind the eye orbits, then more or less straight and in line with the plane of the face
   ... *Oryx*

# Genus *Hippotragus* Sundervall, 1846

Key to the species after Ansell (1972)

1. Colour lighter, pale reddish-brown; ears very long and turned down at the tips; horns shorter; body size larger
   ... *equinus*

   Colour darker, rich chestnut to black; ears pointed, not turned down at the tips and not particularly long; horns longer, body size smaller
   ... *niger*

---

No. 325

## *Hippotragus equinus* (Desmarest, 1804)

## Roan
## Bastergemsbok

Plate 32

---

### Colloquial Name

This refers to the general colour, which is inclined to have a slight strawberry tinge in certain lights.

### Taxonomic Notes

Ansell (1972) listed six subspecies from the continent of which two occur in the Subregion, *H. e. equinus* from the Transvaal, parts of Zimbabwe and perhaps southern Malawi, and *H. e. cottoni* Dollman & Burlace, 1928 from northeastern Zimbabwe, northern Botswana, northeastern Namibia, Angola, southern Zaire, Zambia and perhaps central and northern Malawi. There are wide areas of intergradation of the various subspecies and at the present state of our knowledge it is not possible to set limits to their occurrence except on a very broad basis.

### Description

Roan are very large antelope, surpassed in size only by the eland, *Taurotragus oryx*. The males stand about 1,4 m at the shoulder and have a mass of up to about 270 kg, the females slightly smaller and lighter.

The dark brown body hairs are 35,0±11,3 mm long, the white hairs 28,4±4,8 mm long, large and circular in cross-section, with an irregular waved mosaic scale pattern along the entire length of the hair, which has a rippled scale margin (Fig. XLII.1) (Keogh, 1983). The body colour is greyish-brown, tinged with strawberry, which is more pronounced in some individuals than in others. The West African subspecies is distinctly reddish. The most characteristic features are seen on the face which is black or very dark brown, this colour extending on to the sides of the neck, with a strongly contrasting white patch which extends over the top of the muzzle, around the nostrils, broadly on either side of the lips and on to the chin. A white patch on either side of the face extends from the base of the horns, inside the eyes low down on to the cheeks. The legs are darker brown than the body. The hair of the upstanding mane is pale at the base, broadly dark brown towards the tips. The under parts and rump are lighter in colour than the upper parts of the body. The hair on the neck, especially in the females, is longer than on the body. The insides of the ears are white and they are particularly long, measuring up to 300 mm and have dark brown tassels of long hair on their tips. The tail is black or dark brown, with long black hair towards the tip.

Spoor—Plate IV.

Both sexes carry horns; those of the females are more lightly built. Cylindrical in section, they rise from the top of the head in an even backward curve and are strongly ridged for most of their length, the tips smooth. Best & Best (1977) recorded that the longest horns on record, 0,99 m, came from the Tokwi (Tokwe) Valley, Zimbabwe and are now in the South African Museum, Cape Town.

**Distribution**

Considered as an endangered species in the Republic of South Africa (Smithers, 1986), in the Transvaal encouraging indications have attended conservation efforts by the Transvaal Nature Conservation Division. In 1969 a capture operation established a breeding herd of 21 on a provincial reserve, which by 1983 had increased to 181 animals and from this nucleus viable numbers are being translocated to other reserves with suitable habitat. By November 1985 the number in Transvaal Provincial game reserves was 135, on private properties in the Waterberg 150 and in the Atherstone Game Reserve about 10, a total for the province of 285 (Smithers, 1986). Joubert (1986) reported that in 1985 there were 328 roan in the Kruger National Park, which was a slight drop in the figure of 344 for 1984 and a considerable drop from the figure of 670 given for the Park in 1963 by Pienaar (1963). Some of this drop in numbers was attributable in some measure to an outbreak of anthrax. The situation in West Africa is obscure but they certainly at one time occurred as far west as Gambia from whence Sclater & Thomas (1899) described *H. e. gambianus*, a peculiarly rufous subspecies. In the Subregion, Gordon Cumming (1850) recorded them as far south as Griqualand West but, since those historical times, their limits have shrunk drastically. They no longer occur in the Cape Province, southern Botswana or Swaziland and have disappeared from large parts of the Transvaal and Zimbabwe and, where they do occur, they do so in lesser numbers than in former times.

*South of the Sahara, excluding the Southern African Subregion*

In West Africa they occur from **Gambia** east to **Nigeria** in the Guinea and Sudan savannas; in Nigeria only north of the forest zone in protected areas. They are fairly common in the western parts of the **Central African Republic** and are found in the southeastern **Sudan**, and in western **Ethiopia**. There are records from **Uganda** and they have a restricted distribution in southwestern **Kenya**. They are rare in **Rwanda**, but are widespread in the central and western parts of **Tanzania**. In **Zaire** they occur south of the forest zone, from near Lake Kivu to the extreme southern parts of the **Congo Republic**; throughout **Angola**, excluding the southwestern sector; throughout **Zambia**; in National Parks and Reserves in **Malawi**, and in **Mozambique**, north of the Zambezi River, only in the extreme north and northwest and in the Tete Province.

*Southern African Subregion*

They occur in the extreme northeastern parts of **Namibia**; in northern and northeastern **Botswana**; in **Zimbabwe**, excluding the central plateau and the central western areas along the Botswana border; and in the western parts of **Mozambique**, south of the Zambezi River, as far south as about 24 °S. They occur in the eastern **Transvaal**, in the Kruger National Park, which marks their southern limits of occurrence, and in the Waterberg in the northern Transvaal, from where they have been introduced to Nature Reserves in other parts of the province.

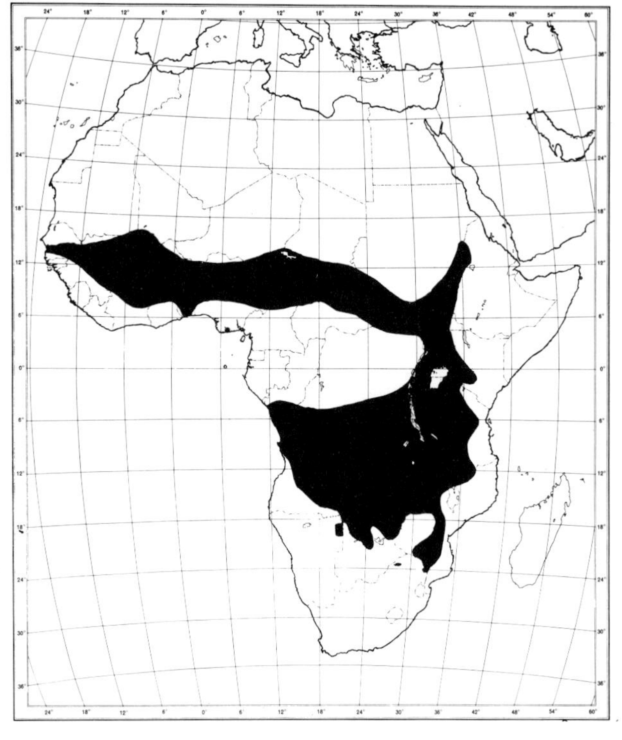

**Habitat**

Throughout their wide distributional range roan are sensitive to changes in their habitat involving either an increase in the woody vegetation or a reduction of the grass cover. Their habitat requirements are critical, their occurrence confined to lightly wooded savanna with extensive open areas of medium to tall grasses, where water is available. In the Kruger National Park, Joubert (1976a) noted that roan avoid woodland where the trees form a closed canopy or where the bush, from the level of 1,5 m to 4 m, forms thick, closed stands. They are tolerant of low bush growth in the grassland up to the level of 1,5 m providing this is open and scattered and remains so. They avoid areas of short grass, open stands of medium to tall grasses being an essential habitat requirement. In the Waterberg, northeastern Transvaal, Ben-Shahar (1986) found that they favoured stony ground on a sandy substrate and that a low tree density did not appear to play a role in their habitat preference.

As a result of these requirements the distribution of roan in the Subregion is patchy and discontinuous. Within a short space of time, their occurrence can be inhibited by factors such as bush encroachment or the over-utilisation of the grassland by other species which, by trampling and eating it down, render it less suitable for the roan.

**Habits**

Roan antelope are gregarious, associating in small herds of about five to 12 individuals. Sometimes the herds are larger, up to 25 individuals, with temporary aggregations of up to 80 on record. The social organisation consists of nursery herds, bachelor groups and solitary bulls. Roan, while not regarded as territorial, in the sense that adult males defend a territory, have nevertheless many attributes of a territorial species. The nursery herds, which may number up to about 20, occupy fixed areas which are largely exclusive to adjoining herds, each nursery herd with a dominant bull.

The herds are stable units and remain within particular areas for long periods, although temporary fragmentation does occur. In the Kruger National Park, Joubert (1970) has records of herds frequenting an area over a period of eight years. This is characteristic of the species and is known to hold for other areas as well. Moore (1938) for example, recorded a herd in East Africa that remained in an area for over 30 years. These areas are known as activity zones (Joubert, 1970) and may be as large as 100 km$^2$. Adjacent herds have similar activity zones which only very rarely overlap. Within the activity zones the herd has a home range which it will occupy for periods and to which it is held by the availability of a plentiful food supply and water, moving to another when water or food supplies become deficient.

Wherever the herd is within its activity zone, the dominant bull defends the females in his herd and an area estimated by Joubert (1970) to be some 300–500 m around them from the trespass of other males. Joubert (1970) called this the intolerance zone.

The essential difference between the roan and some other species is that the dominant bull in the case of the roan is defending his females from the attention of other males, not specifically a demarcated piece of ground within which they are living. Defence of the intolerance zone by the dominant male takes the form of self advertising and fighting. Should a strange male enter the zone and not show submission to the dominant male by lowering of his head, they may horn clash and indulge in pushing bouts with their heads. Should a strange male attempt to oust the dominant male, high intensity fighting may ensue with head-pushing, lunging and horn-clashing, the contestants dropping to their knees to battle. The contest sometimes continues for a lengthy period. Except for damage to the face and neck from the horns, no serious injuries are inflicted and the contest breaks off when one of them submits, and is chased to the perimeter of the intolerance zone.

Trespassing males very often move off purely through the threat attitudes adopted by the territorial male or by visually recognising his presence. They may also appreciate that the area is occupied by the scent marks left by members of the herd. In the threat attitude the dominant bull holds his head high with his neck arched and ears straight out sideways from the head. This is often sufficient to make the trespasser lower his head in submission and move off. All members of the herd will horn bushes and even grass, vigorously thrusting and twisting to strip the leaves and debark the stems or may gently rub their faces on them. They may also horn the ground. These activities serve as visual as well as scent markers denoting their possession of the area. These actions are recognised in other species such as sable (Varian, 1953). Roan have pedal glands which no doubt contribute, along with defecation and urination, to the scent-marking of the area in which they live.

The individual members of roan herds tend to space themselves out with distances of five to 10 m between them, giving the herd the appearance of having a rather loose structure. There is a definite hierarchy among the females and juveniles, with one female becoming dominant over the remainder. This cow usually takes the lead in herd movements and the dominant bull will follow her. In cases where there are several old cows in a herd there may be some sharing of the herd leadership. These old cows contribute to the safety of the herd by acting as sentinels, being found characteristically on its periphery when the herd is grazing or resting (Joubert, 1970). The division of responsibility is thus clearly defined. The dominant bull is responsible for breeding and for the exclusion of other males from his females, and the dominant cow or cows for the choice of the best feeding grounds and the most advantageous situations for resting, sheltering and obtaining water, choices to which the dominant bull submits. Among the juveniles dominance is governed by age. The young bulls are evicted from the nursery herds by the dominant bull at the age of about two years. These then join others to form small bachelor groups of up to about nine individuals. At the age of about five to six years, when they reach maturity, the males become intolerant of other mature males, and either break away from the bachelor herd to live solitary lives or are successful in taking over a nursery herd by ousting its existing dominant bull. Unlike some other species, solitary mature bulls do not join the bachelor herds.

Roan are active from sunrise until about mid-morning and, in hot weather, may not resume feeding until late afternoon, resting up during the day in shade. When feeding the individuals in the herds tend to scatter, giving the appearance of incohesion of the herd.

**Food**

Roan are predominantly grazers, and browse constitutes only a small proportion of their food. From an examination of the availability and palatability of grasses to roan in the Kruger National Park, Joubert (1976a) found that a few species make up the bulk of their diet, although they will utilise a wide variety of different species. They feed on medium to long grass, avoiding areas where the grass is short through over-utilisation by other species or other causes. The availability of the species of grasses plays an important role in food selection. During the most critical period of the year, which falls just before the onset of the rains, red grass, *Themeda triandra; Schmidtia pappophoroides; Setaria woodii*; small buffalo grass, *Panicum coloratum*, and spear grass, *Heteropogon contortus*, ranked high in their diet. During mid-winter *T. triandra, S. pappophoroides* and *P. coloratum* ranked in that order, and in late summer and early autumn they preferred *H. contortus, T. triandra* and woolly fingergrass, *Digitaria pentzii. T. triandra* is an all important grass species in the diet of the roan in the Kruger National Park (Joubert, 1976a).

In the northern Transvaal, Wilson (1975) showed that roan had a marked preference for spear grass, *H. contortus*; Natal red top grass, *Rhynchelytrum repens*; heart-seed lovegrass, *Eragrostis superba*, and autumn grass, *Schizachyrium sanguineum*. In each of these about one-third of the plants was heavily grazed, the remainder moderately or highly grazed. Other well utilised species included thatch grass, *Hyparrhenia hirta*; rolling grass, *Trichoneura grandiglumis*, and red grass, *T. triandra*. Wilson (1975) accounted roan as highly specific in their choice of food plants, even under conditions of stress.

Roan show two peaks of grazing activity, in the early morning and in the late afternoon. They are delicate feeders, utilising the higher parts of grasses to 80 mm above the ground, green shoots being taken as low as 20 mm. They are not close croppers as are wildebeest or zebra and are adapted well to grass of heights up to 1,5 m (Joubert, 1976a). Even when a green flush pervades after burns, roan spend very little time on them, preferring the taller grass stands.

In Zambia, Child & Wilson (1964a), from the examination of 38 stomach contents, found that grass constituted 90% of the content, the remainder being browse. They recorded an unusual observation of two roan standing in water 0,6 m deep feeding on *Equisetum* sp which, to reach, they had to totally immerse their heads.

In the northern Transvaal, Wilson (1975) stated that roan remained in better body condition than sable as they would switch to browse during critical periods. He noted that several species of *Acacia* occurred in their diet together with karee, *Rhus lancea*; wild olive, *Olea africana*; Transvaal beech, *Faurea saligna*; common wild currant, *Rhus pyroides*, and other browse plants.

**Reproduction**

Roan are all the year round breeders and no seasonal peaks have been noted so far (Skinner, 1985). Females conceive at two years of age and, following a gestation period of 276 to 287 days, calve nine months later; a mean calving interval of 317 days has been documented (Joubert, 1976a).

Courtship and mating behaviour follow a distinct pattern. The dominant male approaches a female in the dominant attitude, the head held high, nose and ears pointed forward and the tail slightly extended, the female adopting the attitude of submission by lowering her head. He will then smell her vulva, his light touch causing the female to urinate. Inserting his nose in the stream, he lifts his head and exhibits flehmen, which allows him to judge whether the female is in oestrus or not. If she is not, he ignores her, but if she is, a further pattern of courtship follows. The male repeatedly and gently taps the female between her hind legs with his foreleg. If the female is not receptive she evades his attentions by circling around him, but if she is, then copulation follows.

A few days before the calf is born the female leaves the herd and seeks cover for herself and for concealment of the calf. After it is born she remains with it or nearby for a few days, being particularly alert during this critical time in its life. Thereafter she rejoins the herd, leaving the calf in concealment. The female suckles her calf in the morning and returns to it in the evening. If the female happens to be the dominant female, the whole herd may follow to near where her calf is concealed. Other females may simply leave the herd to visit their calves.

When approaching the calf's place of concealment, the female's presence is usually sufficient to bring it out, but if not she will call it out. She does not return with it, allowing it to choose its own place of concealment, thus avoiding laying a scent trail which might be followed by a predator. Although it has not been ascertained whether the calves are odourless, it has been shown that the interdigital glands in some other species do not function at an early age (Walther, 1969). The assiduous licking of the genitalia by the female may help to lessen the scent of the calf and thus avoid detection. Concealment continues for about six weeks, the calf lying in the cover of grass or underbush. At this early stage the calves are unable to flee in the face of danger and rely on their powers of concealment, lying motionless. If encountered they can be approached and handled. By about the age of two months, the calf starts to move with the herd and to associate more with calves of its own age group than with its mother and, by about six months old, it is weaned. While the association between the female and her heifer calf may persist for a long period, the bond between a female and her bull calf is broken when he is driven from the herd by the bull. Calves are exuberantly playful, running and frolicking among themselves.

The tips of the horns only appear some 40 days after birth. By the age of about 12 months they show the first signs of the ridges and the horns are about 190 mm long. By the age of four to five years the horns show the back curvature and the ridges are clearly distinguishable. The base of the horns is smooth for about 30 mm, a feature which then increases with age.

At birth the calves are light to rich rufous, their colour differing markedly from the adults. The face markings resemble those of the adults. The background of the coat is rufous-brown with less contrast between it and the white pattern than is seen in adults. The first moult takes place at about three months old. At about four months old they resemble the adults.

The females have two pairs of inguinal mammae.

---

No. 326

## *Hippotragus niger* (Harris, 1838)

## Sable
## Swartwitpens

Plate 32

---

### Colloquial Name

The name sable is unfortunate as only old adult bulls are sable in colour. By the same token *swartwitpens* only describes old bulls, but both names are deeply entrenched.

### Taxonomic Notes

Ansell (1972) listed four subspecies from the continent, which included the giant sable, *H. n. variani* Thomas, 1916 from Angola. Of these only one occurs in the Subregion, *H. n. niger*, originally described from the Cashan Mountains (Magaliesberg, west of Pretoria), where they no longer occur.

### Description

Sable are built less robustly and lighter in mass than their close relatives, the roan, *H. equinus*. Adult males stand about 1,35 m at the shoulder and have a mass of about 230 kg. The hairs on the body are 39,9±10,1 mm long, with an irregular waved mosaic cuticular scale pattern along the entire length; the scale margins are rippled to rippled crenate (Fig. XLII.1) (Keogh, 1983). Old adult males are black, with a satiny sheen to their coats. The under parts are pure white, the white on the inner parts of the rump extending upwards to the base of the tail. The face pattern is characteristic, being black with a white chin and a broad white patch extending from the nostrils along the gape of the mouth and broadening towards the angle of the lower jaw. A broad white stripe extends from near the base of the horns downwards in front of the eyes and along the muzzle to meet the white of the lower parts of the face at the nostrils. Giant sable lack the white stripe along the muzzle, although they have the white stripe from the base of the horns extending in front of the eyes.

The tail is fringed and tufted at the tip with long black hair. The basal third of the tail is black or dark brown above and white below, the hairs on the tip reaching to the hocks. The high upstanding mane of black or dark brown hair extends along the top of the neck and on to the shoulders. The ears are narrow and pointed, fringed with white hairs, and are rufous at the back.

In the Subregion, the old adult females are very dark brown, some almost black like the males, but when younger are generally more reddish-brown in colour. In the northern parts of their distributional range on the continent the females never attain the dark colour seen in individuals from the Subregion, tending to remain reddish-brown even when aged. Females of the giant sable, *H. n. variani*, are bright golden-chestnut.

Spoor—Plate IV.

Both sexes carry horns which, in the females, are more slender and less sweepingly curved than in the males. Laterally compressed and heavily ringed in front for most of their length, they sweep backwards in an even curve and are smooth towards the sharp points. The longest horns on record measure 1,543 m which are surpassed by the record of the giant sable at 1,648 m (Best & Best, 1977). The longest horns so far recorded from the Subregion appear to be a pair from Tshokwane, Kruger National Park at 1,47 m (Rowland Ward, 1986).

### Distribution

Historically the first written records of the occurrence of sable are by Cornwallis Harris (1852) who encountered and collected the original type specimen west of Pretoria, which was described in 1838. While they are now extinct in this area, their distributional range in the Subregion is much the same as it was in the past, although they have retreated locally in the face of development. Sable are a savanna woodland species and their distribution is confined, in the southern parts of their distributional range, to the central and eastern parts of the continent. Translocation of sable has taken place in Zimbabwe and the Transvaal to private land and reserves.

*South of the Sahara, excluding the Southern African Subregion*

Their most northerly occurrence on the continent is in the coastal areas of southeastern **Kenya**, as far north as about the Galana River. In **Tanzania** they occur widely, but are absent in the sector immediately east of Lake Victoria and along the Kenyan border until near the coast. They are widespread in **Zambia**, except in parts of the west, and extend into **Zaire** in the southeast and marginally into **Angola** in the extreme southeast, east of the Cuito River. They are widespread in **Mozambique**, north of the Zambezi River, and occur in **Malawi**, predominantly in reserved areas.

The subspecies *H. n. variani*, the giant sable of Angola, which today only occurs in a reserved area between the Cuanza and Luando rivers, had a wider distribution in the past.

*Southern African Subregion*

They occur in northern and northeastern **Botswana** and have a wide distribution in **Zimbabwe**, except on the central plateau from which, unless afforded protection on private lands or in reserves, they have retreated in the face of development. They are confined to the Kruger National Park and the Letaba District in the eastern **Transvaal** and are widespread in **Mozambique**, south of the Zambezi River, although absent in the extreme south and parts of the southeast.

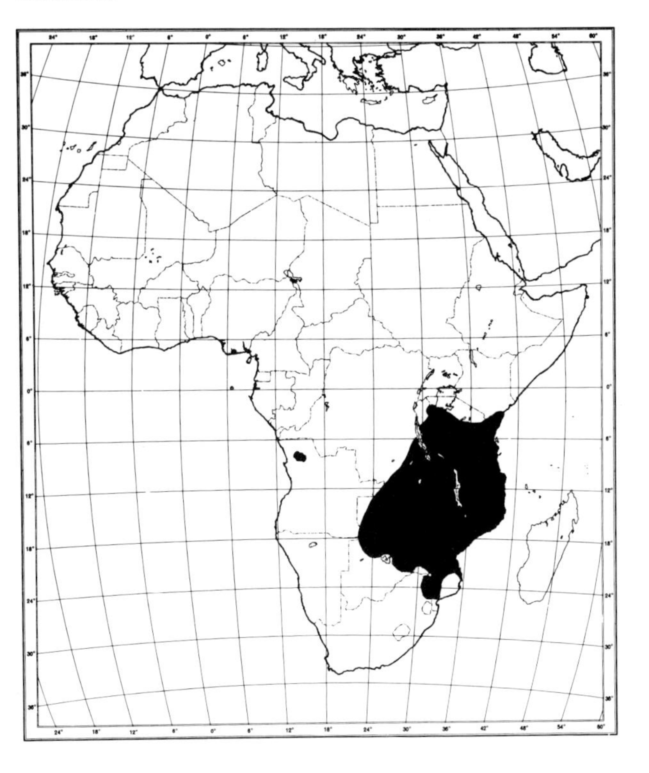

## Habitat

Sable are a savanna woodland species, dependent on cover and the availability of water. They prefer open woodland with adjacent vleis or grassland with medium to high stands of grass. They avoid woodland where the tree density is high and areas where the grass is short, caused by over-utilisation or other causes.

## Habits

Sable are gregarious, occurring in herds of 20 to 30, with very much larger temporary aggregations of up to about 200 on record. Their social organisation consists of territorial bulls, nursery herds and bachelor groups.

The territorial bulls establish territories which, at least during the rut, they defend from the trespass of strange males. Grobler (1974) recognised three categories of territorial bulls in the Matobo National Park, Zimbabwe. The first had territories within the home range of the nursery herds, where the chance of contact with adult females was assured. The second had territories so situated that these contacts were rare, and the third had only the remote possibility of making contact with nursery herds. Territorial bulls defend their territories either by displays leading to intimidation, or by fighting. In the stiff-neck displays the head is held erect, the chin tucked in and the neck muscles contracted. This attitude may be combined with the lateral presentation of the body to the trespasser, the tail held out stiffly and twitching, as the two stand head to tail. Fighting may consist of dropping on to the knees with horn sparring, and may lead to serious fighting. Sometimes this is accompanied by bellowing, much horn-clashing, and slashing with the horns. In disputes over territory, serious fighting can result in the death of contestants (Stevenson-Hamilton, 1947). The long horns with their sharp points are deadly weapons and quick sweeps can cause serious injuries to hunters who have dared to approach too close to wounded sable.

The nursery herds consist of adult females and juveniles of both sexes. Estes & Estes (1970) found that, in the Victoria Falls National Park, the average number in a herd was 29, higher than found in other areas. While the juvenile females may remain with the herd for life, the juvenile males are evicted at the age of about three years by the territorial bull, by a continuing process of threat displays involving charges with horn-sweeping. These juvenile males join the bachelor groups. The nursery herds move around over the territories of the males who, during the rut, will endeavour to retain the females within their territories. This they accomplish by actively herding them into compact groups, rounding them up with loud snorting and vicious horn-sweeps at straying females. This continuing process is exhausting but, if they desist, the herd may move on to another male's territory to be treated similarly.

Within the herd one or more females may establish dominance. These dominant females are the leaders of the herd and are concerned primarily with its welfare. They determine its movements, taking the lead to feeding grounds and water, keeping watch for danger and directing flight from it, but are always subservient to the territorial male. There is a definite hierarchy within the herd, from the dominant females to the lowest category, the young of the year, who sort themselves into a hierarchy based on age (Wilson, 1975). Dominance among the females and young is displayed by the stiff-neck attitude, the young chasing each other and sparring, but serious fighting does not occur.

The young males growing up within the bachelor group, at five or six years of age, will be ready to find a territory of their own, either by challenging and overcoming an already established territorial bull or establishing a new territory for themselves. A bachelor group is an important unit in the social structure as it affords protection to the growing male until he is ready to attempt to stand on his own as a territorial bull.

The nursery herds have home ranges which vary in size from about 0,20–0,40 km$^2$. In the Kruger National Park, Joubert (1974) gave the size of these as 0,20–0,40 km$^2$; in two areas in Zimbabwe 0,24–0,28 km$^2$ (Grobler, 1974), and 0,26–0,47 km$^2$ (Johnstone, 1971), which agree closely with the figure of 0,26 km$^2$ given by Estes & Estes (1970) for Kenya. Within these home ranges they tend to spend a few days in a relatively small area and then move on to another. The home ranges of the territorial bulls are much smaller than those of the nursery herds. Wilson (1975) estimated the size of these as about 0,025–0,040 km$^2$. Grobler (1974) recorded two territorial males that continuously occupied their territories for up to two years.

The breaking of branches of trees and shrubs and the stripping off of bark with the horns, indulged in by territorial bulls, may be a device for boundary-marking of their territories, but this requires study.

Sable are most active in the early mornings and in the late afternoon. Most members of the herds rest during the middle of the day, but there are often some individuals that continue grazing throughout this period. They rest lying down or standing up, often ruminating, usually in the shade of trees during hot weather. The young tend to congregate together. Grobler (1974) could not detect any seasonal change in their activity pattern as is found in some other species of antelope.

## Food

Sable are predominantly grazers, but in some areas will browse to a small extent, especially towards the end of the dry season when the nutritional value of the grasses is low. They are selective feeders with a preference for fresh growth, cropping grasses 40–140 mm above the ground and selecting plant parts with a high crude protein and low crude fibre content (Grobler, 1981b).

Grobler (1974) in Zimbabwe recorded the eating of some 23 species of grass, among which buffalo grass, *Panicum maximum*; spear grass, *Heteropogon contortus; Eragrostis jeffreysii*; red grass, *Themeda triandra*, and *Urochloa oligotricha* were recorded as being utilised on a year-round basis. Wilson (1969a) and Estes & Estes (1970) both added to the list of species utilised in this area. Sable select the greener parts of the grasses, cropping lengths of up to 300 mm. Wilson (1975) recorded that in the northern Transvaal they showed a marked preference for black-footed brachiaria, *Brachiaria nigropedata*, and would also heavily utilise red grass, *T. triandra*; spear grass, *H. contortus*; yellow thatch grass, *Hyperthelia dissoluta*; thatch grass, *Hyparrhenia hirta*; slit grass, *Schizachyrium jeffreysii*; and gum grass, *Eragrostis gummiflua*. In this sector browse was utilised to a very limited extent. In Zimbabwe, Wilson (1969a) included among browse plants utilised sweet thorn, *Acacia karroo; Lippia oatzii*; karee, *Rhus lancea*; silver raisin bush, *Grewia monticola*, and the fruits and leaves of sickle bush, *Dichrostachys glomerata*, and the fruits of buffalo thorn, *Ziziphus mucronata*. Grobler (1974) added wild pear, *Dombeya rotundifolia*; raisin bush, *Grewia flava*; fever tea, *Lippia javanica*, and wild camphor bush, *Tarchonanthus camphoratus*, to the list of browse plants, noting that the last-named is an important species prior to the rains.

Sable are dependent on drinking water and are seldom found more than a distance of about 3 km from it. They drink at least once a day, usually between 10h00 and 16h00, walking into the water knee deep to drink.

### Reproduction

Female sable become sexually mature at two years of age, usually having their first calf at the age of three years and they may continue to have a calf up to an age in excess of 10 years (Grobler, 1974).

Just as in the roan, *H. equinus*, the territorial bull tests the receptiveness of a female by immersing his nose into the urine stream of the female and then exhibiting flehmen. If she is not in a receptive condition the male will disregard her, but if she is, courtship will continue until copulation follows. The gestation period is eight months (Wilson, 1975).

Sable are seasonal breeders, the time of calving varying over the distributional range of the species. In Zimbabwe the calves are born in March (Child & Wilson, 1964; Wilson, 1969a), in northern Botswana from January to early February (Child, 1968b) and in the northern Transvaal from February to April, with a peak in February (Skinner, 1985). The female leaves the nursery herd to have her single calf, which has a mass of between 13 and 18 kg. The calves are reddish-brown in colour, the facial markings barely discernible. Very soon after birth, after being licked clean by the female, the calf suckles and then conceals itself in a shady place in woodland, hidden in patches of grass or in underbush. The female visits it once or twice during the day to suckle, but spends the rest of the day with the herd.

As young sable are unable to avoid danger during their first two weeks of life by running away, they tend to freeze if approached, relying on their concealment and apparent lack of odour to escape detection. At this stage they can be approached and handled. After being suckled and cleaned, the young usually chooses a new hiding place, thus lessening the chance of being scent-trailed by predators. Females have two pairs of inguinal mammae.

## Genus *Oryx* Blainville, 1816

No. 327

## *Oryx gazella* (Linnaeus, 1758)

## Gemsbok
## Gemsbok

Plate 35

### Colloquial Name

The origin of the colloquial name is obscure. The Dutch name *gems* is applied to the chamois, *Rupicapra rupicapra*, of Europe which, morphologically or ecologically, is in no way similar to the gemsbok.

### Taxonomic Notes

Three species of the genus are known, two of which occur on the continent: the gemsbok, *O. gazella*, from the southern part of the species' range and the scimitar-horned oryx, *O. dammah*, from the Sahara. The Arabian oryx, *O. leucoryx*, a small species standing about a metre at the shoulder, is nearly pure white in colour and is considered to be endangered.

Ansell (1972) recognised five subspecies of *O. gazella* from the continent: *O. g. gazella* for populations from the southern range of the species; *O. g. beisa* (Rüppel, 1835) for the Beisa oryx of Ethiopia and Somalia; *O. g. callotis* Thomas, 1892, the fringe-eared oryx of Kenya and Tanzania; *O. g. gallarum* Neumann, 1902 from the Sudan and Ethiopia, and *O. g. annectans* Hollister, 1910 from Kenya and Somalia, with the proviso that the last two named may be synonymous.

### Description

Gemsbok are one of our most handsome species with their long, straight horns, distinctively marked faces and bodies and the long flowing black hair of their tails which contrasts with the pale colour of their bodies. Body hairs are 35,5±9,1 mm long, in cross-section concavo-convex, reniform, with a guttered scale pattern which is regular mosaic along the entire length. The scale margins are smooth, rippled and crenate in the distal half of the hair (Fig. XLII.1) (Keogh, 1983). In the adults, at a distance, the dark brown markings appear black, and contrast with the pale fawn-grey of the body and particularly with the white of the face.

Males stand about 1,2 m at the shoulder and have a mass of up to about 240 kg; females are slightly lighter at about 210 kg. Rowland Ward (1986) recorded that the longest horns on record came from Botswana and measured 1,229 m in length.

The background colour of the upper parts and flanks is a pale fawn-grey. The mane is represented by a ridge of short, dark brown hair. From the shoulders they have a dark brown band of hair down the mid-back which widens out into a saddle on top of the rump and narrows to the base of the tail. The tail is dark brown with a switch of long dark brown hair towards the tip which reaches below the hocks. The under parts of the body are white. On the lower part of the flanks, dividing the pale fawn-grey of the upper parts and the white of the under parts, they have a broad, very distinct dark brown band which, at its anterior end, joins with the dark brown of the upper parts of the front limbs, and at the posterior end with the similar patch of dark brown on the upper parts of the hind limbs. Below the dark brown patches on the upper parts of the limbs, the gemsbok are white, with bands of dark brown on the lower parts of the front of the limbs. The facial markings are characteristic. The background colour is white, with a dark brown patch between the horns, joined to a broad dark brown patch on the top of the muzzle by a thin dark brown line. The anterior part of the muzzle, between the rhinarium and the dark brown muzzle patch, is white. They have a dark brown band from the sides of the horns extending through the eyes to the lower jaw, and a further band of the same colour anterior to this from the dark brown muzzle patch to the lower jaw. They have a distinct dewlap on the throat, with a tuft of long dark brown hair, and a dark brown band down the mid-line of the throat.

The newly born are fawn or reddish-brown in colour, which is replaced at about four to six months of age by the pale fawn-grey adult pelage. At birth the only evidence of the striking adult pattern is a dark brown stripe about 20 mm in width above and running through the eye, and a darker patch on the muzzle.

The spoor is characteristically heart-shaped, the hooves with sharp points and the forehooves larger than the hind (Plate IV).

The straight cylindrical horns are ringed for about one third of their length, the remainder smooth, and are lighter in build but longer in the females than in the males. These arise from above the eye orbits and lie slightly back from the line of the face.

## Distribution

The species *Oryx gazella* occurs in two discrete areas on the continent, separated by some 1 600 km. Their absence from the intervening terrain is due to climatic factors. It is likely that during some time in the Pleistocene Epoch, when this intervening area was drier than it is today, the distribution of the species would have been continuous from southern to northeastern Africa.

In the Subregion they formerly occurred south of the Orange River in Namaqualand, in the northwestern parts of the Cape Province and in the Karoo, but are no longer found so far south (du Plessis, 1969). In Namibia and Botswana there has been little change in the limits within which they formerly occurred, except locally in the face of human development. They are essentially a species of arid terrain. They never occurred much farther east than near the confluence of the Orange and Vaal rivers in the south, the eastern limits of the Kalahari associations in Botswana, and marginally into the Transvaal and Zimbabwe in the dry western sectors.

*South of the Sahara, excluding the Southern African Subregion*

In the northern parts of its distributional range the species is represented by *O. g. beisa*, *O. g. gallarum* and *O. g. callotis*. *O. g. beisa* occurs from the Red Sea coast of northern **Ethiopia** south to parts of **Somalia**; *O. g. gallarum* in central Ethiopia, parts of the **Sudan** and northeastern **Uganda**, extending possibly into parts of Somalia; and *O. g. callotis* occurs in parts of **Kenya** and in northeastern **Tanzania** (Ansell, 1972). The southern *O. g. gazella* extends in its distribution beyond the borders of the Subregion into southwestern **Angola**.

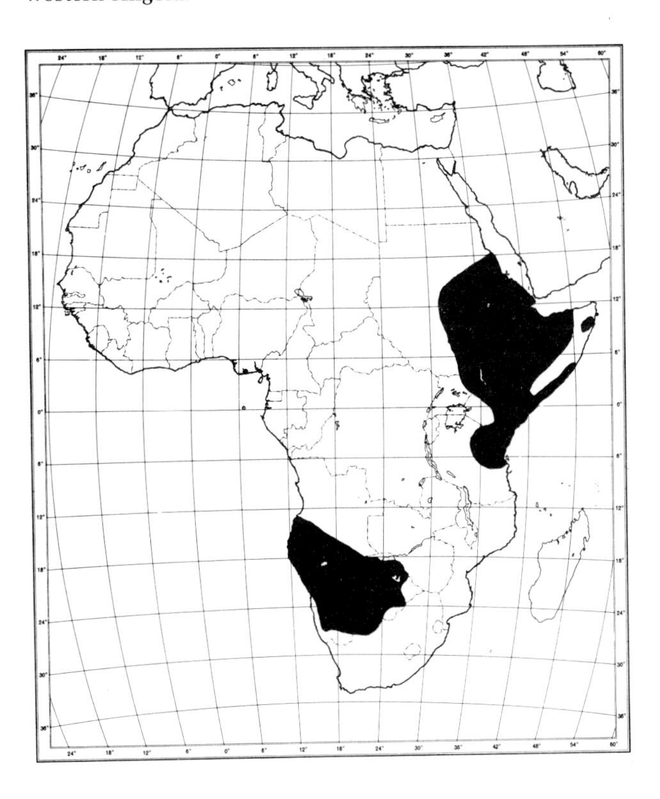

*Southern African Subregion*

Gemsbok occur widely in **Namibia**. They have a wide distribution in **Botswana**, but are confined to the more arid semi-desert areas, and are not found in parts of the south and east of the country. From the northeast of **Botswana** they extend marginally into **Zimbabwe** in the Hwange National Park in the northwest, seldom being found further east of its eastern boundary.

## Habitat

Gemsbok are essentially a species of open, arid country. In Botswana and Namibia they occur in open grassland, open bush savanna and in light open woodland. However, they will penetrate deep into savanna woodland such as *Baikiaea*, *Acacia* and mopane, but are then more often in search of new feeding grounds in the more open areas within them.

In the southern Namib, gemsbok utilise a great diversity of plant communities, such as the extensive dune fields, sand plains and mountain ranges to the north, and the starkly contrasted succulent steppe to the south (Kilian, pers. comm.).

In the Kalahari Gemsbok National Park, gemsbok show a preference for the sand dune country which has only a sparse cover of vegetation. Red sandy soil with short annual grasses such as *Schmidtia kalahariensis*, with scattered *Plinthus* sp, *Hermannia* sp, *Monechma* sp and *Heliotropium* sp, appears to be their preferred habitat in this area.

## Habits

Gemsbok are gregarious, occurring in herds of up to 300 individuals following rainfall in the southern Namib Desert (Kilian, pers. comm.). Smaller herds of two to three and up to 30 animals, as well as solitary males, are also found. Dieckmann (1980) showed that in Namaqualand during the wet season, because the food was dispersed evenly throughout the area, they occurred in large herds, which broke up into smaller herds during the dry season to utilise the less abundant food supply. Similar trends are evident in the Kalahari Gemsbok National Park, gemsbok congregating on the pans and fossil valleys during the wet season and dispersing into the sandveld during the dry season. The soil of the pans and valleys has a high clay content, resulting in a higher nutrient content which supports higher quality veld after rain. The clay soil has a higher wilting point than the sands, so that veld dries out relatively quickly in the dry season. Gemsbok then disperse into the sandveld (Williamson, pers. comm.). Gemsbok congregate in large herds on the plains during the wet season, and disperse into smaller groups in the shrub-coppice dunes with the onset of drier periods. This dispersal pattern is the result of the more abundant food supply in the dunes during dry periods (Kilian, pers. comm.).

They occur in mixed herds, nursery herds and solitary males. The males are territorial. As with springbok, territorial males are much more tolerant of other males than the males of other territorial species. Dieckmann (1980) recorded that in 13% of cases the territorial males were solitary; in 51% they were in mixed herds, and in 3% a territorial male accompanied a nursery herd. All the territorial males were estimated to be between five and seven years old and the non-territorial males between six months and five years. In the mixed herds an absolute dominance hierarchy was established among the non-territorial males, all being subordinate to the territorial male.

Courtship and mating are the prerogative of the territorial male. In Namaqualand, Dieckmann (1980) found that the territories had a mean size of 7,6 $km^2$ (range 4,2 to 9,8 $km^2$), and tended to be delimited by physical features of the terrain such as drainage lines or koppies. The boundaries were not well defined. In the Kalahari Gemsbok National Park territories averaged $25,7 \pm 17,7$ $km^2$, with fairly strictly defined boundaries, while female home ranges averaged $1430,5 \pm 1194,5$ $km^2$ (Knight, pers. comm.). Intrusions by strange territorial males into neighbouring territories were rarely recorded. Territorial males, however, do leave their territories after periods of isolation and, joining with mixed herds, enter strange territories. Dieckmann (1980) recorded a case where, after entering two strange territories, a male was chased back to his own. Territories are known to be maintained for up to three years in the Kalahari Gemsbok National Park (Knight, pers. comm.). As a result of the large size of the territories, observations of interactions between territorial males and trespassing males are rare. Demonstrative-threat advertising is usually sufficient to prevent trespassing. Dieckmann (1980) included in this defecation, pawing and horning of shrubbery. Territorial male gemsbok exhibited a characteristic and specialised defecation posture in the form of a low crouch. This ensured that the fecal pellets lay in a small pile and thus retained their odour longer than if they had been scattered. These dung sites may be located along boundaries or fortuitously throughout the territory and usually were deposited next to trees or large bushes (Knight, pers. comm.). As a prelude to defecation, territorial males frequently paw the ground which transfers secretions from the pedal glands to the ground. Territorial males shrub-horn more frequently than females or bachelor males. In this action, which may accompany defecation and pawing, shrubs are beaten with the horns and sometimes are destroyed totally in the process. Herding of mixed or nursery herds by a territorial male into his territory is of common occurrence.

Taylor (1969) has shown how well their metabolism is adapted to conserving moisture. From experiments in captivity, he showed that when gemsbok are subjected to high temperatures, their body temperature increases. After three or four hours of exposure to high temperatures they lose excess heat by radiation, as ambient temperatures in arid regions decline rapidly after sunset. He concluded that this meant that oryx get past the hottest hours of the day without expending moisture for evaporative cooling, thus saving large amounts of water, even when they are under severe heat load. This is probably one of the most important factors in allowing them to live under desert conditions. Moreover, their kidneys are capable of handling 1,8% brakish water (Giddings, 1990). In addition they have mechanisms to ensure that the temperature of the blood circulating to the brain remains substantially below that of body temperature. The carotid artery, which supplies most of the blood to the brain, divides into retia below the brain, these being surrounded by a sinus of cool venous blood returning from the nasal passages. Panting increases the air flow over the capillaries of the veins in the nasal passages to achieve this cooling process. Gemsbok can also moderate their breathing to reduce the loss of moisture in their respiratory tract. Taylor (1969) found that when gemsbok were deprived of water they did not sweat at all in response to heat, but began to pant when their body temperature exceeded 41 °C.

### Food

Gemsbok are dry-region roughage eaters (Hofmann, 1973), with a great capacity to digest fibre in their fore stomachs and leaves from dwarf species in their hindgut. They are essentially a grazing species, but Dieckmann (1980) recorded that, when introduced to an area where grass cover was minimal, they flourished on a diet consisting principally of browse and ephemeral plants. In the Kalahari Gemsbok National Park summer diets of gemsbok consisted of 89% grass, 7% browse and 4% dicotyledons, while in winter it consisted of 76% grass, 16% browse and 8% dicotyledons (Knight, pers. comm.). On the other hand, in the southern Namib Desert, several shrubs are utilised (Kilian, pers. comm.).

Although drinking water is not essential, gemsbok will dig for succulent subterranean roots, rhizomes and bulbs. In Namaqualand, Dieckmann (1980) recorded that, during the dry season, they would dig for the roots of a small karroid shrub, *Grielum humifusum*, this at a time when there was no sign of the plant above the ground. During the wet season they would eat the whole plant. In the Kalahari Gemsbok National Park they are profilic users of the underground storage organs of plants and Williamson (1987) estimated the mean number of excavations per hectare of such organs by gemsbok as 141, most excavations being clumped in distribution. They dig for tubers of the Gemsbok cucumber, *Acanthosicyos naudinianus* (66% water), *Brachystelma* spp (68%), *Cucumella cinerea* (69%), *Neorautanenia brachypus* (53%) and *Talinum tenuissimum* (62%), and make extensive use of the Tsamma melon, *Citrullus lanatus*.

In arid terrain, such as in the Kalahari Gemsbok National Park, the stomach contents of gemsbok usually have a high moisture content, averaging 82% water (Knight, pers. comm.). Bushmen use the contents as a source of water, squeezing them and straining the liquid through a bunch of grass. When fresh water is available in the Kalahari Gemsbok National Park they will drink 21,65 ± 3,61 l/individual every five days (Dreyer, 1987). This is a similar amount to that required daily by blue wildebeest in the region, indicating that gemsbok are better adapted to life in arid regions, perhaps partially due to their ability to select succulent plant parts in contrast to grazers like wildebeest which have to be content with grass as it lignifies.

### Reproduction

Gemsbok do not have a restricted breeding season, the young being born at any time throughout the year. In the western Transvaal, Skinner, van Zyl & Oates (1974) found a peak in calving about August/September. In the Kalahari Gemsbok National Park, gemsbok calve throughout the year. Although varying from year to year depending on rainfall patterns, calving peaks frequently occur in September. In the early 1980's there was a clear decline in the number of calves born as the drought in the Kalahari Gemsbok National Park intensified (Williamson, pers. comm.). On the extensive plains in the Namib Desert dune fields, there was a peak in calving during May/June/July. This peak corresponds with rainfall and was found to be highly synchronised (Kilian, pers. comm.).

Dieckmann (1980) suggested that females become sexually mature at about two years of age, having their first calf at the age of 29 to 33 months. The territorial males are primarily responsible for mating, and test the females' reproductive status by immersing their noses in their urine streams and exhibiting flehmen. If a territorial male finds that a female is in oestrus, he will court her by tapping between or alongside her hind legs with his forelegs (Laufschlagen). This has the effect of stimulating the female to stand and allow him to copulate with her. Only rarely do non-territorial males manage to copulate with oestrous females. If the female is not receptive she will walk away, circling the male who will follow her if he is persistent. The gestation period is 264 days (Brand, 1963).

At the time of parturition the female may either remain with the herd or leave it to give birth. The young newly-born gemsbok, after being cleaned up by its mother and suckling, hides itself. Usually it does not require prompting from its mother to do this, but in some cases she has to threaten it by butting the calf with her horns or threatening it with a "head low" attitude. The calf lies in a curled up position from which, if it is disturbed, it will adopt an alert position with the head stretched out in front and the ears extended backwards. The mother visits the calf to nurse it, usually walking around the area in which it is concealed and calling it out. The calf may spend the night with its mother. The next concealment site may be up to 3 km from the last one. Concealment of the young may continue for periods of from three to six weeks, after which the mother and calf will join either a mixed or nursery herd. This has given rise to the myth that gemsbok are born with horns because they grow quite rapidly to a length of 20 to 30 mm during this period of concealment, after which the calf is noticed for the first time and believed to be new-born. Females with concealed calves are very wary and will not approach the hiding places if they are aware of the presence of observers.

Nursing of calves within a herd appears to be synchronised as all the young suckle within a period of five or 10 minutes. This is attributed to the fact that nursing takes place after adults have had bouts of resting and ruminating.

**Plate 35**

327. Gemsbok, *Oryx gazella*
Gemsbok
328. African buffalo, *Syncerus caffer*
Afrikaanse buffel

PLATE 35

328

327

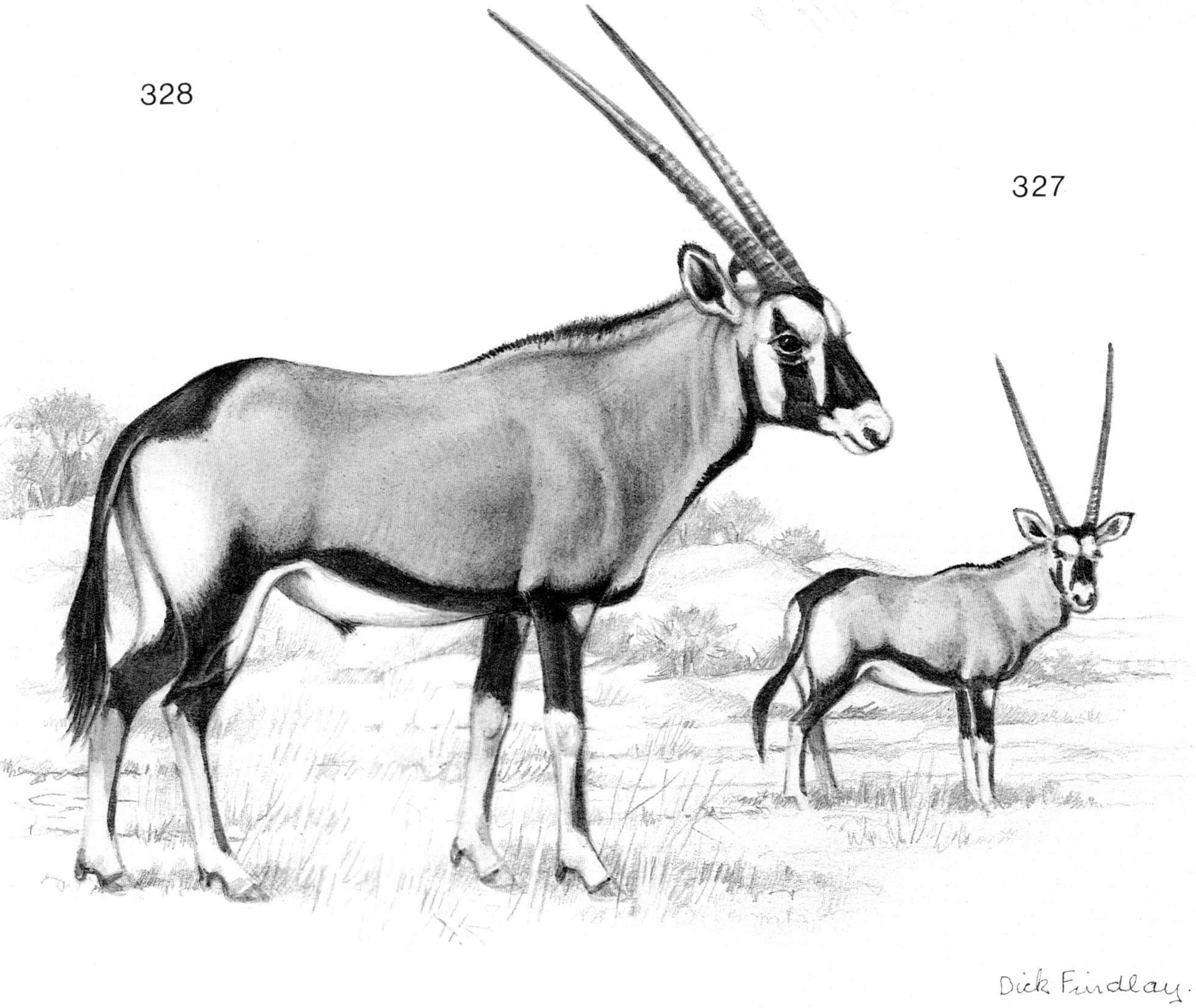

Dick Findlay.

## Subfamily BOVINAE

## Tribe Bovini

## Genus *Syncerus* Hodgson, 1847

No.328

## *Syncerus caffer* (Sparrman, 1779)

## African buffalo
## Afrikaanse buffel

Plate 35

### Colloquial Name

This has its origin from the Portuguese name for the species *bufalo*.

### Taxonomic Notes

Buffalo show a greater range of morphological variation than do any other African mammals. The extremes of this are the small, reddish, lightly built, small-horned buffalo of West Africa, that live in forest and originally were named *S. nanus*, and the much larger, darker and more heavily built, and horned, savanna buffalo, *S. caffer*. Within more recent times it has been shown that there is considerable intergradation of the two, in many areas where their distributions overlap, and generally it is agreed that they are simply subspecies of *S. caffer*, the forest buffalo, *S. c. nanus* (Boddaert, 1785), and the savanna buffalo, *S. c. caffer*. Only the latter is found in the Southern African Subregion.

### Description

Buffalo are very large, heavily built animals. They stand about 1,40 m at the shoulder. Adult males have a mass of up to 800 kg, females up to 750 kg. To support the massive body the legs are correspondingly heavy. The front hooves are distinctly larger than the hind, which show in the spoor and is an indication of the extra mass they carry in the huge head and thick neck (Plate IV).

Body hairs are 50,2±10,6 mm long, large, opaque and circular in cross-section, regular, waved cuticular scale pattern at the base, extremely irregular along shaft and tip which can be used as a diagnostic feature (Fig. XLII.1) (Keogh, 1983). Old adult males are black. Females never attain the same degree of blackness and usually show a tinge of reddish-brown. Juveniles are reddish-brown, the colour darkening with age. While the juveniles are well haired, the adults have only a sparse coating. Aberrant forms are known as, for example, the two specimens in the collection of the National Museum of Zimbabwe from the Luangwa Valley, Zambia which have a broad, pure white band round the middle of the body. A photograph of a similarly marked individual appears in Bainbridge (1969) from the same area.

The muzzle is broad, the rhinarium enclosing the nostrils black and usually shiny, as it remains slightly moist. The ears are large and tipped with a fringe of hair. The tail is long with a terminal tuft of long black or dark brown hair.

**Table 328**

Measurements (mm) and mass (kg) of a series of adult buffalo, *S. c. caffer*, (6,5 years old) from (b) Matusadona National Park, Zimbabwe (Taylor, 1985); (b) Savuti, Chobe National Park, Botswana (Patterson, 1979), and (c) Kruger National Park, South Africa (Pienaar, 1969a) (± S.D.)

| | Males | | Females | |
|---|---|---|---|---|
| | $\bar{x}$ | n | $\bar{x}$ | n |
| HB | 2510±230 | 4 | 2360±110 | 9 |
| Sh.ht | 1450± 80 | 4 | 144± 60 | 9 |
| Mass (a) | 574± 76 | 4 | 433± 40 | 11 |
| (b) | 631± 49 | | 435± 11 | |
| (c) | 590± 21 | | 513± 12 | |

In old adult males the horns are massive, arising from broad, heavy bosses which meet in the centre. They swing outwards and downwards, narrowing from the lowest point, from which they curve upwards and inwards and slightly backwards towards the tips. The bosses and about a third of the inner part of the horns are heavily rugose, the remainder smooth. The tips of the horns are rarely entire, showing abrasions and breaking. The horns of the females are always lighter in build, the bosses flatter, and less rugose. It is difficult to compare buffalo horns as they can be widely diverging in shape, either relatively thin and long or compact and heavy. The greatest length over the outside curve, from the centre of the boss to the tip, recorded from the Subregion, is a trophy measuring 1,295 m (Rowland Ward, 1986).

### Distribution

In historical times in the southern parts of their distributional range buffalo, *S. caffer*, occurred along the southern coast of the Republic of South Africa as far west as about Swellendam. Today, except in the Addo National Park, they are no longer found in the Cape Province.

*South of the Sahara, excluding the Southern African Subregion*

Vagrants may still be found in eastern **Gambia** from time to time, but there is no settled population. In **Guinea Bissau** they still occur in the eastern parts, are not uncommon in **Sierra Leone** and occur sparsely in **Liberia**. They occur in the Niger basin in **Burkina Faso**; in **Togo; Benin**; in many parts of **Ghana**; in **Nigeria**, except in the coastal areas; widely in **Cameroun**, and in southwestern and northeastern **Central African Republic**. They occur in the southern and eastern parts of the **Sudan** and in parts of **Ethiopia**; in **Kenya**, excluding parts of central and northeast Kenya, and in southwestern **Somalia**. They occur in most parts of **Uganda**; in **Zaire; Tanzania; Angola**, excluding the southwestern parts of the country; from **Zambia**, excluding the extreme west; from National Parks and reserves in **Malawi**, and from **Mozambique**, north of the Zambezi River.

*Southern African Subregion*

In **Namibia** they occur from the extreme northeastern parts of the country narrowly along the eastern border south to about 20°, which corresponds with their occurrence in **Botswana**, where they occur throughout the northern parts of the country, in the Okavango Delta, and in the northeast, south to near Lake Ngami and the Makgadikgadi Pan. In **Zimbabwe** they are absent from the central plateau, but occur throughout the northern and northeastern parts of the country and in the southeast, where, however, there are moves afoot to eradicate them from the ranching areas on account of foot and mouth disease. They are patchy in distribution in **Mozambique**; they still occur south of the Zambezi River in the north, central and southwest, with a small population in the southern Inhambane District. They occur in the eastern **Transvaal** south to the Swaziland border. There remains a relict population in the Addo National Park in the **Cape Province** which marks the last remnants of what was once a wide coastal occurrence. From this population, which has grown in numbers with protection, they have been reintroduced to other parts of the province. In **Natal** there are large populations in the Hluhluwe and Umfolozi Game Reserves and in their immediate vicinity.

### Habitat

The habitat requirements of the savanna buffalo, *S. c. caffer*, include a plentiful supply of grass, shade and water. This they find in the better-watered northern, northeastern and eastern parts of the Subregion. They probably never occurred in the Karoo, or on the open grass plains of the Orange Free State and Transvaal, as some, or all, of these essential requirements were not met. However, in historical times they did find suitable habitat in the thick coastal bush along the southern parts of the Subregion, as far west as about Swellendam (Paterson, 1789).

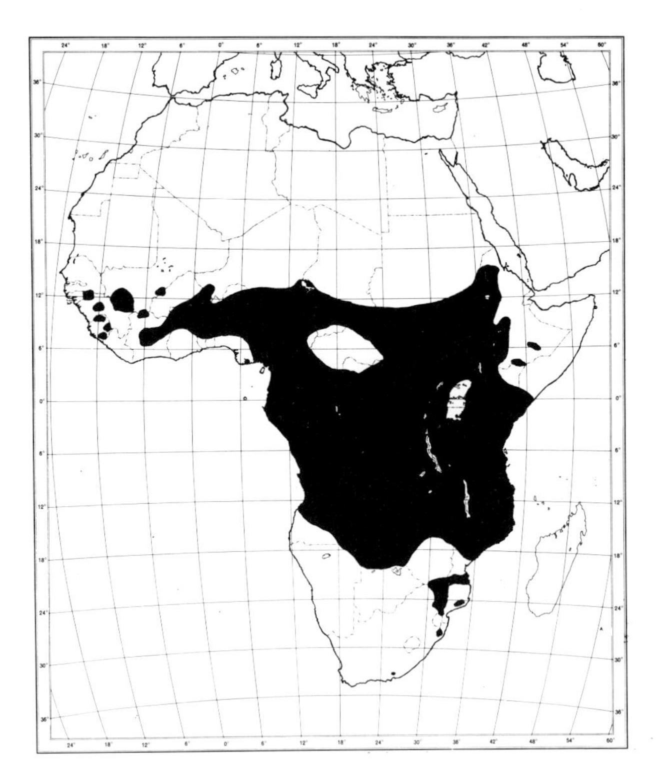

The suitable grasses are found in a variety of types of woodland including mopane, *Baikiaea*, *Acacia* and *Brachystegia* and in the open vleis which occur in association with the last three named. However, they do not frequent wide open areas of grassland or floodplain far from the shade of trees which they require for resting up in during the hotter hours of the day. Nevertheless, the seasonal movements to which they are prone, may carry them on to open grassland in transit or they may utilise it temporarily for a time after sunset or before sunrise. Bachelor males showed a great affinity for the Kariba lakeshore environment in all seasons, while breeding herds were common on the *Panicum repens* grassland along the shore in the hot dry season (Taylor, 1985). Taylor concluded that *P. repens* grassland is the best available buffalo habitat in Matusadona National Park. The next best habitat was the escarpment base woodland savanna ecotone.

Buffalo drink water regularly, generally twice daily, and are inclined to graze in its vicinity, often using the shelter of extensive reed beds in which to rest. Mud-wallowing is engaged in regularly and is important to them in thermoregulation.

### Habits

The savanna buffalo, *S. c. caffer*, is gregarious, occurring in herds of up to several thousand (Hwange, Zimbabwe, 2 500; Savuti, Botswana, 3 000). These herds are relatively stable units, the smaller herds being part of the larger which aggregate and disperse from time to time (Sinclair, 1977). In addition, large herds are subject to seasonal movements. As the country dries up they tend to move to permanently watered areas where there is ample grazing and water, moving out with the onset of the rains about October/November and then tending to fragment into the smaller herds. When resting the larger herds break up into groups, rejoining at the end of the rest period. Sinclair (1977) did not find any clear-cut subgroups within the herd, but did record a distinct family cohesion among the cows that may continue into adult life, but which ceases in the bulls with the onset of puberty at about three years of age. While in allied species such as the water buffalo, *Bubalis bubalis*, there is a system of "leaders" consisting of family groups or individual cows within a group, no such hierarchy has been shown among buffalo so far.

Old and young bulls may leave the herds to form themselves into small, independently living bachelor groups; the two age classes, however, tend to remain apart. Solitary old bulls too are found, these being particularly prone to predation by prides of lions. Grimsdell (1969) found that the old bulls show signs of decreased fertility and have a tendency to remain within very restricted home ranges, some as small as three or four square kilometres. Taylor (1985) also found that bachelor groups in Matusadona occupied areas of 0,5–3 km$^2$ and daily movement of these males was of the order of 1–2 km/day. Within the bachelor groups there is less harassment than would be found if they attempted to return to the herd. Agonistic behaviour, nevertheless, continues within these groups where there is an established hierarchy, this being a continuation of the situation found within the bulls in the herds. Adult bulls may leave the herd seasonally, rejoining it at the rutting season, which coincides with the onset of the rains. Bachelor group size varied from 1,5 in May to 5,5 in October and exceeded four in the hot dry summer months (Taylor, 1985). Because of their small size, these groups could exploit small food niches and remain residential along the lake shore. Breeding herds tended to move around with a home range size estimated at 60–70 km$^2$ for Matusadona. On the other hand, Conybeare (1980) measured home range sizes of 250 km$^2$ in the Sengwa Wildlife Research Area which does not have the *P. repens* grassveld. He also reported an average distance of 6,1 km covered by a herd of buffalo over 24h at Sengwa and 3,4 km at Matusadona.

Within the herd there is a linear hierarchy among the adult bulls which is maintained more by threat behaviour than by serious fighting. This threat is demonstrated by holding the head high, nose pointing to the ground, or a combination of these postures, with a lateral display of the body which emphasises its size. There may also be some head or earth tossing or hooking motions with the horns. If the opponent does not demonstrate submission by holding its head low, with the horns back, and if at close quarters it does not put its nose under the neck or belly of its opponent, fighting may develop. When fighting ensues opponents charge each other, head held out with noses forward, often growling. Just before meeting they lower their heads and take the impact on the boss of the horns. The winner is the one with the greatest power behind this action, the loser turning and being chased off. The cows also exhibit this agonistic behaviour, but to a lesser extent.

Herd size increases in the dry season and is small and fragmented in the wet season in response to scattered water and food resources. This is unrelated to seasonal breeding (Taylor, 1987). Where herds are very large the dominance among the adult bulls is less well defined than in the smaller herds, and in females may not exist at all (Sinclair, 1977). Buffalo herds have clearly defined home ranges which show little overlap with those of neighbouring herds. However, they may vary in size seasonally to include areas where food or water is temporarily plentiful, tending to remain in the vicinity of water in the dry season and to move extensively from this during the rains. Individuals wandering from herds on to the home range of other herds are not accepted by them. The size of the home ranges is variable depending on the availability of food and water, those living in wetter areas having smaller home ranges than those in drier areas.

The herds move to water in the early morning and again in the early evening. Mud-wallowing, especially during the hottest hours of the day, is indulged in by the bulls, but rarely by the cows or young. This wallowing is less effective in temperature regulation than the use of shade (Sinclair, 1977), which the herd normally seeks at this time of the day, individual groups standing or lying down under trees or in patches of tall grass or reed beds. At Matusadona, buffalo spent 76% of their time grazing and ruminating (Taylor, 1985). They did not ruminate more during the dry season as nutrition remained high, unlike other areas, where wallowing or lying in the shade occupied 14,7 % and 26,7% of their time respectively.

Buffalo are inquisitive and individuals will break away from a herd to examine vehicles, advancing with noses outstretched testing the air. If disturbed, they will race to rejoin the herd which is quick to stampede, often in unexpected directions. They have the reputation for being the most dangerous of the African species to hunt. When wounded they have been known to circle and stalk their hunters, lying alert in thick bush and charging out at close range. A charging buffalo with head outstretched is difficult to stop as the heavy boss and wide sweep of the horns cover the shoulders and can deflect or stop even the bullet of a heavy rifle. In attack they are very persistent, and hunters, forced to take to trees, have been kept there for hours while the buffalo stalks underneath, waiting for a chance to attack.

The rinderpest epidemic of the last century which swept through the continent from northeast Africa to the Cape all but exterminated the buffalo. While in parts of their distributional range they were totally wiped out, in others they survived and have recovered in a remarkable way, which is a measure of their power of recuperation as a species. Disease and climatic factors affecting the habitat, rather than predation, are the most serious factors regulating buffalo numbers.

While foot and mouth disease does not necessarily kill buffalo it can cause a drop in condition, when other factors can become lethal to them. Attempts are under way by the Veterinary Department, Zimbabwe to create foot and mouth free buffalo herds for reintroduction into areas free of this disease (Condy & Hedger, 1978). This interesting and so far very successful venture holds promise for their future and would allow their reintroduction into areas where they formerly occurred and where foot and mouth disease is not endemic.

**Food**

In comparison to other wild ruminants buffalo have the most efficient system to digest fibrous food (a grass and roughage feeder—Hofmann, 1973). While fresh, sprouting, young grass on recently burnt areas is attractive to them, as it is to some other species of herbivores, they are less partial to it than most and as readily will feed on old grass. They avoid areas, however, where the grass has been trampled or overgrazed. Their utilisation and trampling of stands of old grass is important to other species in opening them up and making the new growth available to them. Taylor (1985) found that half or more of grazing time (observing bachelor groups at full moon), can take place at night. Individuals have been observed on rare occasions to browse a little.

In seeking areas with a plentiful food supply, buffalo will range over a very wide area away from water but are dependent on regular water intake. Pienaar (1969b) recorded movements of this nature of up to 17 km in the Kruger National Park. They are selective feeders in the rainy season but are non-selective in the dry season, with a preference for grasses such as red grass, *Themeda triandra*; small buffalo grass, *Panicum coloratum*; buffalo grass, *P. maximum*; spear grass, *Heteropogon contortus*, and finger grasses, *Digitaria* spp. On the shoreline of Lake Kariba there is, in parts, a broad fringe of lakeshore grassland of buffalo grass, *P. repens*, and buffalo, which find this grass very attractive, congregate there in large numbers, even crossing to islands to reach it. Sinclair (1977) remarked on the similarity of Pienaar's (1969b) list with the grass species recorded in parts of East Africa.

Although there is a scarcity of information on the changes in food utilised seasonally in the southern parts of their distributional range, analysis of stomach contents in East Africa shows that they select for grass leaf, the degree of this being greater towards the end of the rainy season and declining during the dry season. This reflects an increasing difficulty in finding the preferred types of food and an acceptance of the less preferred (Sinclair, 1977).

Buffalo are sensitive to heat and Sinclair (1977) found that if, while feeding during the day, their subcutaneous temperature approached 40 °C they would cease to graze and move into the shade. Most of their feeding, however, takes place at night, some 85% of the 24 hours being taken up in feeding and ruminating. More time is spent ruminating during the dry season as the food then contains a greater fibre content.

**Reproduction**

At the Matusadona National Park, Zimbabwe, all conceptions occurred in the six months from December to May, with births occurring 11 months later between November and April (Taylor, 1985). Conceptions took place towards the latter half of the rains, with over 60% in February/March, from which a mean conception date of 4 March ± 7 days was calculated. Similarly with 59% of births in January/February, a mean birthdate of 4 February ± 7,2 days was determined. In bulls, seminiferous tubule diameter and testes mass increased from August to peak during and just prior to the breeding season respectively. At no stage in the year did spermatogenesis cease but no conceptions were recorded outside the breeding season.

Carmichael, Patterson, Drager & Breton (1977) found that in northern Botswana the greater bulk of the calf crop was born during the summer months from October to April, with peaks, which varied depending on the vagaries of the season, between about December and February. A few births only were recorded at other times of the year. Pienaar (1969b) found that in the Kruger National Park the majority of calves are born between January and April, and Fairall (1968) showed that there is a peak in January/February. This coincides with the optimum period of the growth of the grass and is at a time when the protein value of the food is high.

Taylor (1985) found the mean age of first ovulation as 3,2 years at a mass of 325–374 kg. Unlike buffalo elsewhere, Matusadona cows ovulated and conceived within the same year. The interval elsewhere was about one year. Buffalo may have their first calf when four to five years old (Carmichael *et al.*, 1977; Taylor, 1985; Mizutani, 1987). In males, spermatogenesis commenced at 2,5 years of age, with testes mass at 130 g, seminiferous tubule diameter at 125 μm and a body mass of 300 kg (Taylor, 1985). In contrast, no males over 10 years were found in breeding herds. While some bulls may reach sexual maturity at three and a half years old and most at five and a half, they are seldom if ever allowed to take part in breeding activity by the more dominant bulls until they are seven to eight years old. The mean gestation period is 335 days (S.D.=10,5; n=3) for males, and 331 (S.D.=8,1; n=3) for females (Attwell, C. in Mizutani, 1987). A single young is produced at birth, with a mass of 31,1 kg (n=22) for males and 31,2 kg (n=9) for females. The calving interval was 509 days (Attwell, C. in Mizutani, 1987). Fecundity among the adult cows may reach 86% under good conditions (Mizutani, 1987), but under suboptimal conditions cows calve every alternate year (Pienaar, 1969a). Carmichael *et al.* (1977) gave a pregnancy rate of 57% for semi-arid savanna which seems reasonable.

Sinclair (1977) noted that births occur either during the afternoon or just before dawn when the herd is resting. At this time the cow remains with the herd. As the calf requires several hours to gain enough strength to follow the herd, the mother and new-born calf often are left behind temporarily. New-born calves are sometimes left in the shelter of thick undergrowth as the mother moves off to graze.

If they lose contact the calf bleats and the mother answers with a croaking call. Suckling continues until it is about 15 months old or when the next calf is born. It may remain with its mother until it is about two years old.

Pienaar (1968) found that, in the Kruger National Park, calf mortality was high, only six to nine of every 20 calves reaching maturity. Sinclair (1977) found that, after two years of age, mortality drops to a low level, probably due to the protection afforded to the calf by the herd. While adult buffalo are a match for hyaenas, lions take toll of the young and two or more of these predators will tackle adults which they cut off or which are separated from the herds. Adult and even old bulls in the smaller bull groups are more vulnerable than individuals in the larger herds. Predation is, however, a lesser factor in mortality than disease or adverse seasonal effects on the habitat.

In the young bulls the bosses of the horns are covered with hair up to the age of about two to three years old. The bosses are not formed properly and do not meet in the mid-line until they are about three to five years old. Females have two pairs of inguinal mammae.

## Tribe Tragelaphini

### Genus *Tragelaphus* Blainville, 1816

Key to the species adapted from Ansell (1972)

1. Size larger, males standing about 1,5 m at the shoulders, females smaller; no inguinal pouches; horns in an open spiral forming one or more complete twists; false hooves of the hind feet with hairy fringed glands

   ... *strepsiceros*

   Size smaller, males standing up to 1,2 m at the shoulders, females smaller; horns in a narrower spiral forming one complete twist; false hooves without hairy fringed glands (except apparently in *angasii*)

   ... 2

2. Hooves elongated, those on forefeet up to about 180 mm in males, 160 mm in females, with the back of the pasterns bare (or with only a small isolated tuft of hair) and rubbery

   ... *spekei*

   Hooves not particularly elongated, back of pasterns fully haired

   ... 3

3. Larger, horns in adults well over 560 mm; well developed mane, throat and ventral fringes of hair in the males, females with a body pattern of vertical stripes; tail long and not very bushy

   ... *angasii*

   Smaller, horns in adults not exceeding 560 mm; males with poorly developed mane, without throat and ventral fringes of hair; females with a pattern of spots and horizontal as well as vertical stripes (in the southern forms the pattern is less well developed); tail shorter and very bushy

   ... *scriptus*

No. 329

## *Tragelaphus strepsiceros* (Pallas, 1766)

## Kudu

## Koedoe

Plate 36

### Colloquial Name

This is derived from the Khoikhoi name *kudu*.

### Taxonomic Notes

The kudu was described originally from a specimen from the "Cape of Good Hope". They never occurred, however, in the vicinity of the Cape Peninsula, the nearest records being from the Kamiesberg in southern Namaqualand (Skead, 1980). Paterson (1789) recorded kudu near Caledon, but this is doubtful as they probably never occurred nearer the Cape in this direction than about the Oudtshoorn district.

Ansell (1972) listed four subspecies from the continent, of which only one, *T. s. strepsiceros*, occurs in the Subregion. The subspecies have been named on the number of light coloured transverse stripes on the body, which Haltenorth (1963) stated is subject to considerable variation.

### Description

To Stevenson-Hamilton (1947) and indeed to many other nature lovers the kudu ranks among our most handsome species. He described the male kudu as the "acme of Nature's efforts to attain perfection of type".

Adult males stand about 1,4 m at the shoulder with masses of up to 250 kg; the females are distinctly smaller with maximum masses of up to about 200 kg and shoulder heights of about 1,25 m (Table 329.1).

Simpson (1966) showed that it was possible to classify immature male kudu into three categories based on the development of the horns, and to age them by months, with an accuracy of about three months. He also found that male kudu could be aged up to about eight years counting the cementum layers in the teeth, and relating these to the "cheeks" or transverse ridging on the horns caused by seasonal fluctuations in growth.

All male members of the genus *Tragelaphus*, which includes the nyala, bushbuck, sitatunga and kudu, have a well developed ridge on their horns which arises from the front of the base of the horns and follows the curving of the horn nearly to its tip. In the case of the kudu it is demarcated clearly.

In the Subregion the body colour is fawn-grey. Body hairs are 20,1±8,8 mm long, oval in cross-section, with a regular waved scale pattern at the base merging into an irregular pattern along the shaft and tip (Fig. XLII.1) (Keogh, 1983). The females are often tinged cinnamon, the juveniles distinctly so. They have a series of five to 14 unevenly spaced white transverse stripes across their backs, from just behind the shoulder to the rump. These tend to lie close together behind the shoulders and are spaced more widely towards the rump. Their elongated necks are greyish, darker in the males than the females, and become dark grey in old males. The lower parts of the legs are lighter in colour than the body with a broad band of dark brown or black just above the hooves. The facial markings vary widely. These consist of a V-shaped white band, the arms of the V arising from just in front of the eyes and continuing across the muzzle, and one or four white patches below the eyes on the sides of the face. The lips and chin are white. The shoulders in both sexes have distinct humps. The hair of the upstanding mane which runs from the back of the head to beyond the shoulders, stands upright on top of this hump, accentuating its height. The hairs of the mane are white tipped and tail off in length behind the hump, continuing as a short white or dark brown crest to near the base of the tail. The tail may be blackish above, or slightly browner than the general colour of the body with a black tip, and reaches nearly to the hocks. Underneath the tail is pure white, making it very conspicuous when curled upwards in flight.

The ears of the kudu are a distinct feature in both sexes. They are particularly large and broad for the size of the head, pink inside, with white hair on their fringes near their notches and on the outside near their rounded tips. At their backs they have fringes of black hair down the sides and encircling the tips.

Adult males have a short beard of dark hair and a fringe of long hair down the mid-throat which extends nearly to the upper chest, reappearing again as a fringe on the mid-belly. The long hairs on this fringe are dark at the base, then with a white band, and end in black tips. The white bands on the hairs, lying in line, give the appearance of a distinct white band down this hairy fringe. In the females the mane and this fringe of long hair are less developed, the fringe down the throat often being white, and they usually lack the fringe on the belly.

The spoor shows the rather elongated marks of the hooves (Plate IV).

**Table 329.1**

Measurements (mm) and mass (kg) of kudu, *T. strepsiceros*, from (a) Zimbabwe (Wilson, 1970); (b) Addo National Park, Eastern Cape Province (May 1987) (Skinner, unpubl.)

**(a)**

| | Males | | | Females | | |
|---|---|---|---|---|---|---|
| | $\bar{x}$ | n | Range | $\bar{x}$ | n | Range |
| TL | 2580 | 7 | 2470–2670 | 2460 | 33 | 2280–2590 |
| T | 430 | 7 | 410–480 | 420 | 33 | 370–470 |
| Hf c/u | 640 | 7 | 620–660 | 600 | 33 | 570–620 |
| E | 253 | 7 | 244–270 | 238 | 33 | 225–250 |
| Mass | 227,8 | 7 | 190,3–258,2 | 157,4 | 33 | 119,6–210,2 |

**(b)**

| | Males | | | Females | | |
|---|---|---|---|---|---|---|
| | $\bar{x}$ | n | Range | $\bar{x}$ | n | Range |
| TL | 2528 | 16 | 2570–2590 | 2315 | 20 | 2125–2310 |
| T | 440 | 16 | 430–510 | 411 | 20 | 380–460 |
| Hf c/u | 522 | 16 | 500–570 | 507 | 20 | 475–530 |
| E | 250 | 16 | 245–260 | 244 | 20 | 230–255 |
| Mass | 220,8 | 16 | 174–268 | 152,1 | 20 | 112–176 |

In the northern Transvaal, Skinner & Huntley (1971) gave the mean mass of 19 bulls as 235,9 kg.

At birth the calf has three incisor milk teeth and a milk canine tooth on either side in the lower jaw and three milk premolars on either side of the upper and lower jaws. The dental formula is:

$i\frac{0}{3}\ c\frac{0}{1}\ p\frac{3}{3} = 20$

The milk incisors and canines start to be replaced by the permanent teeth at an age of about 21 months and are fully replaced by 24 months. The milk premolars start to be replaced at about 29 months and at this stage the three molar teeth on either side of both jaws are fully erupted. By about 34 months of age the individual has its full permanent set of teeth, and the formula is:

$I\frac{0}{3}\ C\frac{0}{1}\ P\frac{3}{3}\ M\frac{3}{3} = 32$ (Simpson, 1966)

The horn buds which first appear between five to six months show as black platelets. Horn growth commences at about five months of age. At first they are seldom more than short spikes that swing outwards from the head. The first curve starts to show as an inward curve at about 14 to 17 months old and this curve is completed by about 21 months. The second outward curve shows by about 30 months. Horn growth continues throughout the life of the individual (Simpson, 1966).

Usually only the males carry horns but rarely the females do as well. These at their maximum development consist of a thin, twisted pair often curling in front of the eyes or forming irregular shapes across the muzzle. They are poor replicas of the stately corkscrew horns of the adult males which can reach a length over the front curve of up to 1,8 m. The world record at the moment is a pair from the northern Transvaal which reached a length of 1,759 m (Rowland Ward, 1986).

**Distribution**

Kudu persist even in the face of heavy hunting pressure and settlement. In this respect they are one of the most resilient of our larger mammalian species. In spite of this there has been some shrinkage of their former distributional range and they have become locally extinct in parts. In the Subregion they have disappeared from parts of Natal and from the eastern parts of the Orange River Valley. In the more arid areas, such as in southern Botswana, they occur widely where there is suitable habitat, but are considered to be uncommon. Within the limits shown on the map they only occur where the habitat is suitable and have never occurred in deserts or in forests.

*South of the Sahara, excluding the Southern African Subregion*

Kudu occur in parts of southeastern **Chad**; in the eastern **Central African Republic**; eastern **Sudan** and in the western and southern parts of **Ethiopia**. They are rare and localised in **Somalia**. They are widespread and localised in northern and southern **Kenya**, with a break in distribution centrally. They occur in northeastern **Uganda** and throughout **Tanzania**, except in the extreme northwest. In **Zaire** they are confined to the southeast, in **Zambia** throughout, except in parts of the Northern Province and western areas abutting on to Angola and Zaire. In **Malawi** they are found in reserves, and are common throughout northern **Mozambique**, north of the Zambezi River. In **Angola** they occur in the southern parts of the country, excluding the coastal desert.

*Southern African Subregion*

They are distributed widely but locally in **Namibia**, except in the coastal Namib Desert and in parts of the south. They are widespread in **Botswana, Zimbabwe** and in **Mozambique**, south of the Zambezi River. In the **Transvaal** they are confined to the western, northern and eastern parts of the province, in **Swaziland** to the eastern sector, south to the northeastern parts of **Natal**. They occur in the northeastern **Cape Province** in the area bordered by Griquatown, Kuruman, Vryburg and Kimberley and in the southeastern parts of the province from about 27 °E westwards to about 22 °E. They have expanded their range in the eastern Cape Province within recent years (Owen-Smith, *in litt.*).

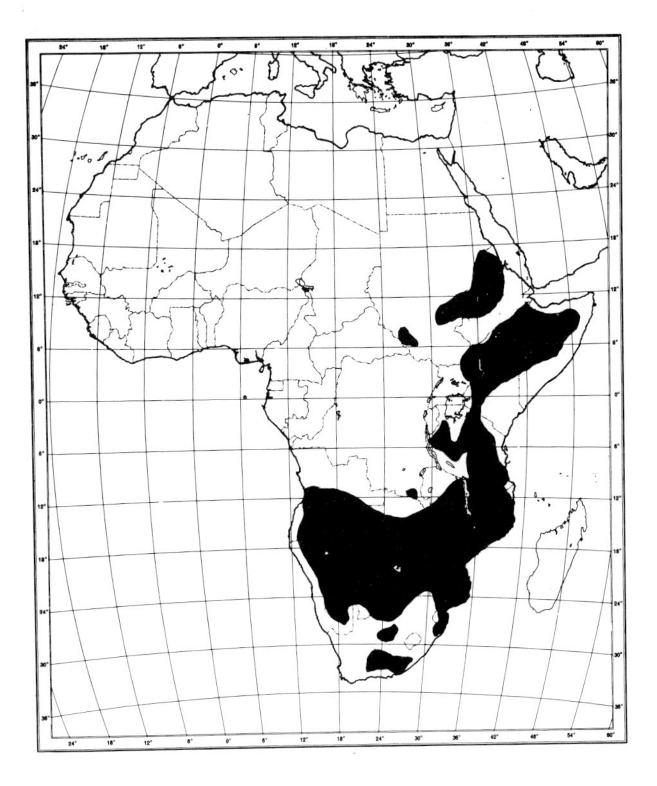

**Habitat**

Kudu are a savanna woodland species that do not occur in desert, forest or in open grassland areas. In semi-desert areas, as for example those lying within the South West Arid Zone, they tend to be localised, only being found where there is sufficient woodland or scrub to afford them protection and food. In the Kruger National Park males have a preference throughout the year for riparian woodland and thickets along drainage lines; the female herds utilise a variety of habitats (du Toit, *in litt.*). In many parts, agricultural developments that lie adjacent to woodland or broken country with thickets, have improved their habitat. In a recent study du Plessis & Skinner (1987) found that the damage kudu inflict on sunflower crops is negligible.

Kudu are partial to areas of broken, rocky terrain, where they have a cover of woodland and a nearby water supply. In arid country they tend to be confined to woodland along water courses or to areas where there are scattered stands of *Acacia* spp woodland, coppice growth of *Terminalia* spp or scrub of sufficient height to provide shelter. Under these conditions they tend to be localised in occurrence and can satisfy their moisture requirements by eating tsamma melons, *Citrullus lanatus*, or cucurbits which are a feature of the vegetation of the sandy, semi-desert areas in the South West Arid Zone. Kudu seldom if ever occur on open grassland except in transit. They do occur, however, in clearings in woodland.

Simpson (1968) showed that, in southwestern Zimbabwe, the preferred habitat throughout the year was riverine *Acacia* thickets. Open mopane, *Colophospermum mopane*, woodland appeared to be the least acceptable. While the males showed least seasonal change in habitat, the females tended to move into the riverine *Acacia* thickets during the dry season where, owing to the subsurface moisture, there was a greater availability of browse and better cover. The availability of a water supply is not an essential habitat requirement in years of normal rainfall as they can obtain their moisture requirements from their food (du Toit, *in litt.*). The highest recorded densities of the species occur in the succulent evergreen thickets of the valley bushveld in the eastern Cape Province (Owen-Smith, *in litt.*).

## Habits

Kudu are gregarious, but herds are usually small, hardly ever numbering more than about 12 individuals and far more commonly only up to about four. In an agriculturally developed area in the Transvaal, near Settlers, du Plessis (1986) recorded a mean herd size of 3,9, with a range of 1–30. At Pretorius Kop in the Kruger National Park, Owen-Smith (1984) found that the largest social unit consisted of 21 individuals and included 11 adult females. These larger units are usually fragmented, the mean group size recorded being a minimum of four during the calving months of January to March, to six to eight during the remainder of the year. Simpson (1968) found that in Zimbabwe the maximum number in a herd was 12. He found that there were two peaks in herd size, the first in November to January just before the females were due to calve, the second in June/July at the time of the rut. During the latter period the greatest number of single individuals was recorded. Outside the rutting period the adult males may remain solitary or may join up to form small bachelor herds of up to about six. At the time of the rut an adult male may be accompanied by a herd of females and their offspring numbering up to about 12 in all. Owen-Smith (1984) recorded a peak in solitary males in the Kruger National Park in February/March just prior to the rut. Most adult males attach themselves to female groups from April to June, and during the remainder of the year form loose all-male groups of two to five, but sometimes up to 16. In the Limpopo valley, Zimbabwe, aggregations of up to 12 males were noted in December (Skinner, unpubl.).

In the Kruger National Park the female groups had home ranges of 3,0 to 25,0 km$^2$; in the eastern Cape Province they were much smaller at about 1,0 km$^2$. In the Park the males move over a larger home range of up to 50 km$^2$.

Kudu are most active in the early morning and late afternoon, lying up during the heat of the day in woodland or in thickets. Where they are subject to disturbance, as for example in farming areas, they are nocturnally active. They are a shy and retiring species and, in traversing open areas or in approaching to drink, they remain constantly on the alert and are cautious and hesitant in their progress. If disturbed they immediately run for the nearest cover without stopping to observe the cause. In woodland they are less nervous and usually stand long enough to assess the situation. Under these circumstances the large rounded ears, especially of the females, are conspicuous, which, when cocked towards the observer, appear to dwarf their heads. They have a heavy and rather clumsy run, curling their tails upwards to show the white hair on their under parts. This is a group coordination display and a visual indication of their direction of flight. When they detect movements without being able to identify the cause, they vocalise with a loud harsh bark (Owen-Smith, *in litt.*), which Dorst & Dandelot (1970) described as the loudest vocalisation made by any antelope. The adult males hold their noses straight forward when running through woodland and so lay their long spiral horns back on to their shoulders to avoid contact with low branches.

Kudu are accomplished jumpers and can surmount a two metre high fence with graceful ease. Stevenson-Hamilton (1947) found that he had to raise his garden fence to 3 m to prevent them raiding during periods of adverse veld conditions.

## Food

Kudu are predominantly browsers, although they may eat fresh grass. They eat a greater variety of browse plants than any other of our Subregion bovids, to the extent that most species that are available are utilised to a greater or lesser degree. Brynard & Pienaar (1960) listed no less than 148 species of plants eaten by kudu in the Kruger National Park. The leaves and shoots are preferred, but they will also eat seed pods of species such as the umbrella thorn, *Acacia tortilis*, either when they are green or dry, the leaves of *Aloe* spp, and many plants generally avoided by other browsing species or known to be poisonous.

Novellie (1983) found that in the Kruger National Park kudu generally favour forbs over woody plants, forbs comprising about 65% of their diet during most of the year, although their utilisation fell to below 20% during the early part of the growing season. At this time early flushing woody species such as knob-thorn, *Acacia nigrescens*, and russet bush-willow, *Combretum hereroense*, offered high quality food, when little else was available, and comprised a high proportion of kudu diet in September to November. Later flushing species such as white-berry, *Securinega virosa*, and sickle-bush, *Dichrostachys cinerea*, increased in importance during December to March. Red bush-willow, *C. apiculatum*, was favoured during the dry season.

The fruits of strychnos, *Strychnos* spp and marula, *Sclerocarya birrea*, as well as the seed pods of *Acacia* spp are highly sought after when available and, in the eastern Cape Province, they eat succulents including *Portulacaria afra* as well as *Aloe* spp and small succulent *Euphorbia* spp (Owen-Smith, *in litt.*).

Du Plessis & Skinner (1987) found that 89% (83–95%) of identifiable material in faeces was dicotyledonous. This was most marked in winter when domestic crop availability was at its lowest and grass species are almost totally lignified. *Acacia tortilis* provided a large prportion of the diet and with other *Acacia* spp. constituted 50% of the diet in August and September. In late winter seed pods, taken from the ground, featured in the diet. Monocotyledons (11% on average) were better represented compared to other studies due to the presence of cultivated species. A marked increase in grazing in September could be attributed to sprouting grass following spring rain and *Acacia* spp shedding their leaves. Damage to maize and sunflowers was negligible. This was in contrast to other reports (Smithers, 1983) describing them as wasteful raiders of grain crops. They do favour vegetables and ornamental plants in some areas.

In the Transvaal kudu feed both during the day and at night. Drinking usually takes place during the late morning (Owen-Smith, *in litt.*).

## Reproduction

The calving period for kudu in southeastern Zimbabwe and the Kruger National Park begins in December or early January, peaks in February and continues for about another three months (Pienaar, 1963; Simpson, 1968). Occasionally calves are born outside this period. Of 16 adult females culled in the Addo National Park in April 1987, none had ovulated yet or were pregnant (Skinner, unpubl.).

Skinner & Huntley (1971) investigated the sexual cycle in the males from a sample collected throughout the year in the northern Transvaal and showed that there was a peak in breeding capability in June, declining to minimal values in November. This correlates with behavioural observations (see **Habits**).

After a gestation period of 270 days (Owen-Smith, *in litt.*), a single calf is born with a mass at birth of about 16 kg (Wilson, 1965). There are no records of twins.

The main calving period falls at a time when the grass is at its tallest. Females break away temporarily from the herd to give birth in the cover of this grass. The females eat the afterbirth although the umbilical cord remains attached to the calf for about 10 days, and after cleaning up their calves leave them hidden for two to three months, after which the calves follow their mothers and rejoin the female herds (Owen-Smith, *in litt.*).

The calves are light cinnamon-fawn in colour with white, clearly marked, lateral stripes. They have a distinct dorsal crest of black hair down the back, except where it is crossed by the lateral stripes, where it is white. The chin, throat,

**Plate IV Spoor**

325. Roan, *Hippotragus equinus*
326. Sable, *Hippotragus niger*
327. Gemsbok, *Oryx gazella*
328. Buffalo, *Syncerus caffer*
329. Kudu, *Tragelaphus strepsiceros*
330. Sitatunga, *Tragelaphus spekei*
331. Nyala, *Tragelaphus angasii*
332. Bushbuck, *Tragelaphus scriptus*
333. Eland, *Taurotragus oryx*

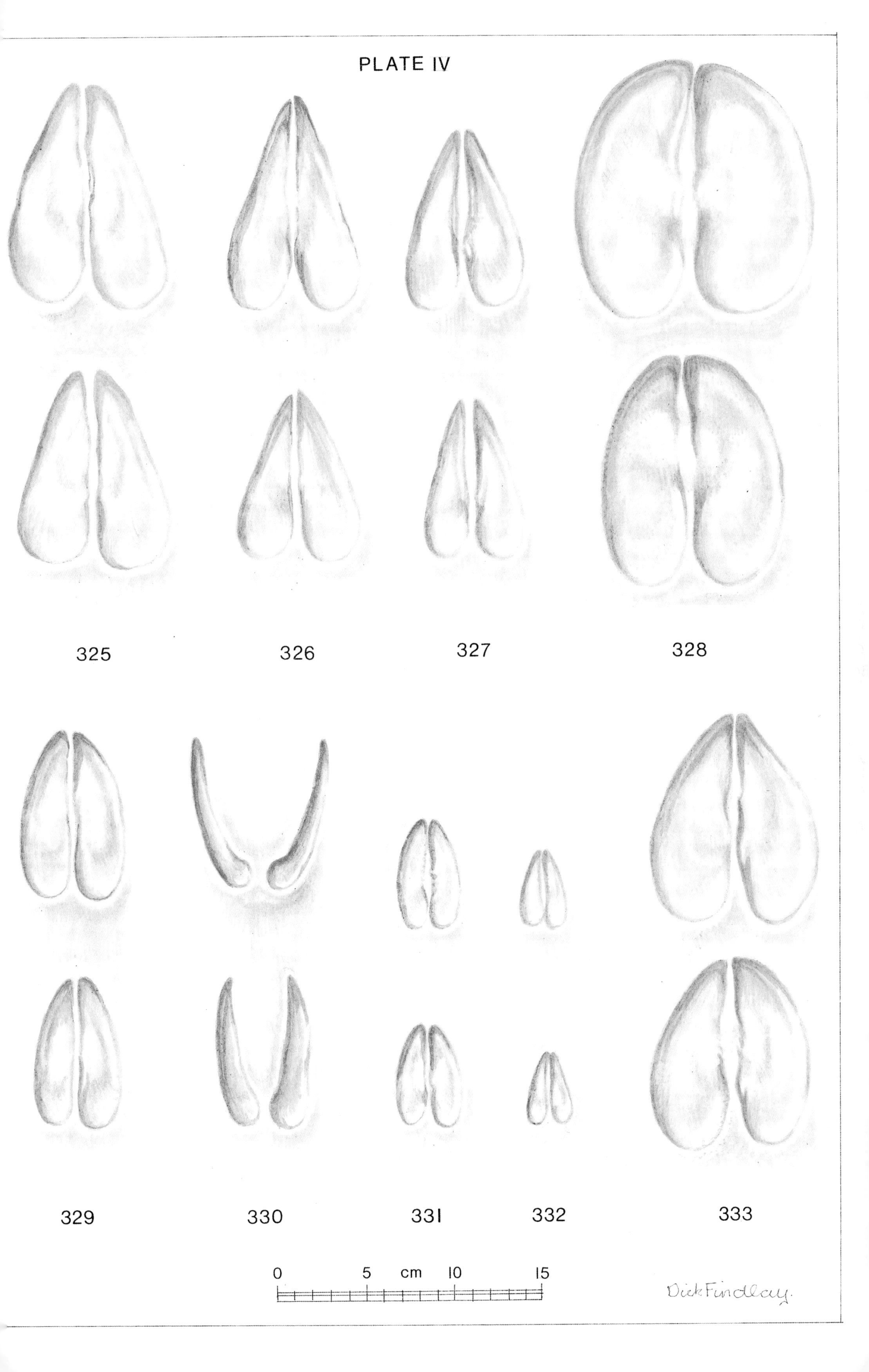
PLATE IV
325
326
327
328
329
330
331
332
333
0
5
cm
10
15
Dick Findlay.

insides of the ears and thighs are white, with white patches on the inside of the upper parts of the forelegs. Just above the hooves on the forelegs there are white patches. The forehead and top of the snout just behind the nostrils are darker than the remainder of the body. The face has a distinct V- shaped marking; the two arms which arise from the front of the eyes join across the muzzle. There are three white marks on either side of the face. The hooves are dark grey, the false hooves black.

In the wild, females live up to about 14 to 15 years, but few males survive longer than six to seven years (Owen-Smith, *in litt.*).

Females have two pairs of inguinal mammae.

---

No. 330

## *Tragelaphus spekei* Speke, 1863

## Sitatunga
## Waterkoedoe

Plate 36

---

### Colloquial Name

The origin of the name sitatunga remains in doubt. It may either be a Lozi name or a Chibemba name which has been corrupted by the baRotse people of Zambia. In the Okavango Delta, Botswana, the Yei name is *naakong* (Campbell, *in litt.*) and the Tswana people use this name. Livingstone (1875) referred to them as *nakong (naakong)*. The name *waterkoedoe* is appropriate as the horns of the males have a similarity to those of the kudu and they are associated particularly with swampy areas.

### Taxonomic Notes

Ansell (1972) listed five subspecies from the continent: *T. s. spekei* of East Africa; *T. s. sylvestris* (Meinertzhagen, 1916), which is endemic to an island in Lake Victoria; *T. s larkeni* (St Leger, 1931) of the Sudan and Zaire; *T. s. gratus* Sclater, 1880 of Zaire and the Central African Republic west to Gambia; and *T. s. selousi* Rothschild, 1898 named after the famous hunter and naturalist, F.C. Selous, which is the only subspecies occurring in the Subregion.

### Description

Throughout their wide distributional range in Africa, south of the Sahara, the colour and pattern of marking of the body and head and the texture of the hair varies considerably. The grey-brown body hairs are $40{,}6 \pm 11{,}7$ mm long, oval in cross-section, having a regular waved mosaic cuticular scale pattern except at the tip; scale margins are smooth to slightly rippled-crenate at the tip (Fig. XLII.1) (Keogh, 1983). In the East African sitatunga, *T. s. spekei*, the adult males are grey-brown, with faint shadow stripes on their bodies and dark dorsal crests. The texture of the hair is silky. In *T. s. larkeni* from the Sudan the body stripes are marked clearly, the hair thin and scanty. In the sitatunga that occur in the Subregion, *T. s. selousi*, the adult males are dark drab brown, with no body stripes. Some individuals have a few diffused yellowish blotches on the mid-back. Their hair is long, coarse and shaggy.

There is considerable variation in the colour of the adult females which may be the same colour as the adult males or redder, with a distinct black dorsal band down the mid-back, four transverse stripes, a white lateral band and white spots on the haunches.

Owen (1970) stated that *T. s. selousi* is larger than the East African *T. s. spekei*, adult males of *T. s. selousi* standing about 0,9 m at the shoulder, with masses of up to 115 kg; the females are distinctly smaller than the males. The upper part of the neck in the males tends to be lighter in colour than the remainder of the upper parts. The limbs are darker where they join the body, the colour lightening towards the hooves. The forehead is dark rufous brown, the cheeks light brown, the top of the snout darker. They have a white chevron marking on top of the muzzle, the arms of which arise in front of the eyes to join on top of the muzzle, with a white spot just below the base of the ears and a second white spot just below this. The front of the upper lip and chin is white. The ears are white inside and are darkly suffused with brown on the back, with broad white margins.

They have two white markings on the under parts of the neck, one just above the chest, the second which is broader between the first stripe and the chin. The tail is dark brown above, white below and black towards the tip. The under parts are darker than the upper parts, with some white hair on the insides of the limbs near the body. The outside of the limbs is slightly paler in colour than the upper parts, with white blazes just above the hooves in front.

The long, coarse hair reaches a length of 70 mm on the neck and is very slightly shorter on the remainder of the upper parts. The hair on the tip of the tail is up to 90 mm in length.

The hooves are a characteristic feature of the species and in adult males reach a length of 180 mm on the front feet and 160 mm on the hind (Fig. 330.1). Between these elongated hooves and the greatly enlarged false hooves the feet are covered with a swollen leathery pad. The function of this is discussed under **Habits**. The spoor on slightly soft ground is quite unmistakable (Plate IV).

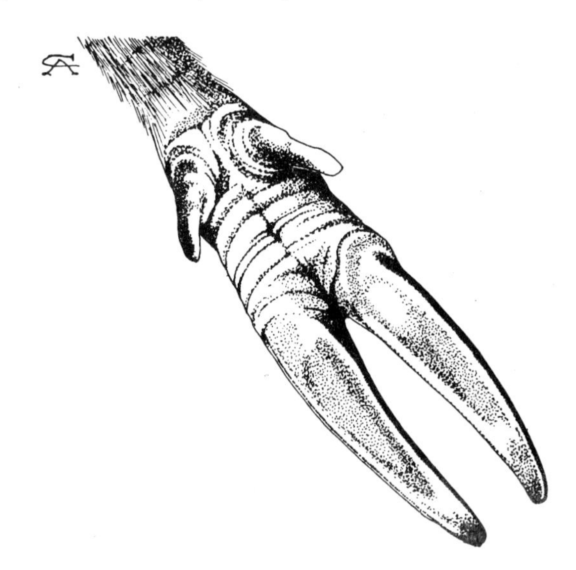

Fig. 330.1. Hoof: sitatunga, *T. spekei*
Right fore foot.

Only the males have horns, which in formation are midway between the bushbuck, *T. scriptus*, and the kudu, *T. strepsiceros*, the spiral consisting of more than one complete twist. They are smooth and end in yellowish-white tips and are nearly triangular in section. Like the other tragelaphine antelopes the horns have a distinct keel which arises in front and at the base of the horns and follows the spiral. The largest horns on record are a pair from the Okavango Swamps, Botswana, which measures 0,825 m (Rowland Ward, 1986).

### Distribution

Owing to their specialised habitat requirements, the distribution of sitatunga, within the limits shown on the map, is patchy and discontinuous.

*South of the Sahara, excluding the Southern African Subregion*

Although the species is believed to have occurred in Guinea Bissau and Guinea, there are no recent records from these countries. They have been recorded in **Togo** and they may still occur in Benin but this is doubtful. In **Nigeria** they occur within the forest zone along rivers and streams in the south, with an isolated population in the vicinity of Lake Chad. Eastwards they occur in **Cameroun**; in the southern parts of the **Central African Republic**; in the southwestern parts of the **Sudan**, and in the Sudd areas of the Nile and its tributaries. They are widespread in **Zaire** and in the **Cabinda Enclave**, and occur in the southern parts of **Uganda** and marginally in **Kenya** in the vicinity of Lake Victoria. In **Tanzania** they occur near Lake Victoria and southwards in the Rift Valley to the Zambian border. In **Zambia** they occur widely west of the Muchinga escarpment but not in the Zambezi Valley. In **Angola** there is an isolated population in the central parts of the country and they occur marginally in the south along the Quito and Cubango rivers.

*Southern African Subregion*

They occur widely throughout the Okavango Delta in **Botswana** and in the swamps associated with the Chobe and Zambezi rivers, both in the **Caprivi Strip** and in Botswana as far east as the western fringes of Imparira Island at the confluence of the Chobe and Zambezi rivers. There are unconfirmed reports of their occurrence on islands in the Zambezi River within Zimbabwean limits (Games, 1983).

Andersson (1856) recorded them from Lake Ngami and they still occurred there as late as 1889, for a live specimen was brought back from there to the Zoological Society's Gardens in London (Bryden, 1893). Selous (in Shortridge, 1934) found them on the Botletle River. Both of these localities are further south than they are recorded today.

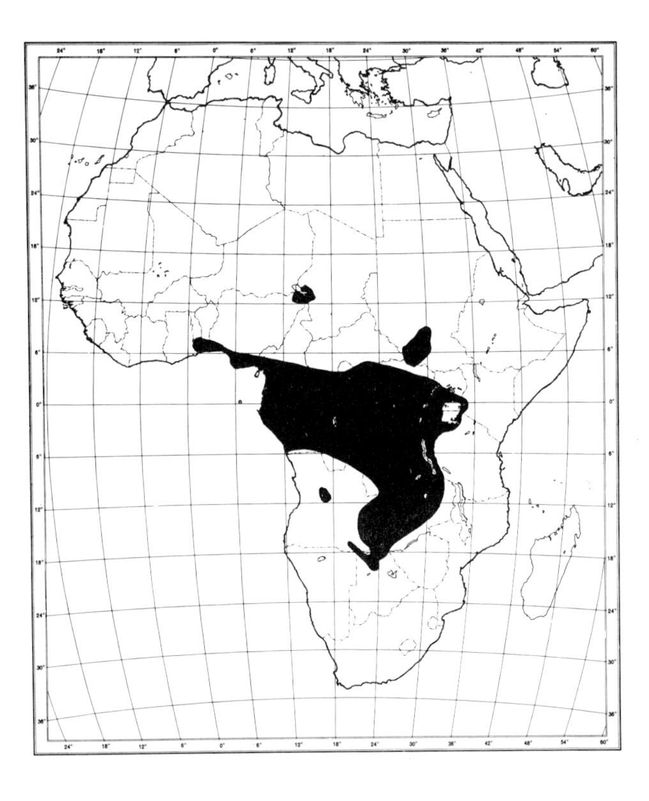

## Habitat

Sitatunga are semi-aquatic, spending the greater part of their lives in dense papyrus, *Cyperus papyrus*, and reed beds, *Phragmites mauritianus*, in swamp areas in water up to about a metre deep. While this applies generally to the species throughout their wide distributional range, one of the East African subspecies, *T. s. sylvestris*, which is found on Nkosi Island in Lake Victoria, has adapted to a life in drier terrain and lives in habitat of the type that, in the Subregion, would be occupied by the bushbuck, *T. scriptus*.

In the Subregion they occur in the swamp areas of the Okavango Delta and along the Chobe River, living deep in the reed beds which are shallowly inundated over huge areas. In times of high flood they are forced out to the shallower fringes of the swamp and then spend their time seasonally among the fringing aquatic grasses. These swamp areas are fringed, on the drier ground, with savanna woodland and floodplain grassland. At night they move out into the woodland but generally avoid the open floodplain except in the immediate vicinity of the reedbeds.

## Habits

In the Okavango Delta sitatunga are active at most times of the day except during the hottest hours when they lie up resting. They are also active at night, moving out from the swamp into the dry fringing woodland. Where they are subject to disturbance, or are hunted, such as in parts of the western Okavango, this movement rarely takes place before midnight. In others where they are undisturbed, such as in the Linyanti Swamp in the eastern Caprivi Strip, they move out of the swamp as early as 22h30. They return to the swamp before first light in the morning.

Sitatunga are very difficult to observe owing to the dense mass of reeds, which may grow up to 5 m above the level of the water. Most sightings are of a dark mass obscured by the reeds. They are very sensitive to noise; any undue splashing or movement of the reeds sends the sitatunga splashing away in great bounds. Normally they do not move far, stopping 50 to 100 m away, alert to further disturbances. If the observer stands still they will recommence feeding after a few minutes, the characteristic "plop" as they break off the fresh shoots of the sprouting reeds showing that they are satisfied that the danger has passed. Within the Linyanti swamp there are many small islands usually with wild fig trees, *Ficus* spp, and palms *Hyphaene* sp, and a dense understorey of low bush and palm scrub on to which sitatunga move at night. Here they are prone to fall prey to lions and leopards which lie up in the dense underbush. Evidence of the latter's activities is manifest on these islands by the bones and horns of sitatunga and lechwe, *K. leche*, on which they have fed. The lions wade and swim to reach these islands and at night it is strange to hear their roaring emanating from the depths of the aquatic environment.

Sitatunga occur in small herds of up to about six. When feeding these are loosely knit as the individual members are scattered. On being disturbed they tend to reform into more closely knit units as they bound off to safety. In the eastern Caprivi Strip these herds usually consisted of an adult male with several females and juveniles. In addition solitary males and females were seen and herds of up to four half-grown calves. At night, in the dry woodland, the herds tend to move in a more closely knit form. In the Linyanti swamp, eastern Caprivi Strip, sitatunga avoided the open stretches of water. They are, however, excellent swimmers and if disturbed readily take to deep, open water to swim to safety. Selous (1908), who was an accurate observer, stated that sitatunga would submerge totally when alarmed, with only their nostrils above the surface. Masubia hunters state that they do this when wounded, usually submerging among the reeds, where, with only their nostrils above water, they are difficult to find. Their more usual reaction, however, is to swim or splash away to safety.

Their resting sites during the hotter hours of the day are on platforms of broken down reed stems or on mats of debris caught up in the papyrus, *Cyperus papyrus*, and *Vossia cuspidata* beds deep in the swamp. These platforms are anchored by the base of the broken down stems or the stems of the reeds and are often in water up to nearly a metre deep. In East Africa, Owen (1970) recorded that they would trample down their own resting platforms and would use these over a period of several consecutive days.

In the Linyanti swamp there are several types of paths through the reed beds. Those made by the movements of hippopotamus are easily recognisable. They are up to 1,5 m wide where the reeds are broken down on either side and about 0,7 m at the level of the muddy bottom, the water in them up to about waist deep. The path in the mud at the bottom is characteristically marked by a central raised ridge, deeper on either side, caused by the spacing of the feet. Other paths are much narrower and less well defined, not more than about 0,5 m wide and not as deep. These presumably are made and used by sitatunga and lechwe. On being disturbed, sitatunga do not appear to use these established tracks as escape routes, but use established paths when moving from the swamp to the woodland as shown by their tracks in the dried mud. They do not use the hippopotamus paths, tending to leap across them. This may have been because these paths are used regularly by crocodiles, or that the water is unduly deep for ease of movement.

Sitatunga bark, especially at night. The bark is reminiscent of that of the bushbuck, *T. scriptus*, but is more drawn out and may be repeated in quick succession.

### Food

Very little information is presently available on the food of sitatunga in the Subregion. In the Linyanti swamp they ate the freshly sprouting tips of reeds, *Phragmites* spp, and bull-rushes, *Typha* sp, as well as aquatic grasses and plants growing in the shallower water. No observations are available as to what they eat at night in the dry woodland. In the Okavango Swamp, Games (1983) recorded their feeding on the umbrels of the papyrus and during high water they also fed on the aquatic grass, *V. cuspidata*. He noted that they actively fed during daylight hours. He also found that young knob thorn, *Acacia nigrescens*, and jackal berry, *Diospyros mespiliformis*, trees on an island showed a distinct browse line. From fecal analysis Games (1983) showed that papyrus occur at a percentage frequency of 45% at times of high water, and that during periods of low water in August to February, virtually their entire diet consists of papyrus. He noted that burning gives sitatunga access to the fresh young shoots of the papyrus as well as to those of a fern, *Cyclosorus interruptus*, and a grass, *Eragrostis inamoena*. They will feed in deep water with their bodies submerged and only the head and top of the back visible. Owen (1970) recorded that in East Africa they would stand on their hind legs and reach like a gerenuk to get at the flowers of sedges, reeds and tall grasses.

### Reproduction

Occasionally calves may be born at any time throughout the year, but the main calf crop is produced during mid-winter. During the Carp Expedition to the eastern Caprivi in June/July, several neonatal calves were brought into the camp, and Shortridge (1934) recorded a young calf in August.

The mothers conceal the newly born young on platforms deep in the swamp or in the high grass on the islands. The young usually make no attempt to escape when approached and are easily caught by hand. Very young sitatunga are unsteady on their feet. Their long thin legs seem all out of proportion to their bodies and, except on open ground, they appear to have trouble in controlling their long hooves and stumble and fall over obstacles and have the greatest trouble in moving through grass or reeds on dry ground. Davison (1950) recorded that when calves do try to get away they tumble awkwardly into the water, swim for a few metres and then dive below the surface.

Females have two pairs of inguinal mammae.

---

No. 331

## *Tragelaphus angasii* Gray, 1849

## Nyala

## Njala

Plate 36

---

### Colloquial Name

The colloquial name originates from the Zulu name for the species, *inxala*. The species was first brought to the notice of European naturalists by Mr Douglas Angas and was at one time known as Angas' bushbuck.

### Taxonomic Notes

No subspecies have been described.

### Description

Nyala are medium-sized antelopes, adult males standing about 1,12 m at the shoulder, with a mean mass of 108 kg; the females are distinctly smaller, with heights at the shoulder of about 0,97 m and a mean mass of 62 kg (Table 331.1).

Body hairs are 34,10±9,4 mm long, oval or oblong in cross-section, with two to three scales across their width; scale margins are smooth at the base, then crenated or rippled crenate towards the tip (Fig. XLII.1) (Keogh, 1983). The predominant colour of females of all ages and males less than eight months old is a rusty red. At about four months the dorsal ridge of the male is still black but becomes more prominent than that of the female and at six months the chevron between the male's eyes becomes more noticeable. By one year the general coat colour is the same, but on the neck the hair has become darker and grown noticeably longer than that in females. Between 14–16 months coat colour becomes greyer (Anderson, 1985). The adult males are slate-grey at two years, varying to dark brown, and in the field, depending on how the light strikes them, they may look black or even tan (Tello & van Gelder, 1975). In the younger males there are up to 14 vertical white stripes on the body, which are reduced in older individuals to three or four, or they may be almost totally absent in some. The forehead is rufous, the cheeks fawn, the upper lip and chin white. They have a distinct white chevron marking on top of the muzzle, the arms of which arise in front of the eyes and which just fail to join on top of the muzzle. They have two or three spots on the sides of the head below the eyes and a white dot on each side of the base of the tail. The bases of the ears at the back are white and they have a distinct white band on the upper chest and a few rather indistinct white spots on the haunches. The under surface of the tail is white, the lower parts of the legs are light-coloured, almost white, and the back of the pasterns black, with two white spots on the front above the hooves.

Adult females are dark rufous on top of the muzzle and forehead, with or without the white chevron in front of the eyes. The white vertical stripes on the body may number up to 18. The lower parts of the legs are slightly lighter in colour than the upper parts, but do not contrast with the colour of the body, as they do in the males. They may or may not have white spots on the haunches.

The males have a dorsal crest of long hair from the back of the head to the base of the tail, which is dark on the neck and broadly tipped white from the shoulders to the base of the tail. On the under parts of the neck and along the middle line of the chest and belly they have a heavy fringe of long hair which is slightly darker in colour than the hair on the body. The long hair on the tail is dark and bushy, white underneath.

The females have a dorsal crest of bristly hair from the back of their heads to the base of the tail, darker in colour than the body, but no long hair on the throat or under parts as in the males.

Tello & van Gelder (1975) reported on a pale yellowish-coloured female and a palomino-coloured male from the Zinave National Park in Mozambique. Aberrant-coloured nyala are known from other areas. Dixon (1964) reported on a male from the Mkuzi Game Reserve which was pale beige in colour, and Dorst & Dandelot (1970) stated that adult males with the bright chestnut colour of the females have been recorded.

Nyala have glands at the base of the false hooves, but no inguinal or preorbital glands (Anderson, 1980). In the spoor the front hooves are slightly larger than the hind (Plate IV).

**Table 331.1**

Measurements (mm) and mass (kg) of adult nyala, *T. angasii*, from Mozambique (Tello & van Gelder, 1975)

| | Males | | | Females | | |
|---|---|---|---|---|---|---|
| | $\bar{x}$ | n | Range | $\bar{x}$ | n | Range |
| TL | 2101 | 20 | 1960–2450 | 1793 | 11 | 1665–1862 |
| T | 428 | 22 | 370–470 | 361 | 10 | 342–399 |
| Hf c/u | 474 | 21 | 425–557 | 423 | 11 | 402–443 |
| E | 194 | 21 | 180–205 | 174 | 11 | 165–183 |
| Sh.ht | 1122 | 17 | 1040–1210 | 966 | 8 | 825–1060 |
| Mass | 107,5 | 13 | 92,5–126,5 | 61,8 | 8 | 54,9–68,1 |

Anderson (1985) established that (for deciduous dentition) the incisors have fully erupted at five months, the first molar erupts at a time when horn buds can be felt on the skull. Horns first became visible between five and six months. At 18 months the permanent incisors have erupted but the deciduous premolars are still present. Adult dentition is attained by the age of 24 months by which time the horns are half-grown, reaching mature size at 4,5 years.

Only the males carry horns which swing back from the head and spiral upwards, curving outwards at the first turn. They have a keel in front and behind, but are otherwise smooth with whitish tips. The world record pair was taken in Natal and measured 0,768 m (Rowland Ward, 1986).

## Distribution

Nyala occur only in the southeastern parts of the continent and, because of their habitat requirements, have a localised distribution. With protection, the species has increased its range in parts during this century, as for example in the Kruger National Park and in parts of Natal (Ansell, 1972). They have been reintroduced to nature reserves in northeastern Swaziland where they occurred previously. They have been introduced to areas outside their normal limits of distribution, for example to the Loskop Dam Nature Reserve, eastern Transvaal, and to parts of the eastern Cape Province in South Africa and to the Kyle Game Reserve in Zimbabwe.

*South of the Sahara, excluding the Southern African Subregion*

In **Malawi** they are confined to the Lengwe and Mwabvi Game Reserves and in **Mozambique**, north of the Zambezi River, to the extreme southeastern extension of the Tete District between the Zambezi River and the Malawi border.

*Southern African Subregion*

In **Zimbabwe** they occur in the northeast in the Zambezi Valley and up the lower reaches of its tributaries. They also occur in the south, in the vicinity of the Limpopo River and its tributaries, e.g. the Umzingwane, Bubye and Nuanetsi rivers and in the Sabi and Lundi rivers in the southeast. In **Mozambique**, south of the Zambezi River, they occur in the southern parts of the Beira and Vila Pery districts, north of the Save River and, south of this, in the northern and western parts of the Gaza and Inhambane districts south to about 24°30′S, with an isolated population in the central Gaza District. They also occur in the extreme southern parts of the Maputo District and from there south to the Natal border. In the **Transvaal** they are restricted to the Limpopo Valley as far west as Swartwater and south of this, along the Mozambique border in the Kruger National Park, to about 24°30′S. In northeastern **Natal** they occur in the Ndumu Game Reserve, in the vicinity of Lake St Lucia and in the Mkuzi, Hluhluwe-Corridor-Umfolozi Game Reserve with their southern limits in this sector on the Umhlatuzi River.

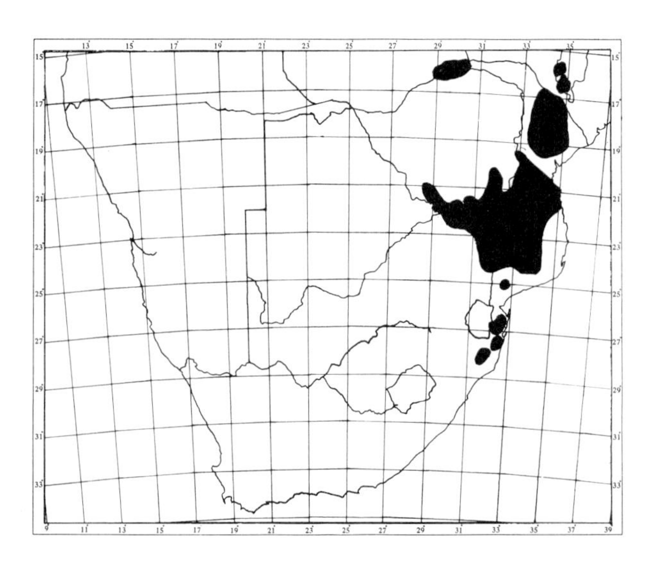

## Habitat

Nyala are associated with thickets in dry savanna woodland. This may take the form of a closed woodland community forming a mosaic with thickets or a very open association, such as is found on floodplains, where there is raised ground or termitaria on which are located a few large trees with a surrounding thicket underbush. Riverine woodland with thickets and dry forest also provide suitable habitat for the species. These associations may abut on to open grassland or floodplain or may have open vlei areas running through them. When the grass is flushing, nyala make wide use of this grassland on which to graze. Their reaction on being disturbed in open areas is to make for the cover of the thicket, and where there is continual disturbance in the form of settlement, they tend to use the open areas at night only. Although nyala occur in a wide variety of habitats, the presence of thickets is important to them. Tello & van Gelder (1975) showed that during their study in Mozambique, in one year 70% of the nyala were observed in association with thickets and 90% in the following year. Although they do occur in the open, they are never more than a few hundred metres from thicket and often remain closer.

In parts of Mozambique, shifting cultivation, with abandonment of lands and consequent bush encroachment, has improved the habitat for nyala. Overgrazing of the grassland by cattle which promotes the invasion of legumes, cucurbits and other herbs, used by nyala as food, has also improved conditions for them (Tello & van Gelder, 1975).

## Habits

Nyala are a gregarious species, occurring in herds numbering up to 30, but more usually in two's and three's. The herds are transient in nature and no long-lasting relationships are evident. Tello & van Gelder (1975) believed that the males have a dominance hierarchy and interpret the agonistic displays between males as challenge and status rituals.

Nyala are not territorial and occupy overlapping home ranges, both between and within the sexes. Anderson (1980) found that in the Hluhluwe Game Reserve, Natal, adult males occupied home ranges of about 0,65 $km^2$, adult females 0,83 $km^2$. Tello & van Gelder (1975) found that in Mozambique adult males had home ranges of about 3,9 $km^2$, adult females 3,6 $km^2$.

In the Hluhluwe Game Reserve, Anderson (1980) recognised nine types of social groupings. He found lone young, still in the lying up stage, and lone females, which may have been tending calves during their lying up stage. Lone males were the most common grouping, and male groups of two or three together were also commonly encountered. These do not correspond to the bachelor groups recorded in other bovids as they are only short term associations, forming and disbanding within a matter of hours. Young males of similar age associate more with each other than they do with older males and these groupings are more permanent than the association between adult males which become more solitary as they grow older. Family groups consist of a female with her offspring or female groups of two or more adult females with their offspring. Family groups meet up to form female groups and female groups break down into family groups. The family group is the most stable of the groupings and there is some evidence that they tend to join up with certain other family groups more often than with others to form the female groups. Female groups may be joined by males to form mixed groups and this is brought about by their association at preferred sites, which may be at water points or at areas with a flush of fresh green grass after rain. Anderson (1980) recorded a mixed group of 31 individuals under these circumstances. Mixed groups centred around a female in oestrus may last for two days, i.e. the duration of the oestrus.

The larger aggregations of nyala were all recorded in open habitat, a feature of bovids that normally live in cover. While this provides greater security from predation, it is a secondary feature and is centred on a preferred feeding site.

Anderson (1980) listed a series of different types of agonistic behaviour recognised in adult males. Ground horning was observed in adults. It generally took place in moist, soft ground and was not necessarily directed as a display at other individuals. Frequently it was executed when the male was alone and, if others were present, they showed no noticeable reaction. Males rub the stems of bushes between the horns and along the sides of the face by moving the head up and down as if marking, but Anderson (1980) could find no trace of scent or secretion. Thrashing of vegetation with the horns takes place in the presence of other nyala, which do not show any obvious reaction. In other cases it is carried out by a male after losing a dominance encounter or prior to an encounter and appears to have an aggressive significance. Pawing of the ground with the forefoot is uncommon, but does occur and is linked with horning and thrashing.

A male may partially raise the dorsal crest of white hair on his back as a sign that he is aware of the presence of another male. This may develop into a display in which the crest is fully raised, the head held high, the legs raised higher than normal, their movements being slow and deliberate. This can develop into a more intense display in which the tail is erected over the rump, the white hairs on its underside fanned out, and the head lowered with the horns pointed forward.

Anderson (1980) witnessed sparring between adult males in the presence of a female in oestrus, which involved head pushing and horn-clashing and a high level of aggression. Serious fighting is uncommon but, when it does take place, Anderson (1980) remarked on the ferocity of the encounter and quoted a case where one of the antagonists was killed by a horn-thrust. Submissive displays in male encounters involve the lowering of the dorsal crest, sweeps with the head and tail, grooming or breaking away to feed. Aggressive behaviour in females is rare, but can involve one contestant butting the other's abdomen with her head. In encounters between males, bodily size appears to be the criterion in deciding the outcome. In adult males the long hair on parts of the body emphasises their size and is to their advantage at these times.

While nyala are usually silent, Anderson (1980) listed three vocalisations. The alarm call is a deep bark which actuates others in the vicinity to take flight. Under stress they bleat, a vocalisation used by calves which have become separated from their mothers. When in oestrus or tending a calf, females make a soft, throaty, clicking sound.

Within the family group, leadership is assumed by the adult female, but when family groups join to form female groups, no ordered leadership was detected (Anderson, 1980).

Nyala are indifferent to the presence of other bovids, but move off if they are approached by them. They react to the alarm calls of impala, baboons and kudu, and impala react to the alarm calls of nyala. Although baboons have been recorded killing and eating small nyala calves, the two species associate when feeding, the nyala eating the fruits and leaves dislodged by the baboons when feeding in the trees overhead.

## Food

Nyala are mixed grazers-browsers, living on the leaves, twigs, flowers and fruits of a wide variety of plants. Their diet, however, includes grass, especially when this is fresh and sprouting after rain. Anderson (in Tello & van Gelder, 1975) found that at this time they would feed on it almost exclusively. Tello & van Gelder (1975) recorded 108 species of browse plants utilised by nyala in Mozambique. They listed as important foods several species of *Acacia* including the fever tree, *A. xanthophloea*; the mustard tree, *Salvadora persica*; tambotie, *Spirostachys africana*; monkey orange, *Strychnos* spp; the cucumber bush, *Thilachium africanum*; the buffalo thorn, *Ziziphus mucronata*, and a variety of legumes. They found *S. persica* showing signs of heavy utilisation, with a browse line of up to 2 m. They eat the bark of the baobab, *Adansonia digitata*, as well as the flowers and fruit. They have been seen to eat the bark stripped from these trees by elephants. Some species of plants are only eaten during the dry season, when the nyala also make wide use of fallen leaves. Other species are only eaten during the wet season from about November to April. Tello & van Gelder (1975) found grass in the stomachs of nyala in most months of the year, this varying from a trace to 65% by volume of the wet contents. In a sample of 20 rumen contents the average amount was 12% of grass and herbs. They observed nyala grazing on the short, sweet grass *Setaria chevalieri*, at the edge of lagoons. Vincent, Hitchins, Bigalke & Bass (1968) found that in the Hluhluwe Game Reserve nyala stomach contents contained 70% browse and 30% grass.

Although nyala are found in areas where water is only available seasonally (southeastern Zimbabwe, Davison, 1971), where it is available they drink daily (Tello & van Gelder, 1975). Its availability is not apparently an essential requirement.

## Reproduction

In Mozambique and in the Ndumu Game Reserve in Natal, nyala breed throughout the year (Tello & van Gelder, 1975; Anderson, 1979). Anderson (1979) showed that there was no seasonal change in the mass of the male testes, which is indicative of a sexual cycle in other bovid species, and that they were capable of breeding at any time of the year. However, there is a major and a false rut in about January to May and October respectively.

The result of this is that, although calves may be born at any time throughout the year, there are two peaks in calving, a major peak in the early part of the summer from about August to December and a minor peak about May.

Female oestrus recurs at approximately 19 day intervals after parturition until conception takes place. Anderson (1980) observed that males test females for signs of oestrus whenever they come into contact. This takes place at points of association such as waterholes or fruiting trees, where there are chances of visual contact between males and family groups. Males smell the vulvas of females and if a female is in oestrus, the male exhibits "flehmen". If she is not in oestrus, the male raises his head and slightly opens his mouth in a less exaggerated manner.

Pro-oestrus lasts nearly two days, with copulation occurring during oestrus which lasts about six hours following this period. If the female is in oestrus, the male aligns his forequarters against her hindquarters, an initial approach that is usually rejected by the female by moving away. Then he follows her with his head and neck stretched forward, pushing his head between her legs. At times this is carried out so violently that the female's hindquarters are lifted off the ground. This courtship has a disruptive effect on the family group, resulting in a temporary break in the female/offspring bond. Anderson (1980) found that in one case this led to the separation of a female and her nine month old calf which did not rejoin for 32 days. During this courtship, which may last for 24 hours or longer, the first male may be supplanted by other more progressively dominant males. When the female is receptive, the male blocks her further movement by standing obliquely to her, shoulder to shoulder, and manoeuvres her into a submissive position, pressing her neck down with his own, a feature of courtship also observed by Tello & van Gelder (1975). He then moves his neck to rest across her withers and copulation follows. The submissive posture of the female with the head lowered is the cue for mating and often males will attempt copulation when a female lowers her head to drink (Anderson, 1980).

Anderson (1979) established that the gestation period is 220 days. A single young is produced at a birth, with a birth mass of 4,2 kg to 5,5 kg (Tello & van Gelder, 1975). The young are usually born in the cover of thickets, although Tello & van Gelder (1975) recorded a birth in the open. The female eats the afterbirth.

Anderson (1980) believed that the lying up period for the calf may last up to 18 days. The female returns to suckle and clean it from time to time. If disturbed in the early stages of its life, the calf lowers its head with its chin on the ground and its ears held flat against the sides of the neck. It may maintain this position for some time. In captivity he recorded a calf holding this position for 11 minutes after being disturbed by a loud noise. Anderson (1980) noted that, in captive individuals, they did not accompany the female until they were between 10 and 14 days old. Females have two pairs of inguinal mammae.

No. 332

## *Tragelaphus scriptus* (Pallas, 1766)

## Bushbuck
## Bosbok

Plate 36

### Colloquial Name

The colloquial name indicates the type of habitat with which this species is closely associated throughout its wide distributional range.

### Taxonomic Notes

Haltenorth (1963) recognised 23 subspecies of bushbuck; Ansell (1972) in his review recognised only nine, of which three occur in the Subregion: *T. s. sylvaticus* (Sparrman, 1780) from southern Natal, the eastern Cape Province and west to Bredasdorp, *T. s. roualeyni* (Gray, 1852) from the Limpopo River drainage, and *T. s. ornatus* Pocock, 1900 from the extreme north, in the Chobe and Zambezi river drainages.

### Description

Bushbuck are medium-sized antelope, adult males standing about 0,8 m at the shoulder (Table 332.1). The females are smaller, standing about 0,7 m at the shoulder. Maximum masses of up to 54 kg are on record (Owen-Smith, *in litt.*).

The body hairs are 24,0±3,61 mm long, oval with a spongy appearance in cross-section. The cuticular scale pattern is regular waved mosaic, with rippled scale margins; there are one or two scales across the hair width (Fig. XLII.1) (Keogh, 1983). Bushbuck, *T. s. sylvaticus*, from the southern parts of the species' range in the Subregion are the darkest in colour of the three subspecies that occur. They lack the white transverse lines on the back so conspicuous in the Chobe bushbuck, *T. s. ornatus*, from the northern areas, and the white spotting on the flanks is confined to a few spots on the sides of the belly and thighs. The adult males are dark brown in colour. The hair on the base of their necks tends to get rubbed off, leaving a collar of a grey-brown colour; the skin shows through the sparse covering of hair. They have a crest of longer white or yellowish-white hair extending from the top of the shoulders to the base of the tail. The top of the tail is the same colour as the body, but is pure white underneath. The sides of the face are lighter in colour than the body. The forehead and top of the muzzle are dark. The lower and upper lips and the chin are white and they have a white spot just below and behind the eyes and another slightly above this towards the base of the ears. They have a white patch on the throat and a band of white below and towards the base of the neck. The ears are rounded and are white inside and dark grey-brown on the back. The upper parts of the limbs are dark like the body, the lower parts tinged light brown and whitish just above the hooves. The insides of the upper part of the forelegs are white, with a central dark brown band.

The adult females are lighter in colour than the males, being a dark fawn. The white markings are similar to those on the males but the spots on the sides of the head are not so distinct.

The subspecies *T. s. ornatus* which occurs in the northern parts of the Subregion is much more colourful than *T. s. sylvaticus*. The adult males are dark red against which the greyish collar, at the base of the neck in older individuals, stands out prominently. A characteristic feature of this subspecies is the pattern of white spots and lines on the body. They may have up to eight distinct white transverse lines, extending from the mid-dorsal band of long white hair on to the upper parts of the flanks, and a series of about six irregularly placed white spots on the shoulders and up to 20 on the hindquarters. Between these clusters of white spots they have a line of white spots along the flanks joining them. The other white markings are the same as *T. s. sylvaticus*, but in addition they have a white patch on the under parts of the neck between the white on the throat and the crescent of white on the lower part of the neck. The females are rich red in colour and have a pattern of white lines and spots as in the males.

The subspecies *T. s. roualeyni* which occupies the zone in the Subregion between the southern Cape bushbuck, *T. s. sylvaticus*, and the Chobe bushbuck, *T. s. ornatus*, is intermediate in colour and body pattern, the males redder than the southern subspecies but not as brightly coloured as the northern. They lack the white lines on the body and are less spotted than *T. s. ornatus*.

The spoor, especially of the hind feet, tend to be heart-shaped (Plate IV).

**Table 332.1**

Measurements (mm) of adult Chobe bushbuck, *T. s. ornatus*, from northeastern Botswana (Simpson, 1974) (to nearest mm), and measurements (mm) from eastern Zambia (Wilson & Child, 1964)

**Botswana**

| | Males | | | Females | | |
|---|---|---|---|---|---|---|
| | $\bar{x}$ | n | Range | $\bar{x}$ | n | Range |
| Hf c/u | 363 | 15 | 335–390 | 335 | 15 | 310–355 |
| E | 145 | 15 | 130–149 | 140 | 15 | 130–149 |
| Sh.ht | 790 | 15 | 730–860 | 692 | 15 | 630–740 |

**Zambia**

| | Males | | | Females | | |
|---|---|---|---|---|---|---|
| | $\bar{x}$ | n | Range | $\bar{x}$ | n | Range |
| TL | 1480 | 15 | 1360–1660 | 1400 | 16 | 1330–1540 |
| T | 210 | 15 | 190–240 | 200 | 16 | 190–220 |
| Hf c/u | 300 | 15 | 290–320 | 280 | 16 | 270–300 |
| E | 135 | 15 | 121–152 | 136 | 16 | 127–152 |

Only the bushbuck males have horns, which are smooth, roughly triangular in section at the base, with keels on the front and hind edges. They spiral upwards from the head, rising roughly parallel to each other (Fig. 332.1). The longest

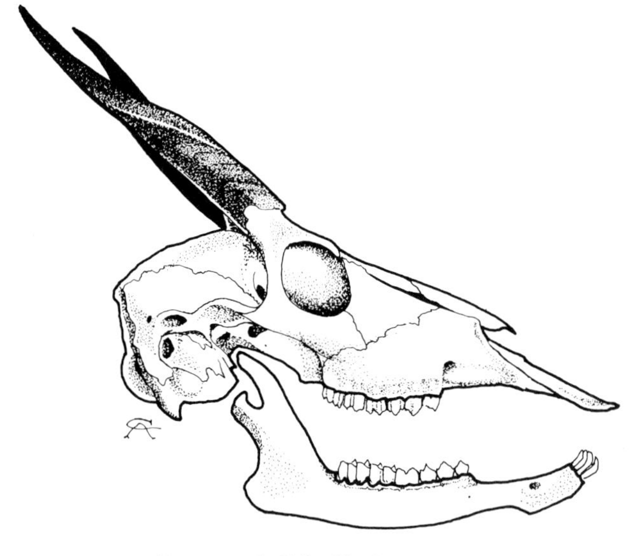

Fig. 332.1. Skull: bushbuck, *T. scriptus*
TL skull 240 mm

**Plate 36**

329. Kudu, *Tragelaphus strepsiceros*
Koedoe
330. Sitatunga, *Tragelaphus spekei*
Waterkoedoe
331. Nyala, *Tragelaphus angasii*
Njala
332. Bushbuck, *Tragelaphus scriptus*
Bosbok
333. Eland, *Taurotragus oryx*
Eland

PLATE 36
333
332
331
329
330
Dick Findlay

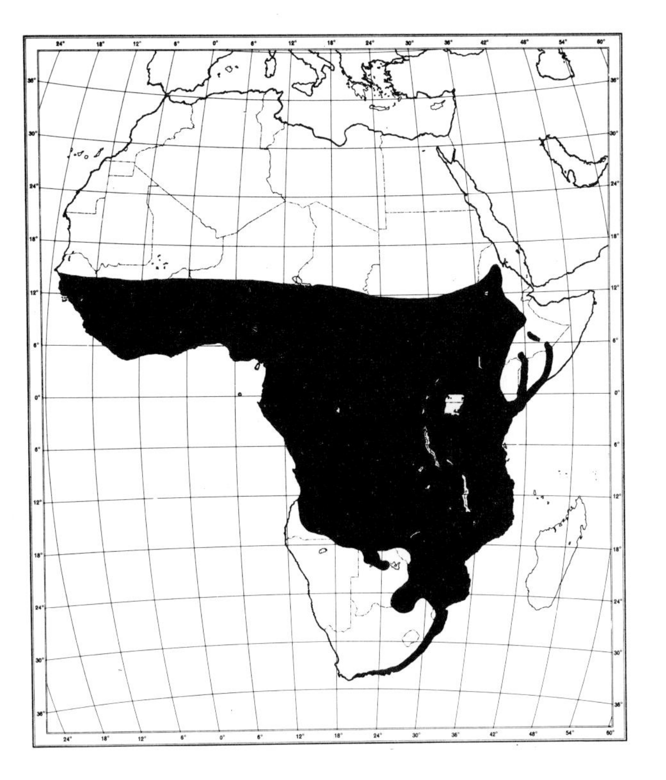

pair of horns of *T. s. sylvaticus* from the Subregion is a pair from Natal which measured 470 mm, and of *T. s. ornatus* from Zimbabwe 463 mm (Rowland Ward, 1986).

## Distribution

Due to their specialised habitat requirements bushbuck only occur within the limits shown on the map where there is suitable habitat. Except where they have been exterminated locally or their habitat destroyed, their overall distribution is very similar to what it was in historical times. Within the Subregion they do not occur in the arid areas and are found only in the Southern Savanna Zone where there is water and cover. Where their distribution covers arid areas, such as in the Somali Arid Zone or in the Sahelian Zone in West Africa, they occur in riverine cover along water courses which may penetrate deep into arid terrain.

*South of the Sahara, excluding the Southern African Subregion*

Bushbuck have a wide distribution in West Africa, occurring from **Senegal** east to **Nigeria**, in the High Forest, Guinea, Sudan and in parts of the Sahelian zones, and extending eastwards to central **Ethiopia** and parts of southwestern **Somalia**. South of this they are recorded from all countries south to **Angola** in the west, where they are absent from the arid southwestern parts of the country. They are recorded from **Zambia, Malawi** and **Mozambique**, north of the Zambezi River.

*Southern African Subregion*

They occur in northeastern **Namibia**; in the Okavango Delta, along the Chobe River and in parts of eastern **Botswana**; widely in **Zimbabwe**, excluding parts of the arid western sector, and in **Mozambique**, south of the Zambezi River. They occur widely in the **Transvaal**, excluding the grassland areas; in parts of eastern, western and northwestern **Swaziland** and in the eastern parts of **Natal**, extending westwards coastally in the **Cape Province** about as far west as the Bredasdorp district.

## Habitat

Throughout their wide distributional range bushbuck are associated closely with riverine or other types of underbush adjacent to permanent water supplies. They exhibit some seasonal movement, dispersing from the riverine underbush in the warm, wet summer months from about September to March, to thickets in the hinterland, where water is temporarily available. Later, as the country dries up, they return to the riverine underbush (Simpson, 1974). Where their habitat provides them with food and water on a year-round basis their movements are restricted noticeably. Where their habitat is opened up by trampling and the food resources heavily utilised by other species such as elephant and domestic stock, bushbuck tend to move to less disturbed areas. They have been known, however, to remain in open underbush until it thickened up with the onset of the rains.

Cover and the availability of water appear to be among the most important habitat requirements for bushbuck.

## Habits

Bushbuck are generally regarded as being solitary animals and lone adult males and females are commonly seen. They occur, however, in small groups of two or three as well; these consist of adult females, or adult females with young or subadults, or two or more adult males may form bachelor groups, but this is of unusual occurrence. Aggregations are found, sometimes numbering up to nine individuals, in favoured areas in riverine underbush (Simpson, 1974).

Bushbuck generally lie up in dense bush during the day, moving and feeding at night or in the early morning or late evening. They may also be active during the day in overcast, cool weather. During the dry season, when they remain in the cover of riverine underbush, their movements are very restricted and their home range is about 0,004 $km^2$ (Simpson, 1974). During the warm, wet months when they tend to move more widely (see **Habitat**), their home ranges are about 0,06 $km^2$.

Bushbuck are shy and retiring, with acute senses of hearing, sight and smell, factors which have allowed them to live in close association with human development. In spite of intensive snaring and hunting with dogs they are still found on the outskirts of large cities such as Port Elizabeth (Fairall, pers. comm.).

When cornered or wounded the males can be dangerous, their aggressiveness under these circumstances being proverbial. In his two-year study of bushbuck on the Chobe River, Botswana, Simpson (1974) found little evidence of fighting between males, but this has been witnessed elsewhere. Stevenson-Hamilton (1947) stated that the males will fight to the death in rivalry for females and he thought that more are killed in this way than any other African antelope.

Both sexes utter a loud, hoarse bark as a warning call, that of the male being louder and harsher than that of the female. They also grunt as a means of maintaining contact in dense bush (Dorst & Dandelot, 1970).

In game rescue operations during the formation of Lake Kariba, Child (1968) recorded that bushbuck took to water readily, were fast, manoeuvrable swimmers, difficult to catch in the water, and could swim up to 3 km without noticeably tiring. They would enter water freely to feed, and under stress would hide in shallows. Because of their limited home range they were reluctant to leave the shrinking islands formed by the flooding and only left these to swim to neighbouring larger islands when they became too small.

Adult bushbuck are subject to predation by the larger carnivores including leopards, *Panthera pardus*; lions, *P. leo*; spotted hyaenas, *Crocuta crocuta*; wild dogs, *Lycaon pictus*; and the lambs by pythons, *Python sebae*, and caracals, *F. caracal* (Wilson & Child, 1964). Because they occur in habitat frequented by tsetse fly, which feed on their blood, they have been the subject of intensive control measures in areas adjacent to those in which there are cattle.

## Food

Bushbuck are browsers, but on rare occasions take some grass (Hofmann, 1973). They are selective feeders but are able to modify their feeding habits qualitatively when necessary for survival in adverse environments (Simpson, 1974). The bulk of the food consists of leaves, but they will also eat the fine twigs with buds attached, and the flowers and fruits of a wide variety of plants. While flowers and fruit are eaten, their seasonal occurrence precludes their use as extensively as leaves. Simpson (1974) showed that bushbuck will choose plants which are not as common as others, thus showing that they have selective feeding habits. Wilson &

Child (1964) noted that they ate fresh green grass in their study area, including buffalo grass, *Panicum maximum*; couch grass, *Cynodon dactylon; Digitaria setivalva*, and heart grass, *Eragrostis superba*, but listing species such as this can be very misleading because the nutritional quality of plant parts differs greatly and has been studied insufficiently. Some concentrate selectors eat plant shoots but are unable to digest plant stems like grazers.

Simpson (1974) recorded a list of over 40 species of browse plants eaten by bushbuck on the Chobe River, Botswana. Of these the leaves, flowers and fruits of the knobbly creeper, *Combretum mossambicense*, were recognised in 69% of a sample of 29 stomach contents. Other browse plants frequently found in stomachs were sausage tree, *Kigelia africana*; white-berry bush, *Securinega virosa*; woolly caperbush, *Capparis tomentosa*, and wild grape, *Cissus cornifolia*, followed by thorn trees, *Acacia* spp; mangosteens, *Garcinia* sp, and others. In northwestern Zimbabwe the highest ranking browse was umbrella thorn, *Acacia tortilis*; followed by sausage tree, *K. africana*, and woolly caperbush, *C. tomentosa*, which were also found in the Chobe River sample.

While the species of browse plants utilised will vary in different parts of the bushbuck's distributional range, among those which are preferred are genera such as *Acacia, Combretum, Kigelia, Ximenia* and *Ziziphus* which have wide distributions in the Subregion and no doubt will be taken wherever they occur in bushbuck habitat.

Bushbuck can become a problem in forestry areas by nipping off the tops of young pine trees and thereby causing branching (eastern Zimbabwe). They can also cause damage in gardens, browsing on shrubs, especially roses and other garden plants.

### Reproduction

The young may be born at any time throughout the year. Simpson (1974) showed, however, that there is a bimodal conceptual pattern in northern Botswana in April/May and October/November, with two related peaks in October/November and April/May respectively. From a sample of only 10 captive births at the East London Zoo, 40% were in February/March and 30% in October/November (von Ketelhodt, 1976). The males become sexually mature at about 10,5 months old, females at 14 months (Morris, 1973; Simpson, 1974). Morris (1973) and Zaloumis & Cross (1974) gave the gestation period as 180 days. A single young is born at a birth, with a mass of between 3,5 to 4,5 kg. The female hides the young in dense underbush, returning to suckle it from time to time until it is strong enough to move freely on its own. The mean lambing interval in captivity was found to be 24 ± 8,6 days. Ewes conceived for the first time at just under one year of age (von Ketelhodt, 1976). Females have two pairs of inguinal mammae.

## Genus *Taurotragus* Wagner, 1855

---

No. 333

## *Taurotragus oryx* (Pallas, 1766)

## Eland
## Eland

Plate 36

---

### Colloquial Name

The name eland is borrowed from the Dutch *eland*, meaning elk.

### Taxonomic Notes

Three subspecies are listed by Ansell (1972), the zones of intergradation between them being broad and ill-defined. *T. o. oryx* occupies the southern part of the species' range on the continent, extending northwards to about the southern parts of Botswana and northern Namibia. *T. o. livingstonii* (P.L. Sclater, 1864) occupies an intermediate area, including parts of Angola, Zambia, southern Zaire, Zimbabwe, Mozambique and Malawi, and *T. o. pattersonianus* (Lydekker, 1906) which is extralimital and occupies the species' range north of *T. o. livingstonii*.

### Description

Eland are the largest of the African antelope, adult males standing about 1,7 m at the shoulder and at an age of six years have a mass of up to 700 kg; females are smaller at about 1,5 m, with masses of up to about 460 kg (Posselt, 1963). Skinner (1967) gave the mean mass of 19 mature bulls as 650 kg (range 425–840 kg).

In the northern parts of their distributional range in Africa eland are rufous-fawn in colour with narrow white stripes down their flanks. In the Subregion, where they formerly had a wider distribution southwards to the Cape, those from the southern part of this range, *T. o. oryx*, were dull fawn in colour, with no white stripes on their bodies and a dark brown mark on the back of the forelegs just above the knees. The body hairs are short, 13,9±4,9 mm, large and circular in cross-section, with an irregular waved mosaic scale pattern along the length of the hair (Fig. XLII.1) (Keogh, 1983).

Eland from the southern parts of their present day range in southern Botswana and northern Namibia are dun-coloured and lack the body stripes. As one moves northwards and eastwards in Botswana, one finds individuals with one or two stripes, and further north still, in Zambia, adult males have six or seven transverse white stripes on the upper parts of the body which, with their dun colour, mark them as the subspecies *T. o. livingstonii*. In these the dark brown mark on the forelegs is generally absent or at most indistinct. There is a wide zone of intergradation of these two subspecies, populations in Zimbabwe and southern Mozambique showing the influence of both. Old adults tend to lose hair and look greyer, because the dark skin shows through the coat.

The hair on the body is short, with a longer tuft of dark brown hair on the forehead, which is often matted and has a strong smell, due to a secretion from a glandular region in the skin at its base.

They have a band of dark brown hair along the back from the neck to near the base of the tail and a tuft of similar and much longer hair on the tip of the tail and hanging from the dewlap. The hair on the sides of the muzzle, on the upper and lower lips, on the lower parts of the legs and the insides of the long pointed ears is whitish.

The hooves mark broadly in the spoor, the front distinctly larger than the hind (Plate IV).

### Skull

In a tame herd in Zimbabwe, Kerr, Wilson & Roth (1970) found that the full adult dentition is attained in their fourth year of life. The dental formula for milk teeth is:

$i\frac{0}{3}\ c\frac{0}{1}\ p\frac{3}{3} = 20$

The dental formula for permanent teeth is:

$I\frac{0}{3}\ C\frac{0}{1}\ P\frac{3}{3}\ M\frac{3}{3} = 30$

The permanent premolars are the second, third and fourth.

Both sexes carry horns, those of the males much heavier than those of the females. Rising in the line of the face, they are nearly straight, slightly diverging, with a heavy spiral ridge at the base. The male horns are normally fairly even; those of the females are often uneven, curving backwards or splayed broadly outwards and lacking the heavy spiral ridge seen in the horns of the males. The world record horns came from Kasane, Botswana and measured 1,023 m (Best & Best, 1977).

At birth the horn buds are clearly visible in both sexes. They grow rapidly up to about seven months of age, thereafter more slowly. At about 15 months of age the horns of the males show the first clear signs of the appearance of the spiral ridge, in the form of bulging outgrowths of the horn bases. At this stage the ridge is ill-defined in the females. At

18 months the horns have attained a length of about 0,75 m. From this time onwards the horns of the males grow progressively heavier, especially towards their bases. For further details see Kerr & Roth (1970) and Jeffery & Hanks (1981).

## Distribution

Eland have a wide distribution in Africa south of Uganda and Kenya, being replaced north of this by the giant eland, *T. derbianus*, which occurs in parts of West and Central Africa and eastwards to the Sudan and possibly in parts of southern Ethiopia. Setzer (1956) believed that the eland occurring in the southern Sudan are allied more closely to *T. derbianus* than to our *T. oryx*, a view that is followed here. This implies that the populations in northern Kenya are similarly more closely allied and are not included, therefore, on the distribution map.

At one time eland were distributed widely in the Republic of South Africa, extending southwestwards to the immediate vicinity of the first settlement at the Cape, where they were common along the Liesbeek and Salt Rivers and at Hout Bay on the Cape Peninsula (Bosman 1952, *ex* van Riebeeck Daghregister, 1652). Today they only occur naturally in the Cape Province in the extreme north, where there are movements into the province from southern Botswana, and in parts of the Transvaal. They have been reintroduced widely and if considered on this basis their distribution today resembles the situation prior to settlement of the Cape, when they occurred throughout what is now the Republic of South Africa.

*South of the Sahara, excluding the Southern African Subregion*

They occur in southern **Uganda** and central and southern **Kenya**; throughout **Tanzania**; in southeastern **Zaire**; in central, southern **Angola**, and throughout **Zambia**. In **Mozambique**, north of the Zambezi River, they occur widely east of Lake Malawi, but are not recorded from the northwestern Tete District, which coincides with their absence from adjacent parts of Zimbabwe.

*Southern African Subregion*

They are confined to the northeastern parts of **Namibia** and southwards along the eastern border to about 23 °S. They are widespread in **Botswana**, but no longer occur in the more developed parts of the eastern sector or in the Okavango Delta. In **Zimbabwe**, where at one time they were widespread, they occur only in the northwest and southeast and marginally in parts of the Eastern Districts. In **Mozambique**, south of the Zambezi River, they are widespread, but no longer occur south of the western parts of the Gaza District or in parts of the Inhambane and Vila Pery districts. In the **Transvaal** they are confined in their distribution to the Kruger National Park and adjacent areas. Stevenson-Hamilton (1947) recorded that in 1910 a herd settled in the Park, near Letaba, from Mozambique. In **Natal** herds have always been present in the Drakensberg foothills.

## Habitat

Eland are versatile in their habitat requirements and, in the past, occurred in the greater part of the South West Arid Zone and in the Southern Savannas, penetrating into the Cape Macchia in the extreme southwestern parts of the continent. They are just as at home in the arid semi-desert scrub associations of Botswana as they are on montane grassland in the western parts of Mozambique. In the Subregion, in addition to this habitat, they occur in various types of woodland including *Baikiaea*, *Acacia* and open *Brachystegia/Julbernardia*. The only part of the Subregion where, historically, they were not found was in the western sector of Namibia where the mean annual rainfall is less than about 300 mm. They occur on the fringes of forests but do not penetrate into them and generally avoid more extensive open, short grass plains, except in transit. As they are predominantly browsers they require trees or bushes to provide for this part of their food requirements. Although today in the Subregion they do not occur coastally, they certainly did so in the past, but they are still found at low

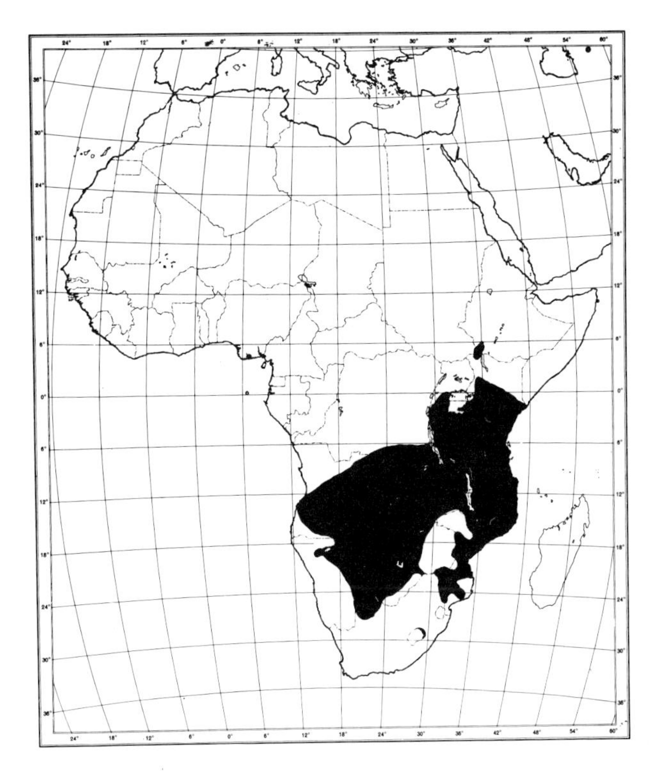

altitudes and occur in eastern Zimbabwe on montane grassland up to about 1 800 m, and in East Africa are recorded up to about 4 000 m.

Where water is available they drink regularly. In the Kalahari, where it may only be available seasonally, they obtain their moisture requirements from their food and the availability of water is not an essential habitat requirement.

## Habits

Eland are a gregarious species usually occurring in small herds, but at times in huge aggregations. Herds of over 700 have been recorded in the Hwange National Park, Zimbabwe (Wilson, 1975), and similar herds in the Kalahari Gemsbok National Park (Skinner unpubl.) and southern Botswana (Smithers, 1971).

In the Subregion the social organisation of a naturally occurring population has not been studied in depth. Interesting pointers to this, however, come from work on a population in the Loskop Dam Nature Reserve by Underwood (1975). This population at the time of his study numbered 70 to 80, all descended from an original herd of 16 introduced in 1963. Underwood found that, at the time of the calving season from August to October, the females formed nursery herds which were joined by yearlings and subadults. These nursery herds showed a marked increase in size at this time. Simultaneously the bulls would associate together. From late October until January the nursery herd was joined by up to six adult bulls to form a breeding herd. This was a relatively peaceful and compact unit, although there was serious fighting within the bull group which remained separated from it. The calves became increasingly independent of their mothers while weaning, from February to April, and the mothers together with the bulls left the nursery herds for gradually increasing periods. By about the end of April the nursery herds consisted mainly of young individuals and they remained as independent units through the winter months to form the nuclei of the following year's nursery herds, when the females rejoined them. During the winter months in Loskop the bulls tended to associate with small groups of females although, in less restricted populations in southern Africa, the bulls remained separate from these. About September/October, which is the peak of the calving period in Loskop, the adult bulls left the females and formed all-male groups. Individuals from these groups rejoined the nursery herds at the time of the rut.

In some areas populations are relatively sedentary, in others they exhibit extensive movements. The movement of large aggregations of eland are well known in southwestern Botswana, the most recent being in 1984 when many hundred died (Knight, pers. comm.) and in 1988 following heavy summer rains (Skinner, unpubl.). The latter grow in numbers as they move southwest across the Kalahari savanna to the Botswana border with the Republic of South Africa. These movements appear to relate to the seasonal availability of food following rains. In mountainous habitat they are known to move up and down the mountains. In other areas the populations are relatively sedentary (southeastern Zimbabwe) but, wherever eland occur, they are great wanderers, if only on a local basis. Some of these movements are directed to preferred feeding areas. They will move on to areas that have been burned in search of fresh, sprouting grass or to areas where shrubs or trees offer palatable seed pods. Underwood (1975) found that, in Loskop, adult dominant individuals were particularly effective in initiating movements, other than food movements. These may be triggered by high winds, or by their seeking shade or shelter from rain.

Dominance in both sexes is displayed by means of various types of ritual behaviour. The use of threats in particular is determined by the reaction of the threatened individual. If it moves on quickly, no further threats or conflict occur. If, however, the retreat is slow, threatening may be followed up by horning, the horns directed upwards and towards the body of the opponent. When closely approached by another, an individual may shake its head which usually is sufficient to make its opponent move off. As an extension of this, individuals may touch the sides of one another with their horns. Cows can be quite savage in repelling strange calves, whipping them with the sides of their horns. Charges are rarely seen but when they occur, with the horns lowered, it is usually sufficient to cause the opponent to move off without contact being established.

If a challenge between bulls is accepted, the contestants lower their horns and eventually interlock them, pushing and heaving forward, twisting their heads and necks until one opponent breaks away by turning his head and body away from his opponent and moving off. In these encounters, which can become intense, a contestant may be fatally injured by the sharp heavy horns of its opponent. Fights between cows follow this pattern, but in a much lower key.

Underwood (1973) could find no evidence of territoriality in eland, in the sense of the defence of a piece of ground. The hierarchy appears to be based on age and size.

All individuals test each other's urine from time to time, sniffing, licking or drinking it and then exhibiting flehmen. In this procedure the lips are curled away from the incisor teeth, the nose held high in the air. Flehmen in the bulls involves turning their heads at right angles to the body which may have a secondary function as a display (Underwood, 1973). Self and mutual grooming is carried out regularly by eland. In the former they scratch their bodies and faces on trees or other objects; in the latter one individual will assiduously lick the sides of the head and neck and the rump of another.

Eland are not entirely diurnal and, particularly during the summer months, will continue to feed after sunset.

While eland are generally silent, Underwood (1973) listed a number of vocalisations. These include the *moo* of the female in communication with her calf, which bleats when calling to her or whimpers on approaching strange calves or when separated from its mother. Adults, usually adult females, bark at strange objects; adult bulls bellow in expressing their dominance or emit a belching grunt in repelling others from food.

When adult eland walk they produce a characteristic clicking noise which can be heard over a considerable distance. What causes this clicking has been the subject of much controversy over the years. Some believe it is caused by the hooves clicking together when walking, others that it emanates from the carpal bones. Posselt (1963) was of the opinion that it comes from the knees, which is most likely to be correct as he worked with tame eland for many years.

In spite of their great size eland are prodigious jumpers, and are capable of clearing obstacles without effort. When jumping fences they will walk slowly up to them, pause, settle back slightly on their hindquarters, then jump, and in this way can clear 2 m with apparent ease. They are timid animals and are quick to gallop off if disturbed. This gallop soon develops into a fast trot which carries them over the ground at a great speed. They are difficult to follow for, even at a walk, they move faster than the good walking pace of a man.

Eland meat is of good quality and no doubt their disappearance from a large part of their former range was due in some measure to over-exploitation. Wild game animals have been the traditional source of meat for indigenous people in Africa, yet it is only within recent years that attempts have been made to utilise them on a sustained yield basis as a source of protein. Eland are docile and tractable and are independent of drinking water. Stevenson-Hamilton had a tame pair as far back as 1906, although larger scale trials were only initiated much later. The pioneer of these trials in the Subregion, John Posselt, established a herd at Lupane, Zimbabwe in 1954 (Posselt, 1963). Their potential appears to be not in supplementing cattle but in complementing them in areas suitable to both (Lightfoot & Posselt, 1976). Eland milk is very high in fat content (8–12%) and is highly nutritious (Uspenskii & Saglanskii, 1952).

Skinner (1967), while acknowledging certain biological advantages of the eland over domestic animals, stated that these advantages have often been overstated. They have a higher reproductive rate and are better adapted to hot, semi-arid environments than domestic animals, and feed on a wider range of plants than cattle. On the other hand, there may be problems in their management as they are seasonally nomadic.

**Food**

Eland which are well adapted to arid environments, apparently cannot subsist in regions where no succulent forage is available, and they occur only as far west as the arid savanna. They are very mobile and adapt their feeding habits to suit the circumstances, requiring a high protein diet, and they graze in summer and browse in winter (Skinner & van Jaarsveld, 1987). Eland have been classified as highly selective mixed feeders (Hofmann, 1973). They are partial to fresh sprouting grass and although grass is only eaten in quantity during the summer months, most stomachs examined from other times of the year contained at least a small percentage of grass.

Hofmeyr (1970) worked with a naturally occurring tame population in Zimbabwe, and listed a total of 60 food plants, including 11 grasses. Mopane, *Colophospermum mopane*, was the most important tree utilized, followed by red bushwillow, *Combretum apiculatum*; raisin bush, *Grewia* spp; African resin tree, *Ozoroa reticulata*, and apple-leaf, *Lonchocarpus capassa*. In the case of mopane, eland avoided certain trees and concentrated on others. In addition to the above foods, they showed a liking for marigold, *Tagestes minuta*; blackjacks, *Bidens pilosa*; starburr, *Acanthospermum* spp, and other forbs. They were seen to eat monkey oranges, *Strychnos* spp; the fruits of the white-berry bush, *Securinega virosa*, as well as the leaves of the raisin bush, *Grewia* spp; mopane, *Colophospermum mopane*; wild syringa, *Kirkia* sp; terminalia, *Terminalia* spp, and the guarri, *Euclea* spp.

During the dry winter months eland are assiduous in their search for green foliage, but at this time will eat the dry fallen leaves of their food plants. Kerr, Wilson & Roth (1970) showed that there are distinct seasonal changes in the percentage of some of the main food plants utilised. In summing up the situation, Posselt (*in litt.*) was of the opinion that there did not appear to be any type of vegetation that eland will not eat, all types being consumed at varying times of the year depending on their availability. When feeding, eland have a tendency to settle in an area, then walk a considerable distance before settling again, the lead in these movements being taken by the dominant individual present. They use their horns very effectively in breaking down the higher branches of shrubs and trees. Inserting the horns on either side of a branch, it is twisted until it either breaks off or hangs loose, when the foliage can be reached conveniently. High branches may also be pulled down by hooking the horns over them. In this manner branches up to 75 mm in diameter are broken. When an individual does this, others gather around to feed, but subordinates are driven off by threatening them with lowered horns or by chasing them in short rushes. Eland are quick feeders, grasping the foliage with the lips, never the tongue, and cutting twigs up to 7 mm thick with the teeth. They may also strip a twig of leaves by drawing it through the lips.

Grasses are not an important part of their diet in the Zimbabwe bushveld and are utilised in quantity only during the wet season from about October to February. Kerr *et al.* (1970) listed among perennial species eaten, *Tricholaena monache*, *Urochloa mosambicensis* and *Schmidtia pappophoroides*, and the annuals, *Brachiaria deflexa*, *Cenchrus biflorus*, and *Chloris virgata*. On the other hand, in the northern Transvaal bushveld, Hofmeyr (1970) found that eland adapt themselves well to what is available and graze constituted 42,5% of total feeding time at certain times of the year. They were particularly partial to *Panicum maximum*. In the western Transvaal, Buys (1987, 1990) found the consumption of dicotyledons increased from February to May, remaining static during winter, and in December there was a sharp decline of 40% in the proportion of browse in the faeces. Five important browse species were identified: *Rhus lancea*, *Grewia flava*, *Diospyros lycioides*, *Tarchonanthus camphoratus* and *Acacia karroo*. Buys (1987) found they adapt their feeding habits to suit the circumstances. They require a high protein diet and in summer tend to graze and in winter to browse. This also enables eland to adopt a more extensive social system and congregate in large herds in early summer; most calves are born then and such large herds afford more protection.

While eland will drink when water is available, they are by no means dependent on drinking water and in some parts of their distributional range they obtain sufficient moisture from their food to enable them to traverse large distances between water points (Taylor, 1969). In the Kalahari Gemsbok National Park, Dreyer (1987) recorded five individuals as drinking an average of 30,2 l of fresh water, but he gave no indication as to the frequency with which they drank.

**Reproduction**

Eland breed throughout the year, with a peak in calving during the early summer months of August to October in the summer rainfall areas (Skinner *et al.*, 1974). Skinner & van Zyl (1969) found that there is a slight difference in the peaks of calving between bushveld and Highveld populations, which they attributed to a difference in the level of nutrition. It also varies slightly in different localities. Female eland frequently have a postpartum oestrus which results in a shorter inter-calving interval. The gestation period is 271 days, birthweight of male calves 30,0 kg and females 25,2 kg. The annual calving percentage is 83% and the calving interval 345,5 days. They breed first at 28 months and cease to breed at 18 years (Skinner, 1988).

The bulls court cows in oestrus by rubbing their heads along their flanks as they walk alongside them and by licking and nuzzling their vulvas. Posselt (1963) recorded horning and pawing the ground as part of the courtship display. Although observed in a non-sexual context as well, the laying of the chin on the lower parts of the back is part of the courtship activities.

Females in oestrus are attended closely by the dominant bull which takes active steps to dissuade other younger bulls from approaching her. He will attack approaching mature bulls actively and there are many cases on record where these have been injured fatally by goring. Roth, Kerr & Posselt (1972) recorded a case where a wild bull broke into the paddock of a tame herd and chased its dominant bull away. In turn it was challenged and killed in a series of fights with another adult bull.

The bulls can mate successfully at 18 months old but normally are not allowed to do so at such an early age owing to the presence of the older dominant bulls. Underwood (1975), in the Loskop Dam Nature Reserve, found that most births take place at night between the hours of 04h00 and 08h00, peaking just at sunrise. Just before giving birth the females become restless and in captivity they are liable to make attempts to escape at this time. The females lie down on their sides to have their calves which, when born, are licked assiduously and the afterbirth eaten by the female. A single calf is produced at a birth, twins being recorded only rarely.

The calves struggle to a standing position very soon after birth and can run within three or four hours. The females communicate with their calves using a series of repeated "clicks" or by mooing and grunting or a combination of these (Underwood, 1975). The calves respond by whimpering or moaning. The respective calls are recognised by both the mother and the calf. Newly born calves have a tendency to follow any moving object larger than themselves but soon learn to follow only their mothers or other larger eland. Small groups of calves thus become associated with a single female temporarily and can be seen strung out in single file in decreasing order of size behind her.

Females only suckle their own calves and, even in the event of losing her calf, will evince no interest in other calves. While it is still very young the female will lead her calf to a suitable lying up place where it will remain while she goes off to feed. Milk-stealing by strange calves does take place but the female drives them off by horning or simply moving away from them. In tame herds the calves are weaned by about four months. During this period the female visits her calf at increasingly infrequent intervals, until she abandons it altogether to its own resources, when it joins up with other weaned calves in the nursery herd. Within these the young tend to form bonds with others which are stronger and more lasting than the mother/calf bond (Underwood, 1975). Females which lose their calves tend to move independently of the nursery herds for a time. The young calves have a coat of much longer hair than the adults. The hair tends to be curly, especially on the back, and is a reddish-fawn colour.

Females have two pairs of inguinal mammae.

## Subfamily REDUNCINAE

Members of this Subfamily are medium to large-sized antelope, the males with medium-sized to long ridged horns, either bowed, lyrate or hooked. Preorbital glands are absent, except in the puku, *Kobus vardonii*, where they are poorly developed, and pedal glands are absent or rudimentary. They have two pairs of mammae. They have medium-length tails which are bushy in some species. Two genera occur in the Subregion, *Kobus* and *Redunca*, the former with three species, the latter with two.

Key to the genera (Meester *et al.*, 1986)

1. Bare patch below the ear; tail bushy
   ... *Redunca*

   No bare patch below the ear; tail not bushy
   ... *Kobus*

## Genus *Redunca* H. Smith, 1827

Key to the species after Meester *et al.* (1986)

1. Larger, shoulder height about 0,75–0,9 m; the horns in adult males 250 mm or more over the outside curve, the horns curving forward well above the level of the tips of the ears; with one pair of inguinal glands
   ... *arundinum*

   Smaller, shoulder height about 0,7–8,8 m; the horns in adult males less than 250 mm over the outside curve, the horns curving forward about the level of the tips of the ears; with two pairs of inguinal glands
   ... *fulvorufula*

No. 334

## *Redunca arundinum* (Boddaert, 1785)

## Reedbuck
## Rietbok

Plate 37

### Colloquial Name

Reedbuck are named from their characteristic association with vleis or reedbeds.

### Taxonomic Notes

Only two subspecies are recognised, a northern *R. a. occidentalis* (Rothschild, 1907) and a southern *R. a. arundinum*, which alone is found in the Subregion.

### Description

Adult male reedbuck stand about 0,9 m at the shoulder and have a mass of up to 68 kg; the females are 0,8 m and have a mass of up to 51 kg (Table 334.1).

The body hairs are 18,4±4,7 mm long, oval or circular in cross-section, with a regular waved mosaic scale pattern along the entire length of the hair (Fig. XLII.1) (Keogh, 1983). The overall colour of the body varies from brown, tending to grey or buffy-grey, to yellow or buffy-yellow or even to greyish-brown. The back is usually slightly darker than the remainder of the upper parts. The upper part of the tail and the neck and head in particular are much lighter. The under sides of the neck and chest are greyish-white or light greyish-brown. The under parts are white, with a clear transition from the colour of the flanks. On the upper parts of the throat there is a distinct half-moon patch which is lighter in colour than the remainder of the neck, which is particularly distinct in adult males. The lips are whitish and the outside of the long ears are pointed and sparsely haired, with the dark skin showing through. There is a distinct, dark brown band down the front of each foreleg extending over the whole length of the leg and a similar but less distinct band on the lower part of the hind legs. The hooves tend to be thin and elongated (Plate V). The bushy tail, which reaches half way down the hock, is buffy-yellow above; the under side is white.

The general colour pattern of darker back, lighter flanks and white under parts has the effect of making the individual seem flat rather than three-dimensional when viewed from the side, due to the unequal reflection of light (Hesse-Dolflein, 1943). This is true for certain other antelope as well. Taken in conjunction with their habit of "freezing" when danger threatens, it is an additional factor in ensuring their survival (Jungius, 1971a).

Juveniles are lighter in colour than adults, lacking the greyness in the coat and appearing more yellowish. In very old individuals the coat tends to be paler. Kirby (1896) reported the shooting of a melanistic reedbuck in the eastern Transvaal and albino specimens have been reported widely.

The glandular, black, hairless patch situated near the base of the ear is conspicuous in some populations of reedbuck (Kruger National Park), but absent in others (Kyle National Park, Zimbabwe). This character has been used in the past to distinguish the reedbuck from its near relative, the mountain reedbuck, but its use for this purpose is invalid.

Reedbuck have inguinal glands situated in the groin region. The males have one pair, while the females sometimes have two. The glandular pouches have a funnel-shaped opening and secrete a yellow waxy substance. They do not have preorbital glands (Pocock, 1910).

**Table 334.1**

Measurements (mm) and mass (kg) of reedbuck, *R. arundinum*, from Zimbabwe (Smithers & Wilson, 1979)

| | Males | | | Females | | |
|---|---|---|---|---|---|---|
| | $\bar{x}$ | n | Range | $\bar{x}$ | n | Range |
| TL | 1600 | 16 | 1560–1785 | 1575 | 20 | 1380–1689 |
| T | 254 | 16 | 215–300 | 245 | 20 | 200–300 |
| Hf c/u | 453 | 16 | 430–475 | 435 | 20 | 397–469 |
| E | 161 | 16 | 153–180 | 159 | 20 | 140–170 |
| Mass | 51,8 | 16 | 42,7–68,2 | 38,2 | 20 | 31,8–50,9 |

Only the males carry horns which rise from the top of the head, curve evenly forward and are ridged and corrugated for the basal two-thirds of their length. The remainder of the horns are smooth and inclined to be hooked forward towards the tips (Fig. 334.1). There is a soft bulbous swelling at the base of each horn which in life is a conspicuous, shining, whitish colour. These appear in the yearling males and are developed most fully in the old adults. They were long thought to be glandular, but Jungius & Claassen (1971) showed that they are composed of tissue from which the horns grow. The whitish colour is caused by small horn particles that are flaking off continually. The greatest horn length recorded from the Subregion is 467 mm (Rowland Ward, 1986).

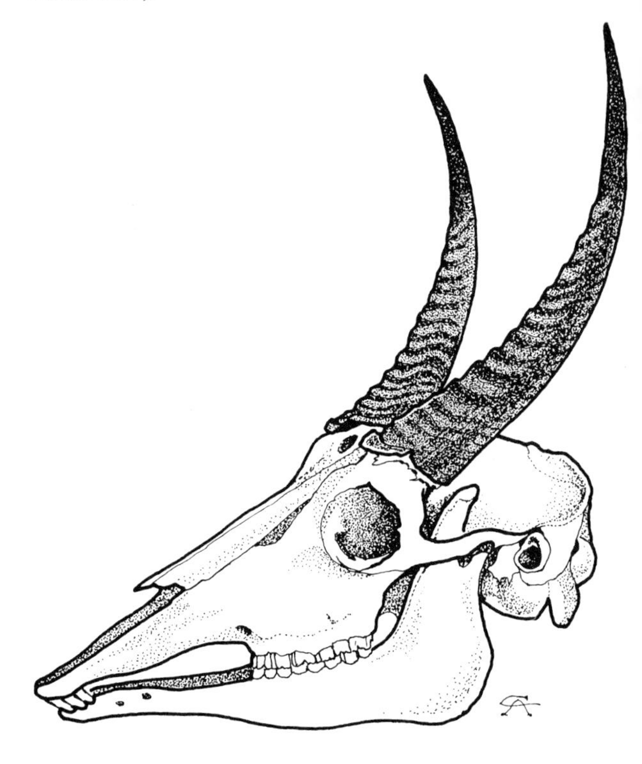

Fig. 334.1. Skull: reedbuck, *R. arundinum*
TL skull 280 mm

### Distribution

Because of their specialised habitat requirements, their distribution within the limits shown is patchy and discontinuous. In the southern parts of their range they are absent from the Zambezi Valley between Zambia and Zimbabwe and in the Limpopo Valley between Zimbabwe and the Transvaal. In Malawi, while widespread, they now remain largely confined to National Parks and other reserved areas. In the Cape Province their distribution has shrunk considerably in historical times. Thunberg (1795) recorded them from Swellendam, but today they do not occur west of the Komgha area in the Eastern Province and numbers there appear to have been reduced seriously within recent years (Lloyd, 1979).

*South of the Sahara, excluding the Southern African Subregion*

They occur in western and southern **Tanzania**; in southern **Zaire**; in **Angola**, excluding the southwestern areas; throughout **Zambia**; in National Parks and reserves throughout **Malawi**, and throughout **Mozambique**, north of the Zambezi River.

*Southern African Subregion*

They occur marginally in northeastern **Namibia** as far west as the Ruacana Falls on the Cunene River; throughout the Okavango Delta, and in the vicinity of the Chobe River in northern **Botswana**, and in the Tati Concession in the northeast of the country. In **Zimbabwe** they occur throughout, except in the Zambezi Valley, in parts of the western border area with Botswana and in the Limpopo Valley. They occur throughout **Mozambique**, south of the Zambezi River. They occur in the central parts of the **Transvaal**, but are absent in the south and in the Limpopo Valley in the north. Although they formerly occurred widely in the **Orange Free State**, they are now virtually extinct, with the possibility that a few may survive in the Golden Gate National Park. They are common in the Ndumu Game Reserve and occur widely in **Natal** below 2 100 m. They occur in considerable numbers on the eastern shores of Lake St Lucia, Natal. Their distribution extends southwards to the **Cape Province** as far as the Komgha district, but they are now extinct west of this.

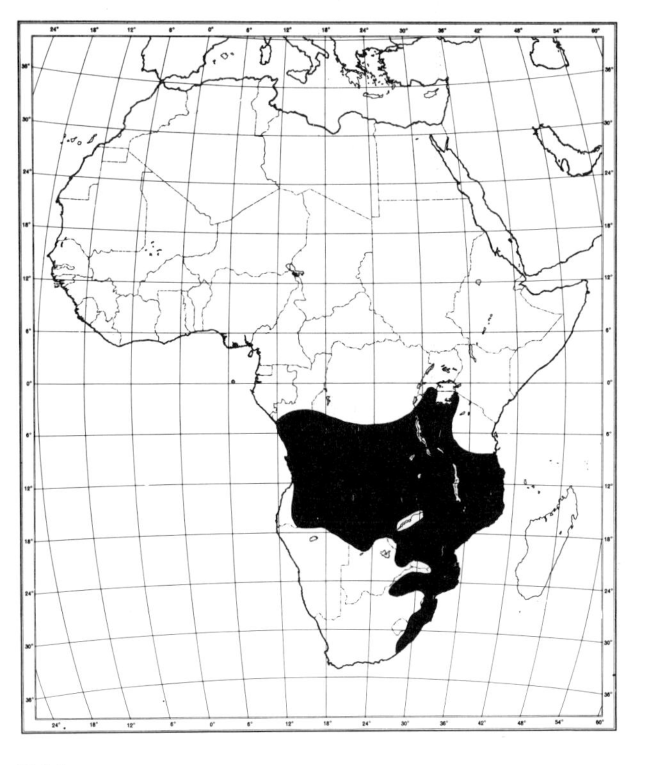

## Habitat

Reedbuck have two essential habitat requirements: tall grass cover or herbaceous cover, preferably with some woody elements, or reedbeds, and a water supply. Vleis with a central, wet drainage area or grassland adjacent to streams, rivers or other areas of permanent water are favoured. In the Drakensberg foothills in Natal, Howard (1986) found that they favour planted pastures adjacent to woody cover in winter, moving to vleis and broken veld (providing adequate cover by way of boulder outcrops, gulleys and ledges supporting rank vegetation) in summer when forage quality improves. They avoid flat open veld and they will vacate areas where bush encroachment has progressed too far. Because of these specialised habitat requirements reedbuck distribution is patchy and discontinuous everywhere. Clean burning will cause them to vacate their habitat, so herbaceous scrub, reedbeds or tall grasses or the wetter central areas of vleis are vital to their continued presence in an area. In the Drakensberg foothills where winters can be severe, herbaceous cover provides shelter against adverse weather conditions and the loss of body heat.

## Habits

Although 15 to 20 may be seen together during the cold, dry months of the year from about May to August, these are purely temporary associations and reedbuck are not a gregarious species. They live in pairs or family parties and never form herds or groups like some other kobs such as waterbuck, *K. ellipsiprymnus*, or lechwe, *K. leche*. Howard (1986) found home range size in Natal varied from 0,73 km$^2$ for adult males to 1,23 km$^2$ for adult females. A pair occupies a territory but, although they move about independently, they maintain contact through numerous olfactory and visual signals (Jungius, 1971a). It is not known whether they associate for more than a single season.

Territorial males on occasion will leave their territory for excursions into adjacent habitat. Contact within the territory is maintained by whistling and they advertise their presence within it by a characteristic rocking canter and "proud" display which emphasises the white throat band (Fig. 334.3). Jungius (1971a) believed that olfactory marking of the territory may also be carried out.

Fig. 334.3 The "proud" display in the territorial male reedbuck, *R. arundinum*.

The territory is defended by the territorial male by means of various threat displays, including defecation and urination in the "proud" attitude in front of the contestant. In this attitude the legs are held stiffly with the head erect. Jungius (1971a) regarded this as one of the strongest forms of threat, releasing either an immediate attack reaction or causing the contestant to move off. Other threats involve horn presentation, with the contestants standing close to each other. When this is carried out with the head close to the ground it may lead to pushing each other with the horns locked and eventually to fighting when, with the ears held back, the opponents lunge forward, the horns clashing together noisily. This may continue at intervals throughout the day, the contestants occasionally breaking off to graze or rest. Fighting is never so fierce as to cause serious injury to the contestants. At the conclusion of fighting the victor sometimes adopts the "proud" attitude and defecates but seldom chases the vanquished. Young males or females may submit to aggressive territorial males by lowering their heads and holding their horns backwards.

Jungius (1971a) showed that the daily activity of reedbuck varies and is governed by factors such as season, weather and disturbance. When good food supplies are available and water is plentiful, reedbuck tend to become nocturnal. During the dry season activity during the day is extended and the time spent in grazing increases because larger quantities of food are required to compensate for its decreased nutritive value. In addition they are forced to visit water supplies more frequently during the dry season, whilst during the wet season a large proportion of their moisture requirements are met from dew and succulent herbage (Jungius, 1971a).

They tend to use fixed trails leading to water. Their approach to it is circumspect, the females usually hanging back, allowing the males and young to make the first approach. They are averse to entering the water, choosing drinking places where they can stand with their feet relatively dry. When a group is at water some individuals remain on the alert while the others drink. The incidence of high wind may prolong their resting periods and reduce the time devoted to grazing. They take little notice of rain.

Reedbuck vocalise in various ways, the best known being the characteristic whistle. This is made with the mouth closed, the air expelled through the nostrils. When whistling the individual holds the head erect with the ears directed forward. All age groups whistle when disturbed, the frequency depending on the degree of alarm. When highly excited the individual may stot and then defecate. As a preliminary to whistling, females may utter a low clicking sound.

When reedbuck are disturbed and take to flight they are inclined to jump, at the same time jerking the hind legs backwards and outwards, which is accompanied by a peculiar "popping" sound. Jungius (1971a) believed this to be caused by the sudden opening of the inguinal pouches. When closely pursued reedbuck gallop, with occasional long jumps, covering several metres, or they may stot, jumping off the ground with the hind legs slightly more pulled up towards the body than the fore. The hindquarters are thrown high and the head held erect, exhibiting the light, crescent-shaped throat marking. At each stot the head is jerked back and they snort loudly.

Social grooming is unknown in reedbuck, but they will lick themselves assiduously, nibble and scratch the neck and head with the hind foot and rub the cheeks on the flanks. The horns are also used for grooming. Normally they rest in the cover of tall grass or reedbeds but will lie out in the full sun. Before lying down they will trample around breaking down the grass to form a bed. When at rest together they lie several metres apart, never close together, the individuals tending to orientate themselves in different directions. They rest on their sides with their heads up, but occasionally with the neck outstretched, the chin on the ground.

### Food

Reedbuck are almost exclusively grazers, although in some areas during the winter months when the nutritional value of the grasses is low, they will eat small quantities of herbs and in other areas may browse extensively. During the dry months they prefer to graze near water, vacating the drier grassland to avail themselves of the greener grasses found there. With the onset of the rains they move back to drier ground. If their habitat is burned and unless patches of tall grass cover of sufficient size remain to provide them with cover, reedbuck will move, the sprouting grass not being a big enough inducement to remain.

While the principal species of grasses utilised vary from area to area, Jungius (1971b), in the Kruger National Park, included yellow thatch grass, *Hyparrhenia dissoluta*; giant spear grass, *Trachypogon capensis*; buffalo grass, *Panicum maximum*, and spear grass, *Heteropogon contortus*, on the higher ground and rice grass, *Leersia hexandra*; red couch grass, *Hemarthria altissima*; cottonwool grass, *Imperata cylindrica*, and the reed, *Phragmites communis*, from the wetter parts of the habitat. In another area of the Park, *Ischaemum brachyatherum*; blue buffalo grass, *Cenchrus ciliaris*, and small buffalo grass, *Panicum coloratum*, were among the most important food plants on the drier areas, and Rhodes' grass, *Chloris gayana*, on the wetter. Water is essential to reedbuck and they cannot survive long without it. If the supply in their habitat dries up, they will move to other areas where it is available.

### Reproduction

Lambs may be born at any time throughout the year, with a peak in births from December to May in the Kruger National Park (Jungius, 1970), while in the Kyle National Park, Zimbabwe, lambs are born two months earlier from September onwards (Ferrar & Kerr, 1971).

When courting, territorial males approach the females with their heads laid back and noses held forward and nuzzle their vulval region. The females may submit to these approaches by lowering their heads and necks, when copulation may take place. The gestation period is about 225 days (Kenneth, 1947). The female gives birth in isolation, the lamb deliberately hiding itself without help from its mother, and is visited by her only once during the day for suckling and cleaning. The adequacy of the habitat in providing suitable sites for concealment is essential as the lambs "lie-out" for some three months (Jungius, 1970; Howard, 1986). The female approaches her lamb quietly and circumspectly and, when she leaves, it normally moves and beds down in a new situation. When it is about three or four months old, the lamb and female rejoin the male. The mother-lamb bond breaks down about the time that she is due to give birth to a new lamb, but if she loses this, the bond may be re-established (Jungius, 1970).

The females have two pairs of inguinal mammae.

---

No. 335

## *Redunca fulvorufula* (Afzelius, 1815)

## Mountain reedbuck
## Rooiribbok

Plate 37

---

### Colloquial Name

This species is closely related to the reedbuck, *R. arundinum*. Throughout its distributional range it is associated with mountains or rocky hills, as opposed to the reedbuck which is a grassland species.

### Taxonomic Notes

Three subspecies are recognised by Ansell (1972): *R. f. adamanae* Pfeffer, 1962 of Cameroun; *R. f. chanleri* (Rothschild, 1895) of East Africa, and *R. f. fulvorufula*, which is the only subspecies found in the Subregion.

### Description

Mountain reedbuck are medium-sized antelope, adult males standing about 0,75 m at the shoulder, with a mean mass of about 30,2 kg, the females slightly smaller and lighter, with a mean mass of 28,6 kg (Table 335.1).

The body hairs are 29,5±6,3 mm long, oval, oblong or concavo-convex in cross-section, some hairs with gutters and with a regular waved mosaic pattern along their entire length (Keogh, 1983). The overall colour is greyish on the upper parts, with pure white under parts. The head and neck are yellowish and the front legs do not have the dark brown line down the front as seen in the reedbuck, *R. arundinum*. The coat is soft and woolly, the tail bushy and the same colour as the upper parts of the body on top and pure white underneath. They have black glandular patches under the ears, which Hofmann (1972) showed had a function in marking.

The spoor shows the rather narrow elongated hooves (Plate V).

**Table 335.1**

Mass (kg) of adult male and female mountain reedbuck, *R. fulvorufula*, from the Mountain Zebra National Park (Skinner, 1980)

| | Males | | | Females | | |
|---|---|---|---|---|---|---|
| | $\bar{x}$ | n | Range | $\bar{x}$ | n | Range |
| Mass | 30,2 | 39 | 24,0–35,5 | 28,6 | 43 | 14,5–33,8 |

**Plate V Spoor**

334.Reedbuck, *Redunca arundinum*
335.Mountain reedbuck, *Redunca fulvorufula*
336.Waterbuck, *Kobus ellipsiprymnus*
337.Red lechwe, *Kobus leche*
338.Puku, *Kobus vardonii*

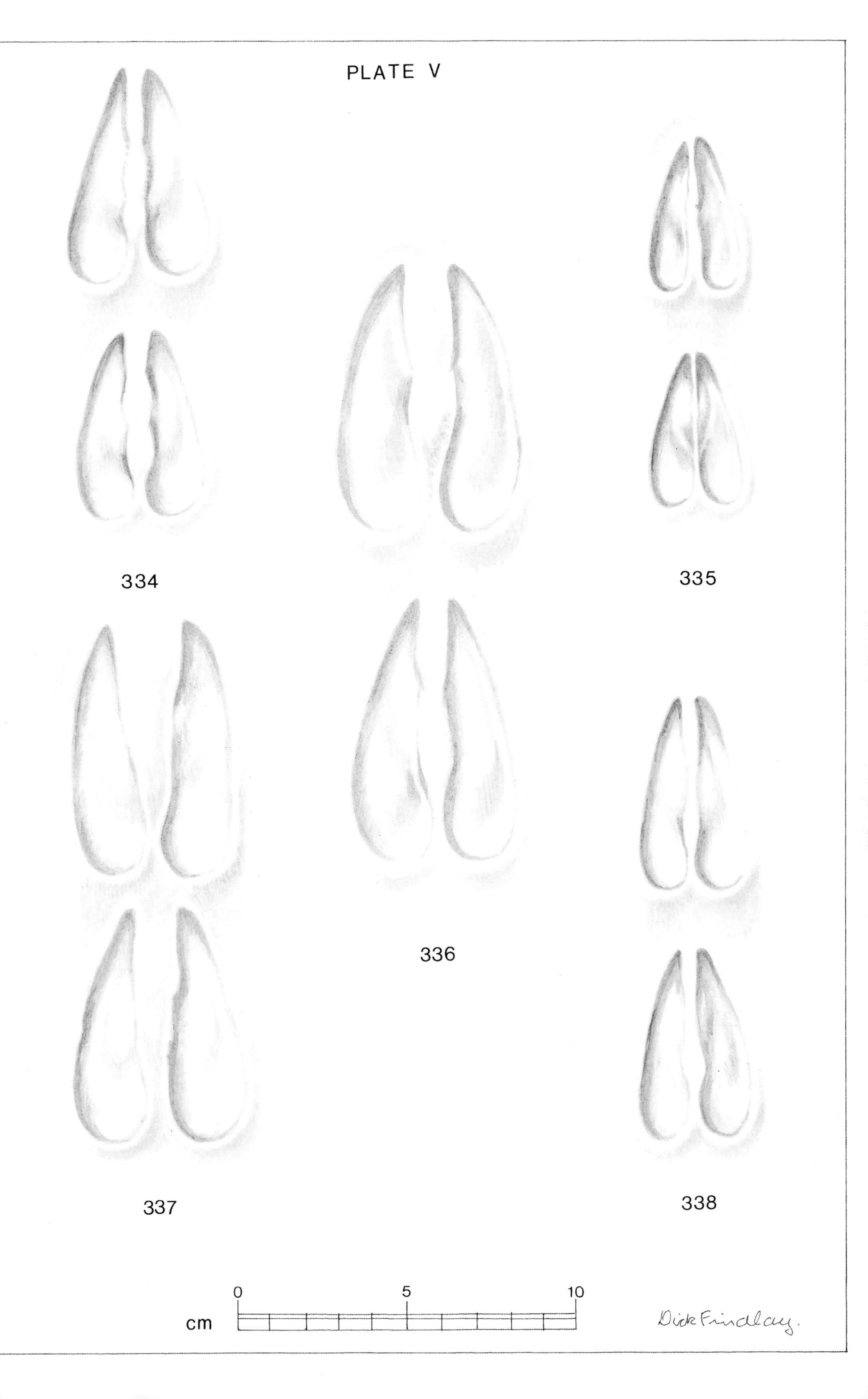
PLATE V
334
335
336
337
338
0
5
10
cm
Dick Findlay.

Only the males carry the short, heavily ridged horns, which rise from the top of the head and hook forward at about the level of the top of the long, narrow ears and end in smooth, rather blunt points (Fig. 335.1.b). The world's record pair, measuring 292 mm over the front curve, originated from Botswana (Rowland Ward, 1986).

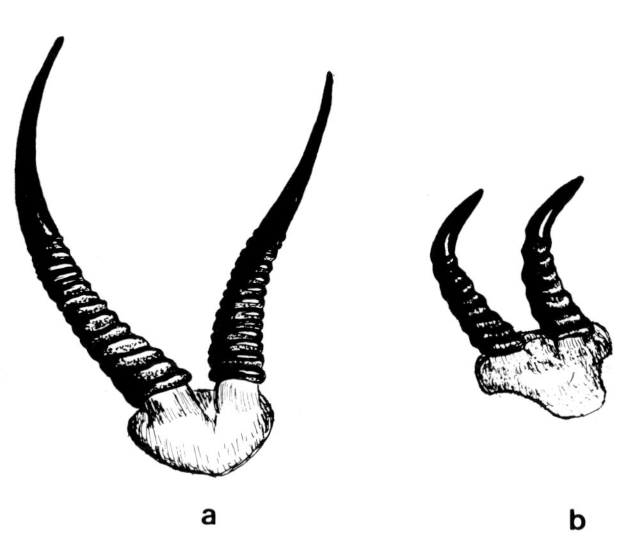


Fig. 335.1. Horns: (a) reedbuck, *R. arundinum* (b) mountain reedbuck, *R. fulvorufula*.

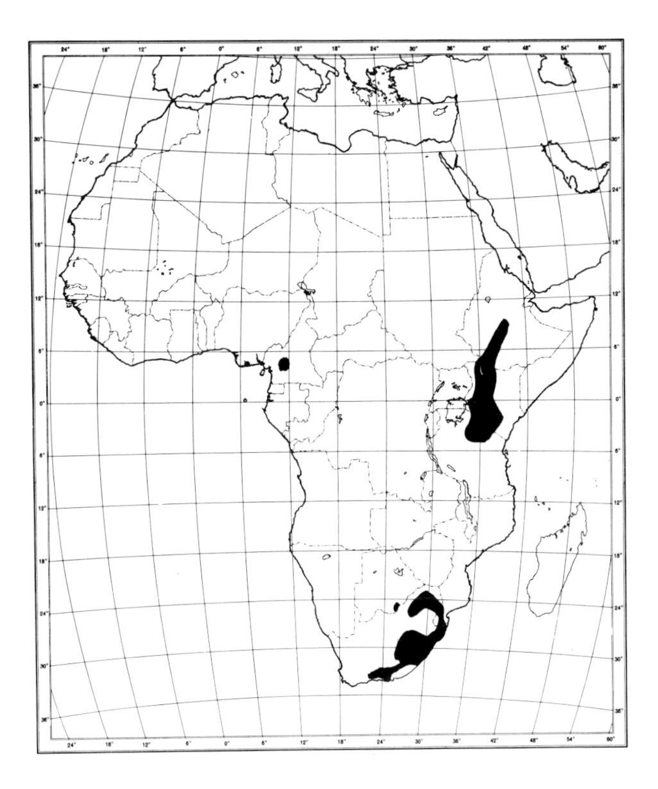

### Distribution

Owing to their specialised habitat requirements the distribution of mountain reedbuck is patchy and discontinuous and they will be found, within the limits shown, only where there is suitable habitat.

In East Africa they occur on Mt Kilimanjaro up to an altitude of 4 560 m; in the Drakensberg to 2 000 m, but generally they are associated with the lower slopes of mountains and stony hills at lower altitudes.

*South of the Sahara, excluding the Southern African Subregion*

The Adamana mountain reedbuck, *R. f. adamanae*, is only known to occur on this massif in **Cameroun**, and is separated from the East African populations by a distance of some 2 000 km. They occur in the southeastern **Sudan**; southern **Ethiopia**; western **Kenya**, and in parts of northern **Tanzania**.

*Southern African Subregion*

They occur in the Ndzindza Nature Reserve in the Lubombo Mountains in eastern **Swaziland** and in the Malolotja Nature Reserve in the northwest. They occur narrowly in the Lobatsi area, in southeastern **Botswana**, and in the Lebombo Mountains in southwestern **Mozambique**. They occur widely in the **Transvaal**, excluding the northeastern and western sectors, and in **Natal**, except in the Ndumu Game Reserve and along the coastal strip. They occur throughout the eastern and southern parts of the **Orange Free State** and in the extreme northeastern and eastern parts of the **Cape Province**, excluding the Eastern Province, east of about 28 °E. There do not appear to be any material records from Lesotho but they probably do occur there.

### Habitat

Mountain reedbuck inhabit the dry, grass-covered, stony slopes of hills and mountains where these provide cover in the form of bushes or scattered trees. They are found infrequently on more open mountain grassland and tend to avoid the bleak open conditions associated with the summits of mountainous areas, preferring the lower slopes, occurring in many areas on low stony hills. They will move on to flats adjacent to their stony habitat to feed or to drink, the availability of water being an essential habitat requirement.

### Habits

Mountain reedbuck occur in small groups of three to eight individuals, increasing up to about 40 individuals in certain seasons (Irby, 1977). The social organisation consists of territorial males, non-territorial males, herds of females with young and bachelor groups. The territorial males occupy their territories all the year round, only moving from them to feed in adjacent areas when their territories get burned out, or to establish temporary contact with other males. If chased out of their territories, they invariably return to them, being nervous and on the alert when outside their limits. Non-territorial males may form into small bachelor groups or they may remain solitary, generally occupying the periphery of the male territories (Irby, 1976).

The herds of females with young are unstable and females, or females with young, move from herd to herd. The females move from one male territory to another. Irby (1976) observed territorial males herding females. The ranges of the female herds are larger than the male territories, several of which they may overlap. In the Loskop Dam Nature Reserve, Irby (1976) found that the mean area of a male territory was 0,28 $km^2$, while the home range of the female herds averaged 0,57 $km^2$.

They are most active in the early mornings, late afternoons and at night, resting during the late mornings and early afternoons in the cover of bushes. When resting they lie up tightly together (Irby, 1981a). They probably feed as much at night as during the day, moving from the hillsides to feed on adjacent flat ground, or to water. If disturbed they give the alarm call, a shrill whistle reminiscent of the reedbuck, *R. arundinum*, which sends the herd running, with their tails upright, along the side of the hill or obliquely downhill. Under similar circumstances the grey rhebok, *Pelea capreolus*, tends to take to the higher slopes. After running off for three or four hundred metres, mountain reedbuck pause and look around for the source of disturbance. It is sometimes possible to halt them in flight by whistling sharply. When running they have a rocking horse motion, bounding along with extended limbs.

They are dependent on drinking water (Norton, 1989) and drink more often during the dry weather than during cold, cloudy weather. They tolerate a wide range of climatic conditions and ignore light rain. In high wind or heavy rainstorms they will orientate themselves with their hindquarters in its direction or will seek sheltered slopes, standing or lying down until the weather conditions improve. They have a tendency to live on the warmer, drier northern or western slopes of their hilly habitat.

**Food**

Their large subdivided rumen with its keratinised mucosa is adapted to digesting a coarse grass diet, of low quality in the dry season (Hofmann & Stewart, 1972). Mountain reedbuck are almost exclusively grazers. From observations on captive individuals, Irby (1976, 1984a) showed that they are selective feeders whose preference for different species of grasses varies seasonally. They almost always feed on the greenest, softest leaves of the grasses and, as long as these remain available, avoid eating the stems. In a study on the Loskop Dam Nature Reserve, Irby (1976) found that of 11 species of grasses recorded in rumen samples, red grass, *Themeda triandra*, and thatch grass, *Hyparrhenia* spp, ranked highly. Other species, common in the area, such as bristle grass, Aristida spp; couch grass, *Cynodon* spp, and love grass, *Eragrostis* spp, were eaten less frequently than was expected. The utilisation of *T. triandra* was high during the wet and early part of the dry season and much lower during the late dry season. During the late dry season Irby (1976) showed that more has to be eaten to compensate for the low food value of the grasses during this period.

**Reproduction**

Mountain reedbuck breed throughout the year, with a peak in breeding activity around April/May. In the Mountain Zebra National Park (Karoo) and the Ohrigstad and Loskop Dam nature reserves (eastern Transvaal), the peak in births occurs from October to January. More recently, in the Karoo, with a large data base, Norton (1989) found 95% of adult and 75% of yearling females were pregnant, with a distinct birth peak in November and a standard deviation of one month around the mean birth date. A single lamb is born (Skinner, 1980), following a gestation period of 236–251 days (Irby, 1979), with a mass of 3,0 kg (Kingdon, 1982). Lambs are hidden for two to three months. Under ideal nutritional conditions, the first oestrus in females can be as early as nine months of age, but normally they do not become reproductively mature until about 12 to 14 months old (Irby, 1979). Thereafter, under good conditions, calves may be born to individual females at intervals of about 12 to 14 months. While spermatozoa are produced by males before they are a year old, sexual maturity and mating ability must await their ability to establish and defend their own territories. When courting, the male approaches a female with his head outstretched. If the female is prepared to accept him, she adopts a submissive posture by lowering her head.

Females leave their group to give birth to their lambs in isolation. The lambs hide themselves and the mother visits her lamb once or twice a day, approaching the hiding place very quietly and circumspectly to suckle and clean it. The female may spend up to half an hour with the lamb and when she leaves, the lamb moves to another hiding place. At this stage the lambs are subject to predation, but the chances of this are reduced by their immobility, their constant changing of hiding places after the females have suckled them, and by the females ingesting their faeces and urine and so reducing the chances of their detection by scent. In spite of this, Irby (1976) recorded that mortality is high during this period. Hiding continues for some two to three months, thereafter the lamb will move with its mother to graze and is soon able to maintain its position in the group. If while in hiding the lamb is in danger or is attacked, it may utter an alarm call which will bring the mother to its aid. The bond between the female and her lamb is broken at the time when the female is about to give birth to her new lamb. If, however, she loses her new lamb the bond may continue over a longer period.

The territorial males tolerate juvenile males up to the age of about six months, but will expel them from the female herds once they have attained an age of nine to 15 months, when they join the bachelor groups. The first dry season following birth is a critical time for the young. They do not have the resilience of the adults with their accumulated fat reserves which were laid down during the preceding wet season. Norton (1989) found that survival depends on rainfall and there was a marked increase in yearling males at the Rolfontein Nature Reserve in the Karoo following good spring rains. This was not confirmed elsewhere and more data are required. In Norton's (1989) study, mortality was 10% for young to medium age adults, particularly amongst males which showed a lower condition index, increasing rapidly after seven years.

Females have two pairs of inguinal mammae.

## Genus *Kobus* A. Smith, 1840

Three species of the genus *Kobus* occur in the Subregion: the red lechwe, *K. leche*; the waterbuck, *K. ellipsiprymnus*, and the puku, *K. vardonii*. The waterbuck is the largest of the three species and is relatively more catholic in its habitat requirements than the other two, which are specialised in this respect. All three have common characteristics: the males are larger than the females; usually only the males have horns, and all three appear to have a poorly developed sense of smell. Waterbuck, however, have no inguinal pouches or infraorbital glands; the lechwe has rudimentary inguinal pouches but no infraorbital glands; the puku has functional inguinal pouches, infraorbital glands and rudimentary pedal glands on the hind feet and in some individuals also on the forefeet (Ansell, 1960b).

Key to the species after Ansell (1972)

1. Size largest; no inguinal pouches; a distinct white ring on the rump

   ... *ellipsiprymnus*

   Size smaller; inguinal pouches present (rudimentary in *K. leche*); no white ring on the rump

   ... 2

2. No preorbital glands; pelage rough; horns long

   ... *leche*

   Preorbital glands present, but rudimentary; pelage smoother; horns much shorter

   ... *vardonii*

No. 336

## *Kobus ellipsiprymnus* (Ogilby, 1833)

## Waterbuck
## Waterbok

Plate 37

**Colloquial Name**

So named as the species is associated with water throughout its distributional range. In Afrikaans *kringgat* is used often and is fully descriptive of the characteristic feature of the waterbuck that occur in the Subregion, the white ring around the rump.

**Taxonomic Notes**

Ansell (1972) considered that the defassa waterbuck, *K. defassa* (Rüppell, 1835), was synonymous with the common waterbuck, *K. ellipsiprymnus*, but noted that it was only in northeastern Tanzania and Kenya that there was overlapping and interbreeding. In Zambia the two occur but are separated either by unsuitable terrain or by the Muchinga escarpment. Individuals of either are found in the other's range, however, and hybrids have been recorded. Ansell (1972) considered the two species as two groups, the *ellipsiprymnus* group with the subspecies listed below and the *defassa* group with nine subspecies, none of which, however, occurs within the limits of the Subregion.

Ansell (1972) listed four in the *ellipsiprymnus* group: *K. e. kondensis* (Matschie, 1911) from southern Tanzania; *K. e. thikae* Matschie, 1910 from parts of Tanzania and Kenya;

*K. e. pallidus* Matschie, 1910 from southern Somalia and *K. l. ellipsiprymnus* from the southern parts of the species' range, which is the only subspecies occurring in the Subregion.

## Description

Waterbuck are large antelope, the males standing about 1,2 m at the shoulder and having a mass of between 250 and 270 kg. The females are smaller and lighter. The body hairs are 41,2±9,6 mm long, large and oval in cross-section, with an irregular waved mosaic cuticular scale pattern along the length; the scale margins are rippled (Fig. XLII.1) (Keogh, 1983). The colour of the upper parts of the body is variable and may be a dark brownish-grey or greyish-brown, in either case grizzled with white and grey hairs. Characteristically they have a broad white ring encircling the rump, the lower portion of which broadens out on the upper parts of the hind legs. The sides of the neck tend to be a shade lighter in colour than the upper parts of the body and the face is darker. They have two elongated patches of white extending from above the eyes around their inner edges on to the muzzle and a white ring just behind the rhinarium encircling the top of the muzzle. The chin is white and they have a collar of white on the sides of the neck and around the throat. Their ears are short and rounded with irregularly placed areas of long white hair on the insides. The tail, which is the same colour as the upper parts of the body, has a tuft of long dark hair which nearly reaches the hocks. They also have a white band encircling the lower part of the legs just above the hooves. The white markings are similar in the females but are less pronounced and never so distinct. The juveniles are reddish in colour. They have coarse shaggy coats, the hair on the middle of the back forming a whorl. The hair on the neck and upper parts of the chest is longer than on the body. Waterbuck have a very strong goat-like smell and the flesh can become tainted if allowed to lie in contact with the hair and external surface of the skin. Often they can be smelt before they are seen.

Spoor—Plate V.

Only the males carry horns, which, arising from the top of the head, sweep forward in a curve. They are heavily ringed for about three-quarters of their length, and are smooth towards the tips. The world record pair originated from the Transvaal and had a length of 0,997 m (Best & Best, 1977).

## Distribution

Although following Ansell (1972) in considering the defassa waterbuck, *K. defassa*, and the common waterbuck, *K. ellipsiprymnus*, as conspecific, for clarity only his grouping *ellipsiprymnus*, that is waterbuck with a white rump ring as we see them in the Subregion, are mapped. The distribution of the *defassa* group is much wider including Angola, most of southern Zaire, western Kenya, Uganda and from Ethiopia west to Senegal in the savanna regions.

*South of the Sahara, excluding the Southern African Subregion*

They occur in southern **Somalia** in the valleys of the Uebi Scebeli and Juba rivers; in southeastern **Kenya**; eastern **Tanzania; Malawi**; in eastern and southern **Zambia** and in **Mozambique**, north of the Zambezi River.

*Southern African Subregion*

They occur in the eastern **Caprivi Strip**; in northern and southeastern **Botswana**; in northern and southern **Zimbabwe**, with isolated pockets of occurrence on the central plateau; in central **Mozambique**, as far south as about the Save River, and excluding a narrow sector of high country along the Zimbabwe border; on the Mlawula Nature Reserve in northeastern **Swaziland** and on the Hlane Game Reserve to the west; in the western, northern and eastern parts of the **Transvaal**, with an isolated island of occurrence in the Hluhluwe and Umfolozi Game Reserves in **Natal**, which marks their furthest southern limits of occurrence on the continent.

## Habitat

Throughout their range waterbuck, as the name suggests, are associated with water, and Taylor, Spinage & Lyman (1969)

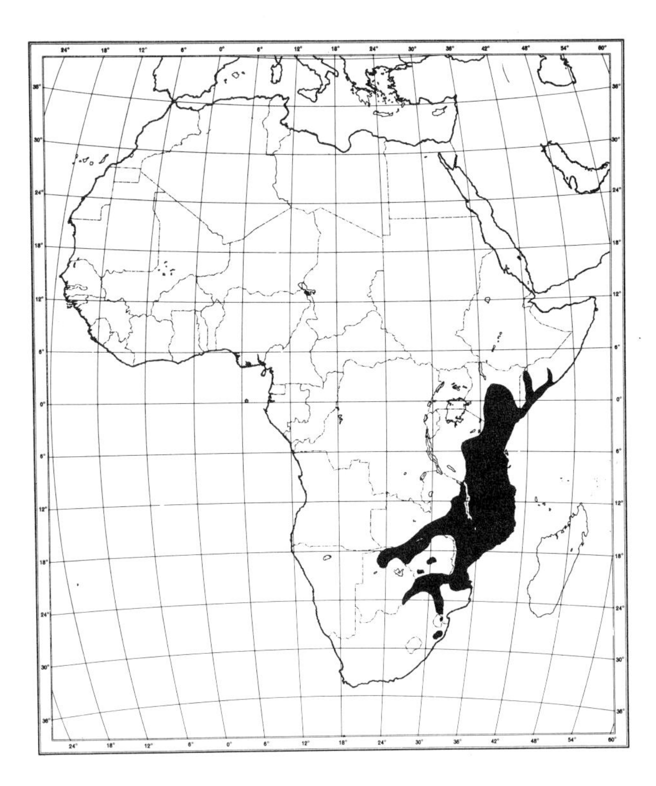

found that they had unusually high water requirements. In East Africa, Lamprey (1963) noted that they remained within about 1,8 km of open water and in the Subregion they occur in its vicinity. While in the Okavango Delta they are commonly found on floodplain and vleis associated with the swamp, along the Zambezi River they also occur in rocky hills near the river. They will take up residence even in areas where only artificial water supplies are available near boreholes and pumps and will only leave these areas if the water is shut off, when they move to other areas where it remains available. Their habitat may be open areas within reed beds as in the case of floodplain or with a woodland cover such as is found along the Zambezi River. Melton (1978) believed that, while no doubt much of the attraction of waterbuck to the type of habitat in which they occur is due to the water itself, a considerable amount is also due to the good quality of the grasses, in particular buffalo grass, *Panicum maximum*, which occurs near water.

Melton (1978) found that in the Umfolozi Game Reserve, Natal, waterbuck were catholic in their habitat requirements but that they tended to be forced out of their prime habitat by nyala, *Tragelaphus angasii*. He placed waterbuck with buffalo, *Syncerus caffer*, and zebra, *Equus burchelli*, in a favourable category as they did not over-utilise grazing areas as did impala, *Aepyceros melampus*, nyala, *T. angasii*, and warthog, *Phacochoerus aethiopicus*.

## Habits

Waterbuck are gregarious, usually occurring in small herds of about six to 12 but occasionally in larger herds of up to 30. The social organisation consists of territorial males, nursery herds and bachelor herds.

Melton (1978) found that, in Natal, there was an increase in group size during the summer months and that group size was a function of the local density of animals. Fragmentation of the herds took place during the winter months which he suggested was due to acceptable food being in low density and scattered in distribution.

Adult males do not achieve the necessary physical status to establish and hold a territory until they are about five or six years old (Spinage, 1982). These territories, which are held throughout the year, are defended from trespass by strange males by a number of intimidatory displays. These include the territorial male adopting a "proud" posture, with frontal and lateral displays. The male stands very erect with head held up. In the frontal display the white on the throat and white between the eyes is displayed prominently. In the lateral display the side is presented and the head turned towards the trespasser which shows the thickness of the neck. Lowering of the head towards the trespasser, with head-shaking is also used. These displays are usually sufficient to frighten off trespassers. Subservient males accept the dominance of a territorial male by lowering the head and body. Serious fighting is commoner with waterbuck than with some other ungulates and can lead to the death of combatants.

In the Transvaal, Herbert (1972) found that the territories varied in size from 1,2–2,8 km in diameter, with no overlapping; Melton (1978) in Natal showed that the mean size was 0,66 km$^2$. The home ranges occupied by the nursery herds may overlap with the territories of several males who will attempt to herd females into their areas. The bachelor herds consist of non-territorial males and juvenile males and sometimes include juvenile females. Young males join the bachelor herds one to two months after weaning. Bachelor herds move widely and may be tolerated by territorial males when they cross into their territories. Young females after weaning remain with their mothers in the nursery herds.

### Food

Waterbuck are pronounced roughage feeders (well developed fibre digestion; Hofmann, 1973). While predominantly grazers, very occasionally they may add browse plants to their diet. Brynard & Pienaar (1960), Child & von Richter (1969) and Herbert (1972) all provided lists of plant species eaten in the Kruger National Park, northeastern Botswana and the eastern Transvaal respectively. While couch grass, *Cynodon dactylon*, ranks high in the diet in Botswana and the eastern Transvaal, it does not appear in the Kruger National Park list. Among other grasses listed buffalo grass, *Panicum maximum*; spear grass, *Heteropogon contortus*; finger grasses, *Digitaria* spp and broad-leaved blue grass, *Andropogon amplectans*, are commonly eaten. Herbert (1972) showed that some grass species are eaten seasonally, others such as couch grass, *C. dactylon*, and red grass, *Themeda triandra*, throughout the year. In the eastern Transvaal, waterbuck ate reeds, *Phragmites communis*, throughout the year, as well as bullrushes, *Typha capensis*, and sedges, and during the dry season browsed on umbrella thorn, *Acacia tortilis*. In the Kruger National Park they ate the fruits of the marula, *Sclerocarya birrea*. In the Hwange National Park, Zimbabwe, Wilson (1975) listed couch grass, *C. dactylon*, and *Digitaria setivalva* as the most favoured grasses.

Melton (1978) examined the nutrient availability of the grasses utilised by waterbuck in the Umfolozi Game Reserve in northern Natal and found that nutritious food represented a limited resource during winter and that they were outcompeted for this by nyala, *Tragelaphus angasii*, and impala, *Aepyceros melampus*. The result of this was that there was high calf mortality due to heavy tick infestation, but that this would not have occurred without the predisposing factor of this interspecific competition for food.

### Reproduction

The territorial males test the reproductive status of the females by smelling their vulvas and urine and then exhibiting flehmen. When testing the urine it is allowed to run over the cupped philtrum of the male before he exhibits flehmen. When in oestrus females tend to hump their backs and extend their tails to one side. The males court the females by rubbing their faces and the base of their horns against the females' backs and, if they are receptive, will rest their heads on the females' backs or tap the females between their hind legs with their forelegs. Copulation may then follow (Spinage, 1982).

The gestation period is 280 days (Spinage, 1982). Throughout their range waterbuck have been shown to breed throughout the year. Pienaar (1963) and Fairall (1968), however, recorded peaks in births in the Kruger National Park in October and again in February/March.

At the time of parturition the female leaves the herd and retires to cover to give birth, eating the afterbirth. Usually a single calf is born but twins have been recorded occasionally and Frechkop (1954) recorded triplets in Zaire. The female leaves the calf to find its own hiding place in underbush or tall grass, visiting it from time to time to suckle and clean it. She calls out the calf by bleating or snorting. At this stage of their lives the calves are at a high risk to predation. By the time they are three to four weeks old they are ready to follow their mothers. The young are weaned at about 276 days, lactation ceasing in the females at about 180 to 210 days (Spinage, 1982).

The young female calves maintain their relationship with the dams for some time after weaning. However, the young males may be separated from them by the territorial males which are antagonistic towards them (Spinage, 1982).

Females have two pairs of inguinal mammae.

---

No. 337

## *Kobus leche* Gray (1850)

## Red lechwe
## Rooi-lechwe

Plate 37

---

### Colloquial Name

The colloquial name is taken from the Tswana name for the species, *leche*.

### Taxonomic Notes

Ansell (1972) listed three extant subspecies, only one of which, *K. l. leche*, occurs in the Subregion. *K. l. robertsi* Rothschild, 1907, which at one time occurred on the Luongo River in northwestern Zambia, is now extinct. The black lechwe, *K. l. smithemani* Lydekker, 1900, is restricted to the Lake Bangweulu area in Zambia, and the Kafue Flats lechwe, *K. l. kafuensis* Haltenorth, 1963, is known only from the Kafue Flats in Zambia. A closely related species, the Nile lechwe, *K. megaceros* (Fitzinger, 1855), occurs in a limited area of swamp in the southern Sudan and western Ethiopia.

### Description

Lechwe are medium-sized antelope, with coats of long, rough hair. They stand about 1,0 m at the shoulder, the hindquarters noticeably higher than the forequarters. Adult males have a mass of about 118,0 kg, females about 80,0 kg (Table 337.1). The body hairs are 62,1±14,0 mm long, circular or oval in cross-section, with an irregular waved mosaic scale pattern along the shaft (Fig. XLII.1) (Keogh, 1983). Lechwe are reddish-yellow on the upper parts of the body and flanks. The white of the under parts extends on to the inside of the limbs, upwards to the base of the tail and as a band up the throat, from the chest to the chin. The fronts of the forelegs are black. In the Kafue Flats lechwe, *K. l. kafuensis*, this black marking extends upwards and broadens out on the shoulder to form a black patch. The lower parts of the front of the hind legs in both subspecies are black. On both the front and hind legs the black encircles the legs between the hooves and the false hooves, except immediately above the hooves where they are encircled with a white band. They have a white patch around the eyes. The tip of the muzzle and chin are white and this extends back along the gape of the mouth.

**Plate 37**

334. Reedbuck, *Redunca arundinum*
 Rietbok
335. Mountain reedbuck, *Redunca fulvorufula*
 Rooiribbok
336. Waterbuck, *Kobus ellipsiprymnus*
 Waterbok
337. Red lechwe, *Kobus leche*
 Rooi-lechwe
338. Puku, *Kobus vardonii*
 Poekoe

PLATE 37
334
335
336
337
338
Dick Findlay.

The hooves of lechwe are distinctly elongated, although not to the extent seen in the sitatunga, *Tragelaphus spekei*. They spread sideways on soft ground, which is advantageous to them in moving on a soft muddy substrate (Plate V).

By plotting horn lengths over estimated age, Robinette (1963) indicated that, on the average, a 12 month old male would have horns about 150 mm long; at 24 months 380 mm; at 36 months 0,57 m and at 4,5 years of age or older would have full length horns which average 0,71 m, with a range of some 0,6 to 0,83 m (n=121). During the first few months of growth the horns are straight and later gradually commence to curve backwards and outwards.

**Table 337.1**

Measurements (mm) and mass (kg) of red lechwe, *K.l. leche*, from Botswana (a) (Williamson, pers. comm.) and (b) three males and one female (Smithers, 1971)

**(a)**

| | Males | | Females | |
|---|---|---|---|---|
| | $\bar{x}$ | n | $\bar{x}$ | n |
| TL | 1640 | 90 | 1530 | 142 |
| Sh.ht | 920 | 90 | 920 | 142 |
| Mass | 118 | 90 | 74 | 142 |

**(b)**

| | Males | | | Females (one only) |
|---|---|---|---|---|
| | $\bar{x}$ | n | Range | $\bar{x}$ |
| TL | 2063 | 3 | 1940–2190 | 1980 |
| Hf c/u | 500 | 3 | 485–515 | 480 |
| E | 150 | 3 | 135–155 | 145 |
| Mass | 126,8 | 3 | 124,6–129,1 | 94,2 |

Only the males carry the lyrate-shaped horns which are heavily ridged and rise from the head to sweep backwards and outwards and then upwards to the smooth, sharp, forwardly curving tips. The world record horns of *K. l. leche* came from Botswana and measure 0,889 m over the front curve (Rowland Ward, 1986).

## Distribution

Because of their highly specialised habitat requirements the distribution of lechwe is discontinuous and patchy.

*South of the Sahara, excluding the Southern African Subregion*

The black lechwe, *K. l. smithemani*, occurs in northeastern **Zambia** only in the vicinity of lake Bangweulu, although at one time they also occurred in the Chinsali District. The red lechwe, *K. l. leche*, occurs in Zambia in the northern parts of the Kawambwa District, on Lake Mweru; in the extreme southeastern parts of **Zaire**, and in western Zambia in restricted areas along the Zambezi and Kwando (Mashi) rivers in the Balovale, Kalabo and Senanga districts. They occur in the northern parts of the Kafue National Park and adjacent areas on the Kafue River, being replaced on the Kafue Flats by the Kafue Flats lechwe, *K. l. kafuensis*. The red lechwe has a marginal distribution in southeastern **Angola** on the Kwando (Mashi) River and, because of their occurrence in western Zambia, might well occur narrowly in other parts of southeastern Angola, but no information is available to confirm this. Mayo (1883) recorded the species from the Cunene River west of Hwmbe, Angola (1614Db) but the record is not mapped as it is doubtful whether they still exist so far west.

*Southern African Subregion*

Only the red lechwe, *K. l. leche*, occurs in the Subregion, being confined to the Okavango Swamps in **Botswana** as far south as about Maun and northeastwards to the swamps along the southern bank of the Chobe River. In the eastern **Caprivi Strip** they are common in the Linyanti Swamp and on the Chobe and Zambezi floodplains.

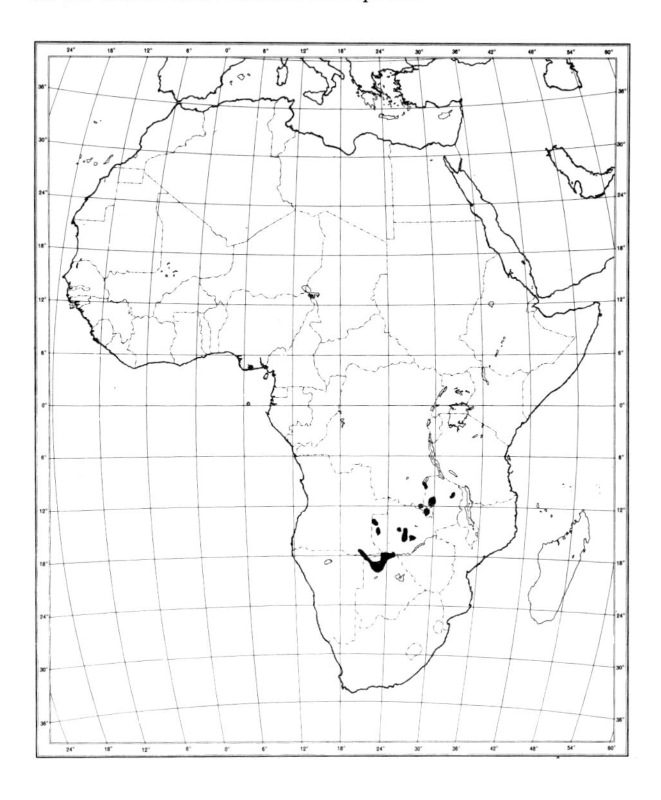

## Habitat

Lechwe are specialised in their habitat requirements and rarely are found more than two or three kilometres from permanent water. They occur characteristically on shallowly inundated floodplains fringing swamps and rivers on the ecotone of the high standing beds of papyrus, *Cyperus papyrus*, reeds, *Phragmites mauritianus*, and high-standing, semi-aquatic grasses such as *Vossia cuspidata*, and the fringes of the dry land. This ecotone has ox-bows and lagoons with permanent water and a lush cover of palatable grasses in water up to about 0,5 m deep. After the sitatunga, *Tragelaphus spekei*, lechwe are associated more closely with this type of wet condition than any other African antelope and in parts of their range the two species occur together. The sitatunga, however, tends to use the deeper water among the papyrus and reed beds and is less prone to use the more open conditions of the ecotone during daylight hours. During times of high flood lechwe move ahead of the flood waters out of the more permanent parts of the swamp on to the shallowly inundated floodplain, retreating again as the floods subside.

## Habits

After the sitatunga, *T. spekei*, the lechwe is the most water-loving antelope. It has no hesitancy about taking to water to escape predators or to feed on semi-aquatic grasses. They are not particularly fast on land and appear to have a poor sense of smell. They are gregarious, occurring in small herds of 15 to 20 and huge aggregations numbering thousands. The herds are loose associations constantly breaking up and reforming. The only close association that persists over a long period is between the female and her lamb.

De Vos & Dowsett (1966) recorded territoriality among the adult males. A number of these, along with herds of females and young, occupy a mating ground of some 0,04 km$^2$ in which the territorial males tend to situate themselves centrally, but not necessarily equidistant, from one another. The dominant ones among these establish themselves near the centre and are aggressive and sexually alert. On the fringe of this mating ground other males establish themselves in small herds. This territorial behaviour may be in evidence for periods of a few days to several months. Williamson (pers. comm.) found that the use of territorial areas depended on water levels in the swamp. As the level of the swamp dropped during the 1980–85 drought, territorial areas were abandoned.

The territorial male will allow other males into his territory provided they remain sexually inactive, but if they show signs of interest in females, he will use the threat display, which usually persuades the trespassers to move off. This display consists of a challenge with head held high and the legs slightly apart, often accompanied by an erection of the penis. It may be performed facing the trespasser or sideways on, in both positions the white throat patch being conspicuously displayed. Territorial males may also move close and parallel to each other along their communal boundary. A high intensity threat display takes the form of sweeping the horns through the grass, which often leaves them festooned with it. Where there is a large surplus of adult males, territorial activity can be intense and vicious fighting can ensue, horn-clashing being heard from distances up to several hundred metres. The territorial males engage in head-pushing with trespassers and this may become so intense that their faces eventually are pressed close to the ground which becomes churned up by their feet. These sparring bouts end with vicious sweeps of the horns and the contestants break away to stand a few metres apart shaking their heads. If one decides to submit he will whirl away quickly to avoid being gored, usually being pursued by the victor. Serious wounds resulting from this fighting may prove fatal. While sparring, the contestants often circle around each other, flicking their tails. During horn-clashing their tails hang down and as soon as they break apart and the tension relaxes, the tails recommence flicking. Sometimes sparring is followed by chasing which may continue up to distances of a kilometre, but quite often sparring takes place without physical contact. The females and young take little notice of these encounters. Between bouts of sparring or threatening, territorial males will often exhibit displacement activity which may take the form of grazing or an alarm display with the head held high, gazing away from the scene of the encounter.

Territorial males remain on the same piece of ground, which has a diameter of some 50 to 100 m, during the period of occupancy of the mating ground, even if the females move elsewhere (Schuster, 1977). In the Okavango, Joubert (1972) recorded that the territories which might or might not have common boundaries were situated invariably along a stretch of open water and never exceeded 150–200 m in diameter.

Female herds move freely within the mating ground unless herded by a territorial male, but the whole herd or individual members may move off his territory if they escape from his herding activities.

Lechwe are active before sunrise and in the early morning and again in the late afternoon for a time after sunset, but some section of a population may continue to be active throughout daylight hours. They normally, however, rest during the hotter hours of the day, lying up in the drier parts of their open habitat, often on islands in the swamp. At night they lie up near the edge of the water. When the herd is disturbed they scatter in small groups and, when chased, usually make for the shelter of their watery habitat. They are relatively slow on dry land, but once in the water they move with a plunging gait. This carries them through the water at a considerable speed and has the advantage over other methods of movement in that it provides better support on the hidden, muddy substrate. David Livingstone (1857) was the first to describe the characteristic behaviour of the lechwe when moving, of lowering the head with the muzzle pointed forward until the neck is nearly parallel with the ground, the horns held low on the shoulders. The alarm call of the lechwe is a "whinny-grunt" which is also used by the territorial males as part of the challenge to trespassing males. They also emit a low whistle which can only be heard at close quarters and a sneeze when the males are disturbed (de Vos & Dowsett, 1966). Lechwe take freely to deep water and swim strongly.

Lechwe are preyed upon widely by lions and leopards. In the Linyanti Swamp in the Caprivi Strip lions regularly penetrate the swamp, wading and swimming to the islands in it where they prey on the lechwe and sitatunga, *Tragelaphus spekei*.

**Food**

Williamson (1979) found that, in northeastern Botswana, red lechwe selected for new growth and that the vegetation of the ecotone between the perennial swamp and the terrestrial plant communities provided their most important food supply. He recorded that couch grass, *Panicum repens*; makoholi lovegrass, *Eragrostis lappula*; and turpentine grass, *Cymbopogon excavatus*, were among the species heavily utilised in this area and provided a list of plants other than grasses eaten, including sedges and other semi-aquatic plants and the shrub stages of the leadwood, *Combretum imberbe*. Williamson (1979) found that during the cool, dry season they rarely drank water, but during the hot, dry season they would drink on an average three times a day.

**Reproduction**

There is a difference between the mating system for the two subspecies of lechwe, Kafue lechwe, *K.l. kafuensis*, and red lechwe, *K.l. leche*, which are separated by some 200 km. Kafue lechwe occur on the Kafue floodplain which is up to 25 km wide and the amplitude of annual flooding is of the order of 5 m. In addition the soils are fertile. These lechwe occur at very high densities (up to 1 000 per km$^2$). They exhibit a classic lek mating system (Schuster, 1976, 1977), namely a cluster of very small territories of less than 0,005 km$^2$ which the males hold for a period of a few days and which females visit apparently only to mate.

Red lechwe occur in the Linyanti Swamp within the Subregion. This swamp is ecologically very different to the Kafue floodplain. The soils are nutrient-poor Kalahari sands and the amplitude of the annual rise in floodwaters is small, approximately 100 mm. As a result the floodplain is seldom more than 1 km wide. In these conditions lechwe occur at much lower densities of the order of 10 per km$^2$, but occasionally in aggregations of up to 100. This lechwe population exhibits resource defence territoriality, in which males defend territories up to 0,05 km$^2$ in area which they may occupy for more than a year depending on water levels in the swamp, and which females visit as a matter of course. As the level of the swamp dropped during the 1980–85 drought, territorial areas were abandoned (Williamson 1979).

Both in Botswana and Zambia calves may be born at any time throughout the year. The main calf crop on the Kafue Flats, Zambia is produced between mid-July and mid-August (Mitchell & Uys, 1961) and in the Okavango Swamp in Botswana the main calf crop is born between August-October and December (Williamson, pers. comm.) when the flood waters are receding and the advent of the rains produces a lush growth of grass on the floodplains.

Females in oestrus are courted by the territorial males who ascertain their reproductive status by sniffing their vulval region. If the female is in oestrus he will move alongside her, lifting his foreleg a few centimetres from the ground and will repeat this behaviour if she moves off or even if she lies down. The male accompanies this leg lifting with grunting and tail-flicking. If the female is receptive, copulation follows, often being preceded by many unsuccessful mountings. Robinette (1963) observed a male mount a single female 20 times.

The gestation period for *K. l. kafuensis* is 225 days (Grimsdell & Bell, 1975). Invariably the foetus is implanted in the right horn of the reproductive tract. A single calf with a mass of about 5 kg is produced at a birth.

When about to give birth the females leave the herd singly or in groups to drop their calves in the cover of tall grass on islands in the swamp or on other dry ground. The calves remain hidden for the first two or three weeks, the females foraging and resting in the open and returning to suckle their calves in the early morning and late afternoon. Mitchell & Uys (1961) stated that, at this time, there is a heavy calf mortality which may amount to as much as 50%.

Robinette (1963) could not fix a definite time for the weaning of the calves, but estimated that this was six to seven months for most of them. Females will continue to suckle calves even when they are up to two to three months pregnant. Only the very young calves accompany their mothers for, as they grow up, the calves move independently and make no attempt to rejoin the mother when the herd is disturbed.

Lechwe can produce calves when they are still yearlings but are not fully productive until they are two years old. Males are capable of breeding from an age of about 15 months but may be debarred from doing so by the territorial males and may not become fully operative until they are four years old.

Females have two pairs of inguinal mammae.

No. 338

## *Kobus vardonii* (Livingstone, 1857)

## Puku

## Poekoe

Plate 37

### Colloquial Name

David Livingstone (1857) who first collected this species on the Zambezi River in Zambia named it *Antilope vardonii* after the African traveller, Major Vardon. Puku is the Tswana and Llozi name.

### Taxonomic Notes

Ansell (1972) listed two subspecies: *K. v. vardonii* from parts of Angola and Zambia and the Chobe River, northeastern Botswana, and *K. v. senganus* Sclater & Thomas, 1897 from northeastern Zambia, Malawi and Tanzania.

### Description

Puku are medium-sized antelope. They are sexually dimorphic, males possessing lyre-shaped horns and are larger in body size than females, weighing 12–16 kg more on average.

The body hairs are 32,3±9,7 mm long, large and oblong in cross-section, with an irregular waved scale pattern along the entire length of the hair (Fig. XLII.1) (Keogh, 1983). The upper parts of the body are a golden-yellow, this colour extending down the outside of the limbs. The sides of the neck are slightly lighter in shade than the upper parts of the body. The forehead tends to be browner in colour than the rest of the body. The face has short white bands extending forward from the top of the eyes to their inner margins. The upper lip is white and they have a white patch just behind the rhinarium on the sides of the muzzle. The throat, under parts of the body and insides of the limbs, are white. The tail is the same colour as the body and has a tuft of long hair towards the tip. They can be distinguished from reedbuck by their non "bushy" tails (Dunham & Tsindi, 1984). Compared with the red lechwe, *K. leche*, puku lack the black bands down the front of the forelegs and are slightly smaller and more brightly coloured.

Puku have active face glands but they are small. The inguinal pouches are well developed and from 40 mm to 80 mm deep. The external opening in the males is 20 mm to 25 mm wide, in females 8 mm to 11 mm (Ansell, 1960a).

Their spoor are illustrated in Plate V.

**Table 338.1**

Measurements (mm) and mass (kg) of puku, *K. vardonii*, from Zambia (a—Ansell, 1960a; 1964), (b—Rosser, 1987)

**(a)**

| | Males | | | Females | | |
|---|---|---|---|---|---|---|
| | $\bar{x}$ | n | Range | $\bar{x}$ | n | Range |
| TL | 1681 | 5 | 1580–1740 | 1602 | 6 | 1545–1740 |
| HB | 1398 | 5 | 1295–1460 | 1311 | 6 | 1260–1420 |
| T | 283 | 5 | 270–290 | 291 | 6 | 265–320 |
| Hf c/u | 419 | 5 | 410–440 | 401 | 6 | 375–420 |
| E | 153 | 5 | 145–159 | 145 | 6 | 135–151 |
| Sh.ht | 809 | 4 | 800–815 | 778 | 6 | 735–830 |
| Mass | 73,8 | 3 | 67,5–77,5 | 61,2 | 5 | 47,6–77,9 |

**(b)**

| | Males | | | Females | | |
|---|---|---|---|---|---|---|
| | $\bar{x}$ | ±S.E. | n | $\bar{x}$ | ±S.E. | n |
| TL | 1467 | ±61,8 | 17 | 1337 | ±138,4 | 27 |
| Sh.ht | 921 | ±28,3 | 17 | 837 | ±34,1 | 27 |
| Mass | 77,3 | ±4,58 | 17 | 61,3 | ±8,38 | 27 |

The horns, which never reach the length seen in the lechwe, are strongly ridged for about two-thirds their length and smooth towards the tips. Rowland Ward (1986) recorded the world record horn length of 0,562 m for a pair from the Luangwa Valley, Zambia.

### Distribution

While in parts of their distributional range, where they have been afforded protection in reserves, puku remain quite common, they have disappeared, nevertheless, from very large parts of their former range and their distribution today is discontinuous and scattered.

The inclusion of the puku in this book results from their marginal occurrence within the borders of the Subregion in northeastern Botswana. In 1874 Selous (1928) stated that puku were very numerous in this sector, which covers the Pookoo Flats on the south bank of the Chobe River where they occurred over a stretch of terrain extending for about 110 km westwards from the Chobe/Zambezi confluence. While no up-to-date survey appears to have been undertaken within recent times, Child & von Richter (1969) stated that, in that year, less than 100 individuals remained, mostly resident along a 16 km stretch of the Chobe River. As this area lies in the Chobe National Park they are protected. At one time they occurred on the north bank of the Chobe River in the Caprivi Strip but by 1969 had disappeared. During the Bernard Carp Expedition of 1947 a number still survived on Imparira Island at the junction of the Chobe and Zambezi rivers (Smithers, unpubl.), but these too have disappeared now, chiefly as a result of settlement (Child & von Richter, 1969).

*South of the Sahara, excluding the Southern African Subregion*

They occur in northeastern **Angola**; in parts of southwestern and southeastern **Zaire**; in southwestern, south central and around the northern tip of Lake Malawi in **Tanzania**; in northwestern and in parts of southwestern **Zambia**, east of the Zambezi River. They have been reintroduced to the Kasungu National Park and natural immigration has taken place to the Vwaza Marsh Game Reserve, Malawi (Bell & Nsanjama, 1985).

*Southern African Subregion*

They have a marginal distribution, occurring on the Pookoo Flats on the Chobe River in northeastern **Botswana**.

### Habitat

Puku favour riverine areas, be they floodplains or plateau dambos, living on grassy areas in the immediate vicinity of rivers. Unlike the lechwe, *K. leche*, which are associated with wide open, grassy floodplains, puku will utilise the narrow stretches of grassland which lie between rivers or swamps and the woodland on the adjacent higher ground. They also frequent narrow, poorly drained depressions in woodland (de Vos & Dowsett, 1966).

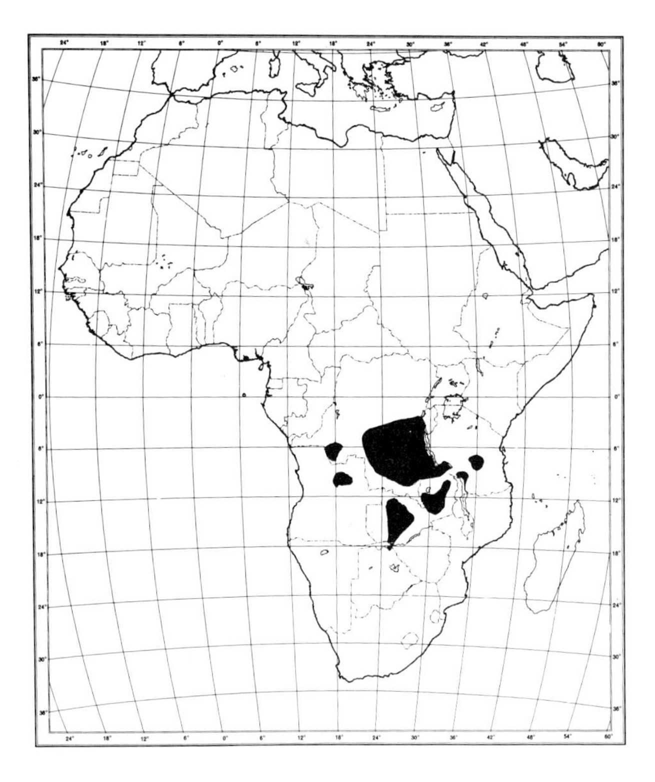

Child & von Richter (1969) recorded that on the Chobe River puku occupied a niche intermediate between the wetter area of the floodplain with its reed beds and open water frequented by lechwe and the drier inland woodland occupied by the waterbuck.

**Habits**

Puku are gregarious, occurring in small herds. In northeastern Botswana, Child & von Richter (1969) recorded that of 221 herds observed over a two year period, the mean number in herds was 5,5, with a range of one to 28. In Zambia, de Vos & Dowsett (1966) recorded herds numbering up to 50, with a high proportion of those numbering one to five, followed by six to 10 and 11 to 15. The herds are not stable units and fluctuations occur as individuals or groups of individuals come and go.

The adult males are territorial. The territories are maintained for periods ranging from a few days to several months, but not always continuously. In the Luangwa Valley, Zambia, de Vos (1965) noted that these territories were established in the more open parts of the area and that sometimes there was overlapping of territories. Defence of the territories was carried out predominantly by display rather than by fighting. The territorial male would face trespassing males, tail-wagging rapidly, or, at closer quarters horn clashing might ensue which usually caused the trespasser to move off, and chasing might then follow. Child & von Richter (1969) recorded that, on the Chobe River, Botswana, a pattern of mutually exclusive territories was established. A territorial male may allow sexually inactive males to remain in his territory, or even to approach his females. Territorial males have a habit of horning grass and raking up dry grass with their horns which may be a defensive behaviour to impregnate the territory with glandular secretions (Rosser, 1987).

Female herds consist of two to 23 adult and juvenile females (de Vos & Dowsett, 1966), which move over the territories of several territorial males. These males herd oestrous females in order to keep them within their territories, but despite these efforts the females may move out (Rosser, pers. comm.). Because of the movement of the female herds a territorial male may have a variable number of females on his territory at any one time. Bachelor herds which may number up to 40 individuals consist of adult and young males which de Vos (1965) in Zambia found had home ranges separate from those of the territorial males and female herds. If bachelor males enter a territorial male's territory, he may disregard them or alternatively may challenge them and chase them off.

The female herds with their young were the commonest association noted in northeastern Botswana (Child & von Richter, 1969).

Puku are crepuscular, with some activity for about an hour after sunset. None of the members of the genus *Kobus* are particularly vocal. Territorial males produce a series of three to four whistles, which are spaced much more closely than alarm whistles. These are probably a form of male/male communication (Rosser, pers. comm.). When they are suddenly disturbed they may hop a few paces with stiff legs in a sort of stotting motion.

De Vos & Dowsett (1966) stated that puku, when compared with lechwe and waterbuck, appeared to have a greater tendency to associate with other mammals such as impala where their ranges overlap.

**Food**

Puku are predominantly a grazing species. In her study in the South Luangwa National Park, Zambia, Rosser (1987) found that monocotyledons comprised more than 88 % of rumen contents of females and 98 % of those of males. Leaf and stem made up similar proportions of the monocotyledon fraction for both sexes but rumens from females contained more dicotyledons. Child & von Richter (1969) recorded that on the Pookoo Flats on the Chobe River, northeastern Botswana, their diet included: lovegrass, *Eragrostis rigidior*; tanner grass, *Brachiaria latifolia*; golden Timothy, *Setaria sphacelata*, and *Vossia cuspidata*, which were among the important species utilised. The utilisation of each of these varied through the year, e.g. *E. rigidior* was utilised more heavily in December and again in July/August; *Vossia cuspidata* in December but otherwise throughout the year to a lesser extent. They listed 14 species of perennial grasses, four annual grasses and two other plants utilised by puku in this area, in addition to those mentioned above. Among these the upright brachiaria, *Brachiaria brizantha*, and makoholi lovegrass, *Eragrostis lappula*, were grazed heavily in July/August, and *Digitaria setivalva* particularly in January. They increased their use of young annual grasses in January for which they had to move to higher ground. Rosser (1987) listed 16 species of monocotyledons and 16 dicotyledons she observed being eaten by puku throughout the year. From January-May female puku preferred the *Echinochloa* communities, from May-October use of swale short grass forb communities increased, while in November-December use of the long grass community increased.

**Reproduction**

Female puku have a protracted calving season and young may be born at any time throughout the year. In Zambia, most births occur over a four month period from January in the wet season (Rosser, 1987). This Rosser (1987) confirmed by observing a peak in conceptions in May/June. Oestrous behaviour rarely lasted more than 24 hours and the length of the oestrous cycle varied from 19–21 days ($n=4$). Sixty-seven percent of Rosser's (1987) marked calves ($n=6$) conceived as yearlings. Gestation length was estimated at eight months and a single weight of 5,8 kg was recorded three days post partum. Calf rate was 76% p.a. and the inter-calving interval was 390 days ($n=12$). A post partum oestrus was possible but usually only at three to four months.

Forty-five percent of the calves died before five months (9% $<1$ month). Calves were weaned at seven months. The calves are left to conceal themselves during the early part of their lives. De Vos & Dowsett (1966) recorded that a close relationship between female and calf was of short duration and the calf did not seem to have a close following reaction to the female. Even very small calves acted independently of their mothers, often running in opposite directions to them when disturbed. When the calf is threatened the female makes no effort to defend it. Within the female herd the calves form loose associations of two or three. Rosser (1987) found that territorial males can be differentiated from bachelor males by physical characteristics, having thickened neck musculature and a glandular secretion on the neck. She suggested that the presence of neck patches from May-November is primarily a form of male/male advertisement. Unlike restricted breeders, territorial males do not greatly decrease their feeding time in the breeding season. As females have an extended breeding season males must minimise energetic costs if they are to retain territories over long periods.

Males herded only oestrous females and approached females with head high, then followed laufschlag, perineal or urine-sniffing and finally flehmen, mounting followed with ejaculation. Territory size varied from $0{,}04 \pm 0{,}02$ km$^2$ in the wet season to $0{,}06 \pm 0{,}04$ km$^2$ in the dry season, with much overlapping. Territories in good quality habitat were smaller than those in poor quality habitat (Rosser, 1987), but the area of the critical swale resource defended in each territory did not differ between good and poor quality habitats. Puku have a resource defence mating system.

Females have two pairs of inguinal mammae.

## SPECIES WHICH HAVE BECOME EXTINCT WITHIN HISTORICAL TIMES

### EXTINCT

## *Equus quagga* Boddaert, 1785

## Quagga
## Kwagga

The colloquial name quagga is imitative of the call of all zebras and while, therefore, it might be used equally well for any of the species, it seems preferable to reserve it for the now extinct *Equus quagga*, more especially as this is its specific name.

It has been suggested recently by Rau (1978; 1983), who based his findings on the variability of the striping on the body, and Higuchi *et al.* (1984) on the basis of comparative DNA analysis, that *E. burchelli* is only subspecifically distinct from *E. quagga*. Recent publications (Lowenstein & Ryder, 1985; George & Ryder, 1986) indicate that the quagga may be related extremely closely to *E. burchelli*. Ansell (1974a) treated *E. burchelli* as a valid species, but Groves (1985) believed that the two species are conspecific, *E. quagga* being the southern end of a cline extending as far north as the Zambezi River. Grubb (1981) retained *E. burchelli* as a valid species but expressed uncertainty as to its relationship with *E. quagga*. Bennett (1980) on the basis of multivariate analysis of skeletal features concluded that the two species are each worthy of specific rank. Meester *et al.* (1986) in reviewing these divergent views, preferred to retain the distinction between the two species, a view that is being queried increasingly (Harley, 1988). Indeed, experiments with colour variants of *E. burchelli* are presently being conducted under the auspices of the Cape Division of Nature Conservation with the objective the possible resuscitation of *E. quagga*.

The early historical record which, in respect of so many other species is accurate and informative, is filled with inconsistencies as far as equids in general are concerned. There was no clear recognition of the differences between mountain zebra, *Equus zebra*; quagga, *E. quagga*, and Burchell's zebra, *E. burchelli*, in fact "horses" and "mules" were the general terms used in the reports of travellers from the settlement in the Cape in early historical times. The name quagga was applied to *E. burchelli* as well, although later *bontquagga* was used. Bryden (1897) commented on this, saying that "it was wrongful and misleading, as quagga should only be applied to the extinct *E. quagga*".

Therefore, the early history of the quagga, *E. quagga*, is largely lost to us and the first records on which we can rely were made in the latter part of the 18th century. William Paterson (1789) recorded large herds of quaggas in 1778 just north of Calvinia and in the same area in later years Barrow (1801) and George Thompson (1827) both recorded their presence. Lichtenstein (1815) recorded herds of 30 to 100 near Carnarvon in 1805 and two months later saw them just west of this town (Skead, 1980). Other recordings include Burchell who saw them near Sutherland in 1811 (Burchell, 1822) and near Victoria West in 1812 (Burchell, 1824). In 1837 Cornwallis Harris (1840) found quaggas in "immense herds" south of the Vaal River. Orpen wrote "I think it was about January 1852 that I saw the true quagga for the last time near Britstown" (Skead, 1980). By 1850 Bryden (1889) reported that they were practically extinct south of the

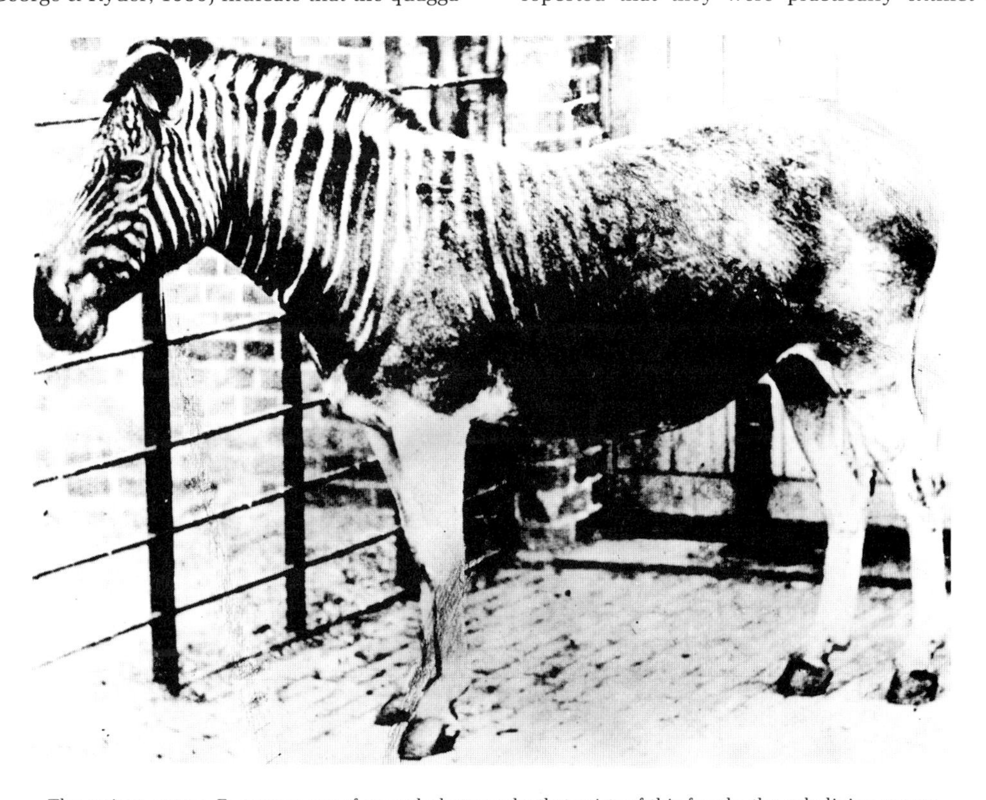

The extinct quagga, *E. quagga*: one of several photographs that exists of this female, the only living quagga ever to be photographed. It lived in the Gardens of the Zoological Society of London from 1851 to 1872. The cause of death was given as old age. Photo: Zoological Society of London.

Orange River and Flower & Lydekker (1891) believed that they only survived there up to about 1878.

There has been some speculation about the colour pattern of the quagga and a publication was recently traced (Morton, 1821) which led to the discovery of two paintings made in 1820 (Plate 38) which may throw more light on this problem. Morton (1821) was experimenting with domesticating the quagga and procured a male which he then crossed with a domestic horse, the progeny of which continued to breed. Apparently the narrow stripes on the forehead with which the quagga is marked were an important characteristic.

Some 23 mounted specimens, including one of a foetus and one a foal, the latter in the collection of the South African Museum, Cape Town, one mounted head, seven skeletons, 20 skulls and two sets of foot bones are all that remain of quaggas (Rau, 1978). Most of these specimens originated from live specimens in zoological gardens in Europe, finding their way into museum collections on their deaths. Ridgeway (1909) reviewed the origin and disposal of these zoo specimens and found that while in some cases their history was well documented, in other cases there were uncertainties or it was not known. Flower & Lydekker (1891) claimed that the last living quagga in captivity died in the Zoological Gardens, Berlin in 1875 and was mounted for exhibition in the Berlin Museum, but it is also recorded that the individual which is mounted in the Amsterdam Museum died on the 12th August 1883. The only photographs that exist of a live quagga were taken of a female in the collection of the Zoological Society of London; this animal lived in their Gardens in London from 1851 to 1872. The mounted skin has always resided in the Royal Museum of Scotland, Edinburgh although it was presumed to have been destroyed. Meanwhile the skeleton was sold to Yale University where it resides in a dusty drawer, complete with the original invoice. Apparently a horse skull was used in mounting the Edinburgh specimen (Kitchener, pers. comm.). Further records and information are contained in Rookmaaker (1989).

Quaggas were variously reported as standing between 1,25 m and 1,35 m (Flower & Lydekker, 1891; Sclater, 1900), with a total length of about 2,57 m. Only the foreparts of the body were striped. Their head, neck and body were dark rufous-brown becoming more fulvous towards the rump which, together with the under parts, was white. They had a broad, dark band extending down the mid-back. The forehead had a pattern of longitudinal buffy stripes, the cheeks with narrow, transverse buffy stripes. The top of the muzzle was black, the neck and anterior half of the body transversely banded with creamy-brown, the bands broader and more regular on the neck and extending to include the erect mane and becoming lost in a series of spots and blotches about half way along the body. The legs, tail and under parts were white, the under parts with a short mid-ventral longitudinal line, and the fetlocks had a dark spot posteriorly. The width and extent of the paler stripes and the amount of the white on the rump, tail and belly were variable and led to a number of subspecies being described.

Schwarz (1912) recorded that the skull was smaller than in other zebra species, the zygomata wider, the bony eye rings narrower, their foreheads broader, their temporal ridges more widely separated. They had small suborbital pits and the posterior borders of the nasals were heart-shaped.

Numbers of subspecies have been described, either from illustrations in literature or from specimens in collections without precise localities. Insufficient material is available from any one locality to allow an assessment of the variation within populations. Judging from the photographs of mounted specimens given by Ridgeway (1891), no two quaggas are marked exactly alike. Roberts (1951) remarked that only one described specimen, *E. q. isabellinus (Hippotigris isabellinus* H. Smith, 1841) stood out, as it had a much paler background colour on the body. From all accounts the quagga was a species which grazed open country, practically the whole of its known historical range lying within the South West Arid Zone and within what is today the Cape Province and the Orange Free State. We have no information on which to assess details of their reproductive cycle.

**EXTINCT**

## *Hippotragus leucophaeus* (Pallas, 1766)

## Blue antelope
## Bloubok

It seems that the processes that eventually led to the extinction of this species were in operation long before the first Europeans set foot in the Subregion. Klein (1974) suggested that this may have been due to the introduction of sheep, which dated from about AD 400 (Schweitzer & Scott, 1973), with the consequent deterioration of the habitat to the detriment of the blue antelope as a grazing species.

The early settlers and travellers, including Thunberg (1793) who encountered the blue antelope just east of the Hottentot Holland Mountains in the early 18th century, accounted them as relatively uncommon, their distributional range then being confined to a triangle of country bounded by Caledon-Swellendam and Bredasdorp. There is little doubt that the advent of Europeans with firearms and the accelerating settlement pressures hastened their extinction. The last records of the species were made somewhere between 1799 and 1800. The blue antelope is therefore the first historically recorded African mammal to become extinct (Klein, 1974).

So many different interpretations of what the blue antelope looked like were given by early writers, either in the form of drawings or descriptions, that for long there remained doubts as to its relationship. The first published account of the blue antelope was provided by Kolb (1719). He portrayed it with a long beard, straight gemsbok-like horns, short ears and a goat-like tail. He thought it was some sort of goat and gave it the name *Capra leucophaea*. However, Le Vaillant (1790) who handled a specimen which he had shot near Riviersonderend, showed in his illustration, which is now in the Parliamentary Library in Cape Town, that it lacked a mane or a beard. As far as bodily shape is concerned his illustration probably gives us the best impression of the species in life.

Mohr (1967) in her monograph on the blue antelope, *H. leucophaeus*, examined four mounted specimens housed in collections in Vienna, Stockholm, Paris and Leiden and a skull in the Hunterian Museum of the University of Glasgow, Scotland. There remains some doubt as to the identification of the skull in the Hunterian collection, which Broom (1949) assigned to the blue antelope, *H. leucophaeus*. Klein (1974) believed that it was that of a sable, *H. niger*. From these, which she illustrated photographically, and the description given by Pallas (1766), blue antelope appear to have been smaller than either roan, *H. equinus*, or sable, *H. niger*, but from the configuration of the horns, and the shape of the skull, they were certainly a member of the same genus, *Hippotragus*. In support of their smaller size, Mohr (1967) gave the following evidence:

| | TL skull (mm) | Height at shoulders (cm) | Horns Length (cm) | Horns Number of rings |
|---|---|---|---|---|
| *H. equinus* | 430–469 | 155 | 50–95 | 20–50 |
| *H. niger* | 420–423 | 127–143 | 70–173 | 35–59 |
| *H. leucophaeus* | 396 | 120 | 50–61 | 20–35 |

**Plate 38**

Quagga, *Equus quagga*
Kwagga
From a painting by Jacques-Laurent Agasse in 1820. Supposedly the closest resemblance to the colour pattern existing. A similar painting by the same artist was used to illustrate his experiments in telegony by the 16th Earl of Morton (1821). By permission of the President and Council of the Royal College of Surgeons of England.

The extinct blue antelope, *Hippotragus leucophaeus*, (after Mohr, 1967), from an illustration by Le Vaillant, now in the Parliamentary Library, Cape Town.

In so far as the ridging of the horns is concerned, those on the horns of the blue antelope are comparable with those on the horns of the roan.

From the evidence that can be gathered from the few specimens of the blue antelope that still exist and the writings and drawings of early travellers, we can build up a picture of their appearance in life. They appear to have been smaller than either of their near relatives the roan, *H. equinus*, or the sable, *H. niger*, with a height at the shoulder of about 1,0 m to 1,2 m, as compared with the roan at 1,6 m and the sable at 1,3 m. Le Vaillant (1790) who shot and preserved the skin of a blue antelope described the colour as faint blue inclining to grey. They had dull whitish under parts which did not specially contrast with the colour of the flanks. The forehead and top of the muzzle were brown and this colour faded into the lighter colour of the sides of the face. They had a distinct white or at least a lighter coloured patch in front of the eyes and a light-coloured upper lip. Their faces lacked the very distinct and extensive pattern of black and white seen in the sable, *H. niger*, or the somewhat similar pattern seen in the roan, *H. equinus*. They had long and rather narrow pointed ears but not as long as in the roan and these lacked the tuft of black hair at the tips seen in the roan. Their horns swept back in an even curve from the top of their heads but were much lighter in build than those of the roan or sable and were flattened slightly on their inner sides as compared with those of the sable, which tend to be flattened on the outer sides, and the roan, which are generally rounder. From the existing material the horns reached a length over the front curve of up to 0,61 m and had a series of 20 to 35 ridges. The limbs had dark bands down their anterior faces. The tail, which just reached the hocks, was tufted. The tuft was darker than the general colour of the body.

From archaeological and palaeontological evidence the blue antelope had a wider distribution and was more numerous in the early Holocene Epoch some 10 000 years ago than recorded at the time of the arrival of the early travellers. At one time they occurred in the Cape Province from Elandsbay in the northwest to near Uniondale in the east, on the coastal side of the inland mountain chain (Klein, 1974). From examination of this material Klein (1974) concluded that the blue antelope could be distinguished from the roan by the possession of substantially smaller premolar and molar teeth and by smaller, more transversely compressed horn cores, and from the sable, *H. niger*, by its larger premolar teeth, by a higher premolar row to molar row length ratio and by having smaller horn cores. This material also shows that at one time the blue antelope was sympatric with the roan coastally in the southwestern Cape Province from Oakhurst (22°30′E) to Uniondale during the early Holocene Epoch. This sympatry shows that the blue antelope was not simply a subspecies of the roan, *H. equinus*, but a valid species in its own right.

# BIBLIOGRAPHY


## A

**Abbott, C.W.** 1968. Observational research on the eland *Taurotragus oryx*. Preliminary Rep. Faculty of Agriculture, University of Natal. Mimeograph.

***Abbot, S. & Fuller, T.** 1971. A fresh look at the cheetah's private life. *Smithsonian* **2**(3): 34–42.

***Ackermann, E.** 1976. The histogenesis of hair follicles in the zebra and giraffe with special reference to pigmentation and cutaneous vasculature. M.Sc. thesis, University of Pretoria.

**Acocks, J.P.H.** 1953. *The veld types of South Africa*. Pretoria: Govt Printer.

**Adamson, J.** 1969. *The spotted sphinx*. London: Collins.

——— 1972. *Pippa's challenge*. London: Collins.

**Aellen, V.** 1952. Contribution à l'etude des Chiroptères du Cameroun. *Mem. Soc. neuchât. Sci. nat.* **8**: 1–121.

——— 1955. *Rhinolophus blasii* Peters (1866) chauve-souris nouvelle pour l'Afrique du Nord. *Mammalia* **19**: 361–366.

——— 1959. Chiroptères nouveaux d'Afrique. *Archs. Sci. Genève* **12**: 217–235.

*——— **& Brosset, A.** 1968. Chiroptères du sud du Congo (Brazzaville). *Rev. suisse Zool.* **75**(14): 435–458.

***Aguayo, A.E.** 1975. Progress report on small cetacean research in Chile. *J. Fish Res. Bd Can.* **32**(7): 1123–1143.

**Aitken, P.F.** 1971. Whales from the coast of South Australia. *Trans. R. Soc. S. Aust.* **95**(2): 95–103.

**Ajayi, S.S.** 1971. Wildlife as a source of protein in Nigeria. *Niger Fld.* **36**(3): 115–127.

*——— 1975. Observations on the biology, domestication and reproductive performance of the African giant rat, *Cricetomys gambianus* Waterhouse in Nigeria. *Mammalia* **39**: 343–364.

*——— 1977. Field observations on the African giant rat *Cricetomys gambianus* Waterhouse in southern Nigeria. *E. Afr. Wildl. J.* **15**: 191–198.

*——— **& Tewe, O.O.** 1978. Distribution of burrows of the African giant rat (*Cricetomys gambianus* Waterhouse) in relation to soil characteristics. *E. Afr. Wildl. J.* **16**: 105–111.

*——— **Tewe, O.O. & Faturoti, E.O.** 1978. Behavioural changes in the African giant rat (*Cricetomys gambianus* Waterhouse) under domestication. *E. Afr. Wildl. J.* **16**: 137–143.

***Aldrich-Blake, F.P.G.** 1970. The ecology and behaviour of the blue monkey *Cercopithecus mitis stuhlmanni*. Ph.D. thesis, University of Bristol.

***Aldridge, H.D.J.N. & Rautenbach, I.L.** 1987. Morphology, echolocation and resource partitioning in insectivorous bats. *J. Anim. Ecol.* **56**: 763–778.

**Alexander, A.J. & Ewer, R.F.** 1959. Observations on the biology and behaviour of the smaller African polecat, *Poecilogale albinucha*. *Afr. wild Life* **13**: 313–320

***Allen, G.M.** 1923. The black finless porpoise, *Meomeris*. *Bull. Mus. comp. Zool.* **65**: 233–256.

——— 1938. Order Pinnipedia (Vol. 11, part 1, p. 490–493). In: The mammals of China and Mongolia. *Am. Mus. Nat. Hist., Nat. Hist. of Central Asia*.

——— 1939 (and reprint 1945). A checklist of African mammals. *Bull. Mus. Comp. Zool. Harv.* **83**: 1–763.

——— 1942. *Extinct and vanishing mammals of the Western Hemisphere with the marine species of all the Oceans*. New York: Am. Com. Int. Wildlife Protection NY. Zool. Park.

——— 1962. *Bats*. New York, Dover.

——— **& Coolidge, H.J.** 1930. Mammals of Liberia, in *The African Republic of Liberia*. Contributions from the Department of Tropical Medicine and the Institute for Tropical Biology and Medicine. Cambridge, Mass.: Harvard University Press.

*——— **& Lawrence, B.** 1936. Scientific results of an expedition to rain forest regions in eastern Africa. *Bull. Mus. comp. Zool.* **79**: 31–126.

——— **& Loveridge, A.** 1927. Mammals from the Uluguru and Usambara Mountains, Tanganyika Territory. *Proc. Boston Soc. nat. Hist.* **38**: 413–441.

*——— **& Loveridge, A.** 1933. Reports on the scientific results of an expedition to the southwestern highlands of Tanganyika Territory. II. Mammals. *Bull. Mus. comp. Zool.* **75**: 47–140.

——— **& Loveridge, A.** 1942. Scientific results of a fourth expedition to forested areas in East and Central Africa. 1. Mammals. *Bull. Mus. comp. Zool. Harv.* **89**: 147–213.

**Allen, J.A.** 1922–1925. The American Museum Congo Expedition collection of: Art. I Insectivora : 1–38. Art. II Sciuridae, Anomaluridae, Idiuridae: 39–72. Art. III Carnivora: 73–282. Art. IV Primates, Index: 283–501. *Bull. Am. Mus. nat. Hist.* **47**.

——— **Lang, H. & Chapin, J.P.** 1917. The American Museum Congo Expedition collection of bats. *Bull. Am. Mus. nat. Hist.* **37**: 405–563.

**Allen, L.D.C.** 1963. The lechwe (*Kobus leche smithemani*) of the Bangweulu Swamps. *Puku* 1: 1–8.

***Allen-Rowlandson, T.S.** 1986. An autecological study of bushbuck and common duiker in relation to forest management. Ph.D. thesis, University of Natal.

***Alling, A.** 1985. Small cetacean entanglement: a case study of the incidental entrapment of cetaceans in Sri Lanka's gillnet fishery. Document SC/37/SM5 presented to the IWC scientific committee, Bournemouth, England. 8pp (unpublished).

**Allsopp, R.** 1971. Seasonal breeding in bushbuck (*Tragelaphus scriptus* Pallas, 1776). *E. Afr. Wildl. J.* **9**: 146–149.

***Alpers, E.A..** 1975. *Ivory and slaves in East Central Africa*. London: Heineman.

**Altmann, S.A. & Altmann, J.** 1973. *Baboon ecology*. Chicago: University Press.

***Altmann, J., Altmann, S.A. & Hausfater, G.** 1978. Primate infant's effects on mother's future reproduction. *Science* **201**: 1028–1030.

**Amtmann, E.** 1966. Zur Systematik Afrikanischer Streifenhörnchen der Gattung *Funisciurus*. *Bonn. zool. Beitr.* **17**(1/2): 1–44.

——— 1975. Family Sciuridae, Part 6.1, pp. 1–12, in *The mammals of Africa: an identification manual*. Eds J. Meester & H.W. Setzer. Washington D.C.: Smithsonian Institution Press.

**Andersen, K.** 1912. *Catalogue of the Chiroptera in the British Museum*. **1** Megachiroptera. London: Trustees British Museum.

**Anderson, A.A.** 1888. *Twenty five years in a wagon. Sport and travel in South Africa*. London: Chapman and Hall.

***Anderson, C.M.** 1981a. Intertroop relations of chacma baboon (*Papio ursinus*). *Int. J. Primatol.* **2**: 285–310.

*——— 1981b. Subtrooping in a chacma baboon (*Papio ursinus*) population. *Primates* **22**: 445–458.

*——— 1982. Baboons below the Tropic of Capricorn. *J. Human Evol.* **11**: 205–217.

*——— 1983. Levels of social organization and male-female bonding in the genus *Papio*. *Am. J. Phys. Anthropol.* **60**: 15–22.

***Anderson, G.D.** 1974. Vegetation composition and elephant damage in the major habitat types of the Sengwa Wildlife Research Area of Rhodesia. M.Sc. thesis, University of Rhodesia.

——— **& Condy, P.R.** 1974. A note on the feral cat and house mouse on Marion Island. *S. Afr. J. Antarct. Res.* **4**: 58–61.

——— **& Walker, B.H.** 1974. Vegetation composition and elephant damage in the Sengwa Wildlife Research Area Rhodesia. *J. sth. Afr. Wildl. Mgmt Ass.* **4**: 1–14.

***Anderson, J.** 1902. Zoology of Egypt. *Mammalia*. London.

**Anderson, J.L.** 1972. Seasonal changes in the social structure and distribution of the impala in Hluhluwe Game Reserve, Natal. *J. sth. Afr. Wildl. Mgmt Ass.* **2**: 16–20.

——— 1979. Reproductive seasonality of the nyala *Tragelaphus angasi*; the interaction of light, vegetation phenology, feeding style and reproductive physiology. *Mammal Rev.* **9**: 33–46.

——— 1980. The social organisation and aspects of behaviour of the nyala, *Tragelaphus angasi* Gray, 1849. *Z. Säugetierk.* **45**: 90–123.

*——— 1985. Age determination of the nyala *Tragelaphus angasii*. *S. Afr. J. Wildl. Res.* **16**: 82–90.

——— **& Pooley, E.S.** 1977. Some plant species recorded from nyala rumens in Ndumu Game Reserve. *Lammergeyer* **23**: 40–45.

***Anderson, K.** 1905a. On some bats of the genus *Rhinolophus* with remarks on their mutual affinities and descriptions of twenty-six new forms. *Proc. zool. Soc. Lond.*: 75–145.

*——— 1905b. A list of species and subspecies of the genus *Rhinolophus* with some notes on their geographical distribution. *Ann. Mag. nat. Hist.* Ser.7, **16**: 648–662.

**Anderson, P.K. & Hill, J.L.** 1965. *Mus musculus*: experimental induction of territory formation. *Science* **148**(3678): 1753–1755.

***Anderson, S.** 1967. Introduction to the rodents, **10** pp. 206–209. In *Recent mammals of the world*. Eds S. Anderson & J. Knox Jones Jr. New York: Ronald Press Co.

*——— **& Jones, J. Knox Jr.** 1967. *Recent mammals of the world*. New York: Ronald Press Co.

***Andersson, A.B.** 1969. Communication in the lesser bushbaby (*Galago senegalensis moholi*). M.Sc. thesis, University of the Witwatersrand.

**Andersson, C.J.** 1856. *Lake Ngami: on explorations and discoveries during four years' wanderings in the wilds of South western Africa*. London: Hurst and Blackett.

**Andrew, R.J.** 1964. The displays of the primates, **2** pp. 227–309. In *Evolutionary and genetic biology of Primates*. Ed. J. Buettner-Janusch. New York: Academic Press.

——— **& Klopman, R.B.** 1974. Urine washing: comparative notes. pp. 303–347. In: *Prosimian Biology*. Eds R.D. Martin, G.A. Doyle & A.C. Walker. London: Duckworth.

**Andrews, R.C.** 1921. A remarkable case of external hind limbs in a humpback whale. *Am. Mus. Novit.* 9: 1–6.

**Angermann, R.** 1975. II. Hares, Rabbits, Pikas. Vol. **12** pp. 419–462. In: *Grzimek's Animal Life Encyclopedia*. Ed. B. Grzimek. London: Van Nostrand Reinhold.

**Anonymous.** 1934. Warthog (*Phacochoerus aethiopicus*). *Niger Fld.* **3**(1): 19–23.

**Anonymous**, 1981. Two or four teats? *Custos* **10**(7): 29–31.

**Anonymous**, 1989. Report of the Sub-committee on Southern Hemisphere minke whales. *Rep. int. Whal. Commn* **39**: 71–83.

**Ansell, A.D.H. & Ansell, P.D.H.** 1969. *Petrodromus tetradactylus* at Ngoma. *Puku* 5: 211–213.

**Ansell, W.F.H.** 1957. Some mammals from Northern Rhodesia. *Ann. Mag. nat. Hist.* **10**(12): 529–551.

——— 1959. Further data on Northern Rhodesian ungulates. *Mammalia* **23**: 332–349.

——— 1960a. *Mammals of Northern Rhodesia*. Lusaka: Government Printer.

——— 1960b. Contributions to the mammalogy of Northern Rhodesia. *Occas. pap. Natl. Mus. Rhod. B., Nat. Sci.* **3**: 351–398.

——— 1960c. Some fruit bats from Northern Rhodesia, with a description of a new race of *Epomophorus gambianus* Ogilby. *Revue Zool. Bot. afr.* **61**: 160–166.

——— 1960d. *Mus minutoides* born in captivity. *J. Mammal.* **41**: 405.

——— 1960e. The African striped weasel, *Poecilogale albinucha* (Gray). *Proc. zool. Soc. Lond.* **134**: 59–64.

——— 1960f. The breeding of some larger mammals in Northern Rhodesia. *Proc. zool. Soc. Lond.* **134**: 251–274.

——— 1963. Additional breeding data on Northern Rhodesian mammals. *Puku* 1: 9–28.

——— 1964a. Captivity behaviour and post-natal development of the shrew *Crocidura bicolor*. *Proc. zool. Soc. Lond.* **142**: 123–127.

——— 1964b. The Kafue Flats lechwe. *Puku* 2: 10–13.

——— 1964c. The preorbital, pedal and preputial glands of *Raphicerus sharpei* Thomas, with a note on the mammae of *Ourebia oribi* Zimmerman. *Arnoldia Rhod.* **1**(18): 1–4.

——— 1964d. Addenda and corrigenda to "Mammals of Northern Rhodesia" No. 1. *Puku* 2: 14–52.

——— 1965. Addenda and corrigenda to "Mammals of Northern Rhodesia" No. 2. *Puku* 3: 14–52.

——— 1965a. Standardisation of field data on mammals. *Zool. Afr.* 1: 97–113.

——— 1967a. Additional records of Zambian Chiroptera. *Arnoldia Rhod.* **2**(38): 1–29.

——— 1967b. An aberrant leopard from Rhodesia. *Arnoldia Rhod.* **3**(3): 1–3.

——— 1969. Addenda and Corrigenda to "Mammals of Northern Rhodesia". No 3. Puku 5: 1–48.

——— 1972. Part 2. 15 Family Artiodactyla, pp. 1–84, in *The Mammals of Africa: an identification manual*. Eds J. Meester & H.W. Setzer. Washington D.C.: Smithsonian Institution Press.

——— 1974a. Order Perissodactyla, Part 14. pp. 1–14, in *The Mammals of Africa: an identification manual*. Eds J. Meester & H.W. Setzer. Washington D.C.: Smithsonian Institution Press.

——— 1974b. Order Proboscidea, Part II, pp. 1–5, in *The Mammals of Africa: an identification manual*. Eds J. Meester & H.W. Setzer. Washington D.C.: Smithsonian Institution Press.

——— 1978. *The Mammals of Zambia*. Chilanga: The National Parks and Wildlife Service.

*——— 1989. *African mammals 1938–1988*. Cornwall: The Trendrine Press.

**Apps, P.** 1982. Possible use of shamming by a brown hyaena in an aggressive encounter with a pride of lions. *S. Afr. J. Zool.* **17**: 91.

***Apps, P.J., Gordon, D.H., Viljoen, H.W. & Pretorius, V.** 1990. Chromatographic analysis of species specific odor profiles in *Mastomys natalensis* and *M. coucha* (Rodentia: Muridae). *J. Chem. Ecol.* (in press).

**Arbousset, T. & Daumas, F.** 1846. *Narrative of an exploratory tour of the north-east of the Colony of Cape of Good Hope*. Facs. reprint. Cape Town: Struik.

**Arbuthnot, T.S.** 1954. *African Hunt*. New York: Norton.

***Arden-Clarke, C.H.G.** 1983. Population density and social organisation of the Cape clawless otter, *Aonyx capensis* Schinz, in the Tsitsikama Coastal National Park. M.Sc. thesis, University of Pretoria.

*——— 1986. Population density, home range size and spatial organization of the Cape clawless otter, *Aonyx capensis*, in a marine habitat. *J. Zool., Lond.* **209**: 201–211.

***Arman, P. & Field, C.R.** 1973. Digestion in the hippopotamus. *E. Afr. Wildl. J.* **11**: 9–17.

***Arnason, U. & Best, P.B.** 1990. Mysticete (whalebone whale) relationships based upon studies of highly repetitive DNA in all extant species. *Systemat. Zool.* (in press).

***Arnbom,T., Papastavrou, V., Weilgart, L.S., & Whitehead, H.** 1987. Sperm whales react to an attack by killer whales. *J. Mammal.* **68**: 450–453.

***Arnold, P., Marsh, H., & Heinsohn, G.** 1987. The occurrence of two forms of minke whales in East Australian waters with a description of external characters and skeleton of the diminutive or dwarf form. *Sci. Rep. Whales Res. Inst., Tokyo* **38**: 1–46.

**Arsenyev, R.K.** 1960. Distribution of *Balaenoptera acutorostrata* Lacép. in the Antarctic. *Norsk Hvalfangsttid.* **49**: 380–382.

***Ascaray, C.M.** 1986. An ecological study of the hairy-footed gerbil, *Gerbillurus paeba* in an eastern Cape duneveld. M.Sc. thesis, University of Port Elizabeth.

**Asdell, S.A.** 1964. *Patterns of Mammalian Reproduction* 2nd edn. London: Constable.

**Asibey, E.O.A.** 1969. Grasscutter *Thryonomys swinderianus* as a source of bushmeat in Ghana. Mimeograph.

——— 1974a. The grasscutter, *Thryonomys swinderianus*, in Ghana. *Symp. zool. Soc. Lond.* **34**: 161–170.

——— 1974b. Reproduction in the grasscutter, *Thryonomys swinderianus* Temminck in Ghana. *Symp. zool. Soc. Lond.* **34**: 251–263.

**Attwell, C.A.M.** 1977. Reproduction and population ecology of the blue wildebeest *Connochaetes taurinus taurinus*, in Zululand. Ph.D. thesis, University of Natal.

——— 1982. Population ecology of the blue wildebeest *Connochaetes taurinus taurinus* in Zululand, South Africa. *Afr. J. Ecol.* **20**: 147–168.

——— **& Bhika, M.** 1985. Feeding ecology of impala on Starvation Island, Lake Kariba. *S. Afr. J. Wildl. Res.* **15**: 41–48.

**Attwell, R.I.G.** 1963. Surveying the Luangwa hippo. Puku 1: 29–50.

——— 1968. Wildlife report. Dept. Nat. Parks and Wildl. Mgmt Rhodesia. Mimeograph.

***Avery, G., Avery, D.M., Braine, S. & Loutit, R.** 1987. Prey of coastal black-backed jackal *Canis mesomelas* (Mammalia, Canidae) in the Skeleton Coast Park, Namibia. *J. Zool., Lond.* **213**: 81–94.

**Azzaroli, A.** 1966. La valeur des charactères craniens clans la classification des éléphants. *Ecol. geol. Helv.* **59**: 541–564.

——— **& Simonetta, A.M.** 1966. Carnivori della Somalia ex-Italiana. *Monitore zool. ital.* (suppl): 101–195.

# B

**Babich, K.** 1964. Animal behaviour with respect to tourists in the Kruger National Park. *Koedoe* **7**: 124–152.

**Backhaus, D.** 1958. Zur Variabilität der auszeren systematischen Merkmale des Afrikanischen Elefanten *Loxodonta*, Cuvier 1825. *Säugetierk. Mitt.* **6**: 166–173.

——— 1959. A hartebeest herd in the Garamba Park (*Alcelaphus buselaphus lelwel*). *Afr. wild Life* **13**: 197–200.

——— 1961. *Beobachtungen an Giraffen in Zoologischen Garten und freier Wildbahn*. Bruxelles: Instit. des Parcs Nat. du Congo et du Ruanda-Urundi.

***Backhouse, J.** 1844. *A narrative of a visit to the Mauritius and South Africa*. London: Hamilton, Adams & Co.

**Backus, D. & Schevill, W.E.** 1972. Physeter clicks, in *Whales, dolphins and porpoises*. Ed. K.S. Norris. Berkeley: University of California Press.

**Bainbridge, W.R.** 1969. A parti-coloured buffalo. Puku **5**: 216.

***Baker, A.N.** 1974. Risso's dolphin in New Zealand waters, and the identity of "Pelorus Jack". *Rec. Dom. Mus.* **8**: 267–276.

*——— 1983. *Whales and dolphins of New Zealand and Australia. An identification guide*. Wellington: Victoria University Press.

***Baker, Carolyn M.** 1981. Agonistic behaviour patterns in slender mongoose, *Herpestes sanguineus*. *S. Afr. J. Zool.* **16**: 263–265.

*——— 1982. Methods of communication exhibited by captive slender mongooses *Herpestes sanguineus*. *S. Afr. J. Zool.* **17**: 143–146.

*——— 1988a. Vocalizations of captive water mongooses, *Atilax paludinosus*. *Z. Säugetierk.* **53**: 83–91.

*——— 1988b. Scent marking behaviour in captive water mongooses (*Atilax paludinosus*). *Z. Säugetierk.* **53**: 358–364.

*——— 1989. Feeding habits of the water mongoose (*Atilax paludinosus*). *Z. Säugetierk.* **54**: 31–39.

*——— **& Meester, J.** 1977. Postnatal physical and behavioural development of *Praomys (Mastomys) natalensis* (A. Smith, 1836). *Z. Säugetierk.* **42**: 295–306.

*——— **& Meester, J.** 1986. Postnatal physical development of the water mongoose (*Atilax paludinosus*). *Z. Säugetierk.* **51**: 236–243.

**Baker, H.G. & Harris, B.J.** 1957. The pollination of *Parkia* by bats and its attendant evolutionary problems. *Evolution, N.Y.* **11**: 449–460.

**Baker, J.R.** 1938. Evolution of Breeding Seasons, in *Evolution: Essays on Aspects of Evolutionary Biology*. London: Clarendon.

**Baker, J.** 1968. Trypanosomes of wild mammals in the neighbourhood of the Serengeti National Park, in *Diseases in free-living wild animals*. Ed. A. McDiarmid. *Symp. zool. Soc. Lond.* **24**: 147–158.

**Baldwin, W.C.** 1894. *African Hunting and Adventure*. London: R. Bently & Sons.

**Balestra, F.A.** 1962. The man-eating hyaenas of Mlanje. *Afr. wild Life* **16**: 25–27.

**Balinsky, B.I.** 1962. Patterns of animal distribution on the African Continent. *Ann. Cape Prov. Mus.* **2**: 299–310.

**Ball, J.H.** 1955. Rearing the two-spotted palm civet (*Nandinia binotata*). *Niger. Fld.* **20**: 64–68.

**Banks, R.C. & Brownell, R.L.** 1969. Taxonomy of the common dolphins of the eastern Pacific Ocean. *J. Mammal.* **50**: 262–271.

***Bannister, J.L., & Baker, A. de C.** 1967. Observations on food and feeding of baleen whales at Durban. *Norsk Hvalfangsttid.* **56**: 78–82.

——— **& Gambell, R.** 1965. The succession and abundance of fin, sei and other whales off Durban. *Norsk. Hvalfangsttid.* **54**: 45–60.

*——— **& Grindley, J.R.** 1966. Notes on *Balaenophilus unisetus* P.O.C. Aurivillius, 1879, and its occurrence in the Southern Hemisphere (Copepoda, Harpacticoida). *Crustaceana* **10**: 296–302.

**Barber, K.B, Buchanan, S.A. & Galbreath, P.F.** 1980. *An ecological survey of the St. Floris National Park, Central African Republic*. Washington D.C.: National Park Service, Dept of the Interior.

***Barclay, R.M.R.** 1985. Foraging behavior of the African insectivorous bat, *Scotophilus leucogaster*. *Biotropica* **17**(1): 65–70.

**Barkalow, F.S. & Shorten, M.** 1973. *The world of the gray squirrel*. New York: Lippencott.

***Barlow, J.** 1984. Reproductive seasonality in pelagic dolphins (*Stenella* spp): implications for measuring rates. *Rep. int. Whal. Commn* (Special Issue **6**): 191–198.

**Barnard, C.J.** 1950. Robert Jacob Gordon se loopbaan aan die Kaap. *Argief-jaarboek vir Suid-Afrikaanse geskiedenis*. Dertiende jaargang, Deel **1**.

**Barnard, K.H.** 1954. *A guide book to South African whales and dolphins*. Guide No. 4. Cape Town: South African Museum.

***Barnes, L.G., Domning, D.P., & Ray, C.E.** 1985. Status of studies on fossil marine mammals. *Mar. Mammal Sci.* **1**: 15–53.

*——— **& McLeod, S.A.** 1984. The fossil record and phyletic relationships of gray whales. pp 3–32. In: The gray whale *Eschrichtius robustus*. Eds M.L. Jones, S.L. Swartz & S. Leatherwood. Florida: Academic Press.

——— **& Mitchell, E.** 1978. Cetacea. In: *Evolution of African mammals*. Eds V. J. Maglio & H.B.S. Cooke. Cambridge, Mass.: Harvard University Press.

***Barnes, R.F.W.** 1982. Mate searching behaviour of elephant bulls in a semi-arid environment. *Anim. Behav.* **30**: 1217–1223.

***Barnett, S.A.** 1973. Maternal processes in the cold adaptation of mice. *Biol. Rev.* **48**: 477–508.

**Barrow, J.** 1801 & 1804. *An account of travels into the interior of southern Africa*. 1801 Vol. **1**, 1804 Vol. **2**. London: Cadell and Davies.

**Bartholomew, G.A.** 1977. Body temperature and energy metabolism, in *Animal Function: Principles and Adaptations* 4th edn. Eds M.S. Gorden, G.A. Bartholomew, A.D. Grinnell, C.B. Jorgensen & F.N. White. New York: MacMillan.

***Basckin, D.R. & Krige, P.D.** 1973. Some preliminary observations on the behaviour of an urban troop of vervet monkeys (*Cercopithecus aethiops*) during the birth season. *J. Behav. Sci.* **1**: 287–296.

**Basilio, R.P.A.** 1952. *La vida animal en la Guinea espanola*. Madrid: Instituto de estudios africanos.

**Basson, P.A., McCully, R.M., Kruger, S.P., van Niekerk, J.W., Young, E., de Vos, V., Keep, M.E. & Ebedes, H.** 1971. Disease conditions of game in Southern Africa: recent miscellaneous findings. *Vet. Med. Rev.* 2/3: 313–340.

**Bateman, J.A.** 1959. Laboratory studies of the golden mole and molerat. *Afr. wild Life* **13**: 65–71.

——— 1960. Observations on young molerats. *Afr. wild Life* **14**: 227–234.

——— 1961. The mammals occurring in the Bredasdorp and Swellendam District, C.P. since European settlement. *Koedoe* **4**: 78-100.

——— 1963. The discovery of elephant remains in the Aberdeen District, C.P. *Ann. Cape Prov. Mus.* **1**: 68–70.

**Bates, G.L.** 1905. Notes on the mammals of the southern Cameroons and the Benito. *Proc. zool. Soc. Lond.*: 65–85.

***Bateson, P.** 1983. Optimal outbreeding, in *Mate Choice*. Ed. P. Bateson. Cambridge: University Press.

**Baudenon, P.** 1958. Note sur le statut des Ongules au Togo. *Mammalia* **22**: 390–398.

**Baxter, R.M., Goulden, E.A. & Meester, J.** 1979. The activity patterns of some southern African *Crocidura* in captivity. *Acta theriol.* **24**: 61–68.

——— **& Meester, J.** 1980. Notes on the captive behaviour of five species of southern African shrews. *Säugetierk. Mitt.* **28**: 55–62.

**Baxter, T.W. & Turner, R.W.S.** 1966. *Rhodesian epic*. Cape Town: Timmins.

**Bearder, S.K.** 1969. Territorial and inter-group behaviour of the lesser bushbaby (*Galago senegalensis moholi* A. Smith) in semi-natural conditions and in the field. M.Sc. thesis, University of the Witwatersrand.

——— 1975a. Aspects of the ecology and behaviour of the thick-tailed bushbaby *Galago crassicaudatus*. Ph.D. thesis, University of the Witwatersrand.

——— 1975b. Inter-relationships between hyaenas and their competitors in the Transvaal Lowveld. *Publs Univ. Pretoria Nuwe Reeks* **97**: 39–47.

——— 1977. Feeding habits of spotted hyaenas in a woodland habitat. *E. Afr. Wildl. J.* **15**: 263–280.

*——— 1987. Lorises, Bushbabies, and Tarsiers: Diverse Societies in Solitary Foragers. In *Primate Societies*. Eds B.B. Smuts, D.L. Cheney, R.M. Seyfarth, R.W. Wrangham & T.T. Struhsaker. Chicago: University Press.

——— **& Doyle, G.A.** 1974. Ecology of bushbabies *Galago senegalensis* and *Galago crassicaudatus*, with some notes on their behaviour in the field, in *Prosimian Biology*. Eds R.D. Martin, G.A. Doyle & A.C. Walker. London: Duckworth.

*——— **& Martin, R.D.** 1979. The social organisation of a nocturnal primate revealed by radio tracking, pp 633–648, in *A handbook on biotelemetry and radio tracking*. Eds C.J. Amlaner & D.W. Macdonald. Oxford: Pergamon Press.

*——— **& Martin R.D.** 1980. *Acacia* gum and its use by bushbabies, *Galago senegalensis* (Primates: Lorisidae). *Int. J. primatol.* **1**: 103–128.

——— **& Randall, R.M.** 1978. The use of fecal marking sites by spotted hyaenas and civets. *Carnivore* **1**(2): 32–48.

**Beaumont, G. de.** 1967. Observations sur les Herpestinae (Viverridae, Carnivora) de l'Oligocene superieure avec quelques remarques sur des Hyaenidae du Neogene. *Archs. Sci., Geneve* **20**(1): 79–108.

***Beeson, M.** 1987. The origins of bark-stripping by blue monkeys (*Cercopithecus mitis*): implications for management. *Zool. J. Linn. Soc.* **91**: 265–291.

**Bell, R.H.V.** 1971. A grazing ecosystem in the Serengeti. *Scient. Am.* **225**: 86–93.

——— **& Grimsdell, J.J.R.** 1973. The persecuted black lechwe of Zambia. *Oryx* **12**(1): 77–92.

*——— **& Nsanjama, H.** 1985. Rhinos. *Swara* **8**: 23–24.

*Bender, P.A. 1990. A reconsideration of the fossil Suidae of the Makapansgat Limeworks, Potgietersrus, Northern Transvaal. M.Sc. thesis, University of the Witwatersrand.

*Bennett, D.K. 1980. Stripes do not a zebra make. A cladistic analysis of Equus. *Systematic Zoology* **29**: 272–287.

*Bennett, N.C. 1988. The trend towards sociality in three species of southern African mole-rats (Bathyergidae): causes and consequences. Ph.D. thesis, University of Cape Town.

*——— 1989. The social structure and reproductive biology of the common mole-rat, *Cryptomys h. hottentotus* and remarks on the trends in reproduction and sociality in the family Bathyergidae. *J. Zool., Lond.* **219**: 45–59.

*——— in press. The behaviour and social organization in a colony of the Damaraland mole-rat *Cryptomys damarensis*. *J. Zool., Lond.*.

*——— **& Jarvis J.U.M.** 1988a. The social structure and reproductive biology of colonies of the mole-rat *Cryptomys damarensis* (Rodentia, Bathyergidae) *J. Mammal.* **69**: 293–302.

*——— **& Jarvis J.U.M.** 1988b. The reproductive biology of the Cape mole-rat, *Georychus capensis* (Rodentia, Bathyergidae) *J. Zool., Lond.* **214**: 95–106.

*——— **Jarvis J.U.M. & Wallace, D.B.** in press. The relative age structure and body masses of complete wild-captured colonies of two social mole-rats, the common mole-rat *Cryptomys hottentotus hottentotus* and the Damaraland mole-rat *Cryptomys damarensis*. *J. Zool., Lond.*.

*Ben-Shahar, R. & Fairall, N. 1987. Comparison of the diurnal activity patterns of blue wildebeest and red hartebeest. *S. Afr. J. Wildl. Res.* **17**: 49–54.

**Benson, C.W.** 1965. The grass owl and the marsh owl. *Puku* **3**: 175–176.

*Ben-Yaacov, Rina & Yom-Tov, Y. 1983. On the biology of the Egyptian mongoose *Herpestes ichneumon* in Israel. *Z. Säugetierk.* **48**: 34–45.

**Bequaert, B.J.** 1922. The predaceous enemies of ants. *Bull. Am. Mus. nat. Hist.* **45**: 271–329.

**Bere, R.M.** 1958. The status of ungulate mammals in the Uganda National Parks. *Mammalia* **23**: 418–426.

——— 1959. Queen Elizabeth National Park, Uganda. The hippopotamus problem and experiment. *Oryx* **5**(3): 116–124.

——— 1962. *The wild mammals of Uganda*. London: Longmans.

*Bergstrom, R. & Skarpe, Christina 1982. Abundance and crowding of some wildlife species in relation to seasons and pans in western Kalahari, Botswana. *Medd. Växtbiol. Inst.*, Uppsala 1982 (3): 36–37.

*Bernard, H.J. & Hohn, A.A. 1989. Differences in feeding habits between pregnant and lactating spotted dolphins (*Stenella attenuata*). *J. Mammal.* **70**: 211–215.

*Bernard, R.T.F. 1980a. Reproductive cycles of *Miniopterus schreibersi natalensis* (Kuhl, 1819) and *M. fraterculus* Thomas & Schwann, 1906. *Ann. Trans. Mus.* **32**: 55–64.

*——— 1980b. Female reproductive anatomy and development of ovarian follicles in *Miniopterus fraterculus*. *S. Afr. J. Zool.* **15**: 111–116.

*——— 1982a. Female reproductive cycle of *Nycteris thebaica* (Microchiroptera) from Natal, South Africa. *Z. Säugetierk.*47: 12–18.

*——— 1982b. Monthly changes in the female reproductive organs and the reproductive cycle of *Myotis tricolor* (Vespertilionidae: Chiroptera). *S. Afr. J. Zool.* **17**: 79–84.

*——— 1983. Reproduction of *Rhinolophus clivosus* (Microchiroptera) in Natal, South Africa. *Z. Säugetierk.* **48**: 321–329.

*——— 1985a. The adaptive significance of reproductive delay phenomena in South African Microchiroptera. *Bat Research News* **26**(4): 55.

*——— 1985b. Reproduction in the Cape horseshoe bat (*Rhinolophus capensis*) from South Africa. *S. Afr. J. Zool.* **20**: 129–135.

*——— 1986a. Male reproduction in the Cape horseshoe bat, *Rhinolophus capensis*. *Arch. Androl.* **17**: 157–158.

*——— 1986b. The natural history of some eastern Cape bats. III. Reproduction and development. *The Naturalist* **30**(3): 55–56.

*——— **& Meester, J.A.J.** 1982. Female reproduction and the female reproductive cycle of *Hipposideros caffer caffer* (Sundevall, 1846) in Natal, South Africa. *Ann. Trans. Mus.* **33**: 131–144.

*——— **& Stuart, C.T.** 1987. Reproduction of the caracal *Felis caracal* from the Cape Province of South Africa. *S. Afr. J. Zool.* **22**: 177–182.

**Berry, H.H.** 1980. Behavioural and eco-physiological studies on blue wildebeest (*Connochaetes taurinus*) at the Etosha National Park. Ph.D. thesis, University of Cape Town.

——— **Siegfried, W.R. & Crowe, T.M.** 1982. Activity patterns in a population of free-ranging wildebeest (*Connochaetes taurinus*) at Etosha National Park. *Z. Tierpsychol.* **59**: 229–246.

*Berry, M.P.S. 1978. Aspects of the ecology and behaviour of the bat-eared fox, *Otocyon megalotis* (Desmarest, 1822), in the upper Limpopo River valley. M.Sc. thesis, University of Pretoria.

**Berry, P.S.M.** 1973. The Luangwa Valley giraffe. *Puku* **7**: 71–92.

*Berry, R.J., Peters, Josephine & van Aarde, R.J. 1978. Sub-antarctic house mice: colonization, survival and selection. *J. Zool., Lond.* **184**: 127–141.

**Bertram, B.C.R.** 1978. *Pride of Lions*. London: J.M. Dent.

——— 1974. Radio-tracking leopards in the Serengeti. *Wildl. News* **9**(2): 7–10.

*——— 1982. Leopard ecology as studied by radio tracking. *Symp. Zool. Soc. Lond.* **49**: 341–352.

**Bertram, C.K.R. & Bertram, R.C.K.** 1966. The dugong. *Nature, Lond.* **209**: 938–939.

*Berzin, A.A. 1972. *The sperm whale*. Israel Program for Scientific Translations, Jerusalem. i-v + 394 pp [transl. from Russian original, 1971].

*——— **& Vladimirov, V.L.** 1983. A new species of killer whale (Cetacea, Delphinidae) from the Antarctic waters. *Zool. Zhur.* **62**: 287–295.

**Besharse, J.C.** 1971. Maturity and sexual dimorphism in the skull mandible and teeth of the beaked whale *Mesoplodon densirostris*. *J. Mammal.* **52**: 297–315.

**Best, A.A. & Best, T.G.W.** 1977. *Rowland Ward's Records of big Game* XVII Edition (Africa). Sussex, England: Rowland Ward.

**Best, E.B., Palmer, A.W., Shepard, T. & Wilson, V.J.** 1970. Some notes on the present day status of roan *Hippotragus equinus* in Rhodesia. *Arnoldia, Rhod.* **5**(2): 1–10.

**Best, P.B.** 1960. Further information on Bryde's whale *Balaenoptera edeni* Anderson from Saldanha Bay, South Africa. *Norsk. Hvalfangsttid.* **49**: 201–215.

——— 1967. Distribution and feeding habits of baleen whales off the Cape Province. *Investl Rep. Div. Sea Fish. S. Afr.* **57**: 1–44.

——— 1968. The sperm whale (*Physeter catodon*) off the west coast of South Africa. No. 2 Reproduction in the female. *Investl Rep. Div. Sea Fish. S. Afr.* **66**: 1–32.

——— 1969a. A dolphin, *Stenella attenuata* from Durban, South Africa. *Ann. S. Afr. Mus.* **52**: 121–135.

——— 1969b. The sperm whale. *Investl Rep. Div. Sea Fish. S. Afr.* **72**: 1–20.

——— 1970a. Records of the pygmy killer whale, *Feresa attenuata*, from southern Africa. *Ann. S. Afr. Mus.* **57**: 1–4.

——— 1970b. Exploitation and recovery of right whales *Eubalaena australis* off the Cape Province. *Investl Rep. Div. Sea Fish. S. Afr.* **80**: 1–15.

——— 1971a. Stalked barnacles, *Conchoderma auritum*, on an elephant seal: occurrence of elephant seals on South African coasts. *Zool. Afr.* **6**: 181–185.

——— 1971b. A leopard seal from Hout Bay, South Africa. *Zool. Afr.* **6**: 177–179.

——— 1971c. Order Cetacea, Part 7, pp. 1–10, in *The Mammals of Africa: an identification manual*. Eds J. Meester & H.W. Setzer. Washington D.C.: Smithsonian Institution Press.

——— 1971d. Order Sirenia, Part 13, pp. 1, in *The Mammals of Africa: an identification manual*. Eds J. Meester & H.W. Setzer. Washington D.C.: Smithsonian Institution Press.

——— 1973a. Status of whale stocks off South Africa. Appendix IV Annex J: 115–126, in *23rd Rep. int. Whal. Comm. Lond.*

——— 1973b. Seals and sealing in South and South West Africa. *The South African Shipping News and Fishing Industry Review*. **28**: 49–55.

*——— 1974. The biology of the sperm whale as it relates to management. pp 257–293. In: *The Whale Problem. A Status Report*. Ed. W.E. Schevill, Harvard University Press, Cambridge, Mass.

——— 1975. Review of world sperm whale stocks. *Advisory Committee on Marine Resources Research*. ACMRR/MM/EC/8 December: 1–35, Mimeograph.

*——— 1977. Two allopatric forms of Bryde's whale off South Africa. *Rep int. Whal. Commn* (Special Issue **1**): 10–38.

*——— 1981. The status of right whales *Eubalaena borealis* of South Africa. *Investl Rep. Div. Sea Fisheries* **123**: 1–44.

*——— 1982. Seasonal abundance, feeding, reproduction, age and growth in minke whales off Durban (with incidental observations from the Antarctic). *Rep. int. Whal. Commn* **32**: 759–786.

*——— 1985. External characters of southern minke whales and the existence of a diminutive form. *Sci. Reports Whales Res. Inst.* 3H: 1–3.

*——— 1986. Fight to save the whales. *Our Living World* No. 6 The Sunday Star, Johannesburg.

*——— 1988a. The external appearance of Heaviside's dolphin, *Cephalorhynchus heavisidii* (Gray, 1828). *Rep. int. Whal. Commn* (Special Issue **9**): 279–299.

*——— 1988b. Right whales (*Eubalaena australis*) at Tristan da Cunha—a clue to the 'non-recovery' of depleted stocks? *Biol. Cons.* **46**: 23–51.

*——— 1990. Natural markings and their use in determining calving intervals in right whales off South Africa. *S. Afr. J. Zool.* **24**: 114–123.

*——— **Butterworth, D.S. & Rickett, L.H.** 1984. An assessment cruise for the South African inshore stock of Bryde's whale (*Balaenoptera edeni*). *Rep. int. Whal. Commn* **34**: 403–423.

*——— **Canham, P.A.S., & MacLeod, N.** 1984. Patterns of reproduction in sperm whales, *Physeter macrocephalus*. *Rep. int. Whal. Commn* (Special Issue **6**): 51–79.

——— **& Rand, R.W.** 1975. Results of a pup-tagging experiment on the *Arctocephalus pusillus* rookery at Seal Island, False Bay, South Africa. *Rapp. P.-v. Reun. Cons. perm. int. Explor. Mer.* **169**: 267–273.

——— **& Ross, G.J.B.** 1977. Exploitation of small cetaceans off southern Africa. *Rep. int. Whal. Commn* **27**: 494–497.

*——— **& Ross, G.J.B.** 1984. Live-capture fishery for small cetaceans in South African waters. *Rep. int. Whal. Commn* **34**: 615–618.

*——— **& Ross, G.J.B.** 1986. Catches of right whales from shore-based establishments in southern Africa, 1792–1975. *Rep. int. Whal. Commn* (Special Issue **10**): 275–289.

——— **& Shaughnessy, P.D.** 1979. An independent account of Captain Benjamin Morrell's sealing voyage to the south-west coast of Africa in the *Antarctic*, 1828/29. *Fish Bull. S. Afr.* **12**: 1–19.

——— **& Shaughnessy, P.D.** 1981. First record of the melon-headed whale, *Peponocephala electra* from South Africa. *Ann. S. Afr. Mus.* **83**: 33–47.

**Best, R.C.** 1981. Foods and feeding habits of wild and captive Sirenia. *Mammal Rev.* **11**: 3–29.

**Best, T.A., Edmond-Blanc, F. & Witting, R.C.** 1962. *Rowland Ward's Records of Big Game*. London: Rowland Ward.

**Bester, J.L.** 1978. Die ekologie en gedrag van die silwerjakkals, *Vulpes chama* (A. Smith, 1833) in die Oranje-Vrystaat. *Vorderingsverslag No. 2* O.V.S. Provinsiale Administrasie: 1–35, Mimeograph.

——— 1979. 'n Studie van die silwerjakkals (*Vulpes chama*) in die Nasionale Kalahari-gemsbokpark. *Vorderingsverslag No. 1* O.V.S. Provinsiale Administrasie: 1–6, Mimeograph.

——— 1980. Gedrag van die silwervos, *Vulpes chama*. *Projek No. 7/7/4* O.V.S. Provinsiale Administrasie: 1–70, Mimeograph.

——— 1982. Die gedragsekologie en bestuur van die silwervos *Vulpes chama* (A. Smith) met spesiale verwysing na die Oranje-Vrystaat. M.Sc. thesis, University of Pretoria.

**Bester, M.N.** 1977. Habitat selection, seasonal population changes, and behaviour of the Amsterdam Island fur seal *Arctocephalus tropicalis* on Gough Island. D.Sc. thesis, University of Pretoria.

——— 1979. A note on winter seal observations in the South Atlantic pack ice. *S. Afr. J. Antarct. Res.* **9**: 27–28.

——— 1980a. Population increase in the Amsterdam Island fur seal *Arctocephalus tropicalis* at Gough Island. *S. Afr. J. Zool.* **15**: 229–234.

——— 1980b. The southern elephant seal *Mirounga leonina* at Gough Island. *S. Afr. J. Zool.* **15**: 235–239.

——— 1981a. Seasonal changes in the population composition of the fur seal, *Arctocephalus tropicalis*, at Gough Island. *S. Afr. J. Wildl. Res.* **11**: 49–55.

*——— 1981b. Fur seals *Arctocephalus gazella* and leopard seals *Hydrurga leptonyx* at the Courbet peninsula, Kerguelen. *S. Afr. J. Antarct. Res* **10/11**: 35–37.

*——— 1982a. The effect of the Subantarctic environment on aspects of the terrestrial phase of fur seal populations. *Can. nat. fr. Rech. Antarctiques* **51**: 469–476.

*——— 1982b. Distribution, habitat selection and colony types of the Amsterdam Island fur seal *Arctocephalus tropicalis* at Gough Island. *J. Zool., Lond.* **196**: 217–232.

*——— 1987. Subantarctic fur seal, *Arctocephalus tropicalis*, at Gough Island (Tristan da Cunha Group). *NOAA Techn. Rep. NMFS* **51**: 57–60.

*——— 1988. Marketing and maintaining studies of the Kerguelen stock of southern elephant seals *Mirounga leonina* and their bearing on biological research in the Vestfold Hills. *Hydrobiologia* **165**: 269–277.

*——— 1989. Movements of southern elephant seals and Subantarctic fur seals in relation to Marion Island. *Mar. Mam. Sci.* **5**: 257–265.

*——— **& Kerley, G.I.H.** 1983. Rearing of twin pups to weaning by Subantarctic fur seal *Arctocephalus tropicalis* female. *S. Afr. J. Wildl. Res.* **13**: 86–87.

*——— **& Langlart, P-Y.** 1982. An analysis of the southern elephant seal *Mirounga leonina* breeding population at Kerguelen. *S. Afr. J. Antarct. Res.* **12**: 11–16.

*——— **& Laycock, P.A.** 1985. Cephalopod prey of the Subantarctic fur seal *Arctocephalus tropicalis* at Gough Island, pp. 551–554, in *Antarctic Nutrient cycles and food webs*. Eds W.R. Siegfried, P.R. Condy & R.M. Laws. Berlin: Springer-Verlag.

*——— **& Roux, J-P.** 1986. Summer presence of leopard seals *Hydrurga leptonyx* at the Courbet Peninsula, Iles Kerguelen. *S. Afr. J. Antarct. Res.* **16**: 29–32.

*——— **& Wilkinson, I.S.** 1989. Field identification of Antarctic and Subantarctic fur seal pups. *S. Afr.J. Wildl. Res.* **19**: 140–144.

**Beuchner, H.K. & Dawkins, H.C.** 1961. Vegetation change induced by elephants and fire in Murchison Falls National Park, Uganda. *Ecology* **42**: 752–766.

***Beukes, P.C.** 1988. Diet of grey rhebuck in the Bontebok National Park. *S. Afr. J. Wildl. Res.* **18**: 11–21.

***Beynon, P. & Rasa, O.A.E.** 1989. Do dwarf mongooses have a language?: warning vocalisations transmit complex information. *S. Afr. J. Sci.* **85**: 447–450.

***Bielert, C. & Busse, C.** 1983. Influences of ovarian hormones on the food intake and feeding of captive and wild female chacma baboons (*Papio ursinus*). *Physiology & Behaviour* **30**: 103–111.

**Bigalke, R.** 1937. The naturalisation of animals with special reference to South Africa. *S. Afr. J. Sci.* **33**: 46–63.

——— 1947. Pretoria Zoo has a baby white rhinoceros. *Anim. Kingd.* **50**: 2.

——— 1955. The bontebok (*Damaliscus pygargus* (Pall.)) with special reference to its history and preservation. *Fauna Flora, Pretoria* **6**: 95–116.

*——— 1956. Die toekoms van die Kaapse bergsebra. *Ons Wild* **1**(1): 6–8.

——— **Steyn, T., de Vos, D. & de Waard, K.** 1950. Observations on a female square-lipped or white rhinoceros, *Ceratotherium simum simum* (Burchell) in the National Zoological Gardens of South Africa. *Proc. zool. Soc. Lond.* **120**: 519–528.

**Bigalke, R.C.** 1958. On the mammillae of the springbok (*Antidorcas marsupialis* Zimmermann). *S. Afr. J. Sci.* **54**: 291.

——— 1963. A note on the reproduction in the steenbok, *Raphicerus campestris* Thunberg. *Ann. Cape Prov. Mus.* **3**: 64–67.

——— 1964. The speed of the cheetah (*Acinonyx jubatus*). *Afr. wild Life* **18**: 257–258.

——— 1966. The springbok. *Nat. Hist., N.Y.* **75**: 20–25.

——— 1970. Observations on springbok populations. *Zool. Afr.* **5**: 59–70.

——— 1972. Observations on the behaviour and feeding habits of the springbok *Antidorcas marsupialis*. *Zool. Afr.* **7**: 333–359.

——— **Liversidge, R. & Schijf, J.** 1975. *Springbok management.* Kimberley: N. Cape Branch Wildlife Society of southern Africa.

***Bigg, M.A.** 1982. An assessment of killer whale (*Orcinus orca*) stocks off Vancouver Island, British Columbia. *Rep. int. Whal. Commn* **32**: 655–666.

*——— **Ellis, G.M., Ford, J.K.B., & Balcomb, K.C.** 1987. *Killer whales. A study of their identification, genealogy and natural history in British Columbia and Washington State.* Nanaimo, British Columbia: Phantom Press & Publishers Inc.

**Bigourdan, J.** 1948. Le phacochere et les suides dans l'ouest Africain. *Bull. Inst. fr. Afr. noire* **10**: 285–360.

——— 1950. Sur quelques caracteres et habitudes de l'orycterope. *Premiere conf. Int. Ouest* **1**: 666.

**Birkenstock, P.J. & Nel, J.A.J.** 1977. Laboratory and field observations on *Zelotomys woosnami* (Rodentia: Muridae). *Zool. Afr.* **12**: 429–443.

**Blackmore, R.P.** 1962. Sable antelope defies pride of lions. *Afr. wild Life* **16**: 228.

**Blamey, A.H.G. & Jackson, W.T.** 1956. The elusive little piti. *Afr. wild Life* **10**: 295–299.

**Blancou, L.** 1958. The African buffaloes. *Anim. Kingd.* **61**: 56–61.

**Bland, K.P.** 1973. Reproduction in the female African tree rat (*Grammomys sudaster*). *J. Zool., Lond.* **171**: 167–175.

**Blower, J.** 1968. The wildlife of Ethiopia. *Oryx* **9**: 276–285.

**Bobrinskii, N.A.** 1944. Pinnipedia (p. 162–168). In: *Mammals of U.S.S.R.* Moscow (Engl. transl. in Oxford Bur. Animal Population).

**Bocage, J.V.B.** 1878. Liste des antilopes d'Angola. *Proc. zool. Soc. Lond.*: 741.

**Bodot, P.** 1967. Cycles saisonniers d'activite collectives des termites des savanes de Basse Cote-D'Ivoire. *Insectes Soc.* **14**: 359–388.

**Boelticher, H. von.** 1933. Die geographische Verbreitung der Afrikanischer Wildschweine und ihre ökologischen Grundlagen. *Jena. Z. Naturw.* **68**: 463–498.

***Böhner, von J., Volger, K., Hendrichs, H.** 1984. Zur Fortpflanzungs-biologie des Blauduckers. *Z. Saügetierk.* **34**: 306–314.

***Boitani, L. & Baretoli, S.** 1983. *Simon and Schuster's guide to the mammals.* New York: Simon & Schuster.

**Bolton, M.** 1973. Notes on the current status and distribution of some large mammals in Ethiopia. *Mammalia* **37**: 562–586.

**Bolwig, N.** 1959. A study of the behaviour of the chacma baboon, *Papio ursinus*. *Behaviour* **14**: 136–163.

***Bond, W., Ferguson, M. & Forsyth, G.** 1980. Small mammals and habitat structure along altitudinal gradients in the southern Cape mountains. *S. Afr. J. Zool.* **15**: 34–43.

***Bond, W.J. & Breytenbach, G.J.** 1985. Ants, rodents and seed predation in Proteaceae. *S. Afr. J. Zool.* **20**: 150–154.

**Bonner, W.N.** 1968. The fur seal of South Georgia. *British Antarctic Survey Sci. Rep.* **56**: 1–81.

——— 1978. Man's impact on seals. *Mammal Rev.* **8**(1/2): 3–13.

**Boomker, E.A.** 1981. A study of the digestive processes of the common duiker *Sylvicapra grimmia* (Linn.). M.Sc. thesis, University of Pretoria.

**Booth, A.H.** 1954. The Dahomey Gap and the mammalian fauna of the West African forests. *Revue Zool. Bot. afr.*: 305–314.

——— 1960. *Small mammals of West Africa.* London: Longmans.

**Booth, V.R.** 1980. A study on Lichtenstein's hartebeest *Alcelaphus lichtensteini* (Peters, 1852) and its habitat in southeastern Rhodesia. M.Sc. thesis, University of Pretoria.

*——— 1986. Some notes on Lichtenstein's hartebeest *Alcelaphus lichtensteini* Peters. *S. Afr. J. Zool.* **20**: 57–60.

**Boschma, H.** 1950. Maxillary teeth in specimens of *Hyperoodon rostratus* (Muller) and *Mesoplodon grayi* von Haast stranded on the Dutch coast. *Proc. K. ned. Akad. Wet.* **53**: 3–14.

**Bosman, D.B.** 1952. *Jan Anthoniez van Riebeek, Dagh Register.* Kaapstad: Die van Riebeek Vereniging.

***Bosman, P. & Hall-Martin, A.J.** 1986. *Elephants of Africa.* Cape Town: Struik.

***Botha, J.** 1985. Reintroduction of Lichtenstein's hartebeest to South Africa. *Afr. wild Life* **39**: 111.

***Botha, S.A.** 1985. The feral pig: an unsuccessful alien in Africa. Abstract of poster for National Synthesis Meeting on the Ecology of Biological invasions. November, 1985.

**Bothma, J. du P.** 1962. The dassie—the elephant's closest relative. *Farmer's Weekly*, November. **14**: 29.

——— 1964. A taxonomic revision of the extant Hyracoidea of southern Africa. M.Sc. thesis, University of Pretoria.

——— 1965. Random observations on the food habits of certain Carnivora (Mammalia) in southern Africa. *Fauna Flora, Pretoria*: **16**: 16–22.

——— 1966a. Colour variation in Hyracoidea from southern Africa. *J. Mammal.* **47**: 687–693.

——— 1966b. Food of the silver fox *Vulpes chama*. *Zool. Afr.* **2**: 205–221.

——— 1966c. Notes on the stomach contents of certain Carnivora (Mammalia) from the Kalahari Gemsbok Park. *Koedoe* **9**: 37–39.

——— 1967. Recent Hyracoidea (Mammalia) of southern Africa. *Ann. Trans. Mus.* **25**: 117–152.

——— 1971a. Order Hyracoidea, Part 12, pp. 1–8, in *The mammals of Africa: an identification manual.* Eds J. Meester & H.W. Setzer. Washington D.C.: Smithsonian Institution Press.

——— 1971b. Food habits of some Carnivora (Mammalia) from southern Africa. *Ann. Trans. Mus.* **27**: 15–26.

——— 1971c. Food of *Canis mesomelas* in South Africa. *Zool. Afr.* **6**: 195–203.

——— 1971d. Notes on movement by black-backed jackal and the aardwolf in the western Transvaal. *Zool. Afr.* **6**: 205–207.

——— 1975. Conservation status of the larger mammals of southern Africa. *Biol. Conserv.* **7**: 87–95.

*——— **& Le Riche, E.A.N.** 1982. Prey preference and hunting efficiency of the Kalahari desert leopard. pp. 389–414, in *Proc. 2nd int. Symposium on cats of the World.* Eds S.D.Miller & D.D.Everett. Nat. Wildlife Fed., Washington DC.

*——— **& Le Riche, E.A.N.** 1984. Aspects of the ecology and behaviour of the leopard *Panthera pardus* in the Kalahari desert. *Koedoe* suppl. **27**: 259–280.

——— **& Nel, J.A.J.** 1980. Winter food and foraging behaviour of the aardwolf, *Proteles cristatus*, in the Namib Naukluft Park. *Madoqua* **12**: 141–149.

*——— **Nel, J.A.J. & MacDonald, A.** 1984. Food niche separation between four sympatric Namib desert carnivores. *J. Zool., Lond.* **202**: 327–340.

**Bourgoin, P.** 1955. *Animaux de chasse d'Afrique.* Paris: La Toison d'or.

**Bourlière, F.** 1948. Sur la reproduction et al croissance du *Cricetomys gambianus*. Terre Vie: 65–68.

——— 1953. *The natural history of mammals.* London: Harrap.

——— 1963. Specific feeding habits of African carnivores. *Afr. wild Life* **17**: 21–27.

——— 1964. Densities and biomass of some ungulate populations in eastern Congo and Rwanda. *Zool. Afr.* **1**: 199–208.

——— **& Verschuren, J.** 1960. *Introduction a l'ecologie des ongules du Parc National Albert.* Brussels: Institut des Parcs Nationaux du Congo Belge.

***Bourquin, O.** 1985. Wild primates and their availability for research purposes in Natal. Mimeograph. Pietermaritzburg: Natal Parks Board.

——— **Vincent, J. & Hitchins, P.M.** 1971. The vertebrates of the Hluhluwe Game Reserve—Corridor (State Land) and Umfolozi Game Reserve Complex. *Lammergeyer* **14**: 5–58.

***Bowland, A.E.** 1986. The effect of the 1982/3 drought on small mammals in Umfolozi Game Reserve. *Cimbebasia* Ser.A **8**: 194–198.

*——— 1987. The blue duiker: Small, beautiful and rare. *Quagga* **18**: 5–6.

***Bowland, A.E.** 1989. Unpublished report. University of Natal.

*——— **& Gordon, D.H.** 1983. The first record of the tree rat *Thallomys paedulcus* in the Hluhluwe Game Reserve. *Lammergeyer* **32**: 53.

***Boyer, D.** 1985. Interaction of two *Gerbillurus* spp in the Namib. *S. Afr. J. Sci.* **81**: 704.

**Braack, H.** 1973. Population dynamics of the blue wildebeest, *Connochaetes taurinus taurinus* (Burchell, 1823), in the Central District of the Kruger National Park. Thesis for Certificate in Field ecology, University of Rhodesia.

**Bradley, R.M.** 1968. Some aspects of the ecology of the warthog. M.Sc. thesis, University of East Africa.

——— 1972. Warthog (*Phacochoerus aethiopicus* Pallas) burrows in Nairobi National Park. *E. Afr. Wildl. J.* **9**: 149–152.

***Braekman, J.C., Daloze, D., Dupont, A., Pasteels, J.M. & Jonsens, G.** 1984. Diterpene composition of defence secretion of four West African *Trinervitermes* soldiers. *J. Chem. Ecol.* **10**: 1363–1370.

***Brain, C.** 1988. Water gathering by baboons in the Namib desert. *S. Afr. J. Sci.* **84**: 590–591

**Brain, C.K.** 1965. Observations on the behaviour of vervet monkeys (*Cercopithecus aethiops*). *Zool. Afr.* **1**: 13–27.

——— 1967. The Transvaal Museum's fossil project at Swartkrans. *S. Afr. J. Sci.* **63**: 378–384.

——— 1970. New finds at the Swartkrans Australopithicine site. *Nature, Lond.* **225**: 1112–1119.

——— 1976. A re-interpretation of the Swartkrans site and its remains. *S. Afr. J. Sci.* **72**: 141–146.

——— 1981. *The hunters or the hunted? An introduction to African cave taphonomy.* Chicago: University Press.

**Brand, D.J.** 1963. Records of mammals bred in the National Zoological Gardens of South Africa during the period 1908–1960. *Proc. zool. Soc. Lond.* **140**: 617–659.

——— 1965. Present numeral status of the white-tailed gnu. *Zoon* **5**: 1–5.

——— **& Cullen, L.** 1967. Breeding of the Cape hunting dog, *Lycaon pictus*, at Pretoria Zoo. *Int. Zoo Yb.* **7**: 124–126.

**Brentjes, B.** 1969. Hirsche in Nubien und Aethiopien. *Säugetierk. Mitt.* **17**: 203–205.

**Breytenbach, G.J.** 1977. An ecological study of the bushpig (*Potamochoerus porcus* L. 1758) on the eastern shores of Lake St Lucia with particular reference to feeding. B.Sc. Hons Project Rep., University of Pretoria.

*——— 1982. Small mammal responses to environmental gradients in the Groot Swartberg of the Southern Cape. M.Sc. thesis, University of Pretoria.

*——— 1986. Impacts of alien organisms on terrestrial communities with emphasis on communities of the south-western Cape. Ch. 18. In: *Ecology and management of biological invasions in southern Africa.* Eds I.A.W. MacDonald, F.J. Kruger & A.A. Ferrar. Pretoria C.S.I.R.

*——— 1988. Diet of the samango monkey in the northern Transvaal. *S. Afr. J. Wildl. Res.* **18**: 113–120.

——— **& Skinner, J.D.** 1982. Diet, feeding and habitat utilization by bushpigs *Potamochoerus porcus* Linnaeus. *S. Afr. J. Wildl. Res.* **12**: 1–7.

**Briand-Petersen, J.C. & Casebeer, R.L.** 1971. A bibliography relating to the ecology and energetics of East African large mammals. *E. Afr. Wildl. J.* **9**: 1–23.

***Bridgeford, P.A.** 1985. Unusual diet of the lion *Panthera leo* in the Skeleton Coast Park. *Madoqua* **14**: 187–188.

**Briggs, K.T. & Morejohn, G.V.** 1976. Dentition, cranial morphology and evolution in elephant seals. *Mammalia* **40**: 199–222.

***Brimley, H.H.** 1943. True's beaked whale *Mesoplodon mirus* True, from North Carolina. *J. Mammal.* **24**: 199–203.

***Britz, M. & Loutit, B.C.** 1989. Monitoring and identification of black rhinoceros *Diceros bicornis* in Damaraland and the compilation of a population register. *Koedoe* **32**: 61–63.

**Brockmann, R.E.D.** 1910. *Mammals of Somaliland.* London: Hurst & Blackett.

***Bronner, G., Rautenbach, I.L. & Meester, J.** 1988. Environmental influence on reproduction in the Natal multimammate mouse *Mastomys natalensis* (A. Smith, 1834). *S. Afr. J. Wildl. Res.* **18**: 142–148.

**Bronson, F.H.** 1979. The reproductive ecology of the house mouse. *Q. Rev. Biol.* **54**: 265–299.

**Brooks, P.M.** 1974. The ecology of the four-striped field mouse *Rhabdomys pumilio* (Sparrman, 1784) with particular reference to a population on the Van Riebeeck Nature Reserve. D.Sc. thesis, University of Pretoria.

*——— 1989. Proposed conservation plan for the black rhinoceros *Diceros bicornis* in South Africa, the TBVC states and Namibia. *Koedoe* **32**: 1–30.

*——— **& MacDonald, I.A.W.** 1983. The Hluhluwe-Umfolozi Reserve: An ecological case history. In *The management of large mammals in African conservation areas*, pp. 51–77. Ed. R.N. Owen-Smith. Pretoria: HAUM.

**Broom, R.** 1909a. On the milk dentition of Orycteropus. *Ann. S. Afr. Mus.* **5**: 381–384.

——— 1909b. On a large extinct species of *Bubalis*. *Ann. S. Afr. Mus.* **7**: 279–280.

——— 1913. Man contemporaneous with extinct mammals in South Africa. *Ann. S. Afr. Mus.* **12**: 13–16.

——— 1934. On the fossil remains associated with *Australopithecus africanus*. *S. Afr. J. Sci.* **31**: 471–480.

——— 1948. Some South African Pliocene and Pleistocene mammals. *Ann. Trans. Mus.* **21**: 1–38.

——— 1949. The extinct blue buck of South Africa. *Nature, Lond.* **164**: 1097–1098.

——— 1950. Some further advances in our knowledge of the Cape golden moles. *Ann. Trans. Mus.* **21**: 234–241.

**Brosset, A.** 1966a. Contribution à la fauna du Congo (Brazzaville) Mission A. Villiers et A. Descarpentries. *Bull. Inst. fr. Afr. noire* **28** Ser A(l): 362–369.

*——— 1966b. Les Chiroptères du Haut-Ivindo (Gabon). *Biol. Gabonica* **2**(1): 47–86.

***Brown, C.H. & Waser, P.M.** 1984. Hearing and communication in blue monkeys (*Cercopithecus mitis*). *Anim. Behav.* **32**: 66–75.

**Brown, D.H. & Norris, K.S.** 1956. Observations of wild and captive cetaceans. *J. Mammal.* **37**: 311–326.

**Brown, G.S., Brownell, R.L., Erikson, A.W., Hofman, R.J., Leano, G.A. & Mackintosh, N.A.** *Antarctic Mammals*. Antarctic map folio series No. 18. New York: American Geographical Society.

**Brown, J.C.** 1964. Observations on the elephant shrews (Macroscelidiidae) of Equatorial Africa. *Proc. zool. Soc. Lond.* **143**: 103–119.

**Brown, K.G.** 1952. Observations on the newly born leopard seal. *Nature, Lond.* **170**: 982.

***Brown, S.G.** 1973. Whale marking—progress report 1972. *Rep. int. Whal. Commn* **23**: 49–54.

**Bruce, W.S.** 1893. Report of the sixty sixth meeting of the British Association. Sept. 1893: 807.

***Bruorton, M.R.** 1989. A comparative morphological and physiological examination of the gastrointestinal tracts of vervet and samango monkeys. M.Sc. thesis, University of Natal.

*——— **& Perrin, M.R.** 1988. The anatomy of the stomach and caecum of the samango monkey, *Cercopithecus mitis erythrarchus* Peters, 1852. *Z. Säugetierk.* **53**: 210–224.

**Bruyns, W.F.J.M.** 1960. The ridge-backed dolphin of the Indian Ocean. *Malay. Nat.* **14**, July: 159–165.

——— 1969. Sight records and notes on the False killer whale *Pseudorca crassidens*. *Säugetierk. Mitt.* **17**: 351–356.

**Bryden, B.R.** 1976. The biology of the African lion (*Panthera leo*, Linnaeus, 1758) in the Kruger National Park. M.Sc. thesis, University of Pretoria.

**Bryden, H.A.** 1889. *Kloof and Karroo: sport, legend and natural history in Cape Colony, with a notice of the game birds and of the present distribution of the antelopes and larger game*. London: Longmans Green.

——— 1893. *Gun and camera in southern Africa*. London: Stanford.

——— 1897. *Nature and sport in South Africa*. London: Chapman & Hall.

——— 1899/1900. *Great and small game of Africa*. London: Rowland Ward.

*——— 1903. The decline and fall of the South African elephant. *Fortnightly Review* **79**: 100–108.

——— 1936. *Wild life in southern Africa*. London: Harrap.

***Bryden, M.M.** 1968. Control of growth in two populations of elephant seals. *Nature, Lond.* **217**: 1106–1108.

——— 1972. Growth and development of marine mammals. pp 1–79. In: *Functional Anatomy of Marine Mammals*. Ed. R.J. Harrison. Academic Press: London.

——— 1972. Body size and composition of elephant seals (*Mirounga leonina*): absolute measurements and estimates from bone dimensions. *J. Zool., Lond.* **167**: 265–276.

——— **& Erickson, A.W.** 1976. Body size and composition of crabeater seals (*Lobodon carcinophagus*) with observations on tissue and organ size in Ross seals (*Ommatophoca rossi*). *J. Zool., Lond.* **179**: 235–247.

——— **Harrison, R.J. & Lear, R.J.** 1977. Some aspects of the biology of *Peponocephala electra* (Cetacea: Delphinidae). 1. General and Reproductive Biology. *Aust. J. mar. Freshwat. Res.* **28**: 703–715.

**Brynard, A.M.** 1954. Die groepverdeling van bergkwaggas in die Nasionale Bergkwaggawildtuin. Report National Parks Board of Trustees, Pretoria. Mimeograph.

——— **& Pienaar, U. de V.** 1960. Annual report of the biologists, 1958/1959. *Koedoe* **3**: 1–205.

**Buchanan, A.** 1921. *Exploration of Aïr. Out of the world north of Nigeria*. London: Murray.

***Buckland, S.T. & Anganuzzi, A.A.** 1988. Estimated trends in abundance of dolphins associated with tuna in the eastern tropical Pacific. *Rep. int. Whal. Commn* **38**: 411–437.

**Buckley, T.E.** 1876. On the past and present geographical distribution of the large mammals of South Africa. *Proc. zool. Soc. Lond.* 277–293.

**Buettner-Janusch, J.** 1964. The breeding of galagos in captivity and some notes on their behaviour. *Folia primatol.* **2**: 93–110.

***Buffenstein, R.** 1984. The importance of microhabitat in thermoregulation and thermal conductance in two Namib rodents—a crevice dweller, *Aethomys namaquensis*, and a burrow dweller, *Gerbillurus paeba*. *J. therm. Biol.* **9**: 235–241.

*——— **Campbell, W.E. & Jarvis, J.U.M.** 1985. Identification of crystalline allantoin in the urine of African Cricetidae (Rodentia) and its role in their water economy. *J. Comp. Physiol.* (B) **155**: 493–499.

**Burchell, W.J.** 1822 & 1824. *Travels in the interior of South Africa*. 1822 Vol. **1**, 1824 Vol. **2**. London: Longman, Hurst, Rees, Orme, Brown & Green.

***Burda, H.** 1989. Reproductive biology (behaviour, breeding and postnatal development) in subterranean molerats, *Cryptomys hottentotus* (Bathyergidae). *Z. Säugetierk.* **54**: 360–376.

**Burney, J. Le B. & Ortiz, C.L.** 1977. Composition of elephant seal milk. *J. Mammal.* **58**: 683–685.

**Burt, W.H. & Grossenheider, R.P.** 1961. *A field guide to the mammals*. Boston: Houghton Mifflin.

**Burton, M.** 1963. The vanishing oribi. *Illus. London News* **242**: 312.

**Buss, I.O.** 1961. Some observations on food habits and behaviour of the African elephant. *J. Wildl. Mgmt* **25**: 131–148.

**Buss, I.O. & Smith, N.S.** 1966. Observations on reproduction and breeding behaviour of the African elephant. *J. Wildl. Mgmt* **30**: 375–388.

***Busse, C.D.** 1984. Spatial structure of chacma baboon groups. *Int. J. Primatol.* **5**: 247–261.

**Butler, H.** 1964. The reproductive biology of a strepsirhine (*Galago senegalensis senegalensis*). *Int. Rev. Gen. Exp. Zool.* **1**: 241–294.

***Butler, P.M.** 1956. The skull of *Ictops* and the classification of the Insectivora. *Proc. zool. Soc. Lond.* **126**: 453–481.

——— 1978. Insectivores and Chiroptera, pp. 56–68, in *Evolution of African mammals*. Eds V.J. Maglio & H.B.S. Cooke. Cambridge, Mass.: Harvard University Press.

***Butterworth, D.S., Duffy, D.C., Best, P.B. & Bergh, M.O.** 1988. On the scientific basis for reducing the South African seal population. *S. Afr. J. Sci.* **84**: 179–188.

**Butynski, T.M.** 1973. Life history and economic value of the springhare (*Pedetes capensis* Forster) in Botswana. *Botswana Notes and Records* **5**: 200–213.

——— 1975. Nocturnal ecology of the springhare, *Pedetes capensis* Forster in Botswana. M.Sc. thesis, Michigan State University.

——— 1978. Ecological studies on the springhare, *Pedetes capensis* in Botswana. Ph.D. thesis, Michigan State University.

——— 1979. Reproductive ecology of the springhare, *Pedetes capensis*, in Botswana. *J. Zool., Lond.* **189**: 221–232.

*——— 1982a. Vertebrate predation by primates: a review of hunting patterns and prey. *J. Human Evol.* **11**: 421–430.

*——— 1982b. Harem-male replacement and infanticide in the blue monkey (*Cercopithecus mitis stuhlmanni*) in the Kibale Forest, Uganda. *Am. J. Primatol.* **3**: 1–22.

*——— 1982c. Blue monkey (*Cercopithecus mitis stuhlmanni*) predation on galagos. *Primates* **23**: 563–566.

——— 1982d. Pelage and moult in the springhare *Pedetes capensis* in Botswana. *Afr. J. Ecol.* **20**: 279–287.

*——— 1982e. Ecology of *Physaloptera capensis* (Nematoda: Spiruroidea) infecting the springhare *Pedetes capensis* (Mammalia) in Botswana. *J. Zool., Lond.* **196**: 233–254.

*——— **& Mattingly, R.** 1979. Burrow structure and fossorial ecology of the springhare, *Pedetes capensis*, in Botswana. *Afr. J. Ecol.* **17**: 205–215.

***Buys, D.** 1987. The ecology of eland (*Taurotragus oryx*) in the western Transvaal Highveld. M.Sc. thesis, University of Pretoria.

*——— 1990. Food selection by eland in the western Transvaal. *S. Afr. J. Wildl. Res.* **20**: 16–20.

*——— **& Keogh, H.J.** 1984. Notes on the microstructure of hair of the Orycteropodidae, Elephantidae, Equidae, Suidae and Giraffidae. *S. Afr. J. Wildl. Res.* **14**: 111–119.

# C

**Cabral, J.C.** 1966. Notes on the taxonomy of *Genetta*. *Zool. Afr.* **2**: 25–26.

——— 1969. As genetas de Angola. *Bol. Inst. Invest. Cient. Ang.* **6**(1): 1–41.

——— 1970. As genetas de Africa Central. *Bol. Inst. Invest. Cient. Ang.* **7**(2): 1–28.

*——— 1989a. Distributional data and notes on Angolan carnivores (Mammalia: Carnivora). I. Small and median-sized species. *Garcia de Orta* Ser. Zool., Lisboa, **14**: 3–27.

*——— 1989b. The prior scientific name of the larger red mongoose (Carnivora: Viverridae: Herpestinae). *Garcia de Orta* Ser. Zool., Lisboa, **14**: 1–2.

**Cabrera, A.** 1932. Los mammiferes de Marruecos. *Trab. Mus. nac. Cienc. nat., Madr. (Serie zoologica)* **57**: 1–362.

*——— 1936. Subspecific and individual variation in the Burchell's zebras. *J. Mammal.* **17**: 89–112.

*——— **& Ruxton, A.E.** 1926. On mammals from Luluabong, southern Congo. *Ann. Mag. nat. Hist.* Ser. 9, **17**: 591–602.

**Cade, C.E.** 1966. A note on the mating behaviour of the Kenya oribi, *Ourebia oribi*, in captivity. *Int. Zoo Yb.* **6**: 205.

***Cadenat, J.** 1949. Notes sur les Cetaces observes sur les cotes du Senegal de 1941 a 1948. *Bull. Inst. fr. Afr. noire* **11**: 1–15.

——— 1958. Notres sur les delphinides ouest-africains. II. Un specimen du genre *Feresa* capture sur les cotes du Senegal. *Bull. Inst. fr. Afr. noire* (A) **20**: 1486–1493.

***Caldwell, D.K., & Brown, D.H.** 1964. Tooth wear as a correlate of described feeding behaviour by the killer whale, with notes on a captive specimen. *Bull. Calif. Acad. Sci.* **63**: 128–140.

——— **& Caldwell, M.C.** 1971. Porpoise fisheries in the southern Caribbean —present utilization and future potentials. *Proc. 23rd Ann. Session Gulf and Caribbean Fisheries Institute*: 195–206.

——— **Caldwell, M.C. & Rice, D.W.** 1966. Behaviour of the sperm whale, in *Whales, dolphins and porpoises*. Ed. K.S. Norris. Berkeley: University of California Press.

**Caldwell, M.C. & Caldwell, D.K.** 1965. Individual whistle contours in bottlenosed dolphins (*Tursiops truncatus*). *Nature, Lond.* **207**: 434–435.

——— **Caldwell, D.K.** 1966. Epimeletic (caregiving) behaviour in Cetacea, in *Whales, dolphins and porpoises*. Ed. K.S. Norris. Berkeley: University of California Press.

***Calef, G.W.** 1988. Maximum rate of increase in the African elephant. *Afr. J. Ecol.* **26**: 323–327.

***Cambefort, J.P.** 1981. A comparative study of culturally transmitted patterns of feeding habits in the chacma baboon *Papio ursinus* and the vervet monkey *Cercopithecus aethiops*. *Folia primatol.* **36**: 243–263.

***Campbell, A.** 1981. A comment on Kalahari wildlife and the Kukhe fence. *Botswana Notes and Records* **13**: 111–118.

**Cansdale, G.S.** 1948. *Provisional Checklist of Gold Coast Mammals*. Accra: Govt. Printing Dept.

**Cansdale, L.S.** 1964. *Management of wild mammals in captivity*. Chicago: University Press.

**Capello, H. & Ivens, R.** 1882. *From Benguella to the territory of the Yacca*. Vol. **1** London: Low, Marston, Searle & Rivington.

***Carleton, M.D. & Musser, G.** 1984. Muroid rodents. In *Orders and Families of recent mammals of the world*. Eds S. Anderson & J. Knox Jones Jnr. New York: John Wiley.

**Carmichael, I.H., Patterson, L., Drager, N. & Breton, D.A.** 1977. Studies on reproduction in the African buffalo (*Syncerus caffer*) in Botswana. *S. Afr. J. Wildl. Res.* **7**: 45–52.

**Carpenter, G.P.** 1970. Some observations on the rusty spotted genet *Genetta rubiginosa zuluensis*. *Lammergeyer* **11**: 60–63.

***Carr, R.D.** 1984. Mammal conservation plan. Department of Nature Conservation, Transvaal Provincial Administration. Mimeograph.

*——— 1986. The distribution and conservation status of tsessebe in the Transvaal. *Project Report TN 6/3/1/39*. Nature Conservation Division, Transvaal Provincial Administration.

**Carrick, R. & Ingham, S.E.** 1962. Studies on the southern elephant seal *M. leonina* (L.). Introduction to the series. *C.S.I.R.O. Wildl. Res.* **7**: 102–118.

——— **Csordas, S.E. & Ingham, S.E.** 1962. Studies on the southern elephant seal *Mirounga leonina* (L.) IV. Breeding and development. *C.S.I.R.O. Wildl. Res.* **7**: 161–197.
***Carruthers, E.J.** 1988. Game protection in the Transvaal 1846–1926. Ph.D. thesis, University of Cape Town.
**Carter, B.** 1970. *Knysna elephant survey.* Knysna: Wildl. Protec. Soc. of S.A., Feb. 1969—Jan. 1970: 1–23.
***Carter, N.** 1971. *The elephants of Knysna.* Cape Town: Purnell.
**Cartmill, M.** 1972. Arboreal adaptations and the origin of the order Primates. pp. 97–122, in *Functional and Evolutionary Biology of Primates.* Ed. R. Tuttle. Chicago: Aldine-Atherton.
**Carvalho, C.T. de.** 1966. Notas sobre *Kogia breviceps* (Cetacea, Physeteridae). *Revta Biol. trop.* **14**: 169–181.
***Castello, H.P. & Pinedo, M.C.** 1977. *Arctocephalus tropicalis*, first record for Rio Grande do Sul coast. *Atlantica, Rio Grande* **2**: 111–119.
**Catto, G.G. & Jacobsen, N.** 1977. Watching the lovable klipspringer. *Fauna Flora, Pretoria* **31**: 19.
***Cave, A.J.E.** 1962. Burchell's original specimens of *Rhinoceros simus. Proc. Zool. Soc. Lond.* **139**: 691–700.
***Channing, A.** 1984. Ecology of the namtap *Graphiurus ocularis* (Rodentia: Gliridae) in the Cedarberg, South Africa. *S. Afr. J. Zool.* **19**: 144–149.
**Chapman, D. & Chapman, N.** 1975. *Fallow deer: their history, distribution and biology.* Lavenham: Terence Dalton.
**Chapman, N.G. & Chapman, D.I.** 1980. The distribution of fallow deer: a worldwide review. *Mamm. Rev.* **10**: 61–138.
***Charles-Dominique, P.** 1977. *Ecology and behaviour of nocturnal primates.* New York: Columbia University Press.
——— **& Bearder, S.K.** 1979. Field studies in lorisid behaviour: methodological aspects, pp. 567–629, in *The study of Prosimian behaviour.* Eds G.A. Doyle & R.D. Martin. London: Academic Press.
***Cheney, D.L.** 1977. The acquisition of rank and the development of reciprocal alliances among free-ranging immature baboons. *Behav. Ecol. Sociobiol.* **2**: 303–318.
*——— **Lee, P.C. & Seyfarth, R.M.** 1981. Behavioral correlates of non-random mortality among free-ranging female vervet monkeys. *Behav. Ecol. Sociobiol.* **9**: 153–161.
*——— **& Seyfarth, R.M.** 1977. Behaviour of adult and immature male baboons during inter-group encounters. *Nature Lond.* **269**: 404–406.
*——— **& Seyfarth, R.M.** 1981. Selective forces affecting the predator alarm calls of vervet monkeys. *Behaviour* **76**: 25–63.
——— **& Seyfarth, R.M.** 1983. Nonrandom dispersal in free-ranging vervet monkeys: social and genetic consequences. *Am. Nat.* **122**: 392–412.
**Chiarelli, A.B.** 1972. *Taxonomic atlas of living Primates.* London: Academic Press.
**Child, G.** 1964. Growth and ageing criteria of impala *Aepyceros melampus. Occas. pap. Natl. Mus. Rhod. B. Nat. sci.* **27**: 128–135.
——— 1968a. Behaviour of large mammals during the formation of Lake Kariba. *Kariba stud.*: 1–123.
——— 1968b. An ecological survey of north-eastern Botswana. Rome: FAO Report No.TA. 2563: 133–182.
——— 1972. Observations on a wildebeest die-off in Botswana. *Arnoldia Rhod.* **5**(31): 1–13.
——— **& Le Riche, J.D.** 1969. Recent springbok treks (mass movements) in south-western Botswana. *Mammalia* **33**: 499–504.
——— **& Mossman, A.** 1965. Right horn implantation in the common duiker. *Science* **149**(3689): 1265–1266.
——— **Parris, R. & Le Riche, E.** 1971. Use of mineralised water by Kalahari wildlife and its effects on habitat. *E. Afr. Wildl. J.* **9**: 125–142.
——— **Robbel, H. & Hepburn, C.P.** 1972. Observations on the biology of tsessebe, *Damaliscus lunatus lunatus*, in northern Botswana. *Mammalia* **36**: 342–388.
——— **Roth, H.H. & Kerr, M.A.** 1968. Reproduction and recruitment patterns in warthog (*Phacochoerus aethiopicus*) populations. *Mammalia* **32**: 6–29.
——— **& Savory, C.R.** 1964. The distribution of large mammal species in Southern Rhodesia. *Arnoldia Rhod.* **1**(14): 1–5.
——— **& von Richter, W.** 1969. Observations on ecology and behaviour of lechwe, puku and waterbuck along the Chobe River, Botswana. *Z. Säugetierk.* **34**: 275–295.
——— **& Wilson, V.J.** 1964a. Observations on ecology and behaviour of roan and sable in three tsetse control areas. *Arnoldia Rhod.* **1**(16):1–8.
——— **& Wilson, V.J.** 1964b. Delayed effects of tsetse control hunting on a duiker population. *J. Wildl. Mgmt* **28**: 866–868.
***Childes, S.L.** 1988. The past history, present status and distribution of the hunting dog *Lycaon pictus* in Zimbabwe. *Biol. Cons.* **44**: 301–316.
**Chilvers, H.E.** 1931. *Huberta goes south; a record of the lone trek of the celebrated Zululand hippopotamus, 1928–1931.* London: Gordon and Gotch.
**Chittleborough, R.G.** 1956. The southern right whale in Australian waters. *J. Mammal.* **37**: 456–457.
——— 1958. The breeding cycle of the female humpback whale, *Megaptera nodosa* (Bonnaterre). *Aust. J. mar. Freshwat. Res.* **9**:1–18.
——— 1965. Dynamics of the populations of the humpback whale, *Megaptera novaeangliae* (Borowski). *Aust. J. mar. Freshwat. Res.* **16**: 33–128.
***Christensen, I.** 1982. Killer whales in Norwegian coastal waters. *Rep. int. Whal. Commn* **32**: 633–642.
***Christian, D.P.** 1978. Effects of humidity and body size on evaporative water loss in three desert rodents. *Comp. Biochem. Physiol.* **60**A: 425–430.
*——— 1979. Physiological correlates of demographic patterns in three sympatric Namib desert rodents. *Physiol. Zool.* **52**: 329–339.
*——— **Enders, J.E. & Shump, K.A. (Jr).** 1977. A laboratory study of caching in *Desmodillus auricularis. Zool. Afr.* **12**: 505–507.
**Chubb, E.C.** 1917. A new bat of the genus *Otomops*, obtained at Durban. *Ann. Durban Mus.* **1**: 433.
**Churcher, C.S.** 1970. The fossil equidae from the Krugersdorp caves. *Ann. Trans. Mus.* **26**: 145–168.
——— 1978. Giraffidae, in *Evolution of African mammals.* Eds J. Maglio and H.B.S. Cooke. Cambridge Mass.: Harvard University Press.
——— **& Richardson, M.L.** 1978. Equidae, in *Evolution of African mammals.* Eds V.J. Maglio & H.B.S. Cooke. Cambridge, Mass.: Harvard University Press.
***Churchfield, S.** 1985. Diets of two syntopic small mammals in the Inyanga National Park, Zimbabwe. *S. Afr. J. Zool.* **20**: 65–67.
***Churchill, J.** 1856. Unpubl. ms. Pretoria: Transvaal Archives.
***Cilliers, A.** 1989. Monitoring methods and techniques for censusing black rhinoceros *Diceros bicornis bicornis* in Etosha National Park. *Koedoe* **32**: 49–60.
**Clarke, J.A.** 1953. The hippopotamus in Gambia, West Africa. *J. Mammal.* **34**: 299–315.
***Clarke, M.R.** 1976. Observation on sperm whale diving. *J. mar. biol. Ass. U.K.* **56**: 809–810.
*——— 1977. Beaks, nets and numbers. *Symp. zool. Soc. Lond.* **38**: 89–126.
*——— 1978. Buoyancy control as a function of the spermaceti organ in the sperm whale. *J. mar. biol. Ass. U.K.* **58**: 27–71.
*——— 1980. Cephalopoda in the diet of sperm whales of the Southern Hemisphere and their bearing on sperm whale biology. *'Discovery' Rep.* **37**: 1–324.
**Clarke, R.** 1956. Sperm whales of the Azores. *'Discovery' Rep.* **28**: 237–298.
——— **Agnayo, A. & Paliza, O.** 1968. Sperm whales of the southeast Pacific. Part l. Introduction; Part 2 Size range, external characters and teeth. *Hvalrad. Skr.* **51**: 1–80.
***Clemens, E.T. & Maloiy, G.M.** 1982. The digestive physiology of three East African herbivores: the elephant, rhinoceros and hippopotamus. *J. Zool., Lond.* **198**: 141–156.
**Cline, D.R., Siniff, D.B. & Erickson, A.W.** 1971. Underwater copulation of the Weddell seal. *J. Mammal.* **52**: 216–218.
***Cloete, G.** 1983. Etho-ecological aspects of the steenbok (*Raphicerus campestris* (Thunberg, 1811)) in the Namib desert, South West Africa. M.Sc. thesis, University of the Orange Free State, Bloemfontein.
*——— **& Kok, O.B.** 1986. Aspects of the water economy of steenbok *Raphicerus campestris* in the Namib desert. *Madoqua* **14**: 375–387.
**Clough, G.** 1969. Some preliminary observations on reproduction in the warthog *Phacochoerus aethiopicus* Pallas. *J. Reprod. Fert. Suppl.* **6**: 323–367.
——— **& Hassan, A.G.** 1970. A quantitative study of the daily activity of the warthog in the Queen Elizabeth National Park, Uganda. *E. Afr. Wildl. J.* **8**: 19–24.
**Coaton, W.G.H.** 1963. Survey of the termites (Isoptera) of the Kalahari thornveld and shrub bushveld of the RSA. *Koedoe* **6**: 38–68.
——— **& Sheasby, J.L.** 1972. Preliminary report on a survey of the termites (Isoptera) of South West Africa. *Cimbebasia Mem.* **2**: 1–219.
——— **& Sheasby, J.L.** 1975. National Survey of the Isoptera of southern Africa. 10. The genus *Hodotermes* Hagen (Hodotermitidae). *Cimbebasia Ser A.* **3**(10): 106–133.
***Cockcroft, V.G., & Ross, G.J.B.** 1990a. Food and feeding of the Indian Ocean bottlenose dolphin off southern Natal, South Africa. pp 295–308. In: *The bottlenose dolphin.* Eds S. Leatherwood & R.R. Reeves. San Diego: Academic Press.
*——— **& Ross, G.J.B.** 1990b. Observations on the early development of a captive bottlenose dolphin calf. pp 461–478. In: *The bottlenose dolphin.* Eds S. Leatherwood & R.R. Reeves. San Diego: Academic Press.
*——— **& Ross, G.J.B.** In press a. Age, growth and reproduction in bottlenose dolphins from the east coast of southern Africa. *Fish. Bull., U.S.*
*——— **Cliff, G. & Ross, G.J.B.** 1989. Shark predation on Indian Ocean bottlenose dolphins *Tursiops truncatus* off Natal, South Africa. *S. Afr. J. Zool.* **24**: 305–310.
**Coe, M.J.** 1967a. Preliminary notes on the eastern Kenya springhare *Pedetes surdaster larvalis* Hollister. *E. Afr. Wildl. J.* **5**: 174–177.
——— 1967b. "Necking" behaviour in the giraffe. *J. Zool., Lond.* **151**: 313–321.
——— 1969. The anatomy of the reproductive tract and breeding in the springhaas, *Pedetes surdaster larvalis* Hollister. *J. Reprod. Fert. Suppl* **6**: 159–174.
——— 1972a. Defaecation by African elephants (*Loxodonta africana africana* Blumenbach). *E. Afr. Wildl. J.* **10**: 165–174.
——— 1972b. The south Turkana expedition. Scientific papers IX. *Geogrl.J.* **138**: 316–338.
*——— 1983. Large herbivores and food quality, pp. 345–368, in *Nitrogen as an ecological factor.* Eds L.J.A. McNeills & I.H. Robinson. London: Blackwell.
*——— **& Carr, R.D.** 1978. The association between dung middens of the blesbok (*Damaliscus dorcas phillipsi* Harper) and mounds of the harvester termite (*Trinervitermes trinervoides* Sjostedt). *S. Afr. J. Wildl. Res.* **8**: 65–70.
*——— **& Carr, R.D.** 1983. The relationship between large ungulate body weight and faecal pellet weight. *Afr. J. Ecol.* **21**: 165–174.
**Coetzee, C.G.** 1963. The prey of owls in the Kruger National Park as indicated by owl pellets collected during 1960–61. *Koedoe* **6**: 115–125.
——— 1969. The distribution of mammals in the Namib Desert and adjoining inland escarpment. *Scient. Pap. Namib Desert Res. Stn* **40**: 23–36.
——— 1970. The relative tail length of striped mice *Rhabdomys pumilio* Sparrman 1784 in relation to climate. *Zool. Afr.* **5**: 1–6.
——— 1977a. Order Carnivora, Part 8, pp 1–42, in *The mammals of Africa: an identification manual.* Eds J. Meester & H.W. Setzer. Washington D.C.: Smithsonian Institution Press.
——— 1977b. Genus *Steatomys*, Part 6.8, pp. 1–4, in *The mammals of Africa: an identification manual.* Eds J. Meester & H.W. Setzer. Washington D.C.: Smithsonian Institution Press.
*——— 1983. The feeding behaviour of *Petromus typicus* A. Smith, 1831 (Rodentia: Petromuridae). *Ann. Mus. Roy. Afr. Centr.* **237**: 203–206.
**Coffey, D.J.** 1977. *The encyclopedia of sea mammals.* London: Hart-Davis.
**Cohen, M.** 1976. The steenbok: a neglected species. *Custos* **5**: 23–26.
——— 1977. The steenbok—hermit of the bush. *Fauna Flora, Pretoria* **30**: 16.
*——— 1987. Aspects of the biology and behaviour of the steenbok, *Raphicerus campestris* (Thunberg, 1811) in the Kruger National Park. D.Sc. thesis, University of Pretoria.
**Colbert, E.H.** 1969. *Evolution of the vertebrates.* New York: J. Wiley.
***Collet, A.** 1981. Biologie du dauphin commun *Delphinus delphis* L. en Atlantique Nord-Est. Thesis presented to the University of Poitiers, La Rochelle, 156 pp.
**Condy, J.B.** 1979. Buffalo and foot-and-mouth disease. *Rhod. Sci. News* **13**(3): 74–75.
——— **& Hedger, R.S.** 1978. Experiences in the establishment of a herd of foot-and-mouth disease-free African buffalo, *Syncerus caffer. S. Afr. J. Wildl. Res..* **8**: 87–92.
**Condy, P.R.** 1973. The population status, social behaviour and daily activity pattern of the white rhino, *Ceratotherium simum simum*, in the Kyle National Park. M.Sc. thesis, University of Rhodesia.
——— 1976. Preliminary guide to the identification of *Arctocephalus tropicalis* and *Arctocephalus gazella* on Marion Island. Internal report, Mammal Research Institute, University of Pretoria. Mimeograph.
——— 1977a. Whale observations in the pack ice off the Fimbul Ice Shelf. *S. Afr. J. Antarct. Res.* **7**: 7–9.
——— 1977b. The ecology of the southern elephant seal *Mirounga leonina* (Linnaeus, 1758) at Marion Island. D.Sc. thesis, University of Pretoria.
——— 1978. Distribution, abundance, and annual cycle of fur seals (*Arctocephalus* spp) on the Prince Edward Islands. *S. Afr. J. Wildl. Res.* **8**: 159–168.
——— 1981. Annual food consumption and seasonal fluctuations in biomass of seals on Marion Island. *Mammalia* **45**: 21–30.
——— **& Burger, A.** 1975. A southern right whale at Marion Island. *S. Afr. J. Sci.* **71**: 349.
——— **& Green, E.D.** 1980. The fur coat of the Amsterdam Island fur seal, *Arctocephalus tropicalis. J. Zool., Lond.* **191**: 85–96.
——— **van Aarde, R.J. & Bester, M.N.** 1978. The seasonal occurrence and behaviour of killer whales, *Orcinus orca*, at Marion Island. *J. Zool., Lond.* **184**: 449–464.
**Conybeare, A.** 1975. Notes on the feeding habits of kudu in the Kalahari sand area of Wankie National Park, Rhodesia. *Arnoldia Rhod.* **7**(14): 1–7.

*——— 1980. Buffalo numbers, home range and daily movement in the Sengwa Wildlife Research Area, Zimbabwe. *S. Afr. J. Wildl. Res.* **10**: 89–93.
**Cooke, H.B.S.** 1947. Some fossil hippotragine antelopes from South Africa. *S. Afr. J. Sci.* **43**: 226–231.
——— **& Wells, L.H.** 1951. Fossil remains from Chelmer, near Bulawayo, Southern Rhodesia. *S. Afr. J. Sci.* **47**: 205–209.
——— **& Wilkinson, A.F.** 1978. Suidae and Tayassuidae, in *Evolution of African mammals*. Eds V.J. Maglio & H.B.S. Cooke. Cambridge Mass.: Harvard University Press.
**Cooper, R.L. & Skinner, J.D.** 1979. Importance of termites in the diet of the aardwolf *Proteles cristatus* in South Africa. *S. Afr. J. Zool.* **14**: 5–8.
***Cooper, Susan M.** 1990a. The hunting behaviour of spotted hyaenas (*Crocuta crocuta*) in the Savuti region of the Chobe National Park, Botswana. Unpublished report, University of the Witwatersrand.
*——— 1990b. Influence of interspecific competition on optimal group size in African predators. Unpubl. Mimeograph, University of the Witwatersrand.
**Copley, H.** 1950. *Small mammals of Kenya*. Nairobi: Highway Press.
**Corbet, G.B.** 1974a. Family Erinaceidae, Part 1.4, pp. 1–3, in *The mammals of Africa: an identification manual*. Eds J. Meester & H.W. Setzer. Washington D.C.: Smithsonian Institution Press.
——— 1974b. Family Macroscelididae, Part 1.5, pp. 1–6, in *The mammals of Africa: an identification manual*. Eds J. Meester & H.W. Setzer. Washington D.C.: Smithsonian Institution Press.
——— 1974c. Subfamily Potamogalinae, Part 1.2, pp. 1–2, in *The mammals of Africa: an identification manual*. Eds J. Meester & H.W. Setzer. Washington D.C.: Smithsonian Institution Press.
——— **& Hanks, J.** 1968. A revision of the elephant shrews, Family Macroscelididae. *Bull. Br. Mus. nat. Hist. (Zool.)* **16**: 5–11.
*——— **& Hill, J.E.** 1980. A world list of mammalian species. British Museum (Natural History) and Cornell University Press, London and Ithaca.
——— **& Jones, L.A.** 1965. The specific characters of the crested porcupines subgenus *Hystrix*. *Proc. zool. Soc. Lond.* **144**: 285–300.
——— **& Neal, B.R.** 1965. The taxonomy of the elephant shrews of the genus *Petrodromus*, with particular reference to the East African coast. *Rev. Zool. Bot. Afr.* **71**: 49–78.
——— **& Yalden, D.W.** 1972. Recent records of mammals (other than bats) from Ethiopa. *Bull. Br. Mus. nat. Hist. (Zool.)* **22**(8): 211–252.
***Cords, M.** 1987. Mixed-species association of *Cercopithecus* monkeys in the Kakamega forest, Kenya. University of California Publications in Zoology Vol. 117. Berkeley: University of California Press.
*——— **& Rowell, T.E.** 1987. Birth intervals of *Cercopithecus* monkeys of the Kakamega Forest, Kenya. *Primates* **28**: 277–281.
**Coryndon, S.C.** 1978. Hippopotamidae: 483–495, in *Evolution of African mammals*. Eds J. Maglio & H.B.S. Cooke. Cambridge, Mass.: Harvard University Press.
***Cotterill, F.P.D. & Giddings, S.R.** 1987. Observations on the activity patterns of the lesser house bat, *Scotophilus viridis*. *S. Afr. J. Zool.* **22**: 175.
***Coulson, D.** 1987. The wild horses of the Namib. *Optima* 35(1): 10–19.
***Courtenay, D.O. & Bearder, S.K.** 1989. The taxonomic status and distribution of bushbabies in Malawi with emphasis on the significance of vocalizations. *Int. J. Primatol.* **10**: 17–34.
**Courtnay-Latimer, M.** 1960. Whales on our coast. *News Bull. zool. Soc. sth. Afr.* **2**: 23–24.
——— 1961. Two rare seal records for South Africa. *Ann. Cape Prov. Mus.* **3**: 122.
——— 1963. Gray's beaked whale, *Mesoplodon grayi*. *Ann. Cape Prov. Mus.* **3**: 122.
**Cowie, M.** 1961. Annual Report, National Parks of Kenya, Nairobi.
——— 1966. *The World of Animals: The African Lion*. New York: Golden Press.
**Cowles, R.B.** 1936. Notes on the mammalian fauna of Umzumbe Valley, Natal, South Africa. *J. Mammal.* **17**: 121–130.
***Cox, G.W.** 1987. The origin of vegetation circles on stoney soil of the Namib desert near Gobabeb, South West Africa, Namibia. *J. Arid. Envir.* **13**: 237–243.
***Cox, J.M.** 1985. A study of Hystricomorph rodent behaviour, especially that of the cane rat (*Thryonomys swinderianus* Temminck). M.Sc. thesis, University of Natal, Durban.
***Craig, G.C.** 1984. Foetal mass and date of conception in African elephants: a revised formula. *S. Afr. J. Sci.* **80**: 512–516.
**Crandall, L.S.** 1964. *The Management of Wild Animals in Captivity*. Chicago: University Press.
***Crawford, R.J.M.** 1984. Activity, group structure and lambing of blue duikers *Cephalophus monticola* in the Tsitsikama National Park, South Africa. *S. Afr. J. Wildl. Res.* **14**: 65–68.
**Crompton, A.W.** 1968. The enigma of the evolution of mammals. *Optima* Sept.: 137–151.
**Cronwright-Schreiner, S.C.** 1925. *The migratory springbucks of South Africa*. London: Fisher Unwin.
***Crook, J.H., Ellis, J.E. & Goss-Custard, J.D.** 1976. Mammalian social systems: structure and function. *Anim. Behav.* **13**: 1–37.
**Crowcroft, P.** 1957. *The life of the shrew*. London: Max Reinhardt.
***Crowe, T.M. & Liversidge, R.** 1977. Disproportionate mortality of males in a population of springbok (Artiodactyla: Bovidae). *Zool. afr.* **12**: 469–473.
***Cruikshank, R.A. & Brown, S.G.** 1981. Recent observations and some historical records of southern right-whale dolphins, *Lissodelphis peronii*. *Fish. Bull. S. Afr.* **15**: 109–121.
**Cullen, A.** 1969. *Window onto Wilderness*, pp. 231. Nairobi: East African Publishing House.
**Cumming, D.H.M.** 1975. A field study of the ecology and behaviour of warthog. *Mus. mem. Natl Mus. Monum. Rhod.* **7**: 1–179.
——— 1981. The management of elephant and other large mammals in Zimbabwe, pp. 91–118. In *Problems in management of locally abundant wild mammals*. Eds P.A. Jewell, S. Holt, & D. Hart. London: Academic Press.
*——— **du Toit, R.F. & Stuart, S.N.** 1990. African Elephants and Rhinos. Status survey and conservation action plan. IUCN/SSC African Elephant and Rhino specialist Group. IUCN, Switzerland.
**Cumming, R.G.** 1850. *Five Years of a Hunter's Life in the Far Interior of South Africa*. (2 volumes) London: J. Murray.
——— 1909. *The lion hunter of South Africa: five years' adventures in the far interior of South Africa with notices of the native tribes and savage animals*. London: J. Murray.
**Cuneo, F.** 1965. Observations on the breeding of the klipspringer antelope, *Oreotragus oreotragus*, and the behaviour of their young born at the Naples Zoo. *Int. Zoo Yb.* **5**: 45–48.
**Curry-Lindahl, K.** 1961. Contribution a l'etude des vertebres terrestres en Afrique tropicale. *Expl. du Parc nat. Albert et du Parc nat. de la Kagera* **II**: 1–331.
**Curtis, B.A. & Perrin, M.R.** 1979. Food preferences of the vlei rat (*Otomys irroratus*) and the four-striped mouse (*Rhabdomys pumilio*). *S. Afr. J. Zool.* **14**: 224–229.
***Cuvier, F. & St. Hilaire, G.** 1825. Histoire Naturelle des Mammiferes. *Bul. Mus. nat. Hist., Paris*.

# D

***D.H.Y. Engineering** 1980. *Countrywide animal and range assessment*. Republic Government Botswana. 5 volumes, volume **iv**.
***Da Costa Leal, F.** 1870. Unpubl. ms. Pretoria: Transvaal Archives.
**Dade, D.J.T.** 1978. Some observations on the Cape grey mongoose (*Herpestes pulverulentus*). Internal Report, Cape Dept. Nat. Conservation. Mimeograph.
**Da Franca, P.** 1967. Sur la presence d'*Arctocephalus pusillus* (Schreber) (Otariidae) et de *Mirounga leonina* (Linne) (Phocidae) au sud d'Angola. *Mammalia* **31**: 50–54.
**Dagg, A.I.** 1959. Food preferences of the giraffe. *Proc. zool. Soc. Lond.* **135**: 640–642.
——— 1962a. Giraffe movement and the neck. *Nat. Hist., N.Y.* **71**(7): 44–51.
——— 1962b. Gaits of the giraffe and okapi. *J. Mammal.* **41**: 282.
——— 1971. *Giraffa camelopardalis*. *Mammalian Species* No. 5. Lawrence, K.S.: Am. Soc. Mammalogists.
——— **& Foster, J.B.** 1976. *The Giraffe: Its Biology, Behaviour and Ecology*. New York: Van Nostrand Reinhold.
**Dalquest, W.W.** 1965. Mammals from the Save River, Mozambique with descriptions of two new bats. *J. Mammal.* **46**: 254–264.
**Dandelot, P.** 1974. Order Primates, Part 3, pp. 1–45, in *The mammals of Africa: an identification manual*. Eds J. Meester & H.W. Setzer. Washington D.C.: Smithsonian Institution Press.
**Daniell, S.** 1804–1805. *African scenery and animals*. London: Samual Daniell.
**Darling, F. Fraser.** 1960. *Wildlife in an African territory*. London: Oxford University Press.
**Darlington, P.J.** 1957. *Zoogeography: the geographical distribution of animals*. New York: J. Wiley.
**Dart, R.A.** 1925a. *Australopithecus africanus*; the man-ape of South Africa. *Nature, Lond.* **115**(2884): 195–199.
——— 1925b. A note on the Taungs skull. *S. Afr. J. Sci.* **26**: 648–658.
——— 1953. The predatory transition from ape to man. *Int. anthrop. ling. Rev.* **6**: 201–218.
*——— 1963. The carnivorous propensity of baboons. *Symp. Zool. Soc. Lond.* **10**: 49–56.
**Da Silva, S.N.** 1970. *A grande fauna selvagem de Angola*. Luanda: Direccao Provincial dos servicos de Veterinaria.
**Dasmann, R.F. & Mossman, A.S.** 1962. Reproduction in some ungulates in Southern Rhodesia. *J. Mammal.* **43**: 533–537.
**David, J.H.M.** 1970. The behaviour of the bontebok *Damaliscus dorcas dorcas* with special reference to territorial behaviour. M.Sc. thesis, University of Cape Town.
——— 1973. The behaviour of the bontebok *Damaliscus dorcas dorcas* (Pallas 1766) with special reference to territoriality. *Z. Tierpsychol.* **33**: 38-107.
——— 1975. Observations on mating behaviour, parturition and the mother-young bond in the bontebok (*Damaliscus dorcas dorcas*). *J. Zool., Lond.* **177**: 203–223.
*——— 1978. A survey of vertebrate fauna on the Rooiberg, Ladysmith, Cape. Unpubl. Rep., Zoology Dept, University of Cape Town.
*——— 1987. South African fur seal, *Arctocephalus pusillus pusillus*. *NOAA Techn. Rep. NMFS* **51**: 65–71.
*——— 1989. Seals Ch. 26 In *Oceans of life off southern Africa*. Cape Town: Vlaeberg.
*——— **& Rand, R.W.** 1986. Attendance behavior of South African fur seals: 126–141, in *Fur seals: maternal strategies on land and at sea*. Eds R.L. Gentry & G.L. Kooyman. Princeton, New Jersey: Princeton University Press.
***Davidson, B.C., Cantrill, R.C. & Varaday, D.** 1986. The reversal of essential fatty acid deficiency symptoms in the cheetah. *S. Afr. J. Zool.* **21**: 161–164.
**Davies, J.L. & Guiler, E.R.** 1957. A note on the pygmy right whale, *Caperea marginata*, Gray. *Proc. zool. Soc. Lond.* **129**: 579–589.
***Davies, K.C. & Jarvis, J.U.M.** 1986. The burrow systems and burrowing dynamics of the mole-rats *Bathyergus suillus* and *Cryptomys hottentotus* in the fynbos of the south-western Cape, South Africa. *J. Zool., Lond.* **209**: 125–147.
***Davies, R.A.G.** 1989. Where dassies dare. *Custos* **17**: 53–54..
*——— **Botha, P. & Skinner, J.D.** 1986. Diet selected by springbok *Antidorcas marsupialis* and Merino sheep *Ovis aries* during Karoo drought. *Trans. Roy. Soc. S. Afr.* **46**: 165–179.
*——— **& Skinner, J.D.** 1986a. Spatial utilisation of an enclosed area of the Karoo by springbok *Antidorcas marsupialis* and Merino sheep *Ovis aries* during drought. *Trans. Roy. Soc. S. Afr.* **46**: 115–132.
*——— **& Skinner, J.D.** 1986b. Temporal activity patterns of springbok *Antidorcas marsupialis* and Merino sheep *Ovis aries* during a Karoo drought. *Tran. Roy. Soc. S. Afr.* **46**: 133–147.
**Davis, D.H.S.** 1942. Rodent damage in plantations and its prevention. *Jl S. Afr. For. Ass.* **8**: 64–69.
——— 1946. A plague survey of Ngamiland, Bechuanaland Protectorate, during the epidemic of 1944–45. *S. Afr. med. J.* **20**: 462–467; 511–515.
——— 1950. Notes on the status of the American grey squirrel, *Sciurus carolinensis* Gmelin in the southwestern Cape (South Africa). *Proc. zool. Soc. Lond.* **120**: 265–268.
——— 1953. Plague in Africa from 1935–1949; a survey of wild rodents in African territories. *Bull. Wld Hlth Org.* **9**: 665–700.
——— 1959. The barn owl's contribution to ecology and paleaecology. *Ostrich* **3**: 144–153.
——— 1962. Distribution patterns of South African Muridae, with notes on some of their fossil antecedents. *Ann. Cape Prov. Mus.* **2**: 56–76.
*——— 1965. Classification problems of African Muridae. *Zool. Afr.* **1**: 121–145.
——— 1974. The distribution of some small southern African mammals (Mammalia: Insectivora, Rodentia). *Ann. Trans. Mus.* **29**: 135–184.
——— 1975a. Genera *Tatera* and *Gerbillurus*, Part 6.4, pp. 1–7, in *The mammals of Africa: an identification manual*. Eds J. Meester & H.W. Setzer. Washington D.C.: Smithsonian Institution Press.
——— 1975b. Genus *Aethomys*, Part 6.6, pp. 1–5, in *The mammals of Africa: an identification manual*. Eds J. Meester & H.W. Setzer. Washington D.C.: Smithsonian Institution Press.
**Davis, R.M.** 1972. Behaviour of the vlei rat, *Otomys irroratus* (Brants, 1827). *Zool. Afr.* 7: 119–140.
——— 1973. The ecology and life history of the vlei rat, *Otomys irroratus* (Brants, 1827) on the Van Riebeeck Nature Reserve, Pretoria. D.Sc. thesis, University of Pretoria.

——— & Meester, J. 1981. Reproduction and postnatal development in the vlei rat, *Otomys irroratus*, on the Van Riebeeck Nature Reserve, Pretoria. *Mammalia* **45**: 99-116.

***Davison, E.** 1950. Wankie Game Reserve. Unpubl. Mimeograph cited by Cumming, 1981.

——— 1950. A maze of reeds: the home of the sitatunga. *Afr. wild Life* **4**: 57–59.

——— 1967. *Wankie*. Cape Town: Books of Africa.

**Davison, G.** 1971. Some observations on a population of nyala, *Tragelaphus angasi* (Gray) in the S.E. Lowveld of Rhodesia. *Arnoldia Rhod.* **5**: 2–8.

**Dawbin, W.H.** 1966. The seasonal migratory cycle of the humpback whales, in *Whales, dolphins and porpoises*. Ed. K.S. Norris. Berkeley: University of California Press.

**Dawson, W.R.** 1925. Bats as *materia medica*. *Ann. Mag. nat. Hist.* **16**: 221–227.

**Day, J., Siegfried, W.R., Louw, G.N. & Jarman, M.L.** 1979. (Eds). *Fynbos ecology: a preliminary synthesis. S. Afr. Nat. Sci. Prog. Rep.* No. 40. Pretoria: CSIR.

**Deane, N.N.** 1960. Hyaena predation. *Lammergeyer* **1**: 36.

——— 1962a. The spotted hyaena *Crocuta crocuta crocuta*. *Lammergeyer* **2**: 26–43.

*——— 1962b. Black rhinoceros, *Diceros bicornis*. *Lammergeyer* **2**: 48.

**Deansley, R.** 1934. The reproductive cycle of the female hedgehog. *Phil. Trans. R. Soc.* **223**: 239–270.

**Dearborn, J.H.** 1965. Food of Weddell seals at McMurdo Sound, Antarctica. *J. Mammal.* **46**: 37–43.

**De Boom, H.P.A.** 1957. Supposed hermaphroditism of the hyaena. *Afr. wild Life* **11**: 284–286.

**De Balzac, Heim.** 1936. Biogeographie des mammifères et des Oiseaux de l'Afrique du nord. *Bull. biol. Fr. Belg. Suppl.* **21**: 1–446.

——— 1948. État actual des connaissances concernant la faune des mammifères du Maroc. *Soc. Sci. nat. Maroc.* Vol. jubil. 1920–1945: 289–303.

——— 1967. Faits nouveaux concernant les *Myosorex* (Soricidae) de l'Afrique Orientale. *Mammalia* **31**: 610–628.

——— & **Lamotte, M.** 1956. Evolution et phylogenie des Soricides Africains. *Mammalia* **20**: 140–167.

——— & **Lamotte, M.** 1957. Evolution et phylogenie des Soricides Africains II. La Lignee *Sylvisorex-Suncus-Crocidura*. *Mammalia* **21**: 15–49.

——— & **Meester, J.** 1977. Order Insectivora, Part 1, pp. 1–29, in *The mammals of Africa: an identification manual*. Eds J. Meester & H.W. Setzer. Washington D.C.: Smithsonian Institution Press.

***Defran, R.H., & Pryor, K.** 1980. The behavior and training of cetaceans in captivity. pp 319–362. In: *Cetacean behavior: mechanisms and functions*. Ed. L.M. Herman. New York: John Wiley.

**De Graaff, G.** 1960a. A preliminary investigation of the mammalian microfauna in Pleistocene deposits of caves in the Transvaal system. *Palaeont. afr.* **7**: 79-118.

——— 1960b. 'n Ontleding van uilklonte van die nonnetjiesuil *Tyto alba*. *Ostrich* **31**: 1–5.

——— 1964. On the parasites associated with the Bathyergidae. *Koedoe* **7**: 113–123.

——— 1965. A systematic revision of the Bathyergidae (Rodentia) of southern Africa. D.Sc. thesis, University of Pretoria.

——— 1972. On the mole-rat (*Cryptomys hottentotus damapensis*) (Rodentia) in the Kalahari Gemsbok National Park. *Koedoe* **15**: 25–35.

——— 1972a. The social behaviour of the bontebok. *Custos* **1**(4): 3–5.

——— 1972b. The social behaviour of the bontebok. *Custos* **1**(6): 24–28.

——— 1973a. The rodents of South Africa: Cape dune mole-rat. *Custos* **2**(7): 22–26.

——— 1973b. The rodents of South Africa: dassie rat. *Custos* **2**(6): 23–26.

——— 1974. The Rodents of South Africa: The South African pygmy gerbil. *Custos* **3**(5): 17–21.

——— 1975a. The red hartebeest. *Custos* **4**(4): 37–41.

——— 1975b. Family Bathyergidae, Part 6.9, pp. 1–5, in *The mammals of Africa: an identification manual*. Eds J. Meester & H.W. Setzer. Washington D.C.: Smithsonian Institution Press.

——— 1978. Notes on the southern African black-tailed tree rat *Thallomys paedulcus* (Sundevall, 1846) and its occurrence in the Kalahari Gemsbok National Park. *Koedoe* **21**: 181–190.

——— 1979. Molerats (Bathyergidae, Rodentia) in South African National Parks: notes on their taxonomic "isolation" and hystricomorph affinities of the Family. *Koedoe* **22**: 89–107.

——— 1981. *The rodents of southern Africa*. Pretoria: Butterworths.

——— & **Nel, J.A.J.** 1965. On the tunnel system of Brants' Karroo rat, *Parotomys brantsi* in the Kalahari Gemsbok National Park. *Koedoe* **8**: 136–139.

——— **Schulz, K.C.A., & Van der Walt, P.T.** 1973. Notes on rumen contents of Cape buffalo *Syncerus caffer* in the Addo Elephant National Park. *Koedoe* **16**: 45–58.

***Degre, A. & Robert, Sylvie** 1987. *Meerkat valley*. Johannesburg: Southern Books.

**Dekeyser, P.L.** 1950. Considerations sur les Chats (*Felis libyca* Forster) de l'Afrique occidentale. *Init. afr.* **12**(3): 700–709.

——— 1955. *Les mammifères de l'Afrique noire*. Dakar: Institute Francais d'Afrique Noire.

**Delany, M.J.** 1975. *The Rodents of Uganda*. London: Trustees of the British Museum (Natural History).

**Delibes, M.** 1974. Sobre alimentacion y biologia de la Gineta (*Genetta genetta* L.) en Espana. *Acta vertebr.* **1**: 143–199.

**Demmer, H.** 1966. Beobachtungen uber das verhalten verschiedener wildlebender Tiere beim Fang in freier Wildbahn in Afrika. *Zool. Gart.* **32**: 210–215.

**De Moor, P.P.** 1969. Seasonal variation in local distribution, age classes and population density of the gerbil, *Tatera brantsi*, on the South African highveld. *J. Zool., Lond.* **157**: 399–411.

***Dempster, Edith R. & Perrin, M.R.** 1989a. The estrous cycle and induction of estrous behaviour in four species of hairy-footed gerbils (genus *Gerbillurus*). *J. Mammal.* **70**: 809–811.

*——— & **Perrin, M.R.** 1989b. Maternal behaviour and neonatal development in three species of Namib Desert rodents. *J. Zool., Lond.* **218**: 407–419.

**Deraniyagda, P.E.P.** 1948. Some scientific results of two visits to Africa. *Spolia zeylan.* **25**(2): 1–42.

***De Villiers, D.J.** 1986. Infanticide in the tree squirrel *Paraxerus cepapi*. *S. Afr. J. Zool.* **21**: 183–184.

*——— 1988. Musth and reproduction in the African elephant *Loxodonta africana*. M.Sc. thesis, University of Pretoria.

*——— & **Skinner, J.D.** 1989. Musth, testosterone concentration and testicular histology in the African elephant *Loxodonta africana*. *Unpubl., submitted.*

*——— **Skinner, J.D. & Hall-Martin, A.J.** 1989. Circulating progesterone concentrations and ovarian functional anatomy in the African elephant (*Loxodonta africana*). *J. Reprod. Fert.* **86**: 195–201.

***De Villiers, P.A. & Kok, O.B.** 1984. Verspreidingspatrone van olifante (*Loxodonta africana*) in Suidwes-Afrika met spesiale verwysing na die Nasionale Etoshawildtuin. *Madoqua* **13**: 281–296.

**De Vore, I. & Hall, K.R.L.** 1965. Baboon ecology. In *Primate behaviour, field studies of monkeys and apes*. New York: Holt Rinehart & Winston.

——— & **Washburn, S.L.** 1963. Baboon ecology and human evolution, pp. 335–367, in *African ecology and human evolution*, Eds F.C. Howell & F. Bourlière. London: Methuen.

**De Vos, A.** 1965. Territorial behaviour among puku in Zambia. *Science* **148**(3678): 1752–1753.

——— & **Dowsett, R.J.** 1966. The behaviour and population structure of three species of the genus *Kobus*. *Mammalia* **30**: 30–55.

**De Winton, W.E.** 1898. Descriptions of three new rodents from Africa. *Ann. Mag. nat. Hist.* **1**: 251–254.

***Diamond, J.M.** 1986. Carnivore dominance and herbivore coexistence in Africa. *Nature, Lond.* **320**: 112.

**Dieckmann, R.C.** 1979. Note on the smaller mammals of the Hester Malan Nature Reserve, Springbok, Namaqualand. *S. Afr. J. Zool.* **14**: 85–89.

——— 1980. The ecology and breeding biology of the gemsbok *Oryx gazella gazella* (Linnaeus, 1758) in the Hester Malan Nature Reserve. M.Sc. thesis, University of Pretoria.

**Dieterlen, F. & Heim de Balsac, H.** 1979. Zur Okologie und Taxonomie der Spitzmause (Soricidae) des Kivu Gebietes. *Säugtierk. Mitt.* **27**: 241–287.

**Dippenaar, N. J.** 1977. Variation in *Crocidura mariquensis* (A. Smith, 1844) in southern Africa, Part I (Mammalia: Soricidae). *Ann. Trans. Mus.* **30**: 163–206.

——— 1978. Dental abnormalities in *Crocidura mariquensis* (A. Smith, 1844) (Mammalia: Soricidae). *Ann. Trans. Mus.* **31**: 165–167.

——— 1979a. Variation in *Crocidura mariquensis* (A. Smith, 1844) in southern Africa, Part 2 (Mammalia: Soricidae). *Ann. Trans. Mus.* **32**: 1–34.

——— 1979b. Notes on the early postnatal development and behaviour of the tiny musk shrew *Crocidura bicolor* Bocage, 1889 (Insectivora: Soricidae). *Mammalia* **43**: 84–91.

——— 1980. A taxonomic revision of the *monax-dolichura, luna-fumosa, glassi*, and *zaodon-poensis* complexes of Afrotropical *Crocidura* (Mammalia: Soricidae). Ph.D. thesis, University of Natal.

*——— **Meester, J., Rautenbach, I.L. & Wolhuter, D.A.** 1983. The status of southern African mammal taxonomy. *Ann. Museé. Roy. de l'Afr. Cont. Sci. Zool.* **237**: 103–107.

**Dittrich, L.** 1969. Breeding the roan antelope, *Hippotragus equinus* at Hanover Zoo. *Int. Zoo Yb.* **12**: 184–187.

**Dixon, J.E.** 1964. Preliminary notes on the mammal fauna of the Mkuzi Game Reserve. *Lammergeyer* **3**: 40–58.

——— 1966. Notes on the mammals of the Ndumu Game Reserve. *Lammergeyer* **6**: 24–40.

**Dobroruka, L.J.** 1966. Ein Beitrag zur Kenntnis süd afrikanischer Leoparden, *Panthera pardus*. *Lynx* **6**: 11–13. *Säugetierk. Mitt.* **14**: 317–324.

——— 1970. Behaviour in the bush squirrel, *Paraxerus cepapi* (A. Smith, 1836). *Revue Zool. Bot. afr.* **82**: 131–141.

***Dobson, G.E.** 1875. Annals and Magazine of Natural History (4) **16**: 122.

***Dohl, T.P., Bonnell, M.L. & Ford, R.G.** 1986. Distribution and abundance of common dolphin, *Delphinus delphis*, in the southern California Bight: a quantitative assessment based upon aerial transect data. *Fish. Bull., U.S.* **84**: 333–343.

*——— **Norris, K.S., & Kang, I.** 1974. A porpoise hybrid: *Tursiops x Steno*. *J. Mammal.* **55**: 217–221.

***Doidge, D.W. & Croxall, J.P.** 1985. Diet and energy budget of the Antarctic fur seal, *Arctocephalus gazella*, at South Georgia. pp. 543–550, in *Antarctic nutrient cycles and food webs*. Eds W.R. Siegfried, P.R. Condy & R.M. Laws. Berlin: Springer-Verlag.

**Dominis, J. & Edey, M.** 1968. *The cats of Africa*. New York: Time-Life Books Inc.

**Donnelly, B.G.** 1969. Further observations on the southern right whale, *Eubalaena australis*, in South African waters. *J. Reprod. Fert.* Suppl. 6: 347–352.

**Dorst, J.** 1948. Les chiroptères du genre *Triaenops* Dobson (Hipposidérinés) *Mammalia* **12**: 15–21.

——— 1953. Considèrations sur le genre *Otomops* et description d'une espèce nouvelle de Madagascar (Chiroptera: Molossidae). *Mem. Inst. scient. Madagascar (A)* **8**: 235–240.

——— & **Dandelot, P.** 1970. *A field guide to the larger mammals of Africa*. London: Collins.

**Douglas-Hamilton, I.** 1973. On the ecology and behaviour of the Lake Manyara elephants. *E. Afr. Wildl. J.* **11**: 401–403.

——— & **Douglas-Hamilton, O.** 1975. *Among the elephants*. London: Collins & Harvill.

***Downs, Colleen T. & Perrin, M.R.** 1989. An investigation of the macro- and micro-environments of four *Gerbillurus* species. *Cimbebasia* **11**: 41–54.

**Dowsett, R.J.** 1966a. Behaviour and population structure of hartebeest in the Kafue National Park. *Puku* **4**: 147–154.

——— 1966b. Wet season game population and biomass in the Ngoma area of the Kafue National Park. *Puku* **4**: 135–145.

——— 1969. Luangwa Valley mammal notes. *Puku* **5**: 220–222.

**Doyle, G.A.** 1974a. The behaviour of prosimians, in *Behaviour of non-human Primates*. Vol. **5**. Eds A.M. Schrier & F. Stollnitz. New York: Academic Press.

——— 1974b. The behaviour of the lesser bushbaby. pp. 213–231, in *Prosimian biology*. Eds R.D. Martin, G.A. Doyle & A.C. Walker. London: Academic Press.

——— 1979. Development of behaviour in prosimians with special reference to the lesser bushbaby, *Galago senegalensis moholi*, in *The Study of Prosimian Behaviour*. Eds G.A. Doyle & R.D. Martin. New York: Academic Press.

——— **Anderson, A. & Bearder, S.K.** 1971. Reproduction in the lesser bushbaby (*Galago senegalensis moholi*) under semi-natural conditions. *Folia primatol.* **14**: 15–22.

——— **Pelletier, A. & Bekker, T.** 1967. Courtship, mating and parturition in the lesser bushbaby (*Galago senegalensis moholi*) under semi natural conditions. *Folia primatol.* **7**: 169–197.

**Drake-Brockman, R.E.** 1910. *The mammals of Somaliland*. London: Hurst & Blackett.

***Dreyer, H. van A.** 1987. Die gebruik van water en soutlekke deur die groter hoefdiere in die Kalahari-Gemsbok Nasionale Park. M.Sc. thesis, University of Stellenbosch.

***Droomer, E.A.** 1985. Volume and value loss owing to samango monkey damage in pine stands in the northern Transvaal. *S. Afr. For. J.* **134**: 47–51.

***Dublin, Holly T.** 1989. Elephant numbers, distributions and trends in the southern African region. A review of census methods and recent population data. African Elephant & Rhino Group, Nairobi. Mimeograph.

**Dücker, G.** 1957. Farb- und Helligkeitssehen und Instinkte bei Viverriden und Feliden. *Zool. Beitr., Berlin* **3**: 25–99.

——— 1960. Beobachtungen uber das Paarungsverhalten des Ichneumons, *Herpestes ichneumon* L. *Z. Säugertierk.* **25**: 47–51.

——— 1965. Colour vision in mammals. *J. Bombay nat. Hist. Soc.* **61**: 572–586.

**Dudok van Heel, W.H.** 1972. Navigation in Cetacea, in *Whales, dolphins and porpoises*. Ed. K.S. Norris. Berkeley: University of California Press.

**Dunbar, R.I. & Dunbar, E.P.** 1974. Social organisation and ecology of the klipspringer (*Oreotragus oreotragus*) in Ethiopia. *Z. Tierpsychol.* **35**: 481–493.

*Dunham, K.M. 1979. The feeding ecology of impala, *Aepyceros melampus* in the Sengwa Wildlife Research Area, Rhodesia. M.Phil. thesis, University of Rhodesia.
*——— 1980. The diet of impala (*Aepyceros melampus*) in the Sengwa Wildlife Research Area, Rhodesia. *J. Zool., Lond.* **192**: 41–57.
*——— 1985. Ages of black rhinos killed by drought and poaching in Zimbabwe. *Pachyderm* **5**: 12–13.
*——— 1986. Movements of elephant cows in the unflooded Middle Zambezi Valley, Zimbabwe. *Afr. J. Ecol.* **24**: 287–291.
*——— 1988. Demographic changes in the Zambezi Valley elephants (*Loxodonta africana*). *J. Zool., Lond.* **215**: 382–388.
*——— **& Murray M.G.** 1982. The fat reserves of impala *Aepyceros melampus*. *Afr. J. Ecol.* **20**: 81–87.
*——— **& Tsindi, N.**. 1984. Record of the puku (*Kobus vardoni*) from Zimbabwe. *The Zimbabwe Science News* **18**: 35.
***Duplaix, Nicole** 1988. Fleas, the lethal leapers. *National Geographic* **174**: 672–694.
***Du Plessis, A.** 1989. Ecophysiology of the bush karoo rat (*Otomys unisulcatus*) and the whistling rat (*Parotomys brantsii*). M.Sc. thesis, University of Port Elizabeth.
***Du Plessis, M.A.** 1986. A note on the social structure of the kudu, *Tragelaphus strepsiceros*, in an agricultural area. *S. Afr. J. Zool.* **21**: 275–276.
*——— **& Skinner, J.D.** 1987. Feeding patterns of the greater kudu *Tragelaphus strepsiceros* in an agricultural area on the Springbok Flats, northern Transvaal. *Trans. Roy. Soc. S. Afr.* **46**: 199–208.
**Du Plessis, S.F.** 1969.The past and present geographical distribution of the Perissodactyla and Artiodactyla in southern Africa. M.Sc. thesis, University of Pretoria.
**Du Plessis, S.S.** 1968. Ecology of blesbok on the Van Riebeeck Nature Reserve, Pretoria with special reference to productivity. D.Sc. thesis, University of Pretoria.
——— 1976. Endangered species of the Transvaal. *Proc. Endangered Wildl. Symp. Pretoria* July 1976; Johannesburg: Endangered Wildlife Trust.
***Du Plooy, J.** 1973. Some observations on the dermatology of the springbok foetus. B.Sc. Hons. Project Report, University of Pretoria.
***Duthie, A.G.** 1989. The ecology of the riverine rabbit *Bunolagus monticularis*. M.Sc. thesis, University of Pretoria.
*——— **& Skinner, J.D.** 1986. Osteophagia in the Cape porcupine *Hystrix africaeaustralis*. *S. Afr. J. Zool.* **21**: 316–318.
*——— **Skinner, J.D. & Robinson, T.J.** 1989. The distribution and status of the riverine rabbit, *Bunolagus monticularis*, in South Africa. *Biol. Conserv.* **47**: 195–202.
***Du Toit, C.F.** 1980. The yellow mongoose *Cynictis penicillata* and other small carnivores in the Mountain Zebra National Park. *Koedoe* **23**: 179–184.
***Du Toit, J.T., Bryant, J.P. & Frisby, Kathleen**. 1990. Regrowth and palatability of *Acacia* shoots following pruning by African savanna browsers. *Ecology* **71**: 149–154.
*——— **Jarvis, J.U.M. & Louw, G.N.** 1985. Nutrition and burrowing energetics of the Cape molerat *Georychus capensis*. *Oecologia* **66**:81–87.
*——— **& Owen-Smith, N.** 1989. Body size, population metabolism, and habitat specialization among large African herbivores. *Am. Nat.* **133**: 736–740.
***Du Toit, R.F.** 1987. African rhino systematics. In: *Proceedings of African Rhino Workshop*. Eds R.F. du Toit, T.J. Foose & D.H.M. Cumming. *Pachyderm* (special issue) No. 9: 3–7.
*——— **Foose, T.J. & Cumming, D.H.M.** 1987. *Proceedings of African Rhino Workshop*. *Pachyderm* (special issue) No. 9: 1–33.
**Dwyer, P.D.** 1963. The breeding biology of *Miniopterus schreibersii blepotis* (Temminck) (Chiroptera) in northeastern New South Wales. *Aust. J. Zool.* **11**: 219–240.
——— 1964. Seasonal changes in activity and weight of *Miniopterus schreibersii blepotis* (Chiroptera) in northeastern New South Wales. *Aust. J. Zool.* **12**: 52–69.
——— 1966. The population pattern of *Miniopterus schreibersii* (Chiroptera) in northeastern New South Wales. *Aust. J. Zool.* **14**: 1073–1137.

# E

***Eaglen, R.H. & Simons, E.L.** 1980. Notes on the breeding biology of thick-tailed and silvery galagos in captivity. *J. Mammal.* **61**: 534–537.
**Earl, S.M.J.A.** 1980. Development of behaviour in the pouched mouse, *Saccostomus campestris*. M.Sc. thesis, University of Pretoria.
**Earl, Z.** 1977. Female *Saccostomus campestris* carrying young in cheek pouches. *J. Mammal.* **58**: 242.
——— 1978. Postnatal development of *Saccostomus campestris*. *Afr. Small Mammal Newsletter* 2: 10–12.
——— **& Nel, J.A.J.** 1976. Climbing behaviour in three African rodent species. *Zool. Afr.* **11**: 183.
***Earlé, R.A.** 1977. Die sosiale- en voedingsgedrag van *Cynictis penicillata* (G. Cuvier) op 'n eiland in die Vaaldam. B.Sc. Honours Project Rep., University of Pretoria.
——— 1981. Aspects of the social and feeding behaviour of the yellow mongoose. *Mammalia* **45**: 143–152.
***East, Marion** 1989. Sympathy for the demon. *BBC Wildlife* Feb. 1989: 88–94.
*——— **Hofer, H. & Turk, Agnes** 1989. Functions of birth dens in spotted hyaenas. *J. Zool., Lond.* **219**: 690–697.
**Eaton, R.L.** 1970a. Hunting behaviour of the cheetah. *J. Wildl. Mgmt* **34**: 56–67.
——— 1970b. Notes on the reproductive biology of the cheetah. *Int. Zoo Yb.* **10**: 86–89.
——— 1974. *The cheetah: the biology, ecology and behavior of an endangered species*. New York: Van Nostrand Reinhold.
**Ebedes, H.** 1970. The nomadic plains zebra (*Equus burchelli antiquorum* H. Smith, 1941) of the Etosha Salina. Report, Director, Nature Conservation, Windhoek, S.W.A. Mimeograph.
**Eccles, D.H., Jensen, R.A.C. & Jensen, M.K.** 1969. Feeding behaviour of the bat hawk. *Ostrich* **40**: 26–27.
**Edmond-Blanc, F.** 1954. *Le grande livre de la fauna Africaine et de sa chasse 1 & 2*. Zurich: Godefroy Schmid.
**Eger, J.L. & Peterson, R.L.** 1979. Distribution and systematic relationship of *Tadarida bivittata* and *Tadarida ansorgei*. *Can. J. Zool.* **57**: 1887–1895.
**Eisenberg, J.F.** 1978. The evolution of arboreal folivores in the class Mammalia, in *The ecology of arboreal folivores*. Ed. G.G. Montgomery. Washington: Smithsonian University Press.
——— **& Kleiman, D.G.** 1972. Olfactory communication in mammals. *Am. Rev. Ecol. Syst.* **3**: 1–32.
**Eisentraut, M.** 1942. Beitrag zur Ockologie Kameruner Chiropteren. *Mitt. zool. Mus. Berl.* **25**: 245–273.
——— 1956. Beitrag zur Chiropteran-Fauna von Kamerun (Westafrika). *Zool. Jb.* **84**: 505–540.
*——— 1960. Zwei neue Rhinolophiden aus Guinea. *Stuttg. Beitr. Naturk.* **39**: 1–7.
*——— 1962. Wie verhalten sich verwandte vertreter von heimischen winterschläfern aus wärmeren gebieten unter veränderten temperaturhedingungen? *Zoologischer Anzeiger* **169**: 429–432.
——— 1964. La faune des Chiroptères de Fernando Po. *Mammalia* **28**: 529–552.
——— **& Knorr, H.** 1957. Les chauves souris Cavernicoles de la Guinee Francaise. *Mammalia* **24**: 321–340.
**Elder, W.H. & Elder, N.L.** 1970. Social groupings and primate associations of the bushbuck (*Tragelaphus scriptus*). *Mammalia* **34**: 356–362.
——— **& Rodgers, D.H.** 1974. Immobilization and marking of African elephants and the prediction of body weight from foot circumference. *Mammalia* **38**: 33–53.
——— **& Rodgers, D.H.** 1975. Body temperature in the African elephant as related to ambient temperature. *Mammalia* **39**: 395–399.
**Ellerman, J.R.** 1940/1949. *The Families and genera of living rodents*. Vol. **1** 1940; Vol. **2** 1941; Vol. **3** 1949. London: Trustees, British Museum (Nat. Hist.).
*——— 1954. Die taksonomie van die Soogdiere van die Unie van Suid-Afrika. *Annale van die Universiteit van Stellenbosch* **30**A(1), 125 pp.
——— **& Morrison-Scott, T.C.S.** 1951. *Check list of Palaearctic and Indian mammals*. 1758–1946. London: Trustees, British Museum (Nat. Hist.).
——— **Morrison-Scott, T.C.S. & Hayman, R.W.** 1953. *Southern African Mammals 1758–1951: a reclassification*. London: Trustees, British Museum (Nat. Hist.).
**Elliott, E.M.N.** 1977. A study of waterbuck ecology in a newly closed area. Ph.D. thesis, University of Cambridge.
***Ellison, G.T.H.** 1990. A note on the small mammal fauna of Vaalkop Dam Nature Reserve. *Koedoe* **33**: 108–110.
*——— 1990. A comparison of thermoregulation and energetics in environmentally separated chromosomal variants of *Saccostomus campestris*. Ph.D. thesis to be submitted, University of Pretoria.
*——— **& Skinner, J.D.** 1990. Thermoregulation and torpor in African woodland dormice, *Graphiurus murinus*, following cold acclimation. *Z. Saügetierk.* (in press).
*——— **& Skinner, J.D.** (in press a). Seasonal energy requirements and thermoregulation in growing pouched mice, *Saccostomus campestris* (Cricetidae). *Int. J. Biometeorol.*
*——— **& Skinner, J.D.** (in press b). The influence of ambient temperature on spontaneous daily torpor in three karyotypic variants of pouched mice (*Saccostomus campestris*) from southern Africa. *J. Therm. Biol.*
*——— **& Westlin-van Aarde, L.** 1990. Ringtail in the pouched mouse (*Saccostomus campestris*). *Laboratory Animals* **24**: 174–175.
**Eloff, A.K.** 1981. The digestion in the hyrax, *Procavia capensis* (Pallas, 1766). M.Sc. thesis, University of Pretoria.
**Eloff, F.C.** 1959. Observations on the migration habits of the antelopes of the Kalahari Gemsbok Park. I and II. *Koedoe* **2**: 1–51.
——— 1961. Observations on the migration and habits of the antelopes of the Kalahari Gemsbok Park. III. *Koedoe* **4**: 18–30.
——— 1962. Observations on the migration and habits of the antelopes of the Kalahari Gemsbok Park. IV. *Koedoe* **5**: 128–136.
——— 1964. On the predatory habits of lions and hyaenas. *Koedoe* **7**: 105–112.
——— 1966. Range extension of the blue wildebeest. *Koedoe* **9**: 34–36.
——— 1971. Ecology and behaviour of the Kalahari lion. In *The World's Cats* Vol. **1**. Ed. R.L. Eaton. Winston Oregon: World Wildlife Safari.
——— 1973a. Lion predation in the Kalahari Gemsbok National Park. *J. sth. Afr. Wildl. Mgmt Ass.* **3**: 59–63.
——— 1973b. Water use by the Kalahari lion, *Panthera leo vernayi*. *Koedoe* **16**: 149–154.
——— 1975. The spotted hyaena *Crocuta crocuta* (Erxleben) in arid regions of southern Africa. *Publ. Univ. Pretoria Nuwe Reeks*, 97: 35–38.
——— 1977. Seven days with a lion family. *Custos* **6**(4): 6–7, 17, 32; **6**(5): 8–9, 22.
——— 1980. Cub mortality in the Kalahari lion, *Panthera leo vernayi* Roberts (1948). *Koedoe* **23**: 163–170.
**Eloff, G.** 1952. Sielkundige aangepastheid van die mol aan onderaardse leefwyse en sielkundige konvergensie. *Tydskr. Wet. Kuns.* **12**:210–225.
***Els, D.A.I.** 1984. Reproduction in *Gerbillurus paeba*. *S. Afr. J. Sci.* **80**: 186.
**Eltringham, S.K. & Woodford, M.H.** 1973. The numbers and distribution of buffalo in the Ruwenzori National Park, Uganda. *E. Afr. Wildl. J.* **11**: 151–164.
**Emmons, L.H.** 1975. Ecology and behaviour of African rainforest squirrels. Ph.D. thesis, Cornell University.
***Emslie, R.H.** 1985. Resource partitioning between the five major grazing ungulates in the Umfolozi Game Reserve, Natal. *S. Afr. J. Sci.* **81**: 698.
*——— **& Adcock, K.** 1990a. Status, history and performance of black rhinoceros populations in South Africa, the TBVC states and Namibia. Unpubl. mimeograph.
*——— **& Adcock, K.** 1990b. Factors influencing the population performance of the black rhinoceros in Zululand : Towards improved management on a national basis. Unpubl. mimeograph.
***Erasmus, B.H.** 1979. Control of the feral cat *Felis catus* (Linnaeus, 1758) population on Marion Island with feline panleucopaenia. M.Sc. thesis, University of Pretoria.
*——— **& Rautenbach, I.L.** 1984. New records of occurrences of six species of small mammals in the northern Cape Province. *S. Afr. J. Wildl. Res.* **14**: 91–96.
**Erickson, A.W., Siniff, D.B., Cline, D.R. & Hofman, R.J.** 1971. Distributional ecology of Antarctic seals, pp. 55–75, in *Proc. SCAR Symposium on Antarctic ice and water masses, Tokyo, Sept. 1970*. Ed. G. Deacon. Cambridge: Sci. Com. Antarct. Res.
***Erskine, St.V.W.** 1875. Journey to Umzila's, south east Africa in 1871–1872. *Journal of the Royal Geographical Society* **45**: 45–128.
**Erz, W.** 1964. Tooth eruption and replacement in Burchell's zebra. *Arnoldia Rhod.* **1**(22): 1–8.
**Esser, J.** 1973. Beiträge zur Biologie des afrikanischen Rhebockes (*Pelea capreolus* Forster, 1790). D.Sc. thesis, Christian Albrechts Universität zu Kiel.
**Estes, R.D.** 1966. Behaviour and life history of the wildebeest (*Connochaetes taurinus taurinus* Burchell). *Nature, Lond.* **212**: 999–1000.
——— 1967. Predators and scavengers. *Nat. Hist., N.Y.* **76**: 38–37.
——— 1969. Territorial behaviour of the wildebeest (*Connochaetes taurinus* Burchell, 1823). *Z. Tierpsychol.* **26**: 284–370.
——— 1972. The role of the vomeronasal organ in mammalian reproduction. *Mammalia* **36**: 315–341.
——— 1974. Social organisation of the African Bovidae, in *The behaviour of ungulates and its relation to management*. Eds V. Geist & F. Walther. IUCN Publication new series No. 24: 166–205.
——— 1976. The significance of breeding synchrony in the wildebeest. *E. Afr. Wildl. J.* **14**: 135–152.
——— **& Buss, I.O.** 1976. Microanatomical structure and development of the African elephant's temporal gland. *Mammalia* **40**: 429–436.
——— **& Estes, R.K.** 1970. The sable in Rhodesia. Progress report to the National Geographic Society No. 2. Mimeograph, pp. 1–25.
——— **& Goddard, J.** 1967. Prey selection and hunting behaviour of the African wild dog. *J. Wildl. Mgmt* **31**: 52–70.
***Evans, G.F.** 1942. Osteology and relationships of the elephant shrews (Macrosceli-

didae). *Bull. Am. Mus. nat. Hist.* **42**: 95–263.
***Evans, W.E.** 1974. Radio-telemetric studies of two species of small odontocete cetaceans. pp 385–394. In: *The whale problem. A status report.* Ed. W.E. Schevill. Cambridge: Harvard University Press.
*——— 1982. Distribution and differentiation of stocks of *Delphinus delphis* Linnaeus in the northeastern Pacific. Mammals in the Seas. *FAO Fish. Ser.* (5) **4**: 45–66.
*——— **Yablokov, A.V., & Bowles, A.E.** 1982. Geographic variation in the color pattern of killer whales (*Orcinus orca*). *Rep. int. Whal. Commn* **32**: 687–694.
**Ewer, R.F.** 1956. The fossil carnivores of the Transvaal caves: Canidae. *Proc. zool. Soc. Lond.* **126**: 97–119.
——— 1963a. A note on the suckling behaviour of the viverrid, *Suricata suricatta* (Schreber). *Z. Tierpsychol.* **20**: 570–607.
——— 1963b. The behaviour of the meerkat, *Suricata suricatta* (Schreber). *Z. Tierpsychol.* **20**: 570–607.
——— 1966. The stokstert meerkat. *Afr. wild Life* **20**: 53–63.
——— 1967. The behaviour of the African giant rat (*Cricetomys gambianus* Waterhouse). *Z. Tierpsychol.* **24**: 6–79.
——— 1968. *Ethology of Mammals.* London: Logos Press.
——— 1969. Form and function in the grass cutter *Thryonomys swinderianus* Temm. **(Rodentia**: Thryonomyidae). *Ghana J. Sci.* **9**: 131–149.
——— 1973. *The Carnivores.* New York: Cornell University Press.
——— **& Wemmer, C.** 1974. The behaviour in captivity of the African civet *Civettictis civetta* (Schreber). *Z. Tierpsychol.* **34**: 359–394.
**Eyre, M.** 1963. A tame otter. *Afr. wild Life* **17**: 49–53.

# F

***Fabricius, C., Lowry, D. & van den Berg, P.** 1988. Fecund black wildebeest x blue wildebeest hybrids. *S. Afr. J. Wildl. Res.* **18**: 35–37.
*——— **van Hensbergen, H.J. & Zucchini, W.** 1989. A discriminant function for identifying hybrid bontebok x blesbok populations. *S. Afr. J. Wildl. Res.* **19**: 61–66.
**Fairall, N.** 1968. The reproductive seasons of some mammals in the Kruger National Park. *Zool. Afr.* **3**: 189–210.
——— 1969. Prenatal development of the impala *Aepyceros melampus* Lichtenstein. *Koedoe* **12**: 97-103.
——— 1970. Research on the reproduction of wild ungulates. *Proc. S. Afr. Soc. Anim. Prod.* **9**: 57–61.
——— 1971. Die geslagsfisiologie van die rooibok. D.Sc. thesis, University of Pretoria.
——— 1972. Behavioural aspects of the reproductive physiology of the impala, *Aepyceros melampus* (Licht.). *Zool. Afr.* **7**: 167–174.
——— 1980. Growth and age determination in the hyrax *Procavia capensis. S. Afr. J. Zool.* **15**: 16–21.
*——— 1983. Production parameters of the impala *Aepyceros melampus. S. Afr. J. Anim. Sci.* **13**: 116–179.
*——— 1985. Manipulation of age and sex ratios to optimize production from impala *Aepyceros melampus* populations. *S. Afr. J. Wildl. Res.* **15**: 85–88.
——— **& McNairn, I.S.** 1981. A metabolic energy conserving strategy in the hyrax, *Procavia capensis. Proc. Wld Furbearer Conf. Univ. Maryland*: 343–354.
*——— **Vermeulen, P.J. & van der Merwe, M.**. 1986. A general model of population growth in the hyrax, *Procavia capensis. Ecol. mod.* **34**: 115–132.
**Feely, J.M.** 1962. Occurrence of the red hare, *Pronolagus crassicaudatus* in the central Zululand Lowveld. *Lammergeyer* **2**: 56.
**Felix, A.** 1953. Notes sur la fauna de Birao. *Mammalia* **17**: 55–66.
**Felton, H.** 1956. Fledermäuse fressen Skorpione. *Natur Volk.* **86**: 53–57.
**Fenton, M.B.** 1975. Observations on the biology of some Rhodesian bats, including a key to the Chiroptera of Rhodesia. *Life Sci. Contr. R. Ont. Mus.* **104**: 1–27.
*——— 1983. Roosts used by the African bat, *Scotophilus leucogaster. Biotropica* **15**(2): 129–132.
*——— 1984. Echolocation: Implications for ecology and evolution of bats. *Q. Rev. Biol.* **59**: 33–53.
*——— **Bell, G.P. & Thomas, D.W.** 1980. Echolocation and feeding behaviour of *Taphozous mauritianus* (Chiroptera: Emballonuridae). *Can. J. Zool.* **58**: 1774–1777.
——— **Boyle, N.G.H., Harrison, T.M. & Oxley, D.J.** 1977. Activity patterns, habitat use and prey selection by some African insectivorous bats. *Biotropica* **9**(2): 73–85.
*——— **Brigham, R.M., Mills, A.M. & Rautenbach, I.L.** 1985. The roosting and foraging areas of *Epomophorus wahlbergi* (Pteropoidae) and *Scotophilus viridis* (Vespertilionidae) in the Kruger National Park. *J. Mammal.* **66**: 461–468.
*——— **& Crerar, L.M.** 1984. Cervical vertebrae in relation to roosting posture in bats. *J. Mammal.* **65**: 395–403.
*——— **Cumming, D.H.M. & Oxley, D.J.** 1978. Prey of bat hawks and availability of bats. *Condor* **79**: 495–497.
*——— **Cumming, D.H.M. Hutton, J.M. & Swanepoel, C.M.** 1987. Foraging and habitat use by *Nycteris grandis* (Chiroptera: Nycteridae) in Zimbabwe. *J. Zool., Lond.* **211**: 709–716.
*——— **Gaudet, C.L. & Leonard, M.L.** 1983. Feeding behaviour of the bats *Nycteris grandis* and *Nycteris thebaica* (Nycteridae) in captivity. *J. Zool., Lond.* **200**: 347–354.
*——— **Merriam, H.G. & Holroyd, G.L.** 1983. Bats of Kootenay, Glacier and Mount Revelstok National Parks in Canada: identification by echolocation calls, distribution, and biology. *Can. J. Zool.* **61**: 2503–2508.
*——— **Rautenbach, I.L.** 1986. A comparison of the roosting and foraging behaviour of three species of African insectivorous bats (Rhinolophidae, Verspertilionidae and Molossidae). *Can. J. Zool.* **64**: 2860–2866.
*——— **Thomas, D.W. & Sasseen, R.** 1981. *Nycteris grandis* (Nycteridae): an African carnivorous bat. *J. Zool., Lond.* **194**: 461–465.
***Ferguson, J.W.H.** 1980. Die ekologie van die rooijakkals *Canis mesomelas* Schreber, 1778 met spesiale verwysing na bewegings en sosiale organisasie. M.Sc. thesis, University of Pretoria.
*——— **Galpin, J.S. & de Wet, M.J.** 1988. Factors affecting the activity patterns of black-backed jackals *Canis mesomelas. J. Zool., Lond.* **214**: 55–69.
*——— **Nel, J.A.J. & de Wet, M.J.** 1983. Social organization and movement patterns of black-backed jackals *Canis mesomelas* in South Africa. *J. Zool., Lond.* **199**: 487–502.
**Ferrar, A.A. & Kerr, M.A.** 1971. A population crash of the reedbuck *Redunca arundinum* (Boddaert) in Kyle National Park, Rhodesia. *Arnoldia Rhod.* **5**(16): 1–19.
——— **& Sherry, B.** 1969. The present status of Lichtenstein's hartebeest in Rhodesia. Ref. D. 955, Dept. Nat. Parks Wild Life Mgmt, Salisbury. Mimeograph.
***Ferreira, N.A.** 1983. The status distribution and habitat requirements of the grey rhebuck, *Pelea capreolus* (Forster 1790) in the Orange Free State. M.Sc. thesis, University of Stellenbosch.
*——— **& Bigalke, R.C.** 1987. Food selection by grey rhebuck in the Orange Free State. *S. Afr. J. Wildl. Res.* **17**: 123–127.
**Fey, V.** 1964. The diet of leopards. *Afr. wild Life* **18**: 105–109.
**Ficheur, E. & Brives, A.** 1900. Sur la decouverte d'une caverne à ossements, à la carrière des Bains-Romains, a l'ouest d'Alger. *C.R. Hebd. Seane Acad. Sci.* **130**: 1485–1487.
**Field, C.R.** 1970. Observations on the food habits of tame warthog and antelope in Uganda. *E. Afr. Wildl. J.* **8**: 1–17.
——— **& Laws, R.M.** 1970. The distribution of the larger herbivores in the Queen Elizabeth National Park, Uganda. *J. Appl. Ecol.* **7**: 273–294.
**Field, C.T., Harrington, G.N. & Pratchett, D.** 1973. A comparison of the grazing preferences of buffalo (*Syncerus caffer*) and Ankole cattle (*Bos indicus*) on three different pastures. *E. Afr. Wildl. J.* **11**: 19–29.
**Findlay, G.H.** 1977. Rhythmic pigmentation in porcupine quills. *Z. Säugetierk.* **42**: 231–239.
*——— 1988. Bicoloured stripes in Hartmann's zebra. *S. Afr. J. Sci.* **84**: 890.
*——— 1989. Development of the springbok skin-colour pattern, hair slope and horn rudiments in *Antidorcas marsupialis. S. Afr. J. Zool.* **24**: 68–73.
***Findlay, K.P.** 1989. The distribution of cetaceans off the coast of South Africa and South West Africa/Namibia. M.Sc. thesis, University of Pretoria.
**Findley, J.S.** 1967. Insectivores and dermopterans, pp. 87-108, in *Recent mammals of the world.* Eds S. Anderson & J.K. Jones. New York: Ronald Press Co.
***Fischer, J.B.** 1829. *Synopsis Mammalium.* Stuttgart.
***Fischer, A.** 1914. Menschen und Tiere in Deutsch-Südwestafrika. Stuttgart: Deutsche Verlag.
**Fisher, J., Simon, N. & Vincent, J.** 1969. *The Red Book, Wildlife in Danger.* London: Collins.
**Fitch, J.E. & Brownell, R.L.** 1968. Fish otoliths in cetacean stomachs and their importance in interpreting feeding habits. *J. Fish. Res. Bd Canada* **25**: 2561–2574.
**Fitzsimons, F.W.** 1919/1920. *The natural history of South Africa.* London: Longmans.
**Fleetwood, J.D.L.** 1962. Notes on mammals new to Kenya. *Durban Mus. Novit.* **6**(17): 205–207.
**Florio, P. & Spinelli, L.** 1967. Successful breeding of a cheetah in a private zoo. *Int. Zoo Yb.* **8**: 76–78.
**Flower, S.S.** 1931. Contribution to our knowledge of the duration of life in vertebrate animals—5 Mammals. *Proc. zool. Soc. Lond.* **100**: 145–234.
——— 1932. Notes on the recent mammals of Egypt, with a list of the species recorded from that Kingdom. *Proc. zool. Soc. Lond.*: 369–450.
**Flower, W.H.** 1869. On the anatomy of proteles, *Proteles cristatus* (Sparrman). *Proc. zool. Soc. Lond.*: 474–496.
——— **& Lydekker, R.** 1891. *An introduction to the study of Mammals, living and extinct.* London: Adam & C. Black.
**Flux, J.E.C.** 1968. Breeding season of hares (*Lepus capensis* L.) near the equator. New Zealand National Research Fellowship Final Report. Mimeograph. pp. 12.
——— 1969. Current work on the reproduction of the African hare, *Lepus capensis*, in Kenya. *J. Reprod. Fert.* Suppl. 6: 225–227.
***Ford, C.E. & Hamerton, J.L.** 1956. Chromosomes of five rodent species. *Nature, Lond.* **177**: 140–141.
**Forster, J.R.** 1781. Natural history and description of the tyger cat of the Cape of Good Hope. *Phil. Trans. R. Soc.* **71**(4): 4–6.
**Forsyth Major, C.I.** 1898. On fossil and recent Lagomorpha. *Trans. Linn. Soc. Lond.* **7**: 433–520.
***Fosbrooke, H.** 1963. The stomoxys plague in Ngorongoro, 1962. *E. Afr. Wildl. J.* **1**: 124–126.
**Fossati, L.** 1937. Abitudini dell'Oritteropo d'Eritrea. *Natura, Milano* **28**: 17–23.
**Foster, J.B.** 1966. The giraffe of Nairobi National Park: home range, sex ratios, the herd, and food. *E. Afr. Wildl. J.* **4**: 139–148.
**Foster, W.E.** 1960. The square-lipped rhinoceros. *Lammergeyer* **1**: 25–35.
**Fourie, L.** 1932. Report on plague in Ovamboland, South West Africa. *Ann. Rept. Dept Pub. Hlth* 1932: 58–60.
*——— 1938. The endemic focus of plague. *S. Afr. med. J.* **12**: 352–358.
**Fourie, P.B.** 1972. A method for trapping the rock dassie (*Procavia capensis*). *J. sth. Afr. Wildl. Mgmt Ass.* **2**: 29–30.
——— 1974. Acoustic communication and social behaviour of the rock dassie, *Procavia capensis* (Pallas) in captivity. M.Sc. thesis, University of Pretoria.
——— 1977. Acoustic communication in the rock hyrax, *Procavia capensis. Z. Tierpsychol.* **44**: 194–219.
——— 1978. The life-span of mammals: estimates for the dassie (*Procavia capensis*). *Jl S. Afr. vet. med. Ass.* **49**: 143–144.
**Fourie, P.F.** 1974. The kudu — a graceful antelope. *Custos* **3**(10): 5–9.
——— 1975. The black-backed jackal. *Custos* **4**(2): 3–6.
——— 1976. Baboons as social animals. Part I *Custos* **5**(8): 17–19; Part II *Custos* **5**(9): 13–15; Part III *Custos* **5**(10): 17–19; Part IV *Custos* **5**(11): 19–20.
**Frade, F.** 1931. Sur l'existence en Afrique de deux especes d'elephants. *Bull. Soc. port. Sci. nat.* **11**: 135.
——— 1936. Distribution geographique des elephants d'Afrique. *C.R. XII Int. Cong. Zool. Lisbonne* 1935: 1191–1202.
——— 1949. Algumas novidades para a fauna da Guine Portuguesa (Aves e Mamiferos). *Anais. Jta. Invest. Ultramar* **4**: 165–186.
——— 1955. Sous-famille des Loxodontinae Osborn 1918. In *Traite de Zoologie.* Ed. P.P. Grasse. **17**(1): 774–780.
**Fradrich, H.** 1965. Zür biologie und Ethologie des Warzenschweines (*Phacochoerus aethiopicus* Pallas) unter Verucksightigung des Verhaltens anderer Suiden. *Z. Tierpsychol.* **22**: 328–393.
**Frame, L.H., Malcolm, J.R., Frame, G.W. & von Luwick, H.** 1979. Social organization of African wild dogs (*Lycaon pictus*) on the Serengeti plains, Tanzania, 1967–1978. *Z. Tierpsychol.* **50**: 225–249.
***Frank, L.G.** 1986. Social organization of the spotted hyaena (*Crocuta crocuta*). II. Dominance and reproduction. *Anim. Behav.* **34**: 1510–1527.
*——— **& Glickman, S.E.** 1989. Neonatal siblicide in the spotted hyena (*Crocuta crocuta*). Abstract of Papers and Posters Vol. II, p.597, Fifth International Theriological Congress, Rome.
**Fraser, A.F.** 1968. *Reproductive behaviour in ungulates.* London: Academic Press.
***Fraser, F.C.** 1940. Three anomalous dolphins from Blacksod Bay, Ireland. *Proc. Royal Irish Acad.* **45** B: 413–455.
——— 1946. Report of Cetacea stranded on the British coasts from 1933–1937. *Bull. Br. Mus. nat. Hist. (Zool.)* **12**: 49–51.
——— 1950. Description of a dolphin *Stenella frontalis* (Cuvier) from the coast of French Equatorial Africa. *Atlantide Rep.* **1**: 61–83.
——— 1955. The southern right whale dolphin, *Lissodelphis peroni* (Lacepede). *Bull. Br. Mus. nat. Hist. (Zool.)* **2**: 341–346.
*——— 1956. A new Sarawak dolphin. *Sarawak Mus. J.* **7**: 478–503.
——— 1964. Whales and whaling, in *Antarctic Research: A review of British*

*scientific achievement in Antarctica*. Eds R. Priestly, R.J. Adie & G. de Q. Robin. London: Butterworths.
——— 1966. Comments on the Delphinoidea, pp. 7–31, in *Whales, dolphins & porpoises*. Ed. K.S. Norris. Berkeley: University of California Press.
——— 1974. Report on Cetacea stranded on the British coasts from 1948–1966. *Bull. Br. Mus. nat. Hist. London (Zool.)* **14**: 1–65.
*——— **& Noble, B.A.** 1970. Variation of pigmentation in Meyer's dolphin, *Stenella coeruleoalba* (Meyer). *Invest. on Cetacea* **2**: 147–164.
——— **& Purves, P.E.** 1955. The "blow" of whales. *Nature, Lond.* **176**: 1221–1222.
**Frechkop, S.** 1944. *Exploration du Parc National de la Kagera. Mammifères Fasc*: 1–55. Bruxelles: Institut des Parcs Nationaux du Congo Belge.
——— 1954. *Exploration du Parc National de l'Upemba. Mammifères Fasc*: 14. Bruxelles: Institut des Parcs Nationaux du Congo Belge.
***Freeman, P.W.** 1981. A multivariate study of the family Molossidae (Mammalia, Chiroptera): morphology, ecology, evolution. Fieldiana, Zoology N.S. **7** (1316): 1–173.
**Fuggle, R.F. & Ashton, E.R.** 1979. Climate, in *Fynbos ecology: a preliminary synthesis*. Eds J. Day, W.R. Siegfried, G.N. Louw & M.I. Jarman. *S. A. Nat. Sci. Prog. Rep. No. 40*. Pretoria: CSIR.
**Fujino, K.** 1960. Immunogenetic and marking approaches to identifying subpopulations of the North Pacific Whales. *Scient. Rep. Whales Res. Inst., Tokyo* **18**: 1–28.
**Fullard, J.H.** 1981. Moths evolve a jamming device to thwart enemy bats, in *The New York Times* June 16, 1981. Ed. M.W. Browne.
**Funaioli, U. & Lanza, B.** 1968. On some bats from Somalia. *Monitore zool. ital. NS2 Suppl.*: 199–202.
——— **& Simonetta, A.M.** 1966. The mammalian fauna of the Somali Republic: status and conservation problems. *Monitore Zool. ital Suppl.*: 285–347.

# G

**Gaerdes, J.H.** 1965. The impala of South West Africa. *Afr. wild Life* **19**: 100–113.
**Gaerdes, F.** 1966. *Tiere im Veld*. Lebensbilder aus der Tierwelt Südwestafrikas. Windhoek, S.W.A.
***Gambell, R.** 1964. A pygmy blue whale at Durban. *Norsk Hvalfangsttid.* **53**: 66–68.
*——— 1966. The dorsal fin of sei and fin whales. *Norsk Hvalfangsttid.* **55**: 177–181.
——— 1967. Seasonal movements in sperm whales. *Symp. zool. Soc. Lond.* **19**: 237–254.
*——— 1968. Seasonal cycles and reproduction in sei whales of the Southern Hemisphere. *'Discovery' Rep.* **35**: 31–134.
——— 1970. Weight of a sperm whale, whole and in parts. *S. Afr. J. Sci.* **66**: 225–227.
*——— 1974. The fin and sei whale stocks off Durban. pp 82–86. In: *The whale problem. A status report*. Ed. W.E. Schevill. Cambridge, Mass.: Harvard University Press.
*——— 1977. Dentinal layer formation in sperm whale teeth. pp 583–590. In: *A voyage of discovery*. Ed. M. Angel. Oxford: Pergamon Press.
——— 1979. The blue whale. *Biologist* **26**: 209–215.
——— **Best, P.B. & Rice, D.W.** 1975. Report on the International Indian Ocean whale marking cruise, 24th Nov 1973—3rd Feb 1974. *Rep. int. Whal. Commn* **25**: 240–252.
**Games, I.** 1983. Observations on the sitatunga (*Tragelaphus spekei selousi*) in the Okavango delta of Botswana. *Biol. Cons.* **27**: 157–170.
**Garber, S.D.** 1977. Bat predation by the American kestrel, *Falco sparvervis* (Aves: Falconiformes). *Bat Research News* **18**(4): 37.
***Gargett, Valerie** 1990. *The black eagle*. Randburg: Acorn Friedman.
**Garner, D.M. & Ridgway, N.M.** 1965. Hydrology of New Zealand offshore waters. *Bull. N.Z. Dept. scient. ind. Res.* **162**: 1–62.
**Garstang, R.** 1982. An analysis of home range utilisation by tsessebe *Damaliscus lunatus lunatus* (Burchell, 1823) in P.W. Willis Private Nature Reserve. M.Sc. thesis, University of Pretoria.
**Gartlan, J.S. & Brain, C.K.** 1968. Ecology and social variability in *Cercopithecus aethiops* and *C. mitis*, in *Primates. Studies in adaptation and variability*. Ed. P.C Jay. New York: Holt Reinhart & Winston.
***Gasaway, W.C., Mossestad, K.T. & Stander, P.E.** 1989. Demography of spotted hyaenas in an arid savanna, Etosha National Park, South West Africa/Namibia. *Madoqua* **16**: 121–127.
**Gaskin, D.E.** 1968. Analysis of sightings and catches of sperm whales (*Physeter catodon* L.) in the Cook Strait area of New Zealand in 1963/64. *N.Z. J. Mar. Freshwat. Res.* **2**: 260–272.
**Gaskin, M.** 1972. *Whales dolphins and seals*. London: Heinemann.
**Gaskin, D.E. & Cawthorn, M.W.** 1967. Squid man. Diet and feeding habits of the sperm whale, *Physeter catodon*, in the Cook Strait region of New Zealand. *N.Z. J. Mar. Freshwat. Res.* **1**: 156–179.
***Gassiott, H.S.** 1852. Notes from a journal kept during a hunting tour in South Africa. *Journal of the Royal Geographical Society* **22**: 137–140.
***Gaudet, C.L. & Fenton, M.B.** 1984. Observational learning in three species of insectivorous bats (Chiroptera). *Anim. Behav.* **32**: 385–388.
**Geertsema, A.** 1976. Impressions and observations on serval behaviour in Tanzania, East Africa. *Mammalia* **40**: 13–19.
***Geertsema, A.A.** 1985. Aspects of the ecology of the serval *Leptailurus serval* in the Ngorogoro Crater, Tanzania. *Netherlands J. Zool.* **35**: 527–610.
**Geiger, R.** 1950. *Climate near the Ground*. Cambridge: Harvard University Press.
**Geigy, R.** 1955. Observations sur les phacocheres du Tanganyika. *Revue suisse Zool.* **62**: 139–163.
**Geist, V.** 1966. The evolution of horn-like organs. *Behaviour* **27**: 175–214.
**Genelly, R.E.** 1965. Ecology of the common mole-rat *Cryptomys hottentotus* in Rhodesia. *J. Mammal.* **46**: 647–665.
**Genest-Villard, H.** 1967. Revision du genre *Cricetomys* (Rongeurs, Cricetidae). *Mammalia* **31**: 390–455.
——— 1969. Particularities des lievres du sud-ouest de l'Angola. *Mammalia* **33**: 124–132.
——— 1978. Revision systematique du genre *Graphiurus* (Rongeurs, Gliridae). *Mammalia* **42**: 391–426.
**Genest, H. & Petter, F.** 1975. Family Tenrecinae, Part 1.1, pp. 1–7, in *The mammals of Africa: an identification manual*. Eds J. Meester & H.W. Setzer. Washington D.C.: Smithsonian Institution Press.
**Gensch, W.** 1968. Notes on breeding timber wolves, *Canis lupus occidentalis*, at Dresden Zoo. *Int. Zoo Yb.* **8**: 15–16.
——— 1969. Veruch der kunstlichen Aufzucht einer giraffe (*Giraffe camelopardalis* L.). *Zool. Gart.* **37**: 231–242.
**Gentry, A.W.** 1972. Genus *Gazella*, Part 15.l, pp. 85–93, in *The mammals of Africa: an identification manual*. Eds J. Meester & H.W. Setzer. Washington D.C.: Smithsonian Institution Press.
——— 1974. A new genus and species of Pliocene boselaphine (Bovidae, Mammalia) from South Africa. *Ann. S. Afr. Mus.* **65**: 145–188.
——— 1978. Bovidae, pp. 540–572, in *Evolution of African Mammals*. Eds V.J. Maglio & H.B.S. Cooke. Cambridge, Mass.: Harvard University Press.
***George, M. & Ryder, O.A.** 1986. Mitochondrial DNA evolution in the Genus *Equus*. *Molec. Biol. Evol.* **3**: 535–546.
***George, W.** 1981. The diet of *Petromus typicus* (Petromuridae, Rodentia) in the Augrabies Falls National Park. *Koedoe* **24**: 159–168.
*——— **& Crowther, G.** 1981. Space partitioning between two small mammals in a rocky desert. *Biol. J. Linn. Soc.* **15**: 195–200.
***Gerneke, W.H.**. 1967. Cytogenetic investigations on normal and malformed animals with special reference to inter-sexes. *Onderstepoort J. vet. Res.* **34**: 219–300.
***Ghiglieri, M.P., Butynski, T.M., Struhsaker, T.T. & Leland, L.**. 1982. Bushpig (*Potamochoerus porcus*) polychromatism and ecology in Kibale Forest, Uganda. *Afr. J. Ecol.* **20**: 231–236.
**Gianuca, N.M. & Castello, H.P.** 1976. First record of the southern bottlenose whale, *Hyperoodon planifrons*, from Brazil. *Scient. Rep. Whales Res. Inst., Tokyo* **28**: 119–126.
***Gibson-Hill, C.A.** 1950. The whales, porpoises and dolphins known in Sarawak waters. *Sarawak Mus. J.* **5**: 288–296.
***Giddings, S.R.** 1990. Water metablism in the gemsbok *Oryx gazella*. M.Sc. thesis, University of Pretoria.
**Gilbert, C. & Gilman, J.** 1951. Pregnancy in the baboon (*Papio ursinus*). *S. Afr. J. med. Sci.* **16**: 115.
**Gilbert, J.R. & Erickson, A.W.** 1976. Distribution and abundance of seals in the pack ice of the Pacific sector of the Southern Ocean. In *Proc. Third Symp. on Antarct. Bio.*, Washington, D.C.
***Gillies, A.** 1988. The effect of seasonal food restriction on the metabolism and circadian activity of the South African hedgehog *Erinaceus frontalis* (Insectivora). B.Sc. Hons Project Rep., University of Pretoria.
**Glass, B.P.** 1965. The mammals of eastern Ethiopia. *Zool. Afr.* **1**: 177–179.
**Gleeson, J.P.** 1981. The ecology of the house mouse *Mus musculus* Linnaeus, on Marion Island. M.Sc. thesis, University of Pretoria.
***Glickman, S.E., Frank, L.G., Davidson, J.M., Smith, E.R. & Siiteri, P.K.** 1987. Androstenedione may organize or activate sex-reversed traits in female spotted hyaenas. *Proc. Natl Acad. Sci., U.S.A.* **84**: 3444–3447.
***Gliwicz, J.** 1985. Rodent community of dry African savanna: population study. *Mammalia* **49**: 509–516.
**Glover, T.D. & Sale, J.B.** 1968. The reproductive system of male rock hyrax (*Procavia* and *Heterohyrax*). *J. Zool., Lond.* **156**: 351–362.
**Goddard, J.** 1966. Mating and courtship of the black rhinoceros in East Tsavo Park, Kenya. *E. Afr. Wildl. J.* **3**: 118–119.
——— 1967. Home range, behaviour, and recruitment rates of two black rhinoceros populations. *E. Afr. Wildl. J.* **5**: 18–23.
——— 1968. Food preferences of two black rhinoceros populations. *E. Afr. Wildl. J.* **6**: 1–18.
——— 1970a. Age criteria and vital statistics of a black rhinoceros population. *E. Afr. Wildl. J.* **8**: 105–121.
——— 1970b. Food preferences of black rhinoceros in the Tsavo National Park. *E. Afr. Wildl. J.* **8**: 145–161.
——— 1970c. A note on age at sexual maturity in the wild black rhinoceros. *E. Afr. Wildl. J.* **8**: 205.
**Gohar, H.A.F.** 1957. The Red Sea dugong. *Publs. mar. biol. Stn Ghardapa* **9**: 3–50.
***Goldsworthy, S.D. & Shaughnessy, P.D.** in press. Subantarctic fur seals *Arctocephalus tropicalis* at Heard Island. *Polar Biol.*
**Golightly, R.T.** 1976. Solar radiation and body temperature in free ranging Abert's squirrels (*Sciurus aberti*). *Am. Soc. Mammal. 56th ann. meeting*, pp. 14.
***Goodall, J.** 1970. Spotted hyaenas. In: *Innocent Killers*, Eds J. Van Lawick-Goodall & H. Van Lawick. Collins: London.
**Goodwin, G.G.** 1945. Record of a porpoise new to the Atlantic. *J. Mammal.* **26**: 195.
——— 1953. Lions—the proud big cats. *Anim. Kingd.* **56**: 119–125.
***Gordon, D.H.** 1978. Distribution of sibling species of the *Praomys (Mastomys) natalensis* group in Rhodesia (Mammalia: Rodentia). *J. Zool., Lond.* **186**: 397–401.
*——— 1984. Evolutionary genetics of the *Praomys (Mastomys) natalensis* species complex (Rodentia: Muridae). Ph.D. thesis: University of the Witwatersrand, Johannesburg.
*——— 1986. Extensive chromosomal variation in the pouched mouse, *Saccostomus campestris* (Rodentia, Cricetidae) from southern Africa: a preliminary investigation of evolutionary status. *Cimbebasia* Ser. A **8**(5): 37–47.
*——— 1988. Discovery of another species of tree rat. *Transvaal Museum Bulletin* **2**: 30–32.
*——— in press. Taxonomic status of *Mastomys shortridgei* from Namibia and comparison of banded chromosomes with *M. coucha*.
*——— **& Griffin, M.** in prep. The identification and distribution of *Mastomys* species in Namibia.
*——— **& Rautenbach, I.L.** 1987. Population cytogenetics of tree rats in southern Africa: evidence for two biological species within the taxon *Thallomys paedulcus*. Fifth Colloquium on Ecology and Taxonomy of African Small Mammals, Rogate, England. Abstr.
*——— **& Watson, C.R.B.** 1986. Identification of cryptic species of rodents (*Mastomys, Aethomys, Saccostomus*) in the Kruger National Park. *S. Afr. J. Zool.*, **21**: 95–99.
***Gorman, M.L. & Mills, M.G.L.** 1984. Scent-marking strategies in hyaena (Mammalia). *J. Zool., Lond.* **202**: 535–547.
**Gosling, L.M.** 1969. Parturition and related behaviour in Coke's hartebeest, *Alcelaphus buselaphus cokei* Gunther. *J. Reprod. Fert. Suppl.* **6**: 265–286.
——— 1972. The construction of antorbital gland marking sites by male oribi (*Ourebia oribi* Zimmermann, 1783). *Z. Tierpsychol.* **30**: 271–276.
***Goss, R.A.** 1986. *Maberly's mammals of southern Africa*. Johannesburg: Delta.
*——— 1987. *The Kwang gang*. Bristol: BBC Natural History Unit.
*——— 1990. *The sisterhood*. Bristol: BBC Natural History Unit.
**Goulden, E.A. & Meester, J.** 1978. Notes on the behaviour of *Crocidura* and *Myosorex* (Mammalia: Soricidae) in captivity. *Mammalia* **42**: 197–207.
**Gouttenoire, G.** 1954. *La chasse en Tunisie in Le grande livre de là fauna Afrique et de sa chasse*. Geneva.
**Grafton, R.N.** 1965. Food of the black-backed jackal: a preliminary report. *Zool. Afr.* **1**: 41–53.
**Graham, A. & Parker, I.** 1965. East African Wildlife Society cheetah survey. Mimeograph.
**Grasse, P.P.** 1955. Ordre des rongeurs, in *Traite de Zoologie*. Eds P.P. Grasse & P.L. Dekeyser. Paris: Masson.
**Gray, J.E.** 1837. Description of some new or little known mammalia principally in the British Museum collection. *Ann. Mag. nat. Hist.* **1**: 586.

——— 1846. Mammalia: on the cetaceous animals. No. 3, vol. 2. In: *The zoology of the voyage of H.M.S. "Erebus" and "Terror" under the command of Captain Sir James Clark Ross R.M. F.R.S. during the years 1839 to 1843*. Eds J. Richardson & J.E. Gray. London: Jansen.

*——— 1866. Catalogue of seals and whales in the British Museum. 2nd edn., London.

***Green, C.A., Keogh, H., Gordon, D.H., Pinto, M. & Hartwig, E.** 1980. The distribution, identification and naming of the *Mastomys natalensis* species complex in southern Africa (Rodentia: Muridae). *J. Zool., Lond.* **192**: 17–23.

**Greenwald, L.I.** 1967. Water economy of the desert dwelling springbok (*Antidorcas marsupialis*). M.Sc. thesis, University of Syracuse.

**Gregory, W.K. & Hellman, M.** 1939. On the evolution and major classification of the civets (Viverridae) and allied fossil and recent Carnivora: a phylogenetic study of the skull and dentition. *Proc. Am. Phil. Soc.* **81**: 309–392.

***Grimbeek, A.M.** 1984. Sitogenetika van die rooibok *Aepyceros melampus*. B.Sc. Hons. Project Report, University of Pretoria.

**Grimpe, G.** 1916. Hyänologische Studien. *Zool. Anz.* **48**: 49–61.

——— 1923. Neues über die Geschlechtsverhaltnisse der gefleckten Hyäne (*Crocuta crocuta* Erxl.). *Verhl. dtsch zool. Ges. Berlin* **28**: 309–392.

***Grimsdell J.J.R. & Bell, H.R.V.** 1975. Ecology of the black lechwe in the Bangweulu Basin of Zambia. National Council for Scientific Research, Zambia. Animal Productivity Report A.R.I.

**Grobler, J.H.** 1973. Biological data on tsessebe, *Damaliscus lunatus* (Mammalia: Alcelaphinae), in Rhodesia. *Arnoldia Rhod.* **6**(12): 1–16.

——— 1974. Aspects of the biology, population ecology and behaviour of the sable *Hippotragus niger niger* (Harris, 1838) in the Rhodes Matopos National Park, Rhodesia. *Arnoldia Rhod.* **7**(6): 1–36.

*——— 1981a. Feeding behaviour of the caracal *Felis caracal* Schreber, 1776 in the Mountain Zebra National Park. *S. Afr. J. Zool.* **16**: 259–262.

*——— 1981b. Feeding behaviour of sable *Hippotragus niger niger* (Harris, 1838) in the Rhodes Matopos National Park, Zimbabwe. *S. Afr. J. Zool.* **16**: 50–58.

——— **& Wilson, V.J.** 1972. Food of the leopard *Panthera pardus* (Linn.) in the Rhodes Matopos National Park, Rhodesia, as determined by faecal analysis. *Arnoldia Rhod.* **5**(35): 1–10.

**Grout, L.** 1862. *Zululand; or life among the Zulu-kafirs of Natal and Zululand, South Africa*. London: Tribner & Co.

***Grove, R.** 1987. Early themes in African conservation, in *Conservation in Africa: peoples, policies and practice*. Cambridge: University Press.

***Groves, C.P.** 1981. Subspecies & clines in the springbok (*Antidorcas marsupialis*). Notes on gazelles, 2. *Z. Säugetierk* **46**: 189–197.

*——— 1985. Was the quagga a species or a subspecies? *African wild Life* **39**: 106–107.

*——— 1987. Geographical variation in the black rhinoceros *Diceros bicornis* (L., 1758). *Z. Säugetierk.* **32**: 267–276.

**Grubb, P.** 1971. Further records of mammals from Ghana, based on the collections of Angus Booth. *Revue Zool. Bot. afr.* **84**: 192–202.

——— 1981. *Equus burchelli*. *Mammalian Species* **157**: 1–9.

**Grzimek, B.** 1970. *Among Animals of Africa*. London: Collins.

——— (ed) 1972–1975. *Grzimek's Animal Life Encyclopedia*. 1972 Mammals I Vol **10**; 1975 Mammals II Vol **11**; 1975 Mammals III Vol **12**; 1972 Mammals IV Vol **13**. London: Van Nostrand Reinhold.

——— **& Grzimek, B.** 1960. A study of the game of the Serengeti Plains. *Z. Säugetierk.* **25**: 1–61.

**Guggisberg, C.A.W.** 1961. *Simba, the life of the lion*. Cape Town: Howard Timmins.

**Guggisberg, C.A.** 1966. *S.O.S. Rhino*. London: Andre Deutsch.

**Guiler, E.R.** 1961. A pregnant female pygmy sperm whale. *Aust. J. Sci.* **24**: 297–298.

——— 1967. Strandings of three species of *Mesoplodon* in Tasmania. *J. Mammal.* **48**: 650–652.

*——— **Burton, H.R. & Gales, N.J.** 1987. On three odontocete skulls from Heard Island. *Sci. Rep. Whales Res. Inst., Tokyo* **38**: 117–124.

**Gundlach, von H.** 1968. Brutfursorge, Brutpflege, Verthaltensontogenese und Tagesperiodik beim Europäischen Wildschwein (*Sus scrofa* L.). *Z. Tierpsychol.* **25**: 955–995.

**Guy, P.** 1974. Feeding behaviour of the African elephant in the Sengwa Research Area of Rhodesia. M.Sc. thesis, University of Rhodesia.

——— 1975. The daily food intake of the African elephant, *Loxodonta africana* Blumenbach, in Rhodesia. *Arnoldia Rhod.* **7**(26): 1–8.

***Guy, P.R.** 1981. Changes in the biomass and productivity of woodlands in the Sengwa Wildlife Research Area, Zimbabwe. *J. Appl. Ecol.* **18**: 507–519.

**Gwynn, A.M.** 1953. The status of the leopard seal at Heard Island and Macquarie Island, 1948–1950. *ANARE Interim Reports* **3**: 1–33.

**Gwynne, M.D. & Bell, R.H.V.** 1968. Selection of vegetation components by grazing ungulates in the Serengeti National Park. *Nature, Lond.* **220**: 390–393.

**Gyldenstolpe, N.** 1934. Travels and collections of Johan August Wahlberg, 1810–1856. *Ibis*: 264–292.

# H

**Haaften, J.L. van** 1974. Zeehonden langs de Nederlandse Kust. *Wetenschappelijke Mededelingen van de Koninklijke Nederlandse Natuurhistorische Vereeniging* No. 101.

**Haagner, A.K.** 1920. *South African Mammals*. London: Witherby.

——— 1940. *South African Mammals*. Cape Town: Maskew Miller.

**Haagner, C.** 1975. Cheetah meets more than its match. *Custos* **4**(7): 20–21.

**Haas, H.** 1959. *We come from the sea*. Doubleday: Garden City N.Y.

**Hafez, E.S.E., Sumption, J.L. & Jackway, J.S.** 1962. The behaviour of swine, in *The Behaviour of Domestic Animals*; Ed. E.S.E. Hafez. London: Balliere, Tindall & Cox.

**Haddon, A.J. & Ellice, J.M.** 1964. Studies on bush-babies (*Galago* spp) with special reference to the epidemiology of yellow fever. *Trans. R. Soc. trop. Med. Hyg.* **58**: 521–538.

***Haim, A. & Fairall, N.** 1986. Physiological adaptations to the subterranean environment by the molerat *Cryptomys hottentotus*. *Cimbebasia* A8: 49–54.

*——— **Skinner, J.D. & Robinson, T.J.** 1987. Bioenergetics, thermoregulation and urine analysis of squirrels from the genus *Xerus* from an arid environment. *S. Afr. J. Zool.* **22**: 45–49.

*——— **van Aarde, R.J. & Skinner, J.D.** 1990a. Metabolism and thermoregulation in the Cape Porcupine, *Hystrix africaeaustralis*. *Physiol. Zool.* **63**: in press.

*——— **van Aarde, R.J. & Skinner, J.D.** 1990b. Metabolic rates, food consumption and thermoregulation in seasonal acclimatization of the Cape porcupine *Hystrix africaeaustralis*. *Oecologia*, in press.

**Hale, H.M.** 1931. Beaked whales—*Hyperoodon planifrons* and *Mesoplodon layardi* from South Australia. *Rec. S. Aust. Mus.* **4**: 291–311.

*——— 1962. Occurrence of the whale *Berardius arnouxi* in southern Australia. *Rec. S. Austr. Mus.* **14**: 231–243.

**Hall, K.R.L.** 1960. Social vigilance behaviour of the chacma baboon *Papio ursinus*. *Behaviour* **16**: 261–294.

——— 1962a. Numerical data, maintenance activities and locomotion of the wild chacma baboon, *Papio ursinus*. *Proc. zool. Soc. Lond.* **139**: 181–220.

——— 1962b. The sexual, agonistic and derived social behaviour patterns of the wild chacma baboon *Papio ursinus*. *Proc. zool. Soc. Lond.* **139**: 283–327.

——— 1963. Variations in the ecology of the chacma baboon. *Symp. zool. Soc. Lond.* 10: 1–28.

——— 1966. Distribution and adaptations of baboons. *Symp. zool. Soc. Lond.* **17**: 49–73.

——— **& De Vore, I.** 1965. Baboon social behaviour, in *Primate behaviour*, Ed. I. de Vore. London: Holt, Reinhart & Winston.

***Hall, M.A. & Boyer, S.D.** 1989. Estimates of incidental mortality of dolphins in the eastern Pacific fishery for tropical tunas in 1987. *Rep. int. Whal. Commn* **39**: 321–322.

***Hall, S.J.** 1986. Age determination of the greater canerat *Thryonomys swinderianus* in Zululand. Unpublished mimeograph submitted to St Stithians College, Johannesburg.

**Hallett, A.F. & Meester, J.** 1971. Early postnatal development of the South African hamster *Mystromys albicaudatus*. *Zool. Afr.* **6**: 221–228.

**Hall-Martin, A.J.** 1974. Food selection by Transvaal lowveld giraffe as determined by analysis of stomach contents. *J. sth Afr. Wildl. Mgmt Ass.* **4**: 191–202.

——— 1975. Studies on the biology and productivity of the giraffe. D.Sc. thesis, University of Pretoria.

——— 1976. Dentition and age determination of the giraffe, *Giraffa camelopardalis*. *J. Zool., Lond.* **180**: 263–289.

*——— 1984. Dzombo, the latest victim of a poaching gang. *Custos* **12**(11): 16–17.

*——— 1987. Role of musth in the reproductive strategy of the African elephant (*Loxodonta africana*). *S. Afr. J. Sci.* **83**: 616–620.

*——— **& Botha, B.P.** 1980. A note of feeding habits, ectoparasites and measurements of the black-backed jackal *Canis mesomelas* from Addo Elephant National Park. *Koedoe* **23**: 157–162.

*——— **Erasmus, T. & Botha, B.P.** 1982. Seasonal variation of diet and faeces composition of black rhinoceros *Diceros bicornis* in the Addo Elephant National Park. *Koedoe* **25**: 63–82.

*——— **& Penzhorn, B.L.** 1977. Behaviour and recruitment of translocated black rhinoceros *Diceros bicornis*. *Koedoe* **20**: 147–162.

——— **& Skinner, J.D.** 1978. Observations on puberty and pregnancy in female giraffe (*Giraffa camelopardalis*). *S. Afr. J. Wildl. Res.* **8**: 91–94.

——— **Skinner, J.D. & Hopkins, B.J.** 1978. The development of the reproductive organs of the male giraffe, *Giraffa camelopardalis*. *J. Reprod. Fert.* **52**: 1–7.

——— **Skinner J. D. & van Dyk, J.M.** 1975. Reproduction in the giraffe in relation to some environmental factors. *E. Afr. Wildl. J.* **13**: 237–248.

*——— **& van der Walt, L.A.** 1984. Plasma testosterone levels in relation to musth in the male African elephant. *Koedoe* **27**: 147–149.

**Haltenorth, T.** 1953. *Die Wildkatzen der Altenwelt*. Leipzig: Geest & Portig.

——— **& Diller, H.** 1980. *A field guide to the mammals of Africa including Madagascar*. London: Collins.

**Hamilton, P.** 1976. The movements of leopards in Tsavo National Park, Kenya as determined by radio-tracking. M.Sc. thesis, University of Nairobi.

**Hamilton, P.H.** 1981. The leopard *Panthera pardus* and the cheetah *Acinonyx jubatus* in Kenya. Report for US Fish and Wildlife Service, the African Wildlife Leadership Foundation and Government of Kenya.

**Hamilton, W.J. Jnr.** 1940. The biology of the smoky shrew (*Sorex fumeus fumeus* Miller). *Zoologica, N.Y.* **15**: 473–492.

***Hamilton, W.J. III & Arrowood, P.C.** 1978. Copulatory vocalizations of chacma baboons (*Papio ursinus*), gibbons (*Hylobates hoolock*) and humans. *Science* **200**: 1405–1409.

*——— **Buskirk, R.E. & Buskirk, W.H.** 1975. Chacma baboon tactics during intertroop encounters. *J. Mammal.* **56**: 857–870.

*——— **Buskirk, R.E. & Buskirk, W.H.** 1976. Defense of space and resources by chacma (*Papio ursinus*) baboon troops in an African desert and swamp. *Ecology* **57**: 1264–1272.

*——— **& Busse, C.** 1982. Social dominance and predatory behavior of chacma baboons. *J. Human Evol.* **11**: 567–573.

*——— **Busse, C. & Smith, K.S.** 1982. Adoption of infant orphan chacma baboons. *Anim. Behav.* **30**: 29–34.

*——— **& Tilson, R.L.** 1982. Solitary male chacma baboons in a desert canyon. *Am. J. Primatol.* **2**: 14–158.

*——— **Tilson, R.L. & Frank, L.G.** 1985. Sexual monomorphism in spotted hyaenas, *Crocuta crocuta*. *Ethology* **71**: 63–73.

**Hamilton, W.R.** 1973. The lower Miocene ruminants of Gebel Zelten, Libya. *Bull. Br. Mus. nat. Hist (Geol.)* **21**: 73–150.

**Handley, C.O.** 1966. A synopsis of the genus *Kogia* (pygmy sperm whales), pp. 62–69, in *Whales, dolphins and porpoises*, Ed. K.S. Norris. Berkeley: University of California Press.

**Hanks, J.** 1969. Recent lechwe counts in Zambia. *Puku* 5: 231–235.

——— 1970. Elephant research project. *Black Lechwe* **8**(1): 14–18.

——— 1971. The elephant problem. *World Wildl. Yb. 1970/71*.

——— 1972. Reproduction of elephant, *Loxodonta africana*, in the Luangwa Valley, Zambia. *J. Reprod. Fert.* **30**: 13–26.

——— 1979. *A struggle for survival: the elephant problem*. Cape Town: C. Struik.

*——— **Cumming, D.H.M., Orpen,J.L., Parry, D.F. & Warren, H.B.** 1976. Growth, condition and reproduction in the impala ram. *J. Zool., Lond.* **179**: 421–435.

——— **& Dowsett, R.J.** 1969. The use of Etorphine (M.99) for the immobilisation and translocation of the puku, *Kobus vardoni*. *Puku* 5: 123–130.

——— **Stanley-Price, M. & Wrangham, R.W.** 1969. Some aspects of the ecology and behaviour of the defassa waterbuck (*Kobus defassa*) in Zambia. *Mammalia* **33**: 471–494.

**Hanney, P.** 1965. The Muridae of Malawi (Africa; Nyasaland). *J. Zool., Lond.* **146**: 577–633.

——— 1975. *Rodents. Their lives and habits*. London: Davis & Charles.

**Hanse, W.A.** 1962. Preliminary studies on the dassie: its relation to farming and methods of control. *Rep. Dept Nat. Conserv.*, Cape Town 19: 108–121.

**Happold, D.C.D.** 1967a. Additional information on the mammalian fauna of the Sudan. *Mammalia* **31**: 605–609.

——— 1967b. Guide to the natural history of Khartoum Province. III. Mammals. *Sudan Notes and News* **48**: 1–22.

*——— **Happold, M. & Hill, J.E.** 1987. The bats of Malawi. *Mammalia* **51**: 337–414.

***Harcourt, C.S.** 1984. The behaviour and ecology of galagos in Kenyan coastal forest. Ph.D. thesis, University of Cambridge.

**Hardley, G.L.** 1950. A dwindling species (the Natal red hartebeest). *Afr. wild Life* **4**: 106–111.

***Harley, E.H.** 1988. The retrieval of the quagga. *S.Afr.J.Sci.* **84**: 158–159.

**Harper, F.** 1935. Extinct and vanishing mammals of the Old World. *Spec. Publs Am. comm. int. wild Life Prot.* **12**: 1–850.

**Harris, B.J. & Baker, H.G.** 1959. Pollination of flowers by bats in Ghana. *Niger Fld.* **24**: 151–159.

**Harris, W.C.** 1840. *Portraits of Game and Wild Animals of Southern Africa.* London: Hullmandel and Walton. Facsimile reprint, 1986. Cape Town: Sable Publishers.

——— 1852. The wild sports of southern Africa. London: Henry G. Bonn. Facsimile reproduction of the fifth edition, 1963. Cape Town: Struik.

**Harrison, D.L.** 1953. Some systematic notes on the long-fingered bats of the genus *Miniopterus* Bonaparte occurring in South Africa and Madagascar. *Durban Mus. Novit.* **4**(5): 65–75.

——— 1955. On a collection of mammals from Oman, Arabia with a description of two new bats. *Ann. Mag. nat. Hist.* (12) **8**: 897.

——— 1957. Some systematic and anatomical notes on the African bats of the genus *Otomops* Thomas. *Durban Mus. Novit.* **5**(2): 17–26.

——— 1959. Report on the bats (Chiroptera) in the collection of the National Museum of Southern Rhodesia, Bulawayo. *Occas. pap. Natl. Mus. Rhod. B., Nat. Sci.* **23**: 217–231.

——— 1960. The occurrence of Bocage's fruit bat *Rousettus (Lissonycteris) angolensis* Bocage, 1898 in southern Rhodesia. *Durban Mus. Novit.* **6**(5): 65–78.

——— 1961. Notes on Southern and East African bats. *Durban Mus. Novit.* **6**: 149–152.

——— 1962. On bats collected on the Limpopo River, with the description of a new race of tomb bat, *Taphosous sudani* Thomas, 1912. *Occas. pap. Natl. Mus. Rhod. B. Nat. Sci.* **26**: 755–769.

——— 1964. *The mammals of Arabia* Vol. 1. London: Ernest Benn.

——— 1968. *The mammals of Arabia Vol. II. Carnivora; Artiodactylia; Hyracoidea.* London: Ernest Benn.

——— 1971. A note on the occurrence of the giant African free-tailed bat *Tadarida africana* (Dobson, 1876), in Tanzania, with some observations on the characters of the species. *Arnoldia Rhod.* **5**(19): 1–5.

——— 1975. The Journal of Oman Studies special report: Mammals obtained by the Expedition. *The Oman Flora and Fauna Survey* : 9–26.

***Harrison, R.J., Boice, R.C., & Brownell, R.L.** 1969. Reproduction in wild and captive dolphins. *Nature, Lond.* **222** (5199): 1143–1147.

**Hart, S.** 1966. *Too Short a Day.* London: Geoffrey Bles.

**Hatt, R.T.** 1934. The pangolins and aardvarks collected by the American Museum Congo Expedition. *Bull. Am. Mus. nat. Hist.* **66**: 643–672.

——— 1940. Mammals collected by the Rockerfeller-Murphy expedition to Tanganyika Territory and the Eastern Belgian Congo. *Am. Mus. Novit.* 1070: 1–8.

**Hauser, W.** 1951. Beobachtungen an einigen Tierformen Angolas in der Natur und nach dem Fang. *Zool. Gart. Lpz.* **18**: 208–210.

**Hausfater, G.** 1974. Dominance and reproduction in baboons (*Papio cynocephalus*): a quantitative analysis. Ph.D. thesis, University of Chicago.

**Hayes, G.D.** 1978. *A guide to Malawi's National Parks and Game Reserves.* Limbe: Montfort Press.

**Hayman, R.W.** 1936. On a collection of mammals from the Gold Coast. *Proc. zool. Soc. Lond.*: 915–937.

——— 1937. A note on *Galago senegalensis inustus* Schwartz. *Ann. Mag. nat. Hist.* Ser. 10, **20**: 149.

——— 1954. Notes on some African bats, mainly from the Belgian Congo. *Revue Zool. Bot. afr.* **50**: 227–295.

——— 1957. Further notes on African bats. *Revue Zool. Bot. afr.* **56**: 41–45.

——— 1960. A note on the bat *Cloeotis percivali* Thomas. *Revue Zool. Bot. afr.* **61**(1/2): 167–172.

——— 1963. Mammals from Angola, mainly from the Luanda District. *Publicacoes cult. Co. Diam. Angola* **66**: 85–138.

——— **& Hill, J.E.** 1971. Order Chiroptera, Part2, pp. 1–73, in *The mammals of Africa: an identification manual.* Eds J. Meester & H.W. Setzer. Washington D.C.: Smithsonian Institution Press.

——— **Misonne, X. & Verheyen, W.N.** 1966. The bats of the Congo and of Rwanda and Burundi. *Annls. Mus. r. Afr. cent. Ser.* 8VO No. 154: i-vii: 1–105.

**Haywood, A.H.W.** 1933. Sierra Leone. The preservation of wild life. *J. Soc. Preserv. Fauna Emp.* **5**(19): 21–23.

**Heck, L.** 1968. 8. Deer: 154–245, in *Grzimek's Animal Life Encyclopedia* **13** Mammals 4. Ed. H.C.B. Grzimek. Zurich: Kindler.

**Hediger, H.** 1950. Gefangenschaftsgeburt eines afrikanischen Springhasen, *Pedetes caffer. Zool.Gart.,Lpz.* **17**: 166–169.

——— 1951. *Observations sur la psychologie animale dans les Parcs Nationaux du* Congo Belge. Bruxelles: Inst. des Parcs Nat. du Congo Belge.

——— 1955. *Studies of the Psychology and Behaviour of Captive Animals in Zoos and Circuses.* London: Butterworth Sci. Publ.

**Heezen, B.C.** 1957. Whales entangled in deep-sea cables. *Deep Sea Res.* **4**: 101–115.

**Heidt, G.A., Petersen, M.K. & Kirkland, G.L.** 1968. Mating behaviour and development of least weasels (*Mustela miralis*) in captivity. *J. Mammal.* **49**: 413–419.

**Heinichen, I.G.** 1969. Karyotype of the South West African plains zebra (*Equus burchelli* Gray, 1824 subsp) and mountain zebra (*Equus zebra hartmannae* Matschie, 1898): their cytogenetic relationship to Chapman's zebra (*Equus burchelli antiquorum* H. Smith, 1841) and the Cradock mountain zebra (*Equus zebra zebra* Linn. 1758). *Madoqua* **1**: 47–52.

——— 1972. Preliminary notes on the suni *Neotragus moschatus* and red duiker *Cephalophus natalensis. Zool. Afr.* **7**: 157–165.

**Heintz, E.** 1975. Origine, migration et paleobiogeographie des Palaeotraginae (Giraffidae, Artiodactyla) antevallesiens de l'ancien monde. *Coll. Internat.*, C.N.R.S. No.218: 723–730.

**Hendey, Q.B.** 1968. The Melkbos site: an upper Pleistocene fossil occurrence in the southwestern Cape Province. *Ann. S. Afr. Mus.* **52**: 89–119.

——— 1969. Quaternary vertebrate fossil sites in the southwestern Cape Province. *S. Afr. Archaeol. Bull.* **24**(3,4): 96–105.

——— 1970. A review of the geology and palaeontology of the Plio/Pliocene deposits at Langebaanweg, Cape Province. *Ann. S. Afr. Mus.* **56**: 75–117.

——— 1973. Fossil occurrences at Langebaanweg, Cape Province. *Nature, Lond.* **244**: 13–14.

——— 1974. The late Cenozoic Carnivora of the southwestern Cape Province. *Ann. S. Afr. Mus.* **63**: 1–369.

——— 1976. The Pliocene fossil occurrences in "E" Quarry, Langebaanweg, Cape Province. *Ann. S. Afr. Mus.* **69**: 215–247.

——— **& Hendey, H.** 1968. New Quaternary fossil sites near Swartklip, Cape Province. *Ann. S. Afr. Mus.* **52**: 43–73.

***Henschel, J.R.** 1986. The socio-ecology of a spotted hyaena *Crocuta crocuta* clan in the Kruger National Park. D.Sc. thesis, University of Pretoria.

——— **David, J.H.M. & Jarvis, J.U.M.** 1982. Age determination and age structure of a striped field mouse, *Rhabdomys pumilio*, population from the Cape Flats. *S. Afr. J. Zool.* **17**: 136–142.

*——— **& Skinner, J.D.** 1987. Social relationships and dispersal patterns in a clan of spotted hyaenas *Crocuta crocuta* in the Kruger National Park. *S. Afr. J. Zool.* **22**: 18–24.

*——— **& Skinner, J.D.** 1990. The diet of the spotted hyaenas *Crocuta crocuta* in the Kruger National Park. *Afr. J. Ecol.* **27**: in press.

*——— **& Skinner, J.D.** Parturition and early maternal care of spotted hyaenas *Crocuta crocuta*: A case report. *J. Zool., Lond.*. in press.

***Henschel & Tilson, 1988. Henschel, J.R. & Tilson, R.L.** 1988. How much does a spotted hyaena eat? Perspective from the Namib Desert. *Afr. J. Ecol.* **26**: 247–255.

**Henschel, J.R., Tilson, R. & von Blottnitz, F.** 1979. Implications of a spotted hyaena bone assemblage in the Namib Desert. *S. Afr. archaeol. Bull.* **34**: 127–131.

***Henwood, R.R.** 1989. Black rhinoceros *Diceros bicornis* capture, transportation and boma management by the Natal Parks Board. *Koedoe* **32**: 43–47.

***Henzi, S.P.** 1981. Causes of testis-abduction in vervet monkeys (*Cercopithecus aethiops pygerythrus*). *Anim. Behav.* **29**: 961–962.

*——— 1985. Genital signalling and the coexistence of male vervet monkeys (*Cercopithecus aethiops pygerythrus*). *Folia primatol.* **45**: 129–147.

*——— 1988. Many males do not a multimale troop make. *Folia Primatol.* **51**: 165–168.

*——— **& Lawes, M.J.** 1987. Breeding season influxes and the behaviour of adult male samango monkeys (*Cercopithecus mitis albogularis*). *Folia primatol.* **48**: 125–136.

*——— **& Lawes, M.J.** 1989. Strategic responses of male samango monkeys (*Cercopithecus mitis*) to a decline in the number of receptive females. *Int. J. Primatol.* **9**: 479–495.

*——— **& Lucas, J.W.** 1980. Observations on the inter-troop movement of adult vervet monkeys (*Cercopithecus aethiops*). *Folia primatol.* **33**: 220–235.

**Herbert, H.J.** 1972. *The population dynamics of the waterbuck Kobus ellipsiprymnus (Ogilby, 1833) in the Sabi Sand Wildtuin.* Mammalia Depicta. Hamburg: Paul Parey.

——— **& Austin, B.** 1972. The past and present distribution of the black and square-lipped rhinoceros in the Wankie National Park. *Arnoldia Rhod.* **5**(26): 1–6.

**Herdman, R.** 1972. Captive cheetah reproduction. *Zoonooz* **45**: 10.

**Herman, L.** 1936–1937. *Travels and adventures in eastern Africa by Nathaniel Isaacs.* 1936 Vol **1** No. 16; 1937 Vol **2** No. 17. Cape Town: Van Riebeeck Society.

***Herman, L.M. & Tavolga, W.N.** 1980. The communication systems of cetaceans. pp 149–209. In: *Cetacean behavior: mechanisms and functions.* Ed. L.M. Herman. New York: John Wiley & Sons.

**Herselman, J.C.** 1980. The distribution and status of bats in the Cape Province. Internal Report, Cape Dept of Nature and Environmental Conservation. Mimeograph.

——— **& Norton, P.M.** 1981. The distribution and status of bats in the Cape Province. Internal Report, Cape Dept of Nature and Environmental Conservation. Mimeograph.

*——— **& Norton, P.M.** 1985. The distribution and status of bats (Mammalia: Chiroptera) in the Cape Province. *Ann. Cape Prov. Mus.* (nat. Hist.) **16**(4): 73–126.

**Hershkowitz, P.** 1963. Notes on S. American dolphins of the genus *Inia, Sotalia* and *Tursiops. J. Mammal.* **44**: 98–103.

——— 1966. Catalogue of living whales. *Bull. U.S. natn. Mus.* **246**: viii : 1–259.

**Herzig-Straschil, B.** 1977. Notes on the feeding habits of the yellow mongoose, *Cynictis penicillata. Zool. Afr.* **12**: 225–256.

——— 1978. On the biology of *Xerus inauris* (Zimmermann, 1980) (Rodentia, Sciuridae). *Z. Säugetierk.* **43**: 262–278.

——— 1979. *Xerus inauris* (Rodentia, Sciuridae)—an inhabitant of the arid regions of Southern Africa. *Folia Zool.* **28**: 119–124.

*——— **& Herzig, A.** 1989. Biology of *Xerus princeps* (Rodentia, Sciuridae). *Madoqua* **16**: 41–46.

*——— **Herzig, A. & Winkler, H.**. Differences in skull morphology and morphometry of *Xerus inauris* and *X. princeps* (Rodentia; Sciuridae). *Z. Säugetierk.* in press.

*——— **& Robinson, G.A.** 1978. On the ecology of the fruit bat, *Rousettus aegyptiacus leachi* (A. Smith, 1829) in the Tsitsikama Coastal National Park. *Koedoe* **21**: 101–110.

**Hesse, P.R.** 1958. Identification of the spoor and dung of East African mammals. Part III. *Afr. wild Life* **12**: 58–63.

**Hewitt, J.** 1931. *A guide to the vertebrate fauna of the Eastern Cape Province.* Grahamstown: Trustees, Albany Museum.

***Hewitt, P.H., Nel, J.J.C., & Schoeman, I.** 1972. The solar and ultraviolet radiation tolerances of several termite species. *J.ent.Soc.sth.Afr.* **35**: 119–121.

***Heyning, J.E.** 1988. Presence of solid food in a young calf killer whale (*Orcinus orca*). *Mar. Mammal Sci.* **4**: 68–71.

**Hickman, G.C.** 1978. Reaction of the bathyergid *Cryptomys hottentotus* to water. *Zool. Afr.* **13**: 319–328.

——— 1979. Burrow system construction of the bathyergid *Cryptomys hottentotus* in Natal, South Africa. *Z. Säugetierk.* **44**: 153–162.

*——— 1980. Locomotory activity of captive *Cryptomys hottentotus* (Mammalia: Bathyergidae), a fossorial rodent. *J. Zool., Lond.* **192**: 225–235.

——— 1982. Copulation of *Cryptomys hottentotus* (Bathyergidae), a fossorial rodent. *Mammalia* **46**: 293–298.

***Higuchi, R., Bowman, B., Freiberger, M., Ryder, O.A. & Wilson, A.C.** 1984. DNA sequences from the quagga, an extinct member of the horse family. *Nature, Lond.* **312**: 282–284.

**Hill, J.E.** 1938. Notes on the dentition of a jumping shrew *Nasilio brachyrhyncha. J. Mammal.* **19**: 465–467.

——— 1968. Bats from the Cameroons, with the description of a new species of *Pipistrellus. Bonn. zool. Beitr.* **19**: 43–48.

——— 1974a. A review of *Laephotis* Thomas, 1901 (Chiroptera: Vespertilionidae). *Bull. Br. Mus. nat. Hist. (Zool.)* **27**: 73–82.

*——— 1974b. A review of *Scotoecus* Thomas, 1901 (Chiroptera: Vespertilionidae). *Bull. Brit. Mus. (Nat. Hist.) Zool.* **27**: 167–188.

——— 1977. African bats allied to *Kerivoula lanosa* (A. Smith, 1847) (Chiroptera: Vespertilionidae). *Rev. zool. Afr.* **91**: 623–633.

*——— 1980. The status of *Vespertilio borbonicus* Geoffroy, 1803 (Chiroptera: Vespertilionidae). *Zool. Mededelingen* **55**(24): 287–295.

*——— 1983. Further records of bats from the Central African Republic (Mammalia: Chiroptera). *Ann. Carnegie Mus.* 52 art. 3: 55–58.

——— **& Carter, T.D.** 1941. The mammals of Angola, Africa. *Bull. Am. Mus. nat. Hist. (Zool.)* **78**: 1–211.

**Hill, W.C.O.** 1945. Notes on the dissection of two dugongs. *J. Mammal.* **26**: 153–175.

——— 1953. *Primates: Comparative Anatomy and Taxonomy.* Vol. **1** *Strepsirhini.* Edinburgh: University Press.

——— 1966. *Primates.* Vol. **VI** *Catarrhini: Cercopithecoidea: Cercopithecinae.* Edinburgh: University Press.

——— 1970. *Primates* Vol. **VIII**. *Cynopithecinae: Papio, Mandrillus, Theropithecus.* Edinburgh: University Press.

——— & Meester, J. 1974. Suborder Prosimii, Part 3.2, pp. 1–5, in *The mammals of Africa: an identification manual.* Eds J. Meester & H.W. Setzer. Washington D.C.: Smithsonian Institution Press.

**Hillman, J.C.** 1974. Ecology and behavior of the wild eland. *Wildl. News* **9**(3): 6–9.

——— 1979. Biology of the eland in the wild. Ph.D. thesis, University of Nairobi.

**Hills, D.M. & Smithers, R.H.N.** 1980. The "king cheetah": a historical review. *Arnoldia Rhod.* **9**(1): 1–23.

**Hinton, M.A.C. & Kershaw, P.S.** 1920. On a collection of mammals from the Dinka country, Bahr-e1-Djebel. *Ann. Mag. nat. Hist.* **6**: 94–101.

**Hirst, S.M.** 1969. Populations in a Transvaal Lowveld Nature Reserve. *Zool. Afr.* **4**: 199–230.

——— 1975. Ungulate-habitat relationships in a South African woodland/savanna ecosystem. *Wildl. monogr.* **44**: 60.

***Hiscocks, K. & Perrin, M.R.** 1987. Feeding observations and diet of black-backed jackals in an arid coastal environment. *S. Afr. J. Wildl. Res.* **17**: 55–58.

**Hitchins, P.M.** 1967. Black and square-lipped rhino count —Hluhluwe Game Reserve and northern Corridor. Natal Parks Board files, Mimeograph.

——— 1968a. Records of plants eaten by mammals in the Hluhluwe Game Reserve, Zululand. *Lammergeyer* **8**: 31–39.

——— 1968b. Liveweights of some mammals from Hluhluwe Game Reserve. *Lammergeyer* **9**: 42.

——— 1968c. Some preliminary findings on the population structure and status of the black rhinoceros *Diceros bicornis* in Hluhluwe Game Reserve, Zululand. *Lammergeyer* **9**: 26–28.

——— 1969. The influence of vegetation types on size of home ranges of black rhinoceros in Hluhluwe Game Reserve, Zululand. *Lammergeyer* **10**: 81–86.

——— 1970. Field criteria for ageing immature black rhinoceros, *Diceros bicornis* L. *Lammergeyer* **12**: 48–55.

——— 1972. Preliminary findings in a radio-telemetric study on the black rhinoceros in Hluhluwe Game Reserve, Zululand: 79–100, in *Proceedings of a Symposium on Biotelemetry, Pretoria, 1971.* Pretoria: CSIR.

——— 1975. The black rhinoceros in South Africa. *Endangered Wildl.* **1**(2): 1–2.

*——— 1989. Census and marking systems for black rhinoceros *Diceros bicornis* with special reference to the Zululand game reserves. *Koedoe* **32**: 84–85.

*——— **& Anderson, J.L.** 1983. Reproduction, population characteristics and management of the black rhinoceros *Diceros bicornis minor* in the Hluhluwe/Corridor/Umfolozi Game Reserve Complex. *S. Afr. J. Wildl. Res.* **13**: 78–85.

——— **& Keep, M.E.** 1970. Observations on skin lesions of the black rhinoceros (*Diceros bicornis* L.). *Lammergeyer* **12**: 56–65.

——— **Keep, M.E. & Rochat, K.** 1972. The capture of black rhinoceros in Hluhluwe Game Reserve and their translocation to the Kruger National Park. *Lammergeyer* **17**: 18–30.

***Hitchins, P. & Vincent, J.** 1972. Observations on range extension & dispersal of impala (*Aepyceros melampus*) in Zululand. *Jl sthn Afr. Wildl. Mgmt. Ass.* **2**: 3–8.

**Hladik, C.M.** 1979. Diet and ecology of prosimians, in *The study of Prosimian behaviour*; Eds G.A. Doyle & R.D. Martin. London: Academic Press.

**Hoeck, H.N.** 1975. Differential feeding behaviour of the sympatric hyrax *Procavia johnstoni* and *Heterohyrax brucei*. *Oecologia (Berl.)* **22**: 15–47.

——— 1977. "Teat order" in hyrax (*Procavia johnstoni* and *Heterohyrax brucei*). *Z. Säugetierk.* **42**: 112–115.

——— 1978. Systematics of the Hyracoidea: toward a clarification. *Bull. Carnegie Mus. Nat. Hist.* **6**: 146–151.

*——— 1982. Population dynamics, dispersal and genetic isolation in two species of hyrax (*Heterohyrax brucei* and *Procavia johnstoni*) on habitat islands in the Serengeti. *Z. Tierpsychol.* **59**: 177–210.

*——— 1989. Demography and competition in hyrax. A 17 years study. *Oecologia* **79**: 353–360.

**Hoesch, W. & Lehmann, E. von.** 1956. Zur saugetier-Fauna Südwestafrikas. *Bonn. zool. Beitr.* **7**: 8–57.

***Hofer, H. & East, Marion.** 1989a. Growth of spotted hyaena cubs in relation to prey availability, litter size and sex of offspring. Abstract of Papers and Posters Vol. II, p. 605, Vth Int. Theriological Congr., Rome.

*——— **& East, Marion** 1989b. Maternal rank and maternal care in spotted hyaenas in a system with fluctuating prey populations. Abstract of Papers and Posters Vol. II, p. 865, Vth Int. Theriological Congr., Rome.

**Hofmann, R.R.** 1972. Zur funktionellen Morphologie der Subaurikularorgans des Ostafrikanischen Bergriedbocks, *Redunca fulvorufula chanleri* (Rothschild, 1895). *Tierärztl. Wochenschrift* **85**: 470–473.

——— 1973. The ruminant stomach. Stomach structure and feeding habits of East African game ruminants. *East African Monographs in Biology Vol.* **2**. pp. 1–354. Nairobi: East African Literature Bureau.

——— **& Stewart, D.R.M.** 1972. Grazer or browser: a classification based on the stomach structure and feeding habits of East African ruminants. *Mammalia* **36**: 226–240.

**Hofmeyr, J.M.** 1970. A review of the food preferences and feeding habits of some indigenous herbivores in the Ethiopian faunal region and some studies on animal: plant relationships. *Proc. S. Afr. Soc. Anim Prod.* **9**: 89–99.

*——— **Ebedes, H., Fryer, R.E.M. & de Bruine, J.R.** 1975. The capture and translocation of the black rhinoceros *Diceros bicornis* Linn. in South West Africa. *Madoqua* **9**: 35–44.

——— **& Skinner, J.D.** 1969. A note on ovulation and implantation in the steenbok and the impala. *Proc. S. Afr. Soc. Anim. Prod.* **8**: 175.

***Hofmeyr, M.D. & Louw, G.N.** 1987. Thermoregulation, pelage conductance and renal function in desert-adapted springbok, *Antidorcas marsupialis*. *J. Arid. Environ.* **13**: 137–151.

**Hoier, R.** 1955. *L'hippopotame, in Le Grande livre de la faune africaine et de sa chasse.* Geneva: Kisten.

**Hollister, N.** 1917. Some effects of environment and habit on captive lions. *Proc. U.S. Natn. Mus.* **53**: 117–193.

——— 1918/24. East African mammals in the United States National Museum. 1918 Part I. Insectivora, Chiroptera and Carnivora: 1–185; 1919 Part II Rodentia, Lagomorpha and Tubulidentata: 1–175; 1924 Part III Primates, Artiodactyla, Perissodactyla, Proboscidea and Hyracoidea: 1–151. *Bull. U.S. Natn. Mus.* **99**.

**Holm, E.** 1969. Contribution to the knowledge of the biology of the Namib desert golden mole *Eremitalpa granti namibensis* Bauer & Niethammer 1959. *Scient. Pap. Namib desert Res. Stn.* **41**: 37–42.

***Holthuis, L.B.** 1987. The scientific name of the sperm whale. *Mar. Mammal Sci.* **3**: 87–88.

**Holub, E.** 1881. *Seven years in South Africa: Travels, researches and hunting adventures, between the diamond fields and the Zambesi (1872–79).* Vols **1** & **2**. London: Sampson Low, Marston, Searle & Rivington.

**Holz, H.** 1964. Zur innerartlichen Variabilitat und phylogenetischen Stellung des Afrikanischen Hyänenhundes *Lycaon pictus*. *Zool. Anz.* **174**: 362–395.

***Honacki, J.H., Kinman, K.E. & Koeppl, J.W.** 1982. *Mammal species of the world; a taxonomic and geographic reference.* Lawrence, Kansas: Allen Press Inc. & The Association of Systematics and Collections.

***Honeycutt, R.L., Edwards S.V., Nelson, K. & Nevo, E.** 1987. Mitochondrial DNA variation and the phylogeny of African mole rats (Rodentia: Bathyergidae). *Syst. Zool.* **36**: 280–292.

**Hoogstraal, H., Wassif, K. & Kaiser, M.N.** 1957. Results of the NAMRU-3 Southeastern Egypt expedition, 1954. *Bull. zool. Soc. Egypt* **13**: 52–57.

**Hooijer, D.A.** 1972. A late Pliocene rhinoceros from Langebaanweg, Cape Province. *Ann. S. Afr. Mus.* **59**: 151–191.

——— 1978. Rhinocerotidae, in *Evolution of African mammals.* Eds V.J. Maglio & H.B.S. Cooke. Cambridge, Mass.: Harvard University Press.

——— **& Patterson, B.** 1972. Rhinoceroses from the Pliocene of northwestern Kenya. *Bull. Mus. comp. Zool. Harv.* **144**: 1–26.

**Hoppe, P.P.** 1977. How to survive heat and aridity: ecophysiology of the dik-dik antelope. *Vet. Med. Rev.* **1**: 77–86.

*——— 1984. Strategies of digestion in African ruminants, pp 222–243. In: *Herbivore Nutrition in the Tropics and Subtropics.* Eds F.M.C. Gilchrist & R.I. Mackie. Craighall, South Africa: Science Press.

*——— **van Hoven, W., Engelhardt, W. von, Prins, R.A., Bronkhorst, A. & Gwynne, M.D.** 1983. Pregastric and caecal fermentation in dikdik (*Madoqua kirki*) and suni (*Neotragus moschatus*). *Comp. Biochem. Physiol.* **75A**(4): 517–524.

**Horning, D.S. & Fenwick, G.D.** 1978. Leopard seals at the Snares Islands, New Zealand. *N.Z. J. Zool.* **5**: 171–172.

***Howard, P.C.** 1986. Habitat preferences of common reedbuck on farmland. *S. Afr. J. Wildl. Res.* **16**: 99–108.

*——— **& Marchant, A.N.** 1984. Distribution and status of some large mammals on private land in Natal. *Lammergeyer* **34**: 1–58.

**Howell, A.** 1944. *Speed in Animals.* Chicago: University Press.

**Howell, F.C.** 1960. European and northwest African Middle Pleistocene hominids. *Curr. Anthrop.* **1**: 195–232.

***Hrdy, S.B.** 1979. Infanticide among animals: a review, classification and examination of the implications for the reproductive strategies of males. *Ethol. Sociobiol.* **1**: 13–40.

**Hubbard, C.A.** 1972. Observations on the life histories and behaviour of some small rodents from Tanzania. *Zool. Afr.* **7**: 419–449.

***Hubert, B.** 1978. Revision of the genus *Saccostomus* (Rodentia: Cricetomyinae) with new morphometric and chromosomal data from specimens from the Lower Omo Valley, Ethiopia. *Bull. Carnegie Mus. Nat. Hist.* **6**: 48–52.

***Huet, P.** 1869. *Het lot der swarten.* Utrecht: Van Peursam.

**Hufnagl, E.** 1972. *Libyan mammals.* Harrow: Oleander Press.

**Huggett, A. St G. & Widdas, W.F.** 1951. The relationship between mammalian foetal weight and conception age. *J. Physiol.* **114**: 306–317.

**Hughes, G.R. & Oxley-Oxland, R.** 1971. A survey of dugong, *Dugong dugon*, in and around Antonio Eres, northern Mocambique. *Biol. Conserv.* **3**: 299–30l.

***Hui, C.A.** 1977. Data preparation and analysis for studies on growth and reproduction of *Delphinus* in the eastern tropical Pacific. Report on contract PO-01-6-200-11439, Southwest Fisheries Center, La Jolla, Calif. 13pp.

*——— 1979. Undersea topography and distribution of dolphins of the genus *Delphinus* in the Southern California Bight. *J. Mammal.* **60**: 521–527.

**Hunter, R.F.** 1964. Home range behaviour in hill sheep, in *Grazing in terrestrial and marine environments.* Ed. D.J. Crisp. *Symp. Br. Ecol. Soc.* **4**: 155–171.

**Huntley, B.J.** 1968. This is the last wilderness. *Afr. wild Life* **22**: 95–103.

——— 1970. Observations on the Percy Fyfe Reserve tsessebe population. *Ann. Trans. Mus.* **27**: 225–239.

——— 1972a. An Eden called Iona. *Afr. wild Life* **26**: 136–141.

——— 1972b. A note on food preferences of a steenbok. *J. sth Afr. Wildl. Mgmt Ass.* **2**: 24–26.

——— 1974. Outlines of wildlife conservation in Angola. *J. sth Afr. Wildl. Mgmt Ass.* **4**: 157–166.

——— 1976. Angola. *Afr. wild Life* **30**: 10–14.

**Husson, A.M. & Holthuis, L.B.** 1974. *Physeter macrocephalus* Linnaeus, 1758, the valid name for the sperm whale. *Zoöl. Meded., Leiden* **48**(19): 205–217.

***Hutton, J.M.** 1986. The status and distribution of bats in Zimbabwe. *Cimbebasia* A. 8 (26): 220–236.

# I

**Ichihara, T.** 1966. The pygmy blue whale, *Balaenoptera musculus brevicauda*, a new subspecies from the Antarctic, pp. 79–113. In *Whales, dolphins and porpoises.* Ed. K.S. Norris. Berkeley: University of California Press.

***Ikeda, H., Izawa, M., Baba, M., Takeishi, M., Doit & Ono, Y.** 1983. Range size and activity pattern of three nocturnal carnivores in Ethiopia by radio-telemetry. *J. Ethol.* **1**: 109–111.

**Ingham, S.E.** 1960. The status of seals (Pinnipedia) at Australian Antarctic Stations. *Mammalia* **24**: 422–430.

**Innis, A.C.** 1958. The behaviour of the giraffe *Giraffa camelopardalis* in the eastern Transvaal. *Proc. zool. Soc. Lond.* **131**: 245–278.

**Ionides, C.J.P.** 1965. *A hunter's story.* London: Allen.

**Irby, L.R.** 1976a. The ecology of mountain reedbuck in southern and eastern Africa. Ph.D. thesis, Texas A & M University, College Station.

*——— 1976b. A note on mountain reedbuck *Redunca fulvorufula fulvorufula* Afzelius in the Kruger National Park. *Koedoe* **19**: 63–66.

*——— 1977. Studies on mountain reedbuck populations with special reference to Loskop Dam Nature Reserve. *S. Afr. J. Wildl. Res.* **7**: 73–86.

*——— 1979. Reproduction in mountain reedbuck (*Redunca fulvorufula*). *Mammalia* **43**: 191–213.

*——— 1981. Mountain reedbuck activity patterns in the Loskop Dam Nature Reserve. *S. Afr. J. Wildl. Res.* **11**: 115–120.

*——— 1984a. Food selection by mountain reedbuck in the Loskop Dam Nature Reserve. *S. Afr. J. Wildl. Res.* **14**: 29–32.

*——— 1984b. Mountain reedbuck reactions to baboon populations exhibiting different levels of predatory behaviour. *S. Afr. J. Wildl. Res.* **14**: 62–64.

**Irving, L., Scholander, P.F. & Grinnell, S.W.** 1941. The respiration of the porpoise *Tursiops truncatus*. *J. cell. comp. Physiol.* **17**: 145–168.

***Isaacson, M.** 1984. A review of some recent developments in human plague with special reference to southern Africa. *Ecology of Disease* **2**: 161–171.

**Ivanova, E.I.** 1961. *Orcinus orca* in the Pacific. *Trudy Inst. Morf. Zhivot* **34**: 205–215.

***Ivashin, M.V.** 1967. [Whale globe-trotter]. *Priroda* **8**: 105–107.

——— **Shevchenko, V.I. & Yukov, V.L.** 1972. Karlikovyi gladkii kit *Caperea marginata* (Cetacea). *Zool. Zh.* **51**: 1715–1723.

# J

*__Jackmann, H.__ 1988. Estimating age in African elephants: a revision of Laws' molar evaluation technique. *Afr. J. Ecol.* **26**: 51–56.

*——— **& Bell, R.H.V.** 1984. The use of elephant droppings in assessing numbers, occupancy and age structure: a refinement of the method. *Afr. J. Ecol.* **22**: 127–141.

*__Jacobs, D.S., Bennett, N.C., Jarvis, J.U.M. & Crowe, T.M.__ 1984. The colony structure and dominance hierarchy of the Damaraland mole-rat, *Cryptomys damarensis* (Rodentia, Bathyergidae). Unpubl.

**Jacobsen, N.H.G.** 1971. Home range, behaviour and feeding preferences of bushbuck in the Lutope River Valley. University of Rhodesia, Salisbury. Mimeograph.

——— 1977. An annotated check list of the amphibians, reptiles and mammals of the Nylsvley Nature Reserve. *S. Afr. Nat. Sci. Prog. Rep.* No. 21. Pretoria: C.S.I.R.

——— 1982a. Observations on the behaviour of slender mongooses, *Herpestes sanguineus*, in captivity. *Säugetierk. Mitt.* **30**: 168–183.

——— 1982b. A note of mating and neonate development of the South African hedgehog (*Erinaceus frontalis*). *Säugetierk. Mitt.* **30**: 199–200.

——— **& du Plessis, E.** 1976. Observations on the ecology and biology of the Cape fruit bat, *Rousettus aegyptiacus leachi*, in the eastern Transvaal. *S. Afr. J. Sci.* **72**: 270–273.

*——— **Viljoen, P.C., Newberry, R.E., de Wet, M.J. & Pietersen, E.** 1987. A contribution to the ecology of the steppe pangolin *Manis temminckii* in the Transvaal. Mimeograph. Division of Nature Conservation, Pretoria.

**Jaeger, E.** 1948. *Tracks and Trailcraft*. New York: MacMillan.

*__Jainudeen, M.R., Katongole, C.B. & Short, R.V.__ 1972. Plasma testosterone levels in relation to musth and sexual activity in the male Asiatic elephant, *Elephas maximus*. *J. Reprod. Fert.* **29**: 99–103.

**Jarman, M.V.** 1970. Attachment to home area in impala. *E. Afr. Wildl. J.* **8**: 198–200.

——— 1976. Impala social behaviour: birth behaviour. *E. Afr. Wildl. J.* **14**: 153–167.

——— **& Jarman, P.J.** 1973. Daily activity of impala. *E. Afr. Wildl. J.* **11**: 75–92.

**Jarman, P.J.** 1971. Diets of large mammals in the woodlands around Lake Kariba, Rhodesia. *Oecologia* **8**: 157–178.

——— 1972. Seasonal distribution of large mammal populations in the unflooded middle Zambezi Valley. *J. Appl. Ecol.* **9**: 277–293.

——— 1974. The social organisation of antelope in relation to their ecology. *Behaviour* **48**: 215–267.

——— **& Jarman, M.V.** 1973. Social behaviour, population structure and reproductive potential in impala. *E. Afr. Wildl. J.* **11**: 329–338.

——— **& Jarman, M.V.** 1974. Impala behaviour and its relation to management, in The behaviour of ungulates and its relation to management. *IUCN Publications, New Series* **24**: 871–881.

**Jarvis, C. & Morris, D.** (eds) 1960. Breeding notes on the hippopotamus and giraffe at Cleveland Zoo. *Int. Zoo Yb.* **2**: 90.

*__Jarvis, J.U.M.__ 1968. The breeding season and litter size of African mole-rats. *J. Reprod. Fert. Suppl.* **6**: 237–248.

——— 1979. Zoogeography, in *Fynbos ecology: a preliminary synthesis*. Eds J. Day, W.R. Siegfried, W.R. Louw & M.L. Jarvis. *S. Afr. Nat. Sci. Prog. Rep.* No. 40. Pretoria: C.S.I.R.

——— **& Sale, J.B.** 1971. Burrowing and burrow patterns of East African molerats, *Tachyoryctes*, *Heliophobius* and *Heterocephalus*. *J. Zool., Lond.* **163**: 451–479.

*__Jeffery, R.C.V. & Hanks, J.__ 1981. Age determination of eland *Taurotragus oryx* (Pallas, 1766) in the Natal Highveld. *S. Afr. J. Zool.* **16**: 113–122.

**Jennison, G.** 1927. *Table of Gestation Periods and Number of Young*. London: Black.

**Jensen, N.** 1977. Game and conservation: bontebok. *Custos* **6**: 42–43.

**Jepsen, G.L.** 1966. Early Eocene bat from Wyoming. *Science, N.Y.* **154**: 1333–1338.

**Jerge, C.R.** 1963. Organisation and function of the trigeminal mesencephalic nucleus. *J. Neurophysiol.* **26**: 379–392.

**Jerison, H.J.** 1973. *Evolution of the brain and intelligence*. New York: Academic Press.

**Jewell, P.A.** 1965. The concept of home range in mammals. *Symp. zool. Soc. Lond.* 18: 85-109.

**Jobaert, A.J.** 1960. Le Lépard. *Zooleo* **56**: 223–230.

*__Johnson, G.L.__. 1901. Contributions to the comparative anatomy of the mammalian eye, chiefly based on opthalmoscopic examination. *Phil. Trans. R. Soc.* (B) **194**: 182.

**Johnston, H.H.** 1884. *The river Congo from its mouth to Bolobo*. London: E.A. Low.

**Johnston, H.J. & Oliff, W.D.** 1954. The oestrous cycle of the female *Rattus (Mastomys) natalensis* as observed in the laboratory. *Proc. zool. Soc. Lond.* **124**: 605–613.

**Johnstone, P.A.** 1971. The sable antelope on Rosslyn Game Ranch in the Matetsi district of Rhodesia. Thesis for Certificate in Field Ecology, University of Rhodesia.

**Jones, C.** 1971. The bats of Rio Muni, West Africa. *J. Mammal.* **52**: 121–140.

——— 1972. Comparative ecology of three pteropid bats in Rio Muni, West Africa. *J. Zool., Lond.* **167**: 353–370.

**Jones, E.C.** 1971. *Isistius brasiliensis*, a squaloid shark, the probable cause of crater wounds on fishes and cetaceans. *Fish. Bull., U.S.* **69**: 791–798.

**Jones, J. & Genoways, H.H.** 1970. Chiropteran systematics. In *About Bats*, pp. 3–21. Eds B.H. Slaughter & D.W. Walton. Dallas: Southern Methodist Press.

**Jones, M.A.** 1978. A scent marking gland in the bushpig *Potamochoerus porcus* (Linn., 1758). *Arnoldia Rhod.* **8**(30): 1–4.

**Jones, O.G.** 1952. Zoo babies. *Zoo news, Adelaide* **3**(6): 130.

**Jones, S.** 1967. Notes on dugong. *Int. Zoo Yb.* **7**: 215–220.

**Jones, T.S.** 1966. Notes on the commoner Sierra Leone mammals. *Niger. Fld.* **31**: 4–17.

**Jonsgard, A. & Lyshoel, P.B.** 1970. A contribution to the knowledge of the biology of the killer whale, *Orcinus orca* (L.). *Nytt Mag. Zool.* **18**: 41–48.

**Joubert, E.** 1969. An ecological study of the black rhinoceros *Diceros bicornis* Linn., 1758 in South West Africa. M.Sc. thesis, University of Pretoria.

*——— 1970. The taxonomic status of the black rhinoceros *D. bicornis* Linn. 1758. *Madoqua* **2**: 27–37.

——— 1971a. Observations on the habitat preferences and population dynamics of the black-faced impala, *Aepyceros petersi* Bocage, 1875 in South West Africa. *Madoqua* **1**: 55–65.

——— 1971b. Ecology, behaviour and population dynamics of the Hartmann zebra, *Equus zebra hartmannae* Matschie, 1898 in South West Africa. D.Sc. thesis, University of Pretoria.

——— 1972. A note on the challenge rituals of territorial male lechwe. *Madoqua* **5**: 63–67.

*——— 1974. Notes on reproduction in the Hartmann zebra *Equus zebra hartmannae* in South West Africa. *Madoqua* ser. **B**: 31–35.

——— **& Eloff, F.C.** 1970. Notes on the ecology and behaviour of the black rhinoceros *Diceros bicornis* Linn. 1758 in South West Africa. *Madoqua* **1**: 5–53.

——— **& Mostert, P.K.N.** 1975. Distribution patterns and status of some mammals in South West Africa. *Madoqua* **9**: 5–44.

**Joubert, S.C.J.** 1970. A study of the social behaviour of the roan antelope, *Hippotragus equinus equinus* (Desmarest, 1804) in the Kruger National Park. M.Sc. thesis, University of Pretoria.

——— 1972. Territorial behaviour of the tsessebe *Damaliscus lunatus lunatus* Burchell in the Kruger National Park. *Zool. Afr.* **7**: 141–156.

——— 1973. The roan antelope. *Custos* **2**(2): 6–13.

——— 1974. The management of rare ungulates in the Kruger National Park. *J. sth Afr. Wildl. Mgmt Ass.* **4**: 67–69.

——— 1976a. The population ecology of the roan antelope. *Hippotragus equinus equinus* (Desmarest, 1804) in the Kruger National Park. D.Sc. thesis, University of Pretoria.

——— 1976b. Rare ungulates and their management in the National Parks of South Africa. Proc. Symp. on Endangered Wildl. in S.A.: Johannesburg: Endangered Wildlife Trust.

*——— 1984. Census and monitoring the herbivorous large mammal populations of the Kruger National Park: 78–99. *Research Report 1983/4*, Research Division, National Parks Board of S.A., Pretoria.

*——— 1986. Censusing and monitoring the herbivorous large mammal populations of the Kruger National Park. *Research Report 1985/86* Research Division, National Parks Board, Skukuza.

——— **& Bronkhorst, P.J.L.** 1977. Some aspects of the history and population ecology of the tsessebe *Damaliscus lunatus lunatus* in the Kruger National Park. *Koedoe* **20**: 125–145.

*__Jouventin, P., Stahl, J-C. & Weimerskirch, H.__ 1982. La recolonisation des iles Crozet par les otaries (*Arctocephalus tropicalis* et *A. gazella*). *Mammalia* **46**: 505–514.

**Jungius, H.** 1970. Studies on the breeding biology of the reedbuck, *Redunca arundinum* Boddaert, 1785 in the Kruger National Park. *Z. Säugetierk.* **35**: 129–146

——— 1971a. *The biology and behaviour of the reedbuck Redunca arundinum Boddaert, 1785 in the Kruger National Park*. Mammalia Depicta. Hamburg: Paul Parey.

*——— 1971b. Studies on the food and feeding behaviour of the reedbuck (*Redunca arundinum* Boddaert, 1785) in the Kruger National Park. *Koedoe* **14**: 56–97.

# K

*__Kamau, J.M.Z.__ 1988. Metabolism and evaporative heat loss in the dik-dik antelope (*Rhynchotragus kirki*). *Comp. Biochem. Physiol.* **89A**: 567–574.

**Kanwisher, J. & Sundnes, G.** 1966. Thermal regulation in cetaceans: pp. 397–409 in *Whales and dolphins* Ed. K.S. Norris. Berkeley: University of California Press.

*__Kasamatsu, F., Hembree, D., Joyce, G., Tsunoda, L., Rowlett, R. & Nakano, T.__ 1988. Distribution of cetacean sightings in the Antarctic: results obtained from the IWC/IDCR minke whale assessment cruises, 1978/79 to 1983/84. *Rep. int. Whal. Commn* **38**: 449–487.

*__Kasuya, T.__ 1975. Past occurrence of *Globicephala melaena* in the western North Pacific. *Sci. Rep. Whales Res. Inst., Tokyo* **27**: 95–110.

*——— 1976. Reconsideration of life history parameters of the spotted and striped dolphins based on cemental layers. *Sci. Rep. Whales Res. Inst., Tokyo* **28**: 73–106.

*——— 1985. Effect of exploitation on reproductive parameters of the spotted and striped dolphins off the Pacific coast of Japan. *Sci. Rep. Whales Res. Inst., Tokyo* **36**: 107–138.

——— **& Ishiara, T.** 1965. Some information on minke whales from the Antarctic. *Scient. Rep. Whales Res. Inst., Tokyo* **19**: 37–43.

*——— **& Marsh, H.** 1984. Life history and reproductive biology of the short-finned pilot whale, *Globicephala macrorhynchus*, off the Pacific coast of Japan. *Rep. int. Whal. Commn* (Special Issue **6**): 259–310.

*——— **& Miyazaki, N.** 1982. The stock of *Stenella coeruleoalba* off the Pacific coast of Japan. Mammals In the Seas. *FAO Fish. Ser.* (5) vol. **4**: 21–37.

*——— **Miyazaki, N. & Dawbin, W.H.** 1974. Growth and reproduction of *Stenella attenuata* in the Pacific coast of Japan. *Sci. Rep. Whales Res. Inst., Tokyo* **26**: 157–226.

*——— **& Ohsumi, S.** 1966. A secondary sexual character of the sperm whale. *Sci. Rep. Whales Res. Inst., Tokyo* **20**: 89–94.

*——— **Sergeant, D.E. & Tanaka, K.** 1988. Re-examination of life history parameters of long-finned pilot whales in the Newfoundland waters. *Sci. Rep. Whales Res. Inst., Tokyo* **39**: 103–119.

**Katsir, Z. & Crewe, R.M.** 1980. Chemical communication in *Galago crassicaudatus*: investigation of the chest gland secretion. *S. Afr. J. Zool.* **15**: 249–254.

**Kayanja, F.I.B.** 1969. The ovary of the impala *Aepyceros melampus* (Lichtenstein 1812). *J. Reprod. Fert. Suppl.* **6**: 311–317.

**Kaufman, G.W., Siniff, D.B. & Reichle, R.** 1975. Colony behaviour of Weddell seals, *Leptonychotes weddelli* at Hutton Cliffs, Antarctica. *Rapp. P-v. Reun. Cons. perm. int. Explor. Mer.* **169**: 228–246.

**Keast, A.** 1965. Interrelationships of two zebra species in an overlap zone. *J. Mammal.* **46**: 53–66.

——— 1972. Comparison of contemporary mammal faunas of southern continents, in *Evolution, mammals and southern Continents*. Eds A. Keast, F.C. Erk & B. Glass. Albany: State University of New York Press.

**Keay, R.W.J.** 1959. *Explanatory notes on vegetation map of Africa south of the Tropic of Cancer (and map 1:10 000 000)*. London: Oxford University Press.

**Keep, M.E.** 1973. Factors contributing to a population crash of nyala in Ndumu Game Reserve. *Ibis* **19**: 16–23.

——— **Barnes, P.R. & Root, A.E.A.** 1974. The marking of male eland to study seasonal movements. *Lammergeyer* **17**: 10–17.

**Kellas, L.M.** 1955. Observations on the reproductive activities, measurements and growth rate of the dik-dik (*Rhynchotragus kirki thomasi*). *Proc. zool. Soc. Lond.* **124**: 751–784.

**Kellogg, A.R.** 1936. A review of the Archaeoceti. *Carnegie Inst. Washington Publ.* **482**(1/15): 1–366.

*__Kemp, A.C. & Rautenbach, I.L.__ 1987. Bat hawks or bat-eating hawks? *Gabar* **2** (2): 4–6.

**Kenmuir, D. & Williams, R.** 1975. *Wild mammals*. Salisbury: Longman.

**Kenneth, J.H.** 1947. Gestation periods. *Tech. Commun. Imp. Bur. Anim. Breed. Genet.*, Edinburgh.

——— **& Ritchie, G.R.** 1953. *Gestation periods: a table and bibliography*. Tech. Commun. No. 5 Imp. Bur. Anim. Breed. Genet. Slough, Bucks: Commonwealth Agricultural Bureaux.

*__Keogh, H.J.__ 1973. Behaviour and breeding in captivity of the Namaqua gerbil *Desmodillus auricularis* (Cricetidae: Gerbillinae). *Zool. Afr.* **8**: 231–240.

——— 1974. Hair characters of thirty-nine species of southern African Muridae and their use as taxonomic criteria. M.Sc. thesis, University of Cape Town.

——— 1979. An atlas of hair from southern African mammal species with reference to its taxonomic and ecological significance. D.Sc. thesis, University of Pretoria.

*Keogh, H.J. 1983. A photographic reference system of the microstructure of the hair of African bovids. S. Afr. J. Wildl. Res. 13: 89–132.
*——— 1985. A photographic reference system based on the cuticular scale patterns and groove of the hair of 44 species of southern African Cricetidae and Muridae. S. Afr. J. Wildl. Res. 15: 109–159.
*Keogh, H. & Price, P.J. 1981. The multimammate mice: a review. S. Afr. J. Sci. 77: 484–488.
Kerbert, C. 1922. Over dracht, geboorte, puberteit en levensduur van Hippopotamus amphibius Linne. Bijdr. Dierk. 22: 185–191.
Kerley, G.I.H. 1981. A guide to the identification of fur seals on Prince Edward Islands. Internal Rep., Mammal Research Institute, University of Pretoria. Mimeograph.
*——— 1983a. Record for the Cape fur seal Arctocephalus pusillus pusillus from subantarctic Marion Island. S. Afr. J. Zool. 18: 139–140.
*——— 1983b. Relative population sizes and trends, and hybridization of fur seals Arctocephalus tropicalis and A. gazella at the Prince Edward Islands, Southern Ocean. S. Afr. J. Zool. 18: 388–392.
*——— 1983c. Comparison of seasonal haul-out patterns of fur seals Arctocephalus tropicalis and A. gazella on subantarctic Marion Island. S. Afr. J. Wildl. Res. 13: 71–77.
*——— 1985. Pup growth in the fur seals, Arctocephalus tropicalis and A. gazella on Marion Island. J. Zool., Lond. 205: 315–324.
*——— 1987. Arctocephalus tropicalis on the Prince Edward Islands. NOAA Techn. Rep. NMFS 51: 61–64.
*——— 1989. Diet of small mammals from the Karoo, South Africa. S. Afr. J. Wildl. Res. 19: 67–72.
*——— & Robinson, T.J. 1987. Skull morphometrics of male Antarctic and Subantarctic fur seals, Arctocephalus gazella and A. tropicalis, and their interspecific hybrids. NOAA Techn. Rep. NMFS 51: 121–131.
Kern, N.G. 1977. The influence of fire on populations of small mammals of the Kruger National Park. M.Sc. thesis, University of Pretoria.
*——— 1981. The influence of fire on populations of small mammals in the Kruger National Park. Koedoe 24: 125–158.
Kerr, M.A. 1965. The age at sexual maturity in male impala. Arnoldia Rhod. 1: 1–6.
*——— 1978. Reproduction of elephant in the Mana Pools National Park, Rhodesia. Arnoldia Rhod. 8: 1–11.
——— & Roth, H.H. 1970. Studies on the agricultural utilization of semi-domesticated eland (Taurotragus oryx) in Rhodesia. 3. Horn development and tooth eruption as indicators of age. Rhod. J. agric. Res. 8: 149–155.
——— & Wilson, V.J. 1967. Notes on reproduction in Sharpe's grysbok. Arnoldia Rhod. 3(17): 1–4.
——— Wilson, V.J. & Roth, H.H. 1970. Studies on the agricultural utilization of semi-domesticated eland (Taurotragus oryx) in Rhodesia. 2. Feeding habits and food preferences. Rhod. J. agric. Res. 8: 71–77.
Kershaw, P.S. 1921. On a collection of South African mammals. Ann. Durban Mus. 3: 27–38.
*——— 1922. On a collection of mammals from Chiromo and Cholo, Ruo, Nyasaland, made by Mr Rodney C. Wood with fieldnotes by the Collector. The Annals and Magazine of Nature History 56: 177–193.
Kettlitz, W.K. 1962a. The distribution of some of the large game mammals in the Transvaal (excluding the Kruger National Park). Ann. Cape Prov. Mus. 2: 118–137.
——— 1962b. Game on farms. Fauna Flora, Pretoria 13: 19–23.
——— 1967. The blesbok, with special reference to the herd in the Percy Fyfe Nature Reserve. Fauna Flora, Pretoria 18: 36–46.
Kiley-Worthington, M. 1965. The waterbuck (Kobus defassa Rüppell, 1835) and K. ellipsiprymnus (Ogilby, 1833) in East Africa: spacial distribution. A study of the sexual behaviour. Mammalia 29: 177–204.
——— 1978. The social organisation of a small captive group of eland, oryx and roan antelope with an analysis of personality profiles. Behaviour 66: 32–55.
King, J.E. 1959a. The northern and southern populations of Arctocephalus gazella. Mammalia 23: 19–40.
——— 1959b. A note on the specific name of the Kerguelen fur seal. Mammalia 23: 381.
——— 1961. The feeding mechanism and jaws of the crabeater seal, Lobodon carcinophagus. Mammalia 25: 462–466.
——— 1964. Seals of the world. London: Trustees of the British Museum (Nat. Hist.).
*——— 1983. Seals of the world, 2nd edn. London: Trustees of the British Museum (Nat. Hist.).
King, J.M. 1965. A field guide to the reproduction of the Grant's zebra and Grevy's zebra. E. Afr. Wildl. J. 3: 99-117.
Kingdon, J. 1971. East African Mammals. Vol. I. (Primates, Hyraxes, Pangolins, Protoungulates, Sirenians). London: Academic Press.
——— 1974. East African Mammals. Vol. IIA (Insectivores & Bats); Part IIB (Hares and Rodents). London: Academic Press.
——— 1977. East African Mammals Vol. IIIA (Carnivores). London: Academic Press.
——— 1979. East African Mammals. Vol. IIIB (Large Mammals). London: Academic Press.
——— 1982. East African Mammals. Vol. IIIC and D. (Bovids). London: Academic Press.
Kirby, F.V. 1896. In Haunts of Wild Game: A hunter naturalist's wanderings from Kahlamba to Libombo. London: Blackwood & Sons.
*——— 1920. The white rhinoceros in Zululand. Ann. Durban Mus. 2: 223–242
*Kleiman, D. 1967. Some aspects of social behavior in the Canidae. Am. Zool. 7: 365–372.
Kleiman, D.G. 1974. Patterns of behaviour in Hystricomorph rodents. Symp. zool. Soc. Lond. 34: 171–209.
*Klein, R.G. 1972. The late quaternary mammalian fauna of Nelson Bay Cave (Cape Province, South Africa): its implications for megafaunal extinctions and environmental and cultural changes. Quat. Res. 2: 135–142.
——— 1974. On the taxonomic status, distribution and ecology of the blue antelope, Hippotragus leucophaeus (Pallas, 1766). Ann. S. Afr. Mus. 65: 99–143.
Klingel, H. 1965. Notes on the biology of the plains zebra (Equus quagga boehmi Matschie). E. Afr. Wildl. J. 3: 86–88.
——— 1967. Soziale Organization und verhalten freilebender Steppenzebras. Z. Tierpsychol. 24: 580–624.
——— 1968. Soziale organization und Verhaltensweissen von Hartman- und Bergzebras (Equus zebra hartmannae und E.z. zebra). Z. Tierpsychol. 25: 76–88.
——— 1969. Reproduction in the plains zebra (Equus burchelli boehmi): behaviour and ecological factors. J. Reprod. Fert. Suppl. 6: 339–346.
——— 1972a. Das Verhalten der Pferde (Equidae). Handb. Zool. 10: 1–66.
——— 1972b. Social behaviour of African Equidae. Zool. Afr. 7: 175–185.
*——— 1979. Social organisation of Hippopotamus amphibius. Verh. Dtsch. Zool. Ges.: 241.
*——— 1983. Life with the gentle giants. Swara 6: 24–27.
*——— 1988. Grossflusspferde (Gattung Hippopotamus). In: Grzimeks Enzyklopädie 5: 64–79.
*——— In press. Social organization and behaviour of Hippopotamus amphibius. Symposium on African Wildlife, Kampala, 1986.
——— & Klingel, U. 1965. Die Geburt eines Zebras (Equus quagga boehmi Matschie). Z. Tierpsychol. 23:72–93.
——— & Klingel, U. 1966a. Tooth development and age determination in the plains zebra (Equus quagga boehmi Matschie). Zool. Gart., Leipzig 33: 34–54.
——— & Klingel, U. 1966b. The rhinoceroses of Ngorongoro Crater. Oryx 8: 302–306.
*Klingelhoeffer, E.W. 1987. Aspects of the ecology of the elephant Loxodonta africana (Blumenbach, 1797) and a management plan for the Tembe Elephant Reserve in Tongaland, KwaZulu. M.Sc. thesis, University of Pretoria.
*Klinowska, M. 1986. The cetacean magnetic sense—evidence from strandings. pp 401–432. In: Research on Dolphins. Eds M.M. Bryden & R. Harrison. Oxford: Clarendon Press.
Knight, M.H. 1984. The ecophysiology of the African giant rat Cricetomys gambianus (Waterhouse). M.Sc. thesis, University of Pretoria.
*——— 1986. Thermoregulation and evaporative water loss in growing African giant rats Cricetomys gambianus. S. Afr. J. Zool. 21: 289–293.
*——— 1987. Food for the Third World. Afr. wild Life 41: 36–41.
*——— 1988. Thermoregulation in the largest African cricetid, the giant rat Cricetomys gambianus. Comp. Biochem. Physiol. 89A: 705–708.
*——— 1989. Rabies outbreak—Kalahari Gemsbok National Park. Int. Union Cons. Nature and Natural Res., Species Survival Commission, Hyaena Specialist Group Newsl. 4: 9–10.
*——— & Knight-Eloff, A.K. 1987. The digestive tract of the African giant rat, Cricetomys gambianus. J. Zool., Lond. 213: 7–22.
*——— & Skinner, J.D. 1981. Thermoregulatory, reproductive and behavioural adaptations of the big-eared desert mouse, Malacothrix typica to its arid environment. J. Arid Environ. 4:137–145.
*——— van Jaarsveld, A.S. & Mills, M.G.L. 1990 submitted. Allo-suckling in spotted hyaenas (Crocuta crocuta): an example of behavioural flexibility in carnivores.
Knobel, R. 1958. The present day status of certain ungulates in the Union of South Africa. Mammalia 22: 498–503.
Kock, D. 1967. Ein Neunachweis von Myotis welwitschi und der Status von Myotis venustus. Senckenberg biol. 48(5/6): 319–325.
——— 1969. Die fledermäus Fauna des Sudan. Frankfurt am Main: W. Kramer.
*Koehler, C. & Richardson, P.R.K. 1990. Proteles cristatus. Mammalian Species. in press.
*Koen, J.H. 1988. Trace elements and some other nutrients in the diet of the Knysna elephants. S. Afr. J. Wildl. Res. 18: 109–110.
*Kofron, C.P. 1987. Seasonal reproduction of the springhare (Pedetes capensis) in southeastern Zimbabwe. Afr. J. Ecol. 25: 185–194.
Kok, O.B. 1975. Gedrag en ekologie van die rooihartbees. Natuurbewaring algemene publikasie Nr. 4, Bloemfontein, Prov. Admin. O.V.S.
——— & Opperman, D.P.J. 1975. Habitatsvoorkeure, tropsamestelling en territoriale status van rooihartbeeste in die Willem Pretorius-wildtuin. J. sth Afr. Wildl. Mgmt Ass. 5: 103–109.
Kok, P.F.D. 1971. The use of anatomical characteristics to identify food plants in the faeces of South African wild animals. Rep., Dept Botany, University of Pretoria. Unpubl. mimeograph.
Kolb, P. 1719. Caput Bonae Spei Hodiernum. Vol. 2. Nurnberg: Monath.
——— 1731. The present state of the Cape of Good Hope: or, a particular account of the several nations of the Hottentots. Vol. 1 and 2. (transl. G. Medley). London: W. Innys.
*Kolbe, F.F. 1983. Dr S.H. Rubidge, on the dassie problem and "lammervanger" controversy 1933–1954. The Naturalist 27: 15–16.
*Koop, K. & Velimirov, B. 1982. Field observations on activity and feeding of bat-eared foxes (Otocyon megalotis) at Nxai Pan, Botswana. Afr. J. Ecol. 20: 23–27.
Koopman, K.F. 1965. Status and forms described or recorded by J.A. Allen in "The American Museum Congo Expedition collection of bats". Am. Mus. Novit. 2219: 1–34.
——— 1966. Taxonomic and distributional notes on Southern African bats. Puku 4: 155–165.
——— 1971. Taxonomic notes on Chalinolobus and Glauconycteris (Chiroptera: Vespertilionidae). Am. Mus. Novit. 2451: 1–10.
——— 1975. Bats of the Sudan. Bull. Am. Mus. nat. Hist. 154: 355–443.
——— Mumford, R.E. & Heisterberg, J.F. 1978. Bat records from Upper Volta, West Africa. Am. Mus. Novit. 2643: 1–6.
Kooyman, G.L. 1967. An analysis of some behavioral and physiological characters related to diving in the Weddell seal, in Antarctic Research Series II. Biology of the Antarctic seas III. Eds G.A. Llano & W.H. Schmitt. Washington D.C.: American Geophysical Union.
*——— 1969. The Weddell seal. Sci. Am. Aug. 1969. 221: 100–106.
*——— 1981. Weddell seal: consummate diver: 1–135. Cambridge: University Press.
*Korn, H. 1986. A case of daily torpor in the golden mole Amblysomus hottentotus (Insectivora) from the Transvaal Highveld, South Africa. Säugetierk. Mittel. 33: 86–87.
*——— 1987. Densities and biomasses of non-fossorial southern African Savanna rodents during the dry season. Oecologia 87: 410–413.
*——— 1989. The annual cycle in body weight of small mammals from the Transvaal, South Africa, as an adaptation to a subtropical seasonal environment. J. Zool., Lond. 218: 223–231.
*——— & Braack, L.E.O. 1987. Survival of wild gerbils (Mammalia: Rodentia) parasitized by larvae of the blowfly Cordylobia anthropophaga (Insecta: Diptera). Z. Säugetierk. 52: 56–57.
*——— & Korn, Ursula 1989. The effect of gerbils (Tatera brantsii) on primary production and plant species composition in a southern African savanna. Oecologia 79: 271–278.
*Kratzing, J.E. & Woodall, P.F. 1988. The rostral nasal anatomy of two elephant shrews. J. Anat. 157: 135–143.
Kritzinger, M.S.B., Steyn, H.A., Schoonees, P.C. & Cronje, W.J. 1968. Groot Woordeboek 10th edn. Pretoria: Van Schaik.
*Kruger, J.C., Skinner, J.D. & Robinson, T.J. 1979. On the taxonomic status of the black and white springbok, Antidorcas marsupialis. S. Afr. J. Sci. 75: 411–412.
*Kruse, S.L., Leatherwood, S., Prematunga, W.P., Mendes, C. & Gamage, A. In press. Records of Risso's dolphins, Grampus griseus, in the Indian Ocean, 1891–1986. Rep. int. Whal. Commn (Special Issue).
Kruuk, H. 1966a. A new view of the hyaena. New Scient. 33: 849–851.

——— 1966b. Clan-system and feeding habits of spotted hyaenas. *Nature, Lond.* **209**: 1257–1258.

——— 1968 Hyaenas, the hunters nobody knows. *Natn. geog. Mag.* **134**(1): 44–57.

——— 1970. Interactions between populations of spotted hyaenas (*Crocuta crocuta* Erx.) and their prey species. *Br. Ecol. Symp.* **10**: 359–374.

——— 1972a. *The spotted hyaena: A Study of predation and social behaviour.* Chicago: University Press.

——— 1972b. Surplus killing by carnivores. *J. Zool., Lond.* **166**: 233–244.

——— **& Sands, W.A.** 1972. The aardwolf (*Proteles cristatus* Sparrman. 1783) as predator of termites. *E. Afr. Wildl. J.* **10**: 211–227.

——— **& Turner, M.** 1967. Comparative notes on predation by lion, leopard, cheetah and wild dog in the Serengeti area, East Africa. *Mammalia* **31**: 1–27.

**Kühme, W.** 1965. Freilandstudien zur Soziologie des Hyänenhundes, *Lycaon pictus lupinus* Thomas, 1902. *Z. Tierpsychol.* **22**: 495–541.

**Kuhn, H.J.** 1965. A provisional check list of the mammals of Liberia. *Senckenberg. biol.* **46**: 321–340.

**Kulzer, von E.** 1958. Untersuchungen über die Biologie von Flughunden der Gatting *Rousettus* Gray. *Z. Morph. Ökol. Tiere* **47**: 374–402.

——— 1962. Fledermäuse aus Tanganyika. *Z. Säugetierk.* **27**: 164–181.

——— 1969. African fruit eating cave bats. Part 1 *Afr. wild Life* **23**: 39–46; Part II *Afr. wild Life* **23**: 129–138.

**Kummer, H.** 1967. Tripartite relations in hamadryas baboons, in *Social communications among Primates.* Ed. S.A. Altmann. Chicago: University Press.

*——— 1968. *Social organisation of hamadryas baboons: A field study.* Chicago: University of Chicago Press.

***Kuntzsch, V. & Nel, J.A.J.**. 1990. Possible thermoregulatory behaviour in *Giraffa camelopardalis. Z. Säugetierk.* **55**: 60–62.

**Kutilek, M.J.** 1975. Feeding strategies and foraging impact of non-migratory African antelope. Ph.D. thesis, Michigan State University.

**Kuyper, M.A.** 1979. A biological study of the golden mole *Amblysomus hottentotus.* M.Sc. thesis, University of Natal.

*——— 1985. The ecology of the golden mole, *Amblysomus hottentotus. Mammal Rev.* **15**: 3–11.

# L

**Labuschagne, W.** 1979. 'n Bio-ekologiese en gedragstudie van die jagluiperd, *Acinonyx jubatus jubatus* (Schreber, 1776). M.Sc. Thesis, University of Pretoria.

**Lack, A.** 1977. Genets feeding on nectar from *Maranthes polyandra* in Northern Ghana. *E. Afr. Wildl. J.* **15**: 233–234.

**Lambert, M.R.K.** 1967. *A report on the Trinity College, Dublin High Atlas & Sahara Expedition, 1966.* London: Fermaprint.

***Lamprecht, J.** 1978. On diet, foraging behaviour and interspecific food competition of jackals in the Serengeti National Park, East Africa. *Z. Saügetierk.* **43**: 210–223.

*——— 1979. Field observations on the behaviour and social system of the bat-eared fox *Otocyon megalotis* Desmarest. *Z. Tierpsychol.* **49**: 260–284.

**Lamprechts, A. von W.** 1971. Getalle en verspreiding van sekere wildsoorte in die Transvaal buite die Nasionale Krugerwildtuin. Unpubl. Research Rep., Transvaal Nature Conservation Division. Mimeograph.

——— 1974. The numerical status of sixteen game species in the Transvaal, excluding the Kruger National Park. *J. sth Afr. Wildl. Mgmt Ass.* **4**: 95–102.

**Lamprey, H.F.** 1963. Ecological separation of the large mammal species in the Tarangire Game Reserve, Tanganyika. *E. Afr. Wildl. J.* **1**: 63–92.

**La Muniere, C.H.** 1962. Notes on hunting and poaching on the Kafue Flats. Unpubl. Research Rep., N. Rhod. Dept Game & Fisheries. Mimeograph.

***Landry, S.O.** 1970. The Rodentia as omnivores. *Quart. Rev. Biol.* **45**: 351–372.

***Lang, T.G. & Norris, K.S.** 1966. Swimming speed of a Pacific bottlenose porpoise. *Science* 151 (3710): 588–590.

*——— **& Pryor, K.** 1966. Hydronamic performance of porpoises (*Stenella attenuata*). *Science* 152 (3721): 531–533.

**Langenegger, O. & Verwoerd, W.J.** 1971. Topographic survey, in *Marion and Prince Edward Islands.* Eds E.M. van Zinderen Bakker, Sr, J.M. Winterbottom & R.A. Dyer. Cape Town: Balkema.

**Langman, V.A.** 1973. Radio-tracking giraffe for ecological studies. *J. sth Afr. Wildl. Mgmt Ass.* **3**: 75–78.

——— 1977. Cow-calf relationship in giraffe. *Z. Tierpsychol.* **43**: 264–286.

——— 1978. Giraffe pica behaviour and pathology as indicators of nutritional stress. *J. Wildl. Mgmt* **42**: 141–147.

**Largen, M.J., Kock, D. & Yalden, D.W.** 1974. Catalogue of the mammals of Ethiopia. I. Chiroptera. *Monitore zool. ital.* N.S. Suppl. 5, **16**: 221–298.

**La Trobe, C.I.** 1818. *Journal of a visit to South Africa in 1815 and 1816 with some account of the missionary settlements of the united brethren, near the Cape of Good Hope.* London: L.B. Seeley.

**Laurie, E.M.O.** 1945. The reproduction of the house mouse (*Mus musculus*) living in different environments. *Proc. zool. Soc. Lond.* **133**: 248–281.

***LaVal, R.K. & LaVal, M.L.** 1977. Reproduction and behaviour of the African banana bat, *Pipistrellus nanus. J. Mammal* **58**: 403–410.

*——— 1980. Prey selection by the slit-faced bat *Nycteris thebaica* (Chiroptera: Nycteridae) in Natal, South Africa. *Biotropica* **12**: 241–246.

**Lavanden, L.** 1926a. *Vertebres du Sahara.* Tunis: Guenard.

——— 1926b. Notes de mammalogie nord-africaine les genettes. *Bull. Soc. Hist. nat. Afr. N.* **17**: 51–54.

***Lawes, M.J.** 1989. Samango monkey radiation in South Africa. pp 60–80 Ch. 6. In: *Biogeography of mixed evergreen forests of southern Africa.* Ed. C.J. Geldenhuys. Report No. 45. Pretoria, Foundation for Research Development.

*——— **Henzi, S.P. & Perrin, M.R.P.** 1990. Diet and feeding behaviour of samango monkeys (*Cercopithecus mitis labiatus*) in Ngoye forest, R.S.A. *Folia primatol.* in press.

**Lawrence, B.** 1964. Notes on the horseshoe bats *Hipposideros caffer, ruber* and *beatus. Breviora* **207**: 1–5.

——— **& Loveridge, A.** 1953. Zoological results of a fifth expedition to East Africa. I. Mammals from Nyasaland and Tete. *Bull. Mus. comp. Zool. Harv.* **110**: 1–80.

**Lawrence, M.J. & Brown, R.W.** 1967. *Mammals of Britain: their tracks, trails and signs.* London: Blandford Press.

***Lawrence, R.F.** 1963. The Solifugae of South West Africa. *Cimbebasia* No. **8**: 1–28.

**Laws, R.M.** 1953. The elephant seal (*Mirounga leonina* Linn.). I. Growth and age. *F.I.D.S. Scientific Reports* **8**: 1–62.

——— 1960. The southern elephant seal (*Mirounga leonina* Linn.) at South Georgia. *Norsk Hvalfangsttid.* **49**: 466–476 & 520–542.

——— 1966. Age criteria for the African elephant *Loxodonta africana. E. Afr. Wildl. J.* **4**: 1–37.

——— 1969a. Tsavo research project. *J. Reprod. Fert.* Suppl. **6**: 495–531.

——— 1969b. Aspects of reproduction in the African elephant, *Loxodonta africana. J. Reprod. Fert.* Suppl. **6**: 193–217.

*——— 1970. Biology of the African elephant. *Sci. Prog. Oxf.* **58**: 251–262.

*——— 1984. Seals: 621–715, in *Antarctic Ecology*, Ed. R.M. Laws. Vol. 2. London: Academic Press.

*——— 1986. Introduction to the Colloquium. A decade of research on Antarctic and sub-Antarctic seals. *S. Afr. J. Sci.* **80**: 25–35.

——— **& Clough, G.** 1966. Observations on reproduction in the hippopotamus, *Hippopotamus amphibius* Linn. *Symp. zool. Soc. Lond.* **15**: 117–140.

——— **& Parker, I.S.C.**. 1968. Recent studies on elephant populations in East Africa. *Symp. zool. Soc. Lond.* **21**: 319.

——— **Parker, I.S.C. & Johnstone, R.C.B.**. 1970. Elephants and habitats in North Bunyoro, Uganda. *E. Afr. Wildl. J.* **8**: 163–180.

——— **Parker, I.S.C. & Johnstone, R.C.B.** 1975. *Elephants and their habitats.* Oxford: Clarendon Press.

——— **& Taylor, R.J.F.** 1957. A mass dying of crabeater seals, *Lobodon carcinophagus* (Gray). *Proc. zool. Soc. Lond.* **129**: 315–324.

***Lawson, D.** 1986. The ecology and conservation of suni in Natal. Ph.D. thesis, University of Natal, Pietermaritzburg.

**Laycock, P.** 1973. Distribution and abundance of bats in the Natal midlands. *Ann. Trans. Mus.* **28**: 207–227.

**Leakey, L.S.B.** 1965. *Olduvai Gorge 1951–1961. Fauna and Background.* Cambridge: University Press.

——— 1969. *Animals of East Africa.* Washington: National Geographic Magazine.

***Leatherwood, S. & Reeves, R.R.** 1983. *The Sierra Club handbook of whales and dolphins.* San Francisco: Sierra Club Books.

*——— **Reeves, R.R., Perrin, W.F. & Evans, W.E.** 1988. *Whales, dolphins and porpoises of the Eastern North Pacific and adjacent Arctic waters: a guide to their identification.* New York: Dover Publications.

——— **& Walker, W.A.** 1979. The northern right whale dolphin *Lissodelphis borealis* Peale in the eastern North Pacific, **3**: 85–141, in *Behaviour of marine mammals: current perspectives in research.* Eds H.W. Winn & B.L. Olla. New York: Plenum.

***Le Boeuf, B.J. & Ortiz, C.L.** 1977. Composition of elephant seal milk. *J. Mammal.* **58**: 683–685.

*——— **Costa, D.P., Huntley, A.C. & Feldkamp, S.D.** 1988. Continuous, deep diving in female northern elephant seals, *Mirounga angustirostris. Can. J. Zool.* **66**: 446–458.

**Ledger, H.P.** 1963. Weights of some East African mammals. *E. Afr. Wildl. J.* **1**: 123–124.

**Ledger, J.A.** 1968. The lice of mammals. *Fauna Flora, Pretoria* **19**: 61–65.

**Leibbrandt, H.C.V.** 1896. *Precis of the archives of the Cape of Good Hope: Letters received, 1695–1708.* Cape Town: Richards & Sons.

——— 1900. *Precis of the archives of the Cape of Good Hope: Letters despatched from the Cape, 1652–1662.* Vols **1, 2, 3**. Cape Town: W.A. Richards & Sons.

**Leistner, O.A.** 1959. Notes on the vegetation of the Kalahari Gemsbok National Park with special reference to its influence on the distribution of antelopes. *Koedoe* **2**: 128–151.

——— 1967. *The plant ecology of the southern Kalahari.* Pretoria: Bot. Survey Mem. 38.

**Leitch, I., Hytten, F.E. & Billewicz, W.Z.** 1959. The maternal and neonatal weights of some Mammalia. *Proc. Zool. Soc. Lond.* **133**: 11–28.

**Lenglart, P.Y. & Bester, M.N.** 1982. Post-weaning dispersion of southern elephant seal *Mirounga leonina* underyearlings at Kerguelen. *Rev. Ecol. (Terre Vie)* **36**: 175–186.

**Lent, P.C.** 1969. A preliminary study of the Okavango lechwe (*Kobus leche leche* Gray). *E. Afr. Wildl. J.* **7**: 147–157.

***Leon, B.** 1980. Fermentation and production of volatile fatty acids in the alimentary tract of the rock hyrax, *Procavia capensis. Comp. Biochem. Physiol.* **A65**: 411–420.

***Leonard, M.L. & Fenton, M.B.** 1984. Echolocation calls of *Euderma maculatum* (Vespertilionidae): Use in orientation and communication. *J. Mammal.* **65**: 122–126.

**Le Riche, M.** 1970. Birth of an oribi. *Africana* **4**: 40–42.

***Le Roux, P.G.** 1988. Report on the 1988 aerial game census, N.E. Tuli Block, Botswana. Unpubl. Report, Mashatu Game Reserve, 4pp.

*——— **& Skinner, J.D.** 1989. A note on the ecology of the leopard (*Panthera pardus* Linnaeus) in the Londolozi Game Reserve, South Africa. *Afr. J. Ecol.* **27**: 167–171.

**Leuthold, B.M. & Leuthold, W.** 1972. Food habits of giraffe in Tsavo National Park, Kenya. *E. Afr. Wildl. J.* **10**: 129–141.

**Leuthold, W.** 1970. Observations on the social organisation of impala (*Aepyceros melampus*) *Z. Tierpsychol.* **27**: 693–721.

——— 1971. Studies on the food habits of lesser kudu in Tsavo National Park, Kenya. *E. Afr. Wildl. J.* **9**: 35–45.

——— 1972. Home range, movements and food of a buffalo herd in Tsavo National Park. *E. Afr. Wildl. J.* **10**: 237–243.

——— **& Sale, J.B.** 1973. Movement and patterns of habitat utilisation of elephant in Tsavo National Park, Kenya. *E. Afr. Wildl. J.* **11**: 369–384.

——— **& Sale, J.B.** 1977. *African ungulates. A comparative review of their ethology and behavioural ecology.* Zoophysiology and Ecology 8, Springer: Berlin.

**Le Vaillant, F.** 1790. *Travels into the interior parts of Africa, 1780, 1785.* Vols **1** and **2**. London: Robinson.

——— 1796. *New travels into the interior parts of Africa by way of the Cape of Good Hope in the years 1783, 1784, 1785.* Vols **1, 2** and **3**. London: Robinson.

**Leyhausen, P.** 1965. The communal organisation of solitary animals. *Symp. zool. Soc. Lond.* **14**: 249–263.

——— **& Toukin, B.** 1966. Breeding of the black-footed cat, *Felis nigripes*, in captivity. *Int. Zoo Yb.* **6**: 178–182.

——— **& Wolff, R.** 1959. Das Revier einer Hauskatze. *Z. Tierpsychol.* **16**: 666–700.

**Lichtenstein, W.H.C.** 1812–1815. *Travels in southern Africa, in the years 1803–1806.* 1812 Vol. **1** 1928 reprinted edition: 1915 Vol. **2** 1930 reprinted edition. Transl. A. Plumtree. Cape Town: Van Riebeeck Society.

***Lichter, A.A.** 1986. Records of beaked whales (Ziphiidae) from the western south Atlantic. *Sci. Rep. Whales Res. Inst.* **37**: 109–127.

*——— **Fraga, F. & Castello, H.P.** 1990. First record of the pygmy killer whale, *Feresa attenuata*, in the southwest Atlantic. *Mar. Mammal Sci.* **6**: 85–86.

**Lightfoot, C.J.** 1970. *Common veld grasses of Rhodesia.* Salisbury: Government Printer.

——— **& Posselt, J.** 1976. Eland (*Taurotragus oryx*) as a ranching animal complementary to cattle in Rhodesia. *Rhodesia agric. J.* **74**: 85–91.

**Ligon, S.** 1976. Aerial survey of the dugong in Kenya. *F.A.O. Ad. Com. on Marine Resources Res.*, Bergen, Norway. Aug/Sept: 1–2.

**Lillie, D.G.** 1915. British Antarctic (Terra Nova) Expedition, 1910. *Nat. Hist. Rep. Br. Antarct. Terra Nova Exped. (Zool.)* **1**: 85–125.

**Lilly, J.C.** 1963. Distress call of the bottlenose dolphin: stimuli and evoked behavioural responses. *Science* **139**: 116–118.

——— & **Miller, A.M.** 1961. Sounds emitted by the bottlenose dolphin. *Science* **133**: 1689–1693.
**Lindeque, M.** 1981. Reproduction in the spotted hyaena, *Crocuta crocuta* (Erxleben). M.Sc. thesis, University of Pretoria.
*——— 1987. Observations on mating behaviour in the common slit-faced bat *Nycteris thebaica*. *Madoqua*. **15**: 183–185.
*——— 1988. Population dynamics of elephants in Etosha National Park, S.W.A./ Namibia. Ph.D. thesis, University of Stellenbosch.
——— & **Skinner, J.D.** 1982a. Aseasonal breeding in the spotted hyaena (*Crocuta crocuta*, Erxleben) in southern Africa. *Afr. J. Ecol.* **20**: 271–278.
——— & **Skinner, J.D.** 1982b. Fetal androgens and sexual mimicry in spotted hyaenas (*Crocuta crocuta*). *J. Reprod. Fert.* **65**: 405–410.
*——— & **Skinner, J.D.** 1984. Size frequency analysis of tooth wear in spotted hyaenas *Crocta crocuta*. *S. Afr. J. Zool.* **19**: 291–294.
*——— **Skinner, J.D. & Millar, R.P.** 1986. Adrenal and gonadal contribution to circulating androgens in spotted hyaenas (*Crocuta crocuta*) as revealed by LHRH, hCG and ACTH stimulation. *J. Reprod. Fert.* **78**: 211–217.
**Lindsey, A.A.** 1937. The Weddell Seal in the Bay of Whales, Antarctica. *J. Mammal.* **18**: 127–144.
——— 1938. Notes on the crabeater seal. *J. Mammal.* **19**: 459–461.
**Linley, T.A.** 1965. Aardwolf at East London Zoo. *Int. Zoo. Yb.* **5**: 145.
***Little, J.S.** 1884. *South Africa: a sketchbook of men, manners and facts.* Vols **1** & **2**. London: Swan, Sonneschein & Co.
**Liversidge, R.** 1968. Problems on the investigation of grazing competition between springbok and sheep. Report, McGregor Museum, Kimberley. Mimeograph.
——— 1970. Identification of grazed grasses using epidermal characters. *Proc. Grassld Soc. S. Afr.* **5**: 153–165.
——— 1973. Cropping springbok. Symp. Wildl. Conserve Util. in Africa. Pretoria. Mimeograph.
*——— & **de Jager** 1984. Reproductive parameters from hand-reared springbok *Antidorcas marsupialis* *S. Afr. J. Wildl. Res.* **14**: 26–27.
**Livingstone, D.** 1857. *Missionary travels and researches in South Africa.* London: Murray.
**Lloyd, P.H.** 1974. Thar project plan. Cape Dept of Nature and Environmental Conservation. Mimeograph.
——— 1975a. A study of Himalayan thar (*Hemitragus jemlahicus*) and its potential effects on the ecology of the Table Mountain range. Cape Dept of Nature and Environmental Conservation. Mimeograph.
——— 1975b. A report on the study of Himalayan thar on Table Mountain. Cape Dept. of Nature and Environmental Conservation. Mimeograph.
——— 1979. A report on reedbuck and suitable habitat in the Komgha area. Research Report, Cape Dept of Nature and Environmental Conservation: 93-105. Mimeograph.
*——— 1984. The Cape mountain zebra. *Afr. wild Life* **38**: 144–147.
——— & **Harper, D.A.** 1980. A case of adoption and rejection of foals in Cape mountain zebra, *Equus zebra zebra*. *S. Afr. J. Wildl. Res.* **10**: 61–62.
*——— & **Rasa, O.A.E.** 1989. Status, reproductive success and fitness in Cape mountain zebra (*Equus zebra zebra*). *Behav. Ecol. Sociobiol.* **25**: 411–420.
**Loche, P.** 1867. Histoire naturelle des mammifères in Exploration scientifique de L'Algerie pendant les années 1840, 1841, 1842. *Sciences physiques Zoologie*: 1–123.
***Lockyer, C.** 1976a. Body weights of some species of large whales. *J. Cons. int. Explor. Mer* **36**: 259–273.
*——— 1977. Observations on diving behaviour of the sperm whale, *Physeter catodon*. pp 591–609. In: *Voyage of Discovery*. Ed. M. Angel. Oxford: Pergamon Press.
*——— 1981a. Growth and energy budgets of large baleen whales from the Southern Hemisphere. Mammals in the Seas. *FAO Fish. Ser.* (5) vol. **3**: 379–487.
——— 1981b. Estimates of growth and energy budget for the sperm whale, *Physeter catodon*. Mammals in the Seas. *F.A.O. Fish Ser.* (5) 489–504.
*——— 1984. Review of baleen whale (Mysticeti) reproduction and implications for management. *Rep. int. Whal. Commn* (Special Issue **6**): 27–50.
**Lombard, G.L.** 1958. The water mongoose, *Atilax paludinosus*. *Fauna Flora, Pretoria* **9**: 25–27.
——— 1961. The Cape fruit bat. *Fauna Flora, Pretoria* **12**: 39–45.
**Longhurst, W.M.** 1958. Wildlife research in Uganda. Progress Report No. 3: 1–44. Mimeograph.
**Lönnberg, E.** 1901. Studies on ruminants. *K. svenska Vetensk. Akad. Handl.* **35**: 21–27.
——— 1908. Notes on some mammals collected in the Congo Free State. *Ark. Zool., Stockholm* **4**: 1–14.
***Lopez, J.C. & Lopez, D.** 1985. Killer whales (*Orcinus orca*) of Patagonia, and their behavior of intentional stranding while hunting nearshore. *J. Mammal.* **66**: 181–183.
***Loskutoff, N.M., Raphael, B.L., Nemec, L.A., Wolfe, B.A., Howard, J.G. & Kraemer, D.C.** 1990. Reproductive anatomy, manipulation of ovarian activity and non-surgical embryo recovery in suni (*Neotragus moschatus zuluensis*). *J. Reprod. Fert.* **88**: 521–532.
**Lousada, A.** 1956. Rearing serval cats. *City Life* **120**: 330–331.
***Loutit, Blythe D.** 1984. A study of the survival means of the black rhino (*Diceros bicornis*) in the arid areas Damaraland and Skeleton Coast Park. *Quagga* **7**: 4–5.
——— & **Lindeque, M.** 1988. A great step for the desert giants. Quagga **22**: 26–28.
*——— **Louw, G.N. & Seely, M.K.** 1987. First approximation of food preferences and the chemical composition of the diet of the desert-dwelling black rhinoceros, *Diceros bicornis* L. *Madoqua* **15**: 35–54.
***Louw, C.J. & Nel, J.A.J.** 1986. Diets of coastal and inland-dwelling water mongoose. *S. Afr. J. Wildl. Res.* **16**: 153–156.
**Louw, E., Louw, G.N. & Retief, C.P.** 1972. Thermoability, heat tolerance and renal function in the dassie or hyrax, *Procavia capensis*. *Zool. Afr.* **7**: 451–469.
**Louw, G.N. & Seely, M.K.** 1982. *The ecology of desert organisms.* London: Longmans.
***Lovegrove, B.G. & Jarvis, J.U.M.** 1986. Co-evolution between mole-rats (Bathyergidae) and a geophyte, *Micranthus* (Iridaceae). *Cimbebasia* A **8**: 79–85.
*——— & **Painting, S.** 1987. Variation in the foraging behaviour and burrow structure of the Damara mole-rat *Cryptomys damarensis* in the Kalahari Gemsbok National Park. *Koedoe* **30**: 149–163.
**Lovejoy, T.E.** 1979. The twenty-first bestiary. *Dodo* **16**: 8–11.
**Loveridge, A.** 1922. Notes on East African mammals (other than horned ungulates) collected or kept in captivity. Part 2. *Jl E. Africa Uganda nat. Hist. Soc.* **17**: 39–69.
——— 1923. Notes on East African mammals collected 1920–1923. *Proc. zool. Soc. Lond.*: 685–739.
——— 1928. Field notes on vertebrates collected by Smithsonian Chrysler East African expedition. *Proc. U.S. Natn. Mus.* **73**: 1–69.
——— 1945. The giraffe at home. *Frontiers (Philadelphia)* **10**: 26–27.
***Lowenstein, J.M. & Ryder, O.A.** 1985. Immunological systematics of the extinct quagga (Equidae). *Experientaia* **41**: 1192–1193.
**Lowther, F. de L.** 1939. The feeding and grooming habits of the Galago. *Zoologica, N.Y.* **24**: 477–480.
——— 1940. A study of the activities of a pair of *Galago senegalensis moholi* in captivity, including the birth and postnatal development of twins. *Zoologica, N.Y.* **25**: 433–462.
**Lundholm, B.G.** 1949. Sable is a prince among antelopes. *Afr. wild Life* **3**: 185–192.
——— 1955a. Description of new mammals. *Ann. Trans. Mus.* **22**: 279–304.
——— 1955b. A taxonomic study of *Cynictis penicillata* (G. Cuvier). *Ann. Trans. Mus.* **22**: 305–320.
**Lups, P.** 1977. Gebiss- und Zahnvariationen an einer Serie von 257 Hauskatzen (*F. catus* L. 1758) (Mammalia, Felidae). *Zool. Abh. Mus. Tierk., Dresden* **34**: 155–165.
***Lydekker, R.** 1904. Note on the skull and markings of the quagga. *Proc. zool. Soc. Lond.*: 426–431.
——— 1908. *The Game Animals of Africa.* London: Rowland Ward.
——— 1916. *Wild Life of the World.* London: Warne.
——— & **Blaine, G.** 1914. *Catalogue of the ungulate mammals in the British Museum (Natural History). Vol.* **3**, Artiodactyla. London: Trustees, British Museum (Nat. Hist.)
**Lynch, C.D.** 1971. A behavioural study of blesbok (*Damaliscus dorcas phillipsi*) with special reference to territoriality. M.Sc. thesis, University of Pretoria.
——— 1974. A behavioural study of blesbok, *Damaliscus dorcas phillipsi* with special reference to territoriality. *Memoir 8, Memoirs of the National Museum, Bloemfontein*: 1–83.
——— 1975. The distribution of mammals in the Orange Free State, South Africa. *Navors. nas. Mus., Bloemfontein* **3**: 109–139.
——— 1979. Ecology of the suricate, *Suricata suricatta*, and yellow mongoose, *Cynictis penicillata*, with special reference to their reproduction. D.Sc. thesis, University of Pretoria.
*——— 1980. Ecology of the suricate, *Suricata suricatta* and yellow mongoose, *Cynictis penicillata*, with special reference to their reproduction. *Mem. nas. Mus., Bloemfontein.* **14**: 1–145.
——— 1981. The status of the Cape grey mongoose, *Herpestes pulverulentus* Wagner, 1839 (Mammalia: Viverridae). *Navors. nas. Mus., Bloemfontein* **4**: 121–168.
*——— 1983. The mammals of the Orange Free State. *Mem. nas. Mus., Bloemfontein* **18**: 1–218.
*——— 1986. The ecology of the lesser dwarf shrew *Suncus varilla* with reference to the use of termite mounds of *Trinervitermes trinervoides*. *Navors. nas. Mus. Bloemfontein* **5**: 278–297.
*——— 1989. The mammals of the north-eastern Cape Province. *Mem. nas. Mus., Bloemfontein* **25**: 1–116.
***Lyons, N.F., Gordon, D.H. & Green, C.A.** 1980. G-banding chromosome analysis of species A of the *Mastomys natalensis* complex (Smith, 1834) (Rodentia: Muridae). *Genetica* **54**: 209–212.
——— **Gordon, D.H., Green, C.A. & Walters, C.R.** 1977. G-banding chromosome analysis of *Praomys natalensis* (Smith) (Rodentia: Muridae) from Rhodesia 1. Chromosome population. *Heredity* **38**: 197–200.

# M

**Maberly, C.T.A.** 1950. The African bushpig—sagacious and intelligent. *Afr. wild Life* **4**: 14–18.
——— 1955. The African civet. *Afr. wild Life* **9**: 55–58.
——— 1959. *Animals of Rhodesia.* Cape Town: Howard Timmins.
——— 1963. *The Game Animals of Southern Africa.* Cape Town: Nelson.
——— 1964. A "predator" duiker. *Afr. wild Life* **18**: 171.
***MacDonald, D.W.** 1984. *The encyclopedia of mammals*, Vol. 1 & 2. London: George Allen & Unwin.
*——— **Ball, F.G. & Hough, N.G.** 1980. The evaluation of home range size and configuration using radio tracking. In *A handbook on Biotelemetry and radio tracking* Eds C.J. Amlaner & D.W. MacDonald. Oxford: Pergamon Press.
***MacDonald, I.A.W.** 1982. The influence of short term climate fluctuations on the distribution of savanna organisms in southern Africa. M.Sc. thesis, University of Natal.
***MacDonald, J.T. & Nel, J.A.J.** 1986. Comparative diets of four sympatric small carnivores. *S. Afr. J. Wildl. Res.* **16**: 115–121.
***Mackay, Margo.** 1983. *The Knysna elephants and their forest home.* Knysna: Wildlife Society of Southern Africa.
**Mackenzie, R.Z.** 1954. Catalogue of mammals of the Sudan. *Sudan Mus. (Nat. Hist.) Publ.* **4**: 1–21.
***Mackie, A.J.** 1988. Bat-eared foxes *Otocyon megalotis* as predators of harvester termites *Hodotermes mossambicus* in the Orange Free State. M.Sc. thesis, University of Stellenbosch.
*——— & **Nel, J.A.J.** 1989. Habitat selection, home range use and group size of bat-eared foxes in the Orange Free State. *S. Afr. J. Wildl. Res.* **19**: 135–139.
**Mackie, C.** 1976. Feeding habits of the hippopotamus on the Lundi river, Rhodesia. *Arnoldia Rhod.* **7**(34): 1–16.
**Mackintosh, N.A.** 1966. The distribution of southern blue and fin whales. In: *Whales, dolphins and porpoises.* Ed. K.S. Norris. Berkeley: University of California Press.
——— 1972. Distribution of Antarctic krill in relation to ice and water conditions. *Discovery Rep.* **36**: 1–94.
——— & **Brown, S.G.** 1974. Whales and whaling, in *Antarctic mammals*. Ed. V.C. Bushnell. New York: American Geographical Society.
**MacClintock, D. & Ferguson, W.** 1970. *Squirrels of North America.* London: Van Nostrand.
**McBride, A.F. & Kritzler, H.** 1951. Observations on pregnancy, parturition and post-natal behaviour in the bottlenose dolphin. *J. Mammal.* **32**: 251–266.
***McBride, C.** 1981. *The white lions of Timbavati.* London: Paddington Press.
***McBride, C.J.** 1982. Age and size categories of lion prey in Chobe National Park, Botswana. *Botswana Notes and Records.* **16**: 139–143.
**McCann, C.** 1975. A study of the genus *Berardius* Duvernoy. *Sci. Rep. Whales Res. Inst. Tokyo* **27**: 111–137.
*——— & **Talbot, F.H.** 1963. The occurrence of True's beaked whale (*Mesoplodon mirus* True) in South African waters, with a key to South African species of the genus. *Proc. Linn. Soc. Lond.* **175** : 137–144.
***McCann, T.S. & Doidge, D.W.** 1987. Antarctic fur seal, *Arctocephalus gazella*. *NOAA Techn. Rep. NMFS* **51**: 5–8.
***McIntosh, B.M., Dickinson, D.B., Meenehan, G.M. & Dos Santos, I.S.L.** 1976. *Culex (Eumelanomyia) rubinotus* Theobald as vector of Banzi, Germiston & Witwatersrand viruses. II. Infections in sentinal hamsters and wild rodents. *J. Med. Entomol.* **12**: 641–644.
***McKenna, M.C.** 1975. Toward a phylogenetic classification of the Mammalia, pp 21–46. In: *Phylogeny of the Primates: a multidisciplinary approach.* Eds W.P. Luckett & S. Szalay. New York: Plenum Publishing.

*McKenzie, A.A. 1989. Do spotted hyaena clans possess social memory? *Int. Union Cons. Nature Natural Res., Species Survival Comm., Hyaena Specialist Group Newsl.* **4**: 11–15.
*——— 1990. The ruminant dental grooming apparatus. *Zool. J. Linn. Soc.*. **99**: 117–128.
**McLaren, I.A.** 1960. Are the Pinnipedia biphyletic? *Syst. Zool.* **9**: 18–28.
**McLachlan, G.R., Liversidge, R. & Tietz, R.M.** 1966. A record of *Berardius arnuxii* from the south-east coast of South Africa. *Ann. Cape Prov. Mus.* **5**: 91–100.
**McLoughlin, R.T.** 1970. Aspects of the biology of the cheetah *Acinonyx jubatus* (Schreber) in Nairobi National Park. M.Sc. thesis, University of Nairobi.
**McMahon, R.P.** 1977. Aspects of the behaviour of samango monkeys (*Cercopithecus (mitis) albogularis labiatus*). M.Sc. thesis, University of Natal.
***McNab, B.K.** 1984. Physiological convergence amongst ant-eating and termite-eating mammals. *J. Zool., Lond.* **203**: 485–510.
**McNairn, I.S. & Fairall, N.** 1979. Relationship between the heart rate and metabolism in the hyrax (*Procavia capensis*) and guineapig (*Cavia porcellus*). *S. Afr. J. Zool.* **14**: 230–232.
*——— **& Fairall, N.** 1984. Metabolic rate and body temperature of adult and juvenile hyrax (*Procavia capensis*). *Comp. Biochem. Physiol.* **A79**: 539–545.
**McSpadden, J.W.** (Ed.) 1917. *Animals of the World*. New York: Garden.
**Maddock, A.H.** 1981. The gastric morphology of the white-tailed rat, *Mystromys albicaudatus* (A. Smith, 1834) and preliminary investigations of its digestive process. M.Sc. thesis, Rhodes University, Grahamstown.
*——— 1986. *Chrysospalax trevelyani*, an unknown and rare mammal endemic to southern Africa. *Cimbebasia* Ser. A **8**: 87–90.
*——— 1989. The wild dog photographic project; final report. *Quagga* **28**: 18–20.
*——— **& Hickman, G.C.** 1985. A preliminary report on locomotory activity in wild and captive *Chrysospalax trevelyani* (Mammalia: Chrysochloridae). *S. Afr. J. Zool.* **20**: 271–273.
**Maddock, I.** 1968. The care and breeding of leopards (*Panthera pardus*) at the Jersey Zoological Park. *Jersey Wildl. Pres. Trust 5th Ann. Rep.* 42–43.
***Maguire, J.M., Pemberton, D. & Collett, M.H.** 1980. The Makapansgat limeworks grey breccia: hominids, hyaenas, hystricids or hillwash? *Palaeont. afr.* **23**: 75–98.
***Maier, W. & Schrenk, F.** 1987. The hystricomorphy of the Bathyergidae, as determined from ontogenetic evidence. *Sonderdruck aus Z. f. Säugetierk.* **52**: 156–164.
**Mainoya, J.R. & Urasa, F.M.** 1982. Occurrence and histology of the sternal gland in the greater bushbaby, *Galago crassicaudatus*. *Afr. J. Ecol.* **20**: 199–205.
***Makacha, S.** 1969. Observations on lions in the Lake Manyara National Park, Tanzania. *E. Afr. Wildl. J.* **7**: 99–103.
**Malbrant, R. & MacLatchy, A.** 1949. Faune de l'equateur africain francais. I. Mammifères. *Encycl. biol.* **36**: 1–323.
***Malcolm, J.R.** 1980. Food caching by African wild dogs. *J. Mammal.* **61**: 743–744.
*——— 1986. Socio-ecology of bat-eared foxes (*Otocyon megalotis*). *J. Zool., Lond.* (A) **208**: 457–467.
**Mallison, J.J.G.** 1969. Notes on the breeding of the African civet, *Viverra civetta* at Jersey Zoo. *Int. Zoo Yb.* **9**: 92–93.
——— 1972. The reproduction of the African civet, *Viverra civetta* at Jersey Zoo. *Int. Zoo Yb.* **14**: 184–187.
**Mandelbrote, J.H.** (translator). 1921, 1925. *A geographical and topographical description of the Cape of Good Hope.* 1921 Vol. **1** Mentzel (1785); 1925 Vol. **2** Mentzel (1787) from original German: Mentzel, O.F. 1785 and 1787. Cape Town: Van Riebeeck Society.
**Mansfield, A.W.** 1958. The breeding behaviour and reproductive cycle of the Weddell seal, *Leptonychotes weddelli*, (Lesson). *Falkland Is. Depend. Surv. Sci. Rep.* **18**: 1–41.
***Manson, J.** 1974. Aspekte van die biologie en gedrag van die Kaapse grysbok, *Raphicerus melanotis* Thunberg. M.Sc. thesis, University of Stellenbosch.
**Marlow, B.J.** 1967. Mating behaviour in the leopard seal, *Hydrurga leptonyx* (Mammalia: Phocidae) in captivity. *Aust. J. Zool.* **15**: 1–5.
*——— 1983. Predation by the ratel *Mellivora capensis* on chicks of the white-backed vulture *Gyps africanus*. *S. Afr. J. Wildl. Res.* **13**: 24.
**Marr, J.W.S.** 1962. The natural history and geography of the Antarctic krill (*Euphausia superba*). *"Discovery" Rep.* 32: 33–464.
**Marsh, H., Spain, A.V. & Heinsohn, G.E.** 1978. Physiology of the dugong. *Comp. Biochem. Physiol.* **61A**: 159–168.
***Martin, A.R., Reynolds, P. & Richardson, M.G.** 1987. Aspects of the biology of pilot whales (*Globicephala melaena*) in recent mass strandings on the British coast. *J. Zool., Lond.* **211**: 11–23.
**Martin, R.B.**. 1978. Aspects of elephant social organisation. *Rhodesia Science News* **12**(8): 184–187.
*——— **Craig, G.C. & Booth, V.R.** 1989. Elephant management in Zimbabwe. pp 1–119. Harare: Dept National Parks & Wildlife Mgmt.
**Martin, R.D.** 1968. Towards a new definition of Primates. *Man* **3**: 377–401.
——— 1972. Adaptive radiation and behaviour of the Malagasy lemurs. *Phil. Trans. R. Soc. Ser. B (Biol. Sci.)* **264**: 295–352.
**Martinez, D.R. & Klinghammer, E.** 1970. The behaviour of the whale *Orcinus orca*: a review of the literature. *Z. Tierpsychol.* **27**: 829–839.
**Mason, D.R.** 1973. Range use and population structure of ungulates in the Jack Scott Nature Reserve. M.Sc. thesis, University of Pretoria.
——— 1982. Studies on the biology and ecology of the warthog *Phacochoerus aethiopicus sundevalli* Lönnberg, 1908 in Zululand. D.Sc. thesis, University of Pretoria.
*——— 1985a. Postnatal growth and physical condition of warthogs *Phacochoerus aethiopicus* in Zululand. *S. Afr. J. Wildl. Res.* **15**: 89–97.
*——— 1985b. Monitoring of ungulate populations in the Kruger National Park —Report on a survey during August, September, October 1984. Cyclostyled Report, Skukuza, National Parks Board.
*——— 1986. Reproduction in the male warthog *Phacochoerus aethiopicus* from Zululand, South Africa. *S. Afr. J. Zool.* **21**: 39–47.
***Masters, Judith C.** 1985. Species within the taxon *Galago crassicaudatus* E. Geoffroy. Ph.D. thesis, University of the Witwatersrand.
*——— 1986. Geographic distributions of karyotypes and morphotypes within the Greater Galagines. *Folia primatol.* **46**: 127–141.
*——— 1988. Speciation in the greater galagos (Prosimii: Galaginae): review and synthesis. *Biol. J. Linn. Soc.* **34**: 149–174.
*——— **Centner, M.R. & Caithness, N.** 1982. Sex ratios in galagos revisited. *S. Afr. J. Sci.* **78**: 198–202.
*——— **& Dunn, D.S.** 1988. Distribution of erythrocytic allozymes in two sibling species of greater galago, *Galago crassicaudatus* E. Geoffroy 1812 and *G. garnettii* (Ogilby 1838). *Am. J. Primatol.* **14**: 235–245.
*——— **& Lubinsky, D.** 1988. Morphological clues to genetic species: multivariate analysis of greater galago sibling species. *Am. J. Physical Anthropology* **75**: 37–52.
*——— **Lumsden, W.H.R. & Young, D.A.** 1989. Reproductive and dietary parameters in wild greater galago populations. *Int. J. Primatol.* **9**: 573–592.
*——— **Stanyon, R. & Romagno, D.** 1987. Standardized karyotypes for the greater galagos, *Galago crassicaudatus* E. Geoffroy, 1812 and *G. garnettii* (Ogilby, 1838) (Primates: Prosimii). *Genetica* **75**: 123–129.
***Mathias, I. & Bourquin, O.** 1984. Capture of blue duiker in Natal. *The Lammergeyer* **33**: 30–34.
**Matschie, P.** 1895. *Säugetiere Deutsch-Ost-Afrikas*. Berlin: Dietrich Reiner.
——— 1900. Geographische Abarten des afrikanischen Elefanten. *Sber. Ges. naturf. Freunde Berl.*: 194.
——— 1915a. Einige Bemerkungen über ältere Arten der Gattung Genetta. *Sber. Ges. naturf. Freunde Berl.*: 107–116.
——— 1915b. Mittlungen über Hyänenhunde. *Sber. Ges. naturf. Freunde Berl.*: 300–391.
**Matthew, W.D.** 1917. A paleocene bat. *Bull. Am. Mus. nat. Hist.* **37**: 569–572.
***Matthews, L.H.** 1937. The humpback whale, *Megaptera nodosa*. *"Discovery" Rep.* **17**: 7–92.
——— 1938. The sperm whale, *Physeter catodon*. *'Discovery' Rep.* **17**: 93–168.
——— 1939a. The bionomics of the spotted hyaena *Crocuta crocuta* (Erxleben). *Proc. zool. Soc. Lond. Ser. A.* **109**: 43–56.
——— 1939b. Reproduction in the spotted hyaena *Crocuta crocuta* (Erxleben). *Phil. Trans. R. Soc. Ser. B.* **230**: 1–78.
——— 1971. *The Life of Mammals*. London: Weidenfeld & Nicholson.
**Matthey, R.** 1954. Nouvelles recherches sur les chromosomes des Muridae. *Caryologia* **6**: 1–44.
——— 1958. Les chromosomes et al position systematique de quelques Murinae Africains. *Acta trop.* **15**: 97-117.
——— 1964. Analyse caryologique de cinq especes de Muridae Africains (Mammalia: Rodentia). *Mammalia* **28**: 403–418.
*——— 1966. Cytogenetique et taxonomic des rats appartenant au sonsgenre *Mastomys* Thomas (Rodentia: Muridae). *Mammalia* **30**: 105–119.
**Maronneaud, P.L.** 1946. Les variations morphologique de la canine chez les Suides. *Mammalia* **10**: 105–121.
**Maugham, R.C.F.** 1906. *Portuguese East Africa*. London: John Murray.
——— 1914. *Wild game in Zambezia*. London: John Murray.
**Maxim, P.E. & Buettner-Janusch, J.** 1963. A field study of the Kenya baboon. *Am. J. phys. Anthrop.* **21**: 165–180.
**Mayo, Earl of** 1883. A journey from Mossamedes to the river Cunene, South West Africa. *Proc. R. geogr. Soc. Lond.*: 458–473.
**Mayr, E., Linsley, E.G. & Usinger, R.L.** 1964. *Methods and principles of systematic zoology*. London: McGraw-Hill.
**Mazak, V.** 1964. Note on the lion's mane. *Z. Säugetierk.* **29**: 124–127.
***Mead, J.G.** 1981. First records of *Mesoplodon hectori* (Ziphiidae) from the Northern Hemisphere and a description of the adult male. *J. Mammal.* **62**: 430–432.
*——— 1984. Survey of reproductive data for the beaked whales (Ziphiidae). *Rep. int. Whal. Commn* (Special Issue **6**): 91–96.
*——— **& Baker, A.N.** 1987. Notes on the rare beaked whale, *Mesoplodon hectori* (Gray). *J. Roy. Soc. N. Z.* **17**: 303–312.
**Measroch, V.** 1954. Growth and reproduction in the females of two species of gerbils, *Tatera brantsi* (A. Smith) and *Tatera afra* (Gray). *Proc. zool. Soc. Lond.* **124**: 631–658.
**Meester, J.** 1953. The genera of African shrews. *Ann. Trans. Mus.* **22**: 205–214.
——— 1958a. Variation in the shrew genus *Myosorex* in southern Africa. *J. Mammal.* **39**: 325–339.
——— 1958b. The fur and moults in the shrew, *Myosorex cafer*. *J. Mammal.* **39**: 494–498.
——— 1960. Early post-natal development of multimammate mice *Rattus (Mastomys) natalensis* (A. Smith). *Ann. Trans. Mus.* **24**: 35–52.
——— 1963. A systematic revision of the shrew genus *Crocidura* in southern Africa. *Transvaal Museum Memoir* No. **13**: 1–126.
——— 1964. Revision of the Chrysochloridae. The desert golden mole *Eremitalpa* Roberts. *Scient. Pap. Namib des. Res. Stn.* **26**: 1–8.
——— 1965. The origins of the southern African mammal fauna. *Zool. Afr.* **1**: 87–95.
——— 1972a. Order Pholidota. Part 4, pp. 1–3, in *The mammals of Africa: an identification manual*. Eds J. Meester & H.W. Setzer. Washington D.C.: Smithsonian Institution Press.
——— 1972b. Order Tubulidentata, Part 10, pp. 1–2, in *The mammals of Africa: an identification manual*. Eds J. Meester & H.W. Setzer. Washington D.C.: Smithsonian Institution Press.
——— 1972c. A new golden mole from the Transvaal (Mammalia: Chrysochloridae). *Ann. Trans. Mus.* **28**: 35–46.
——— 1973. Mammals collected during the Bernard Carp expedition to the Western Province of Zambia. *Puku* **7**: 137–149.
——— 1974. Family Chrysochloridae, part 1.3, pp. 1–7 in *The mammals of Africa: an identification manual*. Eds J. Meester & H.W. Setzer. Washington D.C.: Smithsonian Institution Press.
——— **Davis, D.H.S. & Coetzee, C.G.** 1964. An interim classification of southern African mammals. *Zoological Society of S. Afr.* and *CSIR*. Mimeograph.
——— **& Dippenaar, N.J.** 1978. A new species of *Myosorex* from Knysna, South Africa (Mammalia: Soricidae). *Ann. Trans. Mus.* **31**: 29–43.
——— **& Hallett, A.F.** 1970. Notes on early post natal development in certain African Muridae and Cricetidae. *J. Mammal.* **51**: 703–711.
——— **& Lambrechts, A. von W.** 1971. The southern African species of *Suncus* Ehrenberg (Mammalia: Soricidae). *Ann. Trans. Mus.* **27**: 1–14.
——— **Lloyd, C.N.V. & Rowe-Rowe, D.T.** 1979. A note on the ecological role of *Praomys natalensis*. *S. Afr. J. Sci.* **75**: 183–184.
***Meester, J.A.J., Rautenbach, I.L., Dippenaar, N.J. & Baker, C.M.** 1986. Classification of southern African mammals. *Transvaal Mus. Monogr.* **5**: 1–359.
***Meeuse, A.D.J.** 1955. The aardvark cucumber. *Fmg S. Afr.* **30**: 310–304.
——— 1958. A possible case of interdependence between a mammal and a higher plant. *Arch. Neerl. Zool.* **13** Suppl. **1**: 314–318.
——— 1959. Aardvarken en aardkommer. *Levende Nat.* **62**: 1–7.
*——— 1962. The Cucurbitaceae of southern Africa. *Bothalia* **8**: 1–111.
**Meinertzhagen, R.** 1916. Notes on the sitatunga or marsh antelope of the Sesse Islands, Lake Victoria. *Proc. zool. Soc. Lond.*: 375–381.
**Mejia, C.** 1972. Giraffe behaviour. *Serengeti Research Inst. Ann. Rep.*, 39. Mimeograph.
**Melton, D.A.** 1975. Environmental heterogeneity produced by termitaria in Western Uganda, with special reference to mound usage by vertebrates. M.Sc. thesis, University of British Columbia.
——— 1976. The biology of aardvark (*Tubulidentata* Orycteropodidae). *Mammal Rev.* **6**: 75–88.
——— 1978. Ecology of waterbuck *Kobus ellipsiprymnus* (Ogilby, 1833) in the Umfolozi Game Reserve. D.Sc. thesis, University of Pretoria.

*——— 1985. The status of elephants in northern Botswana. *Biol. Conserv.* : 317–333.
*——— 1987. Habitat selection and resource scarcity. *S. Afr. J. Sci.* **83**: 646–651.
*——— **& Daniels, C.** 1986. A note on the ecology of the aardvark, *Orycteropus afer*. *S. Afr. J. Wildl. Res.* **16**: 112–114.
*——— **Berry, H.H., Berry, C.U. & Joubert, S.M.** 1987. Aspects of blood chemistry of wild lions, *Panthera leo*. *S. Afr. J. Zool.* **22**: 40–45.
*——— **& Melton, C.L.** 1981. Blood parameters of the wild chacma baboon, *Papio ursinus*. *S. Afr. J. Zool.* **17**: 85–90.
***Meltzer, D.G.A.** 1988. Reproduction in the male cheetah, *Acinonyx jubatus jubatus* (Schreber, 1776). M.Sc. thesis, University of Pretoria.
**Mendelssohn, H.** 1965. Breeding the Syrian hyrax *Procavia capensis syriaca* Schreber 1784. *Int. Zoo Yb.* **5**: 116–125.
**Mentis, M.T.** 1970. Estimates of natural biomasses of large herbivores in the Umfolozi Game Reserve area. *Mammalia* **34**: 363–393.
——— 1972. A review of some life history features of the large herbivores of Africa. *Lammergeyer* **16**: 1–89.
——— 1974. Distribution of some wild animals in Natal. *Lammergeyer* **20**: 1–68.
——— 1978. Population limitation in grey rhebuck and oribi in the Natal Drakensberg. *Lammergeyer* **26**: 19–28.
——— **& Duke, R.R.** 1976. Carrying capacities of natural veld in Natal for large wild herbivores. *S. Afr. J. Wildl.Res.* **7**: 65–74.
**Mentzel, O.F.** 1785, 1787. See: Mandelbrote, H.J. 1921, 1925.
***Meredith, C.D.** 1982. Wildlife rabies: past and present in South Africa. *S. Afr. J. Sci.* **78**: 411–415.
**Meredith, D.** (ed.) 1955. *The grasses and pastures of South Africa.* Parow, C.P.: Central News Agency.
**Meyer, G.E.** 1978. Hyracoidea, in *Evolution of African Mammals*, pp. 284–314. Eds V.J. Maglio & H.B.S. Cooke. Cambridge Mass., Harvard University Press.
***Meylan, A.** 1975. Formule chromosomique de *Sylvisorex megalura* (Jentinck) (Mammalia: Insectivora). *Mammalia* **39**: 319–320.
**Michaelis, B.** 1972. Die Schleichkatzen (Viverriden) Afrikas. *Säugetierk. Mitt.* **20**: 1–110.
***Mikhalev, Yu. A., Ivashin, M.V., Savusin, V.P. & Zelenaya, F.E.** 1981. The distribution and biology of killer whales in the Southern Hemisphere. *Rep. int. Whal. Commn* **31**: 551–566.
**Millar, J.C.G.** 1970a. Census of Cape mountain zebra. Part I *Afr. wild Life* **24**: 17–25; Part II *Afr. wild Life* **24**: 105–113.
——— 1970b. The past and present numerical status of the oribi *Ourebia oribi* (Zimmerman) in the Cape Province. *Dept Nature Conservation Investl Rep.* No. 17. Mimeograph.
——— 1971. Certain aspects of the ecology of the American grey squirrel *Sciurus carolinensis carolinensis* Gmelin in South Africa. Cape Dept Nature and Environmental Conservation. First Progress Report. Mimeograph 1–27.
——— 1980. Aspects of the ecology of the American grey squirrel *Sciurus carolinensis* Gmelin in South Africa. M.Sc. thesis, University of Stellenbosch.
——— 1981. Further information on grey squirrels, not included in my thesis. Internal Report, *Cape Dept Nature Conservation.* April 1981. Mimeograph pp. 2.
**Millar, R.P.** 1971. Reproduction in the rock hyrax (*Procavia capensis*). *Zool. Afr.* **6**: 243–261.
——— 1972. Reproduction in the rock hyrax (*Procavia capensis*) with special reference to seasonal sexual activity in the male. Ph.D. thesis, University of Liverpool.
*——— 1973. An unusual light-shielding structure in the eye of the dassie, *Procavia capensis* Pallas (Mammalia: Hyracoidea). *Ann. Trans. Mus.* **28**: 203–205.
**Miller, E.H.** 1975. Annual cycle of fur seals *Arctocephalus forsteri* (Lesson) on the Open Bay Islands, New Zealand. *Pacif. Sciences* **29**(2): 139–152.
**Miller, G.S.** 1907. The Families and genera of bats. *Bull. U.S. natn. Mus.* **57**: 1–282.
——— 1910. The generic name of the house-rats. *Proc. biol. Soc. Wash.* **23**: 57–60.
**Mills, M.G.L.** 1974. Carnivores of the Kalahari, Part I. *Custos* **3**(7): 37–42.
——— 1977. Diet and foraging behaviour of the brown hyaena, *Hyaena brunnea* Thunberg, 1820 in the southern Kalahari. M.Sc. thesis, University of Pretoria.
——— 1978. The comparative socio-ecology of the Hyaenidae. *Carnivore* **1**: 1–6.
*——— 1982. *Hyaena brunnea. Mammalian species* No. 194: 1–5.
*——— 1984a. The comparative behavioural ecology of the brown hyaena *Hyaena brunnea* and the spotted hyaena *Crocuta crocuta* in the southern Kalahari. *Koedoe* **27**: 237–247.
*——— 1984b. Prey selection and feeding habits of the large carnivores in the southern Kalahari. *Koedoe* **27**: 281–294.
*——— 1985a. Hyaena survey of Kruger National Park. *Int. Union Cons. Nature Natural Res. Species Survival Comm., Hyaena Specialist Group Newsl.* **2**: 15–25.
*——— 1985b. Related spotted hyaenas forage together but do not cooperate in rearing young. *Nature, Lond.* **316**: 61–62.
*——— 1987. The behavioural ecology of the spotted hyaena in the southern Kalahari (Kalahari Gemsbok National Park and Gemsbok National Park). Unpubl. Rep. National Parks Board of S.A., Skukuza. Mimeograph.
*——— 1990. *Kalahari hyaenas.* London: Unwin Hyman.
*——— **& Gorman, M.L.** 1987. The scent-marking behaviour of the spotted hyaena *Crocuta crocuta* in the southern Kalahari. *J. Zool., Lond.* **212**: 483–497.
——— **Gorman, M.L. & Mills, E.J.** 1980. The scent marking behaviour of the brown hyaena, *Hyaena brunnea*. *S. Afr. J. Zool.* **15**: 240–248.
*——— **& Mills, M.E.J.** 1977. An analysis of bones collected at hyaena breeding dens in the Gemsbok National Park. *Ann. Trans. Mus.* **30**: 145–155.
*——— **& Retief, P.F.** 1984a. The effect of windmill closure on the movement patterns of ungulates in the Auob riverbed. *Koedoe Suppl.* **27**: 107–118.
*——— **& Retief, P.F.** 1984b. The response of ungulates to rainfall along the riverbeds of the southern Kalahari, 1972–1982. *Koedoe* **27**: 129–142.
**Milstein, P. le S.** 1971. The bushpig *Potamochoerus porcus* as a problem animal in South Africa. Report, Entomological Symposium Pretoria, Mimeograph.
*——— 1989. Historical occurrence of Lichtenstein's hartebeest *Alcelaphus lichtensteini* in the Transvaal and Natal. *Aepyceros* No. 2: 1–141 (Occasional Reports, Transvaal Directorate of Nature and Environmental Conservation, Pretoria).
**Misonne, X.** 1974. Order Rodentia, Part 6, pp 1–39, in *The mammals of Africa: an identification manual.* Eds J. Meester & H.W. Setzer. Washington D.C.: Smithsonian Institution Press.
**Mitchell, B.L.** 1965a. An unexpected association between a plant and an insectivorous animal. *Puku* **3**: 178.
——— 1965b. Breeding, growth and ageing criteria of Lichtenstein's hartebeest. *Puku* **3**: 97–104.
——— **& Uys, J.M.C.** 1961. The problem of the lechwe (*Kobus leche*) on the Kafue Flats. *Oryx* **6**: 171–183.
——— **& Sandbrook, R.** 1980. What shall we do about krill? *Bull. Int. Un. Conserv. Nat.* **11**(7/8): 75–77.
——— **Shenton, J. & Uys, J.** 1965. Predation of large mammals in the Kafue National Park, Zambia. *Zool. Afr.* **1**: 297–318.
**Mitchell, E.** 1970. Pigmentation pattern evolution in delphinid cetaceans: An essay in adaptive coloration. *Can. J. Zool.* **48**: 717–740.
——— 1975a. Report on the meeting on smaller cetaceans, Montreal, April 1–11, 1974. *J. Fish. Res. Bd. Can.* **32**: 889–983.
——— 1975b. Porpoise, dolphin and small whale fisheries of the world. *IUCN Monograph* **3**: 1–129.
*——— **& Baker, A.N.** 1980. Age of reputedly old killer whale, *Orcinus orca*, "Old Tom" from Eden, Twofold Bay, Australia. *Rep. int. Whal. Commn* (Special Issue **3**): 143–154.
**Mitchell, J.A., Pirie, J.H.H. & Ingham, A.** 1927. The plague problem in South Africa: Historical, bacteriological and entomological studies. *Publ. S. Afr. Inst. med. Res.* 30 Vol. **3**: 85–256.
***Mitchell, E. & Tedford, R.H.** 1973. The Enaliarctidae, a new group of extinct aquatic Carnivora and a consideration of the origin of the Otariidae. *Bull. Am. Mus. Nat. Hist.* **151**: 203–284.
**Mivart, St. G.** 1873. On *Lepilemur* and *Cheirogaleus* and on the zoological rank of the Lemuroidea. *Proc. zool. Soc. Lond.*: 484–510.
**Miyazaki, N.** 1977. Growth and reproduction of *Stenella coeruleoalba* off the Pacific coast of Japan. *Scient. Rep. Whales Res. Inst., Tokyo* **29**: 21–48.
*——— 1980. Preliminary note on age determination and growth of the rough-toothed dolphin, *Steno bredanensis*, off the Pacific coast of Japan. *Rep. int. Whal. Commn* (Special Issue 3): 171–179.
*——— 1983. Catch statistics of small cetaceans taken in Japanese waters. *Rep. int. Whal. Commn* **33**: 621–631.
*——— 1984. Further analyses of reproduction in the striped dolphin, *Stenella coeruleoalba*, off the Pacific coast of Japan. *Rep. int. Whal. Commn* (Special Issue 6): 343–353.
*——— **Kusaka, T., & Nishiwaki, M.** 1973. Food of *Stenella caeruleoalba*. *Sci. Rep. Whales Res. Inst., Tokyo* **25**: 265–275.
**Mizue, K. & Yoshida, K.** 1962. Studies on the little toothed whales in the West Sea area of Kyusyu VIII About *Grampus griseus* caught in Goto Is. Nagasaki. *Pref. Bull. Fac. Fish. Nagasaki Univ.* **12**: 45–52.
***Mizutani, Fumi** 1987. Behaviour and patterns of maternal investment in African buffalo *Syncerus caffer* (Sparrman). M.Sc. thesis, University of Zimbabwe.
**Moehlman, P.D.** 1978. Jackals. *Wildl. News, Kenya* **13**: 1–6.
——— 1979. Jackal helpers and pup survival. *Nature, Lond.* **277**(5695): 382–383.
***Moeller, P.** 1899. Journey in Africa through Angola, Ovamboland and Damaraland. Translated from Swedish by Rudner, I. & Rudner, J. 1974. Cape Town: C. Struik.
**Mohr, E.** 1967. *Der Blaubock, Hippotragus leucophaeus (Pallas, 1766)—Eine Dokumentation.* Mammalia Depicta, pp. 1–81. Hamburg: Paul Parey.
**Möhres, F.P.** 1953. Uber der Ultraschallorientierung der Huffeisennasen (Chiroptera —Rhinolophinae). *Z. vergl. Physiol.* **34**: 547–588.
——— **& Kulzer, E.** 1956a. Uber die Orientierung der Flughunde (Chiroptera —Pteropodidae). *Z. vergl. Physiol.* **38**: 1–29.
——— **& Kulzer, E.** 1956b. Untersuchungen über die Ultraschallorientierung von vier afrikanischen Fledermausfamilien. *Verh. dt. zool. Ges.* **19**: 59–65.
**Monard, A.** 1935. Contribution a la mammalogie d'Angola et prodrome d'une fauna d'Angola. *Archos. Mus. Bocage* **6**: 1–314.
——— 1938. Resultats de la mission scientifique du Dr Monard en Guinée Portugaise. *Archos. Mus. Bocage* **9**: 150–196.
——— 1939. Resultats de la mission scientifiques du Dr Monard en Guinée Portugaise 1937–1938 III Chiroptères. *Archos. Mus. Bocage* **10**: 49–80.
——— 1940. Resultats de la mission scientifique du Dr Monard en Guinée Portugaise. *Archos. Mus. Bocage* **11**: 181–208.
***Monath, T.P., Newhouse, V.F., Kemp, G.E., Setzer, H.W. & Cacciapuoti, A.** 1974. Lassa virus from *Mastomys natalensis* rodents during an epidemic in Sierra Leone. *Science* **185**: 263–265.
**Monfort, A. & Monfort, N.** 1973. Quelques observations sur les grands mammifères du Parc National de Tai (Cote d'Ivoire). *Terre Vie* **27**: 499–506.
——— **& Monfort, N.** 1974. Notes sur l'ecologie et là comportment des Oribis (*Ourebia oribi* Zimmermann, 1783). *Terre Vie* **28**: 169–208.
**Monro, R.H.** 1979. A study on the growth, feeding and body condition of impala, *Aepyceros melampus* (Lichtenstein, 1812). M.Sc. thesis, University of Pretoria.
——— 1980. Observations on the feeding ecology of impala. *S. Afr. J. Zool.* **15**: 107–110.
——— **& Skinner, J.D.** 1979. A note on condition indices for adult male impala, *Aepyceros melampus*. *S. Afr. J. Anim. Sci.* **9**: 47–51.
**Monteil, V.** 1951. Contribution a l'etude de la faune du Sahara occidental. Du Sanglier au Phacochère. Catalogue des animaux connus des Tekna, des Rguibat et des Maurers. *Institut des Hautes Etudes marocaines, Notes et Documents* **7**: 1–169.
**Montgomerie, R.D. & Moehlman, P.D.** 1981. Why do jackals help their parents. *Nature, Lond.* **289**(5800): 824–825.
**Moolman, E.** 1975a. Rodents of South Africa: pouch mouse (*Saccostomus campestris*). *Custos* **4**(10): 29.
——— 1975b. Rodents of South Africa: the vlei rat. *Custos* **4**(11): 20.
——— 1975c. Rodents of South Africa: the tree rat (*Thallomys paedulcus*). *Custos* **4**(12): 29–30.
——— 1975d. Rodents of South Africa: Gerbils. *Custos* **4**(9): 25.
——— 1976a. Rodents of South Africa: Spiny mouse. *Custos* **5**(5): 20.
——— 1976b. Rodents of South Africa: *Dendromus melanotis*. *Custos* **5**(4): 30.
——— **& Breytenbach, G.J.** 1976. Stomach contents of the chacma baboon *Papio ursinus* from the Loskop Dam area, Transvaal, South Africa. *S. Afr. J. Wildl. Res.* **6**: 41–43.
***Moolman, L.C.** 1986a. Aspekte van die ekologie en gedrag van die rooikat *Felis caracal* Schreber, 1776 in die Bergkwagga Nasionale Park en op plase daaromheen. *Pelea* **5**: 8–21.
*——— 1986b. Aspekte van die ekologie en gedrag van die rooikat *Felis caracal* Schreber, 1776 in die Bergkwagga Nasionale Park en op die omliggende plase. M.Sc. thesis, University of Pretoria.
**Moore, J.C.** 1959. Relationships among living squirrels of the Sciurinae. *Bull. Am. Mus. nat. Hist.* **118**: 159–206.
——— 1963. The Weddell Sea. *Bull. Chic. Nat. Hist. Mus.* **34**: 6–7.
——— 1966. Diagnoses and distributions of beaked whales of the genus *Mesoplodon* known from Northern American waters, in *Whales, dolphins and porpoises*. Ed. K.S. Norris. Berkeley: University of California Press.
——— 1968. Relationships among the living genera of the beaked whales with classifications, diagnosis and keys. *Fieldiana, Zool.* **53**: 209–298.
**Moreau, R.E.** 1944. Kilimanjaro and Mount Kenya: some comparisons with special reference to mammals and birds. *Tanganyika Notes Rec.* **18**: 28–68.
——— 1952. Africa since the Mesozoic: with particular reference to certain biological problems. *Proc. zool. Soc. Lond.* **121**: 869–913.
***Moreno-Black, G. & Maples, W.R.** 1977. Differential habitat utilization of four Cercopithecidae in a Kenyan Forest. *Folia primatol.* **27**: 85–107.
**Morris, B.** 1962. A denizen of the evergreen forest. *Afr. wild Life* **16**: 117; **17**: 102–107.

——— 1963. Notes on the giant rat (*Cricetomys gambianus*) in Nyasaland. *Afr. wild Life* **17**: 103–107.

**Morris, D.** 1965. *The Mammals*. London: Hodder & Stoughton.

***Morris, D.J. & van Aarde, R.J.** 1985. Sexual behaviour of the female porcupine *Hystrix africaeaustralis*. *Hormones Behav*. **19**: 400–412.

**Morris, N.E.** 1973. A preliminary investigation of the bushbuck population in the Matsikiti area and its relevance to tsetse control hunting. M.Sc. thesis, University of Rhodesia.

**Morris, P.S.** 1966. Occurrence of reedbuck, oribi and hartebeest in the Middle Zambezi Valley. *Puku* **4**: 192–193.

**Morrison-Scott, T.C.S.** 1947. A revision of our knowledge of African elephant's teeth, with notes on forest and "pygmy" elephants. *Proc. zool. Soc. Lond*. **117**: 505–527.

——— 1951. The mummified cats of ancient Egypt. *Bull. Br. Mus. nat. Hist*. 861–867.

——— 1965. *Pan* Oken, 1816 and *Panthera* Oken, 1816 (Mammalia): proposed conservation under the plenary powers. Z.N.(S.) 482. *Bull. zool. Nom*. **22**: 230–232.

**Mortimer, M.A.E.** 1963. Notes on the biology and behaviour of the spotted necked otter, *Lutra maculicollis*. *Puku* **1**: 192–206.

***Morton, Earl of** 1821. A communication of a singular fact in Natural History. *Phil. Trans*. **111**: 20–22.

**Moss, C.** 1976. *Portraits in the Wild*. London: Hamish Hamilton.

**Mossman, H.W.** 1937. Comparative morphogenesis of the fetal membranes and accessory uterine structures. *Publs Carnegie Instn*. **479**: 129–246.

**Mossop, E.E.** (ed.) 1935. *The journal of Hendrik Jacob Wikar (1779) with an English translation by A.W. van der Horst and the journals of Jacobus Coetse Jansz (1790) and Willem van Reenen (1791) with an English translation by Dr E.E. Mossop*. (Van Riebeeck Soc. No. 15). Cape Town: Van Riebeeck Vereniging.

**Mueller, W.W. & Schoop, U.** 1976. Natural resistance of an African rodent *Praomys (Mastomys) natalensis* to rabies infection. *Annls Inst. Pasteur, Paris*: **127A**: 447–453.

**Murray, M.** 1967. The pathology of some diseases found in wild animals in East Africa. *E. Afr. Wildl. J*. **5**: 37–45.

***Murray, M.G.** 1980. Social structure of an impala population. D.Phil. thesis, University of Rhodesia.

*——— 1981. Structure of association of impala *Aepyceros melampus*. *Behav. Ecol. Sociobiol*. **9**: 23–33.

——— 1982a. The rut of impala: Aspects of seasonal mating under tropical conditions. *Z. Tierpsychol*. **59**: 319–337.

*——— 1982b. Home range, dispersal and the clan system of impala. *Afr. J. Ecol*. **20**: 253–269.

**Mutere, F.A.** 1968. The breeding biology of *Rousettus aegyptiacus* living at O°22'S. *Acta trop*. **25**: 112–211.

——— 1973. Reproduction in two species of equatorial free-tailed bats (Molossidae). *E. Afr. Wildl. J*. **11**: 271–280.

**Myers, N.** 1972. *The Long African Day*. New York: MacMillan.

——— 1976. The leopard *Panthera pardus* in Africa. Monograph 4. Gland: Int. Union Cons. Nat.

***Myrick, A.C., Hohn, A.A., Barlow, J. & Sloan, P.A.** 1986. Reproductive biology of female spotted dolphins, *Stenella attenuata*, from the eastern tropical Pacific. *Fish. Bull., U.S*. **84**: 247–259.

# N

**Nader, I.A. & Kock, D.** 1980. First record of *Tadarida nigeriae* (Thomas, 1913) from the Arabian Peninsula. *Senckenbergiana biol*. **60**: 131–135.

***Nash, L.T., Bearder, S.K. & Olson, T.R.** 1989. Synopsis of galago species differences. *Int. J. Primatol*. In press.

**Nash, R.P.** 1972. A new locality record of the Cape grey mongoose. *Lammergeyer* **17**: 64.

**Neal, E.** 1970. The banded mongoose, a little known carnivore. *Animals* **13**: 29–31.

——— 1971. *Uganda Quest*. London: Collins.

**Nel, J.A.J.** 1965. Body lengths and temperatures of the crabeater seal *Lobodon carcinophagus*. *Zool. Afr*. **1**: 319–320.

——— 1966. On the behaviour of the crabeater seal *Lobodon carcinophagus* (Hombron & Jacquinot). *Zool. Afr*. **2**: 91–93.

——— 1967. Burrow systems of *Desmodillus auricularis* in the Kalahari Gemsbok National Park. *Koedoe* **10**: 118–121.

——— 1971. Order Pinnipedia, Part 9, pp. 1–3, in *The mammals of Africa: an identification manual*. Eds J. Meester & H.W. Setzer. Washington D.C.: Smithsonian Institution Press.

——— 1975. Aspects of the social ethology of some Kalahari rodents. *Z. Tierpsychol*. **37**: 322–331.

*——— 1978. Notes on the food and foraging behavior of the bat-eared fox, *Otocyon megalotis*. *Bull. Carnegie Mus. Nat. Hist*. **6**: 132–137.

*——— **& Bester, M.H.** 1983. Communication in the southern bat-eared fox *Otocyon m. megalotis* (Desmarest, 1822) *Z. Säugetierk*. **48**: 277–290.

——— **& Bothma, J. du P.** 1983. Scent marking and midden use by aardwolves (*Proteles cristatus*) in the Namib Desert. *Afr. J. Ecol*. **21**: 25–39.

*——— **Mills, M.G.L. & van Aarde, R.J.** 1984. Fluctuating group size in bat-eared foxes (*Otocyon m. megalotis*) in the south-western Kalahari. *J. Zool., Lond*. **203**: 294–298.

——— **& Rautenbach, I.L.** 1974. Notes on the activity patterns, food and feeding behaviour of *Parotomys brantsi* (Smith, 1840). *Mammalia* **38**: 7–15.

——— **& Rautenbach, I.L.** 1975. Habitat use and community structure of rodents in the southern Kalahari. *Mammalia* **39**: 9–29.

——— **& Stutterheim, C.J.** 1973. Notes on early post-natal development of the Namaqua gerbil, *Desmodillus auricularis*. *Koedoe* **16**: 117–125.

***Nel, J.J.C. & Hewitt, P.H.** 1969. A study of the food eaten by a field population of the harvester termite, *Hodotermes mossambicus* (Hagen) and its relation to population density. *J. ent. Soc. S. Afr*. **32**: 123–131.

**Nemoto, T.** 1964. Schools of baleen whales in the feeding areas. *Scient. Rep. Whales Res. Inst., Tokyo* **18**: 89–110.

***Nevo, E., Capanna, E., Corti, M., Jarvis, J.U.M. & Hickman G.C.** 1986. Karyotype differentiation in the endemic subterranean mole rats of South Africa (Rodentia, Bathyergidae) *Z. Säugetierk*. **51**: 36–49.

*——— **Ben-Shlomo, Beiles, A., Jarvis, J.U.M. & Hickman, G.C.** 1987. Allozyme differentiation and systematics of the endemic subterranean mole rats of Africa (Rodentia, Bathyergidae) *Biochem. Syst. Ecol*. **15**: 489–502.

**Nesbit-Evans, E.M.** 1970. The reactions of a group of Rothschild's giraffe to a new environment. *E. Afr. Wildl. J*. **8**: 53–62.

**Nicholls, J.A. & Eglington, W.** 1892. *The Sportsman in South Africa*. London: British & Colonial.

**Niethammer, G.** 1942. Ueber den Klippspringer Deutch-Südwest Afrikas. *Zool. Gart., Leipzig* **14**(3): 139–149.

**Nishiwaki, M.** 1962. Whales of the world. *Dobutsu to Dobutsu-en* **14**(153): 14–17.

*——— 1963. Taxonomical consideration on genera of Delphinidae. *Scient. Rep. Whales Res. Inst., Tokyo* **17**: 93–103.

——— 1966a. Distribution and migration of the larger cetaceans in the North Pacific as shown by Japanese whaling results, in *Whales, dolphins and porpoises*. Ed. K.S. Norris. Los Angeles: University of California.

——— 1966b. A discussion of rarities among the smaller cetaceans caught in Japanese waters, in *Whales, dolphins and porpoises* Ed. K.S. Norris, Berkeley: University of California Press.

——— 1972. General biology, pp. 3–200, in *Mammals of the sea*, Ed. S.H. Ridgway. Springfield, Ill, USA: C.C. Thomas.

——— **& Handa, C.** 1958. Killer whales caught in the coastal waters off Japan for recent 10 years. *Scient. Rep. Whales Res. Inst., Tokyo* **13**: 85–96.

——— **Hibiya, T. & Ohsumi, S.** 1958. On the sexual maturity of the sperm whale (*Physeter catodon*) found in the North Pacific. *Scient. Rep. Whales Res. Inst., Tokyo* **11**: 39–46.

——— **Kasuya, T., Kamiya, T., Tobayama, T. & Nakajima, M.** 1965. *Feresa attenuata* captured at the Pacific coast of Japan in 1963. *Scient. Rep. Whales Res. Inst., Tokyo* **19**: 65–90.

——— **& Norris, K.S.** 1966. A new genus *Peponocephala* for the odontocete cetacean species *Electra electra*. *Scient. Rep. Whales Res. Inst., Tokyo* **20**: 95–99.

——— **& Oguro, N.** 1971. Baird's beaked whales caught on the coast of Japan in recent 10 years. *Scient. Rep. Whales Res. Inst., Tokyo* **23**: 111–122.

——— **& Oguro, N.** 1972. Catch of Cuvier's beaked whales off Japan in recent years. *Scient. Rep. Whales Res. Inst. Tokyo* **24**: 35–41.

*——— **& Tobayama, T.** 1982. Morphological study of the hybrid between *Tursiops* and *Pseudorca*. *Sci. Rep. Whales Res. Inst., Tokyo* **34**: 109–121.

*——— **& Tobayama, T.** 1984. Hybrids between *Pseudorca crassidens* and *Tursiops truncatus gilli*. *Rep. int. Whal. Commn* (Special Issue 6): 481 [Abstract only].

——— **& Yagi, T.** 1954. On the age determination method of the toothed whale by the study of the tooth. *Proc. Acad*. **30**: 399–404.

**Noack, T.** 1906. Eine Zwergform des afrikanischen Elefanten. *Zool. Anz., Leipzig* **29**: 631.

**Nolte, J.S.** 1973. Epidermal characters of some grasses from De Hoop Nature Reserve. *Cape Provincial Administration Invest. Rep. No. 18*.

***Nordhoff, C.** 1856. *Whaling and Fishing*. Cincinnati: Moore, Wilstach, Keys & Co.

**Norman, J.R. & Fraser, F.C.** 1949. *Field book of giant fishes*. New York: Putnam.

**Norris, K.S.** 1961. Standardised methods for measuring and recording data on small Cetaceans. *J. Mammal*. **42**: 471–476.

*——— **Baldwin, H.A. & Samson, D.J.** 1965. Open ocean diving test with a trained porpoise (*Steno bredanensis*). *Deep-Sea Res*. **12**: 505–509.

*——— **& Harvey, G.W.** 1972. A theory for the function of the spermaceti organ of the sperm whale. In: *Animal Orientation and Navigation*. Eds S.R. Galler, K. Schmidt-Koenig, G.J. Jacobs & R.E. Belleville. NASA Special Publication. 262 pp.

**Norton, P.M.** 1977. Project Plan—The habitat ecology of klipspringer in the Cape Province. Research Rep., Cape Department of Nature Conservation. Mimeograph.

——— 1980. The habitat and feeding ecology of the klipspringer, *Oreotragus oreotragus* (Zimmermann, 1783), in two areas of the Cape Province. M.Sc. thesis, University of Pretoria.

*——— 1989. Population dynamics of mountain reedbuck in three Karoo nature reserves. Ph.D. thesis, University of Stellenbosch.

*——— **& Henley, S.R.** 1987. Home range and movement of male leopards in the Cedarberg Wilderness Area, Cape Province. *S. Afr. J. Wildl. Res*. **17**: 41–48.

*——— **& Lawson, A.B.** 1985. Radio tracking of leopards and caracals in the Stellenbosch area, Cape Province. *S. Afr. J. Wildl. Res*. **15**: 17–24.

*——— **Lawson, A.B., Henley, S.R. & Avery, G.** 1986. Prey of leopards in four mountainous areas of the south-western Cape Province. *S. Afr. J. Wildl. Res*. **16**: 47–52.

——— **& van der Merwe, M.** 1978. Winter activity of bats in a Transvaal Highveld cave. *S. Afr. J. Sci*. **74**: 216–220.

***Novacek, M.J. & Wyss, A.R.** 1986. Higher-level relationships of the recent eutherian orders: morphological evidence. *Cladistics* **2**: 257–287.

**Novellie, P.A.** 1975. Comparative social behaviour of springbok, *Antidorcas m. marsupialis* (Zimmermann, 1780), and blesbok, *Damaliscus dorcas phillipsi* Harper 1939 on the Jack Scott Nature Reserve, Transvaal. M.Sc. thesis, University of Pretoria.

——— 1979. Courtship behaviour of the blesbok (*Damaliscus dorcas phillipsi*). *Mammalia* **43**: 263–274.

——— 1983. Feeding ecology of the kudu *Tragelaphus strepsiceros* (Pallas) in the Kruger National Park. D.Sc. thesis, University of Pretoria.

*——— **Manson, J. & Bigalke, R.C.** 1984. Behavioural ecology and communication in the Cape grysbok. *S. Afr. J. Zool*. **19**: 22–30.

***Novellie, P.** 1986. Relationship between rainfall, population density and size of the bontebok lamb crop in the Bontebok National Park. *S. Afr. J. Wildl. Res*. **16**: 41–46.

# O

**Oboussier, H.** 1966. Zur Kenntnis der Cephalophinae. *Z. Morph. Ökol. Tiere* **57**: 259–273.

——— 1972. Evolution of the mammalian brain, some evidence on the phylogeny of the antelope species. *Acta anat*. **33**: 70–80.

***O'Brien, S.J., Roelke, M.E., Marke, L., Newman, A., Winkler, C.A., Meltzer, D., Colly, L., Everman, J.F., Bush, M. & Wild, D.E.** 1985. Genetic basis for species vulnerability in the cheetah. *Science* **227**: 1428–1434.

*——— **Wildt, D.E. & Busch, M.** 1986. The cheetah in genetic peril. *Scientific American* **254**: 68–76.

**Odendaal, P.B.** 1974. The status of klipspringer, *Oreotragus oreotragus* Zimmerman 1873, on some mountain ranges of the Southern Cape. Res. Report, Dept of Forestry. Mimeograph.

**O'Donohue, P.N.** 1963. Reproduction in the female hyrax (*Dendrohyrax arborea ruwenzorii*). *Proc. zool. Soc. Lond*. **141**: 207–237.

**Offerman, Commandant.** 1939. Note sur la domestication des elephants au Congo belge. Mimeograph.

***Offermans, M. & de Free, F.** 1989. Morphology of the masticatory apparatus in the springhare, *Pedetes capensis*. *J. Mammal*. **70**: 701–711.

**Ogawa, T. & Kamiya, T.** 1957. A case of the cachalot with protruded rudimentary hind limbs. *Scient. Rept. Whales Res. Inst., Tokyo* **12**: 197–208.

**Ogilvie, P.W. & Ogilvie, M.B.** 1964. Observations of a roost of yellow or giant fruit-eating bats, *Eidolon helvum*. *J. Mammal*. **45**: 309–311.

**Ogilvie-Grant, W.R.** 1912. On the birds of Ngamiland: itinerary and field notes of R.B. Woosnam. *Ibis*: 355.

**Ognev, S.I.** 1935. Pinnipedia, Vol. 3, p. 316–600. In: *The mammals of eastern Europe and northern Asia*. Moscow & Leningrad, State Publishing House.
**Ogrizek, D.** (ed.) 1954. *South and Central Africa*. New York: McGraw-Hill.
***Ohsumi, S.** 1958. A descendant of Moby Dick or the white sperm whale. *Scient. Rep. Whales Res. Inst., Tokyo* **13**: 207–209.
——— 1965. A dolphin, *Stenella coeruleoalba*, with protruded rudimentary hind limbs. *Scient. Rept. Whales Res. Inst., Tokyo* **19**: 135–136.
——— **Masaki, Y. & Kawamura, A.** 1970. Stock of Antarctic minke whale. *Scient. Rep. Whales Res. Inst., Tokyo* **22**: 75–126.
——— **Nishiwaki, M. & Kibiya, T.** 1958. Growth of fin whale in Northern Pacific. *Scient. Rep. Whales Res. Inst., Tokyo* **13**: 97–133.
**Oliff, W.D.** 1953. The mortality, fecundity and intrinsic rate of natural increase of the multi-mammate mouse, *Rattus (Mastomys) natalensis* (A. Smith) in the laboratory. *J. Anim. Ecol.* **22**: 217–226.
**Oliver, M.D.N., Short, N.R.M. & Hanks, J.** 1978. Population ecology of oribi, grey rhebuck and mountain reedbuck in Highmoor State Forest Land, Natal. *S. Afr. J. Wildl. Res.* **8**: 95–105.
**Olsen, O.** 1913. On the external characters and biology of Bryde's whale (*Balaenoptera brydei*) a new rorqual from the coast of South Africa. *Proc. zool. Soc. Lond.*: 1073–1090.
——— 1915. Hvaler og Hvalfangsti Sydafrika. *Bergens Mus. Arb.* 1914–1915, **5**: 1–56.
***Olson, T.R.** 1979. Studies on aspects of the morphology and systematics of the genus *Otolemur*. Ph.D. thesis, London University.
**Omura, H.** 1962. Further information on Bryde's whale from the coast of Japan. *Scient. Rep. Whales Res. Inst., Tokyo* 16: 7–18.
——— 1966. Bryde's whale in the northwest Pacific, in *Whales, dolphins and porpoises*, Ed. K.S. Norris. Berkeley: University of California Press.
*——— 1975. Osteological study of the minke whale from the Antarctic. *Scient. Rep. Whales Res. Inst., Tokyo* **27**: 1–36.
——— **Fujino, K. & Kimura, S.** 1955. Beaked whale *Berardius bairdi* of Japan, with notes on *Ziphius cavirostris*. *Scient. Rep. Whales Res. Inst., Tokyo* **10**: 89–132.
***Oosthuizen, W.H. & David, J.H.M.** 1988. Non-breeding colonies of the South African (Cape) fur seal *Arctocephalus pusillus pusillus* in Southern Africa. *Investl Rep. Div. Sea Fish.* **132**: 11–17.
*——— **David, J.H.M. & Ross, G.J.B.** 1988. New records of southern elephant seals *Mirounga leonina* L. on the coast of Southern Africa. *S. Afr. J. mar. Sci.* **7**: 75–86.
***Orford, H.J.L., Perrin, M.R. & Berry, H.H.** 1988. Contraception, reproduction and demography of free-ranging Etosha lions (*Panthera leo*). *J. Zool., Lond.* **216**: 717–733.
**Osmond, E.** 1967. *Animals of Central Asia*. London: Abelard-Schuman.
**Owen, R.** 1866. On some Indian Cetacea collected by Walter Elliott. *Trans. zool. Soc. Lond.* **6**: 17–47.
**Owen, R.E.A.** 1970. Some observations on the sitatunga in Kenya. *E. Afr. Wildl. J.* **8**: 181–195.
**Owen-Smith, N.** 1971. Territoriality in the white rhinoceros (*Ceratotherium simum simum* Burchell). *Nature, Lond.* **231**(5301): 294–296.
——— 1972. Territoriality: the example of the white rhinoceros. *Zool. Afr.* **7**: 273–280.
——— 1973. The behavioural ecology of the white rhinoceros. Ph.D. thesis, University of Wisconsin.
*——— 1984. Demography of greater kudu, *Tragelaphus strepsiceros* in relation to rainfall. *Acta Zool. Fenn.* **172**: 197–199.
*——— 1988. *Megaherbivores. The influence of very large body size on ecology*. Cambridge Studies in Ecology. Cambridge: University Press.
*——— **& Cooper, Susan M.**. 1987. Palatability of woody plants to browsing ruminants in a South African Savanna. *Ecology* **68**: 319–331.
——— **& Novellie, P.** 1982. What should a clever ungulate eat? *Am. Nat.* **119**: 151–178.
**Owens, D.D. & Owens, M.J.** 1978. Feeding ecology and its influence on social organisation in brown hyaenas (*Hyaena brunnea*) of the central Kalahari desert. *E. Afr. Wildl. J.* **16**: 113–136.
——— **& Owens, M.J.** 1979a. Communal denning and clan association in brown hyaena (*Hyaena brunnea* Thunberg) of the central Kalahari desert. *Afr. J. Ecol.* **17**: 35–44.
——— **& Owens, M.J.** 1979b. Notes on the social organisation and behaviour in brown hyaena (*Hyaena brunnea*). *J. Mammal.* **60**: 405–408.
*——— **& Owens, M.J.** 1984. Helping behaviour in brown hyaenas. *Nature, Lond.* **308**: 843–845.

# P

**Palgrave, K.C.** 1977. *Trees of Southern Africa*. Johannesburg: Struik.
***Palmer, R. & Fairall, N.** 1988. Caracal and African wild cat diet in the Karoo National Park and the implications thereof for hyrax. *S. Afr. J. Wildl. Res.* **18**: 30–34.
**Palmer, T.S.** 1904. *Index generum mammalium*. Washington: U.S. Dept Agric.: Div. Biol. Survey North American fauna No. 23.
**Panagis, K.** 1979. Behaviour and postnatal development of *Thamnomys dolichurus* (the African tree rat). B.Sc. Hons. Project Rep., University of Pretoria.
*——— 1981. Local movement of southern elephant seal pups *Mirounga leonina* (Linn.) at Marion Island. *S. Afr. J. Antarct. Res.* **10/11**: 28–30.
*——— 1984. Influence of southern elephant seals, *Mirounga leonina*, on the coastal moulting areas at Marion Island. *S. Afr. J. Sci.* **80**: 30.
——— **& Nel, J.A.J.** 1981. Growth and behavioural development in *Thamnomys dolichurus* (Rodentia: Muridae). *Acta theriol.* **26**: 381–392.
**Panouse, J.B.** 1957. Les mammifères du Maroc. *Trav. Inst. scient. cherif. Serie Zoologie* **5**: 1–206.
**Paradiso, J.L.** 1968. *Walker's mammals of the world* 2nd edn. **2**: 1068–1069. Baltimore: John Hopkins Press.
**Parris, R. & Child, G.** 1973. The importance of pans to wildlife in the Kalahari and the effect of human settlement on these areas. *J. sth Afr. Wildl. Mgmt Ass.* **3**: 1–8.
***Parry, D.** 1984. Man—wildebeest competition in the Lake Xau district, Botswana. B.Sc. Honours Dissertation, University of the Witwatersrand, Johannesburg.
***Paterson, R.A.** 1986. An analysis of four large accumulations of sperm whales observed in the modern whaling area. *Sci. Rep. Whales Re. Inst.* No. **37**: 167–172.
**Paterson, W.** 1789. *A narrative of four journeys into the country of the Hottentots and Caffraria. In the years 1777, 1778 and 1779*. London: J. Johnson.
**Patterson, B.** 1978. Pholidota and Tubulidentata. In *Evolution of African mammals*, Eds V.J. Maglio & H.B.S. Cooke. pp. 268–278. Cambridge, Mass: Harvard University Press.
***Patterson, G.** 1988. *Cry for the lions*. Sandton: Frandson Publishers.
***Patterson, L.** 1979. Studies on the population biology of the African buffalo (*Syncerus caffer*) in Botswana. *Department of Wildlife and National Parks. Government Printer, Gaberone.*
**Payne, H.C.** 1956. Our National Parks. *Afr. wild Life* **10**: 181–186.
——— 1961. Our National Parks—report. *Afr. wild Life* **15**: 181–190.
***Payne, K.B., Langbauer, W.R. Jr & Thomas, E.M.** 1986. Infrasonic calls of the Asian elephant (*Elephas maximus*). *Behav. Ecol. Sociobiol.* **18**: 297–301.
**Payne, M.R.** 1977. Growth of a fur seal population. *Phil. Trans. R. Soc. Lond.* B **279**: 67–79.
——— 1979a. Fur seals, *Arctocephalus tropicalis* and *A. gazella*, crossing the Antarctic Convergence at South Georgia. *Mammalia* **43**: 93–98.
——— 1979b. Growth in the Antarctic fur seal, *Arctocephalus gazella*. *J. Zool., Lond.* **187**: 1–20.
***Payne, R. & Webb, D.** 1971. Orientation by means of long range acoustic signalling in baleen whales. *Ann. N. Y. Acad. Sci.* **188**: 110–142.
**Pearson, O.P.** 1946. Scent glands of the short-tailed shrew. *Anat. Rec.* **94**: 615–629.
***Peddemors, V.M.** 1989. Minimum age at sexual maturation of a female south-east Atlantic bottlenose dolphin *Tursiops truncatus*. *S. Afr. J. Mar. Sci.* **8**: 345–347.
**Peddie, D.A.** 1975. A taxonomic and autecological study of the genus *Pronolagus* in southern Africa. M.Sc. thesis, University of Rhodesia, Salisbury.
**Penrice, G.W.** 1899. *The Great and Small Game of Africa*. London: Rowland Ward.
**Penzhorn, B.L.** 1971. A summary of the reintroduction of ungulates into the South African National Parks (to 31st Dec, 1970). *Koedoe* **14**: 145–159.
——— 1973. Springbok on an integrated livestock-wildlife farm in the Karoo. Symp. Wildl. Conserv. Util. in Afr. Pretoria: South African Wildlife Management Association, Mimeograph.
——— 1975. Behaviour and population ecology of the Cape mountain zebra *Equus zebra zebra* Linn., 1758 in the Mountain Zebra National Park. D.Sc. thesis, University of Pretoria.
——— 1979. Social organisation of the Cape mountain zebra, *Equus z. zebra* in the Mountain Zebra National Park. *Koedoe* **22**: 115–156.
*——— 1982a. Soil eating by Cape mountain zebra *Equus zebra zebra* in the Mountain Zebra National Park. *Koedoe* **25**: 83–88.
*——— 1982b. Age determination in Cape Mountain Zebras *Equus zebra zebra* in the mountain Zebra National Park. *Koedoe* **25**: 89–102.
*——— 1984a. Observations on mortality of free ranging Cape mountain zebra *Equus zebra zebra*. *S. Afr. J. Wildl. Res.* **14**: 89–90.
*——— 1984b. A long-term study of social organisation and behaviour of Cape mountain zebras *Equus zebra zebra*. *Z. Tierpsychol.* **64**: 97–146.
*——— 1984c. Dental abnormalities in free-ranging Cape mountain zebras (*Equus zebra zebra*) *J. Wildl. Diseases*. **20**: 161–166.
*——— 1985a. Reproductive characteristics of a free-ranging population of Cape mountain zebra (*Equus zebra zebra*) *J. Reprod. Fert.* **73**: 51–57.
*——— 1985b. An old reference to hartebeest in the Transvaal Lowveld. *Koedoe* **28**: 69–71.
*——— 1987. Descriptions of incisors of known-age Cape mountain zebras, *Equus zebra zebra*, from the Mountain Zebra National Park. *Onderstepoort J. vet. Res.* **54**: 135–141.
*——— 1988. *Equus zebra*. Mammalian species No. 314 pp. 1–7. *Ann. Soc. Mammal.* Washington.
*——— **& Lloyd, P.H.** 1987. Comparisons of reproductive parameters of two Cape mountain zebra (*Equus zebra zebra*) populations. *J. Reprod. Fert., Suppl.* **35**: 661–663.
*——— **& Rautenbach, I.L.** 1988. Reproduction of the Egyptian fruit bat *Rousettus aegyptiacus leachi* (A. Smith, 1829) (Chiroptera: Pteropodidae) in the southern tropics. *S. Afr. J. Wildl. Res.*. **18**: 88–92.
*——— **& Van der Merwe, N.J.** 1988. Testis size and onset of spermatogenesis in Cape mountain zebras (*Equus zebra zebra*). *J. Reprod. Fert.* **83**: 371–375.
**Percival, A.B.** 1924. *A Game Ranger's Note Book*. New York: George H. Doran.
**Perret, J.L. & Aellen, V.** 1956. Mammifères du Cameroun de la collection J.L. Perret. *Revue suisse Zool.* **63**: 395–450.
***Perrin, M.R.** 1980a. The feeding habits of two co-existing rodents, *Rhabdomys pumilio* (Sparrman, 1784) and *Otomys irroratus* (Brants, 1827). *Acta Oecologia Oecol. Gener.* **1**: 71–89.
*——— 1980b. Seasonal changes in the body fat content of two co-existing rodents, *Rhabdomys pumilio* and *Otomys irroratus*. *S. Afr. J. Wildl. Res.* **11**: 21–27.
*——— 1986. Some perspectives on the reproductive tactics of southern African rodents. *Cimbebasia* **8**: 63–77.
*——— **& Curtis, B.A.** 1980. Comparative morphology of the digestive system of 19 species of South African myomorph rodents in relation to diet evolution. *S. Afr. J. Zool.* **15**: 22–33.
*——— **& Swanepoel, P.** 1987. Breeding biology of the bushveld gerbil *Tatera leucogaster* in relation to diet, rainfall and life history theory. *S. Afr. J. Zool.* **22**: 218–227.
***Perrin, W.F.** 1969. Using porpoise to catch tuna. *World Fishing* (June, 1969): 4 pp.
——— 1970. Colour pattern of the Eastern Pacific spotted porpoise *Stenella graffmani* Lonberg. Cetacea: Delphinidae. *Zoologica, N.Y.* **54**: 135–142.
——— 1972. Colour patterns of spinner porpoises *Stenella c.f. S. longirostris* of the eastern Pacific and Hawaii with comments on delphinid pigmentation. *Fish. Bull. Calif.* **70**: 983–1003.
——— 1975. Variation of spotted and spinner dolphins (genus *Stenella*) in the Eastern Pacific and Hawaii. *Bull. Scripps Instn Oceanogr. tech. Ser.* **21**: 1–206.
*——— 1989. Dolphins, porpoises, and whales. An action plan for the conservation of biological diversity: 1988–1992. 2nd edn. Gland. IUCN.
——— **Best, P.B., Dawbin, W.H., Balcomb, R., Gambell, R. & Ross, G.J.B.** 1973. Rediscovery of Fraser's dolphin *Lagenodelphis hosei*. *Nature, Lond.* **241**: 345–350.
*——— **Brownell, R.L., Zhou, K. & Liu, J.** (eds) 1989. Biology and Conservation of the River Dolphins. *Occ. Pap. I.U.C.N. Spec. Survival Comm.* **3**, i-iv + 173 pp
*——— **Coe, J.M. & Zweifel, J.R.** 1976. Growth and reproduction of the spotted porpoise, *Stenella attenuata*, in the offshore eastern tropical Pacific. *Fish. Bull. U.S.* **74**: 229–269.
*——— **& Henderson, J.R.** 1984. Growth and reproductive rates in two populations of spinner dolphins, *Stenella longirostris*, with different histories of exploitation. *Rep. int. Whal. Commn* (Special Issue 6): 417–430.
*——— **Holts, D.B. & Miller, R.B.** 1977. Growth and reproduction of the eastern spinner dolphin, a geographical form of *Stenella longirostris* in the eastern tropical Pacific. *Fish. Bull. U.S.* **75**: 725–750.
*——— **& Hubbs, C.L.** 1969. Observations on a young pygmy killer whale (*Feresa attenuata* Gray) from the eastern tropical Pacific Ocean. *Trans. San Diego Soc. Nat. Hist.* **15**: 297–308.
*——— **Mitchell, E.D., Mead, J.G., Caldwell, D.K., Caldwell, M.C., Van Bree, P.J.H. & Dawbin, W.H.** 1987. Revision of the spotted dolphins, *Stenella* spp. *Mar. Mammal Sci.* **3**: 99–170.
——— **Mitchell, E.D., van Bree, P.J.H. & Caldwell, D.K.** 1977. Spinner dolphins, *Stenella* spp, in the Atlantic. *Abstr. Proc. 2nd Conf. Biol. Mar. Mammals* Dec.: 12.

*——— **Miyazaki, N. & Kasuya, T.** 1989. A dwarf form of the spinner dolphin (*Stenella longirostris*) from Thailand. *Mar. Mammal Sci.* **5**: 213–227.
*——— **& Reilly, S.B.** 1984. Reproductive parameters of dolphins and small whales of the family Delphinidae. *Rep. int. Whal. Commn* (Special Issue 6): 97–133.
*——— **Smith, T.D. & Sakagawa, G.T.** 1982. Status of populations of spotted dolphin, *Stenella attenuata*, and spinner dolphin, *Stenella longirostris*, in the eastern tropical Pacific. Mammals in the Seas. *FAO Fish. Ser.* (5) vol. 4: 67–83.
——— **Warner, R.R., Fiscus, C.H. & Holts, D.B.** 1973. Stomach contents of porpoise, *Stenella* spp. and yellowfin tuna, *Thunnus albacares*, in mixed species aggregations. *Fish. Bull.* **71**: 1077–1092.
**Perry, J.S.** 1953. The reproduction of the African elephant, *Loxodonta africana*. *Phil. Trans. R. Soc. B.* **239**: 93.
***Perryman, W.L. & Foster, T.C.** 1980. Preliminary report on predation by small whales, mainly the false killer whale, *Pseudorca crassidens*, on dolphins (*Stenella* spp. and *Delphinus delphis*) in the eastern tropical Pacific. *NOAA Admin. Rep.* LJ-80–05, 9 pp.
**Peters, W.H.C.** 1852. *Naturwissenschaftliche Reise nach Mossambique. Zoologie I. Säugetiere.* Berlin: Georg Reimer.
**Peterson, R.** 1964. *Silently by night.* London: Longmans.
**Peterson, R.L.** 1965. A review of the flat-headed bats of the Family Molossidae from South America and Africa. *Occ. Pap. R. Ont. Mus. Zool.* 1–32.
——— 1971. Notes on the African long-eared bats of the genus *Laephotis* (Family Vespertilionidae). *Can.J. Zool.* **49**: 885–888.
——— 1973. The first known female of the African long-eared bat, *Laephotis wintoni* (Vespertilionidae: Chiroptera). *Can. J. Zool.* **51**: 601–603.
——— 1974. Variation in the African bat, *Tadarida lobata*, with notes on habitat and habits (Chiroptera: Molossidae). *Life Sci. Occ. Pap. R. Ont. Mus. No. 24*: 1–8.
——— **& Harrison, D.L.** 1970. The second and third known specimens of the African molossid bat, *Tadarida lobata*. *Life Sci. Occ. Pap. R. Ont. Mus. No. 16*: 1–6.
**Petrides, G.A.** 1965. Advisory report on wildlife and National Parks in Nigeria. *Am. Com. Int. Wild Life Protection spec. Publ.* 18.
——— 1975. Principal foods versus preferred foods and their relations to stocking rate and range condition. *Biol. Conserv.* **7**: 161–169.
**Petter, A. & Petter, J.J.** 1977. Infraorder Lemuriformes, Part 3.1, pp. 1–10, in *The mammals of Africa: an identification manual.* Eds J. Meester & H.W. Setzer. Washington D.C.: Smithsonian Institution Press.
**Petter, F.** 1959. Élèments d'une révision des lièvres africains du sous genre *Lepus*. *Mammalia* **23**: 41–67.
——— 1961. Élèments d'une révision des lièvres europeens et asiatiques du sous-genre *Lepus*. *Z. Säugetierk.* **26**: 1–11.
——— 1963a. Nouveaux élèments d'une révision des lièvres africains. *Mammalia* **27**: 238–255.
——— 1963b. Contribution à la connaissance des souris africaines. *Mammalia* **27**: 602–607.
——— 1966. L'origine des Murides: plan cricetin et plan murins. *Mammalia* **30**: 205–225.
——— 1972. Order Lagomorpha, Part 5, pp. 1–7, in *The mammals of Africa: an identification manual.* Eds J. Meester & H.W. Setzer. Washington D.C.: Smithsonian Institution Press.
——— 1975a. Family Cricetidae, Part 6.2, pp. 1–4, in *The mammals of Africa: an identification manual.* Eds J. Meester & H.W. Setzer. Washington D.C.: Smithsonian Institution Press.
——— 1975b. Subfamily Gerbillinae, Part 6.3, pp. 1–14, in *The mammals of Africa: an identification manual.* Eds J. Meester & H.W. Setzer. Washington D.C.: Smithsonian Institution Press.
——— 1978. Une souris nouvelle du Sud de l'Afrique. *Mammalia* **42**: 377–379.
——— 1981. Remarques sur la systematique des Chrysochlorides. *Mammalia* **45**: 39–43.
——— 1981. Les souris africaines du groupe *sorella* (Rongeursg Muridés). *Mammalia* **45**: 312–320.
——— **& Genest, H.** 1965. Variation morphologique et repartition geographique de *Lepus capensis* dans le Sud-Ouest Africain *Lepus salai=L. capensis*. *Mammalia* **29**: 572–576.
——— **& Matthey, R.** 1975. Genus *Mus*, Part 6.7, pp. 1–4, in *The mammals of Africa: an identification manual.* Eds J. Meester & H.W. Setzer. Washington D.C.: Smithsonian Institution Press.
**Petter, G.** 1969. Interpretive evolution des characters de la dentures des viverrides africaines. *Mammalia* **33**: 607–625.
**Petter, J-J. & Petter-Rousseaux, A.** 1979. Classification of the Prosimians : 1–44, in *The study of prosimian behaviour*, Eds G.A. Doyle & R.D. Martin. London: Academic Press.
**Pettifer, H.L.** 1981a. Aspects on the ecology of cheetah (*Acinonyx jubatus*) on the Suikerbosrand Nature Reserve, in *Worldwide Furbearer Conference Proceedings*, Eds J.A. Chapman & D. Punsley. Virginia: R.R. Donnelley.
——— 1981b. The experimental release of captive-bred cheetah (*Acinonyx jubatus*) into the natural environment, in *Worldwide Furbearer Conference Proceedings.* Eds J.A. Chapman & D. Punsley. Virginia: R.R. Donnelley.
*——— **de Wet, J.I. & Muller, P.J.** 1979. The ecology of cheetah (*Acinonyx jubatus*) on the Suikerbosrand Nature Reserve. Unpubl. Mimeograph, Transvaal Div. Nat. Cons., Pretoria.
***Pettigrew, J.D.** 1986. Flying Primates, Megabats have the advanced pathway from eye to midbrain. *Science* **231**: 1304–1306.
*——— **Jamieson, B.G.M., Robson, S.K., Hall, L.S., Macinally, K.I, & Cooper, H.M.** 1989. Phylogenetic relations between microbats, megabats and primates (Mammalia: Chiroptera & Primates). *Phil. Trans. R. Soc. Lond.* **B325**: 489–559.
*——— **Robson, S.K., Hall, L.S. & Mc Anally, K.L.** 1988. A phylogenetic analysis of flying mammals. Unpubl. Rep. (see Pettigrew *et al.*, 1989).
**Pfeffer, P.** 1962. Une cobe de montagne propre au Cameroun *Redunca fulvorufula adamauae* subspecies nova. *Mammalia* **26**: 64–71.
**Phillips, J.F.V.** 1925. The Knysna elephant: a brief note on their history and habits. *S. Afr. J. Sci.* **22**: 287–293.
——— 1926. Wild pig (*Potamochoerus choiropotamus*) at Knysna: notes by a naturalist. *S. Afr. J. Sci.* **23**: 655–660.
**Pienaar, U. de V.** 1960. Annual Report of the Biologist 1958/59. *Koedoe* **3**: 1–205.
——— 1961a. A supplementary check list of Decapods, fresh water fish, Amphibia, reptiles and small mammals recorded in the Kruger National Park. *Koedoe* **4**: 167–177.
——— 1961b. A second outbreak of anthrax amongst game animals in the Kruger National Park, 5th June to 11th October 1960. *Koedoe* **4**: 4–17.
——— 1963. The large mammals of the Kruger National Park—their distribution and present-day status. *Koedoe* **6**: 1–37.
——— 1964. The small mammals of the Kruger National Park — a systematic list and zoogeography. *Koedoe* **7**: 20.
——— 1967. Operation "Khomandlopfu". *Koedoe* **10**: 158–164.
——— 1969a. Observations on developmental biology, growth and some aspects of the population ecology of African buffalo in the Kruger National Park. *Koedoe* **12**: 29–52.
——— 1969b. Predator-prey relationships amongst the larger mammals of the Kruger National Park. *Koedoe* **12: 108–187.**
——— 1970a. The recolonisation history of the square-lipped (white) rhinoceros *Ceratotherium simum simum* (Burchell) in the Kruger National Park (October 1961–1969). *Koedoe* **13**: 157–169.
——— 1970b. A note on the occurrence of bat-eared fox *Otocyon megalotis* (Desmarest) in the Kruger National Park. *Koedoe* **13**: 23–27.
——— 1974. Habitat preference in South African antelope species and its significance in natural and artificial distribution patterns. *Koedoe* **17**: 185–195.
*——— **Joubert, S.C.J., Hall-Martin, A., de Graaff, G. & Rautenbach, I.L.** 1987. *Field Guide to the Mammals of the Kruger National Park.* Ed. I.L. Rautenbach. Cape Town: Struik.
——— **Rautenbach, I.L. & de Graaff, G.** 1980. *The small mammals of the Kruger National Park.* Pretoria: National Parks Board of South Africa.
——— **van Wyk, P. & Fairall, N.** 1966a. An experimental cropping scheme of hippopotami in the Letaba River of the Kruger National Park. *Koedoe* **9**: 1–33.
——— **van Wyk, P. & Fairall, N.** 1966b. An aerial census of elephant and buffalo in the Kruger National Park. *Koedoe* **9**: 40-107.
**Pike, G.G. & MacAshe, I.B.** 1969. *Orcinus orca* Linnaeus, 1758, killer whale. *Bull. Fish. Res. Bd. Can.* **171**: 19–23.
**Pilleri, G. & Gihr, M.** 1972a. Contribution to the knowledge of the Cetaceans of Pakistan with particular reference to the genera *Neomeris, Sousa, Delphinus* and *Tursiops* and description of a new Chinese porpoise *Neomeris asiaeorientalis*. *Invest. on Cetacea* **4**: 108–162.
——— **& Gihr, M.** 1972b. On the record and taxonomy of *Tursiops gephyreus* Lahille 1908 off the Playa Coronilla, Uruguay. *Invest. on Cetacea* **4**: 173–181.
——— **& Gihr, M.** 1973/74. Contribution to the knowledge of the cetaceans of southwest and monsoon Asia (Persian Gulf, Indus delta, Malabar, Andaman Sea and Gulf of Siam). *Invest. on Cetacea* **5**: 95–149.
**Pilson, R.D. & Pilson, B.M.** 1967. Behaviour studies of *Glossina morsitans* West. *Bull. ent. Res.* **57**: 227–257.
***Pilsworth, H.R.** 1977. Altruistic mongooses tend their sick friend. *New Sci.* **73**: 517.
**Pitman, C.R.S.** 1928. Notes on Nkosi Island and its sitatunga. *Proc. zool. Soc. Lond.*: 655–657.
——— 1931a. *A game warden among his charges.* London: Harmondsworth.
——— 1931b. *Annual Report of the Game Department.* Entebbe, Uganda: Govt Printer.
——— 1934. *A report on a faunal survey of Northern Rhodesia.* Livingstone: Govt Printer.
——— 1942. *A game warden takes stock.* London: Nisbet.
**Player, I.C.** 1972. *The White Rhino Saga.* London: Collins.
——— **& Feely, J.M.** 1960. A preliminary report on the square-lipped rhinoceros (*Ceratotherium simum simum*). *Lammergeyer* **1**: 3–21.
**Plowright, W. & Jessett, D.M.** 1971. Investigations of Allerton-type herpes virus infection in East African game animals and cattle. *J. Hyg.* **69**: 209–222.
**Poche, R.M.** 1975. The bats of National Park W, Niger, Africa. *Mammalia* **39**: 39–50.
***Pocock, R.I.** 1904. The Cape Colony quaggas. *Ann. Mag. nat. Hist.* **14**: 313–338.
——— 1910. On the specialised cutaneous glands in ruminants. *Proc. zool. Soc. Lond.* : 840–986.
——— 1915. On the feet and glands and other external characters of the Viverrinae, with the description of a new Genus. *Proc. zool. Soc. Lond.* : 131–149.
——— 1916a. On the external characters of the mongooses (Mungotidae). *Proc. zool. Soc. Lond.*: 131–149.
——— 1916b. On some external structural characters of the striped hyaena (*Hyaena hyaena*) and related genera and species. *Ann. Mag. Nat. Hist.* **17**: 330–343.
——— 1918a. On the external characters of the lemurs and of *Tarsius*. *Proc. zool. Soc. Lond.*: 19–53.
——— 1918b. On some external characters of ruminant Artiodactyla — Part I Cephalophinae, Neotraginae, Oreotraginae and Madoquinae. *Ann. Mag. nat. Hist.* **1**: 426–435.
——— 1919. The classification of the mongooses (Mungotidae). *Ann. Mag. nat. Hist.* **3**: 515.
——— 1921. On the external characters of the Lutrinae (otters). *Proc. zool. Soc. Lond.*: 535.
——— 1922. On the external characters and classification of the Mustelidae. *Proc. zool. Soc. Lond.*: 803.
*——— 1924. The external characters of the pangolins (Manidae). *Proc. zool. Soc. Lond.*: 707–723.
——— 1925. The external characters of the catarrhine monkeys and apes. *Proc. zool. Soc. Lond.*: 1479.
——— 1927. Description of a new species of cheetah (*Acinonyx*). *Proc. zool. Soc. Lond.*: 530–533.
——— 1932. The leopards of Africa. *Proc. zool. Soc. Lond.*: 544–591.
——— 1939. *The fauna of British India* Vol. I. Primates and Carnivora (in part) Felidae and Viverridae. London: Taylor and Francis.
——— 1944. Three races, one new, of the serval (*Leptailurus*) from North Africa. *Ann. Mag. nat. Hist.* **11**: 690–698.
——— 1951. *Catalogue of the genus Felis.* London: Trustees of the British Museum.
**Pocock, T.N.** 1974. New mammal record for genus *Mus* for southern Africa. *S. Afr. J. Sci.* **70**: 315.
**Poduschka, W.** 1980. Notes on the giant golden mole *Chrysospalax trevelyani* Gunther, 1875 (Mammalia: Insectivora) and its survival chances. *Z. Säugetierk.* **60**: 1–11.
***Poole, Joyce H.** 1982. Musth and male-male competition in the African elephant. Ph.D. thesis, University of Cambridge.
*——— 1987. Rutting behaviour in African elephants: the phenomenon of musth. *Behav.* **102**: 283–316.
*——— 1989a. Announcing intent: the aggressive state of musth in African elephants. *Anim. Behav.* **37**: 140–152.
*——— 1989b. Mate guarding, reproductive success and female choice in African elephants. *Anim. Behav.* **37**: 842–849.
*——— **Kasman, L.H., Ramsay, E.C. & Lasley, B.L.** 1984. Musth and urinary testosterone concentrations in the African elephant (*Loxodonta africana*). *J. Reprod. Fert.* **70**: 255–260.
*——— **& Moss, C.J.** 1981. Musth in the African elephant. *Nature, Lond.* **292**: 830–831.
*——— **Payne, K.B., Langbauer, W.R. Jr & Moss, C.J.** 1988. The social context of some very low frequency calls of African elephants. *Behav. Ecol. Sociobiol.* **22**: 385–392.
**Posselt, J.** 1963. Domestication of the eland. *Rhod. J. agric. Res.* **1**: 81–87.
**Pournelle, G.H.** 1955. Notes on the reproduction of Baringo giraffe. *J. Mammal.* **36**: 574.

——— 1965. Observations on the birth and early development of the spotted hyaena. *J. Mammal.* **46**: 3.
——— 1967. The hyaena and the aardwolf, a family dispute. *Zoonooz.* **40**(11): 8–12.
**Preston, F.W.** 1950. Mongoose luring guineafowl. *J. Mammal.* **31**: 194.
***Prestwich, G.D.** 1983. The chemical defenses of termites. *Sci. Am.* **249**: 68–75.
**Pretorius, P.J.** 1947. *Jungle man.* London: Harrap.
**Prevost, J. & Mougin, J-L.** 1970. *Guide des oiseaux et mammifères des terres Australes et Antarctiques Francaises.* Paris: Delechaux et Niestle.
***Price, J.S., Burton, J.L., Shuster, S. & Wolff, K.** 1976. Control of scrotal colour in the vervet monkey. *J. med. Primatol.* **5**: 296–304.
**Pringle, J.A.** 1963. The red hartebeest of Natal. *Natal Wildl.* **4**: 4–6.
——— 1974. The distribution of mammals in Natal. Part I. Primates, Hyracoidea, Lagomorpha (except *Lepus*), Pholidota and Tubulidentata. *Ann. Natal Mus.* **22**: 173–186.
——— 1977. The distribution of mammals in Natal. Part 2. Carnivora. *Ann. Natal Mus.* **23**: 93–115.
——— 1982. *The conservationists and the killers.* Cape Town: Bulpin.
——— **& Pringle, V.L.** 1979. Observations on the lynx *Felis caracal* in the Bedford district. *S. Afr. J. Zool.* **14**: 1–4.
**Pringle, V.L.** 1981. The caracal. *The Naturalist* **25**: 10–11.
**Proctor, J.** 1963. A contribution to the natural history of the spotted necked otter, *Lutra maculicollis* Lichtenstein. *E. Afr. Wildl. J.* **1**: 93–102.
**Prunier, P.** 1946. Notes sur les Suides savages de Guinée. *Mammalia* **10**: 146–148.
***Pryor, K., Lindbergh, J., Lindbergh, S. & Milano, R.** 1990. A dolphin-human fishing cooperative in Brazil. *Mar. Mammal Sci.* **6**: 77–82.
**Pryor, T., Pryor, K. & Norris, K.S.** 1965. Observations on the pygmy killer whale (*Feresa attenuata* Gray) from Hawaii. *J. Mammal.* **46**: 450–461.
***Purves, P.E. & Pilleri, G.E.** 1978. The functional anatomy and general biology of *Pseudorca crassidens* (Owen) with a review of the hydronamics and acoustics in Cetacea. *Invest. on Cetacea* **9**: 67–227.

# Q

**Qvortrup, S.A. & Blankenship, L.H.** 1974. Food habits of klipspringer. *E. Afr. Wildl. J.* **12**: 79–80.

# R

***Raath, J.P. & Hall-Martin, A.J.** 1989. Transport and boma management techniques for black rhinoceros *Diceros bicornis* as used in the Etosha/Vaalbos operation. *Koedoe* **32**: 69–76.
**Racey, P.A. & Skinner, J.D.** 1979. Endocrine aspects of sexual mimicry in spotted hyaenas, *Crocuta crocuta*. *J. Zool., Lond.* **187**: 315–326.
**Rahm, U. & Christiaensen, A.R.** 1963. Les mammifères de la region occidentale du Lac Kivu. *Annls Mus. r. Afr. cent. Ser. 8 Sci. Zool.* **118** 1–83.
***Rahm, S. & Frewein, J.** 1980. On the anatomy of the gastrointestinal tract in *Procavia, Heterohyrax* and *Dendrohyrax* Hyracoidea. *Zentralblatt fur Veterinarmedizin.* Ser. C. **9**: 307–320.
***Rainy, M. & Rainy, Judy** 1989. High noon on the Maasai Mara. *New Sci.* 9 Dec.: 48–52.
***Ralls, K.** 1976. Mammals in which females are larger than males. *Q. Rev. Biol.* **51**: 245–276.
*——— **Brownell, R.L. & Ballou, J.** 1980. Differential mortality by sex and age in mammals, with specific reference to the sperm whale. *Rep. int. Whal. Commn* (Special Issue 2): 233–243.
**Rand, R.W.** 1954. Notes on the birds of Marion Island. *Ibis* **96**: 173–206.
——— 1955. Reproduction in the female Cape fur seal. *Proc. zool. Soc. Lond.* **124**: 717–740.
——— 1956a. Notes on the Marion Island fur seal. *Proc. zool. Soc. Lond.* **126**: 65–82.
*——— 1956b. The Cape fur seal, *Arctocephalus pusillus* (Schreber). Its general characteristics and moult. *Union South Africa Dep. Com. and Ind., Div. Fish. Investl Rep.*, **21**: 1–52.
——— 1959. The Cape fur seal (*Arctocephalus pusillus*). Distribution, abundance and feeding habits off the south western coast of the Cape Province. *Investl Rep. Div. Sea Fish.* **34**: 1–75.
——— 1967. The Cape fur seal (*Arctocephalus pusillus*). 3. General behaviour on land and sea. *Investl Rep. Div. Sea Fish.* **60**: 1–39.
**Randall, R.M.** 1977. Aspects of the ecology of the civet *Civettictis civetta* (Schreber, 1778). M.Sc. thesis, University of Pretoria.
*——— 1981. Fossil Hyaenidae from the Makapansgat Limeworks deposit, South Africa. *Palaeont. afr.* **24**: 75–85.
***Raper, P. & Boucher, M.** 1988. *Robert Jacob Gordon, Cape travels, 1777 to 1786.* Johannesburg: Brenthurst Press.
**Rasa, O.A.E.** 1973a. Prey capture, feeding technique and their ontogeny in the African dwarf mongoose *Helogale undulata rufula*. *Z. Tierpsychol.* **32**: 449–488.
——— 1973b. Intra-familial sexual repression in the dwarf mongoose *Helogale parvula*. *Naturwissenschaften* **60**: 303–304.
——— 1975. Mongoose sociology and behaviour as related to Zoo exhibition. *Int. Zoo Yb.* **15**: 65–73.
——— 1976a. The ethology and sociology of the dwarf mongoose (*Helogale undulata rufula*). *Z. Tierpsychol.* **43**: 337–406.
——— 1976b. Invalid care in the dwarf mongoose (*Helogale undulata rufula*). *Z. Tierpsychol.* **42**: 337–342
——— 1977a. Differences in group member responses to intruding conspecifics, frightening or potentially dangerous stimuli in dwarf mongoose (*Helogale undulata rufula*). *Z Säugetierk.* **42**: 108–112.
*——— 1977b. The ethology and sociology of the dwarf mongoose, *Helogale undulata rufula*. *Z. Tierpsychol.* **43**: 337–406.
*——— 1983. Dwarf mongoose and hornbill mutualism in the Tara Desert, Kenya. *Behav. Ecol. Sociobiol.* **12**: 181–190.
*——— 1985. *Mongoose watch.* London: John Murray.
*——— 1986. Zwermung as geben Aristoteles recht. *Bild der Wissenschaft* **5**: 18–22.
*——— 1987. The dwarf mongoose: a study of behavior and social structure in relation to ecology in a small social carnivore. *Adv. Study Behav.* **17**: 121–163.
*——— 1989. The costs and effectiveness of vigilance behaviour in the dwarf mongoose: implications for fitness and optimal group size. *Ethology Ecology & Evolution* **1**: 265–282.
**Rattray, J.M.** 1960. The habit, distribution, habitat forage value and veld indicator value of the commoner Southern Rhodesian grasses. *Rhodesia agric. J.* **57**: 424.
***Rau, R.E.** 1974. Revised list of the preserved material of the extinct Cape Colony quagga. *Ann. S. Afr. Mus.* **65**: 41–87.
*——— 1978. Additions to the revised list of observed material of the extinct Cape Colony quagga and notes on the relationship and distribution of southern plains zebras. *Ann. S. Afr. Mus.* **77**: 27–45.
*——— 1983. The coloration of the extinct Cape Colony quagga. *Afr. wild Life* **37**: 136.
**Rautenbach, I.L.** 1971a. Notes on the small mammals of the Kalahari Gemsbok National Park. *Koedoe* **18**: 195–198.
——— 1971b. Ageing criteria in the springbok, *Antidorcas marsupialis* (Zimmermann, 1780) (Artiodactyla: Bovidae). *Ann. Trans. Mus.* **27**: 83–133.
——— 1978a. The Mammals of the Transvaal. Ph.D. thesis, University of Natal.
——— 1978b. A numerical reappraisal of the southern African biotic zones. *Bull. Carnegie Mus. Nat. Hist.* **6**: 175–187.
*——— 1982. The mammals of the Transvaal. Ecoplan Monograph **1**: 111–211.
*——— 1986. Karyotypical variation in southern African Rhinolophidae (Chiroptera) and nongeographic variation in *Rhinolophus denti* Thomas, 1904. *Cimbebasia* Ser A. **8**: 129–139.
——— **& Nel, J.A.J.** 1975. Further records of smaller mammals from the Kalahari Gemsbok National Park. *Koedoe* **18**: 195–198.
——— **& Nel, J.A.J.** 1978. Three species of microchiropteran bats recorded for the first time from the southwest Cape Biotic Zone. *Ann. Trans. Mus.* **31**: 157–161.
——— **& Nel, J.A.J.** 1980. Mammal diversity and ecology in the Cedarberg Wilderness Area, Cape Province. *Ann. Trans. Mus.* **32**: 101–124.
*——— **Schlitter, D.A. & Braack, L.E.O.** 1984. New distributional records of bats for the Republic of South Africa, with special reference to the Kruger National Park. *Koedoe* **27**: 131–135.
——— **Skinner, J.D. & Nel, J.A.J.** 1980. The past and present status of the mammals of Maputaland, in *Studies on the ecology of Maputaland.* Eds M.N. Bruton & K.H. Cooper. Grahamstown: Rhodes University.
***Raven, H.C.** 1942. On the structure of *Mesoplodon densirostris*, a rare beaked whale. *Bull. Am. Mus. Nat. Hist.* **80**: 23–50.
**Raven-Hart, R.** 1967. *Before van Riebeeck.* Cape Town: Struik.
——— 1971. *Cape of Good Hope 1652–1702. The first fifty years of Dutch colonisation as seen by callers.* Vols **1** & **2**. Cape Town: Balkema.
**Rayner, G.W.** 1939. *Globicephala leucosagmaphora* a new species of the genus *Globicephala*. *Ann. Mag. nat. Hist.* **4**: 543–544.
**Rechav, Y., Norval, R.A.I., Tannock, J. & Colborne, J.** 1978. Attraction of the tick *Ixodes meitzi* to twigs marked by the klipspringer antelope. *Nature, Lond.* 275 No.5678: 310–311.
***Redford, K.H.** 1984. Mammalian predation on termites: tests with the burrowing mouse (*Oxymycterus roberti*) and its prey. *Oecologia* **65**: 145–152.
*——— **& Dorea, J.G.** 1984. The nutritional value of invertebrates with emphasis on ants and termites as food for mammals. *J. Zool., Lond.* **203**: 385–395.
**Reich, A.** 1977. Hunting dogs: facts and fiction. *Custos* **6**(7): 9, 21, 41.
——— 1981. The behaviour and ecology of the African wild dog (*Lycaon pictus*) in the Kruger National Park. Ph.D. thesis, University of Yale.
***Reijnders, P.J.H., Plötz, J., Zegers, J. & Gräfe, M.** 1990. Breeding biology of Weddell seals (*Leptonychotes weddellii*) at Drescher Inlet, Riiser Larsen Ice Shelf, Antarctica. *Polar Biol.* **10**: 310–306.
***Reilly, B.K.** 1987. The habit utilisation of the oribi, *Ourebia ourebi ourebi* (Zimmerman, 1783) in the Golden Gate Highlands National Park. M.Sc. thesis, University of Pretoria.
***Reinhardt, J.** 1862. *Pseudorca crassidens. Oversigt Kong. Dansk. Vid. Selsk. Forhandl.*
**Rensch, B. & Dücker, G.** 1959. Die spilele von Mungo and Ichneumon. *Behaviour* **14**: 185–213.
**Repenning, C.A.** 1967. Subfamilies and genera of the Soricidae. *U.S. Geol. Surv.* Professional Paper **565**: 1–74.
——— **Peterson, R.S. & Hubbs, C.L.** 1971. Contributions to the systematics of the southern fur seals, with particular reference to the Juan Fernandez and Guadalupe species, in *Antarctic Pinnipedia*, Ed. W.H. Burt. Washington D.C.: American Geophysical Union. Antarctic Research Series 18.
***Rice, D.W.** 1977. A list of the marine mammals of the world. *NOAA Tech. Rep.* NMFS SSRF-711, 15 pp.
***Rice, F.H. & Saayman, G.S.** 1987. Distribution and behaviour of killer whales (*Orcinus orca*) off the coasts of southern Africa. *Invest. on Cetacea* **20**: 231–250.
**Richardson, P.R.K.** 1980. The natural removal of ungulate carcasses and the adaptive features of the scavengers involved. M.Sc. thesis, University of Pretoria.
*——— 1985. The social behaviour and ecology of the aardwolf, *Proteles cristatus* (Sparrman, 1783) in relation to its food resources. Ph.D. thesis, University of Oxford.
*——— 1986. Aardwolf: African werewolf of the savannas. *Quagga* **14**: 6–10.
*——— 1987a. Food consumption and seasonal variation in the diet of the aardwolf *Proteles cristatus* in southern Africa. *Z. Saugetierk* **52**: 307–325.
*——— 1987b. Aardwolf mating system: overt cuckoldry in an apparently monogamous mammal. *S. Afr. J. Sci.* **83**: 405–410.
*——— 1987c. Aardwolf: The most highly specialized myrmecophagous mammal? *S. Afr. J. Sci* **83**: 643–646.
*——— 1990. The lick of the aardwolf. *Nat. Hist.* **4/90**: 78–87.
*——— **& Bearder, S.K.** 1984. The aardwolf. In: *The Encyclopedia of Mammals,* Vol. 1. Ed. D.W. Macdonald. London: George Allen & Unwin.
*——— **Mundy, P.J. & Plug, I.** 1986. Bone crushing carnivores and their significance to osteodystrophy in griffon vulture chicks. *J. Zool., Lond.* **210**: 23–43.
***Rickart, E.A.** 1981. Demography and activity patterns of some small mammals from the Cape Province, South Africa. *J. Mammal.* **62**: 646–649.
**Ridgeway, W.** 1909. Contributions to the study of the Equidae ii on hitherto unrecorded specimens of *E. quagga*. *Proc. zool. Soc. Lond.*: 563–586.
**Ridgway, S.H.** (ed.) 1972. *Mammals of the sea: biology and medicine.* Springfield Ill.: Thomas.
*——— **& Harrison, R.J.** 1986. Diving dolphins. pp 33–58. In: *Research on dolphins.* Eds M.M. Bryden & R. Harrison. Oxford: Clarendon Press.
**Ried, T.H.** 1958. Giraffes. *Rep. Smithson. Instn.*: 166–167.
**Riney, T. & Child, G.** 1960. Breeding season and ageing criteria for the common duiker (*Sylvicapra grimmia*), 291–299. *Proc. First Fed. Sci. Congr.*, Rhodesian Scientific Association, Salisbury.
——— **& Kettlitz, W.L.** 1964. Management of large mammals in the Transvaal. *Mammalia* **28**: 189–248.
**Ripley, S.D.** 1958. Comments on the black and square-lipped rhinoceros species in Africa. *Ecology* **39**: 172–174.
**Ritchie, A.T.A.** 1963. The black rhinoceros (*Diceros bicornis* L.). *E. Afr. Wildl. J.* **1**: 154–162.
**Roader, J.J.** 1979. La reproduction de la genette (*G. genetta* L.) en captivite. *Mammalia* **43**: 531–542.
**Robbins, C.B.** 1978. Taxonomic identification and history of *Scotophilus nigrita*

(Schreber) (Chiroptera: Vespertilionidae). *J. Mammal.* **59**: 212–213.

*——— & **van der Straaten, E.** 1989. Comments on the systematics of *Mastomys* Thomas, 1915, with the description of a new West African species (Mammalia: Rodentia: Muridae). *Senchenbergiana Biologica* **69**: 1–4.

***Robbins, L.W. & Baker, R.J.** 1978. Karyotypic data for African mammals; with a description of an *in vivo* bone marrow technique. *Bull. Carnegie Mus. Nat. Hist.* **6**: 188–210.

***Roberts, A.** 1917. Fourth supplementary list of mammals in the collection of the Transvaal Museum. *Ann. Trans. Mus.* **5**: 261–278.

——— 1923. The burrowing habits of South African mammals. *S. Afr. Quart. J. Nat. Hist.* **4**: 197.

——— 1933. Eleven new forms of South African mammals. *Ann. Trans. Mus.* **15**: 265–270.

——— 1936a. Report on a survey of the higher vertebrates of north-eastern Zululand. *Ann. Trans. Mus.* **18**: 163–251.

——— 1936b. New South African mammals. *Ann. Trans. Mus.* **18**: 253–254.

——— 1951. *The Mammals of South Africa.* Cape Town: Central News Agency.

**Roberts, K.S.** 1981. The foraging behaviour and strategies of the suricate, *Suricata suricatta* (Erxleben). M.Sc. thesis, University of Pretoria.

**Robertson-Bullock, W.** 1962. The weight of the African elephant *Loxodonta africana*. *Proc. zool. Soc. Lond.* **138**: 133–135.

**Robinette, L.** 1963. Biology of the lechwe (*Kobus leche*) and a proposed game management plan for Lochinvar Ranch, Northern Rhodesia. Research report. Mimeograph.

——— & **Child, G.F.T.** 1964. Notes on biology of the lechwe (*Kobus leche*). *Puku* **2**: 84–117.

**Robinson, G.A.** 1976. Notes on mammals encountered in the Tsitsikama National Parks. *Koedoe* **19**: 145–152.

***Robinson, M.D.** 1977. An observation on parental care of young in the steenbok in South West Africa. *Madoqua* **10**: 215–216.

**Robinson, R.** 1969. The breeding of spotted and black leopards. *J. Bombay Nat. Hist. Soc.* **66**: 423–429.

*——— & **De Vos, V.** 1982. Chinchilla mutant in the lion. *Genetica* **60**: 61–63.

**Robinson, T.J.** 1975. A comparative study of the three subspecies of springbok, *Antidorcas marsupialis marsupialis* (Zimmermann, 1780); *A. m. hofmeyri* Thomas, 1926 and *A. m. angolensis* Blaine, 1922. M.Sc. thesis, University of Pretoria.

——— 1979. Influence of a nutritional parameter on the size differences of the three springbok subspecies. *S. Afr. J. Zool.* **14**: 13–15.

——— 1980. Comparative chromosome studies in the Family Leporidae (Lagomorpha: Mammalia). *Cytogenet. Cell. Genet.* **28**: 64–70.

——— 1981a. Systematics of the South African Leporidae. D.Sc. thesis, University of Pretoria.

——— 1981b. The elusive pondhaas. *Afr. wild Life* **35**: 20–23.

——— 1981c. The bushman hare: 934–938, in *Proc. Wld Lagomorph Conf.*, Guelph, Ontario. Eds K. Myers & C.D. MacInnes. University of Guelph, Ontario.

*——— 1986. Incisor morphology as an aid in the systematics of the South African Leporidae (Mammalia: Lagomorpha). *S. Afr. J. Zool.* **21**: 297–302.

*——— & **Dippenaar, N.J.** 1983. Morphometrics of the South African Leporidae 1. Genus *Pronolagus* Lyon, 1904. *Ann. Mus. Roy. Afr. Centr., Sc. Zool.* **237**: 43–61.

*——— & **Elder, F.F.B.** 1987. Extensive genome reorganization in the African rodent genus *Otomys*. *J. Zool., Lond.* **211**: 735–745.

——— **Elder, F.F.B. & Lopez-Forment, W.** 1981. Banding studies in the volcano rabbit, *Romerolagus diazi*, and Crawshay's hare, *Lepus crawshayi*. *Can. J. Genet. Cytol.* **23**: 469–474.

*——— & **Skinner, J.D.** 1983. Karyology of the riverine rabbit, *Bunolagus monticularis*, and its taxonomic implications. *J. Mammal.* **64**: 678–681.

*——— **Skinner, J.D. & Haim, A.S.** 1986. Close chromosomal congruence in two species of ground squirrel, *Xerus inauris* and *X. princeps* (Rodentia: Sciuridae). *S. Afr. J. Zool.* **21**: 100–106.

***Roche, J., Capanna, E., Civitelli, M.V. & Ceraso, A.** 1984. Caryotypes des rongeurs de Somalie. *Monitore zool. ital.* (NS) Suppl. **19** (7): 259–277.

**Rode, P.** 1943. *Mammifères Ongulés de l'Afrique Noire.* 1–123 en *Fauna de l'Empire français.* Paris: Larose.

**Rodgers, W.A.** 1969. Miombo research Centre, Kingupira. Selous Game Reserve. Ann. Rep. 2. Mimeograph.

**Rodhain, J. & Bequaert, J.** 1916. Observations sur la biologie de *Cyclopodia greeffi* Karsch (Dipt.), Nycteribiide parasite d'une chauve-souris congolaise. *Bull. Soc. zool. Fr.* **40**: 248–262.

***Roe, H.S.J.** 1969. The food and feeding habits of the sperm whales (*Physeter catodon* L.) taken off the west coast of Iceland. *J. du Conseil* **33**: 93–102.

**Roeder, K.D.** 1974. Responses of the less sensitive acoustic sense cells in the tympanic organs of some noctuid and geometrid moths. *J. Insect. Physiol.* **20**: 55–66.

**Romer, A.S.** 1971. *Vertebrate Palaeontology 3rd edn.* Chicago: University Press.

**Rood, J.P.** 1974. Banded mongoose male guard young. *Nature, Lond.* **248**: 176.

——— 1975. Population dynamics and food habits of the banded mongoose. *E. Afr. Wildl. J.* **13**: 89–111.

*——— 1980. Mating relations and breeding suppression in the dwarf mongoose. *Anim. Behav.* **39**: 566–572.

*——— 1990. Group size, survival, reproduction and routes to breeding in dwarf mongooses. *Anim. Behav.* **39**: 566–572.

***Rookmaaker, L.C.** 1989. *The Zoological Exploration of Southern Africa.* Rotterdam: Balkema.

**Roos, J.H., Rethman, N.F.G. & Kotze, G.D.** 1973. Preliminary results on species selection by animals on sour grassveld. *Proc. Grassld Soc. S. Afr.* **8**: 77–81.

**Roosevelt, T.** 1910. *African Game Trails.* New York: Syndicate.

——— & **Heller, E.** 1922. *Life Histories of African Game Animals.* Vol. **2**: 798. London: John Murray.

**Rosenthal, E.** (ed.) 1961. Squirrels, in *Encyclopaedia of Southern Africa.* 5th edn. London: F. Warne & Co.

**Rosenthal, M. & Merritt, D.** 1973a. *The ecology of reproduction in wild and domestic mammals.* London: Methuen.

——— & **Merritt, D.** 1973b. Hand-rearing springhares at Lincoln Park Zoo. *Int. Zoo Yb.* **13**: 135–137.

**Rosevear, D.R.** 1953. *Checklist and atlas of Nigerian mammals.* Lagos: Govt. Printer.

——— 1965. *The Bats of West Africa.* London: Trustees of the Brit. Mus. (Nat. Hist.).

——— 1969. *The rodents of West Africa.* London: Trustees of the Brit. Mus. (Nat. Hist.).

——— 1974. *The carnivores of West Africa.* London: Trustees of the British Museum (Nat. Hist.).

**Ross, G.J.B.** 1969a. The southern elephant seal, *Mirounga leonina*, on South African coasts. *Ann. Cape Prov. Mus. (Nat. Hist.)* **6**: 137–139.

——— 1969b. Evidence for a southern breeding population of True's beaked whale. *Nature, Lond.* **222** No. 56176: 585.

——— 1970. The occurrence of Hector's beaked whale *Mesoplodon hectori* (Gray) in South African waters. *Ann. Cape Prov. Mus. (Nat. Hist.)* **8**: 195–204.

——— 1972. Nuzzling behaviour in captive Cape fur seals, *Arctocephalus pusillus*. *Int. Zoo Yb.* **12**: 183–184.

——— 1973. The taxonomy of bottlenosed dolphins *Tursiops* species in South African waters with notes on their biology. M.Sc. thesis, University of Port Elizabeth.

——— 1977a. The taxonomy of bottlenosed dolphins, *Tursiops* species in South African waters, with notes on their biology. *Ann. Cape Prov. Mus. (Nat. Hist.)* **11**: 135–194.

——— 1977b. The vagrant seal. *Afr. wild Life* **31**: 35.

——— 1979a. The smaller cetaceans of the south east coast of southern Africa. Ph.D. thesis, University of Port Elizabeth.

——— 1979b. Records of pygmy and dwarf sperm whales, genus *Kogia* from southern Africa with biological notes and some comparisons. *Ann. Cape Prov. Mus.* **11**: 259–327.

*——— 1984. The smaller cetaceans of the south east coast of southern Africa. *Ann. Cape Prov. Mus. (Nat. Hist.)* **15**: 173–410.

——— & **Bass, A.J.** 1971. Shark attack on an ailing dolphin, *Stenella coeruleoalba* (Meyer). *S. Afr. J. Sci.* **67**: 413–414.

——— **Best, P.B. & Donnelly, B.G.** 1975. New records of the pigmy right whale (*Caperea marginata*) from South Africa with comments on distribution, migration, appearance and behaviour. *J. Fish. Res. Bd. Can.* **32**: 1005–1017.

*——— **Cockcroft, V.G. & Butterworth, D.S.** 1987. Offshore distribution of bottlenosed dolphins in Natal coastal waters and Algoa Bay, eastern Cape. *S. Afr. J. Zool.* **22**: 50–56.

*——— **Cockcroft, V.G. & Cliff, G.** 1985. Additions to the marine faunas of South Africa and Natal. *Lammergeyer* **35**: 36–40.

*——— **Cockcroft, V.G., Melton, D.A. & Butterworth, D.S.** 1989. Population estimates for bottlenose dolphins *Tursiops truncatus* in Natal and Transkei waters. *S. Afr. J. mar. Sci.* **8**: 119–129.

——— **Shaughnessy, P.D. & Best, P.B.** 1978. New records of crabeater seals, *Lobodon carcinophagus*, from South Africa. *Ann. S. Afr. Mus.* **75**: 153–158.

——— & **Tietz, R.M.** 1972. Records of Cuvier's beaked whale, *Ziphius cavirostris*, from southern Africa. *Ann. Cape Prov. Mus.* **9**: 1–10.

**Ross, J.P.** 1968. A note on the African striped weasel, *Poecilogale albinucha* Gray. *Eastern Cape Naturalist* **34**: 18–19.

***Rosser, Alison M.** 1987. Resource defence in an African antelope, the puku (*Kobus vardoni*). Ph. D. thesis, University of Cambridge.

**Roth, H.H.** 1964. Note on the early growth development of *Hystrix africaeaustralis*. *Z. Säugetierk.* **29**: 313–316.

——— 1965. Observations on growth and ageing of warthog *Phacochoerus aethiopicus* (Pallas, 1766). *Z. Säugetierk.* **30**: 367–380.

——— 1970. Studies on the agricultural utilization of semi-domesticated eland (*Taurotragus oryx*) in Rhodesia. *Rhod. J. agric. Res.* **8**: 67–70.

——— & **Austen, B.** 1966. Twin calves in elephants. *Säugetierk. Mitt.* **4**: 342–345.

——— **Kerr, M.A. & Posselt, J.** 1972. Studies on the utilisation of semi-domesticated eland (*T. oryx*) in Rhodesia. 5: reproduction and herd increase. *Z. Tierzücht. ZüchtBiol.* **89**: 569–583.

**Rourke, J. & Wiens, D.** 1977. Convergent floral evolution in South African and Australian Proteaceae and its possible bearing on pollination by non-flying mammals. *Ann. Mo. bot. Gdn.* **64**: 1–17.

**Rowan, W.** 1926. On photoperiodism, reproductive periodicity and the annual migrations of birds and certain fishes. *Proc. Boston Soc. nat. Hist.* **36**: 147–189.

——— 1929. Experiments in bird migration. I. Manipulation of the reproductive cycle: seasonal histological changes in the gonads. *Proc. Boston Soc. nat. Hist.* **39**: 151–208.

**Rowe-Rowe, D.T.** 1969. Some observations on a captive African weasel, *Poecilogale albinucha*. *Lammergeyer* **10**: 93–96.

——— 1971a. The development and behaviour of a rusty spotted genet, *Genetta rubignosa* Puckeran. *Lammergeyer* **13**: 29–43.

——— 1971b. Sex ratios of steenbok, *Raphicerus campestris* Thunberg, as seen in two South African National Parks. *Koedoe* **14**: 55–59.

——— 1972a. The African weasel, *Poecilogale albinucha* (Gray): observations on behaviour and general biology. *Lammergeyer* **15**: 39–58.

——— 1972b. Distribution of the African weasel, *Poecilogale albinucha* (Gray) in southern Africa. *Lammergeyer* **15**: 59–64.

——— 1972c. Some aspects of antelope ecology in Giant's Castle Game Reserve. Natal Parks, Game and Fish Preservation Board, Pietermaritzburg. Mimeograph.

——— 1974. Game on the Farm, Part 30: Otters and water mongooses. *Farmers' Weekly*, Durban: 35.

——— 1975. Biology of Natal Mustelids. M.Sc. thesis, University of Natal, Durban.

——— 1976. Food of the black-backed jackal in nature conservation and farming areas in Natal. *E. Afr. Wildl. J.* **14**: 345–348.

——— 1977a. Prey capture and feeding behaviour of South African otters. *Lammergeyer* **23**: 13–21.

——— 1977b. Variations in the predatory behaviour of the clawless otter. *Lammergeyer* 23: 22–27.

*——— 1977c. Food ecology of otters in Natal, South Africa. *Oikos* **28**: 210–219.

——— 1978a. Comparative prey capture and food studies of South African mustelines. *Mammalia* **42**: 175–196.

——— 1978b. Reproduction and post-natal development of South African mustelines (Carnivora: Mustelidae). *Zool. Afr.* **13**: 103–114.

——— 1978c. The small carnivores of Natal. *Lammergeyer* **25**: 1–48.

*——— 1983a. Black-backed jackal diet in relation to food availability in the Natal Drakensberg. *S. Afr. J. Wildl. Res.* **13**: 17–23.

*——— 1983b. Habitat preferences of five Drakensberg antelopes. *S. Afr. J. Wildl. Res.* **13**: 1–8.

*——— 1986. Stomach contents of small mammals from the Drakensberg, South Africa. *S. Afr. J. Wildl. Res.* **16**: 32–35.

*——— 1989. Facts about otters. *Technical guides for farmers* No. 10. Pietermaritzburg, Natal Parks Board.

*——— 1990. The African weasel: A Red Data Book species in South Africa. *Mustelid & Viverrid Conservation* No. **2**: 6–7.

*——— & **Meester, J.A.J.** 1982. Habitat preferences and abundance relations of some mammals in the Natal Drakensberg. *S. Afr. J. Zool.* **17**: 202–209.

——— & **Mentis, M.T.** 1973. Some ageing criteria for nyala. *J. sth. Afr. Wildl. Mgmt Ass.* **2**: 17–21.

**Rowell, T.E.** 1966. Forest living baboons in Uganda. *J. Zool. Lond.* **149**: 344–364.

——— 1969. Variability in social organization of primates. In *Primate ethology*, Ed. D. Morris. pp. 283–305. New York: Doubleday & Co.

**Rowland Ward.** See **Ward, Rowland.**

**Rudnai, J.A.** 1970. Social behaviour and feeding habits of lion *Panthera leo massaica* Neumann in Nairobi National Park. M.Sc. thesis, University of Nairobi.

——— 1973a. *The social life of the lion.* Lancaster: Medical & Technical.
——— 1973b. Reproductive biology of lions (*Panthera leo massaica* Neumann) in Nairobi National Park. *E. Afr. Wildl. J.* **11**: 241–253.
——— 1973c. The pattern of lion predation in Nairobi National Park. Mimeograph.
***Rudnai, J.** 1984a. Suckling behaviour in captive *Dendrohyrax arboreus* (Mammalia: Hyracoidea). *S. Afr. J. Zool.* **19**: 121–123.
*——— 1984b. Activity cycle and space utilization in captive *Dendrohyrax arboreus. S. Afr. J. Zool.* **19**: 121–123
***Rüppell, E.** 1827. Atlas zu der Reise im nördlichen Africa von Edward Rüppell. *I. Zoologie.Frankfurt am Main.*
**Rushworth, J.** 1972. Wankie National Park notes. *Dept of Nat. Parks Wildl. Mgmt Rhod.* **6**: 1–8. Mimeograph.
**Ruxton, A.E. & Schwartz, E.** 1929. On hybrid hartebeest and on the distribution of the *Alcelaphus buselaphus* group. *Proc. zool. Soc. Lond*: 567–583.

# S

**Saayman, G.S.** 1968. Oestrogen, behaviour and permeability of a troop of chacma baboons. *Nature, Lond.* **220**: 1339–1340.
——— 1969. Endocrine factors and behaviour in the old-world monkeys. *S. Afr. J. Sci.* **65**: 121–126.
——— 1970. The menstrual cycle and sexual behaviour in a troop of free ranging chacma baboons (*Papio ursinus*). *Folia primatol.* **12**: 81–110.
——— 1971a. Behaviour of chacma baboons. *Afr. wild Life* **25**: 25–29.
——— 1971b. Baboons responses to predators. *Afr. wild Life* **25**: 46–49.
——— 1971c. Aggressive behaviour in free-ranging chacma baboons (*Papio ursinus*). *J. Behav. Sci.* **1**: 77–83.
——— 1971d. Behaviour of the adult males in a troop of free-ranging chacma baboons (*Papio ursinus*). *Folia primatol.* **15**: 36–57.
——— 1971e. Grooming behaviour in a troop of free-ranging chacma baboons (*Papio ursinus*). *Folia primatol.* **16**: 161–178.
——— **Bower, D. & Tayler, C.K.** 1972. Observations on inshore and pelagic dolphins on the south-east Cape coast of South Africa. *Koedoe* **15**: 1–24.
——— **& Tayler, C.K.** 1973. Social organisation of inshore dolphins (*Tursiops aduncus* and *Sousa*) in the Indian Ocean. *J. Mammal.* **54**: 993–996.
*——— **& Tayler, C.K.** 1979. The socioecology of humpback dolphins (*Sousa* sp.). pp 165–226. In: *Behavior of Marine Animals. Current Perspectives in Research. Vol. 3: Cetaceans.* Eds H.E. Winn & B.L. Olla. New York: Plenum Press.
——— **Tayler, C.K. & Bower, D.** 1973. Diurnal activity cycles in captive and free ranging Indian Ocean bottlenose dolphins (*Tursiops aduncus* Ehrenberg). *Behaviour* **44**: 212–233.
**Sachs, R.** 1969. Untersuchungen zur Artbestimmung und Differenzierung der Muskelfinnen ostafrikanischer Wildtiere. *Z. Tropenmed. Parasit.* **20**: 39–50.
**Sadlier, R.** 1966. Notes on reproduction in the larger Felidae. *Int. Zoo Yb.* **6**: 184–187.
**Sale, J.B.** 1965a. Some aspects of the behaviour and ecology of the rock dassies (genera *Procavia* and *Heterohyrax*). Ph.D. thesis, University of London.
——— 1965b. The feeding behaviour of rock hyraces (genera *Procavia* and *Heterohyrax*) in Kenya. *E. Afr. Wildl. J.* **3**: 1–18.
——— 1966a. The habitat of the rock hyrax. *Jl E. Africa nat. Hist. Soc.* **25**, 3(112): 205–214.
——— 1966b. Daily food consumption and mode of ingestion in the hyrax. *Jl E. Africa nat. Hist. Soc.* **25**, 3(112): 215–224.
——— 1969. Breeding season and litter size in Hyracoidea. *J. Reprod. Fert.* Suppl. 6: 249–264.
——— 1970a. Unusual external adaptations in the rock hyrax. *Zool. Afr.* **5**: 101–113.
——— 1970b. The behaviour of the resting hyrax in relation to its environment. *Zool. Afr.* **5**: 87–99.
——— **& Taylor, M.E.** 1969. A new four-toed mongoose from Kenya, *Bdeogale crassicauda nigrescens* ssp. nov. *Jl E. Africa nat. Hist. Soc.* **28**, 2(115): 1–6.
**Sampsell, R.** 1969. Handrearing an aardvark. *Int. Zoo Yb.* **9**: 97–99.
***Sanborn, C.C.** 1951. Chiroptera from Dundo, Lunda, northeastern Angola. *Companhia de diamantes de Angola: Public açaos culturais.* No 18: 53–61.
**Sanderson, I.T.** 1956. *Follow the whale.* Boston: Little, Brown & Co.
**Sauer, E.G.F.** 1973. Zum Sozialverhalten der Kurzohrigen Elefantenspitzmaus. *Z. Säugetierk.* **38**: 65–97.
——— **& Sauer, E.M.** 1963. The South West African bushbaby of the *Galago senegalensis* group. *Jl S. W. Africa scient. Soc.* **16**: 5–36.
*——— **& Sauer, E.M.** 1972. Zur biologie der Kurzohrigen Elefantenspitzmaus, *Macroscelides proboscideus. Z. Kolner Zoo* **15**: 119–139.
**Sauer, J.J.C., Skinner, J.D. & Neitz, R.** 1982. Seasonal utilization of leaves by giraffes *Giraffa camelopardalis* and the relationship of the seasonal utilisation to the chemical composition of the leaves. *S. Afr. J. Zool.* **17**: 210–219.
**Savage, R.J.G.** 1978. Carnivora: 249–267, in *Evolution of African mammals.* Eds V.J. Maglio & H.B.S. Cooke. Cambridge, Mass.: Harvard University Press.
**Savory, J.C.** 1966. Breeding and hand-rearing of the giraffe *Giraffa camelopardalis* at Columbus Zoo. *Int. Zoo Yb.* **6**: 202–204.
**Schaller, G.B.** 1968. Hunting behavior of the cheetah in the Serengeti National Park, Tanzania. *E. Afr. Wildl. J.* **6**: 95–100.
——— 1969. Life with the king of beasts. *Natn. geog. Mag.* **135**(4): 494–519.
——— 1972a. *The Serengeti lion: A study of Predator-prey relations.* Chicago: University Press.
——— 1972b. Predators of the Serengeti. *Nat. Hist.* **81**(2): 49. **81**(3): 60–69. **81**(4): 38–43.
——— 1974. *Golden Shadows, Flying Hooves.* London: Collins.
——— **& Lowther, G.** 1969. The relevance of carnivore behavior to the study of early hominids. *SW. J. Anthrop.* **25**: 307–341.
**Schapera, I. & Farrington, B.** 1933. *The early Cape Hottentots described in the writings of Olfert Dapper (1668), Willem Ten Rhyne (1686) and Johannes Gubielmus de Grevenbroek (1695).* Cape Town: Van Riebeeck Soc.
**Schauenberg, P.** 1977. La stature du chat forestier *Felis silvestris* Schreb. et la variabilite morphologique de l'espere. *Revue suisse Zool.* **84**(2): 323–337.
**Scheffer, V.B.** 1976. Exploring the lives of whales. *Natn. geog. Mag.* **150**: 752–767.
——— **& Rice, D.W.** 1963. A list of marine mammals of the world. *Spec. scient. Rep. U.S. Fish Wildl. Serv.* 431: 1–12.
——— **& Slipp, J.W.** 1948. The whales and dolphins of Washington State, with a key to the cetaceans of the west coast of North America. *Am. Midl. Nat. Monogr.* **39**: 257–337.
**Schenkel, R.** 1966. Zum Problem der Territorialitat und der Markierens bei Säugern am Beispiel des schwarzen Nashorns und des Löwens. *Z. Tierpsychol.* **31**: 593–626.
——— **& Schenkel-Hullinger, L.** 1969. *Ecology and behaviour of the black rhinoceros (Diceros bicornis L.), a field study.* Hamburg: Paul Parey.
***Schevill, W.E.** 1986. The International Code of Zoological Nomenclature and a paradigm: the name *Physeter catodon* Linnaeus 1758. *Mar. Mammal Sci.* **2**: 153–157.
*——— 1987. [The scientific name of the sperm whale] *Mar. Mammal Sci.* **3**: 89–90.
——— **& Watkins, W.A.** 1962. Whale and porpoise noises: a phonograph disk. Woods Hole, Mass. USA: Woods Hole Oceanographic Institute.
**Schillings, C.G.** 1905. *With flashlight and rifle.* London: Hutchinson.
**Schlitter, D.A.** 1973. A new species of gerbil from South West Africa with remarks on *Gerbillurus tytonis* Bauer & Niethammer 1959 (Rodentia: Gerbillinae). *Bull. Sth Calif. Acad. Sci.* **72**: 13–18.
*——— **Robbins, L.W. & Buchanan, S.A.** 1982. Bats of the Central African Republic (Mammalia: Chiroptera). *Ann. Carnegie Mus.* 51 Art **8**: 133–155.
*——— **Rautenbach, I.L. & Coetzee, C.G.** 1984. Karotypes of southern African gerbils, genus *Gerbillurus* Shortridge, 1942 (Rodentia: Cricetidae). *Ann. Carnegie Mus.* **53**: 549–557.
***Schmidt, J.L.** 1984. Common duiker measurements in Natal and Zambia—an example of Bergmann's and Allen's rules. *Lammergeyer* **32**: 8–10.
**Schmidt-Nielson, K.** 1964. *Desert Animals: Physiological problems of heat and water.* Oxford: Clarendon Press.
**Schneider, K.M.** 1926. Über Hyänenzacht. *Peltztierzucht* **2**: 1–4.
——— 1952a. Einige Bilder zur Paarung der Flecken-hyäne *Crocuta crocuta* Erxl. *Zool. Gart.* **19**: 135–149.
——— 1952b. Über Hyänenzucht. *Peltztierzucht* **2**(8): 1–4.
**Schoen, A.** 1972. Studies on the environmental physiology of a semi-desert antelope, the dikdik. *E. Afr. agric. For. J.* **17**: 325–330.
**Scholander, P.F.** 1964. Animals in aquatic environments: adaptation of mammals and birds, in *Handbook of Physiology* Section 4. Adaptation to the environment. Ed. D.B. Dill. Washington D.C.: Am. Physiol. Soc.
——— **& Schevill, W.E.** 1955. Counter current vascular heat exchange in the fins of whales. *J. appl. Physiol.* **8**: 279–282.
**Schoop, U.** 1977. *Praomys (Mastomys) natalensis*: an African mouse capable of sustaining persistent asymptomatic rabies infection. *Annls Inst. Pasteur, Paris*: 289–296.
**Schouteden, H.** 1945. De zoogdieren van Belgisch Congo en van Ruanda-Urundi. *Annls Mus. r. Congo belge* **3**(2): 169–332.
——— 1948. Faune du Congo Belge et du Ruanda Urundi. 1. Mammifères. *Annls Mus. r. Afr. cent.* **8**(1): 1–331.
***Schröder, W. & Mensah, G.A.** 1987. Reproductive biology of *Thryonomys swinderianus* (Temminck). *Z. Säugetierk.* **52**: 164–168.
**Schultz, W.C.** 1966. Breeding and hand-rearing brown hyaena. *Int. Zoo Yb.* **6**: 173–176.
***Schuster, R.** 1976. Lekking behaviour in Kafue lechwe. *Science* **192**: 1240–1242.
*——— 1977. Social organisation of Kafue lechwe. *Black Lechwe.* **12** (3): 40–51.
**Schwarz, E.** 1912. Beiträge zur Kenntnis der Zebras. *Arch. Naturgesch.* **78A** (7): 34–57.
——— 1930. Die Sammlung afrikanischer Säugetiere in Congo Museum. Ginsterkatzen (Gattung *Genetta* Oken). *Revue Zool. Bot. afr.* **19**: 275–286.
——— **& Schwarz, H.K.** 1943. The wild and commensal stocks of the house mouse, *Mus musculus* L. *J. Mammal.* **24**: 59–72.
**Schweitzer, F.R. & Scott, K.J.** 1973. Early occurrence of domestic sheep in sub-Saharan Africa. *Nature, Lond.* **241**: 547–548.
***Sclater, P.L.** 1877. *Felis lanea* the woolly cheetah. *Proc. Zool. Soc. Lond.*: 532–533.
**Sclater, W.L.** 1900/1901. *The Mammals of South Africa* Vol. **I** 1900, Vol. **II** 1901. London: Porter.
**Sclater, P.L. & Thomas, P.** 1899. *Book of Antelopes.* London: R.H. Porter.
**Scorer, J.** 1980. Some factors affecting the feeding ecology and socio-biology of the samango monkey, *Cercopithecus albogularis schwarzi* Roberts, 1931. M.Sc. thesis, University of Pretoria.
**Scotcher, J.S.B.** 1973. Diurnal feeding by bushpig. *Lammergeyer* 19: 33–34.
——— 1978. Hippopotamus numbers and movements in Ndumu Game Reserve. *Lammergeyer* 24: 5–12.
——— **Stewart, D.R.M. & Breen, C.M.** 1978. The diet of the hippopotamus in Ndumu Game Reserve, Natal, as determined by faecal analysis. *S. Afr. J. Wildl. Res.* **8**: 1–12.
***Scott, E.D. & Meester, J.** 1988. Reproduction and postnatal development of the single-striped mouse, *Lemniscomys rosalia. S. Afr. J. Wildl. Res.* **18**: 351–372.
***Scott, M.D. & Cordaro, J.G.** 1987. Behavioral observations of the dwarf sperm whale, *Kogia simus. Mar. Mammal Sci.* **3**: 353–354.
***Scully, W.C.** 1898. *Between sun and sand; a tale of an African desert.* Cape Town: Juta.
——— 1915. *Lodges in the wilderness.* London: Jenkins.
***Seagers, D.J. & Henderson, J.R.** 1985. Cephalopod remains from the stomach of a short finned pilot whale collected near Santa Catalina Island, California. *J. Mammal.* **66**: 777–779.
***Seely, M.K.** 1977. Sand solidified by gemsbok urine as selected burrow sites of gerbils. *Zool. Afr.* **12**: 247–249.
***Seier, J.V.** 1985. Breeding vervet monkeys *Cercopithecus pygerythrus* in a closed environment. Internal Report: National Research Institute for Nutritional Diseases, Tygerberg C.P.
***Selous, F.C.** 1893. *A hunter's wanderings in Africa.* London: Richard Bentley.
——— 1908. *African Nature Notes and Reminiscenses.* London: MacMillan.
——— 1928. *A hunter's wanderings in Africa.* London: MacMillan.
**Semichon, A.** 1923. Le renflement caudal du *Macroscelides rozeti* Duvernoy. *Bull. Soc. zool. Fr.* **47**: 466–469.
**Sergeant, D.E.** 1962. The biology of the pilot or pothead whale *Globicephala melaena* (Traill) in Newfoundland waters. *Bull. Fish. Res. Bd. Can.* **132**: 84.
——— 1963. Minke whales, *Balaenoptera acutirostrata* Lacépède, of the western north Atlantic. *J. Fish. Res. Bd Can.* **20**(6): 1489–1504.
**Setzer, H.W.** 1956. Mammals of the Anglo-Egyptian Sudan. *Proc. U.S. Natn. Mus.* **106**(3377): 447–587.
——— 1957. A review of Libyan mammals. *J. Egypt. publ. Hlth Ass.* **32**(2): 41–82.
——— 1971. New bats of the genus *Laephotis* from Africa (Mammalia: Chiroptera). *Proc. biol. Soc. Wash.* **84**: 259–264.
——— 1975. Genus *Acomys*, Part 6.5, pp. 1–2, in *The mammals of Africa: an identification manual.* Eds J. Meester & H.W. Setzer. Washington D.C.: Smithsonian Institution Press.
**Sewell, G.D.** 1967. Ultrasound in adult rodents. *Nature, Lond.* **215**: 512.
***Seydack, A.H.W.** 1983. Age assessment of the bushpig *Potamochoerus porcus* Linn. 1758 in the southern Cape. M.Sc. thesis, University of Stellenbosch.
***Seyfarth, R.M.** 1980. The distribution of grooming and related behaviours among adult female vervet monkeys. *Anim. Behav.* **28**: 798–813.
*——— **Cheney, D.L. & Marler, P.** 1980. Monkey responses to three different alarm

calls: Evidence of predator classification and semantic communication. *Science* **210**: 801–803.
***Shackleton, C. & Walker, B.H.** 1985. Habitat and dietary species selection by oribi antelope at Mount Sheba Nature Reserve. *S. Afr. J. Wildl. Res.* **15**: 49–53.
***Shallenberger, E.W. & Kang, I.** 1977. Dolphin births at Sea Life Park. pp 77–84. In: *Breeding dolphins; present status, suggestions for the future.* Eds S.H. Ridgway & K. Benirschke. U.S. Dept of Commerce NTIS PB-273 673.
***Shane, S.H., Wells, R.S. & Wursig, B.** 1986. Ecology, behavior and social organization of the bottlenose dolphin: a review. *Mar. Mammal Sci.* **2**: 34–63.
***Sharp, G.J.** 1982. Seasonal variation in the diet and condition of the African elephant in the Sengwa Wildlife Research Area, Zimbabwe. M.Sc. thesis, University of Zimbabwe.
**Shaughnessy, P.D.** 1976. Controversial harvest. *Afr. wild Life* **30**: 26–31.
——— 1979. Cape fur seals in South West Africa. *S.W.A. Jaarboek*: 101–103.
——— 1980. Influence of Cape fur seals on jackass penguin numbers on Sinclair Island. *S. Afr. J. Wildl. Res.* **10**: 18–21.
*——— **& Burton, H.R.** 1986. Fur seals *Arctocephalus* spp. at Mawson Station, Antarctica, and in the Southern Ocean. *Polar Rec.* **23**: 79–81.
*——— **& Fletcher, L.** 1987. Fur seals *Arctocephalus* spp. at MacQuarie Island. *Aust. Mar. Sci. Bull.* **88**: 22.
*——— **& Kerry, K.R.** 1989. Crabeater seals *Lobodon carcinophagus* during the breeding season: observations on five groups near Enderby Land, Antarctica. *Marine Mammal Science* **5**: 68–77.
——— **& Payne, A.I.L.** 1979. Incidental mortality of Cape fur seals during trawl fishing activities in South African waters. *Fish. Bull. Un. S. Afr.* **12**: 20–25.
——— **& Ross, G.J.B.** 1980. Records of the Subantarctic fur seal *Arctocephalus tropicalis* from South Africa with notes on its biology and some observations of captive animals. *Ann. S. Afr. Mus.* **82**: 71–89.
**Shaw, E.H.J.** 1947. The bushbuck. *Afr. wild Life* **1**: 16–19.
***Shepherd, A.J., Leman, P.A. & Hartwig, E.K.** 1983. Analysis of viverrid scats from the northern Orange Free State. *S. Afr. J. Zool.* **18**: 400–401.
**Sheppe, W. & Haas, P.** 1976. Large mammal populations of the lower Chobe River, Botswana. *Mammalia* **40**: 223–243.
**Sheppe, W. & Osborne, T.** 1971. Patterns of use of a flood plain by Zambian mammals. *Ecol. Monogr.* **41**: 179–205.
**Sherry, B.Y.** 1975. Reproduction of elephant in Gonarezhou, south-eastern Rhodesia. *Arnoldia Rhod.* **7**(29): 1–16.
——— 1977. The red squirrel, *Paraxerus palliatus* (Peters), in south-eastern Rhodesia. *Arnoldia Rhod.* **8**(15): 1–7.
***Shoemaker, A.H.** 1983. 1982 Studbook Report on the brown hyena, *Hyaena brunnea*: decline of a pedigree species. *Zoo Biology* **2**: 133–136.
**Short, R.V.** 1966. Oestrus behaviour—ovulation and the formation of the corpus luteum in the African elephant (*Loxodonta africana*). *E. Afr. Wildl. J.* **4**: 56–68.
——— 1972. Species differences, in *Reproduction in mammals: 4. reproductive patterns.* Eds C.R. Austin & R.V. Short. Cambridge: University Press.
**Shorten, M.** 1951. Some aspects of the biology of the grey squirrel, *Sciurus carolinensis* in Great Britain. *Proc. zool. Soc. Lond.* **121**: 427;459.
**Shortridge, G.C.** 1931a. *Felis (Microfelis) nigripes thomasi* subsp. nov. *Rec. Albany Mus.* **4**: 1.
——— 1931b. Field notes on two little known antelopes *Rhynchotragus damarensis* and the Angolan impala *Aepyceros petersi*. *S. Afr. J. Sci.* **28**: 412–417.
——— 1934. *The mammals of South West Africa.* Vols **I** & **II**. London: Heinemann.
——— 1942. Field notes on the first and second expeditions of the Cape Museums mammal survey of the Cape Province, and descriptions of some new subgenera and subspecies. *Ann. S. Afr. Mus.* **36**: 27–100.
**Sidney, J.** 1965. The past and present distribution of some African ungulates. *Trans. zool. Soc. Lond.* **30**: 1–397.
***Siegfried, W.R. & Davies, B.R.** 1982. Conservation of ecosystems. *S. Afr. Nat. Scientific Programmes Report* No. **16**: 1–97. Pretoria: C.S.I.R.
**Sikes, S.K.** 1964. The ratel or honey badger. *Afr. wild Life* **18**: 29–37.
——— 1971. *The natural history of the African elephant.* London: Weidenfeld & Nicholson.
**Simonetta, A.M.** 1968. A new golden mole from Somalia with an appendix on the taxonomy of the Family Chrysochloridae (Mammalia: Insectivora). *Monitore zool. ital.* (NS) 2 (Suppl.): 27–55.
**Simpson, C.D.** 1964a. Notes on the banded mongoose, *Mungos mungo* (Gmelin). *Arnoldia Rhod.* **1**(19): 1–8.
——— 1964b. Observations on courtship behaviour in warthog, *Phacochoerus aethiopicus* Pallas. *Arnoldia Rhod.* **1**(20): 1–4.
——— 1966a. Tooth eruption, growth and ageing criteria in greater kudu, *Tragelaphus strepsiceros* Pallas. *Arnoldia Rhod.* **2**(21): 1–112.
——— 1966b. A key to the identification of carnivore skulls in Rhodesia and Zambia. *Arnoldia Rhod.* **2**(18): 1–32.
——— 1966c. The banded mongoose. *Anim. Kingd.* **69**: 52–57.
——— 1972a. An evaluation of seasonal movement in greater kudu populations —*Tragelaphus strepsiceros* Pallas—in three localities in southern Africa. *Zool. Afr.* **7**: 197–206.
——— 1972b. Some characteristics of Tragelaphine horn growth and their relationship to age in greater kudu and bushbuck. *J. sth Afr. Wildl. Mgmt Ass.* **2**: 1–8.
——— 1974. Ecology of the Zambezi valley bushbuck *Tragelaphus scriptus ornatus* Pocock. Ph.D. thesis, Texas A & M University.
——— 1978. Effects of elephant and other wildlife on the vegetation along the Chobe River, Botswana. *Occ. Pap. Mus. Texas Tech Univ.* **48**: 1–15.
——— **& Cowie, D.** 1967. The seasonal distribution of kudu, *Tragelaphus strepsiceros* Pallas, on a southern Lowveld game ranch in Rhodesia. *Arnoldia Rhod.* **3**(18): 1–13.
——— **& Elder, W.H.** 1968. Lens weight related to estimated age in greater kudu. *J. Wildl. Mgmt* **32**: 764–768.
——— **& Elder, W.H.** 1969. Tooth cementum as an index of age in greater kudu. *Arnoldia Rhod.* **4**(20): 1–10.
**Simpson, G.G.** 1945. The principles of classification and a classification of mammals. *Bull. Am. Mus. nat. Hist.* **85**: 1–350.
——— 1967. The Tertiary lorisiform primates of Africa. *Bull. Mus. comp. Zool. Harv.* **36**: 39–62.
**Sinclair, A.R.E.** 1977a. Lunar and timing of the breeding season in Serengeti wildebeest. *Nature, Lond.* **267**: 832–833.
——— 1977b. *The African buffalo: a study of resource limitation of populations.* Chicago: University Press.
——— **& Duncan, P.** 1972. Indices of condition in tropical ruminants. *E. Afr. Wildl. J.* **10**: 143–149.
——— **& Gwynne, M.D.** 1972. Food selection in the East African buffalo (*Syncerus caffer* Sparrman). *E. Afr. Wildl. J.* **10**: 77–89.
***Singarajah, K.V.** 1984. Observations of the occurrence and behaviour of minke whales off the coast of Brazil. *Sci. Rep. Whales Res. Inst.* 35: 17–38.
**Siniff, D.B. & Bengtson, J.L.** 1977. Observations and hypotheses concerning the interactions among crabeater seals, leopard seals and killer whales. *J. Mammal.* **58**: 414–416.
——— **Stirling, I., Bengtson, J.L. & Reichle, R.A.** 1979. Social behaviour of crabeater seals, *Lobodon carcinophagus*, during the austral spring. *Can. J. Zool.* **57**: 2243–2255.
*——— **& Stone, S.** 1985. The role of the leopard seal in the tropho-dynamics of the Antarctic marine ecosystem. pp 555–560. In: *Antarctic Nutrient Cycles and Food Webs.* Eds W.R. Siegfried, P.R. Condy & R.M. Laws. Berlin: Springer-Verlag.
**Sithu, H.A.A.** 1967. A brief note on dugongs. *Int. Zoo Yb.* **7**: 221.
***Sivasubramanian, K.** 1964. Predation of tuna longline catches in the Indian Ocean by killer whales. *Bull. Fish. Res. Stn Colombo* (17): 221–236.
***Skarpe, C.** 1986. Vegetation ecology in the western Kalahari in relation to large herbivore grazing. *Acta Universitatis Upsaliensis* **33**: 1–22.
*——— 1986. Plant community structure in relation to grazing and environmental changes along a north-south transect in the western Kalahari. *Vegetatio* **68**: 3–18.
*——— **& Bergstrom, R.** 1986. Nutrient content and digestibility of forage plants in relation to plant phenology and rainfall in the Kalahari, Botswana. *J. Arid. Environ.* **11**: 147–164.
**Skaife, S.H.** 1951. Review: The mammals of South Africa by Austin Roberts. *Afr. wild Life* **5**: 348–349.
**Skead, C.J.** 1972. Dassies at Robben Island. *Afr. wild Life* **26**: 54–57.
——— 1973. Zoo historical gazetteer. *Ann. Cape Prov. Mus.* **10**: 1–259.
——— 1980. *Historical mammal incidence in the Cape Province.* Cape Town: Dept Nature and Environmental Conservation.
*——— 1987. Historical mammal incidence in the Cape Province. Vol. **2**. Cape Town, Directorate of Nature & Environmental Conservation.
**Skead, D.M.** 1973. Incidence of calling in the black-backed jackal. *J. sth. Afr. Wildl. Mgmt Ass.* **3**: 28–29.
**Skinner, J.D.** 1966. An appraisal of the eland (*Taurotragus oryx*) for diversifying and improving animal production in Southern Africa. *Afr. wild Life* **20**: 29–40.
——— 1967. An appraisal of the eland as a farm animal in Africa. *Anim. Breed. Abstr.* **35**: 177–186.
*——— 1969. The lifetime production of an impala. *Afr. wild Life* **23**: 79.
——— 1971a. The sexual cycle of the impala ram *Aepyceros melampus* Lichtenstein. *Zool. Afr.* **6**: 75–84.
——— 1971b. Productivity of the eland: an appraisal of the last five years of research. *S. Afr. J. Sci.* **67**: 534–539.
——— 1972a. The springbok: a farm animal of the future. *Afr. wild Life* **26**: 114–115.
——— 1972b. Eland vs. beef. *Afr. wild Life* **26**: 4–9.
——— 1974. "That whimsical compound, the Gnoo". *Afr. wild Life* **28**: 14.
——— 1976. Ecology of the brown hyaena, *Hyaena brunnea*, in the Transvaal with a distribution map for southern Africa. *S. Afr. J. Sci.* **72**: 262–269.
——— 1979. Feeding behaviour in caracal, *Felis caracal*. *J. Zool., Lond.* **189**: 523–525.
——— 1980. Productivity of mountain reedbuck, *Redunca fulvorufula* (Afzelius, 1815) at the Mountain Zebra National Park. *Koedoe* **23**: 123–130.
*——— 1985. Wildlife management in practice: conservation of ungulates through protection and utilization. pp 25–46. In: *Advances in Animal Conservation.* Eds J.P. Hearn & J.K. Hodges. Zoological Society of London. Oxford: Clarendon Press.
*——— 1989. Game ranching in southern Africa. Ch. 15. In: *Animal Production Systems.* Eds R.J. Hudson, K.R. Drew & L.M. Baskin. Cambridge: University Press.
——— **Breytenbach, G.J. & Maberly, C.T.A.** 1976. Observations on the ecology and biology of the bushpig, *Potamochoerus porcus* Linn. in the northern Transvaal. *S. Afr. J. Wildl. Res.* **6**: 123–128.
*——— **Davies, R.A.G., Conroy, A.M. & Dott, H.M.** 1986. Productivity of springbok *Antidorcas marsupialis* and Merino sheep *Ovis aries* during a Karoo drought. *Trans. Roy. Soc. S. Afr.* **46** (2): 149–164.
——— **Davis, S. & Ilani, G.** 1980. Bone collecting by striped hyaenas, *Hyaena hyaena*, in Israel. *Palaeont. afr.* **23**: 99–104.
——— **Dott, H.M., de Vos, V. & Millar, R.P.** 1980. On the sexual cycle of mature bachelor bontebok rams at the Bontebok National Park, Swellendam. *S. Afr. J. Zool.* **15**: 117–120.
——— **Fairall, N. & Bothma, J. du P.** 1977. South African red data book—large mammals. *S. Afr. Nat. Sci. Prog. Rep.* No. 18. Pretoria: CSIR.
——— **& Hall-Martin, A.J.** 1975. A note on foetal growth and development of the giraffe, *Giraffa camelopardalis giraffa*. *J. Zool., Lond.* **177**: 73–79.
*——— **Henschel, J.R. & van Jaarsveld, A.S.** 1986. Bone-collecting habits of spotted hyaenas, *Crocota crocuta* in the Kruger National Park. *S. Afr. J. Zool.* **21**: 303–308.
——— **& Huntley, B.J.** 1971a. The sexual cycle in the blesbok ram, *Damaliscus dorcas dorcas*. *Agroanimalia* **3**: 23–26.
——— **& Huntley, B.J.** 1971b. A report on the sexual cycle in the kudu bull, *Tragelaphus strepsiceros* Pallas, and a description of an inter-sex. *Zool. Afr.* **6**: 293–299.
——— **& Ilani, G.** 1979. The striped hyaena, *Hyaena hyaena*, in the Judean and Negev deserts and a comparison with the brown hyaena, *Hyaena brunnea*. *Israel J. Zool.* **28**: 229–232.
*——— **Monro, R.H. & Zimmerman, J.** 1984. Comparative food intake and growth of cattle and impala on mixed tree savanna. *S.Afr.J.Wildl.Res.* **14**: 1–9.
——— **Nel, J.A.J. & Millar, R.P.** 1977. Evolution of time of parturition and differing litter sizes as an adaptation to changes in environmental conditions. pp 39–44. In: *Reproduction and Evolution.* Eds J.H. Calaby & C.H. Tyndale-Biscoe. *Proc. 4th. Symp. Comp. Biol. Reprod.* Canberra: Australian Acad. Sci.
——— **Scorer, J.A. & Millar, R.P.** 1975. Observations on the reproductive physiological status of mature herd bulls, and young bulls in the hippopotamus, *Hippopotamus amphibius amphibius* Linnaeus. *Gen. Comp. Endocrinol.* **26**: 92–95.
——— **& Skinner, C.P.** 1974. Predation on the cattle egret, *Bubulcus ibis*, and masked weaver, *Ploceus velatus*, by the vervet monkey, *Cercopithecus aethiops*. *S. Afr. J. Sci.* **70**: 157–158.
——— **& van Aarde, R.J.** 1981. The distribution and ecology of the brown hyaena, *Hyaena brunnea*, and spotted hyaena, *Crocuta crocuta*, in the central Namib Desert. *Madoqua* **12**: 231–239.
*——— **& van Aarde, R.J.** 1983. Observations on the trend of the breeding population of southern elephant seals, *Mirounga leonina*, at Marion Island. *J. Appl. Ecol.* **20**: 707–712.
*——— **& van Aarde, R.J.** 1986. The use of space by the aardwolf *Proteles cristatus*. *J. Zool., Lond.* **209**: 299–301.
*——— **van Aarde, R.J. & van Jaarsveld, A.S.** 1984. Adaptations in three species of large mammals *Antidorcas marsupialis, Hystrix africaeaustralis, Hyaena brunnea* to arid environments. *S. Afr. J. Zool.* **19**: 82–86.
——— **van Heerden, J.A.H. & van Zyl, J.H.M.** 1971. The effect of season on the reproductive tract of the eland bull. *S. Afr. J. Anim. Sci.* **1**: 81–84.
——— **& van Zyl, J.H.M.** 1969. Reproductive performance of the common eland, *T. oryx*, in two environments. *J. Reprod. Fert. Suppl.* 6: 319–322.
——— **& van Zyl, J.H.M.** 1970. A study of growth of springbok ewes. *Afr. wild Life* **24**: 149–154.

——— **van Zyl, J.H.M. & Oates, L.G.** 1974. The effect of season on the breeding cycle of plains antelope of the western Transvaal Highveld. *J. sth Afr. Wildl. Mgmt Ass.* **4**: 15–23.

——— **van Zyl, J.H.M. & van Heerden, J.A.H.** 1973. The effect of season on reproduction in the black wildebeest and red hartebeest in South Africa. *J. Reprod. Fert.*, Suppl. 19: 101–110.

——— **von La Chevallerie & van Zyl, J.H.M.** 1971. An appraisal of the springbok for diversifying animal production in Africa. *Anim. Breed. Abstr.* **39**: 215–224.

**Slaughter, B.H.** 1970. Evolutionary trends of Chiropteran dentitions. pp 51–83. In: *About Bats*. Eds B.H. Slaughter & D.W. Walton. Dallas: Southern Methodist Press.

***Sleicher, C.A.** 1973. An attack by jackals on an adult male Thomson's gazelle. *Bull. East. Afr. Nat. Hist. Soc.* **July**: 99–100.

**Slijper, E.J.** 1962. *Whales*. London: Hutchinson.

***Smith, A.** 1834. An epitome of African Zoology; or, a concise description of the objects of the animal kingdom inhabiting Africa, its islands and seas. *S. Afr. Quart. J.*, (2) 2 (3) (2): 234–243.

**Smith, C.C.** 1965. Ageing criteria in the springhare, *Pedetes capensis* Forster. *Arnoldia Rhod.* **1**(26): 1–6.

——— 1968. Adaptive nature of social organization in the genus of tree squirrels *Tamiasciurus*. *Ecol. Monogr.* **38**: 31–63.

**Smith, E.A. & Burton, R.W.** 1970. Weddell seals of Signy Island, in *Antarctic ecology*; Ed. M.W. Holdgate. Vol. **I** pp. 415–428. London: Academic Press.

**Smith, N.B.** 1967. Some aspects of reproduction in the female gray squirrel *Sciurus carolinensis carolinensis* (Gmelin) in Wake County, North Carolina. M.Sc. thesis, State University Raleigh N.C.

**Smith, R.C.** 1967. *Rhodesia—a postal history*. Salisbury: Kingstons.

**Smith, R.L.** 1966. *Ecology and field biology*. London: Harper & Row.

**Smith, R.M.** 1969. Dept of Nat. Parks and Wildl. Mgmt Rhodesia: Wildlife Report Form Punchcard.

*——— 1977. Movement patterns and feeding behaviour of leopard in the Rhodes Matopos National Park. *Arnoldia Rhod.* **8**(13): 1–16.

**Smith, W.W.** 1954. Reproduction in the house mouse, *M. musculus* L., in Mississippi. *J. Mammal.* **35**: 509–515.

**Smithers, R.H.N.** 1938. Notes on the stranding of a school of *Pseudorca crassidens* at the Berg River mouth, December 27, 1936. *Trans. R. Soc. S. Afr.* **25**: 403–411.

——— 1966a. *The Mammals of Rhodesia, Zambia and Malawi*. London: Collins.

——— 1966b. Mutasana—the southern bat-eared fox. *Anim. Kingd.* **79**(6): 162–167.

——— 1971. The Mammals of Botswana. *Mus. mem. Natl Mus. Monum. Rhod.* **4**: 1–340.

——— 1975a. *Guide to the rats and mice of Rhodesia*. Rhodesia: Trustees National Museums and Monuments of Rhodesia.

——— 1975b. Family Felidae, Part 8.1, pp. 1–10, in *The mammals of Africa: an identification manual*. Eds J. Meester & H.W. Setzer. Washington, D.C.: Smithsonian Institution Press.

——— 1978. The serval, *Felis serval* Schreber, 1776. *S. Afr. J. Wildl. Res.* **8**: 29–37.

*——— 1983. *The mammals of the southern African subregion* 1st edn. Pretoria: University of Pretoria.

*——— 1986. South African red data book: terrestrial mammals. *S.A. National Scientific Programmes Report* No. **125**: 1–216. Pretoria: C.S.I.R.

*——— **Meester, J. & Rautenbach, I.L.** 1987. The type locality of *Pipistrellus (Romanica) kuhlii broomi* Roberts, 1948 (Chiroptera: Vespertilionidae). *Mammalia* **51**: 463–465.

——— **& Tello, J.L.P. Lobao.** 1976. Check list and atlas of the mammals of Mozambique. *Mus. mem. Natl Mus. Monum. Rhod.* **8**: 1–184.

——— **& Wilson, V.J.** 1979. Check list and atlas of the mammals of Zimbabwe Rhodesia. *Mus. mem. Natl Mus. Monum. Rhod.* **9**: 1–147.

**Smuts, G.L.** 1972. Seasonal movements, migration and age determination of Burchell's zebra (*Equus burchelli antiquorum*, H. Smith, 1841) in the Kruger National Park (30/ll/72 to 4/12/72). M.Sc. thesis, University of Pretoria.

——— 1974. Growth, reproduction and population characteristics of Burchell's zebra (*Equus burchelli antiquorum* H. Smith, 1841) in the Kruger National Park). D.Sc. thesis, University of Pretoria.

——— 1975. Why we killed those lions. *Afr. wild Life* **29**: 30–32.

——— 1976. Population characteristics and recent history of lions in two parts of Kruger National Park. *Koedoe* **19**: 153–164.

*——— 1982. *Lion*. Macmillan, Johannesburg.

*——— **Hanks, J. & Whyte, I.J.** 1978. Reproduction and social organisation of lions from the Kruger National Park. *Carnivore* **1**: 17–28.

——— **& Whyte, I.J.** 1981. Relationships between reproduction and environment in the hippopotamus *Hippopotamus amphibius* in the Kruger National Park. *Koedoe* **24**: 169–186.

***Smuts, Malie M.S. & Penzhorn, B.L.** 1988. Descriptions of anatomical differences between skulls and mandibles of *Equus zebra* and *E. burchelli* from southern Africa. *S. Afr. J. Zool.* **23**: 328–336.

**Snyman, P.S.** 1940. The study and control of the vectors of rabies in South Africa. *Onderstepoort J. vet. Sci.* **15**: 9–140.

***Sokolov, V.E., Dankova, A.A. & Evgen'eva, T.P.** 1980. Morphology of the subcaudal specific cutaneous gland of the four-toed elephant shrew *Petrodromus tetradactylus*. *Dokl. Biol. Sci.* **250**: 72–75.

**Sommerlatte, M.** 1979. Zur Ökologie des Kronenduckers (*Sylvicapra grimmia* Linne, 1758) in den Kiefernpflanzungen von ost-Transvaal, Südafrika. D.Sc. thesis, Georg August Universität zu Göttingen.

——— **& Woolard, M.D.** 1925a. A monograph of *Orycteropus afer*. 1. Anatomy except the nervous system, sense organs and hair. *Proc. zool. Soc. Lond.* 331–438.

——— **& Woolard, M.D.** 1925b. A monograph of *Orycteropus afer*. II. Nervous system, sense organs and hair. *Proc. zool. Soc. Lond.* 1185–1235.

**Southern, H.N.** 1963. A note on small mammals in East African Forests. *J. Mammal.* **44**: 126–129.

——— 1964. *Handbook of British mammals*. Oxford: Blackwells.

**Sowls, L.K. & Phelps, R.J.** 1968. Observations on the African bushpig, *Potamochoerus porcus* Linn. in Rhodesia. *Zoologica* **53**: 75–84.

**Spallanzani, L.** 1774–1794. Lettere sopra il sospetto di un nuovo senso nei Pipistrelli, in *Le opere di Lazzaro Spallanzani* Vol. **3**, Milano.

**Sparrman, A.** 1786. *A voyage to the Cape of Good Hope, towards the Antarctic polar circle, and round the world: but chiefly into the country of the Hottentots and Caffres, from the year 1772 to 1776*. Vols. **1** & **2**. London: Robinson.

***Spassov, N. & Roche, J.** 1988. Découverte du daman de Johnston, représentant du genre *Procavia*, au Mozambique. *Mammalia* **52**: 169–174.

**Spector, W.S.** 1956. *Handbook of Biological Data*. Philadelphia: Saunders.

**Spillman, F.** 1927. Beitrage zur Biologie des Milchgebisses des Chiropteren. *Senckenberg, naturforsch Gesellsch. Frankfurt a. M.* **40**: 251–255.

**Spinage, C.A.** 1963. Parasites of the giant rat. *Afr. wild Life* **17**: 109.

——— 1968. The life of the waterbuck. *Animals* **11**(6): 257–261.

——— 1969a. Naturalistic observations on the reproductive and maternal behaviour of the Uganda defassa waterbuck, *Kobus defassa ugandae* Neumann. *Z. Tierpsychol.* **26**: 39–47.

——— 1969b. Territoriality and social organization of the Uganda defassa waterbuck *Kobus defassa ugandae*. *J. Zool., Lond.* **159**: 329–361.

——— 1970. Population dynamics of the Uganda defassa waterbuck (*Kobus defassa ugandae* Neumann) in the Queen Elizabeth Park, Uganda. *J. Anim. Ecol.* **39**: 51–78.

*——— 1973. A review of ivory exploitation and elephant trends in Africa. *E. Afr. Wildl. J.* **11**: 281–289.

——— 1982. *A territorial antelope: the Uganda waterbuck*. London: Academic Press.

*——— 1986. *The natural history of Antelopes*. London: Croom Helm.

**St. Leger, Jane.** 1932a. A description of some new mammals from south western Africa. *Ann. Mag. nat. Hist.* **10**: 86–87.

——— 1932b. On *Equus quagga* of south-western and eastern Africa. *Ann. Mag. nat. Hist.* **10**: 587–593.

——— 1935. On some mammals collected by Dr Drake Brockman in Somaliland. *Ann. Mag. nat. Hist.* **15**: 666–673.

**Steen, J.B.** 1971. Secondary adaptions of lung breathers to aquatic life, in *Adaptions to prolonged submersion. Comp. Physiol. of Resper. Mechanism*. London: Academic Press.

**Steinemann, P.** 1963. *Cubs, Calves and Kangaroos*. London: Elek Books.

***Stevenson-Hamilton, J.** 1903. *Transvaal Administration Reports for 1903*. Pretoria: Government Printer.

*——— 1905. *Transvaal Administration Reports for 1905*. Pretoria: Government Printer.

——— 1912. *Animal Life in Africa*. London: Richard Bentley.

——— 1929 & 1934. *The Lowveld, its wild life and peoples*. 1929 First, 1934 Second Edition. London: Cassell & Co.

——— 1947. *Wildlife in South Africa*. London: Cassel.

**Stewart, D.R.M.** 1971. Diet of *Lepus capensis* and *L. crawshayi*. *E. Afr. Wildl. J.* **9**: 161–162.

——— **& Stewart, J.** 1963. The distribution of some large mammals in Kenya. *Jl E. Africa nat. Hist. Soc.* **24**(3) (107): 1–52.

——— **& Steward, J.** 1970. Food preference data by faecal analyses for African plains ungulates. *Zool. Afr.* **5**: 115–130.

**Stiemie, S. & Nel, J.A.J.** 1973. Nest-building behaviour in *Aethomys chrysophilus*, *Praomys (Mastomys) natalensis* and *Rhabdomys pumilio*. *Zool. Afr.* **8**: 91–100.

***Stimson, C. & Goodman, M.** 1966. Chromosomes of the elephant-shrew, *Nasilio brachyrhynchus brachyrhynchus*. *Mamm. chrom. Newsl.* **22**: 188.

**Stirling, I.** 1969a. Distribution and abundance of the Weddell seal in the western Ross Sea, Antarctica. *N. Z. J. Mar. Freshwat. Res.* **3**: 191–200.

——— 1969b. Birth of a Weddell seal pup. *J. Mammal.* **50**: 155–156.

——— 1969c. Tooth wear as a mortality factor in the Weddell seal, *Leptonychotes weddelli*. *J. Mammal.* **50**: 559–565.

——— 1971. Population dynamics of the Weddell seal (*Leptonychotes weddelli*) in McMurdo Sound, Antarctica, in *Antarctic Pinnipedia*, Ed. W.H. Burt. Washington: American Geophysical Union.

——— 1977. Adaptations of Weddell and ringed seals to exploit the Polar fast ice habitat in the absence or presence of surface predators, in *Adaptations within Antarctic Ecosystems*. Houston: Golf Publishing Co.

——— **& Kooyman, G.I.** 1971. The crabeater seal *Lobodon carcinophagus* in McMurdo Sound, Antarctica and the origin of mummified seals. *J. Mammal.* **52**: 175–180.

——— **& Siniff, D.B.** 1979. Underwater vocalisations of leopard seals (*Hydrurga leptonyx*) and crabeater seals (*Lobodon carcinophagus*) near the South Shetland Islands, Antarctica. *Can. J. Zool.* **57**: 1244–1248.

***Stock, A.D.** 1976. Chromosome banding pattern relationships of hares, rabbits and pikas (order Lagomorpha). *Cytogenet. Cell Genetics* **17**: 78–88.

***Stoltz, L.P.** 1977. The population dynamics of baboons in the Transvaal. D.Sc. thesis, University of Pretoria.

*——— **& Keith, M.** 1973. A population survey of chacma baboons in the northern Transvaal. *J. Human Evol.* **2**: 195–212.

——— **& Saayman, G.S.** 1970. Ecology and behaviour of baboons in the Northern Transvaal. *Ann. Trans. Mus.* **26**: 99–143.

**Stoneham, H.** 1955. Meat eating duikers. *Jl E. Afr. Uganda nat. Hist. Soc.* (Nairobi) **22**(5): 205.

**Stott, K.** 1950. Highboys. *Nat. Hist.* **59**: 164–167.

**Straschil, B.** 1974. Albinism in the Cape ground squirrel, *Xerus inauris* (Zimmerman, 1870). *S. Afr. J. Sci.* **70**: 315 .

——— 1975. Sandbathing and marking in *Xerus inauris* (Zimmerman, 1870) (Rodentia, Sciuridae). *S. Afr. J. Sci.* **71**: 215–216.

**Strijbis, C.B.** 1974. More oribi for Golden Gate. *Custos* **3**(11): 10.

——— 1975. Some smaller antelopes. *Custos* **4**(11): 10–11.

——— 1977. Confusion of species avoided. *Custos* **6**(3): 7, 21, 25.

**Stromer, E.** 1926. Reste Land- und Süsswasser-bewohnender Wirbeltiere aus den Diamantenfeldern Deutsch Südwestafrikas. In *Die Diamantenwüste Südwestafrikas* Vol. **2**. Berlin: E. Kaiser.

***Struhsaker, T.T.** 1967. Behavior of vervet monkeys and other Cercopithecines. *Science* **156**: 1197–1203.

**Strum, S.C.** 1975a. Life with the Pumphouse Gang. *Natn. geog. Mag.* **147**(5): 672–691.

——— 1975b. Primate predation: interim report on the development of a tradition in a troop of olive baboons. *Science* **187**: 755–757.

*——— 1981. Processes and products of change: baboon predatory behaviour at Gilgil, Kenya. In *Primate dietary patterns*. Eds R.S.O. Harding & G. Teleki. New York: Columbia University Press.

***Stuart, C.T.** 1975. Preliminary notes on the mammals of the Namib Desert Park. *Madoqua* Ser. II **4**: 5–68.

*——— 1976. Diet of the black-backed jackal *Canis mesomelas* in the Central Namib Desert, South West Africa. *Zool. Afr.* **11**: 193–205.

**Stuart, C.T.** 1977. The distribution, status, feeding and reproduction of carnivores of the Cape Province. *Research Report, Dept Nat. & Environ. Cons. Mammals: 1977*: 91–174.

——— 1980a. The distribution and status of *Manis temmincki* Smuts, 1832 (Pholidota: Manidae). *Z. Säugetierk.* **28**: 123–129.

*——— 1980b. The status of the oribi (*Ourebia ourebi*) in the Cape Province and suggestions for its conservation. Unpubl. mimeograph.

——— 1981. Notes on the mammalian carnivores of the Cape Province, South Africa. *Bontebok* **1**: 1–58.

*——— 1982a. Aspects of the biology of the caracal (*Felis caracal* Schreber, 1776) in the Cape Province, South Africa. M.Sc. thesis, University of Natal.

——— 1982b. The distribution of the small-spotted cat, *Felis nigripes*. *The Naturalist* **26**(3): 8–9.

*——— 1983. Food of the large grey mongoose *Herpestes ichneumon* in the south-west Cape Province. *S. Afr. Zool.* **18**: 401–403.
*——— 1984a. The distribution and status of *Felis caracal* Schreber, 1776. *Säugetierk. Mittel.* **31**: 197–203.
*——— 1984b. Abnormal dental development in male hyrax, *Procavia capensis capensis* (Hyracoidea: Procviidae.) *Säugetierk. Mittel.* **31** (2/3): 268–270.
*——— 1984c. The distribution of the grysbok, *Raphiceros melanotis*, an endemic Cape species. *The Naturalist* **28** (3): 24.
*——— 1985a. More on Cape grysbok, *Raphicerus melanotis*, distribution. *The Naturalist* **29** (1): 22.
*——— 1985b. A note on the bushpig, *Potamocherus porcus* in the Cape Province, South Africa. *The Naturalist* **29** (1): 37–40.
*——— 1985c. The status of two endangered carnivores occurring in the Cape Province, South Africa, *Felis serval*, and *Lutra maculicollis*. Unpubl. mimeograph.
——— **& Lloyd, P.H.** 1979. Preliminary distribution maps of mammals of the Cape Province (excluding Chiroptera, Cetacea and Carnivora). Cape Dept of Nature and Environment Conservation. Mimeograph.
——— **Lloyd, P.H. & Herselman, J.C.** 1980. Preliminary maps of mammals of the Cape Province (excluding Cetacea). Cape Dept of Nature and Environment Conservation. Unpubl. mimeograph.
*——— **Macdonald, I.A.W. & Mills, M.G.L.** 1985. History, current status and conservation of large mammalian predators in Cape Province, Republic of South Africa. *Biol. Conserv.* **31**: 7–19.
——— **& Schneekluth, P.** Undated. Grey rhebok, *Pelea capreolus*, group size and composition in the south-western Cape Province, South Africa. Cape Dept of Nature and Environment Conservation. Unpubl. mimeograph.
*——— **& Wilson, V.J.** 1988. *The cats of southern Africa*. Bulawayo, Chipangali Wildlife Trust.
***Stuhlman, R.A. & Wagner, J.E.** 1971. Ringtail in *Mystromys albicaudatus*: a case report. *Lab. Anim. Sci.* **21**: 585–587.
**Stutterheim, C.J. & Skinner, J.D.** 1973. Preliminary notes on the behaviour and breeding of *Gerbillurus paeba paeba* (A. Smith, 1834) in captivity. *Koedoe* **16**: 127–148.
**Sutcliffe, A.J.** 1970. Spotted hyaena: crusher, gnawer, digester and collector of bones. *Nature, Lond.* **227**: 1110–1113.
**Swanepoel, P.** 1972. The population dynamics of rodents at Pongola, northern Zululand, exposed to dieldrin cover spraying. M.Sc. thesis, University of Pretoria.
*——— 1976. An ecological study of rodents in northern Natal exposed to Dieldrin coverspraying. *Ann. Cape Prov. Mus.* **11** (4): 57–81.
——— **Smithers, R.H.N. & Rautenbach, I.L.** 1980. A checklist and numbering system of the extant mammals of the Southern African Subregion. *Ann. Trans. Mus.* **32**: 156–196.
**Swart, J.N.** 1953. Die Suid-Afrikaanse waaierstertmuise: Fam. Muscardinidae. M.Sc. thesis, University of Pretoria.
**Sweeney, R.C.H.** 1956. Some notes on the feeding habits of the ground pangolin, *Smutsia temminckii* (Smuts). *Ann. Mag. nat. Hist.* 12th Series **9**: 893–896.
——— 1959. *A preliminary annotated check list of the mammals of Nyasaland*. Blantyre: The Nyasaland Soc.
**Swynnerton, G.H.** 1936. The tsetse flies of East Africa. *Trans. R. ent. Soc. Lond.* **84**: 1–579.
——— **& Hayman, R.W.** 1950. A check list of the land mammals of the Tanganyika Territory and the Zanzibar protectorate. *Jl E. Africa nat. Hist. Soc.* **20**(6&7): 274–392.
——— **& Hayman, R.W.** 1958. Additions to checklist of Tanganyika Territory mammals. *Jl E. Africa nat. Hist. Soc.* **23**: 9–10.
***Szalay, F.S.** 1977. Phylogenetic relationships and a classification of the eutherian mammals. In: *Major patterns in vertebrate evolution*. Eds M.K. Hecht, P.C. Goody & B.M. Hecht. *NATO, Advanced Study Inst.* Ser A **14**: 315–374.
——— **& Delson, E.** 1979. *Evolutionary history of the Primates*. New York: Academic Press.

# T

**Tait, W.J.E.** 1969. The elusive and rare oribi. *Afr. wild Life* **23**: 154–160.
**Talbot, F.H.** 1960a. Beaked whale saved for South African Museum. *News Bull. Zool. Soc. S. Afr.* **1**(2): 31.
——— 1960b. True's beaked whale from the south-east coast of South Africa. *Nature, Lond.* **186**: 406.
**Talbot, L.M. & Talbot, M.H.** 1962. Food preferences of some East African wild ungulates. *E. Afr. agric. For. J.* **27**: 131–138.
——— **& Talbot, M.H.** 1963. The wildebeest in western Masailand, East Africa. *Wildl. Monogr.* **12**: 1–88.
**Tandy, J.M.** 1976. Communication in *Galago crassicaudatus*. *Primates* **17**: 523–526.
***Tarpy, C.** 1979. Killer whale attack! *Nat. Geogr. Mag.* **155**: 542–545.
***Taruski, A.G.** 1979. The whistle repertoire of the North Atlantic pilot whale (*Globicephala melaena*) and its relationship to behavior and environment. pp 345–368. In: *Behavior of Marine Animals. Current Perspectives in Research. Vol. 3: Cetaceans*. Eds H.E. Winn & B.L. Olla. New York: Plenum Press.
***Tatham, G.H. & Taylor, R.D.** 1989. The conservation and protection of the black rhinoceros *Diceros bicornis* in Zimbabwe. *Koedoe* **32**: 31–42.
**Tavolga, M.C. & Essapian, F.S.** 1957. The behaviour of the bottlenosed dolphin (*Tursiops truncatus*): mating, pregnancy, parturition and mother-infant behaviour. *Zoologica, N.Y.* **42**: 11–31.
**Taylor, C.R.** 1969. The eland and the oryx. *Scient. Am.* **220**: 89–95.
*——— **Robertshaw, D. & Hofmann, R.R.** 1969. Thermal panting: a comparison of wildebeest and zebu cattle. *Am. J. Physiol.* **217**: 907–910.
——— **Spinage, C.A. & Lyman, C.P.** 1969. Water relations of the waterbuck, an East African antelope. *Am. J. Phys.* **217**: 630–634.
**Taylor, H.C.** 1978. Capensis, in *Biogeography and ecology of southern Africa*, Ed. M.J.A. Werger. The Hague: Junk.
**Taylor, K.D. & Quy, R.J.** 1978. Long distance movements of a common rat (*Rattus norvegicus*) revealed by radio tracking. *Mammalia* **42**: 63–71.
**Taylor, M.E.** 1970. Locomotion in some East African viverrids. *J. Mammal.* **51**: 42–51.
***Taylor, P.J., Jarvis, J.V.M., Crowe, T.M. & Davies, K.C.** 1985. Age determination in the Cape molerat *Georychus capensis*. *S. Afr. J. Zool.* **20**: 261–267.
*——— **& Meester, J.A.J.** 1989. The type locality of *Cynictis penicillata coombsii* Roberts, 1929 and *Gerbillurus paeba coombsii* Roberts, 1929. *Z. Säugetierk.* **54**: 329–330.
***Taylor, R.D.** 1985. The response of buffalo, *Syncerus caffer* (Sparrman), to the Kariba lakeshore grassland (*Panicum repens* L.) in Matusadona National Park. D.Phil. thesis, University of Zimbabwe.
**Taylor, R.H.** 1978. The suni *Neotragus moschatus* van Dueben, 1846. *Natal Parks Board: Research Comm.* 34.
***Taylor, R.J.F.** 1957. An unusual record of three species of whale being restricted to pools in Antarctic sea-ice. *Proc. zool. Soc. Lond.* **129**: 325–331.
**Tedman, R.A. & Bryden, M.M.** 1979. Cow-pup behaviour of the Weddell seal, *Leptonychotes weddelli* (Pinnipedia) in Mc Murdo Sound, Antarctica. *Aust. Wildl. Res.* **6**: 19–37.
**Tello, J.L.P.L.** 1972, 1973. Reconhecimento ecologico da Reserva dos Elefantes du Maputo. *Vet. Mocambicana* **5**(2): 99–122, 1972. **6**(1): 19–76, 1973. **6**(2): 133–186, 1973.
——— **& van Gelder, R.G.** 1975. The natural history of nyala, *Tragelaphus angasi* (Mammalia, Bovidae) in Mozambique. *Bull. Am. Mus. Nat. Hist.* **155**: 323–385.
**Temby, I.D.** 1977. The non-ungulate mammals at Nylsvley. Mammal Research Institute Report: 1–57. Mimeograph.
**Temminck, C.J.** 1827. Monographies de Mammalogie. Paris & Amsterdam.
**Theal, G.M.** 1909. *History and ethnography of Africa south of the Zambesi from the settlement of the Portuguese at Sofala in September* 1505 to the conquest of the Cape Colony by the British in September 1795. Vol. **2**. London: Swan Sonnenschein & Co.
**Theiler, G.** 1962. Baboons on the march. *Afr. wild Life* **16**: 113–115.
***Thenius, E.** 1966. Zur Stammesgeschichte der Hyaenen (Carnivora, Mammalia). *Z. Säugetierk.* **31**: 293–300.
**Thesiger, W.** 1970. Wild dog at 5894 m (19,340 ft). *E. Afr. Wildl. J.* **8**: 202–203.
**Thom, H.B.** (ed.) 1952–1958. *Journal of Jan van Riebeeck*. 1952 Vol. **1**, 1651–1655. 1954 Vol. **2**, 1656–1658. 1958 Vol. **3**, 1659–1662. Cape Town: Balkema for the Van Riebeeck Society.
**Thomas, A.D.** 1964. The Cape dassie. *Afr. wild Life* **1**: 64.
——— **& Kolbe, F.F.** 1942. The wild pigs of South Africa. *Jl S. Afr. vet. med. Ass.* **13**: 1–11.
**Thomas, D.W. & Fenton, M.B.** 1978. Notes on the dry season roosting and foraging behaviour of *Epomophorus gambianus* and *Rousettus aegyptiacus* (Chiroptera: Pteropodidae). *J. Zool., Lond.* **186**: 403–406.
**Thomas, O.** 1894. On the mammals of Nyasaland: third contribution. *Proc. zool. Soc. Lond.*: 136–146.
——— 1895a. On the brush-tailed porcupine of Central Africa. *Ann. Mag. nat. Hist.* **15**: 88–89.
——— 1895b. Diagnosis of two new East-African mammals. *Ann. Mag. nat. Hist.* **15**: 187–188.
——— 1895c. On a new banded mungoose from Somaliland. *Ann. Mag. nat. Hist.* **15**: 531–532.
——— 1896. On the mammals of Nyasaland. *Proc. zool. Soc. Lond.*: 788–798.
——— 1898. On the mammals obtained by Mr A. Whyte in Nyasaland and presented to the British Museum by Sir H.H. Johnston K.C.B., being a fifth contribution to the mammal fauna of Nyasaland. *Proc. zool. Soc. Lond.*: 925–939.
——— 1901. Some new mammals. *Ann. Mag. nat. Hist.* **8**: 32.
——— 1903. On a small collection of mammals from the Rio de Oro, Western Sahara. *Novit. Zool.* **10**: 300.
——— 1909. New African mammals obtained by the Ruwenzori Expedition. *Ann. Mag. nat. Hist.* **19**: 118–123.
——— 1910. New African Mammals IX. *Am. Mus. nat. Hist.* **5**(8): 83–92.
——— 1919. Scientific results from the mammal survey of India, No. 19. A synopsis of the groups of true mice found within the Indian Empire. *J. Bombay nat. Hist. Soc.* **26**: 417–421.
——— 1925. On mammals (other than ruminants) collected by Captain Angus Buchanan during his second Sahara expedition and presented by him to the National Museum. *Ann. Mag. nat. Hist.* **16**: 187–197.
——— 1926. Mammals from Ovamboland and the Cunene River. *Proc. zool. Soc. Lond.*: 285–312.
——— 1929. On mammals from the Kaokoveld, South-West Africa, obtained during Captain Shortridge's fifth Percy Sladen and Kaffrarian Museum Expedition. *Proc. zool. Soc. Lond.*: 109–110.
——— **& Wroughton, R.C.** 1904. On a second collection of mammals obtained by Dr W.J. Ansorge in Angola. *Ann. Mag. nat. Hist.* **16**: 169–178.
——— **& Wroughton, R.C.** 1907–1908. The Rudd exploration of South Africa 1907a VII List of mammals obtained by Mr Grant at Coguno, Inhambane: 285; 1907b VIII. List of mammals obtained by Mr Grant at Beira: 774; 1908a IX. List of mammals obtained by Mr Grant on the Gorongoza Mountains, Portuguese S.E. Africa: 164; 1908b X. List of mammals obtained by Mr Grant near Tette, Zambesia: 535. *Proc. zool. Soc. Lond.* as above.
**Thomas, W.D.** 1962. Post-natal development of a gemsbok. *J. Mammal.* **43**: 98–101.
**Thompson, G.** 1827. *Travels and adventures in southern Africa*, Vol **1** & **2**. 2nd Edn London: Colburn.
**Thompson, P.J.** 1973. Notes on the oribi (Mammalia, Bovidae) in Rhodesia. *Arnoldia Rhod.* **6**(21): 1–5.
——— 1975. The role of elephants, fire and other agents in the decline of *Brachystegia boehmii* woodland. *J. sthn Afr. Wildl. Mgmt Ass.* **5**: 11–18.
**Thorneycroft, G.V.** 1958. African palm civet. *Afr. wild Life* **12**: 81.
**Thunberg, C.P.** 1793 or 1795. *Travels in Europe, Africa and Asia made between the years 1770 and 1779*. Vol. **2** (1773–1775). London: W. Richardson & J. Egerton.
*——— 1820. Beskrifning och teckning pa ett nytt species, *Hyaena brunnea*. *Kg. Vetenskaps. Akademiens Handlingar.* **1820**: 59–65, pl. 2.
**Tietz, R.M.** 1966. The southern bottlenose whale, *Hyperoodon planifrons*, from Humewood, Port Elizabeth. *Ann. Cape Prov. Mus.* **5**: 101–107.
**Tilson, R.L.** 1977. Duetting in Namib Desert klipspringers. *S. Afr. J. Sci.* **37**: 311–315.
*——— **& Hamilton, W.J.** 1984. Social dominance and feeding patterns of spotted hyaenas. *Anim. Behav.* **32**: 715–724.
*——— **& Henschel, J.** 1985. The spotted hyaena—Predator of the Namib night. *Afr. wild Life* **39**: 50–55.
*——— **& Henschel, J.** 1986. Spatial arrangement of spotted hyaena groups in a desert environment, Namibia. *Afr. J. Ecol.* **24**: 173–180.
——— **& Norton, P.M.** 1981. Alarm duetting and pursuit deterrence in an African antelope. *Am. Nat.* **118**: 455–462.
——— **von Blottnitz, F. & Henschel, J.** 1980. Prey selection by spotted hyaena (*Crocuta crocuta*) in the Namib Desert. *Madoqua* **12**: 41–49.
**Tinley, K.L.** 1966. *An ecological reconnaissance of the Moremi Wildlife Reserve, northern Okavango swamps, Botswana*. Cape Town: Okavango Wildlife Society.
——— 1969a. Dikdik, *Madoqua kirkii*, in South West Africa: notes on distribution, ecology and behaviour. *Madoqua* **1**: 7–33.
——— 1969b. First air count of the buffalo of Marromeu. *Veterin. Mocamb.* **1**(2): 155–170.
*——— 1971. Etosha and the Kaokoveld. *Afr. wild Life*. Suppl. **25**: 1–16.
——— 1975a. Marromeu, wrecked by the big dams. *Afr. wild Life* **29**: 22–25.
——— 1975b. Habitat physiognomy, structure and relationships. Publs Univ. Pretoria Nuwe Reeks **97**: 69–77.

——— 1976. *The Ecology of Tongaland*. Durban: Natal Branch of the Wildlife Society. pp. 79.
——— 1977. Framework of the Gorongoza Ecosystem. D.Sc. thesis, University of Pretoria.
**Tobayama, T.M., Nishiwaki, M. & Yang, H.C.** 1973. Records of Fraser's Sarawak dolphin (*Lagenodelphis hosei*) in the western north Pacific. *Scient. Rep. Whales Res. Inst. Tokyo* **25**: 251–263.
***Todd, N.B.** 1977. The dynamics of owned domestic cat populations. *Carniv. Genet. Newsl.* **3**(3): 25.
**Tollu, B.** 1974. The Amsterdam Island fur seal, *Arctocephalus tropicalis tropicalis* (Gray, 1872). Third cycle Doctoral thesis: University of Paris.
***Tomilin, A.G.** 1936. [Cachalots of Kamchatka Sea]. *Zool. Zhur.* **15**: 483–519.
——— 1967. *Mammals of the USSR and adjacent countries*. Vol. **IX**: *Cetacea*. Translation Israeli program for scientific translations, Jerusalem 1967, Publ. for Smithsonian Institution and Natural Science Foundation, Washington D.C. (original published 1957).
**Tomlinson, D.N.S.** 1978. The daily activity and behaviour patterns of waterbuck *Kobus ellipsiprymnus* (Ogilby, 1833) in relation to its seasonal utilization of feeding habitats in the Lake McIlwaine Game Enclosure. M.Sc. thesis, University of Rhodesia, Salisbury.
**Tones, J.** 1850. On the blood coloured exudation from the skin of the hippopotamus. *Proc. zool. Soc. Lond.* **18**: 160–162.
***Torres, D. & Aguayo, A.** 1979. Habitos alimentarios de *Lissodelphis peronii* (Lacepede, 1804) en Chile central (Cetacea: Delphinidae). *Rev. Biol. Mar. Dep. Oceanol. Univ. Chile* **16**: 221–224.
*——— **& Aguayo, A.** 1984. Presence of *Arctocephalus tropicalis* (Gray 1872) at the Juan Fernandez Archipelago, Chile. *Acta Zool. Fenn.* **172**: 133–134.
**Toshi, A.** 1949. Note ecologische su alcuni mammiferi de Olorgesailie. *Ric. Zool. appl. Caccia* **2**: 25–63.
——— 1954. Elenco preliminare dei mammiferi della Libia. *Ric. Zool. appl. Caccia* **2**: 241–273.
**Townsend, C.H.** 1935. The distribution of certain whales as shown by logbook records of American whaleships. *Zoologica, N.Y.* **19**: 1–50.
**Travassos Dias, J.A.** 1968. Fauna selvagem de Mocambique No. 1. *Radio Mocambique Mensario Boletim mensal de Radio Clube de Mocambique*, Lourenco Marques.
**Trouessart, E.L.** 1900. La fauna des mammifères de L'Algerie du Maroc et de là Tunisie. *Causeries scient. Soc. Zool. France* **1**: 353–410.
**True, F.W.** 1889. Contributions to the natural history of the cetaceans. A review of the family Delphinidae. *Bull. U.S. natn. Mus.* **36**: 191 pp.
*——— 1910. An account of the beaked whales of the Family Ziphiidae in the collection of the United States Natural Museum. *Bull. U.S. natn. Mus.* **73**: 1–89.
**Tsutsumi, T., Kamimura, Z. & Mizue, K.** 1954. Studies on the little toothed whales in the West Sea areas of Kyusya. -V About the food of the little toothed whales. *Bull. Fac. Fish. Nagasaki Univ.* **11**: 19–28.
**Tullberg, T.** 1899. Uber das System der Nagetiere: eine phylogenetische Studie. *Nova. Acta. R. Soc. Scient. Upsal.* **3**(18): 1–514.
**Turnbul1-Kemp, P.** 1967. *The Leopard*. Cape Town: Howard Timmins.
**Turner, M.I.M. & Watson, R.M.** 1965a. An introductory study on the ecology of the hyrax (*Dendrohyrax brucei* and *Procavia johnstoni*) in the Serengeti National Park. *E. Afr. Wildl. J.* **3**: 49–60.
——— **& Watson, R.M.** 1965b. Game management and research by aeroplane. *Oryx* **8**: 13–22.
**Twente, J.W. Jnr.** 1954. Predation on bats by hawks and owls. *Wilson Bull.* **66**: 135–136.
——— 1955a. Some aspects of habitat selection and other behaviour of cavern dwelling bats. *Ecology* **36**: 706–732.
——— 1955b. Aspects of population study of cavern dwelling bats. *J. Mammal.* **36**: 379–390.

# U

**Uhlig, H.G.** 1955. The determination of age of nestling and subadult gray squirrels in West Virginia. *J. Wildl. Mgmt* **19**: 479–483.
**Underwood, R.** 1973. Social behaviour of the eland (*Taurotragus oryx*). *Jl sthn Afr. Wildl. Mgmt Ass.* **16**: 1–6.
——— 1975. Social behaviour of the eland (*Taurotragus oryx*) on Loskop Dam Nature Reserve. M.Sc. thesis, University of Pretoria.
——— 1979. Mother-infant relationship and behavioural ontogeny in the common eland (*Taurotragus oryx oryx*). *S. Afr. J. Wildl. Res.* **9**: 27–45.
*——— 1982. Seasonal changes in African ungulate groups. *J. Zool., Lond.* **196**: 191–205.
**Uspenskii, G.A. & Saglanskii, A.A.** 1952. Experimental domestication of the common eland antelope. *CSIR Translation Section* Ref. No. 174, 1961 Priroda 12.
**Uys, C.J.** 1967. Volksrust farmer breeds rare deer. *Farmers Weekly (Durban)* 27th September.

# V

**Valentyn, F.** 1726. *Description of the Cape of Good Hope with the matters concerning it*. Part 1. Van Riebeeck Soc. Second Series No. 2) Cape Town: Van Riebeeck Society.
**Valverde, J.A.** 1957. *Aves del Sahara Espanol*. Madrid: Instituto de estudios Africanos.
***van Aarde, R.J.** 1976. A note on the birth of a giraffe. *S. Afr. J. Sci.* **72**: 307.
——— 1977. Voeding, habitatsvoorkeur en voortplanting van die wilde huiskat *Felis catus* (Linneaus, 1758) op Marioneiland. M.Sc. thesis, University of Pretoria.
*——— 1978. Reproduction and population ecology in the feral house cat on Marion Island. *Carniv. Genet. Newsl.* **3**: 288–316.
*——— 1979. Distribution and density of the feral house cat, *Felis catus*, on Marion Island. *S. Afr. J. Antarct. Res.* **9**: 14–19.
*——— 1980a. The diet and feeding behaviour of feral cats, *Felis catus*, at Marion Island. *S. Afr. J. Wildl. Res.* **10**: 123–128.
——— 1980b. Fluctuations in the population of southern elephant seals, *Mirounga leonina*, at Kerguelen Island. *S. Afr. J. Zool.* **15**: 99–106.
——— 1980c. Harem structure of the southern elephant seal *Mirounga leonina* at Kerguelen Island. *Rev. Ecol. (Terre Vie)* **34**: 31–44.
*——— 1983. Demographic parameters of the feral cat *Felis catus* population at Marion Island. *S. Afr. J. Wildl. Res.* **13**: 12–16.
*——— 1984. Aardvark. pp. 466–467. In: *The encyclopedia of mammals*. Ed. D. MacDonald. London: George Allen & Unwin.
*——— 1985a. Age determination of Cape porcupines, *Hystrix africaeaustralis*. *S. Afr. J. Zool.* **20**: 232–236.
*——— 1985b. Reproduction in captive female Cape porcupines (*Hystrix africaeaustralis*). *J. Reprod. Fert.* **75**: 577–582.
*——— 1985c. Circulating progesterone and oestradiol-17 concentrations in cyclic Cape porcupines, *Hystrix africaeaustralis*. *J. Reprod. Fert.* **75**: 583–591.
*——— 1985d. Husbandry and immobilisation of captive porcupines, *Hystrix africaeaustralis*. *S. Afr. J. Wildl. Res.* **15**: 77–79.
*——— 1985e. Sexual behaviour of the female porcupine, *Hystrix africaeaustralis*. *Hormones & Behaviour* **19**: 400–412.
*——— 1986a. Functional anatomy of the ovaries of pregnant and lactating Cape porcupines, *Hystrix africaeaustralis*. *J. Reprod. Fert.* **76**: 553–559.
*——— 1986b. A case study of an alien predator (*Felis catus*) introduced on Marion Island: selective advantages. *S. Afr. J. Antarct. Res.* **16**: 113–114.
*——— 1987a. Pre- and postnatal growth of the Cape porcupine *Hystrix africaeaustralis*. *J. Zool., Lond.* **211**: 25–33.
*——— 1987b. Reproduction in the Cape porcupine *Hystrix africaeaustralis*: an ecological perspective. *S. Afr. J. Sci.* **83**: 605–607.
*——— 1987c. Demography of a Cape porcupine, *Hystrix africaeaustralis*, population. *J. Zool., Lond.* **213**: 205–212.
*——— **& Potgieter, H.C.** 1986. Circulating progesterone, progesterone binding proteins and oestradiol-17 concentrations in the pregnant Cape porcupine, *Hystrix africaeaustralis*. *J. Reprod. Fert.* **76**: 561–567.
——— **& Robinson, T.J.** 1980. Gene frequencies in feral cats on Marion Island. *J. Hered.* **71**: 366–368.
——— **& Skinner, J.D.** 1981. The feral cat population on Marion Island: characteristics, colonization and control. *Com. nat. fr. Rech. Antarctiques* **51**: 281–288.
*——— **& Skinner, J.D.** 1986a. Reproductive biology of the male Cape porcupine, *Hystrix africaeaustralis*. *J. Reprod. Fert.* **76**: 545–552.
*——— **& Skinner, J.D.** 1986b. Functional anatomy of the ovaries of pregnant and lactating Cape porcupines, *Hystrix africaeaustralis*. *J. Reprod. Fert.* **76**: 553–559.
*——— **& Skinner, J.D.** 1986c. Pattern of space use by relocated servals, *Felis serval*. *Afr. J. Ecol.* **24**: 97–101.
*——— **& van Dyk, Ann** 1986. Inheritance of the king coat colour pattern in cheetahs, *Acinonyx jubatus*. *J. Zool., Lond.* **209**: 573–578.
*——— **Willis, C.K., Skinner, J.D. & Haupt, M.A.** 1990. Range utilisation by the aardvark *Orycteropus* (Pallas, 1766) in the Karoo, South Africa. *J. Arid. Environ.* in press.
**Van Bree, B.J.H., Best, P.B. & Ross, G.J.B.** 1978. Occurrence of the two species of pilot whales (genus *Globicephala*) on the coast of South Africa. FAO Advisory Committee on Marine Resources Research. Scientific consultation on Marine Mammals, Bergen ACMRR/MM/SC/ 128: 1–12.
——— **& Cadenat, J.** 1968. On the skull of *Peponocephala electra* (Gray, 1846) (Cetacea, Globicephalinae) from Senegal. *Beaufortia* **14**(177): 193–202.
***Van Bree, P.J.H. & Gallagher, M.D.** 1978. On the taxonomic status of *Delphinus tropicalis* van Bree, 1971 (Notes on Cetacea, Delphinoidea IX). *Beaufortia* **28** (342): 1–8.
**Van Bree, B.J.H. & Purves, P.E.** 1972. Remarks on the validity of *Delphinus bairdii* (Cetacea: Delphinidae). *J. Mammal.* **53**: 372–374.
**Van Bruggen, A.C.** 1964. A note on *Raphicerus campestris* Thunberg: a challenge to observers. *Koedoe* **7**: 94–98.
**Van der Horst, C.J.** 1941. On the size of the litter and the gestation period of *Procavia capensis*. *Science* **93** 2418: 430–431.
——— 1946. Some remarks on the biology of reproduction in the female of *Elephantulus*. *Trans. R. Soc. S. Afr.* **31**: 181–199.
**Van der Merwe, M.** 1970. Social organisation and seasonal activities of the Natal clinging bat, *Miniopterus schreibersi natalensis* (A. Smith, 1834). M.S. thesis, University of Pretoria.
——— 1973a. Aspects of hibernation and winter activity of the Natal clinging bat, *Miniopterus schreibersi natalensis* (A. Smith, 1834) on the Transvaal Highveld. *S. Afr. J. Sci.* **69**: 116–118.
——— 1973b. Aspects of social behaviour of the Natal clinging bat, *Miniopterus schreibersi natalensis* (A. Smith, 1834). *Mammalia* **37**: 380–389.
——— 1973c. Aspects of temperature and humidity in preferred hibernation sites of the Natal clinging bat, *Miniopterus schreibersi natalensis* (A. Smith, 1834). *Zool. Afr.* **8**: 121–134.
——— 1975. Preliminary study on the annual movements of the Natal clinging bat. *S. Afr. J. Sci.* **71**: 237–241.
——— 1977. Reproduction of the Natal clinging bat, *Miniopterus schreibersi natalensis* (A. Smith, 1834). D.Sc. thesis, University of Pretoria.
——— 1978. Postnatal development and mother-infant relationships in the Natal clinging bat, *Miniopterus schreibersi natalensis* (A. Smith, 1834) pp.309–322. In: Proc. IVth int. Bat Res. Conf. Kenya: National Academy of Arts & Sciences.
——— 1979. Foetal growth curves and seasonal breeding in the Natal clinging bat, *Miniopterus schreibersi natalensis*. *S. Afr. J. Zool.* **14**: 17–21.
——— 1980a. Importance of *Miniopterus schreibersi natalensis* in the diet of barn owls. *S. Afr. J. Wildl. Res.* **10**: 15–17.
*——— 1980b. Delayed implantation in the Natal clinging bat, *Miniopterus schreibersi natalensis* (A. Smith, 1834). In: Proc. Vth Int. Bat Res. Conf. Eds D.E. Wilson & A.L. Gardner. Lubbock: Texas Tech. Press.
*——— 1982. Bat vectors of rabies. *S. Afr. J. Sci.* **78**: 421–422.
*——— 1985a. The vestigial teeth of *Miniopterus schreibersii natalensis* (Mammalia: Chiroptera). *J. Zool. Lond.* **207**: 483–489.
*——— 1985b. The vestigial teeth in *Miniopterus fraterculus* and *Miniopterus inflatus*. *S. Afr. J. Zool.* **20**: 250–252.
*——— 1987. The presence of other bat species in maternity caves occupied by *Moniopterus schreibersii natalensis* (A. Smith, 1834) in the Transvaal. *S. Afr. J. Wildl. Res.* **17**: 25–28.
*——— **Giddings, S.R. & Rautenbach, I.L.** 1987. Post-partum oestrus in the little free-tailed bat, *Tadarida (Chaerephon) pumila* (Microchiroptera: Molossidae) at 24°S. *J. Zool., Lond.* **213**: 317–326.
*——— **& Rautenbach, I.L.** 1986. Multiple births in Schlieffen's bat, *Nycticeius schlieffenii* (Peters, 1859) (Chiroptera: Vespertilionidae) from the Southern African Subregion. *S. Afr. J. Zool.* **21**: 48–50.
*——— **& Rautenbach, I.L.** 1987. Reproduction in Schlieffen's bat, *Nycticeius schlieffenii*, in the eastern Transvaal lowveld, South Africa. *J. Reprod. Fert.* **81**: 41–50.
*——— **Rautenbach, I.L. & van der Colf, W.J.** 1986. Reproduction in females of the little free-tailed bat, *Tadarida (Chaerephon) pumila*, in the eastern Transvaal, South Africa. *J. Reprod. Fert.* **77**: 355–364.
——— **& Skinner, J.D.** 1982. Annual reproductive pattern in the dassie *Procavia capensis*. *S. Afr. J. Zool.* **17**: 130–135.
——— **Skinner, J.D. & Millar, R.P.** 1980. Annual reproductive pattern in the springhaas, *Pedetes capensis*. *J. Reprod. Fert.* **58**: 259–266.
**Van der Merwe, N.J.** 1953. The jackal. *Fauna Flora, Pretoria* **4**: 3–83.
*——— **& Rautenbach, I.L.** 1988. The placenta and foetal membranes of the lesser

yellow house bat, *Scotophilus borbonicus* (Chiroptera: Vespertilionidae). *S. Afr. J. Zool.* **23**: 320–327.
*——— **& Rautenbach, I.L.** 1989. The histology of the testes and the male reproductive pattern of the lesser yellow house bat, *Scotophilus borbonicus* (E. Geoffroy, 1803) (Chiroptera: Vespertilionidae) in the eastern Transvaal Lowveld. *Jl S.A. vet. med. Ass.* **60**: 83–86.
*——— **Rautenbach, I.L. & Penzhorn, B.L.** 1988. A new pattern of early embryonic development in the seasonally breeding non-hibernating lesser yellow house bat, *Scotophilus borbonicus* (E. Geoffroy, 1803) (Chiroptera: Vespertilionidae). *Ann. Trans. Mus.* **34**: 152–156.
***Van der Merwe, P.J.** 1938. *Die trekboer in die geskiedenis van die Kaapkolonie.* Cape Town: Nasionale Pers.
***Van der Veen, H.J. & Penzhorn, B.L.** 1987. The chromosomes of the tsessebe *Damaliscus lunatus*. *S Afr. J. Zool.* **22**: 311–313.
**Van der Werken, H.** 1967. Preliminary report on cheetahs in zoos and in Africa. *R. zool. Soc, Amsterdam*: 1–9.
——— 1968. Cheetahs in captivity. Preliminary report on cheetahs in zoos and in Africa. *Zool. Gart.* **35**(3): 156–161.
**Van der Westhuizen, C.M.** 1974. Squirrels, in *Standard Encyclopedia of Southern Africa* **10**: 236–237. Cape Town: N.A.S.O.U.
**Van der Zee, D.** 1979. Food and status of the Cape clawless otter *Aonyx capensis* Schinz in the Tsitsikama Coastal National Park. M.Sc. thesis, University of Pretoria.
——— **& Skinner, J.D.** 1977. Preliminary observations on samango and vervet monkeys near Lake Sibayi. *S. Afr. J. Sci.* **73**: 381–382.
*——— **& Viljoen, P.J.** 1984. Aspects of the ecology of samango monkeys (*Cercopithecus albogularis*) in the northern Transvaal, South Africa. Unpubl. Report. South African Forestry Research Institute. Mimeograph.
***Van Ee, C.** 1978. Pangolins can't be bred in captivity. *Afr. wild Life* **32**: 24–25.
**Van Eysinga, F.W.B.** 1978. *Geological time table* 3rd edn. Amsterdam: Elsevier Scientific Publishing Company.
**Van Haaften, J.L.** 1974. Zeehonden langs de Nederlandse Kust. *Wetenschappelijke Mededelingen van die Koninklijke Nederlandse Natuurhisjtorische Vereniging* No. 110.
***van Heerden, J.** 1985. Disease and mortality of captive wild dogs *Lycaon pictus*. *S. Afr. J. Wildl. Res.* **16**: 7–11.
*——— **& Dauth, J.** 1987. Aspects of adaptation to an arid environment in free-living ground squirrels *Xerus inauris*. *J. Arid Environm.* **13**: 83–89.
*——— **& Kuhn, F.** 1985. Reproduction in captive hunting dogs *Lycaon pictus*. *S. Afr. J. Wildl. Res.* **15**: 80–84.
***Van Hensbergen, H.J. & Channing, A.** 1989. Habitat preference and use of space by the namtap *Graphiurus ocularis* (Rodentia: Gliridae). *Mammalia* **53**: 25–34.
**Van Horn, R.N. & Eaton, G.G.** 1979. Reproductive physiology and behaviour in Prosimians: 79–120, in *The study of Prosimian behaviour*. Eds G.A. Doyle & R.D. Martin. London: Academic Press.
***Van Hoven, W.** 1974. Ciliate protozoa and aspects of nutrition of the hippopotamus in the Kruger National Park. *S. Afr. J. Sci.* **70**: 107–109.
——— **Hamilton-Attwell, V.L. & Grobler, J.H.** 1979. Rumen ciliate protozoa of the sable antelope *Hippotragus niger*. *S. Afr. J. Zool.* **14**: 37–42.
***Van Jaarsveld, A.S.** 1983. Aspects of the digestion in the Cape porcupine. *S. Afr. J. Anim. Sci.* **13**: 31–33.
*——— **Henschel, J.R. & Skinner, J.D.** 1987. Improved age estimation in spotted hyaenas (*Crocuta crocuta*). *J. Zool., Lond.* **213**: 758–762.
*——— **& Knight-Eloff, A.K.** 1984. Digestion in the porcupine *Hystrix africaeaustralis*. *S. Afr. J. Zool.* **19**: 109–112.
*——— **Mackenzie, A.A. & Meltzer, D.G.A.** 1984. Immobilization and anaesthesia of spotted hyaenas. *S. Afr. J. Wildl. Res.* **14**: 120–122.
*——— **& Skinner, J.D.** 1987. Spotted hyaena monomorphism: an adaptive "phallusy". *S. Afr. J. Sci.* **83**: 612–615.
*——— **Skinner, J.D. & Lindeque, M.** 1988. Growth, development and parental investment in the spotted hyaena, *Crocuta crocuta*. *J. Zool., Lond.* **216**: 45–53.
**Van Lawick, H.** 1977. *Savage Paradise*. London: Collins.
***Van Lawick-Goodall, J.** 1968. The behaviour of free-living chimpanzees in the Gombe Stream Reserve. *Anim. Behav. Monog.* **1**: 161–311.
——— **& Van Lawick, H.** 1970. *Innocent Killers*. London: Collins.
***Van Orsdol, K.G.** 1984. Foraging behaviour and hunting success of lions in Queen Elizabeth National Park, Uganda. *Afr. J. Ecol.* **22**: 79–99.
*——— **Hanby, J.P. & Bygott, J.D.** 1985. Ecological correlates of lion social organization (*Panthera leo*). *J. Zool., Lond.* **206**: 97–112.
***Van Rensburg, P.J.J., Skinner, J.D. & van Aarde, R.J.** 1987. Effects of feline panleucopaenia on the population characteristics of feral cats on Marion Island. *J. appl. Ecol.* **24**: 63–73.
***Van Rooyen, R.J. & Skinner, J.D.** 1989. Dietary differences between the sexes in impala *Aepyceros melampus*. *Trans. Roy. Soc. S. Afr.* **47**: 181–185.
**Van Schaik, B.** 1980. Run for your life rhino. *Environment R.S.A.* **7**(11): 1–2.
**Van Valen, L.** 1963. Notes on the ear region of *Nandinia*. *J. Mammal.* **44**: 273.
***Van Waerbeek, K. & Reyes, J.C.** 1988. First record of the pygmy killer whale, *Feresa attenuata* Gray, 1875 from Peru, with a summary of distribution in the eastern Pacific. *Z. Saugetierk.* **53**: 253–255.
**Van Wyk, P. & Fairall, N.** 1969. The influence of the African elephant on the vegetation of the Kruger National Park. *Koedoe* **12**: 57–89.
**Van Zinderen Bakker Sr, E.M.** 1971. Introduction, in *Marion and Prince Edward Islands*. Eds. E.M. van Zinderen Bakker Sr, J.M. Winterbottom & R.A. Dyer. Cape Town: Balkema.
**Van Zyl, J.H.M.** 1965. The vegetation of the S.A. Lombard Nature Reserve and its utilization by certain antelope. *Zool. Afr.* **1**: 55–71.
——— **& Skinner, J.D.** 1970. Growth and development of the springbok foetus. *Afr. wild Life* **24**: 308–316.
**Varian, H.F.** 1953. The giant sable antelope of Angola. *Afr. wild Life* **7**: 272–283.
**Vaughan, R.W.** 1967. South Georgia elephant seal found in South Africa. *Br. Ant. Sur. Bull.* **14**: 90–91.
**Vaughan, T.A.** 1970. Adaptations for flight in bats : 127–143, in *About Bats*, Eds B.H. Slaughter & D.W. Walton. Dallas: Southern Methodist Press.
——— 1972. *Mammalogy*. London: W.B. Saunders.
***Vaughan-Kirby, F.** 1896. *In haunts of wild game: a hunter naturalist's wanderings from Kahlamba to Libombo*. London: Blackwood & Sons.
***Vaute, A.M.** 1982. First recorded accidental transatlantic bat transport. *Bat. Res. News.* **23**: 16–18.
**Velte, F.F.** 1978. Hand-rearing springhaas, *Pedetes capensis*, at Rochester Zoo. *Int. Zoo Yb.* **18**: 206–208.
**Venter, J.** 1979. Quantity not Quality. *Afr. wild Life* **33**: 30.
**Verheyen, R.** 1951. *Exploration du Parc National de L'Upemba. Contribution a l'étude ethologique des mammifères du Parc de l'Upemba*. Bruxelles: Institute des Parcs Nationeaux du Congo Belge.
***Vermeulen, H.C. & Nel, J.A.J.** 1988. The bush Karoo rat, *Otomys unisulcatus*, on the Cape West coast. *S. Afr. J. Zool.* **23**: 103–111.
**Vernon, C.J.** 1972. An analysis of owl pellets collected in Southern Africa. *Ostrich* **43**: 109–124.
**Verschuren, J.** 1957. *Exploration du Parc National de la Garamba, 7, Chiroptères*. Bruxelles: Institute des Parcs Nationeaux du Congo Belge.
——— 1958. *Exploration du Parc National de la Garamba. Ecologie et biologie des grands mammifères*. Bruxelles: Institute des Parcs Nationeaux du Congo Belge.
***Verwoerd, D.J.** 1987. Observations on the food and status of the Cape clawless otter *Aonyx capensis* at Betty's Bay, South Africa. *S. Afr. J. Zool.* **22**: 33–39.
**Vesey-Fitzgerald, D.F.** 1962. Habitat notes on Central African species of *Crocidura*. *Mammalia* **26**: 171–175.
——— 1964. Mammals of the Rukwa Valley. *Tanganyika Notes and Records* **62**: 61–72.
——— 1966. The habits and habitats of small rodents in the Congo River catchment region of Zambia and Tanzania. *Zool. Afr.* **2**: 111–122.
——— 1969. Utilization of the grazing resources by buffaloes in the Arusha National Park. *E. Afr. Wildl. J.* **7**: 131–145.
**Vidler, B.O., Harthoorn, A.M., Brocklesby, D.W. & Robertshaw, D.** 1963. The gestation and parturition of the African buffalo. *E. Afr. Wildl. J.* **1**: 122.
**Vielliard, J.** 1974. Les Chiroptères du Tchad. *Revue suisse Zool.* **81**: 975–991.
**Viljoen, P.C.** 1975. Ekologie van die oorbietjie, *Ourebia ourebi ourebi* (Zimmerman, 1783) in Transvaal. 3de vorderingsverslag, Transvaalse Afd. Natuurbewaring, Pretoria. Unpubl. mimeograph.
——— 1977. The ecology of the oribi. 2nd int. Symp. Wildl. Ecology, Pretoria. South African Wildlife Management Association. Abstr.
——— 1982. Die gedragsekologie van die oorbietjie *Ourebia ourebi ourebi* (Zimmerman, 1783) in Transvaal. M.Sc. thesis, University of Pretoria.
**Viljoen, P.J.** 1982a. The ecology of the desert-dwelling elephants, black rhinoceroses and giraffes of western Kaokoland and Damaraland, South West Africa. Unpubl. Progress Rep., January 1982, Wildlife Management, University of Pretoria.
*——— 1982b. The distribution and population status of the larger mammals in Kaokoland, South West Africa/Namibia. *Cimbebasia* A **7**: 7–33.
*——— 1987. Status and past and present distribution of elephants in the Kaokoveld, South West Africa/Namibia. *S. Afr. J. Zool.* **22**: 247–257.
*——— 1988. The ecology of the desert dwelling elephants *Loxodonta africana* (Blumenbach, 1797) of western Damaraland & Kaokoland. Ph.D. thesis, University of Pretoria.
**Viljoen, Susan** 1975. Aspects of the ecology, reproductive physiology and ethology of the bush squirrel, *Paraxerus cepapi cepapi* (A. Smith, 1836). M.Sc. thesis, University of Pretoria.
——— 1977a. The yellow-footed squirrel of the bushveld. *Fauna Flora, Pretoria* **28**: 15–16.
——— 1977b. Feeding habits of the bush squirrel *Paraxerus cepapi cepapi* (Rodentia: Sciuridae). *Zool. Afr.* **12**: 459–468.
——— 1977/78. Tree squirrels. *Afr. wild Life* **31**: 36–39.
——— 1978. Notes on the western striped squirrel *Funisciurus congicus* (Kuhl, 1820). *Madoqua* **11**: 119–128.
——— 1980a. A comparative study on the biology of two subspecies of tree squirrels, *Paraxerus palliatus tongensis* Roberts, 1931 and *Paraxerus palliatus ornatus* (Gray, 1864) in Zululand. D.Sc. thesis, University of Pretoria.
*——— 1980b. Environment and reproduction in tree squirrels with special reference to South African squirrels of the genus *Paraxerus*. In: *Environmental factors in mammalian reproduction*. Eds D. Gilmore & B. Cook. London: Macmillan.
*——— 1983a. Activity parameters relative to habitat in southern African tree squirrel species. *S. Afr. J. Zool.* **18**: 378–387.
*——— 1983b. Feeding habits and comparative feeding rates in the southern African arboreal squirrels. *S. Afr. J. Zool.* **18**: 378–398.
*——— 1983c. Communicatory behaviour in four southern African tree squirrels, *Paraxerus palliatus ornatus*, *P. p. tongensis*, *P. c. cepapi* and *Funisciurus congicus*. *Mammalia* **47**: 441–461.
*——— 1985. Comparative thermoregulatory adaptations of southern African tree squirrels from four different habitats. *S. Afr. J. Zool.* **20**: 28–32.
*——— 1986a. Moult of three southern African tree squirrels, *Paraxerus cepapi cepapi*, *P. palliatus ornatus* and *P. p. tongensis*. *Ann. Trans. Mus.* **34**: 245–252.
*——— 1986b. Use of space in southern African tree squirrels. *Mammalia* **50**: 293–310.
*——— 1989. Description, measurements and distribution of the red squirrel *Paraxerus palliatus* in the southern African subregion. *Ann. Trans. Mus.* **35**: 49–60.
——— **& Davis, D.H.S.** 1973. Notes on the stomach content analysis of various carnivores in southern Africa (Mammalia: Carnivora). *Ann. Trans. Mus.* **28**: 353–367.
*——— **& du Toit, S.H.C.** 1985. Postnatal development and growth of southern African tree squirrels in the genera *Funisciurus* and *Paraxerus*. *J. Mammal.* **66**: 119–127.
**Vincent, J.** 1962. The distribution of ungulates in Natal. *Ann. Cape Prov. Mus.* **2**: 110–117.
——— 1972. Reproduction in the impala (*Aepyceros melampus* Lichtenstein), with particular reference to the population in the Mkuzi Game Reserve, Zululand. M.Sc. thesis, University of Pretoria.
——— 1979. The population dynamics of impala *Aepyceros melampus* in Mkuzi Game Reserve. Ph.D. thesis, University of Natal.
——— **Hitchins, P.M., Bigalke, R.C. & Bass, A.J.** 1968. Studies on a population of nyala. *Lammergeyer* **9**: 5–17.
**Visser, J.** 1977. The small cats. *Afr. wild Life* **31**: 26–28.
***Visser, D.S & Robinson, T.J.** 1986. Cytosystematics of the South African *Aethomys* (Rodentia: Muridae). *S. Afr. J. Zool.* **21**: 264–268.
**Vogel, C.** 1962. Einege gefangensch Aftsbeobachtungen am weiblichen Fenek, *Fennecus zerda* (Zinim, 1780). *Z. Säugetierk.* **27**: 193–204.
***Von dem Bussche, G.H. & van der Zee, D.** 1985. Damage by samango monkeys to pine trees in the northern Transvaal. *S. Afr. For. J.* **133**: 43–48.
**Von Gadow, K.** 1978. A pellet count of blue duiker and bushbuck in the Knysna Forests. *S. Afr. For. J.* **107**: 77–81.
**Von Ketelhodt, H.F.** 1973. Breeding notes on blue duiker. *Zool. Afr.* **8**: 138.
*——— 1976. Observations on the lambing interval of the Cape bushbuck *Tragelaphus scriptus sylvaticus*. *Zool. Afr.* **11**: 221–225.
*——— 1977. The lambing interval of the blue duiker, *Cephalophus monticola*, in captivity, with observations on its breeding and care. *S. Afr. J. Wildl. Res.* **7**: 41–43.
**Von Lehmann, E.** 1955. Neue Säugetierrassen aus Sudwest Afrika. *Bonn zool. Beitr.* **6**: 171–172.
**Von Richter, W.** 1971a. Past and present distribution of the black wildebeest, *Connochaetes gnou* Zimmermann (Artiodactyla: Bovidae) with special reference to the history of some herds in South Africa. *Ann. Trans. Mus.* **27**: 35–57.

——— 1971b. Observations on the biology and ecology of the black wildebeest (*Connochaetes gnou*). *J. sth Afr. Wildl. Mgmt Ass.* **1**: 3–16.
——— 1971c. *The black wildebeest.* Nature Cons. Publ. Bloemfontein: Prov. Admin., O.F.S.
——— 1972. Territorial behaviour of the black wildebeest *Connochaetes gnou. Zool. Afr.* **7**: 207–231.
——— 1973. Black and square-lipped rhinoceros in Botswana. *Biol. Conserv.* 5159: 59.
——— 1974. Survey of the adequacy of existing conserved areas in relation to wild animal species. *Koedoe* **17**: 39–70.
——— **Lynch, C.D. & Wessels, T.** 1972. Status and distribution of the larger mammal species on farmland in the Orange Free State. *O.F.S. Prov. Admin. Nat. Conserv. Rep.* 1.
**Von Wolss, J.F.** 1955. *Mammals of Ethiopia and principal reptiles.* Adis Ababa: Ministry of Agriculture.
**Vrba, E.S.** 1971. A new fossil Alcelaphine (Artiodactyla: Bovidae) from Swartkrans. *Ann. Trans. Mus.* **27**: 59–82.
——— 1973. Two species of *Antidorcas* Sundevall at Swartkrans (Mammalia: Bovidae). *Ann. Trans. Mus.* **28**: 287–352.
——— 1975. Some evidence of chronology and palaeoecology of Sterkfontein, Swartkrans and Kromdraai from the fossil Bovidae. *Nature, Lond.* **254**: 301–304.
——— 1976. The fossil Bovidae of Sterkfontein, Swartkrans and Kromdraai. *Trans. Mus. (Pretoria)* Mem. 21.
——— 1979. Phylogenetic analysis and classification of fossil and recent Alcelaphini. Mammalia: Bovidae. *Biol. J. Linn. Soc.* **11**: 207–228.
——— 1984. Evolutionary pattern and process in the sister-group Alcelaphini —Aepycerotini (Mammalia: Bovidae), in *Living fossils*; Eds N. Eldridge & S.M. Stanley. New York: Springer Verlag.

# W

**Walker, A.** 1969. True affinities of *Propotto leakeyi* Simpson, 1967. *Nature, Lond.* **223**: 647–648.
*——— 1979. Prosimian locomotion behaviour: 543–565, in *The study of Prosimian behaviour*, Eds G.A. Doyle & R.D. Martin. London: Academic Press.
**Walker, C.** 1978. Cheetah dilemma. *Afr. wild Life* **32**: 22
——— 1981. The ecology of the desert elephants in western Kaokoland. *Endangered Wildlife Trust No.* 9. pp. 6.
***Walker, E.P.** 1975. *Mammals of the World.* Baltimore: John Hopkins University Press.
——— **Warnick, F., Hamlet, S.E., Lange, K.I., Davis, M.A., Uibele, H.E. & Wright, P.F.** 1964. *Mammals of the world.* Baltimore: John Hopkins Press.
**Walker, H.F.B.** 1917. *A doctor's diary in Damaraland.* London: Arnold.
***Walker, P.L.** 1986. Bushpig distribution and control in Natal. *Lammergeyer* **36**: 40–45.
**Walther, F.** 1966a. Zum Liegeverhalten des Weibchawanzgnus (*Connochaetes gnou* Zimmermann, 1780). *Z. Säugetierk.* **31**: 1–16.
——— 1966b. *Mit Horn und Huf.* Berlin: Paul Parey.
——— 1968. Kuhantilopen, Pferdeböcke und Wasserböcke. *Grzimek's Tierleben* **13**: 437–471.
——— 1969. Flight behaviour and avoidance of predators in Thomson's gazelle. *Behaviour* **34**: 184–221.
**Walton, D.W. & Walton, G.M.** 1970. Post-cranial osteology of bats. pp 93–126. In: *About Bats*, Eds B.H. Slaughter & D.W. Walton. Dallas: Southern Methodist Press.
**Walton, G.A.** 1957. Observations on biological variation in *Ornithodoros moubata* (Murr.) (Argasodae) in East Africa. *Bull. ent. Res.* **48**: 669–710.
**Ward, Rowland** 1896. Lichtenstein's hartebeest. *Records of big game. 2nd Edn.*: 76–78.
***Ward, Rowland** 1984. *Rowland Ward's African records of big game.* San Antonio, Texas: Rowland Ward Publications.
*——— 1986. *Rowland Ward's African records of big game.* San Antonio, Texas: Rowland Ward Publications.
**Warren, H.B.** 1974. Aspects of the behaviour of the impala male *Aepyceros melampus* during the rut. *Arnoldia Rhod.* **6**(27): 1–9.
**Washburn, S.L. & de Vore, I.** 1961. The social life of baboons. *Scient. Am.* **204**: 62–71.
***Wasson, M.** 1990. Hyena kills gnu with unusual death grip. *Gnusletter* **9**(2): 7–9.
***Watkins, W.A.** 1977. Acoustic behavior of sperm whales. *Oceanus* **20**: 50–58.
——— **& Schevill, W.E.** 1979. Aerial observation of feeding behaviour in four baleen whales: *Eubalaena glacialis, Balaenoptera borealis, Megaptera novaeangliae* and *Balaenoptera physalus. J. Mammal.* **60**: 155–163.
***Watson, C.R.B.** 1987. The comparative ecology of two small mammal communities in the Kruger National Park. M.Sc. thesis, University of Pretoria.
*——— **& Watson, R.T.** 1985. Small mammal trapping: analysis of disturbance and methods of trap protection. *S. Afr. J. Wildl. Res.* **15**: 54–58.
*——— **& Watson, R.T.** 1986. Observations on the post natal development of the tiny musk shrew, *Crocidura bicolor. S. Afr. J. Zool.* **21**: 352–354.
**Watson, J.M.** 1950. The wild mammals of Teso and Karamoja. *Uganda J.* **14**(2): 163–203.
***Watson, J.P. & Dippenaar, N.J.** 1987. The species limits of *Galerella sanguinea* (Rüppell, 1836), *G. pulverulenta* (Wagner, 1839) and *G. nigrata* (Thomas, 1928) in southern Africa (Carnivora: Viverridae). *Navors. nas. Mus., Bloemfontein* **5**: 356–413.
**Watson, L.** 1981. *Sea guide to whales of the world.* London: Hutchinson.
**Watson, P.F. & d'Souza, F.** 1975. Detection of oestrus in the African elephant (*Loxodonta africana*). *Theriogenology* **4**: 203–209.
**Watson, R.M.** 1967. The population ecology of the wildebeest (*Connochaetes taurinus albojubatus* Thomas) in the Serengeti. Ph.D. thesis, University of Cambridge.
——— 1969. Reproduction of wildebeest, *Connochaetes taurinus albojubatus* Thomas in the Serengeti region, and its significance to conservation. *J. Reprod. Fert. Suppl.* **6**: 287–310.
**Weinbrenn, C.** 1930. Variations in the skull of *Cercopithecus aethiops pygerythrus. S. Afr. J. Sci.* **27**: 501–520.
***Weir, J.S.** 1969. Chemical properties and occurrence on Kalahari sand of salt licks created by elephants. *J. Zool., Lond.* **15B**: 293–310.
——— 1972. Spatial distribution of elephants in an African National Park in relation to environmental sodium. *Oikos* **23**: 1–13.
——— **& Davison, E.** 1965. Daily occurrence of African game animals at water-holes during the dry weather. *Zool. Afr.* **1**: 353–368.
**Wells, L.H.** 1951. A large fossil klipspringer from Potgietersrust. *S. Afr. J. Sci.* **47**: 167–168.
——— 1967. Antelopes in the Pleistocene of southern Africa. In: *Background to evolution in Africa.* Eds W.W. Bishop & J.D. Clark. Chicago: University Press.
——— **& Cooke, H.B.S.** 1956. Fossil Bovidae from the Limeworks Quarry, Makapansgat, Potgietersrust. *Palaeont. afr.* **4**: 1–55.
**Wells, M.E.** 1968. A comparison of the reproductive tracts of *Crocuta crocuta, Hyaena hyaena* and *Proteles cristatus. E. Afr. Wildl. J.* **6**: 63–70.
***Wenhold, B.A. & Robinson, T.J.** 1987. Comparative karyology of three species of elephant-shrew (Insectivora: Macroscelididae) *Z. Säugtierk.* **52**: 1–9.
*——— 1990. The ethology and social behaviour of the yellow mongoose, *Cynictis penicillata.* M.Sc. thesis, University of Pretoria (to be submitted).
**Werger, M.J.A.** 1978. *Biography and ecology of Southern Africa* Vols. **1** & **2**. Den Haag: Junk.
**Wessels, T.C.** 1978. Bevolkingsdinamika van die vlakhaas *Lepus capensis* L., 1758 in die Willem Pretorius-wildtuin. M.Sc. thesis, University of Pretoria.
**Western, D.** 1971. Giraffe chewing on a Grant's gazelle carcass. *E. Afr. Wildl. J.* **9**: 157.
*——— 1975. Water availability & it's influence in the structure & dynamics of a savanna large mammal community. *E. Afr. Wildl. J.* **13**: 265–286.
*——— **Moss, C.J. & Georgiadis, N.** 1983. Age estimation and population age structure of elephants from footprint dimensions. *J. Wildl. Mgmt* **47**: 1192–1197.
***Westlin-van Aarde, Lilian M.** 1988. Reproduction in a laboratory colony of the pouched mouse, *Saccostomus campestris. J. Reprod. Fert.* **83**: 773–778.
*——— 1989a. Social environment and reproduction in female pouched mice, *Saccostomus campestris. J. Reprod. Fert.* **86**: 367–372.
*——— 1989b. Pregnancy, lactation and the oestrous cycle of the pouched mouse, *Saccostomus campestris. J. Reprod. Fert.* **87**: 155–162.
*——— 1989c. Pre- and post-natal development of pouched mice, *Saccostomus campestris. J. Zool., Lond.* **218**: 47–501.
*——— **van Aarde R.J. & Skinner, J.D.** 1988. Reproduction in female Hartmann's zebra, *Equus zebra hartmannae. J. Reprod. Fert.* **84**: 505–511.
**Whateley, A.** 1980. Comparative body measurements of male and female spotted hyaenas from Natal. *Lammergeyer* **28**: 40–43.
***Whitehead, S.I., Henzi, S.P. & Piper, S.E.** 1990. Estimating the age of infant chacma baboons (*Papio cynocephalus ursinus*). *Folia primatol.* in press.
***Whiten, A., Byrne, R.W. & Henzi, S.P.** 1987. The behavioral ecology of mountain baboons. *Int. J. Primatol.* **8**: 367–388.
**Whitfield, A.K. & Blaber, S.J.M.** 1980. The diet of *Atilax paludinosus* (water mongoose) at St Lucia, South Africa. *Mammalia* **44**: 315–318.
**Whitworth, T.** 1958. Miocene ruminants of East Africa. Fossil Mammals of Africa. *Bull. Br. Mus. nat. Hist.* No. **15**: 1–50.
**Whybrow, H.T.** 1907. Some notes on the antelope of Southern Rhodesia. *Proc. Rhod. Sci. Ass.* **7**(1): 28–58.
***Whyte, I.J.** 1985. The present ecological status of the blue wildebeest (*Connochaetes taurinus taurinus* Burchell, 1823) in the Central District of the Kruger National Park. M.Sc. thesis, University of Natal.
*——— **& Joubert, S.C.J.** 1988. Blue wildebeest population trends in the Kruger National Park and the effects of fencing. *S. Afr. J. Wildl. Res.* **18**: 78–87.
**Wiens, D. & Rourke, J.P.** 1978. Rodent pollination in southern African *Protea* spp. *Nature Lond.* **276**(5683): 71–73.
**Wild, H.& Grandvaux, L.A.** 1967. *Flora Zambesiaca.* Rhodesia: Collins.
***Wildi, H.** 1989. A bibliography of black rhinoceros *Diceros bicornis* (Linnaeus, 1758) and white rhinoceros *Ceratotherium simum* (Burchell, 1817) for southern Africa. *Koedoe* **32**: 89–123.
***Wiles, G.J. & Hill, J.E.** 1986. Accidental aircraft transport of a bat to Guam. *J. Mammal.* **67**: 600–601.
**Wilhelm, J.H.** 1933. Das Wild des Okawangogebiets und des Caprivizipfels. *Jl. S.W. Afr. scient. Soc.* **6**: 51–74.
***Wilkinson, I.S. & Bester, M.N.** in press. Duration of post weaning fast and local dispersion in the southern elephant seal, *Mirounga leonina*, at Marion Island. *J. Zool., Lond.*.
**Willan K. & Meester, J.** 1978. Breeding biology and postnatal development of the African dwarf mouse. *Acta Theriol.* **23**: 55–73.
**Willemse, J.** 1962. An impudent bushpig. *Fauna Flora, Pretoria* **13**: 54.
**Williams, J.G.** 1967. *A field guide to the National Parks of East Africa.* London: Collins.
**Williams, P.E.O.** 1977. Oxford expedition to the Viphya Plateau, Malawi, 1976. *Bull. Oxf. Univ. Explor. Club*, New Series **3**: 55–68.
**Williamson, B.R.** 1975. The condition and nutrition of elephant in Wankie National Park. *Arnoldia Rhod.* **7**(12): 1–20.
*——— 1979. Elephant census, Wankie National Park. Unpubl. Mimeograph. National Parks of Zimbabwe, Harare.
**Williamson, D.T.** 1979. An outline of the ecology and behaviour of the red lechwe (*Kobus leche leche* Gray, 1850). Ph.D. thesis, University of Natal.
*——— 1987. Plant underground storage organs as a source of moisture for Kalahari wildlife. *Afr. J. Ecol.* **25**: 63–64.
*——— **& Mbano, B.** 1983. Wildebeest mortality during 1983 at Lake Xau, Botswana. *Afr. J. Ecol.* **26**: 341–344.
*——— **& Williamson J.** 1985. Botswana's fences and the depletion of Kalahari wildlife. *Parks* **10**: 5–7.
**Williamson, G.R.** 1961. Two kinds of minke whale in the Antarctic. *Norsk. Hvalfangs-tiid.* **50**: 133–140.
*——— 1975. Minke whales off Brazil. *Scient. Rep. Whales Res. Inst., Tokyo* **27**: 37–59.
***Williamson, Jane E.** 1987. Aspects of the behavioural ecology of springbok (*Antidorcas marsupialis* Zimmerman 1780) in the Central Kalahari Game Reserve, Botswana. M.Sc. thesis, University of the Witwatersrand.
***Willis, C.** 1988. Relative importance of ants and termites in the feeding ecology of the aardvark, *Orycteropus afer* Pallas. B.Sc. Hons. Project Rep., University of Pretoria.
***Willis, C.K., Skinner, J.D. & Robertson, H.G.** in prep. Relative importance of ants and termites in the diet of the aardvark *Orycteropus afer.*
**Wilson, D.E.** 1975. Factors affecting roan and sable antelope populations on nature reserves in the Transvaal with particular reference to ecophysiological aspects. D.Sc. thesis, University of Pretoria.
——— **Bartsch, R.C., Bigalke, R.D. & Thomas, S.E.** 1974. Observation on mortality rates and disease in roan and sable antelope on nature reserves in the Transvaal. *J. sth Afr. Wildl. Mgmt Ass.* **4**: 203–206.
——— **& Hirst, S.M.** 1977. Ecology and factors limiting roan and sable antelope populations in South Africa. *Wildl. Monogr.* **54**: 1–111.
**Wilson, D.S. & Clark, A.B.** 1977. Above ground predator defence in the harvester termite, *Hodotermes mossambicus* Hagen. *J. Ent. Soc. S. Afr.* **40**: 271–282.
**Wilson, E.A.** 1907. Mammalia (whales and seals): 1–66, in *National Antarctic Expedition, 1901–1904. Natural History II. Zoology.* London: British Museum (Nat. Hist.).

**Wilson, V.J.** 1965. Observations on the greater kudu *Tragelaphus strepsiceros* Pallas from a tsetse control hunting scheme in Northern Rhodesia. *E. Afr. Wildl. J.* **3**: 27–37.
——— 1966a. Notes on the food and feeding habits of the common duiker, *Sylvicapra grimmia*, in eastern Zambia. *Arnoldia Rhod.* **2**(14): 1–19.
——— 1966b. Predators of the common duiker, *Sylvicapra grimmia*, in eastern Zambia. *Arnoldia Rhod.* **2**(28):1–8.
——— 1966c. Observations on Lichtenstein's hartebeest, *Alcelaphus lichtensteini*, over a three-year period, and their response to various tsetse control measures in Eastern Zambia. *Arnoldia Rhod.* **2**(15):1–13.
——— 1968. Weights of some mammals from eastern Zambia. *Arnoldia Rhod.* **3**(32): 1–20.
——— 1969a. The large mammals of the Rhodes Matopos National Park. *Arnoldia Rhod.* **4**(13): 1–32.
——— 1969b. Eland, *Taurotragus oryx*, in eastern Zambia. *Arnoldia Rhod.* **4**(12): 1–9.
——— 1970. Data from the culling of kudu, *Tragelaphus strepsiceros*, in the Kyle National Park. *Arnoldia Rhod.* **4**(36): 1–26.
——— 1975. Mammals of the Wankie National Park. *Mus. mem. Natl Mus. Mon. Rhod.* **4**: 1–147.
——— **& Clarke, J.E.** 1962. Observations on the common duiker *Sylvicapra grimmia* Linn. based on material collected from a tsetse control game elimination scheme in Northern Rhodesia. *Proc. zool. Soc. Lond.* **138**: 487–497.
——— **& Child, G.F.T.** 1964. Notes on bushbuck (*Tragelaphus scriptus*) from a tsetse fly control area in Northern Rhodesia. *Puku* **2**: 118–128.
——— **& Child, G.F.T.** 1965. Notes on klipspringer from tsetse fly control areas in Eastern Zambia. *Arnoldia Rhod.* **1**(35): 1–9.
——— **& Kerr, M.A.** 1969. Brief notes on reproduction in steenbok, *Raphicerus campestris* Thunberg. *Arnoldia Rhod.* **4**(23): 1–5.
*——— **Schmidt, J.L. & Hanks, J.** 1984. Age determination and body growth of the common duiker. *J. Zool., Lond.* **202**: 283–297.
***Withers, P.C.** 1979. Ecology of a small mammal community on a rocky outcrop on the Namib desert. *Madoqua* **II**: 229–246.
*——— 1983. Seasonal reproduction by small mammals of the Namib Desert. *Mammalia* **47**: 195–204.
*——— **Louw, G.N. & Henschel, J.R.** 1980. Energetics and water relationships of Namib desert rodents. *S. Afr. J. Zool.* **15**: 131–137.
**Wodzicki, K.A.** 1950. *Introduced mammals of New Zealand*. Wellington: N.Z. Department of Science and Industrial Research.
**Wood, A.E.** 1955. A revised classification of the rodents. *J. Mammal.* **36**: 165–187.
——— 1962. The juvenile tooth patterns of certain African rodents. *J. Mammal.* **43**: 310–322.
——— 1974a. The evolution of the Old World and New World hystricomorphs. In: *The biology of hystricomorph rodents*. Eds I.W. Rowlands & Barbara Weir. London: Academic Press.
——— 1974b. The evolution of the Old World and New World Hystricomorphs. *Symp. zool. Soc. Lond.* 34: 21–60.
***Woodall, P.F.** 1987. Digestive tract dimensions and body mass of elephant shrews (Macroscelididae) and the effects of season and habitat. *Mammalia* **51**: 537–545.
*——— **& Currie, G.J.** 1989. Food consumption, assimilation and rate of food passage in the Cape rock elephant shrew, *Elephantulus edwardii* (Macroscelidea, Macroscelidinae). *Comp. Biochem. Physiol.* **92A**: 75–79.
*——— **& Mackie, R.I.** 1987. Caecal size and function in the rock elephant shrew *Elephantulus myurus* (Insectivora, Macroscelididae) and the Namaqua rock mouse *Aethomys namaquensis* (Rodentia, Muridae). *Comp. Biochem. Physiol.* **87A**: 311–314.
*——— **& Skinner, J.D.** 1989. Seasonality of reproduction in male rock elephant shrews, *Elephantulus myurus*. *J. Zool., Lond.* **217**: 203–212.
*——— **Woodall, L.B. & Bodero, D.A.V.** 1989. Daily activity patterns in captive elephant shrews (Macroscelididae). *Afr. J. Ecol.* **27**: 63–76.
***Wrangham, R.W.** 1980. An ecological model of female bonded primate groups. *Behav.* **75**: 262–300.
**Wright, B.S.** 1960. Predation on big game in East Africa. *J. Wildl. Mgmt* **24**: 1–15.
***Wright, P.G.** 1987. Thermoregulation in the hippopotamus on land. *S. Afr. J. Zool.* **22**: 237–242.
*——— **& Luck, C.P.** 1984. Do elephants need to sweat? *S. Afr. J. Zool.* **19**: 270–274.
**Wrogemann, N.** 1975. Cheetah under the sun. Johannesburg: McGraw-Hill.
***Wroughton, R.C.** 1906. Notes on the genus *Otomys*. *Ann. Mag. nat. Hist.* **18**: 264–278.
***Wulff, H., Fabiyi, A. & Monath, T.P.** 1975. Recent isolations of Lassa virus from Nigerian rodents. *Bull. Wld Hlth Org.* **52**: 609–613.
***Wursig, B. & Wursig, M.** 1980. Behavior and ecology of the dusky dolphin, *Lagenorhynchus obscurus*, in the South Atlantic. *Fish. Bull., U.S.* **77**: 871–890.
***Wurster, D.H. & Benirschke, K.** 1968. Chromosome studies in the superfamily Bovoidea. *Chromosoma* **25**: 152–171.
**Wyatt, J.** 1971. Osteophagia in Masai giraffe. *E. Afr. Wildl. J.* **9**: 157.
——— **& Eltringham, S.K.** 1974. The daily activity of the elephant in the Ruwenzori National Park, Uganda. *E. Afr. Wildl. J.* **12**: 273–289.

# Y

**Yalden, D.W., Largen, M.J. & Kock, D.** 1976. Catalogue of the mammals of Ethiopia. 2. Insectivora and Rodentia. *Monitore zool. ital.* (N.S.) Suppl. 8(1): 1–118.
*——— **Largen, M.J. & Kock, D.** 1977. Catalogue of the mammals of Ethiopia 3. Primates. *Monitore zool. ital.* (NS) Suppl **9**: 1–52.
——— **Largen, M.J. & Kock, D.** 1980. Catalogue of the mammals of Ethiopia. 4. Carnivora. *Monitore zool. ital.* (N.S.) Suppl. **13**: 169–272.
*——— **Largen, M.J. & Kock, D.** 1984. Catalogue of the mammals of Ethiopie 5. Artiodactyla. *Monitore zool. ital.* (NS) Suppl. **19**: 67–221.
*——— **Largen, M.J. & Kock, D.** 1986. Catalogue of the mammals of Ethiopia 6. Perissodactyla, Proboscidea, Hyracoidea, Lagomorpha, Tubulidentata, Sirenia and Cetacea. *Monitore zool. ital.* (NS) Suppl. **21**: 31–103.
**Yamada, M.** 1954. An account of a rare porpoise, *Feresa* Gray from Japan. *Scient. Rep. Whales Res. Inst. Tokyo* 9: 59–88.
***Yeaton, R.I.** 1988. Porcupines, fires and the dynamics of the tree layer of the *Burkea africana* savanna. *J. Ecol.* **76**: 1017–1029.
**Yom-Tov, Y.** 1967. On the taxonomic status of the hares (genus *Lepus*) in Israel. *Mammalia* **31**: 246–259.
**York, W.** 1971. A study of serval melanism in the Aberdares Mts., Kenya and some general behavioural information, in *The world's cats* Vol. **1**. Winston Oregon: World Wildlife Safari.
**Yost, R.A.** 1980. The nocturnal behaviour of captive brown hyaenas (*Hyaena brunnea*). *Mammalia* **44**: 27–34.
**Young, E.** 1972a. The value of waterhole counts in estimating wild animal populations. *J. sth Afr. Wildl. Mgmt Ass.* **2**: 22–23.
——— 1972b. Overstraining disease (capture myopathy) in the tsessebe, *Damaliscus lunatus* and oribi, *Ourebia oribi*. *Koedoe* **15**: 143–144.
——— 1972c. Cheetahs. *Custos* **2**(1): 10–12.
**Young, W.C.** 1961. The hormones and mating behaviour : 1173–1239, in *Sex and internal secretions*. Ed. W.C. Young. Baltimore: Williams & Wilkins.

# Z

**Zahavi, A. & Wahrman, J.** 1957. The cytotaxonomy, ecology and evolution of the gerbils and jirds of Israel (Rodentia: Gerbillinae). *Mammalia* **21**: 341–380.
**Zeuner, F.E.** 1963. *The history of domestic animals: the cat*. London: Hutchinson.
***Zhou,K., Li, Y., Qian, W. & Yang, G.** 1979. [Abstract]. Marine Mammal Information (Oregon State University, Sea Grant College Program), December 1979: 46.
***Zimmermann, E., Bearder, S.K., Doyle, G.A. & Andersson, A.B.** 1988. Variations in vocal patterns of Senegal and South African lesser bushbabies and their implications for taxonomic relationships. *Folia primatol.* **51**: 87–105.
**Zuckerman, S.** 1932. *The social life of monkeys and apes*. London: Routledge & Kegan Paul.
——— 1953. The breeding season of mammals in captivity. *Proc. zool. Soc. Lond.* **122**: 827–950.
**Zumpt, F.** (ed.) 1966. The arthropod parasites of vertebrates in Africa south of the Sahara (Ethiopian Region). Vol. **III** Insecta excluding Phthiraptera. *Publs S. Afr. Inst. med. Res.* **13**(52): 1–283.
**Zumpt, I.F.** 1959. Is the multimammate rat a natural reservoir of *Borrelia duttoni*?. *Nature Lond.* **184**: 793.
——— 1968a. The feeding habits of the yellow mongoose, *Cynictis penicillata*, the suricate, *Suricata suricatta*, and the Cape ground squirrel, *Xerus inauris*. *Jl S. Afr. vet. med. Ass.* **39**: 89–91.
——— 1968b. The handling, housing and nutrition of captive wild meerkats. *Jl S. Afr. vet. med. Ass.* **39**: 105–108.
*——— 1969. Factors influencing rabies outbreaks: the age and breeding cycle of the yellow mongoose, *Cynictis penicillata* (G. Cuvier). *Jl S. Afr. vet. med. Ass.* **40**: 319–322.
——— 1970. The ground squirrel. *Afr. wild Life* **24**: 115–121.
*——— 1982. The yellow mongoose as a rabies vector on the central plateau of South Africa. *S. Afr. J. Sci.* **78**: 417–418.

# INDICES

## SCIENTIFIC NAMES

# ENGLISH NAMES

N



O



P



Q



R



S



T

# AFRIKAANS NAME

L



M



N



O



P



R

## Y



## Z

# The Mammal Research Institute

Founded 21 years ago, the University of Pretoria's Mammal Research Institute was set up with the express purposes of providing high-level training for post-graduate students, conducting fundamental research in mammals and furthering international and national liaison with the intention of pooling available knowledge of mammalian systematics, behaviour, physiology, and ecological needs.

With these objectives in mind, intense research has been undertaken over the years with the help of students from the University of Pretoria and post-doctoral researchers from all over the world. In terms of training, the Institute has aimed to turn out top-notch people in this field, and has succeeded consistently in doing so. Today, its graduated students occupy senior positions in a number of conservation organisations and academic institutions in southern Africa, in other African countries and overseas.

The scope of this research and training programme has encompassed the whole of the Southern African Subregion and has extended to the mammal population of the southern oceans. In pursuing this research, the Institute has drawn in expertise from academic departments of the University, from conservation bodies throughout southern Africa and from prestigious institutes in other countries.

A sense of urgency pervades its work since it is recognised that successful conservation cannot precede the acquisition of basic knowledge without risking disastrous errors that may be irreversible. Too often in the past the rash implementation of apparently logical conservation policies have had just such tragic consequences.

The research effort has been both fundamental and dynamic, geared to changing animals in a changing environment, and aimed at the study of ecology, physiology and behaviour patterns of mammals. It has involved intensive work on several endangered species.

Behind the purposeful research of the Institute lies a dedication to meaningful knowledge and the intention to devise successful strategies for conservation and management. Thus strategies have been developed for the conservation of endangered species and other non-utilised wildlife by investigating their environmental needs, their reproductive activities, social behaviour and energy requirements. There is also intense investigation of game as a protein source, based on the concept of conservation through utilisation. Systematic studies are carried out to monitor the variety of mammals in the Southern African Subregion. These led to an appreciation of the need for an up-to-date comprehensive reference work to replace Austin Robert's contribution (1951). To this end the first edition of *Mammals of the Southern African Subregion* was produced, with Reay Smithers taking the major responsibility. The research which made the second edition necessary has been the work of numerous zoologists, mainly either present or former members of the Institute, under the direction of J.D. Skinner.

Among the land mammals of this region research has been carried out on herbivores, as a potential energy source for man, to be utilised in conjunction with domestic livestock. It has also focussed on carnivores, which are largely in conflict with man and therefore more seriously threatened. Research on the sea mammals has dealt with elephant seals, fur seals and whales. This work has concentrated on mammals that are at the top of the food chain and has been undertaken in collaboration with other institutes around the world that do research at the lower levels of the food chain. Research has also been done on terrestrial mammals introduced onto islands used by sea mammals as breeding grounds.

It is vitally important for man to understand his own relationship with the world around him, both in terms of other living things and the environment in which we all live. Consequently, there is a need for basic research and for trained scientists who are exposed to the benefits of international liaison. That is what this Institute is all about.

Deriving its basic funding from the University of Pretoria and from the Council for Scientific and Industrial Research, the Institute nevertheless relies for the maintenance of its student training and research programmes on additional financial and material assistance from individuals and organisations in the private and public sectors. Without their generous response many of its successful enterprises could never have been launched.

Any student or post-graduate scientist interested in doing research at the Mammal Research Institute should write to:

The Director,
Mammal Research Institute,
University of Pretoria,
Pretoria 0002,
Republic of South Africa.